PRENTICE HALL MATHEMATICS

ALGEBRA 2

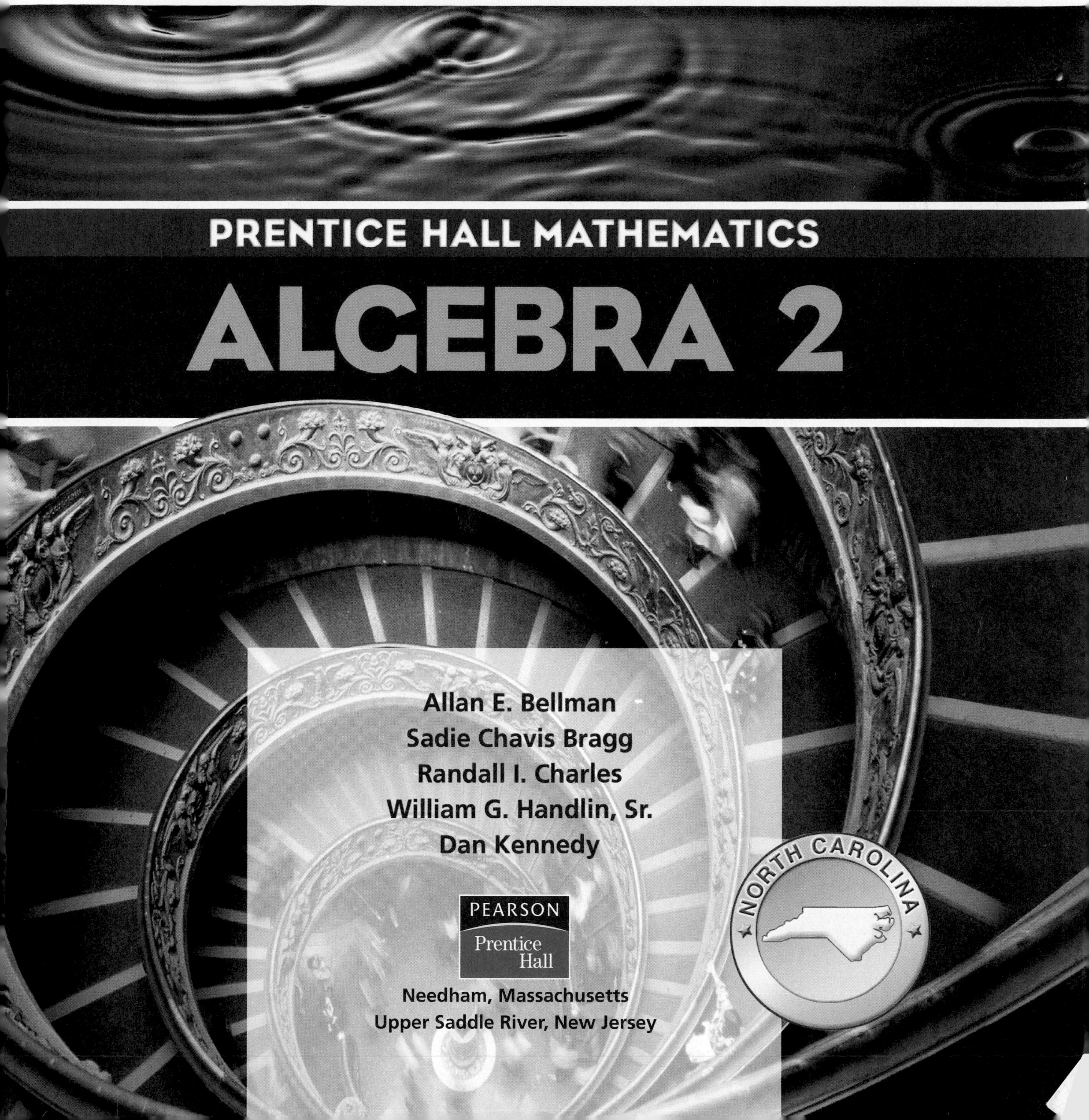

Allan E. Bellman

Sadie Chavis Bragg

Randall I. Charles

William G. Handlin, Sr.

Dan Kennedy

PEARSON

Prentice
Hall

Needham, Massachusetts
Upper Saddle River, New Jersey

NORTH CAROLINA

Dorling Kindersley (DK) is an international publishing company that specializes in the creation of high-quality, illustrated information books for children and adults. Dorling Kindersley's unique graphic presentation style is used in this program to motivate students in learning about real-world applications of mathematics. DK is part of the Pearson family of companies.

ISBN 0-13-180866-4

1 2 3 4 5 6 7 8 9 10   07 06 05 04 03

North Carolina Algebra 2 Standard Course of Study Handbook

Correlation NC4

These pages provide a complete list of the Algebra 2 objectives of the North Carolina Mathematics Standard Course of Study and identify the Prentice Hall Mathematics lessons in this book that address each state objective.

Year-at-a-Glance NC6

These pages provide a brief overview of where each North Carolina mathematics objective is introduced, developed, and concluded in this book.

Lesson-by-Lesson Correlation NC8

These pages list each lesson along with all of the objectives addressed by each lesson. Pacing suggestions for two different teaching schedules – traditional and block – are also offered for each lesson.

Standards Progression NC12

These pages lay out the North Carolina Standard Course of Study for Algebra 2. The pages list the chapters where you can find each objective, as well as a sample item that addresses that objective. Also shown is the progression made in each benchmark from prior years to this year, and then in later years.

North Carolina Standard Course of Study Correlation

This correlation identifies sections on which the North Carolina Standard Course of Study objectives are addressed in this book. With the help of this chart you can find solid, fully developed instruction on any standard.

Standard	Prentice Hall Algebra 2 Lessons
Number & Operations	
1.01 Simplify and perform operations with rational exponents and logarithms (common and natural) to solve problems.	7-1, 7-2, 7-3, 7-4, 8-3, 8-4, 8-5, 8-6
1.02 Define and compute with complex numbers.	5-6, 6-5, 6-6
1.03 Operate with algebraic expressions (polynomial, rational, complex fractions) to solve problems.	1-2, 1-3, 1-4, 5-4, 6-2, 6-3, 6-4, 6-5, 6-6, 6-8, 9-4, 9-5
1.04 Operate with matrices to model and solve problems.	4-1, 4-2, 4-3, 4-4, 4-5, 4-6, 4-7, 4-8
1.05 Model and solve problems using direct, inverse, combined and joint variation.	2-3, 9-1, 9-2
Algebra	
2.01 Use the composition and inverse of functions to model and solve problems; justify results.	7-6, 7-7, 8-3, 8-5, 8-6
2.02 Use quadratic functions and inequalities to model and solve problems; justify results.	
a) Solve using tables, graphs, and algebraic properties.	5-2, 5-3, 5-5, 5-7, 5-8
b) Interpret the constants and coefficients in the context of the problem.	5-1, 5-2, 5-3, 5-7, 5-8
2.03 Use exponential functions to model and solve problems; justify results.	8-1
a) Solve using tables, graphs, and algebraic properties.	8-2
b) Interpret the constants, coefficients, and bases in the context of the problem.	8-2
2.04 Create and use best-fit mathematical models of linear, exponential, and quadratic functions to solve problems involving sets of data.	6-1, 8-1
a) Interpret the constants, coefficients, and bases in the context of the data.	2-4, 8-1
b) Check the model for goodness-of-fit and use the model, where appropriate, to draw conclusions or make predictions.	2-4, 5-1, 6-1

Standard	Prentice Hall Algebra 2 Lessons
Algebra (cont.)	
2.05 Use rational equations to model and solve problems; justify results.	
a) Solve using tables, graphs, and algebraic properties.	9-6
b) Interpret the constants and coefficients in the context of the problem.	9-3, 9-6
c) Identify the asymptotes and intercepts graphically and algebraically.	9-2, 9-3
2.06 Use cubic equations to model and solve problems.	
a) Solve using tables and graphs.	6-1
b) Interpret constants and coefficients in the context of the problem.	6-1
2.07 Use equations with radical expressions to model and solve problems; justify results.	
a) Solve using tables, graphs, and algebraic properties.	7-5, 7-8
b) Interpret the degree, constants, and coefficients in the context of the problem.	7-8
2.08 Use equations and inequalities with absolute value to model and solve problems; justify results.	
a) Solve using tables, graphs, and algebraic properties.	1-5, 2-5, 2-7
b) Interpret the constants and coefficients in the context of the problem.	2-6
2.09 Use the equations of parabolas and circles to model and solve problems; justify results.	
a) Solve using tables, graphs, and algebraic properties.	10-1, 10-2, 10-3, 10-6
b) Interpret the constants and coefficients in the context of the problem.	3-1, 3-2, 3-3, 3-4, 3-6, 4-7, 4-8
2.10 Use systems of two or more equations or inequalities to model and solve problems; justify results. Solve using tables, graphs, matrix operations, and algebraic properties.	7-6, 7-7, 8-3, 8-5, 8-6

North Carolina Standard Course of Study
Year-at-a-Glance

The following chart provides an overview of where within Prentice Hall Algebra 2 each objective in the North Carolina Standard Course of Study is introduced, developed, and concluded.

Standard	PRENTICE HALL ALGEBRA 2 CHAPTERS													
	1	2	3	4	5	6	7	8	9	10	11	12	13	14
Number & Operations														
1.01 Simplify and perform operations with rational exponents and logarithms (common and natural) to solve problems.							I,D	D,C						
1.02 Define and compute with complex numbers.					I	D,C								
1.03 Operate with algebraic expressions (polynomial, rational, complex fractions) to solve problems.	I				D	D			C					
1.04 Operate with matrices to model and solve problems.				I,D,C										
1.05 Model and solve problems using direct, inverse, combined and joint variation.		I,D							D,C					
Algebra														
2.01 Use the composition and inverse of functions to model and solve problems; justify results.							I,D	D,C						
2.02 Use quadratic functions and inequalities to model and solve problems; justify results.														
a) Solve using tables, graphs, and algebraic properties.					I,D,C									
b) Interpret the constants and coefficients in the context of the problem.					I,D,C									
2.03 Use exponential functions to model and solve problems; justify results.								I,D,C						
a) Solve using tables, graphs, and algebraic properties.								I,D,C						
b) Interpret the constants, coefficients, and bases in the context of the problem.								I,D,C						
2.04 Create and use best-fit mathematical models of linear, exponential, and quadratic functions to solve problems involving sets of data.							I,D	D,C						
a) Interpret the constants, coefficients, and bases in the context of the data.		I,D							D,C					
b) Check the model for goodness-of-fit and use the model, where appropriate, to draw conclusions or make predictions.		I			D	C								

I = introduced   D = developed   C = concluded

Standard	PRENTICE HALL ALGEBRA 2 CHAPTERS													
	1	2	3	4	5	6	7	8	9	10	11	12	13	14
2.05 Use rational equations to model and solve problems; justify results.														
a) Solve using tables, graphs, and algebraic properties.									I,D,C					
b) Interpret the constants and coefficients in the context of the problem.									I,D,C					
c) Identify the asymptotes and intercepts graphically and algebraically.									I,D,C					
2.06 Use cubic equations to model and solve problems.						I,D,C								
a) Solve using tables and graphs.						I,D,C								
b) Interpret constants and coefficients in the context of the problem.														
2.07 Use equations with radical expressions to model and solve problems; justify results.							I,D,C							
a) Solve using tables, graphs, and algebraic properties.							I,D,C							
b) Interpret the degree, constants, and coefficients in the context of the problem.														
2.08 Use equations and inequalities with absolute value to model and solve problems; justify results.	I	D,C												
a) Solve using tables, graphs, and algebraic properties.														
b) Interpret the constants and coefficients in the context of the problem.														
2.09 Use the equations of parabolas and circles to model and solve problems; justify results.		I,D,C												
a) Solve using tables, graphs, and algebraic properties.										I,D,C				
b) Interpret the constants and coefficients in the context of the problem.														
2.10 Use systems of two or more equations or inequalities to model and solve problems; justify results. Solve using tables, graphs, matrix operations, and algebraic properties.			I,D	D,C										

North Carolina Standard Course of Study
Lesson-by-Lesson Correlation

This chart provides pacing suggestions based on the objectives of the North Carolina Standard Course of Study for Algebra 2. It is designed to help you maximize your coverage of the objectives.

Chapter 1 Tools of Algebra		North Carolina Course of Study	Pacing	
			Traditional	Block
1-1	Properties of Real Numbers		3 days	2 days
1-2	Algebraic Expressions	1.03	2 days	1 day
1-3	Solving Equations	1.03	3 days	1 1/2 days
1-4	Solving Inequalities	1.03	3 days	1 1/2 days
1-5	Absolute Value Equations and Inequalities	2.08	2 days	1 day
1-6	Probability	Support & Review	2 days	1 day
Testing and Additional Activities			3 days	2 days

Chapter 2 Functions, Equations, and Graphs		North Carolina Course of Study	Pacing	
			Traditional	Block
2-1	Relations and Functions	Support & Review	2 days	1 day
2-2	Linear Equations	Support & Review	2 days	1 day
2-3	Direct Variation	1.05	2 days	1 day
2-4	Using Linear Models	2.04a, b	3 days	1 1/2 days
2-5	Absolute Value Functions and Graphs	2.08a	3 days	1 1/2 days
2-6	Vertical and Horizontal Translations	2.08b	3 days	1 day
2-7	Two-Variable Inequalities	2.08a	2 days	1 day
Testing and Additional Activities			3 days	2 days

Chapter 3 Linear Systems		North Carolina Course of Study	Pacing	
			Traditional	Block
3-1	Graphing Systems of Equations	2.10	2 days	1 day
3-2	Solving Systems Algebraically	2.10	3 days	1 1/2 days
3-3	Systems of Inequalities	2.10	3 days	1 1/2 days
3-4	Linear Programming	2.10	3 days	1 day
3-5	Graphs in Three Dimensions	Support & Review	2 days	1 day
3-6	Systems With Three Variables	2.10	3 days	2 days
Testing and Additional Activities			3 days	2 days

Chapter 4 Matrices		North Carolina Course of Study	Pacing	
			Traditional	Block
4-1	Organizing Data Into Matrices	1.04	2 days	1 day
4-2	Adding and Subtracting Matrices	1.04	2 days	1 day
4-3	Matrix Multiplication	1.04	2 days	1 day
4-4	Geometric Transformations With Matrices	1.04	3 days	1 day
4-5	2×2 Matrices, Determinants, and Inverses	1.04	2 days	1 day
4-6	3×3 Matrices, Determinants, and Inverses	1.04	2 days	1 day
4-7	Inverse Matrices and Systems	1.04, 2.10	3 days	1 1/2 days
4-8	Augmented Matrices and Systems	1.04, 2.10	3 days	1 1/2 days
Testing and Additional Activities			3 days	2 days

NORTH CAROLINA

Chapter 5 Quadratic Equations and Functions	North Carolina Course of Study	Pacing	
		Traditional	Block
5-1 Modeling Data With Quadratic Functions	2.02b, 2.04b	2 days	1 day
5-2 Properties of Parabolas	2.02a, b	3 days	1 day
5-3 Translating Parabolas	2.02a, b	2 days	1 day
5-4 Factoring Quadratic Expressions	1.03	2 days	1 day
5-5 Quadratic Equations	2.02a	2 days	1 day
5-6 Complex Numbers	1.02	2 days	1 day
5-7 Completing the Square	2.02a, b	2 days	1 day
5-8 The Quadratic Formula	2.02a, b	3 days	2 days
Testing and Additional Activities		3 days	2 days

Chapter 6 Polynomials and Polynomial Functions	North Carolina Course of Study	Pacing	
		Traditional	Block
6-1 Polynomial Functions	2.04, 2.06a, b	3 days	1 day
6-2 Polynomials and Linear Factors	1.03	2 days	1 day
6-3 Dividing Polynomials	1.03	2 days	1 day
6-4 Solving Polynomial Equations	1.03	2 days	1 day
6-5 Theorems About Roots of Polynomial Equations	1.02, 1.03	3 days	2 days
6-6 The Fundamental Theorem of Algebra	1.02, 1.03	2 days	1 day
6-7 Permutations and Combinations	Support & Review	2 days	1 day
6-8 The Binomial Theorem	1.03	2 days	1 day
Testing and Additional Activities		3 days	2 days

Chapter 7 Radical Functions and Rational Exponents	North Carolina Course of Study	Pacing	
		Traditional	Block
7-1 Roots and Radical Expressions	1.01	2 days	1 day
7-2 Multiplying and Dividing Radical Expressions	1.01	3 days	1 1/2 days
7-3 Binomial Radical Expressions	1.01	3 days	1 1/2 days
7-4 Rational Exponents	1.01	2 days	1 day
7-5 Solving Radical Equations	2.07a	2 days	1 day
7-6 Function Operations	2.01	2 days	1 day
7-7 Inverse Relations and Functions	2.01	2 days	1 day
7-8 Graphing Radical Functions	2.07a, b	2 days	1 day
Testing and Additional Activities		3 days	2 days

Chapter 8 Exponential and Logarithmic Functions		North Carolina Course of Study	Pacing	
			Traditional	Block
8-1	Exploring Exponential Models	2.03, 2.04, 2.04b	2 days	1 day
8-2	Properties of Exponential Functions	2.03	2 days	1 day
8-3	Logarithmic Functions as Inverses	1.01, 2.01	3 days	1 1/2 days
8-4	Properties of Logarithms	1.01	2 days	1 day
8-5	Exponential and Logarithmic Equations	1.01, 2.01	3 days	1 1/2 days
8-6	Natural Logarithms	1.01, 2.01	2 days	1 day
Testing and Additional Activities			3 days	2 days

Chapter 9 Rational Functions		North Carolina Course of Study	Pacing	
			Traditional	Block
9-1	Inverse Variation	1.05	2 days	1 day
9-2	Graphing Inverse Variations	1.05, 2.05c	2 days	1 day
9-3	Rational Functions and Their Graphs	2.05b, c	2 days	1 day
9-4	Rational Expressions	1.03	2 days	1 day
9-5	Adding and Subtracting Rational Expressions	1.03	2 days	1 day
9-6	Solving Rational Equations	2.05a, b	2 days	1 day
9-7	Probability of Multiple Events	Enrichment	1 day	1 day
Testing and Additional Activities			3 days	2 days

Chapter 10 Quadratic Relations		North Carolina Course of Study	Pacing	
			Traditional	Block
10-1	Exploring Conic Sections	2.09a, b	2 days	1 day
10-2	Parabolas	2.09a, b	3 days	1 1/2 days
10-3	Circles	2.09a, b	3 days	1 1/2 days
10-4	Ellipses	Support & Review	1 day	1/2 day
10-5	Hyperbolas	Support & Review	1 day	1/2 day
10-6	Translating Conic Sections	2.09a, b	2 days	1 day
Testing and Additional Activities			3 days	2 days

Chapter 11 Sequences and Series		North Carolina Course of Study	Pacing	
			Traditional	Block
11-1	Mathematical Patterns	Enrichment and Additional Topics	2 days	1 day
11-2	Arithmetic Sequences	Enrichment and Additional Topics	1 day	1 day
11-3	Geometric Sequences	Enrichment and Additional Topics	2 days	1 day
11-4	Arithmetic Series	Enrichment and Additional Topics	2 days	1 day
11-5	Geometric Series	Enrichment and Additional Topics	1 day	1 day
11-6	Area Under a Curve	Enrichment and Additional Topics	2 days	1 day
Testing and Additional Activities		Enrichment and Additional Topics	3 days	2 days

Chapter 12 Probability and Statistics	North Carolina Course of Study	Pacing	
		Traditional	**Block**
12-1 Probability Distributions	Enrichment and Additional Topics	2 days	1 day
12-2 Conditional Probability	Enrichment and Additional Topics	2 days	1 day
12-3 Analyzing Data	Enrichment and Additional Topics	2 days	1 day
12-4 Standard Deviation	Enrichment and Additional Topics	2 days	1 day
12-5 Working With Samples	Enrichment and Additional Topics	1 day	1 day
12-6 Binomial Distributions	Enrichment and Additional Topics	2 days	1 day
12-7 Normal Distributions	Enrichment and Additional Topics	2 days	1 day
Testing and Additional Activities	Enrichment and Additional Topics	3 days	2 days

Chapter 13 Periodic Functions and Trigonometry	North Carolina Course of Study	Pacing	
		Traditional	**Block**
13-1 Exploring Periodic Data	Enrichment and Additional Topics	1 day	1 day
13-2 Angles and the Unit Circle	Enrichment and Additional Topics	2 days	1 day
13-3 Radian Measure	Enrichment and Additional Topics	1 day	1 day
13-4 The Sine Function	Enrichment and Additional Topics	2 days	1 day
13-5 The Cosine Function	Enrichment and Additional Topics	2 days	1 day
13-6 The Tangent Function	Enrichment and Additional Topics	1 day	1 day
13-7 Translating Sine and Cosine Functions	Enrichment and Additional Topics	2 days	1 day
13-8 Reciprocal Trigonometric Functions	Enrichment and Additional Topics	1 day	1 day
Testing and Additional Activities	Enrichment and Additional Topics	3 days	2 days

Chapter 14 Trigonometric Identities and Equations	North Carolina Course of Study	Pacing	
		Traditional	**Block**
14-1 Trigonometry Identities	Enrichment and Additional Topics	2 days	1 day
14-2 Solving Trigonometric Equations Using Inverses	Enrichment and Additional Topics	2 days	1 day
14-3 Right Triangles and Trigonometric Ratios	Enrichment and Additional Topics	2 days	1 day
14-4 Area and the Law of Sines	Enrichment and Additional Topics	2 days	1 day
14-5 The Law of Cosines	Enrichment and Additional Topics	2 days	1 day
14-6 Angle Identities	Enrichment and Additional Topics	2 days	1 day
14-7 Double-Angle and Half-Angle Identities	Enrichment and Additional Topics	2 days	1 day
Testing and Additional Activities	Enrichment and Additional Topics	3 days	2 days

North Carolina Course of Study

Use these pages to acquaint yourself with the North Carolina Mathematics Standard Course of Study at this grade level with respect to where previous standards have brought the student and where this year's standards will lead their studies going forward.

Number & Operations

Progression

Prior Years	This Year	Going Forward
Students used the laws of exponents to simplify expressions with integer exponents. They are familiar with finding bases and exponents.	They will apply the laws of exponents to rational exponents. They will expand their understanding of exponents to include logarithms, using both 10 and e as bases.	Students will encounter logarithms in many applications in science and calculus. They will use logarithms to solve complex exponential equations and to describe curves and unbounded functions.

1.01 Simplify and perform operations with rational exponents and logarithms (common and natural) to solve problems.

Math Background

Students may have difficulty understanding not only exponents but also the relationship of exponents and logarithms. Essentially they are inverse functions. If $y=b^x$, then $y=\log_b x$.

Working with the basic tools and names of these functions may help. For example, given the function $y=x^2-4$, students need to remember the base is x, the exponent is 2, and the roots are 2 and -2. In addition, graphing exponential and logarithmic functions can help strengthen student understanding.

As students become more comfortable manipulating either purely exponential functions or purely logarithmic functions, then they can move between the two forms.

 What is the logarithmic form of the exponential equation $2^4 = 16$?

A $\log_4 16=2$ B $\log_4 2=16$

C $\log_2 16=4$ D $\log_{16} 2=4$

Answer: C

 Which of the following is equivalent to $\sqrt[3]{125}$?

A 125^3 B $125^{\frac{1}{2}}$

C $125^{\frac{1}{3}}$ D $25^{\frac{1}{5}}$

Answer: C

 Simplify $6^{\frac{1}{5}} \cdot 6^{\frac{3}{10}}$

A $6^{\frac{1}{2}}$ B $6^{-\frac{1}{10}}$

C $6^{\frac{3}{50}}$ D $6^{\frac{2}{3}}$

Answer: A

Progression

Prior Years	This Year	Going Forward
Students focused on understanding real, rational, and irrational numbers. They found square roots of positive integers.	They will expand their understanding to include complex numbers. They will use the imaginary number i to solve simple equations and explore its relationship to roots and real numbers.	Students will continue to use complex numbers in equations and problem-solving. In advanced courses, they will explore how complex numbers can be used to generate common number systems and solution sets.

1.02 Define and compute with complex numbers.

Math Background

Why do we have complex numbers? Isn't math complex enough? Well, complex or not, we need complex numbers.

Students may be interested to learn that although imaginary numbers were invented, so were negative and irrational numbers. These are numbers that students may now accept as being *real,* as students have worked with them quite often.

Students may have difficulty understanding complex numbers because, unlike real numbers, you can't graph them on a number line. So what value do they have? That may be difficult to explain but to solve equations such as $x^2 = -5$, we do need imaginary and, thus, complex numbers.

Find $(6i)(-2i)$.

First, multiply the real numbers. Then, substitute -1 for i^2.

The correct answer is 12.

Write the complex number $\sqrt{-25} + 5$ in the form $a + bi$.

Simplify the radical expression using i: $5i + 5$. Then, write the expression in the form $a + bi$.

The correct answer is $5 + 5i$.

Solve $x^2 + 36 = 0$.

First, isolate x^2. Then find the square root of each side. $x = \pm\sqrt{-36}$.

Simplify using i.

The correct answer is $\pm 6i$.

Progression

Prior Years	This Year	Going Forward
Students learned to simplify polynomials and explored multiplication and division of monomials. They are familiar with the methods of factoring polynomials and using factoring to solve equations.	Using similar methods, students will learn to simplify polynomial, rational, and complex fractions. They will use algebraic expressions to write and solve equations, such as the evaluation of permutations and combinations.	Students will relate operations to properties of graphs. They will explore how certain operations, such as factoring and simplifying, affect graphs by eliminating holes and asymptotes.

1.03 Operate with algebraic expressions (polynomial, rational, complex fractions) to solve problems.

Math Background

Although students should be familiar with algebraic expressions and how to work with them, a refresher, especially on order of operations, is a good way to start the year.

Polynomials are the basic building blocks of algebraic expressions. In working with polynomials, students will need to master (if they have not already) certain skills that are necessary to their work throughout the year. These skills involve combining, simplifying, and factoring polynomials.

Students may be concerned about working with rational expressions (fractions with a variable in the denominator). However, they should consider working with rational expressions as not that much different from working with fractions.

The same is true with a complex fraction—a fraction that has a fraction in its numerator or denominator or in both its numerator and denominator. Students can apply what they know from working with fractions, such as finding the LCD, to working with complex fractions.

Four students compete in a math drill. First, second, and third place ribbons will be awarded to the three most accurate students. How many arrangements of first, second, and third places are possible?

Use the permutation formula:

$$_nP_r = \frac{n!}{(n-r)!}$$

where $n = 4$ and $r = 3$.

Plug in the numbers and compute.

The correct answer is 24.

Which expression can be simplified to $\frac{x-5}{x-2}$?

A $\dfrac{x^2 - 25}{x^2 + 3x - 10}$

B $\dfrac{x^2 - 3x + 25}{x^2 + 3x - 10}$

C $\dfrac{x^2 - 5x + 25}{x^2 - 3x + 10}$

D $\dfrac{x^2 + 25}{x^2 + 3x - 10}$

Answer: A

Progression

Prior Years	This Year	Going Forward
Students focused on using matrices to display and interpret bodies of data. They are familiar with basic operations on matrices.	Students will continue to explore matrix operations. They will use matrices to solve systems of equations and model transformations.	Matrices will be used to model and simplify large, complex bodies of data. Students will learn methods of breaking large matrices into smaller matrices to make them easier to use.

1.04 Operate with matrices to model and solve problems.

Math Background

Students may have difficulty understanding why data is organized into matrices. Organizing data into a matrix facilitates performing operations (addition, subtraction, and so on) on sets of data.

Adding and subtracting matrices should seem natural for most students. Students will need to be reminded to add or subtract corresponding elements and to be sure that the dimensions of the sum or difference match the dimensions of the matrices that are added or subtracted.

Multiplication involving matrices will seem less natural to the students, though the basic principles of multiplication are at work. Students will need to understand the difference between scalar multiplication (multiplying each element by the scalar) and matrix multiplication (multiplying the elements of each row of the first matrix by the elements of each column of the second matrix).

What is the sum of $X + Y$?

$$X = \begin{bmatrix} 2 & 4 & 6 \\ 1 & 10 & -1 \end{bmatrix}$$

$$Y = \begin{bmatrix} -5 & 3 & 1 \\ 3 & -4 & -1 \end{bmatrix}$$

A $\begin{bmatrix} -3 & 7 & 7 \\ 4 & 6 & -2 \end{bmatrix}$

B $\begin{bmatrix} 8 & 2 & 6 \\ -3 & 13 & -1 \end{bmatrix}$

C $\begin{bmatrix} 7 & 7 & 7 \\ 2 & 12 & 2 \end{bmatrix}$

D $\begin{bmatrix} 3 & -5 & 3 \\ -1 & 7 & 7 \end{bmatrix}$

Answer: A

Find the product.

$$5 \begin{bmatrix} 2 & \frac{1}{2} \\ 1.1 & 4 \end{bmatrix}$$

The correct answer is

$$\begin{bmatrix} 10 & \frac{5}{2} \\ 5.5 & 20 \end{bmatrix}$$

Progression

Prior Years	This Year	Going Forward
Students focused on modeling and solving problems using direct variation. They are comfortable with graphing and interpreting linear equations.	Students will learn to identify different kinds of variation (direct, inverse, combined, and joint variation) and represent it in algebraic expressions. They will explore graphs of types of variation.	Different types of variation are used to make predictions about data, to describe trends, and to generate statistics. In calculus, students will explore how types of variation affect derivatives.

1.05 Model and solve problems using direct, inverse, combined and joint variation.

Math Background

Students are probably most familiar with direct variation. Students should know that a direct variation is a linear function defined by an equation in the form of $y = kx$. In other words, students should see that as x increases y increases, and vice versa. A number of common real-life examples will help students remember direct variation (such as wages earned).

An inverse variation is the opposite of a direct variation. In an inverse variation as x increases y decreases and as x decreases y increases. Therefore, an inverse variation has the form $y = \frac{k}{x}$. The graph of an inverse variation is a hyperbola.

A combined variation combines direct and inverse variations in more complicated relationships. A common example of a combined variation is Newton's Law of Universal Gravitation. According to this law, the gravitational force between two objects varies jointly with the masses of the two objects and varies inversely with the square of the distance between the two.

Which equation represents a direct variation between x and y?

A $\quad y = \frac{300a}{x}$ B $\quad xy = 20n$

C $\quad x = \frac{y}{n}$ D $\quad x = -\frac{12w}{y}$

Answer: C

Write a function to model the variation shown in the data table. Then graph the function.

x	0.1	0.3	0.6
y	12	4	2

The function is $y = \frac{1.2}{x}$.

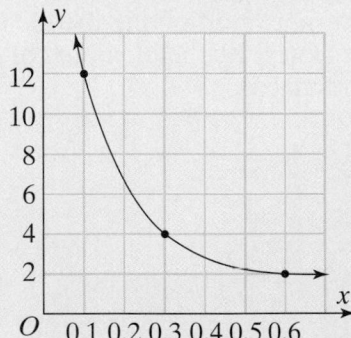

Progression

Prior Years
Students focused on using linear equations or inequalities to model and solve problems. They have used inverse operations and explored inverses of simple linear equations.

This Year
They expand their understanding of inverse operations to finding inverses of relations and functions. They will learn to use the composition of functions and explore the relation between the two operations.

Going Forward
Students will use composition and inverses to simplify and graph functions. They will learn special properties of functions and their inverses. They will learn how operations on a function and its inverse are related.

2.01 Use the composition and inverse of functions to model and solve problems; justify results.

Math Background

Students should think of the composition of functions in terms of input and output. In this case, the output from one function becomes the input for the second function.

Students may find it easier to think of the inverse of a function in terms of a real-life example. You can start by explaining to students the function that describes the distance it takes for a car traveling at a certain speed to skid to a stop, $d = \frac{r^2}{24}$. Then, tell them that the inverse of that function allows police to determine how fast a car was going based on the length of its skid marks.

Find f^{-1} for the following relation.

$f(x) = \pm\sqrt{x + 1}$. Then graph the relation and its inverse on the same coordinate plane.

Rewrite the equation using y:

$y = \pm\sqrt{x + 1}$

Then, interchange x and y:

$x = \pm\sqrt{y + 1}$

Solve for y:

$x^2 = y + 1$

$y = x^2 - 1$

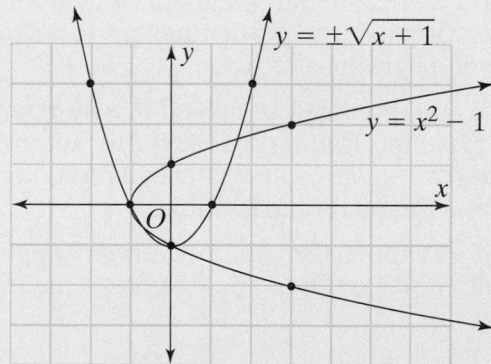

The correct answer is $y = x^2 - 1$.

Progression

Prior Years	This Year	Going Forward
Students focused on graphing, factoring, and evaluating quadratic functions. They are comfortable using linear equations and inequalities to solve problems.	They will use similar methods to solve quadratic equations and inequalities, and they will explore how the constants of equations affect graphs and solutions. They will relate quadratic inequalities to equations and determine when to apply each.	Students will use quadratic equations to describe real world situations, such as problems involving acceleration, and to simplify higher order equations.

2.02 Use quadratic functions and inequalities to model and solve problems; justify results.
  a) Solve using tables, graphs, and algebraic properties.
  b) Interpret the constants and coefficients in the context of the problem.

Math Background

In Algebra 1, students were introduced to the concept of quadratic functions. A quadratic function is a function that can be written in the form $y = f(x) = ax^2 + bx + c$.

The graph of a quadratic function is U-shaped, called a parabola. In Algebra 1, students learned to interpret a graph and use the slope-intercept form to write an equation of a line. Similarly, students will learn to use the vertex form of a quadratic function to write the equation of a parabola.

Quadratic equations can be solved in a number of ways: by graphing, finding square roots, factoring, and completing the square. Quadratic equations can also be solved using the quadratic formula.

Quadratic equations have many everyday applications. One of the more common applications is the flight of a ball.

Sky divers are in free fall from the time they leave the plane until their parachutes open. A diver's height in y feet and t seconds can be modeled with this quadratic function: $y = -16t^2 + 1{,}200$ for a jump from 1,200 feet. How long is the diver in free fall if the parachute opens at 800 feet?

First, plug in 800 for y:
$800 = -16t^2 + 1{,}200$.

Then, solve for t:

$$-400 = -16t^2$$
$$25 = t^2$$
$$5 = t$$

The correct answer is 5 seconds.

What are the solutions of the equation $8x^2 - 200 = 0$?

  A ± 4
  B ± 5
  C ± 8
  D ± 25

Answer: B

Progression

Prior Years

Students learned to evaluate exponents and explored graphs of exponential functions. They are familiar with polynomial equations. Students focused on using linear equations to solve problems. They made linear models of real-world situations given data and evaluated models for accuracy.

This Year

Students will learn to write equations with variable exponents and explore graphs, transformations, and solutions of such equations. They will expand their problem solving skills to include creating models based on linear, exponential, and quadratic functions.

Going Forward

Students will use exponential equations in many real world situations. In calculus, they will continue to explore how operations on an exponential equation affect its graph and solutions. Students will use complicated linear, exponential, and quadratic functions to describe data.

2.03 Use exponential functions to model and solve problems; justify results.
  a) Solve using tables, graphs, and algebraic properties.
  b) Interpret the constants, coefficients, and bases in the context of the problem.
2.04 Create and use best-fit mathematical models of linear, exponential, and quadratic functions to solve problems involving sets of data.
  a) Interpret the constants, coefficients, and bases in the context of the data.
  b) Check the model for goodness-of-fit and use the model, where appropriate, to draw conclusions or make predictions.

Math Background

Remind students that in an exponential function the base is constant and the exponent varies, as in $y = 4^x$. Therefore, an exponential function has the form $y = b^x$, as long as $b > 0$ and $b \neq 1$.

Having students graph various exponential functions with different values for x will help them to see that the graph gets increasingly steeper as x increases.

Help students understand that even though many real-world situations can be modeled by a linear, exponential, or quadratic function, it is unlikely that real world data will fall exactly on a graph of one of these functions. When real-life data are plotted, an approximate line or curve can be drawn or obtained from a graphing calculator.

How is the graph $y = 2^x$ translated from the graph $y = 2^x + 2$? Draw the graph and its translation on the same coordinate plane.

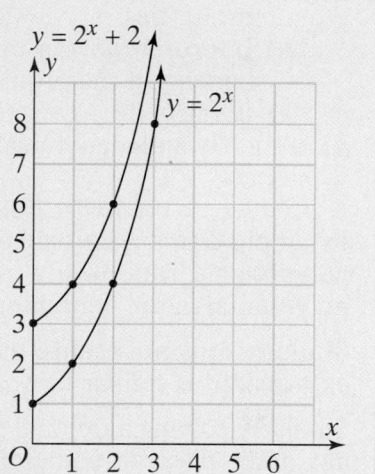

A 2 units right
B 2 units left
C 2 units down
D 2 units up

Answer: C

A car enters a highway 25 miles south of a city. The car travels south at an average speed of 55 miles per hour. Write an equation to model the car's distance from the city after traveling for h hours.

Let d = the car's distance from the city and h = the number of hours spent driving.

The correct answer is $d = 55h + 25$.

Progression

Prior Years
Students focused on using linear equations to solve problems. They are familiar with using graphs and tables of data to predict solutions of linear equations.

This Year
They will use and solve rational equations to model and solve problems. They will learn to identify asymptotes and holes in a graph, and they will use equations with discontinuities to make predictions about data.

Going Forward
Students will use asymptotes and discontinuities to set boundaries in equations and learn to interpret discontinuities in real-world situations. They will learn to write systems of equations to remove discontinuities from a model.

2.05 Use rational equations to model and solve problems; justify results.
  a) Solve using tables, graphs, and algebraic properties.
  b) Interpret the constants and coefficients in the context of the problem.
  c) Identify the asymptotes and intercepts graphically and algebraically.

Math Background

In simple terms, a rational equation is the ratio of two polynomials. Therefore, a rational equation will have a polynomial in the denominator.

Students may not realize that working with rational expressions is similar to working with fractions.

Similarly, solving a rational equation is much like solving any other algebraic equation. Just as in solving algebraic equations, the goal in solving a rational equation is to isolate the variable on one side of the equation.

What are the vertical asymptotes for the graph of the following rational function?

$$y = \frac{x - 1}{(x + 2)(x + 3)}$$

A $x = 2, x = 3$ B $x = 1, x = 2, x = 3$
C $x = -2, x = -3$ D $x = -1, x = 2, x = 3$

Answer: C

What is the horizontal asymptote for the graph of the following rational function? Draw the graph of the function.

$$y = \frac{1}{x}$$

A $y = 0$ B $y = 1$
C $y = 2$ D $y = -1$

Answer: A

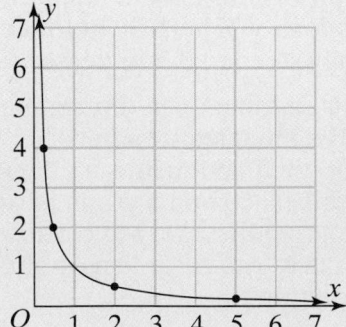

Progression

Prior Years	This Year	Going Forward
Students used linear and quadratic equations to solve problems. They have encountered graphs of cubic equations. Students focused on learning the laws of exponents and simplifying equations with integer exponents.	They will expand their understanding of equations to include cubic equations. They will draw and interpret graphs of cubic equations and relate them to linear and quadratic equations. They will learn to solve equations with radical expressions and rational exponents. They will explore properties of equations with radicals and exponents.	Students will interpret graphs of cubic equations and use them to solve equations of higher order. They will explore methods of manipulating cubic equations to have specific characteristics. Students will interpret the effect of radical expressions on graphs of equations and models of real world situations.

2.06 Use cubic equations to model and solve problems.
  a) Solve using tables and graphs.
  b) Interpret constants and coefficients in the context of the problem.
2.07 Use equations with radical expressions to model and solve problems; justify results.
  a) Solve using tables, graphs, and algebraic properties.
  b) Interpret the degree, constants, and coefficients in the context of the problem.

Math Background

Students have learned that functions in which the highest power is one are linear functions, and those with 2 as the highest power are quadratic functions. Now they will construct and explore functions in which the highest power is three. These functions are known as cubic functions. Cubic functions are written in the form $y = ax^3 + bx^2 + cx + d$.

Graphs of cubic functions have a point of symmetry. The left side of the graph is a rotation of the right side.

A radical expression contains a radical, such as $\sqrt{3}$, $\sqrt{5x}$, and $\sqrt{x + 2}$. An equation that has a variable in a radicand or has a variable with a rational exponent is a radical equation.

Solving a radical equation involves isolating a radical on one side of the equation. Then, after isolating the radical raise both sides of the equation to the same power.

What kind of a model best fits the data?

x	y
0	10.1
5	2.8
10	8.1
15	16.0
20	17.8
25	3.6

A exponential
B linear
C quadratic
D cubic

Answer: D

Solve $2(x - 1)^{\frac{1}{3}} = 2$.

First, divide both sides by 2. Then raise both sides to the 3rd power and simplify.

The correct answer is 2.

Progression

Prior Years	This Year	Going Forward
Students are familiar with algebraic expressions. They have explored absolute value and can evaluate numerical expressions with absolute value.	They will learn to solve equations and inequalities involving absolute value. They will explore characteristics of graphs modeling absolute value equations, and they will begin to explore the meaning of absolute value in real-world situations.	Students will use absolute values to set boundaries for graphs. They will learn to write multiple equations with boundaries in place of absolute value equations to simplify certain calculations.

2.08 Use equations and inequalities with absolute value to model and solve problems; justify results.
  a) Solve using tables, graphs, and algebraic properties.
  b) Interpret the constants and coefficients in the context of the problem.

Math Background

Students will recall that the absolute value of a number is its distance from zero on a number line. Absolute value equations (or inequalities) have variable expressions within the absolute value symbol.

As your students explore absolute value equations (or inequalities), emphasize that the absolute value term must be alone on one side of the equals sign

The graph of an absolute value equation is V-shaped and can point upward or downward.

When solving an absolute value inequality, it may be helpful to sketch an intermediate graph.

Solve $|2x - 1| - 1 = 9$.

First, add 1 to each side. Then, rewrite as two equations and solve both equations.

The correct answer is $x = \frac{11}{2}$ or $-\frac{9}{2}$.

Which graph represents the equation $y \leq |x - 4| + 5$?

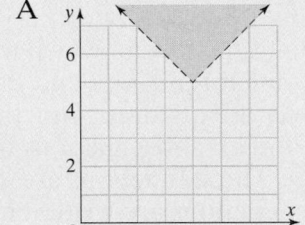

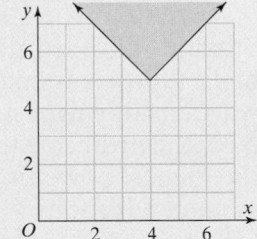
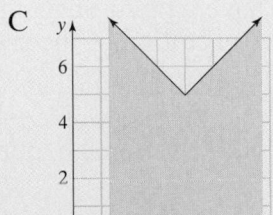
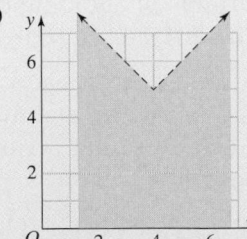

Answer: C.

Progression

Prior Years
Students focused on solving problems using linear, quadratic, and exponential equations and inequalities. They are familiar with geometric properties and descriptions of circles. Students focused on understanding and solving systems of two equations using graphs, substitution, and elimination.

This Year
They will identify key properties of parabolas and circles, and use these characteristics to write equations. They will draw conclusions about graphs from equations, such as radius and center of a circle, and focus of a parabola. Students will use two or more equations in two or more variables to model problems. They will learn new methods of solving systems, such as the use of matrices.

Going Forward
Students will use special properties of circles to solve trigonometric ratios. They will use parabolas to locate maximum and minimum values in problems. In calculus, they will learn methods for evaluating the curve of a parabola. Students will use systems of equations to solve problems with many constraints.

2.09 Use the equations of parabolas and circles to model and solve problems; justify results.
  a) Solve using tables, graphs, and algebraic properties.
  b) Interpret the constants and coefficients in the context of the problem.
2.10 Use systems of two or more equations or inequalities to model and solve problems; justify results. Solve using tables, graphs, matrix operations, and algebraic properties.

Math Background
From their work with quadratic functions, students will recognize that the graph of a quadratic function is a U-shaped curve called a parabola.

Students will need to learn the various properties and parts of a parabola. Parabolas can be folded so that the two sides match exactly—the line that divides the parabola in half is the axis of symmetry. The highest or lowest point of a parabola is called the vertex.

The solution of a system of equations is the point that is common to the equations of both graphs. In other words, the solution is the point where the lines intersect.

Systems of equations can also be solved algebraically, either by using substitution (replacing one variable with an equivalent expression containing the other variable) or by elimination (adding or subtracting equations to eliminate a variable).

Write an equation for a circle with radius 2 and center (0,1).

Use the standard form of the equation of a circle. Use 0 for h, 1 for k, and 2 for r.

The correct answer is

$x^2 + (y - 1)^2 = 4$.

Use a graph to estimate the solution, then solve the system.

$$2x + 6y = 16 \qquad 5x - 3y = 10$$

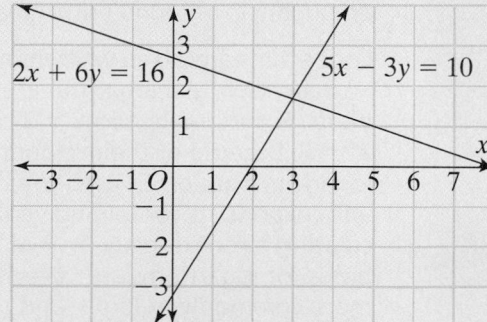

The two graphs intersect at about $(3, 1\frac{1}{2})$.
Use elimination to solve the system.

The correct answer is $x = 3$, $y = \frac{5}{3}$.

North Carolina Course of Study

Here is a complete list of the objectives of the North Carolina Standard Mathematics Course of Study for Algebra 2. These are provided so that you will know what you are expected to learn this year.

Following each objective is an example of how you might see that objective tested. These test questions will become more meaningful to you as the year unfolds. You might want to check back to this section of the book from time to time to check that you understand how to answer the questions.

NUMBER & OPERATION

1.01 Simplify and perform operations with rational exponents and logarithms (common and natural) to solve problems.

What It Means to You

Radical signs, rational exponents and logarithms are ways of writing expressions that include numbers or variables raised to another power. A rational exponent looks like a fraction or a decimal. You may have seen them in science formulas, such as the formulas used to calculate the age of an artifact using carbon dating. The National Weather Service uses rational exponents to calculate wind chill in the formula $35.74 + 0.6215T - 35.75V^{0.16} + 0.4275TV^{0.16} = I$, where T is the temperature, V is the wind velocity, and I is the wind chill index. You will learn that the rules that you used to simplify expressions with integer exponents can also be used with rational exponents.

You may have seen *log* or *ln* in formulas used in discussions of the Richter scale (used to measure earthquakes) and the pH scale (used to measure acidity). The formula $L = 10\log\frac{I}{I_0}$ is used to measure the apparent loudness of sound using measures of intensity.

Logarithms are often written in the form $\log_b x = y$. You can rewrite a logarithmic expression using exponents. For example, $\log_2 8 = 3$ can also be written as $2^3 = 8$. Because of their relationship to exponents, logarithms are often used to simplify expressions with exponents containing variables, rather than calculating a root directly. Two of the most common bases for logarithms are 10—written as $\log_{10} x$ or more commonly as $\log x$—and the irrational number e—written as $\log_e x$ or more commonly as $\ln x$. You will learn how to simplify, add, subtract, multiply, and divide expressions with rational exponents and logarithms this year.

Where You'll Learn This

You will study this in Chapters 7 and 8.

What is the logarithmic form of the exponential equation $3^4 = 81$?

    A $\log_4 81 = 3$

    B $\log_4 3 = 81$

    C $\log_3 81 = 4$

    D $\log_{81} 3 = 4$

Answer: C

Evaluate $\log_5 125$.

    A $\frac{1}{3}$

    B   3

    C   5

    D   25

Answer: B

NUMBER & OPERATION

1.02 Define and compute with complex numbers.

What It Means to You

As you have seen, there are many different types of numbers in mathematics. So far, you have studied types of numbers found in the real numbers, which include integers, rational numbers, and irrational numbers.

You may wonder if there is another type of number not included in the real numbers. Where on a number line do you find $\sqrt{-2}$? Working only in real numbers, you may think $\sqrt{-2}$ does not exist. It is, however, part of another set of numbers called *imaginary numbers*. The imaginary numbers use the symbol i to mean $\sqrt{-1}$, and in the imaginary number system $\sqrt{-2} = 2i$. Real numbers and imaginary numbers together make up a new set of numbers called *complex numbers*. You will learn how to graph complex numbers and use them in calculations.

Where You'll Learn This

You will study this in Chapters 1, 5, and 6.

Find $(2i)(-3i)$. Show your work.

First, multiply the real numbers:
$(2i)(-3i) = -6i^2$

Then, substitute -1 for i^2:
$(2i)(-3i) = -6(-1)$
$(2i)(-3i) = 6$

The correct answer is 6.

1.03 Operate with algebraic expressions (polynomial, rational, complex fractions) to solve problems.

What It Means to You

Sentences often contain a phrase or two. For example, in the sentence "Joe is the student with the highest grade.", "with the highest grade" is a phrase. A phrase in algebra is an algebraic expression. It includes numbers, variables (usually letters), and operation symbols, for example, $4n$, $5x^3$, and $2x^2 + y$. Some may even involve fractions or have more than one variable. One algebraic expression you may be familiar with is the formula for counting permutations, $_nP_r = \frac{n!}{(n-r)!}$. You can also combine expressions and evaluate an expression if you know the value of the variable or variables. You will learn how to add, subtract, multiply, and divide the parts of algebraic expressions in order to solve problems.

Where You'll Learn This

You will study this in Chapters 1, 5, 6, and 9.

Seven students compete in a track meet. First, second, and third place ribbons will be awarded to the three fastest runners. How many arrangements of first, second, and third places are possible? Explain your answer.

One way to approach this problem is to use the permutation formula:
$_nP_r = \frac{n!}{(n-r)!}$

There are seven runners arranged three at a time, so $n = 7$ and $r = 3$.

Plug in the numbers and compute:
$_7P_3 = \frac{7!}{(7-3)!}$
$= \frac{7!}{(4)!} = \frac{5,040}{24} = 210$

The correct answer is 210.

NUMBER & OPERATION

1.04 Operate with matrices to model and solve problems.

What It Means to You

When you use a data table, you organize your data into columns and rows. Like data tables, you can use a matrix to organize data and solve algebra problems.

For example, the number of books sold at two bookstores can be represented as:

	Store 1	Store 2
May	412	902
June	518	321
July	612	602
August	781	819

You can also perform operations with matrices similar to the operations you perform on numbers. For example, suppose you find out that Store 1 and Store 2 each have stores in another town. You can represent the books sold at Store 1b and Store 2b in a matrix. By adding the matrices together, you can find the total number of books sold in both locations for each store.

Store 1	Store 2		Store 1b	Store 2b		Store 1 and 1b	Store 2 and 2b
412	902	+	504	615	=	916	1,517
518	321		320	475		838	796
612	602		600	620		1,212	1,222
781	819		756	750		1,537	1,569

You will learn how to use matrices to represent real-world situations and solve problems. You will also be learning how to use operations, such as addition and multiplication, to develop new matrices and solve problems.

Where You'll Learn This

You will study this in Chapter 4.

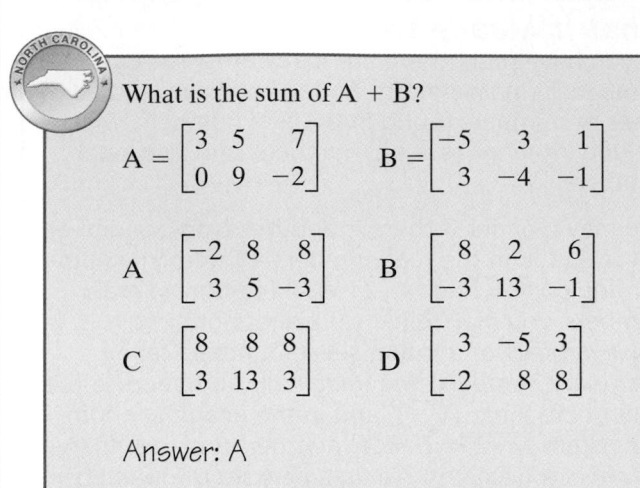

What is the sum of A + B?

$$A = \begin{bmatrix} 3 & 5 & 7 \\ 0 & 9 & -2 \end{bmatrix} \quad B = \begin{bmatrix} -5 & 3 & 1 \\ 3 & -4 & -1 \end{bmatrix}$$

$$A \begin{bmatrix} -2 & 8 & 8 \\ 3 & 5 & -3 \end{bmatrix} \quad B \begin{bmatrix} 8 & 2 & 6 \\ -3 & 13 & -1 \end{bmatrix}$$

$$C \begin{bmatrix} 8 & 8 & 8 \\ 3 & 13 & 3 \end{bmatrix} \quad D \begin{bmatrix} 3 & -5 & 3 \\ -2 & 8 & 8 \end{bmatrix}$$

Answer: A

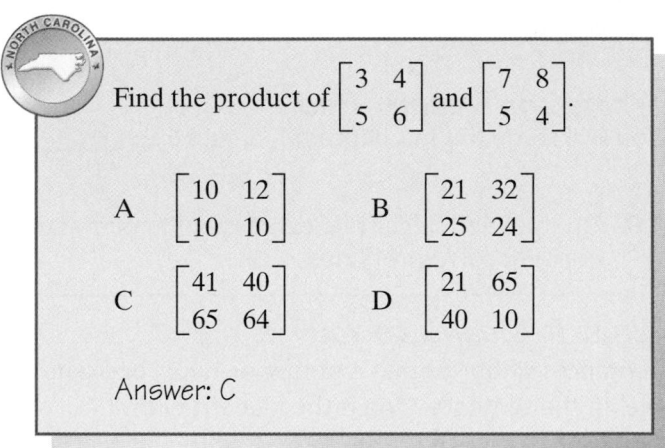

Find the product of $\begin{bmatrix} 3 & 4 \\ 5 & 6 \end{bmatrix}$ and $\begin{bmatrix} 7 & 8 \\ 5 & 4 \end{bmatrix}$.

$$A \begin{bmatrix} 10 & 12 \\ 10 & 10 \end{bmatrix} \quad B \begin{bmatrix} 21 & 32 \\ 25 & 24 \end{bmatrix}$$

$$C \begin{bmatrix} 41 & 40 \\ 65 & 64 \end{bmatrix} \quad D \begin{bmatrix} 21 & 65 \\ 40 & 10 \end{bmatrix}$$

Answer: C

NUMBER & OPERATION

1.05 Model and solve problems using direct, inverse, combined and joint variation.

What It Means to You

You will be learning different ways that variables in algebraic expressions relate to one another. For example, you have worked with direct variation. This is a relationship between two variables in which changing one variable changes the other one at the same rate. In many situations, however, variables in a problem will change at different rates. For example, suppose you have $40 to buy some CDs. One store sells CDs for $12 each. A second store sells CDs for $14 each. You could buy three $12 CDs or two $14 CDs. As the cost of the CDs increases, the number you can buy decreases. This relationship is an example of *inverse variation*. The two variables—the cost of CDs and the number you can buy—do not change at the same rate.

Other types of variation combine direct variation and inverse variation to make more complicated relationships. In some cases with multiple variables, a variable will vary directly with one variable and inversely with another. If you decide to spend your $40 on CDs and books, you will want to consider the relationship between the cost of books and the new variable, the number of books you can buy for a certain price. You will apply what you've learned about direct variation to inverse, combined, and joint variations to model and solve real-world problems. This will involve identifying when variables vary directly and when they vary inversely and representing each in algebraic expressions.

Where You'll Learn This

You will study this in Chapter 9.

Which equation does not represent inverse variation between x and y?

A $\quad y = -\dfrac{2b}{x}$

B $\quad xy = 3n$

C $\quad x = \dfrac{y}{n}$

D $\quad x = -\dfrac{19t}{y}$

Answer: C

How does y vary in relation to z and x in the equation below?

$$y = \frac{kxz}{w}$$

A directly
B inversely
C indirectly
D There is no relationship.

Answer: A

North Carolina Fact

On December 17, 1903, former bicycle mechanics Wilbur and Orville Wright made the first sustained airplane flight when Wilbur kept their fragile plane in the air for 12 seconds.

ALGEBRA

2.01 Use the composition and inverse of functions to model and solve problems; justify results.

What It Means to You

In miniature golf, you often have a two-tiered hole. When you play this hole, your ball goes down one of many chutes and ends up below for you to continue play. Where you continue play depends on where the ball comes out. In a similar fashion, you will encounter situations in which you can combine two functions. In this case, the output of the first function becomes the input for the second function to form a *composite* function. What you put in the first function (which chute your ball goes through) determines what will go in the second function (where you continue to play).

When solving equations, you have explored operations that undo other operations. For example, you can use division to undo multiplication. These are called *inverse operations*. Similarly, you may want to undo an entire function. When you interchange the *x* and *y* values in a function, you get its *inverse*. For a function $f(x)$, you write that its inverse is $f^{-1}(x)$. If you combine a function and its inverse, you will see that they undo each other. For example, if $f(x) = x + 4$, then $f^{-1}(x) = x - 4$. You can use composition to see that these two functions undo each other. You can use the composition and inverse of functions to model and solve problems. These are the types of things you will be learning to do this year.

Where You'll Learn This

You will study this in Chapter 7.

North Carolina Fact

Did you know that the first recorded discovery of gold in the U.S. took place in Carrabus County, North Carolina? John Reed found this treasure in Little Meadow Creek in 1799.

Find f^{-1} for the following function.
$$f(x) = \sqrt{x} - 1$$

Show your work.

Rewrite the equation using *y*:
$$y = \sqrt{x} - 1$$

Then, interchange *x* and *y*:
$$x = \sqrt{y} - 1$$

Square both sides:
$$x^2 = y - 1$$

Solve for *y*:
$$y = x^2 + 1$$

The correct answer is $y = x^2 + 1$.

Find $(f \circ g)(x)$ where:

$$f(x) = \tfrac{1}{x} \qquad g(x) = x^2$$

A $\sqrt{x}$ B $\dfrac{1}{x^2}$

C $\tfrac{1}{2}x$ D $-2x$

Answer: B

ALGEBRA

2.02 Use quadratic functions and inequalities to model and solve problems; justify results.
   a) Solve using tables, graphs, and algebraic properties.
   b) Interpret the constants and coefficients in the context of the problem.

What It Means to You

You're on a trip and you are traveling at an average speed of 60 mi/h. You can write a function $f(x) = 60t$ to determine how far you'll travel in a given amount of time. If you were to graph this function you would get a straight line. Therefore, $f(x) = 60t$ is a linear function. But what about functions whose graph is not a line?

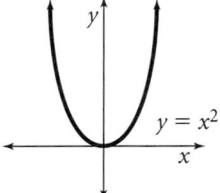

$y = x^2$

Quadratic equations contain a squared variable (x^2) and their graphs are U-shaped. The function used to model the distance an object falls is $d = -16t^2 + h$, where d is the distance the object falls, t is the time it falls, and h is the height from which it is dropped. Many area formulas, such as the area of a circle ($A = \pi r^2$) or a square ($A = s^2$) are quadratic equations.

As with linear functions, each constant and coefficient in a quadratic function has meaning. The number -16 tells you that the U-shape will open downward. The constant, h, is the y-intercept of the graph.

You will learn how to graph these curves and work with their equations in order to solve problems, such as the time it takes a ball to hit the ground when dropped from a specific height. You will also be learning how to use quadratic functions and inequalities to model and solve real-world problems.

Where You'll Learn This

You will study this in Chapter 5.

Sky divers are in free fall from the time they leave the plane until their parachute opens. A diver's height in y feet and t seconds can be modeled with this quadratic function: $y = -16t^2 + 1500$ for a jump from 1,500 feet. How long is the diver in free fall if the parachute opens at 1,000 feet? Show your work.

First, plug in 1,000 for y:
$1,000 = -16t^2 + 1500$

Solve for t:
$-500 = -16t^2$
$31.25 = t^2$
$5.59 = t$

The correct answer is 5.59 seconds.

Graph the equation $y = 2x^2 + 3$.

Answer:

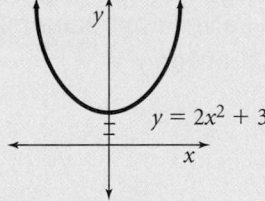

$y = 2x^2 + 3$

Student's Guide

ALGEBRA

2.03 Use exponential functions to model and solve problems; justify results.
    a) Solve using tables, graphs, and algebraic properties.
    b) Interpret the constants, coefficients, and bases in the context of the
       problem.

What It Means to You

In the expression 4^2, the 2 is known as an exponent. You are familiar with evaluating exponents and solving equations with exponents. In some equations, however, the exponent is a variable. For example, a population of bacteria doubles every hour. If you start with a single cell, you can write a function for the population, $y = 2^x$, where x is the number of hours. If you plot the population's growth over time the result is a J-shaped curve.

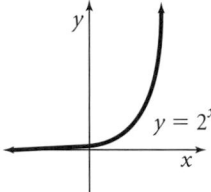

Functions that contain a number raised to another power (a^x) are called exponential functions. Their graphs are steep curves, looking almost like a "j". These functions are used to model rapid growth, such as that of a bacterial population.

As with other functions, the constants and coefficients can help you draw the graph of the function. If the base is greater than 1—as in the model of bacteria population, where the base is 2—the function models growth. If the base is between 0 and 1, the function models decay. For example, a quantity that is halved every hour might be represented with the function $y = \left(\frac{1}{2}\right)^x$.

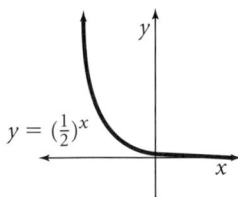

You will learn how to use exponential functions to model data. You will also learn to graph exponential functions and solve exponential equations in order to solve problems.

Where You'll Learn This
You will study this in Chapter 8.

Which function represents exponential growth?

  A $y = -\left(\frac{1}{25^x}\right)$

  B $y = 25^x$

  C $y = -(25^x)$

  D $y = \left(\frac{1}{25}\right)^x$

Answer: B

Graph $y = 2^x + 4$

Answer:

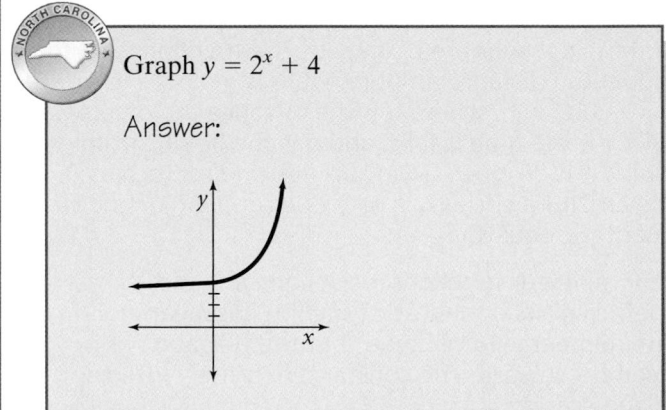

ALGEBRA

2.04 Create and use best-fit mathematical models of linear, exponential, and quadratic functions to solve problems involving sets of data.
    a) Interpret the constants, coefficients, and bases in the context of the data.
    b) Check the model for goodness-of-fit and use the model, where appropriate, to draw conclusions or make predictions.

What It Means to You

Sometimes when you plot data on a graph you can't easily "connect the dots." For example, if you conduct a survey, you may create a scatterplot to display your data. Frequently, the data will not form a straight line. Sometimes, you can identify a trend in data. For example, if you compare time spent studying to grades on an exam, you will see that grades increase as time spent studying increases. You can use the trend to draw a *line of best fit* and use it to estimate what a grade will be given a certain amount of time spent studying.

In some cases, the line of best fit will be a curve or an exponential function, depending on the data you are studying. That's because real-world problems don't always follow a simple equation exactly. However, you can examine data for patterns that look similar to the linear, exponential, and quadratic functions you will be learning about and find a best-fit model. The model you choose will depend on your data and how exact your approximations need to be. Once you have a model to base the data on, you can use the model to draw conclusions or make predictions about the data.

Where You'll Learn This

You will study this in Chapters 2, 6, and 8.

North Carolina Fact

North Carolina's Cape Hatteras National Seashore is one of the longest stretches of undeveloped shoreline along the Atlantic seaboard.

A candle is 10 cm tall after burning for 1 h. After burning for 3 h, it is 9 cm tall. Write a linear equation to model the height y of the candle after burning for *x* hours. Then use your equation to predict how tall the candle will be after burning for 10 hours.

First, find the slope of the model line:

$$m = \frac{10 - 9}{1 - 3} = -\frac{1}{2}$$

Then write a linear equation:

$$y - y_1 = m(x - x_1)$$
$$y - 9 = -\frac{1}{2}(x - 3)$$
$$y = -\frac{1}{2}x + 10.5$$

Finally, use the equation to predict the height of the candle after 10 hours of burning: $x = 10$

$$y = -\frac{1}{2}(10) + 10.5$$
$$y = 5.5$$

The candle will be about 5.5 cm tall after burning for 10 h.

Student's Guide

ALGEBRA

2.05 Use rational equations to model and solve problems; justify results.
  a) Solve using tables, graphs, and algebraic properties.
  b) Interpret the constants and coefficients in the context of the problem.
  c) Identify the asymptotes and intercepts graphically and algebraically.

What It Means to You

When you write a fraction, such as $\frac{2}{3}$, you are writing a type of rational number. A rational expression is similar in that it is a fraction. It is different in that there is a variable in the denominator of the fraction. An inverse variation is one example of a rational equation. In an inverse relationship, as one variable decreases, the other increases proportionally. For example, if you squeeze a balloon the volume will decrease and the pressure exerted will increase. A simple way to write this relationship is $y = \frac{k}{x}$. Many proportions are also forms of rational equations. For example, the relationship $\frac{2}{x+3} = \frac{x+1}{x^2}$ is an example of a proportion that is also a rational equation.

Rational equations also have unique characteristics. Think of the expression $y = \frac{1}{x}$. What will happen to the graph when x is 0?

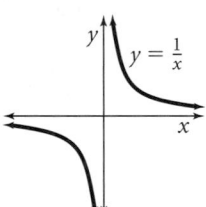

Since $\frac{1}{0}$ is undefined, in this case there will be no y-values for $x = 0$. We call this break a *discontinuity* in the graph. You will learn to identify different types of discontinuities and other properties of graphs of rational equations. You will also be learning how to simplify rational expressions and solve rational equations.

Where You'll Learn This

You will study this in Chapter 9.

Marty has 5,000 summer camp packets to staple. He can staple the packets twice as fast as his sister Maria can. Working together, Marty and Maria can complete the job in 5 hours. How long will it take each of them to do the job alone? Show your work.

Begin by writing down what you know from the problem:

Marty's rate + Maria's rate = combined rate

	Time in hours	Rate (packets per hour)
Marty	x	$\frac{5{,}000}{x}$
Maria	$2x$	$\frac{5{,}000}{2x}$
Combined	5	$\frac{5{,}000}{5} = 1{,}000$

Then, write an equation to model the situation:

$$\frac{5{,}000}{x} + \frac{5{,}000}{2x} = 1{,}000$$

Multiply by $2x$:
$$10{,}000 + 5{,}000 = 2{,}000x$$
$$15{,}000 = 2{,}000x$$
$$7.5 = x$$

Marty could complete the job in 7.5 hours. Maria could do it in about 15 hours.

2.06 Use cubic equations to model and solve problems.
 a) Solve using tables and graphs.
 b) Interpret constants and coefficients in the context of the problem.

What It Means to You

Many real-world situations can be modeled using different kinds of functions. You can use a linear function (whose graph is a line) to model how far you'll travel going a certain rate, an exponential function (whose graph is J-shaped) to model population growth, and quadratic functions (whose graph is U-shaped) to model the flight of a ball thrown in the air. Sometimes, you can fit data more closely if you use a model with a variable raised to a degree of three (x^3). The graph of $y = x^3$ is similar to a quadratic equation that has been turned at the vertex.

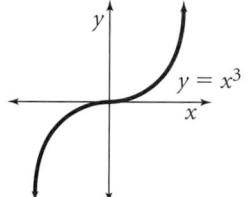

The volume of a rectangular prism with dimensions x, $x + 5$, and $10 - x$ can be modeled with a polynomial of degree three. The equation $y = x(x + 5)(10 - x)$ can be simplified $y = -x^3 + 5x^2 + 50x$. These types of equations are called cubic equations.

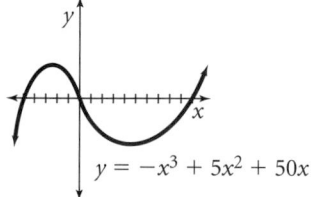

$y = -x^3 + 5x^2 + 50x$

Looking at the shape of this type of cubic equation, you might want to use a cubic equation to find maximum and minimum values. In a cubic equation, however, you will find a *relative* maximum or minimum. This means that the point is the greatest (or least) *y*-value when compared to other points near it, but it is not the greatest point in the graph. You will learn to use cubic equations to model and solve real-world problems.

Where You'll Learn This

You will study this in Chapter 6.

Which model best fits the data in the table?

Data Table

x	y
-2	$-2\frac{2}{3}$
-1	$-\frac{1}{3}$
0	0
1	$\frac{1}{3}$
2	$2\frac{2}{3}$

A $y = x^3$ B $y = 3x^3$

C $y = \frac{1}{3}x^3$ D $y = -\frac{1}{3}x^3$

Answer: C

ALGEBRA

2.07 Use equations with radical expressions to model and solve problems; justify results.

    a) Solve using tables, graphs, and algebraic properties.

    b) Interpret the degree, constants, and coefficients in the context of the problem.

What It Means to You

When you multiply a number by itself, you square the number. The inverse of squaring a number is finding its square root. For example, $4^2 = 16$, and the square root of 16 is 4, or $\sqrt{16} = 4$. Now you will apply what you know to radical expressions and equations.

A radical equation is one that contains a variable under a radical symbol, such as $2 + \sqrt{x} = 12$, or $x^{\frac{2}{3}} = 200$. You often see radical expressions in geometry formulas. For example, the formula for the length of the side of a square given its area is $s = \sqrt{A}$.

You can solve equations with radical expressions using exponents. For example, if $\sqrt{x} = 4$, you can write $(\sqrt{x})^2 = 4^2$, or $x = 16$. You will see that sometimes when you use exponents to solve an equation, *extraneous solutions*, or solutions that fit the squared equation but not the original equation, will appear. In such cases, you will need to check all solutions to eliminate extraneous solutions. This year, you will learn how to work with equations with radical expressions in order to model and solve problems. You will also learn how to transform radical functions using methods similar to those used in linear equations.

Where You'll Learn This

You will study this in Chapter 7.

Solve $5(x - 1)^{\frac{2}{3}} = 125$. Show your work.

First, divide both sides by 5:
$(x - 1)^{\frac{2}{3}} = 25$

Raise both sides to the $\frac{3}{2}$ power:
$(x - 1)^1 = 25^{\frac{3}{2}}$

Simplify:
$x - 1 = 25^{\frac{3}{2}}$

$x - 1 = 125$

$ x = 126$

The correct answer is 126.

When designing a sailboat, an engineer uses the following formula to determine the maximum possible speed that the hull can attain where m is speed in knots and L is the length of the waterline in feet.

$m = 1.35 \cdot \sqrt{L}$

Rounded to the nearest hundredth, what is the length of the waterline of a boat with a maximum speed of 7.9 knots?

A   3.79 ft
B   32.15 ft
C   34.24 ft
D   46.23 ft

Answer: C

ALGEBRA

2.08 Use equations and inequalities with absolute value to model and solve problems; justify results.
  a) Solve using tables, graphs, and algebraic properties.
  b) Interpret the constants and coefficients in the context of the problem.

What It Means to You

You're traveling from your home to your cousin's house. Regardless of the direction in which you go, the distance you travel will be a positive value. Just like distance traveled, the absolute value represents distance on the number line. Because distance traveled cannot be a negative number, the absolute value of a number cannot be a negative number. A number's absolute value is never negative, it is always positive or 0.

You can think of the graph of an absolute value as being the combination of two graphs. Because of this, an absolute value equation is V-shaped. To graph $y = |x|$, you will combine the graphs of $y = x$ (for the right part of the graph) and $y = -x$ (for the left part of the graph).

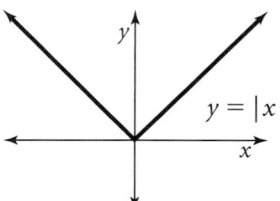

Just as you can use two equations to draw the graph of an absolute value equation, you can use two equations to solve an absolute value equation. Suppose $|x + 2| = 5$. Since $|5| = 5$ and $|-5| = 5$, you know that $x + 2 = 5$ or $x + 2 = -5$ will solve the equation. You can solve the two simpler equations to find solutions for the original equation. You will learn how to solve equations with absolute value to model and solve problems.

Where You'll Learn This

You will study this in Chapter 1.

Solve $2|4x - 1| - 2 = 18$
Show your work.

First, add 2 to each side:
$2|4x - 1| = 20$

Then, divide each side by 2:
$|4x - 1| = 10$

Rewrite as two equations:
$4x - 1 = 10$ or $4x - 1 = -10$

Solve both equations:
$4x = 11$ or $4x = -9$
$x = \frac{11}{4}$ or $x = -\frac{9}{4}$

The correct answer is $x = \frac{11}{4}$ or $-\frac{9}{4}$.

Graph $y = 2|x| + 3$.

Answer:

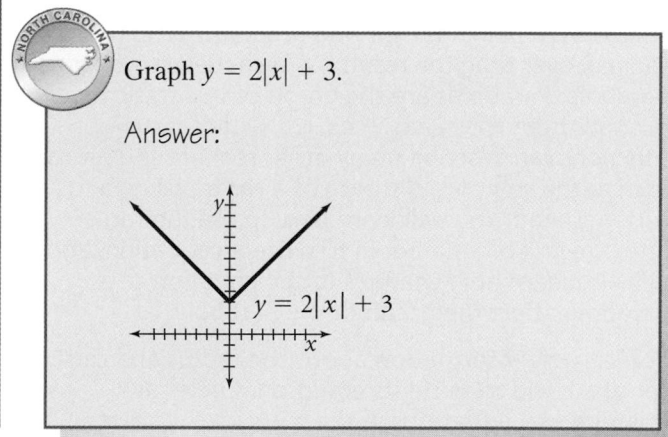

Student's Guide

ALGEBRA

2.09 Use the equations of parabolas and circles to model and solve problems; justify results.

  a) Solve using tables, graphs, and algebraic properties.

  b) Interpret the constants and coefficients in the context of the problem.

What It Means to You

You are familiar with thinking of circles as the set of points in a plane a given distance from a single point. The term *radius* describes the given distance. A parabola, on the other hand, is a set of points in a plane where each point is a given distance from a single line and a fixed point not on that line. The term *focus* describes the fixed point, and the term *directrix* describes the line.

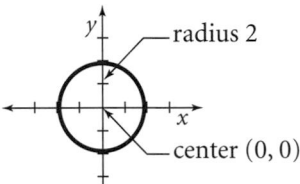

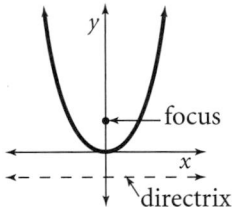

If you toss a ball in the air and graph the height of the ball over time the result is a U-shaped curve, or parabola. Parabolas are the graph of quadratic functions, written $f(x) = ax^2 + bx + c$. Quadratic functions can describe many other real-life situations, such as the stopping distance of a car traveling at a certain speed. You will learn how to use the focus and directrix of a parabola to write an equation. You will also learn how changes to the equation of a parabola affect the graph of the parabola.

You can use information about the radius and center of a circle to write its equation. Circles are described by equations in the form $x^2 + y^2 = r^2$, where r is the radius. You will learn how changes to the equation of a circle can change its size or shape, resulting in larger or smaller circles and ellipses. You will work with equations of parabolas and circles in order to solve problems.

Where You'll Learn This

You will study this in Chapter 10.

Which of the following is the equation of a circle with center $(-2, 3)$ and radius 5?

 A $(x - 3)^2 + (y - 2)^2 = 5$

 B $(x - 2)^2 + (y - 3)^2 = 25$

 C $(x + 2)^2 + (y - 3)^2 = 25$

 D $(x + 2)^2 + (y + 3)^2 = 25$

Answer: C

Find the equation of the parabola described by the following information.

Focus: $(3, 0)$

Vertex: $(0, 0)$

 A $x = \left(\frac{1}{12}\right)y^2$

 B $x = 12y^2$

 C $y = \left(\frac{1}{12}\right)x^2$

 D $y = 12x^2$

Answer: A

ALGEBRA

2.10 Use systems of two or more equations or inequalities to model and solve problems; justify results. Solve using tables, graphs, matrix operations, and algebraic properties.

What It Means to You

You may have seen ads for competing phone services. But which is the better plan? If you model each plan then you have created a system of equations. A system of equations is a set of two or more equations that use the same variables. You will learn how to solve these systems of equations by finding any or all points where the equations intersect.

You have seen how to solve equations by graphing to find where equations or inequalities intersect. In some cases, you will not have the tools to create a graph, or the graphs will be too complex to help determine the solution. In these cases, you may want to solve a single equation for a variable and then substitute that value into other equations. This is called the *substitution method.*

At other times, you will find that equations are too complex to solve for a single variable. Sometimes you will be able to use algebraic properties to convert two or more equations into one equation with one variable. You will learn a method called *elimination*, in which you combine the equations to eliminate a variable.

In situations that involve more than two equations and more than two variables, you may even want to use a matrix to model the equations. You can then perform matrix operations to find solutions for the equations.

You will learn a variety of methods for solving groups (or *systems*) of equations and inequalities in multiple variables. You will then be able to decide which method is appropriate for each problem you encounter.

Where You'll Learn This

You will study this in Chapters 3 and 4.

In order to take swim fitness classes at the Club Pool, you must join the pool and pay a monthly class fee. Two months of classes cost $115. Five months of classes cost $175. What is the cost of joining the pool?

A $20   B $25
C $50   D $75

Answer: D

Solve the system of equations by elimination.

$x^2 + y^2 = 4$

$x^2 + 4y^2 = 16$

A $\{(0,2),(0,-2)\}$
B $\{(0,4),(0,-4)\}$
C $\{(2,0),(-2,0)\}$
D $\{(4,0),(-4,0)\}$

Answer: A

Student's Guide

Teacher's Edition Contents

Prentice Hall Mathematics

A comprehensive program
for North Carolina
Grades 6-12

From middle school math
to high school algebra
and geometry, Prentice Hall
has the solutions you need
to guarantee math success
for all students.

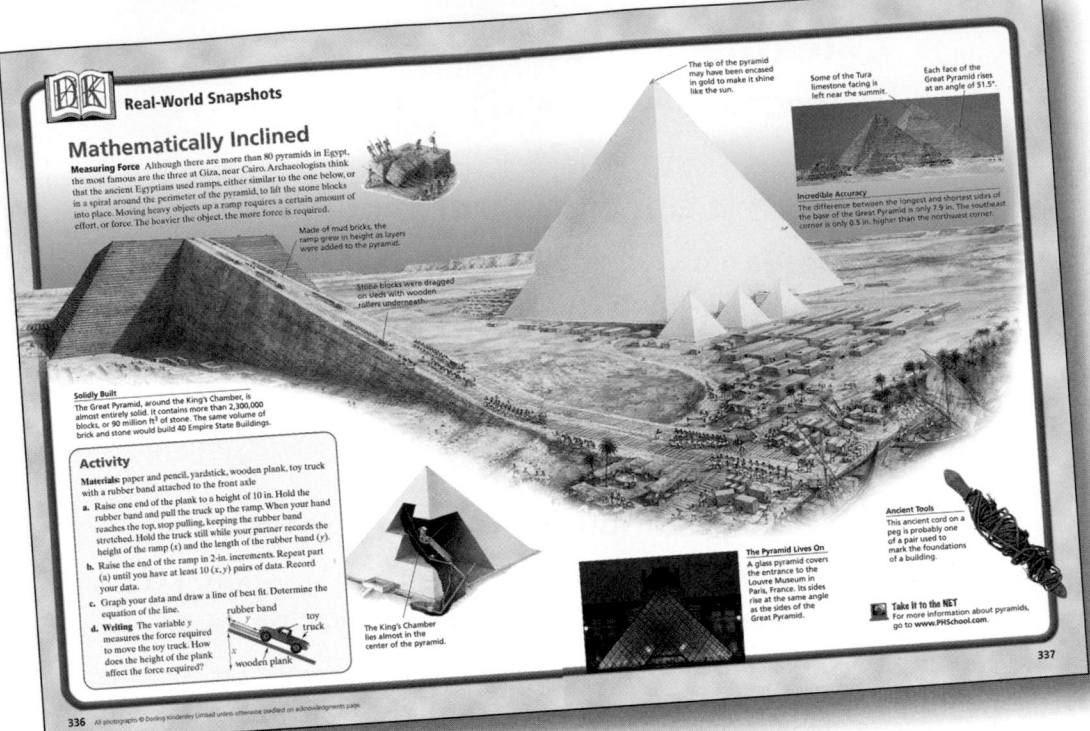

Comprehensive Content Connects to Their World

Our comprehensive scope and sequence of content addresses the North Carolina Standard Course of Study, NAEP, and teacher expectations. Abundant real-world connections reinforce math applications, while unique *Dorling Kindersley Real-World Snapshots* bring math to life.

Empower Them ▶

Give Every North Carolina Student the Opportunity to Succeed

The *Instant Check System™* enables students to check their understanding at key points during instruction. No other program provides such an easy-to-use way to measure students' progress. *Leveled exercise sets* allow you to easily craft just the right assignments for your classes. Plus, we've built in homework helpers along the way.

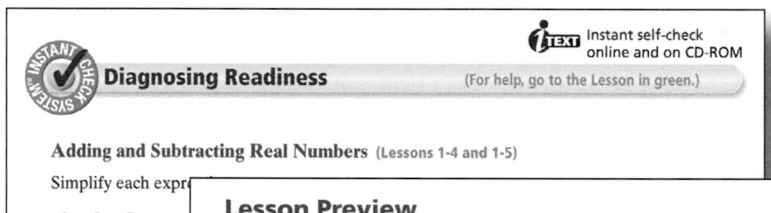

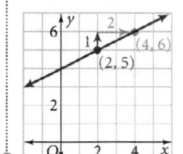

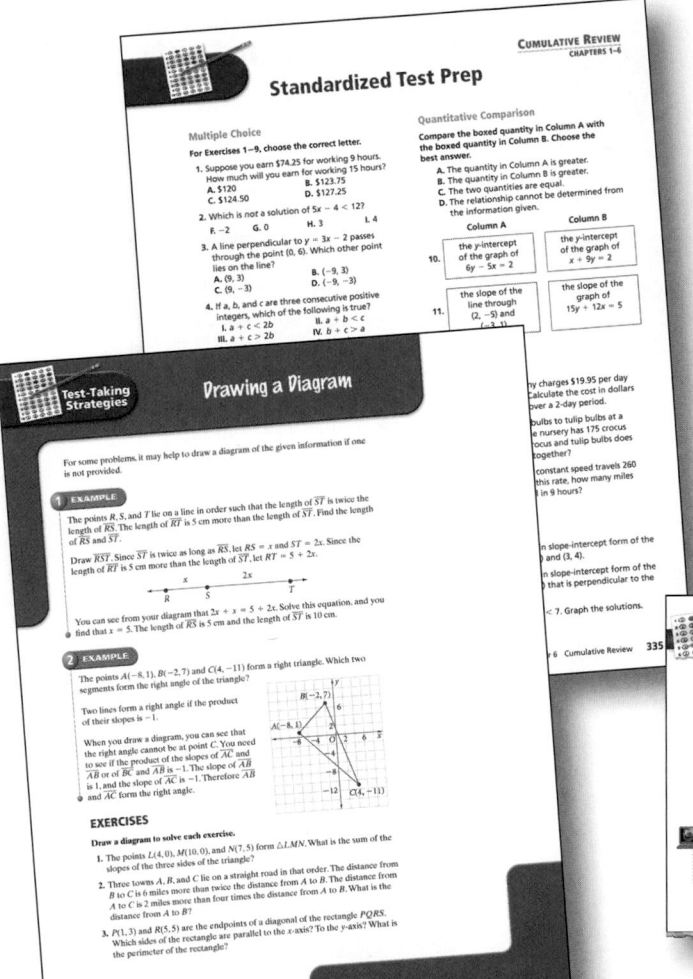

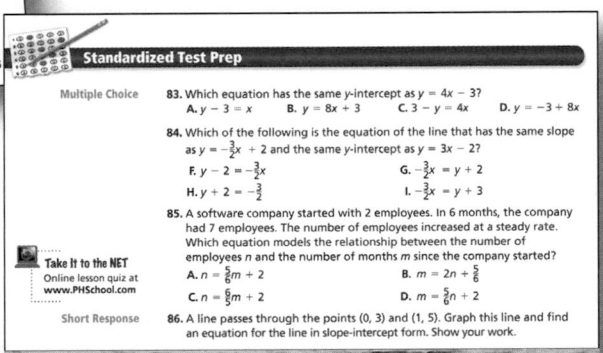

Prepare Them

Test Prep Strand Guarantees EOC and NAEP Success

Reading comprehension activities and test-taking strategies are included throughout the program. Test prep practice in every lesson gives students the confidence they need to succeed on the North Carolina assessments.

And Get the Support You Deserve

Outstanding Teacher Time Savers Allow for Effective Instruction

Our comprehensive *Presentation Assistant Plus!* provides all the material you need to teach every lesson step-by-step from beginning to end, while the unique *PH SuccessNet* unlocks a whole new set of online solutions for teaching success.

OVER 700 transparencies per Grade Level!

Prentice Hall Mathematics

Comprehensive content with a scope and sequence that helps you meet the North Carolina Standard Course of Study while focusing on specific student needs

Content Standards

Careful consideration of the North Carolina Standard Course of Study and the National Assessment of Educational Progress 2005 Guidelines was made prior to developing the scope and sequence of content for each text. In addition, North Carolina teacher input concerning content issues helped to determine the final content coverage of the entire program. Consequently, with *Prentice Hall Mathematics*, you can be assured that new content standards are covered along with the content North Carolina teachers know is important.

Strand Coverage

Important mathematics strands such as number theory, algebra, geometry, measurement, data analysis, statistics, and probability are thoroughly developed as appropriate to each level. Each text from *Pre-Algebra* through *Algebra 2* provides excellent coverage of the topics indicated for that level while other strands are reviewed and reinforced to help students make important connections

Reading and Math

Reading Math lessons are included throughout the program to help students to become more active in the learning process. Reading math vocabulary is carefully developed, and students learn a variety of techniques to help them more effectively read their textbook and mathematical text in general. Reading and Math Literacy Masters are also available.

Alternate Course Planning Guides

A Basic Algebra Planning Guide and an Informal Geometry Planning Guide help you structure alternative courses to meet the needs of less able students. In addition, Connections to Precalculus Masters accompany *Algebra 2* to help you highlight key skills that will ensure success for all your students who continue their study of mathematics.

  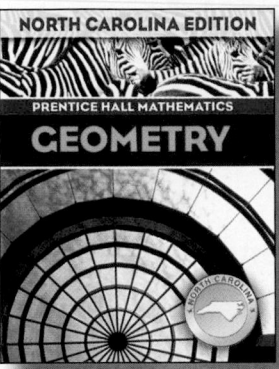 

Complete North Carolina Resources

 North Carolina Student Edition
iText—Interactive text online and on CD-ROM
North Carolina Teacher's Edition
Teaching Resources
- Grab & Go Chapter Support Files
  - Practice
  - Reteaching
  - Enrichment
  - Chapter Projects
  - Checkpoint Quizzes
  - Chapter Tests
  - Alternative Assessment
  - Cumulative Review
- Cumulative Assessment
- Solution Key

Reaching All Students

Practice Workbook
Reading and Math Literacy Masters
Guided Problem-Solving Masters
Hands-on Activities
Technology Activities
Prentice Hall MathNotes Folders
Skills Intervention Kit

**Coming Soon—
Online Intervention**

Teacher Time Savers

Presentation Assistant Plus!
- Additional Examples on Transparencies
- Daily Skills Check and Lesson Quiz Transparencies
- Problem of the Day Transparencies
- Student Edition Answers on Transparencies
- Classroom Aid Transparencies
- Prentice Hall Presentation Pro CD-ROM

Assessment and Test Prep

Prentice Hall Assessment System
- North Carolina Computer Test Generator CD-ROM
- Algebra Readiness Tests
- Assessment Resources
  - Checkpoint Quizzes
  - Chapter Tests, Forms A & B
  - Alternative Assessment
  - Cumulative Assessment
- North Carolina Content Diagnostic Tests
- Skills and Concepts Review
- North Carolina EOC and NAEP Preparation
  Workbook with Teacher's Guide
- Test-Taking Strategies with Transparencies

Spanish Support

Student Edition, Spanish Version
Spanish Practice Workbook
Spanish Reading and Math Literacy Masters
Spanish Assessment Resources

Technology

iText—Interactive text online and on CD-ROM
Prentice Hall Presentation Pro CD-ROM
North Carolina Resource Pro® with
  Planning Express® CD-ROM
North Carolina Computer Test Generator CD-ROM
PH SuccessNet Teacher Center Web Site
PHSchool.com Textbook Site

**Take a virtual tour of the program at
PHSchool.com/northcarolina**

T7

Authors

Series Authors

Dan Kennedy, Ph.D., is a classroom teacher and the Lupton Distinguished Professor of Mathematics at the Baylor School in Chattanooga, Tennessee. A frequent speaker at professional meetings on the subject of mathematics education reform, Dr. Kennedy has conducted more than 50 workshops and institutes for high school teachers. He is co-author of textbooks in calculus and precalculus, and from 1990 to 1994 he chaired the College Board's AP Calculus Development Committee. He is a 1992 Tandy Technology Scholar and a 1995 Presidential Award winner.

Randall I. Charles, Ph.D., is Professor Emeritus in the Department of Mathematics and Computer Science at San Jose State University, San Jose, California. He began his career as a high school mathematics teacher, and he was a mathematics supervisor for five years. Dr. Charles has been a member of several NCTM committees and is the former Vice President of the National Council of Supervisors of Mathematics. Much of his writing and research has been in the area of problem solving. He has authored more than 75 mathematics textbooks for kindergarten through college.

ISBN 0-13-062568-X

1 2 3 4 5 6 7 8 9 10   06 05 04 03 02

Algebra 1 and Algebra 2 Authors

Allan E. Bellman is a Lecturer/Supervisor in the School of Education at the University of California, Davis. Before coming to Davis, he was a mathematics teacher for 31 years in Montgomery County, Maryland. He has been an instructor for both the Woodrow Wilson National Fellowship Foundation and the T^3 program. Mr. Bellman has a particular expertise in the use of technology in education and speaks frequently on this topic. He was a 1992 Tandy Technology Scholar.

Sadie Chavis Bragg, Ed.D., is Professor of Mathematics and Vice President of Academic Affairs at the Borough of Manhattan Community College of the City University of New York. Dr. Bragg is a past president of the American Mathematical Association of Two-Year Colleges (AMATYC), is co-director of the AMATYC project to revise the standards for introductory college mathematics before calculus, and is an active member of the Benjamin Banneker Association. Since 1976, she has co-authored more than 50 mathematics textbooks from kindergarten through college.

William G. Handlin, Sr., is a classroom teacher and Department Chairman of Technology Applications at Spring Woods High School in Houston, Texas. Awarded Life Membership in the Texas Congress of Parent and Teachers Association for his contributions to the well-being of children, Mr. Handlin is also a frequent workshop and seminar leader in professional meetings throughout the world.

Geometry Authors

Laurie E. Bass
Fieldston, the Grades 7–12 Division of
    the Ethical Culture Fieldston School
Riverdale, New York

Art Johnson, Ed.D.
Professor of Mathematics
Boston College
Boston, Massachusetts

Reviewers

North Carolina Math Program Advisors

Kelly S. Crisp
Mathematics Teacher
Buncombe County Schools
Arden, North Carolina

Don McGurrin
Educational Math
Consultant
Clayton, North Carolina

Sheila S. Brookshire
Mathematics Teacher
AC Reynolds Middle School
Asheville, North Carolina

Cynthia Hanner Davis
Mathematics Teacher
Northeast High School
Greensboro, North Carolina

Judy Porter
Leesville Road High School
Raleigh, North Carolina

Dr. Ann R. Crawford
University of North Carolina
   at Wilmington
Wilmington, North Carolina

Algebra 1 Reviewers

Mary Lou Beasley
Southside Fundamental
   Middle School
St. Petersburg, Florida

Jane E. Damaske
Lakeshore Public Schools
Stevensville, Michigan

**Ann Marie Palmieri-
   Monahan**
Director of Mathematics
Bayonne Board of Education
Bayonne, New Jersey

Blanche Smith Brownley
Washington, D.C., Public
   Schools
Washington, D.C.

Stacy A. Ego
Warren Central High School
Indianapolis, Indiana

Marie Schalke
Woodlawn Middle School
Long Grove, Illinois

Joseph Caruso
Somerville High School
Somerville, Massachusetts

Earl R. Jones
Formerly, Kansas City
   Public Schools
Kansas City, Missouri

Julie Welling
LaPorte High School
LaPorte, Indiana

Belinda Craig
Highland West Junior High
   School
Moore, Oklahoma

Jeanne Lorenson
James H. Blake High School
Silver Spring, Maryland

Sharon Zguzenski
Naugatuck High School
Naugatuck, Connecticut

John T. Mace
Hibbett Middle School
Florence, Alabama

Geometry Reviewers

Marian Avery
Great Valley High School
Malvern, Pennsylvania

Mary Emma Bunch
Farragut High School
Knoxville, Tennessee

Karen A. Cannon
K–12 Mathematics Coordinator
Rockwood School District
Eureka, Missouri

Johnnie Ebbert
Department Chairman
DeLand High School
DeLand, Florida

Russ Forrer
Math Department Chairman
East Aurora High School
Aurora, Illinois

Andrea Kopco
Midpark High School
Middleburg Heights, Ohio

Gordon E. Maroney III
Camden Fairview High School
Camden, Arkansas

Charlotte Phillips
Math Coordinator
Wichita USD 259
Wichita, Kansas

Richard P. Strausz
Farmington Public Schools
Farmington, Michigan

Jane Tanner
Jefferson County International
Baccalaureate School
Birmingham, Alabama

Karen D. Vaughan
Pitt County Schools
Greenville, North Carolina

Robin Washam
Math Specialist
Puget Sound Educational
 Service District
Burien, Washington

Algebra 2 Reviewers

Josiane Fouarge
Landry High School
New Orleans, Louisiana

Susan Hvizdos
Math Department Chair
Wheeling Park High School
Wheeling, West Virginia

Kathleen Kohler
Kearny High School
Kearny, New Jersey

Julia Kolb
Leesville Road High School
Raleigh, North Carolina

Deborah R. Kula
Sacred Hearts Academy
Honolulu, Hawaii

Betty Mayberry
Gallatin High School
Gallatin, Tennessee

John L. Pitt
Formerly, Prince William
 County Schools
Manassas, Virginia

Margaret Plouvier
Billings West High School
Billings, Montana

Sandra Sikorski
Berea High School
Berea, Ohio

Tim Visser
Grandview High School
Cherry Creek School District
Aurora, Colorado

Mathematics Content Consultants

Courtney Lewis
Prentice Hall Senior National Consultant
Baltimore, Maryland

Deana Cerroni
Prentice Hall National Consultant
Las Vegas, Nevada

Kim Margel
Prentice Hall National Consultant
Scottsdale, Arizona

Sandra Mosteller
Prentice Hall National Consultant
Anderson, South Carolina

Rita Corbett
Prentice Hall Consultant
Elgin, Illinois

Cathy Davies
Prentice Hall Consultant
Laguna Niguel, California

Sally Marsh
Prentice Hall Consultant
Baltimore, Maryland

Addie Martin
Prentice Hall Consultant
Upper Marlboro, Maryland

Rose Primiani
Prentice Hall Consultant
Brick, New Jersey

Loretta Rector
Prentice Hall Consultant
Foresthill, California

Charlotte Samuels
Prentice Hall Consultant
Lafayette Hill, Pennsylvania

Margaret Thomas
Prentice Hall Consultant
Indianapolis, Indiana

Contents in Brief

Chapter 1

Tools of Algebra

Chapter 2

Functions, Equations, and Graphs

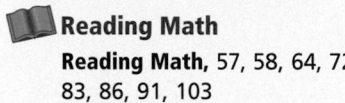

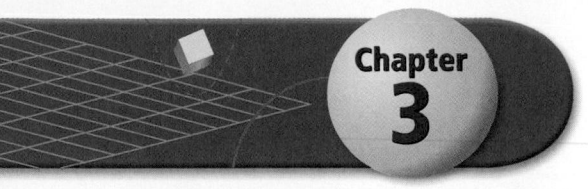

Chapter 3

Linear Systems

Table of Contents

Chapter 4

Matrices

Quadratic Equations and Functions

Table of Contents

Chapter 6

Polynomials and Polynomial Functions

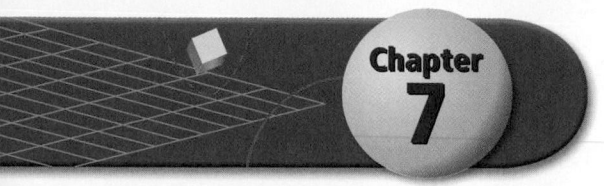

Radical Functions and Rational Exponents

Table of Contents

Contents   **xiii**

Exponential and Logarithmic Functions

Chapter 9

Rational Functions

Student Support

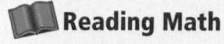

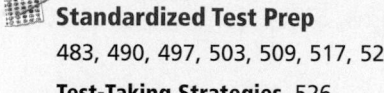

Table of Contents

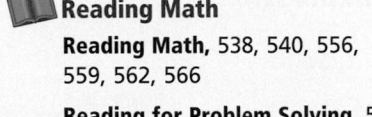

Chapter 10

Quadratic Relations

Chapter 11

Sequences and Series

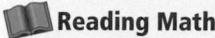
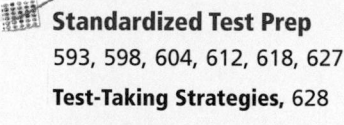
Table of Contents

Chapter 12

Probability and Statistics

Periodic Functions and Trigonometry

Chapter 14

Trigonometric Identities and Equations

Take It to the Net

Throughout this book you will find links to the Prentice Hall Web site for *Algebra 2*. Use the Web Code provided with each link to gain direct access to online material.

Here's how to **Take It to the Net**:
• Go to **PHSchool.com**.
• Enter the Web Code.
• Click Go!

> For a complete list of online features, use Web Code agk-0099

Lesson Quiz Web Codes

There is an online quiz for each lesson. Access these quizzes with Web Codes aga-0101 through aga-1407 for Lesson 1-1 through Lesson 14-7. See page 8.

88 Lesson Quizzes
Web Code format: aga-0204
02 = Chapter 2   04 = Lesson 4

Chapter Resource Web Codes

Chapter	Vocabulary Quizzes *See page 47.*	Chapter Tests *See page 50.*	Dorling Kindersley Real-World Snapshots *See pages 112–113.*	Chapter Projects
1	agj-0151	aga-0152		agd-0161
2	agj-0251	aga-0252	age-0253	agd-0261
3	agj-0351	aga-0352		agd-0361
4	agj-0451	aga-0452	age-0453	agd-0461
5	agj-0551	aga-0552		agd-0561
6	agj-0651	aga-0652	age-0653	agd-0661
7	agj-0751	aga-0752		agd-0761
8	agj-0851	aga-0852	age-0853	agd-0861
9	agj-0951	aga-0952		agd-0961
10	agj-1051	aga-1052	age-1053	agd-1061
11	agj-1151	aga-1152		agd-1161
12	agj-1251	aga-1252	age-1253	agd-1261
13	agj-1351	aga-1352		agd-1361
14	agj-1451	aga-1452	age-1453	agd-1461
End-of-Course		aga-1454		

Additional Resource Web Codes

Data Updates Use Web Code agg-2041 to get up-to-date government data for use in examples and exercises. *See page 83*.

Algebra at Work For information about each Algebra at Work feature, use Web Code agb-2031. *See page 24*.

A Point in Time For information about each A Point in Time feature, use Web Code age-2032. *See page 207*.

Graphing Calculator Procedures There are 27 procedures available online. Use Web Code age-2100 for an index of all the procedures, or Web Codes age-2101 through age-2127 to access individual procedures. *See page 85*.

Table of Contents

Prentice Hall Mathematics programs are research-based and proven to work

The stakes for mathematics educators are high. You are expected to raise student achievement. Prentice Hall understands your dedicated efforts and gives you the confidence to meet this challenge. In developing Prentice Hall programs, the use of research studies is a central, guiding construct. Research on *Prentice Hall Mathematics* indicated key elements of a textbook program that ensure student success: constant review within instruction, support for reading and writing in mathematics, and an ongoing assessment strand. This research was conducted in three phases:

Phase ❶: Exploratory Needs Assessment

Phase ❷: Formative, Prototype Development and Field Testing

Phase ❸: Summative, Validation Research

1 Exploratory Needs Assessment

Along with periodic surveys concerning curriculum issues and challenges, we conducted specific product development research, which included discussions with teachers and advisory panels, focus groups, and quantitative surveys. We explored the specific needs of teachers, students, and other educators regarding each book we developed in *Prentice Hall Mathematics*.

In conjunction with Prentice Hall authors, secondary research was done to explore educational research about learning. This research was incorporated into our instructional strategy and pedagogy to make a more effective mathematics program.

2 Formative, Prototype Development and Field Testing

During this phase of research, we worked to develop prototype materials for each course in *Prentice Hall Mathematics*. Then we tested the materials, including field testing with students and teachers, and qualitative and quantitative evaluations of different kinds. We received solid feedback about our lesson structure in our early prototype testing. Results were channeled back into the program development for improvement. For example, teachers commented positively on motivational quality and richness of the mathematics in the Dorling Kindersley features.

3 Summative, Validation Research

Finally, we conducted and continue to conduct longer-term research based on scientific, experimental designs under actual classroom conditions. This research identifies what works and what can be improved in the next revision of *Prentice Hall Mathematics*. We also continue to monitor the program in the market. We talk to our users about what works, and then we begin the cycle over again. Highlights of this research follow in the next section.

Prentice Hall Research Time Line

Market Needs Assessment
(Quantitative & Qualitative)
- Teacher Interviews
- Classroom Observations
- Mail Surveys
- Conference Participation

Formative Research
(Quantitative & Qualitative)
- Field Testing of Prototypes
- Classroom Observations
- Teacher Reviews
- Supervisor Reviews
- Educator Advisory Panels
- Prentice Hall Sales Force Input

Summative Research
(Experimental and Quasi-Experimental Study Designs & Qualitative Research)
- Pre-Publication Learner Verification Research
- Post-Publication Validation Studies
- Classroom Observations
- Evaluation of In-Market Results on Standardized Tests

Prentice Hall Math programs get results!

Standardized Test End-of-Year Results
(adjusted for differences in pre-test levels)

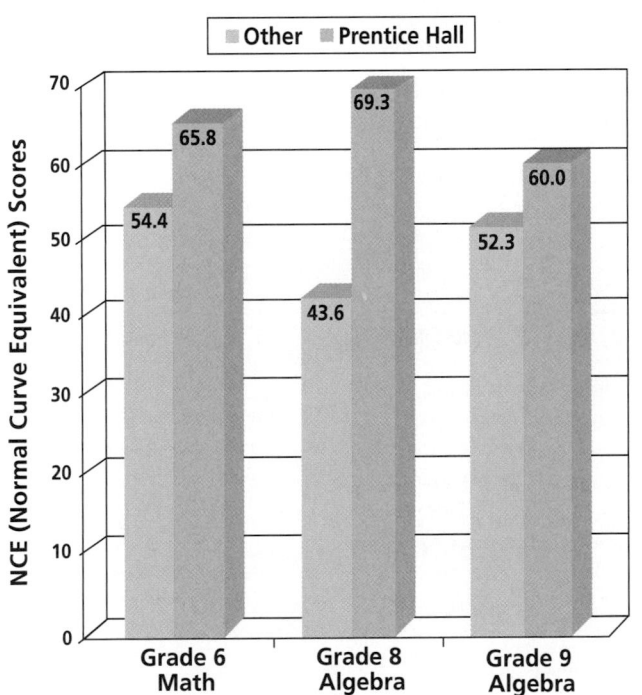

Legend: ▇ Other ▇ Prentice Hall

NCE (Normal Curve Equivalent) Scores

- Grade 6 Math: Other 54.4, Prentice Hall 65.8
- Grade 8 Algebra: Other 43.6, Prentice Hall 69.3
- Grade 9 Algebra: Other 52.3, Prentice Hall 60.0

Prentice Hall mathematics programs are continually researched to determine "what works." Our programs are regularly revised to keep the best of what has worked in prior editions, and to improve them to meet changing market and curriculum needs. For example . . .

In a year-long study conducted in six states, students using Prentice Hall mathematics programs at grades 6, 8 (algebra), and 9 (algebra) outscored students using other math programs on a nationally normed standardized test.

The study followed a scientific, experimental design with two classes per school. The classes selected were of similar ability levels, and the assignment of the Prentice Hall program was done randomly. A total of eight schools (a mix of rural, suburban, and urban) participated, with 350 students involved in the study.

Classes were tested at the beginning of the school year using the TerraNova™ CTBS Basic Battery, and they were re-tested at the end of the school year. The final results, shown in the graph at the left, have been adjusted (via ANCOVA) to eliminate any contribution of higher or lower starting points on the pre-test to the observed post-test score.

All tests were scored by CTB/McGraw-Hill, the publisher of the TerraNova™ exam. Statistical analyses were conducted by an independent statistician from Pulse Analytics, Inc.

Additional studies of program effectiveness are under way, and many districts have demonstrated math improvement since adopting Prentice Hall mathematics programs.

Detailed results of this study can be obtained at **www.PHSchool.com**.

A unique progress-monitoring system that gives every student the opportunity to excel

What Research Indicates: Students' learning progresses to higher levels of understanding only if they have mastered a foundational understanding of preliminary concepts. If students are not functioning at a particular level of understanding, they are not ready to move on. Review plays a key role in promoting retention. Research clearly indicates that review should be systematically planned and incorporated into instruction. Before a new chapter or topic is begun, an inventory can help you ascertain whether any prerequisite knowledge is missing. Review should be continuous for students to attain mastery.

(Suydam, Marilyn N. *The Role of Review in Mathematical Instruction*. Columbus, Ohio: ERIC Clearinghouse for Science, Mathematics, and Environmental Education.)

Prentice Hall's Response: *Prentice Hall Mathematics* provides a unique **Instant Check System™** that is built right into the text to assess mastery and diagnose weaknesses before, during, and after each lesson's instruction. This ongoing monitoring strand allows students to check their understanding of skills before moving on to the next topic. If students have misconceptions or need to reinforce their skills, the green type throughout the text clearly indicates where they can go for help. All the answers for the *Instant Check System™* questions are available at the back of the student edition so students can check their work.

✓ Diagnosing Readiness

At the beginning of every chapter, students complete the *Diagnosing Readiness* exercises to see what prerequisite skills they may need to review before they begin the chapter. The Teacher's Edition prescribes specific *Examples* and *Exercises* that students can do for intervention.

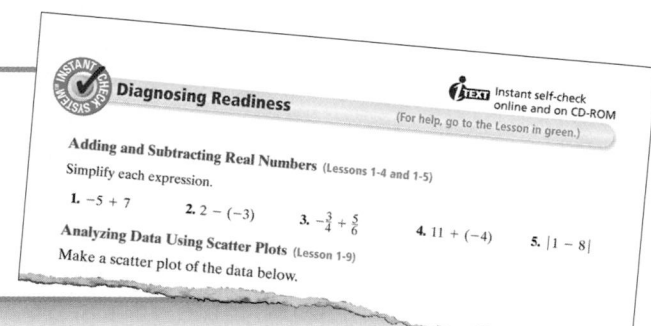

✓ Check Skills You'll Need

To begin each lesson, students complete the *Check Skills You'll Need* exercises to make sure they have the skills needed to successfully learn the concepts in the lesson. These questions with worked-out solutions are conveniently available as transparencies and on CD-ROM.

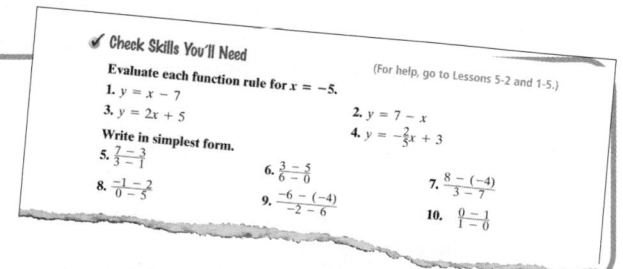

> *"If students do not have the proper level of understanding, they cannot further their knowledge of concepts and relationships in mathematics. Both the Instant Check System and the Diagnosing Readiness feature help teachers assess how well students have achieved understanding of related skills before having them move on to subsequent concepts."*
>
> —Art Johnson, *Prentice Hall Mathematics* program author

✓ Check Understanding

Every lesson includes numerous *Examples*, each followed by *Check Understanding* questions that students can do on their own. As skills and concepts are introduced, these questions focus students on the mathematics being presented and allow them to assess their understanding. More importantly, these questions will raise misconceptions that students have so that you may immediately address them.

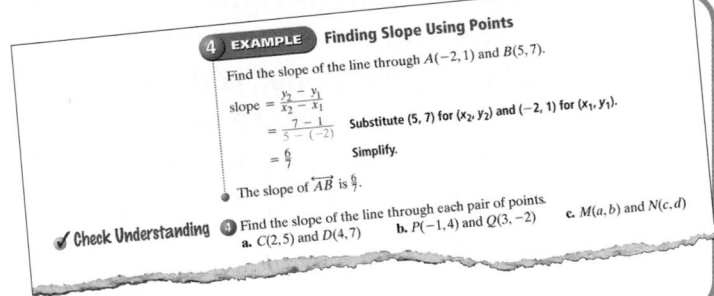

Leveled Exercises

The abundant *Exercises* in every lesson are organized by level to provide ample opportunity for students of all abilities to master the concepts. The *A: Practice by Example* exercises directly relate to the *Examples* in the lesson. The *B: Apply Your Skills* and *C: Challenge* exercises provide richer skill and application problems to extend students' thinking.

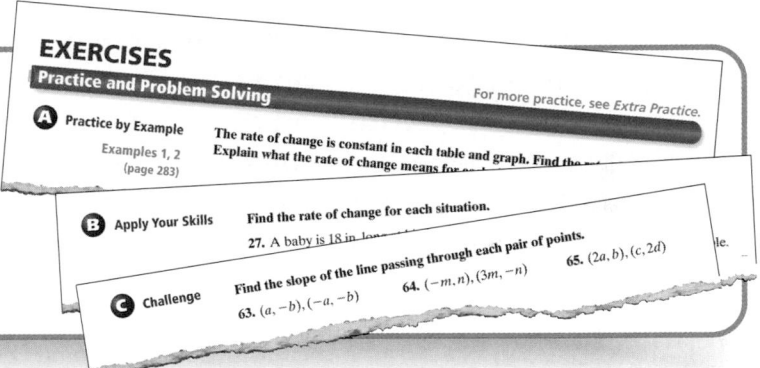

✓ Checkpoint Quizzes

Two *Checkpoint Quizzes* in every chapter provide students with opportunities for ongoing assessment. Each quiz provides a cumulative review of skills within specific lessons. Alternate versions are available in the Teaching Resources and online.

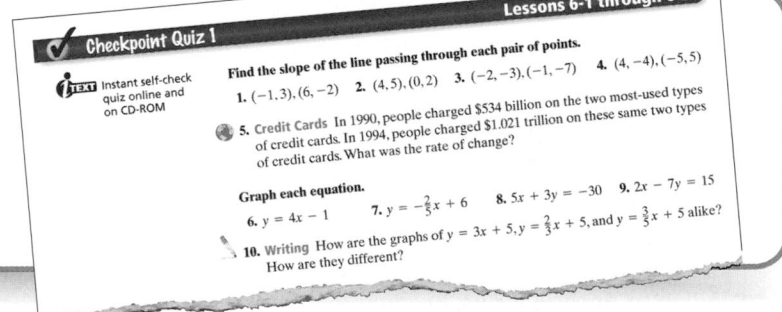

Prentice Hall Mathematics 𝒾TEXT with Self-Grading Assessments

The *iText* provides the complete Student Edition online and on CD-ROM. The unique *Instant Check System*™ is made interactive in the *iText* to allow students ongoing opportunities for checking their learning. Also, the click of a button lets students go back to a lesson or Example for additional help. Students get instant feedback so they know whether they're on track and where to go to get help.

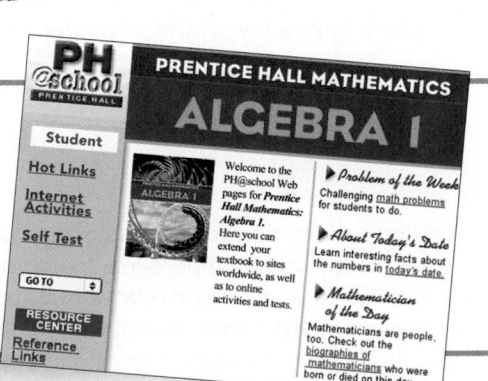

Reading and Writing throughout build communication skills

What Research Indicates: Reading mathematics requires the same skills as reading in other content areas—decoding and comprehending what is read, analyzing and evaluating the content based on one's prior knowledge, and making inferences and generating conclusions. Mathematics text demands that readers also use additional, content-specific reading skills, for example, reading graphs. Students need to learn to focus on significant details, explanations, and the underlying logic in texts where there are more concepts per word, per sentence, and per paragraph than in any other kind of text.

(Barton, Mary Lee & Heidema, Clare. *Teaching Reading in Mathematics:* A Supplement to Teaching Reading in the Content Areas Teacher's Manual, 2nd Ed. Aurora, Colorado: Mid-continent Research for Education and Learning.)

The development of a student's power to use mathematics also involves learning the signs, symbols, and terms of mathematics. This is best accomplished in problem-solving situations in which students have an opportunity to read, write, and discuss ideas so that the use of the language of mathematics becomes natural. As students communicate their ideas, they learn to clarify, refine, and consolidate their thinking.

(*Curriculum and Evaluation Standards for School Mathematics.* Reston, Virginia: The National Council of Teachers of Mathematics, Inc.)

Prentice Hall's Response: *Prentice Hall Mathematics* provides a consistent emphasis on mathematics literacy with a special focus on reading and writing in mathematics. This program integrates even more ways for you to develop your students' ability to read and write mathematically so that they are successful in this course and on state tests.

Reading Math

The *Reading Math* tips within lessons help students to read and understand the language of mathematics. The *Reading Math* features help students read more effectively, so that they can write, speak, and think mathematically. Reading to Analyze Errors, Reading Math Vocabulary, and Reading an Example are just a few of the strategies included.

Reading Math
To set up the subtraction in the slope formula, think of moving from the coordinates of B to the coordinates of A.

$A(-2, 1)$ $B(5, 7)$
$$\frac{7-1}{5-(-2)}$$

Reading Math
You read the coordinates (x_1, y_1) as "x sub 1, y sub 1."

Reading Math

Reading for Problem Solving

FOR USE WITH PAGE 366, EXERCISE 18

Read the exercise below and then follow along with what Bill thinks and writes. Check your understanding by solving the exercise at the bottom of the page.

A garden supply store sells two types of lawn mowers. Total sales of mowers for the year were $8379.70. The total number of mowers sold was 30. The small mowers cost $249.99. The large mowers cost $329.99. Find the number of each type of mower sold.

Writing in Math

Every lesson incorporates *Writing* exercises that help students learn to explain, describe, or compare in a mathematical situation. Special emphasis is also given to writing as it relates to Critical Thinking, Reasoning, and Error Analysis. Instruction in writing answers to rubric-scored questions helps students communicate successfully on today's tests.

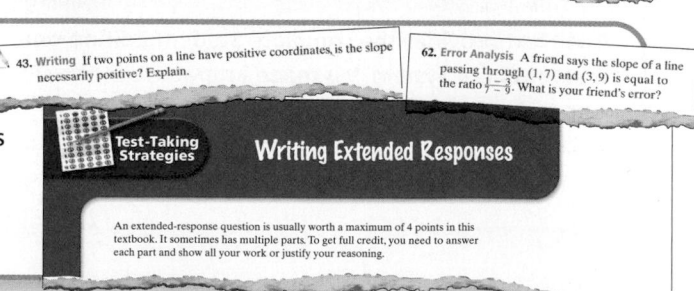

43. Writing If two points on a line have positive coordinates, is the slope necessarily positive? Explain.

62. Error Analysis A friend says the slope of a line passing through (1, 7) and (3, 9) is equal to the ratio $\frac{1}{3} = \frac{7}{9}$. What is your friend's error?

Test-Taking Strategies

Writing Extended Responses

An extended-response question is usually worth a maximum of 4 points in this textbook. It sometimes has multiple parts. To get full credit, you need to answer each part and show all your work or justify your reasoning.

"Success in subsequent mathematics courses and on standardized tests depends greatly on a student's ability to communicate in mathematics. The emphasis on reading and writing in Prentice Hall Mathematics through the Reading Tips and Reading Math features and through the Writing in Math opportunities enables all students to develop their communication skills."

—Randy Charles, *Prentice Hall Mathematics program author*

Understanding Vocabulary

Prentice Hall Mathematics carefully develops the skill of reading math vocabulary. New vocabulary is conveniently listed at the beginning of each chapter and each lesson. Each new term is highlighted in yellow. The Chapter Review includes exercises that help students to correctly use the vocabulary presented in the chapter. The **iTEXT** reinforces students' vocabulary skills with an online vocabulary quiz for every chapter and an audio version of all glossary terms.

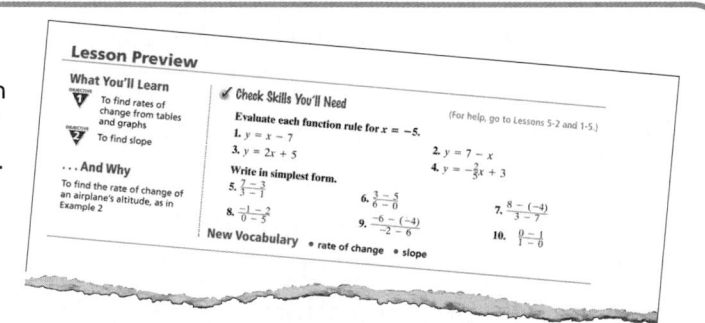

Reading and Math Literacy Masters

These unique blackline masters supplement the coverage of reading and math in the textbook. Students learn a variety of techniques to master mathematics vocabulary and symbols, read for problem solving, and increase comprehension.

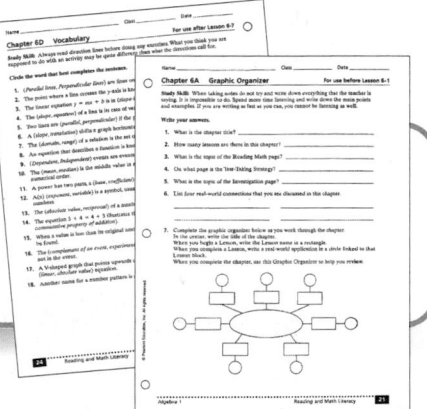

Reading for problem solving through Real-World Connections

Prentice Hall Mathematics incorporates abundant real-world connections within *Examples* and *Exercises* to provide a problem-solving context for applications of mathematics. Dorling Kindersley Real-World Snapshots bring math to life, with activities in which students gather data they need by reading graphic displays and captions.

Ongoing assessment and test preparation guarantee testing success

What Research Indicates: We assess students most fairly when we assess often and with a variety of different answers. Research also shows that assessment needs to measure and describe a student's growth and achievement in all domains of mathematics and at three levels of thinking. Because of this, there should be questions at all levels of thinking, of varying degrees of difficulty, and in all content domains.

(Shafer, Mary C. & Foster, Sherian. "The Changing Faces of Assessment." *Principled Practice in Mathematics and Science Education,* Volume 1, No. 2.)

Prentice Hall's Response: *Prentice Hall Mathematics* provides an ongoing assessment strand that begins within the lesson instruction and continues throughout the program components. The program exposes students to questions of varying difficulty and at different levels of thinking in the daily *Check Understanding* questions and in the leveled *Exercises*.

A variety of question formats, including those found on today's standardized tests, is built into the Student Edition to assess student learning and prepare students for high-stakes tests. The ability to demonstrate knowledge in short-answer and open-ended formats increases opportunities for students to be successful on today's tests and in gaining admission to higher schooling and to the workplace.

✓ Check Understanding

Check Understanding questions after worked-out *Examples* allow students to assess their progress on a daily basis. These questions often emphasize the processes of explaining or reasoning—mirroring the types of questions that students will encounter on today's tests. You can use these questions to address any misconceptions or weaknesses before moving on to new topics.

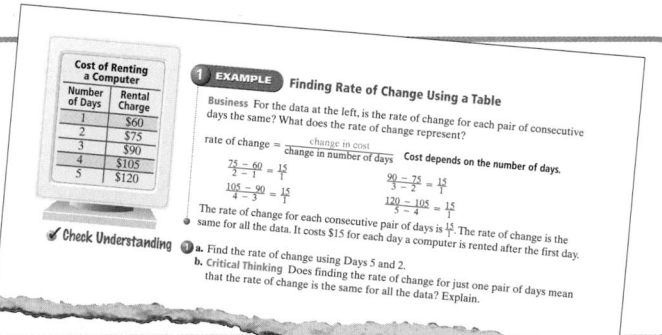

Quizzes and Tests—In Print and Online

You can assess student progress at key points with the *Lesson Quizzes, Checkpoint Quizzes,* and *Chapter Tests.* The Teaching Resources provides additional quizzes and tests, as well as alternative assessments. Online self-grading quizzes and tests are available on the Prentice Hall Web site at **www.PHSchool.com**.

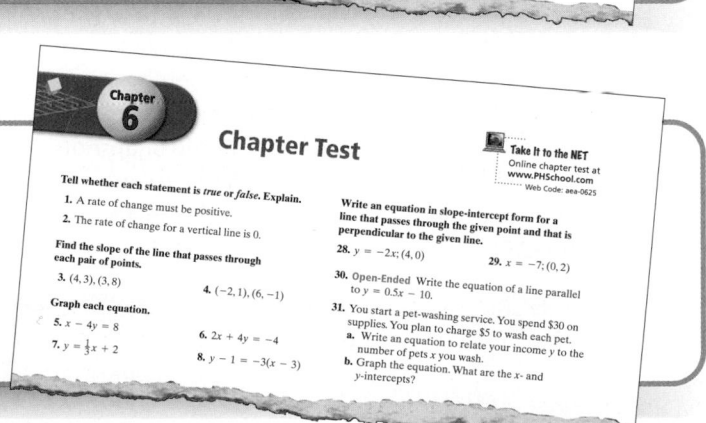

> *"Assessment is an integral part of a mathematics program. Prentice Hall Mathematics provides a strong formative and summative assessment strand. The formative assessment features—before and during instruction—offer a variety of modalities that speak to different kinds of learners. The summative assessment features—after instruction—further prepare students for success on today's tests."*
>
> —Sadie Chavis Bragg, *Prentice Hall Mathematics program author*

Standardized Test Prep Exercises

Standardized Test Prep exercises in every lesson give students daily practice with the types of test item formats that they will encounter on state tests. You can also provide students with the *Standardized Test Prep* page at the end of each chapter.

The daily exercises and the test prep pages include these most common test item formats:

- Multiple Choice
- Gridded Response
- Short Response
- Quantitative Comparison
- Reading Comprehension
- Extended Response

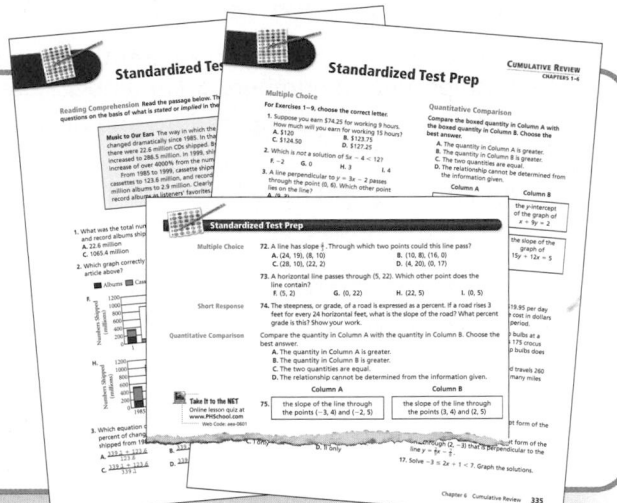

Test-Taking Strategies

Test-Taking Strategies in every chapter teach students strategies to be successful and give them practice in the skills they need to pass state tests and standardized national exams. Several lessons focus on helping students answer rubric-based questions.

The *Test-Taking Strategies With Transparencies* provide instruction on overheads and include additional practice sheets for the strategies taught in each chapter.

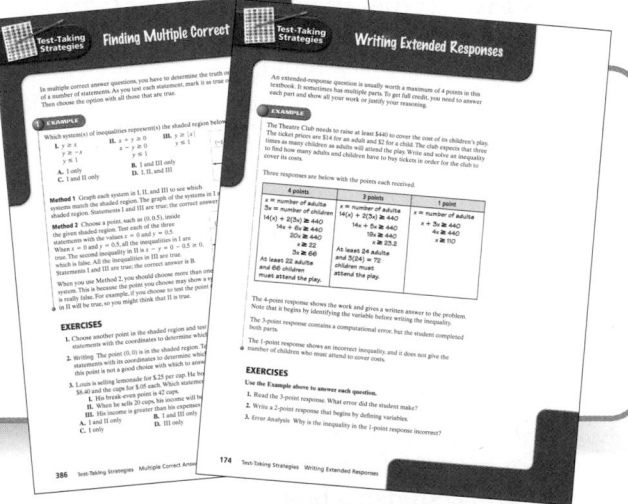

Prentice Hall Assessment System

An innovative *Assessment System* gives you everything you need to assess student progress on the content covered in the course, and to prepare students for high-stakes testing. The system contains the program Assessment Resources and the Computer Test Generator CD-ROM with unlimited questions and ready-to-use Chapter Tests.

In addition, you can diagnose student knowledge with *Content Diagnostic Tests*, prescribe intervention with the *Skills and Concept Review*, and have students practice for standardized assessments with the *Test Preparation* booklet. A *Teacher's Guide* gives you correlations and answers. Also included is the *Test-Taking Strategies With Transparencies* described above.

Research Overview

Mathematical Strands

Overview and Background

Number and Operations

NCTM Standard for Grades 9–12

- Understand numbers, ways of representing numbers, relationships among numbers, and number systems
- Understand meanings of operations and how they relate to one another
- Compute fluently and make reasonable estimates

Key Content in Prentice Hall
Algebra 1, Geometry, Algebra 2

- Represent and compute with rational numbers and real numbers (A1: Ch 1, 11; A2: Ch 1, 7)
- Understand the properties and operations of matrices, vectors, and complex numbers (A1: Ch 1; G: Ch 9; A2: Ch 4, 5)
- Justify relationships within number systems and compare properties of number systems (A1: Ch 1; A2: Ch 1, 4, 5)
- Judge the effects of multiplying, dividing, computing powers, and computing roots on the magnitude of quantities (A1: Ch 8; A2: Ch 7)
- Use counting techniques, including permutations and combinations (A1: Ch 12; A2: Ch 6)
- Judge reasonableness of numerical computations (throughout A1, G, A2)

Background and Progression

Students usually enter an Algebra 1 course having some facility with integers, fractions, and decimals. They have worked with square roots and used the Pythagorean Theorem.

In *Algebra 1,* students build an understanding of real numbers by using symbolic, graphic, and numeric representations as they solve equations and inequalities. Work with rational and radical expressions, equations, and functions builds a wide base of experience with rational and irrational numbers. Matrices are introduced.

In *Geometry,* students' understanding of the properties of real numbers becomes a base for building reasoned geometric arguments. In this year, students first study vectors.

In *Algebra 2,* students study matrices and complex numbers—number systems that do not share all the properties of real numbers (for example, multiplication of matrices is not commutative, and complex numbers cannot be arranged in order).

Data Analysis and Probability

NCTM Standard for Grades 9–12

- Formulate questions that can be addressed with data and collect, organize, and display relevant data to answer them
- Select and use appropriate statistical methods to analyze data
- Develop and evaluate inferences and predictions that are based on data
- Understand and apply basic concepts of probability

Key Content in Prentice Hall
Algebra 1, Geometry, Algebra 2

- Construct and interpret histograms, box plots, and scatterplots (A1: Ch 6; A2: Ch 12)
- Compute statistics, including mean, median, mode, range, and standard deviation (A1: Ch 2; A2: Ch 12)
- Identify trends in bivariate data and find functions that model the data (A1: Ch 6, 10; A2: Ch 2, 5, 6, 8)
- Construct sampling distributions and use them for informal inference about the population (A2: Ch 12)
- Compute probabilities of simple and compound events, geometric probabilities, and conditional probabilities (A1: Ch 4; G: Ch 7; A2: Ch 1, 9, 12)

Background and Progression

In the middle grades, students have gathered, displayed, and interpreted many types of data, including one-variable (for example, test scores), two-variable (height vs. age), and data related to categories (numbers of students who like various foods). They can distinguish appropriate uses of bar, line, and circle graphs, and can find simple probabilities.

In *Algebra 1,* students work with scatter plots and functions to model two-variable, or bivariate, data. They compute probabilities for simple and compound events.

In *Geometry,* students maintain skills, with probability exercises found throughout the text, and are introduced to geometric probability.

In *Algebra 2,* students begin a study of histograms (probability distributions based on experimental results) and theoretical distributions, including binomial (based on two possible outcomes) and normal (representing many real-life random variables, such as adult heights). Students also use tree diagrams to analyze conditional probabilities.

 *For more **Math Background** on every lesson, see page B before each chapter and see each lesson's teaching notes.*

Algebra

NCTM Standard for Grades 9–12

- Understand patterns, relations, and functions
- Represent and analyze mathematical situations and structures using algebraic symbols
- Use mathematical models to represent and understand quantitative relationships
- Analyze change in various contexts

Key Content in Prentice Hall
Algebra 1, Geometry, Algebra 2

- Use various representations of functions and choose types to model quantitative relationships (throughout A1, A2)
- Analyze functions of one variable, including rates of change, intercepts, zeros, and asymptotes (A1: Ch 5, 6, 8, 10; A2: Ch 2, 5–9, 11, 13)
- Combine, compose, and invert common functions (A2: Ch 7, 8, 13, 14)
- Interpret functions of two variables and use parametric forms (A2: Ch 3, 10)
- Understand properties of different types of functions, including linear, quadratic, exponential, polynomial, rational, radical, logarithmic, and periodic functions (A1: Ch 6, 8, 10–12; A2: Ch 2, 5–9, 11, 13)
- Use symbolic algebra to represent and explain mathematical relationships (throughout A1, A2)
- Write equivalent forms of and solve equations, inequalities, and systems (throughout A1, G, A2)

Background and Progression

Today's middle school students are comfortable with tables, graphs, verbal rules, and variables in the representation of simple relationships. Many know how to solve linear equations.

In *Algebra 1,* students use tables, graphs, verbal rules, and symbolic rules to describe linear, quadratic, and exponential functions. They choose a best model for data from among these functions. Rate of change is studied in the context of direct variation, linear equations, and arithmetic and geometric sequences. Students learn how to write equivalent forms of polynomial, radical, and rational expressions.

In *Geometry,* Algebra 1 skills are reinforced with applications involving both linear and quadratic relationships.

In *Algebra 2,* students use multiple representations in studying polynomial, rational, radical, logarithmic, and periodic functions. Using technology, students study residuals as an indicator of the most appropriate model for data. Students first see functions of two variables in the concrete context of linear programming. Trigonometric functions are presented first in the unit circle, and then applied to solving triangles.

Geometry

NCTM Standard for Grades 9–12

- Analyze characteristics and properties of two- and three-dimensional geometric shapes and develop mathematical arguments about geometric relationships
- Specify locations and describe spatial relationships using coordinate geometry and other representational systems
- Apply transformations and use symmetry to analyze mathematical situations
- Use visualization, spatial reasoning, and geometric modeling to solve problems

Key Content in Prentice Hall
Algebra 1, Geometry, Algebra 2

- Analyze properties of plane and space figures. Solve problems involving them, and real-world applications in general (throughout G)
- Explore congruence and similarity (throughout G)
- Use deductive reasoning to establish the validity of conjectures, to prove theorems, and to critique arguments (G: Ch 2–12)
- Use coordinates to analyze shapes, solve problems, and prove relationships (G: Ch 3, 6, 12; A2: Ch 10)
- Understand and represent transformations in the plane using sketches, coordinates, vectors, functions, and matrices (G: Ch 12; A2: Ch 2, 4, 5, 7–10, 13)
- Visualize, draw, and construct plane and space figures, from different perspectives (G: Ch 1, 10; A2: Ch 3, 10)
- Use geometric models to solve problems in other areas of mathematics (A1: Ch 4; G: Ch 7, 9; A2: Ch 14)

Background and Progression

In the middle grades, students have explored various plane and space figures to identify and compare properties. This includes working with similarity, congruence, tessellations, symmetry, slides, flips, turns, and simple figures in the coordinate plane.

In *Algebra 1,* students begin to use geometric models with proportions, percent, and probability. They also explore ways to describe translations of familiar functions in both words and symbols.

In *Geometry,* all key strand content is covered. The first two chapters establish the tools of geometry—methods of reasoning, construction, the coordinate plane, and types of measurement. Subsequent chapters focus on properties and applications of lines, triangles, quadrilaterals, similarity, right triangle trigonometry, circles, and transformations.

In *Algebra 2,* students apply principles of translating in the coordinate plane to functions and conic sections. Geometric models for trigonometric relationships are also utilized.

 *For more **Math Background** on every lesson, see page B before each chapter and see each lesson's teaching notes.*

A1: *Algebra 1;* G: *Geometry;* A2: *Algebra 2*

Mathematical Strands T37

Mathematical Strands

Measurement

NCTM Standard for Grades 9–12

- Understand measurable attributes of objects and the units, systems, and processes of measurement
- Apply appropriate techniques, tools, and formulas to determine measurements

Key Content in Prentice Hall
Algebra 1, Geometry, Algebra 2

- Make decisions about appropriate units and scales in problems involving measurement (A1: Ch 6; G: Ch 8, 10; A2: Ch 1, 13, 14)
- Understand and use formulas for area, surface area, and volume (A1: Ch 2; G: Ch 7, 10; A2: Ch 6, 7)
- Apply concepts of successive approximation, upper and lower bounds, and limits (G: Ch 10; A2: Ch 11, 12)
- Use unit analysis (A1: Ch 4; G: Ch 7)

Background and Progression

Middle school students have usually experienced direct measurements (such as length, mass, and volume), indirect measurements (based on similar triangles), and derived measurements (such as rates). They are familiar with precision and accuracy in measurement, and have developed and used formulas for the perimeters, areas, and volumes of simple figures.

In **Algebra 1,** students make decisions about appropriate scales with graphical representations of data. They use formulas for the perimeters and areas of figures to find missing measures, and use unit analysis (sometimes called dimensional analysis) to help set up proportions and other equations.

In **Geometry,** students justify formulas for perimeter and area and apply them to composite and irregular plane shapes. Students use cross sections to develop formulas for the volumes of prisms, cylinders, pyramids, and cones. The approximation techniques used to help justify the formulas for the surface area and volume of a sphere anticipate calculus. Through work with arc length and the areas of circles and parts of circles, students become comfortable with exact measures (which are irrational and expressed in terms of π) and rational approximations of these measures.

In **Algebra 2,** students use polynomials to express the areas and volumes of figures, and polynomial equations to find missing measures. With geometric sequences they explore successive approximations and the concept of a limit. Various statistical measures lead to the concepts of statistical error and standard deviation. In their study of trigonometry, students learn how to use the parallel measuring scales of degrees and radians, and when to choose one over the other. In "solving" triangles (finding the measures of all sides and angles, and the area), they use trigonometric relationships to make indirect measurements.

Problem Solving

NCTM Standard for Grades 9–12

- Build new mathematical knowledge through problem solving
- Solve problems that arise in mathematics and in other contexts
- Apply and adapt a variety of appropriate strategies to solve problems
- Monitor and reflect on the process of mathematical problem solving

Key Processes in Prentice Hall
Algebra 1, Geometry, Algebra 2

- Solve problems taken from the student's current and future world (Real-World Connection Examples throughout each text)
- Use a variety of appropriate methods to solve problems (Examples showing two methods throughout each text)
- Construct an appropriate expression, equation, or function to solve a problem (Examples using the "Relate-Define-Write" model throughout A1 and A2)
- Use various problem solving strategies as appropriate (reviewed in the Skills Handbook of each text)
- Build understanding of new topics through problem solving (Investigations and Reading for Problem Solving throughout each text)
- Reflect on the process of problem solving (Checks for Reasonableness, Writing, Critical Thinking, Reasoning, and Error Analysis exercises throughout each text)

Background and Progression

The Prentice Hall Mathematics Program for the middle grades contains a rich problem solving strand, including lessons each year covering ten problem solving strategies.

In **Algebra 1, Geometry,** and **Algebra 2,** the strategies are reviewed in the Skills Handbook. In each text, students practice the critical skill of expressing mathematical relationships from real-world problems with symbolic models. Each text contains numerous real-world examples, many of which use the "Relate-Define-Write" format to guide the student in choosing and writing a correct model.

Where possible, examples show more than one method for solving a problem. Many examples include a check for reasonableness. Investigations found throughout each text allow students to form their understanding of a new math topic through guided discovery. The Reading for Problem Solving pages model the thinking of an inquiring student.

Writing, Critical Thinking, Reasoning, and Error Analysis exercises allow students to analyze and verbalize their own understanding of the problem solving process.

 *For more **Math Background** on every lesson, see page B before each chapter and see each lesson's teaching notes.*

Reasoning and Proof

NCTM Standard for Grades 9–12

- Recognize reasoning and proof as fundamental aspects of mathematics
- Make and investigate mathematical conjectures
- Develop and evaluate mathematical arguments and proofs
- Select and use various types of reasoning and methods of proof

Key Processes in Prentice Hall
Algebra 1, Geometry, Algebra 2

- Use inductive reasoning to make and investigate conjectures (Make a Conjecture exercises and Investigation pages throughout each text)
- Develop deductive proof in various formats, including paragraph, flow, two-column, indirect, and coordinate proof (A1: Ch 1; G: Ch 2–12; A2: Ch 6, 14)
- Apply appropriate reasoning to analyze mathematical statements (Checks for Reasonableness, Writing, Critical Thinking, Reasoning, and Error Analysis exercises throughout each text)
- Study and write proofs of geometric theorems (G: Ch 2–12)
- Study and write proofs of algebraic theorems, properties, and equivalences (A1: Ch 1; A2: Ch 6, 8, 14)
- Explain work and justify conclusions (Writing, Critical Thinking, Reasoning, Error Analysis, Short Response, and Extended Response exercises throughout each text)

Background and Progression

In middle grades, students identify the use of Commutative, Associative, Identity, Inverse, and Distributive properties. They use these properties and the Properties of equality to justify steps in solving equations. Students also differentiate deductive and inductive reasoning.

In *Algebra 1,* students solve equations using the properties of real numbers and of equality to justify their steps. These justifications are extended to simple algebraic proofs.

In *Geometry,* students develop an understanding of the structure and concepts of Euclidean plane geometry, building naturally on the step-by-step processes of algebra. They prove theorems in more than one way using paragraph proofs, flow proofs, and two-column proofs.

In *Algebra 2,* students further their understanding and ability to prove concepts not only by deduction but also by using mathematical induction.

Communication

NCTM Standard for Grades 9–12

- Organize and consolidate their mathematical thinking through communication
- Communicate their mathematical thinking coherently and clearly to peers, teachers, and others
- Analyze and evaluate the mathematical thinking and strategies of others
- Use the language of mathematics to express mathematical ideas precisely

Key Processes in Prentice Hall
Algebra 1, Geometry, Algebra 2

- Write about mathematical concepts by summarizing, comparing, analyzing, and explaining (Writing, Critical Thinking, Reasoning, Short Response, and Extended Response exercises throughout each text)
- Understand the language and notations of mathematics (Reading Math notes and Reading for Problem Solving pages throughout each text and Understanding Vocabulary exercises in each Chapter Review)
- Use appropriate notation to express mathematical relationships in real-world contexts (Examples using the "Relate-Define-Write" model throughout A1 and A2, Reading Comprehension exercises, and the Reading for Problem Solving pages in each text)
- Analyze sample work to find errors (Error Analysis exercises throughout each text)

Background and Progression

The Prentice Hall Mathematics Program for the middle grades gives students numerous opportunities to explain and justify their reasoning.

The *Algebra 1, Geometry,* and *Algebra 2* textbooks continue this rich communication strand. In-lesson Investigations and Investigation pages have students develop critical concepts, which students are encouraged first to summarize and then to use in exercises.

The Reading for Problem Solving pages focus on a variety of topics to help students read more effectively, so that they can write, speak, and think mathematically. The Reading Math hints in lessons help students use the language and notation of mathematics correctly and relate new mathematical vocabulary to English terms they already know.

Students are given instruction on answering Short Response questions with two-point rubrics and Extended Response questions with four-point rubrics. Throughout each text, students get ample opportunity to answer rubric-based exercises.

 *For more **Math Background** on every lesson, see page B before each chapter and see each lesson's teaching notes.*

Connections

NCTM Standard for Grades 9–12

- Recognize and use connections among mathematical ideas
- Understand how mathematical ideas interconnect and build on one another to produce a coherent whole
- Recognize and apply mathematics in contexts outside of mathematics

Key Processes in Prentice Hall
Algebra 1, Geometry, Algebra 2

- Solve problems in more than one way (A1 and A2: Examples showing two methods; G: Alternative proofs)
- Solve problems arising from real-world contexts (Real-World Connection Examples, Real-World Snapshots, and application and Reading Comprehension exercises throughout each text)
- Use algebraic concepts such as the coordinate plane, slope, vectors, matrices with transformations, and properties of geometric figures (A1: Ch 5; G: Ch 3, 5, 6, 9, 11,12; A2: Ch 4, 10)
- Use algebraic equations to solve measurement problems in geometry (throughout G)
- Use geometric concepts with probability, systems of equations, functions, and quadratic relations (A1: Ch 7, 10–12; G: Ch 7; A2: Ch 2, 3, 5–13)

Background and Progression

In middle grades, students make connections between geometric and algebraic concepts through graphing geometric figures in the coordinate plane and using slope to investigate the concepts of parallelism and perpendicularity.

In *Algebra 1,* students use algebra to develop formulas for geometric measurement and to describe statistical relationships (lines of best fit). Critical Thinking exercises have students make connections between previously learned material and lesson content. Students understand geometric relationships using slope, midpoint, and distance formulas.

In *Geometry,* students use algebra to interpret and apply geometric relationships. Students take an alternative look at many geometric facts by revisiting them in the coordinate plane.

In *Algebra 2,* students use matrices to describe transformations in the coordinate plane. They extend algebra-geometry connections to reinforce the structure and processes involving functions and conic sections.

Representation

NCTM Standard for Grades 9–12

- Create and use representations to organize, record, and communicate mathematical ideas
- Select, apply, and translate among mathematical representations to solve problems
- Use representations to model and interpret physical, social, and mathematical phenomena

Key Processes in Prentice Hall
Algebra 1, Geometry, Algebra 2

- Organize mathematical information in order to make and support conjectures (Investigations throughout each text)
- Use tables, graphs, verbal rules, and symbolic rules interchangeably as appropriate (A1: Ch 5–8, 10-12; A2: Ch 1, 3, 5, 6, 8–10, 12, 13)
- Choose an appropriate algebraic function model for two-variable measurement data (A1: Ch 10; A2: Ch 2, 5, 8)
- Solve real-world problems by creating a mathematical model to represent the essential mathematics involved (Examples using the "Relate-Define-Write" model in A1 and A2, application exercises, Reading Comprehension exercises, and Real-World Snapshots throughout each text)

Background and Progression

In the middle grades, students have experiences using tables, rules, and graphs to describe functional relationships. They also use tables in problem solving situations to organize real-world data.

In *Algebra 1,* students gain facility in graphing these families of functions: linear, quadratic, exponential, and rational functions. Using tables and graphs, students determine which function best models a given set of data.

In *Geometry,* students learn to recognize, apply, and interpret geometric principles in real-world settings, and frequently use coordinate methods to take another look at these principles.

In *Algebra 2,* students extend their knowledge of the families of functions to polynomial, logarithmic, and trigonometric functions. They also use three-variable equations to model problem situations.

 *For more **Math Background** on every lesson, see page B before each chapter and see each lesson's teaching notes.*

Pacing Options for Algebra 2

Pacing Guide

This chart is provided merely as a guide to help you customize your course. To accommodate flexible scheduling, most lessons are subdivided into objectives. Within the lessons of the Student Edition, these objectives are indicated in red by the symbol ▼. The Assignment Guide for each lesson indicates which exercises in the Student Edition correspond to each objective of the lesson.

Detailed Chapter Pacing Options precede each chapter and give you lesson-by-lesson pacing suggestions for that specific chapter. For information about Block Scheduling, see page A before each chapter.

CHAPTER	Algebra 2 Regular	Algebra 2 With Discrete Math	Algebra 2 With Trigonometry	Algebra 2 Comprehensive Course
1	15 days	12 days	12 days	11 days
2	15 days	13 days	13 days	11 days
3	14 days	11 days	11 days	10 days
4	18 days	16 days	16 days	13 days
5	18 days	15 days	15 days	13 days
6	19 days	16 days	16 days	13 days
7	17 days	15 days	15 days	13 days
8	14 days	11 days	11 days	10 days
9	16 days	14 days	14 days	12 days
10	14 days	12 days	12 days	10 days
11	—	11 days	—	10 days
12	—	14 days	—	12 days
13	—	—	13 days	11 days
14	—	—	12 days	11 days
Total	160 days	160 days	160 days	160 days

Differentiated Scope of Course

R = Regular   D = with Discrete Math   T = with Trigonometry   C = Comprehensive

Chapter 1 Tools of Algebra

	R	D	T	C
1-1: Properties of Real Numbers	✓	✓	✓	✓
• Investigation: Exploring Pi	✓	✓	✓	✓
1-2: Algebraic Expressions	✓	✓	✓	✓
1-3: Solving Equations	✓	✓	✓	✓
• Technology: Spreadsheets		✓		✓
1-4: Solving Inequalities	✓	✓	✓	✓
1-5: Absolute Value Equations and Inequalities	✓	✓	✓	✓
1-6: Probability	✓	✓	✓	✓

Chapter 2 Functions, Equations, and Graphs

	R	D	T	C
• Algebra 1 Review: The Coordinate Plane	✓	✓	✓	✓
2-1: Relations and Functions	✓	✓	✓	✓
2-2: Linear Equations	✓	✓	✓	✓
• Extension: Piecewise Functions		✓		✓
2-3: Direct Variation	✓	✓	✓	✓
2-4: Using Linear Models	✓	✓	✓	✓
• Technology: Finding a Line of Best Fit	✓	✓	✓	✓
2-5: Absolute Value Functions and Graphs	✓	✓	✓	✓
2-6: Vertical and Horizontal Translations	✓	✓	✓	✓
2-7: Two-Variable Inequalities	✓	✓	✓	✓

Chapter 3 Linear Systems

	R	D	T	C
3-1: Graphing Systems of Equations	✓	✓	✓	✓
• Extension: Parametric Equations				✓
3-2: Solving Systems Algebraically	✓	✓	✓	✓
3-3: Systems of Inequalities	✓	✓	✓	✓
3-4: Linear Programming	✓	✓	✓	✓
• Technology: Linear Programming	✓	✓	✓	✓
3-5: Graphs in Three Dimensions	✓	✓	✓	✓
3-6: Systems With Three Variables	✓	✓	✓	✓

Chapter 4 Matrices

	R	D	T	C
4-1: Organizing Data Into Matrices	✓	✓	✓	✓
4-2: Adding and Subtracting Matrices	✓	✓	✓	✓
• Technology: Working With Matrices	✓	✓	✓	✓
4-3: Matrix Multiplication	✓	✓	✓	✓
• Geometry Review: Geometric Transformations	✓	✓	✓	✓
4-4: Geometric Transformations With Matrices	✓	✓	✓	✓
4-5: 2 × 2 Matrices, Determinants, and Inverses	✓	✓	✓	✓
4-6: 3 × 3 Matrices, Determinants, and Inverses	✓	✓	✓	✓

	R	D	T	C
• Extension: Networks				✓
4-7: Inverse Matrices and Systems	✓	✓	✓	✓
4-8: Augmented Matrices and Systems	✓	✓	✓	✓

Chapter 5 Quadratic Equations and Functions

	R	D	T	C
5-1: Modeling Data With Quadratic Functions	✓	✓	✓	✓
• Technology: Using Residuals				✓
5-2: Properties of Parabolas	✓	✓	✓	✓
5-3: Translating Parabolas	✓	✓	✓	✓
5-4: Factoring Quadratic Expressions	✓	✓	✓	✓
• Algebra 1 Review: Square Roots and Radicals	✓	✓	✓	✓
5-5: Quadratic Equations	✓	✓	✓	✓
• Extension: Quadratic Inequalities				✓
5-6: Complex Numbers	✓	✓	✓	✓
• Investigation: Completing the Square	✓	✓	✓	✓
5-7: Completing the Square	✓	✓	✓	✓
5-8: The Quadratic Formula	✓	✓	✓	✓

Chapter 6 Polynomials and Polynomial Functions

	R	D	T	C
6-1: Polynomial Functions	✓	✓	✓	✓
• Extension: End Behavior	✓	✓	✓	✓
6-2: Polynomials and Linear Factors	✓	✓	✓	✓
6-3: Dividing Polynomials	✓	✓	✓	✓
6-4: Solving Polynomial Equations	✓	✓	✓	✓
• Extension: Descartes's Rule of Signs				✓
6-5: Theorems About Roots of Polynomial Equations	✓	✓	✓	✓
6-6: The Fundamental Theorem of Algebra	✓	✓	✓	✓
6-7: Permutations and Combinations	✓	✓	✓	✓
• Investigation: Pascal's Triangle	✓	✓	✓	✓
6-8: The Binomial Theorem	✓	✓	✓	✓

Chapter 7 Radical Functions and Rational Exponents

	R	D	T	C
• Algebra 1 Review: Properties of Exponents	✓	✓	✓	✓
7-1: Roots and Radical Expressions	✓	✓	✓	✓
7-2: Multiplying and Dividing Radical Expressions	✓	✓	✓	✓
7-3: Binomial Radical Expressions	✓	✓	✓	✓
7-4: Rational Exponents	✓	✓	✓	✓
7-5: Solving Radical Equations	✓	✓	✓	✓
7-6: Function Operations	✓	✓	✓	✓
7-7: Inverse Relations and Functions	✓	✓	✓	✓
• Technology: Graphing Inverses				✓
7-8: Graphing Radical Functions	✓	✓	✓	✓

Using Your Book for Success

Welcome to Prentice Hall *Algebra 2*. There are many features built into the daily lessons of this text that will help you learn the important skills and concepts you will need to be successful in this course. Look through the following pages for some study tips that you will find useful as you complete each lesson.

Instant Check System
An *Instant Check System*, built into the text and marked with a ✓, allows you to check your understanding of skills before moving on to the next topic.

✓ Diagnosing Readiness
Complete the *Diagnosing Readiness* exercises to see what topics you may need to review before you begin the chapter.

✓ Check Skills You'll Need
Complete the *Check Skills You'll Need* exercises to make sure you have the skills needed to successfully learn the concepts in the lesson.

New Vocabulary
New Vocabulary is listed for each lesson so you can pre-read the text. As each term is introduced, it is highlighted in yellow.

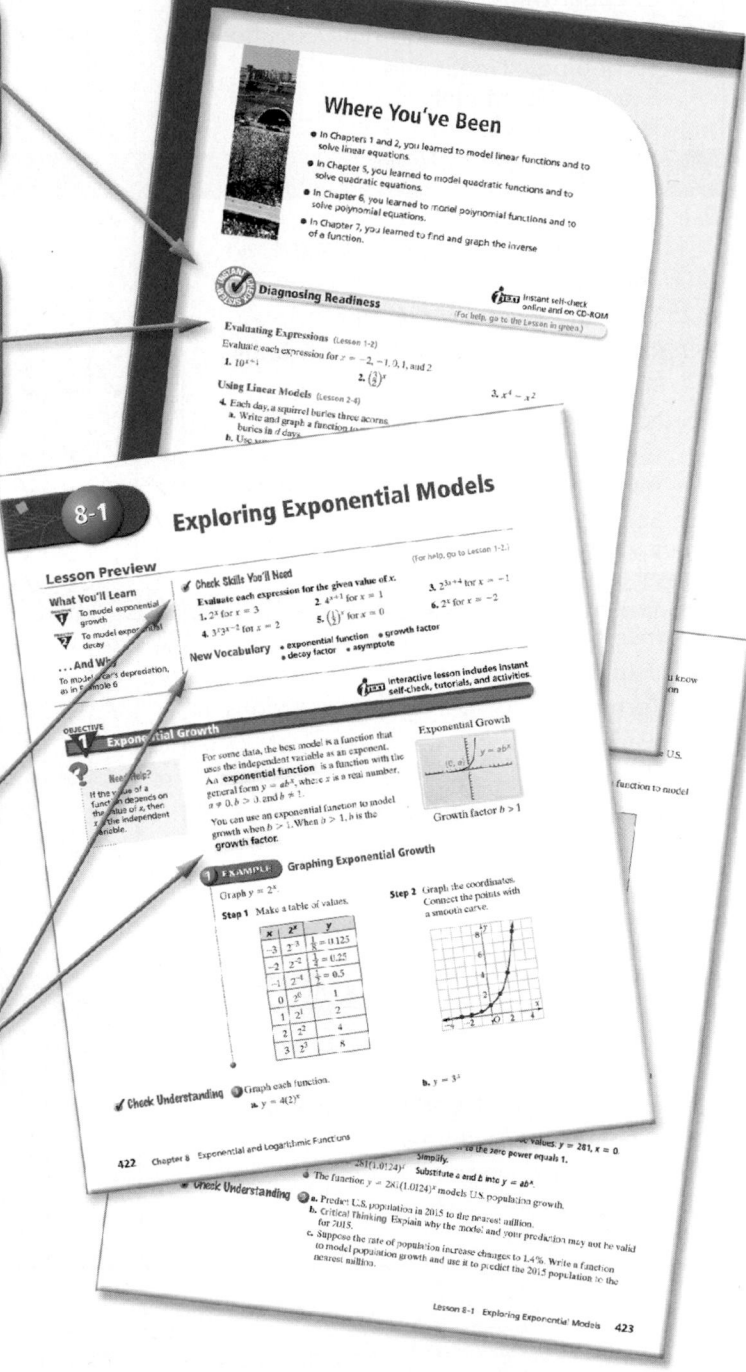

T44

Pacing Options

Need Help?

Need Help? notes provide a quick review of a concept you need to understand the topic being presented. Look for the green labels throughout the text that tell you where to "Go" for help.

✔ Check Understanding

Every lesson includes numerous *Examples*, each followed by a *Check Understanding* question that you can do on your own to see if you understand the skill being introduced. Check your progress with the answers at the back of the book.

Reading Math

The *Reading Math* hints help you to use mathematical notation correctly, understand new mathematical vocabulary, and translate mathematical symbols into everyday English so you can talk about what you've learned.

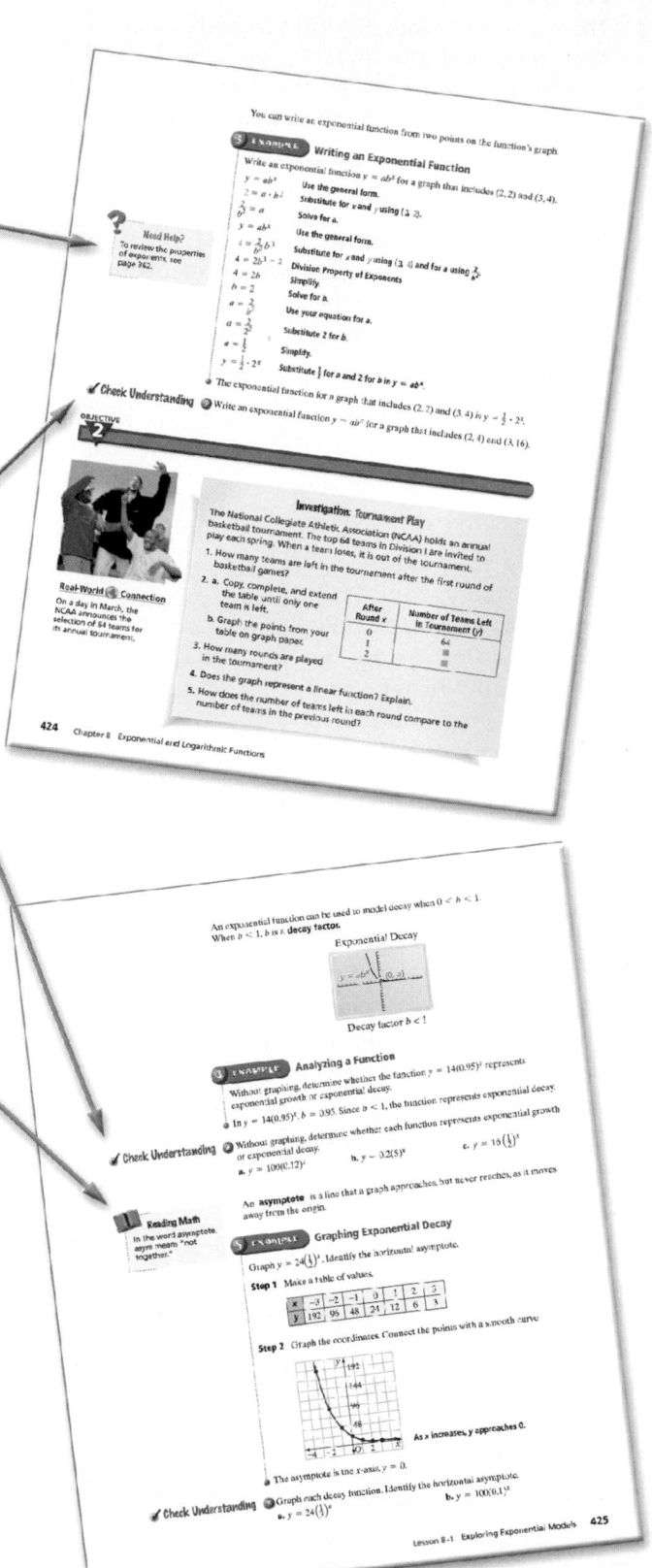

Exercises

There are numerous *Exercises* in each lesson that give you the practice you need to master the concepts in the lesson. Each practice set includes the following sections.

A: Practice by Example

The *A: Practice by Example* exercises refer you back to the Examples in the lesson, in case you need help with completing these exercises.

B: Apply Your Skills

The *B: Apply Your Skills* exercises combine skills from earlier lessons to offer you richer skill exercises and multi-step application problems.

C: Challenge

The *C: Challenge* exercises give you an opportunity to solve problems that extend and stretch your thinking.

Standardized Test Prep

Standardized Test Prep exercises give you daily practice with the types of test question formats that you will encounter on state and national tests.

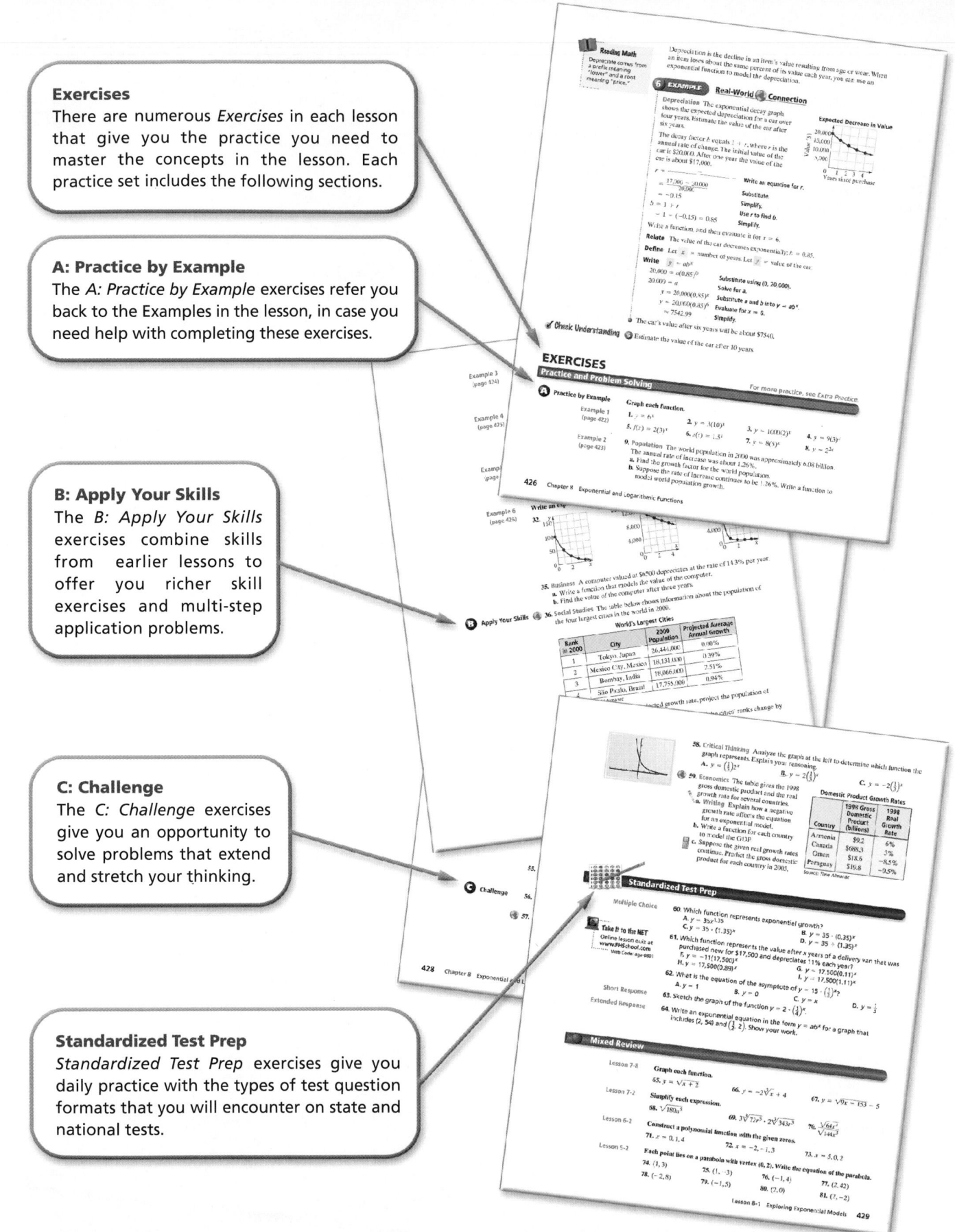

Test-Taking Strategies

Test-Taking Strategies in every chapter teach you strategies to be successful and give you practice in the skills you need to pass state tests and standardized national exams.

Standardized Test Prep

Standardized Test Prep pages in every chapter give you more opportunities to prepare for the tests you will have to take.

Test Item Formats

The *Standardized Test Prep* exercises in your book give you the practice you need to answer all types of test questions.

- *Multiple Choice*
- *Quantitative Comparison*
- *Gridded Response*, for which you write your answer in a grid
- *Short Response*, which are scored using a rubric
- *Extended Response*, which are scored using a rubric
- *Reading Comprehension*

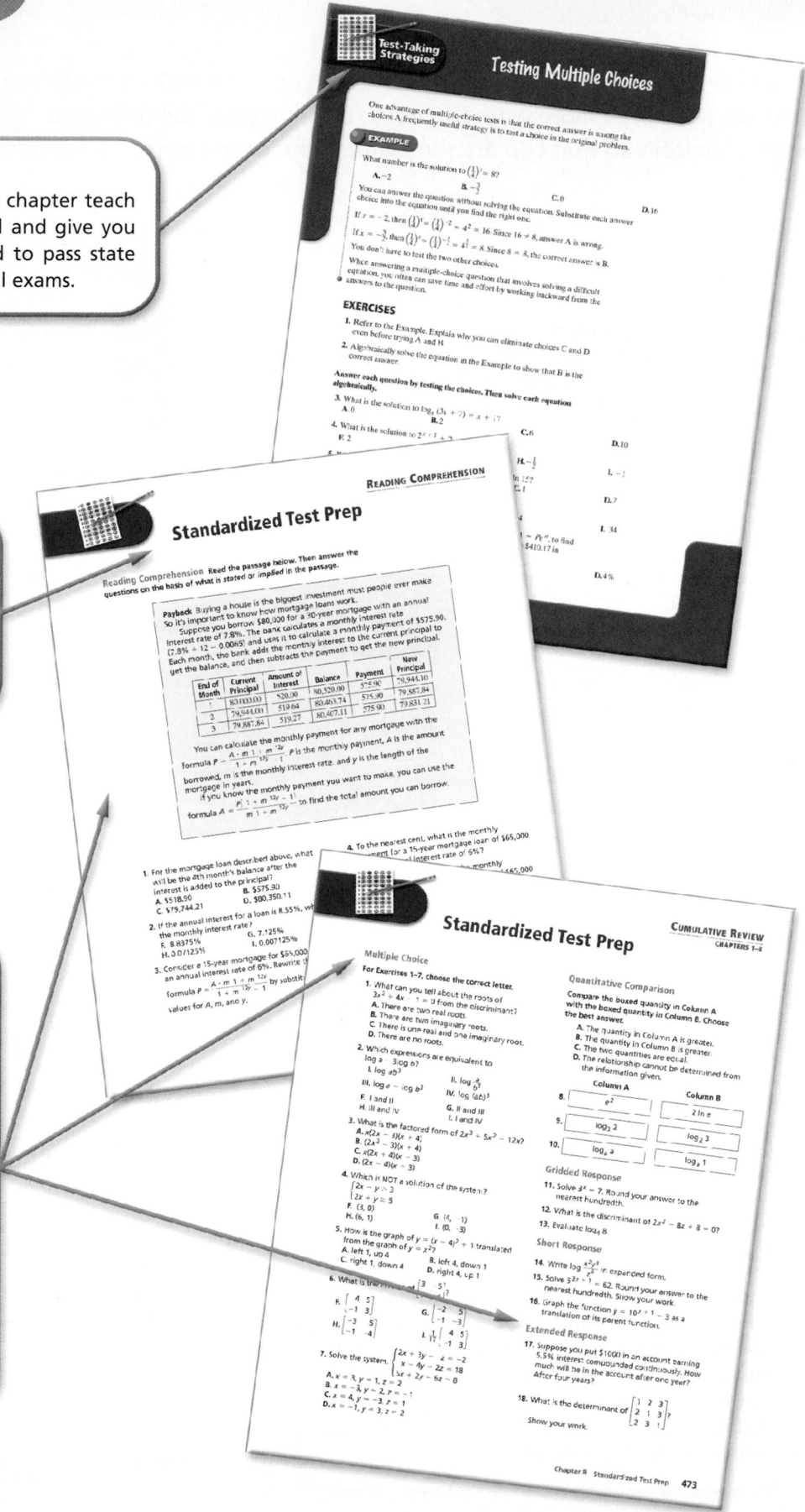

In addition to the Reading Math hints shown on page xxiii, your *Algebra 2* text provides even more ways for you to develop your ability to read mathematically so that you are successful in this course and on state tests.

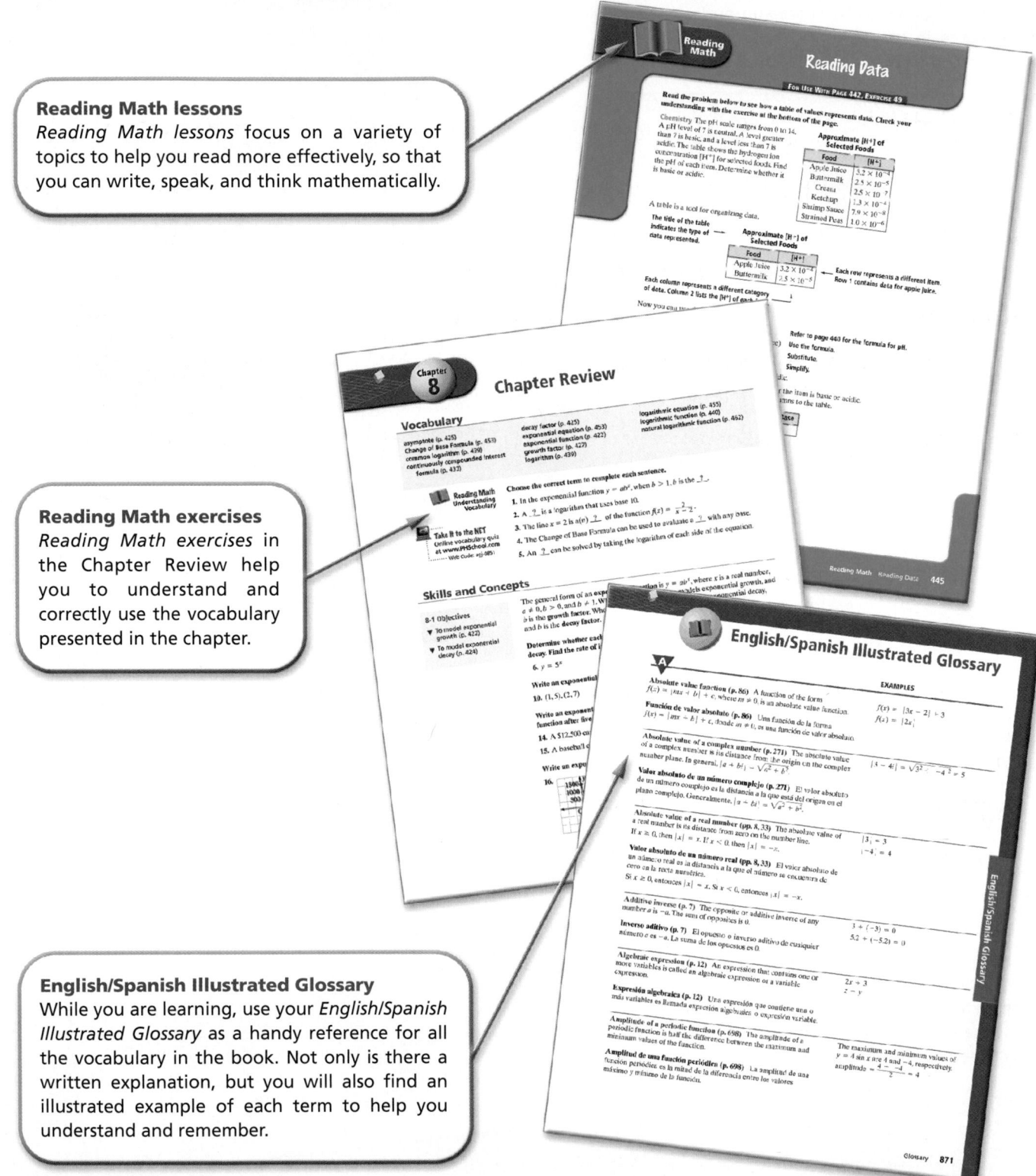

Reading Math lessons
Reading Math lessons focus on a variety of topics to help you read more effectively, so that you can write, speak, and think mathematically.

Reading Math exercises
Reading Math exercises in the Chapter Review help you to understand and correctly use the vocabulary presented in the chapter.

English/Spanish Illustrated Glossary
While you are learning, use your *English/Spanish Illustrated Glossary* as a handy reference for all the vocabulary in the book. Not only is there a written explanation, but you will also find an illustrated example of each term to help you understand and remember.

Dorling Kindersley (DK) is an international publishing company that specializes in the creation of high-quality, illustrated information books for children and adults. DK is part of the Pearson family of companies.

Real-World Snapshots
The *Real-World Snapshots* feature applies the exciting and unique graphic presentation style found in Dorling Kindersley books to show you how mathematics is used in real life.

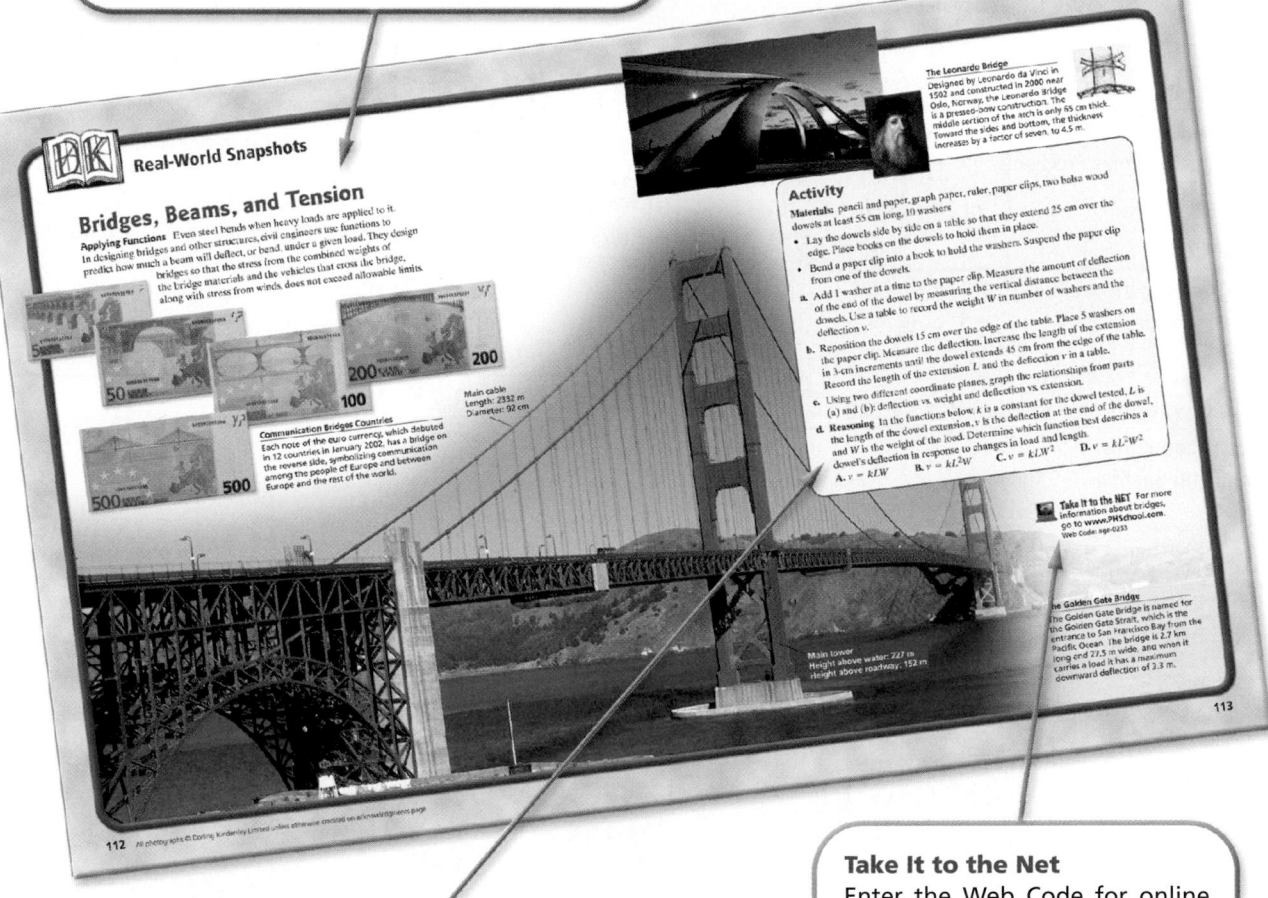

Activities
Using data from these pages and data that you gather, complete the hands-on *Activities* to apply the mathematics you are learning in real-world situations.

Take It to the Net
Enter the Web Code for online information you can use to learn more about the topic of the feature.

Chapter 1

Tools of Algebra

Chapter at a Glance — North Carolina Objectives

1-1 Properties of Real Numbers

| NCTM 1, 2, 8 | ▼ Graphing and Ordering Real Numbers |
| | ▼ Operations With Real Numbers |

1-2 Algebraic Expressions   1.03

| NCTM 2, 3 | ▼ Evaluating Algebraic Expressions |
| | ▼ Simplifying Algebraic Expressions |

1-3 Solving Equations   1.03

| NCTM 1, 3, 9 | ▼ Solving Equations |
| | ▼ Writing Equations To Solve Problems |

1-4 Solving Inequalities   1.03

| NCTM 1, 2, 4, 10 | ▼ Solving and Graphing Inequalities |
| | ▼ Compound Inequalities |

1-5 Absolute Value Equations and Inequalities   2.08a

| NCTM 2, 7, 10 | ▼ Absolute Value Equations |
| | ▼ Absolute Value Inequalities |

1-6 Probability

| NCTM 3, 5, 10 | ▼ Experimental Probability |
| | ▼ Theoretical Probability |

NCTM STANDARDS 2000

1	Number and Operations	6	Problem Solving
2	Algebra	7	Reasoning and Proof
3	Geometry	8	Communication
4	Measurement	9	Connections
5	Data Analysis and Probability	10	Representation

Pacing Options

This chart suggests pacing only for the lessons and their parts. It is provided as a possible guide. It will help you determine how much time you have in your schedule to cover other components, such as the features, Chapter Review, and Chapter Test.

Day	Traditional (45 min.)	Block (90 min.)
1	1-1 ▼	1-1 ▼
2	1-1 ▼ ▼	1-1 ▼
3	1-1 ▼	1-1 ▼
4	1-2 ▼	1-2 ▼ ▼
5	1-2 ▼	1-3 ▼
6	1-3 ▼	1-3 ▼
7	1-3 ▼ ▼	1-4 ▼
8	1-3 ▼	1-4 ▼
9	1-4 ▼	1-5 ▼ ▼
10	1-4 ▼ ▼	1-6 ▼
11	1-4 ▼	1-6 ▼
12	1-5 ▼ ▼	
13	1-6 ▼	
14	1-6 ▼ ▼	
15	1-6 ▼	

NAEP Correlation (National Assessment of Educational Progress 2000 Mathematics Objectives)

1-1	1-2	1-3	1-4	1-5	1-6
N2e, N3a, A3a	N3a, A1f, A5b	M5, G8, N3a	N2e, N3b, A4b	N2e, A3a, A4a	D10a, D10b, D11a

N = Number Sense, Properties, and Operations; **M** = Measurement; **G** = Geometry and Spatial Sense; **D** = Data Analysis, Statistics, and Probability; **A** = Algebra and Functions

Math Background

Chapter Overview

This chapter summarizes and reviews basic concepts and properties of real numbers. The focus is on properties of operations, equality, and inequalities and how these properties are used in solving and graphing one-variable equations and inequalities. Students review absolute value and then solve equations and inequalities that involve absolute value. The chapter concludes with a look at fundamental concepts of experimental, theoretical, and geometric probability.

The ideas and skills discussed in this chapter will be used throughout the course. Appropriate applications to real-world problems are considered at each stage. Many exercises provide good opportunities to relate algebraic to geometric concepts.

Properties of Real Numbers   1-1

Students who have difficulty ordering rational numbers whose absolute values are less than 1 may need extra practice ordering similar irrational numbers. They may also need to discuss the order relation between a number and its square root in terms of whether the number's absolute value is greater than or less than 1.

This lesson defines the absolute value of a number in terms of its distance from 0 on the number line. A more formal algebraic definition of absolute value is given in Lesson 1-2.

Algebraic Expressions   1-2

Some students may need to review the order of operations. A common student error is to misapply the Distributive Property. Students who have difficulty with this property may find it helpful to examine it by using geometric models. They may also find it helpful to express the Distributive Property verbally in their own terms.

The importance of mathematical modeling cannot be overemphasized to students. The ability to create graphs, tables, and equations that reflect real-world situations is a most powerful mathematical tool, important to many business, scientific, and educational endeavors. The model is a shorthand way of approximating a great amount of data. It can be used to interpolate (estimate) data between measured points and to extrapolate (predict) data beyond measured points.

Solving Equations   1-3

Solving equations depends on creating equivalent equations. Students are familiar with the addition, subtraction, multiplication and division properties of equality, but may not realize that they have also been using the other properties. In particular, Substitution seems so apparent that they may not realize it is a necessary justification. You may wish to go through a detailed explanation of a proof step justified by 'Simplify' and show the various substitutions that word summarizes.

Solving Inequalities   1-4

Because the procedures for solving inequalities in one variable are almost identical to solving equations in one variable, the fundamental difference between equations and inequalities may become obscured. It is important to emphasize that equations in one variable have a single solution, while inequalities may have more than one solution. Thus, inequalities are useful in modeling real-world situations where an exact value is not appropriate. For example, in automotive repair, many engine parts have allowable sizes that fall within a range of values.

Absolute Value Equations and Inequalities   1-5

Students who master the logic of 'AND' and 'OR' may enjoy trying to create and solve compound absolute value sentences. They could first consider $|x - 3| > 4$ OR $|2x - 3| \leq 3$ [$x \leq 2$ OR $x > 7$], and then replace OR with AND [no solution].

Probability   1-6

Help students connect their intuitive ideas about probability with the ideas in the lesson. For example, they know from *experience* that for a set of actual tosses, the frequency of heads may not be the same as the frequency of tails.

These exercises give students additional practice in working with numbers derived from realistic settings.

# Ongoing Assessment and Intervention

Tools for Monitoring Student Progress

The Prentice Hall *Algebra 2* program provides you with many options for assessment in the Student Edition, the Teacher's Edition and the teaching resources. From these options you may choose instructional materials and techniques that are appropriate for your students and support your district's curriculum requirements.

 ### Instant Check System™ in Chapter 1

Allows students to check their own learning before, during, and after each lesson.

Diagnosing Readiness before the chapter (p. 2)

Check Skills You'll Need exercises in each lesson (pp. 4, 12, 18, 26, 33, 39)

Check Understanding questions with each Example (pp. 6, 7, 8, 12, 13, 14, 19, 20, 21, 27, 28, 29, 33, 34, 35, 36, 40, 41, 42)

Checkpoint Quiz (pp. 24, 38)

 ### Test Prep in Chapter 1

Teaches students strategies and gives them practice with all the test item formats they will encounter on state tests and standardized national exams.

Standardized Test Prep exercises in each lesson (pp. 10, 17, 23, 31, 38, 45)

Test-Taking Strategies (p. 46)

Standardized Test Prep (p. 51)

All your assessment needs in one place!

Program Assessment

Assess student progress throughout the *Algebra 2* text with blackline masters and CD-ROM.

Assessment Resources

- Checkpoint Quizzes 1 & 2
- Chapter Test, Forms A & B
- Chapter Alternative Assessment

Spanish versions available.

 ### Computer Test Generator

- Unlimited questions of varying difficulty for every lesson objective.
- Create your own practice sheets, quizzes, and tests, or use the pre-made Chapter Tests.
- Diagnose readiness with questions on prerequisite skills.
- Prepare students by making tests based on standardized test objectives.
- Access Algebra 1, Geometry, and Algebra 2 content—all on one CD-ROM.

Test Preparation

A three-step approach to preparing students for high stakes, national, and state exams.

❶ Diagnose & Prescribe

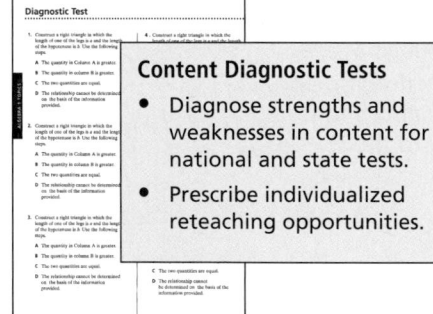

Content Diagnostic Tests
- Diagnose strengths and weaknesses in content for national and state tests.
- Prescribe individualized reteaching opportunities.

❷ Review & Reteach

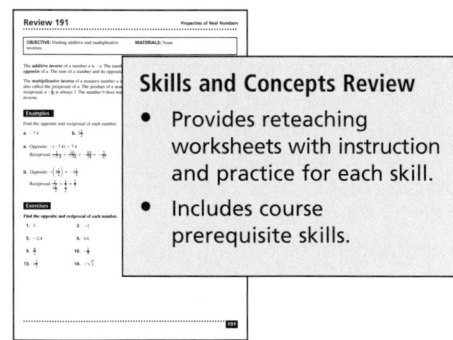

Skills and Concepts Review
- Provides reteaching worksheets with instruction and practice for each skill.
- Includes course prerequisite skills.

❸ Practice & Assess

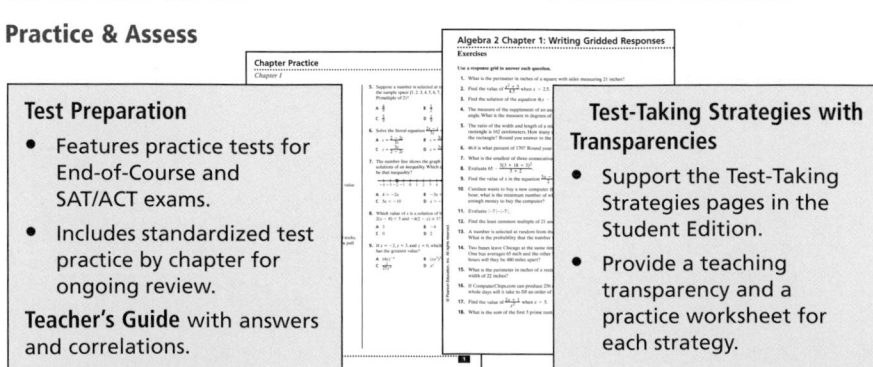

Test Preparation
- Features practice tests for End-of-Course and SAT/ACT exams.
- Includes standardized test practice by chapter for ongoing review.

Teacher's Guide with answers and correlations.

Test-Taking Strategies with Transparencies
- Support the Test-Taking Strategies pages in the Student Edition.
- Provide a teaching transparency and a practice worksheet for each strategy.

 # Reaching All Students

Support in the Student Text and Additional Resources

The textbook, the iText, and other technology components provide numerous opportunities to reach students of various ability levels and learning styles. Each Teacher's Edition lesson suggests how you can help *all* your students be successful and understand the mathematics in Chapter 1.

Below Level

Student Edition
- Diagnosing Readiness*: p. 2
- Check Skills You'll Need*: pp. 4, 12, 18, 26, 33, 39

Reteaching
Chapter 1 Support File: pp. 8–13

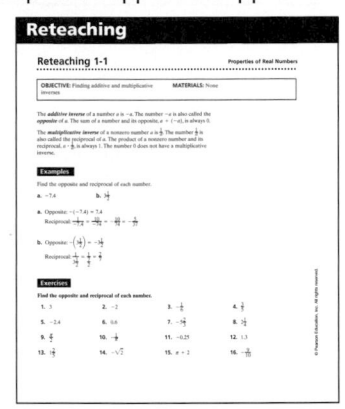

Advanced Learners

Student Edition
- Challenge exercises: pp. 10, 16, 23, 31, 37, 44

Enrichment
Chapter 1 Support File: pp. 14–19

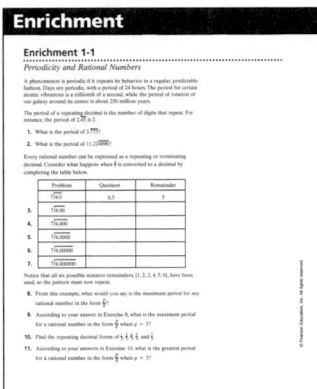

Connections to Precalculus Masters
Chapter 1 Enrichment Topic:
Real Numbers

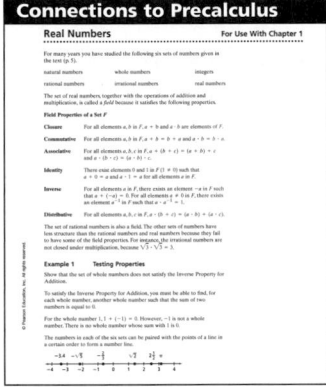

* Can be used with all ability levels to ensure mastery of prerequisite skills.

Reading and Math Literacy

Student Edition
- Vocabulary: pp. 3, 47, *plus* in every Lesson Preview
- Reading Math: pp. 5, 7, 8, 12, 18, 27, 32, 34, 40
- Illustrated Glossary: pp. 871–913

Reading and Math Literacy Masters
Chapter 1: pp. 1–4

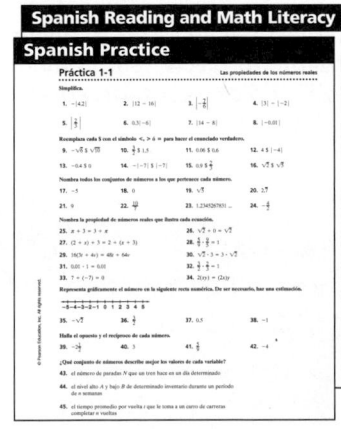

English Learners

Student Edition
- English/Spanish Illustrated Glossary: pp. 871–913

Workbook and Masters
Spanish Practice Workbook: pp. 2–7
Spanish Reading and Math Literacy Masters: pp. 1–4

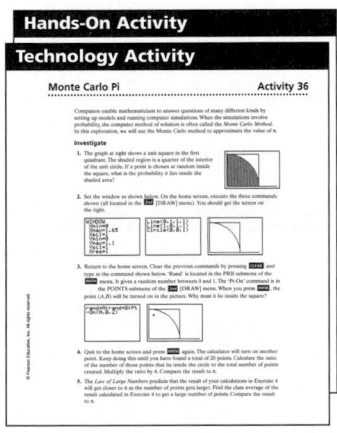

Learning Styles

Student Edition
- Investigation: pp. 4, 11, 39
- Technology: p. 25
- Writing: pp. 10, 11, 17, 23, 25, 30, 37, 44

Activity Masters
Hands-On Activities: 31, 32
Technology Activities: 36

Program Resources

	Teaching Resources in Grab & Go™ Files				Resources for Reaching All Students			Spanish Resources			Transparencies				Presentation Assistant Plus!
	Practice	Reteach	Enrich	Checkpoint Quiz	Reading & Math Literacy	Technology Activities	Hands-On Activities	Practice	Reading & Math Literacy	Checkpoint Quiz	Skills Check	Additional Examples	Answers to Exercises	Lesson Quiz	Prentice Hall Presentation Pro CD-ROM
1-1	■	■	■		■			■	■		■	■	■	■	
1-2	■	■	■				■	■			■	■	■	■	■
1-3	■	■	■	■	■			■	■	■	■	■	■	■	■
1-4	■	■	■					■				■	■	■	■
1-5	■	■	■	■	■			■	■	■	■	■	■	■	■
1-6	■	■	■			■	■	■			■	■	■	■	■
For the chapter	Chapter Tests, Alternative Assessment, Cumulative Review, Cumulative Assessment				Connections to Precalculus Masters			Spanish Chapter Tests, Alternative Assessment, Cumulative Review, Cumulative Assessment			Classroom Aid Transparencies				

Also available for use with the chapter:

  **PRENTICE HALL ASSESSMENT SYSTEM** *See page 2C.*

- Practice Workbook
- Solution Key

- For teacher support and access to student Web site materials, use Web Code agk-5500.
- For additional online and technology resources, see below.

Technology

i TEXT — Online and on CD-ROM

Complete Interactive Student Text online and on CD-ROM—with instant feedback assessment, tutorial help, dynamic activities, instructional and real-world videos, audio, and additional practice.

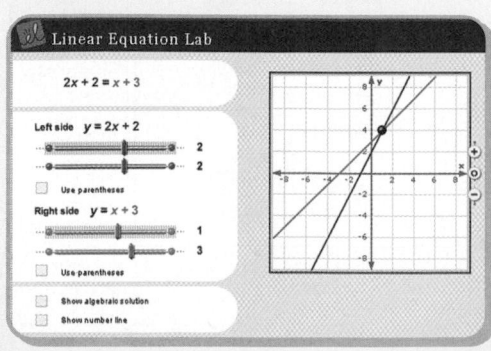

www.PHSchool.com — For Students

Use **Web Codes** for easy access to online activities, chapter projects, self-grading lesson quizzes and chapter tests, vocabulary quizzes, updated data sources, graphing calculator procedures, and more.

PH SuccessNet — For Teachers

Online lesson planning with built-in state correlations, all the teaching resources, complete reference library, your own calendar and Teacher Web page, professional development, and more.

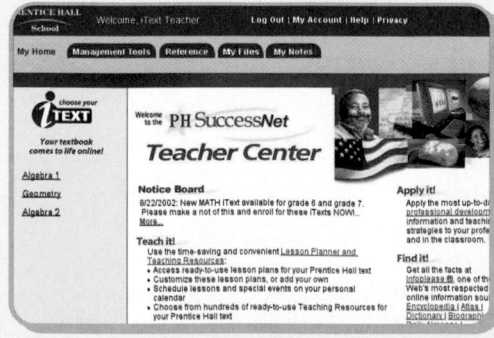

Presentation Assistant Plus!

The Prentice Hall *Presentation Assistant Plus!* provides you with the material you need to teach a lesson from beginning to end. Two easy-to-use formats—Transparencies and CD-ROM—allow you to present a lesson the way you are most comfortable.

 ## Transparencies

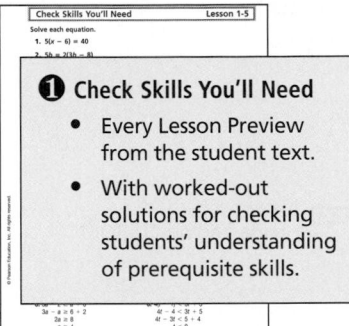

❶ Check Skills You'll Need
- Every Lesson Preview from the student text.
- With worked-out solutions for checking students' understanding of prerequisite skills.

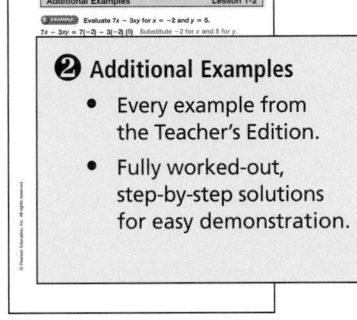

❷ Additional Examples
- Every example from the Teacher's Edition.
- Fully worked-out, step-by-step solutions for easy demonstration.

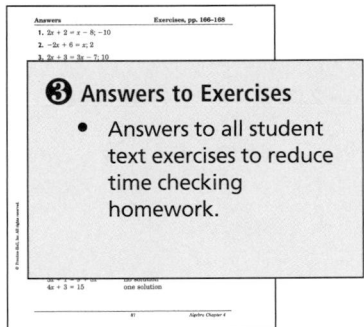

❸ Answers to Exercises
- Answers to all student text exercises to reduce time checking homework.

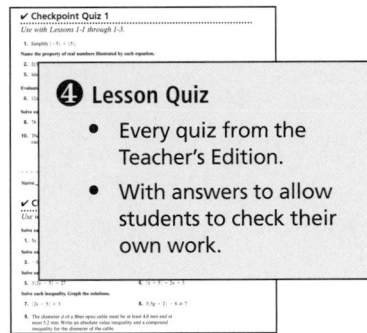

❹ Lesson Quiz
- Every quiz from the Teacher's Edition.
- With answers to allow students to check their own work.

 ## Prentice Hall Presentation Pro CD-ROM

- Includes all Transparencies.
- Conveniently organized by lesson so you can easily ❶ Introduce, ❷ Teach, ❸ Check Homework, and ❹ Assess each lesson.
- Animated examples allow step-by-step instruction at your own pace.
- Easy to edit so you can create custom presentations.

Teaching Chapter 1 Using Presentation Assistant Plus!

	❶ Introduce	❷ Teach	❸ Check Homework	❹ Assess
	Check Skills You'll Need	Additional Examples	Student Edition Answers	Lesson Quiz
1-1	p. 1	pp. 1–2	✔	p. 89
1-2	p. 2	pp. 3–4	✔	p. 89
1-3	p. 3	pp. 4–7	✔	p. 90
1-4	p. 4	pp. 7–9	✔	p. 90
1-5	p. 5	pp. 10–12	✔	p. 91
1-6	p. 6	pp. 12–14	✔	p. 91

 Throughout the Teacher's Edition, this symbol indicates material that is available on transparency in the Presentation Assistant Plus!

 ### Prentice Hall Presentation Pro

CD-ROM with dynamic PowerPoint® presentations for every lesson. Helps you introduce and develop concepts, check homework, and assess progress. Part of Presentation Assistant Plus! *(See above.)*

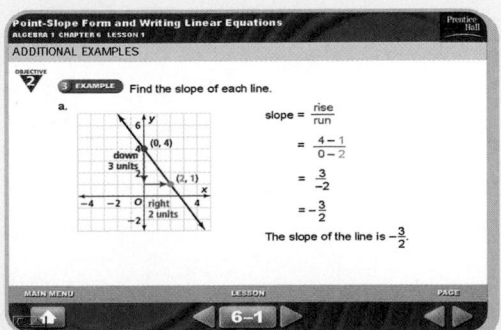

 ### Computer Test Generator

CD-ROM to create practice sheets and tests for course objectives and standardized tests. Includes Instant Chapter Tests™, online testing, and student reports. Part of the PH Assessment System. *(See page 2C.)*

 ### Resource Pro® with Planning Express®

CD-ROM with a lesson planning tool that allows you to import state and local objectives. Includes electronic versions of all the teaching resources.

Tools of Algebra

 Diagnosing Readiness

Students will find answers to these exercises in the back of their textbooks.

For intervention, direct students to:

Adding Rational Numbers
Skills Handbook: p. 845,
Example 1, Exercises 1–10

Subtracting Rational Numbers
Skills Handbook: p. 845,
Example 2, Exercises 2–11

Multiplying and Dividing Rational Numbers
Skills Handbook: p. 845,
Example 3, Exercises 12–20

Using the Order of Operations
Skills Handbook: p. 845,
Example 4, Exercises 21–32

Where You've Been

- In your first course in algebra, you learned to add, subtract, multiply, and divide rational numbers. Rational numbers are the quotients of integers, and they include integers, positive and negative fractions, and positive and negative decimals.

- You have also learned to use the order of operations, which tells how to simplify expressions with grouping symbols, exponents, and operations.

- You have also learned to use algebraic expressions.

 **Instant** **Instant self-check online and on CD-ROM**

Diagnosing Readiness (For help, go to the Skills Handbook.)

Adding Rational Numbers (Skills Handbook page 845)

Find each sum.

1. $6 + (-6)$ **0**
2. $-8 + 6$ **−2**
3. $5.31 + (-7.40)$ **−2.09**
4. $-1.95 + 10$ **8.05**

5. $7\frac{3}{4} + \left(-8\frac{1}{2}\right)$ **−$\frac{3}{4}$**
6. $-2\frac{1}{3} + 3\frac{1}{4}$ **$\frac{11}{12}$**
7. $6\frac{2}{5} + \left(4\frac{3}{10}\right)$ **$10\frac{7}{10}$**
8. $-1\frac{5}{6} + 5\frac{1}{3}$ **$3\frac{1}{2}$**

Subtracting Rational Numbers (Skills Handbook page 845)

Find each difference.

9. $-28 - 14$ **−42**
10. $61 - (-11)$ **72**
11. $-16 - (-25)$ **9**
12. $-6.2 - 3.6$ **−9.8**

13. $-5\frac{2}{3} - \left(-2\frac{1}{3}\right)$ **−$3\frac{1}{3}$**
14. $-2\frac{1}{4} - 3\frac{1}{4}$ **−$5\frac{1}{2}$**
15. $2\frac{2}{3} - 7\frac{1}{3}$ **−$4\frac{2}{3}$**
16. $\frac{5}{2} - \frac{13}{4}$ **−$\frac{3}{4}$**

Multiplying and Dividing Rational Numbers (Skills Handbook page 845)

Find each product or quotient.

17. $-3 \cdot 7$ **−21**
18. $-2.1 \cdot (-3.5)$ **7.35**
19. $-\frac{2}{3} \div 4$ **−$\frac{1}{6}$**
20. $-\frac{3}{8} \div \frac{5}{8}$ **−$\frac{3}{5}$**

Using the Order of Operations (Skills Handbook page 845)

Simplify each expression.

21. $8 \cdot (-3) + 4$ **−20**
22. $3 \cdot 4 - 8 \div 2$ **8**
23. $1 \div 2^2 - 0.54 + 1.26$ **0.97**

24. $9 \div (-3) - 2$ **−5**
25. $5(3 \cdot 5 - 4)$ **55**
26. $1 - (1 - 5)^2 \div (-8)$ **3**

Tools of Algebra

Chapter 1

Key Vocabulary

- absolute value (p. 33)
- absolute value of a real number (p. 8)
- additive inverse (p. 7)
- algebraic expression (p. 12)
- coefficient (p. 13)
- compound inequality (p. 28)
- evaluate (p. 12)
- experimental probability (p. 40)
- extraneous solution (p. 34)
- multiplicative inverse (p. 7)
- opposite (p. 7)
- reciprocal (p. 7)
- sample space (p. 41)
- simulation (p. 40)
- solution of an equation (p. 18)
- term (p. 13)
- theoretical probability (p. 41)
- tolerance (p. 36)
- variable (p. 12)
- variable expression (p. 12)

Where You're Going

- In Chapter 1, you will review and extend your knowledge of algebraic expressions and your skill in solving equations and inequalities.

- You will solve absolute value equations and inequalities by changing them to compound equations and inequalities.

- You will apply theoretical and experimental probabilities to real-world situations such as genetic inheritance.

Real-World Connection Applying what you learn, you will use algebraic expressions on page 13 to solve a problem involving elections.

Chapter 1 Overview

This chapter begins with a review of the properties of real numbers, followed by a review of algebraic expressions. Students are then guided through solving equations, inequalities, and absolute value equations and inequalities. The chapter concludes with a lesson on probability.

Reading Math
- Reading An Example, p. 32

Vocabulary
A complete list of terms, plus vocabulary exercises, appears in the Chapter Review, p. 47.

Illustrated Glossary
Examples for each vocabulary term, plus definitions in both English and Spanish, appear starting on p. 871.

Test-Taking Strategies
Answering Gridded-Response Questions, p. 46

Real-World Connections
Some of the applications you will find in this chapter are recreation (1-1), aeronautics (1-3), basketball (1-5), and biology (1-6).

www.PHSchool.com
Internet support for this chapter includes:
- Self-grading Vocabulary and Chapter 1 Tests
- Chapter Project
- Chapter Planner
- Chapter 1 Resources

Plus

Properties of Real Numbers

1. Plan

Lesson Preview

 **Check Skills You'll Need**

Simplifying Expressions with Integers
Skills Handbook: p. 845
Examples 1–3
Exercises 1–20

Lesson Resources

📁 **Teaching Resources**
Practice, Reteaching, Enrichment

👥 **Reaching All Students**
Practice Workbook 1-1
Spanish Practice Workbook 1-1
Reading and Math Literacy 1A
Spanish Reading & Literacy 1A

⏰ **Presentation Assistant Plus!**
Transparencies
• Check Skills You'll Need 1-1
• Additional Examples 1-1
• Student Edition Answers 1-1
• Lesson Quiz 1-1
PH Presentation Pro CD 1-1

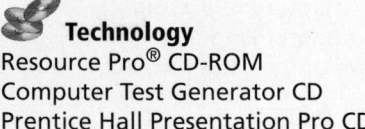 **ASSESSMENT SYSTEM**

Computer Test Generator CD

💿 **Technology**
Resource Pro® CD-ROM
Computer Test Generator CD
Prentice Hall Presentation Pro CD

🖥 **www.PHSchool.com**
Student Site
• Teacher Web Code: agk-5500
• Graphing Calculator, Procedure 1
• Self-grading Lesson Quiz
Teacher Center
• Lesson Planner
• Resources

Plus

Lesson Preview

What You'll Learn

OBJECTIVE 1 To graph and order real numbers

OBJECTIVE 2 To identify and use properties of real numbers

. . . And Why

To classify the numbers used in managing an amusement park, as in Example 1

✓ Check Skills You'll Need

(For help, go to Skills Handbook page 845.)

Simplify.

1. $-(-7.2)$ **7.2**
2. $1 - (-3)$ **4**
3. $-9 + (-4.5)$ **−13.5**
4. $(-3.4)(-2)$ **6.8**
5. $-15 \div 3$ **−5**
6. $\frac{-2}{5} + \frac{3}{-5}$ **−1**

New Vocabulary

• opposite • additive inverse
• reciprocal • multiplicative inverse
• absolute value of a real number

OBJECTIVE 1 **Graphing and Ordering Real Numbers**

 Interactive lesson includes instant self-check, tutorials, and activities.

Real-World Connection

Artists frequently use geometric figures in their work. Juan Gris (1887–1927) used right triangles in this portrait of Picasso.

$\sqrt{2} \approx 1.4; \sqrt{3} \approx 1.7;$
$\sqrt{4} = 2; \sqrt{5} \approx 2.2;$
$\sqrt{6} \approx 2.4; \sqrt{7} \approx 2.6$

Investigation: Estimating Square Roots

1. Use the Pythagorean Theorem to calculate *PB, PC, PD,* and so on, in the figure below.

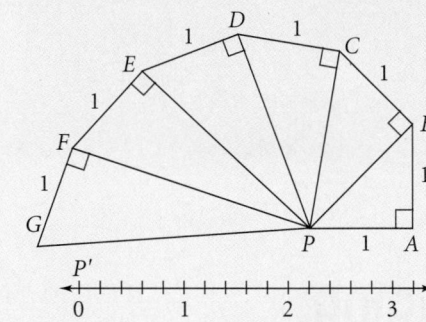

$PB = \sqrt{2}, PC = \sqrt{3},$
$PD = 2, PE = \sqrt{5},$
$PF = \sqrt{6}, PG = \sqrt{7}$

See margin p.5.

2. Copy the number line above. Mark point *B'* so that $P'B' = PB$. Similarly mark points *C', D',* and so on, on your number line.

3. Estimate the decimal coordinates of *B', C', D',* and so on. Copy and complete the table below.

			$\sqrt{3}$	$\sqrt{4}$	$\sqrt{5}$	$\sqrt{6}$
Leg 1	1	$\sqrt{2}$	▪	▪	▪	▪
Leg 2	1	1	1	1	1	1
Hypotenuse	$\sqrt{2} \approx ?$	▪	▪	▪	▪	▪

See left.

4. Evaluate each square root in the table using your calculator. Does the calculator give you exact answers? How do you know? **See margin p. 5.**

4 Chapter 1 Tools of Algebra

Ongoing Assessment and Intervention

Before the Lesson
Diagnose prerequisite skills using:
• Check Skills You'll Need

During the Lesson
Monitor progress using:
• Check Understanding
• Additional Examples
• Standardized Test Prep

After the Lesson
Assess knowledge using:
• Lesson Quiz
• Computer Test Generator CD

Algebra deals with operations and relations among numbers, including real numbers and imaginary numbers. Listed below are some of the subsets of the real numbers. Imaginary numbers will be introduced in Chapter 5.

 Key Concepts

| **Summary** | **Subsets of Real Numbers** |

Natural numbers $1, 2, 3, 4, \ldots$
• Natural numbers are the numbers used for counting.

Whole numbers $0, 1, 2, 3, 4, \ldots$
• Whole numbers are the natural numbers and 0.

Integers $\ldots -3, -2, -1, 0, 1, 2, 3, 4, \ldots$
• The integers are the natural numbers (positive integers), zero, and the negative integers.
• Each negative integer is the opposite, or additive inverse, of a positive integer.

Rational numbers   Examples: $\frac{7}{5}, \frac{-3}{2}, -\frac{4}{5}, 0, 0.3, -1.2, 9$
• Rational numbers are all the numbers that can be written as quotients of integers. Each quotient must have a nonzero denominator.
• Some rational numbers can be written as terminating decimals. For example, $\frac{1}{8} = 0.125$.
• All other rational numbers can be written as repeating decimals. For example, $\frac{1}{3} = 0.\overline{3}$.

Irrational numbers   Examples: $\sqrt{2}, \sqrt{7}, \sqrt{\frac{2}{3}}, \pi, 1.0110111011111011111\ldots$
• Irrational numbers are numbers that cannot be written as quotients of integers.
• Their decimal representations neither terminate nor repeat.
• If a positive rational number is not a perfect square such as 25 or $\frac{4}{9}$, then its square root is irrational.

Reading Math

$\sqrt{2}$ refers to the principal or positive square root of 2. The negative square root of 2 is written as $-\sqrt{2}$.

This diagram shows how the above sets of numbers are related.

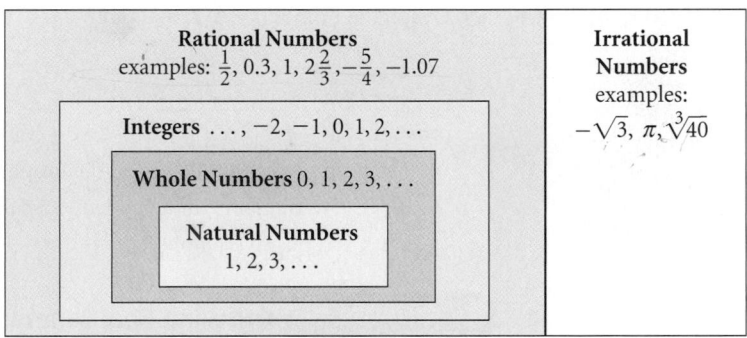

Real Numbers   examples: $-5, -\sqrt{3}, -\frac{1}{2}, 1, \sqrt{5}, \frac{8}{3}$

For example, the diagram shows the following:
• The set of whole numbers is a subset of the set of integers, the set of rational numbers, and the set of real numbers.
• The set of rational numbers and the set of irrational numbers do not intersect.
• The rational numbers and irrational numbers form the set of real numbers.

Professional Development

Math Background

This lesson reviews key concepts from Algebra 1, such as important subsets of the real numbers, ordering real numbers on the number line, and absolute value. It also summarizes fundamental properties of addition and multiplication. Students will find the material in the Key Concepts boxes on pages 5 and 7 helpful for this lesson and for future reference.

OBJECTIVE
1 **Teaching Notes**

Investigation (Optional)
The hypotenuse of each right triangle in the diagram is a leg of the next triangle. If necessary, review how the Pythagorean Theorem is used to find the length of the hypotenuse when the lengths of the legs are known.

In Question 3, students will need to use decimal approximations in the last row of the table. In the top row, if the results are not whole numbers, students should write the square roots in radical form to show exact lengths.

page 4   Investigation

2.

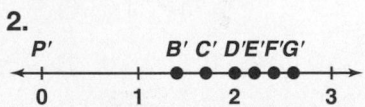

4. **No; squaring the decimals the calculator displays for $\sqrt{2}$, $\sqrt{3}$, $\sqrt{5}$, $\sqrt{6}$, $\sqrt{7}$ will not give a whole number. Only $\sqrt{4}$ is exact; to show that the decimal displayed for $\sqrt{2}$ is not exact, enter the displayed decimal using the keypad and square it to show that the square is not exactly 2.**

👥 Reaching All Students

| **Below Level** Complete the table on p. 4 by working through as many examples as necessary. Show students how to transfer the lengths of the hypotenuses to the number line. | **Advanced Learners** Have students find Pythagorean "triples," whole numbers such as 3, 4, and 5, that make the Pythagorean Theorem true. **Sample: 8, 15, 17** | **Alternative Method** See note on page 6. **Error Prevention** See note on page 9. |

5

2 EXAMPLE Alternative Method

The value of $\sqrt{5}$ can be approximated without a calculator by noting that $2.1^2 = 4.41$, $2.2^2 = 4.84$, and $2.3^2 = 5.29$. Of these three squares, 4.84 comes closest to 5. So, to the nearest tenth, $\sqrt{5} \approx 2.2$.

3 EXAMPLE Alternative Method

Since $y = \sqrt{x}$ is an increasing function, students may also reason that $\sqrt{0.25} > \sqrt{0.01}$ since $0.25 > 0.01$. On the number line, $\sqrt{0.25}$ is to the right of $\sqrt{0.01}$. So $-\sqrt{0.25}$ will lie to the left of $-\sqrt{0.01}$. Therefore, $-\sqrt{0.25} < -\sqrt{0.01}$.

Additional Examples

1 A pilot uses the formula $d = \sqrt{a^2 + 7290a}$ to find the distance d in miles that can be seen when flying at an altitude of a miles. Which set of numbers best describes the values for each variable? **a: rational numbers; d: real numbers**

2 Graph the numbers $-\frac{3}{4}$, $\sqrt{7}$, and 3.6 on a number line.

$$-\frac{3}{4} \qquad \sqrt{7} \quad 3.6$$
$$\begin{array}{c} \longleftarrow\!\!+\!\!+\!\!+\bullet\!\!+\!\!+\!\!+\!\!+\bullet\!\!+\bullet\!\!+\!\longrightarrow \\ -3\ -2\ -1\ \ 0\ \ 1\ \ 2\ \ 3\ \ 4\ \ 5 \end{array}$$

3 Compare -9 and $-\sqrt{9}$. Use the symbols $<$ or $>$. $-9 < -\sqrt{9}$

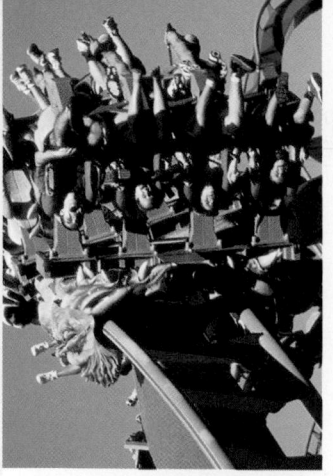

Real-World Connection

The maximum speed of a roller coaster is given by the formula $s = \frac{1200}{\sqrt{h}}$.

---

1 EXAMPLE Real-World Connection

Recreation Many mathematical relationships involving variables are related to amusement parks. Which set of numbers best describes the values for each variable?

a. the cost C in dollars of admission for n people

The cost C of admission is a rational number (such as 7.25), and the number n of people is a whole number.

b. the maximum speed s in meters per second on a roller coaster of height h in meters (Use the formula in the caption of the photograph.)

The height h is measured in rational numbers. Since the speed s is calculated using a formula with a square root, s is an irrational number unless h is the square of a rational number.

c. the park's profit (or loss) P in dollars for each week w of the year

The week number w is one of the first 52 natural numbers, and the profit (or loss) P is a rational number.

✓ **Check Understanding** **1** The number r is the ratio of the number of adult tickets sold to the number of children's tickets sold. Which set of numbers best describes the values of r? Which set of numbers best describes the average cost c per family for tickets?
rational numbers; rational numbers

Real numbers are graphed as points on the number line.

2 EXAMPLE Graphing Numbers on the Number Line⬇

Graph the numbers $-\frac{3}{2}$, $1.\overline{7}$, and $\sqrt{5}$.

Since $-\frac{3}{2} = -1\frac{1}{2}$, $-\frac{3}{2}$ is between -1 and -2. Round $1.\overline{7}$ to 1.8. Use a calculator to find that $\sqrt{5} \approx 2.2$.

$$\begin{array}{c} -\frac{3}{2} \qquad\qquad\qquad 1.\overline{7}\ \ \sqrt{5} \\ \longleftarrow\!\!+\!\!+\bullet\!\!+\!\!+\!\!+\!\!+\!\!+\!\!+\!\!+\bullet\bullet\!\!+\!\!+\longrightarrow \\ -2\quad -1\quad 0\quad 1\quad 2\quad 3 \end{array}$$

✓ **Check Understanding** **2** Graph the numbers $-\sqrt{2}$, $0.\overline{3}$, and $-2\frac{1}{4}$.

$$\begin{array}{c} -2\frac{1}{4}\ \ -\sqrt{2} \qquad\qquad 0.\overline{3} \\ \longleftarrow\!\!+\!\!+\bullet\!\!+\bullet\!\!+\!\!+\!\!+\bullet\!\!+\!\!+\!\!+\!\!+\longrightarrow \\ -3\quad -2\quad -1\quad 0\quad 1\quad 2\quad 3 \end{array}$$

If a and b are real numbers, then $a = b$, $a < b$, or $a > b$. There are several ways to prove that $a < b$:

- The graph of a is to the left of the graph of b on a number line.
- A positive number can be added to a to get b.
- $b - a$ is a positive number.

3 EXAMPLE Ordering Real Numbers

Compare $-\sqrt{0.25}$ and $-\sqrt{0.01}$. Use the symbols $<$ and $>$.

$-\sqrt{0.25} = -0.5$, and $-\sqrt{0.01} = -0.1$. Since $-0.1 - (-0.5)$ is positive, $-0.5 < -0.1$. So $-\sqrt{0.25} < -\sqrt{0.01}$ and $-\sqrt{0.01} > -\sqrt{0.25}$.

✓ **Check Understanding** **3** Compare $-\sqrt{0.08}$ and $-\sqrt{0.1}$ using the symbols $<$ and $>$. $-\sqrt{0.08} > -\sqrt{0.1}$, $-\sqrt{0.1} < -\sqrt{0.08}$

The **opposite** or **additive inverse** of any number a is $-a$. The sum of opposites is 0.

The **reciprocal** or **multiplicative inverse** of any nonzero number a is $\frac{1}{a}$. The product of reciprocals is 1.

Reading Math

Read $-(-3.2)$ as "the opposite of negative 3.2."

Read $\frac{1}{-3.2}$ as "the reciprocal of negative 3.2" or as "1 divided by negative 3.2."

4 EXAMPLE Finding Inverses

Find the opposite and the reciprocal of each number.

a. -3.2

Opposite $-(-3.2) = 3.2$

Reciprocal $\frac{1}{-3.2} = \frac{10}{-32}$
$= -\frac{5}{16}$, or -0.3125

b. $\frac{3}{5}$

Opposite $-\left(\frac{3}{5}\right) = -\frac{3}{5}$

Reciprocal $\frac{1}{\frac{3}{5}} = 1 \cdot \frac{5}{3} = \frac{5}{3}$

Check Understanding **4** Find the opposite and the reciprocal of each number.

a. 400 $-400, \frac{1}{400}$ **b.** $4\frac{1}{5}$ $-4\frac{1}{5}, \frac{5}{21}$ **c.** -0.002 $0.002, -500$ **d.** $-\frac{4}{9}$ $\frac{4}{9}, -\frac{9}{4}\left(\text{or } -2\frac{1}{4}\right)$

You can summarize the properties of real numbers in terms of addition and multiplication.

Key Concepts

Summary	Properties of Real Numbers	

Let $a, b,$ and c represent real numbers.

Property	Addition	Multiplication
Closure	$a + b$ is a real number.	ab is a real number.
Commutative	$a + b = b + a$	$ab = ba$
Associative	$(a + b) + c = a + (b + c)$	$(ab)c = a(bc)$
Identity	$a + 0 = a, 0 + a = a$	$a \cdot 1 = a, 1 \cdot a = a$
Inverse	$a + (-a) = 0$	$a \cdot \frac{1}{a} = 1, a \neq 0$
Distributive	$a(b + c) = ab + ac$	

5 EXAMPLE Identifying Properties of Real Numbers

Which property is illustrated?

a. $6 + (-6) = 0$

Inverse Property of Addition

b. $(-4 \cdot 1) - 2 = -4 - 2$

Identity Property of Multiplication

Check Understanding **5** Which property is illustrated?

a. $(3 + 0) - 5 = 3 - 5$ **b.** $-5 + [2 + (-3)] = (-5 + 2) + (-3)$
  Identity Prop. of Add.   Assoc. Prop. of Add.

4 EXAMPLE Teaching Tip

Point out that reciprocals of rational numbers are usually written in fraction form unless the reciprocal is a terminating decimal with few digits.

5 EXAMPLE Teaching Tip

Invite students to write their own examples of algebraic sentences that illustrate properties in the chart on page 7. Ask them to explain how the form of each sentence can be used to determine which property is illustrated.

6 EXAMPLE Math Tip

Help students understand that the absolute value of a real number is non-negative since distance cannot be negative. This property will help students understand the algebraic definition of absolute value on page 33. Understanding absolute value as a measure of distance will help students in Lesson 1-5.

Additional Examples

4 Find the opposite and the reciprocal of each number.
a. $-3\frac{1}{7}$ $3\frac{1}{7}, -\frac{7}{22}$
b. 4 $-4, \frac{1}{4}$

5 Which property is illustrated?
a. $(-7)(2 \cdot 5) = (-7)(5 \cdot 2)$
Comm. Prop. of Mult.
b. $3 \cdot (8 + 0) = 3 \cdot 8$
Identity Prop. of Add.

6 Find $|4\frac{1}{3}|$, $|-9.2|$, and $|3 - 8|$. $4\frac{1}{3}, 9.2, 5$

Closure

Ask: *If the reciprocal of a number is a rational number, is the number rational or irrational?* **rational**

The **absolute value of a real number** is its distance from zero on the number line.

Assignment Guide

 1 Objective

Ⓐ Ⓑ **Core** 1–33, 61–68, 75–82

2 Objective

Ⓐ Ⓑ **Core** 34–60, 69–74, 83–88

Ⓒ **Extension** 89–94

Standardized Test Prep
95–101

Mixed Review 102–113

Technology Tip

Exercise 30 To help students see that the square root of a number is not always less than the number, have them use graphing calculators to graph $Y_1 = x$ and $Y_2 = \sqrt{x}$. Tell students to set both Xmin and Ymin at 0, and both Xmax and Ymax at 2. Ask: *For which values of x is $\sqrt{x} < x$?* $x > 1$ *For which values of x is $\sqrt{x} \geq x$?* $0 \leq x \leq 1$

📖 Reading Math

Read |3| as "the absolute value of 3."

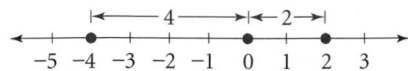
6 EXAMPLE Finding Absolute Value

Find $|-4|$, $|0|$, and $|-1 \cdot (-2)|$.

$|-1 \cdot (-2)| = |2|$ **Simplify within absolute symbols first**

Graph $-4, 0,$ and 2 on a number line.

The distances from the origin are $4, 0,$ and 2. So,

$$|-4| = 4 \qquad |0| = 0 \qquad |-1 \cdot (-2)| = |2| = 2$$

✓ Check Understanding 6 a. Simplify $|-10|$, $|1.5|$, and $|0 - 3|$. **10, 1.5, 3**

b. Critical Thinking For what values of x does $|x| = -x$? **for values of x such that x ≤ 0**

EXERCISES

For more practice, see *Extra Practice*.

Practice and Problem Solving

Ⓐ **Practice by Example**

To which sets of numbers does each number belong? 1–8. See margin.

Example 1
(page 6)

1. 4   **2.** $\sqrt{6}$ **3.** π **4.** -6

5. 0   **6.** $0.\overline{6}$ **7.** $-\sqrt{0.04}$ **8.** $\sqrt{0.4}$

Which set of numbers best describes the value of each variable?

9. the number of times n a cricket chirps; the outdoor temperature T in tenths of a degree **whole numbers; rational numbers**

10. the year y; the median selling price p for a house that year **natural numbers; rational numbers**

11. the time t in seconds an object takes to fall d feet, where $t = \dfrac{\sqrt{d}}{4}$ **real numbers**

Example 2
(page 6)

Graph each number on a number line. 12–16. See margin p. 8–9.

12. 0   **13.** $-\sqrt{24}$ **14.** -2 **15.** $2\frac{1}{2}$ **16.** $-4\frac{2}{3}$

Example 3
(page 6)

Replace each ▧ with the symbol <, >, or = to make the sentence true.

17. $-7 \overset{>}{▧} -9$ **18.** $3 \overset{=}{▧} 3$ **19.** $14 \overset{>}{▧} \sqrt{14}$

20. $\sqrt{6} \overset{<}{▧} \sqrt{10}$ **21.** $0 \overset{<}{▧} 0.\overline{3}$ **22.** $0.8 \overset{=}{▧} \frac{4}{5}$

23. $-18 \overset{>}{▧} -82$ **24.** $0.72737475\ldots \overset{<}{▧} 0.73737373\ldots$

Compare each pair of numbers. Use < and >. 25–33. See margin p. 9.

25. $-\frac{1}{4}, -\frac{1}{3}$ **26.** $0.075, 0.39$ **27.** $-2.\overline{3}, 2.\overline{1}$

28. $-5.2, -4.8$ **29.** $3.0\overline{4}, 3.4$ **30.** $0.4, \sqrt{0.4}$

31. $-4, -\sqrt{4}$ **32.** $\sqrt{5}, \sqrt{7}$ **33.** $-\sqrt{3}, -\sqrt{5}$

---

pages 8–10 Exercises

1. natural numbers, whole numbers, integers, rational numbers, real numbers

2. irrational numbers, real numbers

3. irrational numbers, real numbers

4. integers, rational numbers, real numbers

5. whole numbers, integers, rational numbers, real numbers

6. rational numbers, real numbers

7. rational numbers, real numbers

8. irrational numbers, real numbers

12. [number line showing point at 0, range $-3 -2 -1\ 0\ 1\ 2$]

13. [number line showing point at -5, range $-6 -5 -4 -3 -2 -1\ 0\ 1$]

14. [number line showing point at -2, range $-4 -3 -2 -1\ 0\ 1\ 2$]

Example 4
(page 7)

Find the opposite and the reciprocal of each number.

34. 200 $-200; \frac{1}{200}$ **35.** $3\frac{3}{5}$ $-3\frac{3}{5}; \frac{5}{18}$ **36.** -0.01 $0.01; -100$ **37.** $-\frac{7}{2}$ $\frac{7}{2}; -\frac{2}{7}$

38. $\sqrt{3}$ $-\sqrt{3}; \frac{1}{\sqrt{3}}$ (or $\frac{\sqrt{3}}{3}$) **39.** 2π $-2\pi; \frac{1}{2\pi}$ **40.** -2.34 $2.34; -\frac{50}{117}$ **41.** $\pi - 3$ $3 - \pi; \frac{1}{\pi - 3}$

Example 5
(page 7)

Name the property of real numbers illustrated by each equation. **42–46.**
See margin.

42. $92.5(1) = 92.5$

43. $\pi(a + b) = \pi a + \pi b$

44. $-7 + 4 = 4 + (-7)$

45. $(2\sqrt{10}) \cdot \sqrt{3} = 2(\sqrt{10} \cdot \sqrt{3})$

46. $29\pi = \pi \cdot 29$

47. $-\sqrt{5} + 0 = -\sqrt{5}$

48. $(-8) + [-(-8)] = 0$

49. $\frac{4}{7} \cdot \frac{7}{4} = 1$

47–52.
See margin p.10.

50. $25(2x + 5y) = 50x + 125y$

51. $(-2)(-3) = (-3)(-2)$

52. $(0.5 + 0.25) + (-0.25) = 0.5 + [0.25 + (-0.25)]$

Example 6
(page 8)

Simplify each expression.

53. $|10.3|$ **10.3** **54.** $|-0.06|$ **0.06** **55.** $-|-25|$ **−25** **56.** $0.2|-8|$ **1.6**

57. $\left|-\frac{1}{3}\right|$ $\frac{1}{3}$ **58.** $|7 - 10|$ **3** **59.** $|10 - 7|$ **3** **60.** $|5| - |-7|$
−2

B **Apply Your Skills**

Estimate the numbers graphed at the labeled points. **Exercises 61–68:**
Answers may vary.
Samples are given.

A B C D E F G H

-5 -4 -3 -2 -1 0 1 2 3 4 5

61. point A **−5** **62.** point B **$-3\frac{1}{2}$** **63.** point C **$-1\frac{1}{4}$** **64.** point D **$\frac{1}{2}$**

65. point E **$1\frac{2}{3}$** **66.** point F **$3\frac{1}{3}$** **67.** point G **4** **68.** point H **4.8**

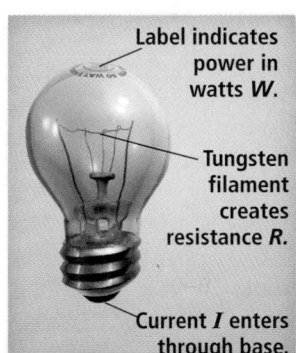

Label indicates power in watts **W**.

Tungsten filament creates resistance **R**.

Current **I** enters through base.

Electric Circuits The electric current I in amperes that flows through an appliance is given by the formula $I = \sqrt{\frac{W}{R}}$, where W is the power in watts and R is the resistance in ohms. Which sets of numbers contain the value of I for the given values of W and R? **69–74. See margin p. 10.**

69. $W = 100, R = 25$ **70.** $W = 100, R = 50$ **71.** $W = 500, R = 100$

72. $W = 50, R = 200$ **73.** $W = 250, R = 100$ **74.** $W = 240, R = 100$

Replace each ■ with the symbol $<$, $>$, or $=$ to make the sentence true.

75. 0 ■ -4
$>$
76. -4 ■ -9
$>$
77. -5.2 ■ -4.8
$<$
78. $|-8|$ ■ $|3|$
$>$

79. $|2|$ ■ $|-6|$
$<$
80. $|7|$ ■ $|-8|$
$<$
81. $-|6|$ ■ $|6|$
$<$
82. $-|-6|$ ■ $|-6|$
$<$

Reasoning Show that each statement is false by finding a counterexample (an example that makes the statement false). **83–87. See back of book.**

83. The reciprocal of each whole number is a whole number.

84. The opposite of each natural number is a natural number.

85. There is no whole number that has an opposite that is a whole number.

86. There is no integer that has a reciprocal that is an integer.

87. The product of two irrational numbers is an irrational number.

88. Open-Ended Write an example of each of the eleven properties of real numbers listed on page 7. **Check students' work.**

Lesson 1-1 Properties of Real Numbers **9**

15.
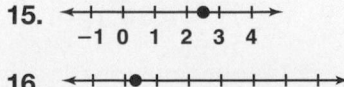
-1 0 1 2 3 4

16.
-6 -5 -4 -3 -2 -1 0 1

25. $-\frac{1}{4} > -\frac{1}{3}, -\frac{1}{3} < -\frac{1}{4}$

26. $0.075 < 0.39,$
$0.39 > 0.075$

27. $-2.\overline{3} < 2.\overline{1}, 2.\overline{1} > -2.\overline{3}$

28. $-5.2 < -4.8,$
$-4.8 > -5.2$

29. $3.0\overline{4} < 3.4, 3.4 > 3.0\overline{4}$

30. $0.4 < \sqrt{0.4}, \sqrt{0.4} > 0.4$

31. $-4 < -\sqrt{4}, -\sqrt{4} > -4$

32. $\sqrt{5} < \sqrt{7}, \sqrt{7} > \sqrt{5}$

Resources

For additional practice with a variety of test item formats:
- Standardized Test Prep, p. 51
- Test-Taking Strategies, p. 46
- Test-Taking Strategies with Transparencies

Exercise 96 Listing a few multiples of 3 and of 5 may help to eliminate some of the choices.

pages 8–10 Exercises

47. Identity Prop. of Add.

48. Inverse Prop. of Add.

49. Inverse Prop. of Mult.

50. Dist. Prop.

51. Comm. Prop. Of Mult.

52. Assoc. Prop. of Add.

69. natural numbers, whole numbers, integers, rational numbers, real numbers

70. irrational numbers, real numbers

71. irrational numbers, real numbers

72. rational numbers, real numbers

73. irrational numbers, real numbers

74. irrational numbers, real numbers

89. all except the Identity Prop. of Add. (since 0 is not in the set of natural numbers) and the inverse properties

90. all except the Inverse Prop. of Mult. and the Inverse Prop. of Add.

91. all except the Inverse Prop. of Mult.

100. [2] The opposite of the reciprocal of 5 is the opposite of $\frac{1}{5}$, or $-\frac{1}{5}$, and the reciprocal of the opposite of 5 is the reciprocal of −5, or $-\frac{1}{5}$.

[1] includes a statement or example that a reciprocal is a multiplicative inverse or that a number times its

C Challenge **Critical Thinking** Review the eleven properties on page 7. Which ones still hold true if *real numbers* is replaced by each of the following? 89–91. See margin.

89. natural numbers   90. whole numbers   91. integers

92. rational numbers   93. irrational numbers
all the properties   **Comm., Asso., and Dist. Prop.**

94. **Writing** Are there two integers with a product of −12 and a sum of −3? Explain. **No; answers may vary. Sample: The only pairs of integers that have a product of −12 are −1 and 12, −2 and 6, −3 and 4, −4 and 3, −6 and 2, and −12 and 1. None of these pairs has a sum of −3.**

Standardized Test Prep

Multiple Choice

95. Which of the following is NOT a rational number? **D**
   A. $\frac{\pi}{2\pi}$ B. $-\sqrt{144}$ C. 3.14   D. $\sqrt{8}$

96. If *p* is a multiple of 3 and *q* is a multiple of 5, which of the following is true? **H**
   F. $p + q$ is even.   G. pq is odd.
   H. $5p + 3q$ is a multiple of 15.   I. $3p + 5q$ is a multiple of 15.

97. The number 8.09 belongs to which sets of numbers? **C**
   A. natural numbers, real numbers
   B. irrational numbers, real numbers
   C. rational numbers, real numbers
   D. whole numbers, integers, rational numbers, real numbers

Take It to the NET

Online lesson quiz at
www.PHSchool.com
Web Code: aga-0101

98. Which shows the numbers -3.5, -4.60, and $-3\frac{1}{4}$ in order from greatest to least? **I**
   F. $-4.60, -3\frac{1}{4}, -3.5$ G. $-4.60, -3.5, -3\frac{1}{4}$
   H. $-3\frac{1}{4}, -4.60, -3.5$ I. $-3\frac{1}{4}, -3.5, -4.60$

99. What is the value of $|3 - 7| - |-11 + 3|$? **A**
   A. −4   B. 4   C. 12   D. 24

Short Response

100. Explain why the *opposite of the reciprocal of 5* is the same as the *reciprocal of the opposite of 5*. **See margin.**

101. Are there any numbers that are their own reciprocals? Explain.
See margin.

Mixed Review

Previous Course   Simplify each expression.

102. $3.6 + (-1.7)$ **1.9**   103. $1.2 - 5$ **−3.8**   104. $(-3)(-9)$ **27**

105. $0(-8)$ **0**   106. $-2.8 \div 7$ **−0.4**   107. $-35 \div (-5)$ **7**

Previous Course   Use the order of operations to simplify each expression.

108. $3 \div 4 + 6 \div 4$ **$\frac{9}{4}$, or $2\frac{1}{4}$**   109. $5[(2 + 5) \div 3]$ **$\frac{35}{3}$, or $11\frac{2}{3}$**

110. $\frac{8 + 5 \cdot 2}{12}$ **$\frac{3}{2}$, or $1\frac{1}{2}$**   111. $(40 + 24) \div 8 - (2^2 - 1)$ **5**

112. $40 + 24 \div 8 - 2^2 - 1$ **38**   113. $40 + 24 \div (8 - 2^2) - 1$ **45**

reciprocal is 1, OR a statement or example that an opposite is an additive inverse or that a number plus its opposite is 0

101. [2] Two numbers are their own reciprocals, 1 and −1. For a number *n* to be equal to its reciprocal, $n = \frac{1}{n}$, which means

$n^2 = 1$. So $n = 1$ or −1.

[1] only includes answer 1 and −1 with no explanation

Exploring Pi

The number π, the ratio of the circumference of a circle to its diameter, has fascinated mathematicians for thousands of years.

Archimedes (about 287−212 B.C.) considered the perimeters of inscribed and circumscribed regular polygons of 96 sides. He found that $\frac{223}{71} < \pi < \frac{22}{7}$.

Seven hundred years later, the Chinese mathematician Tsu Ch'ung-Chi calculated the more precise value $\frac{355}{113}$.

English mathematicians introduced the notation π about 1700. π is the first letter of the Greek word for perimeter.

In 1761, the German mathematician Johann Lambert proved that π is an irrational number.

Although there is no finite formula for calculating π, mathematicians have found many formulas that involve infinite numbers of additions, subtractions, multiplications, or divisions.

diameter = 1

p_1 = perimeter of inscribed polygon

p_2 = perimeter of circumscribed polygon

$p_1 < \pi < p_2$

More than 500 years ago, the Indian mathematician Madhava discovered this formula.

$$\frac{\pi}{4} = \frac{1}{1} - \frac{1}{3} + \frac{1}{5} - \frac{1}{7} + \frac{1}{9} - \frac{1}{11} + \ldots$$

This formula has an infinite number of products.

$$\frac{\pi}{2} = \frac{2}{1} \cdot \frac{2}{3} \cdot \frac{4}{3} \cdot \frac{4}{5} \cdot \frac{6}{5} \cdot \frac{6}{7} \cdot \frac{8}{7} \cdot \frac{8}{9} \cdot \frac{10}{9} \cdot \frac{10}{11} \cdot \ldots$$

And this formula is a continued fraction.

$$\frac{4}{\pi} = 1 + \cfrac{1^2}{3 + \cfrac{2^2}{5 + \cfrac{3^2}{7 + \cfrac{4^2}{9 + \cfrac{5^2}{11 + \ldots}}}}}$$

Now mathematicians have computed π to millions of decimal places using efficient computer algorithms. Here are the first 100 digits.

3.14159265358979323846264338327950288419716939937510
5820974944592307816406286208998628034825342117067

EXERCISES

1. a. Find the average of Archimedes' two approximations. $\frac{3123}{994}$
   b. Compare that average with the computer-generated value of π given above. To which decimal place are they the same? **See margin.**

2. Make the same comparison for Tsu Ch'ung-Chi's approximation. **2–3. See margin.**

3. Compute the value of π using 6 terms, 8 terms, and 10 terms of Madhava's formula. Compare these values with the computer-generated value.

4. Writing Compute approximations of π using the other two formulas. Which formula do you prefer for calculating approximations of π? Explain. **See back of book.**

Investigation

Exploring Pi

Since π is so important in mathematics and its applications, knowing how to approximate its value accurately is worthwhile. Having highly accurate values of π can be helpful in checking the reliability of computer hardware and software programs.

Resources

Any graphing calculator

Teaching Notes

Technology Tip

Exercise 4 Students may be unsure how to work with the continued fraction. Point out that they can use the appropriate keys to display the following expression on the home screen of their calculators:
$1 + (1^2/(3 + (2^2/(5 + (3^2/(7 + (4^2/(9 + (5^2/(11)))))))))$
Pressing ENTER will cause the calculator to display the value of the portion of the continued fraction shown on page 11. Next, press x^{-1} × 4 ENTER to display the desired approximation for π.

3. $\frac{10{,}312}{3465} \approx 2.97604618,$

$\frac{135{,}904}{45{,}045} \approx 3.01707182,$

$\frac{44{,}257{,}352}{14{,}549{,}535} \approx 3.04183962;$

all these approximations are less than the given decimal approximation, but they are getting closer to that approximation as more terms are used.

page 11   Investigation

1b. $\frac{3123}{994} \approx 3.1418511;$ the value $\frac{3123}{994}$ is greater than the given decimal approximation, but it agrees with the approximation through the thousandths place.

2. $\frac{355}{113} \approx 3.14159292;$ this value is also greater than the given decimal approximation, but it agrees with that approximation through the sixth digit to the right of the decimal point.

1-2

1. Plan

Lesson Preview

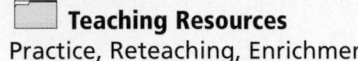
✓ Check Skills You'll Need

Simplifying Expressions with Integers
Skills Handbook: p. 845
Example 4, Exercises 21–32

Lesson Resources

📁 **Teaching Resources**
Practice, Reteaching, Enrichment

👥 **Reaching All Students**
Practice Workbook 1-2
Spanish Practice Workbook 1-2
Hands-On Activities 31

⏱ **Presentation Assistant Plus!**
Transparencies
• Check Skills You'll Need 1-2
• Additional Examples 1-2
• Student Edition Answers 1-2
• Lesson Quiz 1-2
PH Presentation Pro CD 1-2

PRENTICE HALL
ASSESSMENT SYSTEM

Computer Test Generator CD

💿 **Technology**
Resource Pro® CD-ROM
Computer Test Generator CD
Prentice Hall Presentation Pro CD

💻 **www.PHSchool.com**
Student Site
• Teacher Web Code: agk-5500
• Self-grading Lesson Quiz
Teacher Center
• Lesson Planner
• Resources

Plus **iTEXT**

1-2

Algebraic Expressions

1.03 Operate with algebraic expressions (polynomial, rational, complex fractions) to solve problems.

Lesson Preview

What You'll Learn

OBJECTIVE 1 To evaluate algebraic expressions

OBJECTIVE 2 To simplify algebraic expressions

. . . And Why

To use an expression for the number of voters in U.S. elections, as in Example 3

✓ Check Skills You'll Need
(For help, go to Skills Handbook page 845.)

Use the order of operations to simplify each expression.

1. $8 \cdot 3 - 2 \cdot 4$ **16**
2. $8 - 4 + 6 \div 3$ **6**
3. $24 \div 12 \cdot 4 \div 3$ **$\frac{8}{3}$**
4. $3 \cdot 8^2 + 12 \div 4$ **195**
5. $27 + 18 \div 9 - 3^2 + 1$ **21**
6. $(40 + 24) \div 8 - (2^3 + 1)$ **−1**

New Vocabulary • variable • algebraic expression • variable expression • evaluate • term • coefficient

---

OBJECTIVE 1

iTEXT Interactive lesson includes instant self-check, tutorials, and activities.

Evaluating Algebraic Expressions

A **variable** is a symbol, usually a letter, that represents one or more numbers. An expression that contains one or more variables is an **algebraic expression** or a **variable expression.** When you substitute numbers for the variables in an expression and follow the order of operations, you **evaluate** the expression.

❓ **Need Help?**
To review the order of operations, go to page 845.

1 EXAMPLE **Evaluating an Algebraic Expression**

Evaluate $a - 2b + ab$ for $a = 3$ and $b = -1$.

$$a - 2b + ab = 3 - 2(-1) + 3(-1) \quad \text{Substitute 3 for } a \text{ and } -1 \text{ for } b.$$
$$= 3 - (-2) + (-3) \quad \text{Multiply first.}$$
$$= 3 + 2 + (-3) \quad \text{To subtract, add the opposite.}$$
$$= 5 + (-3) \quad \text{Add from left to right.}$$
$$= 2 \quad \text{Add.}$$

✓ **Check Understanding** ❶ Evaluate each expression for $x = 4$ and $y = -2$.
a. $x + y \div x$ **$\frac{7}{2}$**
b. $3x - 4y + x - y$ **26**
c. $x + 2x \div y - 2y$ **4**

2 EXAMPLE **Evaluating an Algebraic Expression with Exponents**

📖 **Reading Math**
Note that $-3^2 \neq (-3)^2$.
$-3^2 = -(3 \cdot 3) = -9$
$(-3)^2 = (-3)(-3) = 9$

Evaluate $-x^2 - 2(x + 1)$ for $x = 3$.

$$-x^2 - 2(x + 1) = -3^2 - 2(3 + 1) \quad \text{Substitute 3 for } x.$$
$$= -9 - 2(4) \quad \text{Simplify the power } 3^2. \text{ Add within the parentheses.}$$
$$= -9 - 8 \quad \text{Multiply.}$$
$$= -17 \quad \text{Subtract.}$$

✓ **Check Understanding** ❷ Evaluate each expression for $c = -3$ and $d = 5$.
a. $c^2 - d^2$ **−16**
b. $c(3 - d) - c^2$ **−3**
c. $-d^2 - 4(d - 2c)$ **−69**

12 Chapter 1 Tools of Algebra

Ongoing Assessment and Intervention

Before the Lesson
Diagnose prerequisite skills using:
• Check Skills You'll Need

During the Lesson
Monitor progress using:
• Check Understanding
• Additional Examples
• Standardized Test Prep

After the Lesson
Assess knowledge using:
• Lesson Quiz
• Computer Test Generator CD

In 1971, the U.S. voting age was lowered from 21 to 18.

3 EXAMPLE Real-World Connection

Elections The expression $-0.3y + 61$ models the percent of eligible voters who voted in presidential elections from 1960 to 2000. In the expression, y represents the number of years since 1960. Find the approximate percent of eligible voters who voted in 1988.

Since $1988 - 1960 = 28$, $y = 28$ represents the year 1988.

$-0.3y + 61 = -0.3(28) + 61$ **Substitute 28 for y.**

≈ 53

● About 53% of the eligible voters voted in the 1988 presidential election.

✔ **Check Understanding** **3** **a.** Assume that the model in Example 3 holds for future years. What percent of the eligible voters will vote in 2012? In 2020? **about 45%; about 43%**

b. **Critical Thinking** Give some reasons that the model may not hold in future years. **Answers may vary. Sample: Changing patterns in minority populations might lead to more voter turnout. Less stable international conditions might arouse voter concerns.**

OBJECTIVE

2 **Simplifying Algebraic Expressions**

In an algebraic expression such as $-4x + 10$, the parts that are added are called terms. A **term** is a number, a variable, or the product of a number and one or more variables. The numerical factor in a term is the **coefficient**. Think of an expression such as $a - 2b$ as the sum $a + (-2b)$ to determine that the coefficient of b is -2.

$$\overbrace{7x^2 + 3y}^{\text{terms}}$$
coefficients

Like terms have the same variables raised to the same powers.

Like terms: $3r^2$ and $-r^2$ $-2xy^3$ and $3xy^3$

You can simplify expressions by combining like terms using the basic properties on page 7 and other properties that can be derived from them. The simplified expressions are equivalent to the original expressions; that is, their values are equal for any replacement of the variables.

 Key Concepts

Summary	Properties for Simplifying Algebraic Expressions
Let a, b, and c represent real numbers.	
Definition of Subtraction	$a - b = a + (-b)$
Definition of Division	$a \div b = \dfrac{a}{b} = a \cdot \dfrac{1}{b}, b \neq 0$
Distributive Property for Subtraction	$a(b - c) = ab - ac$
Multiplication by 0	$0 \cdot a = 0$
Multiplication by -1	$-1 \cdot a = -a$
Opposite of a Sum	$-(a + b) = -a + (-b)$
Opposite of a Difference	$-(a - b) = b - a$
Opposite of a Product	$-(ab) = -a \cdot b = a \cdot (-b)$
Opposite of an Opposite	$-(-a) = a$

Lesson 1-2 Algebraic Expressions   **13**

Math Background

Numerical expressions can be simplified by using properties of operations and the order of operations. Algebraic expressions can be evaluated by substituting specific numbers for each variable and simplifying the resulting numerical expression. The properties for simplifying algebraic expressions are based on those for simplifying numerical expressions.

OBJECTIVE

1 **Teaching Notes**

English Learners

Have students pronounce the word *evaluate* carefully. Point out that in doing so, they can hear the word *value*. Explain that the value of an expression is the number obtained after substituting numbers for the variables and following the Order of Operations.

1 EXAMPLE **Math Tip**

Help students understand that the parentheses around -1 in the first step are necessary to indicate multiplication.

2 EXAMPLE **Teaching Tip**

Stress the importance of the order of operations. Have students demonstrate that performing the subtraction before the multiplication would result in -44. Point out to students that they can check their work by using the distributive property to first rewrite $-x^2 - 2(x + 1)$ as $-x^2 - 2x - 2$ and then substituting 3 for x.

3 EXAMPLE **Math Tip**

Some students may need to be reminded that $\approx$ means "is approximately equal to."

13

Additional Examples

① Evaluate $7x - 3xy$ for $x = -2$ and $y = 5$. **16**

② Evaluate $(k - 18)^2 - 4k$ for $k = 6$. **120**

③ The expression $-0.08y^2 + 3y$ models the percent increase of Hispanic voters in a town from 1990 to 2000. In the expression, y represents the number of years since 1990. Find the approximate percent of increase of Hispanic voters by 1998. **about 19%**

OBJECTIVE

2 **Teaching Notes**

4 **EXAMPLE** **Math Tip**

Some students may not be sure why $-(m + n)$ can be replaced with $-m + (-n)$. Point out that $-(m + n) = (-1)(m + n) = (-1)m + (-1)n = -m + (-n)$.

5 **EXAMPLE** **Tactile Learners**

Have each student trace a finger along the perimeter of the figure. Help students realize that the perimeter of this figure is $2b$ plus the perimeter of the $a \times 2a$ rectangle.

Additional Examples

④ Simplify by combining like terms.
$2h - 3k + 7(2h - 3k)$ **16h − 24k**

⑤ Find the perimeter of this figure. Simplify the answer.
2c + 4d

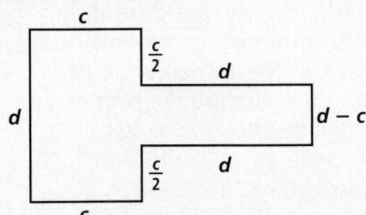

Closure

Ask: *How is the Distributive Property useful in simplifying expressions?* **Answers may vary. Sample: It allows you to combine like terms.**

14

---

4 **EXAMPLE** **Combining Like Terms**

Simplify by combining like terms.

a. $3k - k$

$3k - k = 3k - 1k$ **Identity Property of Multiplication**

$ = (3 - 1)k$ **Distributive Property**

$ = 2k$

b. $5z^2 - 10z - 8z^2 + z$

$5z^2 - 10z - 8z^2 + z = 5z^2 - 8z^2 + (-10z) + z$ **Commutative Property of Addition**

$ = (5 - 8)z^2 + (-10 + 1)z$ **Distributive Property**

$ = -3z^2 - 9z$

c. $-(m - n) + 2(m - 3n)$

$-(m + n) + 2(m - 3n)$

$ = -m + (-n) + 2m + (-6n)$ **Opposite of a Sum, Distributive Property**

$ = -m + 2m + (-n) + (-6n)$ **Commutative Property of Addition**

$ = -1 \cdot m + 2m + (-1 \cdot n) + (-6n)$ **Multiplication by −1**

$ = (-1 + 2)m + [-1 + (-6)]n$ **Distributive Property**

$ = m - 7n$

✓ **Check Understanding** ④ Simplify by combining like terms.

a. $2x^2 + 5x - 4x^2 + x - x^2$ **−3x² + 6x**

b. $-2(r + s) - (2r + 2s)$ **−4r − 4s**

c. $y(1 + y) - 3y^2 - (y + 1)$ **−2y² − 1**

5 **EXAMPLE** **Finding Perimeter**

Geometry Find the perimeter of this figure. Simplify the answer.

$\dfrac{2a - b}{2} + b + b + b + \dfrac{2a - b}{2} + a + 2a + a$

$= \dfrac{2a - b}{2} + \dfrac{2a - b}{2} + 3b + 4a$

$= \dfrac{2(2a - b)}{2} + 3b + 4a$

$= 2a - b + 3b + 4a$

$= 6a + 2b$

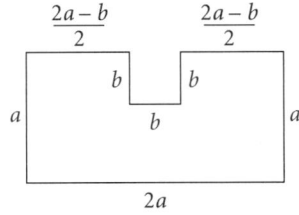

✓ **Check Understanding** ⑤ Find the perimeter of each figure. Simplify the answer.

a. **10x**

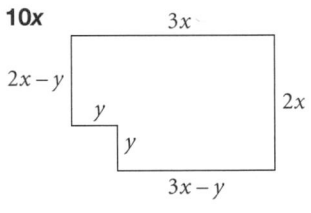

b. **10c + 2d**

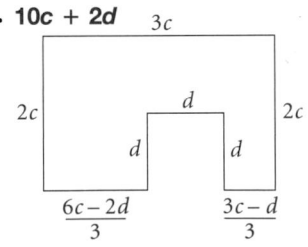

c. Critical Thinking The figure in part (b) is a rectangle with an indentation. By how much does the indentation increase the perimeter of the rectangle? **2d**

Need Help?

When collecting like terms in an algebraic expression, think of it as a sum. For example,

$x^2 - 2 - 3x^2$

$= x^2 + (-2) + (-3x^2)$

$= x^2 + (-3x^2) + (-2)$

$= -2x^2 + (-2)$

$= -2x^2 - 2$

EXERCISES

Practice and Problem Solving

 Practice by Example

Examples 1 and 2
(page 12)

Evaluate each expression for the given values of the variables.

1. $4a + 7b + 3a - 2b + 2a; a = -5$ and $b = 3$ **−30**

2. $5y - 3z + 4y - 1z - 3y; y = 3$ and $z = -2$ **26**

3. $12a^2 - 3ab + 2b; a = -5$ and $b = 4$ **368**

4. $-k^2 - (3k - 5n) + 4n; k = -1$ and $n = -2$ **−16**

5. $3y - (4y + 6x); x = 3$ and $y = -2$ **−16**

6. $3(2c + d) - d; c = 5$ and $d = -1$ **28**

7. $-5(x + 2y) + 15(x + 2y); x = 7$ and $y = -7$ **−70**

8. $4(2m - n) - 3(2m - n); m = -15$ and $n = -18$ **−12**

Example 3
(page 13)

Physics The expression $16t^2$ models the distance in feet that an object falls during t seconds after being dropped. Find the distance an object falls during each time.

9. 0.25 second **1 ft**

10. 0.5 second **4 ft**

11. 2 seconds **64 ft**

12. 10 seconds **1600 ft**

Electrical Engineering The expression $0.01E + 0.003E^2$ gives the thickness in millimeters of the insulation needed for the high voltage cable shown at the left. E is the number of kilovolts carried by the cable. Find the thickness of insulation material needed for each voltage.

13. 1 kilovolt **0.013 mm**

14. 2 kilovolts **0.032 mm**

15. 10 kilovolts **0.4 mm**

16. 20 kilovolts **1.4 mm**

Investing The expression $1000(1.1)^t$ represents the value of a $1000 investment that earns 10% interest per year, compounded annually for t years. Find the value of a $1000 investment at the end of each period.

17. 2 years **$1210**

18. 3 years **$1331**

19. 4 years **$1464.10**

20. 5 years **$1610.51**

Example 4
(page 14)

Simplify by combining like terms.

21. $5a - a$ **4a**

22. $5 + 10s - 8s$ **2s + 5**

23. $-5a - 4a + b$ **−9a + b**

24. $2a + 3b + 4a$ **6a + 3b**

25. $6r + 3s + 2s + 4r$ **10r + 5s**

26. $w + 3z + 5w + 2z$ **6w + 5z**

27. $x^2 + x^2 + x$ **2x² + x**

28. $xy + 2x + x$ **xy + 3x**

29. $0.5x - x$ **−0.5x**

30. $3(2x + 1) - 8$ **6x − 5**

31. $2(5y - 2) + x$ **10y + x − 4**

32. $3y - (4y + 6x)$ **−y − 6x**

33. $7b - (3a - 8b)$ **−3a + 15b**

34. $5 + (4g - 7)$ **4g − 2**

35. $-(3x - 4y + z)$ **−3x + 4y − z**

Example 5
(page 14)

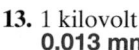 **Geometry** Find the perimeter of each figure. Simplify the answer.

36. **4a**

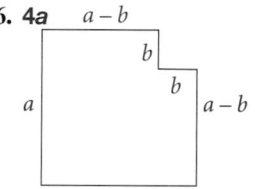

37. **4a**

Assignment Guide

 **Objective**
Ⓐ Ⓑ Core 1–20, 38–46

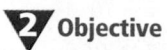 **Objective**
Ⓐ Ⓑ Core 21–37, 47–64
Ⓒ Extension 65–67

Standardized Test Prep 68–73

Mixed Review 74–83

Error Prevention

Exercises 1–8 Remind students that they need to use parentheses around all negative numbers that they substitute into expressions.

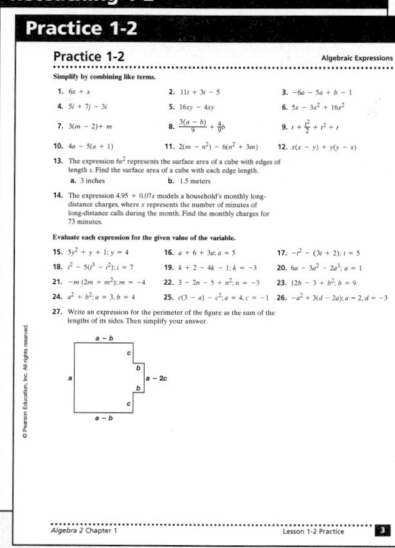

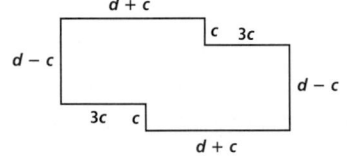
Alternative Assessment

Have students work in pairs. One student writes a simplified expression that contains two variables. The other student creates an expression that can be simplified, using the Distributive Property and combining like terms, to yield the first student's expression. Together, the group checks that its work is reasonable. Then have students substitute several different values for each of the variables into both expressions and verify that both yield the same result. Then, have students switch roles and repeat.

pages 15–17   Exercises

63. Assoc. Prop. of Add.
    Comm. Prop. of Add.
    Assoc. Prop. of Add.
    Identity Prop. of Mult.
    Dist. Prop. of Add.

64. Dist. Prop.
    Dist. Prop.

B Apply Your Skills

Evaluate each expression for the given value of the variable.

38. $|x| + |2x| - |x - 1|$; $x = 2$ **5**

39. $|2z + 3| + |5 - 3z|$; $z = -3$ **17**

40. $3|2a + 5| + 2|3 - a|$; $a = 4$ **41**

41. $6|4b - 5| + 3|2 - 2b|$; $b = -1$ **66**

42. $\dfrac{3(2x + 1) - 2(x - 3)}{x + 6}$; $x = -3$ **−1**

43. $\dfrac{5(2k - 3) - 3(k + 4)}{3k + 2}$; $k = -2$ **$\frac{41}{4}$**

44. $y^2 + 3$; $y = \sqrt{7}$ **10**

45. $5c^3 - 6c^2 - 2c$; $c = -5$ **−765**

46. **Elections** The expression $2.6y + 107$ models the number of eligible voters in millions in the United States from 1960 to 2000. In the expression, y represents the number of years since 1960.   **about 180 million voters**

    a. Find the approximate number of eligible voters in 1988.

    b. Assume that the model continues to hold for future years. How many eligible voters will there be in 2012? In 2020?   **See below left.**

    c. The expression $-0.3y + 61$ models the *percent* of eligible voters who voted in presidential elections from 1960 to 2000. (See Example 3.) Write an expression that models the *number* of voters in presidential elections from 1960 to 2000. **$-0.0078y^2 + 1.265y + 65.27$**

    d. Use your model from (c) to find the approximate number of voters who voted for president in 1980. **about 87 million**

Simplify by combining like terms. 47. $-\frac{3}{4}a^2 + 2b^2$

47. $-a^2 + 2b^2 + \frac{1}{4}a^2$

48. $x + \frac{x^2}{2} + 2x^2 - x$ **$\frac{5x^2}{2}$**

49. $\frac{y^2}{4} + \frac{y}{3} + \frac{y^2}{3} - \frac{y}{5}$ **$\frac{7y^2}{12} + \frac{2y}{15}$**

50. $-(2x + y) - 2(-x - y)$ **y**

51. $x(3 - y) + y(x + 6)$ **$3x + 6y$**

52. $4(2x + y) - 2(2x + y)$ **$4x + 2y$**

53. $\frac{1}{2}(x^2 - y^2) - \frac{5}{2}(x^2 - y^2)$
    $-2x^2 + 2y^2$

Match the property name with the appropriate equation.

54. Definition of Subtraction **F**   A. $2(s - t) = 2s - 2t$

55. Definition of Division **C**   B. $-(a - b) = (-1)(a - b)$

56. Distributive Property **A**   C. $(7 - y) \div (2y) = \dfrac{7 - y}{2y}$

57. Multiplication by 0 **G**   D. $-[-(x - 10)] = x - 10$

58. Multiplication by -1 **B**   E. $-(2t - 11) = 11 - 2t$

59. Opposite of a Sum **H**   F. $2t - 11 = 2t + (-11)$

60. Opposite of a Difference **E**   G. $(4a^2 - 9a)(0) + 5a = 0 + 5a$

61. Opposite of a Product **I**   H. $-[3 + (-y)] = -3 + [-(-y)]$

62. Opposite of an Opposite **D**   I. $-(4z^2) = 4(-z^2)$

63–64. See margin.

Justifying Steps Name the property used in each step of simplification.

63. $(3x + y) + x = 3x + (y + x)$
    $= 3x + (x + y)$
    $= (3x + x) + y$
    $= (3x + 1x) + y$
    $= (3 + 1)x + y$
    $= 4x + y$

64. $2(5 + x) + 4(5 + x) = (2 + 4)(5 + x)$
    $= 6(5 + x)$
    $= 30 + 6x$

C Challenge

65. **Open-Ended** Write four different expressions that simplify to $x^2 - x$. Each expression must have five terms. **See above left.**

Real-World Connection

Each year, millions of U.S. citizens turn 18 and become eligible to vote. Unfortunately, fewer than half of them register.

46b. about 242 million voters; about 263 million voters

65. Answers may vary.
Sample:
$3x^2 + x - 4x^2 + 2x^2 - 2x$,
$x^3 + x^2 + x - x^3 - 2x$,
$-x^2 + 2x^2 + 3x - 3x - x$,
$x^2 - 5x + 4x - x^5 + x^5$,
$3x^2 - x^2 - x^2 + 7x - 8x$

66. Simplify $2(b - a) + 5(b - a)$ and explain each step in your simplification.
See margin.

67. a. Evaluate the expression $2(2x^2 - x) - 3(x^2 - x) + x^2 - x$ for $x = 3$. Do *not* simplify the expression before evaluating it. **18**

$2x^2$; 18

    b. Simplify the expression in (a) and then evaluate your answer for $x = 3$.

    c. Writing Explain why the values in (a) and (b) should be the same. **c–d. See margin.**

    d. Error Analysis A student simplified $2x(x - 6)$ to $2x^2 - 6x$. Should the student check his work by evaluating both expressions for $x = 0$? Explain.

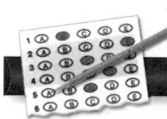

Standardized Test Prep

Multiple Choice

68. Which of the following expressions is NOT equivalent to the others? **B**

    A. $3x - y - x - y$ **B.** $-2(x - y)$

    C. $2(x - y)$ **D.** $2x - 2y$

69. If xy is negative, which one of the following is possible? **G**

    F. $x < y < 0$ **G.** $x < 0 < y$

    H. $x = y$ **I.** $0 \le x \le y$

Short Response

70. For which values of x does $6x(x - 3) = 0$? Explain your answer. **See below left.**

Quantitative Comparison

70. [2] $x = 0$ or $x = 3$ since for $6x(x - 3)$ = 0 either $6x$ or $x - 3$ equals 0.

[1] $x = 0$ and $x = 3$ with no explanation

Compare the boxed quantity in Column A with the boxed quantity in Column B. Choose the best answer.

    A. The quantity in Column A is greater.

    B. The quantity in Column B is greater.

    C. The two quantities are equal.

    D. The relationship cannot be determined from the information given.

Column A	Column B
71. A the perimeter of a square with side 17 in.	the perimeter of an equilateral triangle with side 19 in.
72. D the area of a rectangle with perimeter 24 cm	the area of a rectangle with perimeter 26 cm
73. C the perimeter of a square with area $100a^2b^2$ in.^{2}	the total perimeter of two squares, each with area $25a^2b^2$ in.^{2}

Take It to the NET
Online lesson quiz at
www.PHSchool.com
Web Code: aga-0102

Mixed Review

Lesson 1-1

Order the numbers from least to greatest.

$-4.3, -|3.4|, |-3.4|, |-4.3|$

74. $-1.5, -\sqrt{2}, -1.4, -0.5$ **74.** $-1.5, -0.5, -\sqrt{2}, -1.4$ **75.** $|-4.3|, -4.3, -|3.4|, |-3.4|$

77. $-\sqrt{\frac{1}{8}}, -\sqrt{\frac{1}{10}}, \sqrt{\frac{1}{16}}, \sqrt{\frac{1}{4}}$ **76.** $-\frac{3}{8}, \frac{1}{2}, -\frac{3}{4}, -\frac{5}{6}$ $-\frac{5}{6}, -\frac{3}{4}, -\frac{3}{8}, \frac{1}{2}$ **77.** $\sqrt{\frac{1}{4}}, \sqrt{\frac{1}{16}}, -\sqrt{\frac{1}{8}}, -\sqrt{\frac{1}{10}}$

Lesson 1-1

Replace each ▇ with the symbol <, >, or = to make the sentence true.

78. $|-11| \overset{>}{▇} |9|$ **79.** $|11| \overset{>}{▇} |9|$ **80.** $|-11| \overset{>}{▇} |-9|$

81. $-|-7| \overset{<}{▇} |7|$ **82.** $-|7| \overset{<}{▇} |-7|$ **83.** $-|-7| \overset{=}{▇} -|7|$

Standardized Test Prep

📁 **Resources**

For additional practice with a variety of test item formats:
- Standardized Test Prep, p. 51
- Test-Taking Strategies, p. 46
- Test-Taking Strategies with Transparencies

Exercise 69 Ask students what the given sentence in each choice implies about the sign of the product xy.

Exercise 70 Ask students what they can conclude about the factors if they know that the product is 0.

66. Answers may vary. Sample:
$2(b - a) + 5(b - a)$
  $= (2 + 5)(b - a)$
              Dist. Prop.
  $= 7(b - a)$ **Addition**
  $= 7b - 7a$ **Dist. Prop.**

67c. Properties of operations were used to simplify the original expression. Those properties convert one expression into an equivalent expression, and equivalent expressions have equal values for all replacements of their variables.

d. Answers may vary. Sample: Students should check each step in the simplification; they also should substitute more than one value for x in the original and simplified expressions.

17

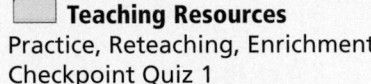
Lesson Preview

✓ **Check Skills You'll Need** 📖

Algebraic Expressions
Lessons 1-2: Example 4
Exercises 21–35
Extra Practice, p. 822

Lesson Resources

📁 **Teaching Resources**
Practice, Reteaching, Enrichment
Checkpoint Quiz 1

👥 **Reaching All Students**
Practice Workbook 1-3
Spanish Practice Workbook 1-3
Reading and Math Literacy 1B
Spanish Reading & Literacy 1B
Spanish Checkpoint Quiz 1

⏱️ **Presentation Assistant Plus!**
Transparencies
• Check Skills You'll Need 1-3
• Additional Examples 1-3
• Student Edition Answers 1-3
• Lesson Quiz 1-3
PH Presentation Pro CD 1-3

PRENTICE HALL
ASSESSMENT SYSTEM

Checkpoint Quiz 1
Computer Test Generator CD

💿 **Technology**
Resource Pro® CD-ROM
Computer Test Generator CD
Prentice Hall Presentation Pro CD

🖥️ **www.PHSchool.com**
Student Site
• Teacher Web Code: agk-5500
• Graphing Calculator, Procedure 7
• Self-grading Lesson Quiz
Teacher Center
• Lesson Planner
• Resources

Plus

18

Solving Equations

 North Carolina Objectives

1.03 Operate with algebraic expressions (polynomial, rational, complex fractions) to solve problems.

Lesson Preview

What You'll Learn

OBJECTIVE 1 To solve equations

OBJECTIVE 2 To solve problems by writing equations

. . . And Why

To solve a problem about aeronautics, as in Example 7

✓ **Check Skills You'll Need** *(For help, go to Lesson 1-2.)*

Simplify each expression.

1. $5x - 9x + 3$ **$-4x + 3$**
2. $2y + 7x + y - 1$ **$7x + 3y - 1$**
3. $10h + 12g - 8h - 4g$ **$8g + 2h$**
4. $\frac{x}{3} + \frac{y}{3} + \frac{2y}{3} - y$ **$\frac{x}{3}$**
5. $(x + y) - (x - y)$ **$2y$**
6. $-(3 - c) - 4(c - 1)$ **$-3c + 1$**

New Vocabulary • solution of an equation

OBJECTIVE 1 **Solving Equations**

📱 **TEXT** Interactive lesson includes instant self-check, tutorials, and activities.

An equation that contains a variable may be true for some replacements of the variable and false for others. A number that makes the equation true is a **solution of the equation.** You can use the properties of equality to solve equations.

🔑 **Key Concepts**

Summary	**Properties of Equality**

Let a, b, and c represent real numbers.

Reflexive Property	$a = a$
Symmetric Property	If $a = b$, then $b = a$.
Transitive Property	If $a = b$ and $b = c$, then $a = c$.
Addition Property	If $a = b$, then $a + c = b + c$.
Subtraction Property	If $a = b$, then $a - c = b - c$.
Multiplication Property	If $a = b$, then $ac = bc$.
Division Property	If $a = b$ and $c \neq 0$, then $\frac{a}{c} = \frac{b}{c}$.
Substitution Property	If $a = b$, then b may be substituted for a in any expression to obtain an equivalent expression.

📖 **Reading Math**

Literally, to solve means "to set apart." Think of solving an equation as setting apart the variable.

1 EXAMPLE **Solving an Equation with a Variable on Both Sides**

Solve $13y + 48 = 8y - 47$.

$13y + 48 = 8y - 47$
$5y + 48 = -47$ **Subtract 8*y* from each side.**
$5y = -95$ **Subtract 48 from each side.**
$y = -19$ **Divide each side by 5.**

Check $13y + 48 = 8y - 47$
$13(-19) + 48 \stackrel{?}{=} 8(-19) - 47$
$-199 = -199$ ✓

18 Chapter 1 Tools of Algebra

⚡ **Ongoing Assessment and Intervention**

Before the Lesson
Diagnose prerequisite skills using:
• Check Skills You'll Need

During the Lesson
Monitor progress using:
• Check Understanding
• Additional Examples
• Standardized Test Prep

After the Lesson
Assess knowledge using:
• Lesson Quiz
• Computer Test Generator CD
• Chapter Checkpoint 1 (p. 24)

① Solve each equation. Check your answers.

    a. $8z + 12 = 5z - 21$ **−11**

    b. $2t - 3 = 9 - 4t$ **2**

---

2 EXAMPLE   **Using the Distributive Property**

Solve $3x - 7(2x - 13) = 3(-2x + 9)$.

$$3x - 7(2x - 13) = 3(-2x + 9)$$

$\quad 3x - 14x + 91 = -6x + 27$ **Distributive Property**

$\quad\quad -11x + 91 = -6x + 27$ **Combine like terms.**

$\quad\quad\quad -5x + 91 = 27$ **Add 6x to each side.**

$\quad\quad\quad\quad -5x = -64$ **Subtract 91 from each side.**

$\quad\quad\quad\quad x = \dfrac{64}{5}$, or 12.8   **Divide each side by −5.**

✓ **Check Understanding** ② Solve each equation. Check your answers.

    a. $2(y - 3) + 6 = 70$ **35**

    b. $6(t - 2) = 2(9 - 2t)$ **3**

When you have a formula or equation that has more than one variable, you can solve for any one of the variables.

---

3 EXAMPLE   **Solving a Formula for One of Its Variables**

Geometry The formula for the area of a trapezoid is $A = \frac{1}{2}h(b_1 + b_2)$. Solve the formula for h.

$$A = \frac{1}{2}h(b_1 + b_2)$$

$\quad 2A = h(b_1 + b_2)$ **Multiply each side by 2.**

$\quad \dfrac{2A}{b_1 + b_2} = h$ **Divide each side by $b_1 + b_2$.**

✓ **Check Understanding** ③ Solve the formula for the area of a trapezoid for b_1. $b_1 = \dfrac{2A}{h} - b_2$

---

4 EXAMPLE   **Solving an Equation for One of Its Variables**

Solve $\frac{x}{a} + 1 = \frac{x}{b}$ for x. Find any restrictions on a and b.

$$\frac{x}{a} + 1 = \frac{x}{b}$$

$ab\left(\dfrac{x}{a}\right) + ab(1) = ab\left(\dfrac{x}{b}\right)$ **Multiply each side by the least common denominator (LCD).**

$\quad\quad bx + ab = ax$ **Simplify.**

$\quad\quad ab = ax - bx$ **Collect terms with x on one side.**

$\quad\quad ab = (a - b)x$ **Distributive Property**

$\quad\quad x = \dfrac{ab}{a - b}$ **Divide each side by $a - b$.**

The denominators cannot be 0, so $a \neq 0$ and $b \neq 0$. Also $a - b \neq 0$, so $a \neq b$.

✓ **Check Understanding** ④ Solve each equation for x. Find any restrictions.

    a. $ax + bx - 15 = 0$

       $x = \dfrac{15}{a + b}, a \neq -b$

    b. $d = \dfrac{2x}{a} + b$

       $x = \dfrac{a(d - b)}{2}, a \neq 0$

Math Background

Many equations in one variable are solved by using basic operations and the properties of equality. As a result, many application problems are solvable once they have been accurately modeled by an equation.

OBJECTIVE

① Teaching Notes

English Learners
Have students look up the words *reflexive, symmetric,* and *transitive* in a dictionary and compare the English meanings to the mathematical properties.

① EXAMPLE   **Math Tip**

Remind students to check their solutions in the original equation since they may have made a mistake at an intermediate step.

③ EXAMPLE   **Teaching Tip**

You may wish to point out that b_1 and b_2 are two different variables, as indicated by their different subscripts. It is not necessary to say that $b_1 \neq -b_2$ since b_1 and b_2 are lengths of segments. This ensures that their sum is not zero.

Additional Examples

① Solve $7x + 3 = 2x - 12$. **−3**

② Solve $4(m + 9) = -3(m - 4)$. $-\dfrac{24}{7}$

③ The formula for the surface area of a rectangular prism is $A = 2(\ell w + \ell h + wh)$. Solve the formula for w. $w = \dfrac{A - 2\ell h}{2\ell + 2h}$

④ Solve $\frac{x}{a} + 8 = b$ for x. Find any restrictions on a and b. $x = ab - 8a; a \neq 0$

👪 Reaching All Students

Below Level Students may have difficulty simplifying expressions containing variables. For these students, work through similar expressions that contain only constants.	**Advanced Learners** Discuss with students whether an expression such as $y = \sqrt{x}$ requires that $x \geq 0$. **If y is to be a real number, $x \geq 0$ must be true.**	**English Learners** See note on page 19. **Error Prevention** See note on page 22.

5 EXAMPLE Teaching Tip

You may want to encourage students to check their solutions algebraically. However, caution students that they may have found correct solutions to incorrect equations, so it is important they they check that their solutions are reasonable.

6 EXAMPLE Teaching Tip

Point out to students that multiplying each number in a ratio of three numbers by x is an extension of the concept of the ratio of two numbers. (If $x \neq 0$, then $a : b = ax : bx$.)

Additional Examples

5 Adrian will use part of a garage wall as one of the long sides of a rectangular rabbit pen. He wants the pen to be 3 times as long as it is wide. He plans to use 68 ft of fencing. Find the dimensions of the pen. **width = $13\frac{3}{5}$ ft, length = $40\frac{4}{5}$ ft**

6 The sides of a quadrilateral are in the ratio 1 : 2 : 3 : 6. The perimeter is 138 cm. Find the lengths of the sides. **11.5 cm, 23 cm, 34.5 cm, 69 cm**

7 A plane takes off from an airport and flies east at a speed of 350 mi/h. Ten minutes later, a second plane takes off from the same airport and flies east at a higher altitude at a speed of 400 mi/h. How long does it take the second plane to overtake the first plane? **$1\frac{1}{6}$ h**

Closure

Have students describe the procedure used to solve an equation for a variable. **Use properties of operations and equality to isolate the variable on one side of the equation. Then, combine like terms and divide both sides by the coefficient of the variable.**

You can write an equation to model and solve a real-world problem.

5 EXAMPLE Real-World Connection

Construction A dog kennel owner has 100 ft of fencing to enclose a rectangular dog run. She wants it to be 5 times as long as it is wide. Find the dimensions of the dog run.

Relate $2 \cdot$ width $+ 2 \cdot$ length $=$ perimeter

Define Let x = the width.

Then $5x$ = the length.

Write $2x + 2(5x) = 100$

$2x + 10x = 100$ **Multiply.**

$12x = 100$ **Combine like terms.**

$x = 8\frac{1}{3}$ **Divide each side by 12.**

$5x = 41\frac{2}{3}$ **Find the length.**

The width is $8\frac{1}{3}$ ft and the length is $41\frac{2}{3}$ ft.

Check Is the answer reasonable? Since the dimensions are about 8 ft and 42 ft, and $2 \cdot 8 + 2 \cdot 42 = 100$, the answer is reasonable.

Real-World Connection

Some states regulate the minimum amount of floor space for animals in kennels.

✓ **Check Understanding** **5** A rectangle is twice as long as it is wide. Its perimeter is 48 cm. Find its dimensions. **8 cm wide; 16 cm long**

Many geometry problems require writing and solving equations.

6 EXAMPLE Using Ratios

Geometry The lengths of the sides of a triangle are in the ratio 3 : 4 : 5. The perimeter of the triangle is 18 in. Find the lengths of the sides.

Relate Perimeter equals the sum of the lengths of the three sides.

Define Let $3x$ = the length of the shortest side.
Then $4x$ = the length of the second side.
Then $5x$ = the length of the third side.

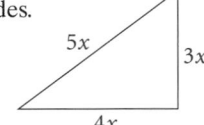

Write $18 = 3x + 4x + 5x$

$18 = 12x$ **Combine like terms.**

$1.5 = x$

$3x = 3(1.5)$ $4x = 4(1.5)$ $5x = 5(1.5)$ **Find the length of each side.**

$= 4.5$ $= 6$ $= 7.5$

The lengths of the sides are 4.5 in., 6 in., and 7.5 in.

Check Is the answer reasonable? Since $5 + 6 + 8 = 19$, the answer is reasonable.

✓ **Check Understanding** **6** The sides of a triangle are in the ratio 12 : 13 : 15. The perimeter is 120 cm. Find the lengths of the sides of the triangle. **36 cm; 39 cm; 45 cm**

7 EXAMPLE Real-World 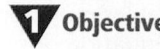 Connection

Aeronautics Radar detected an unidentified plane 5000 mi away, approaching at 700 mi/h. Fifteen minutes later an interceptor plane was dispatched, traveling at 800 mi/h. How long did the interceptor take to reach the approaching plane?

Relate distance for interceptor + distance for approaching plane = 5000 mi

Define Let t = the time in hours for the interceptor.
Then $t + 0.25$ = the time in hours for the approaching plane.

Write $800t + 700(t + 0.25) = 5000$
$\qquad 800t + 700t + 175 = 5000$ **Distributive Property**
$\qquad\qquad\qquad 1500t = 4825$ **Solve for t.**
$\qquad\qquad\qquad\quad t \approx 3.217$ or about 3 h 13 min

Check Is the answer reasonable? In $3\frac{1}{4}$ h, the interceptor flies 2600 mi. In $3\frac{1}{2}$ h, the approaching plane flies 2450 mi. $2600 + 2450 \approx 5000$, so the answer is reasonable.

✓ **Check Understanding** **7** A space probe leaves Earth at the rate of 3 km/s. After 100 days, a radio signal is sent to the probe. Radio signals travel at the speed of light, about 3×10^5 km/s. About how long does the signal take to reach the probe? **about 86.4 seconds, or 1 minute 26.4 seconds**

EXERCISES

For more practice, see *Extra Practice*.

Practice and Problem Solving

A **Practice by Example**

Example 1
(page 18)

Solve each equation. Check your answers.

1. $7w + 2 = 3w + 94$ **23**

2. $15 - g = 23 - 2g$ **8**

3. $43 - 3d = d + 9$ $\frac{17}{2}$

4. $5y + 1.8 = 4y - 3.2$ **−5**

5. $6a - 5 = 4a + 2$ $\frac{7}{2}$

6. $7y + 4 = 3 - 2y$ $-\frac{1}{9}$

7. $5c - 9 = 8 - 2c$ $\frac{17}{7}$

8. $4y - 8 - 2y + 5 = 0$ $\frac{3}{2}$

Example 2
(page 19)

9. $6(n - 4) = 3n$ **8**

10. $2 - 3(x + 4) = 8$ **−6**

11. $5(2 - g) = 0$ **2**

12. $2(x + 4) = 8$ **0**

13. $6(t - 2) = 2(9t - 2)$ $-\frac{2}{3}$

14. $4w - 2(1 - w) = -38$ **−6**

15. $4(k + 5) = 2(9k - 4)$ **2**

16. $10(1 - 2y) = -5(2y - 1)$ $\frac{1}{2}$

Example 3
(page 19)

Solve each formula for the indicated variable.

17. $A = \frac{1}{2}bh$, for h $h = \frac{2A}{b}$

18. $s = \frac{1}{2}gt^2$, for g $g = \frac{2s}{t^2}$

19. $V = \ell wh$, for w $w = \frac{V}{\ell h}$

20. $I = prt$, for r $r = \frac{I}{pt}$

21. $S = 2\pi rh$, for r $r = \frac{S}{2\pi h}$

22. $V = \pi r^2 h$, for h $h = \frac{V}{\pi r^2}$

Example 4
(page 19)

Solve each equation for x. Find any restrictions. **23–28. See margin.**

23. $ax + bx = c$

24. $bx - cx = -c$

25. $\frac{x}{a} + b = c$

26. $\frac{x}{a} - 5 = b$

27. $\frac{x - 2}{2} = m + n$

28. $\frac{2}{5}(x + 1) = g$

Assignment Guide

1 Objective
Ⓐ Ⓑ **Core** 1–28, 36–47, 55–64
Ⓒ **Extension** 65

2 Objective
Ⓐ Ⓑ **Core** 29–35, 48–54
Ⓒ **Extension** 66–68

Standardized Test Prep 69–72

Mixed Review 73–82

Exercises 18–21 Students may find it helpful to first rewrite the expression with the indicated variable as the rightmost factor. For example, in Exercise 20, rewrite $I = prt$ as $I = (pt)r$. This makes it easier to see what to multiply or divide each side by to isolate r.

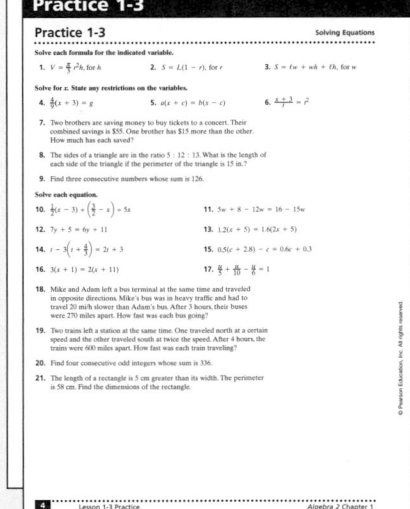

pages 21–24 Exercises

23. $x = \frac{c}{a + b}$, $a \neq -b$

24. $x = \frac{c}{c - b}$, $b \neq c$

25. $x = a(c - b)$ or $ac - ab$, $a \neq 0$

26. $x = a(b + 5)$ or $ab + 5a$, $a \neq 0$

27. $x = 2(m + n) + 2$ or $2m + 2n + 2$

28. $x = \frac{5g}{2} - 1$

21

Examples 5–7
(pages 20, 21)

Write an equation to solve each problem.

29. Two buses leave Houston at the same time and travel in opposite directions. One bus averages 55 mi/h and the other bus averages 45 mi/h. When will they be 400 mi apart? **4 h**

30. Two planes left an airport at noon. One flew east at a certain speed and the other flew west at twice the speed. The planes were 2700 mi apart in 3 h. How fast was each plane flying? **300 mi/h; 600 mi/h**

31. **Geometry** The length of a rectangle is 3 cm greater than its width. The perimeter is 24 cm. Find the dimensions of the rectangle. **width = 4.5 cm; length = 7.5 cm**

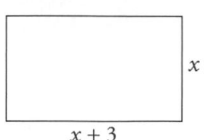

32. **Geometry** One side of a triangle is 1 in. longer than the shortest side and is 1 in. shorter than the longest side. The perimeter is 17 in. Find the dimensions of the triangle. $4\frac{2}{3}$ **in.;** $5\frac{2}{3}$ **in.;** $6\frac{2}{3}$ **in.**

33. **Geometry** The sides of a rectangle are in the ratio 3 : 2. What is the length of each side if the perimeter of the rectangle is 55 cm? **11 cm; 11 cm; 16.5 cm; 16.5 cm**

34. **Geometry** The sides of a triangle are in the ratio 3 : 4 : 5. What is the length of each side if the perimeter of the triangle is 30 cm? **7.5 cm; 10 cm; 12.5 cm**

35. The sum of three consecutive integers is 90. **a–b. See left.**
   a. Find the three numbers by letting x represent the first integer.
   b. Find the three numbers by letting x represent the second integer.

35a. $x + (x + 1) + (x + 2) = 90; 29, 30, 31$
b. $(x − 1) + x + (x + 1) = 90; 29, 30, 31$

B **Apply Your Skills**

Solve each equation. 36. $\frac{46}{39}$**, or** $1\frac{7}{39}$

36. $0.2(x + 3) − 4(2x − 3) = 3.4$

37. $12 − 3(2w + 1) = 7w − 3(7 + w)$ **3**

38. $\frac{27}{5}$**, or** $5\frac{2}{5}$ 38. $3(m − 2) − 5 = 8 − 2(m − 4)$

39. $7(a + 1) − 3a = 5 + 4(2a − 1)$ $\frac{3}{2}$

40. $\frac{x}{2} + \frac{x}{5} + \frac{x}{3} = 31$ **30**

41. $0.5\left(2x + \frac{3}{4}\right) − \frac{1}{3}(0.1 + x) = 1$ $\frac{79}{80}$**, or 0.9875**

Solve each formula for the indicated variable. **42–47. See margin.**

42. $R(r_1 + r_2) = r_1 r_2$, for R

43. $R(r_1 + r_2) = r_1 r_2$, for r_2

44. $S = 2\pi r^2 + 2\pi rh$, for h

45. $h = vt − 5t^2$, for v

46. $v = s^2 + \frac{1}{2}sh$, for h

47. $A = \frac{1}{2}h(b_1 + b_2)$, for b_2

48. **Geometry** The measure of the supplement of an angle is 20° more than three times the measure of the original angle. Find the measures of the angles. **40°, 140°**

49. **Geometry** The measures of an angle and its complement differ by 22°. Find the measures of the angles. **34°, 56°**

50. Michael drove to a friend's house at a rate of 40 mi/h. He returned by the same route at a rate of 45 mi/h. The driving time for the round trip was 4 h. What is the distance Michael traveled? **about 169.4 mi**

51. **Sports** In the 2000 Olympics, Marion Jones of the United States won the gold medal in the 100-meter race with a time of 10.75 seconds. In the 1968 Olympics, Wyomia Tyus, also of the United States, won the gold medal in the 100-meter race in 11.08 seconds. If they ran in the same race repeating their respective times, by how many meters would Jones beat Tyus? **≈2.98 m**

52. **Investments** Suppose you have $5000 to invest. A certificate of deposit (CD) earns 6% annual interest, while bonds, which are more risky, earn 8% annual interest. You decide to invest $2000 in a CD and the rest in bonds. How much interest will you have earned at the end of one year? Of two years? **$360; $746.40**

Left margin

Exercises 42–47 You may wish to have students state any restrictions on the variables.

Error Prevention

Exercise 55 Students should be alerted to the fact that restrictions on variables may stem from the original equation or from expressions in the solution.

Error Prevention

Exercise 67b Students may arrive at the equation $x = \pm\sqrt{\frac{c - b}{a}}$ and say that $c − b$ and a must be perfect squares in order for the two solutions to be rational. Urge them to reassess the possibilities. The quantity $\frac{c - b}{a}$ can be a perfect square even though $c − b$ and a are not. Consider, for example, the case in which $c = 4$, $b = 1$, and $a = 3$.

pages 21–24 Exercises

42. $R = \frac{r_1 r_2}{r_1 + r_2}$

43. $r_2 = \frac{Rr_1}{r_1 - R}$

44. $h = \frac{S - 2\pi r^2}{2\pi r}$

45. $v = \frac{h + 5t^2}{t}$

46. $h = \frac{2(v - s^2)}{s}$

47. $b_2 = \frac{2A}{h} - b_1$

55. $x = ab - b^2 - a, b \neq 0$

56. $x = \frac{c - a}{b - d}, b \neq d$

57. $x = \frac{b + d}{c - a}, a \neq c$

58. $x = \frac{3a - b - 8}{a - b}, a \neq b$

59. $x = \frac{3b + 2c - 5}{b - c}, b \neq c$

60. $x = \frac{2ab - 2c}{3at - cd}, 3at \neq cd$

61. $x = \frac{4a - 3bc}{aq - 5bp}, 5bp \neq aq$

62. $x = \frac{cb}{2da} + 6, a, b, d \neq 0$

63. $x = \frac{10c}{a}, a \neq 0$

64. $x = \frac{a - c}{m} + a, m \neq 0, x \neq a$

22

Bottom

66a. 10 cows; 30 chickens. Sample equation: $4c + 2(40 − c) = 100$, where c is the number of cows

c. Answers may vary. Sample: In all, a repair shop has 11 bicycles and tricycles to repair. These have a total of 26 wheels. How many bicycles and how many tricycles are there? 7 bicycles, 4 tricycles

53. Find 4 consecutive odd integers with a sum of 184. **43, 45, 47, 49**

54. Find 4 consecutive even integers such that the sum of the second and fourth is 76.
34, 36, 38, 40

Solve for x. State any restrictions on the variables. 55–64. See margin p. 22.

55. $\dfrac{x+a}{b} + b = a$

56. $bx + a = dx + c$

57. $cx - b = ax + d$

58. $a(x - 3) + 8 = b(x - 1)$

59. $c(x + 2) - 5 = b(x - 3)$

60. $a(3tx - 2b) = c(dx - 2)$

61. $b(5px - 3c) = a(qx - 4)$

62. $\dfrac{a}{b}(2x - 12) = \dfrac{c}{d}$

63. $\dfrac{3ax}{5} - 4c = \dfrac{ax}{5}$

64. $\dfrac{a-c}{x-a} = m$

C **Challenge**

65. a. $t = \dfrac{s - 1055}{1.1}$
b. about 40.9°F
c. $C = \dfrac{5}{9}(F - 32)$
d. about 4.9°C

65. a. The speed of sound in air s, in ft/s, is given by the formula $s = 1055 + 1.1t$, where t is the temperature in degrees Fahrenheit. Solve the formula for t.
 b. Find the Fahrenheit temperature at which the speed of sound is 1100 ft/s.
 c. The relationship between the temperature in degrees Fahrenheit F and degrees Celsius C is given by the formula $F = \dfrac{9}{5}C + 32$. Solve the formula for C.
 d. Find the Celsius temperature at which the speed of sound is 1100 ft/s.

66. There are 40 cows and chickens in the farmyard. One quiet afternoon, Jack counted and found that there were 100 legs in all. How many cows and how many chickens are there?
 a. Solve this problem by writing and solving an equation. **See margin p. 22.**
 b. Critical Thinking This problem can also be solved by reasoning. Suppose all 40 animals are chickens. How many legs would there be? How many too few legs is that? If one chicken is replaced by one cow, by how many would the number of legs be increased? How many cows would have to replace chickens to get the required 100 legs? **80 legs; 20 legs; 2 legs; 10 cows**
 c. Open-Ended Write a problem about the number of wheels in a group of bicycles and tricycles. Solve your problem. **See margin p. 22.**

67. Assume that $a, b,$ and c are integers and $a \neq 0$.
 a. Proof Prove that the solution of the linear equation $ax - b = c$ must be a rational number. **See margin.**
 b. Writing Describe the values of $a, b,$ and c for which the solutions of $ax^2 + b = c$ are rational. **See back of book.**

68. A tortoise crawling at the rate of 0.1 mi/h passes a resting hare. The hare wants to rest another 30 min before chasing the tortoise at the rate of 5 mi/h. How many feet must the hare run to catch the tortoise? **about 269.4 ft**

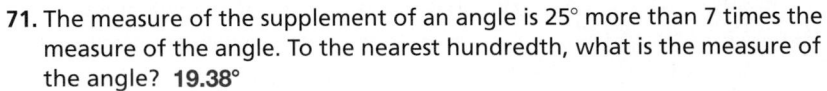

Standardized Test Prep

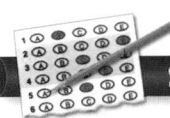
69. What is the only value z for which $6z - 24 = 2z + 50$? Enter your answer as a decimal. **18.5**

70. If 16 less than four times a number is 64, what is the number? **20**

71. The measure of the supplement of an angle is 25° more than 7 times the measure of the angle. To the nearest hundredth, what is the measure of the angle? **19.38°**

72. The sides of a rectangle are in the ratio 5 : 7 and the perimeter of the rectangle is 96 cm. What is the area of the rectangle? **560 cm²**

Lesson 1-3   Solving Equations   **23**

67a. If you solve $ax - b = c$ for x, you get $x = \dfrac{b+c}{a}$. Since b and c are integers, $b + c$ is an integer. But a is a nonzero integer. So $\dfrac{b+c}{a}$ is the quotient of two integers and hence, by the definition of a rational number, $\dfrac{b+c}{a}$ is a rational number.

Chapter Checkpoint 1

To check understanding of Lessons 1-1 to 1-3:

Checkpoint Quiz 1 (p. 24)

📁 **Teaching Resources**
Checkpoint 1 (also in Prentice Hall Assessment System)

👥 **Reaching All Students**
Reading and Math Literacy 1B

Spanish versions available

Mixed Review

Lesson 1-2   **Evaluate each expression for $x = -4$ and $y = 3$.**

73. $x - 2y + 3$ **-7**   **74.** $x + x \div y$ **75.** $3x - 4y - x$ **76.** $x + 2y \div x$
                      $-\frac{16}{3}$, or $-5\frac{1}{3}$ **-20** $-\frac{11}{2}$, or $-5\frac{1}{2}$

Lesson 1-2   **Simplify each expression.**

77. $2x^2 + x + 5x^2 - 3x$ **78.** $ab - a - 5a$ **79.** $-(3x - y + 4x - y)$
   $7x^2 - 2x$ **$ab - 6a$**   **$2y - 7x$**
80. $2(5x - 3) + x$ **81.** $5 - 2(3x + 5)$ **82.** $4r + 2s - (6r + 7s)$
   $11x - 6$ **$-6x - 5$**   **$-2r - 5s$**

✔ Checkpoint Quiz 1   Lessons 1-1 through 1-3

💻 Instant self-check quiz online and on CD-ROM

1. $-1, 0.3, \frac{2}{3}, 7$

2. Comm. Prop. of Add., Assoc. Prop. of Add., Dist. Prop.

1–2. See left.

1. Simplify the numbers and arrange them in order from least to greatest.
    $|4 - 11|$ $0.1|-3|$ $|1 - \frac{1}{3}|$ $|3| - |4|$

2. What three properties of real numbers are needed to simplify $3x + (2 + 5x)$?

Simplify each expression.

3. $-(a + 2b) + 4(a + 2b) - 2(a + 2b)$ **4.** $-3(a^2 + a + 1) - 4(-a^2 - a + 1)$
   $a + 2b$ **$a^2 + a - 7$**

Solve each equation.

5. $2(4x + 1) = 3(4 + 2x)$ **5**   **6.** $12 - 2(3x + 1) = 4x - 5$ $\frac{3}{2}$, or $1\frac{1}{2}$

7. $\frac{1}{2}(4b + 1) = 7 - \frac{1}{4}(6b - 2)$ **2**

Solve for the indicated variable. Find any restrictions. $x = \frac{4b}{7a}, a \neq 0$

8. $A = p(1 + rt)$, for r **9.** $8ax - b = 3b + ax$, for x
   $r = \frac{A - p}{pt}, p \neq 0, t \neq 0$

10. The perimeter of Sportsland Park is 624 yd. The length of the rectangular park is 8 yd more than 3 times the width. Find the dimensions of the park.
                             width = 76 yd, length = 236 yd

Algebra at Work

·········· Wildlife Biologist

Wildlife biologists can model changes in an animal population. An animal population increases rapidly when conditions are good. However, as the number of animals increases, the food supplies decrease. Hunger and disease then lower the population.

    Wildlife biologists take a special interest in extremes of animal populations. If the population of one species becomes too large, it may reduce the population of another species. A continuing decrease may result in an endangered or extinct species.

💻 **Take It to the NET** For more information about wildlife biology, go to **www.PHSchool.com**.
         Web Code: agb-2031

Technology

Spreadsheets

Suppose that you buy an electronic keyboard and sound system for $500 using a credit card. When you get your first monthly statement, the minimum payment is $25. The minimum payment is either 5% of your balance or $15, whichever is greater. Interest is calculated at 1.8% per month. You pay the minimum each month.

EXAMPLE

You can examine the situation described above with a spreadsheet. Write cell formulas for row 3 of the spreadsheet.

	A	B	C	D	E	F	G
1	Month	Balance	Interest	Payment	New Balance	Total Interest	Total Paid
2	1	$500.00	$9.00	$25.00	$484.00	$9.00	$25.00
3	2	$484.00	$8.71	$24.20	$468.51	$17.71	$49.20
4	3	$468.51	$8.43	$23.43	$453.52	$26.15	$72.63

Month	$A3 = A2 + 1$	Increase the month by 1.
Balance	$B3 = E2$	balance from the previous month
Interest	$C3 = B3 \cdot 0.018$	1.8% of the month's balance
Payment	$D3 = B3 \cdot 0.05$	5% of the month's balance
New Balance	$E3 = B3 + C3 - D3$	Add the interest and subtract the payment.
Total Interest	$F3 = F2 + C3$	Add the month's interest to the previous total interest.
Total Paid	$G3 = G2 + D3$	Add the month's payment to the previous total.

EXERCISES

1. Create a spreadsheet for the situation in the Example.
   a. In which month will the minimum payment first be $15? **month 17**
   b. After how many months will the balance reach zero? **41 months**
   c. What is the total interest paid? **$187.74**
   d. What is the total amount you will pay? **$687.74**
   e. How many payments are required to reduce the balance to $400? **7 payments**
   f. Rewrite the right side of $E3 = B3 + C3 - D3$ in terms of B3.
   $E3 = B3 + (B3 \cdot 0.018) - (B3 \cdot 0.05)$, or $B3 \cdot 0.968$
2. Create a new spreadsheet for an account that charges 14.9% annual interest. Use a minimum payment of 10% or $20, whichever is greater. What is the total interest paid for the keyboard and sound system? **$57.34**

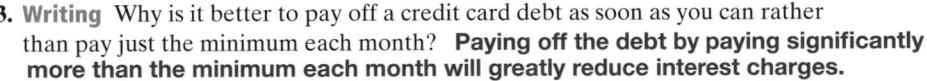

3. **Writing** Why is it better to pay off a credit card debt as soon as you can rather than pay just the minimum each month? **Paying off the debt by paying significantly more than the minimum each month will greatly reduce interest charges.**

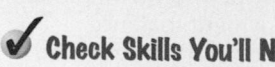
Lesson Preview

 **Check Skills You'll Need**

Properties of Real Numbers
Lesson 1-1: Example 3
Exercises 17–24
Extra Practice, p. 822

Solving Equations
Lesson 1-3: Examples 1, 2
Exercises 1–16
Extra Practice, p. 822

Lesson Resources

📁 **Teaching Resources**
Practice, Reteaching, Enrichment

👥 **Reaching All Students**
Practice Workbook 1-4
Spanish Practice Workbook 1-4

⏰ **Presentation Assistant Plus!**
Transparencies
• Check Skills You'll Need 1-4
• Additional Examples 1-4
• Student Edition Answers 1-4
• Lesson Quiz 1-4
PH Presentation Pro CD 1-4

PRENTICE HALL
ASSESSMENT SYSTEM
Computer Test Generator CD

💿 **Technology**
Resource Pro® CD-ROM
Computer Test Generator CD
Prentice Hall Presentation Pro CD

💻 **www.PHSchool.com**
Student Site
• Teacher Web Code: agk-5500
• Self-grading Lesson Quiz
Teacher Center
• Lesson Planner
• Resources

Plus 📱**TEXT**

1-4

Solving Inequalities

 North Carolina Objectives
1.03 Operate with algebraic expressions (polynomial, rational, complex fractions) to solve problems.

Lesson Preview

What You'll Learn

OBJECTIVE 1 To solve and graph inequalities

OBJECTIVE 2 To solve and write compound inequalities

. . . And Why

To analyze quality control, as in Example 6

✔ **Check Skills You'll Need** (For help, go to Lessons 1-1 and 1-3.)

State whether each inequality is true or false.
1. $5 < 12$ **true**　　**2.** $5 < -12$ **false**　　**3.** $5 \geq 12$ **false**
4. $5 \leq -12$ **false**　　**5.** $5 \leq 5$ **true**　　**6.** $5 \geq 5$ **true**

Solve each equation.
7. $3x + 3 = 2x - 3$ **−6**　　　　　　**8.** $5x = 9(x - 8) + 12$ **15**

New Vocabulary • compound inequality

 Interactive lesson includes instant self-check, tutorials, and activities.

OBJECTIVE 1
Solving and Graphing Inequalities

As with an equation, the solutions of an inequality are the numbers that make it true.

 Need Help?
To review the properties of equality, go to p. 18.

An equation such as $-2x = 10$ has only one solution, -5. On the other hand, the inequality $-2x < 10$ is true for many values of x, such as $-4.99, -1,$ and 100. The solutions of $-2x < 10$ are all the numbers x such that $x > -5$, as shown in the graph at the right.

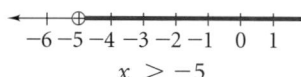
$x > -5$

The properties for solving inequalities are similar to the properties for solving equations. The exception occurs when you multiply or divide each side by a negative quantity. Notice that you can obtain $x > -5$ from $-2x < 10$ by dividing each side by -2 and *reversing* the inequality.

The following properties are for $\leq$. There are similar properties for $<, >,$ and $\geq$.

🔑 **Key Concepts**

Property	**Properties of Inequalities**
Let $a, b,$ and c represent real numbers.	
Transitive Property	If $a \leq b$ and $b \leq c$, then $a \leq c$.
Addition Property	If $a \leq b$, then $a + c \leq b + c$.
Subtraction Property	If $a \leq b$, then $a - c \leq b - c$.
Multiplication Property	If $a \leq b$ and $c > 0$, then $ac \leq bc$. If $a \leq b$ and $c < 0$, then $ac \geq bc$.
Division Property	If $a \leq b$ and $c > 0$, then $\frac{a}{c} \leq \frac{b}{c}$. If $a \leq b$ and $c < 0$, then $\frac{a}{c} \geq \frac{b}{c}$.

←Notice that the inequality is reversed
←when c is negative.

INSTANT CHECK SYSTEM ✔ **Ongoing Assessment and Intervention**

Before the Lesson	**During the Lesson**	**After the Lesson**
Diagnose prerequisite skills using:	**Monitor progress using:**	**Assess knowledge using:**
• Check Skills You'll Need	• Check Understanding	• Lesson Quiz
	• Additional Examples	• Computer Test Generator CD
	• Standardized Test Prep	

① EXAMPLE Solving and Graphing Inequalities

Reading Math

For help with reading and solving Example 1b, see page 32.

Solve each inequality. Graph the solution.

a. $3x - 12 < 3$

$3x - 12 < 3$

$3x < 15$ Add 12 to each side.

$x < 5$ Divide each side by 3.

Graph the solution.
$-1\ 0\ 1\ 2\ 3\ 4\ 5\ 6$

Check First check the boundary point: $3(5) - 12 = 3.$ ✓
Then check another point on the graph, such as 4: $3(4) - 12 < 3.$ ✓

b. $6 + 5(2 - x) \le 41$

$6 + 10 - 5x \le 41$ Distributive Property

$16 - 5x \le 41$ Simplify.

$-5x \le 25$ Subtract 16 from each side.

$x \ge -5$ Divide each side by -5 and reverse the inequality.

Graph the solution.
$-6\ -5\ -4\ -3\ -2\ -1\ 0\ 1$

Check First check the boundary point: $6 + 5[2 - (-5)] = 41.$ ✓
Then check another point, such as -4: $6 + 5[2 - (-4)] \le 41.$ ✓

✓ Check Understanding ① Solve each inequality. Graph the solution.
a. $3x - 6 < 27$ **x < 11**
$5\ 6\ 7\ 8\ 9\ 10\ 11\ 12\ 13$
b. $12 \ge 2(3n + 1) + 22$ **n ≤ −2**
$-6\ -5\ -4\ -3\ -2\ -1\ 0\ 1\ 2$

Some inequalities have no solution, and some are true for all real numbers.

② EXAMPLE No Solutions or All Real Numbers as Solutions

Solve each inequality. Graph the solution.

a. $2x - 3 > 2(x - 5)$

$2x - 3 > 2x - 10$ Distributive Property

$2x > 2x - 7$ Add 3 to each side.

$0 > -7$ Subtract 2x from each side.

The last inequality is always true, so $2x - 3 > 2(x - 5)$ is always true. All real numbers are solutions.
$-3\ -2\ -1\ 0\ 1\ 2\ 3$

b. $7x + 6 < 7(x - 4)$

$7x + 6 < 7x - 28$ Distributive Property

$6 < -28$ Subtract 7x from each side.

The last inequality is always false, so $7x + 6 < 7(x - 4)$ is always false. It has no solution.

All real numbers are solutions.
$-4\ -3\ -2\ -1\ 0\ 1\ 2\ 3\ 4$

✓ Check Understanding ② **a.** Solve $2x < 2(x + 1) + 3$. Graph the solution.
b. Solve $4(x - 3) + 7 \ge 4x + 1$. Graph the solution. **no solutions**
c. Critical Thinking If possible, find values of a such that $2x + a > 2x$ has no solution. Then find values of a such that all real numbers are solutions.
values of a less than or equal to 0; values of a greater than 0

Lesson 1-4 Solving Inequalities   **27**

👥 Reaching All Students

Below Level If students are having difficulty understanding the concept of a solution to an inequality, use substitution to show that many different numbers satisfy the inequality.	**Advanced Learners** Have students try to create inequalities that have a single real-number solution, no solution, or the set of all real numbers as the solution.	**Visual Learners** See note on page 27. **Visual Learners** See note on page 28.

Professional Development

Math Background

Solving inequalities is much like solving equations. An important difference is that multiplying or dividing both sides by a negative number reverses the direction of the inequality symbol.

The work with compound inequalities in this lesson prepares students for solving absolute value inequalities in the next lesson.

OBJECTIVE
① Teaching Notes

① EXAMPLE Teaching Tip

Remind students that when they graph an inequality, they should use an open circle at the boundary point if the boundary point is not a solution.

② EXAMPLE Visual Learners

When an inequality has no solution, students may want to represent this situation graphically by drawing a number line without any shading.

③ EXAMPLE Math Tip

The inequality may also be written as $500 \le 200 + 0.25x$. It is customary (but not necessary) to write the final inequality in the solution so that the variable is on the left side of the inequality symbol.

🖐 Additional Examples

① Solve $-2x < 3(x - 5)$. Graph the solution. **x > 3;**
$-2\ -1\ 0\ 1\ 2\ 3\ 4\ 5\ 6$

② Solve $7x \ge 7(2 + x)$. Graph the solution. **no solution**
$-4\ -3\ -2\ -1\ 0\ 1\ 2\ 3\ 4$

③ A real estate agent earns a salary of $2000 per month plus 4% of the sales. Find the sales if the salesperson is to have a monthly income of at least $5000. **greater than or equal to $75,000**

27

You may wish to use a transparency and erasable color markers to show the graph of $x > -9$ in yellow and the graph of $x < 6$ in blue. The part of the number line that is green is the solution of the compound inequality.

5 EXAMPLE **Teaching Tip**

Adapt the Teaching Tip for Example 4. This time the solution of the compound inequality is any part of the number line that has color.

6 EXAMPLE **Visual Learners**

Invite visual learners to sketch a diagram to illustrate how to trim a 5-in. paper strip so that it is 3 in. long with a tolerance of $\frac{1}{4}$ in.

Additional Examples

4 Graph the solution of $2x - 1 \le 3x$ and $x > 4x - 9$.

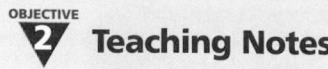

5 Graph the solution of $3x + 9 < -3$ or $-2x + 1 < 5$.

6 A strip of wood is to be 17 cm long with a tolerance of ± 0.15 cm. How much should be trimmed from a strip 18 cm long to allow it to meet specifications? **at least 0.85 cm and no more than 1.15 cm**

Closure

Ask: *What is one important difference between solving equations and solving inequalities?* **Answers may vary. Sample: If you multiply or divide both sides of an inequality by a negative number, you change the direction of the inequality symbol.**

pages 29–31 Exercises

1.

---

3 EXAMPLE **Real-World Connection**

Revenue The band shown at the left agrees to play for $200 plus 25% of the ticket sales. Find the ticket sales needed for the band to receive at least $500.

Relate $200 + 25\%$ of ticket sales $\ge$ $500

Define Let x = ticket sales (in dollars).

Write
$$200 + 0.25x \ge 500$$
$$0.25x \ge 300 \qquad \text{Subtract 200 from each side.}$$
$$x \ge 1200 \qquad \text{Divide each side by 0.25.}$$

● The ticket sales must be greater than or equal to $1200.

✓ **Check Understanding** **3** A salesperson earns a salary of $700 per month plus 2% of the sales. What must the sales be if the salesperson is to have a monthly income of at least $1800?
at least $55,000

OBJECTIVE
2 **Compound Inequalities**

A **compound inequality** is a pair of inequalities joined by *and* or *or*.

Examples:
- $-1 < x$ and $x \le 3$, which you can also write as $-1 < x \le 3$
- $x < -1$ or $x \ge 3$

To solve a compound inequality containing *and*, find all values of the variable that make both inequalities true.

4 EXAMPLE **Compound Inequality Containing *And***

Graph the solution of $3x - 1 > -28$ and $2x + 7 < 19$.

$$3x - 1 > -28 \quad \text{and} \quad 2x + 7 < 19$$
$$3x > -27 \qquad \qquad 2x < 12$$
$$x > -9 \quad \text{and} \qquad x < 6$$

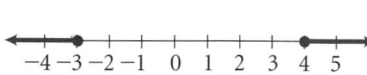

● This compound inequality can be rewritten as $-9 < x < 6$.

✓ **Check Understanding** **4** Graph the solution of $2x > x + 6$ and $x - 7 < 2$.

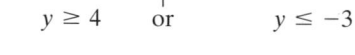

To solve a compound inequality containing *or*, find all values of the variable that make at least one of the inequalities true.

5 EXAMPLE **Compound Inequality Containing *Or***

Graph the solution of $4y - 2 \ge 14$ or $3y - 4 \le -13$.

$$4y - 2 \ge 14 \quad \text{or} \quad 3y - 4 \le -13$$
$$4y \ge 16 \qquad \qquad 3y \le -9$$
$$y \ge 4 \quad \text{or} \qquad y \le -3$$

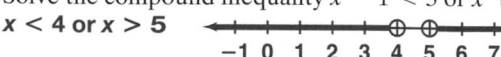

✓ **Check Understanding** **5** Solve the compound inequality $x - 1 < 3$ or $x + 3 > 8$. Graph the solution.
x < 4 or x > 5

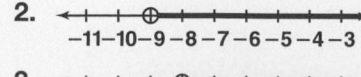

2.

5.

8.

3.

6.

9.

4.

7.

10.

Real-World Connection

When engineers design a part, they specify the allowable variation, or tolerance, in the size of the part.

6 EXAMPLE Real-World  Connection

Quality Control The plans for a gear assembly specify a length of 13.48 cm with a tolerance of ± 0.03 cm. A machinist finds that the part is now 13.67 cm long. By how much should the machinist decrease the length?

Relate   minimum length $\leq$ final length $\leq$ maximum length

Define   Let x = number of centimeters to remove.

Write
$$13.48 - 0.03 \leq 13.67 - x \leq 13.48 + 0.03$$
$$13.45 \leq 13.67 - x \leq 13.51 \quad \textbf{Simplify.}$$
$$-0.22 \leq -x \leq -0.16 \quad \textbf{Subtract 13.67.}$$
$$0.22 \geq x \geq 0.16 \quad \textbf{Multiply by } -1.$$

• The machinist must remove at least 0.16 cm and no more than 0.22 cm.

✓ **Check Understanding** **6** The plans for a circular plastic part in a medical instrument require a diameter of 1.5 in. with a tolerance of ± 0.2 in. A machinist finds that the diameter is now 1.73 in. By how much should the machinist decrease the diameter? **by at least 0.03 in., but by no more than 0.43 in.**

3. Practice

Assignment Guide

1 Objective
   Ⓐ Ⓑ Core 1–17, 29–35, 38–40
   Ⓒ Extension 51–52

2 Objective
   Ⓐ Ⓑ Core 18–28, 36–37, 41–50
   Ⓒ Extension 53–55

Standardized Test Prep 56–61

Mixed Review 62–69

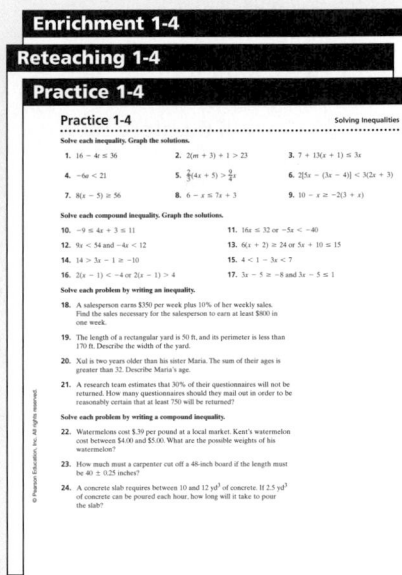

EXERCISES

For more practice, see *Extra Practice*.

Practice and Problem Solving

Ⓐ Practice by Example

Examples 1 and 2
(page 27)

Solve each inequality. Graph the solution. **1–10. See margin p. 28 for graphs. 11–13. See back of book for graphs.**

1. $-12 \geq 24x$ $x \leq -\frac{1}{2}$ **2.** $-7k < 63$ $k > -9$ **3.** $8a - 15 > 73$ $a > 11$

4. $57 - 4t \geq 13$ $t \leq 11$ **5.** $-18 - 5y \geq 52$ $y \leq -14$

6. $14 - 4y \geq 38$ $y \leq -6$ **7.** $4(x + 3) \leq 44$ $x \leq 8$

8. $2(m - 3) + 7 < 21$ $m < 10$ **9.** $4(n - 2) - 6 > 18$ $n > 8$

10. $9(x + 2) > 9(x - 3)$ **All real numbers are solutions.**   **11.** $6x - 13 < 6(x - 2)$ **All real numbers are solutions.**
12. $-6(2x - 10) + 12x \leq 180$ **All real numbers are solutions.**   **13.** $-7(3x - 7) + 21x \geq 50$ **no solutions**

Example 3
(page 28)

Solve each problem by writing an inequality.

14. The length of a picture frame is 3 in. greater than the width. The perimeter is less than 52 in. Describe the dimensions of the frame. **The width is less than 11.5 in., and the length is 3 in. greater than the width.**

15. The lengths of the sides of a triangle are in the ratio 5 : 6 : 7. Describe the length of the longest side if the perimeter is not more than 54 cm. **The longest side is less than 21 cm.**

16. Find the lesser of two consecutive integers with a sum greater than 16. **The smaller number is an integer greater than or equal to 8.**

17. A company estimates that 1% of the computer chips produced in its plant are defective. How many chips must the company make and test in order to be able to ship at least 4500 nondefective chips? **4546 or more chips**

Example 4
(page 28)

Solve each compound inequality. Graph the solution. **18–21. See margin for graphs.**

18. $2x > -10$ and $9x < 18$ $-5 < x < 2$ **19.** $3x \geq -12$ and $8x \leq 16$ $-4 \leq x \leq 2$

20. $6x \geq -24$ and $9x < 54$ $-4 \leq x < 6$ **21.** $7x > -35$ and $5x \leq 30$ $-5 < x \leq 6$

Lesson 1-4   Solving Inequalities   **29**

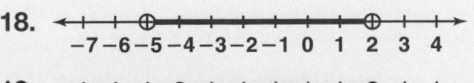

18. ← number line from −7 to 4, open circles at −5 and 2 →

20. ← number line from −5 to 7, closed circle at −4, open circle at 6 →

19. ← number line from −7 to 4, closed circles at −4 and 2 →

21. ← number line from −6 to 7, open circle at −5, closed circle at 6 →

4. Assess

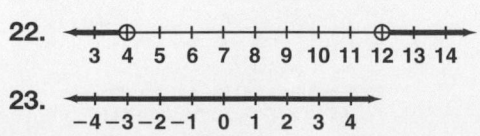
Alternative Assessment

Students work in pairs. They use masking tape to create a number line from -10 to 10 on a desk. Each student places his or her pencil above the number line, using the tip of the pencil as an arrowhead, indicating a single inequality such as $x \geq 3$. Pencils can point in the same or opposite direction and may or may not have an overlapping region. Each group switches stations and writes down two compound inequalities, one inequality assuming that the pencils represent a conjunction and the other assuming a disjunction. Students graph both inequalities and create problems that result in the solution sets represented by the graphs. Students discuss the results.

Example 5
(page 28)

Solve each compound inequality. Graph the solution. See margin for graphs.

22. $4x < 16$ or $12x > 144$ **$x < 4$ or $x > 12$** 23. $3x \geq 3$ or $9x < 54$ **All real numbers are solutions.**

24. $8x > -32$ or $-6x \leq 48$ **$x \geq -8$** 25. $9x \leq -27$ or $4x \geq 36$ **$x \leq -3$ or $x \geq 9$**

Example 6
(page 29)

Solve each problem by writing a compound inequality.

26. A baker needs between 40 lb and 50 lb of a flour-sugar mixture that contains ten times as much flour as sugar. What are the possible weights of flour the baker can use? **between about 36.4 lb and 45.5 lb flour**

27. Between 15,000 yd^3 and 16,000 yd^3 of earth must be trucked away from a construction site. The trucks can remove 1000 yd^3 per day, and 10,500 yd^3 has already been removed. How many days are needed? **between $4\frac{1}{2}$ and $5\frac{1}{2}$ days**

28. By how much should a machinist decrease the length of a rod that is 4.78 cm long if the length must be 4.5 ± 0.02 cm? **between 0.26 cm and 0.30 cm**

B 📝 **Apply Your Skills**

35. **Answers may vary. Sample:** Mario has a coin collection that consists of dimes and nickels. There are half as many dimes as nickels. There are no more than 60 coins in the collection. Describe the collection.

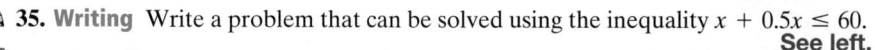

Solve each inequality. Graph the solution. See margin for graphs.

29. $2 - 3z \geq 7(8 - 2z) + 12$ **$z \geq 6$** 30. $17 - 2y \leq 5(7 - 3y) - 15$ **$y \leq \frac{3}{13}$**

31. $\frac{2}{3}(x - 12) \leq x + 8$ **$x \geq -48$** 32. $\frac{3}{5}(x - 12) > x - 24$ **$x < 42$**

33. $3[4x - (2x - 7)] < 2(3x - 5)$ **no solutions** 34. $6[5y - (3y - 1)] \geq 4(3y - 7)$ **All real numbers are solutions.**

35. ✏️ **Writing** Write a problem that can be solved using the inequality $x + 0.5x \leq 60$. **See left.**

36. 📦 **Geometry** The sum of the lengths of any two sides of a triangle is greater than the length of the third side. In $\triangle ABC$, $BC = 4$ and $AC = 8 - AB$. Write an inequality for AB. **$2 < AB < 6$**

37. 🌐 **Construction** A contractor estimated that her expenses for a construction project would be between \$700,000 and \$750,000. She has already spent \$496,000. How much more can she spend and remain within her estimate? **between \$204,000 and \$254,000**

38. **a.** **Error Analysis** Suppose a classmate writes $y \leq 20$ as the solution of $\frac{1}{2}(y - 16) \geq y + 2$. Prove that your classmate's answer is wrong by checking a number that is less than 20. Choose a number that makes the computation easy.
b. Solve $\frac{1}{2}(y - 16) \geq y + 2$. **a. See margin p. 31.**
b. $y \leq -20$

Real-World 🌐 **Connection**

Careers To bid on a job, a construction contractor must consider all the costs of running a business as well as the costs of materials and labor.

45. **All real numbers are solutions.**

47. **All real numbers are solutions.**

Justifying Steps Justify each step by identifying the property used.

39. $3x \leq 4(x - 1) - 8$
$3x \leq 4x - 4 - 8$ **Dist. Prop.**
$3x \leq 4x - 12$ **arithmetic**
$-x \leq -12$ **Subt. Prop. of Ineq.**
$x \geq 12$ **Mult. Prop. of Ineq.**

40. $\frac{1}{2}(y + 3) > \frac{1}{3}(4 - y)$ **Mult. Prop.**
$3(y + 3) > 2(4 - y)$ **of Ineq.**
$3y + 9 > 8 - 2y$ **Dist. Prop.**
$5y + 9 > 8$ **Add. Prop. of Ineq.**
$5y > -1$ **Subt. Prop. of Ineq.**
$y > -0.2$ **Div. Prop. of Ineq.**

Solve each compound inequality. Graph the solutions.
41–49. See margin p. 31 for graphs.

41. $-6 < 2x - 4 < 12$ **$-1 < x < 8$** 42. $11 < 3y + 2 < 20$ **$3 < y < 6$**

43. $-18 > 4x - 3 > -15$ **no solutions** 44. $36 \geq 1 - 5z > -21$ **$-7 \leq z < 4\frac{2}{5}$**

45. $5a - 4 > 16$ or $3a + 2 < 17$ 46. $6b + 3 < 15$ or $4b - 2 > 18$
$b < 2$ or $b > 5$

47. $6c \leq 18$ or $-5c \leq 15$ 48. $8d < -64$ and $5d > 25$
no solutions

49. $4x \leq 12$ or $-7x \leq 21$
All real numbers are solutions. 50. $15x > 30$ and $18x < -36$
no solutions

30   Chapter 1   Tools of Algebra

---

pages 29–31   Exercises

22.
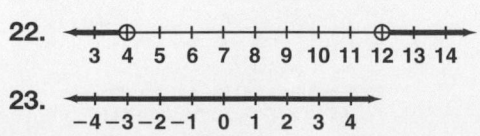

23.
−4−3−2−1 0 1 2 3 4

24.
−8 −6 −4 −2 0 2

25.
−4−3−2−1 0 1 2 3 4 5 6 7 8 9 10

29.
1 2 3 4 5 6 7 8

30.
−3−2−1 0 1 2 3 4 5

31.
−50 −48 −46 −44 −42

32.
39 40 41 42 43 44 45 46

Challenge

51. Answers may vary.
Sample: $2x - 7 \geq -11$

53. Answers may vary.
Sample: $-9 < 5x + 1 < 6$

54. Answers may vary.
Sample: $2x + 4 \leq 0$ or $-3x - 3 \leq 0$

Open-Ended Write an inequality with a solution that matches the graph. At least two steps should be needed to solve your inequality. **Answers may vary.**
Sample: $-3x + 1 > 4$

51.
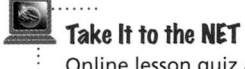
−3 −2 −1 0 1 2 3

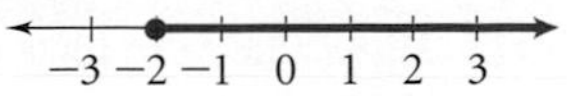

52. 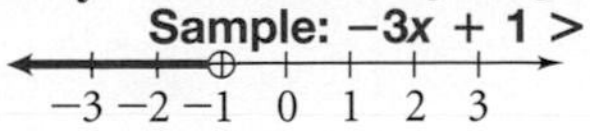
−3 −2 −1 0 1 2 3

53. 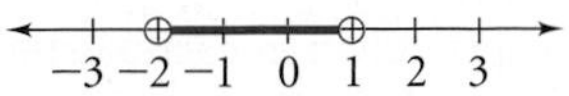
−3 −2 −1 0 1 2 3

54. 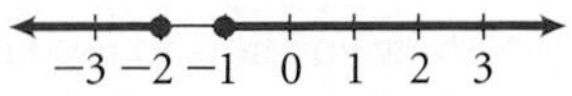
−3 −2 −1 0 1 2 3

55. Critical Thinking Consider the compound inequality $x < 8$ and $x > a$.
   a. Are there any values of a such that all real numbers are solutions of the compound inequality? If so, what are they? **no**
   b. Are there any values of a such that no real numbers are solutions of the compound inequality? If so, what are they? **yes; values of a that are 8 or greater**
   c. Repeat parts (a) and (b) for the compound inequality $x < 8$ or $x > a$.
   a. yes; values of a that are less than 8
   b. no

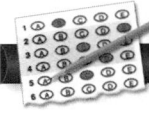

Standardized Test Prep

Multiple Choice

56. Which of the following statements are true? **C**
   I. $-(-6) = 6$ and $-(-4) > -4$
   II. $-(-4) < 4$ or $-10 > 10 - 10$
   III. $5 + 6 = 11$ or $9 - 2 = 11$
   IV. $17 > 2$ or $6 < 9$

   A. I and II only
   B. I, II, and III only
   C. I, III, and IV only
   D. III and IV only

Take It to the NET

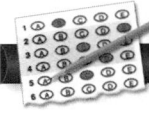

Take It to the NET
Online lesson quiz at
www.PHSchool.com
Web Code: aga-0104

57. What is the solution of the inequality $8 - 3x < -3(1 + x) + 1$? **B**
   A. all real numbers   **B.** no real numbers   **C.** $x > \frac{2}{3}$ **D.** $x < -\frac{11}{6}$

58. What is the solution of the compound inequality $2 < 2(x + 4) < 18$? **H**
   F. all real numbers   **G.** no real numbers   **H.** $-3 < x < 5$ **I.** $-4 < x < 5$

59. What is the solution of the compound inequality $\frac{x}{2} - 4 > 0$ or $\frac{x}{2} + 1 < 0$? **D**
   A. all real numbers
   C. $x > 6$ or $x < 0$
   B. no real numbers
   D. $x > 8$ or $x < -2$

Short Response

60. What is the maximum number of 3- to 5-min songs that fill a 90-min CD? What is the minimum number? Explain your reasoning. **See margin.**

Extended Response

61. Fill each box with the word *and* or *or*, so that the solution of one compound inequality is *all real numbers* and the solution of the other is *no real numbers*. Justify each step of your solution. **See back of book.**

$x + 5 > 0$ ☐ $x - 3 < 0$ $x + 5 < 0$ ☐ $x + 5 > 0$

Mixed Review

Lesson 1-3

Solve each equation. Check your answers.

62. $7x - 6(11 - 2x) = 10$ **4**

63. $10x - 7 = 2(13 + 5x)$ **no solution**

64. $4y - \frac{1}{10} = 3y + \frac{4}{5}$ $\frac{9}{10}$

65. $0.4x + 1.18 = -3.1(2 - 0.01x)$ **−20**

Lesson 1-2

Simplify each expression.

66. $(2a - 4) + (5a + 9)$ **7a + 5**

67. $3(x + 3y) - 5(x - y)$ **−2x + 14y**

68. $\frac{1}{3}(b + 12) - \frac{1}{4}(b + 12)$ $\frac{b + 12}{12}$

69. $0.4(k - 0.1) + 0.5(3.3 - k)$
1.61 − 0.1k

Lesson 1-4 Solving Inequalities **31**

34. 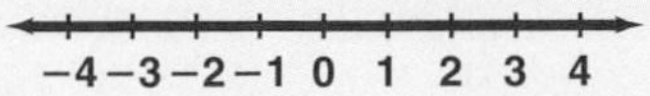
−4 −3 −2 −1 0 1 2 3 4

38a. 0 makes $y \leq 20$ true, but it does not make $\frac{1}{2}(y - 16) \geq y + 2$ true.

41. 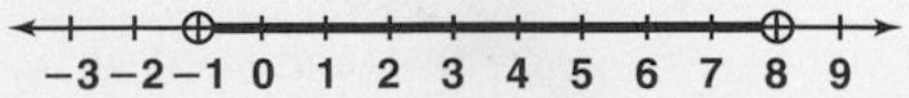
−3 −2 −1 0 1 2 3 4 5 6 7 8 9

42. 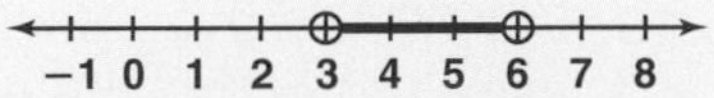
−1 0 1 2 3 4 5 6 7 8

44. 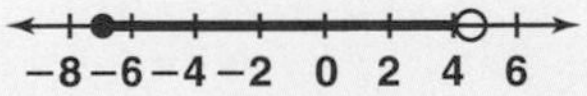
−8 −6 −4 −2 0 2 4 6

45. 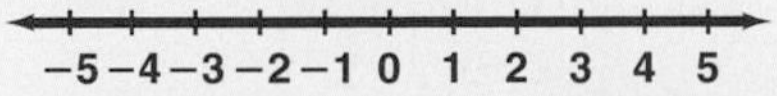
−5 −4 −3 −2 −1 0 1 2 3 4 5

Standardized Test Prep

Resources
For additional practice with a variety of test item formats:
- Standardized Test Prep, p. 51
- Test-Taking Strategies, p. 46
- Test-Taking Strategies with Transparencies

Error Prevention

Exercise 56 Remind students that a compound statement that uses *and* is true only when both component statements are true. A compound statement that uses *or* is true if at least one of the component statements is true.

46.
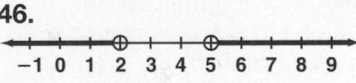
−1 0 1 2 3 4 5 6 7 8 9

47. 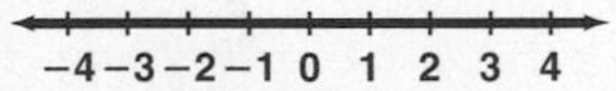
−4 −3 −2 −1 0 1 2 3 4

49. 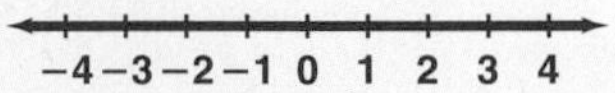
−4 −3 −2 −1 0 1 2 3 4

60. [2] The maximum number of songs can be recorded when the songs are short, so the maximum number of songs is
$$\frac{90 \text{ min}}{3 \text{ min per song}} = 30$$
songs; the minimum number of songs can be recorded when the songs are long, so the minimum number of songs is
$$\frac{90 \text{ min}}{5 \text{ min per song}} = 18$$
songs.

[1] provides 30 and 18 but not the explanation

31

Reading an Example

Students learn how to read information about a concept, interpret an example of the concept, and then work through an example themselves to check their understanding.

Teaching Notes

Ask students to discuss the purpose of an example problem, and how to interpret the steps in the solution of the problem. Then ask students to suggest ways in which they can use an example problem to solve additional problems of the same type.

Math Tip

Remind students that when dividing both sides of an inequality by a negative number, the direction of the inequality must be reversed.

Exercise

Ask students to annotate their work in solving the Exercise problems in a way similar to the example problem.

 **Reading Math**

Reading an Example

Examples show you how to use and apply the concepts taught in each lesson. As you read the example, check your understanding by doing the work yourself.

Before reading an example, read the preceding paragraph for information about the concept. The box on page 26 lists the properties you can use to solve inequalities.

Many examples have two or more parts. Part (b) of Example 1 is examined below.

EXAMPLE **Solving and Graphing Inequalities**

These are the instructions. Read the problem and think about how to solve it. Remember that the goal when solving an equation or inequality is to get the variable by itself.

Solve the inequality. Graph the solution.
$$6 + 5(2 - x) \le 41$$

$$6 + 10 - 5x \le 41 \qquad \text{Distributive Property}$$

This is the first step in the solution. The text at the right explains what was done. Follow along by doing the calculations yourself.

$$16 - 5x \le 41 \qquad \text{Simplify.}$$
$$-5x \le 25 \qquad \text{Subtract 16 from each side.}$$

These are the next steps in the solution. Verify that the work was done correctly.

$$x \ge -5 \qquad \text{Divide each side by } -5 \text{ and reverse the inequality.}$$

This is the last step.

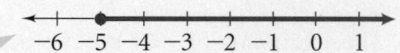
$$-6 \;-5 \;-4 \;-3 \;-2 \;-1 \;\;0 \;\;1$$

Example 1 shows the graph of the inequality. Graph it yourself to check your understanding.

Check First check the boundary point.
$$6 + 5[2 - (-5)] = 41 \checkmark$$
Then check another point on the graph, such as -4.
$$6 + 5[2 - (-4)] \le 41 \checkmark$$

Always check your work.

Questions to check your understanding follow each example. Try the problems that follow this example.

EXERCISE

Solve each inequality. Graph the solution.

a. $3x - 6 < 27$ $x < 11$

8 9 10 11 12

b. $12 \ge 2(3n + 1) + 22$ $-2 \ge n$

$-4 \; -3 \; -2 \; -1 \;\; 0$

1-5 Absolute Value Equations and Inequalities

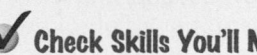
North Carolina Objectives

2.08 Use equations and inequalities with absolute value to model and solve problems; justify results. a) Solve using tables, graphs, and algebraic properties.

Lesson Preview

What You'll Learn

OBJECTIVE 1
To solve absolute value equations

OBJECTIVE 2
To solve absolute value inequalities

. . . And Why

To write specifications for a basketball, as in Example 6

✓ Check Skills You'll Need

(For help, go to Lessons 1-3 and 1-4.)

Solve each equation.

1. $5(x - 6) = 40$ **14**   **2.** $5b = 2(3b - 8)$ **16**   **3.** $2y + 6y = 15 - 2y + 8$ **2.3**

Solve each inequality.

4. $4x + 8 > 20$ **$x > 3$**   **5.** $3a - 2 \geq a + 6$ **$a \geq 4$**   **6.** $4(t - 1) < 3t + 5$ **$t < 9$**

New Vocabulary

● absolute value ● extraneous solution ● tolerance

Lesson Preview

✓ Check Skills You'll Need

Solving Equations
Lesson 1-3: Examples 1, 2
Exercises 1–16
Extra Practice, p. 822

Solving Inequalities
Lesson 1-4: Examples 1, 2
Exercises 1–13
Extra Practice, p. 822

Lesson Resources

📁 **Teaching Resources**
Practice, Reteaching, Enrichment
Checkpoint Quiz 2

👥 **Reaching All Students**
Practice Workbook 1-5
Spanish Practice Workbook 1-5
Reading and Math Literacy 1C
Spanish Reading & Literacy 1C
Spanish Checkpoint Quiz 2

⏱ **Presentation Assistant Plus!**
Transparencies
● Check Skills You'll Need 1-5
● Additional Examples 1-5
● Student Edition Answers 1-5
● Lesson Quiz 1-5
PH Presentation Pro CD 1-5

ASSESSMENT SYSTEM
Checkpoint Quiz 2
Computer Test Generator CD

🖲 **Technology**
Resource Pro® CD-ROM
Computer Test Generator CD
Prentice Hall Presentation Pro CD

💻 **www.PHSchool.com**
Student Site
● Teacher Web Code: agk-5500
● Self-grading Lesson Quiz
Teacher Center
● Lesson Planner
● Resources

Plus

OBJECTIVE 1 **Absolute Value Equations**

 Interactive lesson includes instant self-check, tutorials, and activities.

The **absolute value** of a number is its distance from zero on the number line and distance is nonnegative. So the absolute value of a negative number such as -5 is its opposite, $-(-5)$. For $x < 0$, $|x| = -x$.

🔑 **Key Concepts**

Definition	Algebraic Definition of Absolute Value
● If $x \geq 0$, then $|x| = x$.	● If $x < 0$, then $|x| = -x$.

An absolute value equation such as $|2y - 4| = 12$ has two solutions, since the expression $2y - 4$ can equal 12 or -12.

1 EXAMPLE **Solving Absolute Value Equations**

Solve $|2y - 4| = 12$.

$|2y - 4| = 12$

$2y - 4 = 12$ or $2y - 4 = -12$ The value of $2y - 4$ can be 12 or -12 since $|12|$ and $|-12|$ both equal 12.

$2y = 16$ $2y = -8$ Add 4 to each side of both equations.

$y = 8$ or $y = -4$ Divide each side of both equations by 2.

Check $|2y - 4| = 12$

$|2(8) - 4| \stackrel{?}{=} 12$ $|2(-4) - 4| \stackrel{?}{=} 12$

$|12| = 12$ ✓ $|-12| = 12$ ✓

✓ **Check Understanding** **1** Solve $|3x + 2| = 7$. Check your answer. $\frac{5}{3}$, -3

You will find it easier to solve a multi-step absolute value equation if you first isolate the absolute value expression on one side of the equation.

 Ongoing Assessment and Intervention

Before the Lesson
Diagnose prerequisite skills using:
● Check Skills You'll Need

During the Lesson
Monitor progress using:
● Check Understanding
● Additional Examples
● Standardized Test Prep

After the Lesson
Assess knowledge using:
● Lesson Quiz
● Computer Test Generator CD
● Chapter Checkpoint 2 (p. 38)

2. Teach

Math Background

To solve an equation that involves absolute value, it is possible to rewrite the given equation as two equations by first applying the algebraic definition of absolute value. However, first isolating the absolute value expression on one side of the equal sign and understanding that there may be two solutions leads to an approach that involves less algebraic manipulation.

OBJECTIVE

1 Teaching Notes

1 EXAMPLE Auditory Learners

Help students understand that $|a - b|$ represents the distance between a and b, where a and b are real numbers. Then, tell students that $|2y - 4| = 12$ can be read as "the distance between twice a number and 4 is 12." Help students use this statement to draw a number line and determine the solutions of the equation.

2 EXAMPLE Math Tip

It will be helpful to students to stress that $4w - 1$ can be 5 or -5.

3 EXAMPLE Teaching Tip

Point out that this example makes clear why it is always a good idea to check possible solutions to see whether they really *are* solutions.

Additional Examples

❶ Solve $|15 - 3x| = 6$. **3, 7**

❷ Solve $4 - 2|x + 9| = -5$.
−13.5, −4.5

❸ Solve $|3x - 4| = -4x - 1$. **−5**

---

2 EXAMPLE Solving Multi-Step Absolute Value Equations

Solve $3|4w - 1| - 5 = 10$.

$$3|4w - 1| - 5 = 10$$
$$3|4w - 1| = 15 \qquad \textbf{Add 5 to each side.}$$
$$|4w - 1| = 5 \qquad \textbf{Divide each side by 3.}$$

$4w - 1 = 5 \quad$ or $\quad 4w - 1 = -5 \qquad$ **Rewrite as two equations.**

$4w = 6 \qquad\qquad 4w = -4 \qquad$ **Add 1 to each side of both equations.**

$w = \frac{3}{2} \quad$ or $\qquad w = -1 \qquad$ **Divide each side of both equations by 4.**

Check $\quad 3|4w - 1| - 5 = 10 \qquad\qquad 3|4w - 1| - 5 = 10$

$\qquad\qquad 3|4(\frac{3}{2}) - 1| - 5 \overset{?}{=} 10 \qquad 3|4(-1) - 1| - 5 \overset{?}{=} 10$

$\qquad\qquad\qquad 3|5| - 5 \overset{?}{=} 10 \qquad\qquad 3|-5| - 5 \overset{?}{=} 10$

$\qquad\qquad\qquad\qquad 10 = 10 ✓ \qquad\qquad\qquad 10 = 10 ✓$

✓ Check Understanding ❷ Solve $2|3x - 1| + 5 = 33$. Check your answer. $-\frac{13}{3}, 5$

The equation $|2x + 7| = -2$ has no solution because $|2x + 7|$ cannot be negative. It is important to check possible solutions in the original equation. One or more may be extraneous solutions.

🔑 Key Concepts

Definition	**Extraneous Solution**
An **extraneous solution** is a solution of an equation derived from an original equation that is not a solution of the original equation.	

📖 Reading Math

Extraneous is pronounced ek-STRAY-nee-us.

3 EXAMPLE Checking for Extraneous Solutions

Solve $|2x + 5| = 3x + 4$.

$$|2x + 5| = 3x + 4$$

$2x + 5 = 3x + 4 \quad$ or $\quad 2x + 5 = -(3x + 4) \qquad$ **Rewrite as two equations.**

$-x = -1 \qquad\qquad\qquad 2x + 5 = -3x - 4 \qquad$ **Solve each equation.**

$x = 1 \qquad\qquad\qquad\qquad 5x = -9$

$x = 1 \qquad$ or $\qquad x = -\frac{9}{5}$

Check $\quad |2x + 5| = 3x + 4 \qquad\qquad |2x + 5| = 3x + 4$

$\qquad\qquad |2(1) + 5| \overset{?}{=} 3(1) + 4 \qquad |2(-\frac{9}{5}) + 5| \overset{?}{=} 3(-\frac{9}{5}) + 4$

$\qquad\qquad\qquad |7| \overset{?}{=} 7 \qquad\qquad\qquad |\frac{7}{5}| \overset{?}{=} -\frac{7}{5}$

$\qquad\qquad\qquad 7 = 7 ✓ \qquad\qquad\qquad \frac{7}{5} \neq -\frac{7}{5}$

The only solution is 1. $-\frac{9}{5}$ is an extraneous solution.

✓ Check Understanding ❸ **a.** Solve $|2x + 3| = 3x + 2$. Check for extraneous solutions. **1**
b. Solve $|x| = x - 1$. Check for extraneous solutions. **no solutions**
c. Critical Thinking Find a value for a such that $|x| = x + a$ has exactly one solution. **Answers may vary: any positive real number**

👥 Reaching All Students

Below Level Draw a number line on the board, using inches or centimeters to mark the numbers. Measure the distance of positive and negative numbers from zero.	**Advanced Learners** All sports use specifications such as diameter of carburetor restrictor plates or width of playing field. Find and write such data as an absolute value inequality.	**Auditory Learners** See note on page 34. **Diversity** See note on page 36.

OBJECTIVE 2 — Absolute Value Inequalites

If $|x| > 3$, then x is more than 3 units from 0 on the number line.

$$\xleftarrow{\hspace{0.5em}} \overset{\oplus}{-4}\; \overset{}{-3}\, \overset{}{-2}\, \overset{}{-1}\;\; 0\;\; 1\;\; 2\;\; 3\;\; \overset{\oplus}{4} \xrightarrow{\hspace{0.5em}}$$

This is also the graph of $x < -3$ or $x > 3$. So the absolute value inequality $|x| > 3$ can be rewritten as the compound inequality $x < -3$ or $x > 3$.

4 EXAMPLE — Solving Inequalities of the Form $|A| \ge b$

Solve $|3x + 6| \ge 12$. Graph the solution.

$|3x + 6| \ge 12$

$3x + 6 \le -12$ or $3x + 6 \ge 12$ **Rewrite as a compound inequality.**

$3x \le -18$ or $3x \ge 6$

$x \le -6$ or $x \ge 2$

$$\xleftarrow{\hspace{0.5em}} \overset{}{-7}\; \overset{\bullet}{-6}\, \overset{}{-5}\, \overset{}{-4}\, \overset{}{-3}\, \overset{}{-2}\, \overset{}{-1}\;\; 0\;\; 1\;\; \overset{\bullet}{2}\;\; 3 \xrightarrow{\hspace{0.5em}}$$ **Graph the solution.**

✓ Check Understanding 4 Solve $|2x - 3| > 7$. Graph the solution. $x < -2$ or $x > 5$

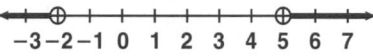

If $|x| < 2$, then x is less than 2 units from 0 on the number line.

$$\xleftarrow{\hspace{0.5em}} \overset{}{-3}\; \overset{\oplus}{-2}\, \overset{}{-1}\;\; 0\;\; 1\;\; \overset{\oplus}{2}\;\; 3 \xrightarrow{\hspace{0.5em}}$$

This is also the graph of $-2 < x < 2$. So the absolute value inequality $|x| < 2$ can be written as the compound inequality $-2 < x < 2$.

Key Concepts

Properties	Absolute Value Inequalities
Let k represent a positive real number.	
$\|x\| \ge k$ is equivalent to	$x \le -k$ or $x \ge k$.
$\|x\| \le k$ is equivalent to	$-k \le x \le k$.

When an absolute value is combined with other operations, first isolate the absolute value expression on one side of the inequality.

? Need Help?
To review the properties of inequalities, go to p. 26.

5 EXAMPLE — Solving Inequalities of the Form $|A| < b$

Solve $3|2x + 6| - 9 < 15$. Graph the solution.

$3|2x + 6| - 9 < 15$

$3|2x + 6| < 24$ **Isolate the absolute value expression. Add 9 to each side.**

$|2x + 6| < 8$ **Divide each side by 3.**

$-8 < 2x + 6 < 8$ **Rewrite as a compound inequality.**

$-14 < 2x < 2$ **Solve for x.**

$-7 < x < 1$

$$\xleftarrow{\hspace{0.5em}} \overset{}{-8}\; \overset{\oplus}{-7}\, \overset{}{-6}\, \overset{}{-5}\, \overset{}{-4}\, \overset{}{-3}\, \overset{}{-2}\, \overset{}{-1}\;\; 0\;\; \overset{\oplus}{1}\;\; 2 \xrightarrow{\hspace{0.5em}}$$

✓ Check Understanding 5 Solve $|5z + 3| - 7 < 34$. Graph the solution. $-8\frac{4}{5} < z < 7\frac{3}{5}$
See margin for graph.

Lesson 1-5 Absolute Value Equations and Inequalities **35**

page 35   Check Understanding

5.
$$\xleftarrow{\hspace{0.5em}} \overset{}{-12}\, \overset{\ominus}{-10}\, \overset{}{-8}\, \overset{}{-6}\, \overset{}{-4}\, \overset{}{-2}\;\; 0\;\; 2\;\; 4\;\; 6\;\; 8\;\; \overset{\ominus}{10} \xrightarrow{\hspace{0.5em}}$$

OBJECTIVE 2 — Teaching Notes

4 EXAMPLE Error Prevention

Encourage students to check that the solutions indicated by their graphs are reasonable. Have students pick a few points in the solution sets and substitute them into the original equation to make certain that the resulting statements are true.

5 EXAMPLE Teaching Tip

You may wish to apply the idea from the Error Prevention in Example 4 to $|2x + 6| < 8$ in Example 5 to help students understand the compound inequality.

6 EXAMPLE Teaching Tip

You may find it helpful to review Example 6 from Lesson 1-4.

Additional Examples

4 Solve $|2x - 5| > 3$. Graph the solution. $x < 1$ or $x > 4$

$$\xleftarrow{\hspace{0.5em}} \overset{}{-2}\; \overset{}{-1}\;\; 0\;\; \overset{\oplus}{1}\;\; 2\;\; 3\;\; \overset{\oplus}{4}\;\; 5\;\; 6 \xrightarrow{\hspace{0.5em}}$$

5 Solve $-2|x + 1| + 5 \ge -3$. Graph the solution. $-5 \le x \le 3$

$$\xleftarrow{\hspace{0.5em}} \overset{}{-6}\; \overset{\bullet}{-5}\, \overset{}{-4}\, \overset{}{-3}\, \overset{}{-2}\, \overset{}{-1}\;\; 0\;\; 1\;\; 2\;\; \overset{\bullet}{3}\;\; 4 \xrightarrow{\hspace{0.5em}}$$

6 The area A in square inches of a square photo is required to satisfy $8.5 \le A \le 8.9$. Write this requirement as an absolute value inequality. $|A - 8.7| \le 0.2$

Closure

Have students describe the procedure used to solve an absolute value equation or inequality. **Isolate the absolute value expression on one side of the equation or inequality. Next, rewrite the result as two equations or as a compound inequality. Then, solve.**

35

Assignment Guide

1 Objective
   A B Core 1–15, 34–43
   C Extension 61–63

2 Objective
   A B Core 16–33, 44–60
   C Extension 64–66

Standardized Test Prep 67–72

Mixed Review 73–83

Connection to Meteorology

Exercise 54 Meteorologists use experimental probability based on previous weather patterns to make forecasts. Students will learn about experimental probability in Lesson 1-6.

Diversity

Exercise 55 Students who are not familiar with sports, may not realize that there are regulations that govern the size of basketballs for men and women. Discuss the regulations and the reasons behind them.

Enrichment 1-5
Reteaching 1-5
Practice 1-5

You can use absolute value inequalities and compound inequalities to specify allowable ranges in measurements. The difference between a desired measurement and its maximum and minimum allowable values is the tolerance. The **tolerance** equals one half of the difference between the maximum and the minimum values.

For example, if a manufacturing specification calls for a dimension d of 10 cm with a tolerance of 0.1 cm, then the allowable difference between d and 10 is less than or equal to 0.1. This specification can be expressed in the following ways.

$|d - 10| \leq 0.1$	absolute value inequality
$d - 10 \leq 0.1$ and $d - 10 \geq -0.1$	equivalent compound inequality
$-0.1 \leq d - 10 \leq 0.1$	equivalent compound inequality
$9.9 \leq d \leq 10.1$	simplified compound inequality

6 EXAMPLE **Real-World Connection**

Basketball The specification for the circumference C in inches of a basketball for men is $29.5 \leq C \leq 30$. Write the specification as an absolute value inequality.

$\dfrac{30 - 29.5}{2} = \dfrac{0.5}{2} = 0.25$ **Find the tolerance.**

$\dfrac{29.5 + 30}{2} = 29.75$ **Find the average of the maximim and minimum values.**

$-0.25 \leq C - 29.75 \leq 0.25$ **Write an inequality.**

$|C - 29.75| \leq 0.25$ **Rewrite as an absolute value inequality.**

✓ **Check Understanding** **6** The specification for the circumference C in inches of a basketball for junior high school is $27.75 \leq C \leq 28.5$. Write the specification as an absolute value inequality.
$|C - 28.125| \leq 0.375$

EXERCISES

For more practice, see *Extra Practice*.

Practice and Problem Solving

A **Practice by Example**

Examples 1 and 2 (pages 33, 34)

Solve each equation. Check your answers.

1. $|3x| = 18$ **−6, 6**   2. $|-4x| = 32$ **−8, 8**   3. $|x - 3| = 9$ **−6, 12**

4. $2|3x - 2| = 14$ **3, $-\frac{5}{3}$**   5. $|3x + 4| = -3$ **no solution**   6. $|2x - 3| = -1$ **no solution**

7. $|x + 4| + 3 = 17$ **−18, 10**   8. $|y - 5| - 2 = 10$ **−7, 17**   9. $|4 - z| - 10 = 1$ **−7, 15**

Example 3 (page 34)

Solve each equation. Check for extraneous solutions.

10. $|x - 1| = 5x + 10$ **$-\frac{3}{2}$**   11. $|2z - 3| = 4z - 1$ **$\frac{2}{3}$**   12. $|3x + 5| = 5x + 2$ **$\frac{3}{2}$**

13. $|2y - 4| = 12$ **−4, 8**   14. $3|4w - 1| - 5 = 10$ **$-1, \frac{3}{2}$**   15. $|2x + 5| = 3x + 4$ **1**

Example 4 (page 35)

Solve each inequality. Graph the solution. **16–23. See margin pp. 36–37.**

16. $|x + 3| > 9$ 17. $|x - 5| \geq 8$ 18. $|y - 3| \geq 12$

19. $|2x + 1| \geq -9$ 20. $3|2x - 1| \geq 21$ 21. $|3z| - 4 > 8$

24–27. See back of book.

Example 5 (page 35)

22. $3|y - 9| < 27$ 23. $|6y - 2| + 4 < 22$ 24. $|3x - 6| + 3 < 15$

25. $\frac{1}{4}|x - 3| + 2 < 1$ 26. $4|2w + 3| - 7 \leq 9$ 27. $3|5t - 1| + 9 \leq 23$

36 Chapter 1 Tools of Algebra

pages 36–38 Exercises

16. $x < -12$ or $x > 6$

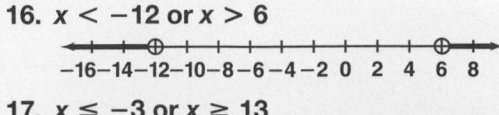

17. $x \leq -3$ or $x \geq 13$

18. $y \leq -9$ or $y \geq 15$

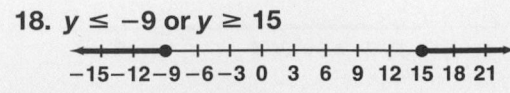

19. all real numbers

Example 6
(page 36)

Write each specification as an absolute value inequality.

28. $1.3 \le h \le 1.5$
$|h - 1.4| \le 0.1$

29. $50 \le k \le 51$
$|k - 50.5| \le 0.5$

30. $27.25 \le C \le 27.75$
$|C - 27.5| \le 0.25$

31. $50 \le b \le 55$
$|b - 52.5| \le 2.5$

32. $1200 \le m \le 1300$
$|m - 1250| \le 50$

33. $0.1187 \le d \le 0.1190$
$|d - 0.11885| \le 0.00015$

 **B** **Apply Your Skills**

Solve each equation.

34. $-|4 - 8b| = 12$ **no solutions**

35. $4|3x + 4| = 4x + 8$ $-\frac{3}{2}, -1$

36. $|3x - 1| + 10 = 25$ $-\frac{14}{3}, \frac{16}{3}$

37. $\frac{1}{2}|3c + 5| = 6c + 4$ $-\frac{1}{3}$

38. $5|6 - 5x| = 15x - 35$ **no solutions**

39. $7|8 - 3h| = 21h - 49$ $\frac{5}{2}$

40. $2|3x - 7| = 10x - 8$ $\frac{11}{8}$

41. $6|2x + 5| = 6x + 24$ $-1, -3$

54. Region 1
$0 \le s \le 0.1$,
$|s - 0.05| \le 0.05$
Region 2
$0.1 \le s \le 1$,
$|s - 0.55| \le 0.45$
Region 3
$1 \le s \le 3$, $|s - 2| \le 1$
Region 4
$3 \le s \le 6$,
$|s - 4.5| \le 1.5$

42. $\frac{1}{4}|4x + 7| = 8x + 16$ $-\frac{57}{28}, -\frac{71}{36}$

43. $\frac{2}{3}|3x - 6| = 4(x - 2)$ **2**

Solve each inequality. Graph the solutions. **44–50. See back of book.**

44. $|3x - 4| + 5 \le 27$

45. $|2x + 3| - 6 \ge 7$

46. $-2|x + 4| < 22$

47. $2|4t - 1| + 6 > 20$

48. $|3z + 15| \ge 0$

49. $|-2x + 1| > 2$

50. $\frac{1}{9}|5x - 3| - 3 \ge 2$

51. $\frac{1}{11}|2x - 4| + 10 \le 11$

52. $\left|\frac{x - 3}{2}\right| + 2 < 6$

53. $\left|\frac{x + 5}{3}\right| - 3 > 6$

51–53. See margin p. 38.

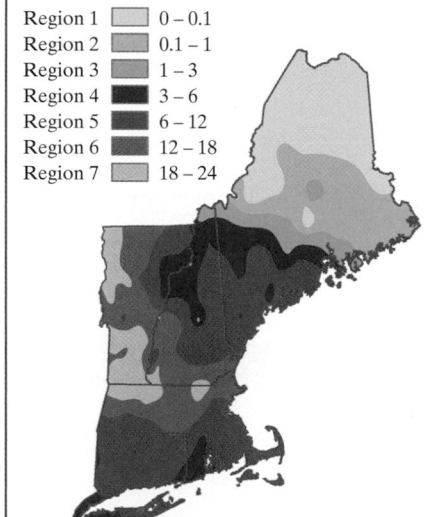

A March Snowfall (inches)

Region 1 ☐ 0 – 0.1
Region 2 ☐ 0.1 – 1
Region 3 ☐ 1 – 3
Region 4 ☐ 3 – 6
Region 5 ☐ 6 – 12
Region 6 ☐ 12 – 18
Region 7 ☐ 18 – 24

Source: Northeast River Forecast Center/NOAA

🌐 **54. Meteorology** Write a compound inequality and an absolute value inequality for the snowfall in regions 1, 2, 3, and 4 in the figure at the left. **See left.**

🌐 **55. Basketball** The circumference of a basketball for women must be from 28.5 in. to 29.0 in. Write an absolute value inequality and a compound inequality for the circumference. $|C - 28.75| \le 0.25; 28.5 \le C \le 29.0$

✎ **56. Writing** Describe the differences in the graphs of $|x| < a$ and $|x| > a$, where a is a positive real number. **See back of book.**

57. Open-Ended Write an absolute value inequality for which every real number is a solution. Write an absolute value inequality that has no solution.
Answers may vary. Sample: $|x - 1| \ge 0$; $|x| < -5$

Write an absolute value inequality and a compound inequality for each length x with the given tolerance.

58. a length of 36.80 mm with a tolerance of 0.05 mm
$|x - 36.8| \le 0.05; 36.75 \le x \le 36.85$

59. a length of 9.55 mm with a tolerance of 0.02 mm
$|x - 9.55| \le 0.02; 9.53 \le x \le 9.57$

60. a length of 100 yd with a tolerance of 4 in.
x is in inches: $|x - 3600| \le 4; 3596 \le x \le 3604$.

C **Challenge** **Solve each equation for x. Assume that a, b, c, and d represent positive real numbers.**

61. $|ax| - b = c$
$-\frac{b + c}{a}, \frac{b + c}{a}$

62. $|cx - d| = ab$
$\frac{ab + d}{c}, \frac{-ab + d}{c}$

63. $a|bx - c| = d$
$\frac{ac + d}{ab}, \frac{ac - d}{ab}$

Graph each solution. **64–66. See back of book.**

64. $|x| \ge 5$ and $|x| \le 6$

65. $|x| \ge 6$ or $|x| < 5$

66. $|x - 5| \le x$

Lesson Quiz 1-5

1. Solve $|3x + 1| = 4$. $-\frac{5}{3}, 1$

2. Solve $|-2x + 3| + 7 > 9$. Graph the solution. $x < \frac{1}{2}$ or $x > \frac{5}{2}$

$\xleftarrow{\hspace{0.3cm}} \underset{-3\,-2\,-1\ \ 0\ \ 1\ \ 2\ \ 3\ \ 4\ \ 5}{\circ\hspace{1.2cm}\circ} \xrightarrow{\hspace{0.3cm}}$

3. Solve $|4x - 12| \le 8$. $1 \le x \le 5$

$\xleftarrow{\hspace{0.3cm}} \underset{-2\,-1\ \ 0\ \ 1\ \ 2\ \ 3\ \ 4\ \ 5\ \ 6}{\bullet\hspace{1.0cm}\bullet} \xrightarrow{\hspace{0.3cm}}$

4. A machinist is to drill a hole with diameter D inches, that satisfies $0.16 \le D \le 0.19$. Express the specification using an absolute value inequality. $|D - 0.175| \le 0.015$

Alternative Assessment

Have students work in pairs. Each student writes two absolute value equations and two absolute value inequalities. Each student then solves his or her partner's equations and inequalities. Then, they check one another's work.

Standardized Test Prep

📁 **Resources**
For additional practice with a variety of test item formats:
- Standardized Test Prep, p. 51
- Test-Taking Strategies, p. 46
- Test-Taking Strategies with Transparencies

Exercise 68 A good first step is to rewrite the absolute value inequality as a compound inequality.

20. $x \le -3$ or $x \ge 4$

$\xleftarrow{\hspace{0.3cm}} \underset{-4\,-2\ \ 0\ \ 2\ \ 4\ \ 6}{\bullet\hspace{1.3cm}\bullet} \xrightarrow{\hspace{0.3cm}}$

21. $z < -4$ or $z > 4$

$\xleftarrow{\hspace{0.3cm}} \underset{-4\hspace{1.4cm}4}{\circ\hspace{1.4cm}\circ} \xrightarrow{\hspace{0.3cm}}$

22. $0 < y < 18$

$\xleftarrow{\hspace{0.3cm}} \underset{-2\ \ 0\ \ 2\ \ 4\ \ 6\ \ 8\ \ 10\ 12\ 14\ 16\ 18\ 20}{\circ\hspace{3.0cm}\circ} \xrightarrow{\hspace{0.3cm}}$

23. $-2\frac{2}{3} < y < 3\frac{1}{3}$

$\xleftarrow{\hspace{0.3cm}} \underset{-5\,-4\,-3\,-2\,-1\ \ 0\ \ 1\ \ 2\ \ 3\ \ 4\ \ 5\ \ 6}{\circ\hspace{2.5cm}\circ} \xrightarrow{\hspace{0.3cm}}$

To check understanding of Lessons 1-4 to 1-5:

Checkpoint Quiz 2 (p. 38)

📁 **Teaching Resources**
Checkpoint Quiz 2 (also in Prentice Hall Assessment System)

👥 **Reaching All Students**
Reading and Math Literacy 1C

Spanish versions available

---

pages 36–38   Exercises

51. $-3.5 \leq x \leq 7.5$
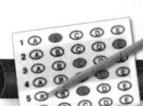
-4 0 4 8

52. $-5 < x < 11$
-8 -4 0 4 8 12

53. $x < -32$ or $x > 22$
-40 -20 0 20

71. [2] $|x - 3| \leq 5$
     $-5 \leq x - 3 \leq 5$
     $-2 \leq x \leq 8$

[1] only includes
    $-2 \leq x \leq 8$ and
    does not show work

72. [4] $3|2x - 4| + 5 < 41$
     $3|2x - 4| < 36$

Subtr. Prop. of Ineq.
     $|2x - 4| < 12$

Div. Prop. of Ineq.
     $-12 < 2x - 4 < 12$

Def. of absolute value
     $-8 < 2x < 16$

Add. Prop. of Ineq.
     $-4 < x < 8$

Div. Prop. of Ineq.

[3] appropriate methods,
    but with one
    computational error

[2] does not include steps

[1] only includes final
    answer of $-4 < x < 8$,
    with no steps or
    justification of steps

38

Multiple Choice

67. Which number is a solution of $|x - 3| = x - 3$? **D**
  A. -3 B. 0 C. 1 D. 3

68. What is the solution of the inequality $\left|\frac{3 - x}{2}\right| < 4$? **F**
  F. $-5 < x < 11$ G. $-11 > x > -5$ H. $5 < x < 11$ I. $11 > x > -1$

💻 ⋯⋯⋯⋯
Take It to the NET
Online lesson quiz at
www.PHSchool.com
⋯⋯⋯ Web Code: aga-0105

69. Which of the following inequalities have the same solutions?   **C**
  I. $|5x - 7| \leq 8$ II. $-8 \leq 5x - 7$ or $5x - 7 \leq 8$
  III. $8 \leq 5x - 7$ and $5x - 7 \geq -8$ IV. $-8 \leq 5x - 7$ and $5x - 7 \leq 8$
  A. I and II   B. I and III   C. I and IV   D. I, III, and IV

70. Which number is a solution of $|9 - x| = 9 + x$?   **G**
  F. -3 G. 0 H. 3 I. 6

Short Response

71. Find all the integers that are solutions of $|x - 3| \leq 5$. Show your work.
See margin.

Extended Response

72. Solve $3|2x - 4| + 5 < 41$. Justify each step of your solution.
See margin.

● **Mixed Review**

Lesson 1-4

Solve each inequality. Graph the solution. **See margin for graphs.**

73. $5y - 10 < 20$ **74.** $-5(4s + 1) < 23$ **75.** $4a + 6 \geq 2a + 14$
    $y < 6$ **$s > -\frac{7}{5}$**   **$a \geq 4$**
76. $0.5x + 5 \geq x - 1$ **77.** $3(4x - 1) \geq 2(4 - x)$ **78.** $4(3t + 2) \leq 43 + 7t$
    $x \leq 12$ **$x \geq \frac{11}{14}$**   **$t \leq 7$**

Lesson 1-2

Evaluate each expression for the given value.

79. $3|4x - 6| - 2x^2$, for $x = -3$ **36**   **80.** $\frac{5r - r^2}{1 - 4r}$, for $r = 4$ $-\frac{4}{15}$

Lesson 1-1

Name the property of real numbers illustrated by each of the following.

81. $16x + (-16x) = 0$ **82.** 5π is a real number.   **83.** $4(x - 9) = (x - 9)4$
    Inverse Prop. of Add.   **Closure Prop. of Mult.**   **Comm. Prop. of Mult.**

✓ **Checkpoint Quiz 2**   **Lessons 1-4 through 1-5**

📱 **iTEXT** Instant self-check
quiz online and
on CD-ROM

Solve each inequality. Graph the solution.   **1–6. See back of book for graphs.**

1. $3x + 10 \leq 25$ $x \leq 5$ **2.** $8x + 15 > 15x - 24$ $x < 5\frac{4}{7}$

3. $z > -1$

4. $w > 1$ or $w < -3$

3. $5z > 2z - 18$ and $3 - 9z < 12$ **4.** $4w > 1 + 3w$ or $12w + 18 < 11w + 15$

5. $2|x + 4| \leq 22$ $-15 \leq x \leq 7$ **6.** $|2x| + 8 > 12$ $x < -2$ or $x > 2$

Solve each equation.

7. $7|3 - 2y| = 56$ $-\frac{5}{2}, \frac{11}{2}$ **8.** $\frac{1}{4}|4x + 2| = 1 - 2x$ $\frac{1}{6}$

9. Write and solve an inequality to find three consecutive whole numbers with a sum between 13 and 16. $13 < 3n + 3 < 16$, $n = 4$

📦 **10. Geometry** The length of a side of any triangle is less than the sum of the lengths of the other two sides. In $\triangle PQR$, $PR = RQ + 4$ and $RQ < 11$. Write and solve an inequality for PQ. $PR - RQ < PQ < PR + RQ$; $4 < PQ < 26$

38   Chapter 1   Tools of Algebra

73.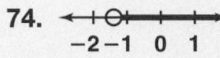
-2 0 2 4 6 8

74.
-2 -1 0 1

75.
-2 0 2 4 6 8

76.
4 6 8 10 12

77.
-1 0 1 2

78.
-4 0 4 8 12

1-6

Probability

1-6

1. Plan

Lesson Preview

What You'll Learn

 OBJECTIVE 1 To find experimental probabilities

OBJECTIVE 2 To find theoretical probabilities

. . . And Why

To find the probabilities of inherited traits, as in Example 4

 Check Skills You'll Need   (For help, go to Skills Handbook page 842.)

Write each number as a percent.

1. $\frac{3}{8}$ **37.5%**

2. $1\frac{5}{6}$ **183$\frac{1}{3}$%**

3. 0.0043 **0.43%**

4. $\frac{1}{400}$ **0.25%**

5. 1.04 **104%**

6. 3 **300%**

New Vocabulary
- experimental probability
- simulation • sample space
- theoretical probability

Lesson Preview

 Check Skills You'll Need

Percent and Percent Applications
Skills Handbook: p. 842
Example 6, Exercises 1–12

Lesson Resources

 Teaching Resources
Practice, Reteaching, Enrichment

 **Reaching All Students**
Practice Workbook 1-6
Spanish Practice Workbook 1-6
Technology Activities 36
Hands-On Activities 32

Presentation Assistant Plus!
Transparencies
- Check Skills You'll Need 1-6
- Additional Examples 1-6
- Student Edition Answers 1-6
- Lesson Quiz 1-6
PH Presentation Pro CD 1-6

 ASSESSMENT SYSTEM
PRENTICE HALL

Computer Test Generator CD

 Technology
Resource Pro® CD-ROM
Computer Test Generator CD
Prentice Hall Presentation Pro CD

 **www.PHSchool.com**
Student Site
- Teacher Web Code: agk-5500
- Graphing Calculator,
  Procedure 15
- Self-grading Lesson Quiz
Teacher Center
- Lesson Planner
- Resources

Plus **iTEXT**

OBJECTIVE 1 **Experimental Probability**

iTEXT Interactive lesson includes instant self-check, tutorials, and activities.

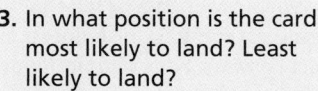

Investigation: *Experimental Probability*

Fold an index card slightly off center, as shown at the left. When you drop the card from a height of several feet, how will it land?

1–5. Check students' work.

1. Drop the card 50 times. Record the number of times the card lands in each position.

2. What percent of the time does the card land on its short side? Find the percents for the other positions.

3. In what position is the card most likely to land? Least likely to land?

4. Suppose that you drop the card another 20 times. Predict how many times it will land in each position.

5. a. Drop the card another 20 times. Record your results.

   b. Compare the results with your prediction from Question 4. Are they close? How could you improve your prediction?

Ongoing Assessment and Intervention

Before the Lesson
Diagnose prerequisite skills using:
- Check Skills You'll Need

During the Lesson
Monitor progress using:
- Check Understanding
- Additional Examples
- Standardized Test Prep

After the Lesson
Assess knowledge using:
- Lesson Quiz
- Computer Test Generator CD

Professional Development

Math Background

Experimental probabilities are calculated on the basis of data from experiments, actual or simulated. Given equally likely outcomes, the basis for calculating theoretical probability is being able to determine the number of ways that an event can occur within these outcomes. Comparisons of measures such as length and area are the basis of geometric probability.

OBJECTIVE

1 Teaching Notes

Investigation (Optional)
You may want students to work on this Investigation with a partner. The results that students obtain may be influenced by a variety of factors, such as how far from the end the card was folded.

1 EXAMPLE Diversity

Invite students who are more familiar with other sports, such as cricket, to suggest examples of experimental probabilities related to those sports.

2 EXAMPLE Alternative Method

Invite students to suggest other simulations such as spinning a two-section spinner.

Additional Examples

1 A player hit the bull's eye on a circular dartboard 8 times out of 50. Find the experimental probability that the player hits the bull's eye. **0.16, or 16%**

2 Describe a simulation you could use that involves flipping a coin to find the experimental probability of guessing exactly 2 answers out of 6 correctly on a true-false quiz. **Answers may vary. Sample: Let heads represent a correct answer. Flip the coin 6 times. Record the number of heads. Repeat 100 times. Divide the number of times you got 2 heads by 100.**

Probability measures how likely to occur an event is. You can express probabilities as percents (0% through 100%) or as real numbers (0 through 1).

The probability of an impossible event is 0 or 0%. The probability of a certain event, which must happen, is 1 or 100%.

When you gather data from observations, you can calculate an experimental probability. Each observation is called an experiment or a trial.

🔑 Key Concepts

Definition	Experimental Probability

experimental probability of event = P(event)

$$= \frac{\text{number of times the event occurs}}{\text{number of trials}}$$

1 EXAMPLE Finding Experimental Probability

A baseball player got a hit 21 times in 60 at-bats. Find the experimental probability of his getting a hit.

📖 Reading Math
Read P(hit) as "probability of a hit."

$$P(\text{hit}) = \frac{21}{60} = 0.35, \text{ or } 35\%$$

✓ Check Understanding **1** A basketball player has made 32 free throws in 50 tries. What is the experimental probability of her making a free throw? $\frac{32}{50}$, **or 0.64, or 64%**

When actual trials are difficult to conduct, you can find experimental probabilities by using a **simulation,** which is a model of one or more events.

2 EXAMPLE Using a Simulation

Suppose you take a four-question true-or-false quiz and guess the answers at random. What is the probability that you will get at least three questions correct?

Step 1 Define how you will do the simulation.
- Generate random numbers on a calculator.
- Since you answer true or false at random, you have a 50% chance of guessing correctly on each question. So let half of the digits represent correct answers. For example, let even digits represent correct answers.
- Since there are four questions, group the random digits in groups of four. List 50 groups to represent taking the test 50 times.

```
rand
        .8767044746
        .7208728315
        .6495877886
        .3462435756
        .8958229562
        .4615208491
■
```

```
        .1214849574
        .5070685798
        .5584414289
        .9071019949
        .1991062533
        .4761581612
        .4792397345
■
```

```
        .6388889895
        .5466561294
        .2840659518
        .2096111775
        .7827769142
        .7787959459
        .6958584068
■
```

Step 2 Conduct the simulation. Underline groups with at least three even digits.

8767	<u>0447</u>	<u>4672</u>	<u>0872</u>	8315	6495	8778	<u>8634</u>	<u>6243</u>	5756
8958	2295	<u>6246</u>	1520	8491	1214	8495	7450	<u>7068</u>	5798
5584	<u>4142</u>	8990	7101	9949	1991	<u>0625</u>	3347	6158	1612
4792	3973	4563	<u>8888</u>	9895	<u>5466</u>	5612	<u>9428</u>	<u>4065</u>	9518
<u>2096</u>	1117	7578	2776	9142	7787	9594	5969	5858	<u>4068</u>

Step 3 Interpret the simulation. Since 15 of the 50 groups represent at least three correct answers, P(at least 3 correct) $= \frac{15}{50} = 0.3$.

The probability that you will get at least three questions correct is 30%.

✓ Check Understanding **2** What is the experimental probability of getting all four answers correct? $\frac{3}{50}$, **or 6%**

👥 Reaching All Students

Below Level Discuss with students why a 50% chance of rain today and a 50% chance of rain tomorrow does not mean it is certain to rain.	**Advanced Learners** To estimate π, drop a toothpick onto parallel lines spaced a toothpick-length apart. Divide twice the number of drops by the number of lines hit. Discuss.	**English Learners** See note on page 43. **Error Prevention** See note on page 42. See note on page 43.

2 Theoretical Probability

When you roll a number cube, the possible outcomes are 1, 2, 3, 4, 5, and 6. The set of all possible outcomes is called the **sample space.** You can calculate theoretical probability as a ratio of outcomes.

Key Concepts

Definition	Theoretical Probability

If a sample space has n equally likely outcomes and an event A occurs in m of these outcomes, then the **theoretical probability** of event A is $P(A) = \frac{m}{n}$.

Sample space: n outcomes

Event A: m outcomes

3 EXAMPLE Finding Theoretical Probability

Find the theoretical probability of getting an even number when you roll a number cube.

The even outcomes are 2, 4, and 6.

3 outcomes result in an even number. $\rightarrow \frac{3}{6} \leftarrow$ **6** equally likely outcomes are in the sample space.

$$= \frac{1}{2}$$

✔ Check Understanding 3 Find the theoretical probability of getting a prime number when you roll a number cube. **$\frac{1}{2}$, or 50%**

4 EXAMPLE Real-World 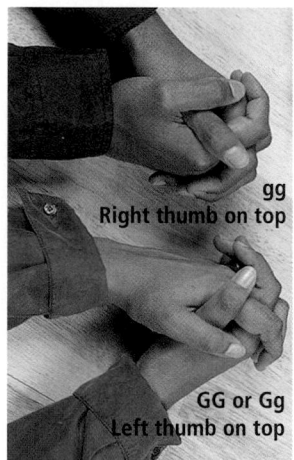 Connection

Biology Fold your hands so your fingers interlace. Do you naturally place your left or right thumb on top? Placing your left thumb on top is a dominant genetic trait.

When a parent has both a dominant and a recessive gene, then the two genes are equally likely to be passed to a child. If you have one or two dominant genes, you normally place your left thumb on top.

Suppose a child has parents who both have just one dominant gene. What is the theoretical probability that the child will naturally place the left thumb on top?

gg
Right thumb on top

GG or Gg
Left thumb on top

Make a table. Let G represent the dominant gene (left thumb on top). Let g represent the recessive gene (right thumb on top).

The sample space {GG, Gg, Gg, gg} contains four equally likely outcomes. Three outcomes have at least one Gg gene. So P(left thumb on top) $= \frac{3}{4}$.

		Gene from Mother	
		G	**g**
Gene from Father	**G**	GG	Gg
	g	Gg	gg

The theoretical probability that the child will naturally place the left thumb on top is $\frac{3}{4}$, or 75%.

✔ Check Understanding 4 What is the theoretical probability that a child of the parents in Example 4 places the right thumb on top? **$\frac{1}{4}$, or 25%**

---

3 EXAMPLE Math Tip

Students need to understand that the theoretical probability of $\frac{1}{2}$ does not mean that, in a particular group of rolls, exactly half the rolls will result in an even number. Probability tells what is *likely* to happen, not what *must* happen.

4 EXAMPLE Career Note

Inherited traits are important in understanding many types of health problems. There are exciting career opportunities in health care and the pharmaceutical industry that are related to genetic research.

5 EXAMPLE Connection to Math

Students may be interested to know that simulations and ideas about geometric probability can be used to find approximate values of areas and important constants such as π.

Additional Examples

3 Find the theoretical probability of rolling a multiple of 3 with a number cube. $\frac{1}{3}$

4 Brown is a dominant eye color for human beings. If a father and mother each carry a gene for brown eyes and a gene for blue eyes, what is the probability of their having a child with blue eyes? $\frac{1}{4}$

5 For the dartboard in Example 5, find the probability that a dart that lands at random on the dartboard hits the outer ring. $\frac{7}{16}$

Closure

Tell students to name two pieces of information that can be used to find the theoretical probability of an event. **number of possible outcomes, number of outcomes representing the event in question**

3. Practice

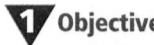

Assignment Guide

1 Objective

A B Core 1–5, 21–23, 40

C Extension 44–45

2 Objective

A B Core 6–20, 24–39, 41–42

C Extension 43

Standardized Test Prep 46–51

Mixed Review 52–63

Technology Tip

Exercises 3, 4 Students can enter the expression randInt(0,1,5) on the home screen of their graphing calculators using the catalog feature. Then they can press ENTER to generate a random sequence of five integers where each integer is either a 0 or 1. Repeatedly pressing ENTER will generate a new sequence each time. Students may wish to use this idea for their simulation.

Error Prevention

Exercises 24–26 Students should not overlook the 31 students who take neither math nor science.

Enrichment 1-6

Reteaching 1-6

Practice 1-6

Practice 1-6 — Probability

1. You select a number at random from the sample space {1, 2, 3, 4, 5}. Find each theoretical probability.
   a. *P*(the number is 2) b. *P*(the number is even)
   c. *P*(the number is prime) d. *P*(the number is less than 5)
2. In a class of 19 students, 10 study Spanish, 7 study French, and 2 study both French and Spanish. One student is picked at random. Find each probability.
   a. *P*(studying Spanish but not French) b. *P*(studying neither Spanish nor French)
   c. *P*(studying both Spanish and French) d. *P*(studying French)
3. In a telephone survey of 150 households, 75 respondents answered "Yes" to a particular question, 50 answered "No," and 25 were "Not sure." Find each experimental probability.
   a. *P*(answer was "Yes") b. *P*(answer was "No")
   c. *P*(answer was "Not sure") d. *P*(answer was not "Not sure")
4. A wallet contains four bills with denominations of $1, $5, $10, and $20. You choose two of the four bills from the wallet at random and add the dollar amounts.
   a. What is the sample space? How many outcomes are there?
   b. What is the probability of getting $15?
   c. What is the probability of getting $50?
   d. What is the probability of getting at least $25?
5. A basketball player has attempted 24 shots and made 13. Find the experimental probability that the player will make the next shot that she attempts.
6. A baseball player attempted to steal a base 70 times and was successful 47 times. Find the experimental probability that the player will be successful on his next attempt to steal a base.

For Exercises 7–8, define a simulation by telling how you represent correct answers, incorrect answers, and the quiz. Use your simulation to find each experimental probability.

7. If you guess the answers at random, what is the probability of getting at least three correct answers on a four-question true-false quiz?
8. A five-question multiple-choice quiz has four choices for each answer. If you guess the answers at random, what is the probability of getting at least four correct answers?
9. A circular pool of radius 12 ft is enclosed within a rectangular yard measuring 50 ft by 100 ft. If a ball from an adjacent golf course lands at a random point within the yard, what is the probability that the ball lands in the pool?
10. Five people each flip a coin. What is the theoretical probability that all five will get heads?

Algebra 2 Chapter 1 — Lesson 1-6 Practice — 7

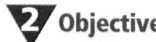

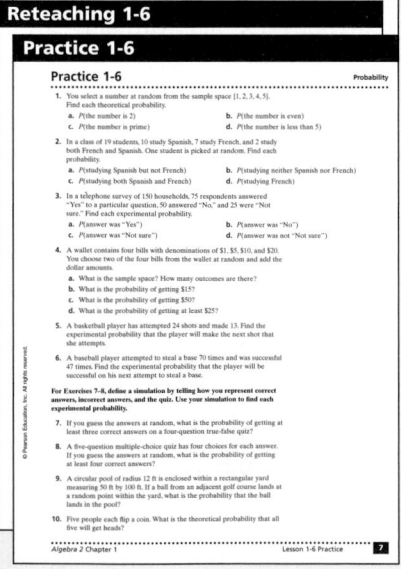

Sometimes you can use areas to find theoretical probability.

5 EXAMPLE Finding Geometric Probability

Geometry Suppose that all the points on the circular dartboard shown at the right are equally likely to be hit by a dart you have thrown. Find the probability of scoring at least ten points.

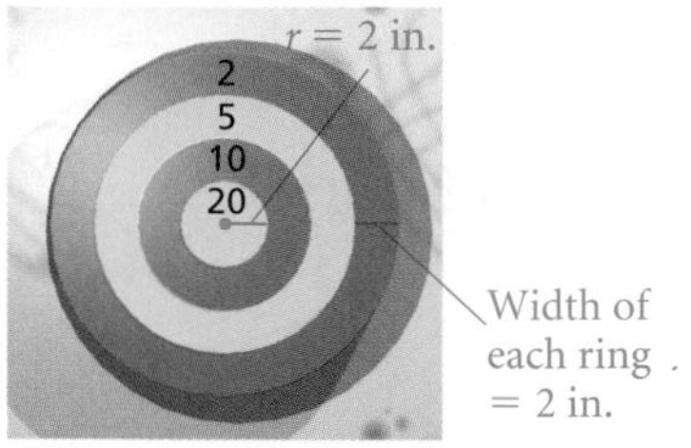

r = 2 in.
2
5
10
20
Width of each ring = 2 in.

$P(\text{at least 10 points})$

$$= \frac{\text{area of circle with radius } 2r}{\text{area of circle with radius } 4r}$$

$$= \frac{\pi(2r)^2}{\pi(4r)^2}$$

$$= \frac{4\pi r^2}{16\pi r^2} = \frac{1}{4}$$

The theoretical probability of scoring at least ten points is $\frac{1}{4}$, or 25%.

Check Understanding 5 Use the dartboard from Example 5. Find each probability.

a. $P(\text{scoring 20 points})$ **$\frac{1}{16}$, or 6.25%**

b. $P(\text{scoring 5 points})$ **$\frac{5}{16}$, or 31.25%**

EXERCISES

For more practice, see *Extra Practice.*

Practice and Problem Solving

A Practice by Example

Example 1 (page 40)

1. A class tossed coins and recorded 161 heads and 179 tails. What is the experimental probability of heads? Of tails? **$\frac{161}{340} \approx 47\%$; $\frac{179}{340} \approx 53\%$**
2. Another class rolled number cubes. Their results are shown in the table. What is the experimental probability of rolling each number? **See margin.**

Number	1	2	3	4	5	6
Occurrences	42	44	45	44	47	46

Example 2 (page 40)

For Exercises 3–5, define a simulation by telling how you represent correct answers, incorrect answers, and the quiz. Use your simulation to find each experimental probability. 3–4. See margin pp. 42–43.

Graphing Calculator Hint

To generate random numbers, press MATH ◄ 1 ENTER.

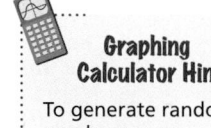

3. If you guess the answers at random, what is the probability of getting at least two correct answers on a five-question true-or-false quiz?
4. If you guess the answers at random, what is the probability of getting at least three correct answers on a five-question true-or-false quiz ?
5. A five-question multiple-choice quiz has five choices for each answer. What is the probability of correctly guessing at random exactly one correct answer? Exactly two correct answers? Exactly three correct answers? (*Hint:* You could let any two digits represent correct answers, and the other digits represent wrong answers.) **See back of book.**

Example 3 (page 41)

A jar contains 30 red marbles, 50 blue marbles, and 20 white marbles. You pick one marble from the jar at random. Find each theoretical probability.

6. $P(\text{red})$ **$\frac{3}{10}$, or 30%**
7. $P(\text{blue})$ **$\frac{1}{2}$, or 50%**
8. $P(\text{not white})$ **$\frac{4}{5}$, or 80%**
9. $P(\text{red or blue})$ **$\frac{4}{5}$, or 80%**

pages 42–45 Exercises

2. the number 1: $\frac{21}{134}$, or about 15.7%; the number 2: $\frac{11}{67}$ or about 16.4%; the number 3: $\frac{45}{268}$ or about 16.8%; the number 4: $\frac{11}{67}$ or about 16.4%; the number 5: $\frac{47}{268}$ or about 17.5%; the number 6: $\frac{23}{134}$ or about 17.2%

3. Answers may vary. Sample: Generate random numbers between 0 and 1 using a graphing calculator. In each random number, examine the first five digits. Let even digits represent correct answers and odd digits incorrect answers. If there

10. $\frac{48}{125}$, or 38.4%

11. $\frac{19}{125}$, or 15.2%

12. $\frac{103}{125}$, or 82.4%

13. $\frac{14}{25}$, or 56%

A bag contains 36 red, 48 green, 22 yellow, and 19 purple blocks. You pick one block from the bag at random. Find each theoretical probability.   **10–13. See left.**

10. P(green)   **11.** P(purple)   **12.** P(not yellow)

13. P(green or yellow)   **14.** P(yellow or not green) $\frac{77}{125}$, **or 61.69%**

Example 4
(page 41)

For each situation, find the sample space and the theoretical probability that a child will naturally place the left thumb on top.

15. The father has gene pair gg and the mother has Gg. **{Gg, Gg, gg};** $\frac{1}{2}$, **or 50%**

16. The father has gene pair gg and the mother has GG.

{Gg, Gg, Gg, Gg}; 1, or 100%

Example 5
(page 42)

17. $\frac{1}{16}$, or 6.25%

18. $\frac{3}{8}$, or 37.5%

19. $\frac{1}{4}$, or 25%

20. $\frac{3}{4}$, or 75%

Geometry Suppose that a dart lands at random on the dartboard shown at the right. Find each theoretical probability.   **17–20. See left.**

17. The dart lands in the bull's-eye.

18. The dart lands in a green region.

19. The dart scores at least 10 points.

20. The dart scores less than 10 points.

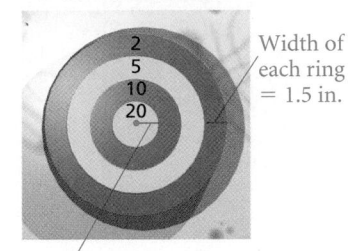
Width of each ring = 1.5 in.

$r = 1.5$ in.

B **Apply Your Skills**

21. The common interpretation of Murphy's Law is, If something can go wrong, it will. Assume that Murphy's Law applies to the following situations, and estimate each probability as either 0 or 1.
   a. P(your dog chews up your homework after you've finished it)   **1**
   b. P(your teacher accepts your excuse for not having your homework)   **0**

22. **Quality Control** Suppose the experimental probability is $\frac{1}{3}$ that a carton of eggs contains at least one broken egg. Use a simulation of 20 trials to find the experimental probability that three cartons selected at random contain only unbroken eggs. (*Hint:* Use any three digits to represent cartons with broken eggs and six other digits to represent cartons with unbroken eggs. Discard the tenth digit.)   **See margin.**

23. Use the random number table at the left to simulate tossing a coin 50 times. Find the experimental probability that the outcome of a coin toss is heads.

See margin.

Random Number Table		
31504	51648	40613
79321	80927	42404
15594	84675	68591
34178	00460	31754
49676	58733	00884
85400	72294	22551
22547	86066	93114
85211	07790	20890
21339	09414	51549
13843	18407	87043
34990	16214	46849
11390	01322	82656
45950	37521	77417

In a class of 147 students, 95 are taking math (M), 73 are taking science (S), and 52 are taking both math and science. One student is picked at random. Find each probability.
24–27. See left.

24. P(taking math or science or both)

25. P(not taking math)

26. P(taking math but not science)

27. P(taking neither math nor science)

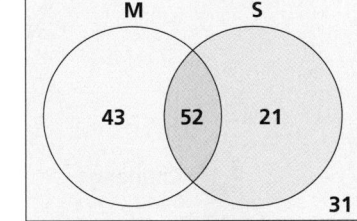

24. $\frac{116}{147}$, or 78.9%

25. $\frac{52}{147}$, or 35.4%

26. $\frac{43}{147}$, or 29.3%

27. $\frac{31}{147}$, or 21.1%

Suppose you roll a number cube. Find each theoretical probability.

28. P(5) $\frac{1}{6}$ **29.** P(an even number) $\frac{1}{2}$

30. P(a number less than 5) $\frac{2}{3}$ **31.** P(8)   **0**

32. P(a number greater than 5) $\frac{1}{6}$ **33.** P(a number less than 8)   **1**

Exercise 36 If necessary, remind students that a prime number is a whole number greater than 1 whose only factors are 1 and itself.

Error Prevention

Exercise 38 It is assumed that the number cubes are distinguishable (for example, of different colors). This means there are *two* ways, not just one, for a pair of numbers such as 2 and 5 to be rolled. It would be beneficial for students to list all the possibilities if they find it difficult to describe the sample space accurately in words.

English Learners

Exercise 44 Be sure students understand that exchanges are distinct from area codes.

22. Answers may vary. Sample: Let the digits 1–6 correspond to good eggs, and 7–9 correspond to bad eggs. Ignoring the digit 0, start in the first row of the table. Circle groups of three digits, 20 groups in all. Tally the circled groups that do not have a 7, 8, or 9. The experimental probability of getting 3 cartons with only unbroken eggs is $\frac{5}{20}$, or $\frac{1}{4}$.

23. Answers may vary. Sample: Let odd digits represent heads and even digits represent tails. Use the first four rows of the table. The experimental probability of heads is $\frac{1}{2}$.

are two or more even digits, make a tally mark for that number. Do this 100 times. Find the total number of tally marks. This, as a percent, gives the experimental probability.

The simulated probability should be about 70%.

4. Answers may vary. Sample: Toss 5 coins. Keep a tally of the times 3 or more heads are tossed. (A head represents a

correct answer.) Do this 100 times. The total number of tally marks, as a percent, gives the experimental probability. The simulated probability should be about 40%.

43

Suppose you select a number at random from the sample space {1, 2, 3, 4, 5, 6, 7, 8, 9}. Find each theoretical probability.

34. P(the number is a multiple of 3) $\frac{1}{3}$ **35.** P(the number is less than 5) $\frac{4}{9}$

36. P(the number is prime) $\frac{4}{9}$ **37.** P(the number is even) $\frac{4}{9}$

38a. (1, 1), (1, 2), (1, 3), (1, 4), (1, 5), (1, 6), (2, 1), (2, 2), (2, 3), (2, 4), (2, 5), (2, 6), (3, 1), (3, 2), (3, 3), (3, 4), (3, 5), (3, 6), (4, 1), (4, 2), (4, 3), (4, 4), (4, 5), (4, 6), (5, 1), (5, 2), (5, 3), (5, 4), (5, 5), (5, 6), (6, 1), (6, 2), (6, 3), (6, 4), (6, 5), (6, 6)

38. Suppose you roll two number cubes.
   a. What is the sample space?
   b. How many outcomes are there? **36 outcomes**
   c. What is the theoretical probability of getting a sum of 12? $\frac{1}{36}$
   d. What is the theoretical probability of getting a sum of 7? $\frac{1}{6}$

 **39. Sports** The batter's strike zone depends on the height and stance of the batter. Find the geometric probability that a baseball thrown at random within the batter's strike zone as shown in the figure below will be "high and inside." This is one of the harder pitches to hit! ≈**6.4%**

40. a. Sports Team A has won one game and team B has won three games in a World Series. What is the experimental probability that team A wins the next game? That team B wins the next game? $\frac{1}{4}; \frac{3}{4}$

   b. Critical Thinking Do you think that experimental probability is a good predictor of the winner of the next game? Explain. **Answers may vary. Sample: Variables such as injuries make probability a poor predictor.**

41. Writing Explain what you would need to know to determine the theoretical probability that a five-digit postal ZIP code ends in 1. **if there are any restrictions on the last digit of a ZIP code**

42. Suppose you choose a two-digit number at random. What is the theoretical probability that its square root is an integer? $\frac{1}{15}$**, or 6.7%**

C Challenge

43a. $\frac{a}{a + b}$

   b. a to $b - a$ or $\frac{a}{b - a}$

   c. A game where the probability of winning is $\frac{1}{2}$; when the odds of winning are $\frac{1}{2}$, the probability of winning is only $\frac{1}{3}$.

43. The odds in favor of an event are the ratio of the number of favorable outcomes to the number of unfavorable outcomes. **See left.**

   a. If the odds in favor of an event are a to b or $\frac{a}{b}$, what is the probability of the event?

   b. If the probability of an event is $\frac{a}{b}$, what are the odds in favor of the event?

   c. Would you rather play a game where your odds of winning are $\frac{1}{2}$, or a game where your probability of winning is $\frac{1}{2}$? Explain.

44. Open-Ended Use a telephone book. Select 50 telephone numbers at random and record the first three digits (the "exchange") of each number. Summarize your results using probability statements. **Check students' work.**

45. On a TV game show, you want to win a prize that is hidden behind one of three doors. You choose one door, but before it is opened the host opens another door and shows that the prize is not there. Now you can switch to the other unopened door or stick with your original choice.

    a. Find the experimental probability of winning the prize if you stick with your original choice. (*Hint:* Simulate the doors with index cards and the prize with a mark on one side of one card. One person can act as the host and another as the contestant.) **about $\frac{1}{3}$**

    b. Find the experimental probability of winning if you switch to the other door. **about $\frac{2}{3}$**

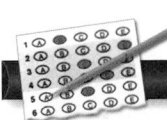

Standardized Test Prep

Multiple Choice

46. What is the theoretical probability of getting a 2 or a 3 when rolling a number cube? **B**

  A. $\frac{1}{2}$ **B.** $\frac{1}{3}$ **C.** $\frac{1}{4}$ **D.** $\frac{1}{6}$

47. How many outcomes are in the sample space for rolling a number cube and tossing a coin? **H**

  F. 2   **G.** 6   **H.** 12   **I.** 24

48–51. See margin.

Short Response

48. What is the sample space for spinning the spinner at the right twice? Are all the outcomes equally likely?

49. What is the probability of spinning a 1 on both of two spins? Explain.

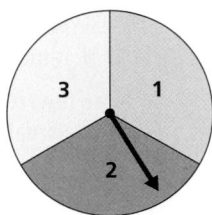

Extended Response

50. Which is more likely on two spins, an even sum or a sum that is not prime? Include all the steps of your solution.

Reading Comprehension

51. Read the passage below. Do you agree with the statement in the last sentence? Explain.

Take It to the NET
Online lesson quiz at
www.PHSchool.com
Web Code: aga-0106

> The chances of the chromosomes being defective are 1 in 250, which sounds like reasonable odds. Except that all odds are, in reality, 50-50: it may happen and it may not.

Mixed Review

Lesson 1-5   **Solve each absolute value equation. Check your answers.**

52. $|x + 3| = 9$ **−12, 6**   **53.** $|3x - 5| = 10$ **$-\frac{5}{3}$, 5**   **54.** $|2x + 7| + 3 = 22$ **−13, 6**

55. $|3x - 6| - 7 = 14$ **−5, 9**   **56.** $|2x + 3| - 9 = 14$ **−13, 10**   **57.** $|6 - 5x| = 18$ **$-\frac{12}{5}$, $\frac{24}{5}$**

Lesson 1-5   **Solve each absolute value inequality.**

58. $2|x| - 3 \geq 5$ **$x \leq -4$ or $x \geq 4$**   **59.** $|2x - 4| + 16 \leq 24$ **$-2 \leq x \leq 6$**   **60.** $|3x - 5| - 2 > 0$ **$x < 1$ or $x > 2\frac{1}{3}$**

61. $|2x + 4| - 6 < 0$ **$-5 < x < 1$**   **62.** $2|x + 3| \geq 10$ **$x \leq -8$ or $x \geq 2$**   **63.** $6|x + 9| \leq 36$ **$-15 \leq x \leq -3$**

Lesson 1-6   Probability   **45**

Standardized Test Prep

Resources
For additional practice with a variety of test item formats:
- Standardized Test Prep, p. 51
- Test-Taking Strategies, p. 46
- Test-Taking Strategies with Transparencies

50. [4] **a.** The favorable outcomes for an even sum are 11, 13, 22, 31, and 33.

    b. The probability of an even sum is $\frac{\text{no. of favorable outcomes}}{\text{total no. of outcomes}} = \frac{5}{9}$.

    c. The favorable outcomes for a composite sum are 13, 22, 31, and 33.

    d. The probability of a composite sum is $\frac{4}{9}$.

    e. $\frac{5}{9} > \frac{4}{9}$, so an even sum is more likely than a composite sum.

[3] omits one of the five parts of the answer

[2] omits two OR three of the five parts of the answer

[1] omits four of the five parts of the answer

51. No; not all odds are 50–50. In this case they are $\frac{1}{249}$, which means 1 out every 250 people will have defective chromosomes.

pages 42–45   Exercises

48. [2] (11, 12, 13, 21, 22, 23, 31, 32, 33); all the pairs are equally likely because the three regions have the same area (or are congruent), and the outcome of the first spin does not affect the outcome of the second spin.

[1] answers one of the two parts

49. [2] $\frac{1}{9}$; the probability of spinning a 1 on each spin is $\frac{1}{3}$. The probability of spinning a 1 on both spins is $\frac{1}{3} \cdot \frac{1}{3}$ or $\frac{1}{9}$.

[1] no explanation included

45

Answering Gridded-Response Questions

This feature helps devise strategies for answering gridded-response questions. The focus of the feature is on recording fractions and decimals in gridded-response blanks after solving equations.

Resources

Test-Taking Strategies with Transparencies
- Transparency 1
- Practice sheet p. 25
- Blank Sheet of Grids, p. vi

Teaching Notes

Students are probably accustomed to changing improper fractions into mixed numbers before recording their answer. Point out that it is best to record improper fractions as a correct response for gridded-response questions.

Test-Taking Strategies with Transparencies

Test-Taking Strategy: Writing Gridded Responses

Learn and practice the proper way to record responses.

Example 1 Answer: $1\frac{1}{2}$

Convert mixed numbers to improper fractions: $1\frac{1}{2} = \frac{3}{2}$

Write answer in boxes. → 3 / 2

Darken matching oval below.

Example 2 Answer: 0.33...

Enter as many decimal places as the grid allows.

Write answer in boxes. → . 3 3 3 3

Darken matching oval below.

Suppose you solve a problem and get each answer below. Show what you would record on an answer grid.

1. Answer: $x = \$554$

(Enter as 554. Can be positioned left, right, or centered.)

2. Answer: $y = \frac{4}{3}$

(Can be recorded as $\frac{4}{3}$. Do not record as $1\frac{1}{3}$ because 11/3 will be interpreted as $\frac{11}{3}$ by the computer.)

Transparency 1

46

Some tests require that you enter numerical answers in a grid. After finding an answer, write it in the top row of the grid. Then fill in the corresponding bubbles below.

EXAMPLE

A rabbit weighs one pound less than eight times the weight of a guinea pig. The rabbit weighs nine pounds. What is the weight in pounds of the guinea pig?

First find the answer by writing and solving an equation.

$8x - 1 = 9$

$\qquad 8x = 10$

$\qquad x = \frac{10}{8}$ or $\frac{5}{4}$ or 1.25

Enter the answer in the grid. You could write it as $\frac{10}{8}$, as $\frac{5}{4}$, or as 1.25. Do not enter the answer as a mixed number. If you enter 1 1/4, it may be interpreted as $\frac{11}{4}$.

Note how to enter fraction bars and decimal points.

EXERCISES

Use a response grid to answer each question. 5, 6. Answers may vary.

1. What is the value of $\frac{x^2 + 1}{2.5}$ when $x = 1.5$? **1.3**

2. A music tape costs a dollar more than half the price of a CD. The music tape costs $9.49. What is the cost in dollars of the CD? **16.98**

3. What is the solution of the equation $3(x - 1) - (x + 2) = 9$? **7**

4. A number is selected at random from the sample space {10, 11, 12, 13, 14, 15}. What is the probability that the number is a multiple of 3? **$\frac{1}{3}$**

5. Write a 4-digit number that is a multiple of both 5 and 6. **4500**

6. Write a rational number between $\sqrt{5}$ and $\sqrt{6}$. **$\frac{12}{5}$**

7. 44.8 is what percent of 128? **35**

8. The length of a picture frame must be at least 4.25 cm greater than the frame's width. The width is 19.5 cm. What is the minimum perimeter, in centimeters, of the picture frame? **86.5**

Chapter Review

Vocabulary

absolute value (p. 33)	evaluate (p. 12)	simulation (p. 40)
absolute value of a real number (p. 8)	experimental probability (p. 40)	solution of an equation (p. 18)
additive inverse (p. 7)	extraneous solution (p. 34)	term (p. 13)
algebraic expression (p. 12)	multiplicative inverse (p. 7)	theoretical probability (p. 41)
coefficient (p. 13)	opposite (p. 7)	tolerance (p. 36)
compound inequality (p. 28)	reciprocal (p. 7)	variable (p. 12)
	sample space (p. 41)	variable expression (p. 12)

Reading Math
Understanding Vocabulary

Choose the correct vocabulary term to complete each sentence.

1. The opposite of a number is also called its _?_ . **additive inverse**

2. The _?_ is the set of all possible outcomes of an experiment. **sample space**

3. The _?_ makes an equation true. **solution of an equation**

4. A pair of inequalities joined by *and* or *or* is called a(n) _?_ **compound inequality**

5. _?_ is another name for a multiplicative inverse of a number. **reciprocal**

6. The _?_ of an event is the ratio of occurrences to trials. **experimental probability**

7. The _?_ of an event is the ratio of possible event outcomes to total possible outcomes. **theoretical probability**

8. A possible solution that does not satisfy the original equation is a(n) _?_ .

9. You can use a(n) _?_ to find experimental probabilities. **simulation**

10. A number's distance from zero on the number line is its _?_ . **absolute value**

Take It to the NET
Online vocabulary quiz at www.PHSchool.com
Web Code: agj-0151

8. **extraneous solution**

Skills and Concepts

1-1 Objectives

▼ To graph and order real numbers (p. 4)

▼ To identify and use properties of real numbers (p. 7)

The natural numbers, whole numbers, integers, rational numbers, and irrational numbers are all subsets of the real numbers. Each real number corresponds to a point on the number line. A real number's distance from zero on the number line is its absolute value.

For both addition and multiplication, real numbers satisfy the properties of closure, associativity, and commutativity. Real numbers have **additive inverses (opposites)** and **multiplicative inverses (reciprocals).** They also have additive and multiplicative identities. Real numbers satisfy the Distributive Property.

To which sets of numbers does each number belong? 11–15. See margin.

11. 8.1π 12. -79 13. $\sqrt{121}$ 14. $\sqrt{200}$ 15. $12\frac{7}{8}$

Compare each pair of numbers. Use < or >.

16. $-\frac{2}{3}, -\frac{3}{2}$ >   17. $\sqrt{6}, 2.\overline{3}$ >   18. $0.45, 0.405$ >   19. $-7, |-7|$ <

pages 47–49 Chapter Review

11. real numbers, irrational numbers

12. real numbers, rational numbers, integers

13. real numbers, rational numbers, integers, whole numbers, natural numbers

14. real numbers, irrational numbers

15. real numbers, rational numbers

20. $3.4; -\frac{1}{3.4}$

-6-4-2 0 2 4 6

21. $-4 - \pi; \frac{1}{4 + \pi}$

-8-6-4-2 0 2 4 6 8

22. $-1\frac{7}{8}; \frac{8}{15}$

-3-2-1 0 1 2 3

23. $-\sqrt{12}; \frac{1}{\sqrt{12}}$

-4-2 0 2 4

Find the opposite and reciprocal of each number. Then graph all three numbers on a number line.   20–23. See margin.

20. -3.4 **21.** $4 + \pi$ **22.** $1\frac{7}{8}$ **23.** $\sqrt{12}$

24–28. Answers may vary.
Open-Ended Write an equation that illustrates each property of real numbers.

24. The Identity Property of Multiplication $(x + 3)(1) = x + 3$

25. The Associative Property of Addition $(2x + 7) + 3y = 2x + (7 + 3y)$

26. The Distributive Property $3(2x - 4) = 6x - 12$

27. The Commutative Property of Multiplication $(5x)(3y) = (3y)(5x)$

28. The Identity Property of Addition $10z + 0 = 10z$

1-2 and 1-3 Objectives

▼ To evaluate algebraic expressions (p. 12)

▼ To simplify algebraic expressions (p. 13)

▼ To solve equations (p. 18)

▼ To solve problems by writing equations (p. 20)

You **evaluate** an **algebraic expression** by substituting numbers for the **variables**. You simplify an algebraic expression by combining like **terms**, using the appropriate properties. To find the **solutions of an equation**, use the properties of equality. To check for **extraneous solutions**, substitute in the original equation. Some equations may have no solutions. Some equations are true for all real numbers.

29. Evaluate $-x^2 + |x - 10|$ for $x = 2$. **4**

30. Evaluate $3t(t + 2) - (3t^2 + 5t)$ for $t = 19$. **19**

31. Simplify $-(3a - 2b) - 3(-a - b)$. **5b**

Solve each equation for x. State any restrictions.

32. $2x - 5 = 17$ **11**   **33.** $8 - \frac{1}{2}x = 3$ **10**

34. $3x = 4x - 5$ **5**   **35.** $0.1x + 1.4 = 1.2x - 3$ **4**

36. $\frac{7 - x}{3} = 5$ **-8**   **37.** $\frac{x + a}{b} = \frac{1}{a}$ $\frac{b - a^2}{a}, a \neq 0, b \neq 0$

Write an equation to solve each problem.

38. **Geometry** The lengths of the sides of a rectangle are in the ratio $5 : 3$. The perimeter of the rectangle is 32 cm. Find the length of each side. **10 cm, 6 cm**

39. Two planes left St. Louis for Los Angeles at the same time. After 4 h they were 700 mi apart. The slower plane traveled at 350 mi/h. What was the speed of the faster plane? **525 mi/h**

40. **Geometry** The measures of an angle and its supplement differ by 40°. Find the measures of the angles. **70°, 110°**

1-4 Objectives

▼ To solve and graph inequalities (p. 26)

▼ To solve and write compound inequalities (p. 28)

You can solve inequalities using properties that are similar to the properties for equations. An important difference is that multiplying or dividing each side of an inequality by a negative number reverses the inequality. Just as with equations, some inequalities are true for all real numbers, and some have no solutions. If a **compound inequality** uses *and*, the solutions must satisfy both inequalities. If a compound inequality uses *or*, the solutions may satisfy either or both of the inequalities.

Solve each inequality. Graph the solution. 41–46. See margin for graphs.

41. $4 - 5z \geq 2$ **42.** $2(5 - 3x) < x - 4(3 - x)$ **43.** $0.3(y - 2) > \frac{1}{2}(6 - y)$
$z \leq \frac{2}{5}$ $x > 2$ $y > 4.5$

Solve each compound inequality. Graph the solution.

44. $5 \leq 9 - 4x \leq 13$ **45.** $3 \geq 2x$ or $x - 4 > 2$ **46.** $6y > 2$ and $y - 5 \geq -2y$
$-1 \leq x \leq 1$ $x \leq \frac{3}{2}$ or $x > 6$ $y \geq \frac{5}{3}$

47. A publisher estimates that the cost of publishing a book is from \$980,000 to \$1,240,000. So far, \$824,150 has been spent. Use a compound inequality to describe the amount A that the publisher can still spend while remaining within the estimate.   **\$155,850 $\leq A \leq$ \$415,850**

1-5 Objectives

▼ To solve absolute value equations (p. 33)

▼ To solve absolute value inequalities (p. 35)

You can rewrite an equation or inequality that involves the absolute value of an **algebraic expression** as a compound sentence. You must consider both cases of the definition of absolute value. Check for **extraneous solutions.**

Solve each equation. Check for extraneous solutions.

48. $|2x + 8| = 3x + 7$ **1**   **49.** $|3x - 5| = 4 + 2x$ $\frac{1}{5}$, **9**   **50.** $|x - 4| + 3 = 1$
                                                              no solution

Solve each inequality. Graph the solution. 51–53. See margin for graphs.

51. $|3x - 2| + 4 \leq 7$ **52.** $4|y - 9| > 36$ **53.** $\frac{2}{5}|3x - 3| - 4 > 2$
$-\frac{1}{3} \leq x \leq \frac{5}{3}$ $y < 0$ or $y > 18$ $x < -4$ or $x > 6$

54. The specification for a length x is 43.6 cm with a tolerance of 0.1 cm. Write the specification as an absolute value inequality. $|x - 43.6| \leq 0.1$

1-6 Objectives

▼ To find experimental probabilities (p. 39)

▼ To find theoretical probabilities (p. 41)

The probability of an event can be expressed as a number from 0% (impossible) to 100% (certain).

Experimental probability is the ratio of two numbers. The first is the observed number of times an experiment results in a particular event. The second is the number of trials. **Simulation** uses random numbers or other models to determine an experimental probability.

Theoretical probability in a sample space of equally likely outcomes is also the ratio of two numbers. The first is the number of outcomes corresponding to the particular event. The second is the number of elements in the sample space, which is the set of all possible outcomes. Geometric probability is computed as a ratio of areas.

Suppose you select a number at random from the sample space $\{-3, -2, -1, 0, 1, 2, 3, 4\}$. Find each probability.

55. P(the number is positive) $\frac{1}{2}$ **56.** P(the number is less than 2) $\frac{5}{8}$

57. P(the number is even) $\frac{1}{2}$ **58.** P(the number is a multiple of 3) $\frac{3}{8}$

🌐 **59. Games** You have won five games of checkers and your opponent has won three. What is the experimental probability of your winning? $\frac{5}{8}$

🌐 **60. Tests** A five-question multiple-choice quiz has four choices for each answer. Find the experimental probability of getting exactly three correct answers if you guess the answers at random. Define a simulation using the random number table on page 43. Use your simulation to find the experimental probability.   **about 9%**

Chapter 1   Chapter Review   **49**

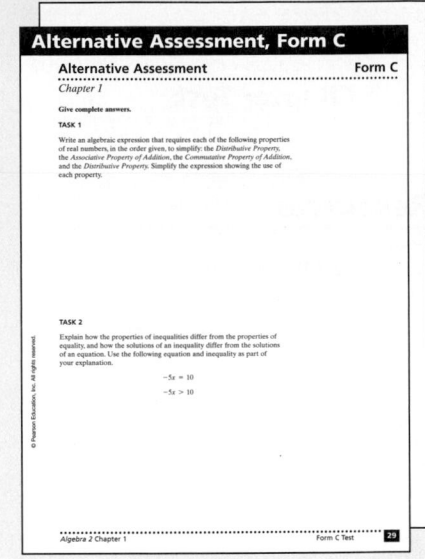
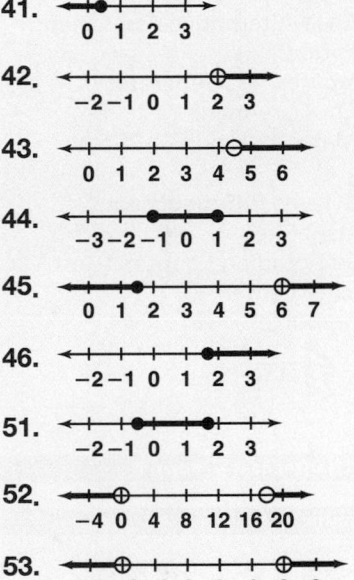

41. (number line: filled dot at 0, arrow right) 0 1 2 3

42. (number line: open circle at 2, arrow right) −2 −1 0 1 2 3

43. (number line: open circle at 4, arrow right) 0 1 2 3 4 5 6

44. (number line: segment from −1 to 1) −3 −2 −1 0 1 2 3

45. (number line) 0 1 2 3 4 5 6 7

46. (number line) −2 −1 0 1 2 3

51. (number line) −2 −1 0 1 2 3

52. (number line) −4 0 4 8 12 16 20

53. (number line) −6 −4 −2 0 2 4 6 8

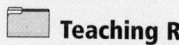

Resources

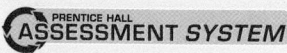

Teaching Resources
Ch. 1 Test, Forms A & B
Ch. 1 Alternative Assessment,
Form C

Reaching All Students
Spanish Ch. 1 Test, Forms A & B
Spanish Ch. 1 Alternative
Assessment, Form C

ASSESSMENT SYSTEM

Assessment Masters
• Ch. 1 Test, Forms A & B
• Ch. 1 Alternative Assessment,
  Form C
Computer Test Generator CD
• Ch. 1 pre-made Test
• Make your own Ch. 1 test

www.PHSchool.com
Student Site
• Self-grading Chapter 1 Test
Teacher Center
• Resources

Plus **iTEXT**

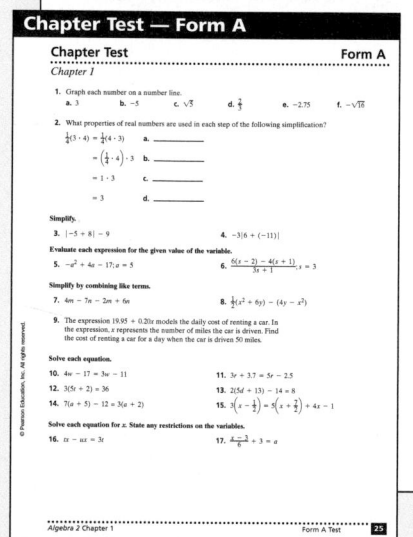

page 50 **Chapter Test**

16. $x = \dfrac{2a}{a - b}, a \neq b$

17. $x = 3c^2, c \neq 0$

18. $x = a(b - 1) + 5, a \neq 0$

19. $x = \dfrac{c - 2}{a - b}, a \neq b$

50

Chapter **1**

Chapter Test

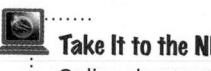
Take It to the NET
Online chapter test at
www.PHSchool.com
Web Code: aga-0152

1. Writing Describe the relationships among these sets of numbers: natural numbers, whole numbers, integers, rational numbers, irrational numbers, and real numbers. **Check students' answers.**

2. Justifying Steps Justify each step by identifying the property used.

$t + 5(t + 1) = t + (5t + 5)$ **Dist. Prop.**
$= (t + 5t) + 5$ **Assoc. Prop. of Add.**
$= (1t + 5t) + 5$ **Identity Prop. of Mult.**
$= (1 + 5)t + 5$ **Dist. Prop.**
$= 6t + 5$ **arithmetic**

Evaluate each expression for $x = 5$.

3. $\frac{5}{3}(3x - 6) - (6 - 4x)$ **29**

4. $3(x^2 - 4) + 7(x - 2)$ **84**

5. $x - 2x + 3x - 4x + 5x$ **15**

Simplify each expression.

6. $a^2 + a + a^2$ **$2a^2 + a$**

7. $2x + 3y - 5x + 2y$ **$-3x + 5y$**

8. $5(a - 2b) - 3(a - 2b)$ **$2a - 4b$**

9. $3[2(x - 3) + 2] + 5(x - 3)$ **$11x - 27$**

Solve each equation.

10. $4y - 6 = 2y + 8$ **7**

11. $3(2z + 1) = 35$ **$\frac{16}{3}$**

12. $5(3w - 2) - 7 = 23$ **$\frac{8}{3}$**

13. $t - 2(3 - 2t) = 2t + 9$ **5**

14. $5(s - 12) - 24 = 3(s + 2)$ **45**

15. $7(3 - 0.5k) = 3k - 5$ **4**

Solve each equation for x. State any restrictions.
16–19. See margin.

16. $ax - bx = 2a$

17. $\frac{x}{c} + c = 4c$

18. $\frac{x - 5}{a} + 1 = b$

19. $ax + 2 = bx + c$

20. The lateral surface area of a cylinder is given by the formula $S = 2\pi rh$. Solve this equation for r.
$r = \dfrac{S}{2\pi h}$

Write an equation to solve each problem.

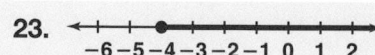

21. Savings Briana and her sister Molly both want to buy the same model bicycle. Briana needs $73 more before she can afford the bike. Molly needs $65 more. If they combine their money, they will have just enough to buy one bicycle that they could share. What is the cost of the bicycle? **$138**

22. Musical There is only one freshman in the cast of the high school musical. There are 6 sophomores and 11 juniors. One third of the cast are seniors. How many seniors are in the musical? **9**

23–31. See margin pp. 50–51 for graphs.
Solve each inequality or equation. Graph the solution.

23. $3x + 17 \geq 5$ **$x \geq -4$**

24. $25 - 2x < 11$ **$x > 7$**

25. $7t > 4t + 3(1 - t)$ **$t > \frac{1}{2}$**

26. $\frac{3}{8}x < -6$ or $5x > 2$ **$x < -16$ or $x > \frac{2}{5}$**

27. $2 < 10 - 4d < 6$ **$1 < d < 2$**

28. $4 - x = |2 - 3x|$ **$-1, \frac{3}{2}$**

29. $|4x + 4| = 8x + 16$ **$-\frac{5}{3}$**

30. $|5 - p| \leq 2$ **$3 \leq p \leq 7$**

31. $5|3w + 2| - 3 > 7$ **$w < -\frac{4}{3}$ or $w > 0$**

Suppose you select a number at random from the sample space {5, 6, 7, 8, 9, 10, 11, 12, 13, 14}. Find each probability.

32. $P(\text{greater than 10})$ **$\frac{2}{5}$**

33. $P(\text{multiple of 30})$ **0**

34. $P(\text{less than 7 or greater than 10})$ **$\frac{3}{5}$**

35. $P(\text{integer})$ **1**

36. Open-Ended Your teacher selects at random two days out of every five days to give a "pop" quiz. Define a simulation to find the experimental probability that you will get a pop quiz on two consecutive days. Then use your simulation to find the probability. **about 40%**

23.
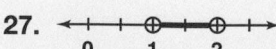
-6 -5 -4 -3 -2 -1 0 1 2

24.
-1 0 1 2 3 4 5 6 7 8 9

25.
-1 0 1 2

26.
-16 -12 -8 -4 0 4

27.
0 1 2

28.
-1 0 1 2

Standardized Test Prep

Reading Comprehension Read the passage below. Then answer the questions on the basis of what is *stated* or *implied* in the passage.

A-Frame Bookshelf Do-it-yourselfers can build large-capacity, self-supporting bookshelves that are easy to set up and break down. They are called A-frame bookshelves, because the frame and shelves form an A.

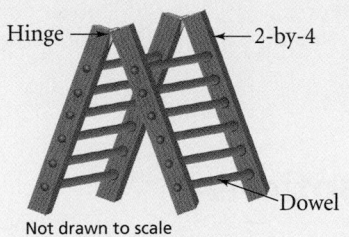

Hinge — 2-by-4

— Dowel

Not drawn to scale

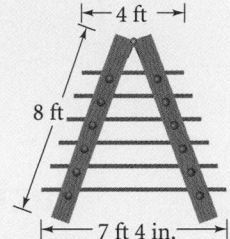

4 ft

8 ft

7 ft 4 in.

The frame uses four 2-by-4's, each 8 feet long. They are joined in pairs by a hinge. Holes are drilled through the 2-by-4's at 1-foot intervals. Round dowels, $\frac{3}{4}$ of an inch in diameter, connect the two parts of the frame.

The shelves are fastened to the dowels. Each shelf is a constant length longer than the shelf above it. In the six-shelf unit shown above, the top shelf is 4 feet long and the bottom shelf is 7 feet 4 inches long.

---

1. What is the difference in length between each shelf and the one directly below it? **C**
   A. 4 in.   B. 6 in.   C. 8 in.   D. $14\frac{2}{3}$ in.

2. How far beyond each edge of the top shelf does each edge of the bottom shelf extend? **H**
   F. 4 in.   G. 8 in.
   H. 1 ft 8 in.   I. 3 ft 6 in.

3. What is the total length of the shelves? **D**
   A. 29 ft 8 in.   B. 32 ft
   C. 33 ft 4 in.   D. 34 ft

4. Suppose you can buy 2-by-4's in any length for $.29 per foot. About how much will you pay for the 2-by-4's for the bookcase? **G**
   F. $5   G. $10   H. $15   I. $20

5. Suppose the 2-by-4's are 2 in. thick, the shelves are 8 in. deep, and the dowels are cut flush with the front and back faces of the bookshelf. If the dowels are sold in 4-ft lengths, how many lengths would you have to buy for the bookcase? **B**
   A. 2   B. 3   C. 4   D. 12

For Questions 6–10, use the information below. Show your work.

A shorter bookshelf uses 2-by-4's that are 6 ft long, and has five shelves. The top shelf is 3 ft long and the bottom shelf is 6 ft 8 in. long.

6. What is the difference in length from each shelf to the one below it? **11 in.**

7. How much does the bottom shelf extend to the right beyond the right-most edge of the top shelf? **1 ft 10 in.**

8. What is the total length of shelving in the bookshelf? **24 ft 2 in.**

9. In a four-shelf bookshelf, the bottom shelf is 8 ft long. The top shelf is 5 ft $1\frac{1}{2}$ in. long. How long are the other two shelves? **7 ft $\frac{1}{2}$ in., 6 ft 1 in.**

10. Which is greater, the average length of the shelves in Questions 6–8 or the average length of the shelves in Question 9? How much greater is it? **The average length of the shelves in Question 9 is greater by 1 ft $8\frac{3}{4}$ in.**

29.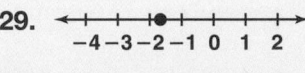
   −4 −3 −2 −1 0 1 2

30. 1 2 3 4 5 6 7 8 9

31. −2 −1 0 1

Students must be able to extract information from reading passages, answer multiple choice questions, and construct responses in order to be successful on current state and national assessments.

To answer the questions, students apply skills and concepts from this chapter and previous chapters.
Multiple Choice: Items 1–5
Extended Response: Items 6–10

Resources

Teaching Resources
Cumulative Review

Reaching All Students
Spanish Cumulative Review

PRENTICE HALL
ASSESSMENT SYSTEM

Standardized Test Prep
• Ch. 1 Standardized Test Practice
Assessment Masters
• Cumulative Review
Computer Test Generator CD
• Standardized Test Practice

www.PHSchool.com
• Standardized Test Practice
• Resources

Plus **iTEXT**

Linear Relationships and Functions

Chapter at a Glance

North Carolina Objectives

2-1	**Relations and Functions**	
NCTM 2, 8, 10	▼ Graphing Relations ▼ Identifying Functions	

2-2	**Linear Equations**	
NCTM 2, 3, 7, 10	▼ Graphing Linear Equations ▼ Writing Equations of Lines	

2-3	**Direct Variation**	1.05
NCTM 1, 2, 8, 9	▼ Writing and Interpreting a Direct Variation	

2-4	**Using Linear Models**	2.04b
NCTM 1, 2, 5, 6, 9	▼ Modeling Real-World Data ▼ Predicting With Linear Models	

2-5	**Absolute Value Functions and Graphs**	2.08a
NCTM 1, 2, 10	▼ Graphing Absolute Value Functions	

2-6	**Vertical and Horizontal Translations**	2.08b
NCTM 2, 3, 10	▼ Translating Graphs Vertically ▼ Translating Graphs Horizontally	

2-7	**Two-Variable Inequalities**	2.08a
NCTM 2, 10	▼ Graphing Linear Inequalities ▼ Graphing Two-Variable Absolute Value Inequalities	

NCTM STANDARDS 2000

1	Number and Operations	6	Problem Solving
2	Algebra	7	Reasoning and Proof
3	Geometry	8	Communication
4	Measurement	9	Connections
5	Data Analysis and Probability	10	Representation

Pacing Options

This chart suggests pacing only for the lessons and their parts. It is provided as a possible guide. It will help you determine how much time you have in your schedule to cover other components, such as the features, Chapter Review, and Chapter Test.

Day	Traditional (45 min.)	Block (90 min.)
1	2-1 ▼	2-1 ▼
2	2-1 ▼ ▼	2-1 ▼
3	2-1 ▼	2-2 ▼
4	2-2 ▼	2-2 ▼
5	2-2 ▼ ▼	2-3 ▼
6	2-2 ▼	2-4 ▼
7	2-3 ▼	2-4 ▼
8	2-4 ▼	2-5 ▼
9	2-4 ▼ ▼	2-6 ▼
10	2-4 ▼	2-6 ▼
11	2-5 ▼	2-7 ▼ ▼
12	2-6 ▼	
13	2-6 ▼ ▼	
14	2-6 ▼	
15	2-7 ▼ ▼	

NAEP Correlation (National Assessment of Educational Progress 2000 Mathematics Objectives)

2-1	2-2	2-3	2-4	2-5	2-6	2-7
A3a, A3c, A11	A3a, A3c, G6a	A1f, N5b, N5c	N2d, A13, D2b	N2d, A3a	A3d	A3a

N = Number Sense, Properties, and Operations; **M** = Measurement; **G** = Geometry and Spatial Sense; **D** = Data Analysis, Statistics, and Probability; **A** = Algebra and Functions

Math Background

Chapter Overview

Relations are defined as sets of ordered pairs and functions are defined as relations that assign exactly one value of the range to each value of the domain. Linear functions are functions whose graphs are lines in the coordinate plane. Students use the concept of slope to write equations for linear functions. They also see how slopes can be used to decide whether two lines in the coordinate plane are parallel or perpendicular.

Direct variations are discussed as a special type of linear function. Students examine mathematical and real-world applications of direct variations.

In the feature following Lesson 2-2, students study piecewise functions. In their study of absolute value functions, students combine what they have learned about linear functions and piecewise functions.

Finally, students examine how the graphs of parent functions of linear functions and of absolute value functions can be translated in the coordinate plane. Translations will be used in later chapters with more complicated graphs.

Relations and Functions   2-1

Notice that relations and functions can be specified by verbal descriptions, lists, tables, and mapping diagrams. Of special interest are relations and functions that are orderly enough to be described by equations.

Linear Equations and Slope   2-2

It is important for students to recognize slope as a rate of change of one variable in terms of another.

Direct Variation   2-3

Direct variations give very clear examples of rates of change. Students who have difficulty using different variables to mean the same thing may not recognize k in $y = kx$ as the slope of the line.

Students who have difficulty with the concept of proportions may find these applications helpful in clarifying their thinking. They should also be aware that the phrases *is directly proportional to, varies directly as,* and *varies directly with* are equivalent.

Using Linear Models   2-4

Even though many real-world situations can be modeled by linear equations, the likelihood that real-world data will fall exactly on the graph of a linear equation is quite low. When real data are recorded as a scatter plot, the approximate line of best fit can be drawn by hand, but a calculator give the actual equation. Students opposed to using calculators may be converted if they research the work needed to actually calculate the line of best fit by hand.

To graph data, one or both axes may be drawn with a break to allow us to see the relevant part of the grid in a reasonably compact space. It is often convenient to use non-unit scales on the axes to accommodate the data of a problem. Different scales may be used for the two axes, but then the apparent slope of a line will be distorted and the slope cannot be calculated by counting grid lines.

Absolute Value Functions and Graphs   2-5

You may wish to show students that the formula $(\frac{-b}{m}, c)$ for the vertex of the graph of an absolute value function need not be memorized, since it is easily derived. For functions of the form $y = |mx + b| + c$, where $m \neq 0$, solving the equation $mx + b = 0$ gives the first coordinate, and c represents the vertical translation of the parent function $y = |x|$.

Vertical and Horizontal Translations   2-6

Students who have difficulty identifying the direction of horizontal translations may be helped by thinking of "speeding up" or "delaying" what happens with values of the function. For example, for $y = |x|$, the value of the function is 0 when $x = 0$. For $y = |x - 3|$, $h = -3$: moving from left to right, you have to "wait 3 units" until you arrive at 3, the number that will make the value of y equal to 0.

Students by now should have a great appreciation of the power that understanding translations gives them to reduce a complicated looking function to the parent function, and so more easily identify various attributes of the function.

Two-Variable Inequalities   2-7

The tolerances involved in many manufacturing and packaging situations can generally be expressed as absolute value inequalities. Skill in applying the logic involved in solving these will also be needed in later courses.

Ongoing Assessment and Intervention

Tools for Monitoring Student Progress

The Prentice Hall *Algebra 2* program provides you with many options for assessment in the Student Edition, the Teacher's Edition and the teaching resources. From these options you may choose instructional materials and techniques that are appropriate for your students and support your district's curriculum requirements.

Instant Check System™ in Chapter 2

Allows students to check their own learning before, during, and after each lesson.

Diagnosing Readiness before the chapter (p. 52)

Check Skills You'll Need exercises in each lesson (pp. 55, 62, 72, 78, 86, 91, 99)

Check Understanding questions with each Example (pp. 55, 56, 57, 58, 63, 64, 65, 66, 67, 72, 73, 74, 78, 79, 80, 87, 88, 91, 92, 93, 94, 95, 100, 101, 102)

Checkpoint Quiz (pp. 77, 98)

Test Prep in Chapter 2

Teaches students strategies and gives them practice with all the test item formats they will encounter on state tests and standardized national exams.

Standardized Test Prep exercises in each lesson (pp. 61, 70, 76, 84, 90, 97, 98, 104)

Test-Taking Strategies (p. 106)

Standardized Test Prep (p. 111)

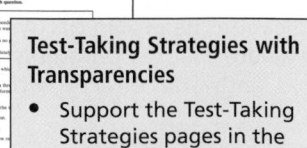

All your assessment needs in one place!

Program Assessment

Assess student progress throughout the *Algebra 2* text with blackline masters and CD-ROM.

Assessment Resources

- Checkpoint Quizzes 1 & 2
- Chapter Test, Forms A & B
- Chapter Alternative Assessment

Spanish versions available.

Computer Test Generator

- Unlimited questions of varying difficulty for every lesson objective.
- Create your own practice sheets, quizzes, and tests, or use the pre-made Chapter Tests.
- Diagnose readiness with questions on prerequisite skills.
- Prepare students by making tests based on standardized test objectives.
- Access Algebra 1, Geometry, and Algebra 2 content—all on one CD-ROM.

Test Preparation

A three-step approach to preparing students for high stakes, national, and state exams.

❶ Diagnose & Prescribe

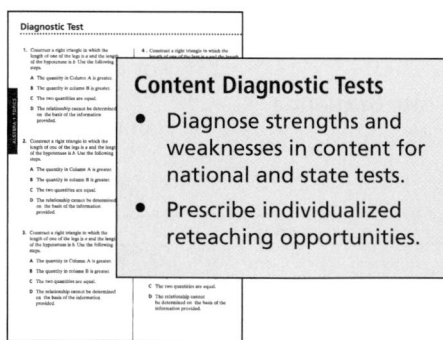

Content Diagnostic Tests
- Diagnose strengths and weaknesses in content for national and state tests.
- Prescribe individualized reteaching opportunities.

❷ Review & Reteach

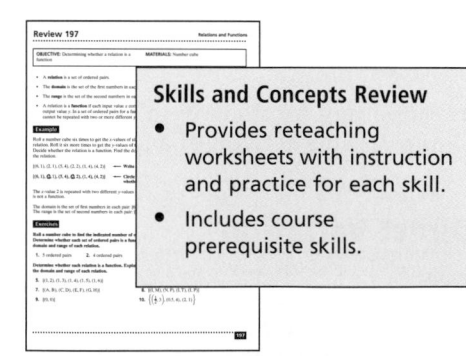

Skills and Concepts Review
- Provides reteaching worksheets with instruction and practice for each skill.
- Includes course prerequisite skills.

❸ Practice & Assess

Test Preparation
- Features practice tests for End-of-Course and SAT/ACT exams.
- Includes standardized test practice by chapter for ongoing review.

Teacher's Guide with answers and correlations.

Test-Taking Strategies with Transparencies
- Support the Test-Taking Strategies pages in the Student Edition.
- Provide a teaching transparency and a practice worksheet for each strategy.

# Reaching All Students

Support in the Student Text and Additional Resources

The textbook, the iText, and other technology components provide numerous opportunities to reach students of various ability levels and learning styles. Each Teacher's Edition lesson suggests how you can help *all* your students be successful and understand the mathematics in Chapter 2.

Below Level

Student Edition
- Diagnosing Readiness*: p. 52
- Check Skills You'll Need*: pp. 55, 62, 72, 78, 86, 91, 99

Reteaching
Chapter 2 Support File: pp. 8–14

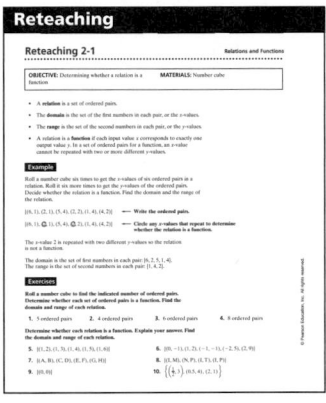

Advanced Learners

Student Edition
- Challenge exercises: pp. 60, 61, 69, 76, 83, 97, 103
- Extension, p. 71

Enrichment
Chapter 2 Support File: pp. 15–21

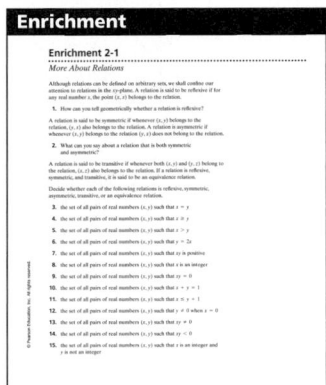

Connections to Precalculus Masters
Chapter 2 Enrichment Topic:
Piecewise Functions

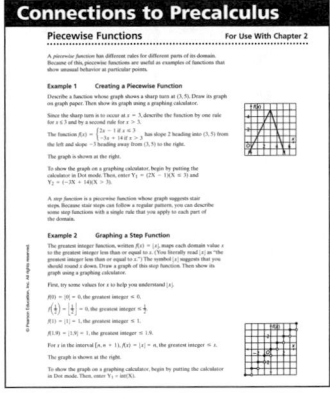

* Can be used with all ability levels to ensure mastery of prerequisite skills.

Reading and Math Literacy

Student Edition
- Vocabulary: pp. 53, 107, *plus* in every Lesson Preview
- Reading Math: pp. 57, 58, 64, 72, 83, 86, 91, 103
- Illustrated Glossary: pp. 871–913

Reading and Math Literacy Masters
Chapter 2: pp. 5–8

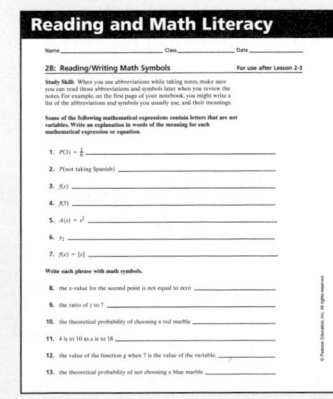

English Learners

Student Edition
- English/Spanish Illustrated Glossary: pp. 871–913

Workbook and Masters
Spanish Practice Workbook: pp. 1–7
Spanish Reading and Math Literacy Masters: pp. 5–8

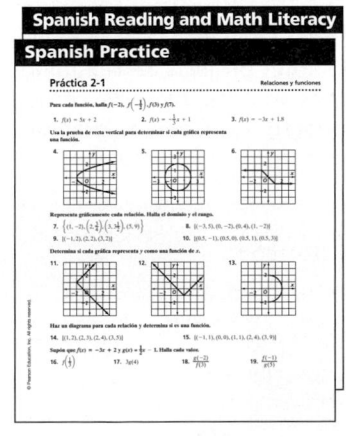

Learning Styles

Student Edition
- Investigation: pp. 64, 99
- Technology: pp. 85, 87
- Writing: pp. 60, 71, 76, 77, 81, 83, 85, 89, 96, 103, 110
- DK Activities: pp. 112–113

Activity Masters
Hands-On Activities: 33, 34, 35
Technology Activities: 1, 2, 3, 6, 27

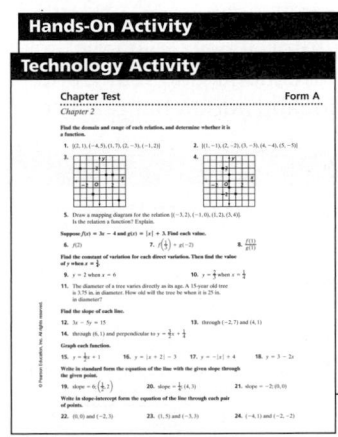

Program Resources

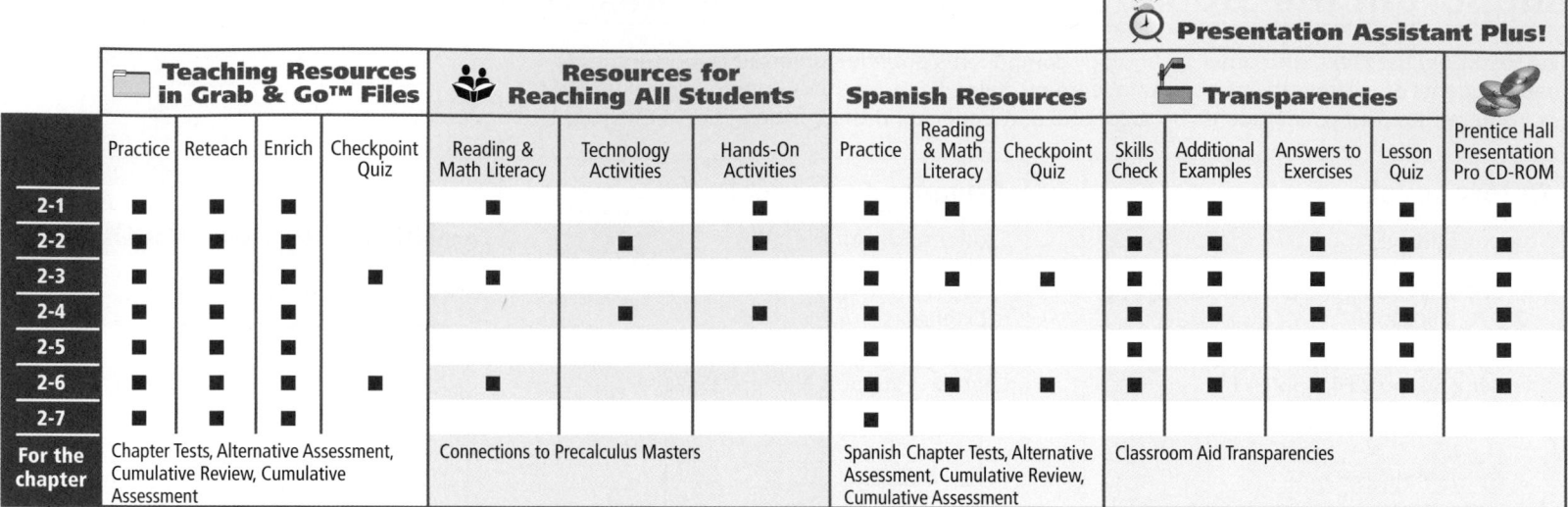

	Practice	Reteach	Enrich	Checkpoint Quiz	Reading & Math Literacy	Technology Activities	Hands-On Activities	Practice	Reading & Math Literacy	Checkpoint Quiz	Skills Check	Additional Examples	Answers to Exercises	Lesson Quiz	Prentice Hall Presentation Pro CD-ROM
2-1	■	■	■		■		■	■			■	■	■	■	■
2-2	■	■	■			■	■	■			■	■	■	■	■
2-3	■	■	■	■	■			■		■	■	■	■	■	■
2-4	■	■	■			■	■	■			■	■	■	■	■
2-5	■	■	■					■			■	■	■	■	■
2-6	■	■	■	■	■			■		■	■	■	■	■	■
2-7	■							■							
For the chapter	Chapter Tests, Alternative Assessment, Cumulative Review, Cumulative Assessment				Connections to Precalculus Masters			Spanish Chapter Tests, Alternative Assessment, Cumulative Review, Cumulative Assessment			Classroom Aid Transparencies				

Teaching Resources in Grab & Go™ Files | **Resources for Reaching All Students** | **Spanish Resources** | **Transparencies** | **Presentation Assistant Plus!**

Also available for use with the chapter:

 PRENTICE HALL ASSESSMENT *SYSTEM*   *See page 52C.*

- Practice Workbook
- Solution Key

- For teacher support and access to student Web site materials, use Web Code agk-5500.
- For additional online and technology resources, see below.

Technology

 Online and on CD-ROM

Complete Interactive Student Text online and on CD-ROM—with instant feedback assessment, tutorial help, dynamic activities, instructional and real-world videos, audio, and additional practice.

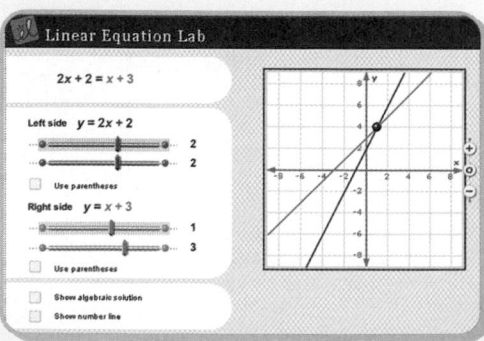

www.PHSchool.com For Students

Use **Web Codes** for easy access to online activities, chapter projects, self-grading lesson quizzes and chapter tests, vocabulary quizzes, updated data sources, graphing calculator procedures, and more.

PH Success*Net* **For Teachers**

Online lesson planning with built-in state correlations, all the teaching resources, complete reference library, your own calendar and Teacher Web page, professional development, and more.

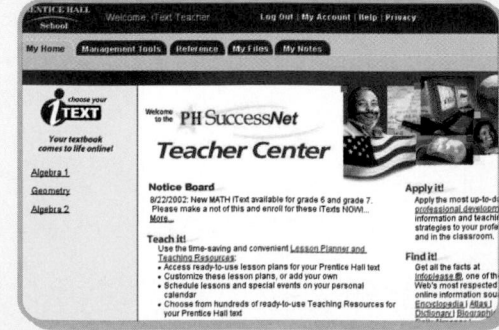

Presentation Assistant Plus!

The Prentice Hall *Presentation Assistant Plus!* provides you with the material you need to teach a lesson from beginning to end. Two easy-to-use formats—Transparencies and CD-ROM—allow you to present a lesson the way you are most comfortable.

Transparencies

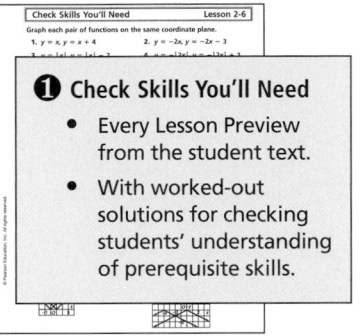

❶ Check Skills You'll Need
- Every Lesson Preview from the student text.
- With worked-out solutions for checking students' understanding of prerequisite skills.

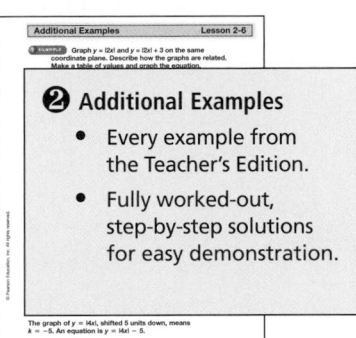

❷ Additional Examples
- Every example from the Teacher's Edition.
- Fully worked-out, step-by-step solutions for easy demonstration.

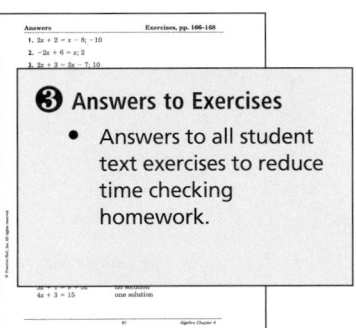

❸ Answers to Exercises
- Answers to all student text exercises to reduce time checking homework.

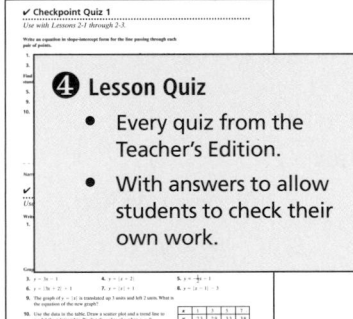

❹ Lesson Quiz
- Every quiz from the Teacher's Edition.
- With answers to allow students to check their own work.

Throughout the Teacher's Edition, this symbol indicates material that is available on transparency in the Presentation Assistant Plus!

Prentice Hall Presentation Pro CD-ROM

- Includes all Transparencies.
- Conveniently organized by lesson so you can easily ❶ Introduce, ❷ Teach, ❸ Check Homework, and ❹ Assess each lesson.
- Animated examples allow step-by-step instruction at your own pace.
- Easy to edit so you can create custom presentations.

Teaching Chapter 2 Using Presentation Assistant Plus!

	❶ Introduce	❷ Teach	❸ Check Homework	❹ Assess
	Check Skills You'll Need	Additional Examples	Student Edition Answers	Lesson Quiz
2-1	p. 7	pp. 15–16	✔	p. 104
2-2	p. 8	pp. 17–21	✔	p. 105
2-3	p. 9	pp. 22–23	✔	p. 106
2-4	p. 10	pp. 24–26	✔	p. 107
2-5	p. 11	pp. 27–28	✔	p. 107
2-6	p. 12	pp. 29–31	✔	p. 108
2-7	p. 13	pp. 32–34	✔	p. 108

Prentice Hall Presentation Pro

CD-ROM with dynamic PowerPoint® presentations for every lesson. Helps you introduce and develop concepts, check homework, and assess progress. Part of Presentation Assistant Plus! *(See above.)*

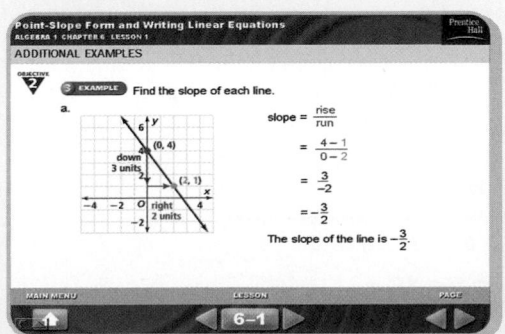

Computer Test Generator

CD-ROM to create practice sheets and tests for course objectives and standardized tests. Includes Instant Chapter Tests™, online testing, and student reports. Part of the PH Assessment System. *(See page 52C.)*

Resource Pro® with Planning Express®

CD-ROM with a lesson planning tool that allows you to import state and local objectives. Includes electronic versions of all the teaching resources.

Chapter 2

Functions, Equations, and Graphs

 Diagnosing Readiness

Students will find answers to these exercises in the back of their textbooks.

For intervention, direct students to:

Graphing Numbers on the Number Line
Lesson 1-1: Example 2
Exercises 12–16
Extra Practice, p. 822

Simplifying Expressions
Lesson 1-2: Example 4
Exercises 21–35
Extra Practice, p. 822

Solving Absolute Value Inequalities
Lesson 1-5: Examples 4–5
Exercises 16–27
Extra Practice, p. 822

Probability
Lesson 1-6: Example 3
Exercises 6–14
Extra Practice, p. 822

Where You've Been

- In first-year algebra, you learned to interpret and solve problems algebraically.

- In geometry, you learned to analyze and manipulate two- and three-dimensional figures.

- In Chapter 1, you learned to represent relationships using variables. You learned to evaluate and simplify variable expressions involving integers and fractions.

 **Diagnosing Readiness** *(For help, go to the Lesson in green.)*

Instant self-check online and on CD-ROM

Graphing Numbers on the Number Line (Lesson 1-1)

Graph each group of numbers on a number line. **1–3. See margin.**

1. $2, -\frac{7}{4}, -1, \frac{15}{2}$ **2.** $0, \frac{2}{3}, -\sqrt{2}, -3$ **3.** $-\frac{5}{4}, \sqrt{7}, 2.\overline{6}, 4$

Simplifying Expressions (Lesson 1-2)

Simplify by combining like terms.

4. $7s - s$ **6s** **5.** $3a + b + a$ **4a + b** **6.** $xy - y + x$ **xy − y + x**

7. $0.5g + g$ **1.5g** **8.** $4t - (t + 3t)$ **0** **9.** $b - 2(1 + c - b)$ **3b − 2c − 2**

10. $5f - (5d - f)$ **6f − 5d** **11.** $2(h + 2g) - (g - h)$**3h + 3g** **12.** $-(3z - 5) + z$ **−2z + 5**

13. $(2 - d)g - 3d(4 + g)$ **14.** $5v - 3(2 - v)$ **15.** $7t - 3s(2 + t) + s$
    2g − 4dg − 12d   **8v − 6**   **7t − 3st − 5s**

Solving Absolute-Value Inequalities (Lesson 1-5)

Solve each absolute-value inequality. Graph the solution. **16–21. See margin.**

16. $|x - 3| < 5$ **17.** $|2a - 1| \geq 2a + 1$ **18.** $|3x + 4| > -4x - 3$

19. $|3x + 1| + 1 > 12$ **20.** $3|d - 4| \leq 13 - d$ **21.** $-\frac{1}{3}|f + 3| + 2 \geq -5$

Probability (Lesson 1-6)

A bag contains 12 red, 15 green, 10 yellow, 25 purple, and 2 black blocks. Find each theoretical probability for one block selected at random.

22. $P(\text{green})$ $\frac{15}{64}$ **23.** $P(\text{black})$ $\frac{1}{32}$ **24.** $P(\text{red or yellow})$ $\frac{11}{32}$
25. $P(\text{not red})$ $\frac{13}{16}$ **26.** $P(\text{not yellow})$ $\frac{27}{32}$ **27.** $P(\text{black or not red})$ $\frac{13}{16}$

---

page 52 Diagnosing Readiness

1.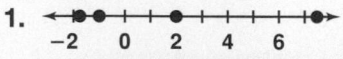
-2 0 2 4 6

2.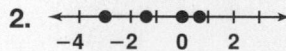
-4 -2 0 2

3.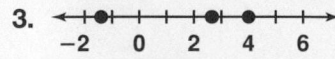
-2 0 2 4 6

16. $-2 < x < 8$
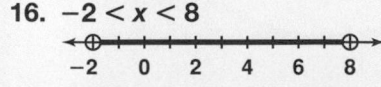
-2 0 2 4 6 8

17. $a \leq 0$
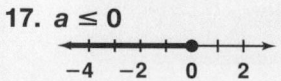
-4 -2 0 2

18. $x > -1$
-2 0 2 4

19. $x < -4$ or $x > \frac{10}{3}$
-6 -4 -2 0 2 4 6

20. $-\frac{1}{2} \leq d \leq \frac{25}{4}$
-2 0 2 4 6 8

21. $-24 \leq f \leq 18$
-30 -20 -10 0 10 20 30

Functions, Equations, and Graphs

Where You're Going

- In Chapter 2, you will move from simplifying variable expressions and solving one-variable equations and inequalities to working with two-variable equations and inequalities.

- You will learn how to represent function relationships by writing and graphing linear equations and inequalities.

- By graphing data and trend lines, you will understand how the slope of a line can be interpreted in real-world situations.

 **Real-World Snapshots** Applying what you learn, on pages 112–113 you will do activities involving bridges.

LESSONS

Key Vocabulary

- absolute value function (p. 86)
- constant of variation (p. 72)
- dependent variable (p. 62)
- direct variation (p. 72)
- domain (p. 56)
- function (p. 57)
- independent variable (p. 62)
- linear equation (p. 62)
- linear function (p. 62)
- linear inequality (p. 99)
- parent function (p. 91)
- point-slope form (p. 65)
- range (p. 56)
- relation (p. 55)
- slope (p. 64)
- slope-intercept form (p. 65)
- standard form (p. 63)
- translation (p. 91)
- vertical-line test (p. 57)
- x-intercept (p. 63)
- y-intercept (p. 63)

Chapter 2 Overview

This chapter begins by introducing students to relations and functions. In the next lesson, students learn about linear equations and slope. Students then study direct variation, and using linear models. Absolute value functions and graphs, and then vertical and horizontal translations, are presented. Students conclude the chapter with a lesson on two-variable inequalities.

Reading Math
Reading for Problem Solving, p. 105

Vocabulary
A complete list of terms, plus vocabulary exercises, appears in the Chapter Review, p. 107.

Illustrated Glossary
Examples for each vocabulary term, plus definitions in both English and Spanish, appear starting on p. 871.

Test-Taking Strategies
Answering short-response questions, p. 106

Real-World Snapshots
See pages 112–113 for a real-world application of functions that utilizes Dorling Kindersley's (DK) unique graphic presentation.

Real-World Connections
Some of the applications you will find in this chapter are art (2-1), transportation (2-2), water conservation (2-3), science (2-4), travel (2-5), fabric design (2-6), and entertainment (2-7).

www.PHSchool.com
Internet support for this chapter includes:
- Self-grading Vocabulary and Chapter 2 Tests
- Chapter Project
- Chapter Planner
- Chapter 2 Resources

Plus

Algebra 1 Review

The Coordinate Plane

In this feature, students review the concept of the coordinate plane by graphing points on the coordinate plane, and writing coordinates for specific points on the coordinate plane in order to identify relations and functions in Lesson 2-1.

Resources

The Coordinate Plane
Skills Handbook: p. 848, Example 1, Exercises 1–12

Teaching Notes

You may wish to give students graph paper on which they can draw their own coordinate planes to practice graphing points.

Auditory Learners

Have students graph points on the coordinate plane as you call out the coordinates. Alternatively, have students call out coordinates and you graph them on a coordinate plane on the chalkboard or overhead projector.

page 54   Algebra 1 Review

1.
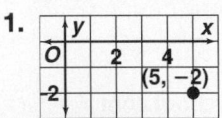

2.
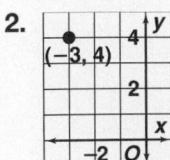

3.
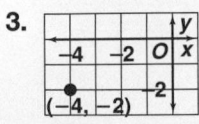

54

There is a one-to-one correspondence between the points in the coordinate plane and the set of ordered pairs (x, y), where x and y are real numbers. The first number is the x-coordinate, or abscissa. The abscissa gives the horizontal position of a point. The second number is the y-coordinate, or ordinate. The ordinate gives the vertical position of a point.

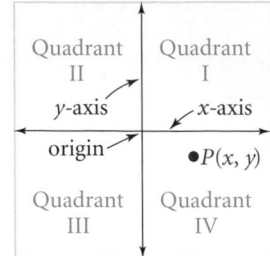

1 EXAMPLE   Graphing Points

Graph $(4, 3)$ and $(-4, -3)$.

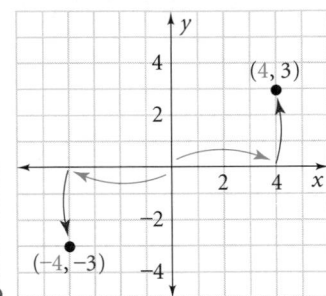

Graph and label each ordered pair.

You can write the coordinates of a point if you are given its graph.

2 EXAMPLE   Writing Coordinates

Write the coordinates of each point in the graph.

The points are $A(2, 4)$, $B(3, 0)$, $C(-4, 0)$, $D(0, -3)$, $E(-5, 4)$, $F\left(4, \frac{1}{2}\right)$, $G(0, 0)$, and $H\left(-3, -3\frac{1}{2}\right)$.

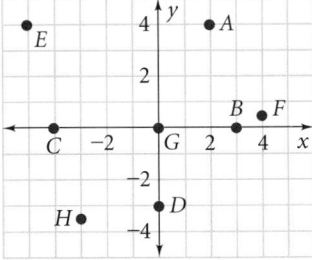

EXERCISES

1–6. See margin for graph.

Graph and label each ordered pair. Name the quadrant or axis where each point lies.

1. $(5, -2)$ **IV**   **2.** $(-3, 4)$ **II**   **3.** $(-4, -2)$ **III**
4. $(5, 0)$ **x-axis**   **5.** $(5, 2)$ **I**   **6.** $(0, -3)$ **y-axis**

Write the coordinates of each point in the graph at the right.

7. C **(4, −4)**   **8.** $G\left(-3, -1\frac{1}{2}\right)$ **9.** J **(3, 2)**   **10.** $A(-1, 4)$

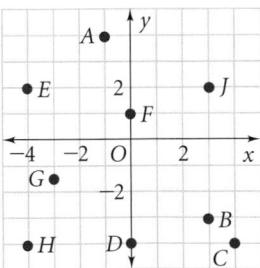

4.
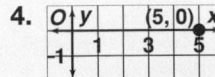

5.
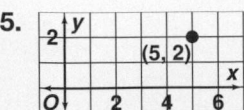

6.
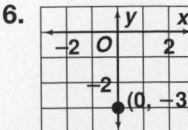

2-1

Relations and Functions

Lesson Preview

What You'll Learn

OBJECTIVE 1 To graph relations

OBJECTIVE 2 To identify functions

. . . And Why

To write a function for the area of a square, as in Example 6

 Check Skills You'll Need (For help, go to Skills Handbook page 848 and Lesson 1-2.)

Graph each ordered pair on the coordinate plane. 1–5. See back of book.

1. $(-4, -8)$ **2.** $(3, 6)$ **3.** $(0, 0)$ **4.** $(-1, 3)$ **5.** $(-6, 5)$

Evaluate each expression for $x = -1, 0, 2,$ and 5.

6. $x + 2$ **7.** $-2x + 3$ **8.** $2x^2 + 1$ **9.** $|x - 3|$
   1, 2, 4, 7   5, 3, -1, -7   3, 1, 9, 51   4, 3, 1, 2

New Vocabulary • relation • domain • range • mapping diagram • function • vertical-line test • function notation

Lesson Preview

 **Check Skills You'll Need**

The Coordinate Plane
Skills Handbook: p. 848
Example 1
Exercises 1–12

Algebraic Expressions
Lesson 1-2: Examples 1, 2
Exercises 1–8
Extra Practice, p. 822

Lesson Resources

📁 **Teaching Resources**
Practice, Reteaching, Enrichment

👥 **Reaching All Students**
Practice Workbook 2-1
Spanish Practice Workbook 2-1
Reading and Math Literacy 2A
Spanish Reading & Literacy 2A
Hands-On Activities 33

⏱ **Presentation Assistant Plus!**
Transparencies
• Check Skills You'll Need 2-1
• Additional Examples 2-1
• Student Edition Answers 2-1
• Lesson Quiz 2-1
PH Presentation Pro CD 2-1

PRENTICE HALL ASSESSMENT SYSTEM
Computer Test Generator CD

Technology
Resource Pro® CD-ROM
Computer Test Generator CD
Prentice Hall Presentation Pro CD

💻 **www.PHSchool.com**
Student Site
• Teacher Web Code: agk-5500
• Graphing Calculator, Procedures 2, 6, 20
• Self-grading Lesson Quiz
Teacher Center
• Lesson Planner
• Resources

Plus 📘 **iTEXT**

📘 **iTEXT** Interactive lesson includes instant self-check, tutorials, and activities.

OBJECTIVE 1 Graphing Relations

A camera recorded the egg's height at various times during its fall.

Suppose you use a motion detector to track an egg as it drops from 10 ft above the ground. The motion detector stores input values (times) and output values (heights). A **relation** is a set of pairs of input and output values. You can write a relation as a set of ordered pairs.

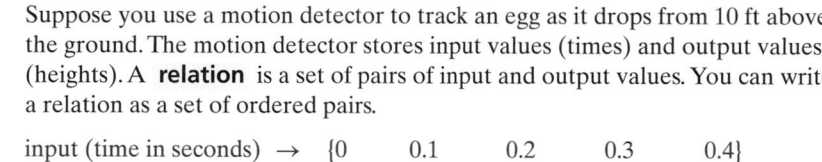

input (time in seconds) → {0   0.1   0.2   0.3   0.4}

relation → {(0, 10), (0.1, 9.8), (0.2, 9.4), (0.3, 8.6), (0.4, 7.4)}

output (height in feet) → {10   9.8   9.4   8.6   7.4}

You can graph a relation on a coordinate plane.

1 EXAMPLE Graphing a Relation

Graph the relation $\{(-2, 4), (3, -2), (-1, 0), (1, 5)\}$.

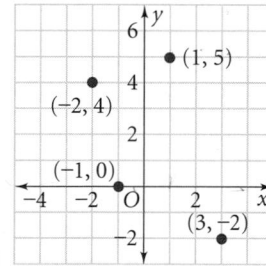

Graph and label each ordered pair.

 **Check Understanding** ① Graph each relation. **a–b. See back of book.**
   a. $\{(0, 4), (-2, 3), (-1, 3), (-2, 2), (1, -3)\}$
   b. $\{(-2, 1), (-1, 0), (0, 1), (1, 2)\}$

Ongoing Assessment and Intervention

Before the Lesson
Diagnose prerequisite skills using:
• Check Skills You'll Need

During the Lesson
Monitor progress using:
• Check Understanding
• Additional Examples
• Standardized Test Prep

After the Lesson
Assess knowledge using:
• Lesson Quiz
• Computer Test Generator CD

Math Background

Professional Development

A relation between two sets of numbers can be represented by a set of ordered pairs. Visually, this set of ordered pairs can be represented by points in the coordinate plane or by a mapping diagram. The first coordinate of the ordered pair is called the input value, or *x*-coordinate. The second coordinate of the ordered pair is called the output value, or *y*-coordinate. It is common to assume that the ordered pairs of a relation are distinct. With this understanding, a function is a relation for which no *x*-coordinate is paired with more than one *y*-coordinate.

OBJECTIVE

1 Teaching Notes

1 EXAMPLE English Learners

The everyday meaning of *relation* may lead students to expect an easily discernable pattern in the coordinates of points for a mathematical relation. Explain that mathematics often uses very broad, inclusive definitions.

2 EXAMPLE Teaching Tip

To help students remember which coordinates to use for the domain and range, use alphabetical order. The letter *d*, for *x*-coordinates, precedes the letter *r*, for *y*-coordinates as *x* precedes *y*.

Backpacks or bookbags are used by 93% of students.

The **domain** of a relation is the set of all inputs, or *x*-coordinates, of the ordered pairs. The **range** of a relation is the set of all outputs, or *y*-coordinates, of the ordered pairs.

You can sometimes find the domain and range of a relation from its graph.

2 EXAMPLE Finding Domain and Range

Write the ordered pairs for the relation shown in the graph. Find the domain and range.

$\{(2, 4), (3, 4.5), (4, 7.5), (5, 7), (6, 5), (6, 7.5)\}$

The domain is $\{2, 3, 4, 5, 6\}$.

The range is $\{4, 4.5, 5, 7, 7.5\}$.

✓ **Check Understanding** ② Find the domain and range of each relation.

a.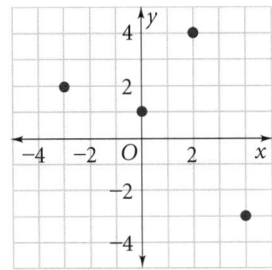

domain $\{-3, 0, 2, 4\}$,
range $\{2, 1, 4, -3\}$

b.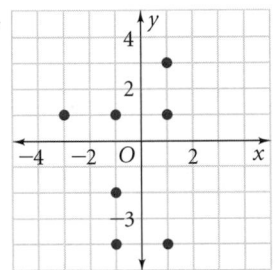

domain $\{-3, -1, 1\}$,
range $\{-4, -2, 1, 3\}$

Another way to show a relation is to use a **mapping diagram,** which links elements of the domain with corresponding elements of the range. Write the elements of the domain in one region and the elements of the range in another. Draw arrows to show how each element from the domain is paired with elements from the range.

3a.   domain   range

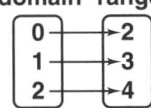

b.   domain   range

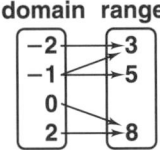

3 EXAMPLE Making a Mapping Diagram

Make a mapping diagram for the relation $\{(-1, -2), (3, 6), (-5, -10), (3, 2)\}$.

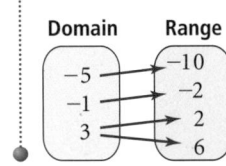

Pair the domain elements with the range elements.

✓ **Check Understanding** ③ Make a mapping diagram for each relation. **See left.**

a. $\{(0, 2), (1, 3), (2, 4)\}$

b. $\{(2, 8), (-1, 5), (0, 8), (-1, 3), (-2, 3)\}$

👥 Reaching All Students

| **Below Level** Explain that all functions are relations, but not all relations are functions. The relation $y = \sqrt{x}$ is not a function because there are two values of *y* for every positive value of *x*. | **Advanced Learners** Have students determine whether the computer spreadsheet function SQRT is a mathematical function. **Yes** | **English Learners** See note on page 56. **Auditory Learners** See note on page 57. |

A **function** is a relation in which each element of the domain is paired with exactly one element in the range.

4 **EXAMPLE** **Identifying Functions**

Determine whether each relation is a function.

a. **Domain** **Range**

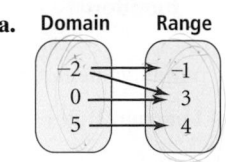

The element −2 of the domain is paired with both −1 and 3 of the range. The relation is *not* a function.

b. **Domain** **Range**

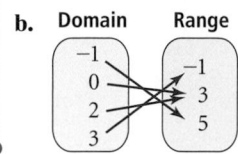

Each element of the domain is paired with exactly one element of the range. The relation is a function.

✓ **Check Understanding** **4** Determine whether each relation is a function.

a. **Domain** **Range** function

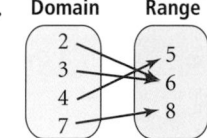

b. **Domain** **Range** not a function

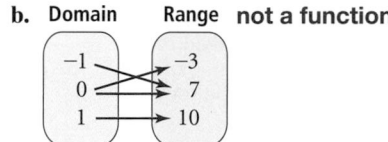

As you saw earlier in this lesson, relations can be represented as discrete data points that may or may not follow a pattern. Relations can also be shown as two-dimensional figures, such as lines or curves.

Reading Math

The word *discrete* means separate. The word *discreet* means careful about what one says or does.

Graphing a relation on a coordinate plane gives you a visual way to tell whether it is a function. You can use the **vertical-line test** to determine whether the relation has at least one element of the domain paired with more than one element of the range. If a vertical line passes through two or more points on the graph, then the relation is *not* a function.

5 **EXAMPLE** **Using the Vertical-Line Test**

Use the vertical-line test to determine whether each graph represents a function.

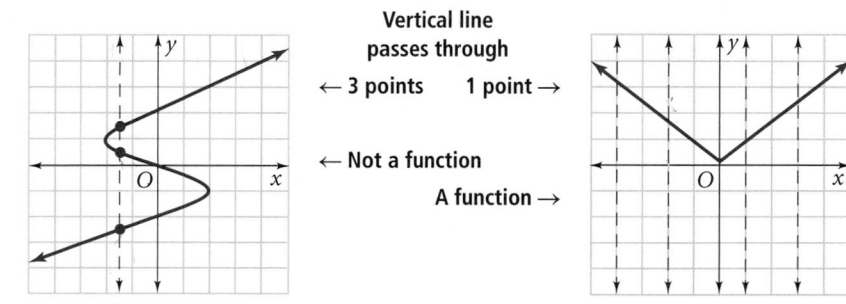

Vertical line passes through
← 3 points   1 point →

← Not a function

A function →

1 Graph the relation {(−3, 3), (2, 2), (−2, −2), (0, 4), (1, −2)}.

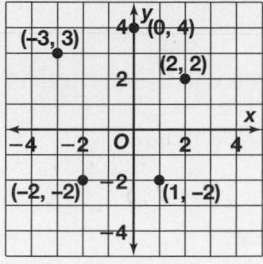

2 Write the ordered pairs for the relation. Find the domain and range.

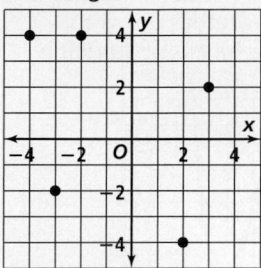

{(−4, 4), (−3, −2), (−2, 4), (2, −4), (3, 2)}; D = {−4, −3, −2, 2, 3}, R = {−4, −2, 2, 4}

3 Make a mapping diagram for the relation {(−1, 7), (1, 3), (1, 7), (−1, 3)}.

Domain **Range**

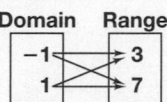

OBJECTIVE
2 **Teaching Notes**

4 **EXAMPLE** **Auditory Learners**

Have students verbalize how the arrows in a mapping diagram can be used to decide whether a relation is a function.

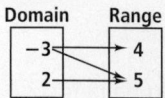
Point out that the input value is 3.5. The output value is $A(3.5)$ or 12.25.

Additional Examples

4 Determine whether the relation is a function. **not a function**

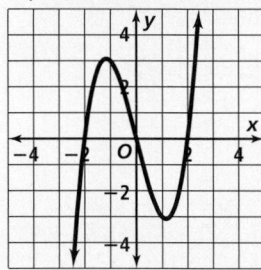

5 Use the vertical-line test to determine whether the graph represents a function. **function**

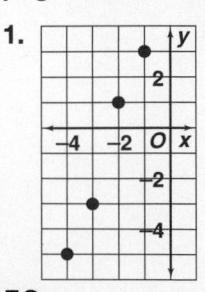

6 Find $f(2)$ for each function.
a. $f(x) = -x^2 + 1$ **−3**
b. $f(x) = |3x|$ **6**
c. $f(x) = \frac{9}{1-x}$ **−9**

Closure

Ask students how functions are different from relations that are not functions. **For a function, each element of the domain is paired with exactly one element of the range. For relations that are not functions, there is at least one element of the domain paired with more than one element of the range.**

pages 59–61 Exercises

1.
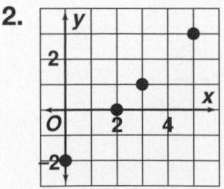

✓ **Check Understanding** **5** Use the vertical-line test to determine whether each graph represents a function.

a.
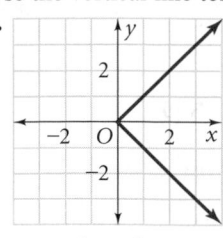
not a function

b.
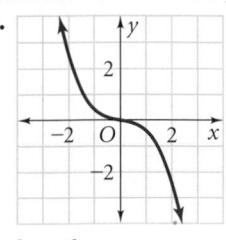
function

c.
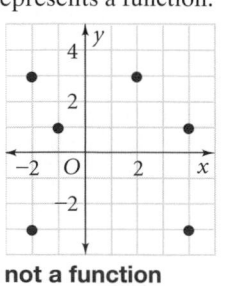
not a function

A function rule expresses an output value in terms of an input value.

Examples of Function Rules

Input	Input	Input
↓	↓	↓
$y = 2x$	$f(x) = x + 5$	$C = \pi d$
↑	↑	↑
Output	Output	Output

You can use $g(x)$, $h(t)$, and so on to represent functions. You read the notation $g(x)$ as "g of x," and the notation $h(t)$ as "h of t."

You read the **function notation** $f(x)$ as "f of x" or "a function of x." Note that $f(x)$ does *not* mean "f times x." When the value of x is 3, $f(3)$, read "f of 3," represents the value of the function at $x = 3$.

Input	Function	Output	Ordered Pair
5 ⟶	Subtract 1 ⟶	4	$(5, 4)$
a ⟶	Add 2 ⟶	$a + 2$	$(a, a + 2)$
3 ⟶	g ⟶	$g(3)$	$(3, g(3))$
x ⟶	f ⟶	$f(x)$	$(x, f(x))$

6 EXAMPLE **Real-World 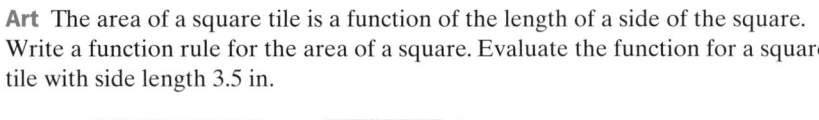 Connection**

Art The area of a square tile is a function of the length of a side of the square. Write a function rule for the area of a square. Evaluate the function for a square tile with side length 3.5 in.

Relate area of a square is $(\text{side length})^2$

Define Let s = the length of one side of the square tile.
Then $A(s)$ = the area of the square tile.

Write
$$A(s) = s^2$$
$$A(3.5) = (3.5)^2 \quad \text{Substitute 3.5 for } s.$$
$$= 12.25 \quad \text{Simplify.}$$

● The area of a square tile with side length 3.5 in. is 12.25 in.^{2}.

Real-World 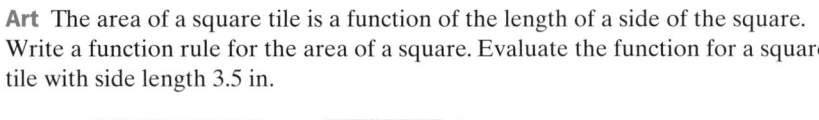 Connection

Square tiles are used as decorative wall and floor coverings.

✓ **Check Understanding** **6** Find $f(-3)$, $f(0)$, and $f(5)$ for each function. **b.** $\frac{-13}{4}$, -1, $\frac{11}{4}$ **c.** $\frac{6}{5}$, $\frac{3}{5}$, $\frac{-2}{5}$
a. $f(x) = 3x - 5$ **b.** $f(a) = \frac{3}{4}a - 1$ **c.** $f(y) = -\frac{1}{5}y + \frac{3}{5}$
−14, −5, 10

2.
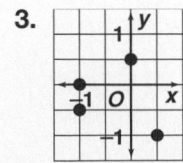

3.

4.
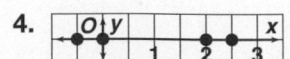

EXERCISES

Practice and Problem Solving

For more practice, see *Extra Practice*.

Ⓐ Practice by Example

Example 1
(page 55)

Graph each relation.   1–7. See margin pp. 58–59.

1. $\{(-1, 3), (-2, 1), (-3, -3), (-4, -5)\}$ **2.** $\{(0, -2), (2, 0), (3, 1), (5, 3)\}$

3. $\left\{(-1, 0), \left(\frac{1}{2}, -1\right), \left(0, \frac{1}{2}\right), \left(-1, -\frac{1}{2}\right)\right\}$ **4.** $\left\{\left(2\frac{1}{2}, 0\right), \left(-\frac{1}{2}, 0\right), (2, 0), (0, 0)\right\}$

Example 2
(page 56)

Write the ordered pairs for each relation. Find the domain and range.

5. 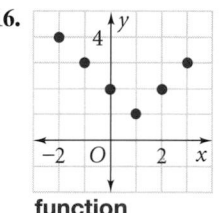   **6.** 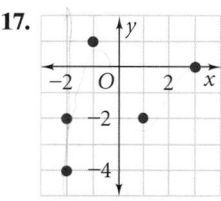   **7.**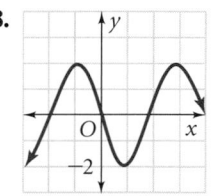

Example 3
(page 56)

Make a mapping diagram for each relation.   8–11. See back of book.

8. $\{(0, 0), (-1, -1), (-2, -8), (-3, -27)\}$ **9.** $\{(-2, 8), (-1, 1), (0, 0), (1, 1), (2, 8)\}$

10. $\{(-\frac{1}{2}, 11), (0, 10), (\frac{1}{2}, 5), (1, 12)\}$ **11.** $\{(5, 10), (10, 5), (15, 20), (20, 15)\}$

Example 4
(page 57)

Determine whether each relation is a function.
not a function
12. $\{(1, -2), (-2, 0), (-1, 2), (1, 3)\}$ **function** **13.** $\{(1, 1), (2, 2), (3, 5), (4, 10), (5, 15)\}$

14. $\left\{\left(17, \frac{15}{4}\right), \left(\frac{15}{4}, 17\right), \left(15, \frac{17}{4}\right), \left(\frac{17}{4}, 15\right)\right\}$ **15.** $\left\{\left(-3, \frac{2}{5}\right), \left(-2, \frac{3}{5}\right), \left(\frac{3}{2}, -5\right), \left(5, \frac{2}{5}\right)\right\}$
function   **function**

Example 5
(page 57)

Use the vertical-line test to determine whether each graph represents a function.

16. 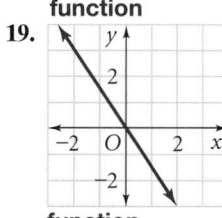   **17.** 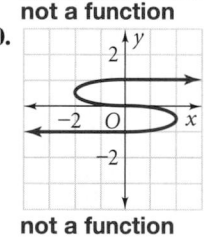   **18.**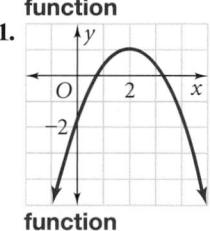
function   not a function   function

19.   **20.**   **21.**
function   not a function   function

Example 6
(page 58)

For each function, find $f(-5)$, $f(-3)$, $f\left(\frac{1}{2}\right)$, and $f(4)$.

22. $f(a) = 2a + 3$ **23.** $f(y) = -3y - 2$ **24.** $f(z) = z + 9.5$

25. $f(x) = -x - 7$ **26.** $f(d) = 1 - 4d$ **27.** $f(x) = 2x - 3$

28. $f(h) = -6h - \frac{2}{3}$ **29.** $f(x) = \frac{5}{6}x + \frac{1}{3}$ **30.** $f(t) = \frac{1}{2}t - 2$
22–30. See back of book.

31. Measurement One meter equals about 39.37 in. Write a function rule for
converting inches to meters. Evaluate the function for 59 in. $y = \frac{x}{39.37}$, where
y is the number of meters and x the number of inches; 1.50 meters

Lesson 2-1   Relations and Functions   **59**

Assignment Guide

1 Objective
Ⓐ Ⓑ **Core** 1–11, 32–35,
40–42

2 Objective
Ⓐ Ⓑ **Core** 12–31, 36–39,
43–54
Ⓒ **Extension** 55–61

Standardized Test Prep 62–65

Mixed Review 66–78

Exercises 5, 7 If a number is the
first element of more than one
ordered pair in a relation, it only
needs to be listed once in the
domain. A similar condition
applies for the range.

Error Prevention

Exercise 3 Point out to students
that a function cannot have two
different *y*-coordinates for the
same *x*-coordinate. Visual learners
will benefit from graphing the
relation and using the vertical line
test to determine if it is a
function.

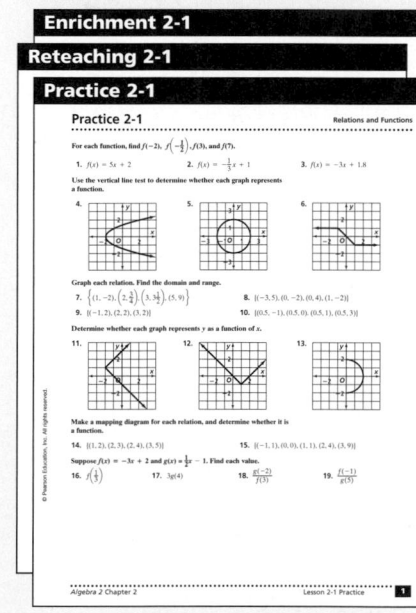

---

5. $(-2, -2), (-1, 1), (1, 1),$
$(1, 0), (3, 3), (3, -2);$
domain $\{-2, -1, 1, 3\}$,
range $\{-2, 0, 1, 3\}$

6. $(-2, 3), (0, 1), (2, -1),$
$(3, -2);$
domain $\{-2, 0, 2, 3\}$,
range $\{-2, -1, 1, 3\}$

7. $(-2, 0), (-1, 2), (0, 3),$
$(1, 2), (2, 0);$
domain $\{-2, -1, 0, 1, 2\}$,
range $\{0, 2, 3\}$

4. Assess

Lesson Quiz 2-1

1. Write the ordered pairs for the relation. Find the domain and range.

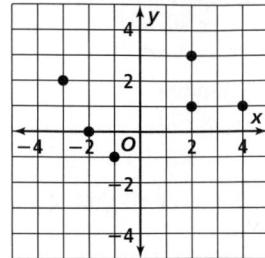

{(−3, 2), (−2, 0), (−1, −1), (2, 1), (2, 3), (4, 1)};
D = {−3, −2, −1, 2, 4},
R = {−1, 0, 1, 2, 3}

2. Determine whether the relation {(−2, 3), (−5, 6), (3, 0), (1, 1)} is a function. **function**

3. Delete one ordered pair so that the relation {(−4, 2), (1, 6), (0, 0), (−4, 6)} is a function. **(−4, 2) or (−4, 6)**

4. Determine whether the graph represents a function. **not a function**

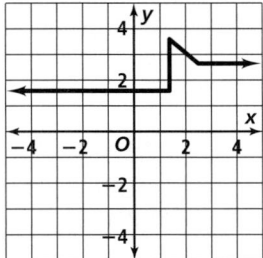

5. Find $f(−5)$ for each function.
   a. $f(x) = 5x + 35$ **10**
   b. $f(x) = x^2 − x$ **30**

pages 59–61 Exercises

32.

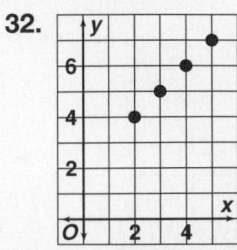

domain {2, 3, 4, 5},
range {4, 5, 6, 7}

60

B **Apply Your Skills**

Graph each relation. Find the domain and range. **32–35. See margin pp. 60-61.**

32. {(2, 4), (3, 5), (4, 6), (5, 7)}   **33.** {(−1, 1), (−2, 2), (−3, 3), (−4, 4)}

34. $\left\{\left(-\frac{1}{2}, 2\right), \left(2, \frac{1}{2}\right), \left(0, -\frac{1}{2}\right), \left(-\frac{1}{2}, -2\right)\right\}$ **35.** $\left\{\left(\frac{3}{2}, -\frac{1}{2}\right), \left(\frac{5}{2}, \frac{1}{2}\right), \left(\frac{1}{2}, \frac{1}{2}\right), \left(-\frac{3}{2}, \frac{1}{2}\right)\right\}$

Find the domain and range of each relation and determine whether it is a function.
36–39. See margin p. 61.

36. {(2, 4), (4, 8), (8, 16)}   **37.** {(−1, 2), (−2, 5), (−2, 7), (0, 2), (9, 2)}

38. 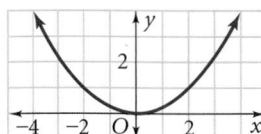   **39.**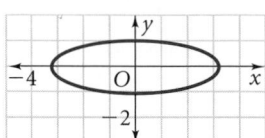

Match each relation with a model.

40. {(1, 2), (−1, −2), (2, −1)} **A**   **41.** {(2, 1), (1, 2), (1, −2)} **B**

42. {(−1, 2), (−2, 1), (−1, −2)} **C**

A. 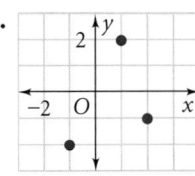   **B.** Domain Range 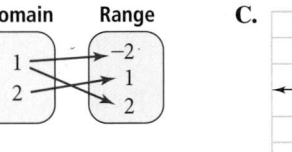   **C.**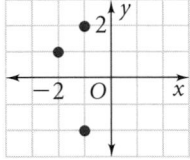

Determine whether each graph represents y as a function of x.

43. 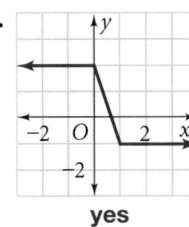   **44.** 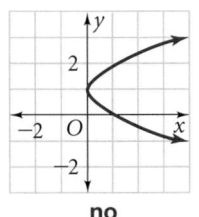   **45.**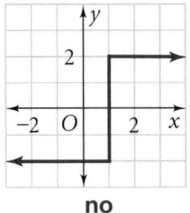

   yes   **no**   **no**

46. Geometry The volume of a cube is a function of the length of a side of the cube. Write a function for the volume of a cube. Find the volume of a cube with a side 13.5 cm long. **$v(s) = s^3$; 2460.375 cm^3**

48. No; since 2 in the domain maps to 1 and 4, it is not a function.

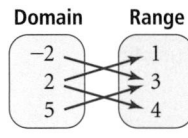

47. Sports The volume of a sphere is a function of the radius of the sphere. Write a function for the volume of a ball. Evaluate the function for a volleyball of radius 10.5 cm. **$v(r) = \frac{4}{3}\pi r^3$; about 4849 cm^3**

48. Writing Does the mapping diagram at the left represent a function? Explain.
See left.

49. Data Collection Draw a graph to show the relationship between the weight of a letter and the cost of postage. Is it a graph of a function? Explain.
Check students' work.

Suppose $f(x) = 2x + 5$ and $g(x) = -\frac{1}{3}x + 2$. Find each value. (*Hint:* For $2g(x)$, find $g(x)$ first, and then multiply the result by 2.)

50. $f(−4)$ **−3** **51.** $2g(7)$ **−$\frac{2}{3}$** **52.** $−2f(x + 1)$ **$-4x - 14$** **53.** $\frac{f(1)}{g(3)}$ **7** **54.** $\frac{f(-2)}{g(f(-2) + 1)}$ **$\frac{3}{4}$**

C **Challenge**

57. Yes; each x is paired with a unique y.

For each relation, determine whether y is a function of x. Explain why or why not.
No; each positive x is paired with two y values.

55. $y = 2x − 3$ **56.** $y^2 = x$ **57.** $x^2 = y − 3$
Yes; each x is paired with a unique y.   **See left.**

33.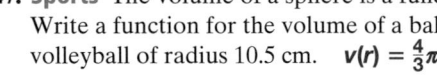

domain {−4, −3, −2, −1},
range {1, 2, 3, 4}

34.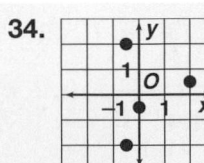

domain $\left\{-\frac{1}{2}, 0, 2\right\}$,

range $\left\{-2, -\frac{1}{2}, \frac{1}{2}, 2\right\}$

Real-World Connection

Careers Chemists use math to predict chemical reactions.

58. Chemistry The time required for a certain chemical reaction is related to the amount of catalyst present during the reaction. The domain of the relation is the number of grams of catalyst, and the range is the number of seconds required for a fixed amount of the chemical to react. The following relation is the data from several reactions: {(2, 180), (2.5, 6), (2.7, 0.05), (2.9, 0.001), (3.0, 6), (3.1, 15), (3.2, 37), (3.3, 176)}. Is the relation a function? If the domain and range were interchanged, would the relation be a function? Explain. **See margin.**

Suppose *a* and *b* are variables representing integers. Find the domain and range of each relation and determine whether it is a function. Justify your reasoning.

59.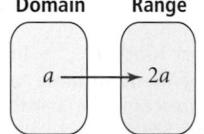

60.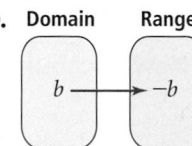

61.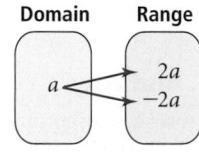

59–61. See back of book.

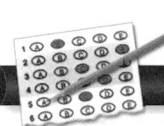

Standardized Test Prep

Multiple Choice

Take It to the NET
Online lesson quiz at
www.PHSchool.com
······· Web Code: aga-0201

62. Which graph models the relation {(−3, −1), (3, 1), (−3, 1), (3, −1)}? **C**

A. 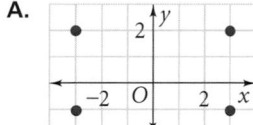 B. 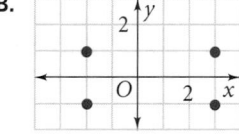 C.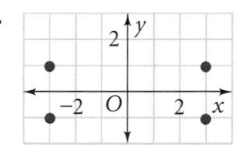

63. Which relation is *not* a function? **G**
   F. {(0, 9), (2, 3), (3, 2), (4, 1)} **G.** {(3, 2), (4, 1), (0, 9), (3, 3)}
   H. {(0, 3), (2, 3), (3, 3), (4, 3)} **I.** {(0, 3), (3, 2), (2, 4), (4, 6)}

Short Response

64. If $f(x) = -2x + 3$ and $g(x) = 4x - 3$, which is greater, $f(5)$ or $g(-2)$? Show your work. **See margin.**

Extended Response

65. Is the total surface area A of a cube a function of the edge c of the cube? If it is not a function, explain why not. If it is a function, write the function rule and then evaluate the function for a cube with edge 2.5 cm. **See back of book.**

Mixed Review

Lesson 1-6

Find each probability for choosing a letter at random from the word *mathematics*.
   66. $P(e)$ $\frac{1}{11}$ **67.** $P(m)$ $\frac{2}{11}$ **68.** $P(vowel)$ $\frac{4}{11}$ **69.** $P(n)$ **0**
   $\frac{6}{11}$ **70.** P(a letter that occurs more than once) **71.** P(consonant) $\frac{7}{11}$ **72.** P(s or t) $\frac{3}{11}$

Lesson 1-5

Solve each equation or inequality. Graph the solution on a number line.
73-75. See back of book.
   73. $|x - 4| = 10$ **74.** $3 + |b| \le 5$ **75.** $|6 - y| > 0$

Previous Course

Find each percent of increase or decrease.
   76. from 9 m to 10 m **11.1% increase**   **77.** from 1 gal to 1.5 gal **50% increase**   **78.** from 2 km to 1.5 km **25% decrease**

Lesson 2-1 Relations and Functions **61**

35. 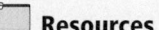 domain $\left\{-\frac{3}{2}, \frac{1}{2}, \frac{3}{2}, \frac{5}{2}\right\}$, range $\left\{-\frac{1}{2}, \frac{1}{2}\right\}$

36. domain {2, 4, 8}, range {4, 8, 16}; function

37. domain {−2, −1, 0, 9}, range {2, 5, 7}; not a function

Alternative Assessment

Have students work in groups of three. Each group creates fifteen distinct ordered pairs. Some ordered pairs should have the same *x*-values and some should have the same *y*-values. Each ordered pair is written on its own piece of paper and placed in a box. Each group picks at least five ordered pairs from the box to form a relation. One group member expresses the relation as a set of ordered pairs. Another group member expresses the relation as a mapping diagram and another expresses the relation as a graph. They share results, determine if the relation is a function, and find the domain and range.

Standardized Test Prep

📁 **Resources**
For additional practice with a variety of test item formats:
• Standardized Test Prep, p. 111
• Test-Taking Strategies, p. 106
• Test-Taking Strategies with Transparencies

Exercise 62 Students may find it helpful to sketch their own graphs and compare them to those in the choices.

38. domain {all real numbers}, range {$y \ge 0$}; function

39. domain {$-3.2 \le x \le 3.2$}, range {$-1 \le y \le 1$}; not a function

58. Function; if the domain and range are interchanged, it is not a function because 6 would be paired with both 2.5 and 3.0.

64. [2] $f(5)$; $f(5) = -2(5) + 3 = -7$ and $g(-2) = 4(-2) - 3 = -11$, and $-7 > -11$.

[1] only includes answer $f(5)$ or $g(-2)$

61

2-2

1. Plan

Lesson Preview

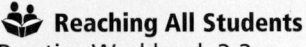 **Check Skills You'll Need**

Algebraic Expressions
Lesson 1-2: Examples 1, 2
Exercises 1–8
Extra Practice, p. 822

Lesson Resources

 **Teaching Resources**
Practice, Reteaching, Enrichment

 **Reaching All Students**
Practice Workbook 2-2
Spanish Practice Workbook 2-2
Technology Activities 1, 2, 3, 27
Hands-On Activities 34

Presentation Assistant Plus!
Transparencies
• Check Skills You'll Need 2-2
• Additional Examples 2-2
• Student Edition Answers 2-2
• Lesson Quiz 2-2
PH Presentation Pro CD 2-2

ASSESSMENT SYSTEM
Computer Test Generator CD

Technology
Resource Pro® CD-ROM
Computer Test Generator CD
Prentice Hall Presentation Pro CD

www.PHSchool.com
Student Site
• Teacher Web Code: agk-5500
• Self-grading Lesson Quiz
Teacher Center
• Lesson Planner
• Resources

Plus *i*TEXT

62

 **2-2**

Linear Equations

Lesson Preview

What You'll Learn

OBJECTIVE 1 To graph linear equations

OBJECTIVE 2 To write equations of lines

. . . And Why

To solve a transportation problem, as in Example 2

✓ **Check Skills You'll Need** (For help, go to Lesson 1-2.)

Evaluate each expression for $x = -2, 0, 1,$ and 4. 1–4. See back of book.

1. $\frac{2}{3}x + 7$ 2. $\frac{3}{5}x - 2$ 3. $3x + 1$ 4. $\frac{1}{2}x - 8$

New Vocabulary
• linear function • linear equation
• dependent variable • independent variable
• x-intercept • y-intercept
• standard form of a linear equation • slope
• point-slope form • slope-intercept form

OBJECTIVE 1 **Graphing Linear Equations**

*i*TEXT Interactive lesson includes instant self-check, tutorials, and activities.

A function whose graph is a line is a **linear function**. You can represent a linear function with a **linear equation**, such as $y = 3x + 2$. A solution of a linear equation is any ordered pair (x, y) that makes the equation true.

You can write the solutions of the equation using set notation as $\{(x, y) \mid y = 3x + 2\}$. Read the notation as "the set of ordered pairs x, y such that $y = 3x + 2$." Because the value of y depends on the value of x, y is called the **dependent variable** and x is called the **independent variable**.

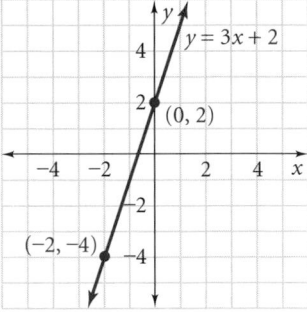

1 EXAMPLE **Graphing a Linear Equation**

Graph the equation $y = \frac{2}{3}x + 3$.

Choose two values for x and find the corresponding values of y. Plot the point for each ordered pair and complete the graph by drawing a line through the points.

x	$\frac{2}{3}x + 3$	y	(x, y)
-3	$\frac{2}{3}(-3) + 3$	1	$(-3, 1)$
3	$\frac{2}{3}(3) + 3$	5	$(3, 5)$

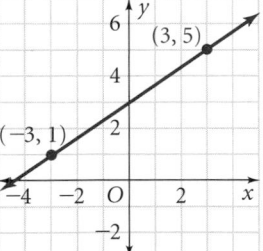

Need Help?

Geometry Since two points determine a line, you can use two points to graph a line. Check your line by finding a third point.

Check Choose a third point on the line and check that its ordered pair satisfies the equation. Since $(0, 3)$ is a point on the line, and $\frac{2}{3}(0) + 3 = 3$, the graph is correct.

Ongoing Assessment and Intervention

Before the Lesson
Diagnose prerequisite skills using:
• Check Skills You'll Need

During the Lesson
Monitor progress using:
• Check Understanding
• Additional Examples
• Standardized Test Prep

After the Lesson
Assess knowledge using:
• Lesson Quiz
• Computer Test Generator CD

Check Understanding **1** Graph each equation. Check your work. **a–c. See left.**

1a.
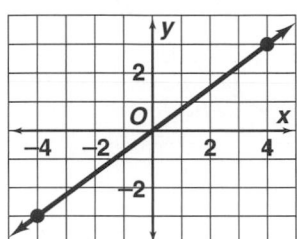

a. $y = \frac{3}{4}x$ **b.** $x + y = -2$ **c.** $y = -\frac{1}{2}x + \frac{1}{2}$

The **y-intercept** of a line is the point at which the line crosses the y-axis. You can use the same term to identify the y-coordinate of this point.

The **x-intercept** of a line is the point at which the line crosses the x-axis. You can use the same term to identify the x-coordinate of this point.

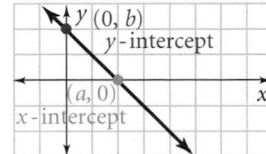

The **standard form of a linear equation** is $Ax + By = C$, where A, B, and C are real numbers, and A and B are not both zero. You can graph a linear equation in standard form by finding the x- and y-intercepts.

b.
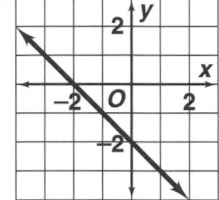

c.
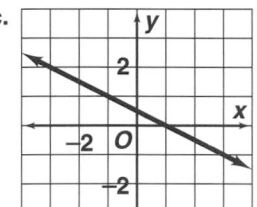

2 **EXAMPLE**   **Real-World** **Connection**

Transportation The equation $3x + 2y = 120$ models the number of passengers who can sit in a train car, where x is the number of adults and y is the number of children. Graph the equation. Describe the domain and the range. Explain what the x- and y-intercepts represent.

Set x or y equal to zero to find each intercept.

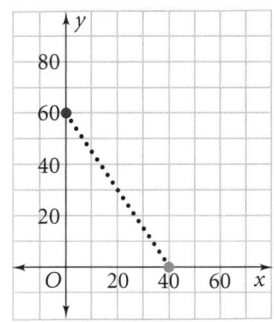

$3x + 2y = 120$	$3x + 2y = 120$
$3x + 2(0) = 120$	$3(0) + 2y = 120$
$3x = 120$	$2y = 120$
$x = 40$	$y = 60$

Use the intercepts to graph the equation. The x-intercept is $(40, 0)$. When 40 adults are seated, no children are seated. The y-intercept is $(0, 60)$. When 60 children are seated, no adults are seated.

The number of people is both discrete and non-negative. Both the domain and the range of the graph are limited to the whole numbers.

 Check Understanding **2 a.** Suppose the train system buys new train cars with molded plastic seats. The model changes to $x + y = 40$. Graph the equation and interpret the x- and y-intercepts. **See back of book.**

2b. Answers may vary. Sample: Each seat holds one person, whether adult or child.

b. Explain how using molded seats changes the number of seated passengers. **See left.**

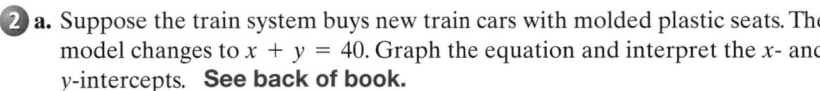

Real-World **Connection**

In Japan, so many people ride public transportation that they need help getting into the trains.

Reaching All Students

Below Level Students may try to identify a single ordered pair as **the** solution of a linear function. Emphasize that many ordered pairs satisfy the equation and that all are solutions.	**Advanced Learners** $Ax + By = C$ and $Dx + Ey = F$ are perpendicular. Find an expression for A. $$A = -\frac{BE}{D}$$	**English Learners** See note on page 63. **Visual Learners** See note on page 64.

 Professional Development

Math Background

A linear function is a function whose graph is a line. When given an equation for a linear function, you can get important information about the graph (slope, intercepts, and so on). Likewise, appropriate information about a line allows you to write an equation for the line.

OBJECTIVE

1 **Teaching Notes**

English Learners

Have students review the mathematical definitions of domain and range. Then, have students look up these words in a dictionary. Help students make the connection between their everyday meanings and their mathematical meanings. Finally, help students see the relationship between the meaning of domain and independent and the meaning of range and dependent.

1 **EXAMPLE** **Math Tip**

Accurate graphs are easy to obtain if the two points used for the line have integer coordinates. To get such points in this example, substitute x-values that are multiples of 3.

2 **EXAMPLE** **Auditory Learners**

Have students verbalize why the graph for this situation is a finite set of discrete points rather than a continuous line.

3 **EXAMPLE** **Alternative Method**

Students need to understand that, when they use two points with the slope formula, either point can be used for (x_1, y_1). The important thing is to subtract corresponding coordinates in the same order when applying the formula. Have students verify that the slope is the same when using $(-9, 6)$ for (x_1, y_1) and $(3, 2)$ for (x_2, y_2).

Additional Examples

1 Graph the equation $y = -\frac{4}{3}x + 2$.

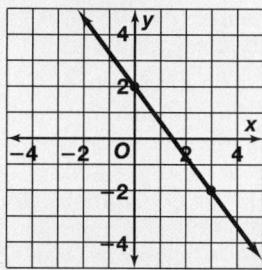

2 The equation $10x + 5y = 40$ models how you can give $.40 change if you have only dimes and nickels. The variable x is the number of dimes, and y is the number of nickels. Graph the equation. Describe the domain and the range. Explain what the x- and y-intercepts represent.

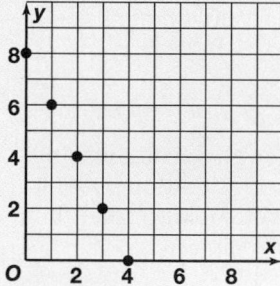

D = {0, 1, 2, 3, 4}, R = {0, 2, 4, 6, 8}; The x-intercept (4, 0) means you use 4 dimes if you give all the change in dimes. The y-intercept (0, 8) means you use 8 nickels if you give all the change in nickels.

3 Find the slope of the line through the points $(-2, 7)$ and $(8, -6)$. $-\frac{13}{10}$

Reading Math

The slope of a line is also the rate of change between two points on the line.

The **slope** of a nonvertical line is the ratio of the vertical change to a corresponding horizontal change. You can calculate slope by subtracting the corresponding coordinates of two points on the line.

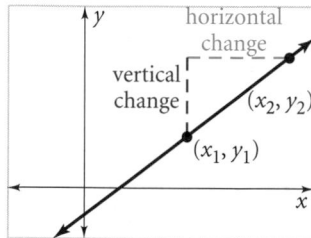

 Key Concepts

Definition	Slope Formula

$$\text{slope} = \frac{\text{vertical change (rise)}}{\text{horizontal change (run)}} = \frac{y_2 - y_1}{x_2 - x_1}, \text{where } x_2 - x_1 \neq 0$$

3 EXAMPLE Finding Slope

Find the slope of the line through the points $(3, 2)$ and $(-9, 6)$.

$\text{slope} = \frac{y_2 - y_1}{x_2 - x_1}$ Use the slope formula.

$= \frac{6 - 2}{-9 - 3}$ Substitute (3, 2) for (x_1, y_1) and (−9, 6) for (x_2, y_2).

$= \frac{4}{-12}$ Subtract.

$= -\frac{1}{3}$ Simplify.

● The slope of the line is $-\frac{1}{3}$.

✓ **Check Understanding** **3** Find the slope of the line through each pair of points.
   a. $(-2, -2)$ and $(4, 2)$ $\frac{2}{3}$ **b.** $(0, -3)$ and $(7, -9)$ $-\frac{6}{7}$

OBJECTIVE

2 **Writing Equations of Lines**

Investigation: Point-Slope Form

1. Make a table of values to graph each line. **1–4. See margin pp. 64–65.**

   a. $y - 1 = -2(x - 2)$ **b.** $y - 2 = \frac{1}{3}(x - 1)$ **c.** $y - 5 = 3(x - 4)$

2. Find the slope of each line. Compare the slope of the line to the red number in the equation of the line. What do you notice?

3. Find the point on the graph of each line with an x-coordinate that is equal to the green number in the equation line. Then compare the y-coordinate of the point to the blue number in the equation of the line. What do you notice?

4. **Make a Conjecture** All three equations in Question 1 are in the form $y - y_1 = m(x - x_1)$. Make a conjecture about how you can use that form to help you graph an equation.

---

page 64 Investigation

1a.

x	y
−5	15
−2	9
0	5
2	1
5	−5

b.

x	y
−5	0
−2	1
1	2
2	$2\frac{1}{3}$
5	$3\frac{1}{3}$

c.

x	y
−4	−19
−2	−13
0	−7
2	−1
4	5

2. $-2, \frac{1}{3}, 3$; the slopes are the same as the red number in the equation.

When you know the slope and a point on a line, you can use the **point-slope form** to write the equation of the line.

 Key Concepts

Definition	Point-Slope Form

The line through point (x_1, y_1) with slope m has the equation below.

$$y - y_1 = m(x - x_1)$$

4 EXAMPLE Writing an Equation Given the Slope and a Point

Write in standard form an equation of the line with slope $-\frac{1}{2}$ through the point $(8, -1)$.

$y - y_1 = m(x - x_1)$ **Use the point-slope equation.**

$y - (-1) = -\frac{1}{2}(x - 8)$ **Substitute $-\frac{1}{2}$ for m, -1 for y_1, and 8 for x_1.**

$y - (-1) = -\frac{1}{2}x - \left(-\frac{1}{2}\right)(8)$ **Distributive Property**

$y + 1 = -\frac{1}{2}x + 4$ **Simplify.**

$\frac{1}{2}x + y = 3$ **Write in standard form.**

✓ **Check Understanding** 4 Write in standard form the equation of each line.

a. slope 2, through $(4, -2)$
$2x - y = 10$

b. slope $\frac{5}{6}$, through $(5, 6)$
$\frac{5}{6}x - y = -\frac{11}{6}$

When you know two points on a line, you can write an equation by using the point-slope equation combined with the slope formula.

5 EXAMPLE Writing an Equation Given Two Points

Write in point-slope form the equation of the line through $(1, 5)$ and $(4, -1)$.

$y - y_1 = m(x - x_1)$ **Write the point-slope equation.**

$y - y_1 = \frac{y_2 - y_1}{x_2 - x_1}(x - x_1)$ **Substitute the slope formula for m.**

$y - 5 = \frac{-1 - 5}{4 - 1}(x - 1)$ **Substitute: $x_1 = 1$, $y_1 = 5$, $x_2 = 4$, $y_2 = -1$.**

$y - 5 = \frac{-6}{3}(x - 1)$ **Simplify.**

$y - 5 = -2(x - 1)$ **Write in point-slope form.**

✓ **Check Understanding** 5 Write in point-slope form the equation of the line through each pair of points.

a. $(5, 0)$ and $(-3, 2)$
$y - 0 = -\frac{1}{4}(x - 5)$

b. $(-2, -1)$ and $(-10, 17)$
$y + 1 = -\frac{9}{4}(x + 2)$

c. $(5, 1)$ and $(-4, -3)$
$y - 1 = \frac{4}{9}(x - 5)$

Another form of the equation of a line is **slope-intercept form,** which you can use to find slope by examining the equation.

 Key Concepts

Definition	Slope-Intercept Form

$$y = \underset{\text{slope}}{mx} + \underset{y\text{-intercept}}{b}$$

3. Where the x-coordinate is the green number, the y-coordinate equals the blue number.

4. Answers may vary. Sample: Using the form $y - y_1 = m(x - x_1)$, you would start at the point (x_1, y_1) and then use m to graph another point. To graph the eq., draw a straight line through the pts.

Investigation (Optional)

Inclusion

Some students may be color-blind or have difficulty discriminating colors. For these students, box the red number, circle the green number, and place a triangle around the blue number. Then, replace the words *red, green,* and *blue* in Questions 2 and 3 with the appropriate shape.

5 EXAMPLE Alternative Method

You may want to have a volunteer show what equation is obtained if $(4, -1)$ is used for (x_1, y_1) and $(1, 5)$ is used for (x_2, y_2). Demonstrate or have a volunteer demonstrate that this new equation and $y - 5 = -2(x - 1)$ can both be rewritten as $2x + y = 7$.

Teaching Tip

You may wish to point out that the slope-intercept form is a special case of the point-slope form. Simply use $(0, b)$ for (x_1, y_1) in the point-slope form.

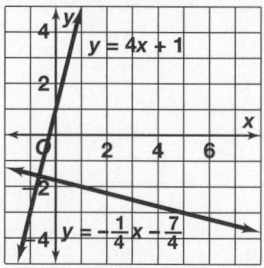
6 EXAMPLE **Finding Slope Using Slope-Intercept Form**

Find the slope of $4x + 3y = 7$.

$4x + 3y = 7$

$\quad 3y = -4x + 7$ **Subtract 4x from each side.**

$\quad\; y = -\frac{4}{3}x + \frac{7}{3}$ **Write in slope-intercept form.**

The slope of the line is $-\frac{4}{3}$.

✓ Check Understanding **6** Find the slope of each line.

   a. $3x + 2y = 1$ $-\frac{3}{2}$ **b.** $\frac{2}{3}x + \frac{1}{2}y = 1$ $-\frac{4}{3}$ **c.** $Ax + By = C$ $-\frac{A}{B}$

Key Concepts

Summary	Equations of a Line	
Point-Slope Form	Standard Form	Slope-Intercept Form
$y - 2 = -3(x + 4)$	$3x + y = -10$	$y = -3x - 10$

The slopes of horizontal, vertical, perpendicular, and parallel lines have special properties.

Horizontal Line

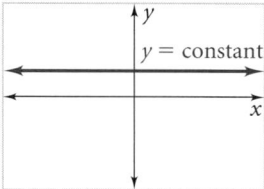

$m = 0$
$y = \text{constant}$

Vertical Line

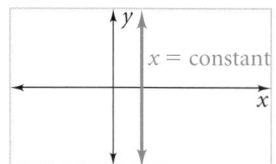

m is undefined.
$x = \text{constant}$

Perpendicular Lines

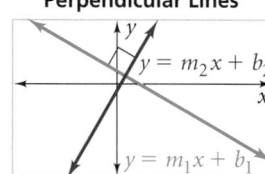

$m_1 \cdot m_2 = -1$
(In other words, m_2 is the negative reciprocal of m_1.)

Parallel Lines

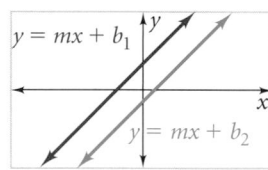

$m = m$
$b_1 \neq b_2$

Real-World Connection

The steel girders of the Eiffel Tower model horizontal, vertical, perpendicular, and parallel lines.

page 67 **Check Understanding**

7a. $y = -\frac{1}{5}x + \frac{14}{5}$    **b.** $y = \frac{2}{3}x - \frac{1}{3}$ 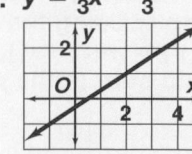   **c.** $x = 5$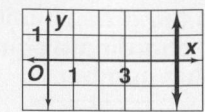

7 EXAMPLE Writing an Equation of a Perpendicular Line

Write an equation of the line through each point and perpendicular to $y = \frac{3}{4}x + 2$.
Graph all three lines.

a. $(0, 4)$

$m = -\left(\dfrac{1}{\frac{3}{4}}\right) = -\dfrac{4}{3}$ Find the negative reciprocal of $\frac{3}{4}$.

$y = mx + b$ Use slope-intercept form.

$y = -\dfrac{4}{3}x + 4$ Substitute: $m = -\frac{4}{3}$ and $b = 4$.

b. $(6, 1)$

$y = -\dfrac{4}{3}x + b$ Slope is $-\frac{4}{3}$.

$1 = -\dfrac{4}{3}(6) + b$ Substitute $(6, 1)$ for (x, y).

$1 = -8 + b$ Simplify.

$9 = b$ Solve for b.

$y = -\dfrac{4}{3}x + 9$ Write the equation.

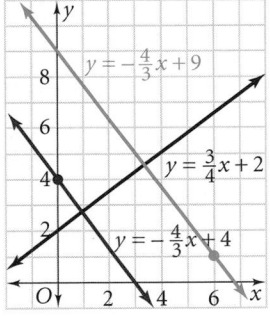

✓ **Check Understanding** **7** Write an equation for each line. Then graph the line. **a–c. See margin p. 66.**
  a. through $(-1, 3)$ and perpendicular to the line $y = 5x - 3$
  b. through $(2, 1)$ and parallel to the line $y = \frac{2}{3}x + \frac{5}{8}$
  c. vertical and through $(5, -3)$

EXERCISES

For more practice, see *Extra Practice*.

Practice and Problem Solving

A Practice by Example

Example 1
(page 62)

Graph each equation. Check your work. **1–8. See back of book.**

1. $y = 2x$ **2.** $y = -3x - 1$ **3.** $y = 3x - 2$ **4.** $y = -4x + 5$

5. $5x - 2y = -4$ **6.** $-2x + 5y = -10$ **7.** $y - 3 = -2x$ **8.** $y + 4 = -3x$

Example 2
(page 63)

9. Cost Analysis The equation $y - 0.23x = 0$ relates the cost of operating a car
to the number of miles driven, where x is the number of miles driven and y is
the cost. **a–b. See margin.**
  a. Graph the equation and determine the domain and range.
  b. Explain what the x- and y-intercepts represent.
  c. Explain what 0.23 represents.
  0.23 represents a cost of $.23 per mile driven.

10. Fund-Raising The school glee club needs a total of $4500 for a trip to Omaha,
Nebraska. To make money, members are selling baseball caps for $4.50 and
sweatshirts for $12.50. **a–b. See back of book.**
  a. Graph the equation $4.5x + 12.5y = 4500$, where x is the number of baseball
  caps and y is the number of sweatshirts sold.
  b. Explain the meaning of the x- and y-intercepts in terms of the fund-raising.

Example 3
(page 64)

Find the slope of the line through each pair of points.

11. $(1, 6)$ and $(8, -1)$ **−1** **12.** $(-3, 9)$ and $(0, 3)$ **−2** **13.** $(0, 0)$ and $(2, 6)$ **3**

14. $(-4, -3)$ and $(7, 1)$ $\frac{4}{11}$ **15.** $(-2, -1)$ and $(8, -3)$ $-\frac{1}{5}$ **16.** $(1, 2)$ and $(2, 3)$ **1**

undefined 17. $\left(\frac{2}{3}, \frac{4}{7}\right)$ and $\left(\frac{2}{3}, \frac{11}{7}\right)$ **18.** $(-3, 5)$ and $(4, 5)$ **0** **19.** $(-5, -7)$ and $(0, 10)$ $\frac{17}{5}$

pages 67–70 Exercises

9a.
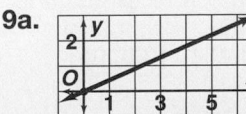

$y = 0.23x$
domain $\{x \mid x \geq 0\}$
range $\{y \mid y \geq 0\}$

b. x-intercept $(0, 0)$,
y-intercept $(0, 0)$; when
no miles have been
driven, there is no cost.

Assignment Guide

1 Objective
  Ⓐ Ⓑ Core 1–19, 42–50,
  63–65, 69–70
  Ⓒ Extension 79–80

2 Objective
  Ⓐ Ⓑ Core 20–41, 51–62,
  66–68, 71–78
  Ⓒ Extension 81–84

Standardized Test Prep 85–90

Mixed Review 91–98

Error Prevention

Exercises 11–19 Remind students
to subtract the x-coordinates in
the same order as they subtract
the y-coordinates and to be
careful when subtracting negative
numbers.

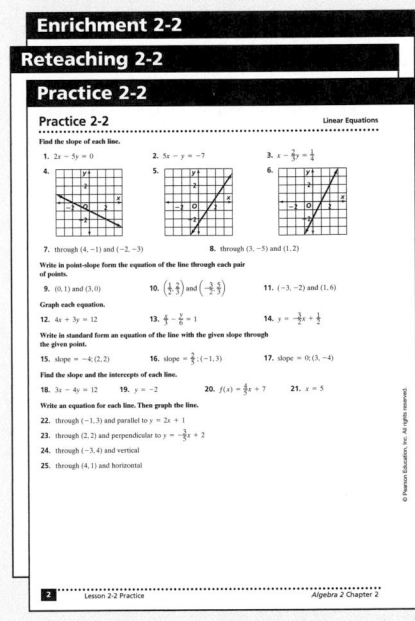

68

Exercises 35, 36 In their answers, students should note any restrictions on A, B, and C.

Exercises 48–50 Remind students that it is a good idea to first multiply each side of the equation by the LCD of all fractions in the equation to clear the equation of fractions.

Math Tip

Exercises 75–77 Even though a standard form of a linear equation uniquely determines a line, be careful to realize that a line does not have a unique standard form.

Example 4
(page 65)

Write in standard form the equation of each line.   20–22. See margin.

20. slope = 3; $(1, 5)$ **21.** slope = $\frac{5}{6}$; $(22, 12)$ **22.** slope = $-\frac{3}{5}$; $(-4, 0)$

23. slope = 0; $(4, -2)$ **24.** slope = -1; $(-3, 5)$ **25.** slope = 5; $(0, 2)$
$y = -2$ $x + y = 2$ $5x - y = -2$

Example 5
(page 65)

Write in point-slope form the equation of the line through each pair of points.
26–28. See margin.

26. $(-10, 3)$ and $(-2, -5)$ **27.** $(1, 0)$ and $(5, 5)$ **28.** $(-4, 10)$ and $(-6, 15)$

29. $(0, -1)$ and $(3, -5)$ **30.** $(7, 11)$ and $(13, 17)$ **31.** $(1, 9)$ and $(6, 2)$
$y + 1 = -\frac{4}{3}(x - 0)$ $y - 11 = 1(x - 7)$ $y - 9 = -\frac{7}{5}(x - 1)$

Example 6
(page 66)

Find the slope of each line.

32. $5x + y = 4$ **−5**   **33.** $-3x + 2y = 7$ $\frac{3}{2}$ **34.** $-\frac{1}{2}x - y = \frac{3}{4}$ **$-\frac{1}{2}$**

35. $Ax + By = C$ $-\frac{A}{B}$ **36.** $Ax - By = C$ $\frac{A}{B}$ **37.** $y = 7$ **0**

Example 7
(page 67)

Write an equation for each line. Then graph the line. 38–39. See margin.

38. through $(-2, 1)$ and parallel to $y = -3x + 1$

39. through $(-3, -1)$ and perpendicular to $y = -\frac{2}{5}x - 4$

40. through $(-7, 10)$ and horizontal **40–41. See back of book.**

41. through $\left(1, -\frac{2}{7}\right)$ and vertical

B **Apply Your Skills**

Graph each equation. 42–50. See back of book.

42. $y = -\frac{3}{5}x - \frac{12}{5}$ **43.** $y = -2x + 3$ **44.** $y = -x + 7$

45. $3y - 2x = -12$ **46.** $4x + 5y = 20$ **47.** $4x - 3y = -6$

48. $\frac{2}{3}x + \frac{y}{3} = -\frac{1}{3}$ **49.** $\frac{3}{5}y - \frac{x}{5} = -\frac{6}{5}$ **50.** $\frac{4}{5} = -\frac{1}{3}x - \frac{3}{4}y$

Find the slope of each line.

51. 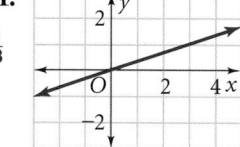   **52.** 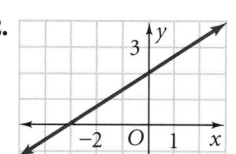   **53.**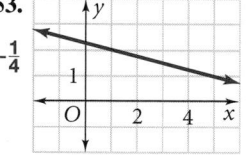

$\frac{1}{3}$ $\frac{2}{3}$ $-\frac{1}{4}$

Find the slope and the intercepts of each line.   54–62. See margin.

54. $f(x) = \frac{2}{3}x + 4$ **55.** $y = -x + 1000$ **56.** $-Rx + Sy = -T$

57. $g(x) = 54x - 1$ **58.** $x = -3$ **59.** $y = 0$

60. $-\frac{1}{3}x - \frac{2}{3}y = \frac{5}{3}$ **61.** $y = 0.4 - 0.8x$ **62.** $\frac{A}{D}x + \frac{B}{D}y = \frac{C}{D}$

Find the slope of the line through each pair of points.

63. $\left(\frac{3}{2}, -\frac{1}{2}\right)$ and $\left(-\frac{2}{3}, \frac{1}{3}\right)$ $-\frac{5}{13}$ **64.** $\left(-\frac{1}{2}, -\frac{1}{2}\right)$ and $\left(-3, \frac{7}{5}\right)$ **65.** $\left(0, \frac{1}{2}\right)$ and $\left(\frac{5}{7}, 0\right)$ $-\frac{7}{10}$
$\frac{7}{5}$

Write an equation for each line. Each interval is 1 unit.

66. 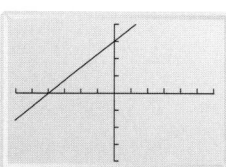   **67.** 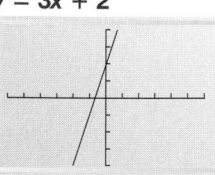 $y = 3x + 2$ **68.** 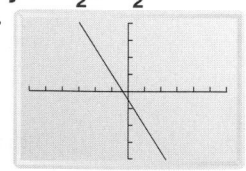 $y = -\frac{3}{2}x - \frac{1}{2}$

$y = \frac{3}{4}x + 3$

pages 67–70   Exercises

20. $3x - y = -2$

21. $\frac{5}{6}x - y = \frac{19}{3}$

22. $\frac{3}{5}x + y = -\frac{12}{5}$

26. $y - 3 = -1(x + 10)$

27. $y - 0 = \frac{5}{4}(x - 1)$

28. $y - 10 = -\frac{5}{2}(x + 4)$

38. $y = -3x - 5$

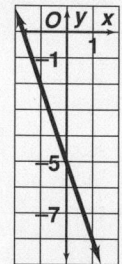

39. $y = \frac{5}{2}x + \frac{13}{2}$

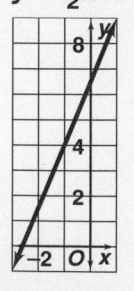

54. $\frac{2}{3}$; $(0, 4)$, $(-6, 0)$

55. -1; $(0, 1000)$, $(1000, 0)$

56. $\frac{R}{S}$; $\left(0, -\frac{T}{S}\right)$, $\left(\frac{T}{R}, 0\right)$

57. 5; $(0, -1)$, $\left(\frac{1}{5}, 0\right)$

58. undefined slope;
no y-intercept, $(-3, 0)$

59. 0; $(0, 0)$, all pts. on x-axis

60. $-\frac{1}{2}$; $\left(0, -\frac{5}{2}\right)$, $(-5, 0)$

61. -0.8; $(0, 0.4)$, $(0.5, 0)$

62. $-\frac{A}{B}$; $\left(0, \frac{C}{B}\right)$, $\left(\frac{C}{A}, 0\right)$

Real-World Connection

You can download data from a motion detector to a computer to produce graphs of distance versus time.

69a. I, II; III; graphs I and II show constant rate of change.

69. Data Analysis Three students moved away from or toward a motion detector, one at a time. Each graph shows distance from the detector as a function of time.

I. 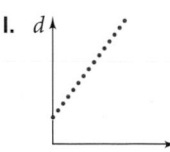   II. 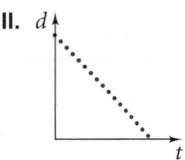   III.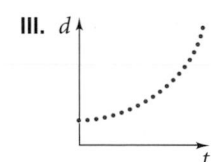

a. Which student(s) moved at a constant rate? Which student(s) did not? Justify your reasoning. **See left.**

b. Which student(s) moved away from the motion detector? **I and III**

c. Which student started farthest from the motion detector? **II**

70. Critical Thinking Most graphing calculators are designed to graph equations that are solved for y. What lines could not be graphed with this method? **Vertical lines cannot be graphed by this method.**

Write an equation for each line. Then graph the line. 71–74. See margin.

71. $m = 0$, through $(5, -1)$ **72.** $m = 2$, through $(1, 3)$

73. $m = \frac{5}{6}$, through $(-4, 0)$ **74.** $m = -\frac{3}{2}$, through $(0, -1)$

Write each equation in standard form.

75. $y = \frac{3}{2}x - 1$ **76.** $x + \frac{1}{3}y = \frac{2}{9}$ **77.** $-\left(\frac{1}{2}x + 2y\right) = \frac{2}{3}$
$3x - 2y = 2$ $9x + 3y = 2$ $3x + 12y = -4$

78. a. Open-Ended Write an equation of a line.

b. Write an equation of the line parallel to the line you wrote in part (a) passing through the point $(0.5, 0.6)$. **a–e. Check students' work.**

c. Write an equation of the line perpendicular to the line you wrote in part (a) passing through the point $\left(\frac{5}{3}, 2\right)$.

d. Write an equation of the line parallel to the line you wrote in part (c) passing through the point $(-3, 1)$.

 **e. Geometry** Graph the lines from parts (a), (b), (c), and (d). If they form a polygon, describe it. **The polygon is a rectangle.**

C Challenge

Points that are on the same line are *collinear*. Use the definition of slope to determine whether the given points are collinear.

79. $(-2, 6), (0, 2), (1, 0)$ **yes**   **80.** $(3, -5), (-3, 3), (0, 2)$ **no**

81. a. Graph $y = 3x + 1$. **See back of book.**

b. Write an equation of the line through point $(-1, 3)$ that is parallel to the line from part (a). Graph the line on the same set of axes. $y = 3x + 6$

c. Write an equation of the line through point $(-1, 3)$ that is perpendicular to the line from part (a). Graph the line on the same set of axes. $y = -\frac{1}{3}x + \frac{8}{3}$

d. What is true about the lines from parts (b) and (c)? Explain. **They are perpendicular.**

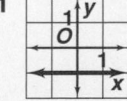 **82. Geometry** Prove that the triangle with vertices $(3, 5), (-2, 6)$, and $(1, 3)$ is a right triangle. **See back of book.**

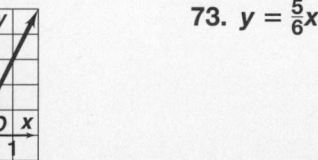 **83. Geometry** Prove that the quadrilateral with vertices $(2, 5), (4, 8), (7, 6)$, and $(5, 3)$ is a rectangle. **See back of book.**

84. Critical Thinking Lines $p, q,$ and r all pass through point $(-3, 4)$. Line p has slope 4 and is perpendicular to line q. Line r passes through Quadrants I and II only. Write an equation for each line. Then graph the three lines on the same coordinate plane. **See back of book.**

Need Help?

The slopes of parallel lines are equal. The slopes of perpendicular lines are negative reciprocals.

Lesson Quiz 2-2

1. Find the slope of the line through the points $(-5, -1)$ and $(2, 3)$. $\frac{4}{7}$

2. Write an equation in standard form for the line with slope 3 through $(9, -4)$. $3x - y = 31$

3. Write in point-slope form an equation of the line through the points $(-3, 8)$ and $(7, 6)$. Use $(-3, 8)$ as the point for the equation. $y - 8 = -\frac{1}{5}(x + 3)$

4. Write the equation $3x - 12y = 6$ in slope-intercept form. $y = \frac{1}{4}x - \frac{1}{2}$

5. What is the slope of a line perpendicular to $y = \frac{2}{3}x - 7$? What is the slope of a line parallel to $y = \frac{2}{3}x - 7$? $-\frac{3}{2}; \frac{2}{3}$

Alternative Assessment

Have students work in pairs. Students use a Geoboard to create a coordinate system by using two red rubberbands, one for the x-axis and one for the y-axis. Each pin along each axis represents one unit. Rubberbands are thought of as representing lines not line segments. One student makes a non-vertical line using a yellow rubberband. The other student names two points on the line, the slope, and the y-intercept, writes an equation of the line perpendicular to the given line at its y-intercept, and graphs this new line using a blue rubberband. Students switch roles and repeat.

71. $y = -1$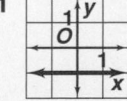

72. $y = 2x + 1$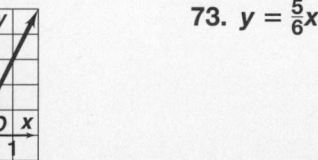

73. $y = \frac{5}{6}x + \frac{10}{3}$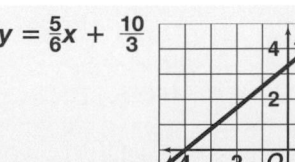

74. $y = -\frac{3}{2}x - 1$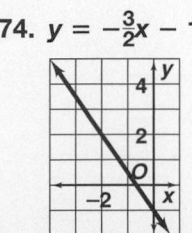

69

Resources

For additional practice with a variety of test item formats:
- Standardized Test Prep, p. 111
- Test-Taking Strategies, p. 106
- Test-Taking Strategies with Transparencies

Exercise 85 Suggest to students that they first determine if any of the given lines pass through (3, 5). Suggest that students write these lines in slope-intercept form and examine their slopes.

Standardized Test Prep

Multiple Choice

85. Which equation represents a line through (3, 5) that is perpendicular to $y = 2x - 5$? **A**

A. $2y = -x + 13$ B. $2y = x + 13$
C. $2y - x = 13$ D. $2y + x = -13$

86. For the equation $3x - 2y = 12$, which has value -6? **G**

F. the x-intercept   G. the y-intercept
H. the slope   I. the origin

Quantitative Comparison

Compare the boxed quantity in Column A with the boxed quantity in Column B. Choose the best answer.

A. The quantity in Column A is greater.
B. The quantity in Column B is greater.
C. The two quantities are equal.
D. The relationship cannot be determined from the information given.

	Column A	Column B
87. C	the slope of $3y + 2x = 4$	the slope of $-3y - 2x = 4$
88. B	the slope of the line through $(-1, 3)$ and $(5, -1)$	the slope of a horizontal line
89. C	the slope of a line perpendicular to $y = -3x + 5$	the slope of a line parallel to $9y = 3x - 20$
90. B	the value of c if the line $2x - 5y = 4$ contains $(-3, c)$	the value of a if the line $\frac{x}{3} - 2y = 10$ contains $(a, -3)$

Take It to the NET
Online lesson quiz at
www.PHSchool.com
Web Code: aga-0202

Mixed Review

Lesson 2-1

Find the domain and range of each relation. Then decide whether it is a function.

91.

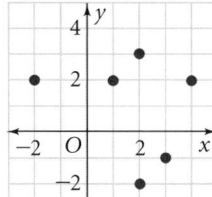

domain {−2, 1, 2, 3, 4},
range {−2, −1, 2, 3};
not a function

92.

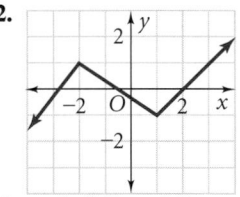

domain {all reals}, range {all reals}; function

93. Domain   Range

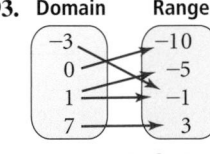

domain {−3, 0, 1, 7},
range {−10, −5, −1, 3};
not a function

Lesson 1-1

Identify each demonstrated property (or properties) of real numbers.

94. $7.4 - 3.4 + 2.6 = 7.4 + 2.6 - 3.4$
Commutative Prop. of Add.

95. $\frac{2}{5} + \frac{27}{5} \cdot \frac{5}{27} = \frac{2}{5} \cdot 1$ **multiplicative inverses**

96. $97(7) = 100(7) - 3(7)$
Distributive Prop.

97. $21 + 19.7 - 19.7 = 21$
additive inverses, additive identity

Previous Course

98. Commission A fabric designer earns a 60% commission for works sold in a textile studio. The studio receives the other 40%. How much does the studio receive for selling a length of fabric that costs $15.65? How much does the designer receive?
studio: $6.26; designer: $9.39

Piecewise Functions

A piecewise function has different rules for different parts of its domain.

1 EXAMPLE Writing a Piecewise Function

Write a piecewise function to represent the graph at the right.

There are three sections on the graph, so there will be three parts to the function. Since $(-2, 3)$ and $(2, -5)$ both lie on two sections of the graph, arbitrarily assign each point to just one section.

When $x \leq -2$, the function is $f(x) = x + 5$. When $-2 < x \leq 2$, the function is $f(x) = -2x - 1$. When $x > 2$, the function is $f(x) = 2x - 9$.

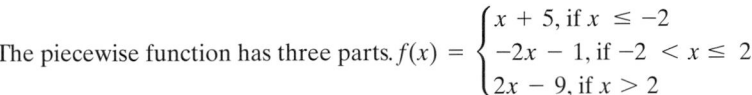

The piecewise function has three parts. $f(x) = \begin{cases} x + 5, \text{ if } x \leq -2 \\ -2x - 1, \text{ if } -2 < x \leq 2 \\ 2x - 9, \text{ if } x > 2 \end{cases}$

Some piecewise functions are step functions. Their graphs look like the steps of a staircase. One step function is the greatest integer function $f(x) = [x]$, where $[x]$ means the greatest integer less than or equal to x.

2 EXAMPLE Graphing a Piecewise Function

Graph the function $f(x) = [x]$.

Step 1 Choose an interval bounded by two consecutive integers. Make a table of values for the interval $0 \leq x \leq 1$.

x	0	0.25	0.5	0.75	1
f(x)	0	0	0	0	1

Each section of the graph ends at the y-value at which it starts. The left endpoint of each "step" is a closed circle. The right endpoint is an open circle.

Step 2 Graph the function.

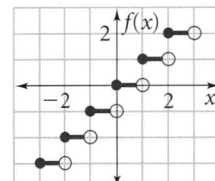

Use closed circles for included endpoints; use open circles for excluded endpoints.

EXERCISES

Graph each piecewise function. **1–6. See margin.**

1. $y = [x] + 2$

2. $f(x) = 3[x]$

3. $y = \begin{cases} x + 4, \text{ if } x \leq -2 \\ -x, \text{ if } x > -2 \end{cases}$

4. $f(x) = \begin{cases} -2x + 1, \text{ if } x < 3 \\ x - 8, \text{ if } x \geq 3 \end{cases}$

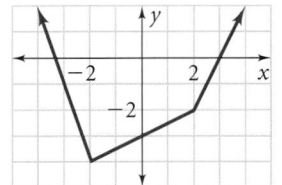

5. Write a piecewise function to represent the graph at the right.

6. Writing Explain how to graph a piecewise function.

page 71   Extension

1.

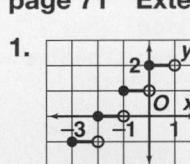

Piecewise Functions

In this extension, students study functions whose graphs are formed by piecing together graphs of two or more linear functions. Such functions are important in many situations where no single linear function can adequately model the situation.

Resources

Technology
Computer Test Generator CD-ROM, Chapter 0, Extension Topics

Teaching Notes

Error Prevention

Exercise 3 Some students may think that $(-2, 2)$ should be marked with an open bullet. This point is, however, part of the final graph, because the value of $x + 4$ is 2 when $x = -2$.

2. 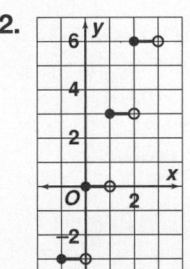 **3.**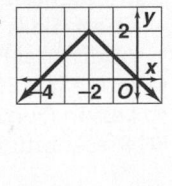

4.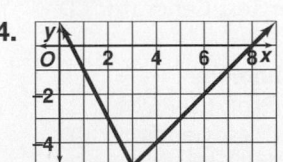

5. $f(x) = \begin{cases} -3x - 10, \text{ if } x \leq -2 \\ \frac{1}{2}x - 3, \text{ if } -2 < x < 2 \\ 2x - 6, \text{ if } x \geq 2 \end{cases}$

6. Answers may vary. Sample: Set up a table for each piece of the function. Choose starting and ending values corresponding to its domain. Substitute to find function values.

71

Lesson Preview

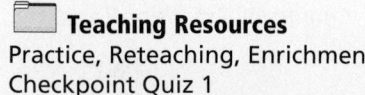 **Check Skills You'll Need**

Solving Equations
Lesson 1-3: Example 1
Exercises 1–8
Extra Practice, p. 822

Proportion
Skills Handbook p. 844
Example 3
Exercises 6–15

Lesson Resources

📁 **Teaching Resources**
Practice, Reteaching, Enrichment
Checkpoint Quiz 1

👥 **Reaching All Students**
Practice Workbook 2-3
Spanish Practice Workbook 2-3
Reading and Math Literacy 2B
Spanish Reading & Literacy 2B
Spanish Checkpoint Quiz 1

⏰ **Presentation Assistant Plus!**
Transparencies
• Check Skills You'll Need 2-3
• Additional Examples 2-3
• Student Edition Answers 2-3
• Lesson Quiz 2-3
PH Presentation Pro CD 2-3

PRENTICE HALL ASSESSMENT SYSTEM

Checkpoint Quiz 1
Computer Test Generator CD

💿 **Technology**
Resource Pro® CD-ROM
Computer Test Generator CD
Prentice Hall Presentation Pro CD

💻 **www.PHSchool.com**
Student Site
• Teacher Web Code: agk-5500
• Self-grading Lesson Quiz
Teacher Center
• Lesson Planner
• Resources

Plus

72

 **2-3**

Direct Variation

1.05   Model and solve problems using direct, inverse, combined and joint variation.

North Carolina Objectives

Lesson Preview

What You'll Learn

▼ OBJECTIVE
1 To write and interpret direct variation equations

...And Why
To model a dripping faucet, as in Example 3

✓ **Check Skills You'll Need**   (For help, go to Lesson 1-3 and Skills Handbook page 844.)

Solve each equation for y.   1–2. See below.

1. $12y = 3x$ **2.** $12y = 5x$ **3.** $\frac{3}{4}y = 15$ **4.** $0.9y = 27x$ **5.** $5y = 35$
$y = 20$ $y = 30x$ $y = 7$

Tell whether each equation is true.

6. $\frac{1}{4} \stackrel{?}{=} \frac{2}{8}$ **true**   **7.** $\frac{2}{5} \stackrel{?}{=} \frac{6}{15}$ **true**   **8.** $\frac{9}{24} \stackrel{?}{=} \frac{12}{36}$ **false**   **9.** $\frac{20}{24} \stackrel{?}{=} \frac{30}{36}$
true

New Vocabulary   • direct variation   • constant of variation

1. $y = \frac{x}{4}$ **2.** $y = \frac{5}{12}x$

 Interactive lesson includes instant self-check, tutorials, and activities.

▼ OBJECTIVE
1   **Writing and Interpreting a Direct Variation**

A linear function defined by an equation of the form $y = kx$, where $k \neq 0$, represents **direct variation**. As with any line, the slope k is constant.

When x and y are variables, you can write $k = \frac{y}{x}$, so the ratio $y : x$ equals the constant k, the **constant of variation**.

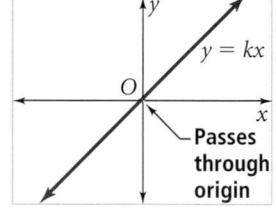

📖 **Reading Math**
You can describe direct variation as "y varies directly as x" or "y varies directly with x."

1 **EXAMPLE**   **Identifying Direct Variation from a Table**

For each function, determine whether y varies directly with x. If so, find the constant of variation and write the equation.

a.

x	y
2	8
3	12
5	20

$\frac{y}{x} = \frac{8}{2} = \frac{12}{3} = \frac{20}{5} = 4$,

so y varies directly with x.
The constant of variation is 4.
The equation is $y = 4x$.

b.

x	y
1	4
2	7
5	16

Since $\frac{4}{1}, \frac{7}{2}$, and $\frac{16}{5}$ are not equal,

$\frac{y}{x}$ is not a constant.

y does *not* vary directly with x.

✓ **Check Understanding** **1** For each function, determine whether y varies directly with x. If so, find the constant of variation and write the equation.

yes; $k = \frac{1}{3}$, $y = \frac{1}{3}x$

a.

x	y
−6	−2
3	1
12	4

b. **no**

x	y
−1	−2
3	4
6	7

c. **no**

x	y
−9	5
3	$-1\frac{2}{3}$
6	$3\frac{5}{8}$

72   Chapter 2   Functions, Equations, and Graphs

 **Ongoing Assessment and Intervention**

Before the Lesson
Diagnose prerequisite skills using:
• Check Skills You'll Need

During the Lesson
Monitor progress using:
• Check Understanding
• Additional Examples
• Standardized Test Prep

After the Lesson
Assess knowledge using:
• Lesson Quiz
• Computer Test Generator CD
• Chapter Checkpoint 1 (p. 77)

You can analyze an equation to determine whether it represents direct variation.

2 EXAMPLE Identifying Direct Variation from an Equation

For each function, determine whether y varies directly with x. If so, find the constant of variation.

a. $3y = 2x$

$3y = 2x$ is equivalent to $y = \frac{2}{3}x$, so y varies directly with x.

The constant of variation is $\frac{2}{3}$.

b. $y = 2x + 3$

Since you cannot write the equation in the form $y = kx$,

y does *not* vary directly with x.

✓ **Check Understanding** ② For each function, determine whether y varies directly with x. If so, find the constant of variation.

a. $y = \frac{x}{2}$
yes; $k = 0.5$

b. $2y - 1 = x$ no

c. $\frac{5}{6}x = \frac{1}{3}y$
yes; $k = \frac{5}{2}$

d. $7x + 4y = 10$
no

You can write an equation to solve a direct variation problem.

3 EXAMPLE Real-World 🌐 Connection

Water Conservation A dripping faucet wastes a cup of water if it drips for three minutes. The amount of water wasted varies directly with the amount of time the faucet drips.

a. Find the constant of variation k and write an equation to model the direct variation.

Relate | water wasted | varies directly | with time

Define Let w = number of cups of water wasted.

Let t = time in minutes the faucet drips.

Write w = k · t

$1 = k(3)$ **Substitute 1 for w and 3 for t.**

$\frac{1}{3} = k$ **Solve for k.**

The constant of variation k is $\frac{1}{3}$. The equation $w = \frac{1}{3}t$ models the direct variation.

b. Find how long the faucet must drip to waste $4\frac{1}{2}$ c of water.

$w = \frac{1}{3}t$ **Use the direct variation.**

$4\frac{1}{2} = \frac{1}{3}t$ **Substitute $4\frac{1}{2}$ for w.**

$\frac{9}{2}(3) = t$ **Solve for t.**

$13\frac{1}{2} = t$ **Simplify.**

The faucet must drip for $13\frac{1}{2}$ min to waste $4\frac{1}{2}$ c of water.

✓ **Check Understanding** ③ **Geometry** The circumference of a circle varies directly with the diameter of the circle. The formula $C = \pi d$ relates the circumference to the diameter.
a. What is the constant of variation? π
b. Find the diameter of a circle with circumference 105 cm to the nearest tenth.
33.4 cm

👐 Reaching All Students

Below Level If students have trouble recognizing direct variation from a table of values, have them graph the number pairs and compare the slopes of the line segments through the pairs.

Advanced Learners The pressure of a gas in a closed container varies directly with the absolute temperature. Have students find other real-world examples of direct variation.

Alternative Method See note on page 73.
Error Prevention See note on page 75.

---

2. Teach

Professional Development

Math Background

If y varies directly as x, then as x increases y increases and as x decreases y decreases. Furthermore, the rate of increase or decrease remains constant. Geometrically, this means that a direct variation is a linear function of the form $y = kx$ for $k \neq 0$.

OBJECTIVE
① **Teaching Notes**

① EXAMPLE Alternative Method

You can also ask whether there is a non-zero number by which all x-values can be multiplied to get the corresponding y-values.

② EXAMPLE Math Tip

Point out that for a linear function to be a direct variation, the graph must be a non-horizontal line through the origin.

③ EXAMPLE Connection to Ecology

Since demands for fresh water are becoming dangerously close to exhausting available resources in many countries, conservation is becoming an increasingly important topic worldwide.

📖 Additional Examples

① For each function, determine whether y varies directly with x. If so, find the constant of variation and write the equation.

a.
x	-1	2	5
y	3	-6	15
no

b.
x	7	9	-4
y	14	18	-8
yes; 2; $y = 2x$

② For each function, tell whether y varies directly with x. If so, find the constant of variation.
a. $3y = 7x + 7$ no
b. $5x = -2y$ yes; $-\frac{5}{2}$

73

Additional Examples

3 The perimeter of a square varies directly as the length of a side of the square. The formula $P = 4s$ relates the perimeter to the length of a side.
a. Find the constant of variation. **4**
b. Find how long a side of the square must be for the perimeter to be 64 cm. **16 cm**

4 Suppose y varies directly with x, and $y = 15$ when $x = 27$. Find y when $x = 18$. **10**

Closure

If a and b are real numbers and if $y = ax + b$ is a direct variation equation, what do you know about a and b? **$a \neq 0$ and $b = 0$**

You can use proportions to solve some direct variation problems. This can save time when the problem does not ask for the constant of variation.

4 EXAMPLE Using a Proportion

Suppose y varies directly with x, and $x = 27$ when $y = -51$. Find x when $y = -17$.

Let $(x_1, y_1) = (27, -51)$ and let $(x_2, y_2) = (x_2, -17)$.

$\dfrac{y_1}{x_1} = \dfrac{y_2}{x_2}$ **Write a proportion.**

$\dfrac{-51}{27} = \dfrac{-17}{x_2}$ **Substitute.**

$-51(x_2) = 27(-17)$ **Write the cross products.**

$x_2 = \dfrac{27(-17)}{-51}$ **Solve for x_2.**

$x_2 = 9$ **Simplify.**

Need Help?
In direct variation, $k = \frac{y}{x}$, so the ratio $y : x$ is constant.

✓ **Check Understanding** **4** Find the missing value for each direct variation.
a. If $y = 4$ when $x = 3$, find y when $x = 6$. **8**
b. If $y = 7$ when $x = 2$, find y when $x = 8$. **28**
c. If $y = 10$ when $x = -3$, find x when $y = 2$. **−0.6**
d. If $y = 1$ when $x = 10$, find y when $x = 2$. **0.2**

EXERCISES

For more practice, see *Extra Practice*.

Practice and Problem Solving

A Practice by Example

For each function, determine whether y varies directly with x. If so, find the constant of variation and write the equation. **1–11. See margin.**

Example 1
(page 72)

1.

x	y
2	4
4	8
16	32

2.

x	y
2	−6
4	−12
5	−15

3.

x	y
11	22
16	32
7	42

4.

x	y
27	9
30	10
60	20

5.

x	y
2	14
3	21
5	35

6.

x	y
3	9
4	13
7	23

7.

x	y
−2	4
−3	6
−5	10

8.

x	y
1	−2
3	−8
5	14

Example 2
(page 73)

Determine whether y varies directly with x. If so, find the constant of variation.

9. $y = 12x$ **10.** $y = 6x$ **11.** $y = -2x$ **12.** $y = 4x + 1$ **no**

13. $y = 4x - 3$ **no**   **14.** $y = -5x$ **yes; $k = -5$**   **15.** $y - 6x = 0$ **yes; $k = 6$**   **16.** $y + 3 = -3x$ **no**

Example 3
(page 73)

For each direct variation, find the constant of variation. Then find the value of y when $x = -5$.

17. $y = 2$ when $x = 7$ $k = \frac{2}{7}; -\frac{10}{7}$ **18.** $y = -5$ when $x = 3$ $k = -\frac{5}{3}; \frac{25}{3}$

19. $y = -2$ when $x = 2$ $k = -1; 5$ **20.** $y = -\frac{2}{3}$ when $x = -\frac{1}{3}$ $k = 2; -10$

21. $y = 17$ when $x = -4$ $k = -\frac{17}{4}; -21\frac{1}{4}$ **22.** $y = \frac{1}{2}$ when $x = -2$ $k = -\frac{1}{4}; 1\frac{1}{4}$

74   Chapter 2   Functions, Equations, and Graphs

pages 74–77 Exercises

1. yes; $k = 2$, $y = 2x$

2. yes; $k = -3$, $y = -3x$

3. no

4. yes; $k = \frac{1}{3}$, $y = \frac{1}{3}x$

5. yes; $k = 7$, $y = 7x$

6. no

7. yes; $k = -2$, $y = -2x$

8. no

9. yes; $k = 12$

10. yes; $k = 6$

11. yes; $k = -2$

46. No; $y = 1.7x$ does not contain the point $(9, -9)$.

47. Yes; $y = -\frac{5}{6}x$ contains the point $(15, -12\frac{1}{2})$.

48. Yes; $y = \frac{7}{2}x$ contains the point $(6\frac{1}{2}, 22\frac{3}{4})$.

23. Environment Suppose you work on a tree farm and you need to find the height of each tree. You know that the length of an object's shadow varies directly with its height. Refer to the diagram.

  a. Find the constant of variation. $k = \frac{13}{36}$

  b. Write an equation to calculate the height of the tree. $s = \frac{13}{36}h$

  c. Find the height of a tree with a shadow 8 ft 4 in. long. ≈ 23 ft 1 in.

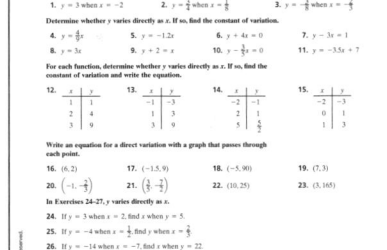

?

6 ft

2 ft 2 in.

8 ft 4 in.

Example 4
(page 74)

For Exercises 24–27, y varies directly with x.

24. If $y = 4$ when $x = -2$, find x when $y = 6$. **−3**

25. If $y = 6$ when $x = 2$, find x when $y = 12$. **4**

26. If $y = 7$ when $x = 2$, find y when $x = 3$. **10.5**

27. If $y = 5$ when $x = -3$, find y when $x = -1$. $\frac{5}{3}$

28. Aviation A speed of 60 mi/h is equal to a speed of 88 ft/s. Find the speed in miles per hour of an aircraft travelling 1000 ft/s. **681.8 mi/h**

B **Apply Your Skills**

For each function, determine whether y varies directly with x. If so, find the constant of variation and write the equation.

yes; $k = 1.3$, $y = 1.3x$

29. yes; $k = \frac{2}{3}$, $y = \frac{2}{3}x$

29.

x	y
9	6
12	8
15	10

30.

x	y
4	1
6	2
8	3

no

31.

x	y
23	24
55	56
66	67

no

32.

x	y
2	2.6
3	3.9
4	5.2

Write an equation for a direct variation with a graph that passes through each point.

33. $(1, 2)$ $y = 2x$ **34.** $(-3, -7)$ $y = \frac{7}{3}x$ **35.** $(2, -9)$ $y = -\frac{9}{2}x$ **36.** $(-0.1, 50)$ $y = -500x$

37. $(-5, -3)$ $y = \frac{3}{5}x$ **38.** $(9, -1)$ $y = -\frac{1}{9}x$ **39.** $(7, 2)$ $y = \frac{2}{7}x$ **40.** $(-3, 14)$ $y = -\frac{14}{3}x$

In Exercises 41–45, y varies directly with x.

41. If $y = 7$ when $x = 3$, find x when $y = 21$. **9**

42. If $y = 25$ when $x = 15$, find x when $y = 10$. **6**

43. If $y = 30$ when $x = -3$, find y when $x = -9$. **90**

44. If $y = -20$ when $x = 2$, find y when $x = 14$. **−140**

45. If $y = 0.9$ when $x = 4.8$, find y when $x = 6.4$. **1.2**

Determine whether a line with the given slope through the given point represents a direct variation. Explain. **46–51. See margin pp. 74–75.**

46. $m = -1.7, (9, -9)$ **47.** $m = -\frac{5}{6}, \left(15, -12\frac{1}{2}\right)$ **48.** $m = \frac{7}{2}, \left(6\frac{1}{2}, 22\frac{3}{4}\right)$

Open-Ended In Exercises 49–51, choose a value of k within the given range. Then write and graph a direct variation using your value for k.

49. $0 < k < 1$ **50.** $3 < k < 4.5$ **51.** $-1 < k < -\frac{1}{2}$

49. Answers may vary.
Sample: $y = 0.5x$

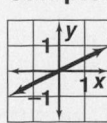

50. Answers may vary.
Sample: $y = 3.2x$

51. Answers may vary.
Sample: $y = -\frac{3}{4}x$

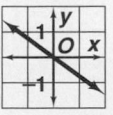

---

3. Practice

Assignment Guide

1 **Objective**

  A **B** Core 1–54
  C Extension 55–59

Standardized Test Prep 60–64

Mixed Review 65–73

Error Prevention

Exercises 1–8 Caution students to check the ratio $\frac{y}{x}$ for each pair of numbers.

Exercises 29–32 One approach is to find the value of k by dividing the y-coordinate of the given point by the x-coordinate. Substitute the resulting value of k in $y = kx$ to get the equation. Another approach is to use the methods of Lesson 2-2 to write an equation for the line through $(0, 0)$ and the given point.

Enrichment 2-3

Reteaching 2-3

Practice 2-3

1. For each function, tell whether y varies directly as x. If so, find the constant of variation and write the equation.

a.

x	y
−4	16
−2	8
8	−32

b.

x	y
2	10
3	15
6	25

yes; −4;
$y = -4x$

no

2. Determine whether y varies directly as x. If so, find the constant of variation.

a. $y = 7x + 4$ **no**

b. $y = \frac{5}{3}x$ **yes; $\frac{5}{3}$**

c. $2y = -12x$ **yes; −6**

3. Assume y varies directly as x. If $y = 8$ when $x = 42$, find y when $x = 126$. **24**

4. How can you tell from the graph of a linear function whether the function is a direct variation? **If the graph is a nonhorizontal line through the origin, then the linear function is a direct variation.**

Alternative Assessment

Have students work in pairs. Each student writes six linear equations, three of which describe direct variations and three of which do not. The other student identifies each direct variation that his or her partner wrote and names the constant of variation.

It takes more effort for an engine to propel a car with underinflated tires. Cars with properly inflated tires get better gas mileage.

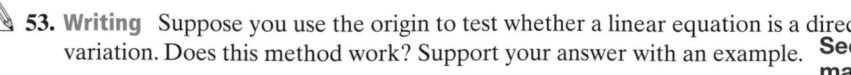

52. **Gas Mileage** Suppose you drive a car 392 mi on one tank of gas. The tank holds 14 gallons. The number of miles traveled varies directly with the number of gallons of gas you use.
   a. Write an equation that relates miles traveled to gallons of gas used. **$y = 28x$**
   b. You only have enough money to buy 3.7 gallons of gas. How far can you drive before refueling? **103.6 mi**
   c. 417.9 gal
   c. Last year you drove 11,700 mi. About how many gallons of gas did you use?
   d. Suppose the price of gas averaged \$1.57 per gallon last year. Find the cost per mile. **\$0.056/mi**

53. **Writing** Suppose you use the origin to test whether a linear equation is a direct variation. Does this method work? Support your answer with an example. **See margin.**

54. **Error Analysis** Find the error in the following computation: If y varies directly with x^2, and $y = 2$ when $x = 4$, then $y = 3$ when $x = 9$. **See margin.**

 **Challenge**

In Exercises 55–58, y varies directly with x.

55. If x is doubled, what happens to y? **y is doubled.**

56. If x is halved, what happens to y? **y is halved.**

57. If x is divided by 7, what happens to y? **y is divided by 7.**

58. If x is multiplied by 10, what happens to y? **y is multiplied by 10.**

59. If z varies directly with the product of x and y ($z = kxy$), then z is said to vary jointly with x and y.
   a. **Geometry** The area of a triangle varies jointly with its base and height. What is the constant of variation? **$\frac{1}{2}$**
   b. Suppose q varies jointly with v and s, and $q = 24$ when $v = 2$ and $s = 3$. Find q when $v = 4$ and $s = 2$. **32**
   c. **Critical Thinking** Suppose z varies jointly with x and y, and x varies directly with w. Show that z varies jointly with w and y. **$z = kxy$, and $x = k_1w$, so $z = kk_1wy$, and z varies jointly with w and y.**

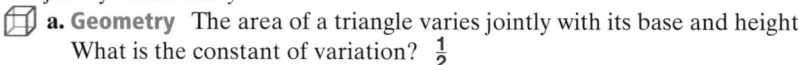 **Standardized Test Prep**

Multiple Choice

60. Which equation does NOT represent a direct variation? **B**
   A. $y - 3x = 0$ **B.** $y + 2 = \frac{1}{2}x$ **C.** $\frac{y}{x} = \frac{2}{3}$ **D.** $y = \frac{x}{17}$

61. Suppose y varies directly with x. If x is 30 when y is 10, what is x when y is 9? **G**
   F. 3   **G.** 27   **H.** 29   **I.** $\frac{300}{9}$

62. Suppose y varies directly with x. If x is −7 when y is 3, what is x when y is −5?
   A. $-11\frac{2}{3}$ **B.** $-4\frac{1}{5}$ **C.** $4\frac{1}{5}$ **D.** $11\frac{2}{3}$ **D**

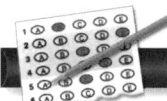

Take It to the NET
Online lesson quiz at
www.PHSchool.com
Web Code: aga-0203

63. Which equation represents the direct variation in the table at the right? **I**

x	3	4	9
y	8.1	10.8	24.3

   F. $4y - 10x = 0$ **G.** $8x = 3y$
   H. $y + 8.1x = 0$ **I.** $10y = 27x$

Short Response

64. Do the values in the table below represent a direct variation? Explain. **See margin.**

x	4	5	7
y	13.1	16.3	22.6

pages 74–77 Exercises

53. **Answers may vary. Sample:** No, the line $y = 0$ passes through the origin, but is not a direct variation.

54. **Answers may vary. Sample:** If y varies directly with x^2, and $y = 2$ when $x = 4$, then $y = 10\frac{1}{8}$ when $x = 9$.

64. **[2] No; the ratio $\frac{y}{x}$ is not constant.**

[1] only has answer no, with no explanation

Lesson 2-2

Use the given information to graph each line. **65–68. See back of book.**

65. slope $= -\frac{3}{5}$, through $(-2, 5)$ **66.** slope $= -\frac{3}{2}$, through $(1, -4)$

67. slope $= -4$, through $(0, -1)$ **68.** slope $= -2$, $(-1, 6)$

Lesson 2-1

Graph each relation. Find the domain and range. **69–72. See margin.**

69. $\{(0, 1), (1, -3), (-2, -3), (3, -3)\}$ **70.** $\{(4, 0), (7, 0), (4, -1), (7, -1)\}$

71. $\{(1, -2), (2, -1), (4, 1), (5, 2)\}$ **72.** $\{(1, 7), (2, 8), (3, 9), (4, 10)\}$

Previous Course **73. Aviation** In 1995, an aircraft set the around-the-world record time for a passenger jet at 31 h, 27 min, 49 s. Six refueling stops took a total of 8 h, 48 min, 8 s. What percent of the time was spent in the air? **≈ 72%**

✓ Checkpoint Quiz 1   Lessons 2-1 through 2-3

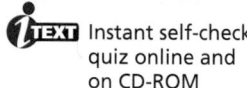 Instant self-check quiz online and on CD-ROM

Find the x- and y-intercepts of each line. **2.** $\left(-\frac{5}{7}, 0\right)$; $(0, 5)$

1. $x - 3y = 9$ **2.** $y = 7x + 5$ **3.** $y = 6x$ **4.** $-4x + y = 10$
   $(9, 0)$; $(0, -3)$ $(0, 0)$; $(0, 0)$ $\left(-\frac{5}{2}, 0\right)$; $(0, 10)$

Write the equation of each line in slope-intercept form.

5. $2x - y = 9$ **6.** $4x = 2 + y$ **7.** $5y = -3x - 10$ **8.** $4x + 6y = 12$
   $y = 2x - 9$ $y = 4x - 2$ $y = -\frac{3}{5}x - 2$ $y = -\frac{2}{3}x + 2$

9. a. A group of friends is going to the movies. Each ticket costs $7.00. Write an equation to model the total cost of the group's tickets. **a–c. See margin.**

     b. Graph the equation. Explain what the x- and y-intercepts represent.

     c. Writing Could the domain include fractions? Explain.

10. Which line is perpendicular to $3x + 2y = 6$? **A**

     A. $4x - 6y = 3$ **B.** $y = -\frac{3}{2}x + 4$ **C.** $2x + 3y = 12$ **D.** $y = \frac{3}{2}x + 1$

Algebra at Work
·· **Miniaturist**

People who make a career out of designing and creating miniature models of an actual object are called miniaturists. They apply direct variations to reproduce realistic models of items such as houses, stores, or scenes. Common scales used to create miniatures are the following.

- the one-inch scale (1 in. : 1 ft or 1 : 12)
- the half-inch scale (0.5 in. : 1 ft or 1 : 24)
- the quarter-inch scale (0.25 in. : 1 ft or 1 : 48)

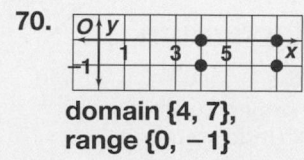 **Take It to the NET** For more information about careers in model design, go to **www.PHSchool.com**.
·········· Web Code: agb-2031

Lesson 2-3   Direct Variation   **77**

69.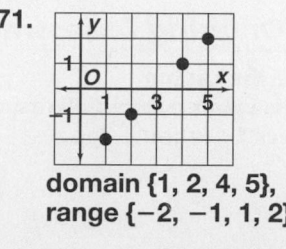
domain $\{0, 1, -2, 3\}$, range $\{1, -3\}$

70.
domain $\{4, 7\}$, range $\{0, -1\}$

71.
domain $\{1, 2, 4, 5\}$, range $\{-2, -1, 1, 2\}$

Standardized Test Prep

📁 Resources
For additional practice with a variety of test item formats:
- Standardized Test Prep, p. 111
- Test-Taking Strategies, p. 106
- Test-Taking Strategies with Transparencies

Exercise 60 Remind students to read carefully and be sure to notice the word *not*.

✓ Chapter Checkpoint 1

To check understanding of Lessons 2-1 to 2-3:

Checkpoint Quiz 1 (p. 77)

📁 Teaching Resources
Checkpoint Quiz 1 (also in Prentice Hall Assessment System)

👥 Reaching All Students
Reading and Math Literacy 2B

Spanish versions available

72.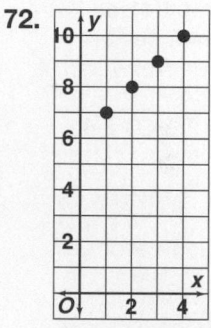
domain $\{1, 2, 3, 4\}$, range $\{7, 8, 9, 10\}$

page 77   Checkpoint Quiz 1

9a. $y = 7x$

b.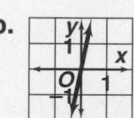

Both intercepts are 0 when no one has bought any tickets.

c. No; the number of people must be a whole number.

✓ Check Skills You'll Need

Relations and Functions
Lesson 2-1: Example 6
Exercises 22–30
Extra Practice, p. 823

Linear Equations
Lesson 2-2: Example 3
Exercises 11–19
Extra Practice, p. 823

Lesson Resources

📁 **Teaching Resources**
Practice, Reteaching, Enrichment

Reaching All Students
Practice Workbook 2-4
Spanish Practice Workbook 2-4
Technology Activities 5
Hands-On Activities 35

Presentation Assistant Plus!
Transparencies
• Check Skills You'll Need 2-4
• Additional Examples 2-4
• Student Edition Answers 2-4
• Lesson Quiz 2-4
PH Presentation Pro CD 2-4

ASSESSMENT SYSTEM
Computer Test Generator CD

Technology
Resource Pro® CD-ROM
Computer Test Generator CD
Prentice Hall Presentation Pro CD

🖥 **www.PHSchool.com**
Student Site
• Teacher Web Code: agk-5500
• Updated data
• Graphing Calculator, Procedure 22
• Self-grading Lesson Quiz
Teacher Center
• Lesson Planner
• Resources

Plus **iTEXT**

2-4

Using Linear Models

 North Carolina Objectives

2.04 Create and use best-fit mathematical models of linear functions to solve problems involving sets of data. b) Check the model for goodness-of-fit and use it to draw conclusions or make predictions.

Lesson Preview

What You'll Learn

OBJECTIVE 1 To write linear equations that model real-world data

OBJECTIVE 2 To make predictions from linear models

. . . And Why

To model a burning candle, as in Example 2

✓ Check Skills You'll Need

(For help, go to Lessons 2-1 and 2-2.)

Find the change in x and the change in y between each pair of points.

1. $(-0.2, 9)$ and $(3.4, 7.3)$ **2.** $(10, 17)$ and $(11.5, 13.5)$ **3.** $\left(0, \frac{3}{10}\right)$ and $\left(-1, \frac{2}{5}\right)$

   3.6, −1.7   **1.5, −3.5**   **−1, $\frac{1}{10}$**

Evaluate each function for the given values.

4. $f(x) = \frac{4}{3}x - 2$ for $x = -3, 0, \frac{1}{2}$ **5.** $g(x) = 3(2 - x)$ for $x = 0, \frac{1}{6}, 1$

   −6, −2, −$\frac{4}{3}$ **6, $\frac{11}{2}$, 3**

New Vocabulary   • scatter plot   • trend line

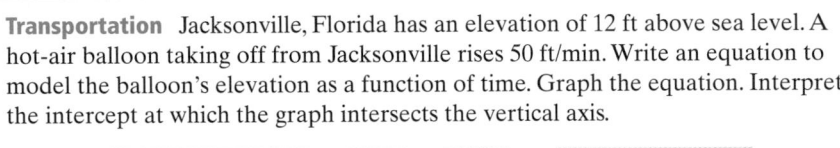

iTEXT Interactive lesson includes instant self-check, tutorials, and activities.

OBJECTIVE 1   **Modeling Real-World Data**

You can write linear equations to model real-world problems.

1 EXAMPLE   **Real-World 🌐 Connection**

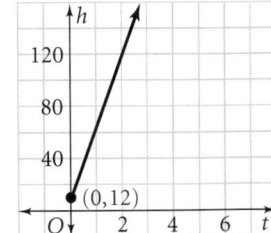

Real-World 🌐 Connection

Careers Hot-air balloonists use mathematics to plot courses, calculate wind speed, and determine their air speed.

Transportation Jacksonville, Florida has an elevation of 12 ft above sea level. A hot-air balloon taking off from Jacksonville rises 50 ft/min. Write an equation to model the balloon's elevation as a function of time. Graph the equation. Interpret the intercept at which the graph intersects the vertical axis.

Relate   balloon's elevation   =   rate   ·   time   +   starting elevation

Define   Let h = the balloon's elevation.

           Let t = time (in minutes) since the hot-air balloon lifted off.

Write h =   50   · t +   12

An equation that models the balloon's elevation is $h = 50t + 12$.

The h-intercept is $(0, 12)$.

The t-coordinate, 0, represents the time at the start of the trip.

The h-coordinate, 12, represents the elevation of the balloon at the start of the trip.

✓ Check Understanding

1 Suppose a balloon begins descending at a rate of 20 ft/min from an elevation of 1350 ft.
   a. Write an equation to model the balloon's elevation as a function of time. What is true about the slope of this line? $h = -20t + 1350$; **the slope is negative.**
   b. Graph the equation. Interpret the h-intercept. **See back of book.**

Ongoing Assessment and Intervention

Before the Lesson	**During the Lesson**	**After the Lesson**
Diagnose prerequisite skills using:	**Monitor progress using:**	**Assess knowledge using:**
• Check Skills You'll Need	• Check Understanding	• Lesson Quiz
	• Additional Examples	• Computer Test Generator CD
	• Standardized Test Prep	

You can use two data points from a linear relationship to write a model.

2 EXAMPLE Real-World  Connection

Science A candle is 6 in. tall after burning for 1 h. After 3 h, it is $5\frac{1}{2}$ in. tall. Write a linear equation to model the height y of the candle after burning x hours.

Step 1 Identify the data points $(1, 6)$ and $\left(3, \frac{11}{2}\right)$ as (x_1, y_1) and (x_2, y_2).

Step 2 Find the slope of the line.

$m = \frac{y_2 - y_1}{x_2 - x_1}$ Use the slope formula.

$m = \frac{\frac{11}{2} - 6}{3 - 1}$ Substitute.

$m = \frac{-\frac{1}{2}}{2}$ Simplify the numerator and denominator.

$m = -\frac{1}{4}$ Simplify.

Step 3 Use one of the points and the point-slope form to write an equation for the line.

$y - y_1 = m(x - x_1)$ Use point-slope form.

$y - 6 = -\frac{1}{4}(x - 1)$ Substitute.

$y = -\frac{1}{4}x + 6\frac{1}{4}$ Solve for y.

An equation of the line that models the height of the candle is $y = -\frac{1}{4}x + 6\frac{1}{4}$.

✓**Check Understanding** **2 a.** **Reasoning** What does the slope $-\frac{1}{4}$ represent? **The candle is burning down at the rate of $\frac{1}{4}$ inch per hour.**
b. What does the y-intercept $6\frac{1}{4}$ represent? **the original height of the candle**
c. Another candle is 7 in. tall after burning for 1 h and 5 in. tall after burning for 2 h. Write a linear equation to model the height of the candle. **$y = -2x + 9$**

6 in. $5\frac{1}{2}$ in.

after 1 h   after 3 h

OBJECTIVE

2 **Predicting With Linear Models**

You can use a linear model to make predictions.

3 EXAMPLE Using a Linear Model

Use the equation from Example 2. When will the candle be 4 in. tall?

$y = -\frac{1}{4}x + 6\frac{1}{4}$ Write the equation.

$4 = -\frac{1}{4}x + 6\frac{1}{4}$ Substitute 4 for y.

$-4\left(4 - 6\frac{1}{4}\right) = x$ Solve for x.

$9 = x$ Simplify.

The candle will be 4 in. tall after burning for 9 h.

✓**Check Understanding** **3 a.** How tall will the candle be after burning for 11 h? **$3\frac{1}{2}$ in.**
b. What was the original height of the candle? **$6\frac{1}{4}$ in.**
c. When will the candle burn out? **after 25 hours**

Math Background

Linear equations are useful in modeling many real-world problems. A scatter plot provides a visual representation of two different sets of data and is useful in determining whether there is a linear relationship between the data sets. A trend line that comes close to the points in a scatter plot can be helpful in studying the related data and in making predictions.

OBJECTIVE

1 Teaching Notes

2 EXAMPLE Auditory Learners

Have students explain aloud why it is reasonable for the slope to be a negative number.

Additional Examples

1 Suppose an airplane descends at a rate of 300 ft/min from an elevation of 8000 ft. Write and graph an equation to model the plane's elevation as a function of the time it has been descending. Interpret the intercept at which the graph intersects the vertical axis. **$d = -300t + 8000$**

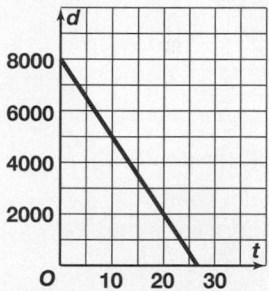

The intercept (0, 8000) shows that the elevation was 8000 ft when the descent began.

👥 **Reaching All Students**

Below Level Because they want to "connect the dots," students may have difficulty drawing trend lines. Emphasize that a trend line is not exact but is an estimate.	**Advanced Learners** Ask students to find the original height of the candle in Check Understanding 2c. **9 in.**	**Auditory Learners** See note on page 79. **Error Prevention** See note on page 81.

2 A spring has a length of 8 cm when a 20-g mass hangs at the bottom end. Each additional gram stretches the spring another 0.15 cm. Write an equation to model the length y of the spring as a function of the mass x of the attached weight. $y = 0.15x + 5$

OBJECTIVE
2 **Teaching Notes**

 Additional Examples

3 Use the equation from Additional Example 2. What mass would be needed to stretch the spring to a length of 9.5 cm? **30 g**

4 An art expert visited a gallery and jotted down her guesses for the selling price of five different paintings. Then, she checked the actual prices. The data points (guess, actual) show the results, where each number is in thousands of dollars {(12, 11), (7, 8.5), (10, 12), (5, 3.8), (9, 10)}.
a. Draw a scatter plot. Decide whether a linear model is reasonable.
b. Draw a trend line. Write the equation of the line.

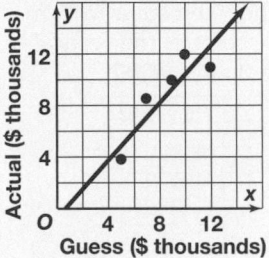

A linear model seems reasonable; Answers may vary. Sample: $y = \frac{10}{9}x - \frac{2}{3}$

Closure

Suppose a linear model seems appropriate for the data represented in a scatter plot. How can you find an equation for a trend line? **Draw a line that comes close to the data points. Use the coordinates of two points on the line to write an equation of the line in point-slope form.**

80

A **scatter plot** is a graph that relates two different sets of data by plotting the data as ordered pairs. You can use a scatter plot to determine a relationship between the data sets.

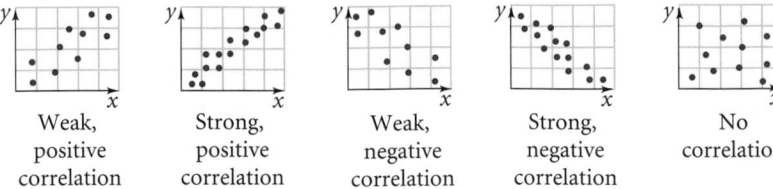

| Weak, positive correlation | Strong, positive correlation | Weak, negative correlation | Strong, negative correlation | No correlation |

A **trend line** is a line that approximates the relationship between the data sets of a scatter plot. You can use a trend line to make predictions.

4 EXAMPLE **Real-World Connection**

Automobiles A woman is considering buying the 1993 car shown in the photo. She researches prices for various years of the same model and records the data in a table.

Model Year	1994	1995	1996	1997	1998
Prices	$5784	$6810	$8237	$9660	$10,948
	$5435	$6207	$7751	$9127	$10,455

a. Let x represent the model year. (Use 4 for 1994, 5 for 1995, and so forth.) Let y be the price of the car. Draw a scatter plot. Decide whether a linear model is reasonable.

A linear model seems reasonable, since the points fall close to a line.

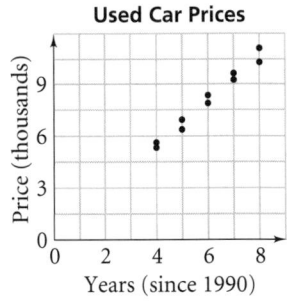

Used Car Prices

b. Draw a trend line. Write the equation of the line. Determine whether the asking price is reasonable.

Draw a line that has about the same number of data points above and below it. Use the slope and the y-intercept to find the equation of the line. Plot the data point for the asking price.

The equation of the trend line in the graph is $y = 1.3x + 0.2$. A fair price would be the value of y for $x = 3$, or about $4100.

The asking price of $4200 is reasonable.

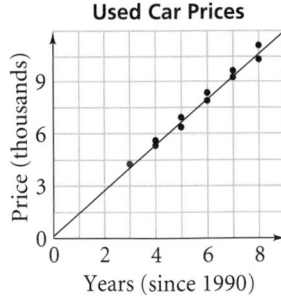

Used Car Prices

✓ Check Understanding **4** Graph each set of data. Decide whether a linear model is reasonable. If so, draw a trend line and write its equation. **a–b. See back of book.**
a. $\{(-7.5, 19.75), (-2, 9), (0, 6.5), (1.5, 3), (4, -1.5)\}$
b. $\{(0, -3), (0.5, -2.5), (1, -1), (3.5, 21.5), (6, 69), (7, 35)\}$

EXERCISES

Practice and Problem Solving

For more practice, see *Extra Practice*.

3. Practice

A Practice by Example

Example 1
(page 78)

1. A car enters an interstate highway 15 mi north of a city. The car travels due north at an average speed of 62.5 mi/h. Write an equation to model the car's distance *d* from the city after traveling for *h* hours. Graph the equation. **1–2. See back of book.**

2. A pump removes 1000 gal of water from a pool at a constant rate of 50 gal/min.
   a. Write an equation to find the amount of water *y* in the pool after *t* minutes.
   b. Graph the equation and interpret the *t*- and *y*-intercepts.

3. A tree 5 ft tall grows an average of 8 in. each year. Write and graph an equation to model the tree's height *h* after *x* years. **See margin.**

Examples 2 and 3
(page 79)

For each situation, find a linear model and use it to make a prediction.

4. There are 2 leaves along 3 in. of an ivy vine. There are 14 leaves along 15 in. of the same vine. How many leaves are there along 6 in. of the vine? $y = x - 1$; **5 leaves**

5. An empty 5-gal water jug weighs 0.75 lb. With 3 c of water inside, the jug weighs 2.25 lb. Predict the weight of the jug with 5 c of water inside. $y = 0.5x + 0.75$; **3.25 lb**

6. There are 55 blades of grass in 1 in.^{2} of lawn. There are 230 blades of grass in 4 in.^{2} of the same lawn. How many blades of grass are in 3 in.^{2} of lawn? $y = 58.\overline{3}x - 3.\overline{3}$; **172 blades of grass**

7. A 2-mi cab ride costs $5.25. A 5-mi cab ride costs $10.50. How much does a 3.8-mi cab ride cost? $y = 1.75x + 1.75$; **$8.40**

Example 4
(page 80)

Graph each set of data. Decide whether a linear model is reasonable. If so, draw a trend line and write its equation. 8–11. See back of book.

8. $\{(0, 11), (2, 8), (3, 7), (7, 2), (8, 0)\}$

9. $\{(1.2, 1), (2.5, 6), (2.5, 7.5), (4.1, 11), (7.9, 19)\}$

10. $\left\{\left(-10, 3\frac{1}{2}\right), \left(-5\frac{1}{2}, 1\frac{1}{2}\right), \left(-\frac{1}{10}, -4\right), \left(3\frac{1}{2}, -7\frac{1}{2}\right), (12, -12)\right\}$

11. $\{(-15, 8), (-8, -7), (-3, 0), (0, 5), (7, -3)\}$

B Apply Your Skills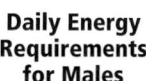

12. **Measurement** The numbering system used in Europe for shoe sizes is different from the system used in the United States. Use the data in the table at the right to create a model for converting between systems. **a. See back of book.**
   a. Graph the data. Is a linear model reasonable?
   b. Find the European equivalent of U.S. size 8. **40**
   c. Writing Explain how to use a model to convert European sizes to U.S. sizes. **See margin.**

Women's Shoe Sizes

U.S. Size	European Size
1	31
3	34
5	36
7	39
9	41
11	44

SOURCE: *Sizes*

Daily Energy Requirements for Males

Age (years)	Energy Needed (Calories)
1	1100
2	1300
5	1800
8	2200
11	2500
14	2800
17	3000

SOURCE: *Go Figure: The Numbers You Need for Everyday Life*

13. **Nutrition** The table at the left shows the average daily energy requirements for male children and adolescents.
   a. Graph the data. Model the data with a linear equation. **See back of book.**
   b. Estimate the daily energy requirements for a male 16 years old. **2930 Cal**
   c. Reasoning Do you think your model also applies to adult males? Explain. **Answers may vary. Sample: No; adults need fewer Calories, not more.**

Assignment Guide

1 Objective
 A B Core 1–3, 15–19
 C Extension 28–29

2 Objective
 A B Core 4–14, 20–26
 C Extension 27

Standardized Test Prep 30–35

Mixed Review 36–46

Error Prevention

Exercise 18 Students may not read the exercise carefully and may find an equation for the line through (3.5, −2.3) and (0, 5.1). Point out that the intercept given is the *x*-intercept, not the *y*-intercept.

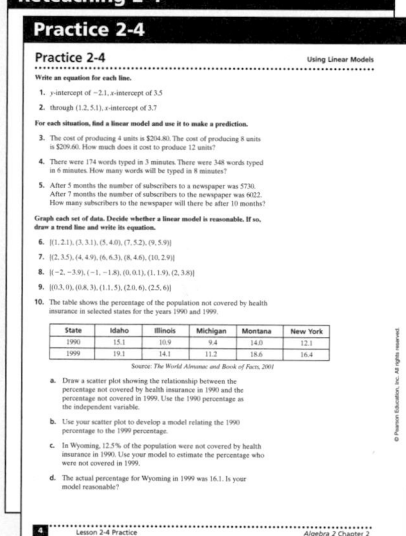

pages 81–84 **Exercises**

3. $h = 8x + 60$

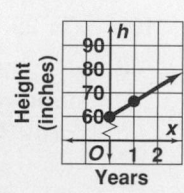

12c. **Answers may vary. Sample: After drawing a trend line, locate the European size on the y-axis. Then find the corresponding U.S. size on the x-axis.**

Careers

Exercise 20 Dietitians and nutritionists plan nutrition programs and supervise the preparation and serving of meals. Some dietitians provide services in institutions such as hospitals and schools. Educational requirements typically include courses in biology, chemistry, physiology, and mathematics.

Connection to Geometry

Exercise 29 Algebra provides many tools that are useful in studying geometric figures. This exercise shows that special lines such as perpendicular bisectors are easy to describe algebraically.

14. Sales Suppose you manufacture and sell tarps. The table displays your current sizes and prices.

Tarps

Size	Price	Size	Price
5 × 7 ft	\$1.39	18 × 20 ft	\$14.39
6 × 8 ft	\$1.99	15 × 30 ft	\$17.99
8 × 10 ft	\$3.19	20 × 30 ft	\$23.99
10 × 12 ft	\$4.79	20 × 40 ft	\$31.99
12 × 16 ft	\$7.69	25 × 45 ft	\$44.99
10 × 20 ft	\$7.99	30 × 50 ft	\$59.99
16 × 20 ft	\$12.79	30 × 60 ft	\$71.99

14a. See back of book.

a. Draw a scatter plot showing the relationship between a tarp's area and its cost. Use area as the independent variable.

14b. Answers may vary. Sample: $c = 0.04A$

b. Use your scatter plot to develop a model relating the area of a tarp to its cost.

14c–d. See margin.

c. How good a model do you feel you have? Explain.

d. Is \$7.00 a reasonable price for a tarp that measures 10 ft by 15 ft? Explain.

e. Using your model and the prices in the table, determine which tarp size varies the most from your predicted price. How great is the discrepancy between your model and the actual price? **6 × 8 ft; \$0.07**

Write an equation for each line.

15. through (2, 2), y-intercept 10 **$y = -4x + 10$**

16. x-intercept – 2, y-intercept –6 **$y = -3x - 6$**

17. y-intercept $-\frac{5}{2}$, x-intercept $-\frac{1}{3}$ **$y = -7.5x - 2.5$**

18. through (3.5, –2.3), x-intercept 5.1 **$y = 1.4375x - 7.33125$**

19. Entertainment Refer to the diagram below. Suppose you are trying to decide whether to subscribe to cable service or just rent videos.

19a–b. See margin.

a. Write an equation to model the cost y of the cable service for 1 month.

b. Write a second equation to model the cost y of renting x movies from the video store. What is the slope? What is the y-intercept?

19c. See back of book.

c. Open-Ended Suppose you currently rent 8 to 12 movies each month. Graph the two equations from parts (a) and (b). Interpret the graph. Use your interpretation to choose between the alternatives. Explain your reasoning.

20. a. Answers may vary. Sample: $y = 0.068x - 7.7$

b. about 15 g

c. 200 Cal; a 200-Cal hamburger has about 6 g of fat.

20. Nutrition The table below shows the relationship between Calories and fat in various fast-food hamburgers.

Hamburger	A	B	C	D	E	F	G	H	I
Calories	720	530	510	500	305	410	440	320	598
Fat (g)	46	30	27	26	13	20	25	13	26

SOURCE: *The Fat Counter*

a. Develop a model for the relationship between Calories and fat.

b. How much fat would you expect a 330–Calorie hamburger to have?

c. Error Analysis A student reports these estimates: 10 g of fat for a 200-Calorie hamburger and 36 g of fat for a 660-Calorie hamburger. Which estimate is *not* reasonable? Explain.

pages 81–84 Exercises

14c. Answers may vary. Sample: The model fits the data very closely.

d. Answers may vary. Sample: No; the area of the tarp is 150 ft^2 so the price should be \$6.00.

19a. $y = 29.95$

b. $y = 2.95x$; slope = 2.95; y-intercept = 0

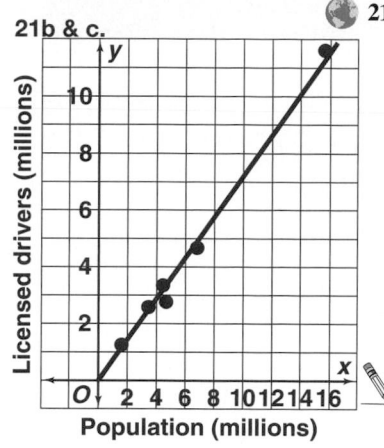

21b & c.

Population (millions) (x-axis label)
Licensed drivers (millions) (y-axis label)

21. **Data Analysis** Is the population of a state related to the number of licensed drivers in that state? The table shows population and licensed-driver statistics from a recent year.
  a. Which variable should be the independent variable? **population**
  b. Draw a scatter plot. **b–c, e.**
  c. Draw a trend line. **See left.**
  d. The population of Oregon was approximately 3 million that year. About how many licensed drivers lived in Oregon that year? **2 million**
  e. **Writing** Is the correlation between population and number of licensed drivers strong or weak? Explain.

State	Population (millions)	Licensed Drivers (millions)
Alabama	4.3	3.2
Florida	14.7	11.6
Louisiana	4.4	2.7
South Carolina	3.8	2.6
Virginia	6.7	4.7
West Virginia	1.8	1.3

SOURCE: U.S. Census Bureau, National Highway Administration. Go to **www.PHSchool.com** for a data update.
Web Code: agg-2041

21e. Answers may vary. Sample: Strong; the points fall close to a straight line.

A linear model for each situation passes through the origin. Find each missing value. Round your answer to the nearest tenth.

22. 47.5 min to jog 5 mi, ▧ min to jog 11 mi **104.5**

23. 8.5 gal of gas to drive 243.1 mi, 3 gal of gas to drive ▧ mi **85.8**

24. 336 words keyboarded in 3.5 min, 624 words keyboarded in ▧ min **6.5**

25. $9.45 to buy 7 lb of apples, $17.55 to buy ▧ lb **13**

26. 567 bricks in a wall 9 ft long, ▧ bricks in a wall 14 ft long **882**

C Challenge **27.** **Social Studies** The table at the right shows per capita revenues and expenditures for selected states from a recent year.
  a. Show the data on a scatter plot. Draw a trend line.
  b. If a state collected revenue of $2000 per capita in taxes, how much would you expect it to spend per capita?
  c. Virginia spent $2654 per capita during that year. According to your model, how much did it collect in taxes per capita? **b–d. See margin.**
  d. In that same year, Alaska collected $2503 per capita in taxes and spent $9274 per capita. Does this information follow the trend? Explain.

27a. See back of book.

Reading Math

Per capita means "for each person". Capita is a form of the Latin word for head.

State	Per Capita Revenue ($)	Per Capita Expenditure ($)
Delaware	2329	4480
Florida	1368	2532
Hawaii	2601	5023
Indiana	1444	2631
Kentucky	1671	3049
Massachusetts	2045	4095
North Carolina	1623	2898
Oklahoma	1399	2807
Tennessee	1163	2599

SOURCE: U.S. Census Bureau. Go to **www.PHSchool.com** for a data update.
Web Code: agg-2041

28. a. Use the first and last data points to find a linear model for the data in the table at the right.
  b. Use the middle two data points to find a linear model for the data.
  c. Which model better represents the data? Can you find a third model that you think best represents the data? Explain.

x	−5	−2	−1	1	3	6
y	22	15	12	8	7	5

a. $y = -\frac{17}{11}x + 14.27$
b. $y = -2x + 10$

Answers may vary. Sample: neither; $y = -1.6x + 11.8$

29. **Geometry** Write the equation of the perpendicular bisector of the segment with endpoints $(-3, 5)$ and $(7, 1)$. $y = \frac{5}{2}x - 2$

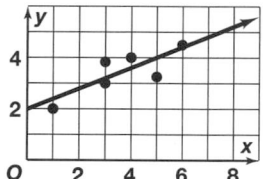

27b. about $3900

  c. about $1400

  d. Answers may vary. Sample: No, expenditure would be predicted to be about $5000.

Lesson Quiz 2-4

1. A family built a house in a beach resort area. In 1990, the house was 430 ft from the water. With erosion, the house was 400 ft from the water in 2000.

  a. Assuming a linear relationship between the number of years x since 1990 and the distance y of the house from the water, write an equation for y as a function of x. $y = -3x + 430$

  b. In what year will the house be only 250 ft from the water? **2050**

2. Graph the set of data. Decide whether a linear model is reasonable. If so, draw a trend line and write its equation.
{(1, 2), (3, 3), (3, 3.75), (4, 4), (5, 3.25), (6, 4.5)}

A linear model seems reasonable; Answers may vary. Sample: $y = 0.4x + 2$

Alternative Assessment

Have students work in pairs. Each student draws a scatter plot of data for which a linear model is reasonable. They trade scatter plots. Each student draws a trend line and finds an equation for the trend line for the scatter plot that the partner drew. Each student checks the other student's work.

A sheet of blank grids is available in the Test-Taking Strategies with Transparencies booklet. Give this sheet to students for practice with filling in the grids.

Resources

For additional practice with a variety of test item formats:
• Standardized Test Prep, p. 111
• Test-Taking Strategies, p. 106
• Test-Taking Strategies with Transparencies

Exercises 30–33 Double check all your calculations for these exercises. Be sure to pay close attention to the placement of decimal points.

pages 81–84 Exercises

40. {−7, −3, −1, 2, 7}

41. {1, 3.5, 5, 6, 8}

42. {3, 4, 5.25, 12, 19}

43. $\left\{-\frac{7}{2}, -\frac{5}{2}, -2, -\frac{5}{4}, 0\right\}$

44. {−299, −99, 1, 151, 401}

45. {1, 6, 9, 11, 15}

Standardized Test Prep

Gridded Response

Each set of three points is collinear. Find each missing x- or y-value. Enter each answer to the nearest hundredth.

30. (2, 3.37), (10, 23.37), (6, y) **13.37**

31. (6, 10.2), (1.5, 3.45), (x, 2.85) **1.10**

32. (0.5, 1), (2.2, y), (1.6, 4.3) **6.10**

33. (x, 0.8), (15, −0.4), (−4, 2.9) **8.09**

Reading Comprehension

Use the newspaper article below for Exercises 34 and 35.

34a. $y = -\frac{16}{3}x + 72.6$, where 1993 corr. to $x = 0$.

b. **35.3 tons**

Take It to the NET
Online lesson quiz at
www.PHSchool.com
Web Code: aga-0204

What's Harming Japan's Oysters?

A 1994 red tide killed off thousands of *akoya* oysters in Japan's Ago Bay. For years following the red tide, oysters continued to die, confounding pearl farmers and scientists alike. Scientists have suggested many possible causes, from a virus to pollutants.

Whatever the reason, in 1996, Japanese pearl farmers harvested only 56.6 tons of pearls from *akoya* oysters, down from 72.6 tons in 1993.

Source: *NOVA,* "The Perfect Pearl"

34. a. Write a linear model for the tons of pearls harvested from *akoya* oysters.
    b. Use your model to estimate the number of tons of pearls harvested in 2000.

35. a. Count the number of words in one line of the article. Then count the number of words in four lines. Write a linear model.
    b. Use your linear model to estimate the number of words in the entire article.
    a. **Answers may vary. Sample:** $y = \frac{16}{3}x + \frac{2}{3}$ b. **70**

Mixed Review

Lesson 2-3

Find each constant of variation. Then find the value of y when $x = -5$.

36. $y = 27$ when $x = -10$ **−2.7; 13.5**   37. $y = -36$ when $x = 12$ **−3; 15**

38. $y = -\frac{2}{5}$ when $x = \frac{1}{3}$ **$-\frac{6}{5}$; 6**   39. $y = -\frac{21}{4}$ when $x = -\frac{5}{8}$ **$\frac{42}{5}$; −42**

Lesson 2-1

Find the range of each function when the domain is {−3, −1, 0, 1.5, 4}.
40–45. See margin.

40. $f(x) = 2x - 1$ 41. $y = -(x - 5)$ 42. $y = x^2 + 3$

43. $g(x) = \frac{x - 4}{2}$ 44. $y = 100x + 1$ 45. $y = 9 - 2x$

Previous Course

46. **Track** Svetlana Masterkova of Russia set a record for running the mile, in 4 minutes 12.56 seconds.   **20.91 ft/s; 2091 ft**
    a. Find Svetlana's rate in feet per second. How far did she run in 100 seconds?
    b. Write an equation that relates the distance she ran to time. Use feet per second as the unit. **$d = 20.91t$**
    c. Calculate Svetlana's speed in miles per hour. **14.25 mi/h**

84   Chapter 2 Functions, Equations, and Graphs

Finding a Line of Best Fit

You can use your graphing calculator to display data sets, draw scatter plots, and draw a line to fit the data. The line is the linear regression line, or line of best fit. The **LinReg** feature on your calculator fits data to the model $y = ax + b$.

Take It to the NET
Graphing Calculator procedures online at
www.PHSchool.com
Web Code: age-2122

EXAMPLE   **Using the LinReg Feature**

The table shows the number of bicycles produced in the United States from 1993 to 1996. Enter the given data on your calculator. Generate a scatter plot of the data and a line of best fit. Then sketch the graph.

Year	Number of Bicycles Produced (millions)
1993	9.9
1994	9.7
1995	8.8
1996	8.0

SOURCE: Bicycle Manufacturers Association of America, Inc.

Step 1 Clear any existing lists or stored equations.

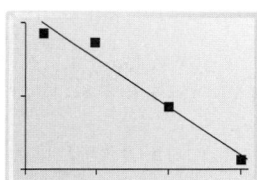

Step 2 Enter data. Press [STAT] [ENTER]. Enter the x-values in L₁ and the y-values in L₂. Let 1990 correspond to $x = 0$.

Step 3 Find the line of best fit. Press [STAT] [▶] 4 [ENTER] to select **LinReg (ax+b)**. Press [Y=] [VARS] 5 [▶] [▶] [ENTER] to enter the regression equation to Y1.

Step 4 Draw the graph. Use the STAT PLOT feature and press 1 [ENTER] to turn on Plot 1.

Use the [▼] key to move down the rows to select a scatter plot using L1 and L2. Then press [ZOOM] 9 to get the scatter plot and the line of best fit.

EXERCISES   4. Answers may vary. Sample: saves time and LinReg feature draws the best-fit line for you.

Find a line of best fit for each set of data. Round to the nearest hundredth.

1. $\{(-5, 6.3), (-4, 5.6), (-3, 4.8), (-2, 3.1), (-1, 2.5), (0, 1.0), (1, -1.4)\}$ $y = -1.24x + 0.66$

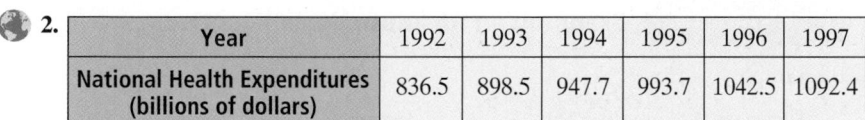

2.

Year	1992	1993	1994	1995	1996	1997
National Health Expenditures (billions of dollars)	836.5	898.5	947.7	993.7	1042.5	1092.4

$y = 50.21x + 742.59$

3.

State	AL	FL	IN	KY	LA	NC	OK	SC	TN	VA
Population (millions)	4.0	12.9	5.5	3.7	4.2	6.6	3.1	3.5	4.9	6.2
Representatives	7	23	10	6	7	12	6	6	9	11

$y = 1.80x - 0.13$

 4. Writing Describe the advantages of using a graphing calculator to draw a line of best fit. **See above.**

Technology

Finding a Line of Best Fit

Students use a graphing calculator to enter data and display a scatter plot. Next, they use the LinReg feature to find an equation of the line of best fit. Finally, they display the graph of the line of best fit along with the scatter plot.

Resources

Students may use any graphing calculator that is able to display scatter plots and generate linear regression equations.

Teaching Notes

In each exercise, rounding the coefficients of the regression equation gives a slightly different line of fit. Students may want to enter the equation with rounded coefficients on the Y= list and display the graph. The graphs of the two equations will be essentially indistinguishable.

Error Prevention

If a student decides, for whatever reason, not to use [ZOOM] 9 to display the scatter plot and line of best fit, it is important to use window settings that include all the x-values and y-values in the data set. Otherwise some of the points of the scatter plot will not be displayed.

1. Plan

Lesson Preview

✓ **Check Skills You'll Need**

Linear Equations
Lesson 2-2: Example 1
Exercises 1–8
Extra Practice, p. 823

Graphing
Skills Handbook: p. 851
Exercises 1–12

Lesson Resources

📁 **Teaching Resources**
Practice, Reteaching, Enrichment

👥 **Reaching All Students**
Practice Workbook 2-5
Spanish Practice Workbook 2-5

⏱ **Presentation Assistant Plus!**
Transparencies
• Check Skills You'll Need 2-5
• Additional Examples 2-5
• Student Edition Answers 2-5
• Lesson Quiz 2-5
PH Presentation Pro CD 2-5

PRENTICE HALL
ASSESSMENT SYSTEM

Computer Test Generator CD

🪙 **Technology**
Resource Pro® CD-ROM
Computer Test Generator CD
Prentice Hall Presentation Pro CD

💻 **www.PHSchool.com**
Student Site
• Teacher Web Code: agk-5500
• Self-grading Lesson Quiz
Teacher Center
• Lesson Planner
• Resources

Plus *i*TEXT

2-5

Absolute Value Functions and Graphs

North Carolina Objectives   **2.08** Use equations and inequalities with absolute value to model and solve problems; justify results. a) Solve using tables, graphs, and algebraic properties.

Lesson Preview

What You'll Learn

OBJECTIVE 1 To graph absolute value functions

. . . And Why

To model distance, as in Example 4

✓ **Check Skills You'll Need**   (For help, go to Lesson 2-2 and Skills Handbook page 851.)

Graph each equation for the given domain and range. **1–2. See below left.**

1. $y = x$ for real numbers x and $y \geq 0$

2. $y = 2x - 4$ for real numbers x and $y \geq 0$

3. $y = -x + 6$ for real numbers x and $y \leq 3$ **See back of book.**

New Vocabulary   • absolute value function   • vertex

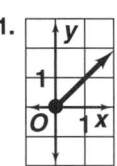

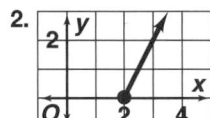

*i*TEXT **Interactive lesson includes instant self-check, tutorials, and activities.**

OBJECTIVE
1 **Graphing Absolute Value Functions**

A function of the form $f(x) = |mx + b| + c$, where $m \neq 0$, is an **absolute value function.** An equation of the form $y = |mx + b| + c$ is an absolute value equation in two variables. Graphs of absolute value equations in two variables look like angles.

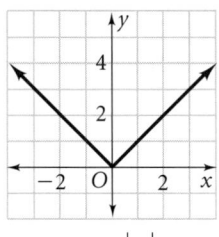
$$y = |x|$$

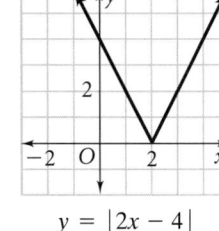
$$y = |2x - 4|$$

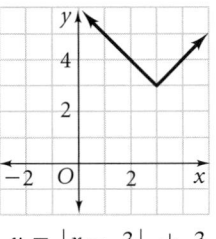
$$y = |x - 3| + 3$$

📖
Reading Math

Vertex means "turning point."

The **vertex** of a function is a point where the function reaches a maximum or minimum. In general, the vertex of $y = |mx + b| + c$ is located at $\left(-\frac{b}{m}, c\right)$. In the middle graph above, the x-coordinate of the vertex is $-\left(\frac{-4}{2}\right) = 2$.

Note that the graph of $y = -|x|$ is a reflection over the x-axis of the graph of $y = |x|$.

1 **EXAMPLE** **Graphing an Absolute Value Function**

Graph $y = |3x + 12|$.

Evaluate the equation for several values of x, beginning with $x = -\frac{b}{m} = -\frac{12}{3} = -4$.

Make a table of values.

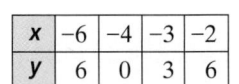

x	−6	−4	−3	−2
y	6	0	3	6

Graph the function.

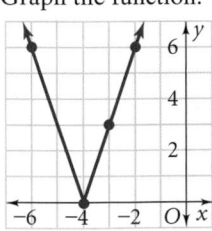

Ongoing Assessment and Intervention

Before the Lesson
Diagnose prerequisite skills using:
• Check Skills You'll Need

During the Lesson
Monitor progress using:
• Check Understanding
• Additional Examples
• Standardized Test Prep

After the Lesson
Assess knowledge using:
• Lesson Quiz
• Computer Test Generator CD

✓ **Check Understanding** ① Graph each equation. **a–b. See margin.**

a. $y = |2x - 5|$

b. $y = -|x + 1| - 2$

You can use a graphing calculator to graph an absolute value equation.

Graphing Calculator Hint

For a calculator screen that shows x- and y-intervals of equal width, press ZOOM, and then select ZSquare.

② **EXAMPLE** Using a Graphing Calculator

Graph $y = -|3x + 4| + 6$ on a graphing calculator.

Use the absolute value key. Graph the equation $Y_1 = -\text{abs}(3X+4)+6$.

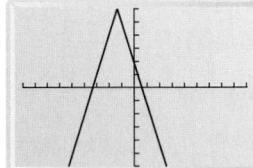

✓ **Check Understanding** ② Graph each equation on a graphing calculator. Then sketch the graph.

a. $y = -|-x| + 5$
See margin.

b. $y = 3 - \left|\dfrac{x}{2}\right|$
See back of book.

You can also graph an absolute value equation by first writing it as two linear equations.

③ **EXAMPLE** Writing Two Linear Equations

Graph $y = |x - 3| + 5$.

Step 1 Isolate the absolute value.

$$y = |x - 3| + 5$$
$$y - 5 = |x - 3|$$

Step 2 Use the definition of absolute value. Write one equation for $x - 3 \geq 0$ and a second equation for $x - 3 < 0$.

when $x - 3 \geq 0$	when $x - 3 < 0$
$y - 5 = x - 3$	$y - 5 = -(x - 3)$
$y = x + 2$	$y = -x + 8$

Step 3 Graph each equation for the appropriate domain.

When $x - 3 \geq 0$, or $x \geq 3$, $y = x + 2$.

When $x - 3 < 0$, or $x < 3$, $y = -x + 8$.

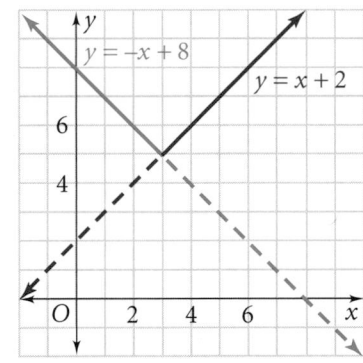

✓ **Check Understanding** ③ Graph each equation by writing two equations.

a. $y = \left|\dfrac{3}{2}x + 4\right| - 3$

b. $y = 2 - |x + 1|$

a–b. See back of book.

 Need Help?

If $x \geq 0$, then $|x| = x$.
If $x < 0$, then $|x| = -x$.

Lesson 2-5 Absolute Value Functions and Graphs   **87**

🙋 Reaching All Students

Below Level Help students understand that, to create a table for the graph, they must choose x-values both less than and greater than the vertex $\frac{-b}{m}$.	**Advanced Learners** Discuss with students the characteristics of the equation of an absolute value function whose vertex angle is a right angle.	**Error Prevention** See note on page 89.

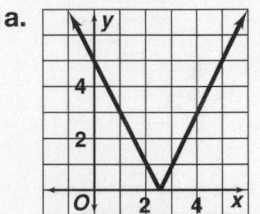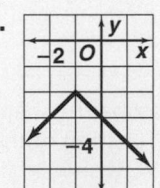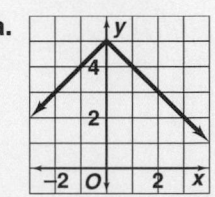

1 Graph $y = |2x - 1|$ by using a table of values.

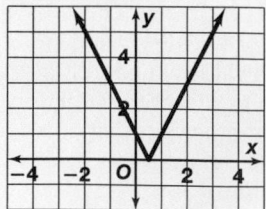

2 Graph $y = |x - 1| - 1$ on a graphing calculator.

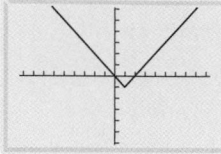

3 Use the definition of absolute value to graph $y = |3x + 6| - 2$.

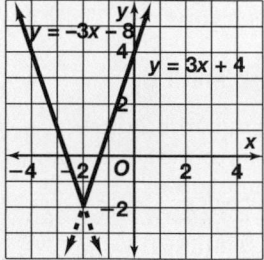

4 A train traveling on a straight track at 50 mi/h passes a certain crossing halfway through its journey each day. Sketch a graph of its trip based on its distance and time from the crossing.

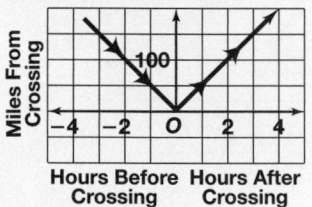

Closure

Have students describe the shape of the graph of a function of the form $y = |mx + b|$, where $m \neq 0$. **The graph looks like an angle.**

Real-World 🌐 Connection

According to legend, Betsy Ross made the first flag of the United States in her house in Philadelphia, Pennsylvania.

You can use absolute value functions to model time-and-distance problems. You can consider the time before you arrive at a destination to be negative.

4 EXAMPLE **Real-World 🌐 Connection**

Travel Suppose you pass the Betsy Ross House halfway along your trip to school each morning. You walk at a rate of one city block per minute. Sketch a graph of your trip to school based on your distance and time from the Besty Ross House.

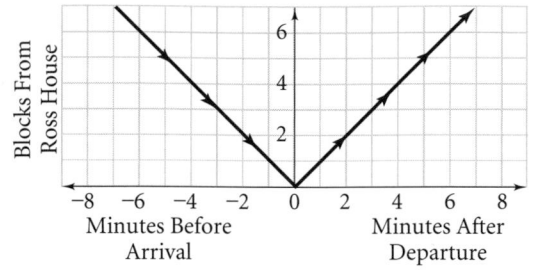

The equation $d = |t|$ models your distance from the Betsy Ross House.

✓ **Check Understanding** **4 a. Critical Thinking** Suppose you ride your bicycle to school at a rate of three city blocks per minute. How would the graph of your trip to school change?
   b. Sketch a new graph. **The graph would get narrower.**

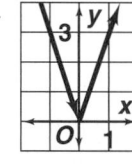

EXERCISES

For more practice, see *Extra Practice*.

Practice and Problem Solving

A Practice by Example

Example 1
(page 86)

Make a table of values for each equation. Then graph the equation.

1. $y = |4x|$ **2.** $y = |4x| - 1$ **3.** $y = |4x - 1|$

4. $y = |-3x|$ **5.** $y = |-3x| + 2$ **6.** $y = |-3x + 2|$

7. $y = -|2x|$ **8.** $y = -|2x| + 5$ **9.** $y = -|2x + 5|$

1–18. See back of book.

Example 2
(page 87)

Graph each equation on a graphing calculator. Then sketch the graph.

10. $y = |x + 2| - 4$ **11.** $y = 4 - |x + 2|$ **12.** $y = 4|x + 2|$

13. $y = \frac{1}{3}|3 - 3x|$ **14.** $y = 3\left|\frac{1}{3} - \frac{1}{3}x\right|$ **15.** $y = \frac{3}{2}|x| - \frac{5}{2}$

16. $y = |x| + \frac{1}{2}|x|$ **17.** $y = \frac{1}{2}|x| - |x|$ **18.** $y = \frac{1}{2}\left|x - \frac{1}{2}\right|$

Example 3
(page 87)

Graph each equation by writing two linear equations. **19–28. See back of book.**

19. $y = |x + 6|$ **20.** $y = |3x + 6|$ **21.** $y = |3x - 6|$

22. $y = -|x - 5|$ **23.** $y = |2x + 1|$ **24.** $y = \frac{3}{2}|3x - 1|$

25. $y = |x - 2| - 6$ **26.** $y = \left|\frac{1}{2}x - 4\right| + 4$ **27.** $y = \frac{1}{2}\left|\frac{1}{2}x + 2\right| - 2$

Example 4
(page 88)

28. Manufacturing The conveyor belt at a factory operates continuously 24 hours a day, carrying vitamin bottles and moving two feet each minute. Sketch a graph showing the distance in feet from the filling arm of one bottle on the conveyor belt before and after it is filled. Use the *x*-axis for time before and after the bottle is filled and the *y*-axis for distance from the filling arm.

B **Apply Your Skills**

Match each equation with its graph. Each interval is 1 unit.

29. $y = |3x| - 4$ **B** **30.** $y = |3x - 4|$ **C** **31.** $y = 3|x - 4|$ **A** **32.** $y = |3x + 12|$ **D**

A.
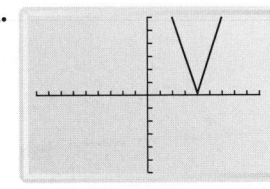

B.
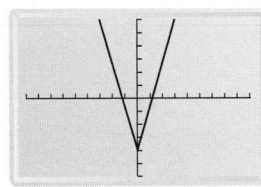

C.
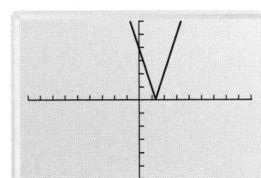

D.
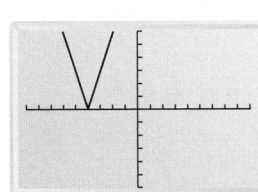

Need Help?

Before graphing, rewrite each equation as two equations.

Graph each absolute value equation. 33–50. See back of book.

33. $y = |4x + 2|$ **34.** $y = |-3x + 5|$ **35.** $y = |4 - 2x|$

36. $y = \left|-\frac{1}{4}x - 1\right|$ **37.** $y = \left|\frac{5}{2}x - 2\right|$ **38.** $y = \left|\frac{3}{2}x + 2\right|$

39. $y = |3x - 6| + 1$ **40.** $y = -|x - 3|$ **41.** $y = |2x + 6|$

42. $y = 2|x + 2| - 3$ **43.** $y = 6 - |3x|$ **44.** $y = 6 - |3x + 1|$

45. $y = -|-2x - 1| + 1$ **46.** $y = 2|x - 3|$ **47.** $y = -\frac{3}{2}\left|\frac{1}{2}x\right|$

48. $2y = \frac{1}{2}|x + 2|$ **49.** $\frac{1}{3}y - 3 = -|x + 2|$ **50.** $-3y = |3x - 6|$

51a. time and distance before and after the roadside stand

51. Travel The graph at the right models a car traveling at a constant speed.

a. Describe the relation shown in the graph.

b. Which equation best represents the relation? **A**

    A. $y = |60x|$

    B. $y = |x + 60|$

    C. $y = |60 - x|$

    D. $y = |x| + 60$

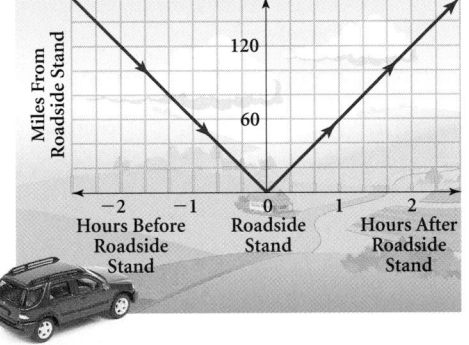

Miles From Roadside Stand

120

60

−2   −1   0   1   2

Hours Before Roadside Stand   Roadside Stand   Hours After Roadside Stand

52. a. Graph the equations $y = \left|\frac{1}{2}x - 6\right| + 3$ and $y = -\left|\frac{1}{2}x + 6\right| - 3$ on the same set of axes. **a–b. See back of book.**

    b. Writing Describe the similarities and differences in the graphs.

C **Challenge** Graph each absolute value equation. 53–58. See back of book.

53. $y = |3x| - x\left|\frac{1}{3}\right|$ **54.** $y = x - |2x|$ **55.** $y = |2x| - x$

56. $y = \frac{1}{2}|x - 3| + 5$ **57.** $y = \frac{1}{2}|x| + 4|x - 1|$ **58.** $y = |x + 1| + |x|$

59. Answers may vary. Samples:

59. a. Open-Ended Find two absolute value equations with graphs that share a vertex. $y = |x|, y = -|x|$

    b. Find two absolute value equations with graphs that share part of a ray. $y = |x|, y = |x - 1| + 1$

Lesson 2-5   Absolute Value Functions and Graphs   **89**

Assignment Guide

1 **Objective**

  A **B** Core 1–52

  C Extension 53–59

Standardized Test Prep 60–66

Mixed Review 67–82

Error Prevention

Exercises 10–18, 29–32 Students should be careful to use parentheses in the appropriate places when they enter the function on the Y= list.

Exercises 53–58 Suggest that students check their graphs by graphing the functions on a graphing calculator.

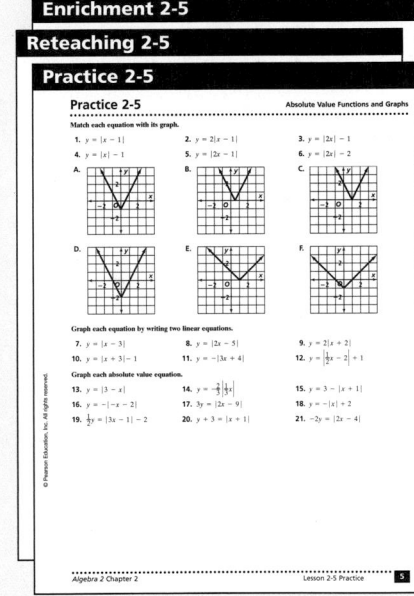

Enrichment 2-5

Reteaching 2-5

Practice 2-5

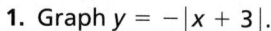

Lesson Quiz 2-5

1. Graph $y = -|x + 3|$.

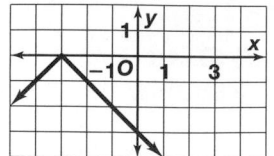

2. Graph $y = |2x - 6| - 2$.

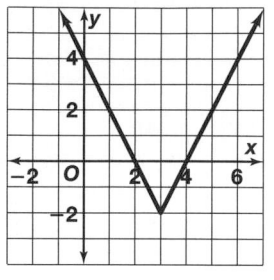

Alternative Assessment

Have students work in pairs. Each student writes a function of the form $y = |mx + b|$ and a function of the form $y = |mx + b| + c$. Students trade functions, and each graphs the functions provided by the partner. Have the partners verify that the graphs are correctly drawn.

Standardized Test Prep

 **Resources**

For additional practice with a variety of test item formats:
• Standardized Test Prep, p. 111
• Test-Taking Strategies, p. 106
• Test-Taking Strategies with Transparencies

Exercise 64 Be careful that, when you use the definition of absolute value, you rewrite the absolute value equation as two linear equations.

Standardized Test Prep

Multiple Choice

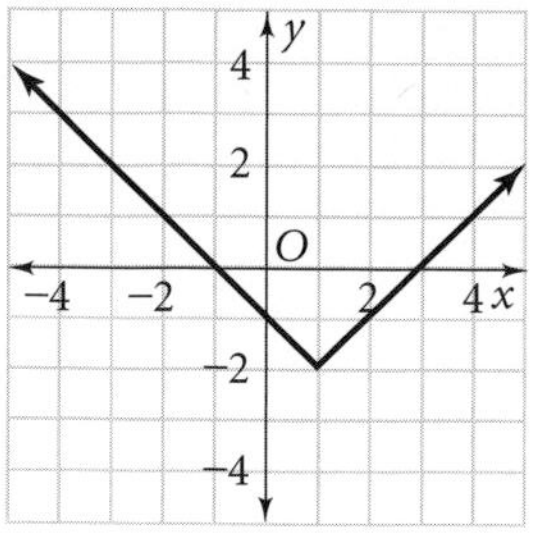

60. The graph at the right models which equation? **B**
    A. $y = |3x - 1| + 2$ B. $y = |x - 1| - 2$
    C. $y = |x - 1| + 2$ D. $y = |3x - 3| - 2$

61. What is the vertex of $y = |x| - 5$? **I**
    F. (5, 0)   G. (−5, 0)
    H. (0, 5)   I. (0, −5)

62. What is the vertex of $y = -|x| - 2$? **A**
    A. (0, −2)   B. (0, 2)
    C. (2, 0)   D. (2, −2)

Take It to the NET
Online lesson quiz at
www.PHSchool.com
Web Code: aga-0205

63. What is the vertex of $y = |x - 3| + 5$? **I**
    F. (−3, 5)   G. (−3, 11)   H. (0, 5)   I. (3, 5)

64. Which pair of linear equations represents the equation $y = |x + 3| - 4$? **C**
    A. $y = x + 1$ for $x \geq 3$ B. $y = x - 1$ for $x \geq 3$
       $y = x - 1$ for $x < 3$ $y = -x - 1$ for $x < 3$
    C. $y = x - 1$ for $x \geq -3$ D. $y = -x - 1$ for $x \geq -3$
       $y = -x - 7$ for $x < -3$ $y = -x + 7$ for $x < -3$

Short Response
65. Explain how to find the x-coordinate of the vertex of $y = |3x - 6|$.
    See margin.

Extended Response
66. How can you graph the equation $y = -|5x + 1|$ by writing two linear equations? Show both equations, and label the coordinates of the vertex in your graph. **See back of book.**

Mixed Review

Lesson 2-4
Graph each set of data. Decide whether a linear model is reasonable. If so, draw a trend line and write its equation. **67–70. See back of book.**

67. $\{(0, -5), (5, 25), (7, 44), (9, 70), (11, 90)\}$

68. $\{(-10, 0), (-4, 4), (-1, 6), (2, 8), (5, 10)\}$

69. $\{(-5, 6), (-1, 4), (0, 5), (3, 8), (4, 7)\}$

70. $\{(0, 7), (2, 6), (5, 4.5), (6, 4), (9, 2.5)\}$

Lesson 2-4
Find the slope of each line.

71. $3x + y = 1$ **−3**   72. $5y - 20x = 6$ **4**   73. $y = \frac{-x}{9}$ $-\frac{1}{9}$

74. $12x = 3y - 2$ **4**   75. $\frac{x}{2} + \frac{y}{3} = 1$ $-\frac{3}{2}$ 76. $0.1y = 0.5x + 0.1$ **5**

77. A tutor earns \$18 per hour. Write a function to model the tutor's earnings after h hours. What kind of function is this? **$y = 18h$; linear**

Lesson 1-3
Solve each equation.

78. $17x = 187$ **11**   79. $13c - 26 = 91$ **9**   80. $2(a - 6) + 11 = 25$ **13**

81. $7(b + 3) - 18(1 - b) = 103$ **4**   82. $6(m + 3) = 3(5 - m) + 66$ **7**

pages 88–90   Exercises

65. **[2]** The vertex of
    $y = |3x - 6|$
    would be where
    $3x - 6 = -(3x - 6)$
    because that would be
    where the graphs
    of both lines meet. In
    this case it is at
    $x = 2$.
    [1] only includes solution
    $x = 2$

Vertical and Horizontal Translations

 North Carolina Objectives

2.08 Use equations and inequalities with absolute value to model and solve problems; justify results. b) Interpret the constants and coefficients in the context of the problem.

Lesson Preview

What You'll Learn

OBJECTIVE 1 To analyze vertical translations

OBJECTIVE 2 To analyze horizontal translations

. . . And Why

To analyze a fabric design, as in Example 6

✓ **Check Skills You'll Need** (For help, go to Lessons 2-2 and 2-5.)

Graph each pair of functions on the same coordinate plane. **1–6. See margin p. 93.**

1. $y = x, y = x + 4$

2. $y = -2x, y = -2x - 3$

3. $y = |x|, y = |x| - 2$

4. $y = -|2x|, y = -|2x| + 1$

5. $y = |x|, y = |x - 1|$

6. $y = -\left|\frac{1}{2}x\right|, y = -\left|\frac{1}{2}x + 2\right|$

New Vocabulary • translation • parent function

✓ **Check Skills You'll Need**

Linear Equations
Lesson 2-2: Example 1
Exercises 1–8
Extra Practice, p. 823

Absolute Value Functions and Graphs
Lesson 2-5: Examples 1–3
Exercises 1–27
Extra Practice, p. 823

Lesson Resources

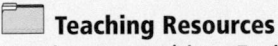 **Teaching Resources**
Practice, Reteaching, Enrichment
Checkpoint Quiz 2

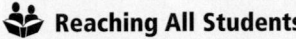 **Reaching All Students**
Practice Workbook 2-6
Spanish Practice Workbook 2-6
Reading and Math Literacy 2C
Spanish Reading & Literacy 2C
Spanish Checkpoint Quiz 2

Presentation Assistant Plus!
Transparencies
• Check Skills You'll Need 2-6
• Additional Examples 2-6
• Student Edition Answers 2-6
• Lesson Quiz 2-6
PH Presentation Pro CD 2-6

 **ASSESSMENT SYSTEM**

Checkpoint Quiz 2
Computer Test Generator CD

 **Technology**
Resource Pro® CD-ROM
Computer Test Generator CD
Prentice Hall Presentation Pro CD

 **www.PHSchool.com**
Student Site
• Teacher Web Code: agk-5500
• Graphing Calculator, Procedures 4, 5
• Self-grading Lesson Quiz
Teacher Center
• Lesson Planner
• Resources

Plus **iTEXT**

Translating Graphs Vertically

📖 **Reading Math**

Translate is a synonym for transfer.

A **translation** is an operation that shifts a graph horizontally, vertically, or both. It results in a graph of the same shape and size, in a different position.

1 EXAMPLE **Comparing Graphs**

Compare the graphs of $y = |x|$ and $y = |x| - 3$. Describe how the graph of $y = |x| - 3$ relates to the graph of $y = |x|$.

x	$y = |x|$	$y = |x| - 3$
-6	6	3
-3	3	0
0	0	-3
3	3	0
6	6	3

Make a table of values and graph the equations.

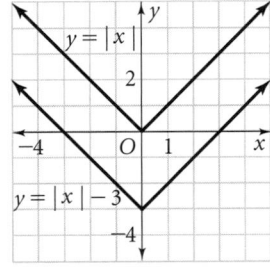

For each value of x, $y = |x| - 3$ is 3 less than the value of $y = |x|$.
● The graph of $y = |x| - 3$ is the graph of $y = |x|$ shifted 3 units down.

✓ **Check Understanding** **1** Compare the graphs of each pair of functions. Describe how the graph of the second function relates to the graph of the first function.

a. $y = x$ and $y = x + 5$
$y = x + 5$ is $y = x$ shifted 5 units up.

b. $f(x) = -|x|$ and $f(x) = -|x| + 2$
$f(x) = -|x| + 2$ is $f(x) = -|x|$ shifted 2 units up.

A family of functions is a group of functions with common characteristics. A **parent function** is the simplest function with these characteristics. A parent function and one or more translations make up a family of functions.

Let k be a positive real number. To graph the functions $y = x + k$ and $y = |x| + k$, translate the graph of the parent function up k units. To graph the functions $y = x - k$ and $y = |x| - k$, translate the graph down k units.

Lesson 2-6 Vertical and Horizontal Translations **91**

Before the Lesson
Diagnose prerequisite skills using:
• Check Skills You'll Need

During the Lesson
Monitor progress using:
• Check Understanding
• Additional Examples
• Standardized Test Prep

After the Lesson
Assess knowledge using:
• Lesson Quiz
• Computer Test Generator CD
• Chapter Checkpoint 2 (p. 98)

2. Teach

Math Background

If $f(x)$ is any function and h is a real number, then the graph of $f(x - h)$ corresponds to a horizontal translation, of h units, of the graph of $f(x)$. If k is a real number, then the graph of $f(x) + k$ corresponds to a vertical translation, of k units, of the graph of $f(x)$.

OBJECTIVE
1 Teaching Notes

1 EXAMPLE Tactile Learners

Students can trace the graph of $y = |x|$ on tracing paper and slide the traced graph straight down 3 units to check that they get the graph of $y = |x| - 3$.

2 EXAMPLE Math Tip

You may want to point out that the graph of $y = -|x|$ can be obtained by reflecting the graph of $y = |x|$ across the x-axis.

3 EXAMPLE Teaching Tip

Students can confirm that the results are correct by graphing the two equations in each part of Example 3 on a graphing calculator.

Additional Examples

1 Graph $y = |2x|$ and $y = |2x| + 3$ on the same coordinate plane. Describe how the graphs are related.

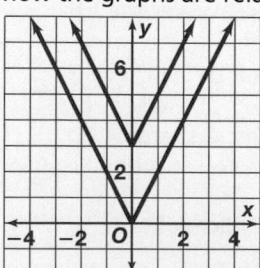

The graph of $y = |2x| + 3$ is the graph of $y = |2x|$ shifted 3 units up.

---

2 EXAMPLE **Graphing a Vertical Translation**

For each function, identify the parent function and the value of k. Then graph the function by translating the parent function.

a. $y = x - 2$

The parent function is $y = x$, and $k = 2$. Translate the graph of $y = x$ *down* 2 units.

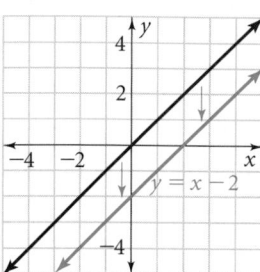

b. $y = -|x| + 3$

The parent function is $y = -|x|$, and $k = 3$. Translate the graph of $y = -|x|$ *up* 3 units.

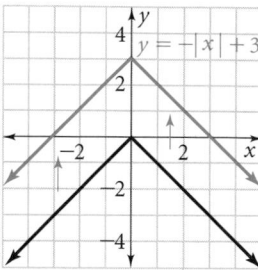

Real-World Connection

Translations of two lines result in the diamond shapes in this window.

✓ **Check Understanding** **2** Identify each parent function and the value of k. Then graph each function by translating the parent function. **See left.**

a. $y = |x| - 1$

b. $y = 3x + 5$

2a. $y = |x|, k = 1$

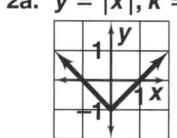

b. $y = 3x, k = 5$

You can write an equation for a translation.

3 EXAMPLE **Writing Equations for Vertical Translations**

Write an equation for each translation.

a. $y = 2x$, 4 units down

The graph of $y = 2x$, shifted 4 units down, means $k = 4$.

An equation is $y = 2x - 4$.

b. $y = \left|\frac{1}{4}x\right|$, $\frac{1}{2}$ unit up

The graph of $y = \left|\frac{1}{4}x\right|$, shifted $\frac{1}{2}$ unit up, means $k = \frac{1}{2}$.

An equation is $y = \left|\frac{1}{4}x\right| + \frac{1}{2}$.

✓ **Check Understanding** **3** Write an equation for each translation.

a. $y = |3x|$, 2 units down

$y = |3x| - 2$

b. $y = \frac{1}{3}x$, 3 units up

$y = \frac{1}{3}x + 3$

OBJECTIVE
2 Translating Graphs Horizontally

Horizontal translations share some of the characteristics of vertical translations.

Let h be a positive real number. Then $y = |x + h|$ translates the graph of $y = |x|$ h units to the left, and $y = |x - h|$ translates the graph h units to the right.

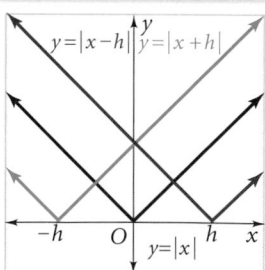

92   Chapter 2   Functions, Equations, and Graphs

Reaching All Students

Below Level As a memory device to help students recognize whether a function is translated horizontally or vertically, the h in $f(x - h)$ could signify a _h_orizontal translation.

Advanced Learners Challenge students to find examples of the artwork of M. C. Escher, and explain how the artist used translations to create his intricate drawings.

Tactile Learners
See note on page 92.
Diversity
See note on page 93.

4 EXAMPLE Graphing Horizontal Translations

For each function, identify the parent function and the value of h. Then graph the function by translating the parent function.

a. $y = |x + 3|$

The parent function is $y = |x|$, and $h = 3$. The plus sign means translate to the left.
Translate the graph of $y = |x|$ *left* 3 units.

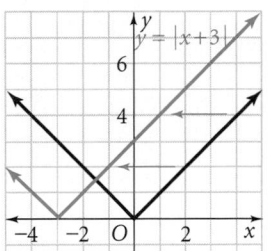

b. $y = -|x - 2|$

The parent function is $y = -|x|$, and $h = 2$. The minus sign means translate to the right.
Translate the graph of $y = -|x|$ *right* 2 units.

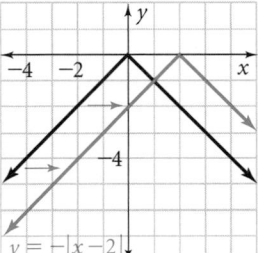

4a. $y = |x|$, $h = 1$

✓ Check Understanding

4 Identify each parent function and the value of h. Then graph each function by translating the parent function.

a. $y = |x - 1|$

b. $y = -\left|x + \frac{5}{2}\right|$

$y = -|x|$, $h = \frac{5}{2}$

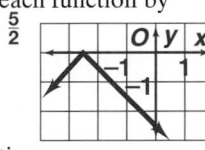

Need Help?

Graph the parent function before you graph the translation.

You can write a horizontal translation from a graph of a function.

5 EXAMPLE Writing Equations for Horizontal Translations

The blue graph at the right is a translation of $y = |x|$. Write an equation for the graph.

This is the graph of $y = |x|$ translated 5 units to the right. A shift to the right calls for an equation of the form $y = |x - h|$. An equation for the graph is $y = |x - 5|$.

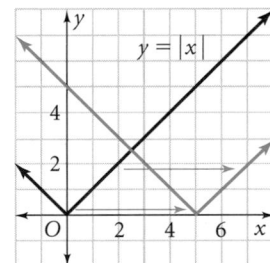

✓ Check Understanding

5 Each graph is a translation of $y = |x|$. Write an equation for each graph.

a.

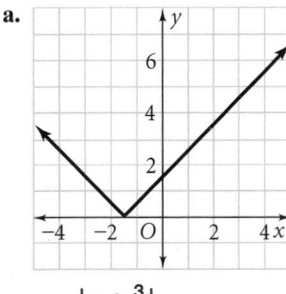

$y = \left|x + \frac{3}{2}\right|$

b.

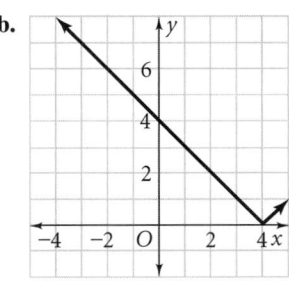

$y = |x - 4|$

Lesson 2-6 Vertical and Horizontal Translations **93**

Additional Examples

2 Identify the parent function for $y = 2x - 3$ and the value of k. Then, graph the function by translating the parent function.
parent function: $y = 2x$; $k = -3$

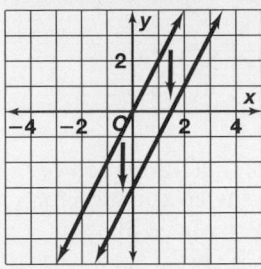

3 Write an equation to translate the graph of $y = |4x|$, down 5 units. $y = |4x| - 5$

OBJECTIVE

2 Teaching Notes

4 EXAMPLE Teaching Tip

Students may find it difficult to understand that the plus sign in part (a) means to move to the left and the minus sign in part (b) means to move to the right. Encourage students to make a table of values for each given function along with its parent function. Have students find an ordered pair for the given function and an ordered pair for the parent function that have the same y-value. Then, have students examine their x-values and discuss how this helps them determine which direction to shift the given function.

6 EXAMPLE Diversity

Invite students to look for patterned textile designs that they can described with translations. Focus on those that might relate to diverse cultural backgrounds.

7 EXAMPLE Math Tip

In each part of the Example, the student can translate the parent graph horizontally and then translate the resulting graph vertically.

---

page 91 Check Skills You'll Need

1.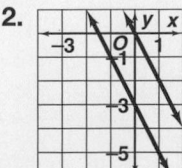

2.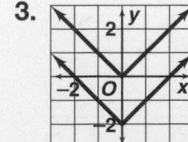

3.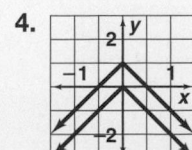

4.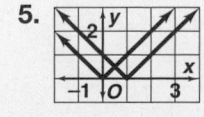

5.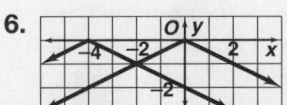

6.

4 Identify the parent function and the value of h for $y = |x - 5|$. Graph both functions.
parent function: $y = |x|$; $h = 5$

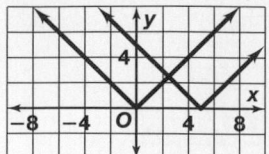

5 The graph is a translation of $y = -|x|$. Write an equation for the graph. $y = -|x + 3|$

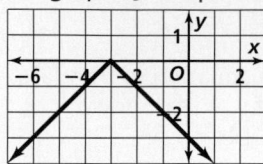

6 Describe a possible translation of Figures M and N in the design shown below.

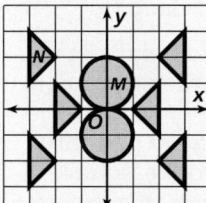

Figure M: 2 units down; Figure N: 4 units down, or else 1 unit right and 2 units down

7 Graph $y = |x + 1| + 2$.

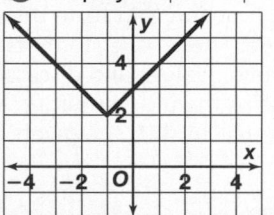

8 Write an equation for each translation of $y = |x|$.
a. 3 units up, 7 units right
$y = |x - 7| + 3$
b. 5 units down, 1 unit left
$y = |x + 1| - 5$

Closure

Suppose h and k are positive numbers. How is the graph of $y = |x - h| + k$ related to the graph of the parent function $y = |x|$? **The graph of $y = |x - h| + k$ is a translation of the parent graph h units right and k units up.**

You can combine vertical and horizontal translations to produce diagonal translations.

6 EXAMPLE Real-World Connection

Fabric Design Describe a possible translation of Figures A and B in the Nigerian textile design below.

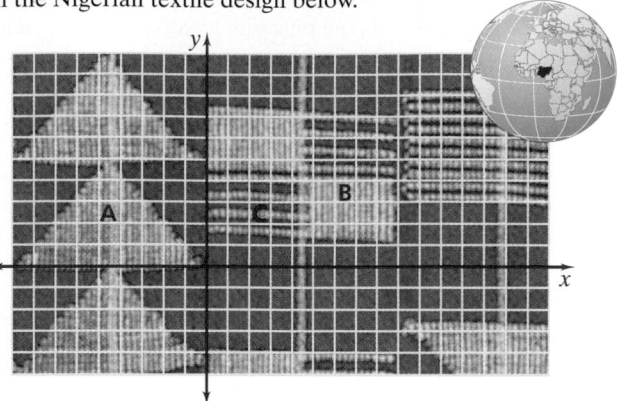

A translation of Figure A: A translation of Figure B:
5 units up or 5 units down   about 5 units left and about 3 units up

✔ **Check Understanding** **6** Describe a possible translation of Figure C in the textile design.
Answers may vary. Sample: 4.5 units right and 3 units up

You can use a parent function to graph a diagonal translation.

7 EXAMPLE Graphing Diagonal Translations

Graph each function.
a. $y = |x - 3| + 1$

The parent function is $y = |x|$, so $h = 3$, and $k = 1$.

The minus sign means move h units to the right. The plus sign means move k units up.

Place the vertex at $(3, 1)$, and draw the graph opening upward.

b. $f(x) = -|x + 2| - 4$

The parent function is $f(x) = -|x|$, so $h = 2$, and $k = 4$.

The plus sign means move h units to the left. The minus sign means move k units down.

Place the vertex at $(-2, -4)$, and draw the graph opening downward.

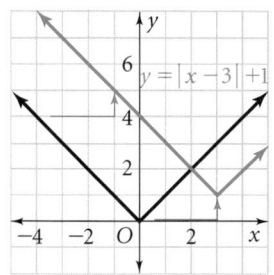

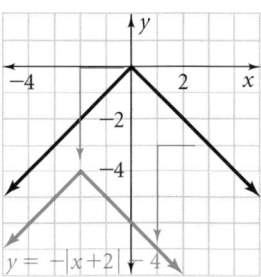

7.

✔ **Check Understanding** **7** Graph the function $f(x) = |x + 5| + 3$. **See left.**

94   Chapter 2   Functions, Equations, and Graphs

pages 95–98   Exercises

5. $y = x, k = 3$

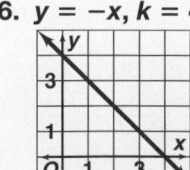

6. $y = -x, k = 4$

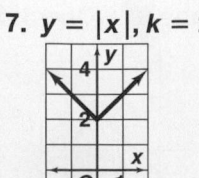

7. $y = |x|, k = 2$

You can write an equation to describe a diagonal translation.

8 EXAMPLE Writing Diagonal Translations

Write an equation for each translation.

a. $y = |x|$, 2 units down, 3 units left

3 units left → $h = 3$; plus sign

2 units down → $k = 2$; minus sign

An equation is $y = |x + 3| - 2$.

b. $f(x) = -|x|$, 1 unit up, $\frac{1}{2}$ unit right

$\frac{1}{2}$ unit right → $h = \frac{1}{2}$; minus sign

1 unit up → $k = 1$; plus sign

An equation is $f(x) = -\left|x - \frac{1}{2}\right| + 1$.

✓ **Check Understanding** **8** Write an equation for each translation.

a. $g(x) = |x|$, 1 unit down, 7 units right

$g(x) = |x - 7| - 1$

b. $y = -|x|$, 4 units up, 3 units right

$y = -|x - 3| + 4$

EXERCISES

For more practice, see *Extra Practice*.

Practice and Problem Solving

A **Practice by Example**

Example 1
(page 91)

Compare the graphs of each pair of functions. Describe how the graph of the second function relates to the graph of the first function.

1. $y = -|x|$, $y = -|x| + 3$ **3 units up**

2. $f(x) = |x|$, $f(x) = |x| - 1$ **1 unit down**

3. $g(x) = |3x|$, $g(x) = |3x| + 2$ **2 units up**

4. $y = \frac{1}{2}|x|$, $y = \frac{1}{2}|x| - \frac{2}{3}$ **$\frac{2}{3}$ units down**

Example 2
(page 92)

For each function, identify the parent function and the value of k. Then graph the function by translating the parent function.   **5–7. See margin p. 94.**

5. $y = x - 3$ **6.** $y = -x + 4$ **7.** $y = |x| + 2$ **8.** $y = -|x| - 6$

See back of book.

Example 3
(page 92)

Write an equation for each vertical translation.

9. $y = x$, $\frac{2}{3}$ units down
$y = x - \frac{2}{3}$

10. $y = |x|$, 4 units up
$y = |x| + 4$

11. $y = -|x|$, 2 units up
$y = -|x| + 2$

Example 4
(page 93)

For each function, identify the parent function and the value of h. Then graph the function by translating the parent function.   **12–15. See margin.**

12. $y = |x - 4|$ **13.** $y = |x + 5|$ **14.** $y = -|x - 1|$ **15.** $y = -|x + 2|$

Example 5
(page 93)

Write an equation for each horizontal translation of $y = |x|$ or $y = -|x|$.

16.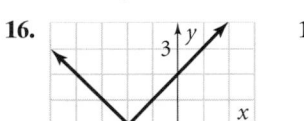

$y = |x + 2|$

17.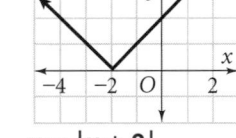

$y = |x - 3|$

18.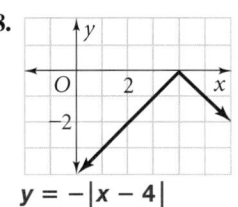

$y = -|x - 4|$

Example 6
(page 94)

Describe a possible translation for each figure.

19. Answers may vary.
Sample: 4.5 units
to the left.

20. Answers may vary.
Sample: $\frac{17}{4}$ units
to the right.

19.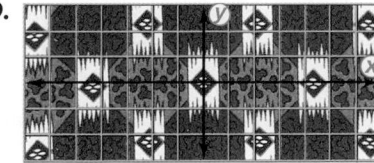

20.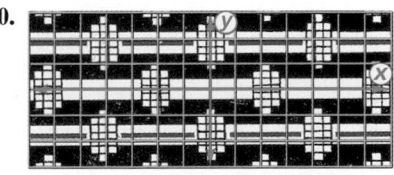

Lesson 2-6 Vertical and Horizontal Translations   **95**

12. $y = |x|$, $h = 4$

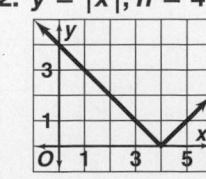

13. $y = |x|$, $h = 5$

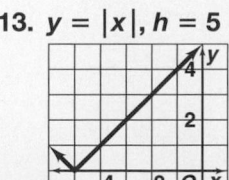

14. $y = -|x|$, $h = 1$

15. $y = -|x|$, $h = 2$

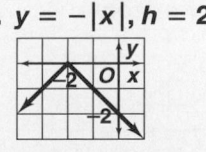

95

3. Practice

Assignment Guide

▼ **1 Objective**
 Ⓐ Ⓑ **Core** 1–11
 Ⓒ **Extension** 56

▼ **2 Objective**
 Ⓐ Ⓑ **Core** 12–55
 Ⓒ **Extension** 57–61

Standardized Test Prep 62–65

Mixed Review 66–72

Error Prevention

Exercises 12–18 Students often forget that when $h > 0$, replacing x with $x - h$ in the parent function translates the graph to the *right*. Replacing x with $x + h$ when $h > 0$ translates the graph to the *left*.

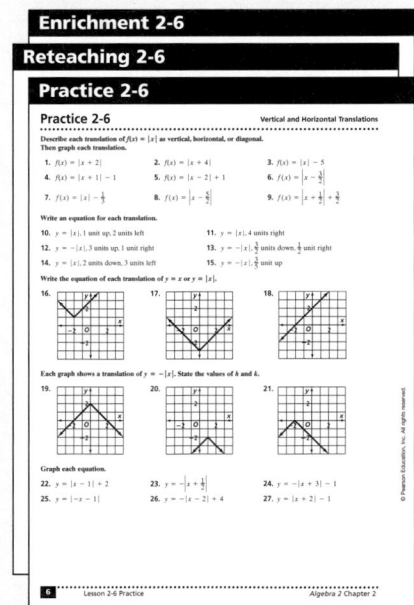

Exercise 26 You may want to point out to students that $y = |x + 2| - 3$ is an equivalent equation to $y = |-x - 2| - 3$ since the absolute values of opposites are equal.

Exercises 31, 35 Students may see that these translations may be viewed either as horizontal or vertical translations.

pages 95–98 Exercises

21.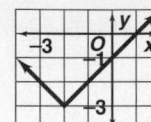

22.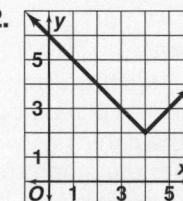

23.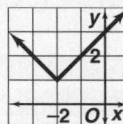

24.

25.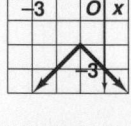

26.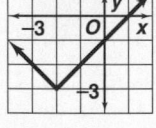

31. vertical
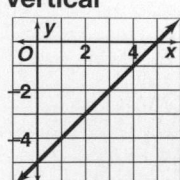

32. diagonal

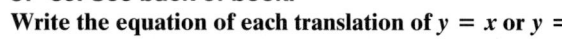

Example 7 (page 94)

Graph each function. 21–26. See margin.

21. $y = |x + 2| - 3$ **22.** $y = |x - 4| + 2$ **23.** $y = |x + 2| + 1$

24. $y = |x - 1| - 2$ **25.** $y = -|x + 1| - 2$ **26.** $y = |-x - 2| - 3$

Example 8 (page 95)

Write an equation for each translation.

27. $y = |x|$, 1 unit down, 3 units right $y = |x - 3| - 1$

28. $y = -|x|$, 2 units up, 1 unit left $y = -|x + 1| + 2$

29. $y = -|x|$, $\frac{1}{2}$ unit up, $2\frac{1}{2}$ units right $y = -|x - \frac{5}{2}| + \frac{1}{2}$

30. $y = |x|$, 3 units up, 7 units right $y = |x - 7| + 3$

 Apply Your Skills

Describe each translation of $f(x) = x$ or $f(x) = |x|$ as *vertical*, *horizontal*, or *diagonal*. Then graph each translation. 31–36. See margin.

31. $f(x) = x - 5$ **32.** $f(x) = |x - 5| + 3$ **33.** $f(x) = |x + 1|$

34. $f(x) = |x| + 1$ **35.** $f(x) = x + \frac{1}{2}$ **36.** $f(x) = |x| - 3$

37. $f(x) = |x - 2| + 3$ **38.** $f(x) = |x + 4| - 2$ **39.** $f(x) = |x - 3| - 6$

37–39. See back of book.

Write the equation of each translation of $y = x$ or $y = |x|$. Each interval is 1 unit.

40. 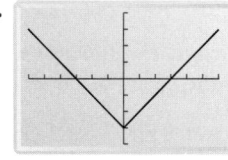   **41.** 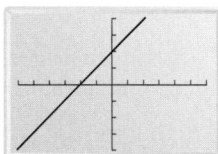   **42.**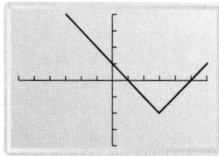

$y = |x| - 3$ $y = x + 2$ $y = |x - 3| - 2$

Each graph shows a translation of $y = -|x|$. State the values of h and k.

43. 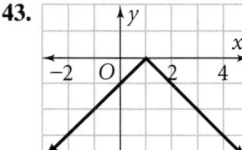   **44.** 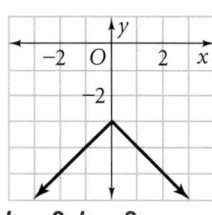   **45.**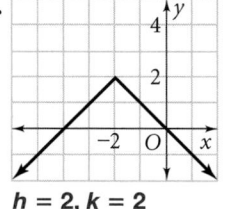

$h = 1, k = 0$ $h = 0, k = 3$ $h = 2, k = 2$

47. Answers may vary. Sample: Since a vert. translation affects only y-values and a horiz. translation affects only x-values, order is irrelevant.

48a.

46. Data Analysis Suppose you plot data with years as the independent variable. What type of translation are you making when you start with $x = 0$ rather than a year such as 1998? Explain. **Horizontal; the graph is shifted left.**

47. Writing Explain why applying a vertical translation and then a horizontal translation produces the same result as applying a horizontal translation and then a vertical translation. **See left.**

48. a. Graph the equation $y = 3x$ on a coordinate plane.
 b. Translate the graph 5 units up. Write an equation for the new line. $y = 3x + 5$
 c. Translate the graph from part (b) 2 units right. Write an equation for the new line. $y = 3x - 1$
 d. Which equation describes the line you graphed in part (c)? **E**
  A. $y = 3x + 5$ **B.** $y = 3x + 2$ **C.** $y = 3x - 2$
  D. $y = 3(x - 5) + 2$ **E.** $y = 3(x - 2) + 5$
 e. Critical Thinking Write the equation of the translation of $y = mx$ that has a graph passing through point (h, k). $y = m(x - h) + k$

49. Open-Ended Draw a figure in Quadrant I. Use a translation to move your figure into Quadrant III. Describe your translation. **Check students' work.**

96   Chapter 2 Functions, Equations, and Graphs

33. horizontal
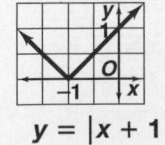
$y = |x + 1|$

34. vertical

35. vertical
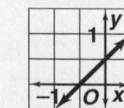

36. vertical
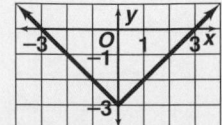

96

Need Help?

Use the form
$y = |x \pm h| \pm k$ for diagonal translations of absolute value functions.

Each graph shows an absolute value function after a translation 4 units up and 3 units left. Write the equation of the original function.

50.

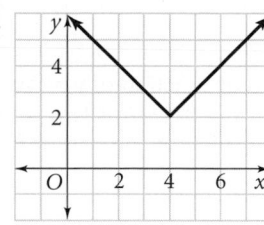

$y = |x - 7| - 2$

51.

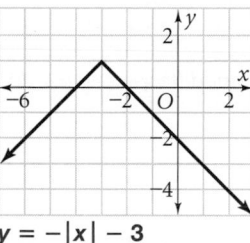

$y = -|x| - 3$

Write an equation for each translation.

52. $y = -|x|$; vertex $(-5, 0)$
$y = -|x + 5|$

53. $y = x$; through $(-4, 3)$ $y = x + 7$

54. $y = |x|$; vertex (a, b)
$y = |x - a| + b$

55. $y = x$; through (p, q)
$y = x + (q - p)$

C **Challenge**

Graph each pair of functions on the same coordinate plane. Describe the translation that takes the first function to the second function.

56. $y = |x + 1|, y = |x - 5|$

57. $y = |x| + 3, y = |x - 4|$

58. $y = |x - 3|, y = |x| + 1$

59. $y = |x + 1| - 1, y = |x - 2| + 2$

56–59. See back of book.

60a.

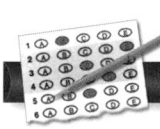

**b. Answers may vary.
Sample: It is a function because each t is paired with a unique height.**

60. Suppose you are playing with a yo-yo, as shown at the right.
a. Sketch a graph of $h(t)$ to show the height h of the yo-yo above the floor over time t. At $t = 0$, the yo-yo leaves your hand.
b. **Critical Thinking** Should your graph be that of a function? Explain.
c. Suppose you demonstrate your yo-yo ability on an auditorium stage that is 5 ft above the floor. Describe the translation of the graph of $h(t)$ that represents the height of the yo-yo above the auditorium floor. **vertical translation 5 ft up**
d. Choose a function $g(t)$ that represents the height of the yo-yo above the auditorium floor when you are on stage. **C**
 A. $g(t) = h(t + 5)$ **B.** $g(t) = h(t - 5)$
 C. $g(t) = h(t) + 5$ **D.** $g(t) = h(t) - 5$

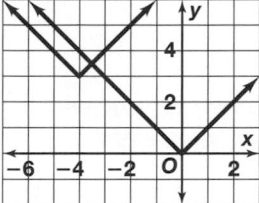

3 ft

61. Use the graph of the function $y = f(x)$ at the right. Sketch the graph of each function.
a. $f(x + 1)$ **a–c. See margin.**
b. $f(x) - 2$
c. $f(x + 2) + 1$

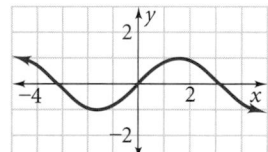

Standardized Test Prep

Multiple Choice

62. Which translation takes $y = |x + 2| - 1$ to $y = |x| + 2$? **C**
 A. 2 units right, 3 units down   **B.** 2 units left, 3 units up
 C. 2 units right, 3 units up   **D.** 2 units left, 3 units down

63. The graph of which equation will NOT have a y-intercept of 5? **H**
 F. $y = |x| + 5$ **G.** $y = |x - 5|$ **H.** $y = |x - 5| + 5$ **I.** $y = |x + 5|$

Lesson 2-6 Vertical and Horizontal Translations **97**

61a.
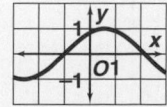

b.
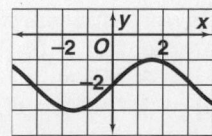

c.
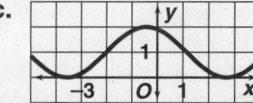

4. Assess

Lesson Quiz 2-6

1. Graph $y = |x|$ and $y = |x + 4| + 3$ on the same coordinate plane. Describe the translation that takes the graph of the parent function to the graph of the other function.

Translate the parent graph 4 units left and 3 units up.

2. Write equations for the graphs obtained by translating $y = |x|$ and $y = -|x|$ as described.

 a. 10 units right
 $y = |x - 10|; y = -|x - 10|$

 b. 4 units down
 $y = |x| - 4; y = -|x| - 4$

 c. 7 units left, 6 units up
 $y = |x + 7| + 6;$
 $y = -|x + 7| + 6$

Alternative Assessment

Have students work in groups of three. Students create six cards, three with $y = |x$ (sign) $h|$ (sign) k and three with $y = -|x$ (sign) $h|$ (sign) k, respectively. They place the cards in a box. Students then create six different positive values of h on one card each and six different positive values of k on one card each and place the values of h in one box and the values of k in another box. In a fourth box students place twelve cards, six with a minus sign written and six with a plus sign. A student draws once from the first three boxes and twice from the fourth box. Then, the student writes and graphs the function represented, using the signs in the order drawn. Students repeat until all cards have been drawn and check each other's work.

97

📁 **Resources**

For additional practice with a variety of test item formats:
- Standardized Test Prep, p. 111
- Test-Taking Strategies, p. 106
- Test-Taking Strategies with Transparencies

Exercise 62 One way to approach this question is first to identify the vertex of each graph. Then, describe the translation that takes the first vertex to the second vertex.

To check understanding of Lessons 2-4 to 2-6:

Checkpoint Quiz 2 (p. 98)

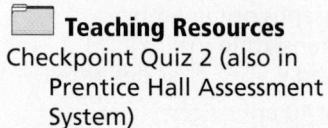 **Teaching Resources**

Checkpoint Quiz 2 (also in Prentice Hall Assessment System)

👥 **Reaching All Students**

Reading and Math Literacy 2C

Spanish versions available

---

pages 95–98 Exercises

65. **[4] The graph of**
$y = |x + 3| - 2$ **is**
$y = |x|$ **first translated 3 units to the left for**
$y = |x + 3|$ **and then 2 units down for**
$y = |x + 3| - 2.$

[3] includes equations and graph with no explanation

[2] includes either the translation equations OR graph

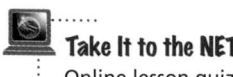
Take It to the NET
Online lesson quiz at
www.PHSchool.com
Web Code: aga-0206

Extended Response

64. The graph of $y = |x - 1|$ is translated 3 units left and 2 units down. What is the equation of the new graph? **A**
   A. $y = |x + 2| - 2$ **B.** $y = |x - 4| - 2$
   C. $y = |x + 4| + 2$ **D.** $y = |x - 4| + 2$

65. Start with the parent function of $y = |x + 3| - 2$. Explain how to describe the graph of $y = |x + 3| - 2$ as two consecutive translations of the parent function. Include graphs of the parent function and each translation. **See margin.**

Mixed Review

Lesson 2-5   Evaluate each function for five values of *x*. Then graph each function.

66. $f(x) = |x - 3| + 2$ 67. $f(x) = |2x + 1| - 3$ 68. $f(x) = \frac{1}{3}\left|\frac{1}{3}x - 3\right|$
66. See margin. 67–71. See back of book.

Lesson 1-4   Solve each inequality. Graph each solution on a number line.

69. $x + 7 \le -3$ 70. $2a + 6 > 15$ 71. $7.5 - 3b < 12$

Lesson 1-3 📦 72. **Geometry** Keiko, an orca whale who starred in a number of movies, moved into an outdoor pool with a volume of 281,250 cubic feet. The pool's surface is 150 ft by 75 ft. Write and solve an equation to find the depth of the pool.
$150 \cdot 75 \cdot x = 281{,}250$; 25 ft

✓ Checkpoint Quiz 2   Lessons 2-4 through 2-6

📱 **ITEXT** Instant self-check quiz online and on CD-ROM

Graph each function. 1–6. See back of book.

1. $y = x - 5$ 2. $y = |x + 1| + 4$ 3. $f(x) = \frac{2}{3}x - 2$
4. $f(x) = |x| - 4$ 5. $y = |2x - 1| - 2$ 6. $y = 3x + 3$

Write an equation for each graph.

7.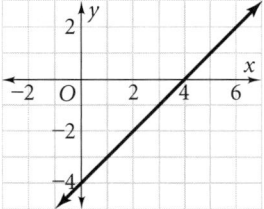
$y = x - 4$

8.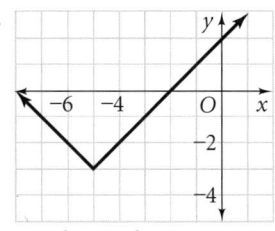
$y = |x + 5| - 3$

9. **a.** Use the table below. Model the relation with a scatter plot and a trend line.
   b. Predict the value of *y* when $x = 10$. **about 7**

9a.
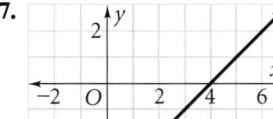

x	1.0	2.0	3.0	4.0	5.0	6.0	7.0
y	−1.5	0.0	1.5	2.0	2.5	3.5	4.0

10. The graph of $y = |x|$ is translated down 5 units and right 4 units. What is the equation of the new graph? **D**
   A. $y = |x + 4| + 5$ **B.** $y = |x + 4| - 5$
   C. $y = |x - 4| + 5$ **D.** $y = |x - 4| - 5$

[1] attempts to interpret the translation for $y = |x + 3| - 2$ **and graphs it but makes an error and does not translate it 3 units left and 2 units down**

66. **Answers may vary. Sample:** $f(0) = 5$; $f(1) = 4$; $f(2) = 3$; $f(3) = 2$; $f(-1) = 6$

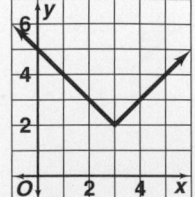

Two-Variable Inequalities

 **North Carolina Objectives**

2.08 Use equations and inequalities with absolute value to model and solve problems; justify results. a) Solve using tables, graphs, and algebraic properties.

Lesson Preview

What You'll Learn

 OBJECTIVE 1 To graph linear inequalities

 OBJECTIVE 2 To graph absolute value inequalities

. . . And Why

To solve problems involving combinations, as in Example 2

✓ **Check Skills You'll Need** (For help, go to Lessons 1-4 and 1-5.)

Solve each inequality. Graph the solution on a number line.

1. $12p \le 15$ **2.** $4 + t > 17$ **3.** $5 - 2t \ge 11$

1–6. See back of book.

Solve and graph each absolute value equation or inequality.

4. $|4c| = 18$ **5.** $|5 - b| = 3$ **6.** $|2h| \ge 7$

New Vocabulary • linear inequality

 TEXT Interactive lesson includes instant self-check, tutorials, and activities.

OBJECTIVE 1 **Graphing Linear Inequalities**

Investigation: Linear Inequalities

1. Graph the line $y = 2x + 3$ on graph paper. **1–2. See back of book.**

2. a. Plot each point listed below.
$(-2, -3), (-2, -1), (-1, -1), (-1, 5), (0, 4), (0, 5), (1, 6), (2, 3), (2, 7)$
b. Classify each point as *on the line*, *above the line*, or *below the line*.

3. Are all the points that satisfy the inequality $y > 2x + 3$ *above*, *below*, or *on* the line? **above the line**

Need Help?

< less than
≤ less than or equal to
> greater than
≥ greater than or equal to
≠ not equal to

A **linear inequality** is an inequality in two variables whose graph is a region of the coordinate plane that is bounded by a line. To graph a linear inequality, first graph the boundary line. Then decide which side of the line contains solutions to the inequality and whether the boundary line is included.

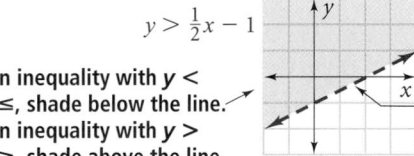

$y > \frac{1}{2}x - 1$

For an inequality with $y <$ or $y \le$, shade below the line. For an inequality with $y >$ or $y \ge$, shade above the line.

A *dashed* boundary line indicates that the line is not part of the solution.

A *solid* boundary line indicates that the line is part of the solution.

Choose a test point above or below the boundary line. The test point $(0, 0)$ makes the inequality true. Shade the region containing this point.

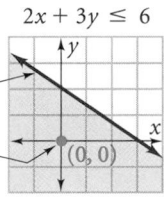

$2x + 3y \le 6$

$(0, 0)$

✓ **Ongoing Assessment and Intervention**

Before the Lesson	**During the Lesson**	**After the Lesson**
Diagnose prerequisite skills using:	**Monitor progress using:**	**Assess knowledge using:**
• Check Skills You'll Need	• Check Understanding	• Lesson Quiz
	• Additional Examples	• Computer Test Generator CD
	• Standardized Test Prep	

---

1. Plan

Lesson Preview

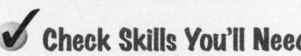 ✓ **Check Skills You'll Need**

Solving Inequalities
Lesson 1-4: Example 1
Exercises 1–6
Extra Practice, p. 822

Absolute Value Equations and Inequalities
Lesson 1-5: Example 4
Exercises 16–21
Extra Practice, p. 822

Lesson Resources

📁 **Teaching Resources**
Practice, Reteaching, Enrichment

👥 **Reaching All Students**
Practice Workbook 2-7
Spanish Practice Workbook 2-7

⏲ **Presentation Assistant Plus!**
Transparencies
• Check Skills You'll Need 2-7
• Additional Examples 2-7
• Student Edition Answers 2-7
• Lesson Quiz 2-7
PH Presentation Pro CD 2-7

 **PRENTICE HALL ASSESSMENT SYSTEM**

Computer Test Generator CD

💿 **Technology**
Resource Pro® CD-ROM
Computer Test Generator CD
Prentice Hall Presentation Pro CD

🖥 **www.PHSchool.com**
Student Site
• Teacher Web Code: agk-5500
• Graphing Calculator, Procedure 8
• Self-grading Lesson Quiz
Teacher Center
• Lesson Planner
• Resources

Plus  **TEXT**

2. Teach

Math Background

Graphing a two-variable inequality is the first step in learning how to graph a system of two-variable inequalities. Such systems play an important role in many applications, including maximizing and minimizing linear functions given a set of linear constants. This topic will be studied in Lesson 3-4.

OBJECTIVE

▼ Teaching Notes

Investigation (Optional)

A vertical line in the coordinate plane will always intersect the graph of $y = 2x + 3$. Points on the vertical line that lie above the point of intersection have coordinates that satisfy $y > 2x + 3$. Points on the vertical line that lie below the point of intersection have coordinates that satisfy $y < 2x + 3$.

1 EXAMPLE Alternative Method

You can also test points to decide which region to shade. Pick a point above the line and a point below the line. The coordinates of the point below the line will satisfy the inequality, but those of the point above the line will not. This tells you that the region below the line is the region to shade.

2 EXAMPLE Teaching Tip

Question 2b in the check understanding part of Example 2 provides a good opportunity to discuss how mathematical results must be interpreted in the light of restrictions imposed by a specific situation.

---

1 EXAMPLE Graphing a Linear Inequality

Graph the inequality $y < \frac{1}{2}x - 3$.

1a.

b.

Step 1 Graph the boundary line $y = \frac{1}{2}x - 3$. Since the inequality is *less than,* not *less than or equal to,* use a dashed boundary line.

Step 2 Since the inequality is *less than,* y-values must be less than those on the boundary line. Shade the region *below* the boundary line.

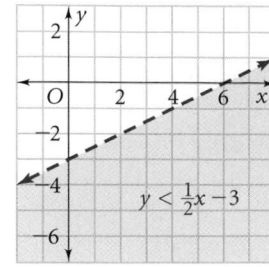

$y < \frac{1}{2}x - 3$

✓ **Check Understanding** ① Graph each inequality.   **a–b. See left.**

a. $4x + 2y \le 4$ **b.** $y \ge 3x$ **c.** $\frac{x}{3} < -y + 2$

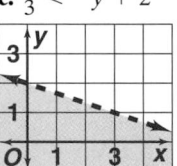

You can use linear inequalities to solve problems.

2 EXAMPLE Real-World 🌐 Connection

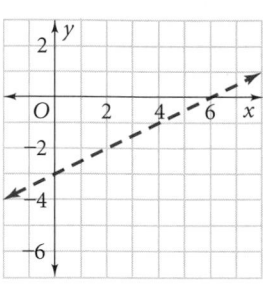

Entertainment At least 35 performers of the Big Tent Circus are in the grand finale. Some pile into cars, while others balance on bicycles. Seven performers are in each car, and five performers are on each bicycle. Draw a graph showing all the possible combinations of cars and bicycles that could be used in the finale.

Relate | the number of performers in cars | plus | the number of performers on bicycles | is greater than or equal to | 35 |

Define Let x = the number of cars.

Let y = the number of bicycles.

Write $7x$ $+$ $5y$ $\ge$ 35

Step 1 Find the intercepts of the boundary line. Use the intercepts to graph the boundary line.

When $y = 0$, $7x + 5(0) = 35$.   When $x = 0$, $7(0) + 5y = 35$.
$7x = 35$ $5y = 35$
$x = 5$ $y = 7$

Graph the intercepts $(5, 0)$ and $(0, 7)$. Since the inequality is *greater than or equal to,* use a solid boundary line.

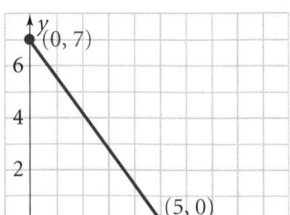

100   Chapter 2   Linear Relationships and Functions

👥 Reaching All Students

| **Below Level** Tell students to look at the inequality symbol to determine whether the boundary line is dashed or solid. The line in the symbol should be a signal to draw a solid line. | **Advanced Learners** Challenge students to explain why the graph of an absolute value function might end at the *x*- or *y*-axis like the graph in Example 2. | **Alternative Method** See note on page 100. **Error Prevention** See note on page 103. |

Step 2 Choose a test point not on the boundary line. The test point $(6, 4)$ makes the inequality true. Shade the region containing $(6, 4)$.

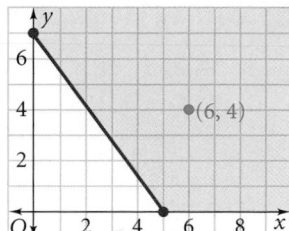

All ordered pairs with whole-number coordinates that are in the shaded area represent a combination of cars x and bicycles y that could be used in the grand finale.

 Check Understanding **2 a.** Find the minimum number of bicycles that will be needed if three cars are available. Then determine three other possible combinations of bicycles and cars. **at least 3; (2, 5), (1, 6), (0, 7)**

b. Critical Thinking Give the domain and range for Example 2. Justify your reasoning. **Domain and range are all whole numbers; only whole numbers of bicycles and cars make sense.**

OBJECTIVE

2 **Graphing Two-Variable Absolute Value Inequalities**

You can graph two-variable absolute value inequalities the same way you graph linear inequalities.

Need Help?

To review graphing absolute value functions, go to Lesson 2-5.

3 **EXAMPLE** **Graphing Absolute Value Inequalities**

Graph each absolute value inequality.

a. $y \leq |x - 4| + 5$

Graph $y = |x - 4| + 5$.
Since the inequality is *less than or equal to,* the boundary is solid and the shaded region is below the boundary.

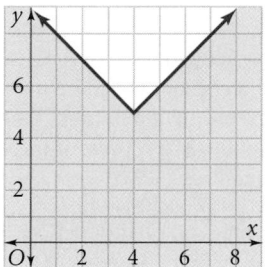

b. $-y + 3 > |x + 1|$

$$-y > |x + 1| - 3$$
$$y < -|x + 1| + 3$$

Graph $y = -|x + 1| + 3$.

Since the inequality is *less than,* the boundary is dashed and the shaded region is below the boundary.

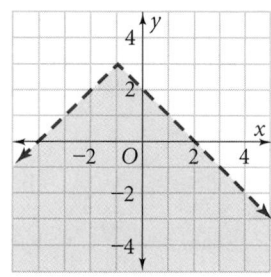

 Check Understanding **3** Graph each absolute value inequality. **See margin.**
a. $y > -|x + 2| - 3$
b. $2y + 3 \leq -|x - 5|$

1 Graph $y > \frac{3}{2}x + 1$.

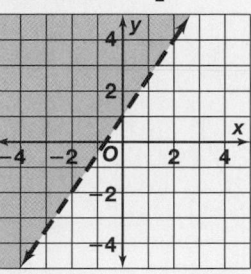

2 A restaurant has only 15 eggs to last until the next delivery. An order of scrambled eggs requires 2 eggs. An omelet requires 3 eggs. Write an inequality to model all possible combinations of orders of scrambled eggs and omelets the restaurant can fill till more eggs arrive. Graph the inequality.
If x = orders of scrambled eggs and y = omelet orders, then $2x + 3y \leq 15$. All ordered pairs with whole-number coordinates in the shaded area and on the line represent a combination of x orders of scrambled eggs and y orders of omelets that the restaurant can fill.

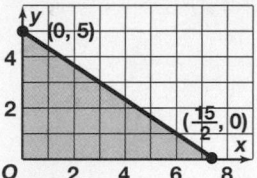

OBJECTIVE

2 **Teaching Notes**

3 **EXAMPLE** **Math Tip**

Verify that the correct region is shaded by picking a point in the shaded region and making sure that it satisfies the inequality.

4 **EXAMPLE** **Math Tip**

Discuss why it is helpful to have the variable y alone on the left side of the inequality.

page 101 **Check Understanding**

3a.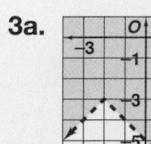

b.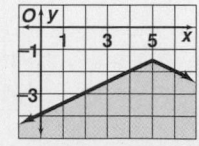

101

3 Graph $y \geq |2x| - 3$.

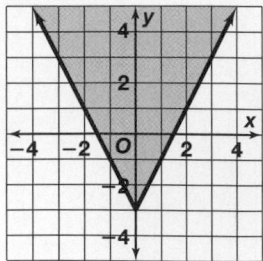

4 Write an inequality for each graph. The boundary line is given.

a. boundary: $y = |x - 2| - 1$

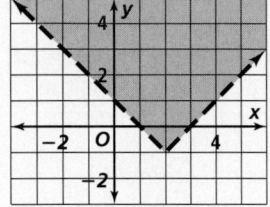

$y > |x - 2| - 1$

b. boundary: $y = -\frac{1}{2}x + 3$

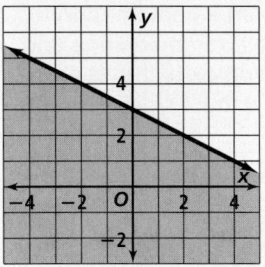

$y \leq -\frac{1}{2}x + 3$

Closure

Suppose y is alone on the left side of an inequality. After you graph the boundary, how can you decide whether to include the boundary in the graph and which region to shade? **Include the boundary if the inequality symbol is $\leq$ or $\geq$. If the symbol is $<$ or $\leq$, shade below the boundary. If the symbol is $>$ or $\geq$, shade above the boundary.**

pages 102–104
Exercises

You can write an inequality by examining a graph.

4 EXAMPLE Writing Inequalities

Write an inequality for each graph. The boundary line is given.

a.
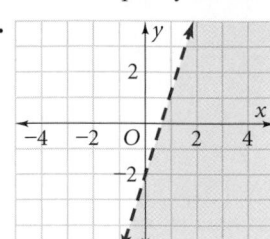

boundary: $y = 3x - 2$

The boundary line is dashed.
The shaded region is below the boundary.
This is the graph of $y < 3x - 2$.

b.
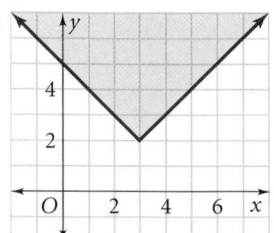

boundary: $y = |x - 3| + 2$

The boundary is solid.
The shaded region is above the boundary.
This is the graph of $y \geq |x - 3| + 2$.

✔ **Check Understanding** **4** Write an inequality for each graph.

a.
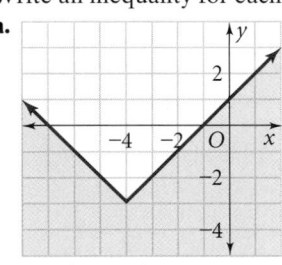

$y \leq |x + 4| - 3$

b.

$y \geq 2x + 5$

EXERCISES

For more practice, see *Extra Practice*.

Practice and Problem Solving

A Practice by Example

Example 1
(page 100)

Graph each inequality. 1–9. See margin pp. 102–103.

1. $y > 2x + 1$ **2.** $y < 3$ **3.** $x \leq 0$

4. $y \leq x - 5$ **5.** $2x + 3y \geq 12$ **6.** $2y \geq 4x - 6$

7. $y > \frac{2}{3}x + \frac{1}{3}$ **8.** $3x - 2y \leq 9$ **9.** $5x > -y + 3$

Example 2
(pages 100–101)

10. Cooking The time needed to roast a chicken depends on its weight. Allow at least 20 min/lb for a chicken weighing up to 6 lb. Allow at least 15 min/lb for a chicken weighing more than 6 lb. **a–b. See back of book.**
  a. Write two inequalities to represent the time needed to roast a chicken.
  b. Graph the inequalities.

Example 3
(page 101)

Graph each absolute value inequality. 11–19. See back of book.

11. $y \geq |2x - 1|$ **12.** $y \leq |3x| + 1$ **13.** $y \leq |4 - x|$

14. $y > |-x + 4| + 1$ **15.** $y - 7 > |x + 2|$ **16.** $y + 2 \leq \left|\frac{1}{2}x\right|$

17. $3 - y \geq -|x - 4|$ **18.** $1 - y < |2x - 1|$ **19.** $y + 3 \leq |3x| - 1$

1.
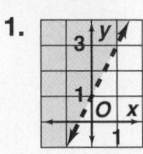

2.
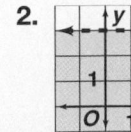

3.

4.
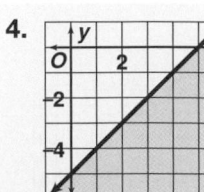

5.
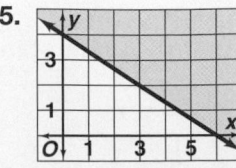

Example 4
(page 102)

Write an inequality for each graph. In each case, the equation for the boundary line is given.

20. $y = -x - 2$

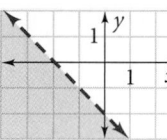

$y < -x - 2$

21. $5x + 3y = 9$

$5x + 3y \leq 9$

22. $2y = |2x + 6|$

$2y \geq |2x + 6|$

B Apply Your Skills

Graph each inequality on a coordinate plane. 23–37. See back of book.

23. $5x - 2y \geq -10$

24. $2x - 5y < -10$

25. $\frac{3}{4}x + \frac{2}{3}y > \frac{5}{2}$

26. $3(x - 2) + 2y \leq 6$

27. $0.5x + 1.2y < 6$

28. $-3x + 4y > -6$

29. $\frac{1}{2}x + \frac{2}{3}y \geq 1$

30. $|x - 1| > y + 7$

31. $y - |2x| \leq 21$

32. $2(x + 3) + y \geq 2$

33. $\frac{1}{4}x - \frac{1}{2}y > 1$

34. $|x + 2| - 3 < y$

35. $\frac{2}{3}x + 2 \leq \frac{2}{9}y$

36. $0.25y - 1.5x \geq -4$

37. $8x - 4y \geq -3$

Write an inequality for each graph.

38. $x > -3$

39. $y \leq \frac{3}{2}x + 2$

40. $y \geq -2x + 4$

41. $y \leq |x + 2|$

42. $y < -|x - 4|$

43. $y > |x + 1| - 1$

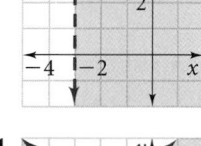 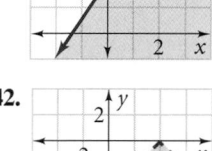 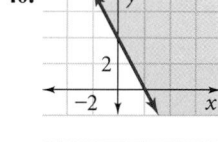

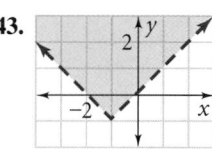

Reading Math

For help with reading and solving Exercise 44, see p. 105.

44. Open-Ended Write an inequality that has $(10, 15)$, $(-10, 20)$, $(-20, -25)$, and $(25, -10)$ as solutions. **Answers may vary. Sample:** $y \leq -\frac{5}{3}x + \frac{95}{3}$

 **45. Business** To raise funds, the junior class plans to sell frozen yogurt cones and sundaes. Each dessert contains one scoop of yogurt.
  a. Write an expression to represent the number of scoops of yogurt used in making c cones and s sundaes. **c + s**
  b. Suppose you have enough yogurt for 200 scoops. Write an inequality to represent all the possible combinations of cones and sundaes. **c + s ≤ 200**
  c. Graph the inequality. Is the point $(20, 50)$ a solution? **See back of book.**
  d. On your graph, find the point representing 60 cones and as many sundaes as possible. What does the s-value of this point represent? **140 sundaes**

C Challenge ✏️ **46. Writing** When you graph an inequality, you can often use the point $(0, 0)$ to test which side of the boundary line to shade. Describe a situation in which you could *not* use $(0, 0)$ as a test point.   **Answers may vary. Sample: when it lies on the boundary line**

🖩 Graph each inequality on a graphing calculator. Then sketch the graph.

47. $y \leq |x + 1| - |x - 1|$

48. $y > |x| + |x + 3|$

49. $y < |x - 3| - |x + 3|$

50. $y < 7 - |x - 4| + |x|$

47–50. See back of book.

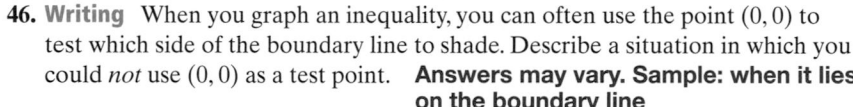

6.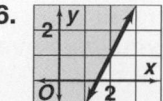

7.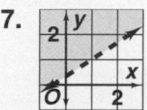

8.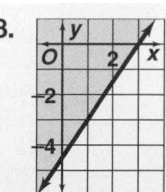

9.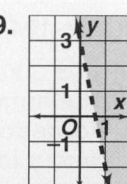

3. Practice

Assignment Guide

▼1 **Objective**
   Ⓐ Ⓑ **Core** 1–10, 23–29, 32–33, 35–40, 44–45
   Ⓒ **Extension** 46

▼2 **Objective**
   Ⓐ Ⓑ **Core** 11–22, 30–31, 34, 41–43
   Ⓒ **Extension** 47–50

Standardized Test Prep 51–56

Mixed Review 57–74

Error Prevention

Exercises 13, 14 Students may find it easier to graph the boundaries if they write the inequalities as $y \leq |x - 4|$ and $y > |x - 4| + 1$. Be sure they understand why this is permissible.

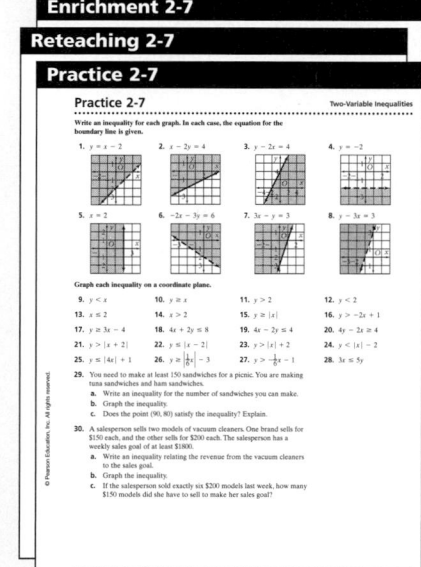

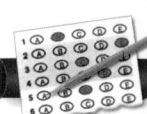

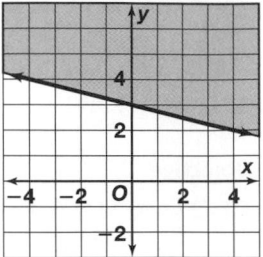

Lesson Quiz 2-7

Graph each inequality.

1. $y \geq -\frac{1}{4}x + 3$

2. $-y + 1 > -|x + 3|$

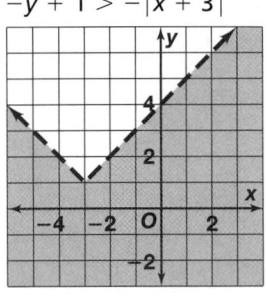

Alternative Assessment

Have students work in pairs. Each student gives the coordinates of two points not on the same vertical line. The partner writes and graphs a linear inequality whose boundary contains the given points. Each partner checks the other's work.

Standardized Test Prep

Resources

For additional practice with a variety of test item formats:
• Standardized Test Prep, p. 111
• Test-Taking Strategies, p. 106
• Test-Taking Strategies with Transparencies

Exercise 53 It will help to rewrite the inequalities in choices B, C, and D so that the variable y is alone on the left side of the inequality symbol. Be careful when dividing both sides by a negative number.

Multiple Choice

51. The graph at the right shows which inequality? **A**
  A. $y > |x + 4| - 4$
  B. $y > |x - 4| + 4$
  C. $y < |x + 4| - 4$
  D. $y < |x - 4| + 4$

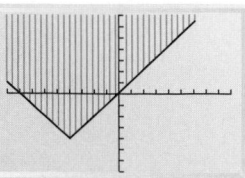

52. The graph of which inequality has its vertex at $\left(2\frac{1}{2}, -5\right)$? **I**
  F. $y < |2x - 5| + 5$ **G.** $y < |2x + 5| - 5$
  H. $y > |2x + 5| - 5$ **I.** $y > |2x - 5| - 5$

Take It to the NET
Online lesson quiz at
www.PHSchool.com
Web Code: aga-0207

53. Which inequality is NOT equivalent to the others? **D**
  A. $y \leq \frac{2}{3}x - 3$ **B.** $3y \leq 2x - 9$
  C. $2x - 3y \geq 9$ **D.** $2x - 3y \leq 9$

54. The graph at the right shows which inequality? **F**
  F. $y \leq -2.5x + 5$
  G. $2.5x + y \geq 5$
  H. $2.5x + y < 5$
  I. $5x + 2y \leq 5$

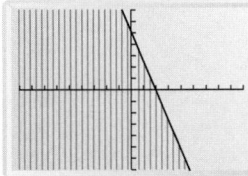

55. Which point(s) are solutions of the inequality $5x + 3y \geq 2$? **C**
  I. $(0, 0)$ **II.** $(-1, 0)$ and $\left(0, -\frac{2}{3}\right)$ **III.** $\left(0, \frac{2}{3}\right)$ and $\left(1, -\frac{2}{3}\right)$
  A. I only   **B.** I and II   **C.** III only   **D.** II and III

Short Response

56. At least 300 tornadoes occur in the United States each year. Write an inequality to model the number of tornadoes that could occur during the next x years. Describe the domain and range of the inequality. **See margin.**

Mixed Review

Lesson 2-6

Graph each function by translating its parent function.

57. $y = 2x + 5$ **58.** $y = |x| - 3$ **59.** $f(x) = |x + 6|$

60. $f(x) = x - 2$ **61.** $y = |x + 2|$ **62.** $y = |x - 1| + 5$
57–62. See margin p. 105.

Lesson 2-3

Determine whether y varies directly with x. If so, find the constant of variation.

63. $y = x + 1$ **no**   **64.** $y = 100x$ **100**   **65.** $5x + y = 0$ **–5**   **66.** $y - 2 = 2x$ **no**

67. $x = \frac{y}{3}$ **yes; 3**   **68.** $-4 = y - x$ **no**   **69.** $y = -10x$ **yes; –10**   **70.** $xy = 1$ **no**

71. Commissions The amount of a commission is directly proportional to the amount of a sale. A realtor received a commission of $13,500 on the sale of a $225,000 house. How much would the commission be on a $130,000 house? **$7800**

Lesson 2-2

Graph each pair of equations on the same coordinate plane.

72. $y = x, y = -x + 5$ **73.** $y = -2x + 1, y = 2x$ **74.** $y = 4x - 1, y = x$
72–74. See margin p. 105.

pages 102–104   Exercises

56. [2] $y \geq 300x$, where y is the number of tornadoes that could occur in the next x years. The domain is all whole numbers greater than 0, since years are whole numbers and can't be negative. The range is whole numbers $\geq$ 300, since you cannot have a fraction of a tornado and in the first year you will have at least 300.

[1] includes only inequality with no explanation of domain and range

Reading for Problem Solving

Read the problem below. Then follow along with Carmen as she solves the problem. Check your understanding with the exercise at the bottom of the page.

Open-Ended Write an inequality that has $(10, 15)$, $(-10, 20)$, $(-20, -25)$, and $(25, -10)$ as solutions.

Reading for Problem Solving

Students read an annotated example problem to determine how to write an inequality that has a set of given points as solutions.

What Carmen Thinks

These points are not necessarily on the same line. I'll plot the points and see where they lie on the coordinate plane.

The problem asks me to write an inequality with these points as solutions. But the graph of a linear inequality has a boundary line with shading on one side. So, I'll have to choose a boundary line.

There are so many possibilities! I need only two points to draw a line, so I'll use $(-20, -25)$ and $(25, -10)$.

The boundary line is solid since the points lie on it. I can include the other two points in the solution set by shading above the boundary line.

Since I have two points, I can use point-slope form to write the equation of the boundary line.

I can substitute the values of m, x, and y into my equation and simplify.

I need to write an inequality. I shaded above the line toward greater y-values, so the inequality includes "greater than." Since I used a solid boundary line, the inequality is "greater than or equal to."

What Carmen Writes

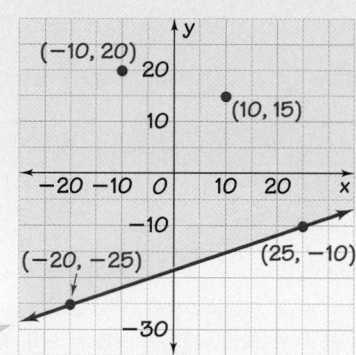

Boundary line through $(-20, -25)$ and $(25, -10)$ has slope $m = \dfrac{-10 - (-25)}{25 - (-20)}$.

$$y - y_1 = m(x - x_1)$$

$$y - (-25) = \frac{-10 - (-25)}{25 - (-20)}(x - (-20))$$

$$y + 25 = \frac{15}{45}(x + 20)$$

$$y = \frac{1}{3}(x + 20) - 25$$

$$y = \frac{1}{3}x - \frac{55}{3} \quad \text{equation of boundary line}$$

$$y \geq \frac{1}{3}x - \frac{55}{3} \quad \text{inequality}$$

Teaching Notes

Point out to students that it does not matter whether the boundary line is above or below the points. However, if the boundary line is above the points, then the area below the line must be shaded. If the line is below the points, then the area above the line must be shaded.

Exercise

Remind students that there are many different solutions to this problem. Caution them that if the boundary line passes through any of the points, then the line must be solid.

61.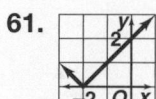

62.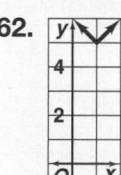

72.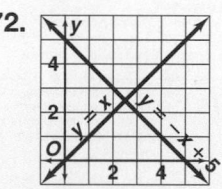

73.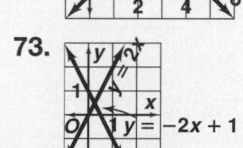

74.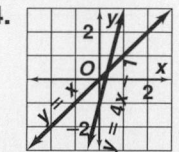

EXERCISE

Write a different inequality that has $(10, 15)$, $(-10, 20)$, $(-20, -25)$, and $(25, -10)$ as solutions. **Answers may vary. Sample: $y < \frac{2}{3}x + 40$**

57.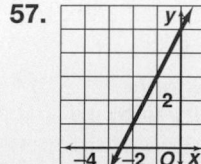

58.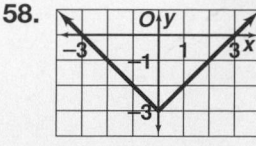

59.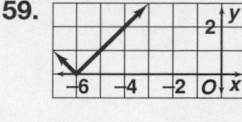

60.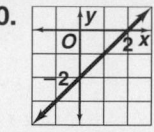

105

Writing Short Responses

This feature explains that in order to receive full credit for short-response questions, students must show their work or justify their reasoning.

Resources

Test-Taking Strategies with Transparencies
- Transparency 2
- Practice sheet p. 26

Teaching Notes

Share your grading policy with regard to giving partial credit for short-response questions. Explain what work or reasoning you expect to see in these types of questions in order to give partial or full credit. Have students record your policy along with examples in their notebooks.

Test-Taking Strategies with Transparencies

Test-Taking Strategy: Writing Short Responses

Della went to the carnival at the county fair. The admission to the carnival was $5.00 and the rides were $1.25 each. Della spent $20 at the carnival. Write and solve an equation to find out how many rides Della rode at the carnival.

Scoring Guide

2	The equation and solution are correct, AND all work is shown.
1	An incorrect equation is used, but the procedure for solving the equation is incorrect.
1	The correct equation or solution is given, but no work is shown.
0	No response, OR completely incorrect response with no work shown.

Answer earning 2 points	In the 2-point response, the student used the correct equation, found the correct answer, AND showed all the work.
$5 + 1.25x = 20$ $1.25x = 15$ $x = 12$ Della rode 12 rides.	

Answer earning 1 point	In this 1-point response, an incorrect equation is used, but the procedure is correct for the used equation.
$1.25x = 20$ $x = 16$ Della rode 16 rides	

Answer earning 1 point	In this 1-point response, the correct solution is given, but no work is shown.
Della rode 12 rides.	

Answer earning 0 points	In the 0-point response, the solution is incorrect, AND no work is shown.
15 rides	

Transparency 2

106

Short-response questions are usually worth two points. To get full credit you must not only give the correct answer, but also show your work or justify your reasoning.

EXAMPLE

A line parallel to $4x - 2y = 5$ passes through the point $(2, -3)$. Write the equation of the line in standard form, $Ax + By = C$.

Study the three responses below. Each received a different score.

2 points	1 point	0 points
$4x - 2y = 5$ $4x - 5 = 2y$ $y = 2x - \frac{5}{2}$ Slope is 2. $y + 3 = 2(x - 2)$ $y + 3 = 2x - 4$ $y = 2x - 7$ $2x - y = 7$	$4x - 2y = 5$ $-2y = 5 + 4x$ $y = -2x - \frac{5}{2}$ Slope is -2. $y = -2x + b$ $-3 = -4 + b$ $1 = b$ $y = -2x + 1$ $2x + y = 1$	$4x - 2y = -3$

In the 2-point response, the student found the correct answer and showed all the work.

In the 1-point response, the student made a computational error in the second line. The final answer is wrong, but still the student received a point because the rest of the work is correct.

In the 0-point response, the student gave an incorrect answer without showing any work. The answer is not far off, so the student probably would have received a point if some work had been shown.

EXERCISES   1–3. See right.

1. At the right is another response to the Example above. How many points does the response deserve? Explain your reasoning.

Answer each question. Show your work.

2. As an orange grows over a five-week period, there is a linear relationship between the volume of the orange and time. At the beginning of the period, the volume is about 34 cm³. Four weeks later, the volume is about 50 cm³. What is the volume at the end of the five-week period?

3. A line perpendicular to $x + 3y = 5$ passes through $(1, -1)$. What is the equation of the line in standard form?

The equation is
$4x - 2y = k$
$4(2) - 2(-3) = k$
$14 = k$
$4x - 2y = 14$

1. **2 points; answer is correct and student showed work.**

2. **[2] slope $= \frac{50 - 34}{4 - 0} = 4$ y-intercept $= 34$ The equation is $V = 4t + 34$, so $V = 4(5) + 34 = 54$ (volume is 54 cm³).**
   [1] incorrect volume OR no work shown

3. **[2] $y = -\frac{1}{3}x + \frac{5}{3}$, so a line perpendicular to it would have a slope of 3. Using the point-slope form $y - (-1) = 3(x - 1)$ you get $3x - y = 4$.**
   [1] incorrect equation OR no work shown

Vocabulary

absolute value function (p. 86)
constant of variation (p. 72)
dependent variable (p. 62)
direct variation (p. 72)
domain (p. 56)
function (p. 57)
function notation (p. 58)
independent variable (p. 62)
linear equation (p. 62)

linear function (p. 62)
linear inequality (p. 99)
mapping diagram (p. 56)
parent function (p. 91)
point-slope form (p. 65)
range (p. 56)
relation (p. 55)
scatter plot (p. 80)
slope (p. 64)

slope-intercept form (p. 65)
standard form (p. 63)
translation (p. 91)
trend line (p. 80)
vertex (p. 86)
vertical-line test (p. 57)
x-intercept (p. 63)
y-intercept (p. 63)

Resources

Student Edition
Extra Practice, Ch. 2, p. 823
English/Spanish Glossary, p. 871
Properties and Formulas, p. 865
Table of Symbols, p. 861

Reaching All Students
Reading and Math Literacy 2D
Spanish Reading and Math
    Literacy 2D

Reading Math
Understanding
Vocabulary

Take It to the NET
Online vocabulary quiz
at www.PHSchool.com
Web Code: agj-0251

Choose the correct term to complete each sentence.

1. In the function $y = f(x)$, y is the (*dependent, independent*) variable. **dependent**

2. All functions are (*relations, domains*). **relations**

3. The graph of a function is (*always, sometimes*) a line. **sometimes**

4. An equation of the form $y - y_1 = m(x - x_1)$ is in (*point-slope, slope-intercept*) form. **point-slope**

5. The vertex of the graph of an absolute value function is (*always, sometimes*) the lowest point on the graph. **sometimes**

PRENTICE HALL
ASSESSMENT SYSTEM

Standardized Test Prep
● Ch. 2 practice in standardized
  test formats

www.PHSchool.com
Student Site
● Self-grading Vocabulary Test
Teacher Center
● Resources

Plus **iTEXT**

Skills and Concepts

2-1 Objectives

▼ To graph relations (p. 55)

▼ To identify functions (p. 57)

A **relation** is a set of ordered pairs that can be represented by points in the coordinate plane or by a **mapping diagram**. The **domain** of a relation is the set of *x*-coordinates. The **range** is the set of *y*-coordinates.

When each element of the domain of a relation is paired with exactly one element of the range, the relation is a **function.** You can write a function using the notation $f(x)$, called **function notation.**

6–10. See margin.

Determine whether each relation is a function. Find the domain and range.

6. $\{(5,0),(8,1),(1,3),(5,2),(3,8)\}$

7. $\{(10,2),(-10,2),(6,4),(5,3),(-6,7)\}$

8.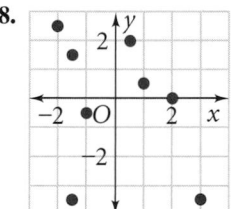

9. Domain Range
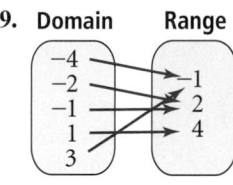

10. Domain Range
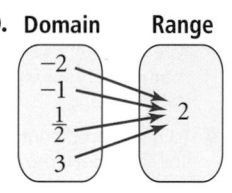

Spanish Reading and Math Literacy

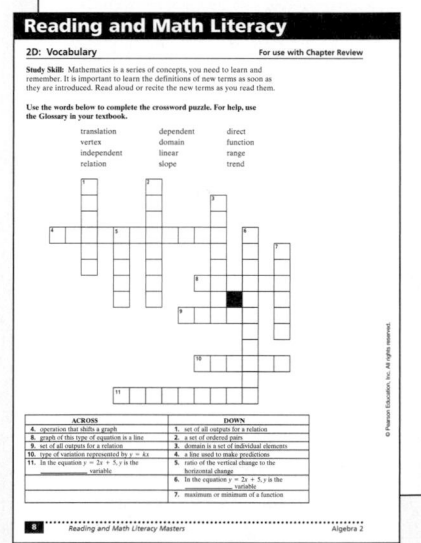

For each function, find $f(-2)$, $f(-0.5)$, and $f(3)$.

11. $f(x) = -x + 4$
   6, 4.5, 1

12. $f(x) = \frac{3}{8}x - 3$
   $-3\frac{3}{4}, -3\frac{3}{16}, -1\frac{7}{8}$

13. $f(x) = -\frac{5}{12}x + 2$
   $2\frac{5}{6}, 2\frac{5}{24}, \frac{3}{4}$

pages 107–109   Chapter Review

6. not a function;
   domain {1, 3, 5, 8},
   range {0, 1, 2, 3, 8}

7. function;
   domain {−10, −6, 5, 6, 10},
   range {2, 3, 4, 7}

8. not a function; domain
   $\left\{-2, -\frac{3}{2}, -1, \frac{1}{2}, 1, 2, 3\right\}$,

range
   $\left\{-\frac{7}{2}, -\frac{1}{2}, 0, \frac{1}{2}, \frac{3}{2}, 2, \frac{5}{2}\right\}$

9. function;
   domain {−4, −2, −1, 1, 3},
   range {−1, 2, 4}

10. function;
   domain $\left\{-2, -1, \frac{1}{2}, 3\right\}$,
   range {2}

26a, b.

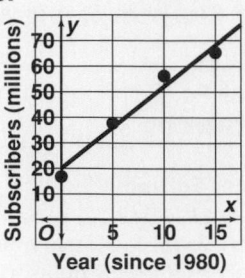

Answers may vary.
Sample:
$y = 3x + 21$

27.

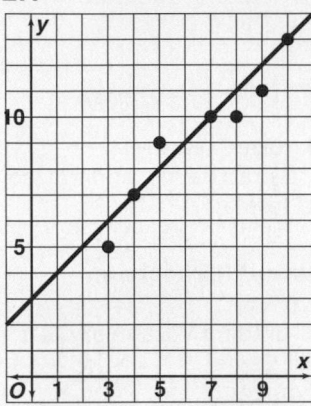

Answers may vary.
Sample: reasonable;
$y = x + 3$; 18

28.

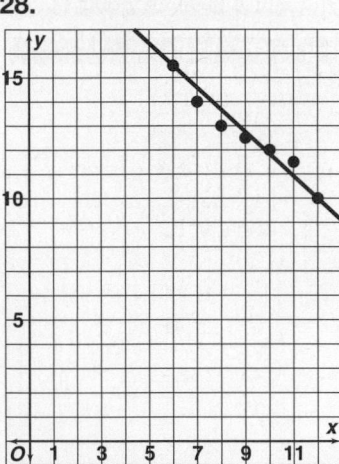

Answers may vary.
Sample: reasonable;
$y = -0.92x + 21$; 7.2

2-2 Objectives

▼ To graph linear equations (p. 62)

▼ To write equations of lines (p. 64)

19c.

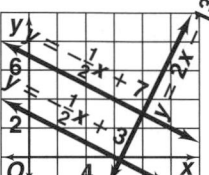

2-3 Objectives

▼ To write and interpret direct variation equations (p. 72)

2-4 Objectives

▼ To write linear equations that model real-world data (p. 78)

▼ To make predictions from linear models (p. 79)

The graph of a **linear function** is a line. You can represent a linear function with a **linear equation.** In a function, the value of y depends on the value of x, so y is the **dependent variable** and x is the **independent variable.**

Given two points on a line, the **slope** of the line is the ratio of the difference of the y-coordinates to the corresponding difference of the x-coordinates. The slope equals the coefficient of x when you write a linear equation in **slope-intercept form.** You can also write a linear equation in **point-slope form** or **standard form.** You can use the slopes of lines to determine whether or not they are parallel, perpendicular, or horizontal. A vertical line has no slope.

Write in standard form an equation for each line.

14. slope $= -3$, through $(4, 0)$
$3x + y = 12$

15. through $(2, 3)$ and $(3, 5)$
$2x - y = 1$

Find the slope, x-intercept, and y-intercept of each line.

16. $4x - 2y = 3$
$2; \left(\frac{3}{4}, 0\right), \left(0, -\frac{3}{2}\right)$

17. $Mx = Ny + P$
$\frac{M}{N}; \left(\frac{P}{M}, 0\right), \left(0, -\frac{P}{N}\right)$

18. $5 - x = y$
$-1; (5, 0), (0, 5)$

19. a. Write an equation of the line parallel to $x + 2y = 6$ through $(8, 3)$.
b. Write an equation of the line perpendicular to $x + 2y = 6$ through $(8, 3)$.
c. Graph the three lines on the same coordinate plane.
a. $y = -\frac{1}{2}x + 7$ **b.** $y = 2x - 13$

A linear equation of the form $y = kx$ represents a **direct variation.** The **constant of variation** is k. You can use proportions to solve some direct variation problems.

For each function, determine whether y varies directly with x. If so, find the constant of variation and write the equation.

20. no

x	y
-2	3
0	4
2	7

21. no

x	y
4	5
6	9
10	17

22. yes; 1, $y = x$

x	y
0	0
1	1
5	5

Find each constant of variation. Then find the value of y when $x = -0.3$.

23. $y = 2$ when $x = -\frac{1}{2}$
-4; 1.2

24. $y = \frac{2}{3}$ when $x = 0.2$
$\frac{10}{3}$; -1

25. $y = 7$ when $x = 2$
$\frac{7}{2}$; $-1\frac{1}{20}$

You can use mathematical models such as **scatter plots** to show relationships between data sets. You can use the models to make predictions about the data set. Sometimes you can draw a **trend line** to model the relation and make predictions.

26. a. Data Analysis Draw a scatter plot of the data below. **a–b. See margin.**
b. Draw a trend line. Write its equation.
c. Estimate the number of cable TV subscribers in 2005. **96.0 million**

Cable TV Subscribers

Year	1980	1985	1990	1995
Millions of Subscribers	17.7	39.9	54.9	63.0

SOURCE: Television Bureau of Advertising

29.

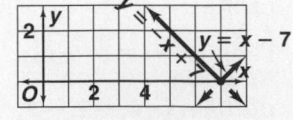
$y = x - 7$

30.

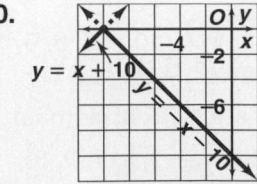
$y = x + 10$

31.

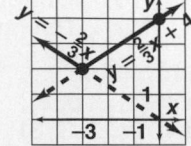

Draw a scatter plot of each set of data. Decide whether a linear model is reasonable. If so, draw a trend line and write its equation. Then predict the value of y when x is 15. 27–28. See margin p. 108.

27.

x	3	4	5	7	8	9	10
y	5	7	9	10	10	11	13

28.

x	6	7	8	9	10	11	12
y	15.5	14.0	13.0	12.5	12.0	11.5	10.0

2-5 and 2-6 Objectives

▼ To graph absolute value functions (p. 86)

▼ To analyze vertical translations (p. 91)

▼ To analyze horizontal translations (p. 92)

The **absolute value function** $y = |x|$ has a graph in the shape of a V. It is the **parent function** for the family of functions of the form $y = |x + h| + k$. The maximum or minimum point of the V is the **vertex** of the graph.

The value of h represents a horizontal translation of the parent graph by h units left (h is positive) or right (h is negative). The k represents a vertical translation of the graph by k units up (k is positive) or down (k is negative). A combination of a horizontal and a vertical translation is a diagonal translation.

Graph each equation by writing two linear equations. 29–31. See margin p. 108.

29. $y = |x - 7|$ **30.** $y = -|x + 10|$ **31.** $y = \frac{1}{3}|2x + 6| + 2$

Describe each translation of $f(x) = |x|$ as vertical, horizontal, or diagonal. Then graph each translation. 32–34. See margin.

32. $f(x) = |x| - 8$ **33.** $f(x) = |x - 5|$ **34.** $f(x) = |x - 3| + 3$

Write an equation for each translation.

35. $y = x$, 2 units down $y = x - 2$ **36.** $y = x$, through $(-3, 2)$ $y = x + 5$

$y = |x - 2| + 4$ **37.** $y = |x|$, 4 units up, 2 units right   **38.** $y = |x|$, vertex $(-3, 0)$ $y = |x + 3|$

39. $y = -|x|$, vertex $(5, 2)$ **40.** $y = -x$, through $(4, 1)$ $y = -x + 5$
$y = -|x - 5| + 2$

2-7 Objectives

▼ To graph linear inequalities (p. 99)

▼ To graph absolute value inequalities (p. 101)

A **linear inequality** describes a region of the coordinate plane that has a boundary. To graph an inequality involving two variables, first graph the boundary. Then decide which side of the boundary contains solutions. Points on a dashed boundary are not solutions. Points on a solid boundary are solutions.

Graph each inequality. 41–45. See margin.

41. $y \geq -2$ **42.** $y < 3x + 1$ **43.** $y \leq -|x - 5|$ **44.** $y > |2x + 1|$

 45. Transportation An air cargo plane can transport as many as 15 regular shipping containers. One super-size container takes up the space of 3 regular containers.
a. Write an inequality to model the situation.
b. Describe the domain and range.
c. Graph the inequality you wrote in part (a).

46. Open-Ended Write an absolute value inequality with a solid boundary that has solutions below the x-axis only. **Answers may vary. Sample:** $y \leq -|x| - 1$

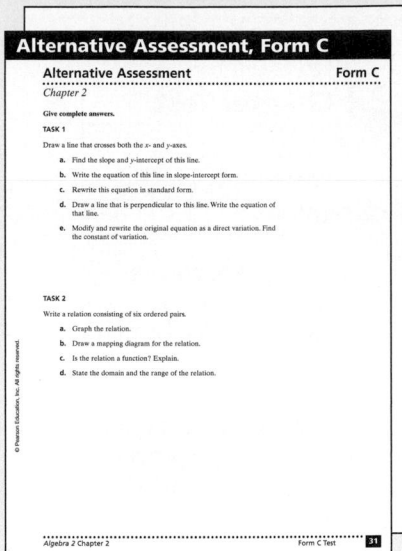
41.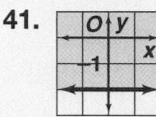

42.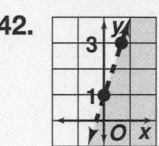

43.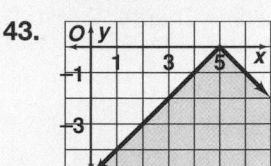

44.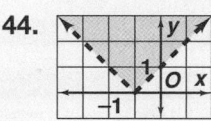

45a. Answers may vary. Sample: $x + 3y \leq 15$

b. Answers may vary. Sample: domain $\{0, 1, 2, 3, 4, 5, 6, 7, 8, 9, 10, 11, 12, 13, 14, 15\}$, **range** $\{0, 1, 2, 3, 4, 5\}$

c.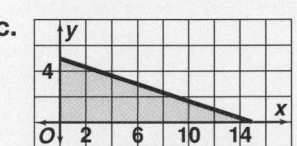

32. vertical

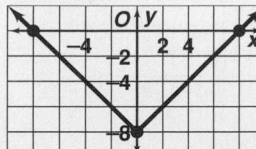

33. horizontal

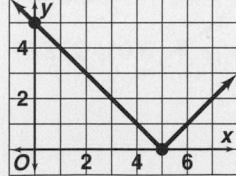

34. diagonal

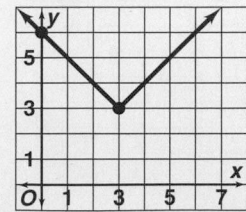

109

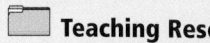
Resources

page 110   Chapter Test

3. domain: $\left\{-2, 1, 3, 4\frac{1}{2}\right\}$,

   range: {1, 2, 3, 4, 5}

110

 # Chapter Test

Find the domain and range. Graph each relation.

1. {(0, 0), (1, −1), (2, −4), (3, −9), (4, −16)} **1–2. See back of book.**

2. {(3, 2), (4, 3), (5, 4), (6, 5), (7, 6)}

3. Domain   Range   4. Domain   Range

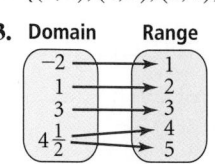   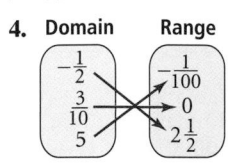

3–4. See margin.

Suppose $f(x) = 2x - 5$ **and** $g(x) = |-3x - 1|$**. Find each value.**

5. $f(3)$ **1**

6. $f(1) + g(2)$ **4**

7. $g(0)$ **1**

8. $g(2) - f(0)$ **12**

9. $f(-1) - g(3)$ **−17**

10. $2g(-4)$ **22**

11. **Open-Ended** Graph a relation that is *not* a function. Find its domain and range.
Check students' work.

Find the slope of each line.

12. through $(3, 5)$ and $(1, 1)$ **2**

13. $4x + 3y = 2$ $-\frac{4}{3}$

14. through $(-0.5, 0.5)$, perpendicular to $y = -2x - 4$ $\frac{1}{2}$

Write in standard form an equation of the line with the given slope through the given point.

15. slope $= -3, (0, 0)$ $3x + y = 0$

16. slope $= \frac{2}{5}, (6, 7)$ $2x - 5y = -23$

17. slope $= 4, (-2, -5)$ $4x - y = -3$

18. slope $= -0.5, (0, 6)$ $x + 2y = 12$

Write in point-slope form an equation of the line through each pair of points. **Answers may vary. Samples:**

19. $(0, 0)$ and $(-4, 7)$ $y = -\frac{7}{4}x$

20. $(-1, -6)$ and $(-2, 10)$ $y + 6 = -16(x + 1)$

21. $(3, 0)$ and $(-1, -2)$ $y = \frac{1}{2}(x - 3)$

22. $(9, 5)$ and $(8, 2)$ $y - 2 = 3(x - 8)$

23. a. **Open-Ended** Write an equation of a line with negative slope. **a–e. See back of book.**
   b. Write an equation of the line perpendicular to the line from part (a) passing through $(-6, 9)$.
   c. Write an equation of the line parallel to the line from part (b) passing through $(12, 12)$.
   d. Write an equation of the line perpendicular to the line from part (c) passing through $(-1, -4)$.
   e. Graph the lines from parts (a), (b), (c), and (d). If they form a polygon, describe it.

For each direct variation, find the constant of variation. Then find the value of y when $x = -0.5$.

24. $y = 4$ when $x = 0.5$ **8; −4**

25. $y = 2$ when $x = 3$ $\frac{2}{3}, -\frac{1}{3}$

🌐 26. **Transportation** The number of minutes a freight train takes to pass an intersection varies directly with the number of cars in the train. A 150-car train passes in 3 min. How long will a 210-car train take to pass? **4.2 min**

Graph each function.   27–30. See back of book.

27. $y = 3x + 4$

28. $y = |5x - 3| + 1$

29. $y = -|x - 3| + 1$

30. $y = 3 - \frac{2}{5}x$

🌐 31. **Recreation** The table displays the amounts the Jackson family spent on vacations during the years 1993–2003.

Jackson Family Vacation Costs

Year	Cost	Year	Cost
1993	$1000	1999	$2750
1994	$1750	2000	$3200
1995	$1750	2001	$2900
1996	$2000	2002	$3100
1997	$2200	2003	$3300
1998	$2700		

a–c. See back of book.
a. Make a scatter plot of the data.
b. Draw a trend line. Write its equation.
c. Estimate the cost to the Jackson family of vacations in 2005.
 d. **Writing** Explain how to use a trend line with a scatter plot. **Check students' work.**

Describe each translation as vertical, horizontal, or diagonal. Then graph each function.
32–37. See back of book.

32. $y = x - 4$

33. $y = |x - 1| - 5$

34. $y = -|x + 4| + 3$

35. $y = x + 1$

36. $y = |x| + 5$

37. $y = -|x + 2| - 3$

Graph each inequality.
38–41. See back of book.

38. $y \geq x + 7$

39. $y > |2x + 3| - 3$

40. $4x + 3y < 2$

41. $y \leq -|x + 1| - 2$

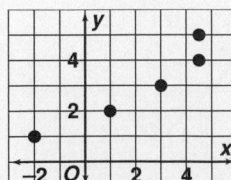

4. domain: $\left\{-\frac{1}{2}, 0.3, 5\right\}$,

   range: {−0.01, 0, 2.5}

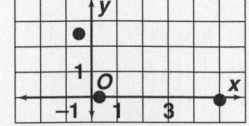

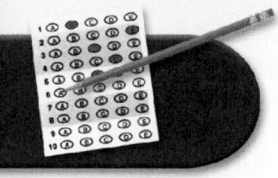

Standardized Test Prep

Multiple Choice

For Exercises 1–8, choose the correct letter. B

1. Which phrase could NOT describe $\sqrt{625}$?
   A. whole number   B. irrational number
   C. integer   D. rational number

2. Which value is in the solution set of **F**
   $4 < -4x - 2 < 8$ and $3 > 4x + 2 > -10$?
   F. -2 G. 0   H. 2   I. 4

3. Which point could NOT be on the graph of a
   function that includes (5, 4), (8, −1), (7, 3), (0, 5),
   and (10, −2)? **B**
   A. (6, 4)   B. (10, 1)   C. (11, −1)   D. (9, 3)

4. Which relations are functions? **F**

   I. 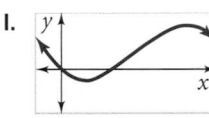   II.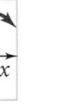

   III. 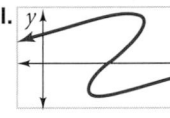   IV.

   F. I and II   G. I and III
   H. II and III   I. II and IV

5. Which lines are parallel? **C**
   I. $y = -2x + 1$ II. $y = x - 4$
   III. $y = -x + 5$ IV. $y = 3 - 2x$
   A. I and II   B. I and III
   C. I and IV   D. II and IV

6. Which values are solutions of $y < 2x + 3$? **H**
   I. (0, 2)   II. (−1, 1)   III. (2, 0)
   F. I only   G. II only
   H. I and III   I. II and III

7. Which line is perpendicular to $y = 2x - 4$? **D**
   A. $y = -2x + 4$ B. $y = -4 - 2x$
   C. $y = -x - 2$ D. $y = -\frac{1}{2}x + 4$

8. Which equation is in standard form? **F**
   F. $x - y = 7$ G. $y = 3x - 1$
   H. $x = 4y + 2$ I. $10 - 5x = 2y$

Quantitative Comparison

**Compare the boxed quantity in Column A with
the boxed quantity in Column B. Choose the
best answer.**

   A. The quantity in Column A is greater.
   B. The quantity in Column B is greater.
   C. The two quantities are equal.
   D. The relationship cannot be determined from
      the information given.

Column A	Column B
9. **B** $\sqrt{27}$	5^2
10. **B** $\sqrt{36}$	6^2
11. **A** the x-intercept of $3x + 4y = 12$	the y-intercept of $3x + 4y = 12$
12. **C** the slope of $y = 3x - 4$	the slope of $2y - 6x = 7$

Gridded Response

13. What is the y-coordinate of the point through **0**
    which the graph of every direct variation passes?

14. In one roll of two number cubes, what is the
    probability that the product of the faces is 12? $\frac{1}{9}$

Short Response   15–16. See back of book.

15. Graph $y < |x + 3|$. Identify the parent function
    of the boundary and describe the translation.

16. Suppose y varies directly as x, and $y = 2$ when
    $x = -2$. Find the constant of variation. Then
    find the value of x when $y = 3$.

Extended Response

17. a. Write an equation of the line through (−2, 6)
       with slope 2. **a–c. See back of book.**
    b. Write an equation of the line through (1, 1)
       perpendicular to the line in part (a).
    c. Graph the two lines on the same set of axes.

Chapter 2   Standardized Test Prep   **111**

Resources

Teaching Resources
Cumulative Review

Reaching All Students
Spanish Cumulative Review

ASSESSMENT SYSTEM

Standardized Test Prep
• Ch. 2 Standardized Test
  Practice
Assessment Masters
• Cumulative Review
Computer Test Generator CD
• Standardized Test Practice

www.PHSchool.com
• Standardized Test Practice
• Resources

Plus **iTEXT**

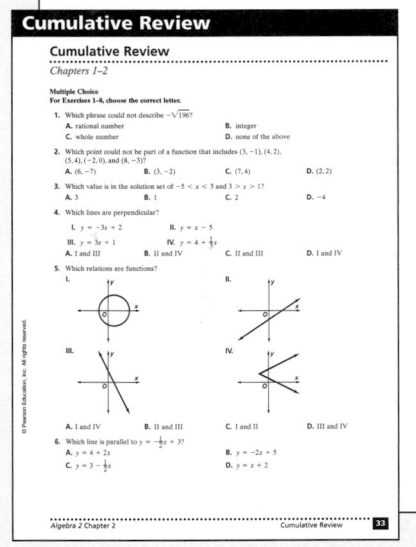

Item	1	2	3	4	5	6	7	8	9	10	11	12	13	14	15	16	17
Lesson	1-1	1-4	2-1	2-1	2-2	1-4	2-2	2-2	1-1	1-1	2-2	2-2	2-3	1-6	2-6	2-3	2-2

Bridges, Beams, and Tension

In this activity students apply their knowledge of functions, equations, and graphs.

Connecting to Prior Knowledge

Have students share their experiences in bending something until it breaks, for example, a pencil or a plastic spoon. Elicit the fact that the bending is the result of force that the person is applying to the material.

Teaching Notes

Have a volunteer read the introductory paragraph. Ask: *What large bridges have you seen? Where are there long or high bridges in our area?*

Teaching Tip

Try this activity yourself before you assign it to students in order to make sure you have thin enough dowels and heavy enough washers to produce a measurable deflection. Make sure that one end of the paper clip fits over the dowel and that the washers can be hung by their center hole on a hook made by bending the other end of the paper clip.

Tactile Learners

In order to give everyone a chance to work with the materials, have students working in pairs or small groups rotate tasks, such as setting up the experiment, making changes, and recording results.

Connection to Science

Have students research famous bridges and share their findings with the class.

English Learners

Use a piece of spaghetti or a strip of heavy cardboard to demonstrate what is meant by the term *deflect*.

112

Real-World Snapshots

Bridges, Beams, and Tension

Applying Functions Even steel bends when heavy loads are applied to it. In designing bridges and other structures, civil engineers use functions to predict how much a beam will deflect, or bend, under a given load. They design bridges so that the stress from the combined weights of the bridge materials and the vehicles that cross the bridge, along with stress from winds, does not exceed allowable limits.

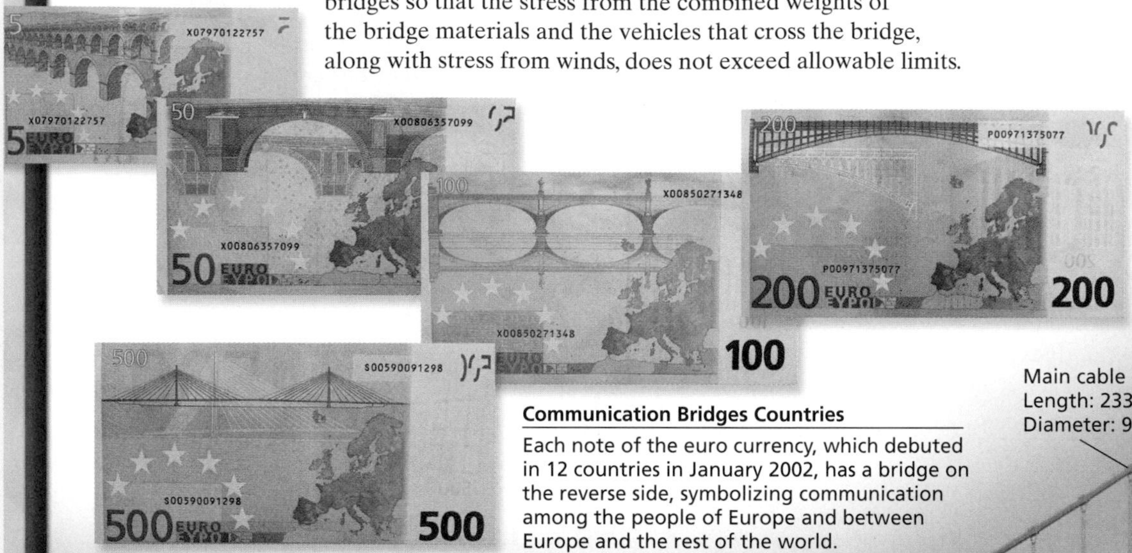

Main cable
Length: 2332 m
Diameter: 92 cm

Communication Bridges Countries

Each note of the euro currency, which debuted in 12 countries in January 2002, has a bridge on the reverse side, symbolizing communication among the people of Europe and between Europe and the rest of the world.

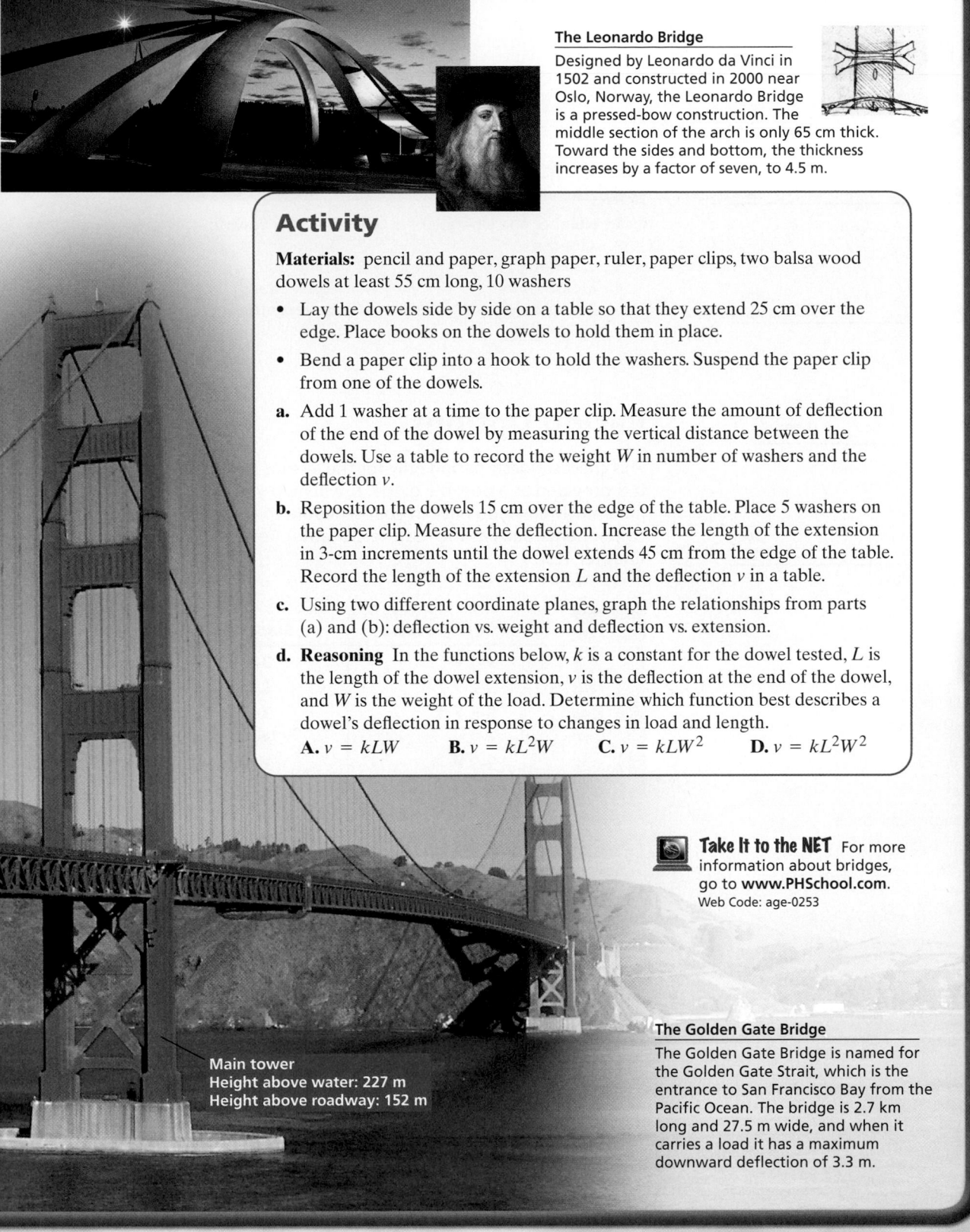

The Leonardo Bridge
Designed by Leonardo da Vinci in 1502 and constructed in 2000 near Oslo, Norway, the Leonardo Bridge is a pressed-bow construction. The middle section of the arch is only 65 cm thick. Toward the sides and bottom, the thickness increases by a factor of seven, to 4.5 m.

Activity

Materials: pencil and paper, graph paper, ruler, paper clips, two balsa wood dowels at least 55 cm long, 10 washers

- Lay the dowels side by side on a table so that they extend 25 cm over the edge. Place books on the dowels to hold them in place.
- Bend a paper clip into a hook to hold the washers. Suspend the paper clip from one of the dowels.

a. Add 1 washer at a time to the paper clip. Measure the amount of deflection of the end of the dowel by measuring the vertical distance between the dowels. Use a table to record the weight W in number of washers and the deflection v.

b. Reposition the dowels 15 cm over the edge of the table. Place 5 washers on the paper clip. Measure the deflection. Increase the length of the extension in 3-cm increments until the dowel extends 45 cm from the edge of the table. Record the length of the extension L and the deflection v in a table.

c. Using two different coordinate planes, graph the relationships from parts (a) and (b): deflection vs. weight and deflection vs. extension.

d. **Reasoning** In the functions below, k is a constant for the dowel tested, L is the length of the dowel extension, v is the deflection at the end of the dowel, and W is the weight of the load. Determine which function best describes a dowel's deflection in response to changes in load and length.

   A. $v = kLW$ **B.** $v = kL^2W$ **C.** $v = kLW^2$ **D.** $v = kL^2W^2$

Take It to the NET For more information about bridges, go to **www.PHSchool.com**. Web Code: age-0253

The Golden Gate Bridge
The Golden Gate Bridge is named for the Golden Gate Strait, which is the entrance to San Francisco Bay from the Pacific Ocean. The bridge is 2.7 km long and 27.5 m wide, and when it carries a load it has a maximum downward deflection of 3.3 m.

Main tower
Height above water: 227 m
Height above roadway: 152 m

113

Before students begin the activity, discuss the illustrations and their captions. Have students work in pairs or in small groups to complete the activities. Have each team read through the activity before beginning to work.

Activity

Materials: paper and pencil, ruler, paper clips, 2 balsa wood dowels, 10 washers

Inclusion

Help students organize their work by making a table for recording the results. Work with students to identify appropriate labels for the rows and columns.

Scoring Rubric

This scoring rubric can be used for evaluating student work on the activity. Share this scoring rubric with students before they begin work.

4 Equations, calculations, and graphs are correct.
Steps are neat, accurate, and clearly show the mathematics. Responses are clearly indicated and give the appropriate units.

3 Equations, calculations, and graphs are mostly correct, with some minor errors. Steps are neat and mostly accurate. Units are not completely accurate.

2 Equations, calculations, and graphs contain both major and minor errors.

1 Correct answer, but no work is shown.

page 113   **Real-World Snapshots**

Activity

a–d. Check students' work.

Chapter 3

Linear Systems

Chapter at a Glance

North Carolina Objectives

3-1	Graphing Systems of Equations	2.10
NCTM 2, 9, 10	Ⅴ Systems of Linear Equations	

3-2	Solving Systems Algebraically	2.10
NCTM 2, 6, 9	Ⅴ Solving Systems by Substitution Ⅴ Solving Systems by Elimination	

3-3	Systems of Inequalities	2.10
NCTM 2, 6, 9, 10	Ⅴ Solving Systems of Inequalities	

3-4	Linear Programming	2.10
NCTM 2, 6, 8	Ⅴ Finding Maximum and Minimum Values Ⅴ Writing Linear Programs	

3-5	Graphs in Three Dimensions	
NCTM 2, 3, 9, 10	Ⅴ Graphing Points in Three Dimensions Ⅴ Graphing Equations in Three Dimensions	

3-6	Systems With Three Variables	2.10
NCTM 2, 6, 9, 10	Ⅴ Solving Three-Variable Systems by Elimination Ⅴ Solving Three-Variable Systems by Substitution	

NCTM STANDARDS 2000

1	Number and Operations	6	Problem Solving
2	Algebra	7	Reasoning and Proof
3	Geometry	8	Communication
4	Measurement	9	Connections
5	Data Analysis and Probability	10	Representation

Pacing Options

This chart suggests pacing only for the lessons and their parts. It is provided as a possible guide. It will help you determine how much time you have in your schedule to cover other components, such as the features, Chapter Review, and Chapter Test.

Day	Traditional (45 min.)	Block (90 min.)
1	3-1 Ⅴ	3-1 Ⅴ
2	3-2 Ⅴ	3-2 Ⅴ
3	3-2 Ⅴ Ⅴ	3-2 Ⅴ
4	3-2 Ⅴ	3-3 Ⅴ
5	3-3 Ⅴ	3-4 Ⅴ
6	3-4 Ⅴ	3-4 Ⅴ
7	3-4 Ⅴ Ⅴ	3-5 Ⅴ
8	3-4 Ⅴ	3-5 Ⅴ
9	3-5 Ⅴ	3-6 Ⅴ
10	3-5 Ⅴ Ⅴ	3-6 Ⅴ
11	3-5 Ⅴ	
12	3-6 Ⅴ	
13	3-6 Ⅴ Ⅴ	
14	3-6 Ⅴ	

NAEP Correlation (National Assessment of Educational Progress 2000 Mathematics Objectives)

3-1	3-2	3-3	3-4	3-5	3-6
D7, A6a	A5b, A5d, A6b	A6a	N4f, A13	A2, A3c	G4a, A5b, A6b

N = Number Sense, Properties, and Operations; **M** = Measurement; **G** = Geometry and Spatial Sense; **D** = Data Analysis, Statistics, and Probability; **A** = Algebra and Functions

Math Background

Chapter Overview

Solutions to many real-world problems and mathematical problems hinge on finding solutions of systems of linear equations or inequalities. Solutions that are adequate for a given situation can often be found graphically. When graphs are not adequate, algebraic methods can be used.

In this chapter, students learn to solve systems of linear equations and inequalities. They learn some of the basics of linear programming. They consider graphs of linear equations in three dimensions. Finally, they extend the algebraic methods they have learned for solving systems of linear equations with two variables to solve systems of linear equations with three variables.

Graphing Systems of Equations   3-1

Students are by now aware that not all systems of linear equations have easily determined solutions.

The system

$$3x + 7y = 5$$
$$6x - 7y = 1$$

has $\left(\frac{2}{3}, \frac{3}{7}\right)$ as its exact solution. If students graph this system using a scale of 1 grid unit $= \frac{1}{21}$ unit (an unlikely choice, seeing only the equations), their solution will be exact. If they graph it using any other scale that is not a multiple of $\frac{1}{21}$, their solution will probably be approximate. If their estimate of the solution, to the nearest hundredth, is (0.67, 0.43), checking these estimates in the equations will yield $5.02 \approx 5$ from the first equation, and $1.01 \approx 1$ from the second equation. Actually, the student is more likely to estimate the solution to the nearest tenth—perhaps (0.7, 0.4)—yielding $4.9 \approx 5$ and $1.4 \approx 1$. The check results are certainly close enough to assure the student that the estimated solution is close to the actual solution. Whether the estimated solution is *close enough* depends on the accuracy appropriate to the actual situation—for example, whether the concern is to build a bridge or a microscope and whether the units are miles or millimeters.

The discussion of independent, dependent, and inconsistent systems will provide convincing evidence of the importance of slope-intercept form in the study of systems of linear equations. Throughout, stress the importance of checking solutions in both equations of the system.

Solving Systems Algebraically   3-2

The Examples and Exercises in this lesson are generally also suitable for solution by graphing. The system

$$y = -0.143x + 294.015$$
$$y = -0.247x + 321.009$$

is more easily recognized as unsuitable for graphical solution. Its solution is (13497/52, 1027593/4000). No matter how carefully students graph this system by hand, their solution is most likely to be approximate and difficult to determine. Checking by substituting their approximations for the coordinates into each equation will most likely lead them to conclude that their work is fairly accurate, but not exact. Students should recognize this system as suitable for the substitution method, since each equation is already solved for y.

Inequalities and Linear Programming   3-3, 3-4

Linear programming is a branch of mathematics that was developed during World War II to cope with the complex task of transporting men and supplies. Analyzing situations to find correct inequalities for the constraints is another important application of mathematical modeling.

Graphs of Systems with Three Variables   3-5, 3-6

The graph of a one-variable equation on the number line is a point. The graph of a two-variable equation on the Cartesian coordinate system is a line. The graph of a three-variable equation in the coordinate space is a plane. Two planes can be parallel, they can intersect in a line, or they can coincide. The graphs of three simultaneous equations in three variables are three planes and they can intersect in one point, a line, a plane, or can have no point of intersection. There is no point of intersection if any two of the planes are parallel, or if each pair of planes intersect in lines that are parallel to each other.

Students who have difficulty visualizing figures in three dimensions may find it helpful to use rectangular boxes or other models to understand points in coordinate space. Finding intercepts for planes is a straightforward extension of the procedure used for finding intercepts for lines in the coordinate plane.

Ongoing Assessment and Intervention

Tools for Monitoring Student Progress

The Prentice Hall *Algebra 2* program provides you with many options for assessment in the Student Edition, the Teacher's Edition and the teaching resources. From these options you may choose instructional materials and techniques that are appropriate for your students and support your district's curriculum requirements.

✔ Instant Check System™ in Chapter 3

Allows students to check their own learning before, during, and after each lesson.

Diagnosing Readiness before the chapter (p. 114)

Check Skills You'll Need exercises in each lesson (pp. 116, 123, 130, 135, 142, 148)

Check Understanding questions with each Example (pp. 117, 118, 123, 124, 125, 131, 136, 137, 143, 144, 149, 150, 151, 152)

Checkpoint Quiz (pp. 134, 147)

Test Prep in Chapter 3

Teaches students strategies and gives them practice with all the test item formats they will encounter on state tests and standardized national exams.

Standardized Test Prep exercises in each lesson (pp. 121, 128, 133, 140, 146, 155)

Test-Taking Strategies (p. 156)

Standardized Test Prep (p. 161)

Program Assessment

Assess student progress throughout the *Algebra 2* text with blackline masters and CD-ROM.

Assessment Resources

- Checkpoint Quizzes 1 & 2
- Chapter Test, Forms A & B
- Chapter Alternative Assessment

Spanish versions available.

Computer Test Generator

- Unlimited questions of varying difficulty for every lesson objective.
- Create your own practice sheets, quizzes, and tests, or use the pre-made Chapter Tests.
- Diagnose readiness with questions on prerequisite skills.
- Prepare students by making tests based on standardized test objectives.
- Access Algebra 1, Geometry, and Algebra 2 content—all on one CD-ROM.

Test Preparation

A three-step approach to preparing students for high stakes, national, and state exams.

❶ Diagnose & Prescribe

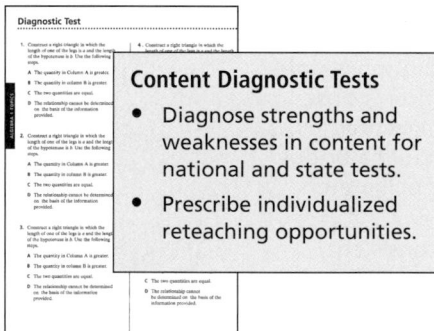

Content Diagnostic Tests

- Diagnose strengths and weaknesses in content for national and state tests.
- Prescribe individualized reteaching opportunities.

❷ Review & Reteach

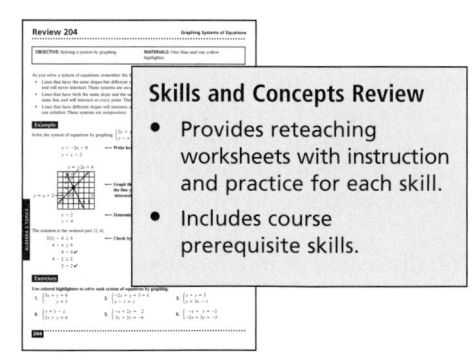

Skills and Concepts Review

- Provides reteaching worksheets with instruction and practice for each skill.
- Includes course prerequisite skills.

❸ Practice & Assess

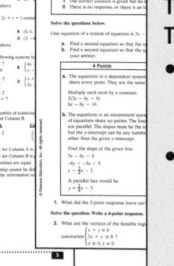

Test Preparation

- Features practice tests for End-of-Course and SAT/ACT exams.
- Includes standardized test practice by chapter for ongoing review.

Teacher's Guide with answers and correlations.

Test-Taking Strategies with Transparencies

- Support the Test-Taking Strategies pages in the Student Edition.
- Provide a teaching transparency and a practice worksheet for each strategy.

🎓 Reaching All Students

Support in the Student Text and Additional Resources

The textbook, the iText, and other technology components provide numerous opportunities to reach students of various ability levels and learning styles. Each Teacher's Edition lesson suggests how you can help *all* your students be successful and understand the mathematics in Chapter 3.

Below Level

Student Edition
- Diagnosing Readiness*: p. 114
- Check Skills You'll Need*: pp. 116, 123, 130, 135, 142, 148

Reteaching
Chapter 3 Support File: pp. 8–13

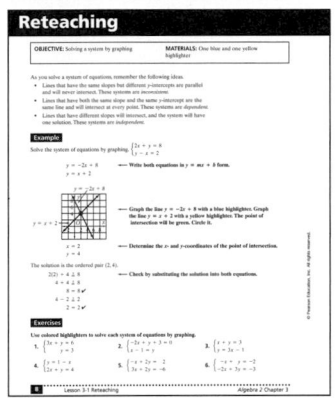

Advanced Learners

Student Edition
- Challenge exercises: pp. 120, 128, 133, 139, 146, 154
- Extension, pp. 122, 141

Enrichment
Chapter 3 Support File: pp. 14–19

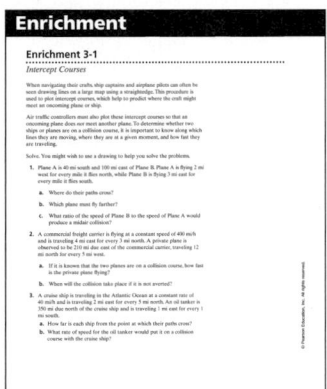

Connections to Precalculus Masters
Chapter 3 Enrichment Topic: Vectors

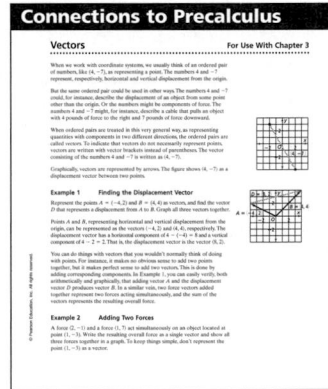

* Can be used with all ability levels to ensure mastery of prerequisite skills.

📖 Reading and Math Literacy

Student Edition
- Vocabulary: pp. 115, 157, *plus* in every Lesson Preview
- Reading Math: pp. 118, 121, 127, 129, 135, 137, 139
- Illustrated Glossary: pp. 871–913

Reading and Math Literacy Masters
Chapter 3: pp. 9–12

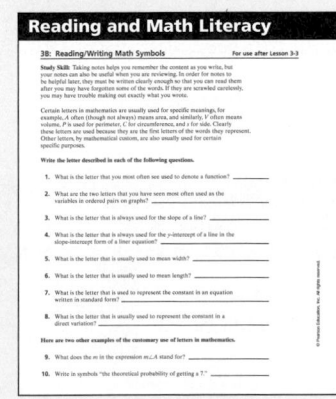

English Learners

Student Edition
- English/Spanish Illustrated Glossary: pp. 871–913

Workbook and Masters
Spanish Practice Workbook: pp. 2–7
Spanish Reading and Math Literacy Masters: pp. 9–12

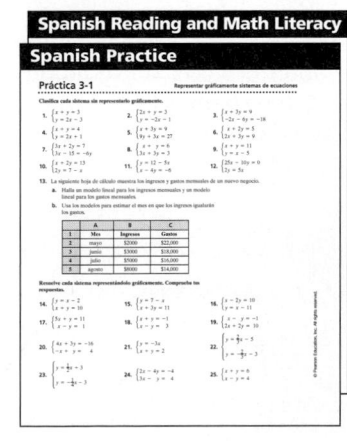

Learning Styles

Student Edition
- Investigation: pp. 116, 135
- Technology: pp. 122, 141
- Writing: pp. 120, 127, 133, 139, 145, 154

Activity Masters
Hands-On Activities: 36, 37
Technology Activities: 4

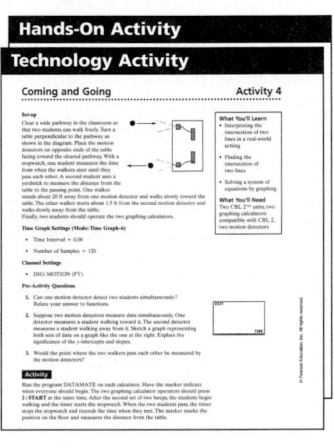

Program Resources

Presentation Assistant Plus!

	Teaching Resources in Grab & Go™ Files				Resources for Reaching All Students			Spanish Resources			Transparencies				Presentation Assistant Plus!
	Practice	Reteach	Enrich	Checkpoint Quiz	Reading & Math Literacy	Technology Activities	Hands-On Activities	Practice	Reading & Math Literacy	Checkpoint Quiz	Skills Check	Additional Examples	Answers to Exercises	Lesson Quiz	Prentice Hall Presentation Pro CD-ROM
3-1	■	■	■		■	■	■	■			■	■	■	■	■
3-2	■	■	■					■				■	■	■	■
3-3	■	■	■	■	■		■	■		■	■	■	■	■	■
3-4	■	■	■					■			■	■		■	■
3-5	■	■	■	■	■			■		■	■	■	■	■	■
3-6	■	■	■					■			■	■	■	■	■
For the chapter	Chapter Tests, Alternative Assessment, Cumulative Review, Cumulative Assessment				Connections to Precalculus Masters			Spanish Chapter Tests, Alternative Assessment, Cumulative Review, Cumulative Assessment			Classroom Aid Transparencies				

Also available for use with the chapter:

 *See page 114C.*

- Practice Workbook
- Solution Key

- For teacher support and access to student Web site materials, use Web Code agk-5500.
- For additional online and technology resources, see below.

  ## Technology

iTEXT — Online and on CD-ROM

Complete Interactive Student Text online and on CD-ROM—with instant feedback assessment, tutorial help, dynamic activities, instructional and real-world videos, audio, and additional practice.

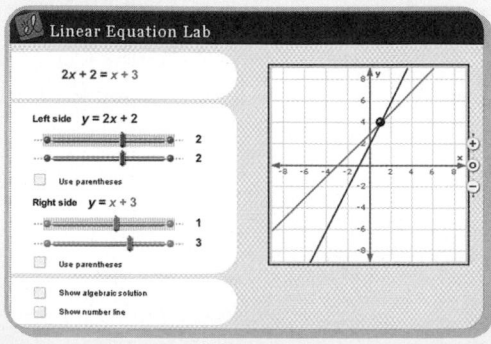

www.PHSchool.com — For Students

Use **Web Codes** for easy access to online activities, chapter projects, self-grading lesson quizzes and chapter tests, vocabulary quizzes, updated data sources, graphing calculator procedures, and more.

PH SuccessNet — For Teachers

Online lesson planning with built-in state correlations, all the teaching resources, complete reference library, your own calendar and Teacher Web page, professional development, and more.

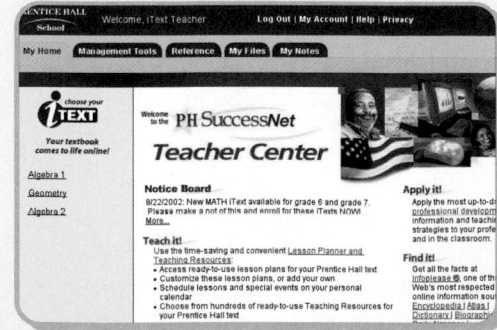

Presentation Assistant Plus!

The Prentice Hall *Presentation Assistant Plus!* provides you with the material you need to teach a lesson from beginning to end. Two easy-to-use formats—Transparencies and CD-ROM—allow you to present a lesson the way you are most comfortable.

 ## Transparencies

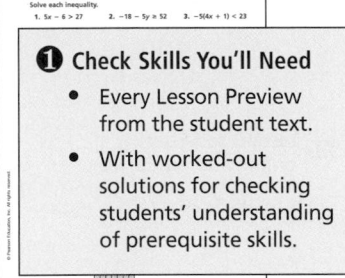

❶ Check Skills You'll Need
- Every Lesson Preview from the student text.
- With worked-out solutions for checking students' understanding of prerequisite skills.

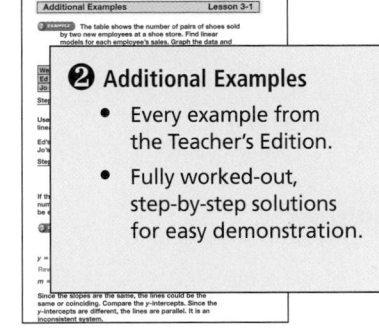

❷ Additional Examples
- Every example from the Teacher's Edition.
- Fully worked-out, step-by-step solutions for easy demonstration.

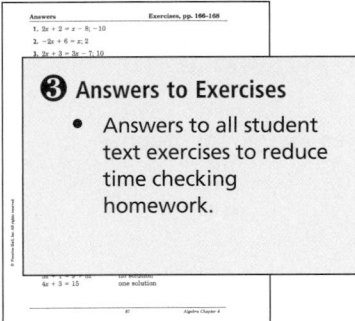

❸ Answers to Exercises
- Answers to all student text exercises to reduce time checking homework.

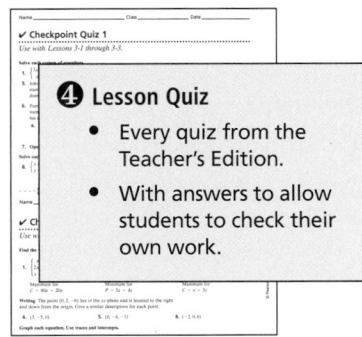

❹ Lesson Quiz
- Every quiz from the Teacher's Edition.
- With answers to allow students to check their own work.

 ## Prentice Hall Presentation Pro CD-ROM

- Includes all Transparencies.
- Conveniently organized by lesson so you can easily ❶ Introduce, ❷ Teach, ❸ Check Homework, and ❹ Assess each lesson.
- Animated examples allow step-by-step instruction at your own pace.
- Easy to edit so you can create custom presentations.

Teaching Chapter 3 Using Presentation Assistant Plus!

	❶ Introduce	❷ Teach	❸ Check Homework	❹ Assess
	Check Skills You'll Need	Additional Examples	Student Edition Answers	Lesson Quiz
3-1	p. 14	pp. 35–36	✔	p. 109
3-2	p. 15	pp. 37–40	✔	p. 109
3-3	p. 16	pp. 41–43	✔	p. 110
3-4	p. 17	pp. 44–45	✔	p. 111
3-5	p. 18	pp. 46–47	✔	p. 112
3-6	p. 19	pp. 48–53	✔	p. 112

 Throughout the Teacher's Edition, this symbol indicates material that is available on transparency in the Presentation Assistant Plus!

 Prentice Hall Presentation Pro

CD-ROM with dynamic PowerPoint® presentations for every lesson. Helps you introduce and develop concepts, check homework, and assess progress. Part of Presentation Assistant Plus! *(See above.)*

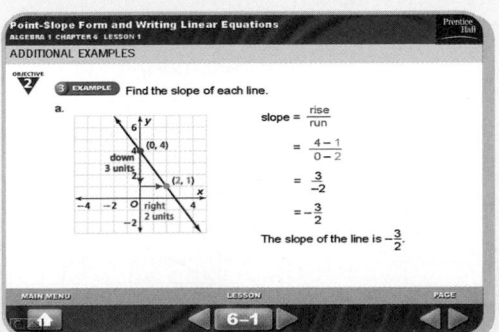

 Computer Test Generator

CD-ROM to create practice sheets and tests for course objectives and standardized tests. Includes Instant Chapter Tests™, online testing, and student reports. Part of the PH Assessment System. *(See page 114C.)*

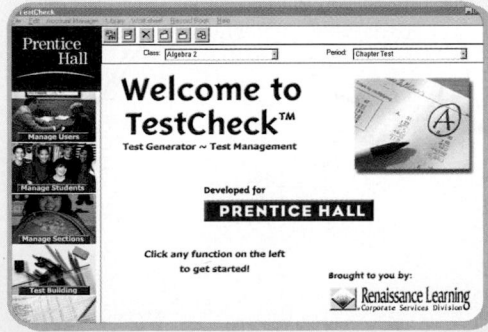

Resource Pro® with Planning Express®

CD-ROM with a lesson planning tool that allows you to import state and local objectives. Includes electronic versions of all the teaching resources.

Linear Systems

page 114   Diagnosing Readiness

5.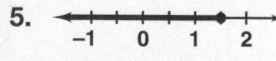

6.

7.

8.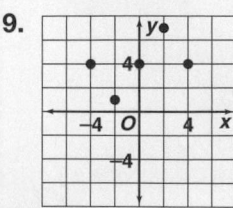

9.

Where You've Been

- In Chapter 1, you learned to write and solve equations and inequalities in one variable.

- In Chapter 2, you learned to write and solve equations and inequalities in two variables.

- In Chapter 2, you learned to graph points and equations in two dimensions.

 Instant self-check online and on CD-ROM

✓ **Diagnosing Readiness**   (For help, go to the Lesson in green.)

Combining Like Terms (Lesson 1-2)

Simplify by combining like terms.

1. $3x + (4x - 1)$
7x − 1

2. $12 - (p + 7)$
5 − p

3. $(2z + 10) - 8z$
−6z + 10

4. $(r - 1) - 3$
r − 4

Solving and Graphing Inequalities (Lesson 1-4)

Solve each inequality. Graph the solutions on a number line.   **5–8. See margin for graphs.**

5. $6a \leq 9$ $a \leq \frac{3}{2}$

6. $8b + 11 > 27$
b > 2

7. $3(24 + 2c) < 0$
c < −12

8. $5(0.2 + d) \leq -4$
d ≤ −1

Graphing Relations (Lesson 2-1)

Graph each relation on a coordinate plane.   **9–10. See margin.**

9. $\{(0, 4), (-2, 1), (2, 7), (-4, 4), (4, 4)\}$

10. $\left\{\left(0, \frac{1}{2}\right), \left(1, \frac{5}{2}\right), \left(2, \frac{9}{2}\right), \left(3, \frac{13}{2}\right), \left(4, \frac{17}{2}\right)\right\}$

Graphing Equations (Lesson 2-2)

Graph each equation on a coordinate plane.   **11–12, 14. See margin.**

11. $y = 4x + 1$

12. $-6y + x = 3$

13. $15x - 3y = 5$
See back of book.

14. $x = 2y - 7$

Writing a Linear Model (Lesson 2-4)

15. Each minute, a toll collector serves an average of six motorists. Write an equation to model the number of motorists this toll collector assists as a function of time. Graph the equation. **See back of book.**

Graphing Inequalities (Lesson 2-7)

Graph each inequality on a coordinate plane.   **16–18. See back of book.**

16. $y > 8x + 3$

17. $2y + x \leq -10$

18. $18x - 9y < 2$

19. $x \geq 4y - 5$
See margin p. 115.

10.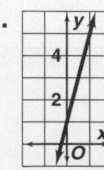

11.

12.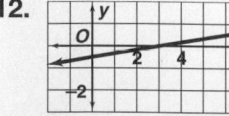

14.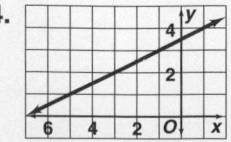

Linear Systems

Where You're Going

- In Chapter 3, you will learn to solve systems of equations and inequalities in two variables algebraically and by graphing.

- You will learn to graph points and equations in three dimensions.

- You will learn to solve systems of equations in three variables.

 Real-World Connection Applying what you learn, on page 139 you will solve a problem about planting trees.

Key Vocabulary

- constraints (p. 135)
- coordinate space (p. 142)
- dependent system (p. 118)
- equivalent systems (p. 125)
- feasible region (p. 136)
- inconsistent system (p. 118)
- independent system (p. 118)
- linear programming (p. 135)
- linear system (p. 116)
- objective function (p. 135)
- ordered triples (p. 142)
- system of equations (p. 116)
- trace (p. 144)

Chapter 3 Overview

This chapter begins by introducing students to the methods of solving systems of equations graphically and algebraically. Students then apply what they learned about systems of equations to solving systems of inequalities. They then learn to model real-world situations with linear programming. Finally, students are introduced to graphs in three dimensions and systems in three variables.

📖 Reading Math

Reading for Problem Solving, p. 129

📖 Vocabulary

A complete list of terms, plus vocabulary exercises, appears in the Chapter Review, p. 157.

📖 Illustrated Glossary

Examples for each vocabulary term, plus definitions in both English and Spanish, appear starting on p. 871.

Test-Taking Strategies

Answering Extended-Response Questions, p. 156

🌐 Real-World Connections

Some of the applications you will find in this chapter are sports (3-1), college admissions (3-3), product design (3-5), and money management (3-6)

💻 www.PHSchool.com

Internet support for this chapter includes:
- Self-grading Vocabulary and Chapter 3 Tests
- Chapter Project
- Chapter Planner
- Chapter 3 Resources

Plus **TEXT**

19.

1. Plan

Lesson Preview

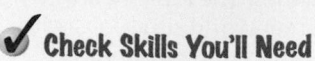

✓ **Check Skills You'll Need**

Linear Equations
Lesson 2-2: Example 1
Exercises 1–8
Extra Practice, p. 823

Lesson Resources

📁 **Teaching Resources**
Practice, Reteaching, Enrichment

👥 **Reaching All Students**
Practice Workbook 3-1
Spanish Practice Workbook 3-1
Reading and Math Literacy 3A
Spanish Reading & Literacy 3A
Technology Activities 4
Hands-On Activities 36

⏰ **Presentation Assistant Plus!**
Transparencies
• Check Skills You'll Need 3-1
• Additional Examples 3-1
• Student Edition Answers 3-1
• Lesson Quiz 3-1
PH Presentation Pro CD 3-1

PRENTICE HALL ASSESSMENT SYSTEM

Computer Test Generator CD

💿 **Technology**
Resource Pro® CD-ROM
Computer Test Generator CD
Prentice Hall Presentation Pro CD

🖥 **www.PHSchool.com**
Student Site
• Teacher Web Code: agk-5500
• Updated Data
• Graphing Calculator,
  Procedure 9
• Self-grading Lesson Quiz
Teacher Center
• Lesson Planner
• Resources

Plus 📱**iTEXT**

116

3-1 Graphing Systems of Equations

North Carolina Objectives

2.10 Use systems of two or more equations or inequalities to model and solve problems; justify results. Solve using tables, graphs, matrix operations, and algebraic properties.

Lesson Preview

What You'll Learn

OBJECTIVE 1
To solve a system by graphing

. . . And Why

To predict sports records, as in Example 2

✓ **Check Skills You'll Need**   (For help, go to Lesson 2-2.)

Graph each equation.   1–6. See back of book.

1. $y = 3x - 2$ **2.** $y = -x$ **3.** $y = -\frac{1}{2}x + 4$

Graph each equation. Use one coordinate plane for all three graphs.

4. $2x - y = 1$ **5.** $2x - y = -1$ **6.** $x + 2y = 2$

New Vocabulary
• system of equations
• linear system
• independent system
• dependent system
• inconsistent system

OBJECTIVE 1   **Systems of Linear Equations**

📱**iTEXT** Interactive lesson includes instant self-check, tutorials, and activities.

Investigation: Analyzing Graphs

1a–c. See back of book.

1. Use a graphing calculator to graph each pair of equations.

a. $y = x + 5$ **b.** $y = 3x + 2$ **c.** $y = -4x - 2$
  $y = -2x + 5$ $y = 3x - 1$ $y = \frac{8x + 4}{-2}$

2. For each pair, answer the following questions. a–b. See back of book.
   a. Do the graphs have any points in common; if so, how many?
   b. Compare the slopes of the graphs. What is the relationship between the slopes and the number of points in common?

3. Copy and complete the table for the graphs of two linear equations.

? ....
Need Help?
If the equation of a line is in the form $y = mx + b$, then the slope is m.

Description of Lines	How Many Points of Intersection?	Equal Slopes? (yes/no)	Same y-intercepts? (yes/no)
intersecting	■ 1	■ no	either
parallel	■ 0	■ yes	■ no
coinciding	■ infinite	■ yes	■ yes

A **system of equations** is a set of two or more equations that use the same variables. If the graph of each equation in a system of two variables is a line, then the system is a **linear system**.

A brace is used to keep the equations of a system together.
$$\begin{cases} y = x + 3 \\ y = -2x + 3 \end{cases}$$

 Ongoing Assessment and Intervention

Before the Lesson	**During the Lesson**	**After the Lesson**
Diagnose prerequisite skills using:	**Monitor progress using:**	**Assess knowledge using:**
• Check Skills You'll Need	• Check Understanding	• Lesson Quiz
	• Additional Examples	• Computer Test Generator CD
	• Standardized Test Prep	

A solution of a system of equations is a set of values for the variables that makes all the equations true. You can solve some linear systems by graphing the equations. The points where both (or all) the graphs intersect represent solutions.

1 EXAMPLE Solving by Graphing

Solve the system by graphing. $\begin{cases} x + 2y = -7 \\ 2x - 3y = 0 \end{cases}$

Graph the equations and find the intersection. The solution appears to be $(-3, -2)$.

Check Show that $(-3, -2)$ makes both equations true.

$$x + 2y = -7 \qquad\qquad 2x - 3y = 0$$
$$-3 + 2(-2) \overset{?}{=} -7 \qquad 2(-3) - 3(-2) \overset{?}{=} 0$$
$$-3 - 4 \overset{?}{=} -7 \qquad\qquad -6 + 6 \overset{?}{=} 0$$
$$-7 = -7 \checkmark \qquad\qquad\quad 0 = 0 \checkmark$$

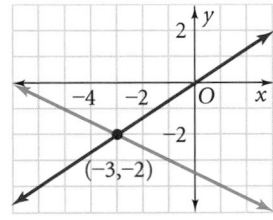

✓ **Check Understanding** ❶ Solve $\begin{cases} 2x + y = 5 \\ -x + y = 2 \end{cases}$ by graphing. Check your solution. **(1, 3)**

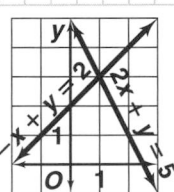

2 EXAMPLE Real-World  Connection

Sports Winning times for the Olympic 400-m run have been decreasing more rapidly for women than for men. Use the data in the table to find linear models for women's and men's times. Predict the year in which the women's winning time could equal that of the men, assuming that current trends continue.

Winning Times for the Olympic 400-Meter Dash (seconds)

Year	1968	1972	1976	1980	1984	1988	1992	1996	2000
Men's Time	43.86	44.66	44.26	44.60	44.27	43.87	43.50	43.49	43.84
Women's Time	52.03	51.08	49.29	48.88	48.83	48.65	48.83	48.25	49.11

SOURCE: *The World Almanac*

Step 1 Let x = number of years since 1968.
Let y = winning times in seconds.

Use the **LinReg** feature of a graphing calculator to find linear models.

Men's time: $y \approx -0.02433x + 44.43$
Women's time: $y \approx -0.08883x + 50.86$

Step 2 Graph each model. Use the Intersect feature on the graphing calculator. The two lines meet at about (99.7, 42.0).

If the trends continue, the times for men and women will be equal about 100 years from 1968, in 2068.

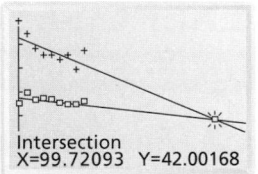
Intersection
X=99.72093 Y=42.00168

✓ **Check Understanding** ❷ **a.** Use the models in Example 2 to predict the winning times for the 400-m run at the Olympics in 2008 and in 2024.

2a. 2008 men: 43.46 s, women: 47.31 s
2024 men: 43.07 s, women: 45.89 s

b. Critical Thinking Example 2 assumes that current trends will continue. Explain why that assumption may not be valid. **It would mean that eventually the 400-m run would be run in zero seconds, and this could not happen.**

Real-World  Connection

Cathy Freeman won the 400-m run in the 2000 Olympics.

👥 Reaching All Students

Below Level Discuss with students the graphs of systems of linear equations that have zero, one, or many solutions.	**Advanced Learners** Have students explain why linear systems must be either independent, dependent, or inconsistent. **The graphs intersect, coincide, or are parallel.**	**English Learners** See note on page 117. **Error Prevention** See note on page 119.

---

2. Teach

Professional Development

Math Background

When you solve a system of equations by graphing, the x- and y-coordinates give an estimated point of intersection which can help verify solutions found using the methods in the following lessons.

OBJECTIVE
1 Teaching Notes

Investigation (Optional)
Some students may think that all lines with equal slopes are parallel. Remind them that the lines might coincide.

1 EXAMPLE Teaching Tip

Point out that when the point of intersection does not have integer coordinates, a graphing calculator may be helpful.

2 EXAMPLE Connection to Physical Education

Every year, more and more girls are joining sports teams. Many are breaking into sports such as football that have generally been thought of as "for boys only."

3 EXAMPLE English Learners

Some students may have a difficult time connecting the phrases *independent system*, *dependent system*, and *inconsistent system* with their graphs. Encourage these students to copy the diagrams and label each system correctly on a piece of paper. Have them refer to this paper as they work the exercises in this lesson.

Closure

Ask students to describe the graph of an independent system of linear equations in two variables. **The graph consists of two lines that intersect in one point.**

117

① Solve the system by graphing.
$$\begin{cases} x + 3y = 2 \\ 3x + 3y = -6 \end{cases} \ (-4, 2)$$

② The table shows the number of pairs of shoes sold by two new employees at a shoe store. Find linear models for each employee's sales. Use the graph of the models to predict the week in which they could sell the same number of pairs of shoes.

Week	1	2	3	4
Ed	50	55	63	67
Jo	40	47	56	62

Ed: $y = 5.9x + 44$;
Jo: $y = 7.5x + 32.5$;
during week 8

③ Classify the system without graphing.
$$\begin{cases} y = 3x + 2 \\ -6x + 2y = 4 \end{cases}$$
dependent system

pages 118–121 Exercises

1. (3, 1)
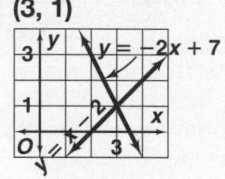

2. (2, 1)
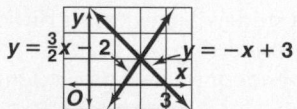

3. (−2, 4)
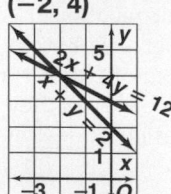

4. (−3, 5)
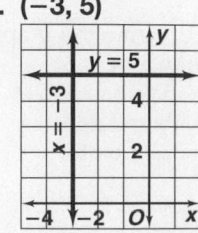

5. no solution
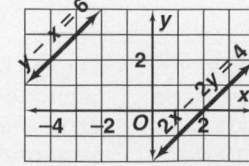

118

 **Reading Math**

Unique means "exactly one."

You can classify a system of two linear equations by the number of solutions. A system that has a unique solution, as in Examples 1 and 2, is an **independent system.** However, not every system has a unique solution.

A **dependent system** does not have a unique solution. An **inconsistent system** is a system that has no solution.

 Key Concepts

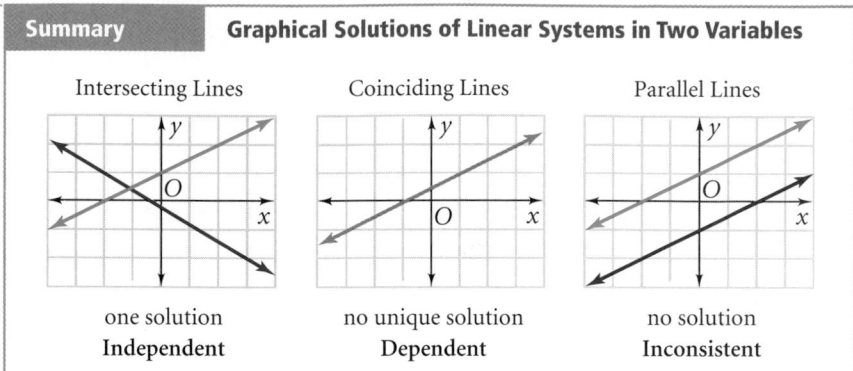

Summary	**Graphical Solutions of Linear Systems in Two Variables**

Intersecting Lines — one solution — Independent

Coinciding Lines — no unique solution — Dependent

Parallel Lines — no solution — Inconsistent

You can also classify a system of equations without graphing. By comparing the slopes and y-intercepts of the equations, you can find the number of solutions.

③ EXAMPLE Classifying Systems Without Graphing

Classify the system without graphing. $\begin{cases} y = 2x + 3 \\ -2x + y = 1 \end{cases}$

$y = 2x + 3$ **Rewrite in slope-intercept form.** → $y = 2x + 1$

$m = 2, b = 3$ **← Find the slope and y-intercept. →** $m = 2, b = 1$

Since the slopes are the same, the lines could coincide. Compare the y-intercepts. Since the y-intercepts are different, the lines are parallel. There is no solution. The system is an inconsistent system.

✔ **Check Understanding** **③** Without graphing, classify each system as *independent*, *dependent*, or *inconsistent*.

a. $\begin{cases} 3x + y = 5 \\ 15x + 5y = 2 \end{cases}$
inconsistent

b. $\begin{cases} y = 2x + 3 \\ -4x + 2y = 6 \end{cases}$
dependent

c. $\begin{cases} x - y = 5 \\ y + 3 = 2x \end{cases}$
independent

EXERCISES

For more practice, see *Extra Practice*.

Practice and Problem Solving

Ⓐ Practice by Example

Solve each system by graphing. Check your answers. **1–5. See margin.**

Example 1
(page 117)

1. $\begin{cases} y = x - 2 \\ y = -2x + 7 \end{cases}$

2. $\begin{cases} y = -x + 3 \\ y = \frac{3}{2}x - 2 \end{cases}$

3. $\begin{cases} 2x + 4y = 12 \\ x + y = 2 \end{cases}$

4. $\begin{cases} x = -3 \\ y = 5 \end{cases}$

5. $\begin{cases} 2x - 2y = 4 \\ y - x = 6 \end{cases}$

6. $\begin{cases} 3x + y = 5 \\ x - y = 7 \end{cases}$

7. $\begin{cases} -5x + y = -9 \\ x + 3y = 21 \end{cases}$

8. $\begin{cases} y = x \\ y - 5x = 0 \end{cases}$

9. $\begin{cases} x = 10 \\ x = y - 10 \end{cases}$

6–9. See back of book.

118 Chapter 3 Linear Systems

12a. **Answers may vary.**
$$\begin{cases} y = 3000x + 5200 \\ y = -900x + 35{,}700 \end{cases}$$

b. If Feb = 1, the revenue will equal expenses in the 7.82 month, or August.

Example 2
(page 117)

For Exercises 10–11, use your graphing calculator. Find linear models for each set of data. Use each model to predict the year in which the quantities will be equal.

10. $\begin{cases} y = 0.174x + 0.1 \\ y = 0.1107x + 2.354 \end{cases}$
about 2005

11. $\begin{cases} y = 0.2182x + 67.52 \\ y = 0.1545x + 75.463 \end{cases}$
about 2095

10.
Annual U.S. Consumption of Vegetables

Year	Broccoli (lb/person)	Cucumbers (lb/person)
1970	0.5	2.6
1975	1.0	2.6
1980	1.4	3.6
1985	2.6	4.0
1990	3.4	4.3
1995	4.4	5.2
2000	5.7	5.8

SOURCE: *Statistical Abstract of the United States.*
Go to **www.PHSchool.com** for a data update.
Web Code: agg-2041

11.
U.S. Life Expectancy at Birth

Year	Men (years)	Women (years)
1970	67.1	74.7
1975	68.8	76.6
1980	70.0	77.4
1985	71.1	78.2
1990	71.8	78.8
1995	72.5	78.9
1997	73.6	79.4

SOURCE: U.S. Census Bureau.
Go to **www.PHSchool.com** for a data update.
Web Code: agg-2041

12. a. **Business** The spreadsheet shows the monthly revenue and monthly expenses for a new business. Find a linear model for monthly revenue and a linear model for monthly expenses. **a–b. See margin p. 118.**
   b. Use the models to predict the month in which revenue will equal expenses.

	A	B	C
1	Month	Revenue	Expenses
2	Feb	8000	35000
3	Mar	12000	33000
4	Apr	13000	34000
5	May	18000	32000
6	Jun	20000	31000

Example 3
(page 118)

Without graphing, classify each system as *independent*, *dependent*, or *inconsistent*.

13. $\begin{cases} 7x - y = 6 \\ -7x + y = -6 \end{cases}$ **dependent**

14. $\begin{cases} -3x + y = 4 \\ x - \frac{1}{3}y = 1 \end{cases}$ **inconsistent**

15. $\begin{cases} 4x + 8y = 12 \\ x + 2y = -3 \end{cases}$ **inconsistent**

16. $\begin{cases} y = 2x - 1 \\ y = -2x + 5 \end{cases}$ **independent**

17. $\begin{cases} x = 6 \\ x = -2 \end{cases}$ **inconsistent**

18. $\begin{cases} 2y = 5x + 6 \\ -10x + 4y = 8 \end{cases}$ **inconsistent**

19. $\begin{cases} x - 3y = 2 \\ 4x - 12y = 8 \end{cases}$ **dependent**

20. $\begin{cases} x + 4y = 12 \\ 2x - 8y = 4 \end{cases}$ **independent**

21. $\begin{cases} 4x + 8y = -6 \\ 6x + 12y = -9 \end{cases}$ **dependent**

22. $\begin{cases} 4y - 2x = 6 \\ 8y = 4x - 12 \end{cases}$ **inconsistent**

23. $\begin{cases} y - x = 0 \\ y = -x \end{cases}$ **independent**

24. $\begin{cases} 2y - x = 4 \\ \frac{1}{2}x - y = 2 \end{cases}$ **inconsistent**

B Apply Your Skills

25–36. See back of book.

Graph and solve each system. Where necessary, estimate the solution.

25. $\begin{cases} 3 = 4y + x \\ 4y = -x + 3 \end{cases}$

26. $\begin{cases} x - 2y + 1 = 0 \\ x + 4y - 6 = 0 \end{cases}$

27. $\begin{cases} 3x + 6y - 12 = 0 \\ x + 2y = 8 \end{cases}$

28. $\begin{cases} -x + 3y = 6 \\ 2x - y = 8 \end{cases}$

29. $\begin{cases} 3x + y = 3 \\ 2x - y = 7 \end{cases}$

30. $\begin{cases} 2x + 3y = 6 \\ 4x = 6y + 3 \end{cases}$

31. $\begin{cases} 10 - 3x = -3y \\ 2 = 2x + y \end{cases}$

32. $\begin{cases} 3x = -5y + 4 \\ 250 + 150x = 300 \end{cases}$

33. $\begin{cases} x + 3y = 6 \\ 6y + 2x = 12 \end{cases}$

34. $\begin{cases} 2y + x = 8 \\ y - 2x = -6 \end{cases}$

35. $\begin{cases} y = -2x + 6 \\ x - 3y = -6 \end{cases}$

36. $\begin{cases} -x - 2 = -2y \\ 2x - 4y - 4 = 0 \end{cases}$

Assignment Guide

▼ **1** Objective
   A **B** Core 1–50
   C Extension 51–55

Standardized Test Prep 56–61

Mixed Review 62–74

Exercise 5 If students draw the graphs correctly, the lines should look parallel. Be sure students understand how slope can be used to confirm that the lines really are parallel.

Error Prevention

Exercises 28, 29, 33 Students can avoid errors by first multiplying both sides of each equation by 10.

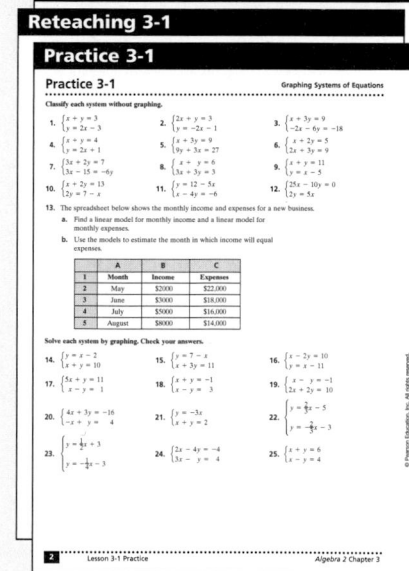

Lesson 3-1 Graphing Systems of Equations **119**

4. Assess

📋 **Lesson Quiz 3-1**

1. Graph and solve the system.
$$\begin{cases} 4x + y = -1 \\ -x + 3y = 10 \end{cases} (-1, 3)$$

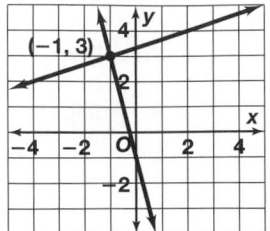

Classify each system without graphing. Tell how many solutions there are.

2. $\begin{cases} 5x + 3y = 10 \\ -x - 0.6y = -2 \end{cases}$
dependent; infinitely many

3. $\begin{cases} 12x - 18y = 9 \\ -6x + 9y = 13 \end{cases}$
inconsistent; no solutions

4. $\begin{cases} 4x + 5y = -10 \\ 3x - 8y = 15 \end{cases}$
independent; one solution

Alternative Assessment

Have students work in groups of three. Students 1 and 2 each write an equation of the form $Ax + By = C$, where A, B, and C are non-zero integers from -9 to 9. Student 3 classifies and graphs the system. If there is a unique solution with integer x- and y-values, student 3 identifies the solution and checks that it is correct. Otherwise, student 3 estimates the solution. Students 1 and 2 then confirm the correctness of the work. Students change roles until each student has graphed two systems.

Exercise 53 Check that students understand what the solution set notation means geometrically.

Real-World 🌐 Connection

Groomers must be able to handle dogs of every breed and temperament.

🅲 **Challenge**

53. Answers may vary. Sample:
$\begin{cases} -10x + 2y = 4 \\ 5x - y = -2 \end{cases}$

120 Chapter 3 Linear Systems

🌐 **37. Banking** To pay your monthly bills, you can either open a checking account or use an online banking service. A local bank charges $3 per month and $.40 per check, while an online services charges a flat fee of $9 per month.
  a. Write and graph a system of linear equations to model the cost c of each service for b bills that you need to pay monthly. **See back of book.**
  b. Find the point of intersection of the two linear models. What does this answer represent? **b–c. See margin.**
  c. If you pay about 12 bills per month, which service should you choose? Explain.

Classify each system without graphing.

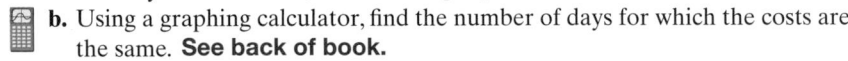

	inconsistent		dependent		independent

38. $\begin{cases} 3x - 2y = 8 \\ 4y = 6x - 5 \end{cases}$ **39.** $\begin{cases} 2x + 8y = 6 \\ x = -4y + 3 \end{cases}$ **40.** $\begin{cases} 3a + 6b = 14 \\ -a + 2b = 3 \end{cases}$

41. $\begin{cases} 3m = -5n + 4 \\ n - \frac{6}{5} = -\frac{3}{5}m \end{cases}$ **42.** $\begin{cases} -12x + 4y = 8 \\ y - 4 = 3x \end{cases}$ **43.** $\begin{cases} -6y + 18 = 12x \\ 3y + 6x = 9 \end{cases}$
  inconsistent   **inconsistent**   **dependent**

🌐 **44. Fees** Suppose you are going on vacation and leaving your dog in a kennel. The Bowowery charges $25 per day, which includes a one-time grooming treatment. The Poochpad charges $20 per day and a one-time fee of $30 for grooming.
  a. Write a system of equations to represent the cost c for d days that your dog will stay at a kennel. **a, c. See margin p. 121.**
  🖩 **b.** Using a graphing calculator, find the number of days for which the costs are the same. **See back of book.**
  c. If your vacation is a week long, which kennel should you choose? Explain.

🌐 **45. Advertising** You and your business partner are mailing advertising flyers to your customers. You address 6 flyers each minute and have already done 80. Your partner addresses 4 flyers each minute and has already done 100. Graph and solve a system of equations to find when the two of you will have addressed equal numbers of flyers. **See back of book.**

Open-Ended Write a second equation for each system so that the system will have the indicated number of solutions. **46–48. Answers may vary. Samples:**

46. one   **47. none**   **48. an infinite number**
$\begin{cases} y = -3x + 2 \\ \underline{\quad?\quad} \end{cases}$ $\begin{cases} y = -4x - 6 \\ \underline{\quad?\quad} \end{cases}$ $\begin{cases} 3y = 6x + 7 \\ \underline{\quad?\quad} \end{cases}$
y = x + 3   **y = -4x + 8**   **y = 2x + $\frac{7}{3}$**

49. Reasoning Is it possible for an inconsistent linear system to consist of two lines with the same y-intercept? Explain.   **No; they would be the same line, and the system would be dependent and consistent.**

✏️ **50. Writing** Summarize the possible relationships for the y-intercepts, slopes, and number of solutions in a system of two linear equations of two variables.   **See margin.**

Open-Ended Write a second equation for each system so that the system will have the indicated number of solutions. **51–52. Answers may vary. Samples:**

51. infinite number of solutions   **52. no solutions**
$\begin{cases} \frac{x}{4} + \frac{y}{3} = 1 \\ \underline{\quad?\quad} \end{cases}$ **3x + 4y = 12** $\begin{cases} 5x + 2y = 10 \\ \underline{\quad?\quad} \end{cases}$ **y = $-\frac{5x}{2}$ + 7**

53. Write a system of linear equations with the solution set $\{(x, y) \mid y = 5x + 2\}$.

54. Critical Thinking Look back through the exercises on the previous two pages to find several dependent systems. What relationship exists between the equations in each system?   **They are the same equation written in different forms.**

pages 118–121 Exercises

37b. (15, 9); the point represents where the cost of using the bank or online service would be the same.

c. The local bank would be cheaper if you only have 12 bills to pay per month.

 55. Economics Research shows that in a certain market only 2000 widgets can be sold at $8 each, but if the price is reduced to $3, then 10,000 can be sold.

  a. Let p represent price and n represent the number of widgets. Identify the independent variable and the dependent variable.

  b. Use the information above to write a linear *demand* equation.

  c. A shop can make 2000 widgets for $5 each and 20,000 widgets for $2 each. Use this information to write a linear *supply* equation.

  d. Find the equilibrium point where supply is equal to demand and profit is a maximum. Explain the meaning of the coordinates of this point within the context of the exercise.

a. p: independent, n: dependent
b. $n = -1600p + 14{,}800$
c. $n = -6000p + 32{,}000$
d. About (3.91, 8545); profits are maximized if about 8545 widgets are sold for about $3.91 each.

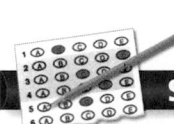

Standardized Test Prep

Multiple Choice

56. Which is an equation for Line 2? **C**
  A. $3x - 5y = 15$ **B.** $3x + 5y = 3$
  C. $3x + 5y = 15$ **D.** $5x + 3y = 15$

57. Which is NOT an equation for Line 1? **G**
  F. $y = x$ **G.** $x + y = 0$
  H. $x - y = 0$ **I.** $y - x = 0$

58. Which point lies on both Line 1 and Line 2? **B**
  A. $(0, 0)$ **B.** $(1.875, 1.875)$
  C. $(1.95, 1.95)$ **D.** $(2, 2)$

Exercises 56–58.

59. What is the solution of the system? $\begin{cases} 5x + 6y = -24 \\ -2x + 3y = 15 \end{cases}$ **H**

  F. $(6, -1)$ **G.** $(6, 1)$ **H.** $(-6, 1)$ **I.** $(-6, -1)$

Short Response

60. Explain how you can use slopes to show that the system $\begin{cases} 2x - 5y = 23 \\ 3y - 7x = -8 \end{cases}$ is NOT inconsistent.

60–61. See margin.

Extended Response

61. One equation of a system of equations is $2x - 3y = 5$.
  a. Find a second equation such that the system is dependent.
  b. Find a second equation such that the system is inconsistent.

Mixed Review

Lesson 2–7
Graph each inequality on a coordinate plane.   **62–64. See back of book.**
  62. $3x - 4y \geq 16$ **63.** $-5x > 8y + 4$ **64.** $x < -4$

Lesson 2–2
Write an equation for each line.
  65. $m = -\frac{2}{3}$; contains $(-9, 4)$ $y = \frac{-2x}{3} - 2$ **66.** $m = 0$; contains $(3, 4)$ $y = 4$

  67. $m = 2$; contains $(-2, -3)$ $y = 2x + 1$ **68.** $m = -\frac{1}{2}$; contains $(2, -6)$ $y = -\frac{1}{2}x - 5$

Lesson 1–3
Solve each equation and check the solution.
  69. $3n = -4(2 + n)$ $-\frac{8}{7}$ **70.** $-4a + a = 7a - 6$ $\frac{3}{5}$ **71.** $\frac{x}{3} + 5 = \frac{1}{6}$ -14.5

  72. $4x - 2 = \frac{1}{2}x$ $\frac{4}{7}$ **73.** $\frac{r}{5} + 5 = r - 3$ 10 **74.** $2(m - 3) = -4$ 1

60. [2] (The slope of $2x - 5y = 23$ is $\frac{2}{5}$ and the slope of $3y - 7x = -8$ is $\frac{7}{3}$. Since the slopes are not equal, the lines are not parallel and they do not coincide. So the lines intersect; the system has exactly one solution and is consistent.
[1] does not include explanation

61. [4] (a) A second equation is $4x - 6y = 10$, or any equation of the form $2ax - 3ay = 5a$.
  (b) A second equation is $2x - 3y = 6$ or any equation of the form $2ax - 3ay = 5b$, where $a \neq b$.
[3] minor error in either part (a) or (b)
[2] minor error in both parts (a) and (b)
[1] only completes part (a) or (b)

44a. $\begin{cases} c = 20d + 30 \\ c = 25d \end{cases}$

  c. The Pooch Pad would be cheaper for a 7-day stay.

50. An independent system has one solution. The slopes are different, but the y-intercepts could be the same. An inconsistent system has no solution. The slopes are the same, and the y-intercept are different. A dependent system has an infinite number of solutions. The slopes and y-intercepts are the same.

121

 Technology

Parametric Equations

Parametric Equations

Students use a graphing calculator to explore graphs of parametric equations.

Resources

Students may use any graphing calculator that has parametric graphing capabilities.

Teaching Notes

You may want to discuss how the flight path looks in three dimensions. The shape of the path in three dimensions is not necessarily a straight line.

English Learners

Discuss with students the meaning of *parameter* and how it relates to the phrase *parametric equation.*

Error Prevention

Be sure students use window settings that allow them to solve the problems they write.

Parametric equations are equations that express the coordinates x and y as separate functions of a common third variable, called the parameter. You can use parametric equations to determine the position of an object over time.

EXAMPLE

Starting from a birdbath 3 ft above the ground, a bird takes flight. Let t equal time in seconds, x equal horizontal distance in feet, and y equal vertical distance in feet. The equations $x(t) = 5t$ and $y(t) = 8t + 3$ model the bird's distance from the base of the birdbath. Graph the equations. Describe the position of the bird at time $t = 3$.

Step 1 Press MODE. Change the function mode to Parametric.

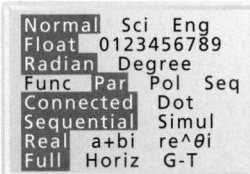

Step 2 Enter the equations. (When you press Y= you will see a list of pairs of equations.)

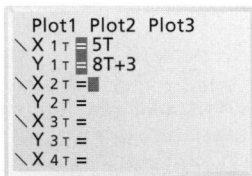

Step 3 Set the window values as shown.

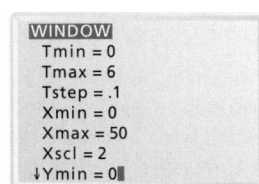

Step 4 Graph the equations. Press TRACE to find $t = 3$.

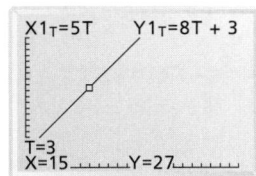

Three seconds after taking flight, the bird is 15 ft horizontally and 27 ft vertically from the base of the birdbath.

EXERCISES   1–4. See margin.

Graph each pair of parametric equations. Set the window with the *t*-values at the right. Find the values of x and y at time $t = 3$.

WINDOW
Tmin = -10
Tmax = 10
Tstep = .1
Xmin = -10
Xmax = 10
Xscl = 1
↓Ymin = -10

1. $x(t) = t$
$y(t) = -t + 6$

2. $x(t) = -3t$
$y(t) = t - 6$

3. $x(t) = |t - 2|$
$y(t) = t + 2$

 4. Writing Write a word problem involving the graph of $x(t) = 3t$ and $y(t) = 10t$. Interpret the x- and y-values at times $t = 0$, $t = 5$, and $t = -2$.

page 122   Technology

1. $x_3 = 3; y_3 = 3$ 2. $x_3 = -9; y_3 = -3$ 3. $x_3 = 1; y_3 = 5$ 4. **Check students' work.**
$x_0 = 0; y_0 = 0$
$x_5 = 15; y_5 = 50$
$x_{-2} = -6; y_{-2} = -20$

Solving Systems Algebraically

2.10 Use systems of two or more equations or inequalities to model and solve problems; justify results. Solve using tables, graphs, matrix operations, and algebraic properties.

Lesson Preview

What You'll Learn

 OBJECTIVE 1 To solve a system by substitution

 OBJECTIVE 2 To solve a system by elimination

. . . And Why

To find the cost of joining a health club, as in Example 2

✓ Check Skills You'll Need

(For help, go to Lessons 1-1 and 1-3.)

Find the additive inverse of each term.

1. 4 **−4**   2. $-x$ **x**   3. $5x$ **−5x**   4. $8y$ **−8y**

Substitute $2y - 1$ for x in each equation. Solve for y.

5. $x + 2y = 3$ **1**   6. $y - 2x = 8$ **−2**   7. $2y + 3x = -5$ **−$\frac{1}{4}$**

New Vocabulary   • equivalent systems

OBJECTIVE **1**

Solving Systems by Substitution

 iTEXT Interactive lesson includes instant self-check, tutorials, and activities.

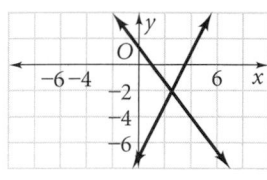

$$\begin{cases} 4x + 3y = 4 \\ 2x - y = 7 \end{cases}$$

Not every system can be solved easily by graphing. Consider the system at the left. Although you can graph each line easily, the exact point of intersection is not obvious. Substitution allows you to find exact solutions without using a graphing calculator.

1 EXAMPLE **Solving by Substitution**

Solve the system by substitution. $\begin{cases} 4x + 3y = 4 \\ 2x - y = 7 \end{cases}$

Step 1 Solve for one of the variables. Solving the second equation for y is easiest.

$$2x - y = 7$$
$$y = 2x - 7$$

Step 2 Substitute the expression for y into the other equation. Solve for x.

$4x + 3y = 4$
$4x + 3(2x - 7) = 4$ **Substitute for y.**
$4x + 6x - 21 = 4$ **Distributive Property**
$4x + 6x = 25$
$x = 2.5$

Step 3 Substitute the value of x into either equation. Solve for y.

$y = 2x - 7$
$y = 2(2.5) - 7$ **Substitute for x.**
$y = -2$

● The solution is $(2.5, -2)$.

✓ **Check Understanding** **1** Solve each system by substitution. Check your answers.

a. $\begin{cases} 2x - 3y = 6 \\ x + y = -12 \end{cases}$ **(−6, −6)**   b. $\begin{cases} 3x - y = 0 \\ 4x + 3y = 26 \end{cases}$ **(2, 6)**

---

1. Plan

Lesson Preview

✓ **Check Skills You'll Need**

Properties of Real Numbers
Lesson 1-1: Example 4
Exercises 37–44
Extra Practice, p. 822

Solving Equations
Lesson 1-3: Example 2
Exercises 5–8
Extra Practice, p. 822

Lesson Resources

Teaching Resources
Practice, Reteaching, Enrichment

Reaching All Students
Practice Workbook 3-2
Spanish Practice Workbook 3-2

Presentation Assistant Plus!
Transparencies
• Check Skills You'll Need 3-2
• Additional Examples 3-2
• Student Edition Answers 3-2
• Lesson Quiz 3-2
PH Presentation Pro CD 3-2

PRENTICE HALL ASSESSMENT SYSTEM

Computer Test Generator CD

Technology
Resource Pro® CD-ROM
Computer Test Generator CD
Prentice Hall Presentation Pro CD

 www.PHSchool.com
Student Site
• Teacher Web Code: agk-5500
• Self-grading Lesson Quiz
Teacher Center
• Lesson Planner
• Resources

Plus  **iTEXT**

Ongoing Assessment and Intervention

Before the Lesson
Diagnose prerequisite skills using:
• Check Skills You'll Need

During the Lesson
Monitor progress using:
• Check Understanding
• Additional Examples
• Standardized Test Prep

After the Lesson
Assess knowledge using:
• Lesson Quiz
• Computer Test Generator CD

Math Background

Solving systems algebraically is more accurate than solving by graphing, if some points of intersection are not integers. The methods of substitution and elimination both result in the solution of an equation in one variable. That solution is then used to find the value of another variable, and so on. The substitution method is most helpful when one equation is presented as solved for one of the variables. The method of elimination is a good way to begin when the coefficients of a variable are opposites.

OBJECTIVE 1 Teaching Notes

1 EXAMPLE Auditory Learners

Have students explain the substitution method orally in their own words.

2 EXAMPLE English Learners

Make sure students understand what an *initiation fee* is. You may want to ask how the term is related to the word *initial*.

Additional Examples

1 Solve the system by substitution. **(2.1, 3.3)**
$$\begin{cases} x + 3y = 12 \\ -2x + 4y = 9 \end{cases}$$

2 At Renaldi's Pizza, a soda and two slices of the pizza-of-the-day cost $10.25. A soda and four slices of the pizza-of-the-day cost $18.75. Find the cost of each item. **soda: $1.75; pizza: $4.25**

---

2 EXAMPLE Real-World Connection

Fees Refer to the photo at the left. The cost of membership in a health club includes a monthly charge and a one-time initiation fee. Find the monthly charge and the initiation fee.

Relate $2 \cdot$ monthly charge $+$ initiation fee $= \$100$

$6 \cdot$ monthly charge $+$ initiation fee $= \$200$

Define Let m = the monthly charge. Let f = the initiation fee.

Write $\begin{cases} 2m + f = 100 \\ 6m + f = 200 \end{cases}$

$2m + f = 100$ Solve for one of the variables.

$f = -2m + 100$

$6m + (-2m + 100) = 200$ Substitute the expression for *f* into the other equation. Solve for *m*.

$m = 25$

$2(25) + f = 100$ Substitute the value of *m* into one of the equations. Solve for *f*.

$f = 50$

● The monthly charge is $25, and the initiation fee is $50.

Health Club Membership Fees
2 months: $100
6 months: $200

✓ **Check Understanding** **2 Shopping** You can buy CDs at a local store for $15.49 each. You can buy them at an online store for $13.99 each plus $6 for shipping. Solve a system of equations to find the number of CDs that you can buy for the same amount at the two stores.
$$\begin{cases} c = 15.49x \\ c = 6 + 13.99x \end{cases}$$ **The number of CDs is 4.**

OBJECTIVE 2
Solving Systems by Elimination

You can solve a system of equations using the Addition Property of Equality. If the quantities you add contain a pair of additive inverses, you can eliminate a variable. You can also eliminate a variable by subtracting like terms.

3 EXAMPLE Solving by Elimination

Use the elimination method to solve the system. $\begin{cases} 4x - 2y = 7 \\ x + 2y = 3 \end{cases}$

$4x - 2y = 7$

$\underline{x + 2y = 3}$ Two terms are additive inverses, so add.

$5x = 10$

$x = 2$ Solve for *x*.

$x + 2y = 3$ Choose one of the original equations.

$2 + 2y = 3$ Substitute for *x*.

$y = \frac{1}{2}$ Solve for *y*.

● The solution is $\left(2, \frac{1}{2}\right)$.

✓ **Check Understanding** **3** Solve each system by elimination.

a. $\begin{cases} 3x - 2y = 14 \\ 2x + 2y = 6 \end{cases}$ **(4, −1)**

b. $\begin{cases} 4x + 9y = 1 \\ 4x + 6y = -2 \end{cases}$ **(−2, 1)**

124 Chapter 3 Linear Systems

👥 Reaching All Students

Below Level Have students use different methods to solve the same system.	**Advanced Learners** You have $13.50 to buy one pound of coffee. Blend A costs $16 a pound. Blend H costs $8 per pound. How many ounces of each can you buy? **11 oz, 5 oz**	**English Learners** See note on page 124. **Auditory Learners** See note on page 129.

Need Help?

The Multiplication Property of Equality states that if $a = b$ then $ac = bc$.

To make two terms additive inverses, you may need to multiply one or both equations in a system by a nonzero number. In doing so, you create a system equivalent to the original one. **Equivalent systems** are systems that have the same solution(s).

4 EXAMPLE Solving an Equivalent System

Solve the system below by elimination.
$$\begin{cases} 3x + 7y = 15 \\ 5x + 2y = -4 \end{cases}$$

To eliminate the y terms, make them additive inverses by multiplying.

① $3x + 7y = 15$	$6x + 14y = 30$	Multiply ① by 2.
② $5x + 2y = -4$	$\underline{-35x - 14y = 28}$	Multiply ② by -7.
	$-29x \qquad = 58$	Add.
	$x = -2$	Solve for x.
	$3x + 7y = 15$	Choose an original equation.
	$3(-2) + 7y = 15$	Substitute the value of x.
	$-6 + 7y = 15$	Simplify.
	$7y = 21$	
	$y = 3$	Solve for y.

● The solution is $(-2, 3)$.

✔ **Check Understanding** ④ Explain how to solve the system in Example 4 by eliminating x. **See left.**

4. Answers may vary. Sample: Multiply (1) by -5. Multiply (2) by 3. Add equations together, solving for y. Substitute the value of y into either original equation and solve for x.

Solving a system algebraically does not always result in a unique solution, as in Examples 3 and 4. You may get an equation that is always true, or one that is never true.

5 EXAMPLE Solving a System Without a Unique Solution

Solve each system by elimination.

a. $\begin{cases} 2x - y = 3 \\ -2x + y = -3 \end{cases}$
$\overline{\qquad 0 = 0 \qquad}$

b. $\begin{cases} 2x - 3y = 18 \\ -2x + 3y = -6 \end{cases}$
$\overline{\qquad 0 = 12 \qquad}$

Elimination gives an equation that is always true. The two equations in the system represent the same line. The system has an infinite number of solutions:
$\{(x, y) \mid y = 2x - 3\}$.

Elimination gives an equation that is always false. The two equations in the system represent parallel lines. The system has no solution.

✔ **Check Understanding** ⑤ Solve each system by substitution or elimination.

a. $\begin{cases} -3x + 5y = 7 \\ 6x - 10y = -14 \end{cases}$
infinite number of solutions $\{(x, y) \mid -3x + 5y = 7\}$

b. $\begin{cases} -2x + 4y = 6 \\ -3x + 6y = 8 \end{cases}$ **no solution**

OBJECTIVE

2 Teaching Notes

3 EXAMPLE Math Tip

Make sure students notice that it helps to write both equations in standard form when using the elimination method.

4 EXAMPLE Teaching Tip

Ask students how they would solve the system by eliminating the x terms. **Answers may vary. Sample: Multiply the first equation by 5, and multiply the second equation by -3.**

5 EXAMPLE Alternative Method

By solving each equation in a system for y, you can determine if the two lines are the same or if they are parallel. Show students that the slope of an equation in standard form is $-\frac{A}{B}$ and the y-intercept is $\frac{C}{B}$. If a student suspects the two lines are the same or parallel, have them find the slopes first. If the slopes are the same, have them use $\frac{C}{B}$ to find the y-intercept.

Additional Examples

❸ Use the elimination method to solve the system. **(-2, -3)**
$\begin{cases} 3x + y = -9 \\ -3x - 2y = 12 \end{cases}$

❹ Solve the system by elimination. **(4, -3)**
$\begin{cases} 2m + 4n = -4 \\ 3m + 5n = -3 \end{cases}$

❺ Solve each system by elimination.

a. $\begin{cases} -3x + 5y = 6 \\ 6x - 10y = 0 \end{cases}$ **no solution**

b. $\begin{cases} -3x + 5y = 6 \\ 6x - 10y = -12 \end{cases}$
$\{(x,y) \mid y = \frac{3}{5}x + \frac{6}{5}\}$

Closure

Have students tell how you know whether a system is ready to be solved by elimination. **The terms involving one of the variables, when written on the same side of the equal sign, are additive inverses.**

125

3. Practice

EXERCISES

For more practice, see *Extra Practice*.

Practice and Problem Solving

Assignment Guide

1 Objective
  Ⓐ Ⓑ **Core** 1–17, 64–65
  Ⓒ **Extension** 66

2 Objective
  Ⓐ Ⓑ **Core** 18–63
  Ⓒ **Extension** 67–69

Standardized Test Prep 70–75

Mixed Review 76–84

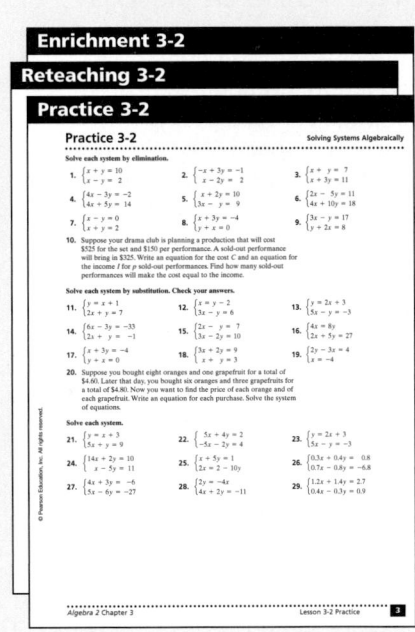

Ⓐ **Practice by Example**

Example 1
(page 123)

Solve each system by substitution. Check your answers.

1. $\begin{cases} 4x + 2y = 7 \\ y = 5x \end{cases}$ **(0.5, 2.5)**

2. $\begin{cases} 3c + 2d = 2 \\ d = 4 \end{cases}$ **(c, d) = (−2, 4)**

3. $\begin{cases} x + 12y = 68 \\ x = 8y − 12 \end{cases}$
   (20, 4)

4. $\begin{cases} 4p + 2q = 8 \\ q = 2p + 1 \end{cases}$
   (p, q) = (0.75, 2.5)

5. $\begin{cases} x + 3y = 7 \\ 2x − 4y = 24 \end{cases}$ **(10, −1)**

6. $\begin{cases} x + 6y = 2 \\ 5x + 4y = 36 \end{cases}$
   (8, −1)

7. $\begin{cases} 3a + b = 3 \\ 2a − 5b = −15 \end{cases}$
   (a, b) = (0, 3)

8. $\begin{cases} t = 2r + 3 \\ 5r − 4t = 6 \end{cases}$
   (r, t) = (−6, −9)

9. $\begin{cases} y = 2x − 1 \\ 3x − y = −1 \end{cases}$
   (−2, −5)

10. $\begin{cases} 2m + 4n = 10 \\ 3m + 5n = 11 \end{cases}$
    (m, n) = (−3, 4)

11. $\begin{cases} −6 = 3x − 6y \\ 4x = 4 + 5y \end{cases}$ **(6, 4)**

12. $\begin{cases} r + s = −12 \\ 2r − 3s = 6 \end{cases}$
    (r, s) = (−6, −6)

Example 2
(page 124)

13a. $\begin{cases} d = 0.50m \\ d = 15 \end{cases}$

13. **Fund-Raising** Suppose you have signed up for a bike-a-thon to raise money for charity. One person is sponsoring you at a rate of $.50 per mile. Each of the other sponsors plans to donate $15 no matter how far you bike.
    a. Write a system of equations to model the donation *d* for *m* miles biked.
    b. For how many miles will all sponsors donate the same amount? **30 miles**

14. **Transportation** A youth group with 26 members is going skiing. Each of the five chaperones will drive a van or a sedan. The vans can seat seven people, and the sedans can seat five people. How many of each type of vehicle could transport all 31 people to the ski area in one trip? **3 vans and 2 sedans, or 4 vans and 1 sedan, or 5 vans and 0 sedans**

15. Suppose you have a part-time job delivering packages. Your employer pays you at a flat rate of $7 per hour. You discover that a competitor pays employees $2 per hour plus $.35 per delivery.

15a. $\begin{cases} p = 28 \\ p = 8 + 0.35d \end{cases}$

   a. Write a system of equations to model the pay *p* for *d* deliveries. Assume a four-hour shift.
   b. How many deliveries would the competitor's employees have to make in four hours to earn the same pay you earn in a four-hour shift? **58**

16. A boat can travel 24 mi in 3 h when traveling with a current. Against the same current, it can travel only 16 mi in 4 h. Find the rate of the current and the rate of the boat in still water. **2 mi/h, 6 mi/h**

17. **Geometry** The measure of one acute angle of a right triangle is 30° more than twice the measure of the other acute angle. Find the measures of the angles. **20°, 70°, 90°**

Example 3
(page 124)

Solve each system by elimination.

18. $\begin{cases} x + y = 12 \\ x − y = 2 \end{cases}$ **(7, 5)**

19. $\begin{cases} x + 2y = 10 \\ x + y = 6 \end{cases}$ **(2, 4)**

20. $\begin{cases} 3a + 4b = 9 \\ −3a − 2b = −3 \end{cases}$ **(a, b) = (−1, 3)**

21. $\begin{cases} 4x + 2y = 4 \\ 6x + 2y = 8 \end{cases}$ **(2, −2)**

22. $\begin{cases} 2w + 5y = −24 \\ 3w − 5y = 14 \end{cases}$
    (w, y) = (−2, −4)

23. $\begin{cases} 3u + 3v = 15 \\ −2u + 3v = −5 \end{cases}$
    (u, v) = (4, 1)

24. $\begin{cases} x + 3y = 11 \\ x + 4y = 14 \end{cases}$ **(2, 3)**

25. $\begin{cases} 5x + 3y = 30 \\ 3x + 3y = 18 \end{cases}$ **(6, 0)**

26. $\begin{cases} x − 14 = −y \\ x − y = 2 \end{cases}$ **(8, 6)**

27. $\begin{cases} 3x + 2y = 6 \\ 3x + 3 = y \end{cases}$ **(0, 3)**

28. $\begin{cases} 5x − y = 4 \\ 2x − y = 1 \end{cases}$ **(1, 1)**

29. $\begin{cases} 2r + s = 3 \\ 4r − s = 9 \end{cases}$
    (r, s) = (2, −1)

pages 126–128 **Exercises**

30. $\{(x, y): −2x + 3y = 13\}$

31. $\{(a, d) \mid −3a + d = −1\}$

32. $(a, b) = (3, 2)$

33. **no solution**

34. **(5, 4)**

35. **no solution**

36. $\left(\frac{20}{17}, \frac{19}{17}\right)$

37. **(−3, 2)**

38. **(r, s) = (4, 1)**

39. **(1, 3)**

40. **no solution**

41. **(m, n) = (1, −4)**

Examples 4, 5
(page 125)

Solve each system by elimination. 30–41. See margin p. 126.

30. $\begin{cases} 4x - 6y = -26 \\ -2x + 3y = 13 \end{cases}$

31. $\begin{cases} 9a - 3d = 3 \\ -3a + d = -1 \end{cases}$

32. $\begin{cases} 2a + 3b = 12 \\ 5a - b = 13 \end{cases}$

33. $\begin{cases} 2x - 3y = 6 \\ 6x - 9y = 9 \end{cases}$

34. $\begin{cases} 20x + 5y = 120 \\ 10x + 7.5y = 80 \end{cases}$

35. $\begin{cases} 6x - 2y = 11 \\ -9x + 3y = 16 \end{cases}$

36. $\begin{cases} 2x - 3y = -1 \\ 3x + 4y = 8 \end{cases}$

37. $\begin{cases} 5x - 2y = -19 \\ 2x + 3y = 0 \end{cases}$

38. $\begin{cases} r + 3s = 7 \\ 2r - s = 7 \end{cases}$

39. $\begin{cases} y = 4 - x \\ 3x + y = 6 \end{cases}$

40. $\begin{cases} 3x + 2y = 10 \\ 6x + 4y = 15 \end{cases}$

41. $\begin{cases} 3m + 4n = -13 \\ 5m + 6n = -19 \end{cases}$

Reading Math

For help with reading
and solving Exercise 42,
see p. 129.

 42. **Elections** In a mayoral election, the incumbent received 25% more votes than the opponent. Altogether, 5175 votes were cast for the two candidates. How many votes did the incumbent mayor receive? **2875 votes**

 43. **Writing** Explain how you decide whether to use substitution or elimination to solve a system. **See margin.**

 B **Apply Your Skills**

Solve each system.

45. $(m, n) = (4, -3)$

46. $\left(-1, -\frac{1}{2}\right)$

47. $(t, v) = (50, 750)$

48. $(0.5, 0.75)$

49. $\left(\frac{3}{11}, -\frac{2}{11}\right)$

44. $\begin{cases} 5x + y = 0 \\ 5x + 2y = 30 \end{cases}$ $(-6, 30)$

45. $\begin{cases} 2m = -4n - 4 \\ 3m + 5n = -3 \end{cases}$

46. $\begin{cases} 7x + 2y = -8 \\ 8y = 4x \end{cases}$

47. $\begin{cases} v = 9t + 300 \\ v = 7t + 400 \end{cases}$

48. $\begin{cases} 80x + 60y = 85 \\ 100x - 40y = 20 \end{cases}$

49. $\begin{cases} 2x + 3y = 0 \\ 7x = 3(2y) + 3 \end{cases}$

50. $\begin{cases} \frac{x}{3} + \frac{4y}{3} = 300 \\ 3x - 4y = 300 \end{cases}$ **(300, 150)**

51. $\begin{cases} 0.02a - 1.5b = 4 \\ 0.5b - 0.02a = 1.8 \end{cases}$ **$(a, b) = (-235, -5.8)$**

52. $\begin{cases} 4y = 2x \\ 2x + y = \frac{x}{2} + 1 \end{cases}$ **(0.5, 0.25)**

53. $\begin{cases} -x + y = 4 \\ 3x - y = 6 \end{cases}$ **(5, 9)**

54. $\begin{cases} \frac{1}{2}x + y = 7 \\ 2x - 3y = 7 \end{cases}$ **(8, 3)**

55. $\begin{cases} 0.4x + 0.1y = 0.6 \\ 0.5x - 0.3y = -0.1 \end{cases}$ **(1, 2)**

For each system, choose the method of solving that seems easier to use. Explain why you made each choice. 56–61. See margin.

56. $\begin{cases} 3x - 5y = 26 \\ -2x - 3y = -11 \end{cases}$

57. $\begin{cases} y = \frac{2}{3}x - 3 \\ -x + 3y = 18 \end{cases}$

58. $\begin{cases} 2m + 3n = 12 \\ -5m + n = -13 \end{cases}$

59. $\begin{cases} 3x - y = 5 \\ y = 4x + 2 \end{cases}$

60. $\begin{cases} 2x - 3y = 4 \\ 2x - 5y = -6 \end{cases}$

61. $\begin{cases} 6x - 3y = 3 \\ 5x - 5y = 10 \end{cases}$

62. **Open-Ended** Write a system of equations in which both equations must be multiplied by a nonzero number before using elimination. Solve your system. **See margin p. 128.**

63. **Critical Thinking** Give an example of a system of equations that would be easier to solve graphically than algebraically. **See margin p. 128.**

 64. **Internet Access** The ads at the left show the costs of Internet access for two companies. **a–d. See margin p. 128.**

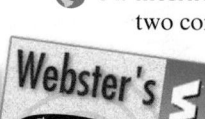

a. Write a system of equations to represent the cost c for t hours of access in one month for each company.

b. Graph the system from part (a). Label each line.

c. For how many hours of use will the costs for the companies be the same? How is this information represented on the graph?

d. If you use the Internet about 20 hours each month, which company should you choose? Explain how you reached an answer.

Lesson 3-2 Solving Systems Algebraically **127**

43. In determining whether to use substitution or elimination to solve an equation, look at the equations to determine if one is solved or can be easily solved for a particular variable. If that is the case, substitution can easily be used. Otherwise, elimination might be easier.

56. Elimination; substitution would be difficult since no coefficient is 1.

57. Substitution; the first equation is solved for y.

Alternative Assessment

Ask three students each to state a different equation in standard form. Write the equations where all students can see them. Instruct half of the students to solve the system by finding x first. Instruct the other half to find y first. Have students compare solutions.

58. **Substitution; the second equation is easily solved for n.**

59. **Substitution; the second equation is solved for y.**

60. **Elimination; $2x$ would be eliminated from the system if the equations were subtracted.**

61. **Elimination; substitution would be difficult since no coefficient is 1.**

127

A sheet of blank grids is available in the Test-Taking Strategies with Transparencies booklet. Give this sheet to students for practice with filling in the grids.

Resources

For additional practice with a variety of test item formats:
- Standardized Test Prep, p. 161
- Test-Taking Strategies, p. 156
- Test-Taking Strategies with Transparencies

pages 126–128   Exercises

62. Answers may vary.
Sample:
$$\begin{cases} -3x + 4y = 12 \\ 5x - 3y = 13 \end{cases}$$
(8, 9)

63. Answers may vary.
Sample:
$$\begin{cases} y = 2x + 1 \\ y = -3x - 4 \end{cases}$$

64a. $c = 9.95 + 2.25t$,
$c = 2.95t$

b.
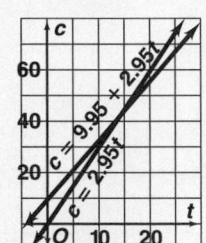

c. 14.2 h; It is where the graphs intersect.

d. Answers may vary.
Sample: Internet Action, because it would cost $4.05 less per month

79. $y = (x + 3) - 4$ or $y = x - 1$

80. $y = |x - 2| + \frac{1}{2}$

81. $y = 2(x - 1) - 4$ or $y = 2x - 6$

82. $y = |x + 3| + 6$

---

65. **Break-Even Point** A theater production costs $40,000 plus $2800 per performance. A sold-out performance brings in $3675. How many sold-out performances will the production need to break even? **46 performances**

C Challenge 66. **Weather** The equation $F = \frac{9}{5}C + 32$ relates temperatures on the Celsius and Fahrenheit scales. Does any temperature have the same number reading on both scales? If so, what is the number? **yes; for −40 degrees**

Find the value of a that makes each system a dependent system.

67. $\begin{cases} y = 3x + a \\ 3x - y = 2 \end{cases}$ **−2**

68. $\begin{cases} 3y = 2x \\ 6y - a - 4x = 0 \end{cases}$ **0**

69. $\begin{cases} y = \frac{x}{2} + 4 \\ 2y - x = a \end{cases}$ **8**

Gridded Response

Use the following system of equations for Exercises 70–73.
$$\begin{cases} 5x - 3y = 11 \\ -x + 12y = 3.5 \end{cases}$$

70. If you want to solve the system by eliminating the x terms (with addition), by what would you multiply the second equation? **5**

71. If you want to solve the system by eliminating the y terms (with addition), by what would you multiply the first equation? **4**

Take It to the NET
Online lesson quiz at
www.PHSchool.com
Web Code: aga-0302

72. What is the value of x in the solution? Enter your answer as a decimal. **2.5**

73. What is the value of y in the solution? Enter your answer as a decimal. **0.5**

Use the following system of equations for Exercises 74–75.
$$\begin{cases} 4x - 10y = -3 \\ 12x + 5y = 12 \end{cases}$$

74. What is the value of x in the solution? Enter your answer as a fraction in simplest form. $\frac{3}{4}$

75. What is the value of y in the solution? Enter your answer as a decimal. **0.6**

Mixed Review

Lesson 3-1   Solve each system of equations by graphing.

76. $\begin{cases} y = 3x + 4 \\ 2y = 6x - 2 \end{cases}$ **no solution**

77. $\begin{cases} -3y = 9x + 1 \\ 6y = -18x - 2 \end{cases}$ **{(x, y) | −9x − 3y = 1}**

78. $\begin{cases} 4x - y = -5 \\ -8x + 2y = 15 \end{cases}$ **no solution**

Lesson 2-6   Write an equation for each diagonal translation. **79–82. See margin.**

79. $y = x$, 4 units down, 3 units left

80. $y = |x|$, $\frac{1}{2}$ unit up, 2 units right

81. $y = 2x - 3$, 1 unit down, 1 unit right

82. $y = |x| + 2$, 4 units up, 2 units left

Lesson 1-1   83. What subset(s) of real numbers contain(s) 6? **natural, whole, integer, rational**

84. The sum of the first and last of four consecutive odd integers is 48. What are the four integers? **21, 23, 25, 27**

Reading For Problem Solving

FOR USE WITH PAGE 127 EXERCISE 42

Read the problem below. Then follow along with David as he solves the problem. Check your understanding with the exercise at the bottom of the page.

Elections In a mayoral election, the incumbent received 25% more votes than the opponent. Altogether, 5175 votes were cast for the two candidates. How many votes did the incumbent mayor receive?

What David Thinks

I'll restate the important information. In the first sentence, 25% more means the greater number is 1.25 times the lesser number.

The second sentence gives me the total number of votes.

What quantities are being used in the problem? I'll assign variables to the number of votes each received.

Now I can write a system of equations.

Great! The first equation defines the value of *n*. I'll solve the system by substituting 1.25*p* from the first equation into the second equation.

The problem asks me to find the number of incumbent votes. That's *n*. I'll use one of the original equations and substitute.

Now I'll write my answer as a sentence.

What David Writes

Incumbent received 25% more votes than opponent.

$$\text{incumbent's votes} = 1.25 \left(\text{opponent's votes} \right)$$

5175 votes total for both candidates.

$$\text{incumbent's votes} + \text{opponent's votes} = 5175$$

n = number of incumbent's votes
p = number of opponent's votes

$$\begin{cases} n = 1.25p \\ n + p = 5175 \end{cases}$$

$$\begin{aligned} n + p &= 5175 \\ 1.25p + p &= 5175 \\ 2.25p &= 5175 \\ p &= 2300 \end{aligned}$$

$$\begin{aligned} n &= 1.25p \\ n &= 1.25(2300) \\ n &= 2875 \end{aligned}$$

The incumbent mayor received 2875 votes.

EXERCISE

Two baseball cards together are worth $30. One card is worth 40% more than the other card. How much is the more expensive card worth? **$17.50**

Reading for Problem Solving

Students read a problem then investigate a sample solution of the problem. They see examples both of what the person who is solving the problem thinks, and of what he writes. Students learn how to restate important information and how to identify the significant quantities given. Finally, they learn how to assign variables to the unknown quantities and then use the given information to solve a system of equations for the unknown quantities.

Teaching Notes

Before students look at how David thinks about or solves the problem, ask them to discuss the problem itself. Ask: *How would you solve the problem? What information in the problem is important?* Then have students compare their thoughts about the problem to the way David handled it.

Math Tip

A more literal way to represent the number of incumbent's votes would be $n = p + 0.25p$, which can then simplify to $n = 1.25p$.

Auditory Learners

Read the problem aloud to the class while they write down any important information that they hear. Repeat sections of the problem as needed.

Exercise

Have students make a two-column table on a sheet of paper. In the left column, ask students to record their thoughts about what they need to do to solve the problem. In the right column, have them record the steps that they follow to solve the problem.

1. Plan

Lesson Preview

 Check Skills You'll Need

Solving Inequalities
Lesson 1-4: Example 1
Exercises 1–9
Extra Practice, p. 822.

Absolute Value Functions and Graphs
Lesson 2-5: Example 1
Exercises 1–9
Extra Practice, p. 823.

Two Variable Inequalities
Lesson 2-7: Example 1
Exercises 1–9
Extra Practice, p. 823.

Lesson Resources

 Teaching Resources
Practice, Reteaching, Enrichment
Checkpoint Quiz 1

Reaching All Students
Practice Workbook 3-3
Spanish Practice Workbook 3-3
Reading and Math Literacy 3B
Spanish Reading & Literacy 3B
Spanish Checkpoint Quiz 1
Hands-On Activities 37

Presentation Assistant Plus!
Transparencies
• Check Skills You'll Need 3-3
• Additional Examples 3-3
• Student Edition Answers 3-3
• Lesson Quiz 3-3
PH Presentation Pro CD 3-3

 ASSESSMENT SYSTEM

Checkpoint Quiz 1
Computer Test Generator CD

 Technology
Resource Pro® CD-ROM
Computer Test Generator CD
Prentice Hall Presentation Pro CD

www.PHSchool.com
Student Site
• Teacher Web Code: agk-5500
• Self-grading Lesson Quiz
Teacher Center
• Lesson Planner
• Resources

 Plus *i*TEXT

Systems of Inequalities

 North Carolina Objectives

2.10 Use systems of two or more equations or inequalities to model and solve problems; justify results. Solve using tables, graphs, matrix operations, and algebraic properties.

Lesson Preview

What You'll Learn

OBJECTIVE 1 To solve systems of linear inequalities

. . . And Why
To model college entrance requirements, as in Example 2

 **Check Skills You'll Need**   (For help, go to Lessons 1-4, 2-5, amd 2-7.)

Solve each inequality.

1. $5x - 6 > 27$ $x > \frac{33}{5}$
2. $-18 - 5y \geq 52$ $y \leq -14$
3. $-5(4x + 1) < 23$ $x > -\frac{7}{5}$

Graph each inequality. **4–9. See back of book.**

4. $y \leq 4x - 1$
5. $3y \geq 6x + 3$
6. $-5y + 2x > -5$
7. $y \leq |x|$
8. $y \geq |x + 3|$
9. $y < |x - 2| + 4$

OBJECTIVE 1 Solving Systems of Inequalities

 *i*TEXT **Interactive lesson includes instant self-check, tutorials, and activities.**

You can solve a system of linear inequalities by graphing. Every point in the region of overlap is a solution of both inequalities and is therefore a solution of the system.

1 EXAMPLE **Solving a System of Inequalities**

Solve the system of inequalities. $\begin{cases} x - 2y < 6 \\ y \leq -\frac{3}{2}x + 5 \end{cases}$

Graph each inequality. First graph the boundary lines. Then decide which side of each boundary line contains solutions and whether the boundary line is included.

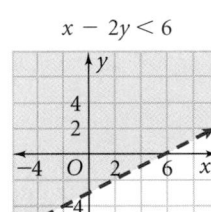 $x - 2y < 6$

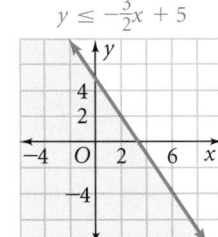 $y \leq -\frac{3}{2}x + 5$

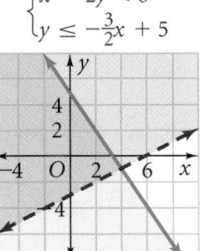 $\begin{cases} x - 2y < 6 \\ y \leq -\frac{3}{2}x + 5 \end{cases}$

Every point in the red region above the dashed line is a solution of $x - 2y < 6$.

Every point in the blue region or on the solid line is a solution of $y \leq -\frac{3}{2}x + 5$.

Every point in the purple region where the red and blue regions intersect is a solution of the system. For example, (1,1) is a solution.

Check Check (1,1) in both inequalities of the system.

$$x - 2y < 6 \qquad\qquad y \leq -\frac{3}{2}x + 5$$
$$1 - 2(1) < 6 \qquad\qquad 1 \leq -\frac{3}{2}(1) + 5$$
$$-1 < 6 \checkmark \qquad\qquad 1 \leq \frac{7}{2} \checkmark$$

? Need Help?
After graphing a boundary line, test whether (0, 0) satisfies the inequality. If it does, shade the side of the line containing (0, 0).

INSTANT CHECK ✓ Ongoing Assessment and Intervention

Before the Lesson	**During the Lesson**	**After the Lesson**
Diagnose prerequisite skills using:	**Monitor progress using:**	**Assess knowledge using:**
• Check Skills You'll Need	• Check Understanding	• Lesson Quiz
	• Additional Examples	• Computer Test Generator CD
	• Standardized Test Prep	• Chapter Checkpoint 1 (p. 134)

✓ **Check Understanding** **1** Solve each system of inequalities.   **a–b. See back of book.**

a. $\begin{cases} y \le -2x + 4 \\ x > -3 \end{cases}$

b. $\begin{cases} y \le 3x - 6 \\ y > -4x + 2 \end{cases}$

2 EXAMPLE **Real-World** **Connection**

College Admissions An entrance exam has two parts, a verbal part and a mathematics part. You can score a maximum total of 1600 points. For admission, the school of your choice requires a math score of at least 600. Write and solve a system of inequalities to model scores that meet the school's requirements.

Relate   verbal score + math score ≤ 1600

math score ≥ 600

Define   Let x = the verbal score.

Let y = the mathematics score.

Write x + y ≤ 1600, or y ≤ 1600 − x

y ≥ 600

The system of inequalities is $\begin{cases} y \le 1600 - x \\ y \ge 600 \end{cases}$.

Xmin = 0	Ymin = 10
Xmax = 1600	Ymax = 1600

Use a graphing calculator. Graph the corresponding equations $y = 1600 - x$ and $y = 600$. Since the first inequality is ≤, shade below the first line. Since the second inequality is ≥, shade above the second line. The region of overlap is a graph of the solution.

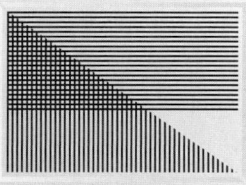

✓ **Check Understanding** **2** Another school requires a math score of at least 550 points and a total score of at least 1100 points. You can score up to 800 points on each part. Write and solve a system of inequalities to model scores that meet the school's requirements.
See back of book.

Some systems consist of linear and absolute value inequalities.

3 EXAMPLE **Solving a Linear Absolute Value System**

Solve the system of inequalities. $\begin{cases} y < 4 \\ y \ge |x - 3| \end{cases}$

$y < 4$ $\qquad$ $y \ge |x - 3|$ $\qquad$ $\begin{cases} y \ge |x - 3| \\ y < 4 \end{cases}$

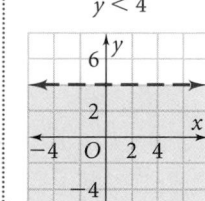 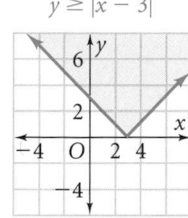 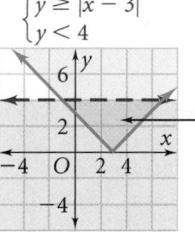

The region of overlap represents the solution.

✓ **Check Understanding** **3** Solve each system of inequalities.   **a–b. See back of book.**

a. $\begin{cases} y \ge x \\ y \le |x + 5| - 2 \end{cases}$

b. $\begin{cases} y \ge -2x + 4 \\ y \le |x - 4| \end{cases}$

Lesson 3-3 Systems of Inequalities   **131**

Real-World **Connection**

Most college admission requirements include standardized test scores.

👪 Reaching All Students

Below Level Try using multiple methods to solve examples, so students can choose the method with which they are most comfortable.	**Advanced Learners** Have students create a real–world example to be solved with a linear system. Let them exchange exercises and solve.	**Tactile Learners** See note on page 131. **Error Prevention** See note on page 132.

Math Background

The graph of a system of inequalities may or may not include parts of the boundaries as part of the solution.

OBJECTIVE

▼ 1 **Teaching Notes**

1 EXAMPLE **Tactile Learners**

Use masking tape to make a large coordinate grid on the floor. Let four students use string to model the two boundaries of the inequalities. Have other students fill in the overlapping area and stand on the "solid" line to model the solution.

2 EXAMPLE **Technology Tip**

Urge students to be careful with boundary points when interpreting graphs that use the shading features of the calculator.

⬡ Additional Examples

1 Solve the system of inequalities.

$\begin{cases} x + y > 3 \\ y > x - 1 \end{cases}$

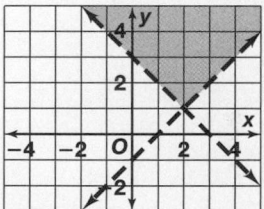

2 Jenna spends at most 150 min a night on math and science homework. She spends at least 60 min on math. Write and solve a system of inequalities to model how she allots her time for these two subjects. **See back of book.**

3 Solve the system.

$\begin{cases} y \ge 3 \\ y > -|x + 2| + 5 \end{cases}$

See back of book.

Closure

Ask: *How do you solve a system of inequalities by graphing?* **Graph the individual inequalities. Shade the region where the graphs overlap.**

131

Assignment Guide

1 Objective

Ⓐ Ⓑ **Core** 1–48
Ⓒ **Extension** 49–52

Standardized Test Prep 53–56

Mixed Review 57–72

Error Prevention

Exercises 8, 12, 13, 15 Students should be careful to have y, not $-y$, on the left side of each inequality when determining whether to shade above or below a boundary line.

Exercises 43-45 Students' diagrams should make it clear that the solutions of the systems are the points whose coordinates satisfy *all three* inequalities.

Enrichment 3-3

Reteaching 3-3

Practice 3-3

Practice 3-3   Solving Systems of Inequalities

EXERCISES

For more practice, see *Extra Practice*.

Practice and Problem Solving

Ⓐ **Practice by Example**

Example 1
(page 130)

Tell whether $(-3, 3)$ is a solution of each system.

1. $\begin{cases} y \geq x + 2 \\ 3y < -6x + 6 \end{cases}$ **yes**
2. $\begin{cases} y - 2x \leq 1 \\ y < -2x - 2 \end{cases}$ **no**
3. $\begin{cases} -2y + x \leq 4 \\ 3y < -9x + 3 \end{cases}$ **yes**

Solve each system of inequalities by graphing. 4–9. See margin pp. 132–133.

4. $\begin{cases} y \leq 2x + 2 \\ y < -x + 1 \end{cases}$
5. $\begin{cases} y > -2 \\ x < 1 \end{cases}$
6. $\begin{cases} y \leq 3 \\ y \leq \frac{1}{2}x + 1 \end{cases}$

7. $\begin{cases} y < 2x \\ y \geq -x + 3 \end{cases}$
8. $\begin{cases} -2y < 4x + 2 \\ y > x + 2 \end{cases}$
9. $\begin{cases} y > x - 5 \\ 3x + y < -2 \end{cases}$

10. $\begin{cases} y \leq 3x + 1 \\ -6x + 2y > 5 \end{cases}$
11. $\begin{cases} x + 2y \leq 10 \\ x + y \leq 3 \end{cases}$
12. $\begin{cases} -x - y \leq 2 \\ y - 2x > 1 \end{cases}$

13. $\begin{cases} y > -2x \\ 2x - y \geq 2 \end{cases}$
14. $\begin{cases} c \geq d - 3 \\ c < \frac{1}{2}d + 3 \end{cases}$
15. $\begin{cases} 2x + y < 1 \\ -y + 3x < 1 \end{cases}$

10–17. See back of book.

Example 2
(page 131)

16. **Fund-Raising** You want to bake at least 6 and at most 11 loaves of bread for a bake sale. You want at least twice as many loaves of banana bread as nut bread.
   a. Write a system of inequalities to model the situation.
   b. Graph the system.

17. **Psychology** A psychologist needs at least 40 subjects for her experiment. She cannot use more than 30 children. Write and graph a system of inequalities.

Example 3
(page 131)

Solve each system of inequalities by graphing. 18–29. See back of book.

18. $\begin{cases} y > 4 \\ y < |x - 1| \end{cases}$
19. $\begin{cases} y < -\frac{1}{3}x + 1 \\ y > |2x - 1| \end{cases}$
20. $\begin{cases} y > x - 2 \\ y \geq |x + 2| \end{cases}$

21. $\begin{cases} y \leq -\frac{4}{3}x \\ y \geq -|x| \end{cases}$
22. $\begin{cases} 3y < -x - 1 \\ y \leq |x + 1| \end{cases}$
23. $\begin{cases} y > -2 \\ y \leq -|x - 3| \end{cases}$

24. $\begin{cases} -2x + y > 3 \\ y \leq -|x + 4| \end{cases}$
25. $\begin{cases} 5y \geq 2x - 5 \\ y < |x + 3| \end{cases}$
26. $\begin{cases} y \geq -3x + 3 \\ y > |x + 2| \end{cases}$

27. $\begin{cases} -2y < 4x + 2 \\ y > |2x + 1| \end{cases}$
28. $\begin{cases} -x \geq 4 - y \\ y \geq |3x - 6| \end{cases}$
29. $\begin{cases} y \leq x - 4 \\ y > |x - 6| \end{cases}$

Ⓑ **Apply Your Skills**

In Exercises 30–39, identify the inequalities A, B, and C for which the given ordered pair is a solution.

A. $x + y \leq 2$ **B.** $y \leq \frac{3}{2}x - 1$ **C.** $y > -\frac{1}{3}x - 2$

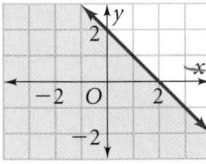   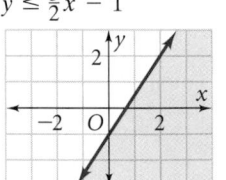   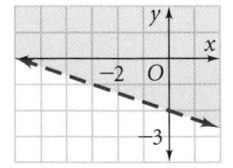

30. $(0, 0)$ **A, C**   31. $(-2, -5)$ **A, B**   32. $(-2, 0)$ **A, C**   33. $(0, -2)$ **A, B**   34. $(-15, 15)$ **A**

35. $(3, 2)$ **B, C**   36. $(2, 0)$ **A, B, C**   37. $(-6, 0)$ **A**   38. $(4, -1)$ **B, C**   39. $(-8, -11)$ **A**

pages 132–134 Exercises

4.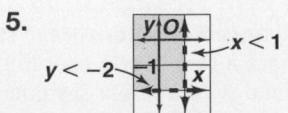
   $y < -x + 1$
   $y \leq 2x + 2$

5. $y < -2$ $x < 1$

6.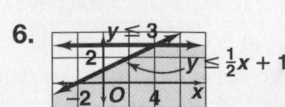
   $y \leq 3$
   $y \leq \frac{1}{2}x + 1$

Real-World Connection

Bake sales are a popular way to raise money.

 40. Fund-Raising Suppose the Student Council has asked you to form a committee to run a bake sale. The committee needs from 7 to 10 members. The number of seniors should be greater than the number of juniors.
  a. Write a system of inequalities to model the problem.
  b. Graph the system and list the combinations of juniors and seniors that may participate in the committee. **a–c. See back of book.**
  c. Critical Thinking Explain why your list in part (b) is finite.

41. Open-Ended Write and graph a system of inequalities for which the solution is bounded by a dashed vertical line and a solid horizontal line.

 **42. Writing** Explain how you determine where to shade when solving a system of inequalities.
41–51. See back of book.

Solve each system of inequalities by graphing.

43. $\begin{cases} x + y < 8 \\ x \ge 0 \\ y \ge 0 \end{cases}$ **44.** $\begin{cases} 2y - 4x \le 0 \\ x \ge 0 \\ y \ge 0 \end{cases}$ **45.** $\begin{cases} y \ge -2x + 4 \\ x > -3 \\ y \ge 1 \end{cases}$

46. $\begin{cases} y \le \frac{2}{3}x + 2 \\ y \ge |x| + 2 \end{cases}$ **47.** $\begin{cases} y < x - 1 \\ y > -|x - 2| + 1 \end{cases}$ **48.** $\begin{cases} 2x + y \le 3 \\ y > |x + 3| - 2 \end{cases}$

C Challenge **Geometry** Write a system of inequalities to describe each shaded figure.

49.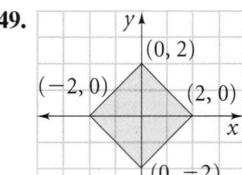
50.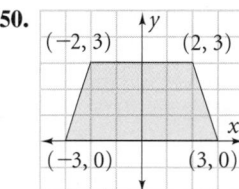
51.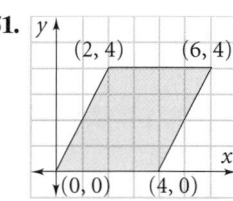

52a.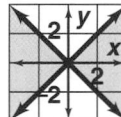

52. a. Graph the "bowtie" inequality, $|y| \le |x|$.
  b. Write a system of inequalities to describe the graph shown at the right.
  Answers may vary.
  Sample: $|y| \le \frac{1}{2}|x|$
  $|x| \le 2$

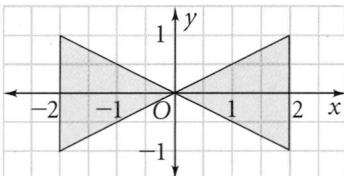

Standardized Test Prep

Multiple Choice

53. When you graph Inequality ① at the right, the boundary line should be _?_ and the shading should be _?_ the line. **B**
  A. dashed, above **B.** dashed, below **C.** solid, above **D.** solid, below

① $\begin{cases} y < -2x + 3 \end{cases}$
② $\begin{cases} y \ge x - 4 \end{cases}$

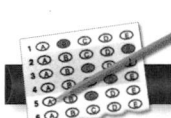
Take It to the NET
Online lesson quiz at
www.PHSchool.com
Web Code: aga-0303

54. When you graph Inequality ②, the boundary line should be _?_ and the shading should be _?_ the line. **H**
  F. dashed, above **G.** dashed, below **H.** solid, above **I.** solid, below

55. What is the x-value of the intersection of the boundary lines? **D**
  A. $\frac{-7}{3}$ **B.** $\frac{-3}{7}$ **C.** $\frac{3}{7}$ **D.** $\frac{7}{3}$

Short Response

56. How would you test whether $(2, -2)$ is a solution of the system?
See back of book.

7.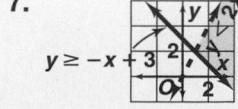
$y \ge -x + 3$

8. $-2y < 4x + 2$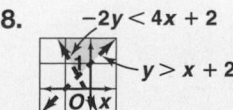
$y > x + 2$

9.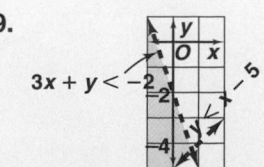
$3x + y < -2$

---

4. Assess

 **Lesson Quiz 3-3**

1. Solve the system of inequalities by graphing.
$\begin{cases} x + y \le 6 \\ -x - 4y < 8 \end{cases}$

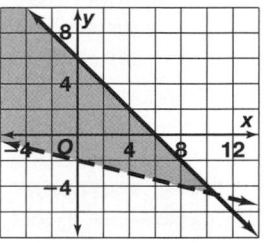

2. A 24-hour radio station plays only classical music, jazz, talk programs, and news. It plays at most 12 h of music per day, of which at least 4 h is classical. Jazz gets at least 25% as much time as classical. Write and graph a system of inequalities.
Let c = hours for classical and j = hours for jazz.
$c + j \le 12, c \ge 4, j \ge 0.25c$

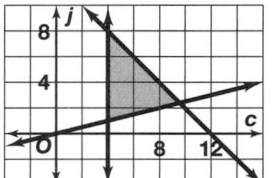

3. Solve the system of inequalities by graphing.
$\begin{cases} y \le x + 3 \\ y \ge |x - 2| + 1 \end{cases}$

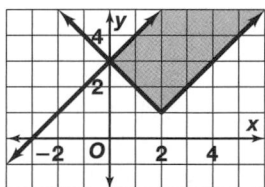

Alternative Assessment

Have students work in pairs. Each student writes one inequality for a system. They combine the two inequalities to make a system, and each graphs the system. They check one another's work.

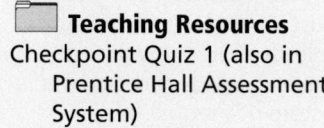
page 134 Checkpoint Quiz 1

7a. $\begin{cases} h \geq 18 \\ s \geq 12 \\ s + h \leq 35 \end{cases}$

b.

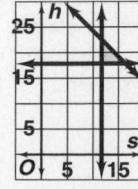

Mixed Review

Lesson 3-2 **Solve each system by elimination or substitution.**

57. $\begin{cases} y = 3x + 1 \\ 2x - y = 8 \end{cases}$ **(−9, −26)** 58. $\begin{cases} 3x + y = 4 \\ 2x - 4y = 7 \end{cases}$ $\left(\frac{23}{14}, -\frac{13}{14}\right)$ 59. $\begin{cases} -x + 5y = 3 \\ 2x - 10y = 4 \end{cases}$ **no solution**

60. $\begin{cases} 2x + 4y = -8 \\ -5x + 4y = 6 \end{cases}$ **(−2, −1)** 61. $\begin{cases} y - 3 = x \\ 4x + y = -2 \end{cases}$ **(−1, 2)** 62. $\begin{cases} 2 = 4y - 3x \\ 5x = 2y - 3 \end{cases}$ $\left(-\frac{4}{7}, \frac{1}{14}\right)$

Lesson 2-3 **For each function, *y* varies directly as *x*.**

63. If $y = -6$ when $x = -2$, find y when $x = 3$. **9**

64. If $y = -8$ when $x = 2$, find x when $y = 2$. $-\frac{1}{2}$

65. If $y = 4$ when $x = 7$, find y when $x = -14$. **−8**

66. If $y = 9$ when $x = 15$, find x when $y = 6$. **10**

Lesson 1-5 **Solve each equation. Check your answers.**

67. $|2x + 5| = 6$ $\frac{1}{2}, -\frac{11}{2}$

68. $|x + 7| = -2$ **no solution**

69. $3|x - 4| + 1 = 13$ **8, 0**

70. $-2|x + 1| - 5 = -7$ **−2, 0**

71. $\frac{1}{2}|3x + 2| - 3 = 4$ $-\frac{16}{3}, 4$

72. $-|2x + 5| = -3$ **−4, −1**

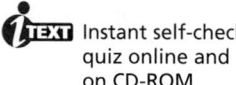 **Checkpoint Quiz 1**   **Lessons 3-1 through 3-3**

Instant self-check quiz online and on CD-ROM

Solve each system of equations.

1. $\begin{cases} 3x + 2y = 6 \\ x - 2y = 10 \end{cases}$ **(4, −3)**

2. $\begin{cases} 4x + 7y = 28 \\ y = 2x - 14 \end{cases}$ **(7, 0)**

3. $\begin{cases} 4x + 5y = -12 \\ 3x - 4y = 22 \end{cases}$ **(2, −4)**

4. $\begin{cases} 3y - 2x = 7 \\ 2y - 2 = 4x \end{cases}$ **(1, 3)**

5. $\begin{cases} 2n + 3m = 158 \\ 2n + 5m = 181 \end{cases}$
$61.75 cost per night
$11.50 cost per meal

5. The Village Inn offers two special packages. For two nights and three meals the cost is $158. For two nights and five meals the cost is $181. Write and solve a system of linear equations to find the costs per night and per meal.

6. **Smart Shopping** An ordinary refrigerator costs $489 and has an estimated annual operating cost of $84. An energy-saving model costs $599, with an estimated annual cost of $61. After how many years will the costs to buy and to operate the two models be equal? **approximately 4.7826 years**

7. Each week you must do a minimum of 18 hours of homework. Participation in sports requires at least 12 hours per week. You have no more than 35 hours per week in total to devote to these activities. **a–b. See margin.**
   a. Write a system of inequalities to model the situation.
   b. Graph and solve the system.

Solve each system of inequalities by graphing. 8–10. See margin.

8. $\begin{cases} y \leq -2 \\ y > |x + 1| \end{cases}$

9. $\begin{cases} 8x + 2y > 5 \\ x + 2y \leq -3 \end{cases}$

10. $\begin{cases} 4y < 3x - 1 \\ y > 2|x| - 3 \end{cases}$

8.
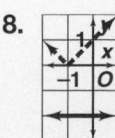

9.
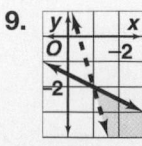

10.
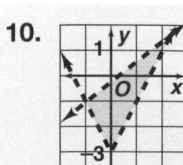

3-4

Linear Programming

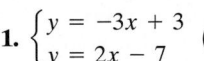
North Carolina Objectives

2.10 Use systems of two or more equations or inequalities to model and solve problems; justify results. Solve using tables, graphs, matrix operations, and algebraic properties.

Lesson Preview

What You'll Learn

OBJECTIVE 1 To find maximum and minimum values

OBJECTIVE 2 To solve problems with linear programming

. . . And Why

To maximize profit, as in Example 2

 Check Skills You'll Need (For help, go to Lessons 3-2 and 3-3.)

Solve each system of equations. **(1, 1)**

1. $\begin{cases} y = -3x + 3 \\ y = 2x - 7 \end{cases}$ **(2, –3)** 2. $\begin{cases} x + 2y = 5 \\ x - y = -1 \end{cases}$ **(1, 2)** 3. $\begin{cases} 4x + 3y = 7 \\ 2x - 5y = -3 \end{cases}$

Solve each system of inequalities by graphing. **4–6. See back of book.**

4. $\begin{cases} x \geq 5 \\ y > -3x + 6 \end{cases}$ 5. $\begin{cases} 3y > 5x + 2 \\ y \leq -x + 7 \end{cases}$ 6. $\begin{cases} x + 3y < -6 \\ 2x - 3y \leq 4 \end{cases}$

New Vocabulary • linear programming • objective function • constraints • feasible region

---

Lesson Preview

 **Check Skills You'll Need**

Graphing Systems of Equations
Lesson 3-1: Example 1
Exercises 1–8
Extra Practice, p. 824

Solving Systems Algebraically
Lesson 3-2: Examples 1, 3
Exercises 1–9, 14–19
Extra Practice, p. 824

Systems of Inequalities
Lesson 3-3: Example 1
Exercises 1–10
Extra Practice, p. 824

Lesson Resources

📁 **Teaching Resources**
Practice, Reteaching, Enrichment

👥 **Reaching All Students**
Practice Workbook 3-4
Spanish Practice Workbook 3-4

⏱ **Presentation Assistant Plus!**
Transparencies
• Check Skills You'll Need 3-4
• Additional Examples 3-4
• Student Edition Answers 3-4
• Lesson Quiz 3-4
PH Presentation Pro CD 3-4

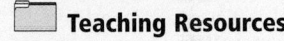
ASSESSMENT SYSTEM

Computer Test Generator CD

💾 **Technology**
Resource Pro® CD-ROM
Computer Test Generator CD
Prentice Hall Presentation Pro CD

💻 **www.PHSchool.com**
Student Site
• Teacher Web Code: agk-5500
• Self-grading Lesson Quiz
Teacher Center
• Lesson Planner
• Resources

Plus

OBJECTIVE 1 **Finding Maximum and Minimum Values**

📱 **Interactive lesson includes instant self-check, tutorials, and activities.**

2.

$\frac{3}{4}x + y \geq 10$

$y \leq 7$

$y \geq 4$

$x \leq 10$

Investigation: Finding a Minimum Value

Music Suppose you want to buy some tapes and CDs. You can afford as many as 10 tapes or 7 CDs. You want at least 4 CDs and at least 10 hours of recorded music. Each tape holds about 45 minutes of music, and each CD holds about an hour.

1. Write a system of inequalities to model the problem. Let x represent the number of tapes purchased. Let y represent the number of CDs purchased.

$\begin{cases} x \leq 10 \\ 4 \leq y \leq 7 \\ \frac{3x}{4} + y \geq 10 \end{cases}$

2. Graph your system of inequalities. **See left.**

3. Does each ordered pair satisfy the system you have graphed?
   a. (4, 7)   **b.** (12, 7)   **c.** (7, 6)   **d.** (9, 4)   **e.** (10, 4)
   yes   **no**   **yes**   **yes**   **yes**

Reading Math

Constraints are sometimes referred to as restrictions.

Linear programming is a technique that identifies the minimum or maximum value of some quantity. This quantity is modeled with an **objective function.** Limits on the variables in the objective function are **constraints,** written as linear inequalities.

The first paragraph of the Investigation describes the constraints on buying tapes and CDs. Suppose you buy x tapes and y CDs. The constraints on x and y can be modeled with inequalities as follows.

as many as 10 tapes $x \leq 10$ at least 4 CDs $y \geq 4$

as many as 7 CDs $y \leq 7$ at least 10 hours $\frac{3}{4}x + y \geq 10$

⚙ **Ongoing Assessment and Intervention**

Before the Lesson	During the Lesson	After the Lesson
Diagnose prerequisite skills using:	**Monitor progress using:**	**Assess knowledge using:**
• Check Skills You'll Need	• Check Understanding	• Lesson Quiz
	• Additional Examples	• Computer Test Generator CD
	• Standardized Test Prep	

Math Background

Linear programming is an extension of solving linear inequalities. You are given constraints represented by linear inequalities that are graphed. All of the points in the overlapping region are solutions, but linear programming problems are usually looking for maximum or minimum values. You substitute the coordinates of the vertices into an objective function to determine which yield the maximum or minimum value.

OBJECTIVE
1 Teaching Notes

Investigation (Optional)
The graph of the system of inequalities encloses a region in the coordinate plane. The only points of this region that make sense for this situation are the points that have whole number coordinates.

1 EXAMPLE Visual Learners

After students have graphed the restrictions, have them graph the lines $3x + 2y = 18$, $3x + 2y = 6$, and $3x + 2y = 0$. Discuss with the students why the maximum and minimum values occur at the vertices.

Additional Examples

1 Find the values of x and y that maximize and minimize P if $P = -5x + 4y$.

$$\begin{cases} y \geq -\frac{2}{3}x + \frac{11}{3} \\ y \leq \frac{1}{4}x + \frac{11}{4} \\ y \geq 3x - 11 \end{cases}$$

maximum of 7 when $x = 1$ and $y = 3$, minimum of -16 when $x = 4$ and $y = 1$

The constraints form the system of inequalities at the right. The red region in the graph, the **feasible region,** contains all the points that satisfy all the constraints.

$$\begin{cases} x \leq 10 \\ y \leq 7 \\ y \geq 4 \\ \frac{3}{4}x + y \geq 10 \end{cases}$$

If you buy tapes at \$8 each and CDs at \$12 each, then the objective function for the total cost C is $C = 8x + 12y$. The blue line is the graph for the total cost \$140. The green line is for the total cost \$112.

Graphs of the objective function for various values of C are parallel lines. Lines closer to the origin represent lower costs. The graph closest to the origin that intersects the feasible region intersects it at the vertex $(8, 4)$. The graph of the objective function farthest from the origin that intersects the feasible region intersects it at the vertex $(10, 7)$. Graphs of an objective function that represent a maximum or minimum value intersect a feasible region at a vertex.

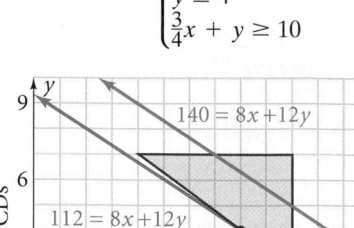
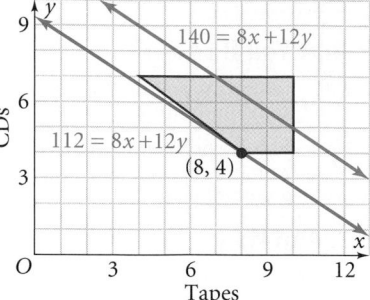

Key Concepts

Property	Vertex Principle of Linear Programming

If there is a maximum or a minimum value of the linear objective function, it occurs at one or more vertices of the feasible region.

1 EXAMPLE Testing Vertices

Find the values of x and y that maximize and minimize P for the objective function $P = 3x + 2y$. What is the value of P at each vertex?

Constraints $\begin{cases} y \geq \frac{3}{2}x - 3 \\ y \leq -x + 7 \\ x \geq 0, y \geq 0 \end{cases}$

Step 1
Graph the constraints.

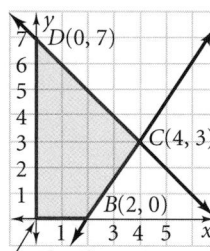

Step 2
Find coordinates for each vertex.

Vertex
$A(0, 0)$
$B(2, 0)$
$C(4, 3)$
$D(0, 7)$

Step 3
Evaluate P at each vertex.

$P = 3x + 2y$
$P = 3(0) + 2(0) = 0$
$P = 3(2) + 2(0) = 6$
$P = 3(4) + 2(3) = 18$
$P = 3(0) + 2(7) = 14$

When $x = 4$ and $y = 3$, P has its maximum value of 18. When $x = 0$ and $y = 0$, P has its minimum value of 0.

✔ Check Understanding **1** Use the constraints in Example 1 with the objective function $P = 2x + 3y$. Find the values of x and y that maximize and minimize P. Find the value of P at each point. **See left.**

1. $P = 2(0) + 3(0) = 0$
$P = 2(2) + 3(0) = 4$
$P = 2(4) + 3(3) = 17$
$P = 2(0) + 3(7) = 21$
When $x = 0$ and $y = 7$, P is maximized at 21.
When $x = 0$ and $y = 0$, P is minimized at 0.

👥 Reaching All Students

Below Level Linear programming can be quite abstract for some students. Carefully review all the vocabulary terms and new concepts.	Advanced Learners Have students use catalogs or the Internet to find products and prices to write a linear programming problem. Have them share the problem and its solution.	Visual Learners See note on page 136. Auditory Learners See note on page 141.

You can use linear programming to solve many real-world problems.

2 EXAMPLE **Real-World** **Connection**

Profit Suppose you are selling cases of mixed nuts and roasted peanuts. You can order no more than a total of 500 cans and packages and spend no more than $600. How can you maximize your profit? How much is the maximum profit?

Mixed Nuts
12 cans per case
You pay ......$24 per case
Sell at ....$3.50 per can
$18 profit per case!

Roasted Peanuts
20 packages per case
You pay ......$15 per case
Sell at ...$1.50 per package
$15 profit per case!

Define Let x = number of cases of mixed nuts ordered.
Let y = number of cases of roasted peanuts ordered.
Let P = total profit.

Relate Organize the information in a table.

	Mixed Nuts	Roasted Peanuts	Total	
Number of Cases	x	y	$x+y$	
Number of Units	$12x$	$20y$	500	constraint
Cost	$24x$	$15y$	600	constraint
Profit	$18x$	$15y$	$18x + 15y$	objective

Write Write and simplify the constraints. Write the objective function.

$$\begin{cases} 12x + 20y \le 500 \\ 24x + 15y \le 600 \\ x \ge 0, y \ge 0 \end{cases} \Rightarrow \begin{cases} 3x + 5y \le 125 \\ 8x + 5y \le 200 \\ x \ge 0, y \ge 0 \end{cases} \qquad P = 18x + 15y$$

Step 1
Graph the constraints.

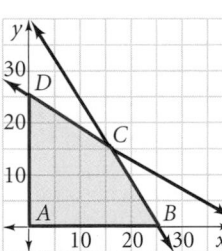

Step 2
Find the coordinates of each vertex.

Vertex
$A(0, 0)$
$B(25, 0)$
$C(15, 16)$
$D(0, 25)$

Step 3
Evaluate P at each vertex.

$P = 18x + 15y$
$P = 18(0) + 15(0) = 0$
$P = 18(25) + 15(0) = 450$
$P = 18(15) + 15(16) = 510$
$P = 18(0) + 15(25) = 375$

You can maximize your profit by selling 15 cases of mixed nuts and 16 cases of roasted peanuts. The maximum profit is $510.

 **Check Understanding** **2** If you sell mixed nuts for $4.25 per can, what should you order to maximize profit?
Order 25 cases of mixed nuts and no cases of roasted peanuts.

---

2 EXAMPLE **Math Tip**

You may wish to point out that the vertices of the feasible region have whole number coordinates and make sense in terms of this situation. If the vertices were not whole numbers, a more detailed analysis would be necessary.

Additional Examples

2 A furniture manufacturer can make from 30 to 60 tables a day and from 40 to 100 chairs a day. It can make at most 120 units in one day. The profit on a table is $150, and the profit on a chair is $65. How many tables and chairs should they make per day to maximize profit? How much is the maximum profit? **60 tables, 60 chairs; $12,900**

Closure

In a linear programming problem, what values do you test to find the values that maximize or minimize the objective function? **the coordinates of each vertex of the feasible region**

Assignment Guide

1 Objective

Ⓐ Ⓑ **Core** 1–9, 12, 14–19

Ⓒ **Extension** 21, 23

2 Objective

Ⓐ Ⓑ **Core** 10–11, 13, 20

Ⓒ **Extension** 22

Standardized Test Prep 24–27

Mixed Review 28–42

Error Prevention

Exercises 1–9 Students may think that the "highest" point on a graph is the maximum. Remind students that the only way to determine a maximum or a minimum is through substitution of the vertices' coordinates into the objective function to find the greatest and least values of the objective function.

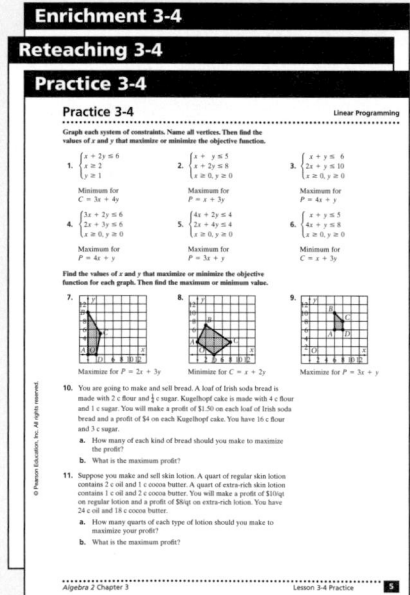

EXERCISES

For more practice, see *Extra Practice*.

Practice and Problem Solving

Ⓐ **Practice by Example**

Example 1
(page 136)

Find the values of *x* and *y* that maximize or minimize the objective function for each graph.   1–3. See left.

1. When *x* = 4 and *y* = 2, *P* is maximized at 16.

2. When *x* = 600 and *y* = 0, *P* is maximized at 4200.

3. When *x* = 6 and *y* = 8, *C* is minimized at 36.

4–9. See back of book.

1.
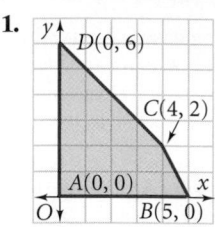
Maximum for
$P = 3x + 2y$

2.
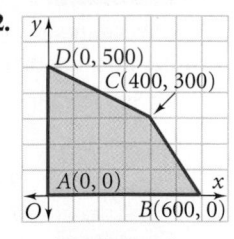
Maximum for
$P = 7x + 4y$

3.
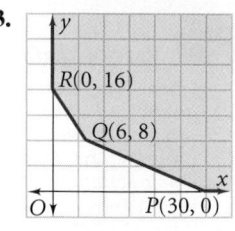
Minimum for
$C = 2x + 3y$

Graph each system of constraints. Name all vertices. Then find the values of *x* and *y* that maximize or minimize the objective function.

4. $\begin{cases} x \le 5 \\ y \le 4 \\ x \ge 0, y \ge 0 \end{cases}$
Maximum for
$P = 3x + 2y$

5. $\begin{cases} x + y \ge 8 \\ y \ge 5 \\ x \ge 0 \end{cases}$
Minimum for
$P = 3x + 2y$

6. $\begin{cases} x + y \le 8 \\ 2x + y \le 10 \\ x \ge 0, y \ge 0 \end{cases}$
Maximum for
$N = 100x + 40y$

7. $\begin{cases} x + y \ge 6 \\ x \le 8 \\ y \le 5 \end{cases}$
Minimum for
$C = x + 3y$

8. $\begin{cases} x + 2y \ge 8 \\ x \ge 2 \\ y \ge 0 \end{cases}$
Minimum for
$C = x + 3y$

9. $\begin{cases} 2 \le x \le 6 \\ 1 \le y \le 5 \\ x + y \le 8 \end{cases}$
Maximum for
$P = 3x + 2y$

Example 2
(page 137)

10. Ecology Teams chosen from 30 forest rangers and 16 trainees are planting trees. An experienced team consisting of two rangers can plant 500 trees per week. A training team consisting of one ranger and two trainees can plant 200 trees per week.

	Experienced Teams	Training Teams	Total
Number of Teams	x	y	$x + y$
Number of Rangers	$2x$	y	30
Number of Trainees	0	$2y$	16
Number of Trees Planted	$500x$	$200y$	$500x + 200y$

10a. $\begin{cases} 2x + y \le 30 \\ 2y \le 16 \\ x \ge 0, y \ge 0 \end{cases}$
$P = 500x + 200y$

a. Write an objective function and constraints for a linear program that models the problem.

b. How many of each type of team should be formed to maximize the number of trees planted? How many trainees are used in this solution? How many trees are planted?   **15 experienced teams, 0 training teams; none; 7500**

c. Find a solution that uses all the trainees. How many trees will be planted in this case?   **11 experienced teams; 8 training teams; 7100 trees**

11. **Air Quality** Trees in urban areas help keep air fresh by absorbing carbon dioxide. A city has \$2100 to spend on planting spruce and maple trees. The land available for planting is 45,000 ft^2. How many of each tree should the city plant to maximize carbon dioxide absorption? **70 spruce; 0 maple**

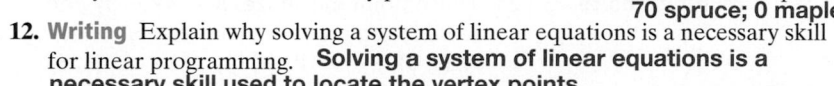

Facts for a Single Tree

	Spruce	Maple
Planting Cost	\$30	\$40
Area Required	600 ft^2	900 ft^2
Carbon Dioxide Absorption	650 lb/yr	300 lb/yr

SOURCES: Auburn University and Anderson & Associates

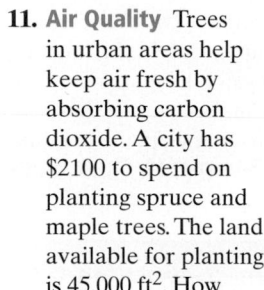

B Apply Your Skills

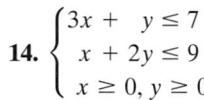

12. **Writing** Explain why solving a system of linear equations is a necessary skill for linear programming. **Solving a system of linear equations is a necessary skill used to locate the vertex points.**

13. **Microbiology** A biologist is developing two new strains of bacteria. Each sample of Type I bacteria produces four new viable bacteria, and each sample of Type II produces three new viable bacteria. Altogether, at least 240 new viable bacteria must be produced. At least 30, but not more than 60, of the original samples must be Type I. Not more than 70 of the samples can be Type II. A sample of Type I costs \$5 and a sample of Type II costs \$7. How many samples of each should be used to minimize cost? **60 samples of Type I and 0 samples of Type II**

Real-World Connection

Careers A microbiologist studies microorganisms, such as bacteria and viruses, to determine their structure and function.

Graph each system of constraints. Name all vertices. Then find the values of x and y that maximize or minimize the objective function. Find the maximum or minimum value. **14–19. See back of book.**

14. $\begin{cases} 3x + y \le 7 \\ x + 2y \le 9 \\ x \ge 0, y \ge 0 \end{cases}$ Maximum for $P = 2x + y$

15. $\begin{cases} 25 \le x \le 75 \\ y \le 110 \\ 8x + 6y \ge 720 \end{cases}$ Minimum for $C = 8x + 5y$

16. $\begin{cases} x + y \le 11 \\ 2y \ge x \\ x \ge 0, y \ge 0 \end{cases}$ Maximum for $P = 3x + 2y$

17. $\begin{cases} 2x + y \le 300 \\ x + y \le 200 \\ x \ge 0, y \ge 0 \end{cases}$ Maximum for $P = x + 2y$

18. $\begin{cases} 5x + y \ge 10 \\ x + y \ge 6 \\ x + 4y \ge 12 \\ x \ge 0, y \ge 0 \end{cases}$ Minimum for $C = 10{,}000x + 20{,}000y$

19. $\begin{cases} 6 \le x + y \le 13 \\ x \ge 3 \\ y \ge 1 \end{cases}$ Maximum for $P = 4x + 3y$

20. **Cooking** Baking a tray of corn muffins takes 4 c milk and 3 c wheat flour. A tray of bran muffins takes 2 c milk and 3 c wheat flour. A baker has 16 c milk and 15 c wheat flour. He makes \$3 profit per tray of corn muffins and \$2 profit per tray of bran muffins. How many trays of each type of muffin should the baker make to maximize his profit? **3 trays of corn muffins and 2 trays of bran muffins**

C Challenge

21. A vertex of a feasible region does not always have whole-number coordinates. Sometimes you may need to round coordinates to find the solution. Using the objective function and the constraints at the right, find the whole-number values of x and y that minimize C. Then find C for those values of x and y. **See back of book.**

$C = 6x + 9y$

$\begin{cases} x + 2y \ge 50 \\ 2x + y \ge 60 \\ x \ge 0, y \ge 0 \end{cases}$

Reading Math

Feasible means "doable" or "suitable."

22. **Open-Ended** Write a system of constraints whose graphs determine a trapezoid. Write an objective function and evaluate it at each vertex. **Check students' work.**

4. Assess

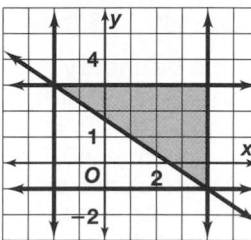

Lesson Quiz 3-4

1. Graph the system of constraints. Name all vertices of the feasible region. Then find the values of x and y that maximize and minimize the objective function $P = 2x + 7y + 4$.
$\begin{cases} -2 \le x \le 4 \\ -1 \le y \le 3 \\ y \ge -\frac{2}{3}x + \frac{5}{3} \end{cases}$

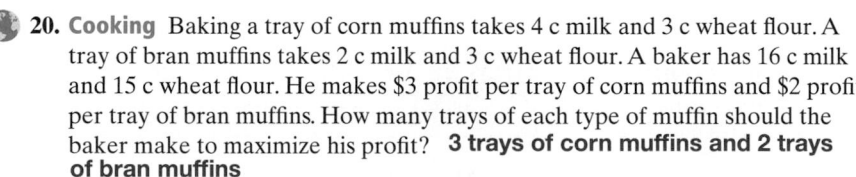

(−2, 3), (4, 3), (4, −1); maximum of 33 when $x = 4$ and $y = 3$, minimum of 5 when $x = 4$ and $y = -1$

2. If the constraint on y in the system for Question 1 is changed to $1 \le y \le 3$, how does the minimum value for the objective function change? **There is a new minimum value of 13 when $x = 1$ and $y = 1$.**

Alternative Assessment

Have students work in small groups. Each group should write and solve a real-world linear programming problem. Groups then exchange problems and solve. Groups should compare answers and resolve any differences.

Standardized Test Prep

Resources

For additional practice with a variety of test item formats:
- Standardized Test Prep, p. 161
- Test-Taking Strategies, p. 156
- Test-Taking Strategies with Transparencies

Exercise 25 It may help to make tables of values that show the value of each objective function for each vertex.

pages 138–140   Exercises

26. **[2]** The boundary line through $R(0, 40)$ and $Q(10, 20)$ is $y = -2x + 40$, so the constraint is $y \geq -2x + 40$. The boundary line through $Q(10, 20)$ and $P(50, 0)$ is $y = -\frac{1}{2}x + 25$, so the constraint is $y \geq -\frac{1}{2}x + 25$.

[1] includes only one of the two parts of the answer above OR makes a minor error in calculation

27. **[4]**

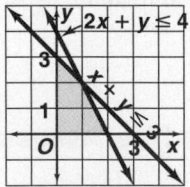

The vertices are $(0, 0)$, $(2, 0)$, $(0, 3)$, and $(1, 2)$.

[3] incorrectly graphs equations, but interprets inequalities correctly

[2] answer of vertices only

[1] only 2 correct vertices with no work shown

28.

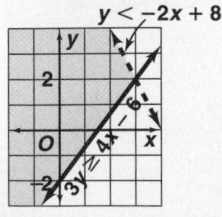

---

23. **Critical Thinking** Sometimes two corners of a graph both yield the maximum profit. In this case, many other points may also yield the maximum profit. Evaluate the profit formula $P = x + 2y$ for the graph shown. Find four points that yield the maximum profit. **Answers may vary. Sample: (4, 6), (6, 5), (9, 3.5), (10, 3)**

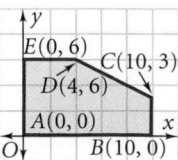

Standardized Test Prep

Multiple Choice

24. Which point maximizes $N = 4x + 3y$ and lies within the feasible region of the constraints at the right?   **C**

$$\begin{cases} y \leq 9 \\ 2x + 2y \leq 18 \\ x \leq 3 \end{cases}$$

   A. $(0, 0)$ **B.** $(9, 0)$ **C.** $(3, 6)$ **D.** $(0, 9)$

Take It to the NET
Online lesson quiz at
www.PHSchool.com
Web Code: aga-0304

25. The vertices of a feasible region are $(0, 0)$, $(0, 2)$, $(5, 2)$, and $(4, 0)$. For which objective function is the maximum cost C found at the vertex $(4, 0)$?   **G**

   E. $C = -2x + 3y$ **F.** $C = 2x + 7y$
   G. $C = 4x - 3y$ **H.** $C = 5x + 3y$

Short Response

26. The figure at the right shows the feasible region for a system of constraints. This system includes $x \geq 0$ and $y \geq 0$. Find the remaining constraint(s). **See margin.**

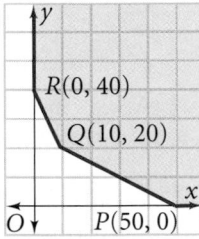

Extended Response

27. What are the vertices of the feasible region bounded by the constraints at the right? **See margin.**

$$\begin{cases} x + y \leq 3 \\ 2x + y \leq 4 \\ x \geq 0, y \geq 0 \end{cases}$$

Mixed Review

Lesson 3-3   Graph each system of inequalities. Indicate any region containing solutions.

28. $\begin{cases} y < -2x + 8 \\ 3y \geq 4x - 6 \end{cases}$ 29. $\begin{cases} x - 2y \geq 11 \\ 5x + 4y < 27 \end{cases}$ 30. $\begin{cases} 2x + 6y > 12 \\ 3x + 9y \leq 27 \end{cases}$

31. $\begin{cases} 2y + x < 4 \\ y - 2x \geq 4 \end{cases}$ 32. $\begin{cases} y + 5 \geq -2x \\ y - x \geq -2 \end{cases}$ 33. $\begin{cases} 2y - 4x < 6 \\ 6x < 3y + 12 \end{cases}$

28–33. See margin pp. 140–141.

Lesson 2-4

34. **Data Analysis** Use the data below.

A Survey of Paperback Books: How Long and How Much?

Pages	326	450	246	427	208	339	367	445	404	465	378	265
Price ($)	7.50	7.99	6.99	7.99	6.99	7.95	7.50	7.95	7.95	7.99	7.99	6.99

Take It to the NET
Graphing Calculator procedures online at
www.PHSchool.com
Web Code: age-2109

   a. Make a scatter plot of the data. **See back of book.**
   b. What kind of correlation do you see? **positive**
   c. Find a linear model. **c–d. See margin p. 141.**
   d. What price would you predict for a paperback containing 100 pages?

Lesson 1-2   Evaluate each expression for $a = 3$ and $b = -5$.

35. $2a + b$ **1**   36. $a - b$ **8**   37. $-4 + 2ab$ **−34**   38. $a + \frac{3b}{a}$ **−2**

39. $3(a - b)$ **24**   40. $4a - 2 + 3b$ **−5** 41. $\frac{a - b}{2a}$ **$\frac{4}{3}$**   42. $b(2b - a)$ **65**

---

27. **[4]**

The vertices are $(0, 0)$, $(2, 0)$, $(0, 3)$, and $(1, 2)$.

[3] incorrectly graphs equations, but interprets inequalities correctly

[2] answer of vertices only

[1] only 2 correct vertices with no work shown

28. $y < -2x + 8$

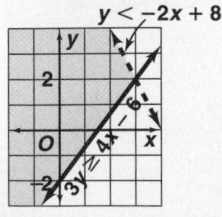

29.

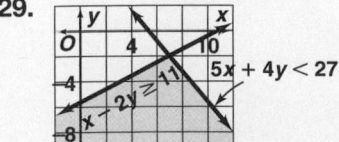

30. $3x + 9y \leq 27$

31.

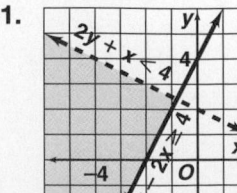

Technology

Linear Programming

Technology

Linear Programming

Students use various **CALC** functions to find the minimum or maximum values of objective functions in linear programming problems.

You can solve linear programming problems with your graphing calculator.

EXAMPLE

Find the values of x and y that will maximize the objective function $P = 13x + 2y$ for the constraints at the right. What is the value of P at this maximum point?

$$\begin{cases} -3x + 2y \leq 8 \\ -8x + y \geq -48 \\ x \geq 0, \ y \geq 0 \end{cases}$$

Resources

Students may use any graphing calculator to explore solving linear programming problems.

Step 1 Rewrite the first two inequalities to isolate y. Enter the inequalities.

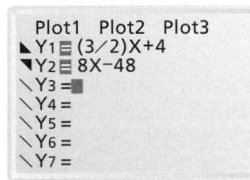

Step 2 Graph, using the window $0 \leq x \leq 12$, $0 \leq y \leq 20$.

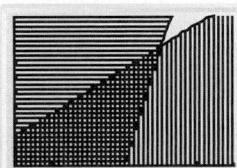

Step 3 Use the value option of **CALC** to find the upper left vertex. Press 0 ENTER.

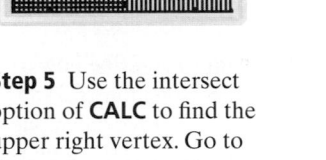

Teaching Notes

Technology Tip
It is important that students include the parentheses around (3/2)X when entering the first inequality. Also, remind students that they must select whether the graph is shaded above or below the line by changing the symbol in front of each equation in the Y= list. For inequalities that are > or ≥, the shading is above the line. For inequalities that are < or ≤, the shading is below the line.

Step 4 Enter the expression for the objective function on the home screen. Press ENTER for the value of P at the vertex.

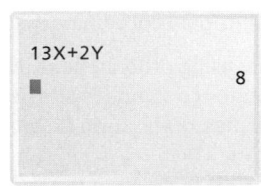

Step 5 Use the intersect option of **CALC** to find the upper right vertex. Go to the home screen and press ENTER for the value of P.

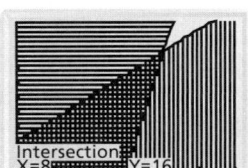

Step 6 Use the zero option of **CALC** to find the lower right vertex. Go to the home screen and press ENTER for the value of P.

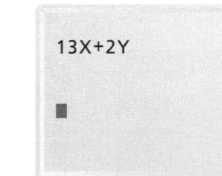

Compare the values of P for the coordinates of the three vertices you found. The objective function has a value of 0 for the vertex located at the origin. The maximum value 136 occurs when $x = 8$ and $y = 16$.

EXERCISES

Find the values of x and y that maximize or minimize the objective function.

1. $\begin{cases} 4x + 3y \geq 30 \\ x + 3y \geq 21 \\ x \geq 0, y \geq 0 \end{cases}$
3, 6; C = 63
Minimum for
$C = 5x + 8y$

2. $\begin{cases} 3x + 5y \leq 35 \\ 2x + y \leq 14 \\ x \geq 0, y \geq 0 \end{cases}$
5, 4; P = 23
Maximum for
$P = 3x + 2y$

3. $\begin{cases} x + y \geq 8 \\ x + 5y \geq 20 \\ x \geq 0, y \geq 2 \end{cases}$
5, 3; C = 27
Minimum for
$C = 3x + 4y$

4. $\begin{cases} x + 2y \leq 24 \\ 3x + 2y \leq 34 \\ 3x + y \leq 29 \\ x \geq 0 \end{cases}$
5, 9.5; P = 38.5
Maximum for
$P = 2x + 3y$

Auditory Learners
Place students in pairs to complete the activity. Have one student read the steps aloud while the other enters the information into the calculator.

34c. $y = 0.0046x + 5.98$, where $x =$ number of pages, $y =$ price in dollars

d. Answers may vary. Sample: using the equation from part (d), $6.44

32.

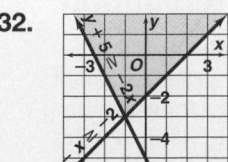

33.

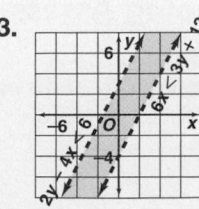

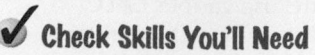 **Check Skills You'll Need**

Linear Equations
Lesson 2-2: Examples 1, 2
Exercises 1–10
Extra Practice, p. 823

Lesson Resources

 **Teaching Resources**
Practice, Reteaching, Enrichment
Checkpoint Quiz 2

Reaching All Students
Practice Workbook 3-5
Spanish Practice Workbook 3-5
Reading and Math Literacy 3C
Spanish Reading & Literacy 3C
Spanish Checkpoint Quiz 2

Presentation Assistant Plus!
Transparencies
• Check Skills You'll Need 3-5
• Additional Examples 3-5
• Student Edition Answers 3-5
• Lesson Quiz 3-5
PH Presentation Pro CD 3-5

ASSESSMENT SYSTEM

Checkpoint Quiz 2
Computer Test Generator CD

Technology
Resource Pro® CD-ROM
Computer Test Generator CD
Prentice Hall Presentation Pro CD

 **www.PHSchool.com**
Student Site
• Teacher Web Code: agk-5500
• Self-grading Lesson Quiz
Teacher Center
• Lesson Planner
• Resources

Plus **iTEXT**

142

Graphs in Three Dimensions

Lesson Preview

 What You'll Learn

OBJECTIVE 1 To graph points in three dimensions

OBJECTIVE 2 To graph equations in three dimensions

. . . And Why

To locate points on a virtual bicycle helmet, as in Example 2

 Check Skills You'll Need *(For help, go to Lesson 2-2.)*

Find the *x*- and *y*-intercepts of the graph of each linear equation.

1. $y = 2x + 6$ ***x*: −3, *y*: 6**   **2.** $2x + 9y = 36$ ***x*: 18, *y*: 4**
3. $3x - 8y = -24$ ***x*: −8, *y*: 3**   **4.** $4x - 5y = 40$ ***x*: 10, *y*: −8**

Graph each linear equation.   5–8. See back of book.

5. $y = 3x$ **6.** $y = -2x + 4$
7. $4y = 3x - 8$ **8.** $-3x - 2y = 7$

New Vocabulary   • coordinate space   • ordered triples   • trace

---

 **Interactive lesson includes instant self-check, tutorials, and activities.**

OBJECTIVE 1   Graphing Points in Three Dimensions

Suppose you want to describe how to get from point *A* to point *B* along the grid shown at the right. You could say "Move down one unit, forward two units, and left three units," or "Move left three units, forward two units, and down one unit."

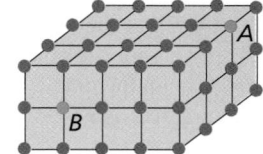

To describe positions in space, you need a three-dimensional coordinate system.

You have learned to graph on an *xy*-coordinate plane using ordered pairs. Adding a third axis, the *z*-axis, to the *xy*-coordinate plane creates **coordinate space.** In coordinate space you graph points using **ordered triples** of the form (x, y, z).

Points in a Plane

+ ↑ *y*-axis
• (2, 3) ← ordered pair
origin
← 3 units up
x-axis
↑ 2 units right

A two-dimensional coordinate system allows you to graph points in a plane.

Points in Space

z-axis⁺ (2, 3, 4) ← ordered triple
origin
← 4 units up
2 units forward
y-axis
x-axis
3 units right

A three-dimensional coordinate system allows you to graph points in space.

In the coordinate plane, point (2, 3) is two units right and three units up from the origin. In coordinate space, point (2, 3, 4) is two units forward, three units right, and four units up.

Real-World 🌐 Connection
The global positioning system locates persons or objects in three dimensions.

Ongoing Assessment and Intervention

Before the Lesson
Diagnose prerequisite skills using:
• Check Skills You'll Need

During the Lesson
Monitor progress using:
• Check Understanding
• Additional Examples
• Standardized Test Prep

After the Lesson
Assess knowledge using:
• Lesson Quiz
• Computer Test Generator CD
• Chapter Checkpoint 2 (p. 147)

1 EXAMPLE Graphing in Coordinate Space

Graph each point in coordinate space.

a. $(0, 3, -2)$
Sketch the axes. From the origin, move right 3 units and down 2 units.

b. $(-2, -1, 3)$
Sketch the axes. From the origin, move back 2 units, left 1 unit, and up 3 units.

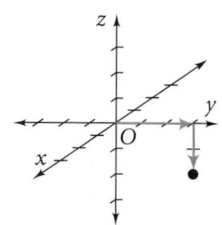

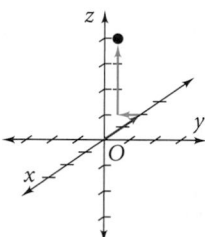

✔ **Check Understanding** ① Graph each point in coordinate space. **a–d. See back of book.**
a. $(0, -4, -2)$ **b.** $(-1, 1, 3)$ **c.** $(3, -5, 2)$ **d.** $(3, 3, -3)$

2 EXAMPLE Real-World Connection

Product Design Computers are used to design three-dimensional objects. Programs allow the designer to view the object from different perspectives. Find coordinates for points A, B, and C in the diagram below.

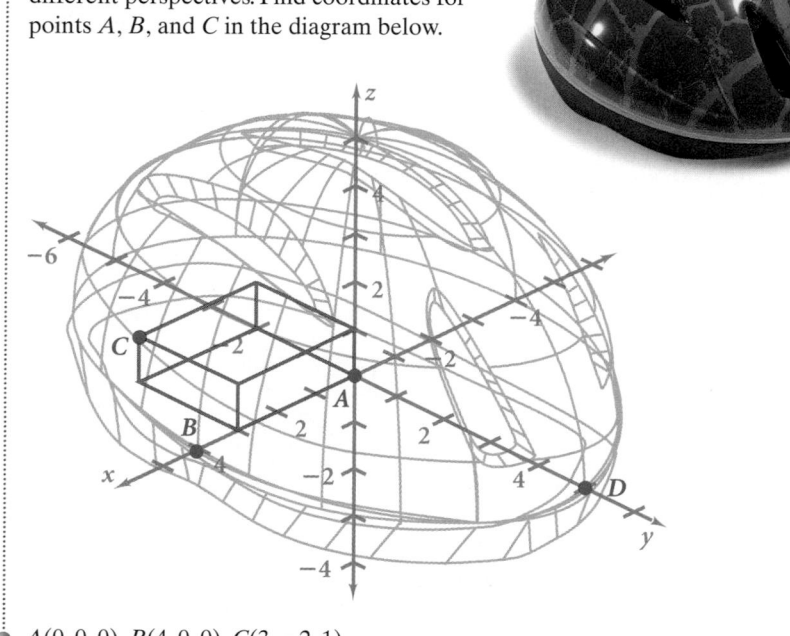

$A(0, 0, 0)$, $B(4, 0, 0)$, $C(3, -2, 1)$

✔ **Check Understanding** ② **a.** Find coordinates for point D in the diagram. **(0, 5, 0)**
b. Does the point $(-3, 2, 4)$ lie inside or outside the helmet? Explain.
outside the helmet, since the helmet is curved

👥 Reaching All Students

| **Below Level** To assist students in visualizing graphs in three dimensions, set up a coordinate system in your classroom. Use tape and string to represent graphs. | **Advanced Learners** Have students research how computer graphics imaging works and share their findings with the class. | **Error Prevention** See note on page 145. |

Math Background

Since space is three-dimensional, a three-dimensional coordinate system describes positions in space. The points in this system have three coordinates, usually x, y, and z. To locate a point in a three-dimensional coordinate system, you start at the origin and first move forward or backward, then right or left, and finally up or down.

OBJECTIVE
▽**1** Teaching Notes

1 EXAMPLE Connection to Geometry

Ask students to name three dimensions used to describe a prism. **length, width, and height**

2 EXAMPLE Careers

Product designers' diagrams have the viewer situated in the part of space where all three coordinates are positive. Ask students why it is important for a designer to be able to view an object from several different perspectives.

⬛ Additional Examples

① Graph each point in coordinate space.
a. $(-3, 3, -4)$ **b.** $(-3, -4, 2)$
See back of book.

② In the diagram, the origin is at the center of a cube that has edges 6 units long. The x-, y-, and z-axes are perpendicular to the faces of the cube. Give the coordinates of the corners of the cube.

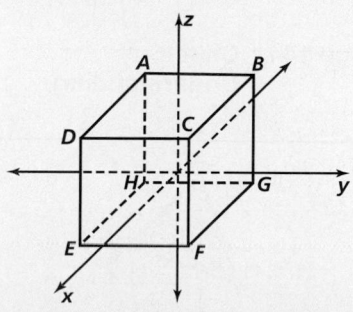

$A(-3, -3, 3)$, $B(-3, 3, 3)$, $C(3, 3, 3)$, $D(3, -3, 3)$, $E(3, -3, -3)$, $F(3, 3, -3)$, $G(-3, 3, -3)$, $H(-3, -3, -3)$

143

Teaching Notes

3 EXAMPLE   Math Tip

Stress similarities with the corresponding concepts for two dimensions. In two dimensions, the intercepts of a line are the points where the line intersects the x- and y-axes. In three dimensions, the intercepts of a plane are the points where the plane intersects the x-, y-, and z-axes. The traces associated with a linear equation $Ax + By + Cz = D$ are the lines that are the intersections of the graph of the equation with the xy-, xz-, and yz-planes.

Additional Examples

3 Sketch the graph of $-3x - 2y + z = 6$.

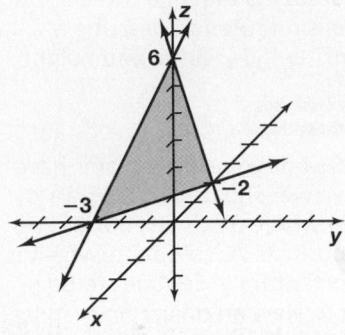

Closure

Describe how you would locate the point $(-2, 4, -3)$ in a three-dimensional coordinate system. **Start at the origin. Move 2 units in the negative direction along the x-axis. Then move parallel to the y-axis 4 units in the positive direction. Then move parallel to the z-axis 3 units in the negative direction.**

page 144   Check Understanding

3a.

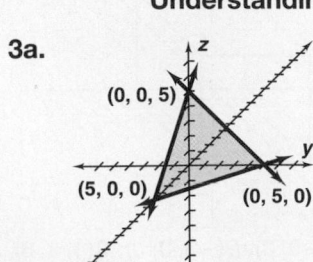

(0, 0, 5)
(5, 0, 0)   (0, 5, 0)

144

The graph of an equation is a picture of all the solutions to the equation. In two dimensions, the graph of $3x - 2y = 6$ is a line. In three dimensions, the graph of $3x - 2y + z = 6$ is a plane, as shown at the right.

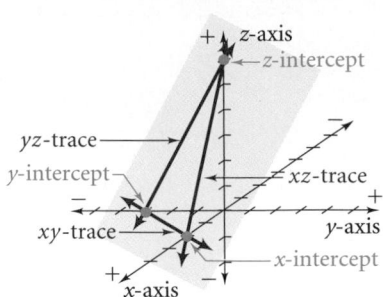

If the graph of a plane intersects one of the coordinate planes in a line, then the line is called a **trace**. For example, the xy-trace is the line in the xy-plane that contains the x- and the y-intercepts. The xz-trace and the yz-trace are defined similarly.

? Need Help?
The x-intercept of a line or plane is the point of intersection with the x-axis.

To sketch a plane, find the x-, y-, and z- intercepts. Then draw the traces and show the plane with shading.

3 EXAMPLE   Sketching a Plane

Sketch the graph of $2x + 3y + 4z = 12$.

Step 1 Find the intercepts.

$$2x + 3y + 4z = 12$$
$$2x + 3(0) + 4(0) = 12 \quad \text{To find the } x\text{-intercept, substitute 0 for } y \text{ and } z.$$
$$2x = 12$$
$$x = 6 \quad \text{The } x\text{-intercept is 6.}$$

$$2(0) + 3y + 4(0) = 12 \quad \text{To find the } y\text{-intercept, substitute 0 for } x \text{ and } z.$$
$$3y = 12$$
$$y = 4 \quad \text{The } y\text{-intercept is 4.}$$

$$2(0) + 3(0) + 4z = 12 \quad \text{To find the } z\text{-intercept, substitute 0 for } x \text{ and } y.$$
$$4z = 12$$
$$z = 3 \quad \text{The } z\text{-intercept is 3.}$$

Step 2 Graph the intercepts.

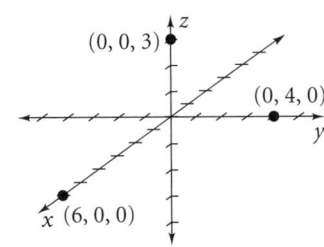

(0, 0, 3)
(0, 4, 0)
(6, 0, 0)

Step 3 Draw the traces. Shade the plane.

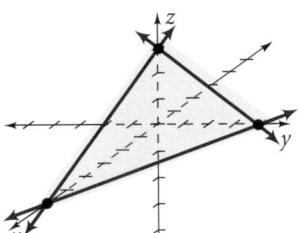

● Each point on the plane represents a solution to $2x + 3y + 4z = 12$.

✓ **Check Understanding** **3** Sketch the graph of each equation.
   a. $x + y + z = 5$ **b.** $2x - y + 3z = 6$ **c.** $x + 2y - z = -4$
   a–c. See margin.

b.

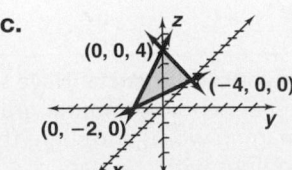

(0, 0, 2)
(0, −6, 0)
(3, 0, 0)

c.

(0, 0, 4)
(−4, 0, 0)
(0, −2, 0)

pages 145–147   Exercises

1. 1 unit back, 5 units right

2. 3 units forward, 3 units left, four units up

EXERCISES

For more practice, see *Extra Practice*.

Practice and Problem Solving

A Practice by Example

Describe the location of each point in coordinate space. 1–7. See margin.

Example 1
(page 143)

1. $(-1, 5, 0)$ **2.** $(3, -3, 4)$

3. $(2, 0, 5)$ **4.** $(-4, -7, -1)$

Graph each point in coordinate space.

5. $(5, 0, -2)$ **6.** $(0, 0, 4)$

7. $(10, -2, -5)$ **8.** $(-1, -1, -1)$

9. $(-4, -5, 3)$ **10.** $(25, 40, -30)$

11. $(1, 1, 0)$ **12.** $(0, -2, 2)$

8–12. See back of book.

Example 2
(page 143)

Find the coordinates of each point in the diagram.

13. A **(0, 0, 0)**   **14.** B **(0, 0, 50)**   **15.** C **(0, 40, 0)**

16. D **(60, 0, 50)**   **17.** E **(0, 80, 100)**   **18.** F **(60, 30, 100)**

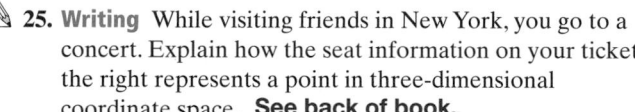

Example 3
(page 144)

Sketch the graph of each equation. 19–24. See back of book.

19. $x + y + 2z = 4$ **20.** $x + y + z = 2$ **21.** $2x + 6y + z = 6$

22. $x - y - 4z = 8$ **23.** $-x + 3y + z = 6$ **24.** $2x - y - 5z = 10$

B Apply Your Skills

25. Writing While visiting friends in New York, you go to a concert. Explain how the seat information on your ticket the right represents a point in three-dimensional coordinate space. **See back of book.**

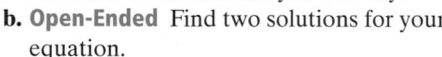
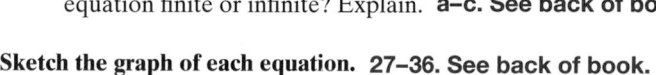

26. a. Party Planning Suppose you have $20 to spend on party decorations. Balloons are $.05 each, streamers are $.25 each, and noisemakers are $.40 each. Write and graph an equation in three variables for the numbers of decorations you can buy.

   b. Open-Ended Find two solutions for your equation.

   c. Critical Thinking Is the number of solutions to your equation finite or infinite? Explain. **a–c. See back of book.**

Sketch the graph of each equation. 27–36. See back of book.

27. $7x + 14y - z = 7$ **28.** $-3x + 5y + 10z = 15$

29. $32x + 16y - 8z = 32$ **30.** $-25x + 30y + 50z = 75$

31. $50x + 25y + 100z = 200$ **32.** $14x - 8y + 28z = 28$

Sketch the graph of each equation and find the equation of each trace.

33. $6x + 6y - 12z = 36$ **34.** $-20x + 10y + 50z = 100$

35. $-12x - 32y - 48z = 96$ **36.** $25x + 125y - 25z = 125$

---

3. 2 units forward, 5 units up

4. 4 units back, 7 units left, 1 unit down

5.
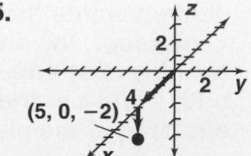

6.
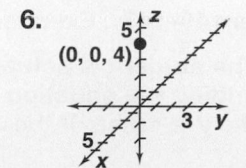

7.

Assignment Guide

1 Objective

A B Core 1–18, 25, 37–46

C Extension 48

2 Objective

A B Core 19–24, 26–36, 47

C Extension 49–52

Standardized Test Prep 53–57

Mixed Review 58–62

Error Prevention

Exercises 5–12 Urge students to be careful to refer to the appropriate axis for each coordinate. Diagrams for three-dimensional coordinate systems do not show the *x*- and *y*-axes in the positions to which students have grown accustomed from their work in two dimensions.

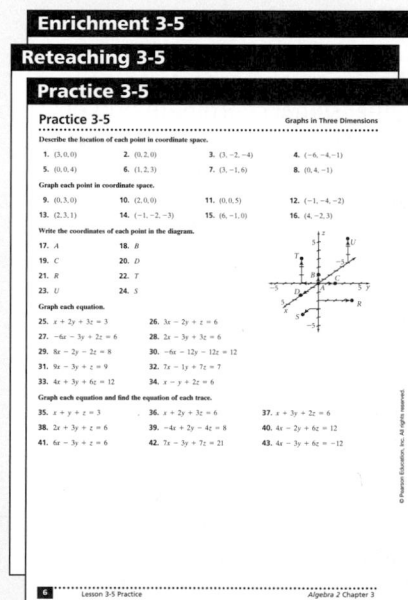

4. Assess

 **Lesson Quiz 3-5**

Graph each point in coordinate space.

1. $(2, -3, 5)$ **2.** $(0, 4, -2)$

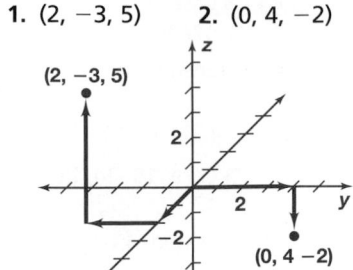

3. Graph $2x + 4y - 4z = 12$.

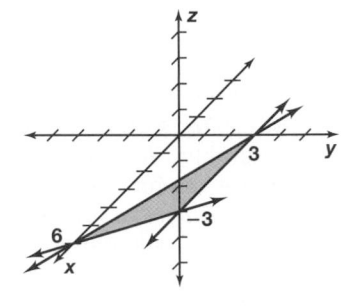

Alternative Assessment

Place a transparency with a three-dimensional coordinate grid on the overhead. Draw a point on the grid and have students describe the location using ordered triples. Repeat a few times. Draw traces representing a plane. Instruct students to find an equation that the plane can represent.

Standardized Test Prep

📁 **Resources**

For additional practice with a variety of test item formats:
- Standardized Test Prep, p. 161
- Test-Taking Strategies, p. 156
- Test-Taking Strategies with Transparencies

Exercise 53 The points that are easiest to test are those containing zeros or ones, such as in choices A, C, and D. Test those points first.

146

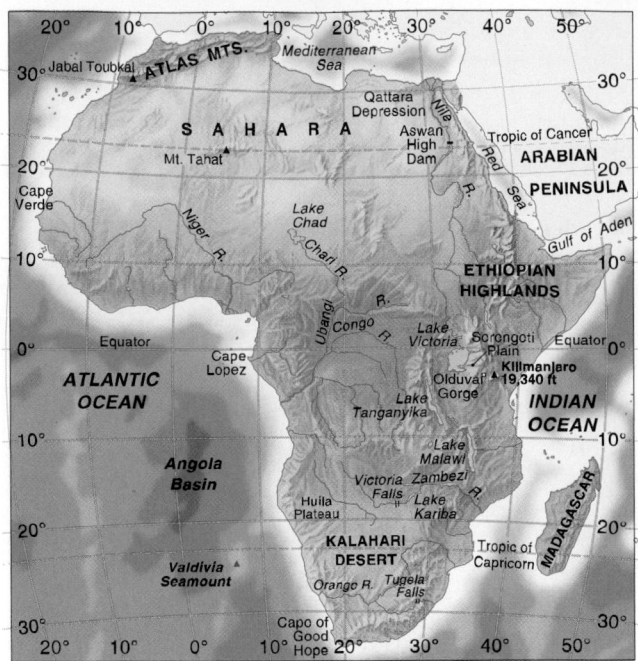

🌐 **Geography** Use the map to identify the geographic feature found at each location.

37. latitude 3° S
longitude 37° E
elevation 19,340 ft
Mt. Kilimanjaro

38. latitude 23° N
longitude 5° E
elevation 9,573 ft
Mt. Tahat

39. latitude 25° S
longitude 6° E
elevation −3,072 ft
Vildivia Seamount

40. latitude 15° N
longitude 18° W
elevation 0 ft
Cape Verde

41. latitude 30° N
longitude 27° E
elevation −440 ft
Qattara Depression

42. latitude 13° N
longitude 14° E
elevation 919 ft
Lake Chad

43. latitude 31° N
longitude 8° W
elevation 49,212 ft
Jabal Toubkal

44. latitude 18° S
longitude 25° E
elevation 2,927 ft
Victoria Falls

45. latitude 22° N
longitude 31° E
elevation 600 ft
Aswan High Dam

46. latitude 1° S
longitude 33° E
elevation 3,720 ft
Lake Victoria

47. Error Analysis A student claims to find the x-intercept of a plane by substituting 0 for x in the equation of the plane. Explain the student's error.
See margin.

C Challenge 📦 **48. a. Geometry** Use the Pythagorean Theorem to find the distance between $(1, 2, 4)$ and $(3, -2, 7)$. (*Hint:* Recall the Distance Formula.) $\sqrt{29}$
b. Make a Conjecture Make a conjecture about how to find the coordinates of the midpoint of a segment in coordinate space. **See margin.**

49. a. Critical Thinking Does every plane have three traces? Explain.
b. Must any two traces of a plane intersect? Explain. **a–b. See margin p. 147.**

Graph each equation in three-dimensional coordinate space.

50. $x = 3$ **51.** $2x + 3y = 6$ **52.** $y = 0$
50–52. See back of book.

Standardized Test Prep

Multiple Choice

53. Which point is NOT on the graph of $2x + 3y - z - 12 = 0$? **D**
A. $(6, 0, 0)$ B. $(3, 3, 3)$ C. $(0, 4, 0)$ D. $(1, 1, 7)$

54. Which point is NOT on the plane with equation $-2x - 3y + 5z = 7$? **G**
F. $(1, 2, 3)$ G. $(-2, -3, 5)$ H. $(-2, 4, 3)$ I. $(-4, 2, 1)$

🖥 **Take It to the NET**
Online lesson quiz at
www.PHSchool.com
········ Web Code: aga-0305

55. What are the intercepts of $-3x + 5y - 2z = 60$? **B**
A. $x = -180, y = 300, z = -120$ B. $x = -20, y = 12, z = -30$
C. $x = -3, y = 5, z = -2$ D. $x = -60, y = 60, z = -60$

56. What is the xy-trace of $2x - 4y + z = 8$? **G**
F. $-4y + z = 8$ G. $x - 2y = 4$ H. $2x + z = 8$ I. $z = 8$

Short Response

57. What is the intersection of the xz-traces for the two planes $2x - 3y - 4z = -4$ and $x + 3y + z = 7$? Explain each step of your answer.
See margin p. 147.

146 Chapter 3 Linear Systems

---

pages 145–147 Exercises

47. The student is actually finding the equation of the y–z–trace. If the student wants the x-intercept, the student should substitute 0 for both y and z in the equation of the plane.

48b. $\left(\dfrac{x_1 + x_2}{2}, \dfrac{y_1 + y_2}{2}, \dfrac{z_1 + z_2}{2}\right)$

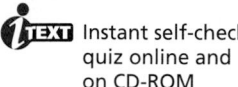
Lesson 3-4

58. Maximize the objective function $P = x + 3y$ under the given constraints. At what vertex does this maximum value occur?
$$\begin{cases} x + y \le 5 \\ x + 2y \le 8 \\ x \ge 0, y \ge 0 \end{cases}$$
$P = 15$ for (0, 4)

Lesson 2-7

Graph each inequality. **59–61. See back of book.**

59. $y \le x - 3$ **60.** $3y - x > -4$ **61.** $2x - y \ge 0$

Lesson 1-6

62. Probability Your town has a drawing for 50 summer jobs. Including you, 150 students apply.
a. What is the probability that you will get one of the jobs? $\frac{1}{3}$
b. You and a friend apply. What is the probability that you both get jobs?
about 0.11

✓ **Checkpoint Quiz 2** **Lessons 3-4 through 3-5**

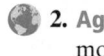 Instant self-check quiz online and on CD-ROM

1. Find the values of x and y that minimize the objective function $C = 2x + 3y$ for the constraints at the right.
$$\begin{cases} y \ge x \\ x + y \le 32 \\ x \ge 5, y \ge 3 \end{cases}$$
$C = 25$ for (5, 5)

🌐 **2. Agriculture** A farmer has at most 400 acres and $45,000 available to grow corn and soybeans. Use the cost and profit information at the right to decide how many acres of each crop will maximize profit.

Cost and Profit for Corn and Soybeans

	Corn	Soybeans
Number of Acres	x	y
Cost	$100x$	$150y$
Profit	$60x$	$75y$

300 acres corn and 100 acres soybeans

Graph each equation. Use traces and intercepts. **3–5. See margin.**

3. $3x + 2y + z = 6$ **4.** $x - y + z = 4$ **5.** $4x + z = 8$

Algebra at Work

· **Radiologist**

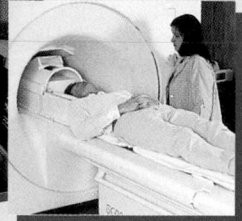

Radiologists are medical doctors who use X-rays, sound waves, and other means to diagnose diseases. Among the radiologist's most powerful diagnostic devices is the CT (computerized tomography) scan. The patient lies on a table while X-rays are beamed through the patient's body from different angles. Images are recorded and fed into a computer. The computer uses a three-dimensional coordinate system to record information and then to produce images of a cross section of the patient's body.

 Take It to the NET For more information about radiology, go to **www.PHSchool.com**.
Web Code: agb-2031

Lesson 3-5 Graphs in Three Dimensions **147**

49a. No, a plane that is parallel to two of the axes (and is therefore perpendicular to the third axis) has only two traces, which are perpendicular.

b. No, a plane that intersects two of the axes and is parallel to the third axis has three traces, two of which are parallel.

 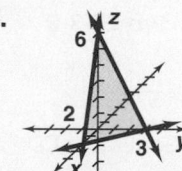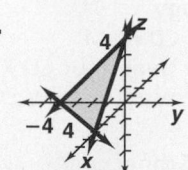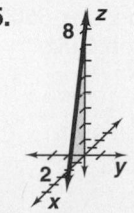

1. Plan

Lesson Preview

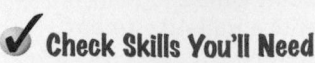
✓ **Check Skills You'll Need**

Solving Equations
Lesson 1-3: Example 2
Exercises 5–8
Extra Practice, p. 822

Graphing Systems of Equations
Lesson 3-1: Example 1
Exercises 1–8
Extra Practice, p. 824

Solving Systems Algebraically
Lesson 3-2: Examples 1, 3–5
Exercises 1–9, 14–25
Extra Practice, p. 824

Lesson Resources

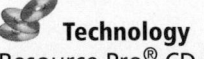
📁 **Teaching Resources**
Practice, Reteaching, Enrichment

👥 **Reaching All Students**
Practice Workbook 3-6
Spanish Practice Workbook 3-6

⏰ **Presentation Assistant Plus!**
Transparencies
• Check Skills You'll Need 3-6
• Additional Examples 3-6
• Student Edition Answers 3-6
• Lesson Quiz 3-6
PH Presentation Pro CD 3-6

PRENTICE HALL
ASSESSMENT SYSTEM

Computer Test Generator CD

💿 **Technology**
Resource Pro® CD-ROM
Computer Test Generator CD
Prentice Hall Presentation Pro CD

💻 **www.PHSchool.com**
Student Site
• Teacher Web Code: agk-5500
• Self-grading Lesson Quiz
Teacher Center
• Lesson Planner
• Resources

Plus

148

3-6

Systems With Three Variables

North Carolina Objectives

2.10 Use systems of two or more equations or inequalities to model and solve problems; justify results. Solve using tables, graphs, matrix operations, and algebraic properties.

Lesson Preview

What You'll Learn

OBJECTIVE 1 To solve systems in three variables by elimination

OBJECTIVE 2 To solve systems in three variables by substitution

. . . And Why

To choose an investment strategy, as in Example 4

✓ **Check Skills You'll Need** (For help, go to Lessons 3-1 and 3-2.)

Solve each system.

1. $\begin{cases} 2x - y = 11 \\ x + 2y = -7 \end{cases}$ **(3, −5)** **2.** $\begin{cases} -x + 6y = 8 \\ 2x - 12y = -14 \end{cases}$ **no solution** **3.** $\begin{cases} 3x + 2y = -5 \\ 4x + 3y = -8 \end{cases}$ **(1, −4)**

Let $y = 4x - 2$. Solve each equation for x.

4. $3x + y = 5$ **1** **5.** $x - 2y = -3$ **1** **6.** $4x + 3y = 2$ $\frac{1}{2}$

Determine whether the given ordered pair is a solution of each equation in the system.

7. $(1, 3)$ $\begin{cases} 2x + 5y = 17 \\ -4x + 3y = 5 \end{cases}$ **yes** **8.** $(-4, 2)$ $\begin{cases} x + 2y = 0 \\ 3x - 2y = -16 \end{cases}$ **yes**

OBJECTIVE 1

iTEXT Interactive lesson includes instant self-check, tutorials, and activities.

Solving Three-Variable Systems by Elimination

You can represent systems of equations in three variables as graphs in three dimensions. As you learned in Lesson 3-5, the graph of any equation of the form $Ax + By + Cz = D$, where A, B, and C are not all zero, is a plane. The solutions of a three-variable system can be shown graphically as the intersections of planes.

❓ **Need Help?**
To review solving systems by graphing, go to Lesson 3-1.

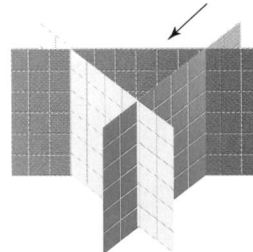

No solution
No point lies in all three planes.

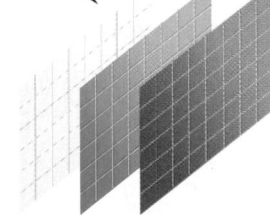

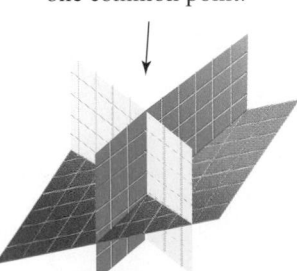

One solution
The planes intersect at one common point.

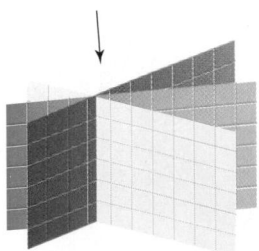

An infinite number of solutions
The planes intersect at all the points along a common line.

⚡ Ongoing Assessment and Intervention

Before the Lesson	**During the Lesson**	**After the Lesson**
Diagnose prerequisite skills using:	**Monitor progress using:**	**Assess knowledge using:**
• Check Skills You'll Need	• Check Understanding	• Lesson Quiz
	• Additional Examples	• Computer Test Generator CD
	• Standardized Test Prep	

When the solution of a system of equations in three variables is represented by one point, you can write it as an ordered triple (x, y, z).

You can solve a system of three equations in three variables by working with the equations in pairs. You will use one of the equations *twice*.

1 EXAMPLE **Solving by Elimination**

Solve the system by elimination. The equations are numbered to make the procedure easy to follow.

① $\begin{cases} x - 3y + 3z = -4 \\ 2x + 3y - z = 15 \\ 4x - 3y - z = 19 \end{cases}$
②
③

Step 1 Pair the equations to eliminate y, because the y terms are already additive inverses.

①$\begin{cases} x - 3y + 3z = -4 \\ 2x + 3y - z = 15 \end{cases}$ **Add.**
②

④ $3x \qquad + 2z = 11$

②$\begin{cases} 2x + 3y - z = 15 \\ 4x - 3y - z = 19 \end{cases}$
③

⑤ $6x \qquad - 2z = 34$

Step 2 Write the two new equations as a system. Solve for x and z.

④$\begin{cases} 3x \qquad + 2z = 11 \\ 6x \qquad - 2z = 34 \end{cases}$
⑤

$9x \qquad\qquad = 45$
$x = 5$

④ $3x + 2z = 11$
$3(5) + 2z = 11$
$2z = -4$
$z = -2$

Substitute the value of *x*.

Step 3 Substitute the values for x and z into one of the original equations (①, ②, or ③) and solve for y.

① $x - 3y + 3z = -4$
$5 - 3y + 3(-2) = -4$
$5 - 3y - 6 = -4$
$-3y = -3$
$y = 1$

The solution of the system is $(5, 1, -2)$.

Check Show that $(5, 1, -2)$ makes each equation true.

$x - 3y + 3z = -4$	$2x + 3y - z = 15$	$4x - 3y - z = 19$
$5 - 3(1) + 3(-2) \overset{?}{=} -4$	$2(5) + 3(1) - (-2) \overset{?}{=} 15$	$4(5) - 3(1) - (-2) \overset{?}{=} 19$
$5 - 3 - 6 \overset{?}{=} -4$	$10 + 3 + 2 \overset{?}{=} 15$	$20 - 3 + 2 \overset{?}{=} 19$
$-4 = -4 ✓$	$15 = 15 ✓$	$19 = 19 ✓$

✓ **Check Understanding** ① Solve each system by elimination. Check your answers.

a. $\begin{cases} 2x + y - z = 5 \\ 3x - y + 2z = -1 \\ x - y - z = 0 \end{cases}$ **(1, 2, −1)**

b. $\begin{cases} 2x - y + z = 4 \\ x + 3y - z = 11 \\ 4x + y - z = 14 \end{cases}$ **(3, 3, 1)**

c. Critical Thinking Suppose one of the equations in a system contains a variable with a coefficient of zero. When pairing the equations to solve the system, would you use that equation twice? Explain.
No; you wouldn't need to use any of the original equations twice.

You can apply the method in Example 1 to any system of three equations in three variables. You may need to multiply one or more of the equations by a nonzero number to create an equivalent system.

Real-World 🌐 Connection

You can use a system in three variables to model the amounts of vitamin C, potassium, and beta carotene in this three-fruit salad.

👥 **Reaching All Students**

| **Below Level** When subtracting equations that contain negative coefficients, suggest that students multiply one equation by −1, and then add the equations. | **Advanced Learners** Challenge students to create and solve a system of four equations in four variables. Promise them that they will learn a simpler method in Chapter 4. | **Inclusion** See note on page 149. **Error Prevention** See note on page 153. |

---

2. Teach

Professional Development

Math Background

Both the elimination method and the substitution method are used to solve systems of three equations in three variables. There is either no solution, one solution, or infinitely many solutions. Numbering the equations helps to avoid confusion.

OBJECTIVE
1 Teaching Notes

1 EXAMPLE **Inclusion**

It may help some students to highlight each equation with a different color. Or, if students are color-blind, it may help to circle the terms of one variable that are additive inverses, and put a square around terms of another variable that are additive inverses.

2 EXAMPLE **Alternative Method**

If some students are already familiar with using matrices on graphing calculators to solve equations, they may prefer this method. First students write a matrix that contains the coefficients of the system of equations. To enter the matrix, press **MATRX** ▷ ▷ **ENTER** 3 **ENTER** 3 **ENTER**. Then enter the coefficients. Each row of the matrix represents one equation.

$A = \begin{bmatrix} 2 & 1 & -1 \\ 1 & 4 & 2 \\ 15 & 6 & -2 \end{bmatrix}$

Press **QUIT**. Now, write a matrix that contains the constants and enter this as matrix **[B]**. Be sure to press 2 for matrix **[B]** before entering the dimensions.

$B = \begin{bmatrix} 5 \\ 16 \\ 12 \end{bmatrix}$

Press **QUIT** again. Tell students that they are going to use the inverse of the coefficient matrix. This is explained in detail in Chapter 4. Now press **MATRX** 1 x^{-1} **MATRX** 2 **ENTER**. The solution is $(-2, 6, -3)$.

149

1 Solve the system by elimination.
$$\begin{cases} -5x + 3y + 2z = 11 \\ 8x - 5y + 2z = -55 \\ 4x - 7y - 2z = -29 \end{cases}$$
$(-2, 5, -7)$

2 Solve the system by elimination.
$$\begin{cases} x + 2y + 5z = 1 \\ -3x + 3y + 7z = 4 \\ -8x + 5y + 12z = 11 \end{cases}$$
$(-1, -9, 4)$

2 EXAMPLE Solving an Equivalent System

Solve the system by elimination. $\begin{array}{l} ① \\ ② \\ ③ \end{array}\begin{cases} 2x + y - z = 5 \\ x + 4y + 2z = 16 \\ 15x + 6y - 2z = 12 \end{cases}$

Step 1 Pair the equations to eliminate z.

$\begin{array}{l} ① \\ ② \end{array}\begin{cases} 2x + y - z = 5 \\ x + 4y + 2z = 16 \end{cases}$

$\begin{array}{rl} 4x + 2y - 2z &= 10 \quad \textbf{Multiply by 2.} \\ x + 4y + 2z &= 16 \\ \hline ④ \quad 5x + 6y &= 26 \end{array}$

$\begin{array}{l} ② \\ ③ \end{array}\begin{cases} x + 4y + 2z = 16 \\ 15x + 6y - 2z = 12 \end{cases}$
$\begin{array}{rl} \hline ⑤ \quad 16x + 10y &= 28 \end{array}$

Step 2 Write the two new equations as a system. Solve for x and y.

$\begin{array}{l} ④ \\ ⑤ \end{array}\begin{cases} 5x + 6y = 26 \\ 16x + 10y = 28 \end{cases}$

$\begin{array}{rl} 25x + 30y &= 130 \quad \textbf{Multiply by 5.} \\ -48x - 30y &= -84 \quad \textbf{Multiply by } -3. \\ \hline -23x &= 46 \\ x &= -2 \end{array}$

$\begin{array}{rl} ④ \quad 5x + 6y &= 26 \\ 5(-2) + 6y &= 26 \quad \textbf{Substitute the value of } x. \\ y &= 6 \end{array}$

Step 3 Substitute the values for x and y into one of the original equations (①, ②, or ③). Solve for z.

$\begin{array}{rl} ① \quad 2x + y - z &= 5 \\ 2(-2) + 6 - z &= 5 \\ z &= -3 \end{array}$

● The solution of the system is $(-2, 6, -3)$.

✔ **Check Understanding** **2** Solve the system by elimination. Check your answers. $\begin{cases} x + 4y - 5z = -7 \\ 3x + 2y + 3z = 7 \\ 2x + y + 5z = 8 \end{cases}$

$(2, -1, 1)$

The graph illustrates the solution to Example 2. Each equation in the system represents a tilted plane. The graph of ① is red, the graph of ② is blue, and the graph of ③ is green. The three planes intersect at $(-2, 6, -3)$.

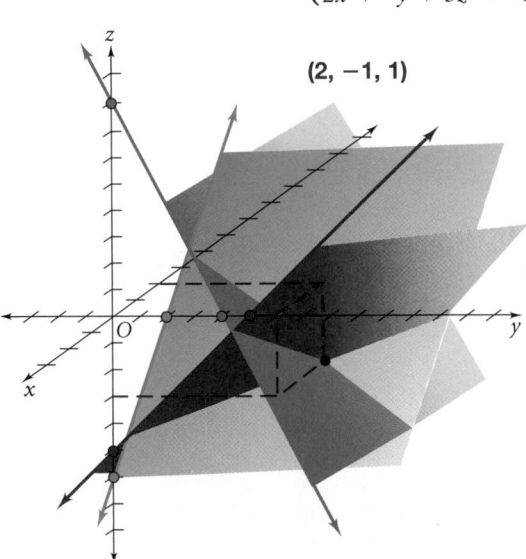

You can also use the substitution method to solve a system of three equations. Substitution is the best method to use when one of the equations can be solved easily for one variable.

3 EXAMPLE **Solving by Substitution**

Solve the system by substitution.

$$\begin{array}{r} ① \quad x - 2y + z = -4 \\ ② \left\{ -4x + y - 2z = 1 \right. \\ ③ \quad 2x + 2y - z = 10 \end{array}$$

Step 1 Choose one equation to solve for one of its variables.

① $x - 2y + z = -4$ **Solve the first equation for x.**

$$x - 2y = -z - 4$$

$$x = 2y - z - 4$$

Step 2 Substitute the expression for x into each of the other two equations.

② $\qquad -4x + y - 2z = 1$ $\qquad\qquad$ ③ $\qquad 2x + 2y - z = 10$

$-4(2y - z - 4) + y - 2z = 1$ **Simplify.** $\quad 2(2y - z - 4) + 2y - z = 10$

$-8y + 4z + 16 + y - 2z = 1$ $\qquad\qquad\quad 4y - 2z - 8 + 2y - z = 10$

$\qquad -7y + 2z + 16 = 1$ $\qquad\qquad\qquad\qquad 6y - 3z - 8 = 10$

④ $\qquad\qquad -7y + 2z = -15$ $\qquad$ ⑤ $\qquad\qquad\qquad 6y - 3z = 18$

Step 3 Write the two new equations as a system. Solve for y and z.

$$\begin{array}{l} ④ \left\{ -7y + 2z = -15 \right. \\ ⑤ \left. \ 6y - 3z = 18 \right. \end{array}$$

$\qquad\qquad -21y + 6z = -45$ **Multiply by 3.**

$\qquad\qquad \underline{\ \ 12y - 6z = \ \ 36}$ **Multiply by 2.**

$\qquad\qquad\qquad -9y \qquad = \ \ -9$

$\qquad\qquad\qquad\qquad y = \ \ 1$

④ $\quad -7y + 2z = -15$

$-7(1) + 2z = -15$ **Substitute the value of y.**

$-7 + 2z = -15$

$2z = -8$

$z = -4$

Step 4 Substitute the values for y and z into one of the original equations (①, ②, or ③). Solve for x.

① $\qquad x - 2y + z = -4$

$x - 2(1) + (-4) = -4$

$x - 2 - 4 = -4$

$x - 6 = -4$

$x = \ \ 2$

The solution of the system is $(2, 1, -4)$.

✓ Check Understanding **3** Solve each system by substitution. Check your answers.

a. $\left\{\begin{array}{l} x - 3y + z = \ \ 6 \\ 2x - 5y - z = -2 \\ -x + y + 2z =. \ \ 7 \end{array}\right.$ **(4, 1, 5)** $\qquad$ **b.** $\left\{\begin{array}{l} 3x + 2y - \ \ z = \ 12 \\ -4x + \ \ y - 2z = \ \ 4 \\ x - 3y + \ \ z = -4 \end{array}\right.$ **(2, 0, −6)**

Teaching Notes

3 EXAMPLE **Teaching Tip**

Have students observe that in Step 1, it would also be easy to solve for y (using equation 2) or for z (using equation 3). The amount of work required for solving the system is about the same no matter which variable is used as the basis for the substitution. Use this example to reinforce the idea that there may be a variety of approaches for solving a system. Ask students if they see another approach for this system. If necessary, point out that an efficient approach would be to add equations 1 and 3. Ask students how they would proceed from that point on.

4 EXAMPLE **Diversity**

Some students may come from backgrounds where they have not been exposed to the various types of funds mentioned and some may come from backgrounds where they have. Help all students feel comfortable by explaining what each type of fund is before reading the example.

Additional Examples

3 Solve the system by substitution.

$$\left\{\begin{array}{l} 12x + 7y + 5z = 16 \\ -2x + y - 14z = -9 \\ -3x - 2y + 9z = -12 \end{array}\right.$$

(7, −9, −1)

151

4 You have $10,000 in a savings account. You want to take most of the money out and invest it in stocks and bonds. You decide to invest nine times as much as you leave in the account. You also decide to invest five times as much in stocks as in bonds. How much will you invest in stocks, how much in bonds, and how much will you leave in savings? **$7500 in stocks, $1500 in bonds, $1000 in savings**

Closure

Describe what you do to solve a system of three linear equations in three variables by elimination. **Answers may vary. Sample: Multiply one or both of two equations, as needed, to make the coefficients of a selected variable additive inverses. Add to eliminate the variable. Follow the same procedure with a different pair of the original equations to eliminate the same variable. Solve the resulting system of two equations in two variables. Substitute the values you get into one of the original equations to find the value of the third variable.**

4 **EXAMPLE** **Real-World Connection**

Money Management Suppose you have saved $3200 from a part-time job and you want to invest your savings in a growth fund, an income fund, and a money market fund. Refer to the graph. To maximize your return, you decide to put twice as much money in the growth fund as in the money market fund. How should you invest the $3200 to get a return of $250 in one year?

Relate growth fund + income fund + money market fund = 3200

growth fund = 2 times money market fund

10% of growth + 7% of income + 5% of money market = 250

Define Let g = amount invested in a growth fund.

Let i = amount invested in an income fund.

Let m = amount invested in a money market fund.

Write
$$① \begin{cases} g + i + m = 3200 \\ ② \quad g = 2m \\ ③ \quad 0.10g + 0.07i + 0.05m = 250 \end{cases}$$

Step 1 Substitute $2m$ for g in equations ① and ③. Simplify.

① $g + i + m = 3200$ ③ $0.10g + 0.07i + 0.05m = 250$

$2m + i + m = 3200$ $0.10(2m) + 0.07i + 0.05m = 250$

④ $\quad 3m + i = 3200$ ⑤ $\quad 0.25m + 0.07i = 250$

Step 2 Write the two new equations as a system. Solve for m and i.

$$④ \begin{cases} 3m + i = 3200 \\ ⑤ \quad 0.25m + 0.07i = 250 \end{cases}$$

     $3m + i = 3200$

     $3m + 0.84i = 3000$ **Multiply by 12.**

           $0.16i = 200$

               $i = 1250$

④ $3m + i = 3200$

     $3m + 1250 = 3200$ **Substitute the value of i.**

           $3m = 1950$

            $m = 650$

Step 3 Substitute the value of m into equation 2 and solve for g.

② $g = 2m$

    $g = 2(650)$

    $g = 1300$

You should invest $1300 in the growth fund, $1250 in the income fund, and $650 in the money market fund to get a return of $250 in one year.

✓ Check Understanding **4** Suppose you discover that your growth fund, income fund, and money market fund return rates are better estimated at 12%, 6%, and 3% per year respectively. How should you invest the $3200 to get a return of $255 in one year?
$1400 growth, $1100 income, and $700 money market
You have learned how to solve systems of equations using the methods of graphing, elimination, and substitution. In Chapter 4, you will learn how to use matrices to solve systems of equations.

152   Chapter 3   Linear Systems

pages 153–155 Exercises

10. (8, −4, 2)

11. $(a, b, c) = (2, 3, −2)$

12. $(r, s, t) = (−2, −1, −3)$

13. (5, 2, 2)

14. (0, 1, 7)

15. (4, 1, 6)

EXERCISES

Practice and Problem Solving

For more practice, see *Extra Practice*.

A Practice by Example

Examples 1 and 2
(pages 149 and 150)

Solve each system by elimination. Check your answers.

1. $\begin{cases} x - y + z = -1 \\ x + y + 3z = -3 \\ 2x - y + 2z = 0 \end{cases}$
   (4, 2, −3)

2. $\begin{cases} x - y - 2z = 4 \\ -x + 2y + z = 1 \\ -x + y - 3z = 11 \end{cases}$
   (0, 2, −3)

3. $\begin{cases} 2x - y + z = -2 \\ x + 3y - z = 10 \\ x + 2z = -8 \end{cases}$
   (2, 1, −5)

4. $\begin{cases} a + b + c = -3 \\ 3b - c = 4 \\ 2a - b - 2c = -5 \end{cases}$
   (a, b, c) = (−3, 1, −1)

5. $\begin{cases} 6q - r + 2s = 8 \\ 2q + 3r - s = -9 \\ 4q + 2r + 5s = 1 \end{cases}$
   (q, r, s) = ($\frac{1}{2}$, −3, 1)

6. $\begin{cases} x - y + 2z = -7 \\ y + z = 1 \\ x = 2y + 3z \end{cases}$
   (0, 3, −2)

7. $\begin{cases} x + y + 2z = 3 \\ 2x + y + 3z = 7 \\ -x - 2y + z = 10 \end{cases}$
   (1, −4, 3)

8. $\begin{cases} 3x - y + z = 3 \\ x + y + 2z = 4 \\ x + 2y + z = 4 \end{cases}$
   (1, 1, 1)

9. $\begin{cases} x - 2y + 3z = 12 \\ 2x - y - 2z = 5 \\ 2x + 2y - z = 4 \end{cases}$
   (4, −1, 2)

Examples 3 and 4
(pages 151 and 152)

Solve each system by substitution. Check your answers.

10–18. See margin pp. 152–153.

10. $\begin{cases} x + 2y + 3z = 6 \\ y + 2z = 0 \\ z = 2 \end{cases}$

11. $\begin{cases} 3a + b + c = 7 \\ a + 3b - c = 13 \\ b = 2a - 1 \end{cases}$

12. $\begin{cases} 5r - 4s - 3t = 3 \\ t = s + r \\ r = 3s + 1 \end{cases}$

13. $\begin{cases} 13 = 3x - y \\ 4y - 3x + 2z = -3 \\ z = 2x - 4y \end{cases}$

14. $\begin{cases} x + 3y - z = -4 \\ 2x - y + 2z = 13 \\ 3x - 2y - z = -9 \end{cases}$

15. $\begin{cases} x - 4y + z = 6 \\ 2x + 5y - z = 7 \\ 2x - y - z = 1 \end{cases}$

16. $\begin{cases} x - y + 2z = 7 \\ 2x + y + z = 8 \\ x - z = 5 \end{cases}$

17. $\begin{cases} x + y + z = 2 \\ x + 2z = 5 \\ 2x + y - z = -1 \end{cases}$

18. $\begin{cases} 5x - y + z = 4 \\ x + 2y - z = 5 \\ 2x + 3y - 3z = 5 \end{cases}$

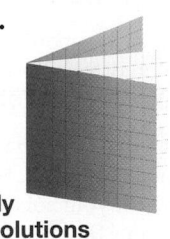

Real-World Connection

Careers Stadium designers must take into account the profitability of different types of seating.

19. **Finance** A company placed $1,000,000 in three different accounts. It placed part in short-term notes paying 4.5% per year, twice as much in government bonds paying 5%, and the rest in utility bonds paying 4%. The income after one year was $45,500. How much did the company place in each account?
    See margin.

20. **Sports** A stadium has 49,000 seats. Seats sell for $25 in Section A, $20 in section B, and $15 in Section C. The number of seats in Section A equals the total number of seats in Sections B and C. Suppose the stadium takes in $1,052,000 from each sold-out event. How many seats does each section hold?
    See margin.

21. A change machine contains nickels, dimes, and quarters. There are 75 coins in the machine, and the value of the coins is $7.25. There are 5 times as many nickels as dimes. Find the number of coins of each type in the machine.
    50 nickels, 10 dimes, and 15 quarters

B Apply Your Skills

Find the number of solutions of each system.

22.
    infinitely many solutions

23.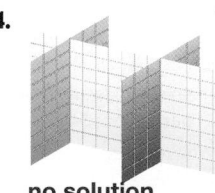
    one solution

24. **no solution**

Lesson 3-6 Systems With Three Variables **153**

Assignment Guide

1 Objective

A B Core 1–9, 22–24, 39–40

C Extension 42, 44

2 Objective

A B Core 10–21, 25–38, 41

C Extension 43, 45

Standardized Test Prep 46–49

Mixed Review 50–67

Error Prevention

Exercises 5–9 When students need to multiply to eliminate a variable, they may not multiply all terms by the number they choose for the multiplication. Urge students to be careful and thorough in using properties of equality and operations.

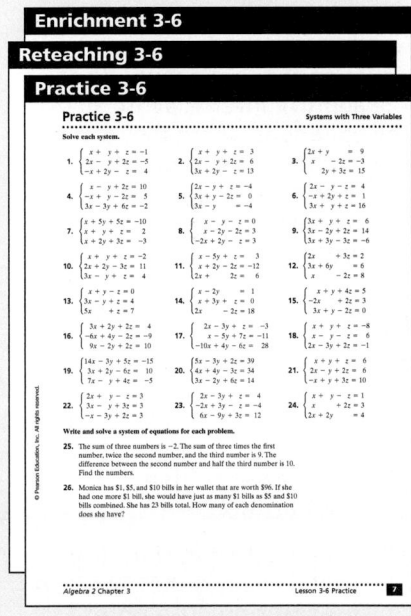

Enrichment 3-6
Reteaching 3-6
Practice 3-6

---

16. **(5, −2, 0)**

17. **(1, −1, 2)**

18. **(1, 3, 2)**

19. **$220,000 was placed in short-term notes. $440,000 was placed in government bonds. $340,000 was placed in utility bonds.**

20. **Section A has 24,500 seats. Section B has 14,400 seats. Section C has 10,100 seats.**

Solve each system by elimination.

1. $\begin{cases} -3x + 2y - 5z = -3 \\ 3x - y + 3z = 4 \\ 3x + 5y - 8z = 6 \end{cases}$
(3, −7, −4)

2. $\begin{cases} 7x - y - z = 2 \\ 13x - 4y + 5z = -7 \\ -4x + 3y - 4z = -5 \end{cases}$
(−2, −11, −5)

3. Solve by substitution.
$\begin{cases} 2x - 3y + 6z = -21 \\ -5x + 4y + z = 3 \\ 7x - 7y - 4z = -6 \end{cases}$
(3, 5, −2)

Alternative Assessment

Ask a student to state a three-variable equation. Ask another student to state a three variable equation that contains an additive inverse of one of the terms in the first equation. Ask another student to state an equation that has a multiple of the additive inverse. Write all of the equations where they can be seen as the students give them to you. Instruct all members of the class to solve the system. Students may want to work in pairs.

pages 153–155   Exercises

41. **Answers may vary.
Sample: When one of the equations can easily be solved for one variable, it is easier to use substitution.**

42. **The student is thinking that 0 means that there is no solution. The point (0, 0, 0) is the solution.**

44. **Answers may vary.
Sample: Solution is (1, 2, 3)**
$x + y + 2 = 6$
$2x - y + 2z = 6$
$3x + 3y + z = 12$

45. **Let E, F, and V represent the numbers of edges,**

Solve each system.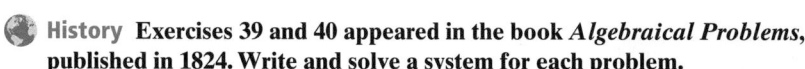

25. $\begin{cases} x - 3y + 2z = 11 \\ -x + 4y + 3z = 5 \\ 2x - 2y - 4z = 2 \end{cases}$ (8, 1, 3)

26. $\begin{cases} x + 2y + z = 4 \\ 2x - y + 4z = -8 \\ -3x + y - 2z = -1 \end{cases}$ (3, 2, −3)

27. $\begin{cases} 4x - y + 2z = -6 \\ -2x + 3y - z = 8 \\ 2y + 3z = -5 \end{cases}$ $\left(\frac{1}{2}, 2, -3\right)$

28. $\begin{cases} 4A + 2U + I = 2 \\ 5A - 3U + 2I = 17 \\ A - 5U = 3 \end{cases}$ (−2, −1, 12)

29. $\begin{cases} 4x - 2y + 5z = 6 \\ 3x + 3y + 8z = 4 \\ x - 5y - 3z = 5 \end{cases}$ no solution

30. $\begin{cases} 2\ell + 2w + h = 72 \\ \ell = 3w \\ h = 2w \end{cases}$ (21.6, 7.2, 14.4)

31. $\begin{cases} 3x + 2y - z = 17.8 \\ x - 3y + 2z = 7.9 \\ 2x + y - 3z = 3.9 \end{cases}$ (6, 1.5, 3.2)

32. $\begin{cases} x + 2y = 2 \\ 2x + 3y - z = -9 \\ 4x + 2y + 5z = 1 \end{cases}$ $\left(-\frac{122}{11}, \frac{72}{11}, \frac{71}{11}\right)$

33. $\begin{cases} 3x + 2y + 2z = -2 \\ 2x + y - z = -2 \\ x - 3y + z = 0 \end{cases}$ $\left(-\frac{10}{13}, -\frac{2}{13}, \frac{4}{13}\right)$

34. $\begin{cases} 6x + y - 4z = -8 \\ \frac{y}{4} - \frac{z}{6} = 0 \\ 2x - z = -2 \end{cases}$ (2, 4, 6)

35. $\begin{cases} 4y + 2x = 6 - 3z \\ x + z - 2y = -5 \\ x - 2z = 3y - 7 \end{cases}$ (−1, 2, 0)

36. $\begin{cases} 5z + 4y = 4 \\ 3x - 2y = 0 \\ x + 3z = -8 \end{cases}$ (4, 6, −4)

37. $\begin{cases} x + 6z = 12 \\ -2x + 3y = 6 \\ y - \frac{z}{2} = \frac{5}{2} \end{cases}$ $\left(2, \frac{10}{3}, \frac{5}{3}\right)$

38. $\begin{cases} 4x - y + z = -5 \\ -x + y - z = 5 \\ 2x - z - 1 = y \end{cases}$ (0, 2, −3)

History Exercises 39 and 40 appeared in the book *Algebraical Problems*, published in 1824. Write and solve a system for each problem.

39. Ten apples cost a penny, and 25 pears cost two pennies. Suppose I buy 100 apples and pears for $9\frac{1}{2}$ pennies. How many of each shall I have?
75 apples; 25 pears

40. A fish was caught whose tail weighed 9 lb. Its head weighed as much as its tail plus half its body. Its body weighed as much as its head and tail. What did the fish weigh? **72 pounds**

43. $x + 2y = 180$
$y + z = 180$
$5z = 540$
$x = 36, y = 72, z = 108$

C Challenge

Need Help?
Sum of angles in a pentagon: 540°

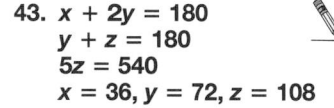
41. **Writing** How do you decide whether substitution is the best method to solve a system in three variables?
See margin.

42. **Error Analysis** A student says that the system consisting of $x = 0$, $y = 0$, and $z = 0$ has no solutions. Explain the student's error. **See margin.**

43. **Geometry** Refer to the regular five-pointed star at the right. Write and solve a system of three equations to find the measure of each labeled angle. **See above left.**

44. **Open-Ended** Write your own system having three variables. Begin by choosing the solution. Then write three equations that are true for your solution. Use elimination to solve the system. **See margin.**

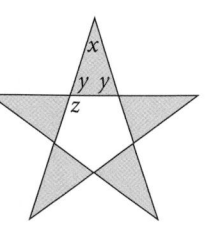

---

faces, and vertices, respectively. From the statement Every face has five edges, and the number of edges is 5 times the number of faces: $E = 5F$. But since

each edge is part of two faces, this counts each edge twice. So $E = \frac{5}{2}F$. Since every face has five vertices and every vertex is shared by three faces, $3V = 5F$ or $V = \frac{5}{3}F$.

Euler's formula:
$V + F = E + 2$. Solving this system of three equations yields
$E = 30$, $F = 12$, and $V = 20$

45. Geometry In the regular polyhedron described below, all faces are congruent polygons. Use a system of three linear equations to find the numbers of vertices, edges, and faces. **See margin p. 154.**

Every face has five edges and every edge is shared by two faces. Every face has five vertices and every vertex is shared by three faces. The sum of the number of vertices and faces is two more than the number of edges.

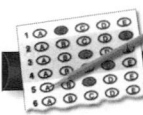

Standardized Test Prep

Multiple Choice

46. What is the solution of the system?
$$\begin{cases} -3x + 2y - z = 6 \\ 3x + y + 2z = 5 \\ 2x - 2y - z = -5 \end{cases} \textbf{B}$$

A. $(6, 5, -3)$ **B.** $(1, 4, -1)$

C. $\left(0, \frac{17}{5}, \frac{4}{5}\right)$ **D.** no solution

47. What is the solution of the system?
$$\begin{cases} x + 3y - 2z = -8 \\ 3x - y + z = 11 \\ 2x + 4y + 2z = 14 \end{cases} \textbf{F}$$

F. $(2, 0, 5)$ **G.** $(-8, 11, 14)$

H. $\left(-2, \frac{4}{3}, 5\right)$ **I.** no solution

Take It to the NET
Online lesson quiz at
www.PHSchool.com
Web Code: aga-0306

48. What is the solution of the system?
$$\begin{cases} y = -2x + 10 \\ -x + y - 2z = -2 \\ 3x - 2y + 4z = 7 \end{cases} \textbf{D}$$

A. $\left(3, -4, \frac{3}{2}\right)$ **B.** $\left(3, 16, \frac{15}{2}\right)$

C. $\left(-3, 16, \frac{15}{2}\right)$ **D.** $\left(3, 4, \frac{3}{2}\right)$

Short Response

49. Why is there no solution to the system? Explain your answer in terms of intersecting planes.
See back of book.
$$\begin{array}{l} ① \\ ② \\ ③ \end{array} \begin{cases} 2x - 3y + z = 5 \\ 2x - 3y + z = -2 \\ -4x + 6y - 2z = 10 \end{cases}$$

Mixed Review

Graph each equation. 50–52. See margin. 53–55. See back of book.

Lesson 3-5

50. $x + y + 4z = 8$ **51.** $2x + 3y - z = 12$ **52.** $-3x + y + 5z = 15$

53. $-2x + 3y - z = 6$ **54.** $6x + 4y - 3z = -12$ **55.** $3x - 6y - 2z = 18$

Graph each equation. 56–61. See margin.

Lesson 2-5

56. $y = |x + 4|$ **57.** $y = |3x - 2|$ **58.** $y = \left|\frac{1}{2}x + 3\right| - 2$

59. $y = |x - 2| + 1$ **60.** $y = |2x + 1|$ **61.** $y = |x + 3| - 2$

Lesson 1-4

Solve each inequality. Graph the solution on a number line. 62–67. See back of book.

62. $-4x + 3 \le 9$ **63.** $-(x + 4) - 3 \ge 11$ **64.** $2(3x - 1) < x - 7$

65. $6 - 2x > 2$ **66.** $3x + 2 < -x + 10$ **67.** $-2(x + 3) \ge x$

50.

51.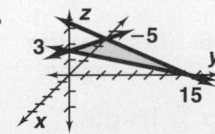

52.

Standardized Test Prep

Resources

For additional practice with a variety of test item formats:

- Standardized Test Prep, p. 161
- Test-Taking Strategies, p. 156
- Test-Taking Strategies with Transparencies

Exercise 48 One approach is to test the answer choices in the equations of the system. A good way to begin is first to test choices in the first equation, since the first equation contains only two of the three variables.

56.

57.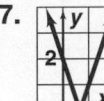

58.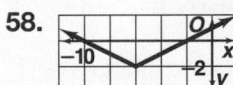

59.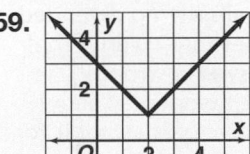

60.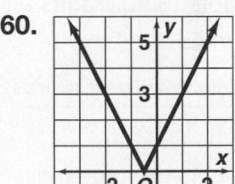

61.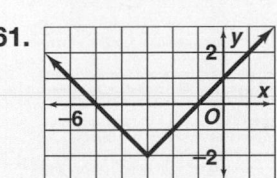

Answering Extended-Response Questions

This feature helps devise strategies for answering extended-response questions. The focus of the feature is on identifying partial and full credit responses to extended response questions.

Resources

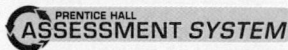
PRENTICE HALL
ASSESSMENT SYSTEM

Test-Taking Strategies with Transparencies
• Transparency 3
• Practice sheet p. 27

Teaching Notes

Point out to students that it is very important to show their work when answering extended-response questions. Even if their eventual answer is wrong, showing their work may allow them to receive partial credit for their response. Partial credit is always preferable to no credit.

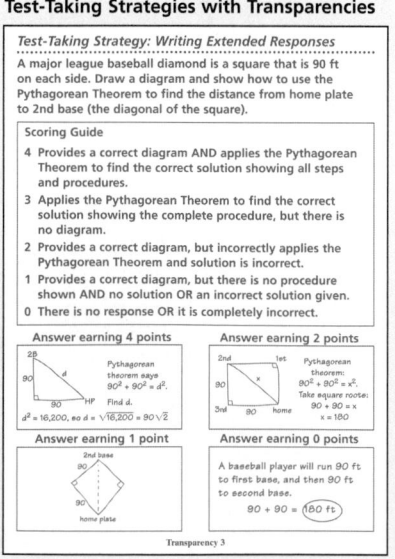

156

Extended-response questions usually are worth 4 points and have multiple parts. If you can't answer one part, you may be able to get partial credit for the other parts.

● EXAMPLE

You plan to put a fence around a rectangular lot. The length of the lot must be at least 52 feet. The cost of the fence along the length of the lot is $2 per foot, and the cost of the fence along the width is $3 per foot. The total cost cannot exceed $360.
a. Use two variables to write a system of inequalities that models the problem.
b. Graph the system, and shade the feasible region.
c. What is the maximum width of the lot if the length is 60 feet?

4 points	3 points	2 points
Let x = length $\quad y$ = width $2(2x) + 3(2y) \le 360$ $\begin{cases} y \le -\frac{2}{3}x + 60 \\ x \ge 52 \quad y \ge 0 \end{cases}$ For $x = 60$, $y \le 20$. Maximum width = 20 ft	$\begin{cases} x \ge 52 \\ y \ge 0 \\ 4x + 6y \le 360 \end{cases}$ When $x = 60$, $y = 20$.	x = length y = width $\begin{cases} 2(2x) + 3(2y) \le 360 \\ x \ge 52 \\ y \ge 0 \end{cases}$ $4x + 6y \le 360$ $4(60) + 6y \le 360$ $6y \le 120$ $y \le 20$ The width must be at most 20 ft.

The 4-point response gives a complete and correct answer to each part. The 3-point response lost credit for not showing all the work. The 2-point response does not include an answer for part (b), but answers the other parts correctly.

EXERCISES

1. What did the 3-point response to the Example leave out?

> 1. Answers may vary. Sample: The 3-point response did not define the variables or answer the question.

2. Open-Ended Describe a response to the Example that would deserve only 1 point. **Answers may vary. Sample: The student answers only 1 part of *a*, *b*, and *c*.**

3. Suppose the minimum length of the lot in the Example is changed to 60 feet, the cost of the fence along the width is changed to $2 per foot, and the cost of the fence along the length is changed to $1.50 per foot. Find the new answers to parts (a), (b), and (c). Show your work. **a, c. See margin.** **b. See back of book.**

---

page 156 **Test-Taking Strategies**

3a. Let x = length,
$\quad\quad y$ = width.

$\begin{cases} x \ge 60 \quad y \ge 0 \\ 1.50(2x) + 2(2y) \le 360 \end{cases}$

$3x + 4y \le 360$
$x = 0, y = 90$
$y = 0, x = 120$

c. for length 60:
$3(60) + 4y \le 360$
$4y \le 180$
$y \le 45$

Chapter Review

Vocabulary

constraints (p. 135)
coordinate space (p. 142)
dependent system (p. 118)
equivalent systems (p. 125)
feasible region (p. 136)

inconsistent system (p. 118)
independent system (p. 118)
linear programming (p. 135)
linear system (p. 116)
objective function (p. 135)

ordered triples (p. 142)
system of equations (p. 116)
trace (p. 144)

 Reading Math
Understanding Vocabulary

Match the vocabulary term in column 1 with the most appropriate phrase in column 2.

Column 1

1. dependent linear systems **A**

2. equivalent systems **D**

3. inconsistent linear systems **B**

4. independent linear systems **E**

5. three-variable systems **C**

Column 2

A. have many solutions

B. have no solutions

C. have solutions that can be shown as the intersection of planes

D. have the same solutions

E. have unique solutions

Take It to the NET
Online vocabulary quiz at www.PHSchool.com
Web Code: agj-0351

Skills and Concepts

3-1 Objectives

▼ To solve a system by graphing (p. 116)

A **system of equations** is a set of two or more equations that use the same variables. The points where all the graphs intersect represent solutions. You must check the coordinates of the points of intersection in the original equations to be sure you have a solution. A **linear system** consists of linear equations.

An **independent system** has a unique solution while a **dependent system** does not have a unique solution. An **inconsistent system** has no solutions.

Solve each system by graphing.

6. $\begin{cases} y = 2x + 1 \\ y = 4x + 5 \end{cases}$ **(−2, −3)** 7. $\begin{cases} y = 3x - 2 \\ y = -2x + 8 \end{cases}$ **(2, 4)** 8. $\begin{cases} y = 3x - 5 \\ 2y = 6x + 4 \end{cases}$ **no solution**

9. $\begin{cases} 3x + 2y = -6 \\ x - y = -2 \end{cases}$ **(−2, 0)** 10. $\begin{cases} 4x - y = 6 \\ -2x + 3y = 12 \end{cases}$ **(3, 6)** 11. $\begin{cases} 12x + 3y = -9 \\ 4x + y = 7 \end{cases}$ **no solution**

Without graphing, classify each system as *independent*, *dependent*, or *inconsistent*.

12. consistent and dependent

12. $\begin{cases} 6x + 3y = 12 \\ y = -2x + 4 \end{cases}$

13. consistent and independent

13. $\begin{cases} y = -x + 5 \\ x - y = -3 \end{cases}$

14. inconsistent

14. $\begin{cases} x + 2y = 2 \\ y = -0.5x - 2 \end{cases}$

 15. Banking Suppose a bank charges a monthly rate of $10 for your checking account. You can switch to a different account that charges $6 plus $.20 per check. For what number of checks is the cost of the two accounts the same? **20 checks**

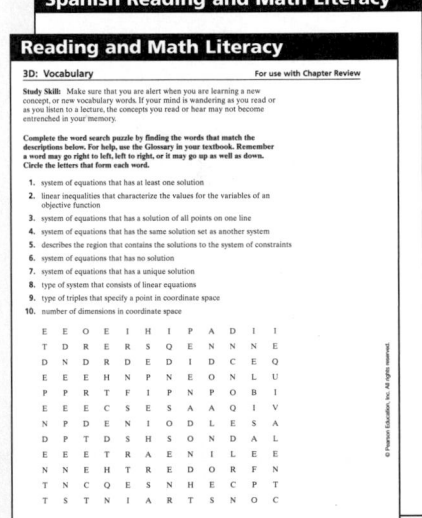

23.

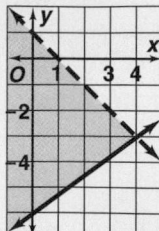

24.

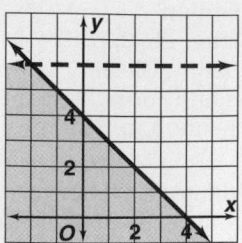

25.

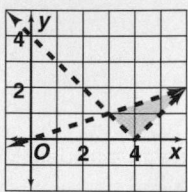

26. Let r = number of gallons of regular coffee, and d = number of gallons of decaffeinated coffee.
$$r + d \le 10$$
$$3r \ge d$$

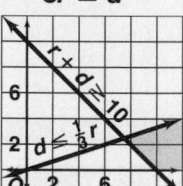

27.

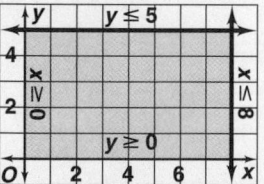

vertices: (0, 0), (8, 0), (8, 5), (0, 5)
$c = 0$ at (0, 0)

28.

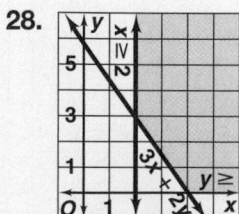

vertices: (4, 0) (2, 3)
$c = 11$ at (2, 3)

3-2 Objectives

▼ To solve a system by substitution (p. 123)

▼ To solve a system by elimination (p. 124)

If you can easily solve one equation in a system of two equations for one of the variables, you can substitute that expression in the other equation. Then you can find the value of the other variable.

Otherwise, you can multiply one or both equations by a nonzero quantity to create two terms that are additive inverses. This creates an **equivalent system** of equations. Adding the two equations then eliminates one variable. Again, you can solve for the other variable.

In either case, you substitute the value of this second variable into either of the original equations to find the value of the first variable. Recall that some systems have an infinite number of solutions and some have no solutions.

Solve using substitution.

16. $\begin{cases} 3x + 5y = 10 \\ y = -4 \end{cases}$
(10, −4)

17. $\begin{cases} 4x + 3y = 12 \\ x = 5y - 20 \end{cases}$
(0, 4)

18. $\begin{cases} 8x + y = 17 \\ x + 4y = 37 \end{cases}$
(1, 9)

Solve using elimination.

19. $\begin{cases} 2x + y = 13 \\ x - y = -4 \end{cases}$
(3, 7)

20. $\begin{cases} 2x + 3y = 4 \\ 4x + 6y = 9 \end{cases}$
no solution

21. $\begin{cases} a + b = \frac{1}{3} \\ a - b = \frac{1}{4} \end{cases}$ $\left(\frac{7}{24}, \frac{1}{24}\right)$

22. Nutrition Roast beef has 25 g of protein and 11 g of calcium per serving. A serving of mashed potatoes has 2 g of protein and 25 g of calcium. How many servings of each are needed to supply exactly 29 g of protein and 61 g of calcium?
1 serving of roast beef and 2 servings of mashed potatoes

3-3 Objectives

▼ To solve systems of linear inequalities (p. 130)

The solution of a system of inequalities is represented on a graph by the region of overlap of the inequalities. To solve a system by graphing, first graph the boundaries for each inequality. Then shade the regions of the plane containing the solutions for both inequalities.

Solve each system by graphing.   23–25. See margin.

23. $\begin{cases} y < -x + 1 \\ y \ge \frac{3}{4}x - 6 \end{cases}$

24. $\begin{cases} x + y \le 4 \\ y < 6 \end{cases}$

25. $\begin{cases} y > |x - 4| \\ y < \frac{1}{3}x \end{cases}$

26. For a community breakfast there should be at least three times as much regular coffee as decaffeinated coffee. A total of ten gallons is sufficient for the breakfast. Model this situation with a system of inequalities. Graph to solve the system.   **See margin.**

3-4 Objectives

▼ To find maximum and minimum values (p. 135)

▼ To solve problems with linear programming (p. 137)

Linear programming is a technique used to find the maximum or minimum value of an **objective function**. Linear inequalities are **constraints** on the variables of the objective function. The solutions to the system of constraints are contained in the **feasible region**. The maximum or minimum value of the objective function occurs at a vertex of the feasible region.

Graph each system of constraints. Find all vertices. Then find the variable values that maximize or minimize the objective function. 27–29. See margin pp. 158–159.

27. $\begin{cases} x \le 8 \\ y \le 5 \\ x \ge 0, y \ge 0 \end{cases}$ 28. $\begin{cases} x \ge 2 \\ y \ge 0 \\ 3x + 2y \ge 12 \end{cases}$ 29. $\begin{cases} 3x + 2y \le 12 \\ x + y \le 5 \\ x \ge 0, y \ge 0 \end{cases}$

Minimum for
$C = x + 5y$

Minimum for
$C = 4x + y$

Maximum for
$P = 3x + 5y$

🌐 **30. Profit** A lunch stand makes \$.75 profit on each chef's salad and \$1.20 profit on each Caesar salad. On a typical weekday, it sells between 40 and 60 chef's salads and between 35 and 50 Caesar salads. The total number sold has never exceeded 100 salads. How many of each type should be prepared in order to maximize profit? **50 of each type**

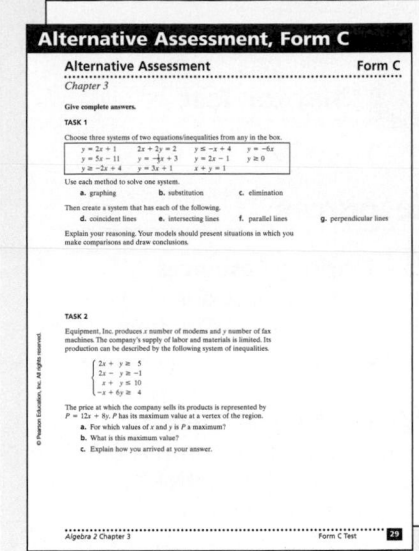

3-5 Objectives

▼ To graph points in three dimensions (p. 142)

▼ To graph equations in three dimensions (p. 144)

You can plot **ordered triples** in **coordinate space.** To sketch a plane that is the graph of an equation in three variables, find the intercepts. To find the x-intercept, substitute 0 for y and z. Then find the other two intercepts. If the plane does not pass through the origin, connect the resulting intercepts on the three axes. These lines are called the **traces** of the plane. **31–35. See margin.**

Graph each point in coordinate space.

31. $(0, 2, 0)$ **32.** $(1, 0, 0)$ **33.** $(0, 0, 3)$ **34.** $(2, 3, 0)$ **35.** $(1, 0, 4)$

Find the coordinates of each point in the diagram at the right.

36. A **(3, 3, 1)**

37. B **(0, −2, 2)**

38. C **(−3, 1, −1)**

39. D **(0, 0, 3)**

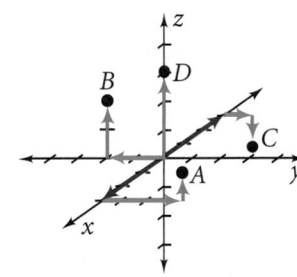

Sketch the graph of each equation. 40–42. See back of book.

40. $x - 2y + z = 4$ **41.** $10x - 4y - 5z = 20$ **42.** $2x + 6y + 3z = 18$

3-6 Objectives

▼ To solve systems in three variables by elimination (p. 148)

▼ To solve systems in three variables by substitution (p. 151)

You can solve systems of three equations in three variables using the technique of substitution you learned in Lesson 3-2.

Elimination with three equations in three variables involves pairing the equations. Use one equation twice. Then eliminate the same variable in both pairs. The result is a system of two equations in two variables. Proceed using the methods you learned in Lesson 3-2.

Solve each system.

43. $\begin{cases} x + y + z = 10 \\ 2x - y + z = 2 \\ -x + 2y - z = 5 \end{cases}$ **44.** $\begin{cases} x + 2y + z = 14 \\ y = z + 1 \\ x = -3z + 6 \end{cases}$ **45.** $\begin{cases} 3x + y - 2z = 22 \\ x + 5y + z = 4 \\ x = -3z \end{cases}$

(2, 5, 3) **no solution** **(6, 0, −2)**

Chapter 3   Chapter Review   **159**

29.
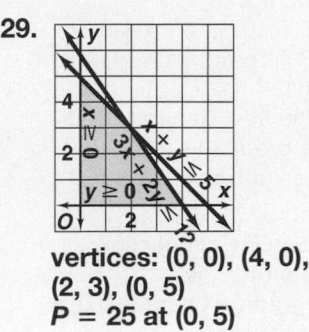
vertices: (0, 0), (4, 0), (2, 3), (0, 5)
P = 25 at (0, 5)

31.
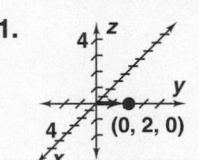

32.
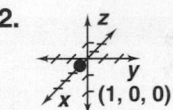

33.
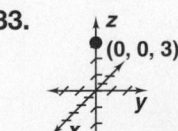

34.
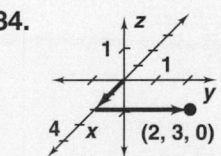

35.
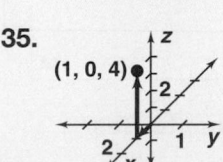

Resources

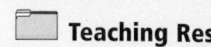

7. Substitution is used when
an equation is easily
solved for one of the
variables.

160

 **Chapter 3**

Chapter Test

Classify each system without graphing. Then graph each system.   1–2. See back of book.

1. $\begin{cases} y = 5x - 2 \\ y = x + 4 \end{cases}$ 2. $\begin{cases} 3x + 2y = 9 \\ 3x + 2y = 4 \end{cases}$

Solve using substitution.

3. $\begin{cases} 3x + 2y = 9 \\ x + y = 4 \end{cases}$ 4. $\begin{cases} 0.3x - y = 0 \\ y = 2 + 0.25x \end{cases}$
(1, 3)   **(40, 12)**

Solve using elimination.

5. $\begin{cases} 3x - y = 1 \\ 2x + y = 14 \end{cases}$ 6. $\begin{cases} 4x - 2y = 3 \\ 2y - 4x = \frac{3}{2} \end{cases}$
(3, 8)   **no solution**

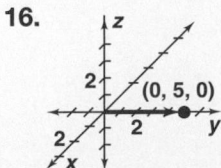 **7. Writing** Describe how to identify situations in which substitution may be the best method for solving a system of equations.   **See margin.**

Graph each system.   8–11. See back of book.

8. $\begin{cases} 2x + y < 3 \\ x < y + 3 \end{cases}$ 9. $\begin{cases} 3y + 9x < 3 \\ y \geq 2 \end{cases}$

10. $\begin{cases} |x + 3| > y \\ y > 2x - 1 \end{cases}$ 11. $\begin{cases} y > -2x + 6 \\ y \leq \frac{1}{4}x - 3 \end{cases}$

Graph each system of constraints. Find all vertices. Evaluate the objective function at each vertex to find the maximum or minimum value.

12. $\begin{cases} x \leq 5 \\ y \leq 4 \\ x \geq 0, y \geq 0 \end{cases}$ 13. $\begin{cases} x + y \leq 8 \\ x + 2y \geq 6 \\ x \geq 0, y \geq 0 \end{cases}$

Maximum for   Minimum for
$P = 2x + y$ $C = x + 3y$
12–13. See back of book.

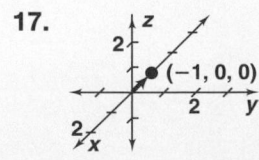 **14. Sales** A pizza shop makes $1.50 on each small pizza and $2.15 on each large pizza. On a typical Friday, it sells between 70 and 90 small pizzas and between 100 and 140 large pizzas. The shop can make no more than 210 pizzas in a day. How many of each size of pizza must be sold in order to maximize profit?   **70 small, 140 large**

15. Open-Ended Write a system of constraints whose graph is a parallelogram.   **Check students' work.**

Graph each point in coordinate space.

16. $(0, 5, 0)$ 17. $(-1, 0, 0)$ 18. $(1, 0, 4)$
19. $(3, 0, -1)$ 20. $(1, 4, -1)$ 21. $(2, -2, 3)$
16–21. See margin pp. 160–161.

Graph each equation. Use intercepts and traces.

22. $x + y + z = 6$ 23. $2x - 3y + z = 6$
24. $-2x + y - 5z = 10$ 25. $x - y + 2z = 8$
22–26. See back of book.

26. You are planning a party. You have $24 to spend on decorations. Balloons cost $.06 each, party favors cost $.48 each, and streamers cost $.08 each. Write and graph an equation for the number of each you can buy.

Solve each system of equations.

27. $\begin{cases} x - y + z = 0 \\ 3x - 2y + 6z = 9 \\ -x + y - 2z = -2 \end{cases}$ 28. $\begin{cases} 2x + y + z = 8 \\ x + 2y - z = -5 \\ z = 2x - y \end{cases}$
(1, 3, 2)   **(2, −1, 5)**

Write a system of equations to solve each problem.

🌐 **29. Investing** A company invested $50,000 in three funds. After a year it had $54,500. The growth fund had a return rate of 12%, the income fund had a return rate of 8%, and the money market fund had a return rate of 5%. The company invested twice as much in the income fund as in the money market fund. How much did the company invest in each fund?   **29–31. See back of book.**

🌐 **30. Earnings** A student can make a weekly salary of $200 plus 15% commission on sales at the Radio Barn or a weekly salary of $300 plus 10% commission on sales at Woofer, Etc. For what amount of sales do these two jobs pay the same?

🌐 **31. Purchasing** To help passengers stranded by bad weather one winter, an airport made the purchases detailed below. Find the cost of a cot, a table, and a chair.

	Number of Cots	Number of Tables	Number of Chairs	Total Costs ($)
Nov	10	10	40	1950
Dec	20	0	20	1800
Jan	10	5	20	1350

16.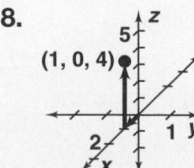
(0, 5, 0)

17.
(−1, 0, 0)

18.
(1, 0, 4)

READING COMPREHENSION

Standardized Test Prep

Reading Comprehension Read the passage below. Then answer the questions on the basis of what is *stated* or *implied* in the passage.

Hot and Cold Do you ever think about the math involved in filling a bathtub? Depending on the location and the season, the temperature of the cold water that enters a home may be 55°F. Some of the water goes to a water heater, where its temperature may be raised to 122°F.

Suppose you want a tub of 22 gallons of water at 78°F. You can write two equations, using x and y to represent the numbers of gallons of cold and hot water.

$x + y = 22$ The full tub contains 22 gal.

$55x + 122y = 22 \cdot 78$ x gal at 55° plus y gal at 122° is equivalent to 22 gal at 78°.

If you solve the system of equations, you find that you need about 14.4 gallons of cold water.

Students must be able to extract information from reading passages, answer multiple choice questions, and construct responses in order to be successful on current state and national assessments.

To answer the questions, students apply skills and concepts from this chapter and previous chapters.
Multiple Choice: Items 1–5
Extended Response: Items 6, 7

Resources

 **Teaching Resources**
Cumulative Review

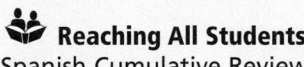 **Reaching All Students**
Spanish Cumulative Review

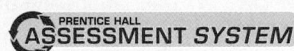 PRENTICE HALL
ASSESSMENT SYSTEM

Standardized Test Prep
• Ch. 3 Standardized Test Practice
Assessment Masters
• Cumulative Review
Computer Test Generator CD
• Standardized Test Practice

www.PHSchool.com
• Standardized Test Practice
• Resources

Plus

1. In the given system of equations, what does x represent? **B**
A. the number of gallons of hot water
B. the number of gallons of cold water
C. the capacity of the tub
D. the temperature of the hot water

2. In the given system of equations, what is the value of y? **I**
F. about 1716   G. about 22
H. about 14.4   I. about 7.6

3. Which equation results from solving for x in the first equation of the system and then substituting that result into the second equation of the system? **B**
A. $55x + 122(22 - x) = 1716$
B. $55(22 - y) + 122y = 1716$
C. $x = \dfrac{1716 - 122y}{55}$
D. $y = \dfrac{1716 - 55x}{122}$

4. Suppose a tub with 22 gallons of water contains a mixture of a gallons of cold water at 60°F and b gallons of hot water at 120°F. The desired bath temperature is 80°F. Which of the following systems models the problem? **H**

F. $a + b = 80$
$60a + 120b = 22(80)$
G. $a + b = 120$
$120a + 60b = 12(80)$
H. $a + b = 22$
$60a + 120b = 22(80)$
I. $a + b = 22$
$120a + 60b = 22(80)$

5. How many gallons of hot water are needed for the bath described in Question 4? **A**
A. $7\frac{1}{3}$
B. 11
C. $14\frac{2}{3}$
D. $16\frac{1}{2}$

6. Suppose a tub with 21 gallons of water contains a mixture of cold water at 65°F and hot water at 128°F. The desired bath temperature is 82°F. Write a system of equations to model the volume h of hot water and the volume c of cold water needed for the bath.
$c + h = 21, 65c + 128h = 21(82)$

7. Consider the bath described in Question 6.
a. How many gallons of hot water are needed?
b. How many gallons of cold water are needed?
a. $5\frac{2}{3}$ gallons   b. $15\frac{1}{3}$ gallons

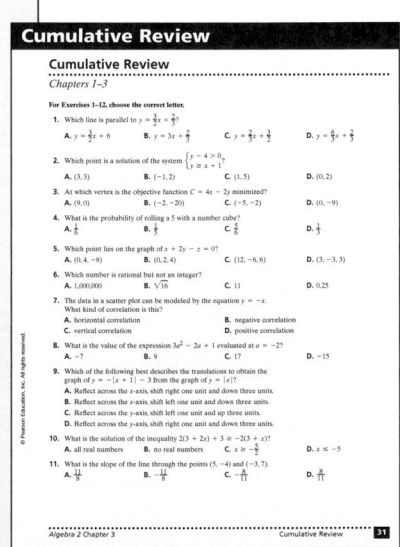

19.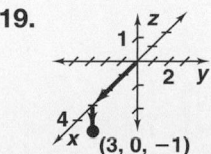

20.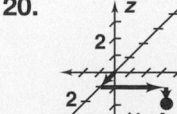

21. (2, −2, 3)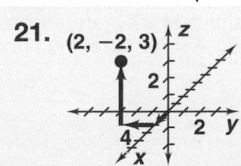

Chapter 4

Matrices

Chapter at a Glance

North Carolina Objectives

4-1		
Organizing Data Into Matrices	1.04	
NCTM 1, 2, 9, 10	▼ Identifying Matrices ▼ Organizing Statistical Data	

4-2		
Adding and Subtracting Matrices	1.04	
NCTM 2, 9, 10	▼ Adding and Subtracting Matrices ▼ Solving Matrix Equations	

4-3		
Matrix Multiplication	1.04	
NCTM 2, 9, 10	▼ Multiplying a Matrix by a Scalar ▼ Multiplying Matrices	

4-4		
Geometric Transformations with Matrices	1.04	
NCTM 3, 7, 9	▼ Translations and Dilations with Matrices ▼ Reflections and Rotations with Matrices	

4-5		
2 × 2 Matrices, Determinants, and Inverses	1.04	
NCTM 2, 3, 7, 9	▼ Evaluating Determinants of 2 × 2 Matrices ▼ Using Inverse Matrices to Solve Equations	

4-6		
3 × 3 Matrices, Determinants, and Inverses	1.04	
NCTM 2, 6, 7, 9	▼ Evaluating Determinants of 3 × 3 Matrices ▼ Using Inverse 3 × 3 Matrices	

4-7		
Inverse Matrices and Systems	1.04, 2.10	
NCTM 2, 10	▼ Solving Systems of Equations Using Inverse Matrices	

4-8		
Augmented Matrices and Systems	1.04, 2.10	
NCTM 2, 8, 9, 10	▼ Solving Systems Using Cramer's Rule ▼ Solving Systems Equations Using Augmented Matrices	

NCTM STANDARDS 2000

1	Number and Operations	6	Problem Solving
2	Algebra	7	Reasoning and Proof
3	Geometry	8	Communication
4	Measurement	9	Connections
5	Data Analysis and Probability	10	Representation

Pacing Options

This chart suggests pacing only for the lessons and their parts. It is provided as a possible guide. It will help you determine how much time you have in your schedule to cover other components, such as the features, Chapter Review, and Chapter Test.

Day	Traditional (45 min.)	Block (90 min.)
1	4-1 ▼ ▼	4-1 ▼ ▼
2	4-2 ▼	4-2 ▼
3	4-2 ▼	4-2 ▼
4	4-3 ▼	4-3 ▼
5	4-3 ▼ ▼	4-3 ▼
6	4-3 ▼	4-4 ▼ ▼
7	4-4 ▼	4-5 ▼
8	4-4 ▼ ▼	4-5 ▼
9	4-4 ▼	4-6 ▼
10	4-5 ▼	4-6 ▼
11	4-5 ▼	4-7 ▼
12	4-6 ▼	4-8 ▼
13	4-6 ▼	4-8 ▼
14	4-7 ▼	
15	4-7 ▼	
16	4-8 ▼	
17	4-8 ▼ ▼	
18	4-8 ▼	

NAEP Correlation (National Assessment of Educational Progress 2000 Mathematics Objectives)

4-1	4-2	4-3	4-4	4-5	4-6	4-7	4-8
A8a, N4b	A8a, A6c	A8a, A6c	G3a, G3b	A8a	A8a	A8a, A6c	A8a, A6c

N = Number Sense, Properties, and Operations; **M** = Measurement; **G** = Geometry and Spatial Sense; **D** = Data Analysis, Statistics, and Probability; **A** = Algebra and Functions

Math Background

Chapter Overview

Matrices and determinants are in large measure the result of efforts to describe, classify, and solve systems of linear equations. The definitions of matrix operations are closely related to those efforts. Matrix operations provide a powerful tool for the investigation of transformations of geometric figures.

Organizing Data into Matrices   4-1

Matrices were first developed to facilitate the work of linear transformations. Later, a formal linear algebra was developed. Linear algebra has widespread applications in other areas of mathematics, including multivariable calculus, differential equations, and probability theory. Diverse applications of linear algebra include linear programming, lines and planes, quadratic forms, graph theory, game theory, least squares, linear economic models, Markov processes, and the Fibonacci sequence.

A standard form for a matrix is $[a_{ij}]$. Make sure students understand that the subscript numbers in the notation a_{23} do not mean "twenty-three" but instead refer to the second row (the 2) and the third column (the 3).

Adding and Subtracting Matrices   4-2

The addition and subtraction operations for matrices will seem natural for most students. The operations are performed on pairs of corresponding elements, and the dimensions of the sum and difference match those of the dimensions of the matrices that are added or subtracted. Students who master this easily may enjoy exploring the properties of the transpose of a matrix, in which rows and columns are interchanged (the first row becomes the first column, and so on). Here are some properties of transposes that some students may enjoy exploring.

1. $(A^T)^T = A$ 2. $(A + B)^T = A^T + B^T$

3. $(AB)^T = B^T A^T$ 4. $(rA)^T = rA^T$

1. and 4. can be convincingly proved discursively.

1. To prove that the transpose of a transpose of a matrix A is the original matrix, consider that row i in A becomes column i in A^T and returns to being row i in $(A^T)^T$.

4. If r is a scalar (a real number, or a variable representing a real number; see Lesson 4-3), then the transpose of the matrix in which every element of A has been multiplied by r is equal to the transpose of A with the r "factored out."

Formal proofs of 2. and 3. are tedious, but demonstrations with 2 by 2 matrices are illustrative, and students can easily produce them.

Matrix Multiplication   4-3

Scalar, as used in this lesson, is related to the ideas of map scales and scaled drawings. For example, if the matrix representation of a parallelogram is multiplied by any number k, clearly the vertices of the figure change, and the area of the parallelogram is multiplied by k^2.

One might wonder why matrix addition is defined in such a natural way while multiplication of two matrices appears to be much more complicated. A thorough understanding of the composition of functions and the relationship between matrices and linear transformations is required to show that the definition of matrix multiplication is the natural one. Most students will probably never *learn* that a linear transformation is a type of function that maps one vector space into another vector space. However, students can *use* linear transformations in many areas of mathematics, as well as in numerous applied problems in the physical sciences, the social sciences, and economics.

Geometric Transformations with Matrices   4-4

The use of matrix operations to perform transformations on geometric figures may help make the definitions of matrix operations more reasonable to students. Encourage the use of diagrams to confirm results obtained by matrix addition and multiplication.

2 × 2 and 3 × 3 Matrices, Determinants, and Inverses   4-5, 4-6

The concept of an $n \times n$ identity matrix for multiplication will probably seem natural to students, as will the concept of a multiplicative inverse for $n \times n$ matrices. The concept and notation of a determinant will be new for most students.

Inverse Matrices and Systems Matrices, Augmented Matrices and Systems   4-7, 4-8

Once students have the knack of matrix multiplication, they will probably have little difficulty moving back and forth between systems of linear equations and the related matrix equations. Lesson 4-7 uses the idea from Lesson 4-6 that the solution of the equation $AX = B$ is given by $X = A^{-1}B$.

Reduced row echelon form can be used for a pencil and paper solution of a system of linear equations. Students should remember that when a system of n equations in n unknowns has a unique solution, the part of the reduced row echelon matrix to the left of the last column will look like an $n \times n$ identity matrix.

# Ongoing Assessment and Intervention

Tools for Monitoring Student Progress

The Prentice Hall *Algebra 2* program provides you with many options for assessment in the Student Edition, the Teacher's Edition and the teaching resources. From these options you may choose instructional materials and techniques that are appropriate for your students and support your district's curriculum requirements.

Instant Check System™ in Chapter 4

Allows students to check their own learning before, during, and after each lesson.

Diagnosing Readiness before the chapter (p. 162)

Check Skills You'll Need exercises in each lesson (pp. 164, 170, 178, 187, 195, 202, 210, 217)

Check Understanding questions with each Example (pp. 164, 165, 166, 171, 172, 173, 178, 179, 180, 181, 182, 188, 189, 190, 191, 196, 197, 198, 199, 203, 204, 210, 211, 212, 213, 217, 218, 219, 220)

Checkpoint Quiz (pp. 185, 207)

Test Prep in Chapter 4

Teaches students strategies and gives them practice with all the test item formats they will encounter on state tests and standardized national exams.

Standardized Test Prep exercises in each lesson (pp. 169, 176, 185, 194, 201, 206, 215, 223)

Test-Taking Strategies (p. 224)

Standardized Test Prep (p. 229)

Program Assessment

Assess student progress throughout the *Algebra 2* text with blackline masters and CD-ROM.

Assessment Resources

- Checkpoint Quizzes 1 & 2
- Chapter Test, Forms A & B
- Chapter Alternative Assessment

Spanish versions available.

Computer Test Generator

- Unlimited questions of varying difficulty for every lesson objective.
- Create your own practice sheets, quizzes, and tests, or use the pre-made Chapter Tests.
- Diagnose readiness with questions on prerequisite skills.
- Prepare students by making tests based on standardized test objectives.
- Access Algebra 1, Geometry, and Algebra 2 content—all on one CD-ROM.

Test Preparation

A three-step approach to preparing students for high stakes, national, and state exams.

❶ Diagnose & Prescribe

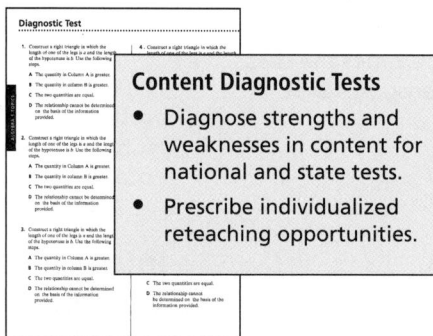

Content Diagnostic Tests
- Diagnose strengths and weaknesses in content for national and state tests.
- Prescribe individualized reteaching opportunities.

❷ Review & Reteach

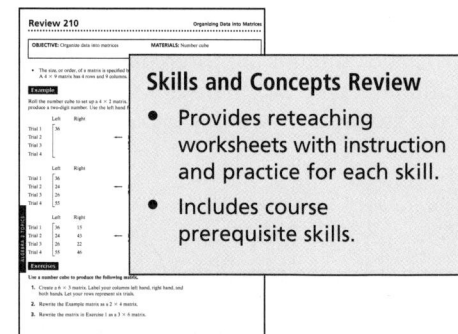

Skills and Concepts Review
- Provides reteaching worksheets with instruction and practice for each skill.
- Includes course prerequisite skills.

❸ Practice & Assess

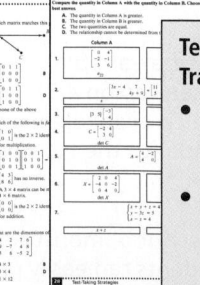

Test Preparation
- Features practice tests for End-of-Course and SAT/ACT exams.
- Includes standardized test practice by chapter for ongoing review.

Teacher's Guide with answers and correlations.

Test-Taking Strategies with Transparencies
- Support the Test-Taking Strategies pages in the Student Edition.
- Provide a teaching transparency and a practice worksheet for each strategy.

All your assessment needs in one place!

🫂 Reaching All Students

Support in the Student Text and Additional Resources

The textbook, the iText, and other technology components provide numerous opportunities to reach students of various ability levels and learning styles. Each Teacher's Edition lesson suggests how you can help *all* your students be successful and understand the mathematics in Chapter 4.

Below Level

Student Edition
- Diagnosing Readiness*: p. 162
- Check Skills You'll Need*: pp. 164, 170, 178, 187, 195, 202, 210, 217

Reteaching
Chapter 4 Support File: pp. 10–17

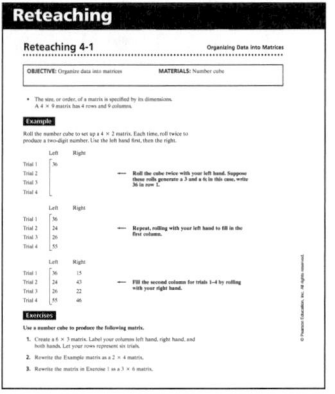

Advanced Learners

Student Edition
- Challenge exercises: pp. 168, 169, 176, 184, 193, 194, 200, 201, 206, 214
- Extension, p. 208

Enrichment
Chapter 4 Support File: pp. 18–25

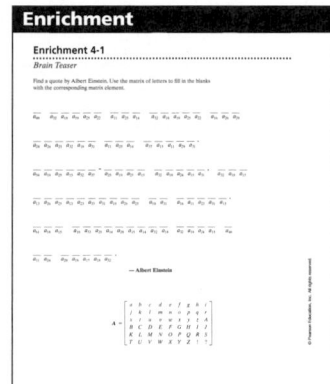

Connections to Precalculus Masters
Chapter 4 Enrichment Topic: Powers of Matrices

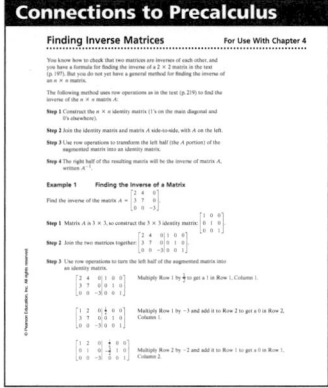

* Can be used with all ability levels to ensure mastery of prerequisite skills.

📖 Reading and Math Literacy

Student Edition
- Vocabulary: pp. 163, 225, *plus* in every Lesson Preview
- Reading Math: pp. 164, 173, 188, 214, 216, 217, 218
- Illustrated Glossary: pp. 871–913

Reading and Math Literacy Masters
Chapter 4: pp. 13–16

English Learners

Student Edition
- English/Spanish Illustrated Glossary: pp. 871–913

Workbook and Masters
Spanish Practice Workbook: pp. 2–9
Spanish Reading and Math Literacy Masters: pp. 13–16

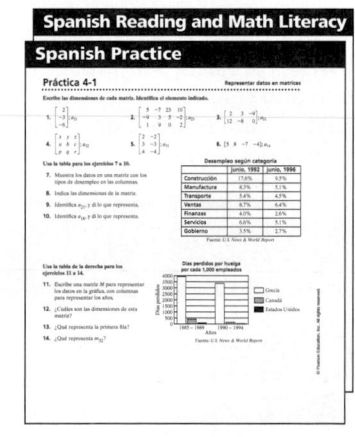

Learning Styles

Student Edition
- Investigation: pp. 180, 187
- Technology: pp. 177, 188, 203, 212, 220
- Writing: pp. 167, 176, 184, 185, 192, 200, 206, 209, 213, 222, 228
- DK Activities: pp. 230–231

Activity Masters
Hands-On Activities: 38, 39
Technology Activities: 28

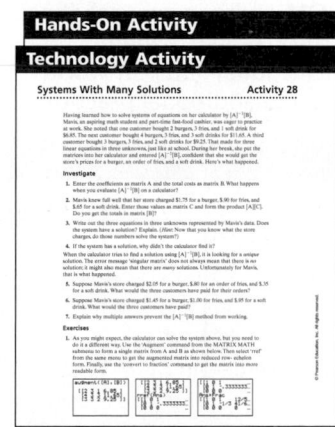

Program Resources

	Teaching Resources in Grab & Go™ Files				Resources for Reaching All Students			Spanish Resources			Transparencies				Presentation Assistant Plus!
	Practice	Reteach	Enrich	Checkpoint Quiz	Reading & Math Literacy	Technology Activities	Hands-On Activities	Practice	Reading & Math Literacy	Checkpoint Quiz	Skills Check	Additional Examples	Answers to Exercises	Lesson Quiz	Prentice Hall Presentation Pro CD-ROM
4-1	■	■	■		■			■			■	■	■	■	■
4-2	■	■	■				■	■			■	■	■	■	■
4-3	■	■	■	■	■		■	■		■	■	■	■	■	■
4-4	■	■	■					■			■	■	■	■	■
4-5	■	■	■					■			■	■	■	■	■
4-6	■	■	■	■	■			■		■	■	■	■	■	■
4-7	■	■	■					■			■	■	■	■	■
4-8	■	■	■			■		■			■	■	■	■	■
For the chapter	Chapter Tests, Alternative Assessment, Cumulative Review, Cumulative Assessment				Connections to Precalculus Masters			Spanish Chapter Tests, Alternative Assessment, Cumulative Review, Cumulative Assessment			Classroom Aid Transparencies				

Also available for use with the chapter:

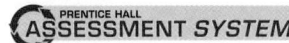 *See page 162C.*

- Practice Workbook
- Solution Key

- For teacher support and access to student Web site materials, use Web Code agk-5500.
- For additional online and technology resources, see below.

  # Technology

 Online and on CD-ROM

Complete Interactive Student Text online and on CD-ROM—with instant feedback assessment, tutorial help, dynamic activities, instructional and real-world videos, audio, and additional practice.

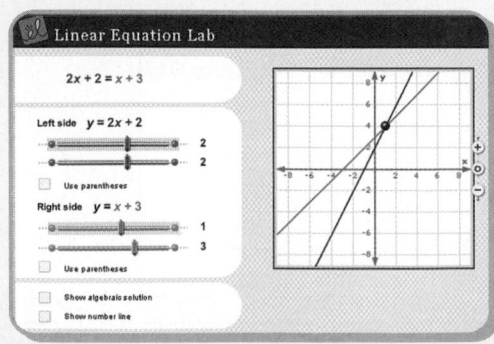

www.PHSchool.com **For Students**

Use **Web Codes** for easy access to online activities, chapter projects, self-grading lesson quizzes and chapter tests, vocabulary quizzes, updated data sources, graphing calculator procedures, and more.

PH SuccessNet **For Teachers**

Online lesson planning with built-in state correlations, all the teaching resources, complete reference library, your own calendar and Teacher Web page, professional development, and more.

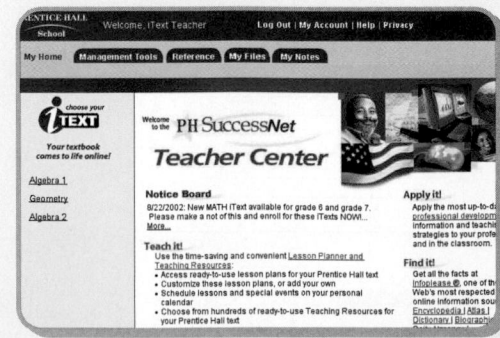

Presentation Assistant Plus!

The Prentice Hall *Presentation Assistant Plus!* provides you with the material you need to teach a lesson from beginning to end. Two easy-to-use formats—Transparencies and CD-ROM—allow you to present a lesson the way you are most comfortable.

Transparencies

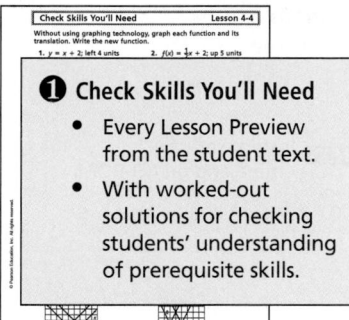

❶ Check Skills You'll Need
- Every Lesson Preview from the student text.
- With worked-out solutions for checking students' understanding of prerequisite skills.

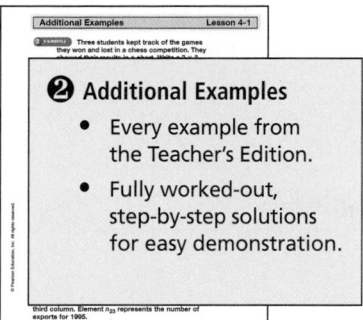

❷ Additional Examples
- Every example from the Teacher's Edition.
- Fully worked-out, step-by-step solutions for easy demonstration.

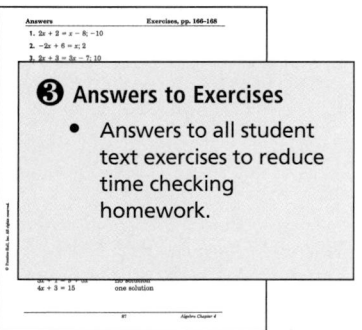

❸ Answers to Exercises
- Answers to all student text exercises to reduce time checking homework.

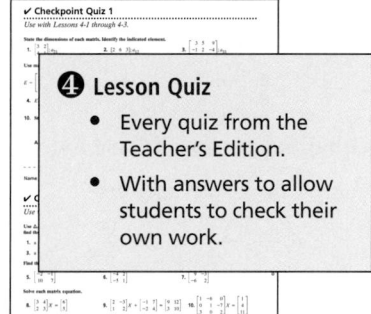

❹ Lesson Quiz
- Every quiz from the Teacher's Edition.
- With answers to allow students to check their own work.

 Throughout the Teacher's Edition, this symbol indicates material that is available on transparency in the Presentation Assistant Plus!

Prentice Hall Presentation Pro CD-ROM

- Includes all Transparencies.
- Conveniently organized by lesson so you can easily ❶ Introduce, ❷ Teach, ❸ Check Homework, and ❹ Assess each lesson.
- Animated examples allow step-by-step instruction at your own pace.
- Easy to edit so you can create custom presentations.

Teaching Chapter 4 Using Presentation Assistant Plus!

	❶ Introduce	❷ Teach	❸ Check Homework	❹ Assess
	Check Skills You'll Need	Additional Examples	Student Edition Answers	Lesson Quiz
4-1	p. 20	pp. 54–55	✔	p. 113
4-2	p. 21	pp. 56–60	✔	p. 114
4-3	p. 22	pp. 61–65	✔	p. 115
4-4	p. 23	pp. 66–69	✔	p. 116
4-5	p. 24	pp. 70–74	✔	p. 117
4-6	p. 25	pp. 75–78	✔	p. 118
4-7	p. 26	pp. 79–81	✔	p. 119
4-8	p. 27	pp. 81–84	✔	p. 120

Prentice Hall Presentation Pro

CD-ROM with dynamic PowerPoint® presentations for every lesson. Helps you introduce and develop concepts, check homework, and assess progress. Part of Presentation Assistant Plus! *(See above.)*

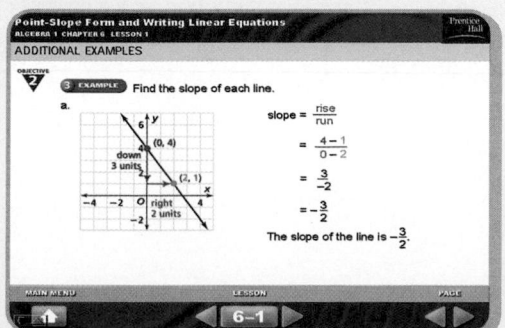

Computer Test Generator

CD-ROM to create practice sheets and tests for course objectives and standardized tests. Includes Instant Chapter Tests™, online testing, and student reports. Part of the PH Assessment System. *(See page 162C.)*

Resource Pro® with Planning Express®

CD-ROM with a lesson planning tool that allows you to import state and local objectives. Includes electronic versions of all the teaching resources.

Matrices

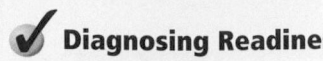

Where You've Been

- In Chapter 1, you learned to represent relationships using variables. You learned to evaluate and simplify variable expressions involving integers and fractions.

- In Chapter 2, you learned to represent two-variable equations in a variety of ways. You learned to graph linear equations and inequalities.

- In Chapter 3, you learned to graph systems of equations and inequalities, including systems of three equations in three variables.

 Instant self-check
online and on CD-ROM

 **Diagnosing Readiness**   (For help, go to the Lesson in green.)

Evaluating Expressions (Lesson 1-2)

Evaluate $ad - bc$ for the given values of the variables.

1. $a = -1, b = -2, c = 5, d = 4$ **6**

2. $a = \frac{1}{2}, b = -1, c = -\frac{2}{3}, d = 2$ **$\frac{1}{3}$**

3. $a = 2, b = \frac{1}{2}, c = \frac{1}{4}, d = -\frac{1}{8}$ **$-\frac{3}{8}$**

4. $a = -\frac{1}{3}, b = \frac{1}{2}, c = \frac{1}{4}, d = -\frac{2}{3}$ **$\frac{7}{72}$**

Solving Equations and Inequalities (Lessons 1-3 and 1-4)

Solve each equation or inequality. Check your answers.

5. $23 - x = 13 + 2x$ **$\frac{10}{3}$**

6. $\frac{x-1}{5} = -2$ **-9**

7. $a + 17 = -3a$ **$-\frac{17}{4}$**

8. $2y - 3 \leq 2y + 5$ **all real numbers**

9. $11 + 3t > -t$ **$t > -\frac{11}{4}$**

10. $\frac{3s-2}{2} < s$ **$s < 2$**

Graphing Equations (Lesson 2-2)

Graph each equation on a coordinate plane. **11–18. See back of book.**

11. $3x - 2y = 4$

12. $-3x = y$

13. $-7x - 3y = 14$

14. $y = \frac{2}{3}x - 3$

15. $y = 2x - 1$

16. $2x - 3y = -6$

17. $-2x = 3y + 12$

18. $-2y - 4x = 15$

Solving Systems of Equations (Lessons 3-2 and 3-6)

Solve each system.

19. $\begin{cases} -2x + y = -5 \\ 4x + y = -2 \end{cases}$ **$\left(\frac{1}{2}, -4\right)$**

20. $\begin{cases} 4x - y = -2 \\ -\frac{1}{2}x - y = 1 \end{cases}$ **$\left(-\frac{2}{3}, -\frac{2}{3}\right)$**

21. $\begin{cases} 3x + y = 5 \\ -x + y = 2 \end{cases}$ **$\left(\frac{3}{4}, \frac{11}{4}\right)$**

22. $\begin{cases} x + y + z = 10 \\ 2x - y = 5 \\ y - z = 15 \end{cases}$ **(7, 9, −6)**

23. $\begin{cases} -x + y + 2z = 16 \\ 2x - 2y - 2z = -16 \\ x + y = 0 \end{cases}$ **(0, 0, 8)**

24. $\begin{cases} -2x + 3y + z = 1 \\ x - 3z = 7 \\ -y + z = -5 \end{cases}$ **(7, 5, 0)**

Matrices

Chapter
4

Where You're Going

- In Chapter 4, you will move from using matrices in organizing data to manipulating matrices through algebra.

- You will learn to represent real-world relationships by writing matrices and using operations such as addition and multiplication to develop new matrices.

- You will learn, by working with geometric figures, how matrices relate to graphic art.

 **Real-World Snapshots** Applying what you learn, on pages 230–231 you will do activities involving the profits and losses of a chocolate-making business.

Key Vocabulary

- augmented matrix (p. 218)
- determinant (p. 196)
- dilation (p. 188)
- equal matrices (p. 173)
- image (p. 188)
- matrix (p. 164)
- matrix addition (p. 170)
- matrix element (p. 165)
- matrix equation (p. 172)
- matrix multiplication (p. 180)
- preimage (p. 188)
- row operations (p. 219)
- scalar product (p. 178)
- transformation (p. 188)
- variable matrix (p. 210)
- zero matrix (p. 171)

Chapter 4 Overview

This chapter introduces students to organizing data into matrices. Students then learn addition and subtraction of matrices, and matrix multiplication. Next, students investigate geometric transformations with matrices. Students also learn about 2 × 2 and 3 × 3 matrices, determinants, and inverses. Finally, students learn about inverse matrices, matrices of systems, and augmented matrices and systems.

📖 Reading Math
Reading for Problem Solving, p. 216

📖 Vocabulary
A complete list of terms, plus vocabulary exercises, appears in the Chapter Review, p. 225.

📖 Illustrated Glossary
Examples for each vocabulary term, plus definitions in both English and Spanish, appear starting on p. 871.

Test-Taking Strategies
Making Quantitative Comparisons, p. 224

Real-World Snapshots
See pages 230–231 for a real-world application of systems of inequalities that utilizes Dorling Kindersley's (DK) unique graphic presentation.

🌐 Real-World Connections
Some of the applications you will find in this chapter are energy and gymnastics (4-1), statistics (4-2), prices and business (4-3), graphic arts (4-4), and cryptology (4-6).

💻 www.PHSchool.com
Internet support for this chapter includes:
- Self-grading Vocabulary and Chapter 4 Tests
- Chapter Project
- Chapter Planner
- Chapter 4 Resources

Plus

4-1

Organizing Data Into Matrices

1.04   Operate with matrices to model and solve problems.

Lesson Preview

Lesson Preview

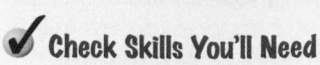 **Check Skills You'll Need**

Percents and Percent Applications
Skills Handbook: p. 842
Example 3, Exercises 19–26

Lesson Resources

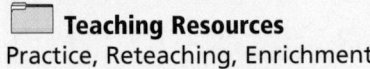 **Teaching Resources**
Practice, Reteaching, Enrichment

Reaching All Students
Practice Workbook 4-1
Spanish Practice Workbook 4-1
Reading and Math Literacy 4A
Spanish Reading & Literacy 4A

Presentation Assistant Plus!
Transparencies
• Check Skills You'll Need 4-1
• Additional Examples 4-1
• Student Edition Answers 4-1
• Lesson Quiz 4-1
PH Presentation Pro CD 4-1

PRENTICE HALL ASSESSMENT SYSTEM

Computer Test Generator CD

Technology
Resource Pro® CD-ROM
Computer Test Generator CD
Prentice Hall Presentation Pro CD

www.PHSchool.com
Student Site
• Teacher Web Code: agk-5500
• Updated Data
• Self-grading Lesson Quiz
Teacher Center
• Lesson Planner
• Resources

Plus

What You'll Learn

OBJECTIVE 1 To identify matrices and their elements

OBJECTIVE 2 To organize data into matrices

… And Why

To organize gymnastics data, as in Example 4

 Check Skills You'll Need   (For help, go to Skills Handbook page 842.)

Use the table at the right.   1–4. See margin p. 166.

1. How many cars were imported to the United States in 1980? How many were imported in 1995?

2. How many more cars were imported in 1990 than in 1980?

3. How many more cars were imported than exported in 1995?

4. Compare the percent increase of imports from 1980 to 1995 with the percent increase of exports from 1980 to 1995.

U.S. Passenger Car Imports and Exports (millions)

	1980	1990	1995
Imports	3.116	3.945	4.115
Exports	0.617	0.794	0.989

SOURCE: U.S. Department of Commerce.
Go to www.PHSchool.com for a data update.
Web Code: agg-2041

New Vocabulary   • matrix   • matrix element

OBJECTIVE 1 **Identifying Matrices**

 Interactive lesson includes instant self-check, tutorials, and activities.

A **matrix** (plural: matrices) is a rectangular array of numbers written within brackets. You represent a matrix with a capital letter and classify it by its dimensions. The number of horizontal rows and the number of vertical columns determine the dimensions of a matrix.

 Reading Math

For matrices, read $\times$ as "by." For example, read 2×3 as "two by three."

3 columns
↓ ↓ ↓

$$A = \begin{bmatrix} 2 & 3 & 4 \\ 6 & 7 & 0 \end{bmatrix} \begin{array}{l} \leftarrow \\ \leftarrow \end{array} 2 \text{ rows}$$ **Matrix A is a 2×3 matrix.**

1 EXAMPLE   **Writing the Dimensions of a Matrix**

Write the dimensions of each matrix.

a. $\begin{bmatrix} 4 & 6 & 5 \\ 2 & -3 & -7 \\ 1 & 0 & 9 \end{bmatrix}$ **b.** $\begin{bmatrix} -4 & \frac{1}{3} & -3 \end{bmatrix}$ **c.** $\begin{bmatrix} 1 \\ 2 \\ 0 \\ 0.5 \end{bmatrix}$

3 rows $\times$ 3 columns   1 row $\times$ 3 columns   4 rows $\times$ 1 column

This is a 3×3 matrix.   This is a 1×3 matrix.   This is a 4×1 matrix.

 Check Understanding **1** Write the dimensions of each matrix.

a. $\begin{bmatrix} 4 & 5 & 0 \\ -2 & 0.5 & 17 \end{bmatrix}$ **2 × 3**   **b.** $\begin{bmatrix} 8 & -3 & 15 \end{bmatrix}$ **1 × 3**   **c.** $\begin{bmatrix} 10 & 0 \\ 1 & -5 \\ -6.2 & 9 \end{bmatrix}$ **3 × 2**

 Ongoing Assessment and Intervention

Before the Lesson
Diagnose prerequisite skills using:
• Check Skills You'll Need

During the Lesson
Monitor progress using:
• Check Understanding
• Additional Examples
• Standardized Test Prep

After the Lesson
Assess knowledge using:
• Lesson Quiz
• Computer Test Generator CD

Each number in a matrix is a **matrix element.** You can identify a matrix element by its position within the matrix. Use a lowercase letter with subscripts. The subscripts represent the element's row number and column number.

2 EXAMPLE **Identifying a Matrix Element**

Identify element a_{13} in matrix A below.

$$A = \begin{bmatrix} 17 & 24 & 3 \\ 10.4 & 12 & 15 \\ 9 & 30 & 15 \end{bmatrix}$$

a_{13} is the element in the first row and the third column.

● Element a_{13} is 3.

✓ **Check Understanding** **2** Identify each matrix element.
    a. a_{33} **15**   **b.** a_{11} **17**   **c.** a_{21} **10.4**   **d.** a_{12} **24**

OBJECTIVE

2 **Organizing Statisical Data**

Successful businesses must track great amounts of data in order to plan the best use of their resources. They use matrices to organize and compare statistical data.

3 EXAMPLE **Real-World Connection**

Energy Energy is often measured in British thermal units (Btus). Write a matrix to represent the data below. Estimate the values from the graph.

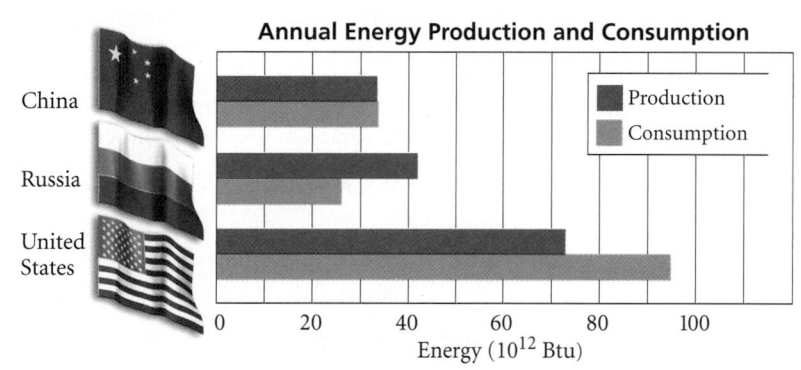

Annual Energy Production and Consumption

SOURCE: Energy Information Administration, International Energy Database.
Go to **www.PHSchool.com** for a data update.
Web Code: agg-2041

Let each row represent a country and each column represent production or consumption levels.

$$\begin{array}{c} \\ \text{China} \\ \text{Russia} \\ \text{United States} \end{array} \begin{array}{cc} \text{Production} & \text{Consumption} \\ \begin{bmatrix} 33 & 34 \\ 41 & 26 \\ 73 & 95 \end{bmatrix} \end{array}$$

Real-World Connection

New appliances have labels that tell how much energy the appliance uses each year.

✓ **Check Understanding** **3 a.** Rewrite the matrix as a 2×3 matrix. Label the rows and columns.
    b. How could you modify your matrix to include data from other countries?
    c. Critical Thinking Explain the difference between a $c \times d$ matrix and a $d \times c$ matrix.
                                       a–c. See back of book.

👥 **Reaching All Students**

| **Below Level** Emphasize that matrices are more than just tables, since they can be added, subtracted, multiplied and divided. | **Advanced Learners** Challenge students to learn how to use the matrix capabilities of their graphing calculators to add, subtract, multiply, divide, and take inverses. | **English Learners** See note on page 165. **Visual Learners** See note on page 165. |

2. Teach

Professional Development

Math Background

Matrices are rectangular arrays of numbers frequently used in organizing and manipulating data. In subsequent lessons students will learn how to interpret the sum, difference, and product of matrices that represent various data. They will also learn how to model geometric transformations with matrices.

OBJECTIVE

1 **Teaching Notes**

1 EXAMPLE **English Learners**

Make sure students understand the words *row* and *column*. Associate *row* with the rows in a theater and *column* with the columns in front of a building.

2 EXAMPLE **Visual learners**

To help students remember that a_{ij} names the element in row i and column j, ask them to think about how they would help someone locate a word on a printed page. Normally, you would tell the person in which line to look and then how far from the beginning of the line.

🛠 **Additional Examples**

1 Write the dimensions of each matrix.
a. $\begin{bmatrix} 7 & -4 \\ 12 & 9 \end{bmatrix}$ **b.** $\begin{bmatrix} 0 & 6 & 15 \end{bmatrix}$
    2×2 1×3

2 Identify each matrix element.
$$K = \begin{bmatrix} 3 & -1 & -8 & 5 \\ 1 & 8 & 4 & 9 \\ 8 & -4 & 7 & -5 \end{bmatrix}$$
a. k_{12} **−1**   **b.** k_{32} **−4**
c. k_{23} **4**   **d.** k_{34} **−5**

OBJECTIVE

2 **Teaching Notes**

3 EXAMPLE **Alternative Method**

Point out that the columns of the matrix may be interchanged provided the labels that go with them are also interchanged. Similarly, rows may be interchanged.

3 Three students kept track of the games they won and lost in a chess competition. They showed their results in a chart. Write a 2×3 matrix to show the data.

✓ = win				✗ = loss		
Ed	✓	✗	✓	✓	✗	✓	✓
Jo	✓	✓	✓	✓	✗	✓	✓
Lew	✗	✓	✗	✗	✓	✓	✗

$$\begin{array}{c} \\ \text{Wins} \\ \text{Losses} \end{array} \begin{array}{ccc} \text{Ed} & \text{Jo} & \text{Lew} \\ \left[\begin{array}{ccc} 5 & 6 & 3 \\ 2 & 1 & 4 \end{array}\right] \end{array}$$

4 Refer to the table at the top of page 166.
a. Write a matrix N to represent the information.

$$\begin{array}{c} \\ \text{Imports} \\ \text{Exports} \end{array} \begin{array}{ccc} 1980 & 1990 & 1995 \\ \left[\begin{array}{ccc} 3.116 & 3.945 & 4.115 \\ 0.617 & 0.794 & 0.989 \end{array}\right] \end{array}$$

b. Which element represents exports for 1995? n_{23}

4 EXAMPLE Diversity

Some students may not be familiar with the sport of gymnastics. Ask·students who are to describe to the class the different types of gymnastic events.

Closure

Ask students what is meant by the *dimensions* of a matrix? **the number of rows and columns in the matrix**

1. 3.116 million cars; 4.115 million cars

2. 0.829 million cars

3. 3.126 million cars

4. The export percent increase of 60.3% was larger than the 32.1% increase for the imports.

You can use matrices to show data from a table.

4 EXAMPLE Real-World Connection

Gymnastics The table below shows scores from the 2000 Olympics in Sydney, Australia.

U.S. Women's Olympic Gymnastics Team Qualification Scores

Gymnast	Floor Exercise	Vault	Balance Beam	Uneven Bars
Amy Chow	9.525	9.468	9.625	9.400
Dominique Dawes	9.087	9.393	8.600	9.675
Kristin Maloney	9.525	9.225	9.312	9.575
Elise Ray	9.225	9.468	9.687	9.687

SOURCE: NBC News

Real-World Connection

Amy Chow was a member of the United States Gymnastics Team at the Olympic Games in 1996 and 2000.

a. Write a matrix W to represent the information. Use a 4×4 matrix.

Each column represents a different event.

$$W = \begin{array}{c} \\ \text{A. Chow} \\ \text{D. Dawes} \\ \text{K. Maloney} \\ \text{E. Ray} \end{array} \begin{array}{cccc} \text{Floor} & & \text{Balance} & \text{Uneven} \\ \text{Exercise} & \text{Vault} & \text{Beam} & \text{Bars} \\ \left[\begin{array}{cccc} 9.525 & 9.468 & 9.625 & 9.400 \\ 9.087 & 9.393 & 8.600 & 9.675 \\ 9.525 & 9.225 & 9.312 & 9.575 \\ 9.225 & 9.468 & 9.687 & 9.687 \end{array}\right] \end{array}$$

← Each row represents a different gymnast.

b. Which element represents Kristin Maloney's score on the vault?

Kristin Maloney's scores are in the third row. The vault scores are in the second column. Element w_{32} represents Kristin's score on the vault.

✓ **Check Understanding** **4 a.** Write a matrix M to represent the information from the table below. **a–b. See**
b. Identify element m_{15}. What does this element represent? **margin.**

U.S. Men's Olympic Gymnastics Team Qualification Scores

Gymnast	Floor Exercise	Pommel Horse	Still Rings	Vault	Parallel Bars	Horizontal Bars
Blaine Wilson	9.025	9.462	9.612	9.800	9.312	9.650
Stephen McCain	9.225	8.850	9.462	8.987	9.500	9.662
Paul Hamm	9.475	9.562	9.512	9.700	9.575	9.612

SOURCE: NBC News

EXERCISES

For more practice, see *Extra Practice*.

Practice and Problem Solving

A Practice by Example

State the dimensions of each matrix.

Example 1 (page 164)

1. $\begin{bmatrix} 4 & -2 & 2 \\ 1 & 4 & 1 \\ 0 & 5 & -7 \end{bmatrix}$ **2.** $\begin{bmatrix} 1 \\ -9 \\ 5 \end{bmatrix}$ **3.** $\begin{bmatrix} 2 & \sqrt{5} \end{bmatrix}$ **4.** $\begin{bmatrix} 3 & 2 & 1 \\ 2 & 0 & -3 \end{bmatrix}$ **5.** $\begin{bmatrix} 2.5 \\ -3 \\ -1.6 \\ 10.0 \end{bmatrix}$

     3×3 3×1 1×2 2×3 4×1

page 166 Check Understanding

4a. $\begin{bmatrix} 9.025 & 9.462 & 9.612 & 9.800 & 9.312 & 9.650 \\ 9.225 & 8.850 & 9.462 & 8.987 & 9.500 & 9.662 \\ 9.475 & 9.562 & 9.512 & 9.700 & 9.575 & 9.612 \end{bmatrix}$

b. 9.312; Blaine Wilson's score on the parallel bars

Example 2
(page 165)

Refer to matrices A and B at the right.
Identify each matrix element.

$$A = \begin{bmatrix} 0 & -1 \\ 1.5 & 3 \\ 7 & -2 \end{bmatrix} \quad B = \begin{bmatrix} 6 & -3 & \frac{1}{2} \end{bmatrix}$$

6. a_{21} **1.5**   **7.** b_{12} **−3**   **8.** a_{31} **7**

9. b_{13} $\frac{1}{2}$ **10.** a_{32} **−2**   **11.** a_{12} **−1**

Example 3
(page 165)

Use the graph below for Exercises 12 and 13.

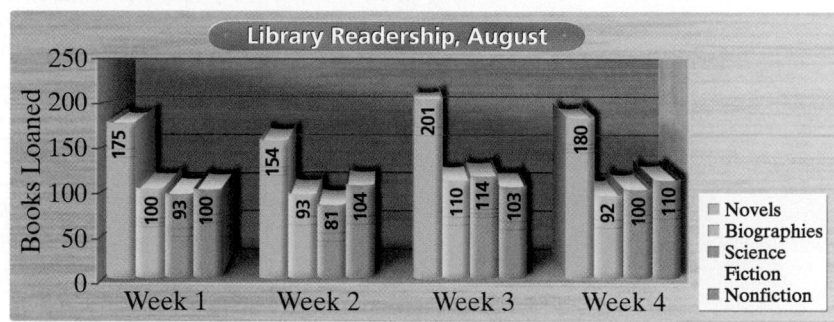

12. Write a matrix to represent the data. Label the rows and columns.
See back of book.
13. Write a different matrix to represent the data. Label the rows and columns.
See back of book.

Example 4
(page 166)

14. a. Write a matrix H to represent the data in the table below. **a–b. See**
  b. Find element h_{23}. What does this element represent? **back of book.**

Technology in Public Schools (millions)

Type of School	Videodisc Players	Modems	Networks	CD-ROMs
Elementary	25.9	35.1	26.4	37.9
Junior High	9.2	11.0	9.0	11.0
Senior High	10.7	14.5	12.9	14.0

SOURCE: Quality Education Data

B **Apply Your Skills**

Use the table below for Exercises 15–17. **15–16. See back of book.**

15. Display the data in a matrix A with columns indicating years. Identify a_{23} and tell what it represents.

U.S. Households with Color TVs and VCRs (millions)

	1980	1985	1990	1992	1995	1997
Color TVs	63	78	90	91	94	97
VCRs	1	18	63	69	77	82

SOURCE: Nielsen Media Research

16. Display the data in a matrix A with rows indicating years. Identify a_{41} and tell what it represents.

17. State the dimensions of the matrices in Exercises 15 and 16. **2 × 6, 6 × 2**

18. The student identified the data in column 3, row 2 when he or she should have looked at row 3, column 2.

18. Error Analysis A student identified element g_{32} from matrix G at the right as -3. What was the student's error?

$$G = \begin{bmatrix} 3 & 2.5 & 4.5 \\ 1.5 & 0 & -3 \\ -3 & 4.5 & 1.5 \end{bmatrix}$$

19. Writing Describe the information necessary to make a matrix containing numerical data meaningful. **You must include what the columns and rows represent.**

Assignment Guide

1 **Objective**
   A **B** **Core** 1–11, 18, 20–25

2 **Objective**
   A **B** **Core** 12–17, 19, 26
   C **Extension** 27–29

Standardized Test Prep 30–33

Mixed Review 34–45

Error Prevention

Exercises 15–17 Students may include the years in the matrices. Remind them that row and column headings do not appear in the matrix. The years are headings, not data.

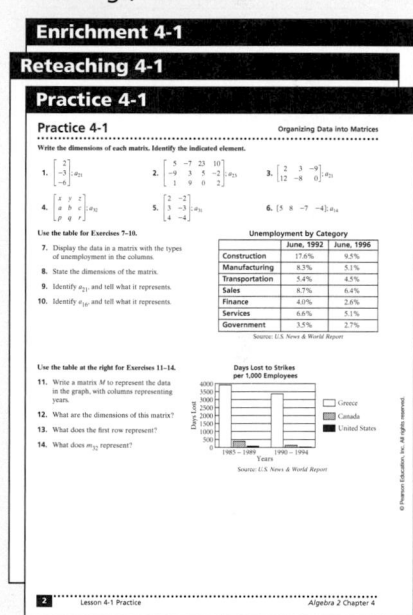

1. Write the dimensions of the matrix.

$$M = \begin{bmatrix} 8 & 4 & 0 & 1 \\ 9 & 3 & -5 & 0 \\ -1 & 2 & 6 & 1 \end{bmatrix} 3 \times 4$$

2. Identify the elements m_{24}, m_{32}, and m_{13} of the matrix M in question 1. **0, 2, 0**

3. The table shows the amounts of the deposits and withdrawals for the checking accounts of four bank customers. Show the data in a 2×4 matrix. Label the rows and columns.

	Deposits	Withdrawals
A	$450	$370
B	$475	$289
C	$364	$118
D	$420	$400

$$\begin{array}{c} \\ \text{Deposits} \\ \text{Withdrawals} \end{array} \begin{array}{cccc} A & B & C & D \\ \end{array}$$

$$\begin{array}{l} \text{Deposits} \\ \text{Withdrawals} \end{array} \begin{bmatrix} 450 & 475 & 364 & 420 \\ 370 & 289 & 118 & 400 \end{bmatrix}$$

Alternative Assessment

Have students work in small groups. They should use almanacs, encyclopedias, or other references to find data that can be presented in a matrix A. They should write the matrix, specify its dimensions, and identify at least four elements of A by using subscript notation.

pages 166–169 Exercises

26a. **Estimates may vary. Sample:**

Types of CDs	Wk 1	Wk 2	Wk 3	Wk 4
Rock	165	150	200	180
R & B	100	94	110	98
Rap	96	90	110	100
Classical	98	97	97	102

State the dimensions of each matrix. Identify the indicated element.

20. 3×3; -7
21. 2×3; 1
22. 3×3; 0

20. $\begin{bmatrix} 4 & 6 & 5 \\ 2 & -3 & -7 \\ 1 & 0 & 9 \end{bmatrix}, a_{23}$ 21. $\begin{bmatrix} -4 & 1 & -3 \\ 2 & 1 & 0 \end{bmatrix}, a_{12}$ 22. $\begin{bmatrix} 1 & 1 & 1 \\ 1 & 0 & 0 \\ 1 & 0 & 0 \end{bmatrix}, a_{32}$

23. $\begin{bmatrix} -4 & 8 & 12 \end{bmatrix}, a_{13}$ 24. $\begin{bmatrix} -5 \\ 4 \\ 3 \end{bmatrix}, a_{31}$ 3×1; 3 25. $\begin{bmatrix} -16 & 24 \\ 8 & -2 \end{bmatrix}, a_{21}$

  1×3; 12 2×2; 8

26. **Retail Sales** The graph shows August sales figures at a music store.

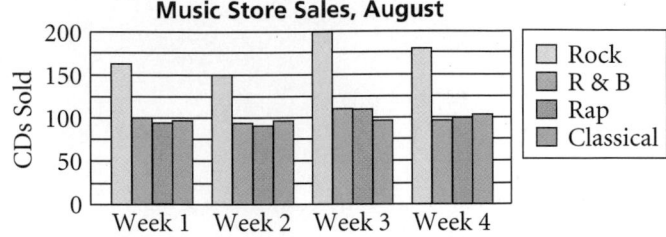

Music Store Sales, August

Legend: Rock, R & B, Rap, Classical

a. **Estimation** Record the data in a table. **a–b. See margin.**
b. Show the data in a matrix. What do the columns represent? What do the rows represent?

C Challenge 27. **Jobs** The four tables display data from a study conducted by a school principal.
  a. Use the information to create four 2×2 matrices. **See margin p. 169.**
  b. How many boys in the school have part-time jobs? **175**
  c. How many girls in the school have part-time jobs? **185**
  d. What percent of the students with part-time jobs are girls? **about 51.4%**

Numbers of Students Who Work Part-time

9th Grade	Has Part-time Job	No Part-time Job		10th Grade	Has Part-time Job	No Part-time Job
Boys	5	95		Boys	35	65
Girls	15	90		Girls	30	55

11th Grade	Has Part-time Job	No Part-time Job		12th Grade	Has Part-time Job	No Part-time Job
Boys	65	35		Boys	70	25
Girls	75	30		Girls	65	45

28. **Transportation Costs** A computer accessory company makes computer carrying cases at four plants located in Atlanta, Boston, Chicago, and Denver. Represent the company's shipping costs in a matrix. Label the rows and columns. **See margin p. 169.**

Shipping Costs

Atlanta to Boston $19
Atlanta to Chicago $12
Atlanta to Denver $23
Boston to Atlanta $19
Boston to Chicago $10
Boston to Denver $21
Chicago to Atlanta $12
Chicago to Boston $10
Chicago to Denver $15
Denver to Atlanta $23
Denver to Boston $21
Denver to Chicago $15

168 Chapter 4 Matrices

b.

$$\begin{array}{l} \text{Rock} \\ \text{R\&B} \\ \text{Rap} \\ \text{Classical} \end{array} \begin{array}{cccc} \text{Wk 1} & \text{Wk 2} & \text{Wk 3} & \text{Wk 4} \\ \end{array}$$

$$\begin{bmatrix} 165 & 150 & 200 & 180 \\ 100 & 94 & 110 & 98 \\ 96 & 90 & 110 & 100 \\ 98 & 97 & 97 & 102 \end{bmatrix};$$

Columns represent the weeks in August and rows are the type of CDs sold.

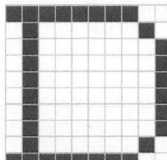

29. a. Open-Ended Using a 10×10 grid, create at least three different letters of the alphabet with a style similar to the one at the left.

b. Technology The tiny lights that make up a computer screen are called pixels. To make a letter, the computer tells the screen which pixels to light up. Represent each letter from part (a) by writing a matrix. Use 1 for a lit pixel and 0 for an unlit pixel. **a–b. See back of book.**

Standardized Test Prep

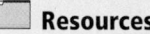 **Resources**

For additional practice with a variety of test item formats:
- Standardized Test Prep, p. 229
- Test-Taking Strategies, p. 224
- Test-Taking Strategies with Transparencies

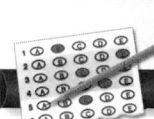

Standardized Test Prep

Multiple Choice

30. Which element in matrix $A = \begin{bmatrix} 5 & -2 & -\frac{1}{2} & 0 \end{bmatrix}$ is the number 0? **C**

A. a_{40} **B.** a_4 **C.** a_{14} **D.** a_{41}

31. In which matrix is the value of a_{32} less than the value of a_{21}? **F**

F. $\begin{bmatrix} -1 & 0 & 5 \\ 4 & 3 & -1 \\ -3 & 2 & 6 \end{bmatrix}$ **G.** $\begin{bmatrix} -1 & 5 & 0 \\ 3 & 4 & -1 \\ -3 & 6 & 2 \end{bmatrix}$ **H.** $\begin{bmatrix} 0 & 5 & -1 \\ -1 & 4 & 3 \\ 6 & 2 & -3 \end{bmatrix}$ **I.** $\begin{bmatrix} 0 & -1 & 5 \\ 0 & 3 & 4 \\ -3 & 1 & 6 \end{bmatrix}$

Quantitative Comparison

Use matrix X at the right. Compare the boxed quantity in Column A with the boxed quantity in Column B. Choose the best answer.

$X = \begin{bmatrix} 3 & 2 & 4 \\ 5 & 0 & 1 \\ 5 & 1 & 0 \end{bmatrix}$

A. The quantity in Column A is greater.
B. The quantity in Column B is greater.
C. The two quantities are equal.
D. The relationship cannot be determined from the information given.

Column A	Column B
32. B the value of x_{12}	the value of x_{21}
33. C the value of x_{21}	the value of x_{31}

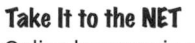

Take It to the NET
Online lesson quiz at
www.PHSchool.com
Web Code: aga-0401

Mixed Review

Lesson 3-6   **Solve each system.**

34. $\begin{cases} 3x + 2y - 2z = -9 \\ 5x \quad\quad - 3z = -7 \\ x + 4y + 3z = 5 \end{cases}$ **(1, −2, 4)**   **35.** $\begin{cases} 2x + 3y + 4z = -1 \\ x - 2y + z = 9 \\ x + 4y - 2z = -12 \end{cases}$ **(2, −3, 1)**

Lesson 3-1   **Solve each system by graphing.**   **36–38. See margin.**

36. $\begin{cases} 2x + y = 8 \\ x - 3y = -3 \end{cases}$ **37.** $\begin{cases} 2x + y = 7 \\ x + y = -5 \end{cases}$ **38.** $\begin{cases} x + 6y = 7 \\ 2x + 4y = -2 \end{cases}$

Lesson 2-3   **Find the constant of variation for a direct variation that includes the given values.**

39. $(2, 4)$ **2**   **40.** $(-1, 7)$ **−7**   **41.** $(-4, -10)$ **$\frac{5}{2}$**   **42.** $(3, 5)$ **$\frac{5}{3}$**   **43.** $\left(\frac{1}{2}, 9\right)$ **18**

In each relation, y varies directly as x. Find y when $x = 9$.

44. $y = 6$ when $x = 4$ **$\frac{27}{2}$**   **45.** $y = 8$ when $x = 4$ **18**

28.

	Atl.	Bos.	Chi.	Denv.
Atl.	0	19	12	23
Bos.	19	0	10	21
Chi.	12	10	0	15
Denv.	23	21	15	0

36.
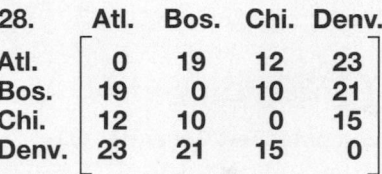

37.
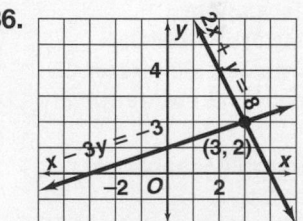

38.
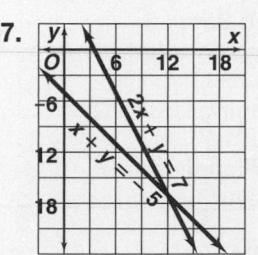

27a.

	Job	No Job
9th gr. boys	5	95
9th gr. girls	15	90

	Job	No Job
11th gr. boys	65	35
11th gr. girls	75	30

	Job	No Job
10th gr. boys	35	65
10th gr. girls	30	55

	Job	No Job
12th gr. boys	70	25
12th gr. girls	65	45

169

1. Plan

4-2 # Adding and Subtracting Matrices

 North Carolina Objectives

1.04 Operate with matrices to model and solve problems.

Lesson Preview

 Check Skills You'll Need

Simplifying Expressions
Skills Handbook: p. 845
Examples 1, 2
Exercises 1–10

Lesson Resources

 Teaching Resources
Practice, Reteaching, Enrichment

 Reaching All Students
Practice Workbook 4-2
Spanish Practice Workbook 4-2
Hands-On Activities 38

 Presentation Assistant Plus!
Transparencies
• Check Skills You'll Need 4-2
• Additional Examples 4-2
• Student Edition Answers 4-2
• Lesson Quiz 4-2
PH Presentation Pro CD 4-2

 **ASSESSMENT SYSTEM**

Computer Test Generator CD

 Technology
Resource Pro® CD-ROM
Computer Test Generator CD
Prentice Hall Presentation Pro CD

 www.PHSchool.com
Student Site
• Teacher Web Code: agk-5500
• Updated Data
• Graphing Calculator, Procedure 13
• Self-grading Lesson Quiz
Teacher Center
• Lesson Planner
• Resources

Plus

Lesson Preview

What You'll Learn

OBJECTIVE 1 To add and subtract matrices

OBJECTIVE 2 To solve certain matrix equations

... And Why

To find SAT score totals, as in Example 1

✓ **Check Skills You'll Need** (For help, go to Skills Handbook page 845.)

Simplify the elements of each matrix. 1–6. See margin p. 171.

1. $\begin{bmatrix} 10+4 & 0+4 \\ -2+4 & -5+4 \end{bmatrix}$

2. $\begin{bmatrix} 5-2 & 3-2 \\ -1-2 & 0-2 \end{bmatrix}$

3. $\begin{bmatrix} -2+3 & 0-3 \\ 1-3 & -5+3 \end{bmatrix}$

4. $\begin{bmatrix} 3+1 & 4+9 \\ -2+0 & 5+7 \end{bmatrix}$

5. $\begin{bmatrix} 8-4 & -5-1 \\ 9-1 & 6-9 \end{bmatrix}$

6. $\begin{bmatrix} 2+4 & 6-8 \\ 4-3 & 5+2 \end{bmatrix}$

New Vocabulary • matrix addition • zero matrix • matrix equation • equal matrices

OBJECTIVE 1 **Adding and Subtracting Matrices**

iTEXT Interactive lesson includes instant self-check, tutorials, and activities.

Sometimes you want to add or subtract matrices to get new information. You perform **matrix addition** on matrices with equal dimensions by adding the corresponding elements, which are elements in the same position in each matrix.

1 EXAMPLE **Real-World Connection**

Statistics Use the data in the table.

a. Write two 2 × 4 matrices to represent the mean verbal and math SAT scores.

Verbal

	1995	1996	1997	1998
Male	505	507	507	509
Female	502	503	503	502

Math

	1995	1996	1997	1998
Male	525	503	530	531
Female	490	502	494	496

Real-World Connection

Many schools have programs for students to help one another prepare for standardized tests.

Mean SAT Scores				
	Verbal		Math	
Year	Male	Female	Male	Female
1995	505	502	525	490
1996	507	503	503	502
1997	507	503	530	494
1998	509	502	531	496

SOURCE: College Entrance Examination Board

b. Find the combined mean SAT scores for each year in the table.

$$\begin{bmatrix} 505 & 507 & 507 & 509 \\ 502 & 503 & 503 & 502 \end{bmatrix} + \begin{bmatrix} 525 & 503 & 530 & 531 \\ 490 & 502 & 494 & 496 \end{bmatrix}$$

$$= \begin{bmatrix} 505+525 & 507+503 & 507+530 & 509+531 \\ 502+490 & 503+502 & 503+494 & 502+496 \end{bmatrix}$$

	1995	1996	1997	1998
Male	1030	1010	1037	1040
Female	992	1005	997	998

Ongoing Assessment and Intervention

Before the Lesson	During the Lesson	After the Lesson
Diagnose prerequisite skills using:	**Monitor progress using:**	**Assess knowledge using:**
• Check Skills You'll Need	• Check Understanding	• Lesson Quiz
	• Additional Examples	• Computer Test Generator CD
	• Standardized Test Prep	

Check Understanding ➊ Find each sum. **See below left.**

a. $\begin{bmatrix} 1 & -2 & 0 \\ 3 & -5 & 7 \end{bmatrix} + \begin{bmatrix} 3 & 9 & -3 \\ -9 & 6 & 12 \end{bmatrix}$

b. $\begin{bmatrix} -12 & 24 \\ -3 & 5 \\ -1 & 10 \end{bmatrix} + \begin{bmatrix} -3 & 1 \\ 2 & -4 \\ -1 & 5 \end{bmatrix}$

🔑 **Key Concepts**

1a. $\begin{bmatrix} 4 & 7 & -3 \\ -6 & 1 & 19 \end{bmatrix}$

b. $\begin{bmatrix} -15 & 25 \\ -1 & 1 \\ -2 & 15 \end{bmatrix}$

Definition	**Matrix Addition**

To add matrices A and B with the same dimensions, add corresponding elements.

$A = \begin{bmatrix} a & b & c \\ d & e & f \end{bmatrix} \qquad B = \begin{bmatrix} r & s & t \\ u & v & w \end{bmatrix}$

$A + B = \begin{bmatrix} a & b & c \\ d & e & f \end{bmatrix} + \begin{bmatrix} r & s & t \\ u & v & w \end{bmatrix} = \begin{bmatrix} a+r & b+s & c+t \\ d+u & e+v & f+w \end{bmatrix}$

The additive identity matrix for the set of all $m \times n$ matrices is the **zero matrix** O, or $O_{m \times n}$, whose elements are all zeros. The opposite, or additive inverse, of an $m \times n$ matrix A is $-A$. $-A$ is the $m \times n$ matrix with elements that are the opposites of the corresponding elements of A.

➋ **EXAMPLE** **Using Identity and Inverse Matrices**

Find each sum.

a. $\begin{bmatrix} 1 & 2 \\ 5 & -7 \end{bmatrix} + \begin{bmatrix} 0 & 0 \\ 0 & 0 \end{bmatrix}$

$= \begin{bmatrix} 1+0 & 2+0 \\ 5+0 & -7+0 \end{bmatrix}$

$= \begin{bmatrix} 1 & 2 \\ 5 & -7 \end{bmatrix}$

b. $\begin{bmatrix} 2 & 8 \\ -3 & 0 \end{bmatrix} + \begin{bmatrix} -2 & -8 \\ 3 & 0 \end{bmatrix}$

$= \begin{bmatrix} 2+(-2) & 8+(-8) \\ -3+3 & 0+0 \end{bmatrix}$

$= \begin{bmatrix} 0 & 0 \\ 0 & 0 \end{bmatrix}$

✓ **Check Understanding** ➋ Find each sum.

2b. $\begin{bmatrix} -1 & 10 & -5 \\ 0 & 2 & -3 \end{bmatrix}$

a. $\begin{bmatrix} 14 & 5 \\ 0 & -2 \end{bmatrix} + \begin{bmatrix} -14 & -5 \\ 0 & 2 \end{bmatrix} \begin{bmatrix} 0 & 0 \\ 0 & 0 \end{bmatrix}$

b. $\begin{bmatrix} 0 & 0 & 0 \\ 0 & 0 & 0 \end{bmatrix} + \begin{bmatrix} -1 & 10 & -5 \\ 0 & 2 & -3 \end{bmatrix}$

Some of the properties of real number addition also apply to matrix addition.

🔑 **Key Concepts**

Properties	**Matrix Addition**

If A, B, and C are $m \times n$ matrices, then

$A + B$ is an $m \times n$ matrix.	Closure Property
$A + B = B + A$	Commutative Property of Addition
$(A + B) + C = A + (B + C)$	Associative Property of Addition
There exists a unique $m \times n$ matrix O such that $O + A = A + O = A$.	Additive Identity Property
For each A, there exists a unique opposite, $-A$. $A + (-A) = O$	Additive Inverse Property

Lesson 4-2 Adding and Subtracting Matrices **171**

👥 **Reaching All Students**

Below Level Emphasize that the zero matrix is not the same as the number zero. There is only one number zero, but there are many different zero matrices of different dimensions.	**Advanced Learners** Have students discuss whether there are any properties of matrix addition that differ from those of integer addition.	**Inclusion** See note on page 171. **Tactile Learners** See note on page 172.

Math Background

One consequence of the definitions of matrix addition and matrix subtraction is that these matrix operations possess many of the properties associated with addition and subtraction of real numbers. This is of great importance in the field of Linear Algebra.

OBJECTIVE
➊ **Teaching Notes**

➊ **EXAMPLE** Inclusion

Adding and subtracting matrices may be difficult for students who are dyslexic. Pair these students with volunteers who can point to elements that the dyslexic student describes by row and column descriptions. This process may be useful throughout this chapter.

Additional Examples

➊ The table shows information on ticket sales for a new movie that is showing at two theaters. Sales are for children (C) and adults (A).

Theater	Matinee		Evening	
	C	A	C	A
1	198	350	54	439
2	201	375	58	386

a. Write two 2×2 matrices to represent matinee and evening sales.

Matinee
C A
$\begin{matrix} 1 \\ 2 \end{matrix} \begin{bmatrix} 198 & 350 \\ 201 & 375 \end{bmatrix}$

Evening
C A
$\begin{matrix} 1 \\ 2 \end{matrix} \begin{bmatrix} 54 & 439 \\ 58 & 386 \end{bmatrix}$

b. Find the combined sales for the two showings.

C A
$\begin{matrix} 1 \\ 2 \end{matrix} \begin{bmatrix} 252 & 789 \\ 259 & 761 \end{bmatrix}$

➋ Find each sum.

a. $\begin{bmatrix} 9 & 0 \\ -4 & 6 \end{bmatrix} + \begin{bmatrix} 0 & 0 \\ 0 & 0 \end{bmatrix} \begin{bmatrix} 9 & 0 \\ -4 & 6 \end{bmatrix}$

b. $\begin{bmatrix} 3 & -8 \\ -5 & 1 \end{bmatrix} + \begin{bmatrix} -3 & 8 \\ 5 & -1 \end{bmatrix} \begin{bmatrix} 0 & 0 \\ 0 & 0 \end{bmatrix}$

171

You can define matrix subtraction by using the Additive Inverse Property.

Key Concepts

Property	Matrix Subtraction

If two matrices, A and B, have the same dimensions, then $A - B = A + (-B)$.

3 EXAMPLE Subtracting Matrices

$A = \begin{bmatrix} 3 & 2 & 4 \\ -1 & 4 & 0 \end{bmatrix}$ and $B = \begin{bmatrix} 1 & 4 & 3 \\ -2 & 2 & 4 \end{bmatrix}$. Find $A - B$.

Method 1 Use additive inverses.

$$A - B = A + (-B) = \begin{bmatrix} 3 & 2 & 4 \\ -1 & 4 & 0 \end{bmatrix} + \begin{bmatrix} -1 & -4 & -3 \\ 2 & -2 & -4 \end{bmatrix} \quad \text{Write the elements of } -B.$$

$$= \begin{bmatrix} 3 + (-1) & 2 + (-4) & 4 + (-3) \\ -1 + 2 & 4 + (-2) & 0 + (-4) \end{bmatrix} \quad \text{Add corresponding elements.}$$

$$= \begin{bmatrix} 2 & -2 & 1 \\ 1 & 2 & -4 \end{bmatrix} \quad \text{Simplify.}$$

Method 2 Use subtraction.

$$A - B = \begin{bmatrix} 3 & 2 & 4 \\ -1 & 4 & 0 \end{bmatrix} - \begin{bmatrix} 1 & 4 & 3 \\ -2 & 2 & 4 \end{bmatrix}$$

$$= \begin{bmatrix} 3 - 1 & 2 - 4 & 4 - 3 \\ -1 - (-2) & 4 - 2 & 0 - 4 \end{bmatrix} \quad \text{Subtract corresponding elements.}$$

$$= \begin{bmatrix} 2 & -2 & 1 \\ 1 & 2 & -4 \end{bmatrix} \quad \text{Simplify.}$$

✔ Check Understanding **3** Find each difference.

a. $\begin{bmatrix} 6 & -9 & 7 \\ -2 & 1 & 8 \end{bmatrix} - \begin{bmatrix} -4 & 3 & 0 \\ 6 & 5 & 10 \end{bmatrix}$ **b.** $\begin{bmatrix} -3 & 5 \\ -1 & 10 \end{bmatrix} - \begin{bmatrix} -3 & 1 \\ 2 & -4 \end{bmatrix}$

$\begin{bmatrix} 10 & -12 & 7 \\ -8 & -4 & -2 \end{bmatrix}$ $\begin{bmatrix} 0 & 4 \\ -3 & 14 \end{bmatrix}$

OBJECTIVE 2 Solving Matrix Equations

A **matrix equation** is an equation in which the variable is a matrix. You can use the addition and subtraction properties of equality to solve matrix equations.

4 EXAMPLE Solving a Matrix Equation

Solve $X - \begin{bmatrix} 1 & 1 \\ 3 & 2 \end{bmatrix} = \begin{bmatrix} 0 & 1 \\ 8 & 9 \end{bmatrix}$ for the matrix X.

$$X - \begin{bmatrix} 1 & 1 \\ 3 & 2 \end{bmatrix} = \begin{bmatrix} 0 & 1 \\ 8 & 9 \end{bmatrix}$$

$$X - \begin{bmatrix} 1 & 1 \\ 3 & 2 \end{bmatrix} + \begin{bmatrix} 1 & 1 \\ 3 & 2 \end{bmatrix} = \begin{bmatrix} 0 & 1 \\ 8 & 9 \end{bmatrix} + \begin{bmatrix} 1 & 1 \\ 3 & 2 \end{bmatrix} \quad \text{Add } \begin{bmatrix} 1 & 1 \\ 3 & 2 \end{bmatrix} \text{ to each side of the equation.}$$

$$X = \begin{bmatrix} 1 & 2 \\ 11 & 11 \end{bmatrix} \quad \text{Simplify.}$$

✔ **Check Understanding** ④ Solve $X + \begin{bmatrix} -1 & 0 \\ 2 & 5 \end{bmatrix} = \begin{bmatrix} 10 & 7 \\ -4 & 4 \end{bmatrix}$. $\begin{bmatrix} 11 & 7 \\ -6 & -1 \end{bmatrix}$

Reading Math

In everyday language, the term *matrix* can be used to describe anything resembling a mathematical matrix, having a rectangular arrangement of elements in rows and columns.

Equal matrices are matrices with the same dimensions and equal corresponding elements.

5 EXAMPLE Determining Equal Matrices

Determine whether the two matrices in each pair are equal.

a. $A = \begin{bmatrix} -0.75 & \frac{1}{5} \\ \frac{1}{2} & -2 \end{bmatrix}$, $B = \begin{bmatrix} -\frac{3}{4} & 0.2 \\ 0.5 & -2 \end{bmatrix}$

$A = \begin{bmatrix} -0.75 & \frac{1}{5} \\ \frac{1}{2} & -2 \end{bmatrix}$ Both *A* and *B* have two rows and two columns, and their corresponding elements are equal. $B = \begin{bmatrix} -\frac{3}{4} & 0.2 \\ 0.5 & -2 \end{bmatrix}$

A and *B* are equal matrices.

b. $X = \begin{bmatrix} -1 & \frac{2}{3} & 2.5 \\ 0 & 1.5 & -\frac{5}{6} \end{bmatrix}$, $Y = \begin{bmatrix} 4-5 & 0.\overline{6} & \frac{5}{2} \\ 0 & 1 & -\frac{2}{3} \end{bmatrix}$

$X = \begin{bmatrix} -1 & \frac{2}{3} & 2.5 \\ 0 & 1.5 & -\frac{5}{6} \end{bmatrix}$ Both *X* and *Y* have three rows and two columns, but $1.5 \neq 1$, and $-\frac{5}{6} \neq -\frac{2}{3}$. $Y = \begin{bmatrix} 4-5 & 0.\overline{6} & \frac{5}{2} \\ 0 & 1 & -\frac{2}{3} \end{bmatrix}$

X and *Y* are *not* equal matrices.

✔ **Check Understanding** ⑤ Determine whether the two matrices in each pair are equal.

a. $\begin{bmatrix} 4 \\ 6 \\ 8 \end{bmatrix}, \begin{bmatrix} \frac{8}{2} & \frac{18}{3} & \frac{16}{2} \end{bmatrix}$ **no**

b. $\begin{bmatrix} -2 & 3 \\ 5 & 0 \end{bmatrix}, \begin{bmatrix} -\frac{8}{4} & 6-3 \\ \frac{15}{3} & 4-4 \end{bmatrix}$ **yes**

6 EXAMPLE Finding Unknown Matrix Elements

Solve the equation $\begin{bmatrix} 2x-5 & 4 \\ 3 & 3y+12 \end{bmatrix} = \begin{bmatrix} 25 & 4 \\ 3 & y+18 \end{bmatrix}$ for *x* and *y*.

$\begin{bmatrix} 2x-5 & 4 \\ 3 & 3y+12 \end{bmatrix} = \begin{bmatrix} 25 & 4 \\ 3 & y+18 \end{bmatrix}$

$2x - 5 = 25$ $3y + 12 = y + 18$ Since the two matrices are equal, their corresponding elements are equal.
$2x = 30$ $2y = 6$
$x = 15$ $y = 3$

6a. $x = 30, y = 2$

b. $x = -3, y = 7$

The solutions are $x = 15$ and $y = 3$.

✔ **Check Understanding** ⑥ Solve each equation for *x* and *y*. **See left.**

a. $\begin{bmatrix} x+8 & -5 \\ 3 & -y \end{bmatrix} = \begin{bmatrix} 38 & -5 \\ 3 & 4y-10 \end{bmatrix}$ **b.** $\begin{bmatrix} 3x & 4 \end{bmatrix} = \begin{bmatrix} -9 & x+y \end{bmatrix}$

⑤ Determine whether the matrices in each pair are equal.

a. $M = \begin{bmatrix} 8+9 & 5 \\ -6 & -1 \\ 0 & 0.\overline{7} \end{bmatrix}$;

$N = \begin{bmatrix} 17 & 5 \\ 4-10 & -2+1 \\ 0 & -\frac{7}{9} \end{bmatrix}$ **no**

b. $P = \begin{bmatrix} 3 & -4 \\ 40 & -3 \end{bmatrix}$;

$Q = \begin{bmatrix} \frac{27}{9} & \frac{-16}{4} \\ \frac{8}{0.2} & \frac{12}{-4} \end{bmatrix}$ **yes**

⑥ Solve the equation
$\begin{bmatrix} 2m-n & -3 \\ 8 & -4m+2n \end{bmatrix} = \begin{bmatrix} 15 & m+n \\ 8 & -30 \end{bmatrix}$ for *m* and *n*.
$m = 4, n = -7$

Closure

Ask students: *How might you solve a matrix equation such as*

$X - \begin{bmatrix} 1 & 4 \\ -3 & 9 \end{bmatrix} + \begin{bmatrix} -4 & 7 \\ 10 & -2 \end{bmatrix} = \begin{bmatrix} 5 & -1 \\ 6 & 3 \end{bmatrix}$?

Add the corresponding elements of the two matrices on the same side of the equal sign. Then use the subtraction property of equality to solve the resulting matrix equation.

Lesson 4-2 Adding and Subtracting Matrices **173**

page 170 Check Skills You'll Need

1. $\begin{bmatrix} 14 & 4 \\ 2 & -1 \end{bmatrix}$

2. $\begin{bmatrix} 3 & 1 \\ -3 & -2 \end{bmatrix}$

3. $\begin{bmatrix} 1 & -3 \\ -2 & -2 \end{bmatrix}$

4. $\begin{bmatrix} 4 & 13 \\ -2 & 12 \end{bmatrix}$

5. $\begin{bmatrix} 4 & -6 \\ 8 & -3 \end{bmatrix}$

6. $\begin{bmatrix} 6 & -2 \\ 1 & 7 \end{bmatrix}$

Assignment Guide

 **Objective**

A B Core 1–9, 18–23,
26–28

C Extension 32

 **Objective**

A B Core 10–17, 24–25,
29–31

C Extension 33–34

Standardized Test Prep 35–38

Mixed Review 39–44

Error Prevention

Exercises 18–22 Suggest students
first make sure the matrices have
the same dimension.

Enrichment 4-2

Reteaching 4-2

Practice 4-2

Practice 4-2   Adding and Subtracting Matrices

Find the value of each variable.

Use the information in the table.

Club Membership at TC High School

Find each sum or difference.

Solve each matrix equation.

**Determine whether the two matrices in each pair are equal.
Justify your reasoning.**

Algebra 2 Chapter 4   Lesson 4-2 Practice   3

pages 174–176 Exercises

2. $\begin{bmatrix} 2 & -3 & 4 \\ 5 & 6 & -7 \end{bmatrix}$

3. $\begin{bmatrix} 1 & 3 \\ 4 & 0 \end{bmatrix}$

4. $\begin{bmatrix} 3.9 & -2.3 \\ -0.6 & 9.1 \end{bmatrix}$

5. $\begin{bmatrix} 0 & 0 \\ 0 & 0 \end{bmatrix}$

6. $\begin{bmatrix} 4 & 3 & 2 \\ 0 & -3 & 5 \end{bmatrix}$

174

EXERCISES

For more practice, see *Extra Practice*.

Practice and Problem Solving

A **Practice by Example**

Example 1
(page 170)

1. **Sports** The modern pentathlon is a grueling all-day competition. Each
member of a team competes in five events: target shooting, fencing, swimming,
horseback riding, and cross-country running. Find the total scores of the U.S.
women's team at the 2000 Olympic Games.

U.S. Women's Pentathlon Scores, 2000 Olympics

Event	Emily deRiel	Mary Beth Iagorashvili
Shoot	1156	964
Fence	800	960
Swim	1182	1205
Ride	1070	1040
Run	1102	960

SOURCE: U.S. Modern Pentathlon Association

a. Write two 5 × 1 matrices to represent the individual scores for each event.
b. Find the total score for the U.S. women's team for each event.
a–b. See back of book.

Examples 2 and 3
(pages 171 and 172)

Find each sum or difference. 2–9. See margin.

2. $\begin{bmatrix} 2 & -3 & 4 \\ 5 & 6 & -7 \end{bmatrix} + \begin{bmatrix} 0 & 0 & 0 \\ 0 & 0 & 0 \end{bmatrix}$

3. $\begin{bmatrix} 1 & 3 \\ 4 & 0 \end{bmatrix} + \begin{bmatrix} 0 & 5 \\ -1 & 2 \end{bmatrix} + \begin{bmatrix} 0 & -5 \\ 1 & -2 \end{bmatrix}$

4. $\begin{bmatrix} 6.4 & -1.9 \\ -6.4 & 0.8 \end{bmatrix} + \begin{bmatrix} -2.5 & -0.4 \\ 5.8 & 8.3 \end{bmatrix}$

5. $\begin{bmatrix} 6 & -3 \\ -7 & 2 \end{bmatrix} + \begin{bmatrix} -6 & 3 \\ 7 & -2 \end{bmatrix}$

6. $\begin{bmatrix} 5 & 4 & 3 \\ 1 & -2 & 6 \end{bmatrix} - \begin{bmatrix} 1 & 1 & 1 \\ 1 & 1 & 1 \end{bmatrix}$

7. $\begin{bmatrix} 2 & 1 & 2 \\ 1 & 2 & 1 \end{bmatrix} - \begin{bmatrix} 2 & 3 & 2 \\ 3 & 2 & 3 \end{bmatrix}$

8. $\begin{bmatrix} 0.5 & 9.5 \\ -3.5 & 5.5 \end{bmatrix} - \begin{bmatrix} 0.5 & 9.5 \\ -3.5 & 5.5 \end{bmatrix}$

9. $\begin{bmatrix} 1.5 & -1.9 \\ 0 & 4.6 \end{bmatrix} - \begin{bmatrix} 8.3 & -3.2 \\ 2.1 & 5.6 \end{bmatrix}$

Example 4
(page 172)

Solve each matrix equation. 10–13. See margin.

10. $\begin{bmatrix} 1 & 2 \\ 2 & 1 \\ -3 & 4 \end{bmatrix} + X = \begin{bmatrix} 5 & -6 \\ 1 & 0 \\ 8 & 5 \end{bmatrix}$

11. $\begin{bmatrix} 2 & 1 & -1 \\ 0 & 2 & 1 \end{bmatrix} - X = \begin{bmatrix} 11 & 3 & -13 \\ 15 & -9 & 8 \end{bmatrix}$

12. $X - \begin{bmatrix} 1 & 4 \\ -2 & 3 \end{bmatrix} = \begin{bmatrix} 5 & -2 \\ 1 & 0 \end{bmatrix}$

13. $X + \begin{bmatrix} 6 & 1 \\ -2 & 3 \end{bmatrix} = \begin{bmatrix} 2 & 0 \\ -3 & 1 \end{bmatrix}$

Example 5
(page 173)

Determine whether the two matrices in each pair are equal. Justify your reasoning.
14–15. See margin
pp. 174–175.

14. $\begin{bmatrix} -2 & 3 \\ 5 & 0 \end{bmatrix}, \begin{bmatrix} 2(-1) & 2(1.5) \\ 2(2.5) & 2(0) \end{bmatrix}$

15. $\begin{bmatrix} 4 \\ -6 \\ -8 \end{bmatrix}, \begin{bmatrix} \sqrt{16} & -6 & \sqrt{64} \end{bmatrix}$

Example 6
(page 173)

Find the value of each variable.

16. $\begin{bmatrix} 2 & 2 \\ -1 & 6 \end{bmatrix} - \begin{bmatrix} 4 & -1 \\ 0 & 5 \end{bmatrix} = \begin{bmatrix} x & y \\ -1 & z \end{bmatrix}$

$x = -2, y = 3, z = 1$

17. $\begin{bmatrix} 2 & 4 \\ 8 & 12 \end{bmatrix} = \begin{bmatrix} 4x - 6 & -10t + 5x \\ 4x & 15t + 1.5x \end{bmatrix}$

$x = 2, t = \frac{3}{5}$

7. $\begin{bmatrix} 0 & -2 & 0 \\ -2 & 0 & -2 \end{bmatrix}$

8. $\begin{bmatrix} 0 & 0 \\ 0 & 0 \end{bmatrix}$

9. $\begin{bmatrix} -6.8 & 1.3 \\ -2.1 & -1 \end{bmatrix}$

10. $\begin{bmatrix} 4 & -8 \\ -1 & -1 \\ 11 & 1 \end{bmatrix}$

11. $\begin{bmatrix} -9 & -2 & 12 \\ -15 & 11 & -7 \end{bmatrix}$

12. $\begin{bmatrix} 6 & 2 \\ -1 & 3 \end{bmatrix}$

13. $\begin{bmatrix} -4 & -1 \\ -1 & -2 \end{bmatrix}$

14. Yes; $-2 = 2(-1)$,
$3 = 2(1.5), 5 = 2(2.5)$,
and $0 = 2(0)$ are
all correct.

B **Apply Your Skills**

Use matrices A, B, C, and D. Find each sum or difference if you can. If you cannot, explain why not. **18–22. See back of book.**

$$A = \begin{bmatrix} 3 & 4 \\ 6 & -2 \\ 1 & 0 \end{bmatrix} \qquad B = \begin{bmatrix} -3 & 1 \\ 2 & -4 \\ -1 & 5 \end{bmatrix} \qquad C = \begin{bmatrix} 1 & 2 \\ -3 & 1 \end{bmatrix} \qquad D = \begin{bmatrix} 5 & 1 \\ 0 & 2 \end{bmatrix}$$

18. $A + B$ **19.** $B + D$ **20.** $C + D$ **21.** $B - A$ **22.** $C - D$

 23. Riding Use the information in the table below.

U.S. Men's Pentathlon Scores, 2000 World Championship

Event	James Gregory	Velizar Iliev	Chad Senior
Shooting	1132	1072	1072
Fencing	760	910	610
Swimming	1173	1177	1285
Riding	1100	1100	1070
Running	1114	1118	1174

Source: U.S. Modern Pentathlon Association

a–c. See back of book.
a. Put the information into three matrices. Label each matrix.
b. Find the total score for the U.S. men's pentathlon team for each event.
c. **Open-Ended** Find the differences between the scores of two of the athletes. In which event were the scores the most different? How different were they?

Real-World Connection

In the riding portion of the modern pentathlon, the athletes are given 20 min to get to know their horses before riding a 400-m course with 15 obstacles.

24. $\begin{bmatrix} 4 & -1 & 11 \\ -8 & -1 & 2 \end{bmatrix}$

25. $\begin{bmatrix} 9 & 62 \\ 125 & -11 \end{bmatrix}$

Solve each matrix equation for X.

24. $\begin{bmatrix} 1 & 2 & -3 \\ 2 & 1 & 3 \end{bmatrix} + X = \begin{bmatrix} 5 & 1 & 8 \\ -6 & 0 & 5 \end{bmatrix}$ **25.** $X - \begin{bmatrix} 4 & 12 \\ 75 & -1 \end{bmatrix} = \begin{bmatrix} 5 & 50 \\ 50 & -10 \end{bmatrix}$

26. Data Analysis Refer to the table.
a. Find the total number of people participating in each activity.
b. Find the difference between the numbers of males and females participating in each activity.
c. **Reasoning** In part (b), does the order of the matrices matter? Explain. **a–c. See margin.**

U.S. Participation in Selected Leisure Activities (millions)

Activity	Male	Female
Movies	62.2	65.9
Exercise Programs	70.7	78.1
Sports Events	46.2	34.5
Home Improvement	66.9	61.9

Source: U.S. National Endowment for the Arts.
Go to www.PHSchool.com for a data update.

27. Manufacturing The table below shows the number of beach balls produced during one shift at two manufacturing plants. Plant 1 has two shifts per day and Plant 2 has three shifts per day.

Beach Ball Production Per Shift

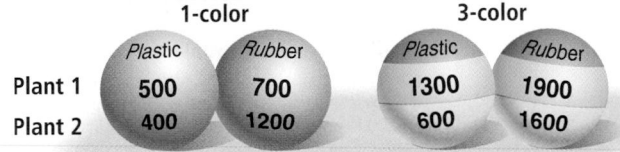

	1-color		3-color	
	Plastic	Rubber	Plastic	Rubber
Plant 1	500	700	1300	1900
Plant 2	400	1200	600	1600

a–b. See back of book.
a. Write matrices to represent one day's total output at the two plants.
b. Use your results from part (a). Find the difference between production totals at the plants. Which plant produces more three-color plastic balls? Which plant produces more one-color rubber balls?

Lesson 4-2 Adding and Subtracting Matrices **175**

15. No; the matrices have different dimensions.

26a. $\begin{bmatrix} 128.1 \\ 148.8 \\ 80.7 \\ 128.8 \end{bmatrix}$ **b.** $\begin{bmatrix} -3.7 \\ -7.4 \\ 11.7 \\ 5 \end{bmatrix}$

c. Yes, order matters because subtraction is not commutative.

---

4. Assess

Lesson Quiz 4-2

Find each sum or difference.

1. $\begin{bmatrix} 2 & 8 \\ 0 & -12 \end{bmatrix} + \begin{bmatrix} -9 & 6 \\ 6 & -5 \end{bmatrix}$

$\begin{bmatrix} -7 & 14 \\ 6 & -17 \end{bmatrix}$

2. $\begin{bmatrix} -3 & 1 \\ 4 & 8 \\ -5 & 4 \end{bmatrix} - \begin{bmatrix} -3 & -2 \\ 9 & 5 \\ 4 & -6 \end{bmatrix}$

$\begin{bmatrix} 0 & 3 \\ -5 & 3 \\ -9 & 10 \end{bmatrix}$

3. What is the additive identity for 2×4 matrices?

$\begin{bmatrix} 0 & 0 & 0 & 0 \\ 0 & 0 & 0 & 0 \end{bmatrix}$

4. Solve the equation for x and y.

$\begin{bmatrix} -2x & -1 \\ 5 & x + y \end{bmatrix} = \begin{bmatrix} 18 & -3x + 4y \\ x - 2y & -16 \end{bmatrix}$

$x = -9, y = -7$

5. Are the following matrices equal?

$\begin{bmatrix} 3 & 0.5 \\ \frac{2}{5} & -\frac{2}{3} \end{bmatrix}; \begin{bmatrix} \frac{6}{2} & 0.50 \\ 0.4 & -0.6 \end{bmatrix}$ **no**

6. Solve $X - \begin{bmatrix} 4 & 3 \\ 1 & 5 \end{bmatrix} = \begin{bmatrix} 2 & 7 \\ 0 & 6 \end{bmatrix}$ for the matrix X.

$\begin{bmatrix} 6 & 10 \\ 1 & 11 \end{bmatrix}$

Alternative Assessment

Have students work in pairs. Each student writes a 3×2 matrix. Next, each student subtracts the matrix that he or she wrote from the matrix that the partner wrote. They add their results. The sum should be the 3×2 additive identity matrix. If it is not, each student needs to check the other's work to discover where the errors occurred.

175

Standardized Test Prep

 **Resources**

For additional practice with a variety of test item formats:
- Standardized Test Prep, p. 229
- Test-Taking Strategies, p. 224
- Test-Taking Strategies with Transparencies

Exercises 37, 38 Encourage students to write a matrix for the sum on the left side of the equation. Then solve for any variables.

pages 174–176   Exercises

28a. To find $A + B$ you would add the corresponding elements. To find $A - B$ you would subtract the elements in B from the corresponding elements in A.

b. Matrix C would be the same dimension as A. Its elements would be the opposites of the corresponding elements in A.

29. $a = 2, b = \frac{9}{4}, c = -1$, $d = 0, f = \frac{1}{2}, g = -4$

30. $x = \pm3, y = 0$ or 5

31. $c = \frac{5}{2}, d = \frac{2}{5}, f = 7$, $g = 5, h = -1$

33. Consider any two 2×2 matrices, $A = \begin{bmatrix} a & b \\ c & d \end{bmatrix}$ and $B = \begin{bmatrix} w & x \\ y & z \end{bmatrix}$. By the def. of matrix addition and the Comm. Prop. of Add.,

$A + B = \begin{bmatrix} a & b \\ c & d \end{bmatrix} + \begin{bmatrix} w & x \\ y & z \end{bmatrix} =$

$\begin{bmatrix} a + w & b + x \\ c + y & d + z \end{bmatrix} =$

$\begin{bmatrix} w + a & x + b \\ y + c & z + d \end{bmatrix} = B + A$

34. Consider any three 2×2 matrices

$A = \begin{bmatrix} a & b \\ c & d \end{bmatrix}, B = \begin{bmatrix} e & f \\ g & h \end{bmatrix}$,

and $C = \begin{bmatrix} w & x \\ y & z \end{bmatrix}$.

By the definition of matrix addition and the Assoc. Prop. of Add.,

$A + (B + C) =$

176

---

 28. Writing Suppose A and B are two matrices with the same dimensions.
   a. Explain how to find $A + B$ and $A - B$.   **a–b. See margin.**
   b. Explain how to find a matrix C such that $A + C = O$.

Solve each equation for each variable.   29–31. See margin.

29. $\begin{bmatrix} 4b + 2 & -3 & 4d \\ -4a & 2 & 3 \\ 2f - 1 & -14 & 1 \end{bmatrix} = \begin{bmatrix} 11 & 2c - 1 & 0 \\ -8 & 2 & 3 \\ 0 & 3g - 2 & 1 \end{bmatrix}$

30. $\begin{bmatrix} x^2 & 4 \\ -2 & y^2 \end{bmatrix} = \begin{bmatrix} 9 & 4 \\ -2 & 5y \end{bmatrix}$

31. $\begin{bmatrix} 4c & 2 - d & 5 \\ -3 & -1 & 2 \\ 0 & -10 & 15 \end{bmatrix} = \begin{bmatrix} 2c + 5 & 4d & g \\ -3 & h & f - g \\ 0 & -4c & 15 \end{bmatrix}$

C **Challenge**

32. Find the sum of $E = \begin{bmatrix} 3 \\ 4 \\ 7 \end{bmatrix}$ and the additive inverse of $G = \begin{bmatrix} -2 \\ 0 \\ 5 \end{bmatrix}$. $\begin{bmatrix} 5 \\ 4 \\ 2 \end{bmatrix}$

33. Prove that matrix addition is commutative for 2×2 matrices.   **See margin.**

34. Prove that matrix addition is associative for 2×2 matrices.   **See margin.**

Standardized Test Prep

Multiple Choice

Use matrices $A = \begin{bmatrix} 5 & 7 & 3 \\ -1 & 0 & -4 \end{bmatrix}$ and $C = \begin{bmatrix} -7 & 4 & 2 \\ 1 & -2 & -3 \end{bmatrix}$ for Exercises 35 and 36.

35. What is the sum $A + C$? **B**
   A. The matrices cannot be added.

   B. $\begin{bmatrix} -2 & 11 & 5 \\ 0 & -2 & -7 \end{bmatrix}$ **C.** $\begin{bmatrix} 12 & 3 & 1 \\ -2 & 2 & -1 \end{bmatrix}$ **D.** $\begin{bmatrix} -35 & 28 & 6 \\ -1 & 0 & 12 \end{bmatrix}$

Take It to the NET
Online lesson quiz at
www.PHSchool.com
Web Code: aga-0402

36. What is matrix Y if $Y - A = \begin{bmatrix} 1 & 0 & 1 \\ 0 & 1 & 0 \end{bmatrix}$? **G**

   F. $\begin{bmatrix} 4 & 7 & 2 \\ -1 & -1 & -5 \end{bmatrix}$ **G.** $\begin{bmatrix} 6 & 7 & 4 \\ -1 & 1 & -4 \end{bmatrix}$ **H.** $\begin{bmatrix} -6 & 4 & 3 \\ 1 & -1 & -3 \end{bmatrix}$ **I.** $\begin{bmatrix} -4 & -7 & -2 \\ 1 & 1 & 5 \end{bmatrix}$

Short Response

Find the value of each variable.   **37–38. See margin.**

37. $\begin{bmatrix} x & y - 2 \\ z & w + 4 \end{bmatrix} + \begin{bmatrix} 2 & 5 \\ -2 & 4 \end{bmatrix} = \begin{bmatrix} 6 & 1 \\ 4 & 8 \end{bmatrix}$ **38.** $\begin{bmatrix} x & 3 \\ x & -2 \end{bmatrix} + \begin{bmatrix} y & 6 \\ -y & 3 \end{bmatrix} = \begin{bmatrix} 6 & 9 \\ 4 & 1 \end{bmatrix}$

Mixed Review

Lesson 4-1

39. Open-Ended Write a real-world problem that you can represent with a matrix. Write a matrix for the problem. Label the rows and columns.
   Check students' work.

Lesson 3-2 **40. Business** Your friend's mother plans to open a restaurant. The initial investment is $90,000. Weekly expenses will be about $8200. If the weekly income is about $8900, in how many weeks will she get back her investment?
   about 129 weeks

Lesson 2-2 **Find the slope and y-intercept of the graph of each function.**

41. $y = 2x - 6$ **42.** $3y = 6 + 2x$ **43.** $-x - 2y = 12$ **44.** $y = 5x$
   2, −6 $\frac{2}{3}, 2$ $-\frac{1}{2}, -6$ **5, 0**

$\begin{bmatrix} a & b \\ c & d \end{bmatrix} + \left(\begin{bmatrix} e & f \\ g & h \end{bmatrix} + \begin{bmatrix} w & x \\ y & z \end{bmatrix} \right)$

$= \begin{bmatrix} a & b \\ c & d \end{bmatrix} + \begin{bmatrix} e + w & f + x \\ g + y & h + z \end{bmatrix}$

$= \begin{bmatrix} a + (e + w) & b + (f + x) \\ c + (g + y) & d + (h + z) \end{bmatrix}$

$= \begin{bmatrix} (a + e) + w & (b + f) + x \\ (c + g) + y & (d + h) + z \end{bmatrix}$

$= \begin{bmatrix} a + e & b + f \\ c + g & d + h \end{bmatrix} + \begin{bmatrix} w & x \\ y & z \end{bmatrix}$

$= (A + B) + C$

37. [2] $x = 4, y = -2$, $w = 0, z = 6$
   [1] contains a minor error

38. [2] $x = 5, y = 1$
   [1] contains a minor error

Working With Matrices

FOR USE WITH LESSON 4-2

You can use a graphing calculator to work with matrices. First you need to enter the matrix into the calculator.

Take It to the NET
Graphing Calculator procedures online at **www.PHSchool.com**
Web Code: age-2113

1 EXAMPLE

Enter matrix $A = \begin{bmatrix} -3 & 4 \\ 7 & -5 \\ 0 & -2 \end{bmatrix}$ into your graphing calculator. Select the **EDIT** option of

the **MATRX** feature to edit matrix [A]. Specify a 3×2 matrix by pressing 3 ENTER 2 ENTER.

Enter the matrix elements one row at a time, pressing ENTER after each element. Then use the **QUIT** feature to return to the main screen.

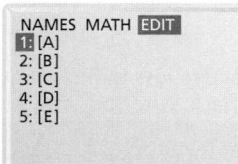 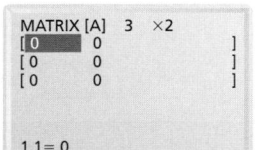 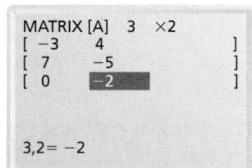

You can use a graphing calculator to perform matrix operations.

2 EXAMPLE

Perform each operation for matrix $A = \begin{bmatrix} -3 & 4 \\ 7 & -5 \\ 0 & -2 \end{bmatrix}$ and matrix $B = \begin{bmatrix} 10 & -7 \\ 4 & -3 \\ -12 & 11 \end{bmatrix}$.

a. $A + B$

Use the **EDIT** option to select the matrices you want to add. Press ENTER to see the sum.

```
[A] + [B]
    [[  7     -3  ]
     [ 11     -8  ]
     [ -12     9  ]]
```

b. $A - B$

Use the **EDIT** option to select the matrices you want to subtract. Press ENTER to see the difference.

```
[A] - [B]
    [[ -13    11  ]
     [  3     -2  ]
     [ 12    -13  ]]
```

EXERCISES

Find each sum or difference. 1–6. See margin.

1. $\begin{bmatrix} 0 & -3 \\ 5 & -7 \end{bmatrix} - \begin{bmatrix} -5 & 3 \\ 4 & 10 \end{bmatrix}$

2. $\begin{bmatrix} 3 & 5 & -7 \\ 0 & -2 & 0 \end{bmatrix} + \begin{bmatrix} -1 & 6 & 2 \\ -9 & 4 & 0 \end{bmatrix}$

3. $\begin{bmatrix} 3 \\ 5 \end{bmatrix} - \begin{bmatrix} -6 \\ 7 \end{bmatrix}$

4. $\begin{bmatrix} 3 & 5 & -8 \end{bmatrix} + \begin{bmatrix} -6 & 4 & 1 \end{bmatrix}$

5. $\begin{bmatrix} 17 & 8 & 0 \\ 3 & -5 & 2 \end{bmatrix} - \begin{bmatrix} 4 & 6 & 5 \\ 2 & -2 & 9 \end{bmatrix}$

6. $\begin{bmatrix} -9 & 6 & 4 \end{bmatrix} + \begin{bmatrix} -3 & 8 & 4 \end{bmatrix}$

Technology

Working With Matrices

Students enter matrices on a graphing calculator and use the calculator to calculate sums and differences of matrices. Calculators can be especially useful in later lessons where students consider matrix multiplication, determinants, and inverse matrices.

Resources

Students may use any graphing calculator with matrix calculation capabilities.

Teaching Notes

Technology Tip

Point out that the NAMES menu on the 2nd [MATRX] screen shows the dimensions of the matrices currently stored in the calculator. This listing can be helpful when you want to check quickly whether there has been an error entering the dimensions of a matrix.

Error Prevention

Students will find it a good idea to check that they have entered all elements correctly in the matrices before they perform calculations on the matrices. They can do this by returning to the appropriate matrix edit screen or by pressing 2nd [MATRX], the key for the name of the matrix they wish to check, and the ENTER key. The calculator will display the matrix on the home screen.

---

page 177   Technology

1. $\begin{bmatrix} 5 & -6 \\ 1 & -17 \end{bmatrix}$

2. $\begin{bmatrix} 2 & 11 & -5 \\ -9 & 2 & 0 \end{bmatrix}$

3. $\begin{bmatrix} 9 \\ -2 \end{bmatrix}$

4. $\begin{bmatrix} -3 & 9 & -7 \end{bmatrix}$

5. $\begin{bmatrix} 13 & 2 & -5 \\ 1 & -3 & -7 \end{bmatrix}$

6. $\begin{bmatrix} -12 & 14 & 8 \end{bmatrix}$

177

Lesson Preview

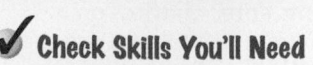 **Check Skills You'll Need**

Adding and Subtracting Matrices
Lesson 4-2: Example 2
Exercises 2–9
Extra Practice, p. 825

Lesson Resources

Teaching Resources
Practice, Reteaching, Enrichment
Checkpoint Quiz 1

Reaching All Students
Practice Workbook 4-3
Spanish Practice Workbook 4-3
Reading and Math Literacy 4B
Spanish Reading & Literacy 4B
Spanish Checkpoint Quiz 1
Hands-On Activities 39

Presentation Assistant Plus!
Transparencies
• Check Skills You'll Need 4-3
• Additional Examples 4-3
• Student Edition Answers 4-3
• Lesson Quiz 4-3
PH Presentation Pro CD 4-3

ASSESSMENT SYSTEM

Checkpoint Quiz 1
Computer Test Generator CD

Technology
Resource Pro® CD-ROM
Computer Test Generator CD
Prentice Hall Presentation Pro CD

www.PHSchool.com
Student Site
• Teacher Web Code: agk-5500
• Self-grading Lesson Quiz
Teacher Center
• Lesson Planner
• Resources

Plus

4-3

Matrix Multiplication

1.04 Operate with matrices to model and solve problems.

North Carolina Objectives

Lesson Preview

What You'll Learn

OBJECTIVE 1 To multiply a matrix by a scalar

OBJECTIVE 2 To multiply two matrices

. . . And Why

To calculate the gross income of a record store, as in Example 5

New Vocabulary • scalar • scalar product • matrix multiplication

✓ **Check Skills You'll Need** (For help, go to Lesson 4-2.)

Find each sum.

1. $\begin{bmatrix} 3 & 5 \\ 2 & 8 \end{bmatrix} + \begin{bmatrix} 3 & 5 \\ 2 & 8 \end{bmatrix} + \begin{bmatrix} 3 & 5 \\ 2 & 8 \end{bmatrix}$ $\begin{bmatrix} 9 & 15 \\ 6 & 24 \end{bmatrix}$

2. $\begin{bmatrix} -4 \\ 7 \end{bmatrix} + \begin{bmatrix} -4 \\ 7 \end{bmatrix} + \begin{bmatrix} -4 \\ 7 \end{bmatrix} + \begin{bmatrix} -4 \\ 7 \end{bmatrix} + \begin{bmatrix} -4 \\ 7 \end{bmatrix}$ $\begin{bmatrix} -20 \\ 35 \end{bmatrix}$

3. $\begin{bmatrix} -1 & 3 & 4 \\ 0 & -2 & -5 \end{bmatrix} + \begin{bmatrix} -1 & 3 & 4 \\ 0 & -2 & -5 \end{bmatrix} + \begin{bmatrix} -1 & 3 & 4 \\ 0 & -2 & -5 \end{bmatrix} + \begin{bmatrix} -1 & 3 & 4 \\ 0 & -2 & -5 \end{bmatrix}$

3. $\begin{bmatrix} -4 & 12 & 16 \\ 0 & -8 & -20 \end{bmatrix}$

iTEXT Interactive lesson includes instant self-check, tutorials, and activities.

OBJECTIVE 1 **Multiplying a Matrix by a Scalar**

You can multiply a matrix by a real number.

$$3\begin{bmatrix} 3 & 5 \\ 2 & 8 \end{bmatrix} = \begin{bmatrix} 9 & 15 \\ 6 & 24 \end{bmatrix}$$

The real number factor (such as 3) is called a **scalar.**

Key Concepts

Definition	Scalar Multiplication

Suppose c is a scalar (real number) and A is a matrix. You find the **scalar product** cA by multiplying each element of A by c.

1 EXAMPLE **Real-World Connection**

Prices Use the price list. The cafeteria plans to raise the cost of each beverage to one and a half times the current cost. How much will each beverage cost?

$$1.5\begin{bmatrix} 0.35 & 0.67 \\ 0.65 & 0.89 \\ 0.58 & 0.75 \end{bmatrix} = \begin{bmatrix} 1.5(0.35) & 1.5(0.67) \\ 1.5(0.65) & 1.5(0.89) \\ 1.5(0.58) & 1.5(0.75) \end{bmatrix}$$ Multiply each element by 1.5.

$$\approx \begin{bmatrix} 0.53 & 1.01 \\ 0.98 & 1.34 \\ 0.87 & 1.13 \end{bmatrix}$$ Simplify.

	SMALL	LARGE
LOWFAT MILK	$.35	$.67
ORANGE JUICE	$.65	$.89
TOMATO JUICE	$.58	$.75

Milk will cost $.53 and $1.01. Orange juice will cost $.98 and $1.34. Tomato juice will cost $.87 and $1.13.

✓ **Check Understanding** ● **1** Find $-3\begin{bmatrix} 15 & -12 & 10 & 0 \\ 20 & -10 & 7 & 0 \end{bmatrix}$. $\begin{bmatrix} -45 & 36 & -30 & 0 \\ -60 & 30 & -21 & 0 \end{bmatrix}$

178 Chapter 4 Matrices

Ongoing Assessment and Intervention

Before the Lesson
Diagnose prerequisite skills using:
• Check Skills You'll Need

During the Lesson
Monitor progress using:
• Check Understanding
• Additional Examples
• Standardized Test Prep

After the Lesson
Assess knowledge using:
• Lesson Quiz
• Computer Test Generator CD
• Chapter Checkpoint 1 (p. 185)

You can find sums and differences of scalar products.

2 EXAMPLE Using Scalar Products

Find the difference $5A - 3B$ for $A = \begin{bmatrix} 2 & 3 & -7 \\ 1 & 4 & 5 \end{bmatrix}$ and $B = \begin{bmatrix} 3 & 0 & 6 \\ -1 & 8 & 2 \end{bmatrix}$.

$5A - 3B = 5\begin{bmatrix} 2 & 3 & -7 \\ 1 & 4 & 5 \end{bmatrix} - 3\begin{bmatrix} 3 & 0 & 6 \\ -1 & 8 & 2 \end{bmatrix}$

$= \begin{bmatrix} 10 & 15 & -35 \\ 5 & 20 & 25 \end{bmatrix} - \begin{bmatrix} 9 & 0 & 18 \\ -3 & 24 & 6 \end{bmatrix} = \begin{bmatrix} 1 & 15 & -53 \\ 8 & -4 & 19 \end{bmatrix}$

2a. $\begin{bmatrix} 7 & -12 & 58 \\ -9 & 24 & -10 \end{bmatrix}$

b. $\begin{bmatrix} 20 & 3 & 29 \\ -5 & 52 & 17 \end{bmatrix}$

 Check Understanding **2** Use matrices A and B from Example 2. Find each sum or difference.
 a. $5B - 4A$ **b.** $A + 6B$

 Key Concepts

Properties	**Scalar Multiplication**

If A, B, and O are $m \times n$ matrices and c and d are scalars, then

cA is an $m \times n$ matrix.	Closure Property
$(cd)A = c(dA)$	Associative Property of Multiplication
$c(A + B) = cA + cB$ $(c + d)A = cA + dA$	Distributive Property
$1 \cdot A = A$	Multiplicative Identity Property
$0 \cdot A = O$ and $cO = O$	Multiplicative Property of Zero

Need Help?

O is the $m \times n$ matrix with every element zero.

You can use the properties of scalar multiplication to solve matrix equations.

3 EXAMPLE Solving Matrix Equations with Scalars

Solve $4X + 2\begin{bmatrix} 3 & 4 \\ -2 & 1 \end{bmatrix} = \begin{bmatrix} 10 & 0 \\ 4 & 2 \end{bmatrix}$.

$4X + 2\begin{bmatrix} 3 & 4 \\ -2 & 1 \end{bmatrix} = \begin{bmatrix} 10 & 0 \\ 4 & 2 \end{bmatrix}$

$4X + \begin{bmatrix} 6 & 8 \\ -4 & 2 \end{bmatrix} = \begin{bmatrix} 10 & 0 \\ 4 & 2 \end{bmatrix}$ Scalar multiplication

$4X = \begin{bmatrix} 10 & 0 \\ 4 & 2 \end{bmatrix} - \begin{bmatrix} 6 & 8 \\ -4 & 2 \end{bmatrix}$ Subtract $\begin{bmatrix} 6 & 8 \\ -4 & 2 \end{bmatrix}$ from each side.

$4X = \begin{bmatrix} 4 & -8 \\ 8 & 0 \end{bmatrix}$ Simplify.

$X = \frac{1}{4}\begin{bmatrix} 4 & -8 \\ 8 & 0 \end{bmatrix} = \begin{bmatrix} 1 & -2 \\ 2 & 0 \end{bmatrix}$ Multiply each side by $\frac{1}{4}$ and simplify.

Check $4X + 2\begin{bmatrix} 3 & 4 \\ -2 & 1 \end{bmatrix} = \begin{bmatrix} 10 & 0 \\ 4 & 2 \end{bmatrix}$

$4\begin{bmatrix} 1 & -2 \\ 2 & 0 \end{bmatrix} + 2\begin{bmatrix} 3 & 4 \\ -2 & 1 \end{bmatrix} \stackrel{?}{=} \begin{bmatrix} 10 & 0 \\ 4 & 2 \end{bmatrix}$ Substitute.

$\begin{bmatrix} 4 & -8 \\ 8 & 0 \end{bmatrix} + \begin{bmatrix} 6 & 8 \\ -4 & 2 \end{bmatrix} \stackrel{?}{=} \begin{bmatrix} 10 & 0 \\ 4 & 2 \end{bmatrix}$ Multiply.

$\begin{bmatrix} 10 & 0 \\ 4 & 2 \end{bmatrix} = \begin{bmatrix} 10 & 0 \\ 4 & 2 \end{bmatrix}$ ✓   Simplify.

Reaching All Students

Below Level Carefully demonstrate how, in a matrix product, the number of columns of the first matrix must equal the number of rows of the second.	**Advanced Learners** Have students find examples of matrices A and B where $AB = BA$, and where AB and BA exist, but $AB \neq BA$.	**Visual Learners** See note on page 180. **Auditory Learners** See note on page 180.

2. Teach

 Professional Development

Math Background

Matrices are typically students' first exposure to a set with addition and multiplication operations that do not satisfy all the usual properties of real numbers. For instance, matrix multiplication is not commutative. Also, multiplicative inverses only exist for $n \times n$ matrices with nonzero determinants. Nevertheless, matrices play an extremely important role in applications, from those seen throughout this chapter to more sophisticated applications such as data compression.

OBJECTIVE
1 **Teaching Notes**

1 EXAMPLE Connection to Algebra

Relate scalar multiplication to the Distributive Property. You multiply the scalar by each element inside the matrix brackets.

 **Additional Examples**

1 The table shows the salaries of the three managers (M1, M2, M3) in each of two branches (A and B) of a retail clothing company. The president of the company has decided to give each manager an 8% raise. Show the new salaries in a matrix.

Store	M1	M2	M3
A	$38,500	$40,000	$44,600
B	$39,000	$37,800	$43,700

$\begin{matrix} \ \ \text{M1} & \ \ \text{M2} & \ \ \text{M3} \\ \begin{bmatrix} 41,580 & 43,200 & 48,168 \\ 42,120 & 40,824 & 47,196 \end{bmatrix} \begin{matrix} \text{A} \\ \text{B} \end{matrix} \end{matrix}$

2 Find the sum $-3M + 7N$ for $M = \begin{bmatrix} 2 & -3 \\ 0 & 6 \end{bmatrix}$ and $N = \begin{bmatrix} -5 & -1 \\ 2 & 9 \end{bmatrix}$.

$\begin{bmatrix} -41 & 2 \\ 14 & 45 \end{bmatrix}$

3 Solve the equation for Y.

$-3Y + 2\begin{bmatrix} 6 & 9 \\ -12 & 15 \end{bmatrix} = \begin{bmatrix} 27 & -18 \\ 30 & 6 \end{bmatrix}$

$\begin{bmatrix} -5 & 12 \\ -18 & 8 \end{bmatrix}$

179

Math Tip

Students may have difficulty understanding why one matrix is written as a single row and the other as a single column. It may help to point out that this format emphasizes that the matrices represent different categories of data—the costs of lunches and the number of lunches sold.

4 EXAMPLE Visual Learners

Suggest students imagine that they are physically lifting a column of elements out of the second factor and turning it to fit on a row of the first factor. Help students relate this procedure to the definition of matrix multiplication that follows the example.

5 EXAMPLE Auditory Learners

Students may find it helpful to explain orally what each term represents in the matrix after the first equal sign.

6 EXAMPLE Visual Learners

To decide whether a matrix product is or is not defined, students may find it helpful to write the dimensions of the matrices side by side and ring the two middle numbers. If these numbers are equal, then the product exists. If they are not equal, then the product does not exist.

Additional Examples

4 Find the product of $\begin{bmatrix} -2 & 5 \\ 3 & -1 \end{bmatrix}$ and $\begin{bmatrix} 4 & -4 \\ 2 & 6 \end{bmatrix}$.

$\begin{bmatrix} 2 & 38 \\ 10 & -18 \end{bmatrix}$

page 180   Investigation

2b. For each lunch, multiply the number of lunches sold by the cost per lunch. Then add the three products.

✓ **Check Understanding**   **3** Solve each equation. Check your answer.

a. $2X = \begin{bmatrix} 4 & 12 \\ 1 & -4 \end{bmatrix} + \begin{bmatrix} -2 & 0 \\ 3 & 4 \end{bmatrix}$ **b.** $-3X + \begin{bmatrix} 7 & 0 & -1 \\ 2 & -3 & 4 \end{bmatrix} = \begin{bmatrix} 10 & 0 & 8 \\ -19 & -18 & 10 \end{bmatrix}$

3a. $\begin{bmatrix} 1 & 6 \\ 2 & 0 \end{bmatrix}$ **3b.** $\begin{bmatrix} -1 & 0 & -3 \\ 7 & 5 & -2 \end{bmatrix}$

OBJECTIVE
2 **Multiplying Matrices**

Investigation: Using Matrices

Use the data in the table.

	Lunch 1	Lunch 2	Lunch 3
Cost per Lunch	$2.50	$1.75	$2.00
Number Sold	50	100	75

1. How much money did the cafeteria collect selling lunch 1? Selling lunch 2? Selling lunch 3? **$125; $175; $150**

2. a. How much did the cafeteria collect selling all three lunches? **$450**
 b. Explain how you used the data in the table to find your answer. **See margin.**

3. a. Write a 1 × 3 matrix to represent the cost of the lunches.
 b. Write a 3 × 1 matrix to represent the number of lunches sold.
 c. Writing Describe a procedure for using your matrices to find how much money the cafeteria collected from selling all three lunches. Use the words *row*, *column*, and *element*.
 a–c. See margin pp. 180–181.

Graphing Calculator Hint

You can use the MATRX feature of a graphing calculator to multiply matrices.

To perform **matrix multiplication,** multiply the elements of each *row* of the first matrix by the elements of each *column* of the second matrix. Add the products.

4 EXAMPLE   Multiplying Matrices

Find the product of $\begin{bmatrix} -1 & 0 \\ 3 & -4 \end{bmatrix}$ and $\begin{bmatrix} -3 & 3 \\ 5 & 0 \end{bmatrix}$.

Multiply a_{11} and b_{11}. Then multiply a_{12} and b_{21}. Add the products.

$\begin{bmatrix} -1 & 0 \\ 3 & -4 \end{bmatrix}\begin{bmatrix} -3 & 3 \\ 5 & 0 \end{bmatrix} = \begin{bmatrix} ? & \blacksquare \\ \blacksquare & \blacksquare \end{bmatrix}$ $(-1)(-3) + (0)(5) = 3$

The result is the element in the first row and first column.
Repeat with the rest of the rows and columns.

$\begin{bmatrix} -1 & 0 \\ 3 & -4 \end{bmatrix}\begin{bmatrix} -3 & 3 \\ 5 & 0 \end{bmatrix} = \begin{bmatrix} 3 & ? \\ \blacksquare & \blacksquare \end{bmatrix}$ $(-1)(3) + (0)(0) = -3$

$\begin{bmatrix} -1 & 0 \\ 3 & -4 \end{bmatrix}\begin{bmatrix} -3 & 3 \\ 5 & 0 \end{bmatrix} = \begin{bmatrix} 3 & -3 \\ ? & \blacksquare \end{bmatrix}$ $(3)(-3) + (-4)(5) = -29$

$\begin{bmatrix} -1 & 0 \\ 3 & -4 \end{bmatrix}\begin{bmatrix} -3 & 3 \\ 5 & 0 \end{bmatrix} = \begin{bmatrix} 3 & -3 \\ -29 & ? \end{bmatrix}$ $(3)(3) + (-4)(0) = 9$

The product of $\begin{bmatrix} -1 & 0 \\ 3 & -4 \end{bmatrix}$ and $\begin{bmatrix} -3 & 3 \\ 5 & 0 \end{bmatrix}$ is $\begin{bmatrix} 3 & -3 \\ -29 & 9 \end{bmatrix}$.

	Lunch 1	Lunch 2	Lunch 3

3a. A = Cost per lunch   [2.50   1.75   2.00]

b.   Number Sold

$B = \begin{matrix} \text{Lunch 1} \\ \text{Lunch 2} \\ \text{Lunch 3} \end{matrix} \begin{bmatrix} 50 \\ 100 \\ 75 \end{bmatrix}$

c. Multiply each element in the row of matrix A by the corresponding element in the column for matrix B. Then add the 3 products to find the amount collected from all 3 lunches.

4 a. Find the product of $\begin{bmatrix} -3 & 3 \\ 5 & 0 \end{bmatrix}$ and $\begin{bmatrix} -1 & 0 \\ 3 & -4 \end{bmatrix}$. **a–b. See margin.**

b. Critical Thinking Is matrix multiplication commutative? Explain.

Key Concepts

Definition	Matrix Multiplication

To find element c_{ij} of the product matrix AB, multiply each element in the ith row of A by the corresponding element in the jth column of B, and then add.

You can use matrix multiplication to solve problems.

5 EXAMPLE **Real-World Connection**

Real-World Connection

The music on an LP record (a) plays continuously as the stylus travels along the groove. The music on a CD (b) plays in discrete intervals read by a laser.

a   b

Business A used-record store sells tapes, LP records, and compact discs. The matrices show today's information. Find the store's gross income for the day.

Prices

Tapes LPs CDs
$\begin{bmatrix} \$8 & \$6 & \$13 \end{bmatrix}$

Number of Items Sold

$\begin{matrix} \text{Tapes} \\ \text{LPs} \\ \text{CDs} \end{matrix} \begin{bmatrix} 9 \\ 30 \\ 20 \end{bmatrix}$

Multiply each price by the number of items sold and add the products.

$$\begin{bmatrix} 8 & 6 & 13 \end{bmatrix} \begin{bmatrix} 9 \\ 30 \\ 20 \end{bmatrix} = [8(9) + 6(30) + 13(20)] = [512]$$

The store's gross income for the day was $512.

 Check Understanding

5 Find each product.

a. $\begin{bmatrix} 12 & 3 \end{bmatrix} \begin{bmatrix} 10 \\ -5 \end{bmatrix}$ **[105]**

b. $\begin{bmatrix} 10 \\ -5 \end{bmatrix} \begin{bmatrix} 12 & 3 \\ 0 & 0 \end{bmatrix}$ **Matrix does not exist.**

The product of two matrices A and B exists only if the number of *columns* of A is equal to the number of *rows* of B.

Key Concepts

Property	Dimensions of a Product Matrix

If matrix A is an $m \times n$ matrix and matrix B is an $n \times p$ matrix, then the product matrix AB is an $m \times p$ matrix.

Example   matrix A •   matrix B

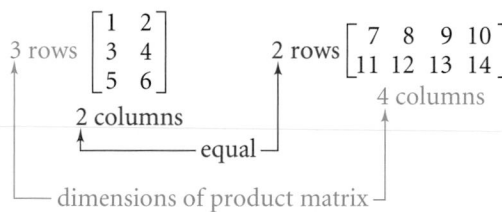

The dimensions of product matrix AB is 3×4.

---

5 Matrix A gives the prices of shirts and jeans on sale at a discount store. Matrix B gives the number of these items sold on one day. Find the income for the day from the sale of the shirts and jeans.

$\begin{matrix} & \text{Shirts} & \text{Jeans} \end{matrix}$
$A = \begin{bmatrix} \$18 & \$22 \end{bmatrix}$

$B = \begin{matrix} \text{Shirts} \\ \text{Jeans} \end{matrix} \begin{bmatrix} 109 \\ 76 \end{bmatrix}$ **$3634**

6 Use the Matrices

$P = \begin{bmatrix} 3 & -1 & 2 \\ 5 & 9 & 0 \\ 0 & 1 & 8 \end{bmatrix}$ and

$Q = \begin{bmatrix} 6 & 5 & 7 & 0 \\ 2 & 0 & 3 & 1 \\ 1 & -1 & 5 & 2 \end{bmatrix}$.

Determine whether PQ and QP are defined or undefined. Determine the dimensions of each product. **PQ is defined and is a 3×4 matrix. QP is undefined.**

Closure

Ask students how to determine whether a matrix product AB is defined. **The number of columns in A must be the same as the number of rows in B.**

page 181 Check Understanding

4a. $\begin{bmatrix} 12 & -12 \\ -5 & 0 \end{bmatrix}$

b. No; explanations may vary. Sample: For the matrices in part (a),

$AB = \begin{bmatrix} 12 & -12 \\ -5 & 0 \end{bmatrix}$.

However,

$BA = \begin{bmatrix} 3 & -3 \\ -29 & 9 \end{bmatrix}$,

so $AB \ne BA$.

3. Practice

Assignment Guide

 **Objective**

Ⓐ Ⓑ **Core** 1–10, 30–32, 35–37

 **Objective**

Ⓐ Ⓑ **Core** 11–29, 33–34, 38–54

Ⓒ **Extension** 55–60

Standardized Test Prep 61–64

Mixed Review 65–72

Error Prevention

Exercise 9 Remind students to perform the scalar multiplication before using the Subtraction Property.

Enrichment 4-3

Reteaching 4-3

Practice 4-3

Practice 4-3   Matrix Multiplication

[worksheet image]

pages 182–185 Exercises

1. $\begin{bmatrix} 9 & 12 \\ 18 & -6 \\ 3 & 0 \end{bmatrix}$

2. $\begin{bmatrix} -12 & 4 \\ 8 & -16 \\ -4 & 20 \end{bmatrix}$

3. $\begin{bmatrix} -3 & -6 \\ 9 & -3 \end{bmatrix}$

4. $\begin{bmatrix} -5 & -1 \\ 0 & -2 \end{bmatrix}$

182

---

6 **EXAMPLE** **Determining Whether a Product Matrix Exists**

Use matrices $G = \begin{bmatrix} 2 & 3 \\ -1 & 8 \\ 4 & 0 \end{bmatrix}$ and $H = \begin{bmatrix} 8 & 0 \\ 2 & -5 \end{bmatrix}$. Determine whether products GH and HG are *defined* (exist) or *undefined* (do not exist).

Find the dimensions of each product matrix.

GH	HG
$(3 \times 2)(2 \times 2) \rightarrow 3 \times 2$	$(2 \times 2)(3 \times 2)$
↑ ↑ product	↑ ↑
equal matrix	*not* equal

Product GH is defined and is a 3×2 matrix. Product HG is undefined, because the number of columns of H is not equal to the number of rows of G.

✔ **Check Understanding** **6** Let $R = \begin{bmatrix} 4 & -2 \\ 5 & -4 \end{bmatrix}$ and $S = \begin{bmatrix} 8 & 0 & -1 & 0 \\ 2 & -5 & 1 & 8 \end{bmatrix}$.

6a. *RS* is defined, but *SR* is undefined.

a. Determine whether products *RS* and *SR* are *defined* or *undefined*.

b. Find each defined product.

b. $RS = \begin{bmatrix} 28 & 10 & -6 & -16 \\ 32 & 20 & -9 & -32 \end{bmatrix}$

Matrix multiplication has some of the properties of real number multiplication.

 Key Concepts

Properties	**Matrix Multiplication**
If A, B, and C are $n \times n$ matrices, then	
AB is an $n \times n$ matrix.	Closure Property
$(AB)C = A(BC)$	Associative Property of Multiplication
$A(B + C) = AB + AC$ $(B + C)A = BA + CA$	Distributive Property
$OA = AO = O$, where O has the same dimensions as A.	Multiplicative Property of Zero

EXERCISES

For more practice, see *Extra Practice*.

Practice and Problem Solving

Ⓐ **Practice by Example**

Examples 1 and 2 (pages 178 and 179)

1–8. See margin.

Use matrices A, B, C, and D. Find each scalar product, sum, or difference.

$A = \begin{bmatrix} 3 & 4 \\ 6 & -2 \\ 1 & 0 \end{bmatrix}$ $B = \begin{bmatrix} -3 & 1 \\ 2 & -4 \\ -1 & 5 \end{bmatrix}$ $C = \begin{bmatrix} 1 & 2 \\ -3 & 1 \end{bmatrix}$ $D = \begin{bmatrix} 5 & 1 \\ 0 & 2 \end{bmatrix}$

1. $3A$ **2.** $4B$ **3.** $-3C$ **4.** $-D$

5. $A - 2B$ **6.** $3A + 2B$ **7.** $4C + 3D$ **8.** $2A - 5B$

Example 3 (page 179)

Solve each equation. Check your answers. **9–10. See margin.**

9. $3\begin{bmatrix} 2 & 0 \\ -1 & 5 \end{bmatrix} - 2X = \begin{bmatrix} -10 & 5 \\ 0 & 17 \end{bmatrix}$

10. $5X - \begin{bmatrix} 1.5 & -3.6 \\ -0.3 & 2.8 \end{bmatrix} = \begin{bmatrix} 0.2 & 1.3 \\ -5.6 & 1.7 \end{bmatrix}$

182 Chapter 4 Matrices

5. $\begin{bmatrix} 9 & 2 \\ 2 & 6 \\ 3 & -10 \end{bmatrix}$

6. $\begin{bmatrix} 3 & 14 \\ 22 & -14 \\ 1 & 10 \end{bmatrix}$

7. $\begin{bmatrix} 19 & 11 \\ -12 & 10 \end{bmatrix}$

8. $\begin{bmatrix} 21 & 3 \\ 2 & 16 \\ 7 & -25 \end{bmatrix}$

9. $\begin{bmatrix} 8 & -2.5 \\ -1.5 & -1 \end{bmatrix}$

10. $\begin{bmatrix} 0.34 & -0.46 \\ -1.18 & 0.9 \end{bmatrix}$

Example 4
(page 180)

Find each product. 11–18. See margin.

11. $\begin{bmatrix} -3 & 4 \\ 5 & 2 \end{bmatrix}\begin{bmatrix} 1 & 0 \\ 2 & -3 \end{bmatrix}$

12. $\begin{bmatrix} 1 & 0 \\ 2 & -3 \end{bmatrix}\begin{bmatrix} -3 & 4 \\ 5 & 2 \end{bmatrix}$

13. $\begin{bmatrix} 0 & 2 \\ -4 & 0 \end{bmatrix}\begin{bmatrix} 0 & 2 \\ -4 & 0 \end{bmatrix}$

14. $\begin{bmatrix} -3 & 5 \end{bmatrix}\begin{bmatrix} -3 \\ 5 \end{bmatrix}$

15. $\begin{bmatrix} -3 & 5 \end{bmatrix}\begin{bmatrix} -3 & 0 \\ 5 & 0 \end{bmatrix}$

16. $\begin{bmatrix} -3 & 5 \end{bmatrix}\begin{bmatrix} 0 & -3 \\ 0 & 5 \end{bmatrix}$

17. $\begin{bmatrix} 0 & -3 \\ 0 & 5 \end{bmatrix}\begin{bmatrix} -3 & 0 \\ 5 & 0 \end{bmatrix}$

18. $\begin{bmatrix} 1 & 0 \\ -1 & -5 \\ 0 & 3 \end{bmatrix}\begin{bmatrix} -1 & 0 \\ 0 & -1 \end{bmatrix}$

Example 5
(page 181)

19. **Business** A florist creates three special floral arrangements. One uses three lilies. The second uses three lilies and four carnations. The third uses four daisies and three carnations. Lilies cost $2.15 each, carnations cost $.90 each, and daisies cost $1.30 each.
  a. Write a matrix to represent the number of each type of flower in each arrangement.
  b. Write a matrix to represent the cost of each type of flower.
  c. Find the matrix representing the cost of each floral arrangement. **a–c. See back of book.**

Example 6
(page 182)

Determine whether each product is defined or undefined.

$F = \begin{bmatrix} 2 & 3 \\ 6 & 9 \end{bmatrix}$ $G = \begin{bmatrix} -3 & 6 \\ 2 & -4 \end{bmatrix}$ $H = \begin{bmatrix} -5 \\ 6 \end{bmatrix}$ $J = \begin{bmatrix} 0 & 7 \end{bmatrix}$

20. *FG*
  defined
21. *GF*
  defined
22. *FH*
  defined
23. *HF*
  undefined
24. *GH*
  defined
25. *HG*
  undefined
26. *FJ*
  undefined
27. *JF*
  defined
28. *HJ*
  defined
29. *JH*
  defined

B **Apply Your Skills**

Mental Math Find each product. 30–34. See margin.

30. $2\begin{bmatrix} -1 & 4 \\ 2 & 5 \end{bmatrix}$

31. $-3\begin{bmatrix} 6 & -3 \\ -7 & 4 \end{bmatrix}$

32. $-1\begin{bmatrix} 9 & -7 & -4 \\ -8 & -2 & 3 \end{bmatrix}$

33. $\begin{bmatrix} -1 & 0 \\ 0 & -1 \end{bmatrix}\begin{bmatrix} -1 & 0 & 1 \\ 0 & -1 & 1 \end{bmatrix}$

34. $\begin{bmatrix} 1 & 0 \\ 0 & -1 \end{bmatrix}\begin{bmatrix} -1 & 0 \\ 0 & -1 \end{bmatrix}$

Find each product.

35. $-1\begin{bmatrix} 7.5 & 6.2 & 4.0 \\ 6.7 & 8.2 & 0 \end{bmatrix}$

36. $\frac{1}{4}\begin{bmatrix} 4 & 0 & -3 & 1 \\ 12 & 16 & 6 & -4 \\ 0 & -2 & 5 & 8 \end{bmatrix}$

37. $0.5\begin{bmatrix} 3 & 14 \\ 7 & -4 \end{bmatrix}$

35–37. See margin.

Find the dimensions of each product matrix. Then find each product. 38–41. See margin.

38. $\begin{bmatrix} 5 & 7 & 0 \\ -\frac{4}{5} & 3 & 6 \\ 0 & -\frac{2}{3} & 4 \end{bmatrix}\begin{bmatrix} 2 & -1 \\ 1 & 1 \\ 0 & -1 \end{bmatrix}$

39. $\begin{bmatrix} 0 & -1 & 3 \\ 0 & -5 & 2 \\ 0 & 0 & 2 \\ 1 & 0 & -3 \end{bmatrix}\begin{bmatrix} -1.5 & 4.3 & 0 \\ 1.6 & -2.2 & 1.8 \\ 1 & 0 & -1.2 \end{bmatrix}$

40. $\begin{bmatrix} w & x \\ y & z \end{bmatrix}\begin{bmatrix} 9 & -7 \\ 3 & 1 \end{bmatrix}$

41. $\begin{bmatrix} 1 & 0 & 0 \\ 1 & 0 & -2 \\ 0 & 0 & 2 \\ -1 & 0 & 1 \end{bmatrix}\begin{bmatrix} a & 0 & b & 0 \\ 0 & c & 0 & d \\ e & 0 & 0 & f \end{bmatrix}$

30. $\begin{bmatrix} -2 & 8 \\ 4 & 10 \end{bmatrix}$

31. $\begin{bmatrix} -18 & 9 \\ 21 & -12 \end{bmatrix}$

32. $\begin{bmatrix} -9 & 7 & 4 \\ 8 & 2 & -3 \end{bmatrix}$

33. $\begin{bmatrix} 1 & 0 & -1 \\ 0 & 1 & -1 \end{bmatrix}$

34. $\begin{bmatrix} -1 & 0 \\ 0 & 1 \end{bmatrix}$

35. $\begin{bmatrix} -7.5 & -6.2 & -4.0 \\ -6.7 & -8.2 & 0 \end{bmatrix}$

36. $\begin{bmatrix} 1 & 0 & -0.75 & 0.25 \\ 3 & 4 & 1.5 & -1 \\ 0 & -0.5 & 1.25 & 2 \end{bmatrix}$

37. $\begin{bmatrix} 1.5 & 7 \\ 3.5 & -2 \end{bmatrix}$

38. $3 \times 2;$ $\begin{bmatrix} 17 & 2 \\ \frac{7}{5} & -\frac{11}{5} \\ -\frac{2}{3} & -\frac{14}{3} \end{bmatrix}$

39. $4 \times 3;$ $\begin{bmatrix} 1.4 & 2.2 & -5.4 \\ -6 & 11 & -11.4 \\ 2 & 0 & -2.4 \\ -4.5 & 4.3 & 3.6 \end{bmatrix}$

40. $2 \times 2;$ $\begin{bmatrix} 9w+3x & -7w+x \\ 9y+3z & -7y+z \end{bmatrix}$

41. $4 \times 4;$ $\begin{bmatrix} a & 0 & b & 0 \\ a-2e & 0 & b & -2f \\ 2e & 0 & 0 & 2f \\ -a+e & 0 & -b & f \end{bmatrix}$

Lesson 4-3 Matrix Multiplication **183**

11. $\begin{bmatrix} 5 & -12 \\ 9 & -6 \end{bmatrix}$

12. $\begin{bmatrix} -3 & 4 \\ -21 & 2 \end{bmatrix}$

13. $\begin{bmatrix} -8 & 0 \\ 0 & -8 \end{bmatrix}$

14. $\begin{bmatrix} 34 \end{bmatrix}$

15. $\begin{bmatrix} 34 & 0 \end{bmatrix}$

16. $\begin{bmatrix} 0 & 34 \end{bmatrix}$

17. $\begin{bmatrix} -15 & 0 \\ 25 & 0 \end{bmatrix}$

18. $\begin{bmatrix} -1 & 0 \\ 1 & 5 \\ 0 & -3 \end{bmatrix}$

pages 182–185 Exercises

42. $\begin{bmatrix} 1 & -6 & -5 \\ 6 & 1 & -5 \\ -3 & -12 & 0 \end{bmatrix}$

43. $\begin{bmatrix} 9 & -6 \\ 15 & -3 \\ -6 & -12 \end{bmatrix}$

44. $\begin{bmatrix} 17 & -24 \\ -33 & -7 \\ 69 & -18 \end{bmatrix}$

45. $\begin{bmatrix} 17 & -24 \\ -33 & -7 \\ 69 & -18 \end{bmatrix}$

46. $\begin{bmatrix} -3 & 12 & -1 \\ -2 & 3 & 5 \\ -4 & -3 & -4 \end{bmatrix}$

For Exercises 42–49, use matrices D, E, and F shown below. Perform the indicated operations if they are defined. If an operation is not defined, label it undefined.

$$D = \begin{bmatrix} 1 & 2 & -1 \\ 0 & 3 & 1 \\ 2 & -1 & -2 \end{bmatrix} \quad E = \begin{bmatrix} 2 & -5 & 0 \\ 1 & 0 & -2 \\ 3 & 1 & 1 \end{bmatrix} \quad F = \begin{bmatrix} -3 & 2 \\ -5 & 1 \\ 2 & 4 \end{bmatrix}$$

42. DE 43. $-3F$ 44. $(DE)F$ 45. $D(EF)$

46. $D - 2E$ 47. $(E - D)F$ 48. D^2E 49. $(2D)(3F)$

42–49. See margin.

🌐 50. **Business** A hardware store chain displays prices in a 1 × 3 matrix and daily purchases at its three stores in a 3 × 3 matrix.

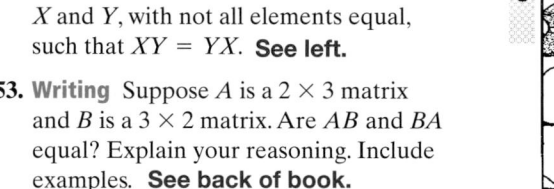

	Prices			Number of Items Sold		
				Store A	Store B	Store C
Hammers	Flashlights	Lanterns	Hammers	10	9	8
[$3	$5	$7]	Flashlights	3	14	6
			Lanterns	2	5	7

a. Find the product of the two matrices. Explain what the product represents.
b. How would you find the total gross revenue from all three stores?
c. Find the total gross revenue from the flashlights sold at all three stores.
a–c. See margin p. 185.

🌐 51. **Math in the Media** Refer to the cartoon. An algorithm is a step-by-step description of a calculation rule. What is the algorithm for matrix multiplication? **See left.**

51. **Answers may vary. Sample:** Multiply the elements in each row of the first matrix by the elements in each column of the second matrix. Then add to get the corresponding entry in the resultant matrix.

52. **Open-Ended** Find two 2 × 2 matrices X and Y, with not all elements equal, such that $XY = YX$. **See left.**

52. **Answers may vary. Sample:**

$\begin{bmatrix} 1 & 0 \\ 0 & 1 \end{bmatrix}$ and $\begin{bmatrix} 0 & 1 \\ 1 & 0 \end{bmatrix}$

✏️ 53. **Writing** Suppose A is a 2 × 3 matrix and B is a 3 × 2 matrix. Are AB and BA equal? Explain your reasoning. Include examples. **See back of book.**

🌐 54. **Revenue** Write a matrix that represents the daily revenue from the play. **See back of book.**

Ticket Prices		
Orchestra	Mezzanine	Balcony
$7.00	$6.00	$5.00

Number of Tickets Sold			
Location	Thursday	Friday	Saturday
Orchestra	150	130	160
Mezzanine	125	130	175
Balcony	60	52	80

🔵 **Challenge**

Solve for x and y.

55. $\begin{bmatrix} 2x & 1 \\ 2 & 0 \end{bmatrix}\begin{bmatrix} 1 & 3 \\ 2 & -y \end{bmatrix} = \begin{bmatrix} -4 & -9 \\ 2 & 6 \end{bmatrix}$
$x = -3, y = -9$

56. $\begin{bmatrix} 2x & 1 \\ 2 & 0 \end{bmatrix}\begin{bmatrix} 0 & 3 \\ 2x & -y \end{bmatrix} = \begin{bmatrix} -4 & -9 \\ 0 & 6 \end{bmatrix}$
$x = -2, y = -3$

For Exercises 57–60, use matrices P, Q, R, S, and I. Determine whether the two expressions in each pair are equal.

$$P = \begin{bmatrix} 3 & 4 \\ 1 & 2 \end{bmatrix} \quad Q = \begin{bmatrix} -1 & 0 \\ 3 & -2 \end{bmatrix} \quad R = \begin{bmatrix} 1 & 4 \\ -2 & 1 \end{bmatrix} \quad S = \begin{bmatrix} 0 & 1 \\ 2 & 0 \end{bmatrix} \quad I = \begin{bmatrix} 1 & 0 \\ 0 & 1 \end{bmatrix}$$

57. $(P + Q)R$ and $PR + QR$ **yes** 58. $(P + Q)I$ and $PI + QI$ **yes**

59. $(P + Q)(R + S)$ and $(P + Q)R + (P + Q)S$ **yes**

60. $(P + Q)(R + S)$ and $PR + PS + QR + QS$ **yes**

47. $\begin{bmatrix} 34 & -1 \\ 6 & -13 \\ -7 & 16 \end{bmatrix}$

48. $\begin{bmatrix} 16 & 20 & -15 \\ 15 & -9 & -15 \\ 2 & 11 & -5 \end{bmatrix}$

49. $\begin{bmatrix} -90 & 0 \\ -78 & 42 \\ -30 & -30 \end{bmatrix}$

Multiple Choice

61. Which product is NOT defined? **B**

A. $\begin{bmatrix} -1 \\ 2 \end{bmatrix}\begin{bmatrix} -1 & 2 \end{bmatrix}$
B. $\begin{bmatrix} -1 & 2 \\ -1 & 2 \end{bmatrix}\begin{bmatrix} -1 & 2 \end{bmatrix}$
C. $\begin{bmatrix} -1 & 2 \\ -1 & 2 \end{bmatrix}\begin{bmatrix} 2 & -1 \\ 2 & -1 \end{bmatrix}$
D. $\begin{bmatrix} -1 & 2 \end{bmatrix}\begin{bmatrix} -1 \\ 2 \end{bmatrix}$

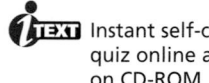

Take It to the NET
Online lesson quiz at
www.PHSchool.com
Web Code: aga-0403

62. Given $P = \begin{bmatrix} 4 & 3 & -2 \\ -1 & 0 & 5 \end{bmatrix}$ and $Q = \begin{bmatrix} 3 & -2 & -5 \\ -1 & -2 & -1 \end{bmatrix}$, what is $2P - 3Q$? **H**

F. $\begin{bmatrix} 1 & -5 & 3 \\ 0 & -2 & 6 \end{bmatrix}$
G. $\begin{bmatrix} 17 & 0 & 19 \\ -5 & 6 & 7 \end{bmatrix}$
H. $\begin{bmatrix} -1 & 12 & 11 \\ 1 & 6 & 13 \end{bmatrix}$
I. $\begin{bmatrix} 1 & 5 & 3 \\ 0 & 2 & 6 \end{bmatrix}$

Short Response

63. Solve $3Y + 2\begin{bmatrix} -1 & -3 \\ 2 & 5 \end{bmatrix} = \begin{bmatrix} 13 & -9 \\ 4 & 16 \end{bmatrix}$. Show the steps of your solution.
See back of book.

Extended Response

64. Given $M = \begin{bmatrix} -3 & 4 \\ 1 & -2 \end{bmatrix}$ and $N = \begin{bmatrix} 0 & 1 \\ -2 & 5 \end{bmatrix}$, does $M \times N = N \times M$? Explain.
See back of book.

Mixed Review

Lesson 4-2

Add or subtract. **65–66. See margin.**

65. $\begin{bmatrix} -1 & 2 \\ 0 & 17 \end{bmatrix} - \begin{bmatrix} 32 & 14 \\ 6 & -10 \end{bmatrix}$

66. $\begin{bmatrix} 0 & -1 & 5 \\ 6 & 10 & 12 \end{bmatrix} + \begin{bmatrix} 9 & -5 & 7 \\ -4 & 10 & 0 \end{bmatrix}$

Lesson 3-4

Graph each system of constraints. Find all vertices. Then find the values of x and y that maximize or minimize the objective function. 67–69. See back of book.

67. $\begin{cases} x + y \le 3 \\ x \ge 0 \\ y \le 2 \end{cases}$
Maximize for
$P = 3x + 4y$.

68. $\begin{cases} x + 2y \le 8 \\ x \ge 2 \\ y \ge 0 \end{cases}$
Minimize for
$C = x + 3y$.

69. $\begin{cases} x + y \le 6 \\ 2x + y \le 10 \\ x \ge 0, y \ge 0 \end{cases}$
Maximize for
$P = 4x + y$.

Lesson 2-7

Graph each inequality. 70–72. See back of book.

70. $y < 4x - 1$
71. $y \le -3x + 8$
72. $y \ge |2x + 5| - 3$

Checkpoint Quiz 1   Lessons 4-1 through 4-3

TEXT Instant self-check quiz online and on CD-ROM

State the dimensions of each matrix. Identify the indicated element.

1. $\begin{bmatrix} 5 & 2 \\ -8 & 3 \\ 10 & 1 \end{bmatrix}; a_{32}$
$3 \times 2; 1$

2. $\begin{bmatrix} 9 & 1 & 7 \\ 6 & -2 & 4 \end{bmatrix}; a_{22}$
$2 \times 3; -2$

3. $\begin{bmatrix} 8 & 1 & 5 \\ 9 & 4 & 2 \\ 7 & 0 & 3 \end{bmatrix}; a_{13}$
$3 \times 3; 5$

Use matrices A, B, C, and D. Perform each operation.

$A = \begin{bmatrix} 3 & 1 \\ 5 & 7 \end{bmatrix}$
$B = \begin{bmatrix} 4 & 6 \\ 1 & 0 \end{bmatrix}$
$C = \begin{bmatrix} -5 & 3 \\ 1 & 9 \end{bmatrix}$
$D = \begin{bmatrix} 1.5 & 2 \\ 9 & -6 \end{bmatrix}$

4. $A + C$ **5.** $B - A$ **6.** $3D$ **7.** BA **8.** $C(DB)$
4–10. See margin.

9. Writing How do you decide whether two matrices can be multiplied?

10. Open-Ended Write a matrix equation with solution $\begin{bmatrix} 12 & 7 & -3 & 8 \\ 9 & 0 & -11 & 1 \end{bmatrix}$.

50a. [59 132 103]; the elements are the total sales for the three items at each store.

b. Add the elements of the product matrix in part (a).

c. $115

65. $\begin{bmatrix} -33 & -12 \\ -6 & 27 \end{bmatrix}$

66. $\begin{bmatrix} 9 & -6 & 12 \\ 2 & 20 & 12 \end{bmatrix}$

📁 **Resources**
For additional practice with a variety of test item formats:
- Standardized Test Prep, p. 229
- Test-Taking Strategies, p. 224
- Test-Taking Strategies with Transparencies

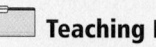 **Chapter Checkpoint 1**

To check understanding of Lessons 4-1 to 4-3:

Checkpoint Quiz 1 (p. 185)

📁 **Teaching Resources**
Checkpoint Quiz 1 (also in Prentice Hall Assessment System)

👥 **Reaching All Students**
Reading and Math Literacy 4B

Spanish versions available

---

page 185   Checkpoint Quiz 1

4. $\begin{bmatrix} -2 & 4 \\ 6 & 16 \end{bmatrix}$

5. $\begin{bmatrix} 1 & 5 \\ -4 & -7 \end{bmatrix}$

6. $\begin{bmatrix} 4.5 & 6 \\ 27 & -18 \end{bmatrix}$

7. $\begin{bmatrix} 42 & 46 \\ 3 & 1 \end{bmatrix}$

8. $\begin{bmatrix} 50 & 117 \\ 278 & 495 \end{bmatrix}$

9. Make sure that the number of columns in the first matrix is the same as the number of rows in the second matrix.

10. Answers may vary. Sample:
$2X + \begin{bmatrix} 1 & 2 & 2 & 4 \\ 0 & 3 & 0 & 5 \end{bmatrix} = \begin{bmatrix} 25 & 16 & -4 & 20 \\ 18 & 3 & -22 & 7 \end{bmatrix}$

Geometry Review

Geometric Transformations

Students will find it helpful to review basic terminology about geometric transformations before they begin Lesson 4-4.

Teaching Notes

Teaching Tip

You may wish to discuss some of the key features of the four kinds of transformations. For example, translations, reflections and rotations do not change the size or shape of a figure. Dilations do not change the shape of a figure, though they usually change its size. Reflections change orientation, whereas the other transformations do not.

Error Prevention

Exercise 5a You may wish to tell students that vertices of the preimage can be assumed to be at points with integer coordinates or midway between two points with integer coordinates.

Tactile Learners

Allow students to perform transformations with cut-outs, blocks, or algebra tiles. The actual manipulation of the objects will reinforce the concepts for students.

page 186   Geometry Review

5a. Answers may vary. Sample: For the blue image in Exercise 3, the vertices are (−0.5, 0.5), (−1.5, 0.5), (−1.5, 1.5), (−1.75, 1.5), (−1, 3), (−0.25, 1.5), and (−0.5, 1.5). For the black pre-image, the corresponding vertices are (−0.5, −0.5), (−1.5, −0.5), (−1.5, −1.5), (−1.75, −1.5), (−1, −3), (−0.25, −1.5), and (−0.5, −1.5).

186

Geometric Transformations

FOR USE WITH LESSON 4-4

Geometric patterns, such as those formed by geese flying south for the winter or tiles on a plane surface, can be described using geometric transformations. A transformation is a change made to a figure. There are four types.

A translation slides a figure a given distance and direction without changing its size or shape.

preimage

image

A rotation turns a figure through a given angle about a point called the center.

preimage

image

A reflection flips a figure over a given line called its axis of reflection.

preimage

image

A dilation enlarges or reduces a figure by a given scale factor.

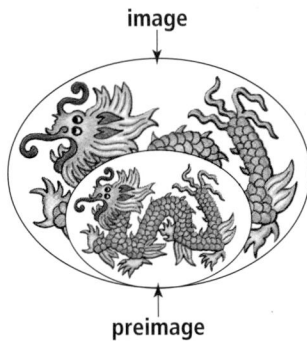
image

preimage

EXERCISES

Describe each transformation from the black figure to the blue figure as a *translation*, *rotation*, *reflection*, or *dilation*.

1.

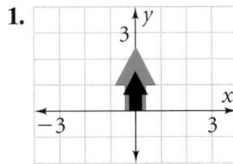

dilation

2.

translation

3.

reflection

4.

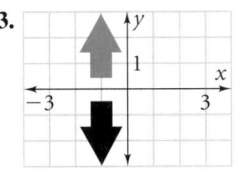

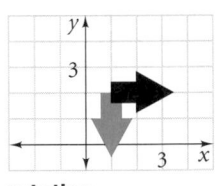

rotation

5. a. Open-Ended List the coordinates of the vertices of one black figure above. List the coordinates of the corresponding blue figure.   **a–b. See margin.**

   b. Make a Conjecture How do the coordinates of the black figure relate to the coordinates of the corresponding blue figure? Use examples to verify your conjecture.

b. For each vertex in the preimage and its corresponding vertex in the image, the *x*-coordinates are equal and the *y*-coordinates are opposites. For example, this is true for the corresponding vertices (−0.5, 0.5) and (−0.5, −0.5). It is also true for (−1, 3) and (−1, −3).

Geometric Transformations with Matrices

North Carolina Objectives   1.04 Operate with matrices to model and solve problems.

Lesson Preview

What You'll Learn

 OBJECTIVE 1
To represent translations and dilations with matrices

 OBJECTIVE 2
To represent reflections and rotations with matrices

. . . And Why

To transform a photo, as in Example 2

✓ Check Skills You'll Need

(For help, go to Lesson 2-6.)

Without using graphing technology, graph each function and its translation. Write the new function. 1–6. See back of book.

1. $y = x + 2$; left 4 units

2. $f(x) = \frac{1}{2}x + 2$; up 5 units

3. $g(x) = |x|$; right 3 units

4. $y = x$; down 2 units

5. $y = |\frac{1}{3}x - 3|$; down 2 units

6. $f(x) = |-2x|$; right 2 units

New Vocabulary
- transformation
- image
- preimage
- translation
- dilation
- reflection
- rotation
- center of rotation

 Interactive lesson includes instant self-check, tutorials, and activities.

OBJECTIVE

1 **Translations and Dilations with Matrices**

Investigation: Translating a Geometric Figure

Geometry In Chapter 2 you used vertical and horizontal translations to graph functions. A translation shifts a graph without changing its size or shape. **2–7. See back of book.**

1. Draw the figure on a coordinate grid as shown. **Check students' work.**

2. Translate the figure 4 units right and 6 units down. Label the new figure.

3. Identify the coordinates of the vertices of the original figure and the new figure.

4. How does the translation *4 units right and 6 units down* relate the coordinates of the new figure to the coordinates of the original figure?

5. Without graphing, identify the coordinates that result from a translation of the original figure 10 units right and 3 units up.

6. Suppose the original figure is translated so that two vertices have coordinates (0, 0) and (2, 0). Find two possible translations. Write the coordinates for the vertices of each translated figure.

7. **Critical Thinking** What translations of the original figure will result in a tessellation?

8. **Open-Ended** Design another simple figure that will tessellate the plane. Describe the translations needed to fill the plane.
   Check students' work.

? Need Help?

A tessellation is a repeating pattern of figures that covers a plane, without gaps or overlaps.

---

1. Plan

Lesson Preview

✓ Check Skills You'll Need

Vertical and Horizontal Translations
Lesson 2-6: Examples 2–5
Exercises 5–18
Extra Practice, p. 823

Lesson Resources

📁 **Teaching Resources**
Practice, Reteaching, Enrichment

👥 **Reaching All Students**
Practice Workbook 4-4
Spanish Practice Workbook 4-4

⏱ **Presentation Assistant Plus!**
Transparencies
- Check Skills You'll Need 4-4
- Additional Examples 4-4
- Student Edition Answers 4-4
- Lesson Quiz 4-4
PH Presentation Pro CD 4-4

PRENTICE HALL ASSESSMENT SYSTEM

Computer Test Generator CD

💿 **Technology**
Resource Pro® CD-ROM
Computer Test Generator CD
Prentice Hall Presentation Pro CD

💻 **www.PHSchool.com**
Student Site
- Teacher Web Code: agk-5500
- Self-grading Lesson Quiz
Teacher Center
- Lesson Planner
- Resources

Plus

✓ Ongoing Assessment and Intervention

Before the Lesson	During the Lesson	After the Lesson
Diagnose prerequisite skills using:	**Monitor progress using:**	**Assess knowledge using:**
• Check Skills You'll Need	• Check Understanding • Additional Examples • Standardized Test Prep	• Lesson Quiz • Computer Test Generator CD

2. Teach

Professional Development

Math Background

Matrices are a powerful tool to represent translations, dilations, reflections, and rotations. Understanding these fundamental concepts can help students to grasp the idea of how compressing music files into a mp3 format will allow a 700 MB CD to hold 200 songs.

OBJECTIVE

▽1 Teaching Notes

Investigation (Optional)

When you discuss Question 4, be sure students understand that *4 units right* signifies a change in each *x*-coordinate and that *6 units down* signifies a change in each *y*-coordinate.

1 EXAMPLE **English Learners**

Ask students who are having difficulty with the vocabulary to list terms whose meanings are unclear to them and write the definitions. Encourage them to refer to their lists to provide special help as needed.

2 EXAMPLE **Tactile Learners**

Draw a polygon very closely centered on a piece of plain paper. Make several photocopies on graph paper. Now make more photocopies of the polygon on plain paper at various enlargement and reduction sizes. On each photocopy, note the enlargement or reduction setting you used. Organize the class into small groups. Give each group one copy at the original size and one that you have enlarged or reduced. Instruct students to copy or trace the copy onto graph paper. Ask students to use approximate coordinates and determine if the photocopier did the enlargement or reduction correctly. Have students exchange photocopies so that each group does one enlargement and one reduction.

188

You can write the vertices of a figure as a matrix. For example, the matrix below represents the vertices of figure *ABCD*.

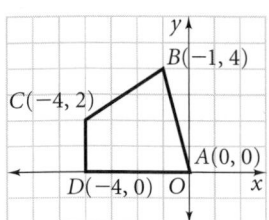

$$\begin{array}{c} \\ x\text{-coordinate} \\ y\text{-coordinate} \end{array} \begin{array}{cccc} A & B & C & D \\ \begin{bmatrix} 0 & -1 & -4 & -4 \\ 0 & 4 & 2 & 0 \end{bmatrix} \end{array}$$

A **transformation** is a change made to a figure. The transformed figure is called the **image**. The original figure is called the **preimage**. A **translation** is a transformation that slides a figure without changing the size or shape of the figure. You can use matrix addition to translate all the vertices of a figure in one step.

1 EXAMPLE **Translating a Figure**

Geometry Quadrilateral *ABCD* above has vertices $A(0, 0)$, $B(-1, 4)$, $C(-4, 2)$, and $D(-4, 0)$. Use a matrix to find the coordinates of the vertices of the image translated 6 units right and 2 units down. Then graph *ABCD* and its image $A'B'C'D'$.

Vertices of the Quadrilateral	Translation Matrix	Vertices of the Image

Add 6 to each *x*-coordinate.

↓ ↓ ↓ ↓

$$\begin{array}{cccc} A & B & C & D \\ \begin{bmatrix} 0 & -1 & -4 & -4 \\ 0 & 4 & 2 & 0 \end{bmatrix} \end{array} + \begin{bmatrix} 6 & 6 & 6 & 6 \\ -2 & -2 & -2 & -2 \end{bmatrix} = \begin{array}{cccc} A' & B' & C' & D' \\ \begin{bmatrix} 6 & 5 & 2 & 2 \\ -2 & 2 & 0 & -2 \end{bmatrix} \end{array}$$

↑ ↑ ↑ ↑

Subtract 2 from each *y*-coordinate.

The vertices of the image are $A'(6, -2)$, $B'(5, 2)$, $C'(2, 0)$, and $D'(2, -2)$.

Graph both quadrilaterals.

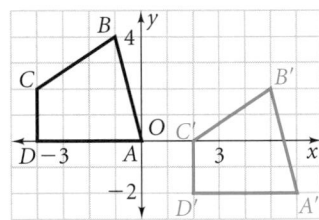

✓ **Check Understanding** **1** **a.** **Critical Thinking** Explain how to translate quadrilateral $A'B'C'D'$ from Example 1 so that its image is quadrilateral *ABCD*. **a–c. See margin.**

b. What matrix would you use to translate the vertices of a pentagon 3 units left and 2 units up?

c. Use your answer to part (b) to translate the pentagon with vertices $(0, -5)$, $(-1, -1)$, $(-5, 0)$, $(1, 3)$, and $(4, 0)$. Find the coordinates of the vertices of the image. Graph the preimage and the image.

A **dilation** is a transformation that changes the size of a figure. When the center of the dilation is the origin, you can use scalar multiplication to find the coordinates of the vertices of an image. All dilations in this book are centered at the origin.

Reading Math

Read the notation A' as "A prime," A'' as "A double prime," etc. The prime symbol tells you that something happened to point *A* to change it to point A'.

Graphing Calculator Hint

Enter the preimage and translation matrices as [A] and [B]. Use matrix addition to find the coordinates of the image.

188   **Chapter 4** Matrices

👥 Reaching All Students

Below Level The mathematical meanings of the terms *transformation*, *translation*, and *rotation* may be unfamiliar to students. For each term, have a student act out the movement.	**Advanced Learners** Have students find the factor by which an 11 × 17 inch photo must be reduced to fit onto an 8.5 × 11 piece of paper. **0.64**	**English Learners** See note on page 188. **Tactile Learners** See note on page 188.

2 EXAMPLE Real-World Connection

Graphic Arts An artist sends you a photo electronically. You increase the size of the photo by a factor of 1.2. Find the coordinates of the vertices of the enlargement.

Write a matrix to represent the coordinates of the vertices, which are at $(0, 0)$, $(0, 5.875)$, $(9.75, 5.875)$, and $(9.75, 0)$. Then multiply by the factor 1.2.

$$1.2 \begin{bmatrix} 0 & 0 & 9.75 & 9.75 \\ 0 & 5.875 & 5.875 & 0 \end{bmatrix} = \begin{bmatrix} 0 & 0 & 11.7 & 11.7 \\ 0 & 7.05 & 7.05 & 0 \end{bmatrix}$$

● The new coordinates are $(0, 0)$, $(0, 7.05)$, $(11.7, 7.05)$, and $(11.7, 0)$.

✓ **Check Understanding** ❷ The coordinates of the vertices of figure ABC are $A(-5, 0)$, $B(8, -1)$, and $C(4, 5)$. Find the coordinates of each image under the following dilations. Then graph each image and its preimage on the same coordinate plane. **a–c. See margin.**

a. 4   b. $\frac{1}{5}$ c. -1.5

OBJECTIVE

2 Reflections and Rotations with Matrices

A **reflection**, or flip, is a transformation that creates symmetry on the coordinate plane. A reflection maps a point in the plane to its mirror image, using a specific line as the mirror. The lines used in this book are the x- and y-axes and the lines $y = x$ and $y = -x$.

You can use matrix multiplication to graph reflections in the coordinate plane.

🔑 **Key Concepts**

Properties	Matrices for Reflections in the Coordinate Plane		
Reflection in the y-axis	Reflection in the x-axis	Reflection in the line $y = x$	Reflection in the line $y = -x$
$\begin{bmatrix} -1 & 0 \\ 0 & 1 \end{bmatrix}$	$\begin{bmatrix} 1 & 0 \\ 0 & -1 \end{bmatrix}$	$\begin{bmatrix} 0 & 1 \\ 1 & 0 \end{bmatrix}$	$\begin{bmatrix} 0 & -1 \\ -1 & 0 \end{bmatrix}$

Lesson 4-4 Geometric Transformations with Matrices **189**

Additional Examples

❶ Triangle ABC has vertices $A(1, -2)$, $B(3, 1)$, and $C(2, 3)$. Use a matrix to find the coordinates of the vertices of the image translated 3 units left and 1 unit up. Graph ABC and its image $A'B'C'$.

Vertices: $A'(-2, -1)$, $B'(0, 2)$, $C'(-1, 4)$

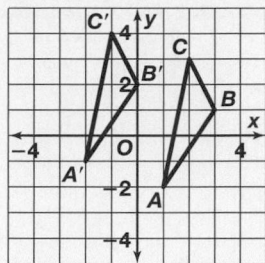

❷ The figure in the diagram is to be reduced by a factor of $\frac{2}{3}$. Find the coordinates of the vertices of the reduced figure.

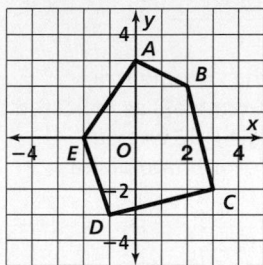

$A'(0, 2)$, $B'\left(\frac{4}{3}, \frac{4}{3}\right)$, $C'\left(2, -\frac{4}{3}\right)$, $D'\left(-\frac{2}{3}, -2\right)$, $E'\left(-\frac{4}{3}, 0\right)$

---

pages 188–189 Check Understanding

1a. Subtract 6 from each x-coordinate and add 2 to each y-coordinate.

b. $\begin{bmatrix} -3 & -3 & -3 & -3 & -3 \\ 2 & 2 & 2 & 2 & 2 \end{bmatrix}$

c. $(-3, -3)$, $(-4, 1)$, $(-8, 2)$, $(-2, 5)$, $(1, 2)$

See back of book for graph.

2a–c. **See back of book for graphs.**

2a. $(-20, 0)$, $(32, -4)$, $(16, 20)$

b. $(-1, 0)$, $(1.6, -0.2)$, $(0.8, 1)$

c. $(7.5, 0)$, $(-12, 1.5)$, $(-6, -7.5)$

189

Additional Examples

3 Reflect the triangle with coordinates $A(2, -1)$, $B(3, 0)$, and $C(4, -2)$ in each line. Graph triangle ABC and each image on the same coordinate plane.

a. x-axis
$$\begin{bmatrix} 2 & 3 & 4 \\ 1 & 0 & 2 \end{bmatrix}$$

b. y-axis
$$\begin{bmatrix} -2 & -3 & -4 \\ -1 & 0 & -2 \end{bmatrix}$$

c. $y = x$
$$\begin{bmatrix} -1 & 0 & -2 \\ 2 & 3 & 4 \end{bmatrix}$$

d. $y = -x$
$$\begin{bmatrix} 1 & 0 & 2 \\ -2 & -3 & -4 \end{bmatrix}$$

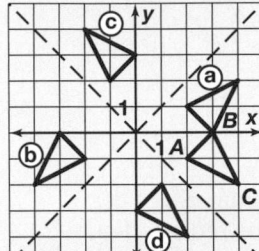

4 Rotate the triangle from Additional Example 3 as indicated. Graph triangle ABC and each image on a coordinate plane.

a. 90°
$$\begin{bmatrix} 1 & 0 & 2 \\ 2 & 3 & 4 \end{bmatrix}$$

b. 180°
$$\begin{bmatrix} -2 & -3 & -4 \\ 1 & 0 & 2 \end{bmatrix}$$

c. 270°
$$\begin{bmatrix} -1 & 0 & -2 \\ -2 & -3 & -4 \end{bmatrix}$$

d. 360°
$$\begin{bmatrix} 2 & 3 & 4 \\ -1 & 0 & -2 \end{bmatrix}$$

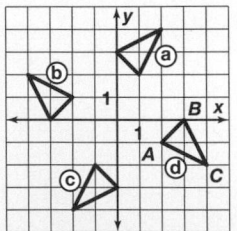

Closure

Ask students what matrix operations you can use to translate, dilate, reflect, and rotate figures in the coordinate plane. **addition, scalar multiplication, matrix multiplication**

190

---

3 **EXAMPLE** **Reflecting a Figure**

Reflect the triangle with coordinates $A(0, 0)$, $B(2, 5)$, and $C(-2, 3)$ in each line. Then graph each pair of triangles on the same coordinate plane.

a. y-axis
$$\begin{bmatrix} -1 & 0 \\ 0 & 1 \end{bmatrix}\begin{bmatrix} 0 & 2 & -2 \\ 0 & 5 & 3 \end{bmatrix} = \begin{bmatrix} 0 & -2 & 2 \\ 0 & 5 & 3 \end{bmatrix}$$

b. x-axis
$$\begin{bmatrix} 1 & 0 \\ 0 & -1 \end{bmatrix}\begin{bmatrix} 0 & 2 & -2 \\ 0 & 5 & 3 \end{bmatrix} = \begin{bmatrix} 0 & 2 & -2 \\ 0 & -5 & -3 \end{bmatrix}$$

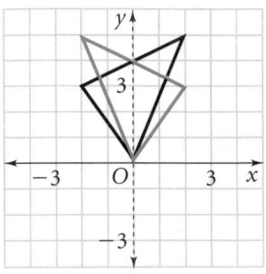 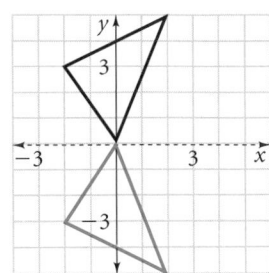

c. $y = x$
$$\begin{bmatrix} 0 & 1 \\ 1 & 0 \end{bmatrix}\begin{bmatrix} 0 & 2 & -2 \\ 0 & 5 & 3 \end{bmatrix} = \begin{bmatrix} 0 & 5 & 3 \\ 0 & 2 & -2 \end{bmatrix}$$

d. $y = -x$
$$\begin{bmatrix} 0 & -1 \\ -1 & 0 \end{bmatrix}\begin{bmatrix} 0 & 2 & -2 \\ 0 & 5 & 3 \end{bmatrix} = \begin{bmatrix} 0 & -5 & -3 \\ 0 & -2 & 2 \end{bmatrix}$$

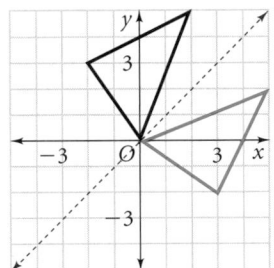 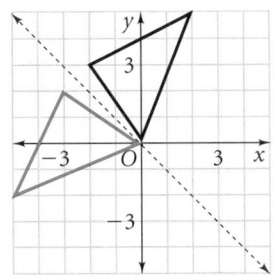

✓ **Check Understanding** **3** Reflect the triangle with coordinates $D(-3, 0)$, $E(-4, 4)$, and $F(1, 1)$ in each line. Then graph each pair of triangles on the same coordinate plane.

a. y-axis   **b.** x-axis   **c.** $y = x$ **d.** $y = -x$

a–d. See margin.

Need Help?

There are 360 degrees in a circle.

A **rotation** is a transformation that turns a figure about a fixed point called the **center of rotation.** You can rotate a figure as much as 360 degrees. In this book, all rotations are counterclockwise about the origin.

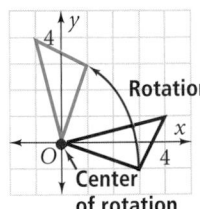

Rotation

Center of rotation

  Key Concepts

Properties	Matrices for Rotations in the Coordinate Plane			
Rotation of 90°	Rotation of 180°	Rotation of 270°	Rotation of 360°
$\begin{bmatrix} 0 & -1 \\ 1 & 0 \end{bmatrix}$	$\begin{bmatrix} -1 & 0 \\ 0 & -1 \end{bmatrix}$	$\begin{bmatrix} 0 & 1 \\ -1 & 0 \end{bmatrix}$	$\begin{bmatrix} 1 & 0 \\ 0 & 1 \end{bmatrix}$

190   Chapter 4   Matrices

pages 190–191 **Check Understanding**

3, 4. See back of book for graphs.

3a. $\begin{bmatrix} 3 & 4 & -1 \\ 0 & 4 & 1 \end{bmatrix}$

b. $\begin{bmatrix} -3 & -4 & 1 \\ 0 & -4 & -1 \end{bmatrix}$

c. $\begin{bmatrix} 0 & 4 & 1 \\ -3 & -4 & 1 \end{bmatrix}$

d. $\begin{bmatrix} 0 & -4 & -1 \\ 3 & 4 & -1 \end{bmatrix}$

4 EXAMPLE Rotating a Figure

Rotate the triangle with coordinates $A(0,0)$, $B(2,5)$, and $C(-2,3)$. Then graph each pair of triangles on the same coordinate plane.

a. 90°

$$\begin{bmatrix} 0 & -1 \\ 1 & 0 \end{bmatrix}\begin{bmatrix} 0 & 2 & -2 \\ 0 & 5 & 3 \end{bmatrix} = \begin{bmatrix} 0 & -5 & -3 \\ 0 & 2 & -2 \end{bmatrix}$$

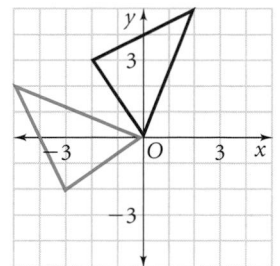

b. 180°

$$\begin{bmatrix} -1 & 0 \\ 0 & -1 \end{bmatrix}\begin{bmatrix} 0 & 2 & -2 \\ 0 & 5 & 3 \end{bmatrix} = \begin{bmatrix} 0 & -2 & 2 \\ 0 & -5 & -3 \end{bmatrix}$$

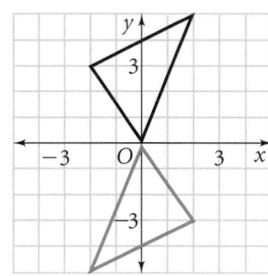

c. 270°

$$\begin{bmatrix} 0 & 1 \\ -1 & 0 \end{bmatrix}\begin{bmatrix} 0 & 2 & -2 \\ 0 & 5 & 3 \end{bmatrix} = \begin{bmatrix} 0 & 5 & 3 \\ 0 & -2 & 2 \end{bmatrix}$$

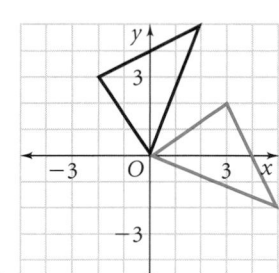

d. 360°

$$\begin{bmatrix} 1 & 0 \\ 0 & 1 \end{bmatrix}\begin{bmatrix} 0 & 2 & -2 \\ 0 & 5 & 3 \end{bmatrix} = \begin{bmatrix} 0 & 2 & -2 \\ 0 & 5 & 3 \end{bmatrix}$$

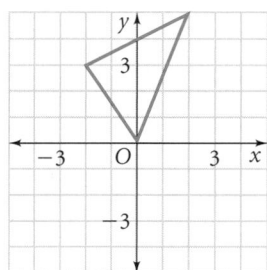

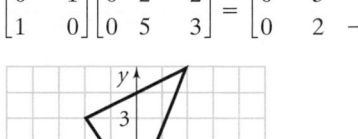

Real-World Connection

The triangles in the windmill have 90° rotational symmetry.

✓ **Check Understanding** ④ Rotate the quadrilateral with coordinates $A(1,1)$, $B(3,1)$, $C(6,4)$, and $D(1,3)$. Then graph each pair of quadrilaterals on the same coordinate plane.
a. 90°　　　　**b.** 180°　　　　**c.** 270°　　　　**d.** 360°
a–d. See margin.

EXERCISES

For more practice, see *Extra Practice*.

Practice and Problem Solving

Ⓐ Practice by Example

Example 1
(page 188)

Use matrix addition to find the coordinates of each image after a translation of 3 units left and 5 units up. If possible, graph each pair of figures on the same coordinate plane. **1–4. See margin.**

1. $A(1,-3)$, $B(1,1)$, $C(5,1)$, $D(5,-3)$　　**2.** $G(0,0)$, $H(4,4)$, $I(4,-4)$, $J(8,0)$

3. $J(-10,2)$, $K(-16,a)$, $L(12,-5)$　　**4.** $R(9,3)$, $S(3,6)$, $T(3,3)$, $U(6,-3)$

5–9. See back of book.

Example 2
(page 189)

Graph each figure and its image after the given dilation.

5. $\begin{bmatrix} 0 & 2 & 5 & 8 \\ 0 & 4 & 5 & 1 \end{bmatrix}, 2$　　**6.** $\begin{bmatrix} -7 & -3 & 4 \\ -5 & 4 & 0 \end{bmatrix}, 0.5$　　**7.** $\begin{bmatrix} 0 & -2 & -5 \\ 0 & 0 & 5 \end{bmatrix}, \frac{9}{10}$

8. $\begin{bmatrix} -10 & -5 & 0 & 5 & 10 \\ 8 & 16 & 20 & 16 & 8 \end{bmatrix}, \frac{1}{4}$　　**9.** $\begin{bmatrix} -8 & 2 & 3 & 1 & -2 \\ 6 & 4 & 0 & -4 & 0 \end{bmatrix}, 1.5$

Lesson 4-4 Geometric Transformations with Matrices　**191**

4a. $\begin{bmatrix} -1 & -1 & -4 & -3 \\ 1 & 3 & 6 & 1 \end{bmatrix}$

b. $\begin{bmatrix} -1 & -3 & -6 & -1 \\ -1 & -1 & -4 & -3 \end{bmatrix}$

c. $\begin{bmatrix} 1 & 1 & 4 & 3 \\ -1 & -3 & -6 & -1 \end{bmatrix}$

d. $\begin{bmatrix} 1 & 3 & 6 & 1 \\ 1 & 1 & 4 & 3 \end{bmatrix}$

pages 191–194　Exercises

1, 2, 4. *See back of book for graphs.*

3. Practice

Assignment Guide

1 Objective

Ⓐ Ⓑ Core 1–9, 24–30, 35–37, 43–44

Ⓒ Extension 45–46

2 Objective

Ⓐ Ⓑ Core 10–23, 31–34, 38–42

Ⓒ Extension 47–50

Standardized Test Prep 51–54

Mixed Review 55–63

Error Prevention

Exercises 1–4 Suggest that students write "– 3" below each x-coordinate and "+ 5" below each y-coordinate.

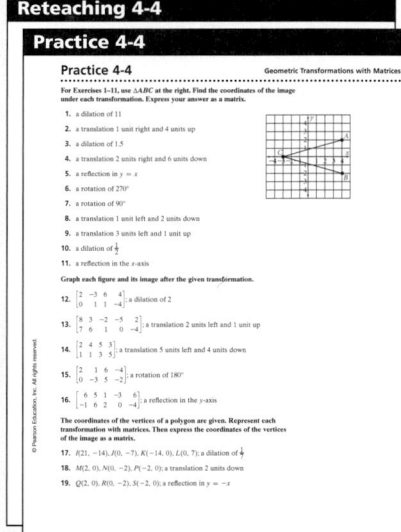

1. $\begin{bmatrix} -2 & -2 & 2 & 2 \\ 2 & 6 & 6 & 2 \end{bmatrix}$

2. $\begin{bmatrix} -3 & 1 & 1 & 5 \\ 5 & 9 & 1 & 5 \end{bmatrix}$

3. $\begin{bmatrix} -13 & -19 & 9 \\ 7 & a+5 & 0 \end{bmatrix}$; graph not possible

4. $\begin{bmatrix} 6 & 0 & 0 & 3 \\ 8 & 11 & 8 & 2 \end{bmatrix}$

pages 191–194   Exercises

10.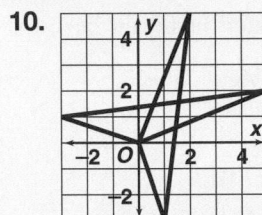

11.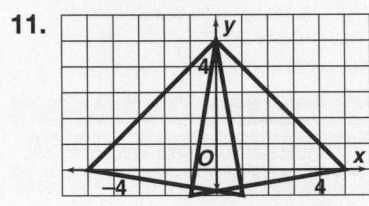

12.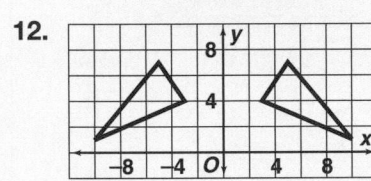

13. $\begin{bmatrix} 3 & -3 & -3 & 3 \\ -3 & -6 & -3 & -6 \end{bmatrix}$

14. $\begin{bmatrix} 0 & 4 & 8 & 6 \\ 0 & -4 & -4 & -2 \end{bmatrix}$

15. $\begin{bmatrix} 3 & 2 & 2 & 3 & 5 \\ 1 & 2 & 3 & 4 & 2.5 \end{bmatrix}$

16. $\begin{bmatrix} -1 & -2 & -4 & -6 & -2 \\ 4 & 0 & 0 & 3 & 4 \end{bmatrix}$

20. $\begin{bmatrix} -3 & 3 & 3 & -3 \\ -3 & -6 & -3 & -6 \end{bmatrix}$

21. $\begin{bmatrix} 0 & 4 & 8 & 6 \\ 0 & 4 & 4 & 2 \end{bmatrix}$

22. $\begin{bmatrix} -1 & -2 & -3 & -4 & -2.5 \\ -3 & -2 & -2 & -3 & -5 \end{bmatrix}$

Example 3
(page 190)

Graph each figure and its image after reflection in the given line.   10–12. See margin.

10. $\begin{bmatrix} 0 & -3 & 5 \\ 0 & 1 & 2 \end{bmatrix}; y = x$
11. $\begin{bmatrix} -1 & 0 & 5 \\ -1 & 5 & 0 \end{bmatrix}; y\text{-axis}$
12. $\begin{bmatrix} -3 & -5 & -10 \\ 4 & 7 & 1 \end{bmatrix}; x\text{-axis}$

Find the coordinates of each image after reflection in the given line.   13–16. See margin.

13. $\begin{bmatrix} 3 & 6 & 3 & 6 \\ -3 & 3 & 3 & -3 \end{bmatrix}; y = -x$
14. $\begin{bmatrix} 0 & 4 & 8 & 6 \\ 0 & 4 & 4 & 2 \end{bmatrix}; x\text{-axis}$

15. $\begin{bmatrix} 1 & 2 & 3 & 4 & 2.5 \\ 3 & 2 & 2 & 3 & 5 \end{bmatrix}; y = x$
16. $\begin{bmatrix} -1 & -2 & -4 & -6 & -2 \\ -4 & 0 & 0 & -3 & -4 \end{bmatrix}; x\text{-axis}$

Example 4
(page 191)

Graph each figure and its image after the given rotation.

17. $\begin{bmatrix} 0 & -3 & 5 \\ 0 & 1 & 2 \end{bmatrix}; 90°$
18. $\begin{bmatrix} -1 & 0 & 5 \\ -1 & 5 & 0 \end{bmatrix}; 180°$
19. $\begin{bmatrix} -5 & 6 & 0 \\ -1 & 2 & 4 \end{bmatrix}; 90°$

17–19. See back of book.

Find the coordinates of each image after the given rotation.   20–23. See margin.

20. $\begin{bmatrix} 3 & 6 & 3 & 6 \\ -3 & 3 & 3 & -3 \end{bmatrix}; 270°$
21. $\begin{bmatrix} 0 & 4 & 8 & 6 \\ 0 & 4 & 4 & 2 \end{bmatrix}; 360°$

22. $\begin{bmatrix} 1 & 2 & 3 & 4 & 2.5 \\ 3 & 2 & 2 & 3 & 5 \end{bmatrix}; 180°$
23. $\begin{bmatrix} -1 & -2 & -4 & -6 & -2 \\ -4 & 0 & 0 & -3 & -4 \end{bmatrix}; 270°$

B **Apply Your Skills** **Geometry** Each matrix represents the vertices of a polygon. Translate each figure 5 units left and 1 unit up. Express your answer as a matrix.   24–26. See margin.

24. $\begin{bmatrix} -3 & -3 & 2 & 2 \\ -2 & -4 & -2 & -4 \end{bmatrix}$
25. $\begin{bmatrix} -3 & 0 & 3 & 0 \\ -9 & -6 & -9 & -12 \end{bmatrix}$
26. $\begin{bmatrix} 0 & 1 & -4 \\ 0 & 3 & 5 \end{bmatrix}$

For Exercises 27–34, use $\triangle ABC$. Write the coordinates of each image in matrix form.   27–30. See margin.

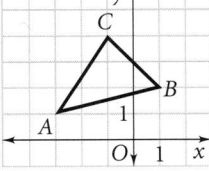

27. a dilation four times the original size
28. a translation 2 units left and 3 units down

29. a dilation half the original size
30. a translation 1 unit right and 7 units up

31. a rotation of 90°
32. a reflection in $y = x$ **31–34. See margin p. 193.**

33. a rotation of 180°
34. a reflection in the x-axis

35. a. Graph $\begin{bmatrix} 9 & 10 & 6 \\ 1 & -3 & -2 \end{bmatrix}$ and $2\begin{bmatrix} 9 & 10 & 6 \\ 1 & -3 & -2 \end{bmatrix}$.

   b. Writing Compare the graphs in part (a). Generalize how a dilation changes a graph.   **a–b. See back of book.**

Need Help?

A tessellation is a repeating pattern of figures that covers a plane, without gaps or overlap.

36. Geometry Create a tessellation based on the quadrilateral $\begin{bmatrix} 0 & -3 & -5 & 0 \\ 1 & 3 & -1 & -1 \end{bmatrix}$.

   Translate the quadrilateral using $\begin{bmatrix} 5 & 5 & 5 & 5 \\ 2 & 2 & 2 & 2 \end{bmatrix}$ and $\begin{bmatrix} 3 & 3 & 3 & 3 \\ -4 & -4 & -4 & -4 \end{bmatrix}$.
   See back of book.

37. Writing Explain why you might want to represent a transformation as a matrix.   **Check students' work.**

38. Find $\begin{bmatrix} -3 & 0 \\ 0 & -3 \end{bmatrix}\begin{bmatrix} 1 & -2 & 4 \\ 1 & -1 & 2 \end{bmatrix}$ and $-3\begin{bmatrix} 1 & -2 & 4 \\ 1 & -1 & 2 \end{bmatrix}$. What do you notice?
   Both products are equal.

23. $\begin{bmatrix} -4 & 0 & 0 & -3 & -4 \\ 1 & 2 & 4 & 6 & 2 \end{bmatrix}$
25. $\begin{bmatrix} -8 & -5 & -2 & -5 \\ -8 & -5 & -8 & -11 \end{bmatrix}$
27. $\begin{bmatrix} -12 & 4 & -4 \\ 4 & 8 & 16 \end{bmatrix}$

24. $\begin{bmatrix} -8 & -8 & -3 & -3 \\ -1 & -3 & -1 & -3 \end{bmatrix}$
26. $\begin{bmatrix} -5 & -4 & -9 \\ 1 & 4 & 6 \end{bmatrix}$
28. $\begin{bmatrix} -5 & -1 & -3 \\ -2 & -1 & 1 \end{bmatrix}$

Use matrices to represent the vertices of graph *f* and graph *g*. Name each transformation. 39–44. See back of book.

39.
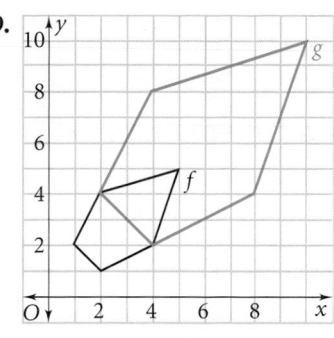

40.
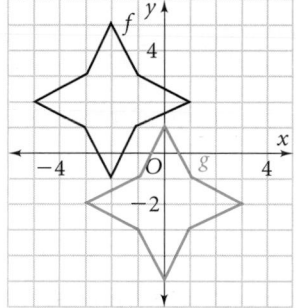

41.
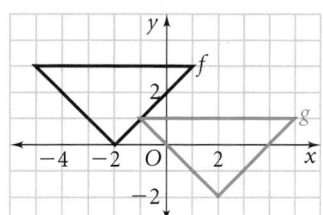

42.
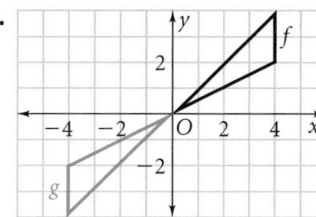

Graph each triangle and its translation on the same coordinate plane.

43. $\begin{bmatrix} 0 & 2 & 3 \\ 0 & 0 & 5 \end{bmatrix}$; 3 units right, 4 units down

44. $\begin{bmatrix} -5 & 3 & 4 \\ 5 & 1 & -4 \end{bmatrix}$; 2 units left, 5 units up

 **Challenge**

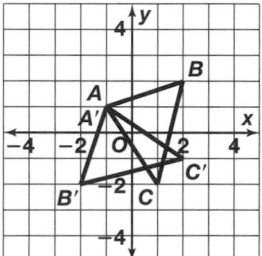 **45. Architecture** Use the pattern of brown tiles shown.
  a. Copy the graph. Mark scales on the axes so that the dimensions of the square tiles are 1 unit by 1 unit.
  b. Write a matrix for the translation of tile *ABCD* to tile *A'B'C'D'*. What are the coordinates of the vertices of the preimage and the image?
  c. A brown tile is 6 units right and 6 units down from tile *ABCD*. Write a matrix to represent the coordinates of its vertices. **a–c. See back of book.**
  d. A tile has vertices at $(-6, 9), (-6, 8), (-7, 9),$ and $(-7, 8)$. What translation of tile *ABCD* results in these coordinates? **Translate the vertices of *ABCD* left 12 units.**

Geometry Each matrix represents the vertices of a polygon. Write a matrix to represent the vertices of the image after each transformation. 46–49. See back of book.

46. $\begin{bmatrix} -3 & 0.5 & -5 \\ 0 & 3 & 3 \end{bmatrix}$; dilation of 2

47. $\begin{bmatrix} 4 & 7 & 10 \\ 0 & 2 & 0 \end{bmatrix}$; rotation of 270°

48. $\begin{bmatrix} 17 & 6 & 6 & 2 \\ 5 & 10 & 2 & 6 \end{bmatrix}$; reflection in $y = x$

49. $\begin{bmatrix} 3 & 4.5 & 5 & 3.5 \\ 3 & 1.5 & 2 & 4 \end{bmatrix}$; rotation of 90°

Lesson 4-4 Geometric Transformations with Matrices **193**

29. $\begin{bmatrix} -1.5 & 0.5 & -0.5 \\ 0.5 & 1 & 2 \end{bmatrix}$

30. $\begin{bmatrix} -2 & 2 & 0 \\ 8 & 9 & 11 \end{bmatrix}$

31. $\begin{bmatrix} -1 & -2 & -4 \\ -3 & 1 & -1 \end{bmatrix}$

32. $\begin{bmatrix} 1 & 2 & 4 \\ -3 & 1 & -1 \end{bmatrix}$

33. $\begin{bmatrix} 3 & -1 & 1 \\ -1 & -2 & -4 \end{bmatrix}$

34. $\begin{bmatrix} -3 & 1 & -1 \\ -1 & -2 & -4 \end{bmatrix}$

For additional practice with a
variety of test item formats:
• Standardized Test Prep, p. 229
• Test-Taking Strategies, p. 224
• Test-Taking Strategies with
  Transparencies

Exercise 51 Examine the answer
choices. You will notice that you
can identify the correct choice
without finding the reflection
image of all the given points
because the only correct
coordinates of X' appear in
answer choice B.

pages 191–194 Exercises

50a. 3 2 1 0 1 2 3

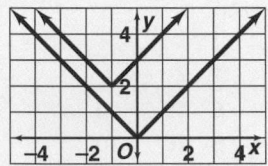

53. [2] $\begin{bmatrix} -2 & -2 & -2 \\ 6 & 6 & 6 \end{bmatrix}$;

(–6, 2), (–4, 8), (2, 3)

[1] **does not represent
the combined
transformation in
matrix form OR
does not state new
vertices**

54a. [4]

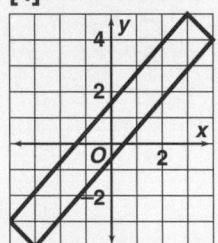

b. $\begin{bmatrix} -5 & -4 & 4 & 3 \\ 3 & 4 & -3 & -4 \end{bmatrix}$

c.

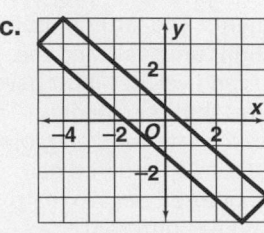

d. **90° rotation**

---

50. Let the matrix $\begin{bmatrix} x \\ y \end{bmatrix}$ represent points on the graph $y = |x|$.
   a. Complete the table. Sketch the graph. **See margin.**

x	-3	-2	-1	0	1	2	3
y	■	■	■	■	■	■	■

   3   2   1   0   1   2   3

   b. **Critical Thinking** What does the matrix addition $\begin{bmatrix} x \\ y \end{bmatrix} + \begin{bmatrix} -1 \\ 2 \end{bmatrix}$ represent?
   Show your answer on your graph from part (a).
   **Answers may vary. Sample: The addition represents a
   translation of the pt. (x, y) 1 unit to the left and 2 units up.**

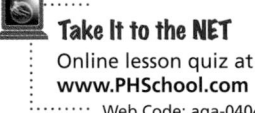

Standardized Test Prep

Multiple Choice

51. What are the coordinates of $X(5, 1)$, $Y(-5, -3)$, and $Z(-1, 3)$ reflected in
   the line $y = x$? **B**
   A. $X'(-5, -1)$, $Y'(5, 3)$, $Z'(1, -3)$ B. $X'(1, 5)$, $Y'(-3, -5)$, $Z'(3, -1)$
   C. $X'(-1, -5)$, $Y'(3, 5)$, $Z'(-3, 1)$ D. $X'(5, 1)$, $Y'(-5, -3)$, $Z'(-1, 3)$

52. Reflection in which line takes the figure with vertices $A(0, 0)$, $B(-2, 4)$,
   $C(-4, 2)$, and $D(-3, 0)$ to $A'(0, 0)$, $B'(-2, -4)$, $C'(-4, -2)$, and $D'(-3, 0)$? **F**
   F. x-axis   G. y-axis   H. $y = x$ I. $y = -x$

Short Response

53. Each vertex of the triangle at the right is
   transformed by *right 3, up 2* and then by
   left 5, up 4. What is a matrix for the combined
   transformation? What are the coordinates of
   the vertices of the final triangle? **See margin.**

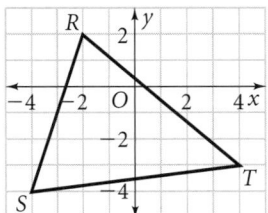

Extended Response

54. A quadrilateral has coordinates $\begin{bmatrix} 3 & 4 & -3 & -4 \\ 5 & 4 & -4 & -3 \end{bmatrix}$.
   a. Graph the quadrilateral.
   b. Find the product $\begin{bmatrix} 0 & -1 \\ 1 & 0 \end{bmatrix}\begin{bmatrix} 3 & 4 & -3 & -4 \\ 5 & 4 & -4 & -3 \end{bmatrix}$.
   c. Graph the result as a new quadrilateral.
   d. What is the relationship between the quadrilaterals in parts (a) and (c)?
   a–d. See margin.

Take It to the NET
Online lesson quiz at
www.PHSchool.com
Web Code: aga-0404

Mixed Review

Lesson 4-3

If possible, find the dimensions of each product matrix; then find each product. If
the product is not defined, explain why not.   **55–56. See back of book.**

55. $\begin{bmatrix} 1 & 0 & -5 \\ 2 & -1 & 6 \end{bmatrix}\begin{bmatrix} 2 & 4 & -2 \\ 0 & 10 & 4 \\ 0 & 1 & -7 \end{bmatrix}$ 56. $\begin{bmatrix} 0 & 7 & k & 5 \\ 0 & 6 & 0 & 5 \end{bmatrix}\begin{bmatrix} 9 & -1 & 3 & 0 \\ 7 & 0 & 7 & 0 \end{bmatrix}$

Lesson 3-5

Graph each equation.   **57–59. See back of book.**

57. $x + y - z = 5$ 58. $2x - y + 3z = 12$ 59. $-x + 4y - z = -6$

Lesson 2-1

Make a mapping diagram for each relation. Determine whether it is a function.

60. $(-2, 4), (-1, 1), (0, 0), (1, 1), (2, 4)$ **yes**   61. $(27, -2), (3, -1), (0, 0), (3, 1), (27, 2)$ **no**

62. $(-2, 15), (-1, 1), (0, -3), (1, 3), (2, 15)$**yes** 63. $(-3, 8), (-2, 1), (1, -2), (0, -1), (1, 4)$
no
60–63. See back of book for diagram.

[3] **appropriate methods,
but with one
computational error in
determining the product**

[2] **unable to graph matrix
or unable to recognize
transformation**

[1] **correct graph in part (a),
but with the rest
completed incorrectly**

2 × 2 Matrices, Determinants, and Inverses

 North Carolina Objectives

1.04   Operate with matrices to model and solve problems.

Lesson Preview

What You'll Learn

 OBJECTIVE 1
To evaluate determinants of 2 × 2 matrices and find inverse matrices

OBJECTIVE 2
To use inverse matrices in solving matrix equations

... And Why

To predict cell phone ownership, as in Example 5

 Check Skills You'll Need   (For help, go to Skills Handbook page 845.)

Simplify each group of expressions.

1. **a.** $3(4)$ **12**   **b.** $2(6)$ **12**   **c.** $3(4) - 2(6)$ **0**

2. **a.** $3(-4)$ **−12**   **b.** $2(-6)$ **−12**   **c.** $3(-4) - 2(-6)$ **0**

3. **a.** $-3(-4)$ **12**   **b.** $2(-6)$ **−12**   **c.** $-3(-4) - 2(-6)$ **24**

4. **a.** $-3(4)$ **−12**   **b.** $-2(-6)$ **12**   **c.** $-3(4) - (-2)(-6)$ **−24**

New Vocabulary   • square matrix   • multiplicative identity matrix
    • multiplicative inverse of a matrix   • determinant

---

1. Plan

Lesson Preview

 **Check Skills You'll Need**

Simplifying Expressions with Integers
Skills Handbook: p. 845
Example 3
Exercises 11, 13, 15–16, 18

Lesson Resources

Teaching Resources
Practice, Reteaching, Enrichment

Reaching All Students
Practice Workbook 4-5
Spanish Practice Workbook 4-5

Presentation Assistant Plus!
Transparencies
• Check Skills You'll Need 4-5
• Additional Examples 4-5
• Student Edition Answers 4-5
• Lesson Quiz 4-5
PH Presentation Pro CD 4-5

 **PRENTICE HALL ASSESSMENT SYSTEM**

Computer Test Generator CD

 Technology
Resource Pro® CD-ROM
Computer Test Generator CD
Prentice Hall Presentation Pro CD

 **www.PHSchool.com**
Student Site
• Teacher Web Code: agk-5500
• Self-grading Lesson Quiz
Teacher Center
• Lesson Planner
• Resources

Plus **iTEXT**

 OBJECTIVE 1

Evaluating Determinants of 2 × 2 Matrices

iTEXT Interactive lesson includes instant self-check, tutorials, and activities.

A **square matrix** is a matrix with the same number of columns as rows.

For any real number a, the number 1 is the multiplicative identity of a, since $a \cdot 1 = 1 \cdot a = a$. Square matrices also have a multiplicative identity.

Key Concepts

| **Definition** | **Multiplicative Identity Matrix** |

For an $n \times n$ square matrix, the **multiplicative identity matrix** is an $n \times n$ square matrix I, or $I_{n \times n}$, with 1's along the main diagonal and 0's elsewhere.

$$I_2 = \begin{bmatrix} 1 & 0 \\ 0 & 1 \end{bmatrix}, \qquad I_3 = \begin{bmatrix} 1 & 0 & 0 \\ 0 & 1 & 0 \\ 0 & 0 & 1 \end{bmatrix}, \qquad \text{and so forth}$$

If the product of the real numbers a and b is 1, then a and b are multiplicative inverses. Some, but not all, square matrices have multiplicative inverses.

Key Concepts

| **Definition** | **Multiplicative Inverse of a Matrix** |

If A and X are $n \times n$ matrices, and $AX = XA = I$, then X is the multiplicative inverse of A, written A^{-1}.

$$AA^{-1} = A^{-1}A = I$$

If B is the multiplicative inverse of A, then A is the multiplicative inverse of B. To show that A and B are multiplicative inverses, show that $AB = I$ or that $BA = I$.

 ## Ongoing Assessment and Intervention

Before the Lesson	**During the Lesson**	**After the Lesson**
Diagnose prerequisite skills using:	**Monitor progress using:**	**Assess knowledge using:**
• Check Skills You'll Need	• Check Understanding	• Lesson Quiz
	• Additional Examples	• Computer Test Generator CD
	• Standardized Test Prep	

Professional Development

Math Background

Many $n \times n$ matrices have multiplicative inverses. Inverse matrices play a central role in answering questions about the existence of solutions for systems of linear equations. For square matrices, verifying either that $AB = I$ or that $BA = I$ is sufficient to show that A and B are inverses of each other.

OBJECTIVE

1 Teaching Notes

2 EXAMPLE Auditory Learners

Students may want to set the products ad and bc equal to each other as is done when solving proportions. Emphasize to students that they should find the *difference* of the products when evaluating a *determinant*. Stress the initial *d* in each word.

3 EXAMPLE Alternative Method

Point out that the quickest way to determine if a 2×2 matrix has an inverse is to determine whether $ad - bc = 0$, or equivalently $ad = bc$. If $ad = bc$ there is no inverse.

 Need Help?

To review the multiplicative inverse of a number, go to Lesson 1-1.

1 EXAMPLE Verifying Inverses

Show that B is the multiplicative inverse of A.

$$A = \begin{bmatrix} 2 & 3 \\ 1 & 2 \end{bmatrix} \qquad B = \begin{bmatrix} 2 & -3 \\ -1 & 2 \end{bmatrix}$$

$$AB = \begin{bmatrix} 2 & 3 \\ 1 & 2 \end{bmatrix}\begin{bmatrix} 2 & -3 \\ -1 & 2 \end{bmatrix} = \begin{bmatrix} 2(2) + 3(-1) & 2(-3) + 3(2) \\ 1(2) + 2(-1) & 1(-3) + 2(2) \end{bmatrix} = \begin{bmatrix} 1 & 0 \\ 0 & 1 \end{bmatrix}$$

$AB = I$, so B is the multiplicative inverse of A. A is also the multiplicative inverse of B.

Check $BA = \begin{bmatrix} 2 & -3 \\ -1 & 2 \end{bmatrix}\begin{bmatrix} 2 & 3 \\ 1 & 2 \end{bmatrix} = \begin{bmatrix} 2(2) + (-3)(1) & 2(3) + (-3)(2) \\ -1(2) + 2(1) & -1(3) + 2(2) \end{bmatrix} = \begin{bmatrix} 1 & 0 \\ 0 & 1 \end{bmatrix}$ ✓

✓ **Check Understanding** **1** Show that the matrices are multiplicative inverses.

a. $\begin{bmatrix} 2 & 1 \\ 2.5 & 1 \end{bmatrix}$ and $\begin{bmatrix} -2 & 2 \\ 5 & -4 \end{bmatrix}$ **b.** $\begin{bmatrix} -2 & -5 \\ -3 & -8 \end{bmatrix}$ and $\begin{bmatrix} -8 & 5 \\ 3 & -2 \end{bmatrix}$

a–b. See margin p. 197.

Every square matrix with real-number elements has a real-number determinant. Determinants can help you find inverses.

Write	Read	Evaluate
↓	↓	↓
$A = \begin{bmatrix} a & b \\ c & d \end{bmatrix}$ $\det A = \begin{vmatrix} a & b \\ c & d \end{vmatrix}$	the determinant of A	 $= ad - bc$

🔑 **Key Concepts**

Definition	**Determinant of a 2 × 2 Matrix**

The **determinant** of a 2×2 matrix $\begin{bmatrix} a & b \\ c & d \end{bmatrix}$ is $ad - bc$.

Symbols for the determinant of a matrix

↓   ↓

$\det A$ $\begin{vmatrix} a & b \\ c & d \end{vmatrix}$

2 EXAMPLE Evaluating the Determinant of a 2 × 2 Matrix

Evaluate each determinant.

a. $\det \begin{bmatrix} -3 & 4 \\ 2 & -5 \end{bmatrix} = \begin{vmatrix} -3 & 4 \\ 2 & -5 \end{vmatrix} = (-3)(-5) - (4)(2) = 15 - 8 = 7$

b. $\det \begin{bmatrix} 2 & -3 \\ 3 & -2 \end{bmatrix} = \begin{vmatrix} 2 & -3 \\ 3 & -2 \end{vmatrix} = (2)(-2) - (-3)(3) = -4 - (-9) = 5$

c. $\det \begin{bmatrix} a & 0 \\ 0 & a \end{bmatrix} = \begin{vmatrix} a & 0 \\ 0 & a \end{vmatrix} = a^2 - 0 = a^2$

✓ **Check Understanding** **2** Evaluate the determinant of each matrix.

a. $\begin{bmatrix} 4 & 2 \\ 4 & 2 \end{bmatrix}$ 0   **b.** $\begin{bmatrix} 8 & 7 \\ 2 & 3 \end{bmatrix}$ 10   **c.** $\begin{bmatrix} k & 3 \\ 3 - k & -3 \end{bmatrix}$ −9

👥 **Reaching All Students**

Below Level Students may confuse a matrix with its determinant because they look similar. Remind students that the determinant of a matrix is a real number, not a matrix.	**Advanced Learners** Have students use the definition of A^{-1} to prove that, if A^{-1} exists, $AA^{-1} = A^{-1}A = I$.	**Auditory Learners** See note on page 196. **Error Prevention** See note on page 199.

The following test will help you determine whether a 2 × 2 matrix has an inverse. The test will also help you find the inverse, if it exists.

Key Concepts

| Definition | Inverse of a 2 × 2 Matrix |

Let $A = \begin{bmatrix} a & b \\ c & d \end{bmatrix}$. If det $A \neq 0$, then A has an inverse.

If det $A \neq 0$, then $A^{-1} = \dfrac{1}{\det A}\begin{bmatrix} d & -b \\ -c & a \end{bmatrix} = \dfrac{1}{ad - bc}\begin{bmatrix} d & -b \\ -c & a \end{bmatrix}$.

3 EXAMPLE Finding an Inverse Matrix

Determine whether each matrix has an inverse. If an inverse matrix exists, find it.

a. $M = \begin{bmatrix} -2 & 2 \\ 5 & -4 \end{bmatrix}$ $ad - bc = (-2)(-4) - (2)(5)$ Find det M.

$= -2$ Simplify.

Since det $M \neq 0$, the inverse of M exists.

Change signs.

$M^{-1} = \begin{bmatrix} -2 & 2 \\ 5 & -4 \end{bmatrix}^{-1}$

Switch positions.

$= \dfrac{1}{\det M}\begin{bmatrix} -4 & -2 \\ -5 & -2 \end{bmatrix}$ Use the determinant to write the inverse.

$= \dfrac{1}{-2}\begin{bmatrix} -4 & -2 \\ -5 & -2 \end{bmatrix}$ Substitute −2 for det M.

$= \begin{bmatrix} 2 & 1 \\ 2.5 & 1 \end{bmatrix}$ Multiply.

b. $N = \begin{bmatrix} 3 & 9 \\ 2 & 6 \end{bmatrix}$ $ad - bc = (3)(6) - (9)(2)$ Find det N.

$= 0$ Simplify.

Since det $N = 0$, the inverse of N does *not* exist.

3a. yes; $\begin{bmatrix} 1.5 & -2 \\ -0.5 & 1 \end{bmatrix}$

b. yes; $\begin{bmatrix} -\frac{24}{11} & \frac{23}{33} \\ \frac{10}{11} & \frac{-5}{33} \end{bmatrix}$

✓ **Check Understanding** **3** Determine whether each matrix has an inverse. If an inverse matrix exists, find it.

a. $\begin{bmatrix} 2 & 4 \\ 1 & 3 \end{bmatrix}$ **b.** $\begin{bmatrix} 0.5 & 2.3 \\ 3 & 7.2 \end{bmatrix}$ **a–b. See left.**

OBJECTIVE

2 Using Inverse Matrices to Solve Equations

If the inverse of matrix A exists, you can use it to solve matrix equations of the form $AX = B$. Multiply each side of the equation by A^{-1} to find X.

$AX = B$

$A^{-1}(AX) = A^{-1}B$ Multiply each side by A^{-1}.

$(A^{-1}A)X = A^{-1}B$ Associative Property of Multiplication

$IX = A^{-1}B$ definition of multiplicative inverse

$X = A^{-1}B$ definition of multiplicative identity

1 Show that the matrices are multiplicative inverses.

$A = \begin{bmatrix} 3 & -1 \\ 7 & 1 \end{bmatrix}$

$B = \begin{bmatrix} 0.1 & 0.1 \\ -0.7 & 0.3 \end{bmatrix}$

Both **AB** and **BA** are equal to $\begin{bmatrix} 1 & 0 \\ 0 & 1 \end{bmatrix}$.

2 Evaluate each determinant.

a. det $\begin{bmatrix} 7 & 8 \\ -5 & -9 \end{bmatrix}$ **−23**

b. det $\begin{bmatrix} 4 & -3 \\ 5 & 6 \end{bmatrix}$ **39**

c. det $\begin{bmatrix} a & -b \\ b & a \end{bmatrix}$ **$a^2 + b^2$**

3 Determine whether each matrix has an inverse. If it does, find it.

a. $\begin{bmatrix} 12 & 4 \\ 9 & 3 \end{bmatrix}$ **no**

b. $\begin{bmatrix} 6 & 5 \\ 25 & 20 \end{bmatrix}$ **yes;** $\begin{bmatrix} -4 & 1 \\ 5 & -1.2 \end{bmatrix}$

page 196   Check Understanding

1a. $\begin{bmatrix} 2 & 1 \\ 2.5 & 1 \end{bmatrix}\begin{bmatrix} -2 & 2 \\ 5 & -4 \end{bmatrix} =$

b. $\begin{bmatrix} -2 & -5 \\ -3 & -8 \end{bmatrix}\begin{bmatrix} -8 & 5 \\ 3 & -2 \end{bmatrix} =$

$\begin{bmatrix} 2(-2) + 1(5) & 2(2) + 1(-4) \\ 2.5(-2) + 1(5) & 2.5(2) + 1(-4) \end{bmatrix} = \begin{bmatrix} 1 & 0 \\ 0 & 1 \end{bmatrix}$

$\begin{bmatrix} -2(-8) + (-5)(3) & -2(5) + (-5)(-2) \\ -3(-8) + (-8)(3) & -3(5) + (-8)(-2) \end{bmatrix} = \begin{bmatrix} 1 & 0 \\ 0 & 1 \end{bmatrix}$

197

Transition matrices can be useful in predicting results such as market penetration over short periods of time. The study of transition matrices is closely linked to Markov chains, which students may encounter in their future work in mathematics.

Additional Examples

4 Solve $\begin{bmatrix} 9 & 25 \\ 4 & 11 \end{bmatrix} X = \begin{bmatrix} 3 \\ -7 \end{bmatrix}$ for

the matrix X. $\begin{bmatrix} -208 \\ 75 \end{bmatrix}$

5 In a city with a stable group of 45,000 households, 25,000 households use long distance carrier A, and 20,000 use long distance carrier B. Over a 1-year period, 84% of the households remain with carrier A, while 16% switch to B. 93% of the households using B stay with B, while 7% switch to A.

a. Write a matrix to represent the changes in long distance carriers.

From
  A   B
To A $\begin{bmatrix} 0.84 & 0.07 \\ 0.16 & 0.93 \end{bmatrix}$
   B

b. Predict the number of households that will be using long distance carrier B next year.
22,600 households
c. Use the inverse of the matrix from part a to find, to the nearest hundred households, how many households used carrier A last year.
about 28,500 households

Closure

How can you find out whether a 2 × 2 matrix has an inverse? If it does, how can you find the inverse? **Calculate the determinant of the matrix. If the determinant is not 0, then the matrix has an inverse. If a 2 × 2 matrix $\begin{bmatrix} a & b \\ c & d \end{bmatrix}$ does have an inverse, you can find it by multiplying the matrix $\begin{bmatrix} d & -b \\ -c & a \end{bmatrix}$ by the reciprocal of the determinant of $\begin{bmatrix} a & b \\ c & d \end{bmatrix}$.**

198

4a. $\begin{bmatrix} 0 & -2 \\ 0 & 4 \end{bmatrix}$

b. $\begin{bmatrix} -2 \\ 1 \end{bmatrix}$

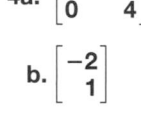

Real-World Connection

Martin Cooper invented the portable cellular radio telephone in 1973.

---

4 EXAMPLE Solving a Matrix Equation

Solve $\begin{bmatrix} -2 & -5 \\ 1 & 3 \end{bmatrix} X = \begin{bmatrix} -2 \\ 2 \end{bmatrix}$ for the matrix X.

The matrix equation has the form $AX = B$. First find A^{-1}.

$A^{-1} = \frac{1}{ad - bc} \begin{bmatrix} d & -b \\ -c & a \end{bmatrix} = \frac{1}{-2(3) - (-5)1} \begin{bmatrix} 3 & 5 \\ -1 & -2 \end{bmatrix}$ Use the definition of inverse.

$= \begin{bmatrix} -3 & -5 \\ 1 & 2 \end{bmatrix}$ Simplify.

Use the equation $X = A^{-1}B$. $X = \begin{bmatrix} -3 & -5 \\ 1 & 2 \end{bmatrix} \begin{bmatrix} -2 \\ 2 \end{bmatrix}$ Substitute.

$= \begin{bmatrix} -3(-2) + -5(2) \\ 1(-2) + 2(2) \end{bmatrix} = \begin{bmatrix} -4 \\ 2 \end{bmatrix}$ Multiply and simplify.

Check $\begin{bmatrix} -2 & -5 \\ 1 & 3 \end{bmatrix} X = \begin{bmatrix} -2 \\ 2 \end{bmatrix}$ Use the original equation.

$\begin{bmatrix} -2 & -5 \\ 1 & 3 \end{bmatrix} \begin{bmatrix} -4 \\ 2 \end{bmatrix} \stackrel{?}{=} \begin{bmatrix} -2 \\ 2 \end{bmatrix}$ Substitute.

$\begin{bmatrix} -2(-4) + (-5)(2) \\ 1(-4) + 3(2) \end{bmatrix} \stackrel{?}{=} \begin{bmatrix} -2 \\ 2 \end{bmatrix}$ Multiply.

$\begin{bmatrix} -2 \\ 2 \end{bmatrix} = \begin{bmatrix} -2 \\ 2 \end{bmatrix} \checkmark$ Simplify.

✔ Check Understanding **4** Solve each matrix equation in the form $AX = B$. Use the equation $X = A^{-1}B$.

a. $\begin{bmatrix} 3 & -4 \\ 4 & -5 \end{bmatrix} X = \begin{bmatrix} 0 & -22 \\ 0 & -28 \end{bmatrix}$ **b.** $\begin{bmatrix} 7 & 5 \\ 3 & 2 \end{bmatrix} X = \begin{bmatrix} -9 \\ -4 \end{bmatrix}$ a–b. See left.

You can use matrices to make predictions about trends.

5 EXAMPLE Real-World Connection

Communications The diagram shows the trends in cell phone ownership over four consecutive years.

a. Write a matrix to represent the changes (or transitions) in cell phone use.

From
No cell   Cell
To   No cell $\begin{bmatrix} 0.57 & 0.13 \\ 0.43 & 0.87 \end{bmatrix}$ **Write the percents as decimals.**
    Cell

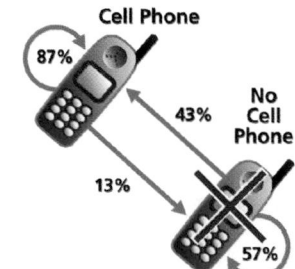

Cell Phone

87%

43%   No Cell Phone

13%

57%

b. In a stable population of 16,000 people, 9927 own cell phones, while 6073 do not. Assume the trends continue. Predict the number of people who will own cell phones next year.

No cell $\begin{bmatrix} 6073 \\ 9927 \end{bmatrix}$ **Write the information in a matrix.**
  Cell

$\begin{bmatrix} 0.57 & 0.13 \\ 0.43 & 0.87 \end{bmatrix} \begin{bmatrix} 6073 \\ 9927 \end{bmatrix} \approx \begin{bmatrix} 4752 \\ 11,248 \end{bmatrix}$ **Use the transition matrix from part (a). Multiply.**

Next year, about 11,248 people in the population will own cell phones.

---

pages 199–201 **Exercises**

14. yes; $\begin{bmatrix} 0 & 1 \\ -1 & 2 \end{bmatrix}$

15. yes; $\begin{bmatrix} -1 & 3 \\ 1 & -2 \end{bmatrix}$

16. yes; $\begin{bmatrix} 2 & -1.5 \\ -1 & 1 \end{bmatrix}$

17. yes; $\begin{bmatrix} 0 & \frac{1}{2} \\ \frac{1}{3} & -\frac{1}{6} \end{bmatrix}$

18. no

c. Use the inverse of the matrix from part (a) to find the number of people who owned cell phones last year.

$$\begin{bmatrix} 0.57 & 0.13 \\ 0.43 & 0.87 \end{bmatrix}^{-1} \begin{bmatrix} 6073 \\ 9927 \end{bmatrix} = \begin{bmatrix} 9075 \\ 6925 \end{bmatrix}$$

● Last year, 6925 people owned cell phones.

✓ Check Understanding **5 a.** **Critical Thinking** Find the percent of the population owning cell phones last year, this year, and next year. Estimate the percent two years from now.
b. Use the answer to Example 5, part (b), and the transition matrix to predict the number of people who will own cell phones two years from now.
c. Use the answer to Example 5, part (c), and the inverse of the transition matrix to estimate the number of people who owned cell phones two years ago.

5. a. 43.3%, 62.0%, 70.3%; 73.9%

b. about 11,829 people

c. about 102 people

EXERCISES

For more practice, see *Extra Practice*.

Practice and Problem Solving

 **Practice by Example**

Show that the matrices are multiplicative inverses. **1–3. See back of book.**

Example 1
(page 196)

1. $\begin{bmatrix} 3 & 2 \\ 4 & 3 \end{bmatrix}, \begin{bmatrix} 3 & -2 \\ -4 & 3 \end{bmatrix}$ **2.** $\begin{bmatrix} -3 & 7 \\ -2 & 5 \end{bmatrix}, \begin{bmatrix} -5 & 7 \\ -2 & 3 \end{bmatrix}$ **3.** $\begin{bmatrix} \frac{1}{5} & -\frac{1}{10} \\ 0 & \frac{1}{4} \end{bmatrix}, \begin{bmatrix} 5 & 2 \\ 0 & 4 \end{bmatrix}$

Example 2
(page 196)

Evaluate the determinant of each matrix.

4. $\begin{bmatrix} 7 & 2 \\ 0 & -3 \end{bmatrix}$ −21 **5.** $\begin{bmatrix} 6 & 2 \\ -6 & -2 \end{bmatrix}$ 0 **6.** $\begin{bmatrix} 0 & 0.5 \\ 1.5 & 2 \end{bmatrix}$ −0.75 **7.** $\begin{bmatrix} \frac{1}{2} & \frac{2}{3} \\ \frac{3}{5} & \frac{1}{4} \end{bmatrix}$ −$\frac{11}{40}$ **8.** $\begin{bmatrix} -1 & 3 \\ 5 & 2 \end{bmatrix}$ −17

9. $\begin{bmatrix} -2 & 0 \\ 2 & -1 \end{bmatrix}$ 2 **10.** $\begin{bmatrix} 5 & 3 \\ -2 & 1 \end{bmatrix}$ 11 **11.** $\begin{bmatrix} 5 & 2 \\ 1 & 3 \end{bmatrix}$ 13 **12.** $\begin{bmatrix} 2 & -1 \\ 5 & -4 \end{bmatrix}$ −3 **13.** $\begin{bmatrix} -4 & 3 \\ 2 & 0 \end{bmatrix}$ −6

Example 3
(page 197)

Determine whether each matrix has an inverse. If an inverse matrix exists, find it. **14–21. See margin pp. 198–199.**

14. $\begin{bmatrix} 2 & -1 \\ 1 & 0 \end{bmatrix}$ **15.** $\begin{bmatrix} 2 & 3 \\ 1 & 1 \end{bmatrix}$ **16.** $\begin{bmatrix} 2 & 3 \\ 2 & 4 \end{bmatrix}$ **17.** $\begin{bmatrix} 1 & 3 \\ 2 & 0 \end{bmatrix}$

18. $\begin{bmatrix} 6 & -8 \\ -3 & 4 \end{bmatrix}$ **19.** $\begin{bmatrix} 4 & 8 \\ -3 & -2 \end{bmatrix}$ **20.** $\begin{bmatrix} -1.5 & 3 \\ 2.5 & -0.5 \end{bmatrix}$ **21.** $\begin{bmatrix} 1 & -2 \\ 3 & 0 \end{bmatrix}$

Example 4
(page 198)

Solve each matrix equation. If an equation cannot be solved, explain why. **22–24. See margin.**

22. $\begin{bmatrix} 12 & 7 \\ 5 & 3 \end{bmatrix} X = \begin{bmatrix} 2 & -1 \\ 3 & 2 \end{bmatrix}$ **23.** $\begin{bmatrix} 0 & -4 \\ 0 & -1 \end{bmatrix} X = \begin{bmatrix} 0 \\ 4 \end{bmatrix}$ **24.** $\begin{bmatrix} 5 & -3 \\ 4 & -2 \end{bmatrix} X = \begin{bmatrix} 5 \\ 10 \end{bmatrix}$

Example 5
(pages 198–199)

25. **Data Analysis** Use the information in the diagram.
a. Write a transition matrix to represent the changes in cable television subscribers. **a–c. See back of book.**
b. In a stable population of 30,000 people, 20,000 people subscribe to cable television, while 10,000 do not. Predict the number of people who will subscribe to cable television next year.
c. Use the inverse of the matrix from part (a) to find the number of people who subscribed to cable television last year.

Cable TV — 99.5% → No Cable TV
2% ← , 0.5% , 98%

Lesson 4-5 2 × 2 Matrices, Determinants, and Inverses **199**

3. Practice

Assignment Guide

1 **Objective**
Ⓐ Ⓑ **Core** 1–21, 26–41, 44
Ⓒ **Extension** 46, 49–51

2 **Objective**
Ⓐ Ⓑ **Core** 22–25, 42–43, 45
Ⓒ **Extension** 47–48

Standardized Test Prep 52–55

Mixed Review 56–63

Error Prevention

Exercises 14–21 Students need to be cautious when calculating inverses of matrices. Urge them to be especially careful when writing the matrix that is to be multiplied by the reciprocal of the determinant. They may forget to switch the elements on the main diagonal of the original. Also, they may forget to use the opposites of the elements on the other diagonal.

19. yes; $\begin{bmatrix} -\frac{1}{8} & -\frac{1}{2} \\ \frac{3}{16} & \frac{1}{4} \end{bmatrix}$

20. yes; $\begin{bmatrix} \frac{2}{27} & \frac{4}{9} \\ \frac{10}{27} & \frac{2}{9} \end{bmatrix}$

21. yes; $\begin{bmatrix} 0 & \frac{1}{3} \\ -\frac{1}{2} & \frac{1}{6} \end{bmatrix}$

22. $\begin{bmatrix} -15 & -17 \\ 26 & 29 \end{bmatrix}$

23. No solutions; the determinant of $\begin{bmatrix} 0 & -4 \\ 0 & -1 \end{bmatrix}$ **is 0.**

24. $\begin{bmatrix} 10 \\ 15 \end{bmatrix}$

4. Assess

pages 199–201 Exercises

32. No; answers may vary.
    Sample: the product is $\begin{bmatrix} 23 & 8 \\ -46 & -16 \end{bmatrix}$.

33. No; answers may vary.
    Sample: the product is $\begin{bmatrix} 0 & 1 \\ 1 & 0 \end{bmatrix}$.

34. yes; $\begin{bmatrix} -3 & 4 \\ 1 & -1 \end{bmatrix}$

35. yes; $\begin{bmatrix} -5 & 7 \\ 3 & -4 \end{bmatrix}$

200

B Apply Your Skills

Evaluate each determinant.

26. $\begin{vmatrix} 4 & 5 \\ -4 & 4 \end{vmatrix}$ **36**

27. $\begin{vmatrix} -3 & 10 \\ 6 & 20 \end{vmatrix}$ **−120**

28. $\begin{vmatrix} -\frac{1}{2} & 2 \\ -2 & 8 \end{vmatrix}$ **0**

29. $\begin{vmatrix} 2 & 0 \\ 0 & 1 \end{vmatrix}$ **2**

30. $\begin{vmatrix} 6 & 9 \\ 3 & 6 \end{vmatrix}$ **9**

Determine whether the matrices are multiplicative inverses. If they are not, explain why not. 32–33. See margin.

31. $\begin{bmatrix} 2 & 0.5 \\ 5 & 1 \end{bmatrix}, \begin{bmatrix} -2 & 1 \\ 10 & -4 \end{bmatrix}$ **yes**

32. $\begin{bmatrix} -3 & 4 \\ 6 & -8 \end{bmatrix}, \begin{bmatrix} -1 & 0 \\ 5 & 2 \end{bmatrix}$

33. $\begin{bmatrix} -2 & -5 \\ -2 & -4 \end{bmatrix}, \begin{bmatrix} -2.5 & 2 \\ 1 & -1 \end{bmatrix}$

Determine whether each matrix has an inverse. If an inverse matrix exists, find it. If it does not exist, explain why not. 34–41. See margin.

34. $\begin{bmatrix} 1 & 4 \\ 1 & 3 \end{bmatrix}$

35. $\begin{bmatrix} 4 & 7 \\ 3 & 5 \end{bmatrix}$

36. $\begin{bmatrix} -3 & 11 \\ 2 & -7 \end{bmatrix}$

37. $\begin{bmatrix} 2 & 0 \\ 0 & 2 \end{bmatrix}$

38. $\begin{bmatrix} 0 & 3 \\ 3 & 0 \end{bmatrix}$

39. $\begin{bmatrix} -1 & 3 \\ 2 & 0 \end{bmatrix}$

40. $\begin{bmatrix} 1 & 2 \\ 2 & 1 \end{bmatrix}$

41. $\begin{bmatrix} 3 & 0 \\ 6 & 0 \end{bmatrix}$

Solve each matrix equation.

42. $\begin{bmatrix} 4 & 7 \\ 1 & 2 \end{bmatrix}X + \begin{bmatrix} 2 & 7 \\ -3 & 4 \end{bmatrix} = \begin{bmatrix} 6 & 2 \\ -2 & 3 \end{bmatrix}$

43. $\begin{bmatrix} 1 & 9 \\ 6 & -6 \end{bmatrix} = \begin{bmatrix} -7 & -9 \\ 4 & 5 \end{bmatrix}X + \begin{bmatrix} 3 & 4 \\ 4 & -3 \end{bmatrix}$

44. **Writing** Suppose $A = \begin{bmatrix} a & b \\ c & d \end{bmatrix}$ has an inverse. In your own words, describe how to switch or change the elements of A to write A^{-1}. **See margin p. 201.**

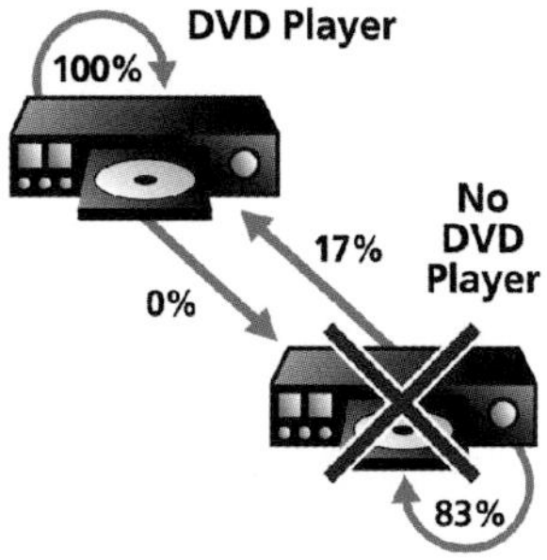

45. **Entertainment** Use the information in the diagram at the left.
    a. Write a transition matrix to represent the changes in DVD-player ownership.
    b. In a stable population of 30,000 people, 7000 people own DVD players, while 23,000 do not. Predict the number of people in the population who will own DVD players next year. **about 10,910 people**
    c. Use the inverse of the matrix from part (a) to estimate the number of people in the population who owned DVD players last year.
    d. **Error Analysis** A student estimated that the number of people in the population who owned DVD players last year was 8434. What was the student's error? **a, c–d. See margin p. 201.**

C Challenge

46. **Critical Thinking** Suppose $A = \begin{bmatrix} a & b \\ c & d \end{bmatrix}$. For what values of $a, b, c,$ and d will A be its own inverse? (*Hint:* There is more than one correct answer.)
    Answers may vary. Sample: $a = \pm1, d = \pm1, b = c = 0$

Solve each matrix equation.

47. $-2\begin{bmatrix} -2 & 0 \\ 0 & -1 \end{bmatrix} + \begin{bmatrix} 0 & -3 \\ 5 & -4 \end{bmatrix}X + \begin{bmatrix} 0 & -3 \\ 5 & -4 \end{bmatrix} = \begin{bmatrix} 19 & -27 \\ 10 & -24 \end{bmatrix}\begin{bmatrix} -3 & 2 \\ -5 & 8 \end{bmatrix}$

48. $\begin{bmatrix} 0 & -6 \\ 1 & 2 \end{bmatrix} - \begin{bmatrix} 5 & 2 \\ 4 & 3 \end{bmatrix}X - \begin{bmatrix} 2 & -26 \\ 3 & -18 \end{bmatrix} = \begin{bmatrix} 3 & 25 \\ 2 & 24 \end{bmatrix}\begin{bmatrix} -1 & -1 \\ 0 & 0 \end{bmatrix}$

49. **Critical Thinking** Explain why $A_{2 \times 3}$ does not have a multiplicative inverse. **See margin.**

50. Let $M = \begin{bmatrix} a & b \\ c & d \end{bmatrix}$ and $N = \begin{bmatrix} e & f \\ g & h \end{bmatrix}$. Prove that the product of the determinants of M and N equals the determinant of the matrix product MN. **See back of book.**

200   Chapter 4   Matrices

---

42. $\begin{bmatrix} 1 & -3 \\ 0 & 1 \end{bmatrix}$

43. $\begin{bmatrix} 8 & -2 \\ -6 & 1 \end{bmatrix}$

DVD Player
100%
17% **No DVD Player**
0%
83%

36. yes; $\begin{bmatrix} 7 & 11 \\ 2 & 3 \end{bmatrix}$

37. yes; $\begin{bmatrix} 0.5 & 0 \\ 0 & 0.5 \end{bmatrix}$

38. yes; $\begin{bmatrix} 0 & \frac{1}{3} \\ \frac{1}{3} & 0 \end{bmatrix}$

39. yes; $\begin{bmatrix} 0 & \frac{1}{2} \\ \frac{1}{3} & \frac{1}{6} \end{bmatrix}$

40. yes; $\begin{bmatrix} -\frac{1}{3} & \frac{2}{3} \\ \frac{2}{3} & -\frac{1}{3} \end{bmatrix}$

41. No; the determinant is 0.

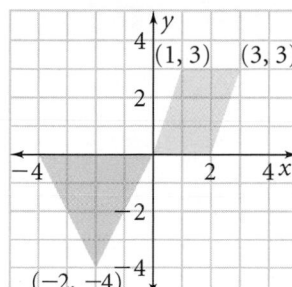

(1, 3)   (3, 3)

(−2, −4)

51. a. Coordinate Geometry Find the area of the parallelogram at the left. **6 units²**

   b. Evaluate the determinant $\begin{vmatrix} 2 & 0 \\ 1 & 3 \end{vmatrix}$. Compare the value of the determinant to the area from part (a). **6; it is the same.**

   c. Make a Conjecture Consider the triangle at the left to be half a parallelogram. Make a conjecture about its area and the value of

$$\frac{1}{2}\begin{vmatrix} -4 & 0 \\ -2 & -4 \end{vmatrix}.$$ **They are the same.**

   d. Open-Ended Graph a different triangle with one vertex at the origin. Find the area of the triangle by writing and evaluating a determinant. **Check students' work.**

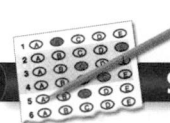

Standardized Test Prep

Gridded Response

Take It to the NET
Online lesson quiz at
www.PHSchool.com
Web Code: aga-0405

52. What is the determinant of $\begin{bmatrix} -2 & -3 \\ 5 & 0 \end{bmatrix}$? **15**

53. What is the determinant of $\begin{bmatrix} \frac{1}{10} & \frac{1}{5} \\ \frac{1}{8} & \frac{1}{3} \end{bmatrix}$? Enter your answer as a fraction. $\frac{1}{120}$

54. If $A = \begin{bmatrix} 4 & 2 \\ -3 & -1 \end{bmatrix}$, and the inverse of A is $x\begin{bmatrix} -1 & -2 \\ 3 & 4 \end{bmatrix}$, what is the value of x? Enter your answer as a fraction. $\frac{1}{2}$

55. If $B = \begin{bmatrix} 4 & -1 \\ 2 & 0 \end{bmatrix}$, what is det B^{-1}? $\frac{1}{2}$

Mixed Review

Lesson 4-4

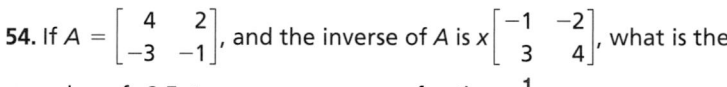

Each matrix represents the vertices of a polygon. Write a matrix to represent the vertices of the image after each transformation. **56–59. See margin.**

56. $\begin{bmatrix} 0 & 0 & 5 \\ 0 & -4 & 0 \end{bmatrix}$; rotation of 90°

57. $\begin{bmatrix} -2 & -5 & 0 \\ 0 & 3 & 5 \end{bmatrix}$; reflection in $y = x$

58. $\begin{bmatrix} 5 & 3 & 2 \\ 7 & 1 & 3 \end{bmatrix}$; 2 units left, 1 unit down

59. $\begin{bmatrix} -3 & -2 & -1 \\ 4 & 1 & 5 \end{bmatrix}$; dilation of 2

Lesson 3-6

Solve each system by substitution. $\left(\frac{70}{11}, -\frac{10}{11}, \frac{50}{11}\right)$ $\left(\frac{36}{13}, \frac{9}{13}, \frac{18}{13}\right)$

60. $\begin{cases} x = 5 \\ x - y + z = 5 \\ x + y - z = -5 \end{cases}$ **no solution**

61. $\begin{cases} x - 3y = 2z \\ x + 2y - z = 0 \\ x + y + z = 10 \end{cases}$

62. $\begin{cases} 3x + 3y - z = 9 \\ 2y = x - z \\ x - y + 5z = 9 \end{cases}$

Lesson 2-4 **63. a. Exercise** Suppose you begin a training program by walking 2 miles every day. During the first week, the walk takes you 40 minutes per day. Each week after that, you reduce your time by one minute. Write a linear model for the number of minutes you take to walk 2 miles in week w. **a–b. See margin.**

   b. Critical Thinking Can you continue to improve at the same rate? Explain.

44. Answers may vary. Sample: Form a new matrix by switching the element in row 1, column 1 with the element in row 2, column 2. Then replace the other two elements with their opposites. Finally divide each element by the determinant of the original matrix.

Lesson Preview

 **Check Skills You'll Need**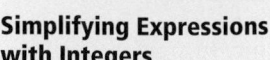

Simplifying Expressions with Integers
Skills Handbook: p. 845
Example 3
Exercises 11, 13, 15–16, 18

Lesson Resources

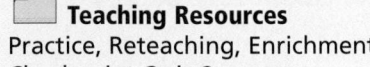 **Teaching Resources**
Practice, Reteaching, Enrichment
Checkpoint Quiz 2

Reaching All Students
Practice Workbook 4-6
Spanish Practice Workbook 4-6
Reading and Math Literacy 4C
Spanish Reading & Literacy 4C
Spanish Checkpoint Quiz 2

Presentation Assistant Plus!
Transparencies
• Check Skills You'll Need 4-6
• Additional Examples 4-6
• Student Edition Answers 4-6
• Lesson Quiz 4-6
PH Presentation Pro CD 4-6

 **ASSESSMENT SYSTEM**

Checkpoint Quiz 2
Computer Test Generator CD

Technology
Resource Pro® CD-ROM
Computer Test Generator CD
Prentice Hall Presentation Pro CD

 **www.PHSchool.com**
Student Site
• Teacher Web Code: agk-5500
• Self-grading Lesson Quiz
Teacher Center
• Lesson Planner
• Resources

Plus **iTEXT**

202

4-6 · 3 × 3 Matrices, Determinants, and Inverses

North Carolina Objectives   1.04 Operate with matrices to model and solve problems.

Lesson Preview

What You'll Learn

OBJECTIVE 1
To evaluate determinants of 3 × 3 matrices

OBJECTIVE 2
To use inverse matrices in solving matrix equations

. . . And Why

To decode messages, as in Example 5

✔ Check Skills You'll Need   (For help, go to Skills Handbook page 845.)

Find the product of the red elements in each matrix.

1. $\begin{bmatrix} 2 & 3 & 0 \\ -1 & 3 & -2 \\ 4 & -3 & -4 \end{bmatrix}$ **−24**

2. $\begin{bmatrix} 2 & 3 & 0 \\ -1 & 3 & -2 \\ 4 & -3 & -4 \end{bmatrix}$ **0**

3. $\begin{bmatrix} 2 & 3 & 0 \\ -1 & 3 & -2 \\ 4 & -3 & -4 \end{bmatrix}$ **−24**

4. $\begin{bmatrix} 2 & 3 & 0 \\ -1 & 3 & -2 \\ 4 & -3 & -4 \end{bmatrix}$ **12**

5. $\begin{bmatrix} 2 & 3 & 0 \\ -1 & 3 & -2 \\ 4 & -3 & -4 \end{bmatrix}$ **12**

6. $\begin{bmatrix} 2 & 3 & 0 \\ -1 & 3 & -2 \\ 4 & -3 & -4 \end{bmatrix}$ **0**

 Interactive lesson includes instant self-check, tutorials, and activities.

OBJECTIVE 1

Evaluating Determinants of 3 × 3 Matrices

As you learned in Lesson 4-5, the determinant of a matrix helps you to find an inverse matrix and solve a matrix equation.

Key Concepts

Definition	The Determinant of a 3 × 3 Matrix

The determinant of a 3 × 3 matrix $\begin{bmatrix} a_1 & b_1 & c_1 \\ a_2 & b_2 & c_2 \\ a_3 & b_3 & c_3 \end{bmatrix}$ is

$$\begin{vmatrix} a_1 & b_1 & c_1 \\ a_2 & b_2 & c_2 \\ a_3 & b_3 & c_3 \end{vmatrix} = (a_1 b_2 c_3 + a_2 b_3 c_1 + a_3 b_1 c_2) - (a_1 b_3 c_2 + a_2 b_1 c_3 + a_3 b_2 c_1)$$

Visualize the pattern this way:

$$\begin{matrix} a_1 & b_1 & c_1 \\ a_2 & b_2 & c_2 \\ a_3 & b_3 & c_3 \end{matrix} \quad - \quad \begin{matrix} a_1 & b_1 & c_1 \\ a_2 & b_2 & c_2 \\ a_3 & b_3 & c_3 \end{matrix}$$

---

1 EXAMPLE   **Evaluating the Determinant of a 3 × 3 Matrix**

Evaluate the determinant of $F = \begin{bmatrix} -1 & 3 & 5 \\ 2 & -4 & 6 \\ 0 & 1 & -1 \end{bmatrix}$.

$$\begin{vmatrix} -1 & 3 & 5 \\ 2 & -4 & 6 \\ 0 & 1 & -1 \end{vmatrix} = [-1(-4)(-1) + 2(1)(5) + 0(3)(6)] \quad \text{Use the definition.}$$
$$- [-1(1)(6) + 2(3)(-1) + 0(-4)(5)]$$
$$= [-4 + 10 + 0] - [-6 + (-6) + 0] \quad \text{Multiply.}$$
$$= 6 - (-12) = 18 \quad \text{Simplify.}$$

The determinant of F is 18.

✔ Ongoing Assessment and Intervention

Before the Lesson	**During the Lesson**	**After the Lesson**
Diagnose prerequisite skills using:	**Monitor progress using:**	**Assess knowledge using:**
• Check Skills You'll Need	• Check Understanding	• Lesson Quiz
	• Additional Examples	• Computer Test Generator CD
	• Standardized Test Prep	• Chapter Checkpoint 2 (p. 207)

✓ **Check Understanding** ❶ Evaluate each determinant.

a. $\begin{vmatrix} -3 & 4 & 0 \\ 2 & -5 & 1 \\ 0 & 2 & 3 \end{vmatrix}$ **27**   b. $\begin{vmatrix} 1 & -1 & 2 \\ 0 & 4 & 2 \\ 3 & -6 & 10 \end{vmatrix}$ **22**   c. $\begin{vmatrix} 2 & 0 & -1 \\ 0 & 0 & 0 \\ 1 & -5 & 3 \end{vmatrix}$ **0**

You can use a graphing calculator to evaluate the determinant of a 3 × 3 matrix.

❷ **EXAMPLE** **Using a Graphing Calculator**

Enter matrix A into your graphing calculator. Use the matrix submenus to evaluate the determinant of A.

$A = \begin{bmatrix} 1 & 7 & 2 \\ -1 & 1 & -2 \\ 1 & 1 & 1 \end{bmatrix}$

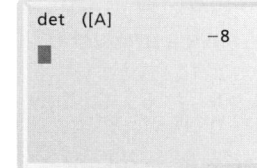

```
NAMES MATH EDIT
1:det(
2: T
3:dim(
4:Fill(
5:identity(
6:randM(
7:augment(
```

```
NAMES MATH EDIT
1:[A]    3×3
2:[B]
3:[C]
4:[D]
5:[E]
```

```
det ([A]
                 -8
■
```

✓ **Check Understanding** ❷ Use a graphing calculator to evaluate the determinant of $\begin{bmatrix} 13 & 21 & 11 \\ -2 & 4 & -1 \\ 17 & -2 & 0 \end{bmatrix}$.
−1087

OBJECTIVE

2 **Using Inverse 3 × 3 Matrices**

Like 2 × 2 matrices, some 3 × 3 matrices do not have inverses.

❸ **EXAMPLE** **Verifying Inverses**

Determine whether the matrices are multiplicative inverses.

Need Help?
If A and B are inverse matrices, then
$AB = BA = I$.

a. $A = \begin{bmatrix} 1 & 5 & -1 \\ 1 & 0 & -1 \\ 1 & 0 & 0 \end{bmatrix}, B = \begin{bmatrix} 0 & 0 & 1 \\ 0.2 & -0.2 & 0 \\ 0 & -1 & 1 \end{bmatrix}$

$\begin{bmatrix} 1 & 5 & -1 \\ 1 & 0 & -1 \\ 1 & 0 & 0 \end{bmatrix}\begin{bmatrix} 0 & 0 & 1 \\ 0.2 & -0.2 & 0 \\ 0 & -1 & 1 \end{bmatrix} = \begin{bmatrix} 1 & 0 & 0 \\ 0 & 1 & 0 \\ 0 & 0 & 1 \end{bmatrix}$

Since $AB = I$, A and B are multiplicative inverses.

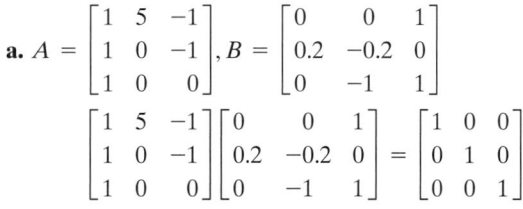

b. $C = \begin{bmatrix} 3 & 4 & 1 \\ -2 & 0 & 2 \\ 1 & 5 & 3 \end{bmatrix}, D = \begin{bmatrix} 0 & 1 & 0 \\ 1 & 0 & 1 \\ 0 & 1 & 0 \end{bmatrix}$

$\begin{bmatrix} 3 & 4 & 1 \\ -2 & 0 & 2 \\ 1 & 5 & 3 \end{bmatrix}\begin{bmatrix} 0 & 1 & 0 \\ 1 & 0 & 1 \\ 0 & 1 & 0 \end{bmatrix} = \begin{bmatrix} 4 & 4 & 4 \\ 0 & 0 & 0 \\ 5 & 4 & 5 \end{bmatrix}$

Since $CD \neq I$, C and D are not multiplicative inverses.

✓ **Check Understanding** ❸ a. Verify that A and B are inverses by showing that $BA = I$.
b. Verify that C and D are not inverses by showing that $DC \neq I$.
a–b. See back of book.

Lesson 4-6 3 × 3 Matrices, Determinants, and Inverses **203**

👪 **Reaching All Students**

| **Below Level** A 3 × 3 determinant can be determined using the diagonals of the array a_1 b_1 c_1 a_1 b_1 a_2 b_2 c_2 a_2 b_2 a_3 b_3 c_3 a_3 b_3. | **Advanced Learners** Ask students to research expanding a 3 × 3 determinant by its 'minors' and compare the result to the definition. | **Error Prevention** See note on page 205. |

2. Teach

Professional Development

Math Background

This lesson extends the work in Lesson 4-5 to 3 × 3 matrices. Calculating the inverse of a 3 × 3 matrix is rather complicated. Students are therefore encouraged to use graphing calculators for many of the calculations in this lesson. Calculators are essential in finding the inverse of an $n \times n$ matrix for large values of n.

OBJECTIVE

1 **Teaching Notes**

❶ **EXAMPLE** **Technology Tip**

After entering matrix A, be sure to press 2nd [QUIT] before using the matrix submenus.

 Additional Examples

❶ Evaluate the determinant of
$\begin{bmatrix} 8 & -4 & 3 \\ -2 & 9 & 5 \\ 1 & 6 & 0 \end{bmatrix}$. **−323**

❷ Use a graphing calculator to evaluate the determinant of
$\begin{bmatrix} 4 & 2 & 3 \\ -2 & -1 & 5 \\ 1 & 3 & 6 \end{bmatrix}$. **−65**

OBJECTIVE

2 **Teaching Notes**

❺ **EXAMPLE** **Teaching Tip**

It is crucial that the message first be written in a matrix that has 3 rows. Use 0 for a space between words and for spaces at the end of the message if the message does not fill the last row of the matrix. Multiply E by the matrix just constructed to obtain the coded message.

203

a. $\begin{bmatrix} 0.5 & 0 & 0 \\ 0 & 0 & 0.5 \\ 0 & 1 & 1 \end{bmatrix}$; $\begin{bmatrix} 2 & 0 & 0 \\ 0 & 2 & 1 \\ 0 & 2 & 0 \end{bmatrix}$ **no**

b. $\begin{bmatrix} 0 & 0 & 1 \\ 0 & 1 & 0 \\ 1 & 0 & -1 \end{bmatrix}$; $\begin{bmatrix} 1 & 0 & 1 \\ 0 & 1 & 0 \\ 1 & 0 & 0 \end{bmatrix}$ **yes**

4 Solve the equation.

$\begin{bmatrix} 2 & 0 & 1 \\ 0 & 1 & 4 \\ 1 & 0 & 0 \end{bmatrix} X = \begin{bmatrix} -1 \\ 8 \\ -2 \end{bmatrix}$ $\begin{bmatrix} -2 \\ -4 \\ 3 \end{bmatrix}$

5 Use the alphabet table on page 204 and the encoding matrix

$K = \begin{bmatrix} 0.5 & 0.25 & 0.25 \\ 0.25 & -0.5 & 0.5 \\ 0.5 & 1 & -1 \end{bmatrix}$.

a. Find the decoding matrix K^{-1}.

$\begin{bmatrix} 0 & 2 & 1 \\ 2 & -2.5 & -0.75 \\ 2 & -1.5 & -1.25 \end{bmatrix}$

b. Decode the following text.

$\begin{bmatrix} 11.25 & 16.75 & 24.5 \\ 5.75 & 17 & 5.5 \\ 1.5 & -12 & 15 \end{bmatrix}$

NEAT CODE

Closure

Ask: *How do you determine whether two 3 × 3 matrices are inverses of each other?* **Multiply them to see if the product is**

$\begin{bmatrix} 1 & 0 & 0 \\ 0 & 1 & 0 \\ 0 & 0 & 1 \end{bmatrix}$.

You can use 3 × 3 matrices to solve matrix equations.

4 **EXAMPLE** **Solving a Matrix Equation**

Solve the equation $\begin{bmatrix} 0 & 0 & 2 \\ 1 & 3 & -2 \\ 1 & -2 & 1 \end{bmatrix} X = \begin{bmatrix} 6 \\ -11 \\ 8 \end{bmatrix}$.

Let $A = \begin{bmatrix} 0 & 0 & 2 \\ 1 & 3 & -2 \\ 1 & -2 & 1 \end{bmatrix}$. Find A^{-1}.

[A]$^{-1}$
[[.1 .4 .6]
 [.3 .2 -.2]
 [.5 0   0]]

$X = \begin{bmatrix} 0.1 & 0.4 & 0.6 \\ 0.3 & 0.2 & -0.2 \\ 0.5 & 0 & 0 \end{bmatrix} \begin{bmatrix} 6 \\ -11 \\ 8 \end{bmatrix}$ ← Use the equation $X = A^{-1}C$.

Multiply. →

[A]$^{-1}$[C]
[[1]
 [-2]
 [3]]

$X = \begin{bmatrix} 1 \\ -2 \\ 3 \end{bmatrix}$

✓ **Check Understanding** 4 a. Verify that A and A^{-1} are inverses. **See left.**

b. Solve the equation $\begin{bmatrix} 0 & 0 & 2 \\ 1 & 3 & -2 \\ 1 & -2 & 1 \end{bmatrix} X = \begin{bmatrix} 0 \\ -6 \\ 19 \end{bmatrix}$. $\begin{bmatrix} 9 \\ -5 \\ 0 \end{bmatrix}$

4a. The matrices
$\begin{bmatrix} 0 & 0 & 2 \\ 1 & 3 & -2 \\ 1 & -2 & 1 \end{bmatrix}$ and
$\begin{bmatrix} 0.1 & 0.4 & 0.6 \\ 0.3 & 0.2 & -0.2 \\ 0.5 & 0 & 0 \end{bmatrix}$
have a product of
$\begin{bmatrix} 1 & 0 & 0 \\ 0 & 1 & 0 \\ 0 & 0 & 1 \end{bmatrix}$, so they
are inverses.

You can use 3 × 3 matrices to encode and decode messages.

A	26	N	13
B	25	O	12
C	24	P	11
D	23	Q	10
E	22	R	9
F	21	S	8
G	20	T	7
H	19	U	6
I	18	V	5
J	17	W	4
K	16	X	3
L	15	Y	2
M	14	Z	1

$E = \begin{bmatrix} 0.5 & 0.5 & 0.5 \\ 0.25 & 0.25 & -0.25 \\ 0.5 & 0 & -0.5 \end{bmatrix}$

5 **EXAMPLE** **Real-World Connection**

Cryptography Use the alphabet table and the encoding matrix at the left.

a. Find the decoding matrix E^{-1}.

[E]$^{-1}$
[[1 -2 2]
 [0 4 -2]
 [1 -2 0]]

Use a graphing calculator.

b. Decode $\begin{bmatrix} 22.5 & 26 & 15.5 \\ 0.25 & 9 & 7.75 \\ -4 & 9 & 3.5 \end{bmatrix}$. Zero indicates a space holder.

$\begin{bmatrix} 1 & -2 & 2 \\ 0 & 4 & -2 \\ 1 & -2 & 0 \end{bmatrix} \begin{bmatrix} 22.5 & 26 & 15.5 \\ 0.25 & 9 & 7.75 \\ -4 & 9 & 3.5 \end{bmatrix} = \begin{bmatrix} 14 & 26 & 7 \\ 9 & 18 & 24 \\ 22 & 8 & 0 \end{bmatrix}$ **Use the decoding matrix from part (a). Multiply.**

The numbers 14 26 7 9 18 24 22 8 0 correspond to the letters MATRICES.

✓ **Check Understanding** 5 **Literature** Use the information from Example 5. Decode the matrix at the right, which gives the title of a Pablo Neruda poem. Zero indicates a space between words. **POETRY**

$\begin{bmatrix} 21 & 10.5 \\ 6 & 4.25 \\ 1 & 5 \end{bmatrix}$

3. Practice

 A **Practice by Example**

Evaluate the determinant of each matrix.

Example 1
(page 202)

1. $\begin{bmatrix} 1 & 2 & 5 \\ 3 & 1 & 0 \\ 1 & 2 & 1 \end{bmatrix}$ **20**

2. $\begin{bmatrix} 1 & 4 & 0 \\ 2 & 3 & 5 \\ 0 & 1 & 0 \end{bmatrix}$ **−5**

3. $\begin{bmatrix} -2 & 4 & 1 \\ 3 & 0 & -1 \\ 1 & 2 & 1 \end{bmatrix}$ **−14**

4. $\begin{bmatrix} 2 & 3 & 0 \\ 1 & 2 & 5 \\ 7 & 0 & 1 \end{bmatrix}$ **106**

Example 2
(page 203)

Use a graphing calculator to evaluate the determinant of each 3 × 3 matrix.

5. $\begin{bmatrix} 1 & 0 & 0 \\ 0 & 1 & 0 \\ 0 & 0 & 1 \end{bmatrix}$ **1**

6. $\begin{bmatrix} 0 & -2 & -3 \\ 1 & 2 & 4 \\ -2 & 0 & 1 \end{bmatrix}$ **6**

7. $\begin{bmatrix} 12.2 & 13.3 & 9 \\ 1 & -4 & -17 \\ 21.4 & -15 & 0 \end{bmatrix}$

−7314.14

Example 3
(page 203)

Determine whether the matrices are multiplicative inverses.

8. $\begin{bmatrix} 1 & 2 & -1 \\ -1.5 & -3 & 1.75 \\ 0 & -1 & 0.5 \end{bmatrix}, \begin{bmatrix} 1 & 0 & 2 \\ 3 & 2 & -1 \\ 6 & 4 & 0 \end{bmatrix}$
yes

9. $\begin{bmatrix} 2 & 2 & 2 \\ -2 & 2 & -2 \\ -2 & -2 & -2 \end{bmatrix}, \begin{bmatrix} 2 & 2 & 2 \\ -2 & 2 & -2 \\ -2 & -2 & -2 \end{bmatrix}$
no

Example 4
(page 204)

Solve each equation.

10. $\begin{bmatrix} 5 & 1 & -4 \\ 2 & -3 & -5 \\ 7 & 2 & -6 \end{bmatrix} X = \begin{bmatrix} 5 \\ 2 \\ 5 \end{bmatrix}$ $\begin{bmatrix} 3 \\ -2 \\ 2 \end{bmatrix}$

11. $\begin{bmatrix} 6 & 10 & -13 \\ 4 & -2 & 7 \\ 0 & 9 & -8 \end{bmatrix} X = \begin{bmatrix} 84 \\ 18 \\ 56 \end{bmatrix}$ $\begin{bmatrix} 5 \\ 8 \\ 2 \end{bmatrix}$

Example 5
(page 204)

Literature Use the information from Example 5. Decode each title.

12. Emily Dickinson, $\begin{bmatrix} 23.5 & 12.5 \\ 4.75 & -0.25 \\ 6 & -3.5 \end{bmatrix}$
AUTUMN

13. E. E. Cummings, $\begin{bmatrix} 18 & 14 & 17.5 \\ 0 & 3.5 & 8.75 \\ -3.5 & 2.5 & 4.5 \end{bmatrix}$
PORTRAIT

 **B** **Apply Your Skills**

14–16. For each matrix the determinant equals zero.

Verify that each matrix has no inverse.

14. $\begin{bmatrix} 1 & 0 & 1 \\ 0 & 1 & 0 \\ 1 & 0 & 1 \end{bmatrix}$

15. $\begin{bmatrix} 0 & 1 & 0 \\ 1 & 0 & 1 \\ 0 & 1 & 0 \end{bmatrix}$

16. $\begin{bmatrix} 0 & 1 & 0 \\ 0 & 1 & 0 \\ 1 & 1 & 1 \end{bmatrix}$

17. **Cryptography** Two members of the Hopewell High School math club share messages in code. They use the alphabet table from Example 5.
   a. One of the students has lost her encoding matrix. Luckily, she remembers that the decoding matrix is   **a–b. See margin.**

   $E^{-1} = \begin{bmatrix} 1 & -1 & 0 \\ 0 & 1 & -1 \\ 0 & 0 & 1 \end{bmatrix}$. Compute E to find the encoding matrix.

   b. Use your answer to part (a) to encode the message MATH IS COOL.
   c. **Open-Ended** Use the encoding matrix from part (a) to encode a short sentence. Use the decoding matrix to check your work.
   Check students' work.

Evaluate the determinant of each matrix.

18. $\begin{bmatrix} 0 & 2 & -3 \\ 1 & 2 & 4 \\ -2 & 0 & 1 \end{bmatrix}$ **−30**

19. $\begin{bmatrix} 5 & 1 & 0 \\ 0 & 2 & -1 \\ -2 & -3 & 1 \end{bmatrix}$ **−3**

20. $\begin{bmatrix} 4 & 6 & -1 \\ 2 & 3 & 2 \\ 1 & -1 & 1 \end{bmatrix}$ **25**

21. $\begin{bmatrix} -3 & 2 & -1 \\ 2 & 5 & 2 \\ 1 & -2 & 0 \end{bmatrix}$ **1**

Real-World Connection

During World War II, these Navaho code talkers transmitted messages in an unbreakable code.

Assignment Guide

1 Objective
  A B Core 1–7, 14–16, 18–21, 26

2 Objective
  A B Core 8–13, 17, 22–25
  C Extension 27–30

Standardized Test Prep 31–33

Mixed Review 34–39

Error Prevention

Exercises 1–4 Urge students to show all their work when they apply the definition of the determinant of a 3 × 3 matrix. The visual pattern that accompanies the definition may be helpful. Students may choose to use a graphing calculator to check their final answers.

---

pages 205–207 Exercises

17a. $\begin{bmatrix} 1 & 1 & 1 \\ 0 & 1 & 1 \\ 0 & 0 & 1 \end{bmatrix}$

b. $\begin{bmatrix} 38 & 56 & 27 & 34 \\ 24 & 30 & 20 & 15 \\ 24 & 12 & 12 & 15 \end{bmatrix}$

Lesson Quiz 4-6

1. Use pencil and paper to evaluate the determinant of
$\begin{bmatrix} -2 & -4 & 2 \\ 3 & 1 & 0 \\ 5 & -6 & -2 \end{bmatrix}$. **−66**

2. Determine whether the matrices are multiplicative inverses.
$\begin{bmatrix} 1 & 1 & -1 \\ -1 & 0 & 1 \\ 0 & -1 & 1 \end{bmatrix}; \begin{bmatrix} 1 & 0 & 1 \\ 1 & 1 & 0 \\ 1 & 1 & 1 \end{bmatrix}$
yes

3. Solve the equation.
$\begin{bmatrix} -1 & -1 & 1 \\ 1 & 2 & -1 \\ 0 & -1 & 1 \end{bmatrix} M = \begin{bmatrix} -1 \\ -4 \\ 3 \end{bmatrix}$
$\begin{bmatrix} 4 \\ -5 \\ -2 \end{bmatrix}$

Alternative Assessment

Have each student create and encode a message using the alphabet table and encoding matrix in Example 5. Direct students to exchange coded messages and decode them.

Standardized Test Prep

📁 **Resources**
For additional practice with a variety of test item formats:
• Standardized Test Prep, p. 229
• Test-Taking Strategies, p. 224
• Test-Taking Strategies with Transparencies

Exercises 32, 33 Many standardized tests now permit the use of graphing calculators. If you do these exercises with a graphing calculator, display the matrices to be sure you entered them correctly. Then evaluate the determinants.

pages 205–207 Exercises

22. $\begin{bmatrix} -4 & -3.5 & 2 \\ -5 & -5 & 3 \\ 2 & 2 & -1 \end{bmatrix}$

Find the inverse of each matrix, if it exists. 22–24. See margin.

22. $\begin{bmatrix} -2 & 1 & -1 \\ 2 & 0 & 4 \\ 0 & 2 & 5 \end{bmatrix}$ **23.** $\begin{bmatrix} 2 & 0 & -1 \\ -1 & -1 & 1 \\ 3 & 2 & 0 \end{bmatrix}$ **24.** $\begin{bmatrix} 0 & 0 & 2 \\ 1 & 4 & -2 \\ 3 & -2 & 1 \end{bmatrix}$ **25.** $\begin{bmatrix} 1 & 2 & 6 \\ 1 & -1 & 0 \\ 1 & 0 & 2 \end{bmatrix}$
no inverse

✏️ **26. Writing** Evaluate the determinant of each matrix. Describe any patterns.

a. $\begin{bmatrix} 1 & 2 & 3 \\ 1 & 2 & 3 \\ 1 & 2 & 3 \end{bmatrix}$ **0** **b.** $\begin{bmatrix} -1 & -2 & -3 \\ -3 & -2 & -1 \\ -1 & -2 & -3 \end{bmatrix}$ **0** **c.** $\begin{bmatrix} 1 & 2 & 3 \\ 2 & 3 & 1 \\ 1 & 2 & 3 \end{bmatrix}$ **0** **d.** $\begin{bmatrix} -1 & 2 & -3 \\ 2 & -3 & -1 \\ -1 & 2 & -3 \end{bmatrix}$ **0**

See margin for pattern.

C Challenge 📟 **Literature** Use the table and decoding matrix from Example 5. Decode each title.

Maya Angelou—poet, educator, historian, novelist, actress, and playwright

27. Maya Angelou, $\begin{bmatrix} 26.5 & 28 & 15.5 & 16.5 & 13.5 \\ 0.25 & 2 & -3.25 & 8.25 & 6.75 \\ -6 & -6 & -6.5 & 6.5 & 9 \end{bmatrix}$ **MORNING GRACE**

28. Oliver Wendell Holmes, $\begin{bmatrix} 19 & 24 & 24.5 & 18.5 & 26.5 & 13.5 & 19.5 & 20 \\ 6.5 & 8.5 & 3.25 & 1.75 & 10.25 & 2.75 & 9.75 & 10 \\ 0.5 & 6 & 2 & -7.5 & 9 & 5.5 & 13 & 7 \end{bmatrix}$
THE CHAMBERED NAUTILUS

📟 Solve each equation.

29. $\begin{bmatrix} 7 & -5 & 3 \\ 0 & 1 & 3 \\ 8 & 4 & -2 \end{bmatrix} X + \begin{bmatrix} 5 \\ -9 \\ 0 \end{bmatrix} = \begin{bmatrix} 54 \\ -12 \\ 96 \end{bmatrix}$ $\begin{bmatrix} 10 \\ 3 \\ -2 \end{bmatrix}$

30. $\begin{bmatrix} -1 & 0 & 2 \\ -6 & -5 & 0 \\ 1 & 4 & 1 \end{bmatrix} - \begin{bmatrix} -4 & 0 & 2 \\ 0 & 3 & 6 \\ 0 & 5 & 0 \end{bmatrix} X = \begin{bmatrix} -21 & 10 & 26 \\ -54 & 1 & -15 \\ 1 & 4 & -24 \end{bmatrix}$ $\begin{bmatrix} -1 & 2 & 6 \\ 0 & 0 & 5 \\ 8 & -1 & 0 \end{bmatrix}$

Standardized Test Prep

Multiple Choice **31.** What is the determinant of $\begin{bmatrix} 5 & 0 & 0 \\ 0 & 5 & 0 \\ 0 & 0 & 5 \end{bmatrix}$? **C**

A. 5 **B.** 25 **C.** 125 **D.** 555

Quantitative Comparison Compare the boxed quantity in Column A with the boxed quantity in Column B. Choose the best answer.
A. The quantity in Column A is greater.
B. The quantity in Column B is greater.
C. The two quantities are equal.
D. The relationship cannot be determined from the information given.

Column A	Column B
32. **C** $\begin{vmatrix} 1 & 0 & 5 \\ -5 & 0 & -1 \\ 0 & 5 & 0 \end{vmatrix}$	$\begin{vmatrix} -1 & 0 & -5 \\ -5 & 0 & -1 \\ 0 & -5 & 0 \end{vmatrix}$
33. **A** $\begin{vmatrix} 2 & 0 & 3 \\ 4 & 0 & 1 \\ 0 & 2 & 1 \end{vmatrix}$	$\begin{vmatrix} -2 & 0 & -3 \\ -4 & 0 & -1 \\ 0 & -2 & -1 \end{vmatrix}$

💻 **Take It to the NET**
Online lesson quiz at
www.PHSchool.com
Web Code: aga-0406

206 Chapter 4 Matrices

23. $\begin{bmatrix} 0.4 & 0.4 & 0.2 \\ -0.6 & -0.6 & 0.2 \\ -0.2 & 0.8 & 0.4 \end{bmatrix}$

24. $\begin{bmatrix} 0 & \frac{1}{7} & \frac{2}{7} \\ \frac{1}{4} & \frac{3}{14} & -\frac{1}{14} \\ \frac{1}{2} & 0 & 0 \end{bmatrix}$

26d. Answers may vary. Sample: When the top row and bottom row are identical and the middle row has the same numbers as both rows, then the determinant is zero.

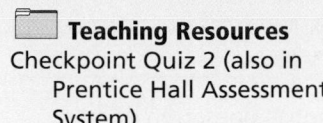
Mixed Review

Lesson 4-5 **Determine whether each matrix has an inverse. If an inverse matrix exists, find it.**

34. $\begin{bmatrix} -9 & 3 \\ 4 & 2.5 \end{bmatrix}$ **35.** $\begin{bmatrix} 2 & 3 \\ 8 & 12 \end{bmatrix}$ **36.** $\begin{bmatrix} -3 & 4 \\ 9 & 10 \end{bmatrix}$ **37.** $\begin{bmatrix} 0 & -1 \\ -1 & 0 \end{bmatrix}$

34–37. See margin.

Lesson 3-1 **Solve each system of equations.**

38. $\begin{cases} 2x + 2y = 10 \\ 3x - y = 4 \end{cases}$ $\left(\frac{9}{4}, \frac{11}{4}\right)$ **39.** $\begin{cases} -x + y + z = 5 \\ 2x + y - z = 2 \\ 3x + 2y + 4z = 0 \end{cases}$

$\left(-\frac{13}{8}, \frac{69}{16}, -\frac{15}{16}\right)$

✓ Checkpoint Quiz 2   Lessons 4-4 through 4-6

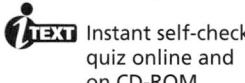 Instant self-check quiz online and on CD-ROM

Use △ABC at the right. Find the coordinates of the image under each transformation. 1–4. See margin.

1. a dilation twice the original size

2. a translation 3 units left and 3 units up

3. a rotation of 270°

4. a reflection in $y = -x$

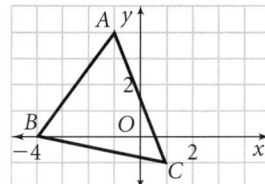

Solve each matrix equation. 5–7. See margin.

5. $\begin{bmatrix} 0 & 3 \\ 5 & 0 \end{bmatrix} X = \begin{bmatrix} -12 & -15 \\ 10 & 15 \end{bmatrix}$ **6.** $\begin{bmatrix} -1 & 2 & 3 \\ 0 & 3 & 2 \\ 3 & -2 & 0 \end{bmatrix} X = \begin{bmatrix} 17 \\ 18 \\ 11 \end{bmatrix}$ **7.** $\begin{bmatrix} 4 & 5 \\ -1 & 5 \end{bmatrix} X = \begin{bmatrix} 32 \\ 42 \end{bmatrix}$

Evaluate the determinant of each matrix.

8. $\begin{bmatrix} -2 & 3 \\ 0 & 5 \end{bmatrix}$ **−10**   **9.** $\begin{bmatrix} 0 & 5 & 4 \\ -1 & -1 & 3 \\ 2 & 5 & 0 \end{bmatrix}$ **18**   **10.** $\begin{bmatrix} -3 & 2 & 0 \\ 4 & 17 & 10 \\ 1 & -5 & -1 \end{bmatrix}$ **−71**

⋯A P●int in Time

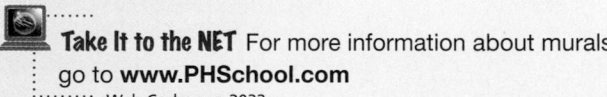

```
1500   1600   1700   1800   1900   2000
```

An artist who paints murals creates a sketch and then uses a dilation of the sketch for the actual mural. Judith Francisca Baca is a muralist who serves as the artistic director of the Great Wall of Los Angeles. The 13-ft-by-2400-ft mural, which depicts California's multicultural history, has involved over 400 youths, 100 scholars, and 50 assisting artists.

Take It to the NET For more information about murals, go to **www.PHSchool.com**
Web Code: age-2032

Lesson 4-6 3 × 3 Matrices, Determinants, and Inverses   **207**

---

34. yes; $\begin{bmatrix} -\frac{5}{69} & \frac{2}{23} \\ \frac{8}{69} & \frac{6}{23} \end{bmatrix}$

35. no

36. yes; $\begin{bmatrix} -\frac{5}{33} & \frac{2}{33} \\ \frac{3}{22} & \frac{1}{22} \end{bmatrix}$

37. yes; $\begin{bmatrix} 0 & -1 \\ -1 & 0 \end{bmatrix}$

To check understanding of Lessons 4-4 to 4-6:

Checkpoint Quiz 2 (p. 207)

📁 **Teaching Resources**
Checkpoint Quiz 2 (also in Prentice Hall Assessment System)

👥 **Reaching All Students**
Reading and Math Literacy 4C

Spanish versions available

page 207 Checkpoint Quiz 2

1. $A'(-2, 8)$, $B'(-8, 0)$, $C'(2, -2)$

2. $A'(-4, 7)$, $B'(-7, 3)$, $C'(-2, 2)$

3. $A'(4, 1)$, $B'(0, 4)$, $C'(-1, -1)$

4. $A'(-4, 1)$, $B'(0, 4)$, $C'(1, -1)$

5. $\begin{bmatrix} 2 & 3 \\ -4 & -5 \end{bmatrix}$

6. $\begin{bmatrix} 5 \\ 2 \\ 6 \end{bmatrix}$

7. $\begin{bmatrix} -2 \\ 8 \end{bmatrix}$

207

Overview

The smooth operation of many of the systems we depend on in everyday life often require detailed analyses of how various locations are linked by channels of transportation or communication. Matrices are helpful in developing mathematical models for such studies.

Resources

Technology
Computer Test Generator
CD-ROM, Chapter 0, Extension
Topics

Teaching Notes

1 EXAMPLE Teaching Tip

Expand on the comment at the end of the example. Point out that N_1 and N_4 are not directly linked by a single path. You can get from N_1 to N_4 only by way of other points.

2 EXAMPLE Teaching Tip

Ask students what type of situation might yield a graph of this kind. There are various possibilities. The arrows could indicate traffic flow along streets in a city. They could indicate who provides information to whom within an organization.

3 EXAMPLE Teaching Tip

You may again wish to ask for real-world examples. One possibility is that arrows indicate payees for checks written by three people.

pages 208–209 Extension

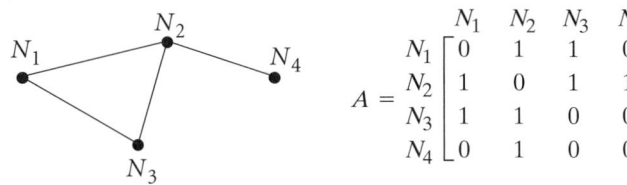
A finite graph is a set of points, called vertices, connected by curves, or paths.

You can use a matrix to describe a finite graph. A 1 indicates a path between two vertices or one vertex and itself. A 0 indicates that no path exists between two vertices or from one vertex to itself.

1 EXAMPLE

Write a matrix A to represent the finite graph. Explain the significance of element a_{41}.

$$A = \begin{array}{c} \\ N_1 \\ N_2 \\ N_3 \\ N_4 \end{array} \begin{array}{cccc} N_1 & N_2 & N_3 & N_4 \\ \begin{bmatrix} 0 & 1 & 1 & 0 \\ 1 & 0 & 1 & 1 \\ 1 & 1 & 0 & 0 \\ 0 & 1 & 0 & 0 \end{bmatrix} \end{array}$$ ← **There is a path from N_2 to N_4.**

Element a_{41} is 0. It indicates that there is no path between N_4 and N_1.

Directed graphs are finite graphs that indicate the direction of a path. The directed graph at the right below represents the information in the map.

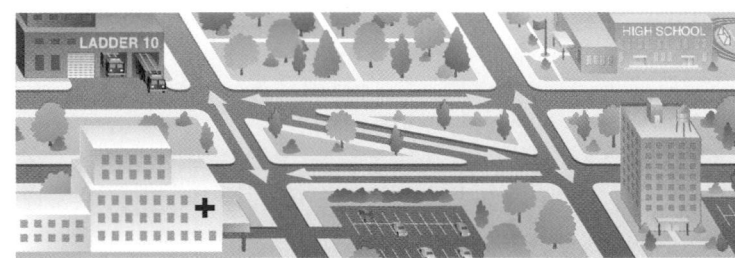

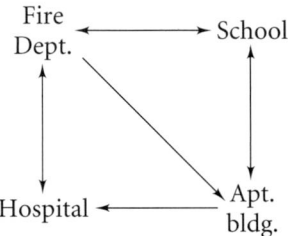

You can use a matrix to represent the information in a directed graph.

2 EXAMPLE

Write a matrix B to represent the information from the directed graph. Compare elements b_{12} and b_{21}.

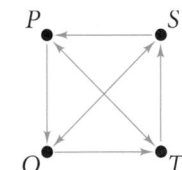

$$B = \begin{array}{c} \\ P \\ Q \\ S \\ T \end{array} \begin{array}{cccc} \text{To} \to & P & Q & S & T \\ \text{From} \to & & & & \\ \begin{bmatrix} 0 & 1 & 0 & 1 \\ 0 & 0 & 1 & 1 \\ 1 & 1 & 0 & 0 \\ 1 & 0 & 1 & 0 \end{bmatrix} \end{array}$$

Element b_{12} is 1, and element b_{21} is 0. The path between P and Q is one way from P to Q.

208 Extension Networks

1.
$$\begin{array}{c} \\ N_1 \\ N_2 \\ N_3 \\ N_4 \end{array} \begin{array}{cccc} N_1 & N_2 & N_3 & N_4 \\ \begin{bmatrix} 0 & 1 & 0 & 1 \\ 1 & 0 & 1 & 1 \\ 0 & 1 & 0 & 1 \\ 1 & 1 & 1 & 0 \end{bmatrix} \end{array}$$

2.
$$\begin{array}{c} \\ S \\ T \\ U \\ V \end{array} \begin{array}{cccc} S & T & U & V \\ \begin{bmatrix} 0 & 0 & 1 & 0 \\ 0 & 0 & 1 & 0 \\ 1 & 1 & 0 & 1 \\ 0 & 0 & 1 & 0 \end{bmatrix} \end{array}$$

3.
$$\begin{array}{c} \\ V_1 \\ V_2 \\ V_3 \\ V_4 \\ V_5 \end{array} \begin{array}{ccccc} V_1 & V_2 & V_3 & V_4 & V_5 \\ \begin{bmatrix} 0 & 1 & 0 & 0 & 0 \\ 1 & 0 & 1 & 0 & 0 \\ 0 & 1 & 0 & 1 & 1 \\ 0 & 0 & 1 & 0 & 1 \\ 0 & 0 & 1 & 1 & 0 \end{bmatrix} \end{array}$$

4.
$$\begin{array}{c} \\ A \\ B \\ C \\ D \\ E \end{array} \begin{array}{ccccc} A & B & C & D & E \\ \begin{bmatrix} 0 & 1 & 0 & 0 & 1 \\ 1 & 0 & 1 & 0 & 0 \\ 0 & 1 & 0 & 1 & 0 \\ 0 & 0 & 0 & 0 & 1 \\ 0 & 0 & 0 & 1 & 0 \end{bmatrix} \end{array}$$

You can use information in a matrix to draw a directed graph.

③ EXAMPLE

Draw a directed graph to represent the information in the matrix.

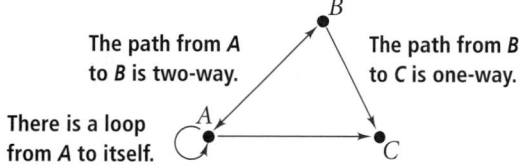

$$\begin{array}{c} \text{To} \to \ A \ B \ C \\ \begin{array}{c} A \\ \text{From} \to B \\ C \end{array} \begin{bmatrix} 1 & 1 & 1 \\ 1 & 0 & 1 \\ 0 & 0 & 0 \end{bmatrix} \end{array}$$

The path from *A* to *B* is two-way.

The path from *B* to *C* is one-way.

There is a loop from *A* to itself.

EXERCISES

Write a matrix to represent each finite or directed graph. 1–6. See margin pp. 208–209.

1.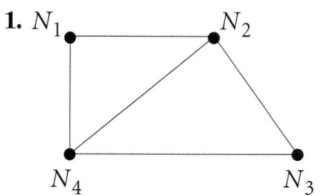

2.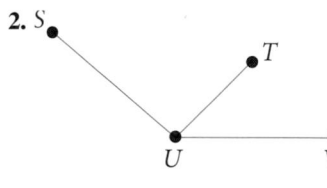

3.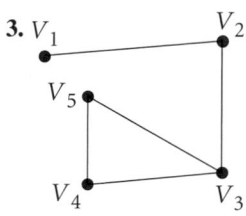

4.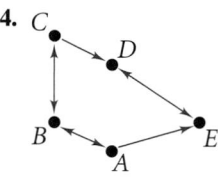

5.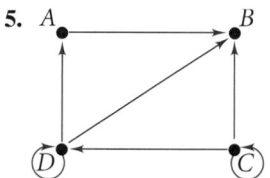

6.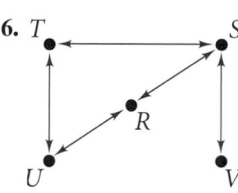

Draw a directed graph to represent the information in each matrix. 7–10. See back of book.

7.
$$\begin{array}{c} \ \ J \ K \ L \ M \\ \begin{array}{c} J \\ K \\ L \\ M \end{array} \begin{bmatrix} 0 & 0 & 0 & 1 \\ 0 & 0 & 1 & 1 \\ 0 & 1 & 0 & 1 \\ 1 & 1 & 1 & 0 \end{bmatrix} \end{array}$$

8.
$$\begin{array}{c} \ \ A \ B \ C \ D \\ \begin{array}{c} A \\ B \\ C \\ D \end{array} \begin{bmatrix} 0 & 0 & 1 & 1 \\ 1 & 1 & 0 & 0 \\ 0 & 1 & 0 & 1 \\ 1 & 0 & 1 & 0 \end{bmatrix} \end{array}$$

9.
$$\begin{array}{c} \ \ N_1 \ N_2 \ N_3 \ N_4 \\ \begin{array}{c} N_1 \\ N_2 \\ N_3 \\ N_4 \end{array} \begin{bmatrix} 1 & 1 & 1 & 1 \\ 0 & 0 & 1 & 1 \\ 1 & 0 & 0 & 0 \\ 0 & 0 & 1 & 0 \end{bmatrix} \end{array}$$

10. Travel Alice and Becky live on Parkway East, at the intersections of Owens Bridge and Bay Bridge, respectively. Carl and David live on Parkway West, at the intersections of Bay Bridge and Owens Bridge, respectively. Parkway East is a one-way street running east. Parkway West is one way running west. Both bridges are two way.
   a. Draw a directed graph indicating road travel between the houses.
   b. Write a matrix T to represent the information in the directed graph.
   c. Writing Calculate T^2. What does the new matrix model? Explain.

5.
$$\begin{array}{c} \ \ A \ B \ C \ D \\ \begin{array}{c} A \\ B \\ C \\ D \end{array} \begin{bmatrix} 0 & 1 & 0 & 0 \\ 0 & 0 & 0 & 0 \\ 0 & 1 & 1 & 1 \\ 1 & 1 & 0 & 1 \end{bmatrix} \end{array}$$

6.
$$\begin{array}{c} \ \ S \ T \ U \ V \ R \\ \begin{array}{c} S \\ T \\ U \\ V \\ R \end{array} \begin{bmatrix} 0 & 1 & 0 & 1 & 1 \\ 1 & 0 & 1 & 0 & 0 \\ 0 & 1 & 0 & 0 & 1 \\ 1 & 0 & 0 & 0 & 0 \\ 1 & 0 & 1 & 0 & 0 \end{bmatrix} \end{array}$$

● **Extension**

📘 **Additional Examples**

① Write a matrix to represent the finite graph.

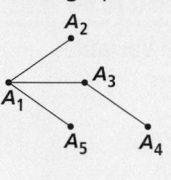

$$\begin{array}{c} \ \ \ A_1 \ A_2 \ A_3 \ A_4 \ A_5 \\ \begin{array}{c} A_1 \\ A_2 \\ A_3 \\ A_4 \\ A_5 \end{array} \begin{bmatrix} 0 & 1 & 1 & 0 & 1 \\ 1 & 0 & 0 & 0 & 0 \\ 1 & 0 & 0 & 1 & 0 \\ 0 & 0 & 1 & 0 & 0 \\ 1 & 0 & 0 & 0 & 0 \end{bmatrix} \end{array}$$

② Write a matrix to represent the information in the directed graph.

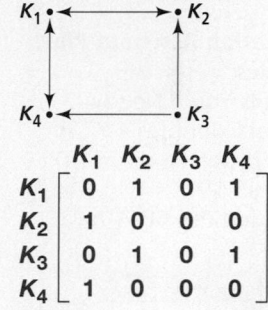

$$\begin{array}{c} \ \ \ K_1 \ K_2 \ K_3 \ K_4 \\ \begin{array}{c} K_1 \\ K_2 \\ K_3 \\ K_4 \end{array} \begin{bmatrix} 0 & 1 & 0 & 1 \\ 1 & 0 & 0 & 0 \\ 0 & 1 & 0 & 1 \\ 1 & 0 & 0 & 0 \end{bmatrix} \end{array}$$

③ Draw a directed graph to represent the information in the matrix.

$$\begin{array}{c} \ \ \ A_1 \ A_2 \ A_3 \ A_4 \\ \begin{array}{c} A_1 \\ A_2 \\ A_3 \\ A_4 \end{array} \begin{bmatrix} 0 & 1 & 1 & 0 \\ 1 & 1 & 1 & 0 \\ 0 & 0 & 0 & 1 \\ 0 & 1 & 0 & 1 \end{bmatrix} \end{array}$$

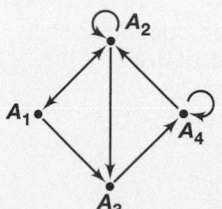

209

4-7

1. Plan

 Lesson Preview

 Check Skills You'll Need

Systems With Three Variables
Lesson 3-6: Examples 1–3
Exercises 1–15
Extra Practice, p. 824

 Lesson Resources

 Teaching Resources
Practice, Reteaching, Enrichment

Reaching All Students
Practice Workbook 4-7
Spanish Practice Workbook 4-7

Presentation Assistant Plus!
Transparencies
• Check Skills You'll Need 4-7
• Additional Examples 4-7
• Student Edition Answers 4-7
• Lesson Quiz 4-7
PH Presentation Pro CD 4-7

 PRENTICE HALL
ASSESSMENT SYSTEM

Computer Test Generator CD

 Technology
Resource Pro® CD-ROM
Computer Test Generator CD
Prentice Hall Presentation Pro CD

 **www.PHSchool.com**
Student Site
• Teacher Web Code: agk-5500
• Graphing Calculator,
  Procedures 14, 25
• Self-grading Lesson Quiz
Teacher Center
• Lesson Planner
• Resources

Plus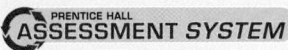

210

4-7

Inverse Matrices and Systems

1.04 Operate with matrices to model and solve problems.
2.10 Use systems of two or more equations to model and solve problems. Solve using matrix operations and algebraic properties.

Lesson Preview

What You'll Learn

 **OBJECTIVE 1** To solve systems of equations using inverse matrices

. . . And Why

To calculate business costs, as in Example 4

✔ **Check Skills You'll Need**   (For help, go to Lesson 3-6.)

Solve each system.

1. $\begin{cases} 5x + y = 14 \\ 4x + 3y = 20 \end{cases}$

2. $\begin{cases} x - y - z = -9 \\ 3x + y + 2z = 12 \\ x = y - 2z \end{cases}$

3. $\begin{cases} -x + 2y + z = 0 \\ y = -2x + 3 \\ z = 3x \end{cases}$

(2, 4)   **(0, 6, 3)**   **(3, −3, 9)**

New Vocabulary   • coefficient matrix   • variable matrix   • constant matrix

---

Interactive lesson includes instant self-check, tutorials, and activities.

OBJECTIVE

1   **Solving Systems of Equations Using Inverse Matrices**

You can represent a system of equations with a matrix equation.

System of equations	**Matrix equation**
$\begin{cases} x + 2y = 5 \\ 3x + 5y = 14 \end{cases}$	$\begin{bmatrix} 1 & 2 \\ 3 & 5 \end{bmatrix}\begin{bmatrix} x \\ y \end{bmatrix} = \begin{bmatrix} 5 \\ 14 \end{bmatrix}$

Each matrix in an equation of the form $AX = B$ has a name.

Coefficient matrix A **Variable matrix** X **Constant matrix** B

$\begin{bmatrix} 1 & 2 \\ 3 & 5 \end{bmatrix}$ $\begin{bmatrix} x \\ y \end{bmatrix}$ $\begin{bmatrix} 5 \\ 14 \end{bmatrix}$

?
Need Help?
To review the definitions of *coefficient* and *variable*, go to Lesson 1-2.

1 **EXAMPLE**   **Writing a System as a Matrix Equation**

Write the system $\begin{cases} -b + 2c = 4 \\ a + b - c = 0 \\ 2a + 3c = 11 \end{cases}$ as a matrix equation. Then identify the coefficient matrix, the variable matrix, and the constant matrix.

Matrix equation: $\begin{bmatrix} 0 & -1 & 2 \\ 1 & 1 & -1 \\ 2 & 0 & 3 \end{bmatrix}\begin{bmatrix} a \\ b \\ c \end{bmatrix} = \begin{bmatrix} 4 \\ 0 \\ 11 \end{bmatrix}$

Coefficient matrix   Variable matrix   Constant matrix

$\begin{bmatrix} 0 & -1 & 2 \\ 1 & 1 & -1 \\ 2 & 0 & 3 \end{bmatrix}$ $\begin{bmatrix} a \\ b \\ c \end{bmatrix}$ $\begin{bmatrix} 4 \\ 0 \\ 11 \end{bmatrix}$

✔ **Check Understanding**  **1** Write each system as a matrix equation. Identify the coefficient matrix, the variable matrix, and the constant matrix. **a–b. See back of book.**

a. $\begin{cases} 3x + 2y = 16 \\ y = 5 \end{cases}$

b. $\begin{cases} x - y + z = 0 \\ x - 2y - z = 5 \\ 2x - y + 2z = 8 \end{cases}$

210   Chapter 4   Matrices

 Ongoing Assessment and Intervention

Before the Lesson	**During the Lesson**	**After the Lesson**
Diagnose prerequisite skills using:	**Monitor progress using:**	**Assess knowledge using:**
• Check Skills You'll Need	• Check Understanding	• Lesson Quiz
	• Additional Examples	• Computer Test Generator CD
	• Standardized Test Prep	

Sometimes you can find the inverse of the coefficient matrix. Then you can use it to solve systems of equations quickly.

EXAMPLE Solving a System of Two Equations

Solve the system $\begin{cases} 2x + 3y = 11 \\ x + 2y = 6 \end{cases}$.

$\begin{bmatrix} 2 & 3 \\ 1 & 2 \end{bmatrix}\begin{bmatrix} x \\ y \end{bmatrix} = \begin{bmatrix} 11 \\ 6 \end{bmatrix}$ **Write the system as a matrix equation.**

$A^{-1} = \begin{bmatrix} 2 & -3 \\ -1 & 2 \end{bmatrix}$ **Find A^{-1}.**

$\begin{bmatrix} x \\ y \end{bmatrix} = A^{-1}B = \begin{bmatrix} 2 & -3 \\ -1 & 2 \end{bmatrix}\begin{bmatrix} 11 \\ 6 \end{bmatrix} = \begin{bmatrix} 4 \\ 1 \end{bmatrix}$ **Solve for the variable matrix.**

The solution of the system is $(4, 1)$.

Check	$2x + 3y = 11$	$x + 2y = 6$	**Use the original equations.**
	$2(4) + 3(1) \stackrel{?}{=} 11$	$4 + 2(1) \stackrel{?}{=} 6$	**Substitute.**
	$8 + 3 = 11 ✓$	$4 + 2 = 6 ✓$	**Simplify.**

✓ **Check Understanding** **2** Solve each system. Check your answers.

a. $\begin{cases} 5a + 3b = 7 \\ 3a + 2b = 5 \end{cases}$ **(−1, 4)**   b. $\begin{cases} x + 3y = 22 \\ 3x + 2y = 10 \end{cases}$ **(−2, 8)**

You can use a graphing calculator to solve a system of three equations.

3 **EXAMPLE** Solving a System of Three Equations

Solve the system $\begin{cases} 2x + y + 3z = 1 \\ 5x + y - 2z = 8. \\ x - y - 9z = 5 \end{cases}$

Step 1 Write the system as a matrix equation.

$\begin{bmatrix} 2 & 1 & 3 \\ 5 & 1 & -2 \\ 1 & -1 & -9 \end{bmatrix}\begin{bmatrix} x \\ y \\ z \end{bmatrix} = \begin{bmatrix} 1 \\ 8 \\ 5 \end{bmatrix}$

Step 2 Store the coefficient matrix as matrix A and the constant matrix as matrix B.

```
[A]⁻¹[B]
        [[4  ]
         [−10]
         [1  ]]
```

The solution is $(4, -10, 1)$.

✓ **Check Understanding** **3** **a.** Check the solution from Example 3 in each of the original equations. **See left.**

b. Solve the system $\begin{cases} x + y + z = 2 \\ 2x + y = 5. \\ x + 3y - 3z = 14 \end{cases}$ Check your solution. **(1.25, 2.5, −1.75)**

3a. $2(4) + (-10) + 3(1) \stackrel{?}{=} 1$
$8 - 10 + 3 \stackrel{?}{=} 1$
$1 = 1$
$5(4) + (-10) - 2(1) \stackrel{?}{=} 8$
$20 - 10 - 2 \stackrel{?}{=} 8$
$8 = 8$
$4 - (-10) - 9(1) \stackrel{?}{=} 5$
$4 + 10 - 9 \stackrel{?}{=} 5$
$5 = 5$

Need Help?

The inverse of $\begin{bmatrix} a & b \\ c & d \end{bmatrix}$ is

$\dfrac{1}{ad - bc}\begin{bmatrix} d & -b \\ -c & a \end{bmatrix}$.

The matrix $\begin{bmatrix} a & b \\ c & d \end{bmatrix}$ has

no inverse when $ad - bc = 0$.

Lesson 4-7 Inverse Matrices and Systems **211**

2. Teach

Professional Development

Math Background

A system of n linear equations in n variables can be represented by a matrix equation of the form $AX = B$, where A is an $n \times n$ matrix and B is an $n \times 1$ matrix. If A has an inverse, then the solution of the system can be found by solving $A^{-1}B = X$ for X.

OBJECTIVE

1 Teaching Notes

3 **EXAMPLE** **Teaching Tip**

After discussing the example, ask students whether the matrix method, the substitution method, or the elimination method requires less work.

Additional Examples

1 Write the system

$\begin{cases} 3x - 4y + 5z = 11 \\ -2x + 7y = -6 \\ -5x + y - z = 20 \end{cases}$

as a matrix equation. Then identify the coefficient matrix, the variable matrix, and the constant matrix.

$\begin{bmatrix} 3 & -4 & 5 \\ -2 & 7 & 0 \\ -5 & 1 & -1 \end{bmatrix}\begin{bmatrix} x \\ y \\ z \end{bmatrix} = \begin{bmatrix} 11 \\ -6 \\ 20 \end{bmatrix}$

The first matrix is the coefficient matrix, the second is the variable matrix, and the third is the constant matrix.

2 Solve the system.

$\begin{cases} 2x + 3y = -1 \\ x - y = 12 \end{cases}$ **(7, −5)**

3 Solve the system.

$\begin{cases} 7x + 3y + 2z = 13 \\ -2x + y - 8z = 26 \\ x - 4y + 10z = -13 \end{cases}$

(9, −12, −7)

Reaching All Students

Below Level Remind students that each equation must be written with the variables in the same order and zeroes must be written as coefficients of missing variables.

Advanced Learners Challenge students to research and explain how to find the inverses of larger square matrices. Have the students share their results with the class.

Error Prevention
See note on page 212.
Error Prevention
See note on page 213.

211

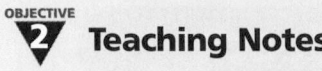
5 EXAMPLE Error Prevention

Urge students to be cautious when they use the determinant of the coefficient matrix to make statements about the number of solutions of a system. If the determinant is zero, the only thing you can be sure of is that there is not a *unique* solution. There could be no solutions or there could be infinitely many solutions.

Additional Examples

4 A linen shop has several tables of sheets and towels on special sale. The sheets are all priced the same, and so are the towels. Mario bought 3 sheets and 5 towels at a cost of $137.50. Marco bought 4 sheets and 2 towels at a cost of $118.00. Find the price of each item. **sheets: $22.50; towels: $14.00**

5 Write the coefficient matrix for each system. Use it to determine whether the system has a unique solution.

a. $\begin{cases} 4x - 2y = 7 \\ -6x + 3y = 5 \end{cases}$

$\begin{bmatrix} 4 & -2 \\ -6 & 3 \end{bmatrix}$; **no**

b. $\begin{cases} 12x + 8y = -3 \\ 3x - 7y = 50 \end{cases}$

$\begin{bmatrix} 12 & 8 \\ 3 & -7 \end{bmatrix}$; **yes**

Closure

Ask students to describe how to find the solution of a system of three linear equations in three variables. (Assume there is exactly one solution.) **Answers may vary. Sample: Write each equation so that all the variables are on the left side of the equal sign and all constants on the right side of the equal sign. Represent the system by a matrix equation of the form $AX = B$, where A is the coefficient matrix and B is the constant matrix. Then calculate $A^{-1}B$.**

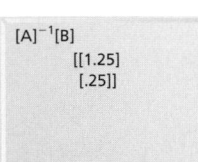

$3.25

$4.75

There are many business applications for matrices of systems of equations.

4 EXAMPLE **Real-World Connection**

Business A bead store has a sale on certain beads. Find the price of each size of bead.

Relate   2 large beads and 3 small beads cost $3.25.
             3 large beads and 4 small beads cost $4.75.

Define   Let x = the price of one large bead.
             Let y = the price of one small bead.

Write $\begin{bmatrix} 2 & 3 \\ 3 & 4 \end{bmatrix}\begin{bmatrix} x \\ y \end{bmatrix} = \begin{bmatrix} 3.25 \\ 4.75 \end{bmatrix}$ Write the system as a matrix equation.

$[A]^{-1}[B]$
$\quad [[1.25]$
$\quad\ [.25]]$

Use a graphing calculator. Store the coefficient matrix as matrix A and the constant matrix as matrix B.

● The price of a large bead is $1.25. The price of a small bead is $.25.

✔ **Check Understanding** **4** Suppose the sale is over, and the price of each package increases. The price of a package of two large beads and three small beads increases to $5.55. The price of a package of three large beads and four small beads increases to $8.05. Find the new price of each type of bead. **one large bead = $1.95, one small bead = $.55**

When the coefficient matrix of a system has an inverse, the system has a unique solution. Similarly, when the coefficient matrix does *not* have an inverse, the system does *not* have a unique solution. In that case, the system either has no solution or has an infinite number of solutions.

5 EXAMPLE **Unique Solutions**

Write the coefficient matrix for each system. Use it to determine whether the system has a unique solution.

a. $\begin{cases} x + y = 3 \\ x - y = 7 \end{cases}$

$A = \begin{bmatrix} 1 & 1 \\ 1 & -1 \end{bmatrix}$; $\det A = \begin{vmatrix} 1 & 1 \\ 1 & -1 \end{vmatrix} = 1(-1) - 1(1) = -2$

Since $\det A \neq 0$, the matrix has an inverse, so the system has a unique solution.

b. $\begin{cases} x + 2y = 5 \\ 2x + 4y = 8 \end{cases}$

$A = \begin{bmatrix} 1 & 2 \\ 2 & 4 \end{bmatrix}$; $\det A = \begin{vmatrix} 1 & 2 \\ 2 & 4 \end{vmatrix} = 1(4) - 2(2) = 0$

Since $\det A = 0$, the matrix does not have an inverse and the system does *not* have a unique solution.

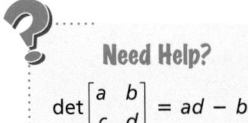

Need Help?

$\det\begin{bmatrix} a & b \\ c & d \end{bmatrix} = ad - bc$

✓ **Check Understanding** **5** **a.** Determine whether the system $\begin{cases} 3x + 5y = 1 \\ 2x - y = -8 \end{cases}$ has a unique solution. **yes**

b. You can use an inverse matrix to solve a system of equations. What happens when you try to do this with a graphing calculator and the system does not have a unique solution? **The graphing calculator indicates that there is a "singular matrix" error.**

EXERCISES

For more practice, see *Extra Practice*.

Practice and Problem Solving

A **Practice by Example**

Example 1 (page 210)

Write each system as a matrix equation. Identify the coefficient matrix, the variable matrix, and the constant matrix. **1–6. See back of book.**

1. $\begin{cases} x + y = 5 \\ x - 2y = -4 \end{cases}$

2. $\begin{cases} y = 3x - 7 \\ x = 2 \end{cases}$

3. $\begin{cases} 3a + 5b = 0 \\ a + b = 2 \end{cases}$

4. $\begin{cases} x + 3y - z = 2 \\ x + 2z = 8 \\ 2y - z = 1 \end{cases}$

5. $\begin{cases} r - s + t = 150 \\ 2r + t = 425 \\ s + 3t = 0 \end{cases}$

6. $\begin{cases} x + 2y = 11 \\ 2x + 3y = 18 \end{cases}$

Examples 2 and 3 (page 211)

Solve each system of equations. Check your answers.

7. $\begin{cases} x + 3y = 5 \\ x + 4y = 6 \end{cases}$ **(2, 1)**

8. $\begin{cases} p - 3q = -1 \\ -5p + 16q = 5 \end{cases}$ **(−1, 0)**

9. $\begin{cases} 300x - y = 130 \\ 200x + y = 120 \end{cases}$ **($\frac{1}{2}$, 20)**

10. $\begin{cases} x + 5y = -4 \\ x + 6y = -5 \end{cases}$ **(1, −1)**

11. $\begin{cases} 2x + 3y = 12 \\ x + 2y = 7 \end{cases}$ **(3, 2)**

12. $\begin{cases} 2x + 3y = 5 \\ x + 2y = 6 \end{cases}$ **(−8, 7)**

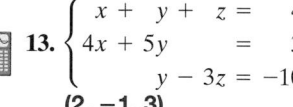 **13.** $\begin{cases} x + y + z = 4 \\ 4x + 5y = 3 \\ y - 3z = -10 \end{cases}$ **(2, −1, 3)**

14. $\begin{cases} 9y + 2z = 18 \\ 3x + 2y + z = 5 \\ x - y = -1 \end{cases}$ **(−3, −2, 18)**

15. $\begin{cases} 9y + 2z = 14 \\ 3x + 2y + z = 5 \\ x - y = -1 \end{cases}$ **(1, 2, −2)**

Example 4 (page 212)

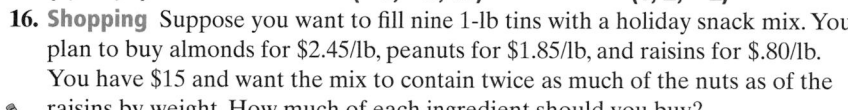 **16. Shopping** Suppose you want to fill nine 1-lb tins with a holiday snack mix. You plan to buy almonds for $2.45/lb, peanuts for $1.85/lb, and raisins for $.80/lb. You have $15 and want the mix to contain twice as much of the nuts as of the raisins by weight. How much of each ingredient should you buy?

a. Writing Explain how each equation in the system at the right relates to the problem. What does each variable represent?

$\begin{cases} x + y + z = 9 \\ 2.45x + 1.85y + 0.8z = 15 \\ x + y = 2z \end{cases}$

b. Solve the system. **See margin.** **(2.5, 3.5, 3)**

Example 5 (page 212)

Determine whether each system has a unique solution.

17. $\begin{cases} 20x + 5y = 240 \\ y = 20x \end{cases}$ **yes**

18. $\begin{cases} 20x + 5y = 145 \\ 30x - 5y = 125 \end{cases}$ **yes**

19. $\begin{cases} y = 2000 - 65x \\ y = 500 + 55x \end{cases}$ **yes**

20. $\begin{cases} y = \frac{2}{3}x - 3 \\ y = -x + 7 \end{cases}$ **yes**

21. $\begin{cases} 3x + 2y = 10 \\ 6x + 4y = 16 \end{cases}$ **no**

22. $\begin{cases} x + 2y + z = 4 \\ y = x - 3 \\ z = 2x \end{cases}$ **yes**

B **Apply Your Skills**

Solve each matrix equation. If the coefficient matrix has no inverse, write *no unique solution.*

25. (16, −22)

23. $\begin{bmatrix} 1 & 1 \\ 1 & 2 \end{bmatrix} \begin{bmatrix} x \\ y \end{bmatrix} = \begin{bmatrix} 8 \\ 10 \end{bmatrix}$ **(6, 2)**

24. $\begin{bmatrix} 2 & -3 \\ -4 & 6 \end{bmatrix} \begin{bmatrix} a \\ b \end{bmatrix} = \begin{bmatrix} 1 \\ -2 \end{bmatrix}$ **no unique solution**

25. $\begin{bmatrix} 2 & 1 \\ 4 & 3 \end{bmatrix} \begin{bmatrix} x \\ y \end{bmatrix} = \begin{bmatrix} 10 \\ -2 \end{bmatrix}$ **See left.**

Lesson 4-7 Inverse Matrices and Systems **213**

Assignment Guide

1 **Objective**

A **B** Core 1–37

C Extension 38–42

Standardized Test Prep 43–48

Mixed Review 49–56

Error Prevention

Exercises 17–22 Suggest that students first write each equation of the system in the form $Ax + By = C$. This will help ensure that they use the correct coefficient matrix.

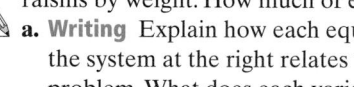

---

pages 213–215 Exercises

16a. *x* is the number of pounds of almonds, *y* is the number of pounds of peanuts, and *z* is the number of pounds of raisins that must be bought. The first equation states that the total weight will be 9 pounds. The second equation states that the total cost will be $15. The third equation states that the combined weights of almonds and peanuts should be double the weight of the raisins.

Alternative Assessment

Have each student write a system of two linear equations in two variables and a system of three linear equations in three variables. Each student then solves the systems using matrices. If a system does not have exactly one solution, the student should explain how he or she knows that this is the case.

pages 213–215   Exercises

41. The tea temperature was 126°F and the milk temperature was 36°F.

42a. Let c = lb of chicken, r = lb of rice, and s = lb of shellfish.

$\begin{cases} c + r + s = 18 \\ 1.50c + 0.40r + 6.00s \\ \quad = 29.50 \\ 100c + 20r + 50s \\ \quad = 850 \end{cases}$

b. (5, 10, 3); 5 lb of chicken, 10 lb of rice, 3 lb of shellfish

26. (−2, −1)

27. (2, 4)

28. (−1, 0)

29. (4, 1, 3)

30. (5, 0, 1)

31. (−19, 22, 13)

Reading Math
For help with reading and solving Exercise 36, see p. 216.

C Challenge

Solve each system.

26. $\begin{cases} -3x + 4y = 2 \\ x - y = -1 \end{cases}$

27. $\begin{cases} x + 2y = 10 \\ 3x + 5y = 26 \end{cases}$

28. $\begin{cases} x - 3y = -1 \\ -6x + 19y = 6 \end{cases}$

29. $\begin{cases} x = 5 - y \\ 3y = z \\ x + z = 7 \end{cases}$

30. $\begin{cases} -x = -4 - z \\ 2y = z - 1 \\ x = 6 - y - z \end{cases}$

31. $\begin{cases} -b + 2c = 4 \\ a + b - c = -10 \\ 2a + 3c = 1 \end{cases}$

32. $\begin{cases} x + y + z = 4 \\ 4x + 5y = 4 \\ y - 3z = -9 \end{cases}$ **(1, 0, 3)**

33. $\begin{cases} x + y + z = 4 \\ 4x + 5y = 3 \\ y - 3z = -10 \end{cases}$ **(2, −1, 3)**

34. $\begin{cases} -2w + x + y = 0 \\ -w + 2x - y + z = 1 \\ -2w + 3x + 3y + 2z = 6 \\ w + x + 2y + z = 5 \end{cases}$

(1, 1, 1, 1)

35. $\begin{cases} -2w + x + y = -2 \\ -w + 2x - y + z = -4 \\ -2w + 3x + 3y + 2z = 2 \\ w + x + 2y + z = 6 \end{cases}$

(2, 0, 2, 0)

36. Coordinate Geometry The coordinates (x, y) of a point in a plane are the solution of the system $\begin{cases} 2x + 3y = 13 \\ 5x + 7y = 31 \end{cases}$. Find the coordinates of the point. **(2, 3)**

37. Geometry A rectangle is twice as long as it is wide. The perimeter is 840 ft. Find the dimensions of the rectangle. **length = 280 ft, width = 140 ft**

Open-Ended Complete each system for the given number of solutions.

39–40. Answers may vary.

38. infinitely many

$\begin{cases} x + y = 7 \\ 2x + 2y = \blacksquare \end{cases}$ **14**

39. one solution

$\begin{cases} x + y + z = 7 \\ y + z = \blacksquare \\ z = \blacksquare \end{cases}$ **0**
0

40. no solution

$\begin{cases} x + y + z = 7 \\ y + z = \blacksquare \\ y + z = \blacksquare \end{cases}$ **0**
1

41. Physics When you mix hot and cold liquids, you can find the temperature of the mixture by using the formula $T = \dfrac{ah + bc}{a + b}$, where T is the temperature of the mixture, h is the temperature of the hot liquid, c is the temperature of the cold liquid, and a and b represent the amounts of hot and cold liquids. Suppose you mix hot tea and cold milk in a ratio $a : b$ of $9 : 1$, and find that the temperature of the mixture is $117°F$. You then change the tea : milk ratio to $2 : 1$, and the temperature drops to $96°F$. Find the initial temperatures of the tea and the milk. **See margin.**

42. Nutrition A caterer combines ingredients to make a paella, a Spanish fiesta dish. The paella weighs 18 lb, costs $29.50, and supplies 850 g of protein.
a. Write a system of three equations to find the weight of each ingredient.
b. Solve the system. How many pounds of each ingredient did she use? **a–b. See margin.**

Paella Nutrition Chart

Food	Cost/lb	Protein/lb
Chicken	$1.50	100 g
Rice	$.40	20 g
Shellfish	$6.00	50 g

48. [2] First write each equation in standard form. Then place the coefficients in a matrix, with the coefficients of x in the first column, the coefficients of y in the second column, and the coefficients of z in the third:

$\begin{bmatrix} 2 & -3 & 1 \\ 1 & 4 & -2 \\ -3 & -2 & 3 \end{bmatrix}$

Multiple Choice

43. Which matrix equation represents the system $\begin{cases} 2x - 3y = -3 \\ -5x + y = 14 \end{cases}$? **B**

A. $\begin{bmatrix} x \\ y \end{bmatrix} \begin{bmatrix} 2 & -3 \\ -5 & 1 \end{bmatrix} = \begin{bmatrix} -3 \\ 14 \end{bmatrix}$

B. $\begin{bmatrix} 2 & -3 \\ -5 & 1 \end{bmatrix} \begin{bmatrix} x \\ y \end{bmatrix} = \begin{bmatrix} -3 \\ 14 \end{bmatrix}$

C. $\begin{bmatrix} 2 & -3 \\ -5 & 1 \end{bmatrix} \begin{bmatrix} -3 \\ 14 \end{bmatrix} = \begin{bmatrix} x \\ y \end{bmatrix}$

D. $\begin{bmatrix} -3 \\ 14 \end{bmatrix} [x \ y] = \begin{bmatrix} 2 & -3 \\ -5 & 1 \end{bmatrix}$

44. What is the solution to the matrix equation $\begin{bmatrix} 3 & -1 \\ -1 & 2 \end{bmatrix} \begin{bmatrix} a \\ b \end{bmatrix} = \begin{bmatrix} 7 \\ -9 \end{bmatrix}$? **I**

F. $a = 7, b = -9$ G. $a = 2, b = 1$ H. $a = \frac{7}{3}, b = -\frac{9}{2}$ I. $a = 1, b = -4$

Use the system $\begin{cases} 2x - 3y + z = 6 \\ x + 2y - 4z = 5 \\ -3x - 2y + 3z = -5 \end{cases}$ for Exercises 45–47.

45. Which matrix is the coefficient matrix for the system? **C**

A. $\begin{bmatrix} 2 & 3 & 1 \\ 1 & 2 & 4 \\ 3 & 2 & 3 \end{bmatrix}$ B. $\begin{bmatrix} 2 & -3 & 1 & 6 \\ 1 & 2 & -4 & 5 \\ -3 & -2 & 3 & -5 \end{bmatrix}$ C. $\begin{bmatrix} 2 & -3 & 1 \\ 1 & 2 & -4 \\ -3 & -2 & 3 \end{bmatrix}$ D. $\begin{bmatrix} 6 \\ 5 \\ -5 \end{bmatrix}$

46. Which matrix is the constant matrix for the system? **I**

F. $\begin{bmatrix} 2 & 3 & 1 \\ 1 & 2 & 4 \\ 3 & 2 & 3 \end{bmatrix}$ G. $\begin{bmatrix} 2 & -3 & 1 & 6 \\ 1 & 2 & -4 & 5 \\ -3 & -2 & 3 & -5 \end{bmatrix}$ H. $\begin{bmatrix} 2 & -3 & 1 \\ 1 & 2 & -4 \\ -3 & -2 & 3 \end{bmatrix}$ I. $\begin{bmatrix} 6 \\ 5 \\ -5 \end{bmatrix}$

Take It to the NET
Online lesson quiz at
www.PHSchool.com
Web Code: aga-0407

47. What is the determinant of the coefficient matrix? **B**

A. -150 B. -27 C. 6 D. 29

Short Response

48. How can you write the three equations at the right as a matrix equation for a system? Explain your steps.
See margin.

$2x - 3y + z + 10 = 0$
$x + 4y = 2z + 11$
$-2y + 3z + 7 = 3x$

Standardized Test Prep

📁 **Resources**
For additional practice with a variety of test item formats:
● Standardized Test Prep, p. 229
● Test-Taking Strategies, p. 224
● Test-Taking Strategies with Transparencies

Exercise 48 Tell students to be sure to include an explanation of everything they do to the equations before writing the matrix equation.

Mixed Review

Lesson 4-6 **Evaluate the determinant of each matrix.**

49. $\begin{bmatrix} -1 & 3 & 7 \\ 5 & -4 & -2 \\ 0 & 2 & 10 \end{bmatrix}$ **-44** **50.** $\begin{bmatrix} 17 & 0 & 0 \\ 0 & 17 & 0 \\ 0 & 0 & 17 \end{bmatrix}$ **4913** **51.** $\begin{bmatrix} -3 & 0 & 5 \\ 5 & -3 & 2 \\ -3 & -5 & -2 \end{bmatrix}$ **-218**

Lesson 4-2 **Add or subtract.**

52. $\begin{bmatrix} 5 & -3 \\ 4 & 11 \end{bmatrix} + \begin{bmatrix} 4 & 0 \\ -9 & 1 \end{bmatrix}$ $\begin{bmatrix} 9 & -3 \\ -5 & 12 \end{bmatrix}$

53. $\begin{bmatrix} -1 & 2 & 0 \\ 10 & -5 & 15 \\ 17 & 3 & -4 \end{bmatrix} - \begin{bmatrix} 0 & 6 & -3 \\ 4 & -7 & 11 \\ -9 & 10 & -1 \end{bmatrix}$
See margin.

Lesson 2-6 **Describe each translation of** $f(x) = |x|$ **as** *vertical, horizontal,* **or** *diagonal.* **Then graph the translation.** **54–56. See margin.**

54. $f(x) = |x + 4|$ **55.** $f(x) = |x| - 3$ **56.** $f(x) = |x - 5| + 3$

53. $\begin{bmatrix} -1 & -4 & 3 \\ 6 & 2 & 4 \\ 26 & -7 & -3 \end{bmatrix}$

54. horizontal
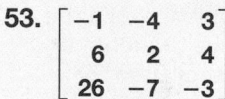

55. vertical
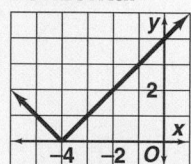

56. diagonal
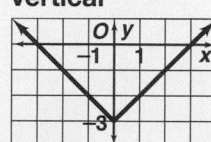

Finally, put this in an equation with the variable matrix $\begin{bmatrix} x \\ y \\ z \end{bmatrix}$ and the constant matrix $\begin{bmatrix} -10 \\ 11 \\ -7 \end{bmatrix}$, to get $\begin{bmatrix} 2 & -3 & 1 \\ 1 & 4 & -2 \\ -3 & -2 & 3 \end{bmatrix} \begin{bmatrix} x \\ y \\ z \end{bmatrix} = \begin{bmatrix} -10 \\ 11 \\ -7 \end{bmatrix}$.

[1] answer only, without explanation of steps

Reading For Problem Solving

In this problem solving example, students not only see how a sample problem is worked out, but they also see the thought processes of the person who is working out the problem. The notes in the left-hand column explain the actions taken in the right-hand column.

Teaching Notes

Tell students to read through the example, looking carefully at both how the problem is worked out, and what Jaime thinks as he works out the problem. Tell students to look back at the examples in this lesson if they do not recall how to find the reciprocal of a matrix, or how to multiply matrices by their reciprocals.

Exercise

Place students in pairs. Have one student record the steps used in solving the problem, while the other records the thought processes that they used for each step.

Read the problem below. Then follow along with Jaime as he solves the problem. Check your understanding with the exercise at the bottom of the page.

Coordinate Geometry The coordinates (x, y) of a point in a plane are the solution of the system $\begin{cases} 2x + 3y = 13 \\ 5x + 7y = 31 \end{cases}$. Find the coordinates of the point.

What Jaime Thinks

The problem tells me that the solution of this system is (x, y). I could graph the lines to see where they intersect, but that's not necessary when I can solve the system with matrices. I'll rewrite the system as a matrix equation.

To solve for the variable matrix that includes x and y, I should multiply each side of the equation by the inverse of the coefficient matrix. I'll use the formula on page 197.

Now that I have the inverse, I can multiply.

Something is wrong. I can't multiply the matrices on the right side of this equation because the dimensions don't match.

Oh!!! I have to multiply the inverse matrix on the left, because matrix multiplication is not commutative!

I'll rewrite the equation correctly. The result will be a 2 × 1 matrix.

This means the x-coordinate is 2 and the y-coordinate is 3. I'll write my answer in a sentence.

What Jaime Writes

$$\begin{cases} 2x + 3y = 13 \\ 5x + 7y = 31 \end{cases} \quad \begin{bmatrix} 2 & 3 \\ 5 & 7 \end{bmatrix}\begin{bmatrix} x \\ y \end{bmatrix} = \begin{bmatrix} 13 \\ 31 \end{bmatrix}$$

Inverse of
$$\begin{bmatrix} 2 & 3 \\ 5 & 7 \end{bmatrix} = \frac{1}{(2)(7) - (5)(3)}\begin{bmatrix} 7 & -3 \\ -5 & 2 \end{bmatrix}$$
$$= -1\begin{bmatrix} 7 & -3 \\ -5 & 2 \end{bmatrix} = \begin{bmatrix} -7 & 3 \\ 5 & -2 \end{bmatrix}$$

$$\begin{bmatrix} -7 & 3 \\ 5 & -2 \end{bmatrix}\begin{bmatrix} 2 & 3 \\ 5 & 7 \end{bmatrix}\begin{bmatrix} x \\ y \end{bmatrix} = \begin{bmatrix} 13 \\ 31 \end{bmatrix}\begin{bmatrix} -7 & 3 \\ 5 & -2 \end{bmatrix}$$
$$\qquad\qquad\qquad\qquad\qquad 2 \times 1 \quad 2 \times 2$$
doesn't work!

$$\begin{bmatrix} -7 & 3 \\ 5 & -2 \end{bmatrix}\begin{bmatrix} 2 & 3 \\ 5 & 7 \end{bmatrix}\begin{bmatrix} x \\ y \end{bmatrix} = \begin{bmatrix} -7 & 3 \\ 5 & -2 \end{bmatrix}\begin{bmatrix} 13 \\ 31 \end{bmatrix}$$

$$\begin{bmatrix} x \\ y \end{bmatrix} = \begin{bmatrix} (-7)(13) + (3)(31) \\ (5)(13) + (-2)(31) \end{bmatrix} = \begin{bmatrix} 2 \\ 3 \end{bmatrix}$$

The coordinates of the point are (2, 3).

EXERCISE

Coordinate Geometry The coordinates (x, y) of a point in a plane are the solution of the system $\begin{cases} 12x + 13y = 14 \\ 5x + 7y = 9 \end{cases}$. Find the coordinates of the point. **(−1, 2)**

4-8 Augmented Matrices and Systems

 North Carolina Objectives

1.04 Operate with matrices to model and solve problems.
2.10 Use systems of two or more equations to model and solve problems. Solve using matrix operations and algebraic properties.

Lesson Preview

What You'll Learn

OBJECTIVE 1 To solve a system of equations using Cramer's Rule

OBJECTIVE 2 To solve a system of equations using augmented matrices

. . . And Why

To solve systems of three equations, as in Example 2

✓ **Check Skills You'll Need** (For help, go to Lessons 4-5 and 4-6.)

Evaluate the determinant of each matrix.

1. $\begin{bmatrix} -1 & 2 \\ 0 & 3 \end{bmatrix}$ −3

2. $\begin{bmatrix} 0 & 1 \\ -1 & 3 \end{bmatrix}$ 1

3. $\begin{bmatrix} 2 & 1 \\ -1 & 5 \end{bmatrix}$ 11

4. $\begin{bmatrix} 0 & 1 & -3 \\ 4 & 5 & -1 \\ -1 & 0 & 1 \end{bmatrix}$ −18

5. $\begin{bmatrix} 3 & 4 & 5 \\ -1 & 2 & 0 \\ 0 & -1 & 1 \end{bmatrix}$ 15

6. $\begin{bmatrix} 0 & 2 & -1 \\ 3 & 4 & 0 \\ -2 & -1 & 5 \end{bmatrix}$ −35

New Vocabulary • Cramer's Rule • augmented matrix • row operations

---

 Interactive lesson includes instant self-check, tutorials, and activities.

OBJECTIVE

1 Solving Systems Using Cramer's Rule

You can solve a system of linear equations that has a unique solution by using determinants and a pattern called Cramer's Rule.

 Key Concepts

Definition	Cramer's Rule

System

Use the x- and y-coefficients.
↓

Replace the x-coefficients with the constants.
↓

Replace the y-coefficients with the constants.
↓

$$\begin{cases} ax + by = m \\ cx + dy = n \end{cases} \quad D = \begin{vmatrix} a & b \\ c & d \end{vmatrix} \quad D_x = \begin{vmatrix} m & b \\ n & d \end{vmatrix} \quad D_y = \begin{vmatrix} a & m \\ c & n \end{vmatrix}$$

The solution of the system is $x = \dfrac{D_x}{D}$ and $y = \dfrac{D_y}{D}$, or $\left(\dfrac{D_x}{D}, \dfrac{D_y}{D}\right)$.

 Reading Math

Cramer's Rule was developed in 1750 by the Swiss mathematician Gabriel Cramer.

1 EXAMPLE Using Cramer's Rule

Use Cramer's Rule to solve the system $\begin{cases} 3x + 2y = 0 \\ x - y = -5 \end{cases}$.

Evaluate three determinants. Then find x and y.

$$D = \begin{vmatrix} 3 & 2 \\ 1 & -1 \end{vmatrix} = -5 \qquad D_x = \begin{vmatrix} 0 & 2 \\ -5 & -1 \end{vmatrix} = 10 \qquad D_y = \begin{vmatrix} 3 & 0 \\ 1 & -5 \end{vmatrix} = -15$$

$$x = \frac{D_x}{D} = \frac{10}{-5} = -2 \qquad y = \frac{D_y}{D} = \frac{-15}{-5} = 3$$

● The solution of the system is $(-2, 3)$.

✓ **Check Understanding** **1** Use Cramer's Rule to solve the system $\begin{cases} 3x + y = 5 \\ 2x + 3y = 8 \end{cases}$. **(1, 2)**

 Ongoing Assessment and Intervention

Before the Lesson	During the Lesson	After the Lesson
Diagnose prerequisite skills using:	**Monitor progress using:**	**Assess knowledge using:**
• Check Skills You'll Need	• Check Understanding	• Lesson Quiz
	• Additional Examples	• Computer Test Generator CD
	• Standardized Test Prep	

---

1. Plan

Lesson Preview

✓ **Check Skills You'll Need**

2 × 2 Matrices, Determinants, and Inverses
Lesson 4-5: Example 2
Exercises 4–13
Extra Practice, p. 825

3 × 3 Matrices, Determinants, and Inverses
Lesson 4-6: Example 1
Exercises 1–4
Extra Practice, p. 825

Lesson Resources

📁 **Teaching Resources**
Practice, Reteaching, Enrichment

👥 **Reaching All Students**
Practice Workbook 4-8
Spanish Practice Workbook 4-8
Technology Activities 28

⏱ **Presentation Assistant Plus!**
Transparencies
• Check Skills You'll Need 4-8
• Additional Examples 4-8
• Student Edition Answers 4-8
• Lesson Quiz 4-8
PH Presentation Pro CD 4-8

 PRENTICE HALL **ASSESSMENT SYSTEM**

Computer Test Generator CD

 Technology
Resource Pro® CD-ROM
Computer Test Generator CD
Prentice Hall Presentation Pro CD

 **www.PHSchool.com**
Student Site
• Teacher Web Code: agk-5500
• Self-grading Lesson Quiz
Teacher Center
• Lesson Planner
• Resources

Plus **iTEXT**

Math Background

Cramer's Rule and using row operations on augmented matrices are tools for solving linear systems. Augmented matrices can yield information about systems that have no solution or infinitely many solutions. For instance, 2×2 matrices having final augmented matrices of the form $\begin{bmatrix} 1 & 0 & | & a \\ 0 & 1 & | & b \end{bmatrix}$, $\begin{bmatrix} 1 & c & | & a \\ 0 & 0 & | & b \end{bmatrix}$, and $\begin{bmatrix} 1 & d & | & a \\ 0 & 0 & | & 0 \end{bmatrix}$, represent systems with one solution, no solutions, and infinitely many solutions, respectively. Interested students may wish to investigate that aspect of augmented matrices further.

OBJECTIVE 1 Teaching Notes

2 EXAMPLE Error Prevention

When writing matrices for three-variable systems, students may place coefficients in the wrong columns. Encourage students to write the variable letters over the appropriate columns when writing the coefficient matrix.

Additional Examples

1 Use Cramer's Rule to solve the system.
$$\begin{cases} 7x - 4y = 15 \\ 3x + 6y = 8 \end{cases} \left(\frac{61}{27}, \frac{11}{54} \right)$$

2 Find the y-coordinate of the solution of the system.
$$\begin{cases} -2x + 8y + 2z = -3 \\ -6x \quad\quad + 2z = \quad 1 \quad -\frac{5}{6} \\ -7x - 5y + z = \quad 2 \end{cases}$$

218

You can also use Cramer's Rule to solve a system of three equations.

2 EXAMPLE Using Cramer's Rule with Three Equations

Find the x-coordinate of the solution of the system $\begin{cases} y + 4z = 5 \\ x + y + z = 8. \\ 2x - 5y = 7 \end{cases}$

$D = \begin{vmatrix} 0 & 1 & 4 \\ 1 & 1 & 1 \\ 2 & -5 & 0 \end{vmatrix} = -26$ **Evaluate the determinant.**

$D_x = \begin{vmatrix} 5 & 1 & 4 \\ 8 & 1 & 1 \\ 7 & -5 & 0 \end{vmatrix} = -156$ **Replace the x-coefficients with the constants and evaluate again.**

$x = \dfrac{D_x}{D} = \dfrac{-156}{-26} = 6$ **Find x.**

● The x-coordinate of the solution is 6.

✓ **Check Understanding** **2 a. Critical Thinking** How would you modify the determinant D to find D_z?
b. Solve the system for y and z.

a. In D, replace the coefficients of z with the constants.
b. $y = 1, z = 1$

OBJECTIVE
2 Solving Systems Using Augmented Matrices

Reading Math

Augmented means "enlarged."

You can solve some linear systems by using an augmented matrix. An **augmented matrix** contains the coefficients and the constants from a system of equations. Each row of the matrix represents an equation.

3 EXAMPLE Writing an Augmented Matrix

Write an augmented matrix to represent the system $\begin{cases} -6x + 2y = 10 \\ 4x = -20 \end{cases}$.

System of equations $\begin{cases} -6x + 2y = 10 \\ 4x = -20 \end{cases}$

x-coefficients ↕   ↕ y-coefficients ↕ constants

Augmented matrix $\begin{bmatrix} -6 & 2 & | & 10 \\ 4 & 0 & | & -20 \end{bmatrix}$

         └── **Draw a vertical bar to separate the coefficients from the constants.**

An augmented matrix that represents the system is $\begin{bmatrix} -6 & 2 & | & 10 \\ 4 & 0 & | & -20 \end{bmatrix}$.

✓ **Check Understanding** **3** Write an augmented matrix to represent each system.

3b. $\begin{bmatrix} 1 & 2 & 3 & | & -4 \\ 0 & 1 & -2 & | & 8 \\ 0 & 0 & 1 & | & -3 \end{bmatrix}$

a. $\begin{cases} x - 5y = 15 \\ 3x + 3y = 3 \end{cases}$ $\begin{bmatrix} 1 & -5 & | & 15 \\ 3 & 3 & | & 3 \end{bmatrix}$

b. $\begin{cases} x + 2y + 3z = -4 \\ y - 2z = 8 \\ z = -3 \end{cases}$ **See left.**

An augmented matrix contains an entry of zero for any term missing from the system. You can write a system of equations from an augmented matrix.

👥 Reaching All Students

Below Level It may help students to write the identity matrix so they can check that they are computing 1s and 0s in the proper places.	**Advanced Learners** Discuss the advantage of using an augmented matrix instead of the technique of elimination to solve a system of equations.	**English Learners** See note on page 219. **Error Prevention** See note on page 220.

4 EXAMPLE Writing a System from an Augmented Matrix

Write a system of equations for the augmented matrix $\begin{bmatrix} 6 & 0 & | & 3 \\ 1 & 1 & | & -5 \end{bmatrix}$.

Augmented matrix
$$\begin{bmatrix} 6 & & 0 & & | & & 3 \\ 1 & & 1 & & | & & -5 \end{bmatrix}$$

x-coefficients $\updownarrow$ $\updownarrow$ y-coefficients $\updownarrow$ constants

System of equations $\begin{cases} 6x & + & & = & 3 \\ x & & y & = & -5 \end{cases}$

✓ **Check Understanding** 4 Write a system of equations for each augmented matrix.

4b. $\begin{cases} -x + & 3z = -4 \\ 7x + 2y - & z = 0 \\ & y + 2z = -3 \end{cases}$

a. $\begin{bmatrix} 5 & 7 & | & -3 \\ 0 & -8 & | & 6 \end{bmatrix}$ $\begin{cases} 5x + 7y = -3 \\ -8y = 6 \end{cases}$

b. $\begin{bmatrix} -1 & 0 & 3 & | & -4 \\ 7 & 2 & -1 & | & 0 \\ 0 & 1 & 2 & | & -3 \end{bmatrix}$

See left.

In Chapter 3 you learned how to solve systems of equations by using multiples of one or more of the equations to eliminate variables. You can do the same thing to an augmented matrix by using row operations.

🔑 **Key Concepts**

Definition	**Row Operations**

To solve a system of equations using an augmented matrix, you can use one or more of the following **row operations.**

- Switch any two rows.
- Multiply a row by a constant.
- Add one row to another.
- Combine one or more of these steps.

5 EXAMPLE Using an Augmented Matrix

Use an augmented matrix to solve the system $\begin{cases} x + 2y = -1 \\ 2x + 5y = -4 \end{cases}$.

$\begin{bmatrix} 1 & 2 & | & -1 \\ 2 & 5 & | & -4 \end{bmatrix}$ **Write an augmented matrix.**

$\begin{bmatrix} 1 & 2 & | & -1 \\ 0 & 1 & | & -2 \end{bmatrix}$
$\begin{array}{r} -2(1 \quad 2 \quad -1) \\ 2 \quad 5 \quad -4 \\ \hline 0 \quad 1 \quad -2 \end{array}$ **Multiply Row 1 by –2 and add it to Row 2. Write the new augmented matrix.**

$\begin{bmatrix} 1 & 0 & | & 3 \\ 0 & 1 & | & -2 \end{bmatrix}$
$\begin{array}{r} 1 \quad 2 \quad -1 \\ -2(0 \quad 1 \quad -2) \\ \hline 1 \quad 0 \quad 3 \end{array}$ **Multiply new Row 2 by –2 and add it to Row 1. Write the final augmented matrix.**

The solution to the system is $(3, -2)$.

Check $x + 2y = -1$ $2x + 5y = -4$ **Use the original equations.**

$3 + 2(-2) \stackrel{?}{=} -1$ $2(3) + 5(-2) \stackrel{?}{=} -4$ **Substitute.**

$3 + (-4) \stackrel{?}{=} -1$ $6 + (-10) \stackrel{?}{=} -4$ **Multiply.**

$-1 = -1$ ✓ $-4 = -4$ ✓   **Simplify.**

✓ **Check Understanding** 5 Solve $\begin{cases} x + y = -10 \\ -x + y = 20 \end{cases}$. Check your solution. **(−15, 5)**

OBJECTIVE
 2 Teaching Notes

3 EXAMPLE English Learners

As the text states, *augmented* means enlarged. It has a similar meaning in music. Working with a partner who is involved in music, have students find this meaning in a dictionary or book on music. **a perfect or major interval that has been enlarged by a semitone** Relating a word to more than one subject may help students remember the meaning.

6 EXAMPLE Technology Tip

Tell students that if the calculator displays a matrix with elements that are lengthy decimals, they can press MATH 1 ENTER to see if the calculator can change the decimals to fractions. Otherwise, they can adjust the decimal display.

📋 Additional Examples

3 Write an augmented matrix to represent the system.
$$\begin{cases} -7x + 4y = -3 \\ x + 8y = 9 \end{cases}$$
$$\begin{bmatrix} -7 & 4 & | & -3 \\ 1 & 8 & | & 9 \end{bmatrix}$$

4 Write a system of equations for the augmented matrix.
$$\begin{bmatrix} 9 & -7 & | & -1 \\ 2 & 5 & | & -6 \end{bmatrix}$$
$$\begin{cases} 9x - 7y = -1 \\ 2x + 5y = -6 \end{cases}$$

5 Use an augmented matrix to solve the system.
$$\begin{cases} x - 3y = -17 \\ 4x + 2y = 2 \end{cases} \text{ (−2, 5)}$$

6 Use the rref feature on a graphing calculator to solve the system.
$$\begin{cases} 4x + 3y + z = -1 \\ -2x - 2y + 7z = -10 \\ 3x + y + 5z = 2 \end{cases}$$
(7, −9, −2)

Closure

Ask: *In an initial augmented matrix, where do you find the coefficients of the variables for the related system of equations?* **to the left of the vertical bar**

219

Assignment Guide

▼1 Objective

Ⓐ Ⓑ **Core** 1–5, 24–28, 32–34

Ⓒ **Extension** 40–41

▼2 Objective

Ⓐ Ⓑ **Core** 6–23, 29–31, 35–39

Ⓒ **Extension** 42–45

Standardized Test Prep 46–49

Mixed Review 50–57

Error Prevention

Exercises 12–17 Students will find it helpful to follow the lead of Example 5 and write notes indicating what row operations they used at each stage.

You can use augmented matrices and row operations to solve systems of three equations. Graphing calculators have a feature that uses row operations to simplify matrices.

Graphing Calculator Hint

To find rref([A]), select B from the MATH option of the MATRX feature. (rref stands for "reduced row-echelon form.")

6 EXAMPLE   Using a Graphing Calculator

Use a graphing calculator to solve the system $\begin{cases} 2x + 3y - z = 11 \\ 3x - 2y + 4z = 10. \\ x + 4y - 2z = 8 \end{cases}$

Step 1 Enter the augmented matrix as matrix A.

Step 2 Use the rref feature of your graphing calculator.

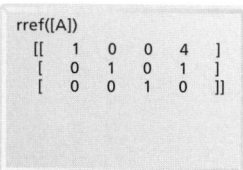

[A]
[[2   3   -1   11]
 [3 -2   4   10]
 [1   4   -2   8]]

rref([A])
[[1   0   0   4]
 [0   1   0   1]
 [0   0   1   0]]

The simplified augmented matrix is equivalant to $\begin{cases} x = 4 \\ y = 1. \\ z = 0 \end{cases}$ The solution is $(4, 1, 0)$.

Partial Check

$$2x + 3y - z = 11 \quad \text{Use the first equation.}$$
$$2(4) + 3(1) - (0) \overset{?}{=} 11 \quad \text{Substitute.}$$
$$8 + 3 - 0 \overset{?}{=} 11 \quad \text{Multiply.}$$
$$11 = 11 \checkmark \quad \text{Simplify.}$$

✓ **Check Understanding** **a.** Check the solution to Example 6 in the remaining two equations. **See margin.**

b. Use a graphing calculator to solve the system $\begin{cases} x + 4y - z = 4 \\ x - 2y + z = -2. \\ 5x - 3y + 8z = 13 \end{cases}$ Check your answer. **(−1, 2, 3)**

EXERCISES

For more practice, see *Extra Practice*.

Practice and Problem Solving

Ⓐ **Practice by Example**

Examples 1 and 2
(pages 217 and 218)

Use Cramer's Rule to solve each system.

(3, 1)

1. $\begin{cases} 2x + y = 4 \\ 3x - y = 6 \end{cases}$ **(2, 0)**

2. $\begin{cases} 2x + y = 7 \\ -2x + 5y = -1 \end{cases}$ **(3, 1)**

3. $\begin{cases} 2x + 4y = 10 \\ 3x + 5y = 14 \end{cases}$

4. $\begin{cases} y + 4z = 5 \\ x + y + z = 8 \\ 2x - 5y = 7 \end{cases}$ **(6, 1, 1)**

5. $\begin{cases} 2x + 3y + z = 5 \\ x + y - 2z = -2 \\ -3x + z = -7 \end{cases}$ **(3, −1, 2)**

Example 3
(page 218)

Write an augmented matrix for each system. **6–8. See margin.**

6. $\begin{cases} 3x - 4y = 17 \\ 8x + y = -3 \end{cases}$

7. $\begin{cases} 3x - 7y + 3z = -3 \\ x + y + 2z = -3 \\ 2x - 3y + 5z = -8 \end{cases}$

8. $\begin{cases} -x + 5y = -1 \\ x - 2y = 1 \end{cases}$

Enrichment 4-8
Reteaching 4-8
Practice 4-8

Practice 4-8

Augmented Matrices and Systems

Write a system of equations for each augmented matrix.

1. $\begin{bmatrix} 4 & -2 & | & 3 \\ 6 & 11 & | & 9 \end{bmatrix}$ 2. $\begin{bmatrix} 12 & 6 & | & -4 \\ -1 & 0 & | & 2 \end{bmatrix}$ 3. $\begin{bmatrix} -2 & 9 & -2 & | & 20 \\ 3 & -1 & 2 & | & 29 \\ 6 & 5 & 5 & | & -4 \end{bmatrix}$

Use Cramer's Rule to solve each system.

4. $\begin{cases} 2x + y = 1 \\ 3x - y = 9 \end{cases}$ 5. $\begin{cases} 2x - y = 10 \\ x - 3y = 0 \end{cases}$ 6. $\begin{cases} 3x + 5y = 1 \\ x + 6y = 9 \end{cases}$

7. $\begin{cases} x + y + z = 1.28 \\ x - 3y + 2z = 1.26 \\ 3x + 2y + 4z = 4.06 \end{cases}$ 8. $\begin{cases} 2x + y - z = 0.75 \\ 3x + 3y + 2z = 4 \\ x - 5y + 3z = -2 \end{cases}$ 9. $\begin{cases} x + y - z = 6 \\ 3x - 9y + z = -2 \\ 0.2x - 0.3y + 0.71z = -1.12 \end{cases}$

Write an augmented matrix for each system.

10. $\begin{cases} -3x + 4y = -8 \\ 2x - 8y = 16 \end{cases}$ 11. $\begin{cases} x + 3z = -30 \\ 4a + v = 1 \end{cases}$ 12. $\begin{cases} x - 4y + z = -9 \\ 3x + 2y - 3z = 9 \\ 4x + 2z = -4 \end{cases}$

Use an augmented matrix to solve each system.

13. $\begin{cases} x + y + z = 0 \\ 2x - 2y + 3z = 46 \\ 3x + 7y + 11z = 80 \end{cases}$ 14. $\begin{cases} 3x + y + z = 18 \\ 4x + 2y + 3z = 12 \\ 7x + 9y + 5z = 9 \end{cases}$ 15. $\begin{cases} 3x + 7y + 10z = 28 \\ 0.7x - 0.6y + 0.8z = 4.3 \\ 12x - 7y - 9z = 77 \end{cases}$

16. $\begin{cases} x - 2y - 3z = 2 \\ 2x + x - 5z = 30 \\ 7x - 11y - z = -48 \end{cases}$ 17. $\begin{cases} x + y + z = 6.5 \\ 3x - 5y + 6z = -35 \\ 5x + 2y + 2z = 10 \end{cases}$ 18. $\begin{cases} -x + y - z = -2 \\ 3x + 2y + 0.5z = -1.5 \\ 21x + 19y - 2z = -45 \end{cases}$

Use a graphing calculator to solve each system.

19. $\begin{cases} 4x - 2y + 3z = -2 \\ 2x + 2y + 5z = 16 \\ 8x - 5y + 11z = 4 \end{cases}$ 20. $\begin{cases} x + y + z = -1 \\ 3x + 5y + 4z = 2 \\ 3x + 6y + 5z = 0 \end{cases}$ 21. $\begin{cases} x + 3y - 2z = -3 \\ 2x + y - z = -6 \\ 3x - 2y + 4z = 8 \end{cases}$

Algebra 2 Chapter 4   Lesson 4-8 Practice   9

---

page 220   Check Understanding

6a. $3(4) - 2(1) + 4(0) \overset{?}{=} 10$
$12 - 2 + 0 \overset{?}{=} 10$
$10 = 10 \checkmark$
$4 + 4(1) - 2(0) \overset{?}{=} 8$
$4 + 4 - 0 \overset{?}{=} 8$
$8 = 8 \checkmark$

220

pages 220–223   Exercises

6. $\begin{bmatrix} 3 & -4 & | & 17 \\ 8 & 1 & | & -3 \end{bmatrix}$

7. $\begin{bmatrix} 3 & -7 & 3 & | & -3 \\ 1 & 1 & 2 & | & -3 \\ 2 & -3 & 5 & | & -8 \end{bmatrix}$

8. $\begin{bmatrix} -1 & 5 & | & -1 \\ 1 & -2 & | & 1 \end{bmatrix}$

Careers

Exercise 33 Financial planners can use matrices to help find the best way to invest money. Many have computer programs that have been programmed to perform the functions of these matrices.

Example 4
(page 219)

Write a system of equations for each augmented matrix. 9–11. See margin.

9. $\begin{bmatrix} 5 & 1 & | & -3 \\ -2 & 2 & | & 4 \end{bmatrix}$

10. $\begin{bmatrix} -1 & 2 & | & -6 \\ 1 & 1 & | & 7 \end{bmatrix}$

11. $\begin{bmatrix} 2 & 1 & 1 & | & 1 \\ 1 & 1 & 1 & | & 2 \\ 1 & -1 & 1 & | & -2 \end{bmatrix}$

Example 5
(page 219)

Use an augmented matrix to solve each system.

(5, −2.5)
12. $\begin{cases} 2x - 2y = 15 \\ 4x + 4y = 10 \end{cases}$

(−2, −6)
13. $\begin{cases} 2x - 4y = 20 \\ 4x + 2y = -20 \end{cases}$

(−3, 3)
14. $\begin{cases} x + 2y = 3 \\ 4x + 2y = -6 \end{cases}$

15. $\begin{cases} x + 5y = -25 \\ 5x + y = 25 \end{cases}$

16. $\begin{cases} -x + 5y = 15 \\ 2x + 3y = 9 \end{cases}$

17. $\begin{cases} 3x + 6y = 2 \\ 2x - y = 3 \end{cases}$

(6.25, −6.25)

(0, 3)

$(\frac{4}{3}, -\frac{1}{3})$

Example 6
(page 220)

Solve each system.

18. (1, 1, 0)

19. (3, 1, 1)

20. no unique solution

18. $\begin{cases} x + y + z = 2 \\ 2y - 2z = 2 \\ x - 3z = 1 \end{cases}$

19. $\begin{cases} x - y + z = 3 \\ x + 3z = 6 \\ y - 2z = -1 \end{cases}$

20. $\begin{cases} x + y - z = -1 \\ 3x + 4y - z = 8 \\ 6x + 8y - 2z = 16 \end{cases}$

21. $\begin{cases} x + y - z = 1 \\ 3x + 3y + z = 3 \\ 2x + 2y - 2z = 2 \end{cases}$

22. $\begin{cases} x + y = 1 \\ y + z = 2 \\ x - z = -1 \end{cases}$

23. $\begin{cases} x + z = -4 \\ y - z = 1 \\ x + y = -3 \end{cases}$

no unique solution

no unique solution

no unique solution

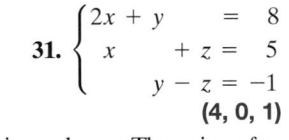

B Apply Your Skills

Use Cramer's Rule to solve each system.

24. $\begin{cases} 0.5x + 1.5y = 7 \\ 2.5x - 3.5y = -9 \end{cases}$

25. $\begin{cases} -1.2x - 0.3y = 2.1 \\ -0.2x + 0.8y = 4.6 \end{cases}$

26. $\begin{cases} \dfrac{x}{5} - \dfrac{2y}{5} = 4 \\ \dfrac{2x}{5} - \dfrac{3y}{5} = 5 \end{cases}$

(2, 4)

(−3, 5)

(−10, −15)

27. $\begin{cases} \dfrac{x}{2} + \dfrac{y}{4} = 4 \\ \dfrac{x}{4} - \dfrac{3y}{8} = -2 \end{cases}$

28. $\begin{cases} 2x + 3y + 5z = 12 \\ 4x + 2y + 4z = -2 \\ 5x + 4y + 7z = 7 \end{cases}$

(4, 8)

(−4, 5, 1)

Use an augmented matrix to solve each system.

29. $\begin{cases} x + y + z = 1 \\ y - 3z = 4 \\ x - z = 2 \end{cases}$

30. $\begin{cases} x + y + z = 0 \\ y + 4z = -6 \\ 2x - 2z = 4 \end{cases}$

31. $\begin{cases} 2x + y = 8 \\ x + z = 5 \\ y - z = -1 \end{cases}$

(1, 1, −1)

(0, 2, −2)

(4, 0, 1)

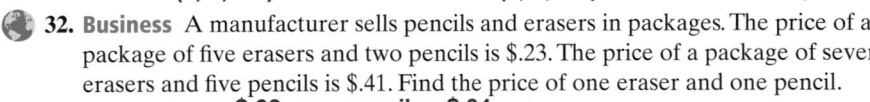

32. **Business** A manufacturer sells pencils and erasers in packages. The price of a package of five erasers and two pencils is $.23. The price of a package of seven erasers and five pencils is $.41. Find the price of one eraser and one pencil.
one eraser = $.03, one pencil = $.04

33. **Investments** Suppose you invested $5000 in three different mutual funds for one year. The funds paid simple interest of 8%, 10%, and 7%, respectively. The total interest at the end of one year was $405. You invested $500 more at 10% than at 8%. How much did you invest in each mutual fund?
$1000, $1500, $2500

34. **Open-Ended** Write and solve a system of three equations in three unknowns using Cramer's Rule. **Check students' work.**

Solve each system.

35. $\begin{cases} 2x - 3y + 2z = 10 \\ x + 3y + 4z = 14 \\ 3x - y + z = 9 \end{cases}$

36. $\begin{cases} 4x - y + z = 3 \\ x + 2y + z = 0 \\ 3x + 7y - 3z = 6 \end{cases}$

37. $\begin{cases} x + 2y + z = 4 \\ 3x + 6y + 3z = 2 \\ x - y + z = 3 \end{cases}$

(2, 0, 3)

(1, 0, −1)

no unique solution

9. $\begin{cases} 5x + y = -3 \\ -2x + 2y = 4 \end{cases}$

10. $\begin{cases} -x + 2y = -6 \\ x + y = 7 \end{cases}$

11. $\begin{cases} 2x + y + z = 1 \\ x + y + z = 2 \\ x - y + z = -2 \end{cases}$

221

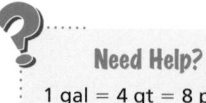

4. Assess

Alternative Assessment

Have each student write a system of two equations in two variables and a system of three equations in three variables. Then solve the systems. They should use Cramer's Rule for one system and an augmented matrix for the other system.

pages 220–223 Exercises

38a. Let r = price of 1 pt of red and let y = price of 1 pt of yellow.

$$\begin{cases} 2r + 6y = 25 \\ 5r + 3y = 28 \end{cases}$$

c. A quart of red paint = $7.75 and a quart of yellow paint = $5.75.

44a. Let a, b, and c be the number of portions per day of food sources A, B, and C.

$10a + 4b + 12c = 120$
$11a + 77b \qquad = 220$
$4a + b + 16c = 80$

c. Answers may vary. Sample: Adding 12 more portions of food A would compensate for C running out.

🌐 **38. Colors** A hardware store mixes paints in a ratio of two parts red to six parts yellow to make pumpkin orange. A ratio of five parts red to three parts yellow makes red-pepper red. A gallon of pumpkin orange sells for $25, and a gallon of red-pepper red sells for $28. **a, c. See margin.**
 a. Write a system of equations to model the situation.
 b. Solve the system. **(3.875, 2.875)**
 c. Find the cost of 1 qt of red paint and the cost of 1 qt of yellow paint.

🌐 **39. Sales** Refer to the signs below. Find the price per pound of each type of nut.
 almonds: $2/lb, pecans: $4/lb, pistachios: $6/lb

2 lb almonds
3 lb pecans
only $16

1 lb almonds
1 lb pecans
1 lb pistachios
only $12

3 lb pecans
2 lb pistachios
only $24

ⓒ Challenge Solve using Cramer's Rule. (*Hint:* Start by substituting $m = \frac{1}{x}$ and $n = \frac{1}{y}$.)

40. $\begin{cases} \dfrac{4}{x} + \dfrac{1}{y} = 1 \\ \dfrac{8}{x} + \dfrac{4}{y} = 3 \end{cases}$ **(8, 2)**

41. $\begin{cases} \dfrac{4}{x} - \dfrac{2}{y} = 1 \\ \dfrac{10}{x} + \dfrac{20}{y} = 0 \end{cases}$ **(5, −10)**

🖩 **Solve each system.**

42. $\begin{cases} w + x + y + z = 3 \\ -w + x - 2y + z = -2 \\ 2x - y + z = 1 \\ w + y - z = 2 \end{cases}$
(1, 1, 1, 0)

43. $\begin{cases} 2x + 2y + z = 4 \\ w + y - z = -2 \\ w + x + y + z = 3 \\ -4w + z = 2 \end{cases}$
(0, 1, 0, 2)

🌐 **44. Nutrition** While stranded on an island, the crew of a sailboat has access to only three sources of food, as shown in the table below. One of the crew members designs a daily diet to supply each person with 120 g of fat, 220 g of carbohydrates, and 80 g of protein.

	A	B	C
Fat	10 g	4 g	12 g
Carbohydrates	11 g	77 g	0 g
Protein	4 g	1 g	16 g

 a. Write a system of three equations in three variables to find the number of portions of each food each person must have to meet the daily diet.
 b. Use an augmented matrix to solve the system of equations from part (a). Round each answer to the nearest tenth. **about (7.8, 1.7, 3.0)**
 c. Writing Suppose food C runs out. How would this change the number of portions of food required each day?

45. Geometry The perimeter of the rectangle at the right is 28 cm. The perimeter of each of the triangles is 24 cm. The diagonal of the rectangle is 2 cm longer than the longer side of the rectangle.

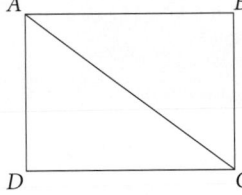

   a. Write a system of three equations in three unknowns. **a–c. See margin.**

   b. Simplify the system to a system of two equations in two unknowns.

   c. Write an augmented matrix for the system in part (b).

   d. Find the dimensions of the rectangle. **6 cm × 8 cm**

   e. Find the length of the diagonal. **10 cm**

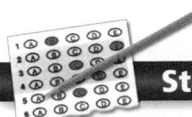

Standardized Test Prep

Multiple Choice

Use the system $\begin{cases} 5x - 4y = -13 \\ -3x + 6y = 6 \end{cases}$ for Exercises 46 and 47.

46. Which is the determinant D_x? **B**

   A. $\begin{vmatrix} 5 & -4 \\ -3 & 6 \end{vmatrix}$ **B.** $\begin{vmatrix} -13 & -4 \\ 6 & 6 \end{vmatrix}$ **C.** $\begin{vmatrix} 5 & -13 \\ -3 & 6 \end{vmatrix}$ **D.** $\begin{vmatrix} 5 & 4 & -13 \\ -3 & 6 & 6 \end{vmatrix}$

47. What is the solution of the system? **H**

   F. $(-13, 6)$ **G.** $\left(-\frac{13}{5}, 1\right)$ **H.** $\left(-3, -\frac{1}{2}\right)$ **I.** $2x + 2y = -7$

Use the system $\begin{cases} 2x + y - 3z = -2 \\ 4x - 3y + 6z = 9 \\ -2x - 2y + 9z = 7 \end{cases}$ for Exercises 48 and 49.

48. What is the value of the determinant D_y? **D**

   A. -36 **B.** -24 **C.** -18 **D.** 36

Take It to the NET
Online lesson quiz at
www.PHSchool.com
Web Code: aga-0408

49. What is the value of the determinant D_z? **G**

   F. -36 **G.** -24 **H.** -18 **I.** 36

Mixed Review

Lesson 4-7   Solve each system of equations by using the inverse of the coefficient matrix.

50. $\begin{cases} x + 4y + 3z = 3 \\ 2x - 5y - z = 5 \\ 3x + 2y - 2z = -3 \end{cases}$ **(1, −1, 2)**   **51.** $\begin{cases} x + y + z = -1 \\ y + 3z = -5 \\ x + z = -2 \end{cases}$ **(0, 1, −2)**

Lesson 3-3   Solve each system of inequalities by graphing.   **52–54. See margin.**

52. $\begin{cases} 2x + y < 3 \\ -x - y \geq 1 \end{cases}$ **53.** $\begin{cases} 2x \leq 0 \\ -x + y > -1 \end{cases}$ **54.** $\begin{cases} x < 3 \\ y \geq -4 \\ -x + y < 5 \end{cases}$

Lesson 2-2   Write in point-slope form the equation of the line through each pair of points.

55. $(0, 1)$ and $(2, -5)$ **56.** $(-9, 3)$ and $(-4, -4)$ **57.** $(1, 8)$ and $(7, 2)$

   $y - 1 = -3x$ $y - 3 = \frac{-7}{5}(x + 9)$ $y - 8 = -(x - 1)$

Lesson 4-8 Augmented Matrices and Systems   **223**

Resources
For additional practice with a variety of test item formats:
- Standardized Test Prep, p. 229
- Test-Taking Strategies, p. 224
- Test-Taking Strategies with Transparencies

Exercise 47 Sometimes you can immediately eliminate answer choices. Eliminate answer choice I since it is an equation rather than an ordered pair. For answer choice G to be correct, the y-coordinate would have to be 0.

45a. Let $x = $ the width of the rectangle, let $y = $ the length of the rectangle, and let $z = $ the diagonal.

$$\begin{cases} 2x + 2y = 28 \\ x + y + z = 24 \\ x - z = -2 \end{cases}$$

b. $\begin{cases} 2x + 2y = 28 \\ 2x + y = 22 \end{cases}$

c. $\begin{bmatrix} 2 & 2 & 28 \\ 2 & 1 & 22 \end{bmatrix}$

52.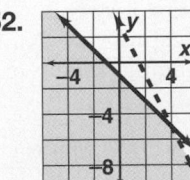

53.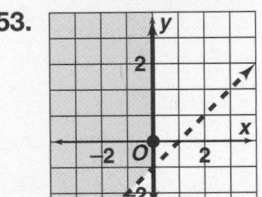

54.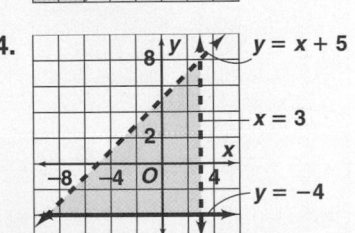

223

Making Comparison Questions

This feature explains how to answer a multiple-choice test item in which students must compare two given quantities.

Resources

PRENTICE HALL
ASSESSMENT SYSTEM

Test-Taking Strategies with Transparencies
- Transparency 4
- Practice sheet p. 30

Teaching Notes

Make sure students understand that there are two tasks in quantitative comparison questions. The first task is simplifying the expression. Only then can they compare the two given quantities.

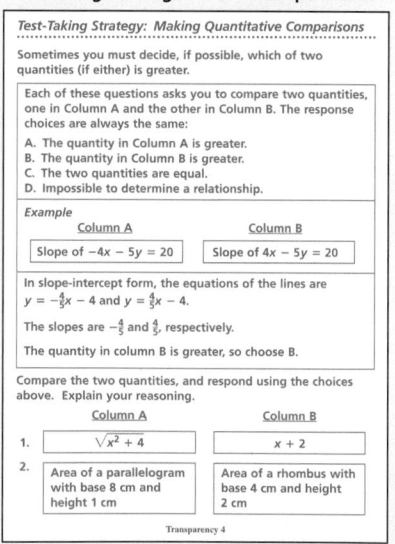

To answer Quantitative Comparison questions, you usually need to simplify, rewrite, or evaluate a given equation or the expressions in Columns A and B. Then choose the answer that correctly compares the values:

A. The quantity in Column A is greater.
B. The quantity in Column B is greater.
C. The two quantities are equal.
D. The relationship cannot be determined from the information given.

EXAMPLE

$$\begin{bmatrix} 0 & x \\ -1 & 0 \end{bmatrix}^2 = y\begin{bmatrix} 1 & 0 \\ 0 & 1 \end{bmatrix}$$

Column A	**Column B**
x^2	y^2

To find and compare x^2 and y^2, first simplify both sides of the given equation.

$$\begin{bmatrix} 0 & x \\ -1 & 0 \end{bmatrix}^2 = y\begin{bmatrix} 1 & 0 \\ 0 & 1 \end{bmatrix}$$

$$\begin{bmatrix} 0 & x \\ -1 & 0 \end{bmatrix}\begin{bmatrix} 0 & x \\ -1 & 0 \end{bmatrix} = \begin{bmatrix} y & 0 \\ 0 & y \end{bmatrix}$$

$$\begin{bmatrix} -x & 0 \\ 0 & -x \end{bmatrix} = \begin{bmatrix} y & 0 \\ 0 & y \end{bmatrix}$$

Since $-x = y$, $x^2 = y^2$. The quantities are equal. The answer is C.

EXERCISES

Compare the boxed quantity in Column A with the boxed quantity in Column B. Choose the best answer.

A. The quantity in Column A is greater.
B. The quantity in Column B is greater.
C. The two quantities are equal.
D. The relationship cannot be determined from the information given.

1.
B

$$x > 0$$

$$\begin{bmatrix} 1 & x \\ 0 & 1 \end{bmatrix}^2 = \begin{bmatrix} 1 & y \\ 0 & 1 \end{bmatrix}$$

Column A	**Column B**
x	y

2.
B

$$\begin{bmatrix} 1 & 1 & 1 \\ 0 & 1 & 1 \\ 0 & 0 & 1 \end{bmatrix} \cdot \begin{bmatrix} x \\ y \\ z \end{bmatrix} = \begin{bmatrix} 1 \\ 2 \\ 3 \end{bmatrix}$$

Column A	**Column B**
$x + y$	z

Chapter Review

Vocabulary

augmented matrix (p. 218)	matrix (p. 164)	rotation (p. 190)
center of rotation (p. 190)	matrix addition (p. 170)	row operations (p. 219)
coefficient matrix (p. 210)	matrix element (p. 165)	scalar (p. 178)
constant matrix (p. 210)	matrix equation (p. 172)	scalar product (p. 178)
Cramer's Rule (p. 217)	matrix multiplication (p. 180)	square matrix (p. 195)
determinant (p. 196)	multiplicative identity matrix (p. 195)	transformation (p. 188)
dilation (p. 188)	multiplicative inverse matrix (p. 195)	translation (p. 188)
equal matrices (p. 173)	preimage (p. 188)	variable matrix (p. 210)
image (p. 188)	reflection (p. 189)	zero matrix (p. 171)

Reading Math
Understanding
Vocabulary

Choose the correct vocabulary term to complete each sentence.

1. A _?_ is a rectangular array of numbers. **matrix**

2. Translations, dilations, reflections and rotations are all _?_. **transformations**

3. Cramer's Rule uses _?_ to solve a system of equations. **determinants**

4. If corresponding elements of matrices are equal, the matrices are _?_. **equal matrices**

5. The additive identity of a matrix is the _?_. **zero matrix**

6. A _?_ consists of a coefficient matrix, a variable matrix, and a constant matrix. **matrix equation**

7. An $n \times n$ matrix is called a _?_. **square matrix**

8. The image of a figure is a transformation of the _?_. **preimage**

9. The product of a real number and a matrix is called a _?_. **scalar product**

10. A matrix is the inverse of another matrix if their product is the _?_. **multiplicative identity matrix**

Take It to the NET
Online vocabulary quiz
at **www.PHSchool.com**
Web Code: agj-0451

Skills and Concepts

4-1 Objectives

▼ To identify and classify matrices and their elements (p. 164)

▼ To organize data into matrices (p. 165)

It is often useful to organize data into matrices. A **matrix** is a rectangular array of numbers classified by its dimensions. An $m \times n$ matrix has m rows and n columns. A **matrix element** a_{ij} is in the ith row and jth column of matrix A.

State the dimensions of each matrix A. Identify the indicated element.

11. $\begin{bmatrix} 5 & 8 & -7 \\ 1 & 11 & 3 \end{bmatrix}; a_{13}$
    2×3; -7

12. $\begin{bmatrix} 3 & 1 \\ -5 & 0 \\ 7 & 6 \end{bmatrix}; a_{21}$
    3×2; -5

13. $\begin{bmatrix} 5 & 1 & -2 \\ 4 & -7 & 12 \\ 0 & 78 & 3 \end{bmatrix}; a_{32}$
    3×3; 78

Use the matrix at the right for Exercises 14–16.

14. How many points has Tamika scored? **226**

15. How many three-point shots has Tran made? **50**

16. What percent of Johanna's points were from one-point shots? **about 9%**

	1-pt Shots	2-pt Shots	3-pt Shots
Tamika	22	30	48
Johanna	21	31	48
Tran	21	29	50

Resources

Student Edition
Extra Practice, Ch. 4, p. 825
English/Spanish Glossary, p. 871
Properties and Formulas, p. 865
Table of Symbols, p. 861

 Reaching All Students
Reading and Math Literacy 4D
Spanish Reading and Math
    Literacy 4D

ASSESSMENT *SYSTEM*

Standardized Test Prep
• Ch. 4 practice in standardized test formats

 **www.PHSchool.com**
Student Site
• Self-grading Vocabulary Test
Teacher Center
• Resources

Plus **TEXT**

Spanish Reading and Math Literacy

23. $\begin{bmatrix} 18 & 3 & 0 & 24 \\ -12 & 9 & 21 & 33 \end{bmatrix}$

24. $\begin{bmatrix} -9 & 7 \\ -8 & -8 \end{bmatrix}$

25. **does not exist**

26. $\begin{bmatrix} -6 & 10 & 21 & 41 \\ -28 & 10 & 28 & 28 \end{bmatrix}$

27. $\begin{bmatrix} -14 & -2 \\ 43 & -7 \end{bmatrix}$

28. $\begin{bmatrix} 4 & -1 & 2 \\ -1 & -2 & 3 \end{bmatrix}$

29. $\begin{bmatrix} 0 & -5 & -2 \\ 5 & 4 & 9 \end{bmatrix}$

30. $\begin{bmatrix} -3 & 2 & -1 \\ 1 & 0 & 5 \end{bmatrix}$

31. $\begin{bmatrix} 1 & 0 & 5 \\ 3 & -2 & 1 \end{bmatrix}$

32. $\begin{bmatrix} 1 & 0 & 5 \\ -3 & 2 & -1 \end{bmatrix}$

33. $\begin{bmatrix} 1.5 & -1 & 0.5 \\ 0.5 & 0 & 2.5 \end{bmatrix}$

34. $\begin{bmatrix} 6 & -4 & 2 \\ 2 & 0 & 10 \end{bmatrix}$

35. $\begin{bmatrix} -1 & 0 & -5 \\ 3 & -2 & 1 \end{bmatrix}$

4-2 and 4-3 Objectives

▼ To add and subtract matrices (p. 170)

▼ To solve some matrix equations (p. 172)

▼ To multiply a matrix by a scalar (p. 178)

▼ To multiply two matrices (p. 180)

To perform **matrix addition** or subtraction, add or subtract the corresponding elements in the matrices. To obtain the **scalar product** of a matrix and a **scalar,** multiply each matrix element by the scalar. **Matrix multiplication** uses both multiplication and addition. The element in the ith row and jth column of the product of two matrices is the sum of the products of each element of the ith row of the first matrix and each element of the jth column of the second matrix. The first matrix must have the same number of columns as the second has rows.

Two matrices are **equal matrices** when corresponding elements are equal and they have the same dimensions. This principle is used to solve a **matrix equation.**

Solve each matrix equation for matrix X.

17. $[2 \quad -6 \quad 8] + [-1 \quad -2 \quad 4] = X$
$[1 \quad -8 \quad 12]$

18. $\begin{bmatrix} t \\ 6 \end{bmatrix} - \begin{bmatrix} 1 \\ 3 \end{bmatrix} = X \quad \begin{bmatrix} t-1 \\ 3 \end{bmatrix}$

19. $\begin{bmatrix} 7 & -1 \\ 0 & 8 \end{bmatrix} + X = \begin{bmatrix} 4 & 9 \\ -3 & 11 \end{bmatrix} \begin{bmatrix} -3 & 10 \\ -3 & 3 \end{bmatrix}$

20. $X - \begin{bmatrix} -7 & 13 & 5 \\ 31 & 0 & -4 \end{bmatrix} = \begin{bmatrix} 9 & -5 & 8 \\ 2 & 0 & -3 \end{bmatrix}$ $\begin{bmatrix} 2 & 8 & 13 \\ 33 & 0 & -7 \end{bmatrix}$

Solve for each variable.

21. $\begin{bmatrix} x-5 & 9 \\ 4 & t+2 \end{bmatrix} = \begin{bmatrix} -7 & w+1 \\ 8-r & 1 \end{bmatrix}$
$x = -2, w = 8, r = 4, t = -1$

22. $\begin{bmatrix} -4+t & 2y \\ r & w+4 \end{bmatrix} = \begin{bmatrix} 2t & 11 \\ -2r+12 & 9 \end{bmatrix}$
$t = -4, y = \frac{11}{2}, r = 4, w = 5$

Use matrices $A, B, C,$ and D. Find each scalar product, sum, or difference, if possible. If an operation is not defined, label it *undefined*. 23–27. See margin.

$A = \begin{bmatrix} 6 & 1 & 0 & 8 \\ -4 & 3 & 7 & 11 \end{bmatrix}$ $B = \begin{bmatrix} 1 & 3 \\ -2 & 4 \end{bmatrix}$ $C = \begin{bmatrix} -2 & 1 \\ 4 & 0 \\ 2 & 2 \\ 1 & 1 \end{bmatrix}$ $D = \begin{bmatrix} 5 & -2 \\ 3 & 6 \end{bmatrix}$

23. $3A$ 24. $B - 2D$ 25. AB 26. BA 27. $AC - BD$

4-4 Objectives

▼ To represent translations and dilations with matrices (p. 187)

▼ To represent reflections and rotations with matrices (p. 189)

A **transformation** is a change made to a figure. The original figure is the **preimage,** and the transformed figure is the **image.** A **translation** slides a figure without changing its size or shape. A **dilation** changes the size of a figure. You can use matrix addition to translate a figure and scalar multiplication to dilate a figure.

You can use multiplication by the appropriate matrix to perform transformations that are specific **reflections** or **rotations.** For example, to reflect a figure in the y-axis, multiply by $\begin{bmatrix} -1 & 0 \\ 0 & 1 \end{bmatrix}$. To rotate a figure 180°, multiply by $\begin{bmatrix} -1 & 0 \\ 0 & -1 \end{bmatrix}$.

For Exercises 28–35, use $\triangle ABC$ with vertices $A(3, 1)$, $B(-2, 0)$, and $C(1, 5)$. Write the coordinates of each image in matrix form. 28–35. See margin.

28. a translation 1 unit right and 2 units down

29. a translation 3 units left and 4 units up

30. a reflection in the y-axis

31. a reflection in the line $y = x$

32. a rotation of 270°

33. a dilation half the original size

34. a dilation twice the original size

35. a rotation of 90°

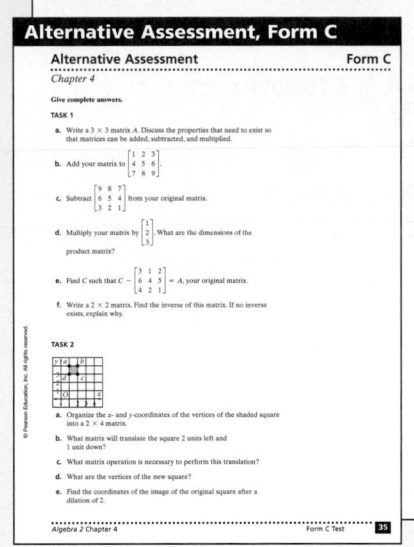

4-5, 4-6 and 4-7 Objectives

▼ To evaluate determinants of 2 × 2 matrices and find inverse matrices (p. 195)

▼ To use inverse matrices in solving matrix equations (pp. 197 and 203)

▼ To evaluate determinants of 3 × 3 matrices (p. 202)

▼ To solve systems of equations using inverse matrices (p. 210)

A **square matrix** with 1's along its main diagonal and 0's elsewhere is the **multiplicative identity matrix,** I. If A and X are square matrices such that $AX = I$, then X is the **multiplicative inverse matrix** of A, A^{-1}.

You can use formulas to evaluate the determinants of 2 × 2 and 3 × 3 matrices.

$$\begin{vmatrix} a & b \\ c & d \end{vmatrix} = ad - bc \qquad \begin{vmatrix} a_1 & b_1 & c_1 \\ a_2 & b_2 & c_2 \\ a_3 & b_3 & c_3 \end{vmatrix} = \begin{array}{l} a_1b_2c_3 + a_2b_3c_1 + a_3b_1c_2 \\ - a_1b_3c_2 - a_2b_1c_3 - a_3b_2c_1 \end{array}$$

You can use a calculator to find the inverse of a matrix. The inverse of a 2 × 2 matrix can be found by using its determinant. $\begin{bmatrix} a & b \\ c & d \end{bmatrix}^{-1} = \dfrac{1}{ad - bc}\begin{bmatrix} d & -b \\ -c & a \end{bmatrix}$

You can use inverse matrices to solve some matrix equations.

You can also use inverse matrices to solve some systems of equations. When equations in a system are in standard form, the product of the **coefficient matrix** and the **variable matrix** equals the **constant matrix.** You solve the equation by multiplying both sides of the equation by the inverse of the coefficient matrix. If that inverse does not exist, the system does not have a unique solution.

Evaluate the determinant of each matrix, and find the inverse, if possible. 36–39. See margin.

36. $\begin{bmatrix} 6 & 1 \\ 0 & 4 \end{bmatrix}$ 37. $\begin{bmatrix} 5 & -2 \\ 10 & -4 \end{bmatrix}$ 38. $\begin{bmatrix} 10 & 1 \\ 8 & 5 \end{bmatrix}$ 39. $\begin{bmatrix} 1 & 0 & 2 \\ -1 & 0 & 1 \\ -1 & -2 & 0 \end{bmatrix}$

Use an inverse matrix to solve each equation or system. 40–43. See margin.

40. $\begin{bmatrix} 3 & 5 \\ 6 & 2 \end{bmatrix} X = \begin{bmatrix} -2 & 6 \\ 4 & 12 \end{bmatrix}$ 41. $\begin{cases} x - y = 3 \\ 2x - y = -1 \end{cases}$ 42. $\begin{bmatrix} 4 & 1 \\ 2 & 1 \end{bmatrix}\begin{bmatrix} x \\ y \end{bmatrix} = \begin{bmatrix} 10 \\ 6 \end{bmatrix}$

43. $\begin{bmatrix} -6 & 0 \\ 7 & 1 \end{bmatrix} X = \begin{bmatrix} -12 & -6 \\ 17 & 9 \end{bmatrix}$ 44. $\begin{cases} x + 2y = 15 \\ 2x + 4y = 30 \end{cases}$    45. $\begin{cases} a + 2b + c = 14 \\ b = c + 1 \\ a = -3c + 6 \end{cases}$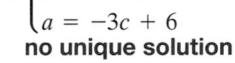
           no unique solution   **no unique solution**

 46. **Physical Fitness** A club of 17 students is going on a canoe trip. The group of people on the trip includes 5 chaperones, one for each canoe. Some canoes hold 5 people, while some hold 4 people. How many of each kind of canoe should the group rent? **3 small canoes, 2 large canoes**

4-8 Objectives

▼ To solve a system of equations using Cramer's Rule (p. 217)

▼ To solve a system of equations using augmented matrices (p. 218)

Cramer's Rule for solving systems of equations uses determinants to solve for each variable. D is the determinant of the coefficient matrix. D_y is the determinant formed by replacing the coefficients of y in D with the constant terms.

You can also use **row operations** on an augmented matrix to solve a system.

Solve each system using Cramer's Rule. Check your answers by solving each system using an augmented matrix.

47. $\begin{cases} 2x - y = 15 \\ x + 3y = -17 \end{cases}$
   (4, −7)

48. $\begin{cases} 3r + s - 2t = 22 \\ r + 5s + t = 4 \\ r = -3t \end{cases}$
   (6, 0, −2)

Chapter 4 Chapter Review **227**

---

36. $24;\ \begin{bmatrix} \frac{1}{6} & -\frac{1}{24} \\ 0 & \frac{1}{4} \end{bmatrix}$

37. 0; does not exist

38. $42;\ \begin{bmatrix} \frac{5}{42} & -\frac{1}{42} \\ -\frac{4}{21} & \frac{5}{21} \end{bmatrix}$

39. $6;\ \begin{bmatrix} \frac{1}{3} & -\frac{2}{3} & 0 \\ -\frac{1}{6} & \frac{1}{3} & -\frac{1}{2} \\ \frac{1}{3} & \frac{1}{3} & 0 \end{bmatrix}$

40. $\begin{bmatrix} 1 & 2 \\ -1 & 0 \end{bmatrix}$

41. (−4, −7)

42. $\begin{bmatrix} 2 \\ 2 \end{bmatrix}$

43. $\begin{bmatrix} 2 & 1 \\ 3 & 2 \end{bmatrix}$

Chapter Test

Take It to the NET
Online chapter test at
www.PHSchool.com
Web Code: aga-0452

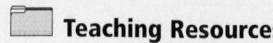
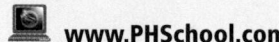

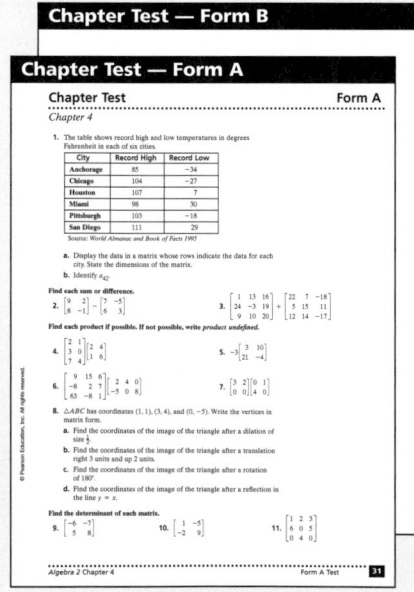
History Use the table below for Exercises 1–3.

President	Years	Vetoes	Overrides
Kennedy	3	21	9
Johnson	5	30	0
Nixon	5.5	43	7
Ford	2.5	66	12
Carter	4	31	2
Reagan	8	78	9
G.H.W. Bush	4	46	1
Clinton	8	38	2

SOURCE: Congressional Research Service.
Go to www.PHSchool.com for a data update.
Web Code: agg-2041

1. Display the data in a matrix in which each row represents a president. **See back of book.**

2. State the dimensions of the matrix. **8 × 3**

3. Find and identify a_{32}. **43, the number of Nixon's vetoes**

Find each sum or difference.

4. $\begin{bmatrix} 4 & 7 \\ -2 & 1 \end{bmatrix} - \begin{bmatrix} -9 & 3 \\ 6 & 0 \end{bmatrix}$ $\begin{bmatrix} 13 & 4 \\ -8 & 1 \end{bmatrix}$

5. $\begin{bmatrix} 4 & -5 & 1 \\ 10 & 7 & 4 \\ 21 & -9 & -6 \end{bmatrix} + \begin{bmatrix} -7 & -10 & 4 \\ 17 & 0 & 3 \\ -2 & -6 & 1 \end{bmatrix}$ **See margin.**

Find each product. **6–8. See margin.**

6. $\begin{bmatrix} 2 & 6 \\ 1 & 0 \end{bmatrix}\begin{bmatrix} -1 & 5 \\ 3 & 1 \end{bmatrix}$

7. $2\begin{bmatrix} -8 & 5 & -1 \\ 0 & 9 & 7 \end{bmatrix}$

8. $\begin{bmatrix} 0 & 3 \\ -4 & 9 \end{bmatrix}\begin{bmatrix} -4 & 6 & 1 & 3 \\ 9 & -8 & 10 & 7 \end{bmatrix}$

Parallelogram $ABCD$ has coordinates $A(2, -1)$, $B(4, 3)$, $C(1, 5)$, and $D(-1, 1)$. Write a matrix for the vertices of its image after each transformation.

9. a dilation of size $\frac{2}{3}$ **See margin.**

10. a translation right 2 units and down 4 units

11. a reflection in $y = x$ **12.** a rotation of 270°

13. Graph parallelogram $ABCD$ and its image from Question 11 on the same coordinate plane.
10–14. See back of book.

14. Open-Ended Write a matrix that has no inverse.

15. Writing Explain how to determine whether two matrices can be multiplied and what the dimensions of the product matrix will be.
See back of book.

16. Find the value of each variable.
$\begin{bmatrix} x & 1 & y \\ 2 & 0 & 1 \end{bmatrix} = \begin{bmatrix} 1-x & z & 2 \\ 2+w & 4-t & 1 \end{bmatrix}$
$x = \frac{1}{2}, z = 1, y = 2, w = 0, t = 4$

Find the determinant of each matrix.

17. $\begin{bmatrix} 1 & 0 & 0 \\ 0 & 1 & 0 \\ 0 & 0 & 1 \end{bmatrix}$ **1** **18.** $\begin{bmatrix} 2 & 3 & 0 \\ -1 & 1 & 0 \\ 4 & 2 & 1 \end{bmatrix}$ **5** **19.** $\begin{bmatrix} 8 & -3 \\ 2 & 9 \end{bmatrix}$ **78**

20. $\begin{bmatrix} 0 & 3 \\ x & t \end{bmatrix}$ **−3x** **21.** $\begin{bmatrix} \frac{1}{2} & -1 \\ 3 & 0 \end{bmatrix}$ **3**

22–26. See back of book.

Find the inverse of each matrix, if it exists.

22. $\begin{bmatrix} 3 & 8 \\ -7 & 10 \end{bmatrix}$ **23.** $\begin{bmatrix} 0 & -5 \\ 9 & 6 \end{bmatrix}$ **24.** $\begin{bmatrix} \frac{1}{2} & -1 \\ 0 & 4 \end{bmatrix}$

25. $\begin{bmatrix} -8 & 4 & -11 \\ 5 & 2 & 9 \\ -5 & 6 & 2 \end{bmatrix}$ **26.** $\begin{bmatrix} 1 & 1 & 2 \\ 2 & 1 & 3 \\ 2 & 1 & 1 \end{bmatrix}$

Solve each matrix equation.

27. $\begin{bmatrix} 3 & -8 \\ 10 & 5 \end{bmatrix} - X = \begin{bmatrix} 2 & 8 \\ -1 & 12 \end{bmatrix}$ $\begin{bmatrix} 1 & -16 \\ 11 & -7 \end{bmatrix}$

28. $\begin{bmatrix} 3 & 2 \\ -1 & 5 \end{bmatrix}X = \begin{bmatrix} -10 & -11 \\ 26 & -36 \end{bmatrix}$ $\begin{bmatrix} -6 & 1 \\ 4 & -7 \end{bmatrix}$

29. $2X - \begin{bmatrix} -2 & 0 \\ 1 & 4 \end{bmatrix} = \begin{bmatrix} 5 & 10 \\ -15 & 9 \end{bmatrix}$ $\begin{bmatrix} \frac{3}{2} & 5 \\ -7 & \frac{13}{2} \end{bmatrix}$

Solve each system using inverse matrices.

30. $\begin{cases} 2x - y = 5 \\ x + 4y = 7 \end{cases}$ **(3, 1)**

31. $\begin{cases} x + 2y + z = -1 \\ 4x - y - z = -1 \\ 2z = -3y \end{cases}$ **(0, −2, 3)**

32. Solve $\begin{cases} -2x + 7y = 19 \\ x + 3y = 10 \end{cases}$ using Cramer's Rule. **(1, 3)**

33. Solve the system using an augmented matrix. **(7, −8, 10)**
$\begin{cases} x + y + z = 9 \\ 4x + 3y - z = -6 \\ -x - y + 2z = 21 \end{cases}$

page 228 Chapter Test

5. $\begin{bmatrix} -3 & -15 & 5 \\ 27 & 7 & 7 \\ 19 & -15 & -5 \end{bmatrix}$

6. $\begin{bmatrix} 16 & 16 \\ -1 & 5 \end{bmatrix}$

7. $\begin{bmatrix} -16 & 10 & -2 \\ 0 & 18 & 14 \end{bmatrix}$

8. $\begin{bmatrix} 27 & -24 & 30 & 21 \\ 97 & -96 & 86 & 51 \end{bmatrix}$

9. $\begin{bmatrix} \frac{4}{3} & \frac{8}{3} & \frac{2}{3} & -\frac{2}{3} \\ -\frac{2}{3} & 2 & \frac{10}{3} & \frac{2}{3} \end{bmatrix}$

Standardized Test Prep

Multiple Choice

For Exercises 1–8, choose the correct letter.

1 Which number is irrational? **D**
A. $8.\overline{12}$ B. $\sqrt{121}$ C. -5 D. $\sqrt{35}$

2. Which numbers are solutions of $\frac{5}{4}|2x - 9| = 5$? **G**
F. $\frac{11}{8}, \frac{61}{8}$ G. $\frac{5}{2}, \frac{13}{2}$ H. $\frac{8}{5}, \frac{28}{5}$ I. 2, 7

3. Which equation represents the xy-trace of **A**
$20x - 70y - 50z = 100$?
A. $2x - 7y = 10$ B. $-7y - 5z = 10$
C. $2x - 5z = 10$ D. $5z = -10$

4. Which ordered pair is *not* a solution of **H**
the system $\begin{cases} x + y \le 4 \\ 2x - y \ge -3 \end{cases}$?

F. $(1, 1)$ G. $(0, 3)$ H. $(-5, -1)$ I. $(3, 0)$

5. What is the solution of $\begin{cases} 2x - y = 4 \\ y = 2 - x \end{cases}$? **B**

A. $(0, 2)$ B. $(2, 0)$ C. $(2, 4)$ D. $(0, -4)$

6. Which lines are perpendicular to $y = 3x - 8$? **I**
I. $y = \frac{1}{3}x - 1$ II. $y = -\frac{1}{3}x + 1$
III. $y = 3x + 2$ IV. $y = 6x + 4$

F. I only   G. III and IV   H. I and II   I. II only

7. What is the sum $\begin{bmatrix} 3 & 7 & -2 \\ 0 & 10 & 5 \end{bmatrix} + \begin{bmatrix} 6 & -8 & 1 \\ 9 & -4 & 11 \end{bmatrix}$? **A**

A. $\begin{bmatrix} 9 & -1 & -1 \\ 9 & 6 & 16 \end{bmatrix}$ B. $\begin{bmatrix} 9 & 15 & -1 \\ 9 & 6 & 16 \end{bmatrix}$

C. $\begin{bmatrix} 9 & 15 & -3 \\ 9 & 6 & 16 \end{bmatrix}$ D. $\begin{bmatrix} -3 & 1 & -3 \\ -9 & 14 & -6 \end{bmatrix}$

8. Which equation has the solution $\begin{bmatrix} 1 & -2 & 0 \\ -5 & 4 & 7 \end{bmatrix}$? **H**

F. $\begin{bmatrix} 7 & -2 & -3 \\ 0 & 1 & 8 \end{bmatrix} - X = \begin{bmatrix} 8 & -4 & -3 \\ -5 & 5 & 15 \end{bmatrix}$

G. $\begin{bmatrix} 10 & -8 & 12 \\ 4 & 0 & 5 \end{bmatrix} - \begin{bmatrix} -9 & -6 & 12 \\ -1 & -4 & -2 \end{bmatrix} = X$

H. $\begin{bmatrix} 0 & 6 & 5 \\ 2 & -1 & -9 \end{bmatrix} + X = \begin{bmatrix} 1 & 4 & 5 \\ -3 & 3 & -2 \end{bmatrix}$

I. $X - \begin{bmatrix} 3 & 7 & 4 \\ 8 & -6 & 1 \end{bmatrix} = \begin{bmatrix} 2 & -5 & 4 \\ -3 & 2 & 6 \end{bmatrix}$

Quantitative Comparison

Compare the boxed quantity in Column A with the boxed quantity in Column B. Choose the best answer.

A. The quantity in Column A is greater.
B. The quantity in Column B is greater.
C. The two quantities are equal.
D. The relationship cannot be determined from the information given.

Column A	Column B
$P = \begin{bmatrix} 4 & 1 & 9 \\ -5 & 3 & 2 \\ 7 & -4 & 1 \end{bmatrix}$	$Q = \begin{bmatrix} 4 & -5 & 7 \\ 1 & 3 & -4 \\ 9 & 2 & 1 \end{bmatrix}$

9. **A** | p_{13} | p_{31} |

10. **C** | p_{13} | q_{31} |

11. **C** | det P | det Q |

Gridded Response

12. What is the slope of the graph of $8x + 2y = 3$? **−4**

13. What is the value of $\begin{vmatrix} 7 & -1 \\ 3 & 2 \end{vmatrix}$? **17**

Short Response

14. Write a matrix to translate $\begin{bmatrix} -1 & 4 & 5 \\ 0 & 7 & 2 \end{bmatrix}$ 7 units left and 2 units up. Use the matrix to find the coordinates of the image. **See back of book.**

Extended Response

15. A dietitian wants to prepare a meal with 24 g of protein, 27 g of fat, and 20 g of carbohydrates, using the three foods shown in the table.

Food	Protein	Fat	Carbohydrates
A	2 g/oz	3 g/oz	4 g/oz
B	3 g/oz	3 g/oz	1 g/oz
C	3 g/oz	3 g/oz	2 g/oz

a–c. See back of book.
a. Set up a matrix equation for the data.
b. Solve the matrix equation.
c. How many ounces of each food are needed?

Resources

 Teaching Resources
Cumulative Review
Quarter 1 Test, Forms A & B

 Reaching All Students
Spanish Cumulative Review
Spanish Quarter 1 Test,
Forms A & B

ASSESSMENT SYSTEM

Standardized Test Prep
• Ch. 4 Standardized Test Practice
Assessment Masters
• Cumulative Review
• Quarter 1 Test, Forms A & B
Computer Test Generator CD
• Standardized Test Practice

 www.PHSchool.com
• Standardized Test Practice
• Resources

Plus **iTEXT**

Item	1	2	3	4	5	6	7	8	9	10	11	12	13	14	15
Lesson	1-1	1-5	3-5	3-3	2-2	4-2	4-3	4-2	4-1	4-1	4-6	1-6	4-5	4-4	3-6

Building a Business

In these activities students apply their knowledge of inequalities, systems of inequalities, and linear programming.

Connecting to Prior Knowledge

Have students research the different kinds of chocolate (milk, dark, white) and forms (cocoa, bars, syrup), what products contain chocolate, what countries grow the cacao tree, and how the beans are processed.

Teaching Notes

Have a volunteer read the introductory paragraph. Ask: *Has anyone ever visited a factory or a bakery that produces a large quantity of a product each day?* Have students describe the various processes they observed.

Teaching Tip

Discuss how students might conduct a test to compare the tastes of two or more chocolate bars, including hiding the brand names for a blind test, and recording the various responses in such a way that they can be analyzed numerically.

Connection to Science

Have students research recent findings about the chemical contents of chocolate and its effects, including whether eating chocolate may be a cause of complexion or skin problems.

English Learners

Have volunteers describe what is meant by *the efficiency of a factory* and *maximizing profits*.

Real-World Snapshots

Building a Business

Applying Inequalities The efficiency of a factory depends on how you divide limited resources among the products produced. The bad news is that in any factory you have a limited number of machines and raw materials available. The good news is that these limitations lead to inequalities that you can use to decide how to maximize your profits.

1 The cacao tree grows in tropical jungles. It produces melonlike fruits, each containing 20–40 cocoa beans.

3 The inside of the cocoa bean is ground into a concentrated chocolate liquid.

2 After roasting, cocoa beans pass through a machine that separates the shell from the inside of the bean.

Activity

You are in charge of a small private chocolate factory that makes two popular and profitable chocolate bars, Cocoa Bar and Choco-Lot. Your goal is to figure out how many of each type of chocolate bar you should produce each day to maximize your company's profits.

Here are a few key pieces of information:

- The success of your chocolate recipes lies in your use of two secret ingredients, referred to as Flavor A and Flavor B to protect the company's interests. The table shows the production rate and requirements of the flavors.

	Flavor A	Flavor B
Production rate	126 kg/day	136 kg/day
Cocoa Bar requirements	1.8 g/bar	4.0 g/bar
Choco-Lot requirements	2.8 g/bar	1.7 g/bar

- One machine wraps both candy bars. It can wrap 50,000 chocolate bars per day.
- Your profit on each Cocoa Bar bar is 14¢, and your profit on each Choco-Lot bar is 12¢.

a. Write inequalities to describe each objective and constraint.

b. Graph the inequalities you wrote in part (a).

c. Find the quantity of each chocolate bar you should manufacture to maximize your daily profit. Calculate the profit you will earn.

pages 230–231 **Real-World Snapshots**

Activity

a. Let B = number of Cocoa Bar bars, L = number of Choco-Lot bars.
Constraints:

$B \geq 0; L \geq 0$
$B + L \leq 50{,}000$
$1.8B + 2.8L \leq 126{,}000$
$4.0B + 1.7L \leq 136{,}000$
Objective:
maximize $0.14B + 0.12L$

b.

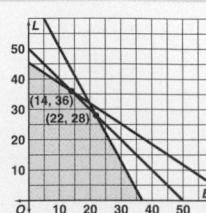

(14, 36)
(22, 28)

230

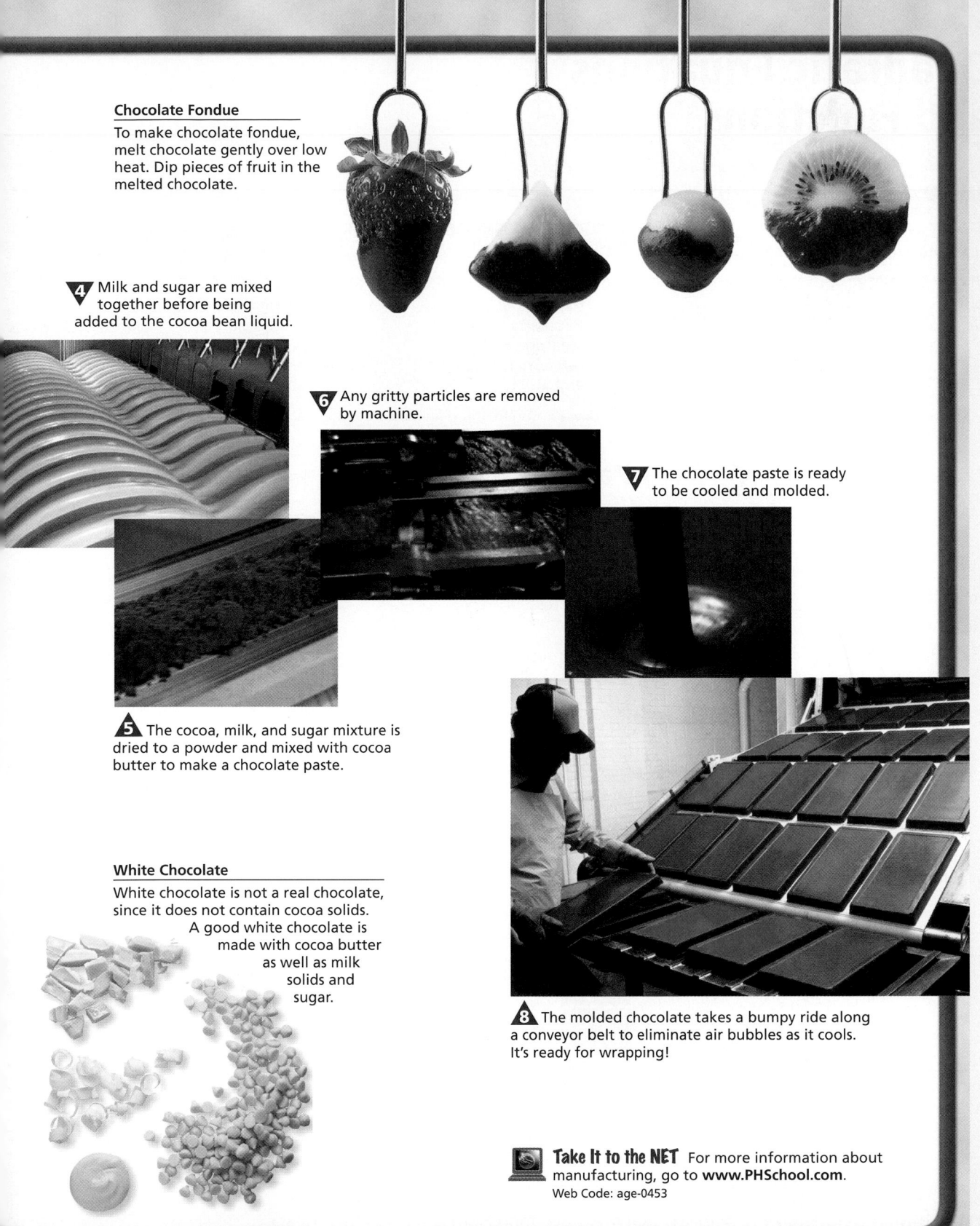

Chocolate Fondue

To make chocolate fondue, melt chocolate gently over low heat. Dip pieces of fruit in the melted chocolate.

4 Milk and sugar are mixed together before being added to the cocoa bean liquid.

6 Any gritty particles are removed by machine.

7 The chocolate paste is ready to be cooled and molded.

5 The cocoa, milk, and sugar mixture is dried to a powder and mixed with cocoa butter to make a chocolate paste.

White Chocolate

White chocolate is not a real chocolate, since it does not contain cocoa solids. A good white chocolate is made with cocoa butter as well as milk solids and sugar.

8 The molded chocolate takes a bumpy ride along a conveyor belt to eliminate air bubbles as it cools. It's ready for wrapping!

Take It to the NET For more information about manufacturing, go to **www.PHSchool.com**.
Web Code: age-0453

c. $L = 28{,}000$; $B = 22{,}000$; $6440

Chapter 5

Quadratic Equations and Functions

Chapter at a Glance

North Carolina Objectives

5-1	Modeling Data With Quadratic Functions	2.02b
NCTM 2, 5, 10	▼ Quadratic Functions and Their Graphs ▼ Using Quadratic Models	

5-2	Properties of Parabolas	2.02a, b
NCTM 2, 3, 6, 10	▼ Graphing Parabolas ▼ Finding Maximum and Minimum Values	

5-3	Translating Parabolas	2.02a, b
NCTM 2, 3, 10	▼ Using Vertex Form	

5-4	Factoring Quadratic Expressions	1.03
NCTM 1, 2, 7	▼ Finding Common and Binomial Factors ▼ Factoring Special Expressions	

5-5	Quadratic Equations	2.02a
NCTM 2, 3, 6, 9	▼ Solving by Factoring and Finding Square Roots ▼ Solving by Graphing	

5-6	Complex Numbers	1.02
NCTM 1, 2, 10	▼ Identifying Complex Numbers ▼ Operations With Complex Numbers	

5-7	Completing the Square	2.02a, b
NCTM 2, 6, 7	▼ Solving Equations by Completing the Square ▼ Rewriting a Function by Completing the Square	

5-8	The Quadratic Formula	2.02a, b
NCTM 2, 6, 7	▼ Using the Quadratic Formula ▼ Using the Discriminant	

NCTM STANDARDS 2000

1	Number and Operations	6	Problem Solving
2	Algebra	7	Reasoning and Proof
3	Geometry	8	Communication
4	Measurement	9	Connections
5	Data Analysis and Probability	10	Representation

Pacing Options

This chart suggests pacing only for the lessons and their parts. It is provided as a possible guide. It will help you determine how much time you have in your schedule to cover other components, such as the features, Chapter Review, and Chapter Test.

Day	Traditional (45 min.)	Block (90 min.)
1	5-1 ▼	5-1 ▼
2	5-1 ▽	5-1 ▽
3	5-2 ▼	5-2 ▼
4	5-2 ▼ ▽	5-2 ▽
5	5-2 ▽	5-3 ▼
6	5-3 ▼	5-4 ▼
7	5-3 ▼	5-4 ▽
8	5-4 ▼	5-5 ▼
9	5-4 ▽	5-5 ▽
10	5-5 ▼	5-6 ▼ ▽
11	5-5 ▽	5-7 ▼
12	5-6 ▼	5-7 ▽
13	5-6 ▽	5-8 ▼ ▽
14	5-7 ▼	
15	5-7 ▽	
16	5-8 ▼	
17	5-8 ▼ ▽	
18	5-8 ▽	

NAEP Correlation (National Assessment of Educational Progress 2000 Mathematics Objectives)

5-1	5-2	5-3	5-4	5-5	5-6	5-7	5-8
D1b, D1c, A13	A3a	A3a, A3c, A3d	N3a, A9	N3a, A9	N3a, G6b, A9	N3a, A9	N3a, A9

N = Number Sense, Properties, and Operations; **M** = Measurement; **G** = Geometry and Spatial Sense;
D = Data Analysis, Statistics, and Probability; **A** = Algebra and Functions

Math Background

Chapter Overview

Students study the symmetry of parabolas and learn to locate their maximum or minimum points. They learn that the graph of a function $y = a(x - h)^2 + k$ is a translation image of the graph of $y = ax^2$.

There is a detailed discussion of factoring quadratic expressions. Students then solve quadratic equations by factoring. After learning about complex numbers, students go on to solve quadratic equations by completing the square and by using the quadratic formula.

Modeling Data with Quadratic Functions   5-1

Students see how a system of linear equations can be used to find a quadratic function whose graph passes through three noncollinear points. They should enjoy this blending of their new skill and finding quadratic models for data in real-world situations. To graph data, one or both axes may be drawn with a break to indicate skipped values. It is often convenient to use non-unit scales on the axes to accommodate the data of a problem. Different scales may used for the two axes, but then the apparent slope of a line will be distorted and the slope cannot be calculated by counting grid lines.

Properties of Parabolas   5-2

Students must recognize that, just as the graph of a linear function is always a line, the graph of a quadratic function is always a parabola. Emphasize that a parabola is a curve and has no section that is linear, even when several plotted points appear to be collinear.

Translating Parabolas   5-3

Students should be able to establish the relationship between the two forms used to write quadratic functions, and relate h, k, a, b, and c. Clearly the a in each equation is the same; $a = a$. Rewriting will show that $b = -2ah$ and $c = ah^2 + k$.

Factoring Quadratic Expressions   5-4

Usually, when we ask for the factors of a number such as 28, we expect the answer 1, 2, 4, 7, 14, and 28 because those are the whole-number factors. However, when factoring a trinomial such as

$$x^2 - 3x + 2$$

we factor 2 with respect to the integers as -1×-2 to get $(x - 1)(x - 2)$. When we factor

$$x^2 - 0.25$$

we factor 0.25 with respect to the rational numbers as -0.5×0.5 to get $(x - 0.5)(x + 0.5)$. We could *factor* $x^2 - 3$ by factoring 3 with respect to the real numbers, yielding $(x - \sqrt{3})(x + \sqrt{3})$.

You may wish to introduce students to the method of substituting values for the variables as another way to check factoring. This type of check will generally reveal an error, but does not guarantee correctness.

To check

$$pg - 2g + 6 - 3p = (p - 2)(g - 3)$$

choose values for p and g that make the computations easy. If 2 is substituted for p and 1 is substituted for g, the right side of the equation is easily seen to equal 0. The left side yields $2 \cdot 1 - 2 \cdot 1 + 6 - 3 \cdot 2 = 0$. The values of the two sides of the equation are equal, suggesting that the factoring is probably correct.

Quadratic Equations   5-5

Sometimes the word *or* indicates one of two possibilities but not both of them. In the principle of zero products (if $ab = 0$, then $a = 0$ or $b = 0$) the *or* is used inclusively to mean that $a = 0$ or $b = 0$ or that both a and b equal 0. When we solve the equation $(x - 1)(x - 2) = 0$ and say that $x = 1$ or $x = 2$, the "or" is not inclusive; we mean that both 1 and 2 are solutions of the equation. The solution set is {1,2}. You may wish to point out to students that using graphs to find approximate solutions is often the best way to arrive at useful information about a problem.

Complex Numbers   5-6

Students may be surprised to learn that numbers are actually invented or defined. Negative numbers were invented to solve equations like $x + 8 = 1$. Irrational numbers were invented to solve equations like $x^2 = 2$. And imaginary numbers were invented to solve equations like $x^2 = -3$, using the definition $i^2 = -1$, or equivalently, $i = \sqrt{-1}$. Although i looks like a variable, and we can manipulate it as we do a variable, it is a number. It does not make sense to order the complex numbers; there is no way to graph them on the real number line.

Completing the Square, The Quadratic Formula   5-7, 5-8

Students can see that the technique of completing the square yields the vertex form of a parabola. In some countries, the standard form of a quadratic equation is $x^2 + 2bx + c = 0$. Completing the square gives a slightly simpler formula for the roots: $x = -b \pm \sqrt{b^2 - c}$. Students should not have much difficulty showing that, for this form, the sum of the roots written in this way is $-2b$, the product of the roots is c, and the axis of symmetry and x-coordinate of the vertex are $x = -b$.

# Ongoing Assessment and Intervention

Tools for Monitoring Student Progress

The Prentice Hall *Algebra 2* program provides you with many options for assessment in the Student Edition, the Teacher's Edition and the teaching resources. From these options you may choose instructional materials and techniques that are appropriate for your students and support your district's curriculum requirements.

Instant Check System™ in Chapter 5

Allows students to check their own learning before, during, and after each lesson.

Diagnosing Readiness before the chapter (p. 232)

Check Skills You'll Need exercises in each lesson (pp. 234, 241, 248, 255, 263, 270, 278, 285)

Check Understanding questions with each Example (pp. 235, 236, 241, 242, 243, 249, 250, 251, 255, 256, 257, 258, 259, 264, 265, 270, 271, 272, 273, 278, 279, 280, 281, 286, 287, 288)

Checkpoint Quiz (pp. 254, 276)

Test Prep in Chapter 5

Teaches students strategies and gives them practice with all the test item formats they will encounter on state tests and standardized national exams.

Standardized Test Prep exercises in each lesson (pp. 239, 247, 254, 261, 268, 276, 283, 291)

Test-Taking Strategies (p. 292)

Standardized Test Prep (p. 297)

All your assessment needs in one place!

Program Assessment

Assess student progress throughout the *Algebra 2* text with blackline masters and CD-ROM.

Assessment Resources

- Checkpoint Quizzes 1 & 2
- Chapter Test, Forms A & B
- Chapter Alternative Assessment

Spanish versions available.

Computer Test Generator

- Unlimited questions of varying difficulty for every lesson objective.
- Create your own practice sheets, quizzes, and tests, or use the pre-made Chapter Tests.
- Diagnose readiness with questions on prerequisite skills.
- Prepare students by making tests based on standardized test objectives.
- Access Algebra 1, Geometry, and Algebra 2 content—all on one CD-ROM.

Test Preparation

A three-step approach to preparing students for high stakes, national, and state exams.

❶ Diagnose & Prescribe

Content Diagnostic Tests
- Diagnose strengths and weaknesses in content for national and state tests.
- Prescribe individualized reaching opportunities.

❷ Review & Reteach

Skills and Concepts Review
- Provides reaching worksheets with instruction and practice for each skill.
- Includes course prerequisite skills.

❸ Practice & Assess

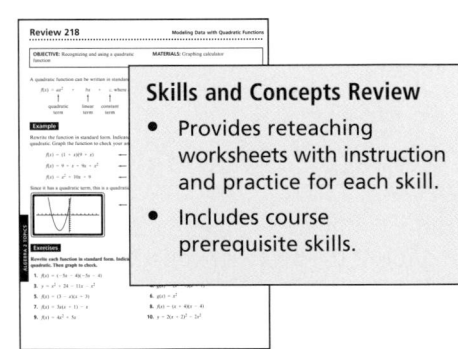

Test Preparation
- Features practice tests for End-of-Course and SAT/ACT exams.
- Includes standardized test practice by chapter for ongoing review.

Teacher's Guide with answers and correlations.

Test-Taking Strategies with Transparencies
- Support the Test-Taking Strategies pages in the Student Edition.
- Provide a teaching transparency and a practice worksheet for each strategy.

# Reaching All Students

Support in the Student Text and Additional Resources

The textbook, the iText, and other technology components provide numerous opportunities to reach students of various ability levels and learning styles. Each Teacher's Edition lesson suggests how you can help *all* your students be successful and understand the mathematics in Chapter 5.

Below Level

Student Edition
- Diagnosing Readiness*: p. 232
- Check Skills You'll Need*: pp. 234, 241, 248, 255, 263, 270, 278, 285

Reteaching
Chapter 5 Support File: pp. 10–17

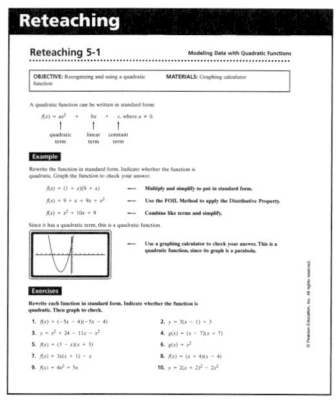

Advanced Learners

Student Edition
- Challenge exercises: pp. 239, 246, 253, 261, 267, 275, 283, 291
- Extension, p. 269

Enrichment
Chapter 5 Support File: pp. 18–25

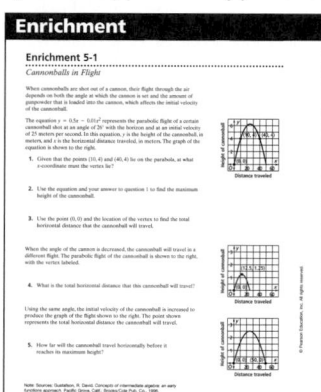

Connections to Precalculus Masters
Chapter 5 Enrichment Topic: Systems of Equations

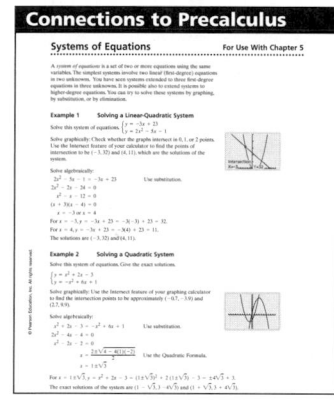

* Can be used with all ability levels to ensure mastery of prerequisite skills.

Reading and Math Literacy

Student Edition
- Vocabulary: pp. 233, 293, *plus* in every Lesson Preview
- Reading Math: pp. 241, 243, 249, 256, 278, 282, 284
- Illustrated Glossary: pp. 871–913

Reading and Math Literacy Masters
Chapter 5: pp. 17–20

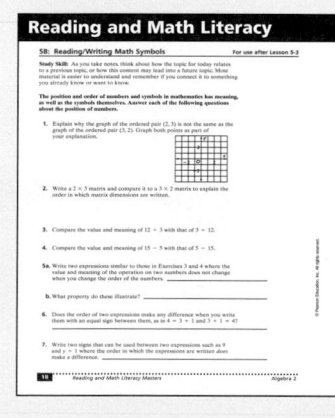

English Learners

Student Edition
- English/Spanish Illustrated Glossary: pp. 871–913

Workbook and Masters
Spanish Practice Workbook: pp. 2–9
Spanish Reading and Math Literacy Masters: pp. 17–20

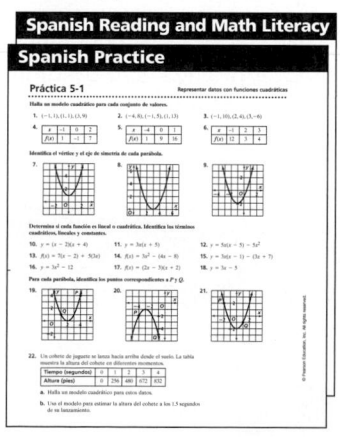

Learning Styles

Student Edition
- Investigation: pp. 248, 255, 277
- Technology: pp. 240, 253
- Writing: pp. 238, 246, 253, 260, 267, 274, 282, 290

Activity Masters
Hands-On Activities: 40, 41, 42
Technology Activities: 5, 7, 9, 10

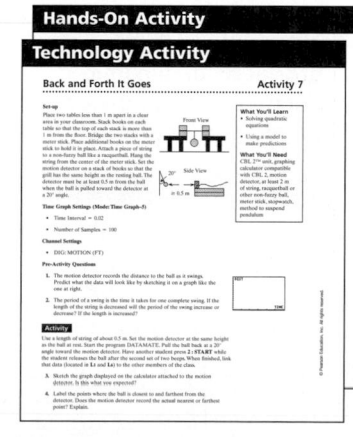

Program Resources

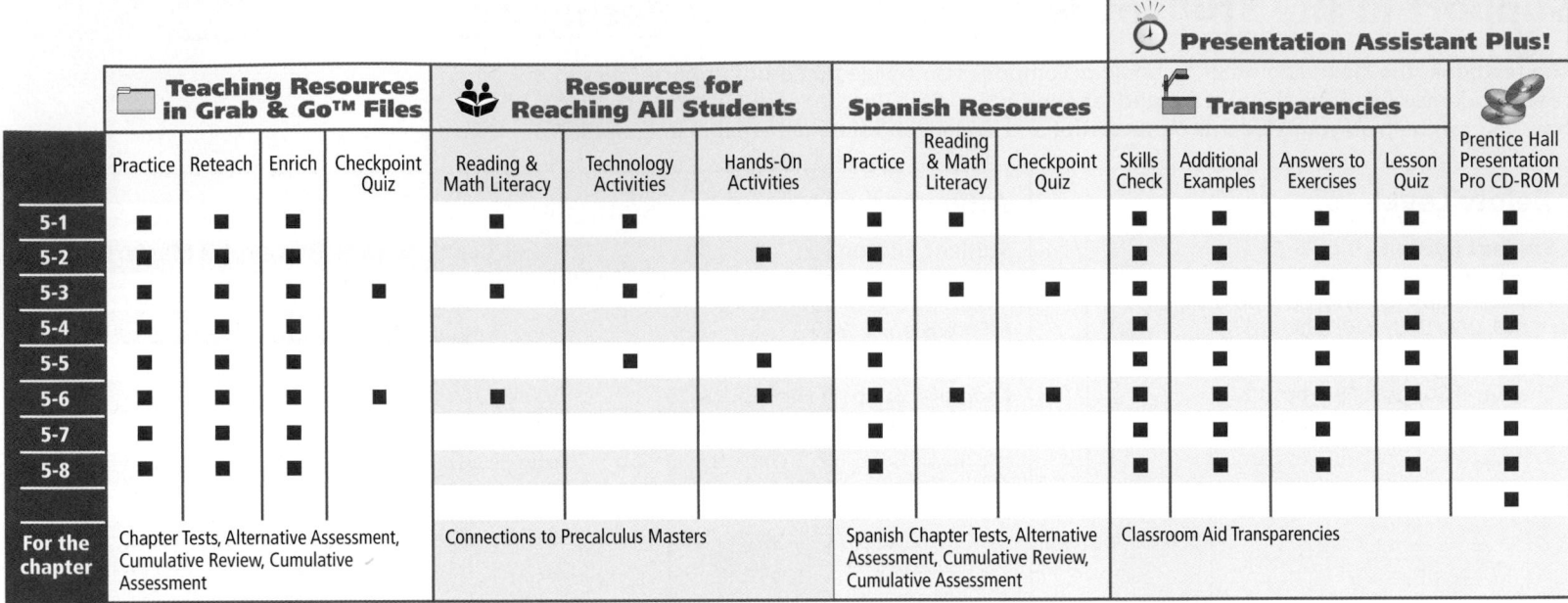

	Teaching Resources in Grab & Go™ Files				Resources for Reaching All Students			Spanish Resources			Presentation Assistant Plus! — Transparencies				Prentice Hall Presentation Pro CD-ROM
	Practice	Reteach	Enrich	Checkpoint Quiz	Reading & Math Literacy	Technology Activities	Hands-On Activities	Practice	Reading & Math Literacy	Checkpoint Quiz	Skills Check	Additional Examples	Answers to Exercises	Lesson Quiz	
5-1	■	■	■		■	■		■			■	■	■	■	■
5-2	■	■	■					■			■	■	■	■	■
5-3	■	■	■	■	■	■		■	■	■	■	■	■	■	■
5-4	■	■	■					■			■	■	■	■	■
5-5	■	■	■			■	■	■			■	■	■	■	■
5-6	■	■	■	■	■		■	■		■	■	■	■	■	■
5-7	■	■	■					■			■			■	■
5-8	■	■	■					■			■	■	■	■	■
															■
For the chapter	Chapter Tests, Alternative Assessment, Cumulative Review, Cumulative Assessment				Connections to Precalculus Masters			Spanish Chapter Tests, Alternative Assessment, Cumulative Review, Cumulative Assessment			Classroom Aid Transparencies				

Also available for use with the chapter:

 *See page 232C.*

- Practice Workbook
- Solution Key

- For teacher support and access to student Web site materials, use Web Code agk-5500.
- For additional online and technology resources, see below.

  **Technology**

iTEXT Online and on CD-ROM

Complete Interactive Student Text online and on CD-ROM—with instant feedback assessment, tutorial help, dynamic activities, instructional and real-world videos, audio, and additional practice.

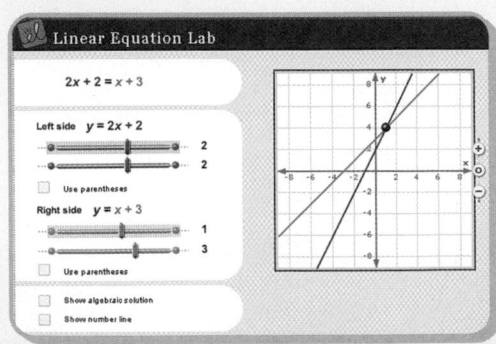

www.PHSchool.com For Students

Use **Web Codes** for easy access to online activities, chapter projects, self-grading lesson quizzes and chapter tests, vocabulary quizzes, updated data sources, graphing calculator procedures, and more.

PH SuccessNet For Teachers

Online lesson planning with built-in state correlations, all the teaching resources, complete reference library, your own calendar and Teacher Web page, professional development, and more.

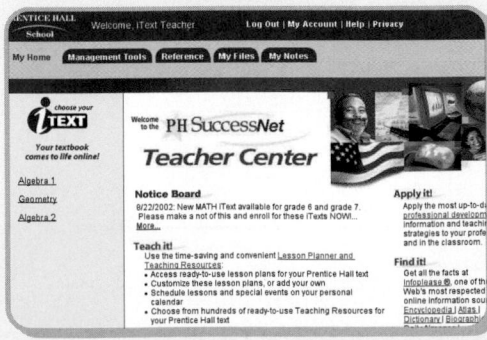

Presentation Assistant Plus!

The Prentice Hall *Presentation Assistant Plus!* provides you with the material you need to teach a lesson from beginning to end. Two easy-to-use formats—Transparencies and CD-ROM—allow you to present a lesson the way you are most comfortable.

Transparencies

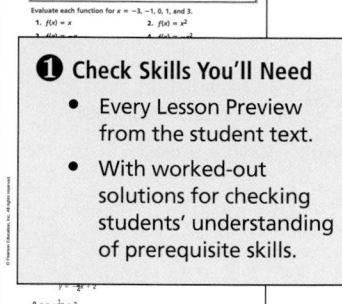

❶ Check Skills You'll Need
- Every Lesson Preview from the student text.
- With worked-out solutions for checking students' understanding of prerequisite skills.

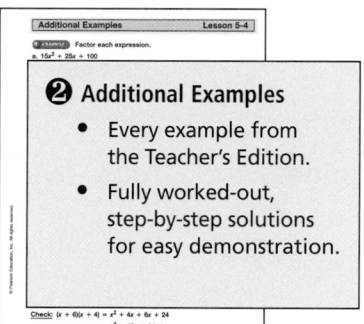

❷ Additional Examples
- Every example from the Teacher's Edition.
- Fully worked-out, step-by-step solutions for easy demonstration.

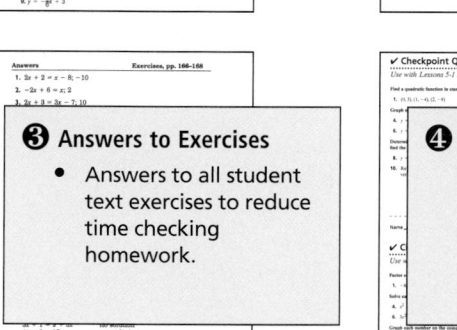

❸ Answers to Exercises
- Answers to all student text exercises to reduce time checking homework.

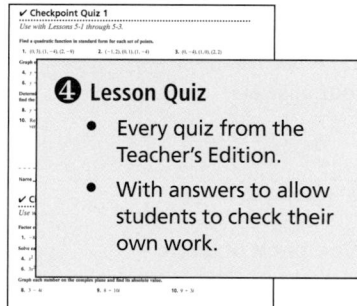

❹ Lesson Quiz
- Every quiz from the Teacher's Edition.
- With answers to allow students to check their own work.

 Throughout the Teacher's Edition, this symbol indicates material that is available on transparency in the Presentation Assistant Plus!

Prentice Hall Presentation Pro CD-ROM

- Includes all Transparencies.
- Conveniently organized by lesson so you can easily ❶ Introduce, ❷ Teach, ❸ Check Homework, and ❹ Assess each lesson.
- Animated examples allow step-by-step instruction at your own pace.
- Easy to edit so you can create custom presentations.

Teaching Chapter 5 Using Presentation Assistant Plus!

	❶ Introduce	❷ Teach	❸ Check Homework	❹ Assess
	Check Skills You'll Need	Additional Examples	Student Edition Answers	Lesson Quiz
5-1	p. 28	pp. 85–87	✔	p. 121
5-2	p. 29	pp. 88–91	✔	p. 122
5-3	p. 30	pp. 92–93	✔	p. 122
5-4	p. 31	pp. 94–98	✔	p. 123
5-5	p. 32	pp. 99–101	✔	p. 123
5-6	p. 33	pp. 102–104	✔	p. 124
5-7	p. 34	pp. 105–108	✔	p. 124
5-8	p. 35	pp. 109–112	✔	p. 125

Prentice Hall Presentation Pro

CD-ROM with dynamic PowerPoint® presentations for every lesson. Helps you introduce and develop concepts, check homework, and assess progress. Part of Presentation Assistant Plus! *(See above.)*

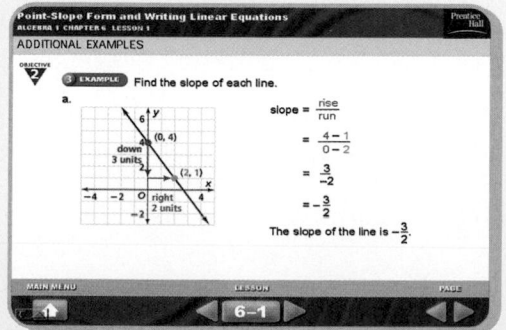

Computer Test Generator

CD-ROM to create practice sheets and tests for course objectives and standardized tests. Includes Instant Chapter Tests™, online testing, and student reports. Part of the PH Assessment System. *(See page 232C.)*

Resource Pro® with Planning Express®

CD-ROM with a lesson planning tool that allows you to import state and local objectives. Includes electronic versions of all the teaching resources.

Chapter 5

Quadratic Equations and Functions

 Diagnosing Readiness

Students will find answers to these exercises in the back of their textbooks.

For intervention, direct students to:

Simplifying Expressions
Lesson 1-2: Example 4
Exercises 21–35
Extra Practice, p. 822

Solving Linear Equations
Lesson 1-3: Examples 1, 2
Exercises 1–16
Extra Practice, p. 822

Graphing Linear Equations
Lesson 2-2: Example 1
Exercises 1–8
Extra Practice, p. 823

Using Linear Models
Lesson 2-4: Example 4
Exercises 8–11
Extra Practice, p. 823

Graphing Translations
Lesson 2-6: Example 4
Exercises 12–15
Extra Practice, p. 823

Where You've Been

- In Chapter 1, you learned to write and solve linear equations.
- In Chapter 2, you learned to graph linear functions.
- In Chapter 2, you learned to use linear functions to model real-world data.

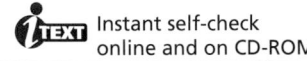 **TEXT** Instant self-check online and on CD-ROM

 **Diagnosing Readiness** (For help, go to the Lesson in green.)

Simplifying Expressions (Lesson 1-2)

Simplify each expression.

1. $x^2 + 3x^2 - 5x$ $4x^2 - 5x$

2. $\frac{x^2}{2} - \frac{x^2}{3} + \frac{x^2}{5}$ $\frac{11x^2}{30}$

3. $-6x(x + 2) - x(x + 1)$
$-7x^2 - 13x$

Solving Linear Equations (Lesson 1-3)

Solve each equation. Check your answers.

4. $4 - 2x = x + 2$ $\frac{2}{3}$

5. $6x + 2.5 = 4x - 1.1$ -1.8

6. $3(x - 1) = 8(2x - 2)$ 1

Graphing Linear Functions (Lesson 2-2)

Graph each function.   **7–12. See back of book.**

7. $y = -5x - 1$

8. $y = 3x + 12$

9. $y = -6x + 6$

10. $2x - 3y = -4$

11. $-3x + 9y = -12$

12. $y - 1 = -4x$

Using Linear Models (Lesson 2-4)

Graph each set of values. Decide whether a linear model is reasonable. If so, draw a trend line and write its equation.   **13–15. See back of book.**

13. $\{(0, 12), (2, 17), (4, 25), (6, 29), (8, 36)\}$

14. $\{(5.5, 16), (6.8, 18.4), (7.5, 19.3), (8, 20), (8.5, 20.8)\}$

15. Each second, a car that begins with a speed of 40 ft/s increases its speed by 6 ft/s. Write and graph an equation to model the car's speed at s seconds.

Graphing Translations (Lesson 2-6)

16. Identify the parent function of $y = |x - 5|$. Graph $y = |x - 5|$ by translating its parent function.   **See back of book.**

Quadratic Equations and Functions

Where You're Going

- In Chapter 5, you will learn to use quadratic functions to model real-world data.

- You will learn to graph and to solve quadratic equations.

- You will learn to graph complex numbers and to use them in solving quadratic equations.

 Real-World Connection Applying what you learn, on page 265 you will solve a problem involving art.

Key Vocabulary

- axis of symmetry (p. 235)
- completing the square (p. 278)
- complex number (p. 271)
- complex number plane (p. 271)
- difference of two squares (p. 259)
- discriminant (p. 287)
- factoring (p. 255)
- i (p. 270)
- imaginary number (p. 270)
- parabola (p. 235)
- perfect square trinomial (p. 258)
- Quadratic Formula (p. 285)
- quadratic function (p. 234)
- standard form of a quadratic function (p. 234)
- vertex form of a quadratic function (p. 248)
- zero of a function (p. 264)
- Zero Product Property (p. 263)

233

Chapter 5 Overview

This chapter begins by introducing the concept of modeling data with quadratic functions. Students then learn about the properties of parabolas, and how to translate parabolas. Next, students are introduced to factoring quadratic expressions, followed by a lesson on solving quadratic equations by factoring or finding square roots. The chapter continues by introducing students to complex numbers. Students complete the chapter with lessons on solving quadratic equations by completing the square and by using the quadratic formula.

 **Reading Math**
Reading Formulas, p. 284

Vocabulary
A complete list of terms, plus vocabulary exercises, appears in the Chapter Review, p. 293.

Illustrated Glossary
Examples for each vocabulary term, plus definitions in both English and Spanish, appear starting on p. 871.

Test-Taking Strategies
Using a Variable, p. 292

Real-World Connections
Some of the applications you will find in this chapter are hydraulics (5-1), civil engineering (5-3), firefighters (5-5), fractals (5-6), and art (5-8).

 **www.PHSchool.com**
Internet support for this chapter includes:
- Self-grading Vocabulary and Chapter 5 Tests
- Chapter Project
- Chapter Planner
- Chapter 5 Resources

Plus **TEXT**

North Carolina
Objectives
2.02b

1. Plan

Lesson Preview

✓ **Check Skills You'll Need**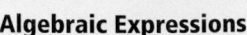

Algebraic Expressions
Lesson 1-2: Examples 1 and 2
Exercises 1–4
Extra Practice, p. 822

Linear Equations
Lesson 2-2: Example 6
Exercises 32–37
Extra Practice, p. 823

Lesson Resources

📁 **Teaching Resources**
Practice, Reteaching, Enrichment

👥 **Reaching All Students**
Practice Workbook 5-1
Spanish Practice Workbook 5-1
Reading and Math Literacy 5A
Spanish Reading & Literacy 5A
Technology Activities 5, 9

🕐 **Presentation Assistant Plus!**
Transparencies
• Check Skills You'll Need 5-1
• Additional Examples 5-1
• Student Edition Answers 5-1
• Lesson Quiz 5-1
PH Presentation Pro CD 5-1

PRENTICE HALL
ASSESSMENT SYSTEM

Computer Test Generator CD

💿 **Technology**
Resource Pro® CD-ROM
Computer Test Generator CD
Prentice Hall Presentation Pro CD

💻 **www.PHSchool.com**
Student Site
• Teacher Web Code: agk-5500
• Graphing Calculator,
  Procedure 23
• Self-grading Lesson Quiz
Teacher Center
• Lesson Planner
• Resources

Plus

5-1 Modeling Data With Quadratic Functions

North Carolina Objectives 2.02 Use quadratic functions and inequalities to model and solve problems; justify results. b) Interpret the constants and coefficients in the context of the problem.

Lesson Preview

What You'll Learn

OBJECTIVE 1 To identify quadratic functions and graphs

OBJECTIVE 2 To model data with quadratic functions

... And Why

To model the flow of water from a container, as in Example 4

✓ Check Skills You'll Need   (For help, go to Lessons 1-2 and 2-2.)

Evaluate each function for $x = -3, -1, 0, 1,$ and 3.

1. $f(x) = x$ −3, −1, 0, 1, 3

2. $f(x) = x^2$ 9, 1, 0, 1, 9

3. $f(x) = -x$ 3, 1, 0, −1, −3

4. $f(x) = -x^2$ −9, −1, 0, −1, −9

5. $f(x) = \frac{1}{3}x^2$ 3, $\frac{1}{3}$, 0, $\frac{1}{3}$, 3

6. $f(x) = -\frac{1}{3}x^2$ −3, −$\frac{1}{3}$, 0, −$\frac{1}{3}$, −3

Write each equation in slope-intercept form.

7. $3x + 4y = 8$
$y = -\frac{3}{4}x + 2$

8. $2x - y = -7$
$y = 2x + 7$

9. $\frac{1}{2}x + 3y = 9$
$y = -\frac{1}{6}x + 3$

New Vocabulary • quadratic function • standard form of a quadratic function • parabola • axis of symmetry • vertex of a parabola

---

OBJECTIVE 1 Quadratic Functions and Their Graphs

📱 Interactive lesson includes instant self-check, tutorials, and activities.

A **quadratic function** is a function that can be written in the standard form $f(x) = ax^2 + bx + c$, where $a \neq 0$.

🔑 **Key Concepts**

Definition	Standard Form of a Quadratic Function
$f(x) = \underset{\text{quadratic term}}{ax^2} + \underset{\text{linear term}}{bx} + \underset{\text{constant term}}{c}$	

The condition $a \neq 0$ gives every quadratic function a quadratic term, but not necessarily a linear term or a constant term. If $a = 0$, then the function has no quadratic term, and it is not a quadratic function.

❓ **Need Help?**

You can use the FOIL method to multiply.

$$y = (2x + 3)(x - 4)$$

First — Last
Inner
Outer

1 EXAMPLE Classifying Functions

Determine whether each function is linear or quadratic. Identify the quadratic, linear, and constant terms.

a. $y = (2x + 3)(x - 4)$
$= 2x^2 - 8x + 3x - 12$ **Multiply.**
$= 2x^2 - 5x - 12$ **Write in standard form.**

This is a quadratic function.
Quadratic term: $2x^2$
Linear term: $-5x$
Constant term: -12

b. $f(x) = 3(x^2 - 2x) - 3(x^2 - 2)$
$= 3x^2 - 6x - 3x^2 + 6$
$= -6x + 6$

This is a linear function.
Quadratic term: none
Linear term: $-6x$
Constant term: 6

Ongoing Assessment and Intervention

Before the Lesson
Diagnose prerequisite skills using:
• Check Skills You'll Need

During the Lesson
Monitor progress using:
• Check Understanding
• Additional Examples
• Standardized Test Prep

After the Lesson
Assess knowledge using:
• Lesson Quiz
• Computer Test Generator CD

✓ **Check Understanding** ❶ Determine whether each function is linear or quadratic. Identify the quadratic, linear, and constant terms. **See below left.**
a. $f(x) = (x^2 + 5x) - x^2$ b. $f(x) = (x - 5)(3x - 1)$ c. $f(x) = x(x + 3)$

Real-World Connection

Objects tossed into the air follow parabolic paths.

1a. linear; none, 5x, none

b. quadratic; $3x^2$, $-16x$, 5

c. quadratic; x^2, 3x, none

The graph of a quadratic function is a **parabola.** The **axis of symmetry** is the line that divides a parabola into two parts that are mirror images. The **vertex of a parabola** is the point at which the parabola intersects the axis of symmetry. The y-value of the vertex of a parabola represents the maximum or minimum value of the function.

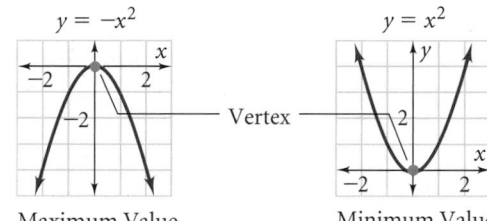

Maximum Value   Minimum Value

The axis of symmetry of the graph of a quadratic function is always a vertical line defined by the x-coordinate of the vertex. In each graph above, the axis of symmetry is the y-axis, $x = 0$.

Each point of the parabola has a corresponding point on its mirror image. Two corresponding points are the same distance from the axis of symmetry.

❷ **EXAMPLE** **Points on a Parabola**

Below is the graph of $y = 2x^2 - 8x + 8$. Identify the vertex and the axis of symmetry. Identify points corresponding to P and Q.

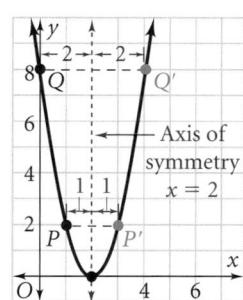

The vertex is $(2, 0)$.

The axis of symmetry is $x = 2$, the vertical line passing through the vertex.

$P(1, 2)$ is one unit to the left of the axis of symmetry. Corresponding point $P'(3, 2)$ is one unit to the right of the axis of symmetry.

$Q(0, 8)$ is two units to the left of the axis of symmetry. Corresponding point $Q'(4, 8)$ is two units to the right of the axis of symmetry.

✓ **Check Understanding** ❷ Identify the vertex and the axis of symmetry of each parabola. Identify points corresponding to P and Q.

a.
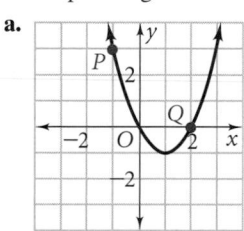

b.
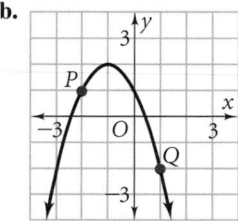

$(1, -1), x = 1; P'(3, 3),$
$Q'(0, 0)$

$(-1, 2), x = -1; P'(0, 1),$
$Q'(-3, -2)$

Lesson 5-1 Modeling Data with Quadratic Functions   **235**

Professional Development

Math Background

The study of quadratic equations and their graphs plays an important role in many applications. For instance, physicists can model the height of an object over time t with quadratic equations. Economists can model revenue and profit functions with quadratic equations. Using such models to determine important values such as maximum height, maximum revenue, or maximum profit, depends on understanding the nature of a parabolic graph.

OBJECTIVE

❶ **Teaching Notes**

❶ **EXAMPLE** Math Tip

The key point to remember is that $f(x) = ax^2 + bx + c$ is a quadratic function if and only if $a \neq 0$. Though the function in part b is initially defined as an expression with x^2 terms, there are no x^2 terms when the expression is simplified. The expression is thus linear.

Additional Examples

❶ Determine whether each function is linear or quadratic. Identify the quadratic, linear, and constant terms.
a. $f(x) = (2x - 1)^2$
quadratic; $4x^2$, $-4x$, 1
b. $f(x) = x^2 - (x + 1)(x - 1)$
linear; none, 0x (or 0), 1

❷ Below is the graph of $y = x^2 - 6x + 11$. Identify the vertex and the axis of symmetry. Identify points corresponding to P and Q.

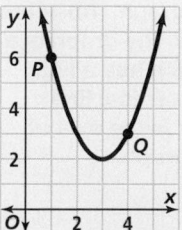

$(3, 2), x = 3; P'(5, 6), Q'(2, 3)$

235

4 **EXAMPLE** **Technology Tip**

Remind students that they can press the ZOOM key and use ZoomStat to have the calculator automatically select an appropriate window setting.

Additional Examples

3 Find a quadratic function to model the values in the table.

x	−2	1	5
y	−17	10	−10

$y = -2x^2 + 7x + 5$

4 The table shows data about the wavelength x (in meters) and the wave speed y (in meters per second) of deep water ocean waves. Model the data with a quadratic function. Graph the data and the function. Use the model to estimate the wave speed of a deep water wave that has a wavelength of 6 meters.

Wavelength x (m)	Wave speed y (m/s)
3	6
5	16
7	31
8	40

$y = 0.59x^2 + 0.34x - 0.33$

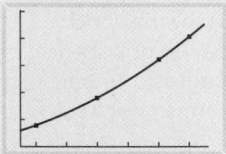

about 23 m/s

Closure

Have students describe the shape of the graph of a quadratic function, then state basic properties of the graph. **Answers may vary. Sample: The graph is a parabola. The graph has a high or low point. The vertical line through this point is the axis of symmetry of the graph.**

You have already learned to use linear functions to model data. Some data can be modeled with a quadratic function.

3 **EXAMPLE** **Finding a Quadratic Model**

Find a quadratic function to model the values in the table.

x	y
2	3
3	13
4	29

Substitute the values of x and y into $y = ax^2 + bx + c$. The result is a system of three linear equations.

$y = ax^2 + bx + c$

$3 = a(2)^2 + b(2) + c = 4a + 2b + c$ Use (2, 3).

$13 = a(3)^2 + b(3) + c = 9a + 3b + c$ Use (3, 13).

$29 = a(4)^2 + b(4) + c = 16a + 4b + c$ Use (4, 29).

Using one of the methods of Chapter 3, solve the system. $\begin{cases} 4a + 2b + c = 3 \\ 9a + 3b + c = 13 \\ 16a + 4b + c = 29 \end{cases}$

The solution is $a = 3, b = -5, c = 1$. Substitute these values into standard form.

$y = (3)x^2 + (-5)x + (1)$

The quadratic function is $y = 3x^2 - 5x + 1$.

✓**Check Understanding** **3** Find a quadratic function with a graph that includes $(1, 0)$, $(2, -3)$, and $(3, -10)$.

$y = -2x^2 + 3x - 1$

You can use the quadratic regression feature of a graphing calculator to find and graph a quadratic model.

4 **EXAMPLE** **Real-World** 🌎 **Connection**

Hydraulics The table at the left shows the height of a column of water as it drains from its container. Model the data with a quadratic function. Graph the data and the function. Use the model to estimate the water level at 35 seconds.

Elapsed Time	Water Level
0 s	120 mm
10 s	100 mm
20 s	83 mm
30 s	66 mm
40 s	50 mm
50 s	37 mm
60 s	28 mm

Step 1 Enter the data. Use **QuadReg**.

Step 2 Graph the data and the function.

Step 3 Use the table feature to find $f(35)$.

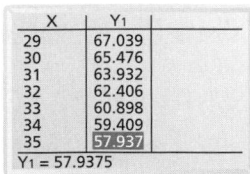

```
QuadReg
y = ax² + bx + c
a = .0091666667
b = ⁻2.103571429
c = 120.3333333
```

X	Y₁
29	67.039
30	65.476
31	63.932
32	62.406
33	60.898
34	59.409
35	57.937

$Y_1 = 57.9375$

An approximate model of the quadratic function is $y = 0.009167x^2 - 2.10x + 120$. At 35 seconds the water level is approximately 58 mm.

4c. No; the tank is empty at 109 seconds.

✓**Check Understanding** **4** **a.** Use the quadratic model to estimate the water level at 25 seconds. **73 mm**
b. Use the quadratic model to predict the water level at 3 minutes. **39 mm**
c. **Critical Thinking** Is your prediction in part (b) reasonable? Explain. **See left.**

pages 237–239 Exercises

1. linear; none, x, 4

2. quadratic; $2x^2$, $-3x$, 5

3. quadratic; $3x^2$, $-6x$, none

4. quadratic; x^2, none, -7

EXERCISES

Practice and Problem Solving

For more practice, see *Extra Practice*.

For more practice, see *Extra Practice*.

(A) Practice by Example

Example 1
(page 234)

Determine whether each function is linear or quadratic. Identify the quadratic, linear, and constant terms.   1–9. See margin pp. 236–237.

1. $y = x + 4$
2. $y = 2x^2 - (3x - 5)$
3. $y = 3x(x - 2)$

4. $f(x) = x^2 - 7$
5. $y = (x - 2)(x + 5)$
6. $g(x) = -7(x - 4)$

7. $h(x) = (3x)(2x) + 6$
8. $y = x(1 - x) - (1 - x^2)$ **9.** $f(x) = -x(2x + 8)$

Example 2
(page 235)

Identify the vertex and the axis of symmetry of each parabola.

10.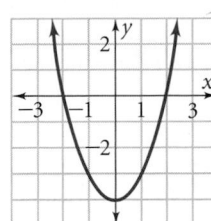

11.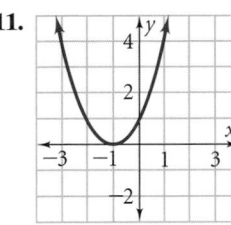

12.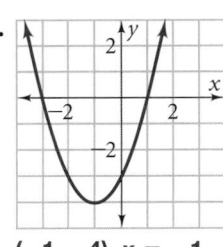

$(0, -4), x = 0$ $(-1, 0), x = -1$ $(-1, -4), x = -1$

For each parabola, identify points corresponding to P and Q.

13.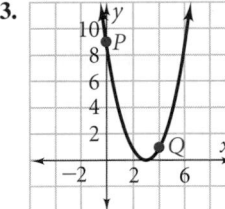

14.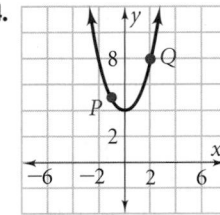

15.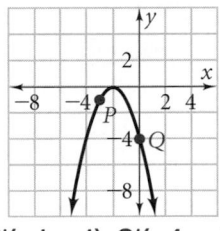

$P'(6, 9), Q'(2, 1)$ $P'(1, 5), Q'(-2, 8)$ $P'(-1, -1), Q'(-4, -4)$

Example 3
(page 236)

Find a quadratic model for each set of values.   16–18. See margin.

16. $(1, -2), (2, -2), (3, -4)$ **17.** $(1, -2), (2, -4), (3, -4)$ **18.** $(-1, 6), (1, 4), (2, 9)$

19.

x	−1	1	2
f(x)	−1	3	8

$y = x^2 + 2x$

20.

x	−1	1	2
f(x)	17	17	8

$y = -3x^2 + 20$

Example 4
(page 236)

21. Physics A man throws a ball off the top of a building. The table shows the height of the ball at different times.
 a. Find a quadratic model for the data. **See margin.**
 b. Use the model to estimate the height of the ball at 2.5 seconds. **28.5 ft**

Height of a Ball

Time	Height
0 s	46 ft
1 s	63 ft
2 s	48 ft
3 s	1 ft

22. Communications The table shows the percent of U.S. houses with cable TV.
 a. Find a quadratic model using 1960 as year 0, 1970 as year 10, and so on.
 b. Use the model to estimate the percent of households with cable TV in 1995.

Television Cable Access

Year	1960	1970	1980	1990	2000
% of Households	0	7	20	56	68

Source: *Time Almanac*

22a. $y = 0.0236x^2 + 0.907x - 2.09$

b. **58.5%**

Lesson 5-1   Modeling Data with Quadratic Functions   **237**

---

5. quadratic; x^2, $3x$, −10

6. linear; none, −7x, 28

7. quadratic; $6x^2$, none, 6

8. linear; none, x, −1

9. quadratic; $-2x^2$, −8x, none

16. $y = -x^2 + 3x - 4$

17. $y = x^2 - 5x + 2$

18. $y = 2x^2 - x + 3$

21a. $y = -16x^2 + 33x + 46$, where x is the number of seconds after release and y is height in ft.

Assignment Guide

1 Objective
 (A)(B) Core 1–15, 27–29, 39
 (C) Extension 41

2 Objective
 (A)(B) Core 16–26, 30–38
 (C) Extension 40, 42–43

Standardized Test Prep 44–48

Mixed Review 49–58

Error Prevention

Exercises 1–9 Tell students to simplify the expression on the right side of each equation before they attempt to classify the function.

Teaching Tip

Exercises 23–26 Help students recall that $f(x) = ax^2 + bx + c$ is a quadratic function if and only if $a \neq 0$.

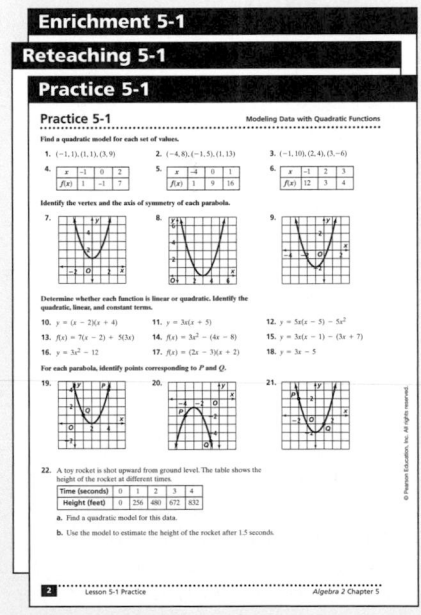

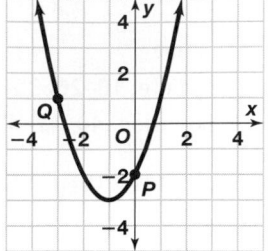
Alternative Assessment

Have each student write a quadratic function and create a table listing at least three pairs of corresponding x- and y-values for the function. Instruct students to exchange tables only. Direct students to find a quadratic model for the set of values in the table. They can check their quadratic model with the student who wrote the quadratic function.

pages 237–239 Exercises

31c. Never; the quadratic model is useful over a limited number of years,

---

B **Apply Your Skills**

Determine whether a quadratic model exists for each set of values. If so, write the model.

$$y = 4x^2$$
23. $f(-2) = 16, f(0) = 0, f(1) = 4$

$$y = -2x^2 + 3x + 5$$
24. $f(0) = 5, f(2) = 3, f(-1) = 0$

25. $f(-1) = -4, f(1) = -2, f(2) = -1$
no

26. $f(-2) = 7, f(0) = 1, f(2) = 0$
$$y = \tfrac{5}{8}x^2 - \tfrac{7}{4}x + 1$$

27. $\left(-\tfrac{1}{2}, -\tfrac{1}{2}\right), x = -\tfrac{1}{2}$

28. $(-1, 4), x = -1$

29. $\left(\tfrac{1}{2}, 0\right), x = \tfrac{1}{2}$

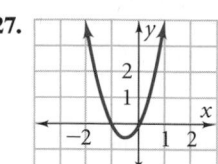

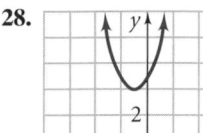

Real-World 🌐 Connection

Aremy McCann won a stamp-design competition sponsored by the U.S. government.

Identify the vertex and the axis of symmetry for each function.

27.   **28.**   **29.**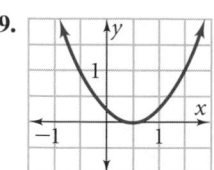

📦 **30. a. Geometry** Copy and complete the table. It shows the total number of segments that can be drawn among x points, no three of which are collinear.
x: 4, 5; y: 6, 10

Number of points, x	2	3	▪	▪
Number of segments, y	1	3	▪	▪

b. Write a quadratic model for the data. $y = \tfrac{1}{2}x^2 - \tfrac{1}{2}x$

c. Predict the number of segments that can be drawn among ten points.
45 segments

📱 **31. a. Postal Rates** Find a quadratic model for the data. Use 1974 as year 0.
$$y = -0.0112x^2 + 1.24x + 9.97$$

Price of First-Class Stamp

Year	1974	1978	1981	1983	1988	1995	2001	2002
Price (cents)	10	15	18	20	25	32	34	37

b. Estimation Estimate when first-class postage was 29¢. **1992**

c. Predict when first-class postage will be 50¢. Explain why your prediction may not be valid. **See margin.**

The graph of each function contains the given point. Find the value of c.

32. $y = x^2 + c; (0, 3)$ **3**

33. $y = x^2 - c; (4, 8)$ **8**

34. $y = -5x^2 + c; (2, -14)$ **6**

35. $y = 2x^2 + c; \left(-\tfrac{3}{4}, -\tfrac{1}{4}\right)$ $-\tfrac{11}{8}$

36. $y = -\tfrac{3}{4}x^2 + c; \left(3, -\tfrac{1}{2}\right)$ $\tfrac{25}{4}$

37. $y = (x + c)^2; (10, 0)$ **−10**

📱 **38. Road Safety** The table below gives the stopping distance for an automobile under certain road conditions.

Speed (mi/h)	20	30	40	50	55
Stopping Distance (ft)	17	38	67	105	127

a. Find a linear model for the data. $y = 3.157x - 52.34$

✏️ **b.** Find a quadratic model for the data. $y = 0.04243x^2 - 0.04080x + 0.8890$

c. Writing Compare the models. Which is better? Explain. **See margin.**

39. Open-Ended Write three different quadratic functions, each with a graph that includes $(0, 0)$ and $(5, -1)$. **See margin.**

but because it increases and then decreases, it does not model the data after 2021.

38c. Answers may vary. Sample: Quadratic; the quadratic model comes closer to most data points than the linear model because the data follow a curve.

39. Answers may vary. Sample: $y = -\tfrac{1}{25}x^2$, $y = \tfrac{1}{25}x^2 - \tfrac{2}{5}x$, $y = \tfrac{1}{5}x^2 - \tfrac{6}{5}x$

C Challenge

40. **Critical Thinking** What is the minimum number of data points you need to find a quadratic model for a data set? Explain. **See margin.**

41. How are the graphs of $y = x^2$ and $y = |x|$ similar? How are they different? **See margin.**

42. A parabola contains the points $(0, -4)$, $(2, 4)$, and $(4, 4)$. Find the vertex. **(3, 5)**

43. A model for the height of an arrow shot into the air is $h(t) = -16t^2 + 72t + 5$, where t is time and h is height. Without graphing, consider the function's graph.
    a. What can you learn by finding the graph's intercept with the h-axis?
    b. What can you learn by finding the graph's intercept(s) with the t-axis?
    a–b. See margin.

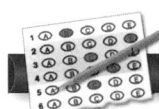

Standardized Test Prep

Multiple Choice

44. For which quadratic function is -3 the constant term? **A**
    A. $y = (3x + 1)(-x - 3)$ **B.** $y = x^2 - 3x + 3$
    C. $f(x) = (x - 3)(x - 3)$ **D.** $g(x) = -3x^2 + 3x + 9$

45. The vertex of a parabola is $(3, 2)$. A second point on the parabola is $(1, 7)$. Which point is also on the parabola? **H**
    F. $(-1, 7)$ **G.** $(3, 7)$ **H.** $(5, 7)$ **I.** $(3, -2)$

Take It to the NET
Online lesson quiz at
www.PHSchool.com
Web Code: aga-0501

46. The graph of a quadratic function has vertex $(-3, -2)$. What is the axis of symmetry? **A**
    A. $x = -3$ **B.** $x = 3$ **C.** $y = -2$ **D.** $y = 2$

47. Which function is NOT a quadratic function? **I**
    F. $y = (x - 1)(x - 2)$ **G.** $y = x^2 + 2x - 3$
    H. $y = 3x - x^2$ **I.** $y = -x^2 + x(x - 3)$

Extended Response

48. What is the quadratic function with a graph that includes $(1, 6)$, $(2, 11)$, and $(3, 20)$? Find the function by writing and solving a system of equations. Write the function in standard form. Show all your work. **See margin.**

Mixed Review

Lesson 4-8 Write the augmented matrix for each system. Then solve the system.
49–50. See margin.

49. $\begin{cases} 3x - y = 7 \\ 2x + 2y = 10 \end{cases}$

50. $\begin{cases} 3x + y - 2z = -3 \\ x - 3y - z = -2 \\ 2x + 2y + 3z = 11 \end{cases}$

Lesson 4-3 Find each product.

51. $[2 \;\; -3] \begin{bmatrix} 3 & -2 & 4 & 1 \\ 2 & 0 & -3 & 2 \end{bmatrix}$
    $[0 \;\; -4 \;\; 17 \;\; -4]$

52. $\begin{bmatrix} 3 & 10 \\ 1 & 5 \end{bmatrix} \begin{bmatrix} -7 & 2 \\ 8 & 4 \end{bmatrix}$ $\begin{bmatrix} 59 & 46 \\ 33 & 22 \end{bmatrix}$

Lesson 3-2 Solve each system by elimination.

53. $\begin{cases} x + y = 7 \\ 5x - y = 5 \end{cases}$ **(2, 5)**

54. $\begin{cases} 2x - 3y = -14 \\ 3x - y = 7 \end{cases}$ **(5, 8)**

55. $\begin{cases} x - 3y = 2 \\ x - 2y = 1 \end{cases}$ **(−1, −1)**

Lesson 2-3 For each direct variation, find the value of y when $x = 2$.

56. $y = 2$ when $x = 5$ $\frac{4}{5}$

57. $y = 1$ when $x = 4$ $\frac{1}{2}$

58. $y = -2$ when $x = 4$ $\frac{-1}{4}$

Lesson 5-1 Modeling Data with Quadratic Functions **239**

Standardized Test Prep

📁 **Resources**
For additional practice with a variety of test item formats:
• Standardized Test Prep, p. 297
• Test-Taking Strategies, p. 292
• Test-Taking Strategies with Transparencies

Exercise 46 It may help students to make a rough sketch of the graph, with a vertical line through the point for the vertex.

43a. You can find how high the arrow was when it was released.

b. The negative intercept tells you how much earlier you would have to shoot the arrow from height zero for its height to be described by the same function. The positive intercept tells you how many seconds after the release the arrow will take to hit the ground.

48. [4] System:
$a(1)^2 + b(1) + c = 6$,
$a(2)^2 + b(2) + c = 11$,
$a(3)^2 + b(3) + c = 20$;
$a = 2, b = -1, c = 5$;
$y = 2x^2 - x + 5$

[3] appropriate methods, but with one computational error

[2] incorrect system solved correctly OR correct system solved incorrectly

[1] correct function, without work shown

49. $\begin{bmatrix} 3 & -1 & | & 7 \\ 2 & 2 & | & 10 \end{bmatrix}$; (3, 2)

50. $\begin{bmatrix} 3 & 1 & -2 & | & -3 \\ 1 & -3 & -1 & | & -2 \\ 2 & 2 & 3 & | & 11 \end{bmatrix}$;
(1, 0, 3)

40. **Answers may vary. Sample:** You need at least 3 points; you are going to substitute x- and y-values into $y = ax^2 + bx + c$ to set up and solve a linear system for finding values of a, b, and c.

41. **Answers may vary. Sample:** They are similar in that both are symmetric with respect to the y-axis, have only non-negative y-values, lie in Quadrants I and II, and have minimums at $(0, 0)$; they are different in that the graph of $y = x^2$ rises more steeply, while $y = |x|$ rises at a steady rate as $|x|$ increases.

239

Modeling Using Residuals

Students use a graphing calculator to compare the residuals for a linear and a quadratic model for a set of data.

Resources

Students may use any graphing calculator with regression capabilities.

Teaching Notes

Students who want to duplicate the work in the example on their calculators can have the calculator enter the linear model into Y1 by having the cursor next to Y1 in the Y = window and then pressing **VARS** 5 ▶ ▶ 1 immediately after finding the linear model. They can then find the quadratic model and follow the same procedure to enter the quadratic model for Y2.

Error Prevention

Students should follow the procedure in the teaching note to get the best results. The values of the residuals can be affected greatly if the student rounds the coefficients in the models. Students can appreciate this fact by comparing the residuals for the quadratic model in the example to those for a model such as $y = -0.05x^2 + 9.57x - 416.96$, which uses rounded coefficients.

Modeling Using Residuals

FOR USE WITH LESSON 5-1

You can use more than one model for a set of data. You can determine which is a better model by analyzing the differences between the y-values of the data and the y-values of each model. These differences are called residuals. The better model will have residuals that are closer to zero.

EXAMPLE

The calculator screen shows the graphs of a linear model and a quadratic model for the data below. Which model better fits the data?

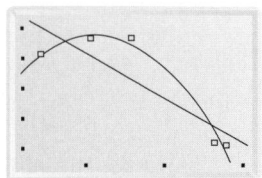

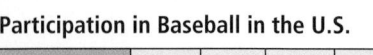

Participation in Baseball in the U.S.

Year (0 = 1900)	87	90	93	98	99
Millions of Participants	15.1	15.5	15.6	12.3	12.1

Step 1 Press **STAT** **ENTER** to enter the data in L_1 and L_2. Then use the LinReg and QuadReg features to find linear and quadratic models.

Step 2 Enter the linear model as Y_1 and the quadratic model as Y_2.

Step 3 To find the residuals of the linear model and store the differences in L_3, enter L_2 − **VARS** ▶ 1 1 **(** L_1 **)** **STO▶** L_3 **ENTER**.

Step 4 Find the residuals of the quadratic model. Store the differences in L_4.

Step 5 Compare the residuals in L_3 and L_4. The values in L_4 are closer to zero, so the quadratic model is the better fit.

L2	L3	L4	4
15.1	-.9205	.0409	
15.5	.37034	-.1797	
15.6	1.3612	.25141	
12.3	-.454	-.3816	
12.1	-.357	.26904	
------	------	------	

L4(6) =

EXERCISES

For each set of data, find a linear model and a quadratic model. Which model is the better fit? Justify your reasoning.

1. **Money Spent in the U.S. on Personal Technology**

Year (0 = 1970)	0	10	20	22	24	26
Billions of Dollars	8.8	17.6	53.8	61.2	78.5	89.7

1. linear: $y = 3.090x - 0.9375$; quadratic: $y = 0.1457x^2 - 0.6930x + 9.0852$; the quadratic model is better. The residuals are closer to zero for the quadratic model.

2. **Fishing Licenses Sold**

Year (0 = 1970)	0	5	10	15	20	25
Millions Sold	31.1	34.9	35.2	35.7	37.0	37.9

2. linear: $y = 0.2331x + 32.39$; quadratic: $y = -0.0075x^2 + 0.4206x + 31.76$; the quadratic model seems slightly better. The residuals seem a bit closer to zero for the quadratic model.

Properties of Parabolas

 North Carolina Objectives

2.02 Use quadratic functions and inequalities to model and solve problems. a) Solve using graphs. b) Interpret the constants and coefficients in the context of the problem.

Lesson Preview

What You'll Learn

OBJECTIVE 1 To graph quadratic functions

OBJECTIVE 2 To find maximum and minimum values of quadratic functions

...And Why

To maximize a company's revenue

✓ Check Skills You'll Need   (For help, go to Lessons 2-2 and 2-5.)

Find the y-intercept of the graph of each function.

1. $y = 3x + 3$ **3**   **2.** $y = -2x - 1$ **−1**   **3.** $4x - 3y = 12$ **−4**

Find the vertex of the graph of each function.

4. $y = |-2x|$ **(0, 0)**   **5.** $y = \left|-\frac{2}{3}x - 1\right|$ $\left(-\frac{3}{2}, 0\right)$ **6.** $y = |3x + 7|$ $\left(-\frac{7}{3}, 0\right)$

Graph each equation. **7–9. See back of book.**

7. $y = -4x - 3$ **8.** $\frac{1}{2}x + y = -2$ **9.** $y = |5x - 5|$

Lesson Preview

✓ Check Skills You'll Need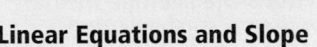

Linear Equations and Slope
Lesson 2-2: Examples 1 and 2
Exercises 1–10
Extra Practice, p. 823

Absolute Value Functions and Graphs
Lesson 2-5: Example 1
Exercises 1–9
Extra Practice, p. 823

Lesson Resources

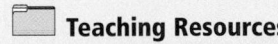 **Teaching Resources**
Practice, Reteaching, Enrichment

Reaching All Students
Practice Workbook 5-2
Spanish Practice Workbook 5-2
Hands-On Activities 40

Presentation Assistant Plus!
Transparencies
• Check Skills You'll Need 5-2
• Additional Examples 5-2
• Student Edition Answers 5-2
• Lesson Quiz 5-2
PH Presentation Pro CD 5-2

ASSESSMENT SYSTEM

Computer Test Generator CD

Technology
Resource Pro® CD-ROM
Computer Test Generator CD
Prentice Hall Presentation Pro CD

 **www.PHSchool.com**
Student Site
• Teacher Web Code: agk-5500
• Self-grading Lesson Quiz
Teacher Center
• Lesson Planner
• Resources

Plus

OBJECTIVE

1 Graphing Parabolas

The standard form of a quadratic function is $y = ax^2 + bx + c$. When $b = 0$, the function simplifies to $y = ax^2 + c$.

The graph of $y = ax^2 + c$ is a parabola with an axis of symmetry $x = 0$, the y-axis. The vertex of the graph is the y-intercept $(0, c)$.

Reading Math

The word *symmetry* comes from a prefix meaning "same" and a root meaning "measure."

1 EXAMPLE  **Graphing a Function of the Form $y = ax^2 + c$**

Graph $y = -\frac{1}{2}x^2 + 2$.

Step 1 Graph the vertex, which is the y-intercept $(0, 2)$.

Step 2 Make a table of values to find some points on one side of the axis of symmetry $x = 0$. Graph the points.

x	1	2	3	4
y	$1\frac{1}{2}$	0	$-2\frac{1}{2}$	-6

Step 4 Graph corresponding points on the other side of the axis of symmetry.

Step 5 Sketch the curve.

✓ Check Understanding  **a.** Graph $y = 2x^2 - 4$.
b. Graph $y = -5 + 3x^2$. **a–b. See back of book.**
c. Reasoning What are the coordinates of the vertex of the graph of a function in the form $y = ax^2$? **(0, 0)**

✓ Ongoing Assessment and Intervention

Before the Lesson
Diagnose prerequisite skills using:
• Check Skills You'll Need

During the Lesson
Monitor progress using:
• Check Understanding
• Additional Examples
• Standardized Test Prep

After the Lesson
Assess knowledge using:
• Lesson Quiz
• Computer Test Generator CD

2. Teach

Professional Development

Math Background

An intuitive approach to locating the vertex of a parabola can be seen by examining the graph of a function such as $f(x) = x^2 - 2x$. It is evident that the x-coordinate of the vertex is the average of the x-intercepts. However, such an approach depends on the ability to locate the intercepts, a topic discussed in subsequent lessons. An alternative method, using $x = -\frac{b}{2a}$ to find the x-coordinate of the vertex, depends only on the ability to identify a and b in the standard form of a quadratic equation.

OBJECTIVE

1 **Teaching Notes**

1 EXAMPLE Math Tip

Point out that the graph of $y = ax^2 + c$ is the graph of $y = ax^2$ translated up if $c > 0$ or down if $c < 0$.

Additional Examples

1 Graph $y = \frac{1}{3}x^2 + 1$.

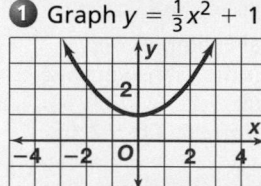

2 Graph $y = \frac{1}{2}x^2 + x + 3$. Label the vertex and axis of symmetry.

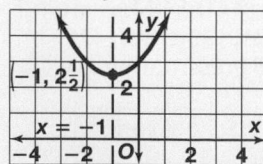

When $b \neq 0$ in the standard form of a quadratic function, $y = ax^2 + bx + c$, the values of both a and b affect the position of the axis of symmetry.

You can use the values of a, b, and c to find characteristics of the graph of a quadratic function.

🔑 **Key Concepts**

❓ **Need Help?**

The y-intercept is the point at which a line crosses the y-axis.

Properties	Graph of a Quadratic Function in Standard Form

The graph of $y = ax^2 + bx + c$ is a parabola when $a \neq 0$.

- When $a > 0$, the parabola opens up. When $a < 0$, the parabola opens down.
- The axis of symmetry is the line $x = -\frac{b}{2a}$.
- The x-coordinate of the vertex is $-\frac{b}{2a}$. The y-coordinate of the vertex is the value of y when $x = -\frac{b}{2a}$, or $y = f\left(-\frac{b}{2a}\right)$.
- The y-intercept is $(0, c)$.

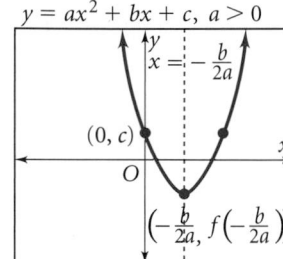

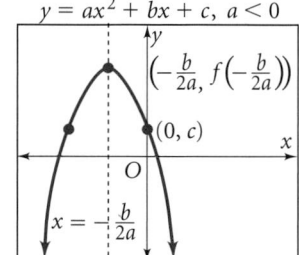

2 EXAMPLE **Graphing a Function of the Form $y = ax^2 + bx + c$**

Graph $y = x^2 - 2x - 3$. Label the vertex and the axis of symmetry.

Step 1 Find and graph the axis of symmetry.
$$x = -\frac{b}{2a} = -\frac{(-2)}{2(1)} = 1$$

Step 2 Find and graph the vertex. The x-coordinate of the vertex is $-\frac{b}{2a}$, or 1.

The y-coordinate is $y = (1)^2 - 2(1) - 3 = -4$. So the vertex is $(1, -4)$.

Step 3 Find and graph the y-intercept and its reflection. Since $c = -3$, the y-intercept is $(0, -3)$ and its reflection is $(2, -3)$.

Step 4 Evaluate the function for another value of x, such as $y = (3)^2 - 2(3) - 3 = 0$. Graph $(3, 0)$ and its reflection $(-1, 0)$.

Step 5 Sketch the curve.

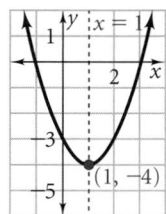

Since $a > 0$, the graph opens up.

✔ **Check Understanding** **2** Graph each function. Label the vertex and the axis of symmetry.
a. $y = -x^2 + 4x + 2$ **a–b. See margin page 243.**
b. $y = -\frac{1}{3}x^2 - 2x - 3$

242 Chapter 5 Quadratic Equations and Functions

👥 Reaching All Students

Below Level Sketch parabolas illustrating why a quadratic equation might have two real roots, one real root, or no real roots, or use a graphing calculator to display graphs.	**Advanced Learners** Have students determine what happens to the graph of the equation $y = x^2 - 2x - 3$ when the signs of any of the coefficients are changed.	**Visual Learners** See note on page 243. **Error Prevention** See note on page 245.

The y-coordinate of the vertex of a parabola represents the maximum or minimum value of a quadratic function.

3 **EXAMPLE** **Finding a Minimum Value**

Graph $y = 3x^2 + 12x + 8$. What is the minimum value of the function?

Since $a > 0$, the graph of the function opens up, and the vertex represents the minimum value. Find the coordinates of the vertex.

$x = -\frac{b}{2a} = -\frac{12}{2(3)} = -2$ **Find the x-coordinate of the vertex.**

$y = 3(-2)^2 + 12(-2) + 8 = -4$ **Find the y-coordinate of the vertex.**

Graph the vertex and the axis of symmetry $x = -2$. Graph two points on one side of the axis of symmetry, such as $(0, 8)$ and $(-1, -1)$. Then graph corresponding points $(-4, 8)$ and $(-3, -1)$.

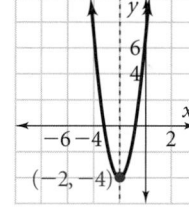

• The minimum value of the function is -4.

✓ **Check Understanding** **3** **a.** Graph $y = 2x^2 + 8x - 1$. Find the minimum value of the function. **See margin.**
    b. **Critical Thinking** What is the maximum value of the function? **none**

You can find a maximum or minimum value without graphing the function.

4 **EXAMPLE** **Real-World** **Connection**

Economics The number of items a company sells frequently is a function of the item's price. The revenue from sales of the item is the product of the price and the number sold. Refer to the photo. What price will maximize the company's revenue from unicycle sales? What is the maximum revenue?

Relate   revenue equals price times number of unicycles sold

Define Let R = revenue. Let p = price of a unicycle.

        Let $-2.5p + 500$ = number of unicycles sold.

Write $R = p(-2.5p + 500)$

        $= -2.5p^2 + 500p$ **Write in standard form.**

Find the maximum value of the function. Since $a < 0$, the graph of the function opens down, and the vertex represents a maximum value.

$p = -\frac{b}{2a} = -\frac{500}{2(-2.5)} = 100$ **Find p at the vertex.**

$R = -2.5(100)^2 + 500(100)$ **Evaluate R for p = 100.**

    $= 25,000$ **Simplify.**

• A price of $100 will maximize revenue. The maximum revenue is $25,000.

✓ **Check Understanding** **4** The number of widgets the Woodget Company sells can be modeled by $-5p + 100$, where p is the price of a widget. What price will maximize revenue? What is the maximum revenue? **$10; $500**

Lesson 5-2 Properties of Parabolas   **243**

Real-World **Connection**

The number of unicycles a company sells can be modeled by $-2.5p + 500$.

2a.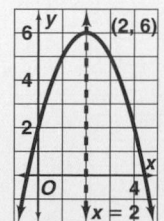

2b. (graph)

3a. (graph)

minimum: -9

3 **EXAMPLE** **Alternative Method**

Discuss with students the fact that the y-coordinate of the vertex of a quadratic function is always going to represent the maximum or minimum, depending on which way the parabola opens. Thus, they can substitute $-\frac{b}{2a}$ for x in the equation to find the minimum or maximum for the equation, without graphing.

4 **EXAMPLE** **Visual Learners**

Suggest that students graph the function on a graphing calculator and press 2nd [CALC] 4, then 90 ENTER 110 ENTER ENTER so they can see that the maximum of the graph actually lies at $25,000.

Additional Examples

3 Graph $y = -\frac{1}{4}x^2 + 2x - 3$. What is the maximum value of the function? **1**

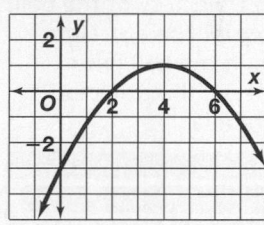

4 The number of weekend getaway packages a hotel can sell can be modeled by $-0.12p + 60$, where p is the price of a get-away package. The revenue is the product of the price and the number of packages sold. What price will maximize the revenue? What is the maximum revenue? **$250; $7500**

Closure

Ask students how to determine whether a quadratic function has a maximum or minimum and how to find it. **If $a > 0$, the value is a minimum. If $a < 0$, the value is a maximum. Substitute $x = -\frac{b}{2a}$ into the function to find the maximum or minimum value.**

243

For more practice, see *Extra Practice*.

EXERCISES

Practice and Problem Solving

Assignment Guide

1 Objective

A B Core 1–21, 31–34, 37–40, 44–53, 57–66

C Extension 67–70

2 Objective

A B Core 22–30, 35–36, 41–43, 54–56

C Extension 71–73

Standardized Test Prep 74–79

Mixed Review 80–83

Connection to Physics

Exercise 29 Students should note that the function given in the exercise does not describe the shape of the trajectory of the ball. The trajectory will be a straight vertical path. If the ball is not fired straight up, the trajectory will be a parabola.

A Practice by Example

Example 1 (page 241)

Graph each function. 1–9. See margin pp. 244–245.

1. $y = -x^2 + 1$ 2. $y = -x^2 - 1$ 3. $y = 2x^2 + 4$

4. $y = 3x^2 - 6$ 5. $y = -\frac{1}{3}x^2 - 1$ 6. $y = -5x^2 + 12$

7. $y = \frac{1}{2}x^2 + 3$ 8. $y = \frac{1}{4}x^2 - 3$ 9. $y = -2x^2 + \frac{3}{4}$

Example 2 (page 242)

Graph each function. Label the vertex and the axis of symmetry. 10–21. See back of book.

10. $y = x^2 + 2x + 1$ 11. $y = -x^2 + 2x + 1$

12. $y = x^2 + 4x + 1$ 13. $y = x^2 + 6x + 9$

14. $y = -x^2 - 3x + 6$ 15. $y = 2x^2 + 4x$

16. $y = 4x^2 - 12x + 9$ 17. $y = -6x^2 - 12x - 1$

18. $y = -\frac{3}{4}x^2 + 6x + 6$ 19. $y = 3x^2 - 12x + 10$

20. $y = \frac{1}{2}x^2 + 2x - 8$ 21. $y = -4x^2 - 24x - 36$

Example 3 (page 243)

Graph each function. If $a > 0$ find the minimum value. If $a < 0$ find the maximum value. 22–27. See back of book.

22. $y = -x^2 + 2x + 5$ 23. $y = 3x^2 - 4x - 2$

24. $y = -2x^2 - 3x + 4$ 25. $y = \frac{1}{3}x^2 + 2x + 5$

26. $y = -x^2 - x + 6$ 27. $y = 2x^2 + 5$

Example 4 (page 243)

28. **Revenue** A model for a company's revenue is $R = -15p^2 + 300p + 12{,}000$, where p is the price in dollars of the company's product. What price will maximize revenue? Find the maximum revenue. **$10; $13,500**

29. **Physics** The equation for the motion of a projectile fired straight up at an initial velocity of 64 ft/s is $h = 64t - 16t^2$, where h is the height in feet and t is the time in seconds. Find the time the projectile needs to reach its highest point. How high it will go? **2 s; 64 ft**

30. **Manufacturing** The equation for the cost in dollars of producing automobile tires is $C = 0.000015x^2 - 0.03x + 35$, where x is the number of tires produced. Find the number of tires that minimizes the cost. What is the cost for that number of tires? **1000 tires; $20**

B Apply Your Skills

Sketch each parabola using the given information. 31–34. See margin p. 245.

31. vertex $(3, 6)$, y-intercept 2   32. vertex $(-1, -4)$, y-intercept 3

33. vertex $(0, 5)$, point $(1, -2)$ 34. vertex $(2, 3)$, point $(6, 9)$

35. Find a pair of numbers with a sum of 26 and a product that is a maximum. Find the maximum product. **13, 13; 169**

36. Find two numbers with a difference of 10 and a product that is a minimum. Find the minimum product. **−5, 5; −25**

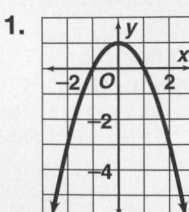
pages 244–247   Exercises

1.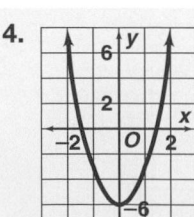

Match each function with its graph.

37. $y = x^2 + 4x + 1$ **B**   **38.** $y = -x^2 - 4x + 1$ **C**   **39.** $y = -\frac{1}{2}x^2 - 2x + 1$ **A**

A.
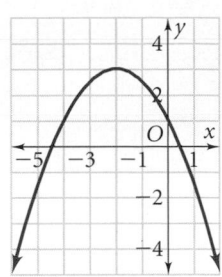

B.
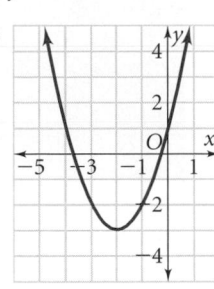

C.
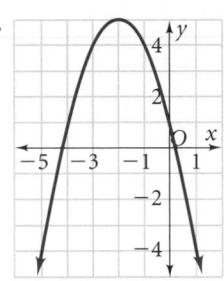

Teaching Tip
Exercise 42 Students can assume that the fence is straight and that the plane of the fence is perpendicular to the plane of the parabola.

Error Prevention
Exercises 48–53 Be sure students understand that each function is to have the form $y = ax^2 + c$.

Error Prevention
Exercise 55 Be sure students do not think that all four sides of the playground are bounded by fencing. Stress the importance of reading the problem carefully.

40. Answers may vary.
Sample:
$y = x^2 + 20x + 96$

Real-World Connection

Careers Picture framers choose the dimensions of frames that best suit works of art.

40. Open-Ended Write the equation of a parabola symmetric about $x = -10$.

41. Woodworking Suppose you want to frame a collage of pictures. You have a 9-ft strip of wood for the frame. What dimensions of the frame give you the maximum area for the collage? What is the maximum area?
2.25 ft by 2.25 ft; 5.0625 ft²

42. Physics Suppose you throw a ball over a 10-ft fence. Barely clearing the fence, the ball reaches its highest point directly above the fence and lands 10 ft from the fence. Using the fence as the axis of symmetry, write a quadratic function that models the ball's height. $y = -\frac{1}{10}x^2 + 10$

43. Packaging The bottom of a box is to be a rectangle with a perimeter of 36 cm. The box must be 4 cm high. What dimensions give the maximum volume?
length = 9 cm, width = 9 cm

For each function, the vertex of the function's graph is given. Find c.

44. $y = x^2 - 6x + c; (3, -4)$ **5**   **45.** $y = -3x^2 + 6x + c; (1, 0)$ **−3**

46. $y = x^2 + 10x + c; (-5, -27)$ **−2**   **47.** $y = c - x^2 - 2x; (-1, 3)$ **2**

Find the quadratic function $y = ax^2 + c$ with a graph that has the given points.
48–53. See margin.

48. $(0, 2), (3, 5)$ **49.** $(0, -3), (1, -7)$ **50.** $\left(2, \frac{5}{2}\right), \left(0, -\frac{1}{2}\right)$

51. $(-3, 89), (2, 39)$ **52.** $(-2, -10), (4, -40)$ **53.** $(-1, 14), (4, 104)$

54. A rock club's profit from booking local bands depends on the ticket price. Using past receipts, the owners find that the profit p can be modeled by the function $p = -15t^2 + 600t + 50$, where t represents the ticket price in dollars.
a. What price yields the maximum profit? **$20**
b. What is the maximum profit? **$6050**
c. Open-Ended What price would you pay to see your favorite local band? How much profit would the club owner make using that ticket price?
Check students' work.

55. Landscape Design A town is planning a child-care facility. It wants to fence in a rectangular playground using one of the walls of the building. What is the largest playground that can be fenced in using 100 ft of donated fencing?
25 ft by 50 ft, area = 1250 ft²

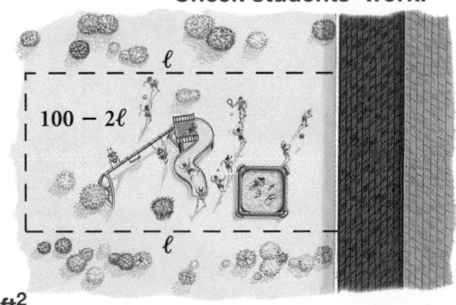

31.
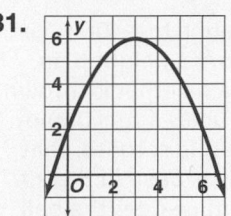

32.
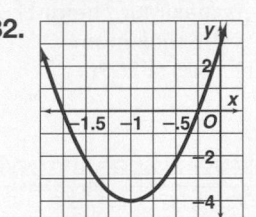

33.
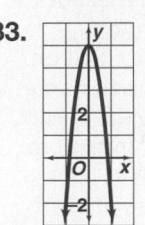

34.
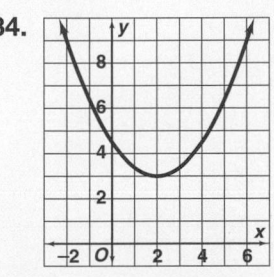

48. $y = \frac{1}{3}x^2 + 2$

49. $y = -4x^2 - 3$

50. $y = \frac{3}{4}x^2 - \frac{1}{2}$

51. $y = 10x^2 - 1$

52. $y = -\frac{5}{2}x^2$

53. $y = 6x^2 + 8$

6.
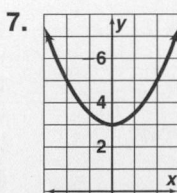

7.

8.

9.

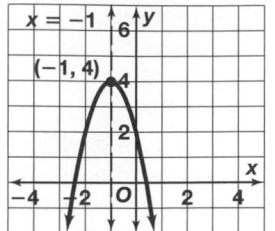

Alternative Assessment

Let a volunteer write a quadratic function on the board or overhead transparency. Call on students one at a time to name the axis of symmetry, the vertex, and the maximum or minimum. Repeat until all students have answered the same number of times.

Real-World Connection

The archaeological remains of the Harappan city Mohenjo Daro show the thick walls that were built to keep out the hot sun.

56. **History** Around 2500 B.C. in the Indus Valley of South Asia, the Harappan people built one of the first cities. The Harappans built rectangular houses that had open central courtyards surrounded by solid brick walls.
   a. Suppose you build a model of a Harappan house. For the outer walls you plan to use 2400 bricks. The walls of the model are 10 bricks high and 1 brick thick. Draw several possible floor plans.   **Check students' work.**
   b. Find the dimensions of the floor plan that give the model of maximum area.
   60 bricks by 60 bricks

Each point lies on a parabola that has its vertex at (0, 1). Write the equation of the parabola. Indicate whether the graph opens up or down.   57–64. See margin.

57. $(-3, 10)$ 58. $(-1, 6)$ 59. $(2, -1)$ 60. $(4, -7)$

61. $(3, 4)$ 62. $(5, -4)$ 63. $(8, -15)$ 64. $(-6, -2)$

65. **Construction** A construction worker places his toolbox on a board that rests on two cement posts 10 ft apart. The toolbox is halfway between the posts. Under the weight of the toolbox, the board sags by one quarter inch. Model the shape of the board in three different ways by writing a function whose graph satisfies each condition below.   **a–c. See margin.**
   a. The origin of the graph corresponds to the position of the toolbox.
   b. The origin of the graph corresponds to the position of the post on the left.
   c. The origin of the graph corresponds to the position of the post on the right.

|←——— 10 ft ———→|

66. A student says that the graph of $y = ax^2 + bx + c$ gets wider as a increases.
   a. **Error Analysis** Use examples to show that the student is wrong.
   b. **Writing** Summarize the relationship between $|a|$ and the width of the graph of $y = ax^2 + bx + c$.   **a–b. See margin.**

C Challenge

For each function, the vertex of the function's graph is given. Find a and b.

67. $y = ax^2 + bx - 27; (2, -3)$ **−6, 24**   68. $y = ax^2 + bx + 5; (-1, 4)$ **1, 2**

69. $y = ax^2 + bx + 8; (2, -4)$ **3, −12**   70. $y = ax^2 + bx; (-3, 2)$ $-\frac{2}{9}, -\frac{4}{3}$

The formula for the area enclosed by a parabola and the x-axis from x-intercepts x_1 to x_2 is $A = \frac{2}{3}h(x_2 - x_1)$, where h is the height. Find the enclosed area for each parabola.

71.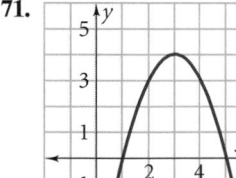

72.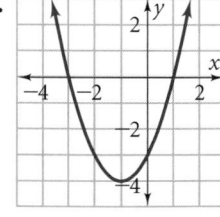

73.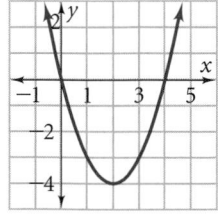

$10\frac{2}{3}$ square units $10\frac{2}{3}$ square units $10\frac{2}{3}$ square units

pages 244–247   Exercises

57. $y = x^2 + 1$; up

58. $y = 5x^2 + 1$; up

59. $y = -\frac{1}{2}x^2 + 1$; down

60. $y = -\frac{1}{2}x^2 + 1$; down

61. $y = \frac{1}{3}x^2 + 1$; up

62. $y = -\frac{1}{5}x^2 + 1$; down

63. $y = -\frac{1}{4}x^2 + 1$; down

64. $y = -\frac{1}{12}x^2 + 1$; down

65a. $y = \frac{1}{14,400}x^2$

b. $y = \frac{1}{14,400}x^2 - \frac{1}{120}x$

c. $y = \frac{1}{14,400}x^2 + \frac{1}{120}x$

66a. Check students' work.

b. Answers may vary. Sample: The widths of

$y = ax^2 + bx + c$ and $y = -ax^2 + bx + c$ are the same. As $|a|$ increases, the widths of $y = ax^2 + bx + c$ and $y = -ax^2 + bx + c$ decrease.

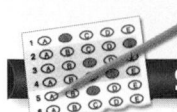
Multiple Choice

74. What is the vertex of $y = -2x^2 - 4x - 5$? **D**

    A. $(-2, -3)$ **B.** $(1, -3)$ **C.** $(1, -11)$ **D.** $(-1, -3)$

75. What is the y-intercept of $y = (x + 1)^2 - 2$? **F**

    F. $(0, -1)$ **G.** $(0, -3)$ **H.** $(0, 1)$ **I.** $(0, -2)$

76. What is the maximum area in square units of a rectangle with a perimeter of 128 units? **B**

    A. 4096   **B.** 1024   **C.** 256   **D.** 32

77. The vertex of the graph of $y = -x^2 - 16x - 62$ lies in which quadrant? **H**

    F. IV   **G.** III   **H.** II   **I.** I

78. What percent of nonzero integers have squares that are odd numbers? **B**

    A. 25   **B.** 50   **C.** 75   **D.** 100

Short Response

79. Sketch the graph of $y = x^2 - 6x + 2$. Explain how to identify the vertex and two other points on the parabola. **See margin.**

Mixed Review

Lesson 5-1

Answers may vary. Sample: $y = -0.14857x^2 + 5.1714x + 16.9714$

80. Find a quadratic model for the values in the table.

x	0	5	10	15	20
y	17	39	54	61	61

Lesson 4-2

Solve each equation.

81. $X + \begin{bmatrix} 0 & 4 \\ -2 & 1 \end{bmatrix} = \begin{bmatrix} 3 & 0 \\ 1 & 1 \end{bmatrix} \begin{bmatrix} 3 & -4 \\ 3 & 0 \end{bmatrix}$ **82.** $X - \begin{bmatrix} 3 & 3 \\ -2 & -1 \end{bmatrix} = \begin{bmatrix} 1 & 0 \\ 0 & 1 \end{bmatrix} \begin{bmatrix} 4 & 3 \\ -2 & 0 \end{bmatrix}$

Lesson 3-3 **83. Manufacturing** A new factory will require at least 40,000 ft² of storage space. No more than 25,000 ft² of the space will be covered with a roof. Write a system of inequalities to represent the constraints. Solve the system by graphing. **See margin.**

Algebra at Work

············**Landscape Architect**

Landscape architects create outdoor environments for parks, office buildings, and homes. They plan walls, staircases, pools, walkways, and plantings. Landscape architects blend ideas from art, science, nature, and math in their work. They need training in all three areas before they begin their careers. For example, when planning a decorative fountain, an architect needs to predict the parabolic path of the spray. The height and distance of the spray depend on the speed of the water and the angle at which it exits a pipe. Basic principles of physics often help architects. By making adjustments to a model, they can plan the effect they want.

Lesson 5-2   Properties of Parabolas   **247**

📁 **Resources**

For additional practice with a variety of test item formats:

- Standardized Test Prep, p. 297
- Test-Taking Strategies, p. 292
- Test-Taking Strategies with Transparencies

Teaching Tip

Exercise 74 To limit work time, students should first just find the value of x and eliminate answer choices. In this case, they do not need to find the value of y.

79. **[2]**

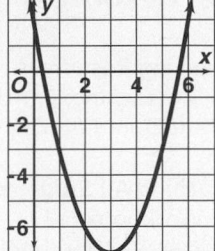

The axis of symmetry is $x = -\frac{b}{2a}$ or $x = 3$. The y-coordinate of the vertex is $3^2 - 6 \cdot 3 + 2 = -7$. So the vertex is $(3, -7)$. The y-intercept is where $x = 0$ or $0^2 - 6 \cdot 0 + 2 = 2$. So $(0, 2)$ is on the parabola. The point corresponding to $(0, 2)$ with respect to $x = 3$ is $(6, 2)$ so $(6, 2)$ is also on the parabola.

[1] incorrect graph OR no explanation

83. **Let x = amount of storage space and y = amount of space to be covered by the roof.**
$$x \geq 40{,}000$$
$$y \leq 25{,}000$$

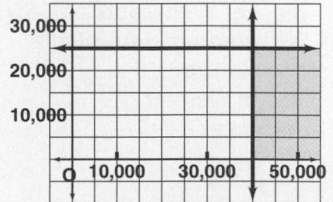

1. Plan

Check Skills You'll Need

Vertical and Horizontal Translations
Lesson 2-6: Examples 2, 4, 7
Exercises 5–8; 12–15; 21–26
Extra Practice, p. 823

Lesson Resources

Teaching Resources
Practice, Reteaching, Enrichment
Checkpoint Quiz 1

Reaching All Students
Practice Workbook 5-3
Spanish Practice Workbook 5-3
Reading and Math Literacy 5B
Spanish Reading & Literacy 5B
Spanish Checkpoint Quiz 1
Technology Activities 10

Presentation Assistant Plus!
Transparencies
• Check Skills You'll Need 5-3
• Additional Examples 5-3
• Student Edition Answers 5-3
• Lesson Quiz 5-3
PH Presentation Pro CD 5-3

ASSESSMENT SYSTEM

Checkpoint Quiz 1
Computer Test Generator CD

Technology
Resource Pro® CD-ROM
Computer Test Generator CD
Prentice Hall Presentation Pro CD

www.PHSchool.com
Student Site
• Teacher Web Code: agk-5500
• Self-grading Lesson Quiz
Teacher Center
• Lesson Planner
• Resources

Plus *iTEXT*

5-3

Translating Parabolas

2.02 Use quadratic functions and inequalities to model and solve problems. a) Solve using graphs. b) Interpret the constants and coefficients in the context of the problem.

Lesson Preview

What You'll Learn

OBJECTIVE 1 To use the vertex form of a quadratic function

. . . And Why
To model a suspension bridge, as in Example 3

✔ Check Skills You'll Need

(For help, go to Lesson 2-6.)

Identify the parent function of each function. Then graph the function by translating the parent function. 1–3. See back of book.

1. $y = -x + 2$ **2.** $y = |3x| + 2$ **3.** $y = -|x + 1| - 1$

Write an equation for each translation.

4. $y = 2x$, 2 units down $y = 2x - 2$ **5.** $y = x$, 4 units up, 1 unit right $y = x + 3$

New Vocabulary • vertex form of a quadratic function

OBJECTIVE

1 **Using Vertex Form**

iTEXT Interactive lesson includes instant self-check, tutorials, and activities.

Investigation: Vertex Form

1. Each function in the first column is written in standard form. In the second column, each function has been rewritten in vertex form. Use multiplication to verify that the functions in each row are equivalent. **1–2. See back of book.**

Standard Form $y = ax^2 + bx + c$	$-\dfrac{b}{2a}$	Vertex Form $y = a(x - h)^2 + k$	h
$y = x^2 - 4x + 4$		$y = (x - 2)^2$	
$y = x^2 + 6x + 8$		$y = (x + 3)^2 - 1$	
$y = -3x^2 - 12x - 8$		$y = -3(x + 2)^2 + 4$	
$y = 2x^2 + 12x + 19$		$y = 2(x + 3)^2 + 1$	

2. a. Patterns Copy and complete the table.
b. Compare the values of $-\dfrac{b}{2a}$ and h in each row. Write a formula to show the relationship between $-\dfrac{b}{2a}$ and h.

Need Help?
A translation shifts a graph horizontally, or vertically, or both.

In Chapter 2, you learned to graph linear functions and absolute value functions as translations of their parent functions. Similarly, you can graph a quadratic function as a translation of the parent function $y = ax^2$.

To translate the graph of a quadratic function, you can use the **vertex form of a quadratic function,** $y = a(x - h)^2 + k$.

Ongoing Assessment and Intervention

Before the Lesson Diagnose prerequisite skills using:	**During the Lesson** Monitor progress using:	**After the Lesson** Assess knowledge using:
• Check Skills You'll Need	• Check Understanding • Additional Examples • Standardized Test Prep	• Lesson Quiz • Computer Test Generator CD • Chapter Checkpoint 1 (p. 254)

Key Concepts

The graph of $y = a(x - h)^2 + k$ is the graph of $y = ax^2$ translated h units horizontally and k units vertically.

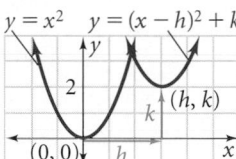

- When h is positive the graph shifts right; when h is negative the graph shifts left.
- When k is positive the graph shifts up; when k is negative the graph shifts down.
- The vertex is (h, k), and the axis of symmetry is the line $x = h$.

Reading Math

Vertex means "turning point."

A function in vertex form is easy to graph.

1 EXAMPLE **Using Vertex Form to Graph a Parabola**

Graph $y = -\frac{1}{2}(x - 2)^2 + 3$.

The graph of $y = -\frac{1}{2}(x - 2)^2 + 3$ is a translation of the graph of the parent function $y = -\frac{1}{2}x^2$. You can graph it by translating the parent function or by finding the vertex and the axis of symmetry.

1a.

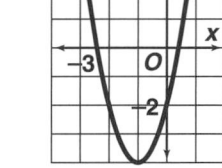

Step 1 Graph the vertex $(2, 3)$. Draw the axis of symmetry $x = 2$.

Step 2 Find another point. When $x = 0$, $y = -\frac{1}{2}(0 - 2)^2 + 3 = 1$. Graph $(0, 1)$.

Step 3 Graph the point corresponding to $(0, 1)$. It is 2 units to the right of the axis of symmetry at $(4, 1)$.

Step 4 Sketch the curve.

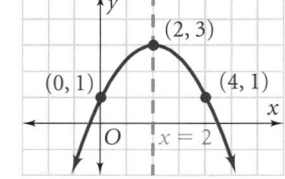

Check Understanding **1** **a.** Graph $y = 2(x + 1)^2 - 4$. **See left.**
b. In graphing the function in part (a), which method did you use—translating the parent function, or graphing the vertex and axis of symmetry of the given function? Explain the reasons for your choice. **Check Students' work**

You can use the vertex form to write the equation of a parabola. Substitute values for h, k, and a point (x, y). Then solve for a.

2 EXAMPLE **Writing the Equation of a Parabola**

Write the equation of the parabola at the right.

$y = a(x - h)^2 + k$ Use the vertex form.
$y = a(x - 3)^2 + 4$ Substitute $h = 3$ and $k = 4$.
$-4 = a(5 - 3)^2 + 4$ Substitute $(5, -4)$.
$-8 = 4a$ Simplify.
$-2 = a$ Solve for a.

The equation of the parabola is $y = -2(x - 3)^2 + 4$.

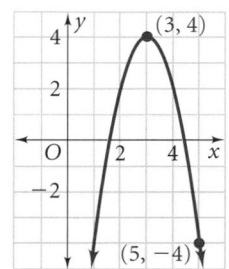

Lesson 5-3 Translating Parabolas   **249**

Math Background

The vertex form of a quadratic equation can be used when analyzing data that form a quadratic pattern. That is, given a set of points in the plane that form an approximately parabolic pattern, a quadratic function that approximately models the data can be found if the vertex of the model is known and one other point on the graph. This is an alternative to having to solve a system of three equations in three unknowns.

OBJECTIVE
1 **Teaching Notes**

Investigation (Optional)
Ask students if they can make a conjecture to explain why $y = a(x - h)^2 + k$ is called *vertex form*. **The coordinates of the vertex are shown.**

1 EXAMPLE **Alternative Method**

You can also graph the function by translating $y = -\frac{1}{2}x^2$ right 2 units and up 3 units. The vertex of the parent function is at $(0, 0)$, and two other points on its graph are $(-2, -2)$ and $(2, -2)$. If you translate these three points 2 units right and 3 units up, you get the points $(2, 3)$, $(0, 1)$, and $(4, 1)$. Plot the points and sketch the curve.

4 EXAMPLE **Math Tip**

Students should note that the value of a is always the same whether the equation is in vertex form or in standard form.

👥 Reaching All Students

| **Below Level** On a coordinate grid on the overhead projector place the graph of a parabola. Have students identify the vertex and axis of symmetry for different positions of the parabola. | **Advanced Learners** After Example 3, have students research other suspension bridges, and attempt to model the suspension cables with quadratic functions. | **Visual Learners** See note on page 252. **Error Prevention** See note on page 251. |

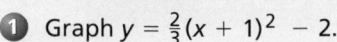
1 Graph $y = \frac{2}{3}(x + 1)^2 - 2$.

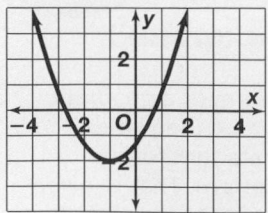

2 Write the equation of the parabola shown below.

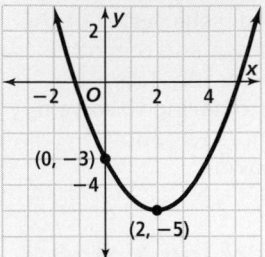

$y = \frac{1}{2}(x - 2)^2 - 5$

3 A long strip of colored paper is attached as a party decoration at the top corners of a wall of a rectangular room. The strip approximates a parabola with equation $y = 0.008(x - 25)^2 + 10$. The bottom left corner of the wall is the origin, and x and y are measured in feet. How far apart are the corners? How high are they? **50 ft; 15 ft**

4 Write $y = -7x^2 - 70x - 169$ in vertex form. $y = -7(x + 5)^2 + 6$

Closure

Ask: *How can you use the values of a, b, and c to write a quadratic function in vertex form? Find h by evaluating $-\frac{b}{2a}$. Substitute this for x in the standard form equation and use the result as the value of k. Substitute the values of a, h, and k into the vertex form $y = a(x - h)^2 + k$.*

page 251–254 Exercises

1.
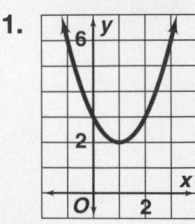

✓ Check Understanding **2** Use vertex form to write the equation of the parabola below. $y = 2(x + 1)^2$

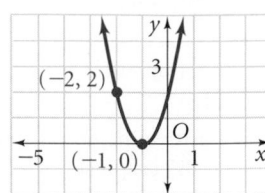

You can use vertex form to model real-world problems.

3 **EXAMPLE** **Real-World** 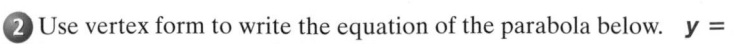 **Connection**

Civil Engineering The photo shows the Verrazano–Narrows Bridge in New York, which has the longest span of any suspension bridge in the United States. A suspension cable of the bridge forms a curve that resembles a parabola. The curve can be modeled with the function $y = 0.0001432(x - 2130)^2$, where x and y are measured in feet.

The origin of the function's graph is at the base of one of the two towers that support the cable. How far apart are the towers? How high are they?

Start by drawing a diagram.

The function is in vertex form. Since $h = 2130$ and $k = 0$, the vertex is at $(2130, 0)$. The vertex is halfway between the towers, so the distance between the towers is $2(2130 \text{ ft}) = 4260 \text{ ft}$.

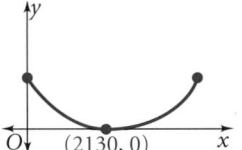

To find the tower's height, find y for $x = 0$.

$$y = 0.0001432(0 - 2130)^2$$
$$y = 0.0001432(-2130)^2$$
$$\approx 650$$

● The towers are 4260 ft apart and about 650 ft high.

✓ Check Understanding **3** Suppose the towers in Example 3 are 4000 ft apart and 600 ft high. Write a function that could model the curve of the suspension cable. $y = 0.00015(x - 2000)^2$

Both the vertex form and the standard form give useful information about a parabola. The standard form makes it easy to identify the y-intercept. The vertex form makes it easy to identify the vertex and to graph the parabola as a translation. The graph shows the relationship between the two forms.

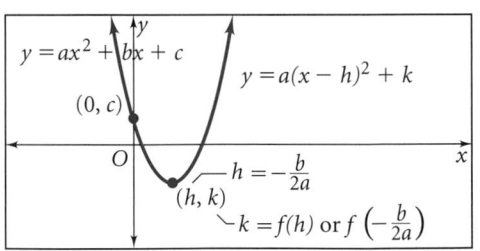

2.
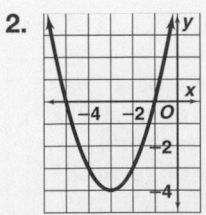

3.
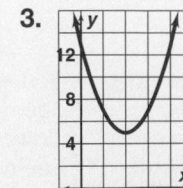

4.
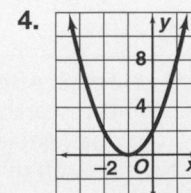

5.
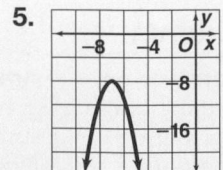

6.
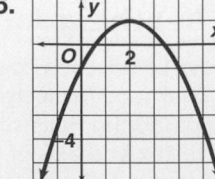

You can convert a function from standard form to vertex form.

4 EXAMPLE Converting to Vertex Form

Write $y = 2x^2 + 10x + 7$ in vertex form.

$x = -\dfrac{b}{2a}$ **Find the *x*-coordinate of the vertex.**

$= -\dfrac{10}{2(2)}$ **Substitute for *a* and *b*.**

$= -2.5$

$y = 2(-2.5)^2 + 10(-2.5) + 7$ **Find the *y*-coordinate of the vertex.**

$= -5.5$

The vertex is at $(-2.5, -5.5)$.

$y = a(x - h)^2 + k$ **Write the vertex form.**

$= 2(x - (-2.5))^2 - 5.5$ **Substitute for *a*, *h*, and *k*.**

$= 2(x + 2.5)^2 - 5.5$ **Simplify.**

● The vertex form of the function is $y = 2(x + 2.5)^2 - 5.5$.

✓ **Check Understanding**   4   Write $y = -3x^2 + 12x + 5$ in vertex form. $y = -3(x - 2)^2 + 17$

EXERCISES

For more practice, see *Extra Practice*.

Practice and Problem Solving

A Practice by Example

Graph each function. 1–12. See margin pp. 250–251.

Example 1
(page 249)

1. $y = (x - 1)^2 + 2$ **2.** $y = (x + 3)^2 - 4$

3. $y = 2(x - 2)^2 + 5$ **4.** $y = 2(x + 1)^2$

5. $y = -3(x + 7)^2 - 8$ **6.** $y = -\frac{1}{2}(x - 2)^2 + 1$

7. $y = (x - 5)^2 - 3$ **8.** $y = (x + 2)^2 - 3$

9. $y = -(x - 1)^2 + 4$ **10.** $y = 3(x + 5)^2 - 8$

11. $y = -(x - 7)^2 + 10$ **12.** $y = -4(x + 8)^2 - 6$

Example 2
(page 249)

Write the equation of each parabola in vertex form.

13.
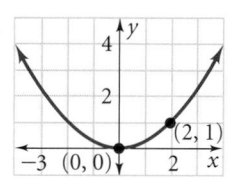
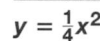
$y = \frac{1}{4}x^2$

14.
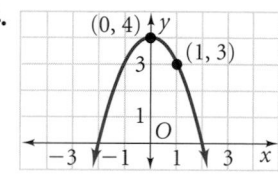
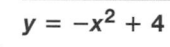
$y = -x^2 + 4$

15.
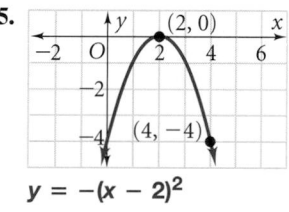
$y = -(x - 2)^2$

16.
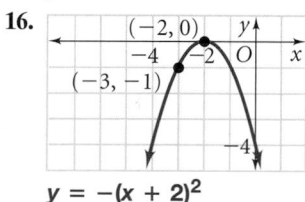
$y = -(x + 2)^2$

Lesson 5-3   Translating Parabolas   **251**

7.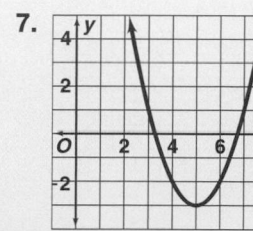

8.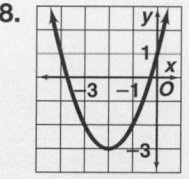

9.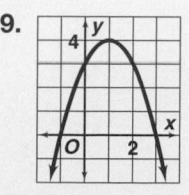

10.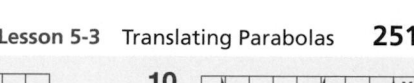

11.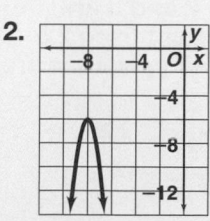

12.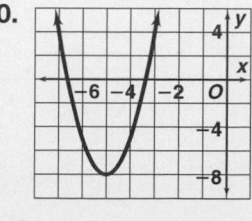

3. Practice

Assignment Guide

▼ **1 Objective**
   Ⓐ Ⓑ **Core** 1–77
   Ⓒ **Extension** 78–84

Standardized Test Prep 85–90

Mixed Review 91–96

Error Prevention

Exercises 1–12 Remind students that the sign of *h* is the opposite of the sign in the parentheses, while the sign of *k* is the same as the sign before it.

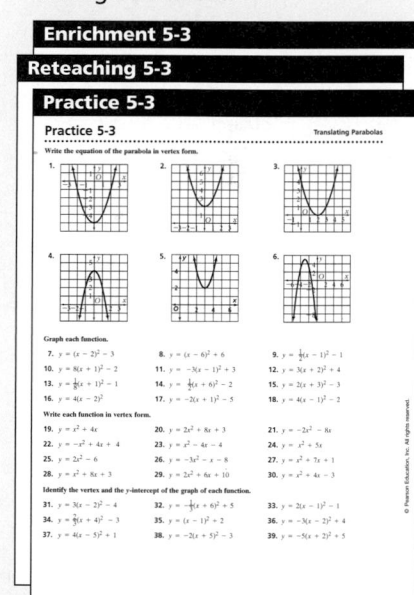

Visual Learners

Exercise 57 It may help students to sketch graphs if they do not immediately see how to use the spreadsheets alone to find the axes of symmetry.

pages 251–254 Exercises

27. $y = (x - 2)^2 + 2$

28. $y = (x + 1)^2 + 4$

29. $y = 6x^2 - 10$

30. $y = -5x^2 + 12$

31. $y = 4\left(x + \frac{7}{8}\right)^2 - \frac{49}{16}$

32. $y = 2\left(x + \frac{1}{4}\right)^2 - \frac{1}{8}$

33. $y = 2\left(x - \frac{5}{4}\right)^2 + \frac{71}{8}$

34. $y = -2(x - 2)^2 + 11$

35. $y = \frac{9}{4}\left(x + \frac{2}{3}\right)^2 - 2$

42a. **All nonnegative numbers; a price cannot be negative; it would imply that the bakery pays people to take bread.**

43. $y = -7(x - 1)^2 + 2$

44. $y = -\frac{4}{9}(x - 3)^2 + 6$

45. $y = -\frac{1}{2}(x + 3)^2 + 6$

46. $y = \frac{3}{2}(x + 2)^2 + 6$

47. $y = 7(x + 1)^2 - 4$

48. $y = -7x^2 + 5$

49. $y = -10\left(x - \frac{1}{10}\right)^2 - \frac{9}{10}$

50. $y = 8\left(x - \frac{1}{4}\right)^2 - \frac{3}{2}$

57a. **first: $x = 4$, second: $x = 2.5$**

b. **For the first spreadsheet the x_1-values 3 and 5 are equidistant from 4 and their y_1-values are both -3. In the second spreadsheet, the x_2-values 2 and 3 are equidistant from 2.5 and their y_2-values are both 2.**

c. $y = -4(x - 4)^2 + 1;$
$y = 4\left(x - \frac{5}{2}\right)^2 + 1$

252

Write the equation of each parabola in vertex form.

17. $y = (x - 2)^2$
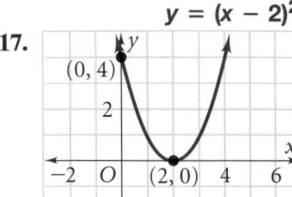

18. $y = -2x^2$
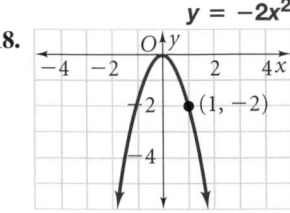

19. $y = 6(x + 3)^2 - 2$
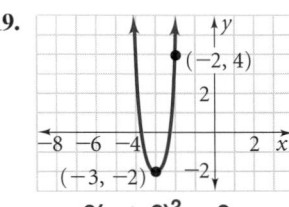

20. $y = -(x - 1)^2 + 2$
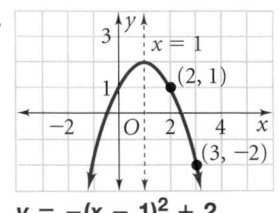

Example 3
(page 250)

Identify the vertex and the y-intercept of the graph of each function.

21. $y = -1.5(x + 20)^2$ **(−20, 0), −600**

22. $y = 0.1(x - 3.2)^2$ **(3.2, 0), 1.024**

23. $y = 24(x + 5.5)^2$ **(−5.5, 0), 726**

24. $y = 0.0035(x + 1)^2 - 1$
(−1, −1), −0.9965

25. $y = -(x - 4)^2 - 25$ **(4, −25), −41**

26. $y = (x - 125)^2 + 125$
(125, 125), 15,750

Example 4
(page 251)

Write each function in vertex form. 27–35. See margin.

27. $y = x^2 - 4x + 6$

28. $y = x^2 + 2x + 5$

29. $y = 6x^2 - 10$

30. $y = -5x^2 + 12$

31. $y = 4x^2 + 7x$

32. $y = 2x^2 + x$

33. $y = 2x^2 - 5x + 12$

34. $y = -2x^2 + 8x + 3$

35. $y = \frac{9}{4}x^2 + 3x - 1$

B **Apply Your Skills**

Sketch each parabola. 36–41. See back of book.

36. $y = 2(x + 2)^2 - 3$

37. $y = -3(x - 2)^2$

38. $y = 5(x + 0.3)^2 - 10$

39. $y = -0.5(x - 2)^2 - 5$

40. $y = -2(x + 1)^2 + 1$

41. $y = 0.2(x - 12)^2 + 0.2$

42. **Business** The Big Brick Bakery sells more bagels when it reduces its prices, but then its profit changes. The function $y = -1000(x - 0.55)^2 + 300$ models the bakery's daily profit in dollars, from selling bagels, where x is the price of a bagel in dollars. The bakery wants to maximize the profit. **See margin.**
a. What is the domain of the function? Can x be negative? Explain. **$277.50;**
b. Find the daily profit for selling bagels for $.40 each; for $.85 each. **$210.00**
c. What price should the bakery charge to maximize its profit from bagels? **$0.55**
d. What is the maximum profit? **$300.00**

Write the equation of each parabola in vertex form. 43–50. See margin.

Real-World Connection

Bagel sales in the United States total nearly $3 billion each year.

43. vertex $(1, 2)$, point $(2, -5)$

44. vertex $(3, 6)$, y-intercept 2

45. vertex $(-3, 6)$, point $(1, -2)$

46. vertex $(-2, 6)$, y-intercept 12

47. vertex $(-1, -4)$, y-intercept 3

48. vertex $(0, 5)$, point $(1, -2)$

49. vertex $\left(\frac{1}{10}, -\frac{9}{10}\right)$, y-intercept -1

50. vertex $\left(\frac{1}{4}, -\frac{3}{2}\right)$, point $(1, 3)$

Write each function in standard form.

51. $y = 25x^2 + 60x + 27$

52. $y = -9x^2 + 24x - 10$

53. $y = 2x^2 + 22x$

54. $y = \frac{1}{2}x^2 - 5x + \frac{35}{2}$

55. $y = -10x^2 - 40x - 40$

56. $y = 16x^2 - 8x + 2$

Write each function in standard form.

51. $y = (5x + 6)^2 - 9$

52. $y = -(3x - 4)^2 + 6$

53. $y = 2x(x + 7) + 8x$

54. $y = \frac{1}{2}(x - 5)^2 + 5$

55. $y = -0.1(10x + 20)^2$

56. $y = (1 - 4x)^2 + 1$

 57. a. **Technology** Determine the axis of symmetry for each parabola defined by the spreadsheet values at the right.

b. How could you use the spreadsheet columns to verify that the axes of symmetry are correct?

c. Write functions in vertex form that model the data. Check that the axes of symmetry are correct.
a–c. See margin p. 252.

	A	B
1	X1	Y1
2	1	−35
3	2	−15
4	3	−3
5	4	1
6	5	−3

	A	B
1	X2	Y2
2	1	10
3	2	2
4	3	2
5	4	10
6	5	26

58. **Writing** Describe the steps you would take to sketch the graph of $y = -2(x - 3)^2 + 4$. **See margin.**

Determine whether each function is written in vertex form. If a function is not in vertex form, rewrite the function.

61. no; $y = -3\left(x + \frac{1}{3}\right)^2 + \frac{4}{3}$

63. no; $y = (x + 1)^2 + 7$

67. no; $y = 100\left(x - \frac{1}{5}\right)^2 + 6$

59. $y = -2x^2 + 35$ **yes**

60. $y = -8x^2$ **yes**

61. $y = -3x^2 - 2x + 1$

62. $y = -2(x + 1)^2 - 1$ **yes**

63. $y = x^2 + 2x + 8$

64. $y = \frac{3}{10}x^2 - 1$ **yes**

65. $y = -4x^2 + 6x + 3$
no; $y = -4\left(x - \frac{3}{4}\right)^2 + \frac{21}{4}$

66. $y = 0.5x^2 + 10$ **yes**

67. $y = 100x^2 - 40x + 10$

Determine a and k so both points are on the graph of the function.
68–73. See margin.

68. $(0, 1), (2, 1); y = a(x - 1)^2 + k$

69. $(-3, 2), (0, 11); y = a(x + 2)^2 + k$

70. $(1, 11), (2, -19); y = a(x + 1)^2 + k$

71. $(-2, 6), (3, 1); y = a(x - 3)^2 + k$

72. $(-2, 10), (1, -34); y = a(2x + 2)^2 + k$

73. $(4, 26), (5, -25); y = a(x - 30)^2 + k$

74. The equation of one of the parabolas in the graph at the right is $y = (x - 4)^2 + 2$. Write the equation of the other parabola in vertex form. $y = -(x - 4)^2 + 2$

75. **Open-Ended** Write a quadratic function in vertex form for which the graph has a vertex at $(-2, 5)$. Rewrite the function in standard form.
Check students' work.

76. Determine whether the function $f(x) = 0.25(2x - 15)^2 + 150$ has a maximum or a minimum value. Then find the value.
minimum; 150

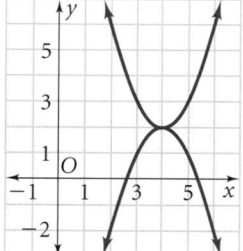

77. **Critical Thinking** Describe the differences between the graphs of $y = (x + 6)^2$ and $y = (x - 6)^2 + 7$. **See margin.**

C Challenge

78. a. In the function $y = ax^2 + bx + c$, c represents the y-intercept. Find the value of the y-intercept in the function $y = a(x - h)^2 + k$. $ah^2 + k$

b. Under what conditions does k represent the y-intercept? $h = 0$ or $a = 0$
(Note, however, that if $a = 0$, the function will not be quadratic.)

Find the quadratic function $y = a(x - h)^2$ for which the graph includes the given points. **79–84. See margin.**

79. $(-2, 1), (2, 1)$

80. $(-5, 2), (-1, 2)$

81. $(-1, -4), (7, -4)$

82. $(2, -1), (4, 0)$

83. $(-2, 18), (1, 0)$

84. $(1, -64), (-3, 0)$

58. **Answers may vary. Sample: The vertex is (3, 4), so graph that point first. Then substitute 2 for x to find (2, 2) is on the graph. Plot that point and the symmetrically**

opposite point from the line of symmetry, (4, 2), and sketch the parabola. Plot more and more symmetric pairs if a more accurate curve is desired.

68. **Any real numbers a and k such that $a + k = 1$ will work. However, if $a = 0$ and $k = 1$, the function will be linear rather than quadratic.**

Lesson Quiz 5-3

1. Graph the function $y = 4(x - 3)^2$.

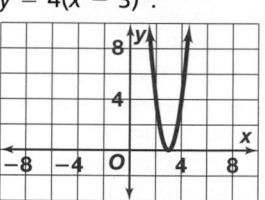

2. Identify the vertex and the y-intercept of the graph of $y = -2(x + 5)^2 + 8$.
(−5, 8), −42

3. Write the equation $y = 3x^2 + 12x - 1$ in vertex form.
$y = 3(x + 2)^2 - 13$

Alternative Assessment

Give students the coordinates of a point (a, b) in the coordinate plane. Then give them the coordinates of another point (c, d), for which $c \neq a$ and $d \neq b$. Have students write an equation for a parabola having vertex (a, b) and passing through (c, d), and an equation for a parabola having vertex (c, d) and passing through (a, b).

69. $a = 3, k = -1$

70. $a = -6, k = 35$

71. $a = \frac{1}{5}, k = 1$

72. $a = -\frac{11}{3}, k = \frac{74}{3}$

73. $a = 1, k = -650$

77. **Answers may vary. Sample: The graph of $y = (x - 6)^2 + 7$ is the graph of $y = (x + 6)^2$ translated right 12 units and up 7 units.**

79. $y = \frac{1}{4}x^2$

80. $y = \frac{1}{2}(x + 3)^2$

81. $y = -\frac{1}{4}(x - 3)^2$

82. $y = -\frac{1}{4}(x - 4)^2$

83. $y = 2(x - 1)^2$

84. $y = -4(x + 3)^2$

253

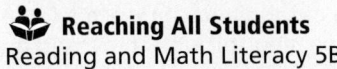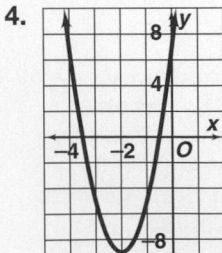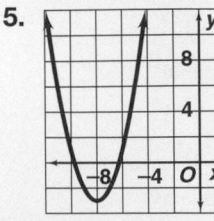

Standardized Test Prep

Gridded Response

Take It to the NET
Online lesson quiz at
www.PHSchool.com
Web Code: aga-0503

Use the following information about quadratic functions for Exercises 85–90.

vertex form: $y = a(x - h)^2 + k$ standard form: $y = ax^2 + bx + c$

85. When $y = -3x^2 - 18x - 23$ is written in vertex form, what is the value of k? **4**

86. When $y = 2(x - 3)(x + 5)$ is written in standard form, what is the value of b? **4**

87. When $y = -2(x + 3)^2 + 25$ is written in standard form, what is the value of c? **7**

88. For $y = 3x^2 - 7x + 5$, what is the x-value of the vertex? Enter your answer as an improper fraction in simplest form. $\frac{7}{6}$

89. What is the y-coordinate of the vertex of $y = -2(x + 1)^2 - 3$? **−3**

90. How many units down must you shift the graph of $y = 3(x + 3)^2$ to get the graph of $y = 3(x + 3)^2 - 2$? **2**

Mixed Review

Lesson 5-2   Graph each function.   91–93. See back of book.

91. $y = x^2 - 5$ **92.** $y = x^2 - 4x + 8$ **93.** $y = 3x^2 + 6x + 5$

Lesson 4-5   Solve each matrix equation.

94. $\begin{bmatrix} 0 & 1 \\ -1 & 2 \end{bmatrix} X = \begin{bmatrix} 20 \\ 10 \end{bmatrix} \begin{bmatrix} 30 \\ 20 \end{bmatrix}$

95. $\begin{bmatrix} -1 & 3 \\ 1 & -2 \end{bmatrix} X = \begin{bmatrix} 4 \\ -4 \end{bmatrix} \begin{bmatrix} -4 \\ 0 \end{bmatrix}$

Lesson 3-4   **96.** Find the maximum and minimum values of the objective function $P = 2x + y$, under the constraints at the right.   **max: 6, min: 0**
$\begin{cases} y \geq 2x - 2 & x \geq 0 \\ y \leq -x + 4 & y \geq 0 \end{cases}$

Checkpoint Quiz 1   Lessons 5-1 through 5-3

 Instant self-check quiz online and on CD-ROM

Find a quadratic model in standard form for each set of values.

1. $(0, 3), (1, 10), (2, 19)$
$y = x^2 + 6x + 3$

2. $(-2, -15), (0, 1), (2, 1)$
$y = -2x^2 + 4x + 1$

3. $(0, 0), (1, -5), (2, 0)$
$y = 5x^2 - 10x$

Graph each function.   4–6. See margin.

4. $y = 4x^2 + 16x + 7$ **5.** $y = (x + 8)^2 - 3$ **6.** $y = -(x + 2)^2 - 7$

Determine whether each function has a maximum or minimum value. Then find the value.

7. $y = -x^2 + 6x + 5$ **max.; 14**   **8.** $y = \frac{1}{2}(x - 6)^2 + 7$ **min.; 7**

9. Rewrite the equation $y = -3x^2 - 6x - 8$ in vertex form. Identify the vertex and the axis of symmetry. $y = -3(x + 1)^2 - 5; (-1, -5); x = -1$

10. Answers may vary.
Sample:
$y = (x - 3)^2 + 2;$
$x = 3; (0, 11), (6, 11)$

10. Open-Ended Write the equation of a parabola with a vertex at $(3, 2)$. Write the axis of symmetry and the coordinates of two other points on the graph.

6.
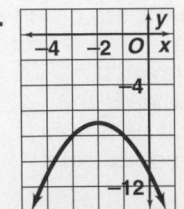

Factoring Quadratic Expressions

1.03 Operate with algebraic expressions (polynomial, rational, complex fractions) to solve problems.

Lesson Preview

What You'll Learn

OBJECTIVE 1 To find common and binomial factors of quadratic expressions

OBJECTIVE 2 To factor special quadratic expressions

...And Why

To model the cross section of a pipe, as in Example 8

✓ Check Skills You'll Need

(For help, go to Lessons 1-2 and 5-1.)

Simplify each expression.

1. $x^2 + x + 4x - 1$
$x^2 + 5x - 1$

2. $6x^2 - 4(3)x + 2x - 3$
$6x^2 - 10x - 3$

3. $4x^2 - 2(5 - x) - 3x$
$4x^2 - x - 10$

Multiply.

4. $2x(5 - x)$
$-2x^2 + 10x$

5. $(2x - 7)(2x - 7)$
$4x^2 - 28x + 49$

6. $(4x + 3)(4x - 3)$
$16x^2 - 9$

New Vocabulary • factoring • greatest common factor (GCF) of an expression • perfect square trinomial • difference of two squares

---

OBJECTIVE 1 Finding Common and Binomial Factors

iTEXT Interactive lesson includes instant self-check, tutorials, and activities.

Investigation: Factoring

1. Since $6 \cdot 3 = 18$, 6 and 3 make up a factor pair for 18.
 a. Find the other factor pairs for 18, including negative integers.
 b. Find the sum of the integers in each factor pair for 18.
  $-19, -11, -9, 19, 11, 9$

2. a. Does 12 have a factor pair with a sum of -8? A sum of -9? **yes; no**
 b. Using all the factor pairs of 12, how many sums are possible? **6**
 c. How many sums are possible for the factor pairs of -12? **6**

1a. -1 and -18, -2 and -9, -3 and -6, 1 and 18, 2 and 9

Need Help?

One number is a factor of another if the first divides into the second with no remainder.

Factoring is rewriting an expression as the product of its factors. The **greatest common factor (GCF) of an expression** is the common factor with the greatest coefficient and the greatest exponent. You can factor any expression with terms having a GCF greater than 1.

1 EXAMPLE Finding Common Factors

Factor each expression.

a. $4x^2 + 20x - 12$

$4x^2 + 20x - 12 = 4x^2 + 4(5x) - 4(3)$ **Factor out the GCF, 4.**

$= 4(x^2 + 5x - 3)$ **Rewrite using the Distributive Property.**

b. $9n^2 - 24n$

$9n^2 - 24n = 3n(3n) - 3n(8)$ **Factor out the GCF, 3n.**

$= 3n(3n - 8)$ **Rewrite using the Distributive Property.**

✓ Check Understanding ❶ Factor each expression.

a. $9x^2 + 3x - 18$
$3(3x^2 + x - 6)$

b. $7p^2 + 21$
$7(p^2 + 3)$

c. $4w^2 + 2w$
$2w(2w + 1)$

Lesson 5-4 Factoring Quadratic Expressions **255**

---

1. Plan

Lesson Preview

✓ Check Skills You'll Need

Algebraic Expressions
Lesson 1-2: Example 4
Exercises 17–38
Extra Practice, p. 822

Modeling Data With Quadratic Functions
Lesson 5-1: Example 1
Exercises 1–9
Extra Practice, p. 826

Lesson Resources

📁 **Teaching Resources**
Practice, Reteaching, Enrichment

Reaching All Students
Practice Workbook 5-4
Spanish Practice Workbook 5-4

⏱ **Presentation Assistant Plus!**
Transparencies
• Check Skills You'll Need 5-4
• Additional Examples 5-4
• Student Edition Answers 5-4
• Lesson Quiz 5-4
PH Presentation Pro CD 5-4

ASSESSMENT SYSTEM
Computer Test Generator CD

Technology
Resource Pro® CD-ROM
Computer Test Generator CD
Prentice Hall Presentation Pro CD

🖥 **www.PHSchool.com**
Student Site
• Teacher Web Code: agk-5500
• Self-grading Lesson Quiz
Teacher Center
• Lesson Planner
• Resources

Plus **iTEXT**

🕐 Ongoing Assessment and Intervention

Before the Lesson	During the Lesson	After the Lesson
Diagnose prerequisite skills using:	**Monitor progress using:**	**Assess knowledge using:**
• Check Skills You'll Need	• Check Understanding • Additional Examples • Standardized Test Prep	• Lesson Quiz • Computer Test Generator CD

Math Background

A quadratic function of the form $f(x) = ax^2 + bx + c$ factors into two linear factors, say $mx + p$ and $nx + q$, if and only if $mq + pn = b$ and $(mq)(pn)$ or $(mn)(pq) = ac$. This is shown by the following:

$$f(x) = ax^2 + bx + c$$
$$= (mx + p)(nx + q)$$
$$= mnx^2 + mqx + pnx + pq$$
$$= mnx^2 + (mq + pn)x + pq$$

Thus, when trying to factor a quadratic function, we look for two factors whose sum is b and whose product is ac. (In the above notation these two factors are represented by mq and pn.)

OBJECTIVE 1 Teaching Notes

Investigation (Optional)
In order to factor quadratic expressions, students must be able to find factor pairs for integers. Have students complete the Investigation to practice finding factor pairs. Tell students it is important to include negative factors.

1 EXAMPLE English Learners

Be sure students understand the meaning of the terms *factoring* and *greatest common factor*. Use integer examples and algebraic expressions to illustrate the meaning of each term.

2 EXAMPLE Math Tip

In the first part of Step 2, show students that the order in which they write the addends is important. The goal is to have the first two terms and the last two terms have a common factor.

3 EXAMPLE Error Prevention

Some students may look for any numbers whose sum is -17. Remind them that only the factor pair in the table with a sum of -17 can be used to factor the expression.

256

Reading Math

A monomial is an expression with one term. A binomial has two terms, and a trinomial has three terms.

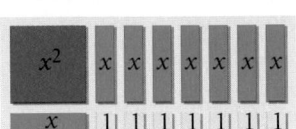

You can use algebra tiles to factor the expression in Example 2.

A quadratic trinomial is an expression in the form $ax^2 + bx + c$. You can factor many quadratic trinomials into two binomial factors. First find two factors with a product ac and a sum b. Then find common factors.

If ac and b are positive, then the factors of ac are both positive.

2 EXAMPLE   Factoring When $ac > 0$ and $b > 0$

Factor $x^2 + 8x + 7$.

Step 1 Find factors with product ac and sum b.

Since $ac = 7$ and $b = 8$, find positive factors with product 7 and sum 8.

Factors of 7	1, 7	These are the only positive factors of 7.
Sum of factors	8	

Step 2 Rewrite the term bx using the factors you found. Group the remaining terms and find the common factors for each group. After removing common factors from each group, you should find two identical binomials.

$x^2 + 8x + 7$

$x^2 + x + 7x + 7$ **Rewrite bx: $8x = x + 7x$.**

$x(x + 1) + 7(x + 1)$ **Find common factors.**

Step 3 Rewrite the expression as the product of two binomials.

$x(x + 1) + 7(x + 1)$

$(x + 1)(x + 7)$ **Rewrite using the Distributive Property.**

Check $(x + 1)(x + 7) = x^2 + 7x + x + 7$
$$= x^2 + 8x + 7 ✓$$

✓ Check Understanding **2** Factor each expression. Check your answers.
  a. $x^2 + 6x + 8$ **b.** $x^2 + 12x + 32$ **c.** $x^2 + 14x + 40$
  $(x + 2)(x + 4)$ $(x + 4)(x + 8)$ $(x + 4)(x + 10)$

If ac is positive and b is negative, then the factors of ac are both negative.

3 EXAMPLE   Factoring When $ac > 0$ and $b < 0$

Factor $x^2 - 17x + 72$.

Step 1 Find factors with product ac and sum b.

Since $ac = 72$ and $b = -17$, find negative factors with product 72 and sum -17.

Factors of 72	−1, −72	−2, −36	−3, −24	−4, −18	−6, −12	−8, −9
Sum of factors	−73	−38	−27	−22	−18	−17

Step 2 Rewrite the term bx using the factors you found. Then find common factors and rewrite the expression as the product of two binomials.

$x^2 - 17x + 72$

$x^2 - 8x - 9x + 72$ **Rewrite bx.**

$x(x - 8) - 9(x - 8)$ **Find common factors.**

$(x - 9)(x - 8)$ **Rewrite using the Distributive Property.**

🤝 Reaching All Students

Below Level Have students make a table summarizing the procedures in the examples for various combinations of signs of ac and b.	**Advanced Learners** Challenge students to use a spreadsheet program to create tables like those used in the examples for finding the sum of possible factors.	**English Learners** See note on page 256. **Inclusion** See note on page 259.

✓ **Check Understanding** ❸ Factor each expression.

a. $x^2 - 6x + 8$
$(x - 2)(x - 4)$

b. $x^2 - 7x + 12$
$(x - 3)(x - 4)$

c. $x^2 - 11x + 24$
$(x - 3)(x - 8)$

Note in Example 3 that the factors of c, -9 and -8, appear in the binomials of the factored form, $(x - 9)(x - 8)$. That is also the case for the factors in Example 2, and it is the case whenever $a = 1$. So when $a = 1$, you can skip a few steps in factoring. See Example 4.

If ac is negative, then the factors of ac have different signs.

❹ EXAMPLE Factoring When $ac < 0$

Factor $x^2 - x - 12$.

Step 1 Find factors with product ac and sum b.

Since $ac = -12$ and $b = -1$, find factors with product -12 and sum -1.

Factors of −12	1, −12	−1, 12	2, −6	−2, 6	3, −4	−3, 4
Sum of factors	−11	11	−4	4	−1	1

Step 2 Since $a = 1$, you can write binomials using the factors you found.

$x^2 - x - 12$

● $(x - 4)(x + 3)$ **Use the factors you found.**

✓ **Check Understanding** ❹ Factor each expression.

a. $x^2 - 14x - 32$
$(x + 2)(x - 16)$

b. $x^2 + 3x - 10$
$(x + 5)(x - 2)$

c. $x^2 + 4x - 5$
$(x + 5)(x - 1)$

If ac is positive, as in Examples 2 and 3, then the factors of ac have the same sign. This is true even when $a \neq 1$.

❺ EXAMPLE Factoring When $a \neq 1$ and $ac > 0$

Factor $3x^2 - 16x + 5$.

Step 1 Find factors with product ac and sum b.

Since $ac = 15$ and $b = -16$, find negative factors with product 15 and sum -16.

Factors of 15	−1, −15	−3, −5
Sum of factors	−16	−8

Step 2 Rewrite the term bx using the factors you found. Then find common factors and rewrite the expression as the product of two binomials.

$3x^2 - 16x + 5$

$3x^2 - x - 15x + 5$ **Rewrite bx.**

$x(3x - 1) - 5(3x - 1)$ **Find common factors.**

● $(x - 5)(3x - 1)$ **Rewrite using the Distributive Property.**

✓ **Check Understanding** ❺ Factor each expression. Check your answers.

a. $2x^2 + 11x + 12$
$(x + 4)(2x + 3)$

b. $4x^2 + 7x + 3$
$(x + 1)(4x + 3)$

c. $2x^2 - 7x + 6$
$(x - 2)(2x - 3)$

Lesson 5-4 Factoring Quadratic Expressions   **257**

❹ EXAMPLE Math Tip

Placement of the signs is very important. To emphasize this, have students switch the signs in the binomial factors and multiply.

❻ EXAMPLE Alternative Method

Have students draw a square with four sections, such as the one shown. Then follow these steps:

1. Write the first and the last term as shown.

$4x^2$	
	-15

2. Multiply a and c. Then find factors of the product that have a sum of b.

$4(-15) = -60$

$6(-10) = -60$

and $6 + (-10) = -4$

3. Write the factors with their signs and variables in the other two boxes. Order does not matter. Then find the GCF of each column and each row. A GCF is negative if both terms are negative.

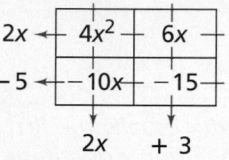

$(2x - 5)(2x + 3)$

Additional Examples

❶ Factor each expression.

a. $15x^2 + 25x + 100$

$5(3x^2 + 5x + 20)$

b. $8m^2 + 4m$ $4m(2m + 1)$

❷ Factor $x^2 + 10x + 24$.

$(x + 4)(x + 6)$

❸ Factor $x^2 - 14x + 33$.

$(x - 3)(x - 11)$

❹ Factor $x^2 + 3x - 28$.

$(x - 4)(x + 7)$

❺ Factor $6x^2 - 31x + 35$.

$(3x - 5)(2x - 7)$

❻ Factor $6x^2 + 11x - 35$.

$(3x - 5)(2x + 7)$

Point out that you can only use this formula for the *difference* of two squares. If it was the *sum* of two squares, the last term would be positive. Therefore the signs in the factors would have to be the same resulting in a middle term when multiplied.

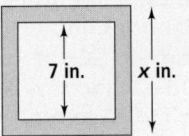
Additional Examples

7 Factor $100x^2 + 180x + 81$.
$(10x + 9)^2$

8 A square photo is enclosed in a square frame, as shown in the diagram. Express the area of the frame (the shaded area) in completely factored form.
$(x + 7)(x - 7)$ in.^{2}

7 in.   *x in.*

Closure

Ask: *What is usually the first step in factoring a quadratic trinomial that is not a perfect square trinomial and whose terms have no common factor greater than 1?* Find two integers that have product *ac* and sum *b*.

Again, if *ac* is negative, then the factors of *ac* have different signs.

6 EXAMPLE   **Factoring When $a \neq 1$ and $ac < 0$**

Factor $4x^2 - 4x - 15$.

Step 1 Find factors with product *ac* and sum *b*.

Since $ac = -60$ and $b = -4$, find factors with product -60 and sum -4.

Factors of −60	1, −60	−1, 60	2, −30	−2, 30	3, −20	−3, 20
Sum of factors	−59	59	−28	28	−17	17
Factors of −60	4, −15	−4, 15	5, −12	−5, 12	6, −10	−6, 10
Sum of factors	−11	11	−7	7	−4	4

Step 2 Rewrite the term *bx* using the factors you found. Then find common factors and rewrite the expression as the product of two binomials.

$4x^2 - 4x - 15$
$4x^2 + 6x - 10x - 15$ **Rewrite *bx*.**
$2x(2x + 3) - 5(2x + 3)$ **Find common factors.**
$(2x - 5)(2x + 3)$ **Rewrite using the Distributive Property.**

 Check Understanding **6** Factor each expression.
  a. $2x^2 + 7x - 9$ **b.** $3x^2 - 16x - 12$ **c.** $4x^2 + 5x - 6$
  $(x - 1)(2x + 9)$ $(x - 6)(3x + 2)$ $(x + 2)(4x - 3)$

A **perfect square trinomial** is the product you obtain when you square a binomial. An example is $x^2 + 10x + 25$, which can be written as $(x + 5)^2$. The first term and the third term of the trinomial are always positive, as they represent the squares of the two terms of the binomial. The middle term of the trinomial is two times the product of the terms of the binomial.

Key Concepts

Property	Factoring Perfect Square Trinomials
$a^2 + 2ab + b^2 = (a + b)^2$	$a^2 - 2ab + b^2 = (a - b)^2$

7 EXAMPLE   **Factoring a Perfect Square Trinomial**

Factor $9x^2 - 42x + 49$.

$9x^2 - 42x + 49 = (3x)^2 - 42x + 7^2$ **Rewrite the first and third terms as squares.**

$= (3x)^2 - 2(3x)(7) + 7^2$ **Rewrite the middle term to verify the perfect square trinomial pattern.**

$= (3x - 7)^2$ $a^2 - 2ab + b^2 = (a - b)^2$

Check Understanding **7** Factor each expression.
  a. $4x^2 + 12x + 9$ **b.** $64x^2 - 16x + 1$ **c.** $25x^2 + 90x + 81$
  $(2x + 3)^2$ $(8x - 1)^2$ $(5x + 9)^2$

An expression of the form $a^2 - b^2$ is defined as the **difference of two squares**. It also follows a pattern that makes it easy to factor.

 Key Concepts

Property	Factoring a Difference of Two Squares
	$a^2 - b^2 = (a + b)(a - b)$

3. Practice

8 **EXAMPLE** **Real-World** **Connection**

Hydraulics The photo at the right shows the cross-section of a pipe. Express the pipe's cross-sectional area in completely factored form.

Relate   pipe's area equals   the outer area

minus   the inner area

Define Let $r =$ inner radius in feet.

Write   area = $\pi(3)^2$ − πr^2

area = $\pi(3)^2 - \pi r^2$

$= \pi(3^2 - r^2)$

$= \pi(3 + r)(3 - r)$

 3 ft

● The cross-sectional area of the pipe in factored form is $\pi(3 + r)(3 - r)$ ft^2.

 Need Help?

For a circle, $A = \pi r^2$.

✓ **Check Understanding** **8** Factor each expression.

a. $x^2 - 64$
$(x - 8)(x + 8)$

b. $4a^2 - 49$
$(2a + 7)(2a - 7)$

Assignment Guide

1 **Objective**
Ⓐ Ⓑ Core 1–36, 48–50, 67–70
Ⓒ Extension 71

2 **Objective**
Ⓐ Ⓑ Core 37–47, 51–66
Ⓒ Extension 72–78

Standardized Test Prep 79–84

Mixed Review 85–91

Inclusion
Exercises 7–45 Pair students who have difficulty remembering their multiplication facts with students who know them well.

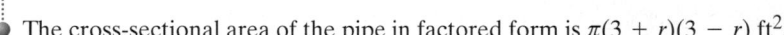

EXERCISES

For more practice, see *Extra Practice*.

Practice and Problem Solving

 **Practice by Example**

Example 1
(page 255)

Find the GCF of each expression. Then factor the expression.

1. $3a^2 + 9$ **3;** $3(a^2 + 3)$ **2.** $25b^2 - 35$ **5;** $5(5b^2 - 7)$ **3.** $x^2 - 2x$ $x;$ $x(x - 2)$

4. $5t^2 + 7t$ $t;$ $t(5t + 7)$ **5.** $14y^2 + 7y$ **7y;** $7y(2y + 1)$**6.** $27p^2 - 9p$
$9p;$ $9p(3p - 1)$

Factor each expression. 7–30. See margin.

Example 2
(page 256)

7. $x^2 + 3x + 2$ **8.** $x^2 + 5x + 6$ **9.** $x^2 + 7x + 10$

10. $x^2 + 10x + 16$ **11.** $y^2 + 15y + 36$ **12.** $x^2 + 22x + 40$

Example 3
(page 256)

13. $x^2 - 3x + 2$ **14.** $x^2 - 13x + 12$ **15.** $r^2 - 11r + 18$

16. $x^2 - 10x + 24$ **17.** $d^2 - 12d + 27$ **18.** $x^2 - 13x + 36$

Example 4
(page 257)

19. $x^2 - 5x - 14$ **20.** $x^2 + x - 20$ **21.** $x^2 - 3x - 40$

22. $c^2 + 2c - 63$ **23.** $x^2 + 10x - 75$ **24.** $t^2 - 7t - 44$

Example 5
(page 257)

25. $3x^2 + 31x + 36$ **26.** $2x^2 - 19x + 24$ **27.** $5r^2 + 23r + 26$

28. $2m^2 - 11m + 15$ **29.** $5t^2 + 28t + 32$ **30.** $2x^2 - 27x + 36$

pages 259–261   Exercises

7. $(x + 1)(x + 2)$

8. $(x + 2)(x + 3)$

9. $(x + 2)(x + 5)$

10. $(x + 2)(x + 8)$

11. $(y + 3)(y + 12)$

12. $(x + 2)(x + 20)$

13. $(x - 1)(x - 2)$

14. $(x - 12)(x - 1)$

15. $(r - 2)(r - 9)$

16. $(x - 4)(x - 6)$

17. $(d - 3)(d - 9)$

18. $(x - 4)(x - 9)$

19. $(x - 7)(x + 2)$

20. $(x + 5)(x - 4)$

21. $(x - 8)(x + 5)$

22. $(c + 9)(c - 7)$

23. $(x + 15)(x - 5)$

24. $(t - 11)(t + 4)$

25. $(3x + 4)(x + 9)$

26. $(x - 8)(2x - 3)$

27. $(r + 2)(5r + 13)$

28. $(m - 3)(2m - 5)$

29. $(t + 4)(5t + 8)$

30. $(x - 12)(2x - 3)$

259

Alternative Assessment

Have students work in pairs. Each student multiplies five pairs of binomials of the form $mx + n$, where m and n are nonzero integers. Tell students to write only the trinomial products (without the factors) on a sheet of paper. Students trade the sheets that have the products written on them. Have each student then factor the products that he or she received. Then ask the partners to make sure that the factorization is complete and correct.

Error Prevention

Exercises 51–65 Students may forget to factor out the GCF of the terms of the given expression. Remind them that if they do not factor out the GCF, the expression has not been factored completely.

pages 259–261   Exercises

31. $(x + 4)(3x - 5)$

32. $(y + 4)(5y - 8)$

33. $(x - 2)(7x + 6)$

34. $(z + 4)(2z - 7)$

35. $(x + 4)(3x - 4)$

36. $(4k + 3)(7k - 2)$

Example 6
(page 258)

Factor each expression.   31–45. See margin.

31. $3x^2 + 7x - 20$
32. $5y^2 + 12y - 32$
33. $7x^2 - 8x - 12$
34. $2z^2 + z - 28$
35. $3x^2 + 8x - 16$
36. $28k^2 + 13k - 6$

Example 7
(page 258)

37. $x^2 + 2x + 1$
38. $t^2 - 14t + 49$
39. $x^2 - 18x + 81$
40. $4n^2 - 20n + 25$
41. $9x^2 + 48x + 64$
42. $81z^2 + 36z + 4$
43. $x^2 - 4$
44. $c^2 - 64$
45. $9x^2 - 1$

Example 8
(page 259)

46. **Manufacturing** Refer to the diagram at the right. A machine will cut a small square of plastic from a larger square. Write an expression for the remaining area. Factor the expression. $x^2 - 16$; $(x + 4)(x - 4)$

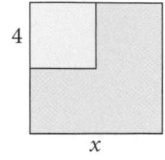

4

x

47. The area in square centimeters of a square mat is $25x^2 - 10x + 1$. Find the dimensions of the mat in terms of x. **5x − 1 by 5x − 1**

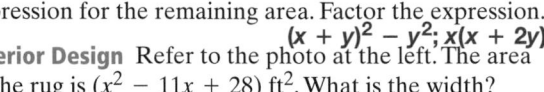 **B** **Apply Your Skills**

48. The area of a rectangular cloth is $(6x^2 - 19x - 85)$ cm². The length is $(2x + 5)$ cm. Find the width. **(3x − 17) cm**

49. Refer to the diagram at the right. Suppose you cut a small square from a square sheet of cardboard. Write an expression for the remaining area. Factor the expression.
   $(x + y)^2 - y^2$; $x(x + 2y)$

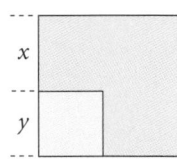

x

y

 50. **Interior Design** Refer to the photo at the left. The area of the rug is $(x^2 - 11x + 28)$ ft². What is the width?
   (x − 7) ft

Factor each expression completely.   51–65. See margin.

51. $9x^2 - 36$
52. $18z^2 - 8$
53. $12y^2 - 75$
54. $64t^2 - 16$
55. $12x^2 + 36x + 27$
56. $16x^2 - 80x + 100$
57. $2a^2 - 16a + 32$
58. $3x^2 - 24x - 27$
59. $18b^2 + 24b - 10$
60. $4n^2 - 20n + 24$
61. $3y^2 + 24y + 45$
62. $-x^2 + 5x - 4$
63. $4x^2 - 22x + 10$
64. $\frac{1}{2}x^2 - \frac{1}{2}$
65. $-6z^2 - 600$

 66. **Geometry** Express the volume of the shaded pipe at the right in completely factored form. $\pi h(R + r)(R - r)$

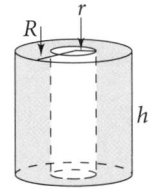

R r h

 67. **Agriculture** The area in square feet of a rectangular field is $x^2 - 120x + 3500$. The width in feet is $x - 50$. Find the length. **(x − 70) ft**

68. **Writing** Explain how to factor $3x^2 + 6x - 72$ completely.
   See margin p. 261.

69. **Open-Ended** Write a quadratic trinomial that can be factored, where $a \neq 1$, $ac > 0$, and $b < 0$. Factor the expression. **Check students' work.**

70. **Error Analysis** Find the error below. Then factor the expression correctly.
   The third line should be $x(2x - 5) - (2x - 5)$, and the final line should be $(x - 1)(2x - 5)$.

   $2x^2 - 7x + 5$
   $2x^2 - 5x - 2x + 5$
   $x(2x - 5) + (2x - 5)$
   $(x + 1)(2x - 5)$

(x − 4) ft

37. $(x + 1)^2$
38. $(t - 7)^2$
39. $(x - 9)^2$
40. $(2n - 5)^2$
41. $(3x + 8)^2$
42. $(9z + 2)^2$
43. $(x + 2)(x - 2)$
44. $(c + 8)(c - 8)$
45. $(3x + 1)(3x - 1)$
51. $9(x + 2)(x - 2)$
52. $2(3z + 2)(3z - 2)$
53. $3(2y + 5)(2y - 5)$
54. $16(2t + 1)(2t - 1)$
55. $3(2x + 3)^2$
56. $4(2x - 5)^2$

C Challenge   **71. Critical Thinking** Explain how to factor $4x^4 + 24x^3 + 32x^2$. **See margin.**

Factor each expression completely. 72–76. See margin.

72. $0.25t^2 - 0.16$ **73.** $8100x^2 - 10,000$ **74.** $3600z^2 - 4900$

75. $(x + 3)^2 + 3(x + 3) - 54$ **76.** $(x - 2)^2 - 15(x - 2) + 56$

77. $6(x + 5)^2 - 5(x + 5) + 1$ **78.** $3(2a - 3)^2 + 17(2a - 3) + 10$
(2x + 9)(3x + 14)   **2(a + 1)(6a − 7)**

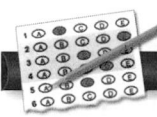

Standardized Test Prep

Multiple Choice   **79.** Which term is NOT a common factor of $4a^2c^2 + 2a^2c - 6ac^2$? **A**
    A. $4c$ **B.** $2a$ **C.** $2ac$ **D.** ac

80. How can you write $(m - 5)(m + 4) + 8$ as a product of two binomials? **G**
    F. $(m - 1)(m + 8)$ **G.** $(m - 4)(m + 3)$
    H. $(m + 8)(m + 8)$ **I.** $(m - 5)(8m + 32)$

Take It to the NET
Online lesson quiz at
www.PHSchool.com
.... Web Code: aga-0504

81. What is the factored form of $4x^2 + 15x - 4$? **D**
    A. $(2x + 2)(2x - 2)$ **B.** $(2x - 4)(2x + 1)$
    C. $(4x + 1)(x - 4)$ **D.** $(4x - 1)(x + 4)$

82. Which is a factored form of $0.81p^2 - 0.09$? **H**
    F. $(0.9p + 0.045)(0.9p - 0.045)$ **G.** $(0.09p + 0.03)(0.09p - 0.03)$
    H. $(0.9p + 0.3)(0.9p - 0.3)$ **I.** $(0.9p + 0.81)(0.9p - 0.81)$

Short Response   **83.** Explain how to rewrite the expression $a^2 - 2ab + b^2 - 25$ as the product of two trinomial factors. **See margin.**

Extended Response   **84.** Suppose you hit a baseball and its flight takes a parabolic path. The height of the ball at certain times appears in the table below. **a–b.**
See back of book.

Time (s)	0.5	0.75	1	1.25
Height (ft)	10	10.5	9	5.5

a. Find a quadratic model for the ball's height as a function of time.
b. Write the quadratic function in factored form.

Mixed Review

Lesson 5-3   **Write each function in vertex form.**

85. $y = x^2 - 2x + 1$ **86.** $y = -2x^2 + 2x + 5$ **87.** $y = 5x^2 - 1$
    $y = (x - 1)^2$ $y = -2\left(x - \frac{1}{2}\right)^2 + \frac{11}{2}$ $y = 5x^2 - 1$

Lesson 4-6   **Evaluate each determinant.**

88. $\begin{vmatrix} 2 & -1 & 0 \\ 1 & 0 & 3 \\ 4 & -2 & 1 \end{vmatrix}$ **1**   **89.** $\begin{vmatrix} 1 & 5 & 0 \\ 3 & 3 & 5 \\ 0 & 1 & 2 \end{vmatrix}$ **−29**   **90.** $\begin{vmatrix} 0 & 4 & 1 \\ 1 & 0 & 1 \\ 1 & 2 & 1 \end{vmatrix}$ **2**

Lesson 3-6 🌐 **91. Coins** The combined mass of a penny and a nickel and a dime is 9.8 g. Ten nickels and three pennies have the same mass as 25 dimes. Fifty dimes have the same mass as 18 nickels and 10 pennies. Write and solve a system of equations to find the mass of each type of coin. **penny: 2.5 g, nickel: 5 g, dime 2.3 g**

Lesson 5-4 Factoring Quadratic Expressions **261**

57. $2(a - 4)^2$

58. $3(x - 9)(x + 1)$

59. $2(3b - 1)(3b + 5)$

60. $4(n - 2)(n - 3)$

61. $3(y + 3)(y + 5)$

62. $-(x - 1)(x - 4)$

63. $2(x - 5)(2x - 1)$

64. $\frac{1}{2}(x + 1)(x - 1)$

65. $-6(z^2 + 100)$

68. Factor 3 from the terms to get $3(x^2 + 2x - 24)$. Look for numbers whose product is -24 and whose sum is 2. The numbers -4 and 6 work. The complete factorization is $3(x - 4)(x + 6)$.

Standardized Test Prep

☐ **Resources**
For additional practice with a variety of test item formats:
• Standardized Test Prep, p. 297
• Test-Taking Strategies, p. 292
• Test-Taking Strategies with Transparencies

Exercise 81 Point out that choices A and B can be eliminated immediately since they are not completely factored expressions. Explain that to choose between C and D, you can mentally multiply the outer and inner terms to see if the result is the required middle term.

71. First factor out $4x^2$ to get $4x^2(x^2 + 6x + 8)$. To factor $x^2 + 6x + 8$, note that the numbers 2 and 4 have a product of 8 and a sum of 6. The complete factorization is $4x^2(x + 2)(x + 4)$.

72. $(0.5t + 0.4)(0.5t - 0.4)$

73. $100(9x - 10)(9x + 10)$

74. $100(6z - 7)(6z + 7)$

75. $(x + 12)(x - 3)$

76. $(x - 10)(x - 9)$

83. [2] First separate out -25 so it reads $(a^2 - 2ab + b^2) - 25$, and then factor $a^2 - 2ab + b^2$. This leaves you with $(a - b)^2 - 25$. Factor this as the difference of 2 perfect squares and you get $(a - b + 5)$ $(a - b - 5)$.

[1] no work shown, only answer, OR work shown with minor error

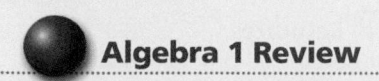
Square Roots and Radicals

Students will find this a helpful review of square roots and simplifying radical expressions. They will be using square roots in the remaining lessons of this chapter.

Resources

Technology

Computer Test Generator CD-ROM, Chapter 0, Integer, Decimal, and Fraction Operations

Teaching Notes

1 EXAMPLE Alternative Method

Another way to find the principal square root of a number is to first list the prime factorization of the number. Find pairs of matching prime factors and take the square root of each pair. For example, the principal square root of (2×2) is 2. Find the product of all the square roots of all the pairs. Write this product in front of a radical sign. Write the product of the non-paired prime factors inside the radical sign.
$48 = (2 \times 2) \times (2 \times 2) \times 3$
$\sqrt{48} = 2 \times 2\sqrt{3} = 4\sqrt{3}$

2 EXAMPLE Math Tip

Remind students that expressions that have a radical as a denominator are not considered to be in simplest form. To simplify, multiply by 1 in the form of the denominator divided by itself.

Square Roots and Radicals

FOR USE WITH LESSON 5-5

A radical symbol $\sqrt{}$ indicates a square root. The expression $\sqrt{16}$ means the principal, or positive, square root of 16. The expression $-\sqrt{16}$ means the negative square root of 16.

Properties	Square Roots

Multiplication Property of Square Roots

For any numbers $a \geq 0$ and $b \geq 0$, $\sqrt{ab} = \sqrt{a} \cdot \sqrt{b}$.

Division Property of Square Roots

For any numbers $a \geq 0$ and $b > 0$, $\sqrt{\dfrac{a}{b}} = \dfrac{\sqrt{a}}{\sqrt{b}}$.

You can use the properties of square roots to simplify radical expressions.

1 EXAMPLE Radical Expressions Containing Perfect Squares

Simplify $\sqrt{48}$.

$\sqrt{48} = \sqrt{16} \cdot \sqrt{3}$ Multiplication Property of Square Roots

$\phantom{\sqrt{48}} = 4\sqrt{3}$ Simplify.

2 EXAMPLE Denominators Containing Radical Expressions

Simplify $-\sqrt{\dfrac{5}{7}}$.

$-\sqrt{\dfrac{5}{7}} = -\dfrac{\sqrt{5}}{\sqrt{7}}$ Division Property of Square Roots

$\phantom{-\sqrt{\dfrac{5}{7}}} = -\dfrac{\sqrt{5}}{\sqrt{7}} \cdot \dfrac{\sqrt{7}}{\sqrt{7}}$ Multiply both the numerator and the denominator by $\sqrt{7}$.

$\phantom{-\sqrt{\dfrac{5}{7}}} = -\dfrac{\sqrt{35}}{\sqrt{49}}$ Multiplication Property of Square Roots

$\phantom{-\sqrt{\dfrac{5}{7}}} = -\dfrac{\sqrt{35}}{7}$ Simplify.

EXERCISES

Simplify each radical expression.

1. $\sqrt{18}$ $3\sqrt{2}$

2. $\sqrt{75}$ $5\sqrt{3}$

3. $-\sqrt{32}$ $-4\sqrt{2}$

4. $\sqrt{\dfrac{3}{5}}$ $\dfrac{\sqrt{15}}{5}$

5. $-\sqrt{\dfrac{7}{12}}$ $-\dfrac{\sqrt{21}}{6}$

6. $\sqrt{\dfrac{3}{8}}$ $\dfrac{\sqrt{6}}{4}$

7. $-\sqrt{200}$ $-10\sqrt{2}$

8. $5\sqrt{320}$ $40\sqrt{5}$

9. $(2\sqrt{27})^2$ 108

10. $-\sqrt{10^4}$ -100

11. $\sqrt{x^2 y^2}$ xy

12. $\sqrt{\dfrac{8}{x^2}}$ $\dfrac{2\sqrt{2}}{x}$

Quadratic Equations

 North Carolina Objectives

2.02 Use quadratic functions and inequalities to model and solve problems; justify results. a) Solve using tables, graphs, and algebraic properties.

Lesson Preview

What You'll Learn

 OBJECTIVE 1 To solve quadratic equations by factoring and by finding square roots

 OBJECTIVE 2 To solve quadratic equations by graphing

. . . And Why

To solve equations involving art, as in Example 5

✓ Check Skills You'll Need

(For help, go to Lessons 5-2 and 5-4.)

Factor each expression.

1. $x^2 + 5x - 14$
$(x + 7)(x - 2)$

2. $4x^2 - 12x$
$4x(x - 3)$

3. $9x^2 - 16$
$(3x - 4)(3x + 4)$

Graph each function. 4–6. See margin p. 265.

4. $y = x^2 - 2x - 5$

5. $y = x^2 - 4x + 4$

6. $y = x^2 - 4x$

New Vocabulary

- standard form of a quadratic equation
- Zero-Product Property • zero of a function

 Interactive lesson includes instant self-check, tutorials, and activities.

OBJECTIVE

1 Solving by Factoring and Finding Square Roots

The **standard form of a quadratic equation** is $ax^2 + bx + c = 0$, where $a \neq 0$. You can solve some quadratic equations in standard form by factoring the quadratic expression and then using the Zero-Product Property.

 Key Concepts

Property	Zero-Product Property
If $ab = 0$, then $a = 0$ or $b = 0$.	
Example	If $(x + 3)(x - 7) = 0$, then $(x + 3) = 0$ or $(x - 7) = 0$.

1 EXAMPLE Solving by Factoring

Solve $2x^2 - 11x = -15$.

$2x^2 - 11x + 15 = 0$ Write in standard form.

$2x^2 - 5x - 6x + 15 = 0$ Rewrite the bx term.

$x(2x - 5) - 3(2x - 5) = 0$ Find common factors.

$(x - 3)(2x - 5) = 0$ Rewrite using the Distributive Property.

$x - 3 = 0$ or $2x - 5 = 0$ Use the Zero-Product Property.

$x = 3$ or $x = \frac{5}{2}$ Solve for x.

The solutions are 3 and $\frac{5}{2}$.

Check
$$2x^2 - 11x = -15$$
$$2(3)^2 - 11(3) \stackrel{?}{=} -15$$
$$18 - 33 \stackrel{?}{=} -15$$
$$-15 = -15 ✓$$

$$2x^2 - 11x = -15$$
$$2\left(\frac{5}{2}\right)^2 - 11\left(\frac{5}{2}\right) \stackrel{?}{=} -15$$
$$\frac{25}{2} - \frac{55}{2} \stackrel{?}{=} -15$$
$$-15 = -15 ✓$$

Lesson 5-5   Quadratic Equations   **263**

Lesson Preview

 ✓ **Check Skills You'll Need**

Properties of Parabolas
Lesson 5-2: Example 2
Exercises 10–21
Extra Practice, p. 826

Factoring Quadratic Expressions
Lesson 5-4: Examples 2, 3
Exercises 7–18
Extra Practice, p. 826

Lesson Resources

📁 **Teaching Resources**
Practice, Reteaching, Enrichment

👥 **Reaching All Students**
Practice Workbook 5-5
Spanish Practice Workbook 5-5
Hands-On Activities 41
Technology Activities 7

⏱ **Presentation Assistant Plus!**
Transparencies
- Check Skills You'll Need 5-5
- Additional Examples 5-5
- Student Edition Answers 5-5
- Lesson Quiz 5-5
PH Presentation Pro CD 5-5

PRENTICE HALL ASSESSMENT SYSTEM

Computer Test Generator CD

 Technology
Resource Pro® CD-ROM
Computer Test Generator CD
Prentice Hall Presentation Pro CD

 www.PHSchool.com
Student Site
- Teacher Web Code: agk-5500
- Self-grading Lesson Quiz
Teacher Center
- Lesson Planner
- Resources

Plus

✓ **Ongoing Assessment and Intervention**

Before the Lesson
Diagnose prerequisite skills using:
- Check Skills You'll Need

During the Lesson
Monitor progress using:
- Check Understanding
- Additional Examples
- Standardized Test Prep

After the Lesson
Assess knowledge using:
- Lesson Quiz
- Computer Test Generator CD

263

2. Teach

Math Background

The use of the Zero-Product Property allows students to solve quadratic equations that can be factored. Other useful techniques include finding square roots and graphing. However, each of these techniques has limitations. This should begin to convince students of the need for a method without limitations. Such a method is presented in Lesson 5-8. The idea of building upon previous knowledge and trying to discover new ideas and more general techniques is fundamental to the development of mathematics.

OBJECTIVE
▼ 1 Teaching Notes

1 EXAMPLE Connection to Logic

Point out that the word *or* is the appropriate word to use when the Zero-Product Property is being used. This is so, because $x = 3$ and $x = \frac{5}{2}$ cannot simultaneously be true. On the other hand, the word *and* is the appropriate word when you are listing the solutions, because each of the numbers will make the original equation true.

3 EXAMPLE Careers

This example demonstrates just how important Algebra is to smoke jumpers or any other skydivers. Without equations such as these, they would not know when to release their parachutes, possibly endangering their lives.

Additional Examples

1 Solve $3x^2 - 20x - 7 = 0$. $-\frac{1}{3}$, 7

2 Solve $6x^2 - 486 = 0$. ± 9

3 The function $y = -16x^2 + 270$ models the height y in feet of a heavy object x seconds after it is dropped from the top of a building that is 270 feet tall. How long does it take the object to hit the ground? **about 4.1 s**

264

✓ **Check Understanding** **1** Solve each equation by factoring. Check your answers.

  a. $x^2 + 7x = 18$ **b.** $2x^2 + 4x = 6$ **c.** $16x^2 = 8x$
  $-9, 2$ $-3, 1$ $0, \frac{1}{2}$

You can solve an equation in the form $ax^2 = c$ by finding square roots.

2 EXAMPLE Solving by Finding Square Roots

Solve $5x^2 - 180 = 0$.

$5x^2 - 180 = 0$
$\qquad 5x^2 = 180$ Rewrite in the form $ax^2 = c$.
$\qquad \dfrac{5x^2}{5} = \dfrac{180}{5}$ Isolate x^2.
$\qquad\quad x^2 = 36$ Simplify.
$\qquad\quad\ x = \pm 6$ Take the square root of each side.

✓ **Check Understanding** **2** Solve each equation by finding square roots.
  a. $4x^2 - 25 = 0$ $-\frac{5}{2}, \frac{5}{2}$ **b.** $3x^2 = 24$ $-2\sqrt{2}, 2\sqrt{2}$ **c.** $x^2 - \frac{1}{4} = 0$ $-\frac{1}{2}, \frac{1}{2}$

3 EXAMPLE Real-World  Connection

Firefighting Smoke jumpers are in free fall from the time they jump out of a plane until they open their parachutes. The function $y = -16t^2 + 1600$ models a jumper's height y in feet at t seconds for a jump from 1600 ft. How long is a jumper in free fall if the parachute opens at 1000 ft?

$\qquad\quad y = -16t^2 + 1600$
$\quad 1000 = -16t^2 + 1600$ **Substitute 1000 for y.**
$\quad -600 = -16t^2$ **Isolate t^2.**
$\quad\ 37.5 = t^2$
$\quad \pm 6.1 \approx t$ **Take the square root of each side.**

The jumper is in free fall for about 6.1 seconds.

Check Is the answer reasonable? The negative number -6.1 is also a solution to the equation. However, since a negative value for time has no meaning in this case, only the positive solution is reasonable.

Real-World Connection

Careers Smoke jumpers are firefighters who parachute into areas near forest fires.

✓ **Check Understanding** **3 a.** A smoke jumper jumps from 1400 ft. The function describing the height is $y = -16t^2 + 1400$. Using square roots, find the time during which the jumper is in free fall if the parachute opens at 1000 ft. **5 s**
  b. Solve the equation in part (a) by factoring. Which method do you prefer—using square roots or factoring? Explain. **$t = 5$ or $t = -5$, and use positive solution because it describes time; check students' work.**

OBJECTIVE
2 Solving by Graphing

Not every quadratic equation can be solved by factoring or by taking the square root. You can solve a quadratic equation in standard form by graphing its related quadratic function $y = ax^2 + bx + c$. When the graph of the function intersects the x-axis, the value of the function is zero, and each x-value is a zero of the function. A **zero of a function** is a solution of the equation $ax^2 + bx + c = 0$.

264   Chapter 5   Quadratic Equations and Functions

👥 Reaching All Students

| **Below Level** Remind students that finding square roots yields two possible solutions to an equation. $x^2 = 4$ has two solutions, $x = \pm 2$. | **Advanced Learners** Have students research the trajectory of a specific projectile, and graph the equation. | **Error Prevention** See note on page 266. |

4 EXAMPLE Solving by Graphing

Solve $x^2 - 5x + 2 = 0$.

Graph the related function $y = x^2 - 5x + 2$ with a graphing calculator. Use the **CALC** feature to find the two zeros of the function.

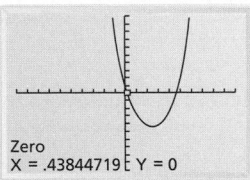
Zero
X = .43844719 Y = 0

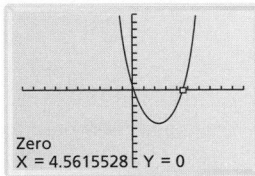
Zero
X = 4.5615528 Y = 0

● The solutions are $x \approx 0.44$ and $x \approx 4.56$.

✓ **Check Understanding** ④ Use a graphing calculator to solve each equation. When necessary, round your answers to the nearest hundredth.

a. $x^2 + 6x + 4 = 0$ b. $3x^2 + 5x - 12 = 8$ c. $x^2 = -2x + 7$
   −5.24, −0.76   **−3.55, 1.88**   **−3.83, 1.83**

5 EXAMPLE Real-World Connection

Art Artists often use a golden rectangle in their work because forms based on it are visually pleasing. You can divide a golden rectangle into a square of side length one and a smaller rectangle that is similar to the original one. The ratio of the longer side to the shorter side of a golden rectangle is the golden ratio. Use the figure at the right to find the golden ratio.

Need Help?

Two rectangles are similar if their corresponding sides are in proportion.

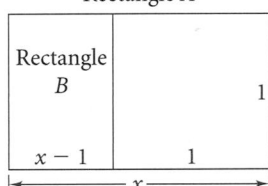
Rectangle A

Rectangle B   1

$x - 1$ 1

x

Relate $\dfrac{\text{longer side of } A}{\text{shorter side of } A} = \dfrac{\text{longer side of } B}{\text{shorter side of } B}$

Define Let x = longer side of rectangle A. Then $x - 1$ = shorter side of rectangle B.

Write $\dfrac{x}{1} = \dfrac{1}{x - 1}$

$x^2 - x = 1$ **Find cross-products.**

$x^2 - x - 1 = 0$ **Write in standard form.**

Graph the related function $y = x^2 - x - 1$. Use the CALC feature to find the positive solution.

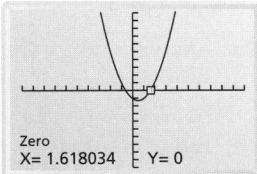
Zero
X = 1.618034   Y = 0

● The ratio is about $1.62 : 1$.

✓ **Check Understanding** ⑤ Solve each equation. When necessary, round to the nearest hundredth.

a. $x^2 - 2x = 4$ **−1.24, 3.24**   b. $x^2 + \frac{1}{2}x - \frac{1}{4} = 0$ **−0.81, 0.31**

Real-World Connection

Francisco José de Goya y Lucientes (1746–1828) was a Spanish painter. In *Portrait of a Man,* Goya placed the most significant elements of the painting within golden rectangles.

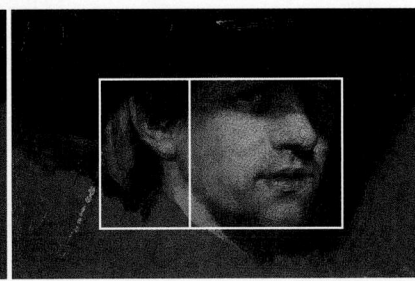

Lesson 5-5 Quadratic Equations **265**

page 263 **Check Skills You'll Need**

4.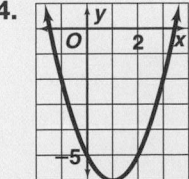
5.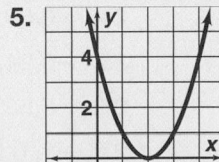
6.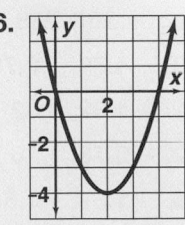

OBJECTIVE 2 Teaching Notes

5 EXAMPLE Connection to Algebra

The golden ratio has an interesting relation to the famous Fibonacci sequence. The Fibonacci sequence is the infinite sequence 1, 1, 2, 3, 5, 8, . . . that has 1 as its first two terms and thereafter has new terms formed by adding the two immediately preceding terms. If the nth term is denoted by F_n, then the ratios $\dfrac{F_n}{F_{n-1}}$ approach the golden ratio as n is increased.

Additional Examples

④ Use a graphing calculator to solve $2x^2 + 7x - 1 = 0$. Round the solutions to the nearest hundredth. **−3.64, 0.14**

⑤ A carpenter wants to cut a piece of plywood in the shape of a right triangle. The carpenter wants the hypotenuse of the triangle to be 6 feet long and the legs to be as shown in the diagram. About how long should the perpendicular sides be?

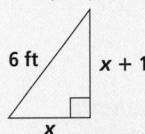
6 ft $x + 1$
x

about 3.7 ft and 4.7 ft

Closure

Ask students how factoring can be used to solve a quadratic equation? **Write the equation in standard form. Factor to express the quadratic expression as the product of two linear factors. Set each factor equal to zero and solve each equation for the variable. Or graph the function and find the zeros.**

265

Assignment Guide

1 Objective
A B **Core** 1–19, 33–35,
54–61
C **Extension** 62

2 Objective
A B **Core** 20–32, 36–53
C **Extension** 63–66

Standardized Test Prep 67–73

Mixed Review 74–83

Technology Tip

Exercises 20–31 If students use the zero feature on the CALC menu, it is crucial to select the left bound first and the right bound second. Selecting the bounds in the opposite order will result in an error message. Remind students to repeat the procedure for each point where the parabola crosses the x-axis.

Error Prevention

Exercise 62 Be sure students understand that the matrix on the left is to be multiplied by itself. The exponent does *not* indicate that the individual elements of the matrix are to be squared.

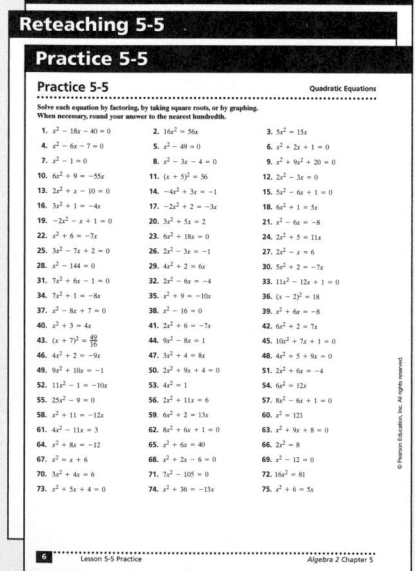

EXERCISES

For more practice, see *Extra Practice*.

Practice and Problem Solving

A Practice by Example

Example 1
(page 263)

Solve each equation by factoring. Check your answers.

1. $x^2 + 6x + 8 = 0$ **−4, −2** **2.** $x^2 + 18 = 9x$ **3, 6** **3.** $2x^2 - x = 3$ **−1, $\frac{3}{2}$**

4. $x^2 - 10x + 25 = 0$ **5** **5.** $2x^2 + 6x = -4$ **−2, −1** **6.** $3x^2 = 16x + 12$ **$-\frac{2}{3}$, 6**

Example 2
(page 264)

Solve each equation by finding square roots.

7. $5x^2 = 80$ **−4, 4** **8.** $x^2 - 4 = 0$ **−2, 2** **9.** $2x^2 = 32$ **−4, 4**

10. $9x^2 = 25$ **$-\frac{5}{3}, \frac{5}{3}$** **11.** $3x^2 - 15 = 0$ **$-\sqrt{5}, \sqrt{5}$** **12.** $5x^2 - 40 = 0$ **$-2\sqrt{2}, 2\sqrt{2}$**

Example 3
(page 264)

Solve each equation by factoring or by taking square roots.

13. $x^2 - 4x = 0$ **0, 4** **14.** $6x^2 + 4x = 0$ **$-\frac{2}{3}$, 0** **15.** $12x^2 - 147 = 0$ **$-\frac{7}{2}, \frac{7}{2}$**

16. $3x^2 = 48$ **−4, 4** **17.** $2x^2 = x + 3$ **−1, $\frac{3}{2}$** **18.** $4x^2 - 80 = 0$ **$-2\sqrt{5}, 2\sqrt{5}$**

19. Firefighters A smoke jumper jumps from a plane that is 1700 ft above the ground. The function $y = -16t^2 + 1700$ gives the jumper's height y in feet at t seconds.
a. How long is the jumper in free fall if the parachute opens at 1000 ft? **about 6.61 s**
b. How long is the jumper in free fall if the parachute opens at 940 ft? **about 6.89 s**

Examples 4 and 5
(page 265)

Solve each equation by graphing. If necessary, round your answer to the nearest hundredth. **20–31. See margin.**

20. $x^2 + 5x + 3 = 0$ **21.** $x^2 - 7x = 11$ **22.** $2x^2 - x = 2$

23. $6x^2 = -19x - 15$ **24.** $3x^2 - 5x - 4 = 0$ **25.** $5x^2 - 7x - 3 = 8$

26. $6x^2 + 31x = 12$ **27.** $1 = 4x^2 + 3x$ **28.** $\frac{1}{2}x^2 - x = 8$

29. $x^2 = 4x + 8$ **30.** $x^2 + 4x = 6$ **31.** $2x^2 - 2x - 5 = 0$

B Apply Your Skills

32a. Answers may vary.
Sample:
$\frac{\ell}{w} \approx \frac{7.2}{4.4} \approx 1.6$

b. the tree trunk

32. a. Art Verify that the Chinese painting at the right is a golden rectangle. **a–b. See left.**
b. What element in the painting divides it into a square and another golden rectangle?

33. Physics The period of a pendulum is the time the pendulum takes to swing back and forth. The function $\ell = 0.81t^2$ relates the length ℓ in feet of a pendulum to the time t in seconds that it takes to swing back and forth.
a. Find the period of a pendulum that is 2.5 ft long.
b. The convention center in Portland, Oregon, has the longest pendulum in the United States. The pendulum's length is 90 ft. Find the period. **a–b. See margin pp. 266–267.**

34. Open-Ended Write an equation in standard form that you can solve by factoring and an equation that you cannot solve by factoring. **Check students' work.**

pages 266–268 **Exercises**

20. −4.30, −0.70

21. −1.32, 8.32

22. −0.78, 1.28

23. −1.67, −1.5

24. −0.59, 2.26

25. −0.94, 2.34

26. −5.53, 0.36

27. −1, 0.25

28. −3.12, 5.12

29. −1.46, 5.46

30. −5.16, 1.16

31. −1.16, 2.16

33a. $\frac{5\sqrt{10}}{9}$ or about 1.76 s

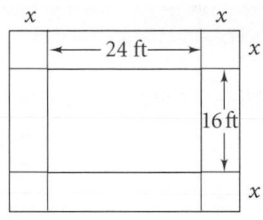

35. Gardening Suppose you want to expand the garden shown at the right by planting a border of flowers. The border will be of the same width around the entire garden. The flowers you bought will fill an area of 276 ft². How wide should the border be? **3 ft**

Solve each equation by factoring, by taking square roots, or by graphing. If necessary, round your answer to the nearest hundredth. **36–53. See margin.**

36. $x^2 + 6x + 5 = 45$ **37.** $x^2 - 11x + 24 = 0$ **38.** $3x^2 = 27$

39. $2x^2 - 5x - 3 = 0$ **40.** $x^2 + 2x = 6 - 6x$ **41.** $6x^2 + 13x + 6 = 0$

42. $2x^2 + 8x = 5x + 20$ **43.** $7x^2 - 243 = 0$ **44.** $3x^2 + 7x = 9$

45. $12x^2 - 154 = 0$ **46.** $x^2 + 4x = 0$ **47.** $x^2 = 8x - 7$

48. $x^2 + 2x = 15$ **49.** $x^2 + 11x + 10 = 0$ **50.** $4x^2 + 4x = 3$

51. $(x + 3)^2 = 9$ **52.** $2x^2 - 6x = 8$ **53.** $2x^2 + x - 28 = 0$

57. To find the *x*-coordinates, set the right side of the first equation equal to the right side of the second equation and solve for *x*. Then find the corresponding *y*-values by substituting each solution into the simpler of the two original equations.

Critical Thinking The graphs of each pair of functions intersect. Find their points of intersection without using a calculator. (*Hint*: Solve as a system using substitution.)

54. $y = x^2$
$y = -\frac{1}{2}x^2 + \frac{3}{2}x + 3$
(−1, 1), (2, 4)

55. $y = x^2 - 2$
$y = 3x^2 - 4x - 2$
(0, −2), (2, 2)

56. $y = -x^2 + x + 4$
$y = 2x^2 - 6$
$\left(-\frac{5}{3}, -\frac{4}{9}\right)$, **(2, 2)**

 57. Writing Explain how you found the intersections in Exercises 54–56.
See left.

Open-Ended Write a quadratic equation with the given solutions.
58–61. See margin.
58. 3 and 5   **59.** −3 and 2   **60.** −1 and −6   **61.** $\frac{1}{2}$ and $\frac{2}{3}$

© Challenge

62. Matrices Find the possible values of *x* and *y*.

$$\begin{bmatrix} x & 2 \\ 3 & y \end{bmatrix}^2 = \begin{bmatrix} 22 & 10 \\ 15 & \blacksquare \end{bmatrix} \quad \text{x = 4, y = 1 or x = −4, y = 9}$$

63a. $y = x^2 + 6x + 14$

63. a. Write the equation of a parabola with vertex $(-3, 5)$ passing through $(-4, 6)$.
b. Find the values of *x* when $y = 8$.   **about −4.732, about −1.268**

64. The equation $x^2 - 10x + 24 = 0$ can be written in factored form as $(x - 4)(x - 6) = 0$. How can you use this fact to find the vertex of the graph of $y = x^2 - 10x + 24$? **See back of book.**

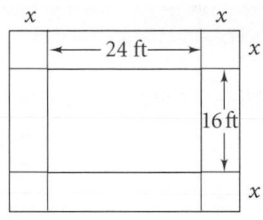 **65. Physics** Suppose you throw a ball straight up from the ground with a velocity of 80 ft/s. As the ball moves upward, gravity slows it. Eventually the ball begins to fall back to the ground. The height *h* of the ball after *t* seconds in the air is given by the quadratic function $h(t) = -16t^2 + 80t$.
a. How high does the ball go? **100 ft**
b. For how many seconds is the ball in the air before it hits the ground? **5 s**

66. a. Let $a > 0$. Use algebraic or arithmetic ideas to explain why the lowest point on the graph of $y = a(x - h)^2 + k$ must occur when $x = h$.
b. Suppose that the function in part (a) is $y = a(x - h)^3 + k$. Is your reasoning still valid? Explain. **a–b. See back of book.**

Lesson 5-5   Quadratic Equations   **267**

 Lesson Quiz 5-5

Solve each equation by factoring.
1. $4x^2 - 17x - 15 = 0$ $-\frac{3}{4}, 5$
2. $10x^2 + 19x + 6 = 0$ $-\frac{3}{2}, -\frac{2}{5}$
3. Solve $3x^2 = 4800$ by using square roots. **±40**
4. Use a graphing calculator to solve $2x^2 + 5x - 9 = 0$. Round the solutions to the nearest hundredth. **−3.71, 1.21**

Alternative Assessment

Give students a quadratic equation to solve and ask them to solve it both by factoring and by graphing with a graphing calculator. Ask students to write a short paragraph explaining which method they prefer, and why. Then ask students to explain why the graphing method might be easier for some problems, while factoring might be easier for others.

49. −10, −1
50. −1.5, 0.5
51. −6, 0
52. −1, 4
53. −4, 3.5
58–61. Answers may vary. Samples are given.
58. $x^2 - 8x + 15 = 0$
59. $x^2 + x - 6 = 0$
60. $x^2 + 7x + 6 = 0$
61. $6x^2 - 7x + 2 = 0$

33b. $\frac{10\sqrt{10}}{3}$ or about 10.54 s
36. −10, 4
37. 3, 8
38. −3, 3
39. $-\frac{1}{2}$, 3
40. −8.69, 0.69
41. $-\frac{3}{2}, -\frac{2}{3}$
42. $-4, \frac{5}{2}$
43. −5.89, 5.89
44. −3.25, 0.92
45. −3.58, 3.58
46. −4, 0
47. 1, 7
48. −5, 3

Exercise 68 Point out that students can divide both sides of the equation by 3 to get the simpler equation $2x^2 + 3x - 5 = 0$. They can then solve by factoring, or by substituting the numbers given in the choices.

Standardized Test Prep

Multiple Choice

67. What are the values of x that satisfy the equation $3 - 27x^2 = 0$? **B**

  A. $x = \pm 3$ **B.** $x = \pm\frac{1}{3}$

  C. $x = \frac{1}{9}$ or $x = -\frac{1}{9}$ **D.** $x = 2\sqrt{6}$ or $x = -2\sqrt{6}$

68. What are the solutions of the equation $6x^2 + 9x - 15 = 0$? **G**

  F. $1, -15$ **G.** $1, -\frac{5}{2}$

  H. $-1, -5$ **I.** $3, \frac{5}{2}$

69. For which equation is -3 NOT a solution? **D**

  A. $x^2 - 2x - 15 = 0$ **B.** $x^2 - 21 = 4x$

  C. $2x^2 + 12x = -18$ **D.** $9 + x^2 = 0$

Quantitative Comparison

Compare the boxed quantity in Column A with the boxed quantity in Column B. Choose the best answer.

  A. The quantity in Column A is greater.
  B. The quantity in Column B is greater.
  C. The two quantities are equal.
  D. The relationship cannot be determined from the information given.

73. [2] $6x^2 - 15x - 9$
$= 0\ 3(2x^2 - 5x - 3)$
$= 0\ 3(2x + 1)(x - 3)$
$= 0$

[1] solution only, no work shown

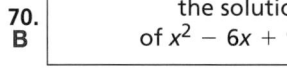
Take It to the NET
Online lesson quiz at
www.PHSchool.com
Web Code: aga-0505

	Column A	Column B
70. **B**	the solution of $x^2 - 6x + 9 = 0$	the solution of $x^2 - 10x + 25 = 0$
71. **A**	the sum of the solutions of $x^2 - 8x + 15 = 0$	the product of the solutions of $x^2 - 8x - 9 = 0$
72. **B**	the sum of the solutions of $x^2 + x - 6 = 0$	the product of the solutions of $x^2 + 6x + 9 = 0$

Short Response

73. What are the solutions of the quadratic equation $6x^2 - 15x - 9 = 0$? Show the steps of your solution. **See left.**

Mixed Review

Lesson 5-4   **Factor each expression.**

74. $3x^2 - 4x + 1$ **75.** $25z^2 - 9$ **76.** $6s^2 + 9s$
   $(3x - 1)(x - 1)$ $(5z + 3)(5z - 3)$ $3s(2s + 3)$

Lesson 4-1   **State the dimensions of each matrix. Identify the indicated element.**

77. $\begin{bmatrix} 4 & 6 & 5 \\ 1 & -3 & 0 \\ 1 & 1 & 9 \end{bmatrix}; a_{13}$ **78.** $\begin{bmatrix} 4 & -1 & 6 \\ 2 & 0 & 0 \end{bmatrix}; a_{21}$ **79.** $\begin{bmatrix} -9 & 1 & -1 \\ 0 & 6 & 0 \\ 1 & 0 & -2 \end{bmatrix}; a_{32}$

      $3 \times 3; 5$ $2 \times 3; 2$ $3 \times 3; 0$

Lesson 1-1   **Name the property of real numbers illustrated by each equation.**

80. **Distributive Property**   **80.** $3(2x + y) = 6x + 3y$ **81.** $3x^2 + 7y = 7y + 3x^2$

81. **Comm. Prop. of Add.**   **82.** $4(3x) = (4 \cdot 3)x$ **83.** $3 + (-3) = 0$
                                 Assoc. Prop. of Mult.   **Additive Inverse Prop.**

Quadratic Inequalities

You can use a graphing calculator to graph quadratic inequalities and to solve systems of quadratic inequalities.

1 EXAMPLE

Graph $y \leq x^2 - 5x - 6$.

Enter the corresponding equation as shown. Place the cursor to the left of Y_1 and press ENTER three times to produce shading *below* the graph. The solution is represented by all the points in the shaded region. Solutions to $y = x^2 - 5x - 6$ are also part of the solution.

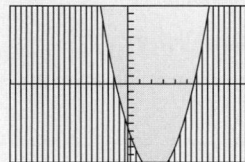

2 EXAMPLE

Solve $y \geq x^2 + 8x + 17$ and $y \leq -x^2 - 6x - 3$.

Enter the corresponding equations. For each equation, choose shading that corresponds to the inequality sign. The solution consists of all points within the double-shaded region.

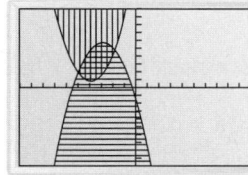

You can also use the **Shade** command from the **DRAW** menu. This command instructs the calculator to shade only the region of the intersection of the graphs.

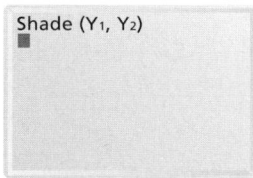
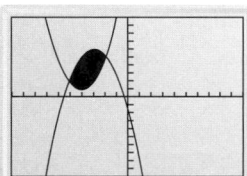

EXERCISES

Graph each quadratic inequality. **1–6. See margin.**

1. $y \geq 2x^2 + 7x - 4$

2. $y < -x^2 - 5x$

3. $y > -1.4x^2 + 2x + 7$

Solve each system of quadratic inequalities graphically.

4. $y \geq x^2 - 6x + 5$
$y \leq -x^2 + 6x$

5. $y \geq x^2 - x - 6$
$y \geq -x^2 - x + 6$

6. $y \geq x^2$
$y \geq (x - 3)^2$

Extension   Quadratic Inequalities   **269**

page 269   Extension

1.
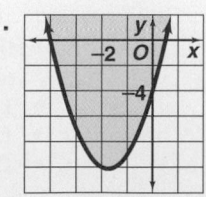

2.
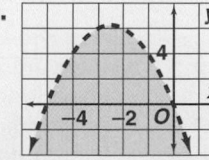

3.
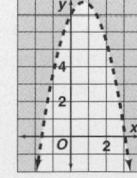

Extension

Quadratic Inequalities

Students use a graphing calculator to graph individual quadratic inequalities and systems of quadratic inequalities in the coordinate plane.

Resources

Technology
Computer Test Generator CD-ROM, Chapter 0, Extension Topics

Teaching Notes

By using the shading options on the Y= screen, students have a visual reminder of which part of the coordinate plane they have chosen to shade for each function.

Technology Tip

Students should be careful to use the function names in the correct order. Shade (Y1, Y2) and Shade (Y2, Y1) will produce different results.

4.
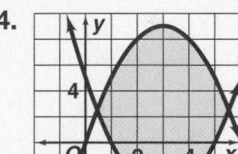

5.
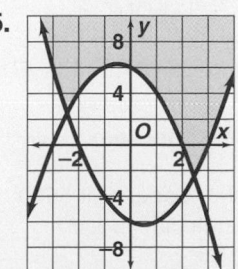

6.
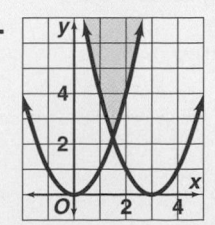

269

North Carolina
Objectives
1.02

1. Plan

Lesson Preview

 Check Skills You'll Need

Operations with Radicals
Skills Handbook, p. 855
Example 1
Exercises 1–7

Lesson Resources

 Teaching Resources
Practice, Reteaching, Enrichment
Checkpoint Quiz 2

 Reaching All Students
Practice Workbook 5-6
Spanish Practice Workbook 5-6
Reading and Math Literacy 5C
Spanish Reading & Literacy 5C
Spanish Checkpoint Quiz 2
Hands-On Activities 42

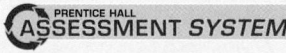 **Presentation Assistant Plus!**
Transparencies
• Check Skills You'll Need 5-6
• Additional Examples 5-6
• Student Edition Answers 5-6
• Lesson Quiz 5-6
PH Presentation Pro CD 5-6

 PRENTICE HALL
ASSESSMENT SYSTEM

Checkpoint Quiz 2
Computer Test Generator CD

 Technology
Resource Pro® CD-ROM
Computer Test Generator CD
Prentice Hall Presentation Pro CD

 **www.PHSchool.com**
Student Site
• Teacher Web Code: agk-5500
• Graphing Calculator,
  Procedure 26
• Self-grading Lesson Quiz
Teacher Center
• Lesson Planner
• Resources

Plus **iTEXT**

270

5-6

Complex Numbers

1.02 Define and compute with complex numbers.

 North Carolina Objectives

Lesson Preview

What You'll Learn

OBJECTIVE 1 To identify and graph complex numbers

OBJECTIVE 2 To add, subtract, and multiply complex numbers

. . . And Why

To explore fractals, as in Example 8

 Check Skills You'll Need (For help, go to Skills Handbook page 855.)

Simplify each expression.

1. $\sqrt{3^2 + 4^2}$ **5**   **2.** $\sqrt{(-2)^2 + 8^2}$ $2\sqrt{17}$ **3.** $\sqrt{5^2 + (-12)^2}$ **13**

4. $\sqrt{6^2 + 10^2}$ $2\sqrt{34}$ **5.** $\sqrt{x^2 + x^2}$ $x\sqrt{2}$ **6.** $\sqrt{(3x)^2 + (4x)^2}$ **5x**

New Vocabulary • *i* • imaginary number • complex numbers
• complex number plane
• absolute value of a complex number

OBJECTIVE
1   **Identifying Complex Numbers**

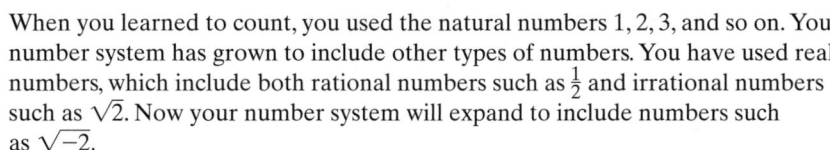 **iTEXT** Interactive lesson includes instant self-check, tutorials, and activities.

When you learned to count, you used the natural numbers 1, 2, 3, and so on. Your number system has grown to include other types of numbers. You have used real numbers, which include both rational numbers such as $\frac{1}{2}$ and irrational numbers such as $\sqrt{2}$. Now your number system will expand to include numbers such as $\sqrt{-2}$.

The imaginary number *i* is defined as the number whose square is −1. So $i^2 = -1$ and $i = \sqrt{-1}$. An **imaginary number** is any number of the form $a + bi$, where $b \neq 0$.

 Key Concepts

Property	**Square Root of a Negative Real Number**

For any positive real number a, $\sqrt{-a} = i\sqrt{a}$.

Example $\sqrt{-4} = i\sqrt{4} = i \cdot 2 = 2i$
Note that $(\sqrt{-4})^2 = (i\sqrt{4})^2 = i^2\sqrt{4}^2 = -1 \cdot 4 = -4$ (not 4).

1 **EXAMPLE**   **Simplifying Numbers Using *i***

Simplify $\sqrt{-8}$ by using the imaginary number *i*.

$\sqrt{-8} = \sqrt{-1 \cdot 8}$ Factor −8 as −1 · 8.
$= \sqrt{-1} \cdot \sqrt{8}$ Use the Multiplication Property of Square Roots.
$= i \cdot \sqrt{8}$ Substitute *i* for $\sqrt{-1}$.
$= i \cdot 2\sqrt{2}$ Simplify $\sqrt{8}$.
$= 2i\sqrt{2}$ Use the Commutative Property.

1a. $i\sqrt{2}$
b. $2i\sqrt{3}$
c. $6i$

 Check Understanding **1** Simplify each number by using the imaginary number *i*.
a. $\sqrt{-2}$ **b.** $\sqrt{-12}$ **c.** $\sqrt{-36}$

Ongoing Assessment and Intervention

Before the Lesson	**During the Lesson**	**After the Lesson**
Diagnose prerequisite skills using:	**Monitor progress using:**	**Assess knowledge using:**
• Check Skills You'll Need	• Check Understanding	• Lesson Quiz
	• Additional Examples	• Computer Test Generator CD
	• Standardized Test Prep	• Chapter Checkpoint 2 (p. 276)

Imaginary numbers and real numbers together make up the set of **complex numbers.**

 Key Concepts

Definition	**Complex Numbers**

A complex number can be written in the form $a + bi$, where a and b are real numbers, including 0.

$$a \;+\; b i$$
Real part   Imaginary part

2 EXAMPLE   **Simplifying Imaginary Numbers**

Write the complex number $\sqrt{-9} + 6$ in the form $a + bi$.

$\sqrt{-9} + 6 = 3i + 6$ **Simplify the radical expression.**

$= 6 + 3i$ **Write in the form $a + bi$.**

✓ **Check Understanding**   **2** Write the complex number $\sqrt{-18} + 7$ in the form $a + bi$.   **$7 + 3i\sqrt{2}$**

The diagram below shows the sets of numbers that are part of the complex number system, and examples of each set.

Complex Numbers

Real Numbers: -5, $-\sqrt{3}$, 0, $\sqrt{5}$, $\frac{8}{3}$, 9	Imaginary Numbers:

Rational Numbers: -5, 0, $\frac{8}{3}$, 9 Irrational Numbers: $-4i$

Integers: -5, 0, 9 $-\sqrt{3}$ $3 + 2i$

Whole Numbers: 0, 9 $\sqrt{5}$ $2i\sqrt{2}$

Natural Numbers: 9

You can use the **complex number plane** to represent a complex number geometrically. Locate the real part of the number on the horizontal axis and the imaginary part on the vertical axis. You graph $3 - 4i$ in the same way you would graph $(3, -4)$ on the coordinate plane.

The **absolute value of a complex number** is its distance from the origin on the complex number plane. You can find the absolute value by using the Pythagorean Theorem. In general,
$|a + bi| = \sqrt{a^2 + b^2}$.

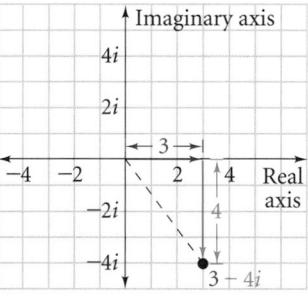

? Need Help?

The Pythagorean Theorem: $c^2 = a^2 + b^2$ and $c = \sqrt{a^2 + b^2}$

3 EXAMPLE   **Finding Absolute Value**

a. Find $|5i|$.

$5i$ is 5 units from the origin on the imaginary axis. So $|5i| = 5$.

b. Find $|3 - 4i|$.

$|3 - 4i| = \sqrt{3^2 + (-4)^2}$

$= \sqrt{9 + 16} = 5$

3a. $2\sqrt{13}$

b. $\sqrt{29}$

c. 4

✓ **Check Understanding**   **3** Find the absolute value of each complex number.

a. $|6 - 4i|$ **b.** $|-2 + 5i|$ **c.** $|4i|$

Lesson 5-6   Complex Numbers   **271**

2. Teach

 Professional Development

Math Background

Imaginary numbers, by name, are typically believed by students to not exist or to be "made up." However, they arise naturally from trying to find solutions to equations such as $x^2 + 1 = 0$.

OBJECTIVE

1   **Teaching Notes**

1 EXAMPLE   **Teaching Tip**

Some students may find the example easier to follow if you insert a third line such as $\sqrt{i^2} \cdot \sqrt{8}$. This will help students see the substitution of i^2 for -1.

2 EXAMPLE   **Teaching Tip**

Students are used to algebraic expressions with the variable terms written before the constant. Explain that i is not a variable. In the standard form of a complex number, the imaginary portion (in this case, $3i$) always comes after the real portion.

3 EXAMPLE   **Error Prevention**

A common error in finding the absolute value of a complex number is to somehow include i in the formula $\sqrt{a^2 + b^2}$. Emphasize that the distance formula does NOT include i.

Additional Examples

1 Simplify $\sqrt{-54}$ by using the imaginary number i.   **$3i\sqrt{6}$**

2 Write the complex number $\sqrt{-121} - 7$ in the form $a + bi$.   **$-7 + 11i$**

3 Find each absolute value.

a. $|-7i|$ **7**

b. $|10 + 24i|$ **26**

👥 Reaching All Students

Below Level Have students graph 3, 4, and $3 + 4$ on a real number line, and then graph $3 + 4i$ on the complex plane. Discuss the fact that $3 + 4i$ cannot be simplified.	**Advanced Learners** Discuss the difference between $\sqrt{-2} \cdot \sqrt{-3}$ and $\sqrt{(-2)(-3)}$ and have students check their understanding by using a calculator.	**Alternative Method** See note on page 272. **Error Prevention** See note on page 274.

OBJECTIVE 2

Teaching Notes

4 EXAMPLE Math Tip

Students should observe that the additive inverse of $a + bi$ is $-a + (-bi)$ or $-a - bi$.

5 EXAMPLE Connection to Algebra

Point out that you are basically combining like terms. In the case of complex numbers, first add or subtract the real components, then add or subtract the imaginary components.

6 EXAMPLE Alternative Method

Instead of using FOIL, you can use FLOI when multiplying $(a + bi)(a - bi)$ to keep the pairs of real and imaginary numbers side-by-side.

Additional Examples

4 Find the additive inverse of $-7 - 9i$. **$7 + 9i$**

5 Simplify the expression $(3 + 6i) - (4 - 8i)$. **$-1 + 14i$**

6 Find each product.
a. $(3i)(8i)$ **-24**
b. $(3 - 7i)(2 - 4i)$ **$-22 - 26i$**

OBJECTIVE 2

Operations With Complex Numbers

You can apply the operations of real numbers to complex numbers.

If the sum of two complex numbers is 0, then each number is the opposite, or additive inverse, of the other.

4 EXAMPLE Additive Inverse of a Complex Number

Find the additive inverse of $-2 + 5i$.

$-2 + 5i$

$-(-2 + 5i)$ **Find the opposite.**

$2 - 5i$ **Simplify.**

Check Understanding 4 Find the additive inverse of each number.

a. $-5i$ **$5i$** **b.** $4 - 3i$ **$-4 + 3i$** **c.** $a + bi$ **$-a - bi$**

To add or subtract complex numbers, combine the real parts and the imaginary parts separately.

5 EXAMPLE Adding Complex Numbers

Simplify the expression $(5 + 7i) + (-2 + 6i)$.

$(5 + 7i) + (-2 + 6i) = 5 + (-2) + 7i + 6i$ **Use commutative and associative properties.**

$= 3 + 13i$ **Simplify.**

Check Understanding 5 Simplify each expression.

a. $(8 + 3i) - (2 + 4i)$ **$6 - i$** **b.** $7 - (3 + 2i)$ **$4 - 2i$** **c.** $(4 - 6i) + 3i$ **$4 - 3i$**

For two imaginary numbers bi and ci, $(bi)(ci) = bc(i)^2 = bc(-1) = -bc$.

You can multiply two complex numbers of the form $a + bi$ by using the procedure for multiplying binomials.

6 EXAMPLE Multiplying Complex Numbers

a. Find $(5i)(-4i)$.

$(5i)(-4i) = -20i^2$ **Multiply the real numbers.**

$= -20(-1)$ **Substitute -1 for i^2.**

$= 20$ **Multiply.**

b. Find $(2 + 3i)(-3 + 5i)$.

$(2 + 3i)(-3 + 5i) = -6 + 10i - 9i + 15i^2$ **Multiply the binomials.**

$= -6 + 10i - 9i + 15(-1)$ **Substitute -1 for i^2.**

$= -21 + i$ **Simplify.**

Check Understanding 6 Simplify each expression.

a. $(12i)(7i)$ **-84** **b.** $(6 - 5i)(4 - 3i)$ **$9 - 38i$** **c.** $(4 - 9i)(4 + 3i)$ **$43 - 24i$**

Some quadratic equations have solutions that are complex numbers.

7 EXAMPLE Finding Complex Solutions

Solve $4x^2 + 100 = 0$.

$$4x^2 + 100 = 0$$

$$4x^2 = -100 \qquad \text{Isolate } x^2.$$

$$x^2 = -25$$

$$x = \pm\sqrt{-25} \qquad \text{Find the square root of each side.}$$

$$= \pm 5i \qquad \text{Simplify.}$$

Check
$$4x^2 + 100 = 0$$
$$4(5i)^2 + 100 \overset{?}{=} 0$$
$$4(25i^2) \overset{?}{=} -100$$
$$100(-1) \overset{?}{=} -100$$
$$-100 = -100 \checkmark$$

$$4x^2 + 100 = 0$$
$$4(-5i)^2 + 100 \overset{?}{=} 0$$
$$4(25i^2) \overset{?}{=} -100$$
$$100(-1) = -100$$
$$-100 = -100 \checkmark$$

✓ **Check Understanding** 7 Solve each equation. Check your answers.

a. $3x^2 + 48 = 0$ **b.** $-5x^2 - 150 = 0$ **c.** $8x^2 + 2 = 0$
    $\pm 4i$ $\pm i\sqrt{30}$ $\pm\frac{1}{2}i$

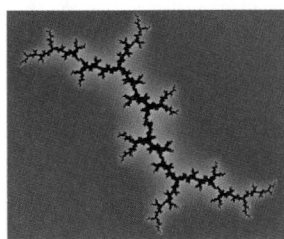

Functions of the form $f(z) = z^2 + c$ where c is a complex number generate fractal graphs on the complex plane like the one at the left. To test if z belongs to the graph, use z as the first input value and repeatedly use each output as the next input. If the output values do not become infinitely large, then z is on the graph.

8 EXAMPLE Real-World 🌐 Connection

Fractals Find the first three output values for $f(z) = z^2 + i$.

$$f(z) = z^2 + i$$

$$f(0) = 0^2 + i \qquad \text{Use } z = 0 \text{ as the first input value.}$$

$$= i$$

$$f(i) = i^2 + i \qquad \text{First output becomes second input. Evaluate for } z = i.$$

$$= -1 + i$$

$$f(-1 + i) = (-1 + i)^2 + i \qquad \begin{array}{l}\text{Second output becomes third input.}\\ \text{Evaluate for } z = -1 + i.\end{array}$$

$$= [(-1)^2 + (-1)(i) + (-1)(i) + (i)^2] + i$$

$$= (1 - 2i - 1) + i$$

$$= -i \qquad \text{Third output would be next input.}$$

The first three output values are i, $-1 + i$, and $-i$.

✓ **Check Understanding** 8 Find the first three output values for $f(z) = z^2 - 1 + i$.
                               $-1 + i, -1 - i, -1 + 3i$

Lesson 5-6 Complex Numbers   **273**

For more practice, see *Extra Practice*.

EXERCISES

Practice and Problem Solving

Assignment Guide

1 Objective
  Ⓐ Ⓑ Core 1–23, 53–55
  Ⓒ Extension 73

2 Objective
  Ⓐ Ⓑ Core 24–52, 56–70
  Ⓒ Extension 71–72, 74–75

Standardized Test Prep 76–80

Mixed Review 81–89

Error Prevention

Exercises 20–23 Remind students that the absolute value of a complex number is its distance from the origin in the complex plane. Thus, in Exercise 20, $|5 + 12i|$ is not $|5| + |12i| = 17$ but rather $\sqrt{5^2 + 12^2} = 13$.

Exercise 35 Avoid saying that the exercise involves multiplying a negative by a positive imaginary number. The terms *positive* and *negative* connote *greater than 0* and *less than 0*. The order relations $<$, $\le$, $>$, and $\ge$ are undefined for imaginary numbers. They are meaningful only for real numbers.

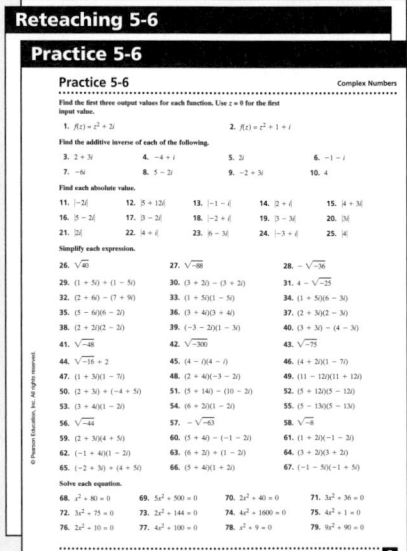

Ⓐ **Practice by Example**

Example 1
(page 270)

Simplify each number by using the imaginary number i.

1. $\sqrt{-4}$ **$2i$**   2. $\sqrt{-7}$ **$i\sqrt{7}$**   3. $\sqrt{-15}$ **$i\sqrt{15}$** 4. $\sqrt{-81}$ **$9i$**   5. $\sqrt{-50}$ **$5i\sqrt{2}$**

6. $\sqrt{-16}$ **$4i$**   7. $\sqrt{-32}$ **$4i\sqrt{2}$** 8. $3\sqrt{-9}$ **$9i$**   9. $-\sqrt{-100}$ **$-10i$**   10. $\sqrt{-72}$ **$6i\sqrt{2}$**

Example 2
(page 271)

Write each number in the form $a + bi$. 11–18. See margin.

11. $2 + \sqrt{-3}$ 12. $\sqrt{-8} + 8$ 13. $6 - \sqrt{-28}$ 14. $\sqrt{-4} + 3$

15. $7 - \sqrt{-25}$ 16. $\sqrt{-1} + 2$ 17. $-\sqrt{-50} - 2$ 18. $\sqrt{-72} + 4$

Example 3
(page 271)

Find the absolute value of each complex number.

19. $|2i|$ **2**   20. $|5 + 12i|$ **13** 21. $|2 - 2i|$ **$2\sqrt{2}$**   22. $|1 - 4i|$ **$\sqrt{17}$**   23. $|3 - 6i|$ **$3\sqrt{5}$**

Example 4
(page 272)

Find the additive inverse of each number.

24. $4i$ **$-4i$**   25. $5 - 3i$ **$-5 + 3i$**   26. $9 + i$ **$-9 - i$** 27. $-3 - 2i$ **$3 + 2i$**   28. $-4 + 7i$ **$4 - 7i$**

Example 5
(page 272)

Simplify each expression. 29–40. See margin p. 274–275.

29. $(2 + 4i) + (4 - i)$ 30. $(-3 - 5i) + (4 - 2i)$ 31. $(7 + 9i) + (-5i)$

32. $6 - (8 + 3i)$ 33. $(12 + 5i) - (2 - i)$ 34. $(-6 - 7i) - (1 + 3i)$

Example 6
(page 272)

35. $(-2i)(5i)$ 36. $(4 - 3i)(5 + 2i)$ 37. $(8 + i)(2 + 7i)$

38. $(-6 - 5i)(1 + 3i)$ 39. $(-6i)^2$ 40. $(9 + 4i)^2$

Example 7
(page 273)

Solve each equation. Check your answers.

41. $x^2 + 25 = 0$ **$\pm 5i$**   42. $2x^2 + 1 = 0$ **$\pm\frac{i\sqrt{2}}{2}$**   43. $3s^2 + 2 = -62$ **$\pm\frac{8i\sqrt{3}}{3}$**

44. $x^2 = -7$ **$\pm i\sqrt{7}$**   45. $x^2 + 36 = 0$ **$\pm 6i$**   46. $-5x^2 - 3 = 0$ **$\pm\frac{i\sqrt{15}}{5}$**

Example 8
(page 273)

Find the first three output values of each fractal-generating function. Use $z = 0$ as the first input value.

47. $z^2 - i$ **$-i, -1 - i, i$**   48. $f(z) = z^2 - 2i$ **$-2i, -4 - 2i, 12 + 14i$**   49. $f(z) = z^2 + 1 - i$ **$1 - i, 1 - 3i, -7 - 7i$**

Ⓑ **Apply Your Skills**

Solve each equation.

50. $x^2 + 16 = -49$ **$\pm i\sqrt{65}$** 51. $x^2 - 30 = -79$ **$\pm 7i$**   52. $3x^2 + 1 = x^2 - 1$ **$\pm i$**

53. **Writing** In reality, is it possible for Mr. Milde's average to be an imaginary number? Explain. **See margin p. 275.**

ROBOTMAN by Jim Meddick

 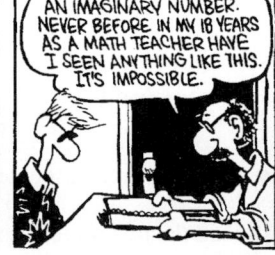 

pages 274–276 Exercises

11. $2 + i\sqrt{3}$

12. $8 + 2i\sqrt{2}$

13. $6 - 2i\sqrt{7}$

14. $3 + 2i$

15. $7 - 5i$

16. $2 + i$

17. $-2 - 5i\sqrt{2}$

18. $4 + 6i\sqrt{2}$

29. $6 + 3i$

30. $1 - 7i$

31. $7 + 4i$

32. $-2 - 3i$

33. $10 + 6i$

54. a. Name the complex number represented by each point on the graph at the right.
  b. Find the additive inverse of each number. **a–b. See margin.**

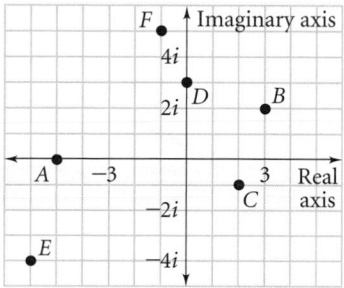

55. a. Open-Ended Name eight complex numbers that have absolute values of 10. Plot them in a complex number plane.
  b. Geometry What is the geometric figure that contains *all* the points that have absolute values of 10? **a–b. See margin.**

56. Solve $(x + 3i)(x - 3i) = 34.$ **−5, 5**

Simplify each expression.

57. $(8i)(4i)(-9i)$ **288i**

58. $(2 + \sqrt{-1}) + (-3 + \sqrt{-16})$ **−1 + 5i**

59. $(4 + \sqrt{-9}) + (6 - \sqrt{-49})$

60. $(10 + \sqrt{-9}) - (2 + \sqrt{-25})$

61. $(8 - \sqrt{-1}) - (-3 + \sqrt{-16})$

62. $2i(5 - 3i)$ **6 + 10i**

63. $-5(1 + 2i) + 3i(3 - 4i)$ **7 − i**

64. $(3 + \sqrt{-4})(4 + \sqrt{-1})$ **10 + 11i**

65. $(-2 + \sqrt{-9})(6 + \sqrt{-25})$ **−27 + 8i**

66. $(1 - \sqrt{-4})(-3 - \sqrt{-25})$ **−13 + i**

67. a. Copy and complete the table.
  b. Number pairs such as p and q in the table are complex conjugates. Describe at least three patterns you see in complex conjugate pairs.

Values of p and q	$p + q$	$p \cdot q$	$\|p\|$	$\|q\|$
$p = 1 + 2i, q = 1 - 2i$	■	■	■	■
$p = 3 - i, q = 3 + i$	■	■	■	■
$p = -6 + 8i, q = -6 - 8i$	■	■	■	■

  c. Plot each pair of conjugates. How are the points of each pair related?
  d. True or false: The conjugate of an additive inverse is equal to the additive inverse of the conjugate. Explain your answer. **a–d. See back of book.**

Two complex numbers $a + bi$ and $c + di$ are equal when $a = c$ and $b = d$. Solve each equation for x and y.

68. $2x + 3yi = -14 + 9i$
  $x = -7, y = 3$

69. $3x + 19i = 16 - 8yi$
  $x = \frac{16}{3}, y = -\frac{19}{8}$

70. $-14 - 3i = 2x + yi$
  $x = -7, y = -3$

 Challenge

71. Show that the product of a nonzero complex number $a + bi$ and its conjugate (as described in Exercise 67) is a real number. **See margin.**

72. Fractals The fractal at the left can be described by the function $f(z) = z^2 + c$. If $c = 0.383 + 0.11i$, find the first two output values of the function. Use $z = 0$ as the first input value.
  0.383 + 0.11i, 0.517589 + 0.19426i

73. For what real values of x and y is $(x + yi)^2$ an imaginary number? **nonzero real numbers x and y**

74. Complex numbers can be used to generate interesting patterns. Here is a pattern generated by powers of $1 + 3i$. **See back of book.**

$(1 + 3i)^1 = 1 + 3i$ and $1^2 + 3^2 = 10$
$(1 + 3i)^2 = -8 + 6i$ and $(-8)^2 + 6^2 = 10^2$
$(1 + 3i)^3 = -26 - 18i$ and $(-26)^2 + (-18)^2 = 10^3$
$(1 + 3i)^4 = 28 - 96i$ and $28^2 + (-96)^2 = 10^4$

Find the powers of $3 + 4i$ through $(3 + 4i)^5$. Generate and verify a similar pattern.

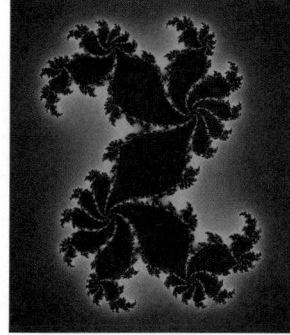

Exercise 72

34. $-7 - 10i$

35. 10

36. $26 - 7i$

37. $9 + 58i$

38. $9 - 23i$

39. −36

40. $65 + 72i$

53. No; the test scores were real numbers. He added the scores and divided

by the number of scores. The set of real numbers is closed with respect to addition and division so he should have gotten a real number

Lesson Quiz 5-6

1. Simplify $-\sqrt{-169}$. **−13i**
2. Find $|-1 + i|$. **$\sqrt{2}$**

Simplify each expression.

3. $(-7i)(-3i)$ **−21**
4. $(9 + 10i) + (-7 + 4i)$
   2 + 14i
5. $(-3 + 4i) - (-3 - 8i)$ **12i**
6. $(-5 + 2i)(7 - 4i)$
   −27 + 34i
7. Solve $\frac{1}{2}x^2 + 2 = 0$. **±2i**

Alternative Assessment

Ask each student to write two complex numbers, where a and b are nonzero, on a sheet of paper. Students trade papers. Each student then adds, subtracts, and multiplies the numbers on the paper he or she received. Students also find the absolute value of each complex number. Students check one another's work.

54a. A: −5, **B:** 3 + 2i,
  C: 2 − i, **D:** 3i,
  E: −6 − 4i,
  F: −1 + 5i

  b. 5, −3 − 2i, −2 + i,
  6 + 4i, 1 − 5i

55a. Check students' work.

  b. a circle with radius 10 and center at the origin

71. $(a + bi)(a - bi) =$
  $a^2 + b^2$; since a and b are real, so is $a^2 + b^2$.

275

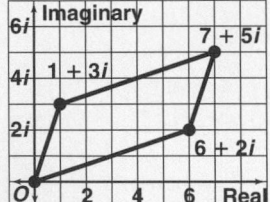
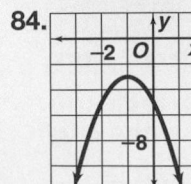
75. Critical Thinking Graph $1 + 3i$ and $6 + 2i$. Also graph their sum. Draw the quadrilateral that has these three points and the origin as vertices. Repeat with other complex numbers. What do you notice?   **See margin.**

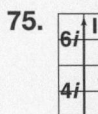

Standardized Test Prep

Multiple Choice

76. What is the number $\sqrt{-225} + 36$ when written in the form $a + bi$? **D**
   A. $-15 + 6i$ **B.** $6 + 15i$ **C.** $6 - 15i$ **D.** $36 + 15i$

77. How can you rewrite the expression $(8 - 5i)^2$ in the form $a + bi$? **G**
   F. $39 + 80i$ **G.** $39 - 80i$ **H.** $69 + 80i$ **I.** $69 - 80i$

Take It to the NET
Online lesson quiz at
www.PHSchool.com
Web Code: aga-0506

78. What are the solutions of $-4x^2 - 72 = 0$? **B**
   A. $\pm2i\sqrt{3}$ **B.** $\pm3i\sqrt{2}$ **C.** $\pm2\sqrt{3}$ **D.** $\pm3\sqrt{2}$

79. Which description of the graph of $y = ax^2 + bx + c$ is NOT possible? **H**
   F. There are two x-intercepts, the vertex is below the x-axis, and $a > 0$.
   G. There is one x-intercept and the vertex is on the x-axis.
   H. There are two x-intercepts, the vertex is below the x-axis, and $a < 0$.
   I. There are no x-intercepts, the vertex is above the x-axis, and $a > 0$.

Extended Response

80. Use factoring to find all complex solutions to $x^4 - 16 = 0$. Show your work.
   See back of book.

Mixed Review

Lesson 5-5   Solve each equation using a graphing calculator.

81. $2x^2 + 3x - 4 = 0$ **82.** $4x^2 + x = 1$ **83.** $x^2 = -7x - 8$
   $-2.351, 0.851$ $-0.640, 0.390$ $-5.562, -1.438$

Lesson 5-2   Graph each function.   **84–86. See margin.**

84. $y = -2(x + 1)^2 - 3$ **85.** $y = \frac{1}{2}(x - 4)^2 + 1$ **86.** $y = 3(x - 1)^2 - 5$

Lesson 3-5   Graph each point in coordinate space.   **87–89. See margin p. 276–277.**

87. $(2, 0, -4)$ **88.** $(0, -3, 5)$ **89.** $(9, -1, 0)$

✓ Checkpoint Quiz 2   Lessons 5-4 through 5-6

iTEXT Instant self-check quiz online and on CD-ROM

Factor each quadratic expression.

1. $2x^2 + x - 6$ **2.** $5x^2 - 45$ **3.** $4x^2 - 36x + 81$
   $(2x - 3)(x + 2)$ $5(x + 3)(x - 3)$ $(2x - 9)^2$

Solve each equation.

4. $(3x - 3)(2x + 8) = 0$ **5.** $x^2 - 2x + 1 = 0$ **1**   **6.** $x^2 + 121 = 0$ **±11i**
   $-4, 1$

Find the absolute value of each number.

7. $5 - 2i$ $\sqrt{29}$ **8.** $9 - i$ $\sqrt{82}$ **9.** $7 + 4i$ $\sqrt{65}$

10. Can you solve the equation $x^2 + 7x + 14 = 0$ by graphing the related function $y = x^2 + 7x + 14$? Explain. **No; the graph does not intersect the x-axis.**

85.

86.

87.

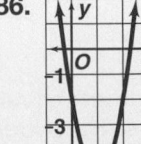

$(2, 0, -4)$

Completing the Square

Use tiles or draw a diagram. Copy the model below.

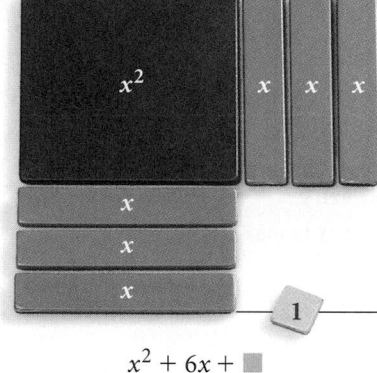

$x^2 + 6x + \blacksquare$

1. a. Add unit tiles until you have a complete square. How many tiles did you add? **9**
   b. Write an expression to represent the sum of the areas of the tiles. $x^2 + 6x + 9$
   c. Write an expression to represent the length times the width of the completed square. $(x + 3)(x + 3)$
   d. How do the six x-tiles in the model relate to the length of the sides of the completed square? To the number of unit tiles used? **See margin.**

2. Suppose the expression $x^2 + 8x + \blacksquare$ can also be modeled by a complete square of tiles. **a. See margin.**
   a. Draw a diagram or use tiles to find the missing value.
   b. What is the coefficient of x in the expression? **8**
   c. Critical Thinking How can you use the coefficient of x to find the length of the completed square? **Add half the coefficient of x to x.**

3. Suppose $x^2 - 4x + \blacksquare$ can be modeled by a complete square of tiles. Using red to represent negative values, draw a diagram or use tiles to find the missing value. **See margin.**

EXERCISES

Complete each square. Then write an expression that represents the sum of the areas of the tiles and an expression that represents the length times the width of the completed square. **1–3. See back of book.**

1.

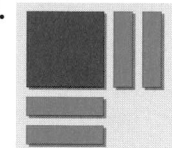

2.

3.

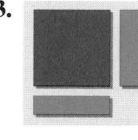

Assume that each expression can be modeled by a complete square of tiles. Find the missing value.

4. $x^2 + 14x + \blacksquare$ **49**   **5.** $x^2 + 20x + \blacksquare$ **100**

6. $x^2 + 10x + \blacksquare$ **25**   **7.** $x^2 + 100x + \blacksquare$ **2500**

8. $x^2 + 32x + \blacksquare$ **256**   **9.** $x^2 - 8x + \blacksquare$ **16**

10. Make a Conjecture In Lesson 5-5, you solved quadratic equations by taking square roots. How could you use that method together with completing the square to solve $x^2 + 6x + 6 = 0$? **See back of book.**

Investigation

Completing the Square

Using algebra tiles for demonstrating the process of completing the square is very helpful to both visual and tactile learners. They make and see the square.

Resources

Students may use algebra tiles or diagrams for the work in this investigation.

Teaching Notes

Inclusion
Students who have difficulty drawing diagrams will find it helpful to use algebra tiles for this investigation.

Error Prevention
Exercise 10 Some students may try to get a perfect-square trinomial on the left side by rewriting the equation as $x^2 + 4x + 4 = -2x - 2$. Help students see why this leads to a dead end.

page 277 Investigation

1d. Half of the six x-tiles complete the length of each side of the square; the square of this number is the number of unit tiles.

2a.

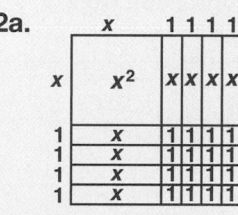

16

3.

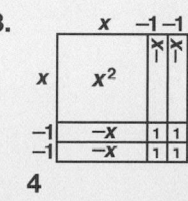

4

88.

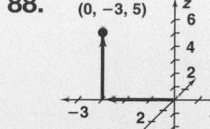

89.

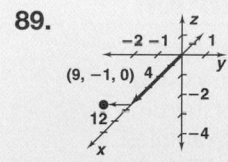

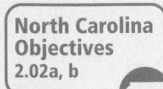

Lesson Preview

 Check Skills You'll Need

Modeling Data With Quadratic Functions
Lesson 5-1: Example 1
Exercises 1–9
Extra Practice, p. 826

Lesson Resources

 Teaching Resources
Practice, Reteaching, Enrichment

 Reaching All Students
Practice Workbook 5-7
Spanish Practice Workbook 5-7

 **Presentation Assistant Plus!**
Transparencies
• Check Skills You'll Need 5-7
• Additional Examples 5-7
• Student Edition Answers 5-7
• Lesson Quiz 5-7
PH Presentation Pro CD 5-7

ASSESSMENT SYSTEM

Computer Test Generator CD

 Technology
Resource Pro® CD-ROM
Computer Test Generator CD
Prentice Hall Presentation Pro CD

 www.PHSchool.com
Student Site
• Teacher Web Code: agk-5500
• Self-grading Lesson Quiz
Teacher Center
• Lesson Planner
• Resources

Plus **iTEXT**

278

5-7

Completing the Square

2.02 Use quadratic functions and inequalities to model and solve problems. a) Solve using algebraic properties. b) Interpret the constants and coefficients in the context of the problem.

Lesson Preview

What You'll Learn

 OBJECTIVE 1
To solve equations by completing the square

 OBJECTIVE 2
To rewrite functions by completing the square

. . . And Why

To find a price to maximize profit, as in Example 7

✓ **Check Skills You'll Need** (For help, go to Lesson 5-1 and page 262.)

Simplify each expression.

1. $(x - 3)(x - 3)$ $x^2 - 6x + 9$ **2.** $(2x - 1)(2x - 1)$ $4x^2 - 4x + 1$

3. $(x + 4)(x + 4) - 3$ $x^2 + 8x + 13$ **4.** $\pm\sqrt{25}$ ± 5

5. $\pm\sqrt{48}$ $\pm 4\sqrt{3}$ **6.** $\pm\sqrt{-4}$ $\pm 2i$ **7.** $\pm\sqrt{\frac{9}{16}}$ $\pm\frac{3}{4}$

New Vocabulary   • completing the square

iTEXT Interactive lesson includes instant self-check, tutorials, and activities.

You can solve an equation in which one side is a perfect square trinomial by taking the square root of each side.

1 **EXAMPLE**   **Solving a Perfect Square Trinomial Equation**

Solve $x^2 + 10x + 25 = 36$.

$x^2 + 10x + 25 = 36$

$(x + 5)^2 = 36$ **Factor the trinomial.**

$x + 5 = \pm 6$ **Find the square root of each side.**

$x + 5 = 6$ or $x + 5 = -6$ **Solve for x.**

$x = 1$ or $x = -11$

✓ **Check Understanding** ❶ Solve $x^2 - 14x + 49 = 81$.   **−2, 16**

 Reading Math
Quadratic comes from the Latin word for "square."

If one side of an equation is not a perfect square trinomial, you can convert it into a perfect square trinomial by rewriting the constant term. The process of finding the last term of a perfect square trinomial is called **completing the square.** Use the following relationship to find the term that will complete the square.

$$x^2 + bx + \left(\frac{b}{2}\right)^2 = \left(x + \frac{b}{2}\right)^2$$

2 **EXAMPLE**   **Completing the Square**

Find the missing value to complete the square: $x^2 - 8x + \blacksquare$.

$\left(\frac{b}{2}\right)^2 = \left(\frac{-8}{2}\right)^2 = 16$ **Find $\left(\frac{b}{2}\right)^2$. Substitute −8 for b.**

$x^2 - 8x + 16$ **Complete the square.**

✓ **Check Understanding** ❷ Find the missing value to complete the square: $x^2 + 7x + \blacksquare$. $\frac{49}{4}$

278   Chapter 5   Quadratic Equations and Functions

 Ongoing Assessment and Intervention

Before the Lesson
Diagnose prerequisite skills using:
• Check Skills You'll Need

During the Lesson
Monitor progress using:
• Check Understanding
• Additional Examples
• Standardized Test Prep

After the Lesson
Assess knowledge using:
• Lesson Quiz
• Computer Test Generator CD

You can solve any quadratic equation by completing the square.

3 EXAMPLE Solving by Completing the Square

Solve $x^2 - 12x + 5 = 0$.

$\left(\dfrac{-12}{2}\right)^2 = 36$ Find $\left(\dfrac{b}{2}\right)^2$.

$x^2 - 12x = -5$ Rewrite so all terms containing x are on one side.

$x^2 - 12x + 36 = -5 + 36$ Complete the square by adding 36 to each side.

$(x - 6)^2 = 31$ Factor the perfect square trinomial.

$x - 6 = \pm\sqrt{31}$ Find the square root of each side.

$x = 6 \pm\sqrt{31}$ Solve for x.

Check

$x^2 - 12x + 5 \stackrel{?}{=} 0$

$(6 +\sqrt{31})^2 - 12(6 +\sqrt{31}) + 5 \stackrel{?}{=} 0$

$6^2 + 2(6\sqrt{31}) + (\sqrt{31})^2 - 72 - 12\sqrt{31} + 5 \stackrel{?}{=} 0$

$36 + 12\sqrt{31} + 31 - 72 - 12\sqrt{31} + 5 \stackrel{?}{=} 0$

$(36 + 31 - 72 + 5) + (12\sqrt{31} - 12\sqrt{31}) \stackrel{?}{=} 0$

$0 = 0 \checkmark$

$x^2 - 12x + 5 \stackrel{?}{=} 0$

$(6 -\sqrt{31})^2 - 12(6 -\sqrt{31}) + 5 \stackrel{?}{=} 0$

$6^2 - 2(6\sqrt{31}) + (\sqrt{31})^2 - 72 + 12\sqrt{31} + 5 \stackrel{?}{=} 0$

$36 - 12\sqrt{31} + 31 - 72 + 12\sqrt{31} + 5 \stackrel{?}{=} 0$

$(36 + 31 - 72 + 5) - (12\sqrt{31} - 12\sqrt{31}) \stackrel{?}{=} 0$

$0 = 0 \checkmark$

This stamp commemorates the 1200th birthday of al-Khwarizmi (780-850), who showed how to solve equations by completing the square. His book *Al-jabr w'al muqabala* gave algebra its name.

✓ Check Understanding **3** Solve each equation. Check your solution.
a. $x^2 + 4x - 4 = 0$ $-2 \pm 2\sqrt{2}$ **b.** $x^2 - 2x - 1 = 0$ $1 \pm \sqrt{2}$

By completing the square, you can solve equations that cannot be solved by factoring, taking square roots, or graphing.

4 EXAMPLE Finding Complex Solutions

Solve $x^2 - 8x + 36 = 0$.

$\left(\dfrac{-8}{2}\right)^2 = 16$ Find $\left(\dfrac{b}{2}\right)^2$.

$x^2 - 8x = -36$ Rewrite so all terms containing x are on one side.

$x^2 - 8x + 16 = -36 + 16$ Complete the square by adding 16 to each side.

$(x - 4)^2 = -20$ Factor the perfect square trinomial.

$x - 4 = \pm\sqrt{-20}$ Find the square root of each side.

$x = 4 \pm 2i\sqrt{5}$ Solve for x and simplify.

✓ Check Understanding **4 a.** Check the solution to Example 4.   **a–b. See back of book.**
b. Try solving the same equation with a graphing calculator. Explain your results.
c. Solve $x^2 + 6x = -34$. $-3 \pm 5i$

👥 Reaching All Students

| **Below Level** Have students explain why the constant term, *c*, must be greater than or equal to zero in order for the trinomial to be a perfect square. | **Advanced Learners** Have students derive the quadratic formula, solving $ax^2 + bx + c = 0$ by factoring after completing the square. | **English Learners** See note on page 279. **Auditory Learners** See note on page 279. |

---

2. Teach

Professional Development

Math Background

Completing the square provides a useful tool for locating the vertex of a quadratic function. This method explains the formula $x = -\dfrac{b}{2a}$ that was used in Lesson 5-2. Also, completing the square and the square root technique learned in Lesson 5-5 combine in the proof of the quadratic formula in Lesson 5-8. This is the method that will allow students to solve any quadratic equation.

OBJECTIVE

1 Teaching Notes

1 EXAMPLE English Learners

Be sure students understand that a *perfect square trinomial* is the product of a squared binomial.

2 EXAMPLE Auditory Learners

Help students understand that $\left(\dfrac{b}{2}\right)^2$ is actually taking half of *b* and squaring it. Have them repeat the phrase "take half of *b* and square it" a few times to help them remember what to do.

3 EXAMPLE Teaching Tip

Explain to students that the purpose of completing the square is to transform the trinomial side of the equation into a perfect square, not both sides. Therefore, the right side of the equation may still have a radical or complex number when it is completely simplified.

4 EXAMPLE Error Prevention

It is a common error to forget to add 16 to both sides. Remind students of the Addition Property of Equality. You cannot add an amount to only one side of an equation and preserve equality.

🖊 Additional Examples

1 Solve $x^2 - 12x + 36 = 9$.   **3, 9**

2 Find the missing value to complete the square: $x^2 + 20x + \blacksquare$.   **100**

279

3 Solve $x^2 + 4x + 1 = 0$.
$-2 \pm \sqrt{3}$

4 Solve $x^2 + 6x + 12 = 0$.
$-3 \pm i\sqrt{3}$

5 Solve $2x^2 = -7x + 1$.
$-\frac{7}{4} \pm \frac{\sqrt{57}}{4}$

OBJECTIVE

2 Teaching Notes

6 **EXAMPLE** Math Tip

Point out that the technique used in this example can be combined with the technique used in Example 5 to rewrite, in vertex form, an equation in which $a \neq 1$, such as $y = 4x^2 + 9x + 3$.

7 **EXAMPLE** Teaching Tip

You may want to start with a simpler example with a leading coefficient of -1, such as $P = -x^2 - 6x + 3$. Then move on to the more difficult function in the example.

 Additional Examples

6 Write $y = x^2 + 5x + 2$ in vertex form.
$y = \left(x + \frac{5}{2}\right)^2 - \frac{17}{4}$

7 The monthly profit P from the sale of rugs woven by a family rug-making business depends on the price r that they charge for a rug. The profit is modeled by $P = -r^2 + 500r - 59,500$. Write the function in vertex form. Use the vertex form to find the price that yields the maximum monthly profit and the amount of the maximum profit.
$P = -(r - 250)^2 + 3000$;
price = $250, profit = $3000

Closure

Ask: *If a quadratic expression is not a perfect-square trinomial, how can you find the number you would add to each side to get a perfect-square trinomial on the left side of the equation?* **Divide each side by the coefficient of x^2. Then find half the coefficient of x and square the result. Add this value to each side.**

280

When the quadratic term has a coefficient that is not 1, you can still solve by completing the square. First divide each side of the equation by the coefficient.

5 **EXAMPLE** Solving When $a \neq 1$

Solve $5x^2 = 6x + 8$.

$$5x^2 = 6x + 8$$

$$x^2 = \frac{6}{5}x + \frac{8}{5} \quad \text{Divide each side by 5.}$$

$$x^2 - \frac{6}{5}x = \frac{8}{5} \quad \text{Rewrite so all terms containing } x \text{ are on one side.}$$

$$\left(\frac{-\frac{6}{5}}{2}\right)^2 = \left(-\frac{3}{5}\right)^2 = \frac{9}{25} \quad \text{Find } \left(\frac{b}{2}\right)^2.$$

$$x^2 - \frac{6}{5}x + \frac{9}{25} = \frac{8}{5} + \frac{9}{25} \quad \text{Complete the square by adding } \frac{9}{25} \text{ to each side.}$$

$$\left(x - \frac{3}{5}\right)^2 = \frac{49}{25} \quad \text{Factor the perfect square trinomial.}$$

$$x - \frac{3}{5} = \pm\sqrt{\frac{49}{25}} \quad \text{Find the square root of each side.}$$

$$x = \frac{3}{5} \pm \frac{7}{5} \quad \text{Solve for } x.$$

$$x = 2, -\frac{4}{5} \quad \text{Simplify.}$$

✓ **Check Understanding** **5** Solve each quadratic equation by completing the square.
a. $2x^2 + x = 6$ $-2, \frac{3}{2}$ **b.** $2x^2 = 3x - 4$ $\frac{3}{4} \pm \frac{i\sqrt{23}}{4}$

OBJECTIVE

2 **Rewriting a Function by Completing the Square**

Need Help?

Vertex form of a quadratic function:
$y = a(x - h)^2 + k$

In Lesson 5-3 you converted quadratic functions into vertex form by using $x = -\frac{b}{2a}$ to find the x-coordinate of the parabola's vertex. Then, by substituting for x, you found the y-coordinate of the vertex. Another way of rewriting a function is to complete the square.

When completing the square, it is convenient to work with just one side of a function equation. For example, $y = x^2 + 6x + 2$ is equivalent to $y = x^2 + 6x + 9 + 2 - 9$. When you add 9 to the right side of the equation, you must remember to subtract 9 to keep the equality true.

6 **EXAMPLE** Rewriting in Vertex Form

Write $y = x^2 + 6x + 2$ in vertex form.

$y = x^2 + 6x + 2$

$= x^2 + 6x + 3^2 + 2 - 3^2 \quad$ **Complete the square. Add and subtract 3^2 on the right side.**

$= (x + 3)^2 + 2 - 9 \quad$ **Factor the perfect square trinomial.**

$= (x + 3)^2 - 7 \quad$ **Simplify.**

The vertex form is $y = (x + 3)^2 - 7$.

✓ **Check Understanding** **6** Write each equation in vertex form.
a. $y = x^2 - 10x - 2$ $y = (x - 5)^2 - 27$ **b.** $y = x^2 + 5x + 3$ $y = \left(x + \frac{5}{2}\right)^2 - \frac{13}{4}$

280 Chapter 5 Quadratic Equations and Functions

---

pages 281–283 Exercises

13. $-4, 7$

14. $-1, 4$

15. $-3 \pm 4i\sqrt{2}$

When the coefficient of the quadratic term is not 1, factor out the coefficient from the quadratic and linear terms. Remember that the factored coefficient is distributed to all terms within the parentheses.

3. Practice

7 EXAMPLE Real-World  Connection

Handmade Clothing The profit P from handmade sweaters depends on the price s at which each sweater is sold. The function $P = -s^2 + 120s - 2000$ models the monthly profit from sweaters for one custom tailor. Write the function in vertex form. Use the vertex form to find the price that yields the maximum monthly profit and the amount of the maximum profit.

$P = -s^2 + 120s - 2000$

$= -(s^2 - 120s) - 2000$ **Factor -1 from the first two terms.**

$= -[s^2 - 120s + (-60)^2] - 2000 + (-60)^2$ **Add and subtract $(-60)^2$ on the right side.**

$= -(s - 60)^2 - 2000 + 3600$ **Factor the perfect-square trinomial.**

$= -(s - 60)^2 + 1600$ **Simplify in vertex form.**

Careers Custom tailors use math to design clothing and to calculate profit.

The vertex is $(60, 1600)$. A price of \$60 per sweater gives a maximum monthly profit of \$1600.

✓ **Check Understanding** **7** **a.** Use vertex form to find the vertex of $P = -\frac{1}{2}s^2 + 280s - 1200$. **(280, 38,000)**
   b. How do you know the vertex represents a maximum point?
   The coefficient of s^2 is negative, so the parabola opens downward.

Assignment Guide

▼**1 Objective**
   Ⓐ Ⓑ **Core** 1–27, 40–48, 51–56

▼**2 Objective**
   Ⓐ Ⓑ **Core** 28–39, 49–50
   Ⓒ **Extension** 57–63

Standardized Test Prep 64–68

Mixed Review 69–77

Error Prevention

Exercises 21–27 Students may add the wrong amount to the right side of the equation when they are completing the square. Caution them to remember to use the Distributive Property in deciding what number they should add on the right side.

EXERCISES

For more practice, see *Extra Practice*.

Practice and Problem Solving

Ⓐ **Practice by Example**

Example 1 (page 278)

Solve each equation.

1. $x^2 + 6x + 9 = 1$ **−4, −2**
2. $x^2 - 4x + 4 = 100$ **−8, 12**
3. $x^2 - 2x + 1 = 4$ **−1, 3**

4. $x^2 + 8x + 16 = \frac{16}{9}$ $-\frac{16}{3}, -\frac{8}{3}$
5. $4x^2 + 4x + 1 = 49$ **−4, 3**
6. $x^2 - 12x + 36 = 25$ **1, 11**

Example 2 (page 278)

Complete the square.

7. $x^2 + 18x + \blacksquare$ **81**
8. $x^2 - x + \blacksquare$ $\frac{1}{4}$
9. $x^2 - 24x + \blacksquare$ **144**

10. $x^2 + 20x + \blacksquare$ **100**
11. $m^2 - 3m + \blacksquare$ $\frac{9}{4}$
12. $x^2 + 4x + \blacksquare$ **4**

Examples 3 and 4 (page 279)

Solve each quadratic equation by completing the square.

13. $x^2 - 3x = 28$
14. $x^2 - 3x = 4$
15. $x^2 + 6x + 41 = 0$

13–27. See margin.

16. $x^2 - 2x = -2$
17. $w^2 - 8w - 9 = 0$
18. $x^2 + 6x = -22$

19. $x^2 + 4 = 0$
20. $-x^2 - 2x = 5$
21. $6x - 3x^2 = -12$

Example 5 (page 280)

22. $2p^2 = 6p - 20$
23. $3x^2 - 12x + 7 = 0$
24. $4c^2 + 10c = -7$

25. $2x^2 + x - 28 = 0$
26. $9x^2 - 12x + 5 = 0$
27. $4x^2 + 4x = 3$

Example 6 (page 280)

Rewrite each equation in vertex form. **28–33. See margin.**

28. $y = x^2 + 4x - 7$
29. $y = -x^2 + 4x - 1$
30. $y = -2x^2 + 6x + 1$

31. $y = x^2 + 4x + 1$
32. $y = 2x^2 - 8x + 1$
33. $y = -x^2 - 2x + 3$

Lesson 5-7   Completing the Square   **281**

16. $1 \pm i$
17. $-1, 9$
18. $-3 \pm i\sqrt{13}$
19. $\pm 2i$

20. $-1 \pm 2i$
21. $1 \pm \sqrt{5}$
22. $\frac{3}{2} \pm \frac{i\sqrt{31}}{2}$
23. $2 \pm \frac{\sqrt{15}}{3}$

24. $-\frac{5}{4} \pm \frac{i\sqrt{3}}{4}$
25. $-4, \frac{7}{2}$
26. $\frac{2}{3} \pm \frac{1}{3}i$
27. $-\frac{3}{2}, \frac{1}{2}$

28. $y = (x + 2)^2 - 11$
29. $y = -(x - 2)^2 + 3$
30. $y = -2\left(x - \frac{3}{2}\right)^2 + \frac{11}{2}$
31. $y = (x + 2)^2 - 3$
32. $y = 2(x - 2)^2 - 7$
33. $y = -(x + 1)^2 + 4$

281

Alternative Assessment

Give students several quadratic equations to solve by completing the square. When students have solved the problems, ask them to use graphing calculators to check their solutions. If they have any discrepancies, ask them to work through the problem again to find their mistakes.

Diversity

Exercise 39 Some students may not be familiar enough with football to understand the terms used in this exercise. Ask for a volunteer to explain the meaning of *punted football, defensive player,* and *block the punt.*

pages 281–283 Exercises

34. $y = -4\left(x + \frac{5}{8}\right)^2 + \frac{73}{16}$;
$\left(-\frac{5}{8}, \frac{73}{16}\right)$

35. $y = \frac{1}{2}(x - 5)^2 - \frac{1}{2}$;
$\left(5, -\frac{1}{2}\right)$

36. $y = -\frac{1}{5}(x - 2)^2 + 3$;
(2, 3)

38. Add −11 to each side of the given equation to obtain $x^2 + 8x = -11$. Then add the square of half the coefficient of x to each side to obtain $x^2 + 8x + 4^2 = -11 + 4^2$, or $x^2 + 8x + 16 = 5$. Rewrite the left side of the last equation as $(x + 4)^2$ to obtain $(x + 4)^2 = 5$.

39e. Answers may vary. Sample: The path is parabolic. Also, the linear model does not predict that the ball will eventually hit the ground.

Example 7
(page 281)

Rewrite each equation in vertex form. Then find the vertex of the graph.
34–36. See margin.

34. $y = -4x^2 - 5x + 3$ 35. $y = \frac{1}{2}x^2 - 5x + 12$ 36. $y = -\frac{1}{5}x^2 + \frac{4}{5}x + \frac{11}{5}$

37. **Manufacturing** An electronics company has a new line of portable radios with CD players. Their research suggests that the daily sales s for the new product can be modeled by $s = -p^2 + 120p + 1400$, where p is the price of each unit.
   a. Find the vertex of the graph of the function by completing the square.
   b. Find the maximum daily sales. **$5000**   a. (60, 5000)
   c. What price will result in that maximum? **$60**

38. **Writing** Explain the process of rewriting $x^2 + 8x + 11 = 0$ as $(x + 4)^2 = 5$.
See margin.

Reading Math

For help in reading and solving Exercise 39, see page 284.

39. **Sports** The height of a punted football can be modeled with the quadratic function $h = -0.01x^2 + 1.18x + 2$. The horizontal distance in feet from the point of impact with the kicker's foot is x, and h is the height of the ball in feet.

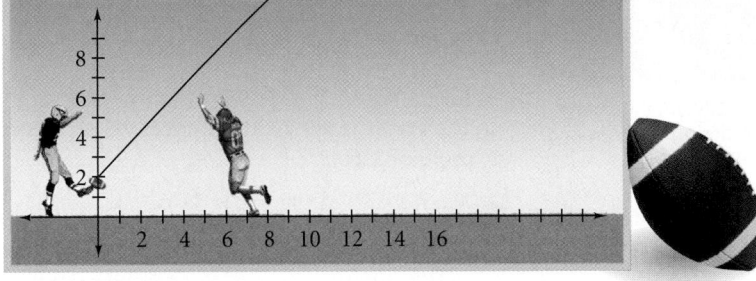

(59, 36.81)
   a. Find the vertex of the graph of the function by completing the square.
   b. What is the maximum height of the punt? **36.81 ft**
   c. The nearest defensive player is 5 ft horizontally from the point of impact. How high must the player reach to block the punt? **7.65 ft**
   d. Suppose the ball was not blocked but continued on its path. How far down field would the ball go before it hit the ground? **about 120 ft**
   e. **Critical Thinking** The linear equation $h = 1.13x + 2$ could model the path of the football shown in the graph. Why is this not a good model?
See margin.

B **Apply Your Skills**

Find the value of k that would make the left side of each equation a perfect square trinomial.

       −10, 10   −20, 20   −22, 22
40. $x^2 + kx + 25 = 0$ 41. $x^2 - kx + 100 = 0$ 42. $x^2 - kx + 121 = 0$
       −16, 16   −18, 18   −10, 10
43. $x^2 + kx + 64 = 0$ 44. $x^2 - kx + 81 = 0$ 45. $25x^2 - kx + 1 = 0$
       −1, 1   −12, 12   −12, 12
46. $x^2 + kx + \frac{1}{4} = 0$ 47. $9x^2 - kx + 4 = 0$ 48. $36x^2 - kx + 1 = 0$

49. **Geometry** The table shows some possible dimensions of rectangles with a perimeter of 100 units. Complete the table.   **a–e. See back of book.**

Width	1	2	3	4	5	6	7	8	9	10
Length	49	48	■	■	■	■	■	■	■	■
Area	49	■	■	■	■	■	■	■	■	■

   a. Plot the points (width, area). Find a model for the data set.
   b. Find another point in the data set and use it to verify your model.
   c. What is a reasonable domain for this function? Explain.
   d. Find the maximum possible area. Find its dimensions.
   e. Find an equation for area in terms of width without using the table. Do you get the same equation as in part (a)? Explain.

Gateway Arch in St. Louis

50. Architecture The shape of the Gateway Arch in St. Louis, Missouri, is a catenary curve, which closely resembles a parabola. The function $y = -\frac{2}{315}x^2 + 4x$ models the shape of the arch, where y is the height in feet and x is the horizontal distance from the base of the left side of the arch in feet.
  a. Graph the function and find its vertex. **See margin.**
  b. According to the model, what is the maximum height of the arch? **630 ft**
  c. What is the width of the arch at the base? **630 ft**

Solve each quadratic equation by completing the square. 51–56. See margin.

51. $\frac{1}{3}x^2 + 8x - 3 = 0$ **52.** $\frac{1}{2}x^2 + 4x = 2$ **53.** $x^2 - \frac{1}{2}x = \frac{1}{3}$

54. $3x^2 + x = \frac{2}{3}$ **55.** $2x^2 - \frac{1}{2}x = \frac{1}{8}$ **56.** $x^2 + \frac{3}{4}x = \frac{1}{2}$

⊙ Challenge   **Solve for x in terms of a. 57–62. See margin.**

57. $2x^2 - ax = 6a^2$ **58.** $3x^2 + ax = a^2$ **59.** $2a^2x^2 - 8ax = -6$

60. $4a^2x^2 + 8ax + 3 = 0$ **61.** $3x^2 + ax^2 = 9x + 9a$ **62.** $6a^2x^2 - 11ax = 10$

63. Solve $x^2 = \left(6\sqrt{2}\right)x + 7$ by completing the square.
  $-5 + 3\sqrt{2}, 5 + 3\sqrt{2}$

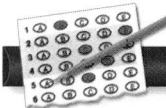

Standardized Test Prep

Multiple Choice

64. What can you add to $x^2 + 5x$ to get a perfect square trinomial? **A**
  A. $\frac{25}{4}$ **B.** $\frac{25}{2}$ **C.** 25   **D.** $2.5x$

Take It to the NET
Online lesson quiz at
www.PHSchool.com
Web Code: aga-0507

65. How can you rewrite the equation $x^2 + 12x + 5 = 3$ so the left side of the equation is in the form $(x + a)^2$? **G**
  F. $(x - 6)^2 = 28$ **G.** $(x + 6)^2 = 34$
  H. $(x + 6)^2 = 39$ **I.** $(x + 12)^2 = -2$

66. What are the solutions of the equation $x^2 + 10x + 40 = 5$? **C**
  A. $10 \pm i\sqrt{5}$ **B.** $5 \pm i\sqrt{10}$ **C.** $-5 \pm i\sqrt{10}$ **D.** $-10 \pm i\sqrt{5}$

Short Response   **67.** Solve $14x = x^2 + 36$. Show your work. **See back of book.**

Extended Response   **68.** List the steps for solving the equation $3x^2 - 6 = -7x$ by the method of completing the square. Explain each step. **See back of book.**

Mixed Review

Lesson 5-6   **Simplify each expression.**

69. $(2 - 3i) + (-4 + 5i)$ **70.** $(7 + 3i) - (2 + i)$ **71.** $(4 - 9i)(3 + 8i)$
    $-2 + 2i$ $5 + 2i$ $84 + 5i$

Lesson 5-1   **Find a quadratic model for each set of data.**

72. $(-4, 3), (-3, 3), (-2, 4)$ **73.** $\left(-1, \frac{1}{2}\right), (0, 2), (2, 2)$ **74.** $(0, 2), (1, 0), (2, 4)$
    $y = \frac{1}{2}x^2 + \frac{7}{2}x + 9$ $y = -\frac{1}{2}x^2 + x + 2$ $y = 3x^2 - 5x + 2$

Lesson 4-8   **Use Cramer's Rule to solve each system.**

75. $\begin{cases} 2x + y = 4 \\ 3x - y = 6 \end{cases}$ **(2, 0)**   **76.** $\begin{cases} 2x + y = 7 \\ -2x + 5y = -1 \end{cases}$ **(3, 1)**   **77.** $\begin{cases} 2x + 4y = 10 \\ 3x + 5y = 14 \end{cases}$ **(3, 1)**

Standardized Test Prep

🗂 **Resources**
For additional practice with a variety of test item formats:
• Standardized Test Prep, p. 297
• Test-Taking Strategies, p. 292
• Test-Taking Strategies with Transparencies

Exercise 65 Emphasize that answer choices F and I can be eliminated because neither -6 nor 12 is half of 12.

50a.
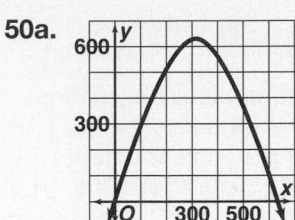

(315, 630)

51. $-12 \pm 3\sqrt{17}$

52. $-4 \pm 2\sqrt{5}$

53. $\frac{1}{4} \pm \frac{\sqrt{57}}{12}$

54. $-\frac{2}{3}, \frac{1}{3}$

55. $\frac{1}{8} \pm \frac{\sqrt{5}}{8}$

56. $-\frac{3}{8} \pm \frac{\sqrt{41}}{8}$

57. $-\frac{3}{2}a, 2a$

58. $\frac{-a \pm a\sqrt{13}}{6}$

59. $\frac{3}{a}, \frac{1}{a}, a \neq 0$

60. $-\frac{3}{2a}, -\frac{1}{2a}, a \neq 0$

61. $3, -\frac{3a}{a + 3}, a \neq -3$

62. $-\frac{2}{3a}, \frac{5}{2a}, a \neq 0$

283

Reading Math

Reading Formulas

Students learn how to read and interpret formulas that are mathematical relationships among quantities. The example involves a formula for the height of the football to the horizontal distance traveled.

Teaching Notes

Make sure students understand that in this formula, h is equivalent to y in a standard quadratic equation, and the h-axis is the same as the y-axis.

Explain that the ball is two feet above the ground when it is kicked because the punter holds the ball and then drop-kicks in during a punt. During a place kick, the ball is kicked from the ground.

For part c, explain that the defensive player is five feet horizontally, or directly in front of, the punter when the ball is kicked. How high must the defensive player reach in order to touch, or block the ball after it has been kicked, assuming that the player is still five feet from where the ball was kicked?

Kinesthetic Learners

Have students model the kick outdoors with an actual football to get a better understanding of the fact that the point of impact is two feet off the ground, and that the flight of the football after it is kicked actually resembles a parabola.

Exercises

Remind students that the quantities in the formula are in feet, not yards, so the answers should be in feeet, or in both feet and yards.

Sports The height of a punted football can be modeled with the quadratic function $h = -0.01x^2 + 1.18x + 2$. The horizontal distance in feet from the point of impact with the kicker's foot is x, and h is the height of the ball in feet.
   a. Find the vertex of the graph of the function by completing the square.
   b. What is the maximum height of the punt?
   c. The nearest defensive player is 5 ft horizontally from the point of impact. How high must the player reach to block the punt?

To understand a formula, identify the formula and its parts.

From the problem, the formula is $h = -0.01x^2 + 1.18x + 2$. The problem gives you some information. You can find other information from the graph.

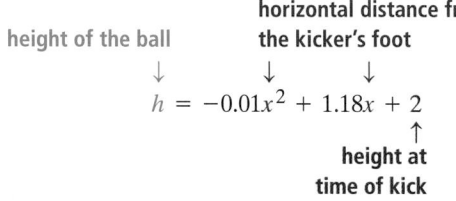

Part (a) of the problem asks you to find the vertex of the graph. By completing the square, you can get an equation in vertex form.

$$h = -0.01(x - 59)^2 + 36.81 \qquad \textbf{vertex form}$$

x-coordinate   **y-coordinate**

Since the y-coordinate of the vertex is 36.81, you know that the maximum height of the football is 36.81 ft. That answers part (b).

To block the punt, the defensive player must touch the football along its path. To answer part (c), find the height of the ball (and the height of the defensive player's hand) when it is horizontally 5 ft from the kicker, or when $x = 5$.

$$
\begin{aligned}
h(5) &= -0.01x^2 + 1.18x + 2 & \textbf{Use the formula.} \\
&= -0.01(5)^2 + 1.18(5) + 2 & \textbf{Substitute.} \\
&= 7.65 & \textbf{Simplify.}
\end{aligned}
$$

The defensive player must reach 7.65 ft above the ground to block the punt.

EXERCISES

1. What is the ball's height when it has traveled 20 yd (60 ft) downfield? **36.8 ft**

2. How far downfield has the ball traveled when it reaches its maximum height? **59 ft**

3. **a.** How far downfield has the ball traveled when it reaches a height of 6 ft?   **3.49 ft, 114.51 ft**
   b. **Reasoning** Explain why part (a) has more than one answer. **The ball reaches 6 ft on the way up and on the way down.**

The Quadratic Formula

 North Carolina Objectives

2.02 Use quadratic functions and inequalities to model and solve problems. a) Solve using algebraic properties. b) Interpret the constants and coefficients in the context of the problem.

1. Plan

Lesson Preview

What You'll Learn

 OBJECTIVE 1
To solve quadratic equations by using the Quadratic Formula

 OBJECTIVE 2
To determine types of solutions by using the discriminant

. . . And Why

To investigate the motion of a field hockey ball, as in Example 5

✓ **Check Skills You'll Need** (For help, go to Lessons 1-2 and 5-1.)

Write each quadratic equation in standard form. 1–4. See margin p. 286.

1. $y = 8 - 10x^2$

2. $y = (x + 2)^2 - 1$

3. $y = -2x(x - 1) + (x + 1)^2$

4. $y = (3x)^2 - (x - 1)^2$

Evaluate the expression $b^2 - 4ac$ for the given values of a, b, and c.

5. $a = 1, b = 6, c = 3$ **24**

6. $a = -5, b = 2, c = 4$ **84**

7. $a = 3, b = -6, c = 7$ **−48**

8. $a = 2, b = 3, c = -10$ **89**

New Vocabulary
• Quadratic Formula • discriminant

Lesson Preview

✓ **Check Skills You'll Need**

Algebraic Expressions
Lesson 1-2: Example 2
Exercises 3, 4
Extra Practice, p. 822

Modeling Data With Quadratic Formulas
Lesson 5-1: Example 1
Exercises 1–9
Extra Practice, p. 826

Lesson Resources

📁 **Teaching Resources**
Practice, Reteaching, Enrichment

👥 **Reaching All Students**
Practice Workbook 5-8
Spanish Practice Workbook 5-8

⏱ **Presentation Assistant Plus!**
Transparencies
• Check Skills You'll Need 5-8
• Additional Examples 5-8
• Student Edition Answers 5-8
• Lesson Quiz 5-8
PH Presentation Pro CD 5-8

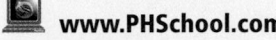 **ASSESSMENT SYSTEM**

Computer Test Generator CD

💿 **Technology**
Resource Pro® CD-ROM
Computer Test Generator CD
Prentice Hall Presentation Pro CD

 **www.PHSchool.com**
Student Site
• Self-grading Lesson Quiz
Teacher Center
• Lesson Planner
• Math Background
• Resources

Plus **iTEXT**

 Interactive lesson includes instant self-check, tutorials, and activities.

OBJECTIVE

1 Using the Quadratic Formula

You can derive a formula for solving quadratic equations by completing the square. Below is the equation $2x^2 + 6x + 1 = 0$. Next to it is the general form of a quadratic equation, $ax^2 + bx + c = 0$. Each equation is solved for x.

$$2x^2 + 6x + 1 = 0$$
$$x^2 + 3x + \tfrac{1}{2} = 0$$
$$x^2 + 3x = -\tfrac{1}{2}$$
$$x^2 + 2\left(\tfrac{3}{2}\right)x + \left(\tfrac{3}{2}\right)^2 = \left(\tfrac{3}{2}\right)^2 - \tfrac{1}{2}$$
$$\left(x + \tfrac{3}{2}\right)^2 = \tfrac{9}{4} - \tfrac{2}{4}$$
$$\left(x + \tfrac{3}{2}\right)^2 = \tfrac{7}{4}$$
$$x + \tfrac{3}{2} = \pm\sqrt{\tfrac{7}{4}}$$
$$x = -\tfrac{3}{2} \pm \tfrac{\sqrt{7}}{2}$$
$$x = \frac{-3 \pm \sqrt{7}}{2}$$

$$ax^2 + bx + c = 0$$
$$x^2 + \tfrac{b}{a}x + \tfrac{c}{a} = 0$$
$$x^2 + \tfrac{b}{a}x = -\tfrac{c}{a}$$
$$x^2 + 2\left(\tfrac{b}{2a}\right)x + \left(\tfrac{b}{2a}\right)^2 = \left(\tfrac{b}{2a}\right)^2 - \tfrac{c}{a}$$
$$\left(x + \tfrac{b}{2a}\right)^2 = \tfrac{b^2}{4a^2} - \tfrac{c}{a}$$
$$\left(x + \tfrac{b}{2a}\right)^2 = \tfrac{b^2 - 4ac}{4a^2}$$
$$x + \tfrac{b}{2a} = \pm\sqrt{\tfrac{b^2 - 4ac}{4a^2}}$$
$$x = -\tfrac{b}{2a} \pm \tfrac{\sqrt{b^2 - 4ac}}{2a}$$
$$x = \frac{-b \pm \sqrt{b^2 - 4ac}}{2a}$$

 Key Concepts

Theorem	**Quadratic Formula**

A quadratic equation written in standard form $ax^2 + bx + c = 0$ can be solved with the Quadratic Formula.

$$x = \frac{-b \pm \sqrt{b^2 - 4ac}}{2a}$$

 Ongoing Assessment and Intervention

Before the Lesson
Diagnose prerequisite skills using:
• Check Skills You'll Need

During the Lesson
Monitor progress using:
• Check Understanding
• Additional Examples
• Standardized Test Prep

After the Lesson
Assess knowledge using:
• Lesson Quiz
• Computer Test Generator CD

Professional Development

Math Background

The development of the quadratic formula, which provides a solution to any quadratic equation in terms of its coefficients, leads one to ask whether or not such formulas exists for cubic and quartic equations. Formulas that depend solely on the coefficients do exist, but are not as straight-forward as the quadratic formula. These methods were first published in Cardano's book *Ars magna* in 1545.

OBJECTIVE

 Teaching Notes

1 EXAMPLE Visual Learners

Stress the importance of substituting correctly and being careful with the calculations. Enclosing the values of a, b, and c in parentheses can be visually helpful at the substitution stage, especially when some of the values are negative.

2 EXAMPLE Math Tip

Stress to students the importance of first writing the equation in standard form.

3 EXAMPLE Teaching Tip

Have students refer to Example 5 on page 265 to refresh their memories on how to obtain the equation $x^2 - x - 1 = 0$.

page 285 Check Skills You'll Need

1. $y = -10x^2 + 8$

2. $y = x^2 + 4x + 3$

3. $y = -x^2 + 4x + 1$

4. $y = 8x^2 - 2x - 1$

page 286 Check Understanding

2b.

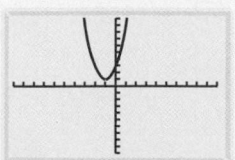

The graph does not intersect the x-axis.

286

---

1 EXAMPLE Using the Quadratic Formula

Use the Quadratic Formula to solve $3x^2 - 5x = 2$.

$3x^2 - 5x - 2 = 0$ **Write in standard form.**

$a = 3, b = -5, c = -2$ **Find the values of a, b, and c.**

$x = \dfrac{-b \pm \sqrt{b^2 - 4ac}}{2a}$ **Write the Quadratic Formula.**

$= \dfrac{-(-5) \pm \sqrt{(-5)^2 - 4(3)(-2)}}{2(3)}$ **Substitute.**

$= \dfrac{5 \pm \sqrt{25 - (-24)}}{6}$ **Simplify.**

$= \dfrac{5 \pm \sqrt{49}}{6}$

$= \dfrac{5 \pm 7}{6}$

$= \dfrac{12}{6}$ or $\dfrac{-2}{6}$

$= 2$ or $-\dfrac{1}{3}$

Check

$3x^2 - 5x = 2$	$3x^2 - 5x = 2$
$3(2)^2 - 5(2) \stackrel{?}{=} 2$	$3\left(-\dfrac{1}{3}\right)^2 - 5\left(-\dfrac{1}{3}\right) \stackrel{?}{=} 2$
$12 - 10 \stackrel{?}{=} 2$	$\dfrac{1}{3} + \dfrac{5}{3} \stackrel{?}{=} 2$
$2 = 2$ ✓	$2 = 2$ ✓

✓ **Check Understanding 1** Use the Quadratic Formula to solve $3x^2 - x = 4$. Check your solutions. $-1, \dfrac{4}{3}$

The Quadratic Formula will give you complex solutions that you cannot find by graphing or factoring.

2 EXAMPLE Finding Complex Solutions

Solve $2x^2 = -6x - 7$.

$2x^2 + 6x + 7 = 0$ **Write in standard form.**

$a = 2, b = 6, c = 7$ **Find the values of a, b, and c.**

$x = \dfrac{-(6) \pm \sqrt{(6)^2 - 4(2)(7)}}{2(2)}$ **Substitute.**

$= \dfrac{-6 \pm \sqrt{36 - 56}}{4}$ **Simplify.**

$= \dfrac{-6 \pm \sqrt{-20}}{4}$

$= \dfrac{-6 \pm 2i\sqrt{5}}{4}$

$= -\dfrac{3}{2} \pm \dfrac{i\sqrt{5}}{2}$

Need Help?

$\sqrt{-1} = i$

✓ **Check Understanding 2 a.** Use the Quadratic Formula to solve $-2x^2 = 4x + 3$. $-1 \pm \dfrac{i\sqrt{2}}{2}$

b. Graph the related quadratic function $y = 2x^2 + 4x + 3$. Explain why you cannot use the graph to find the solution. **See margin.**

🤝 Reaching All Students

Below Level Students may make fewer errors if they memorize the quadratic formula as $\dfrac{-b}{2a} \pm \dfrac{\sqrt{b^2 - 4ac}}{2a}$.	**Advanced Learners** Have students rewrite the quadratic formula for the special cases $b = 0$ or $c = 0$. Ask them to describe how these cases fit into the summary on p. 289.	**Visual Learners** See note on page 286. **Tactile Learners** See note on page 287.

In Lesson 5-5, you found an approximate value for the golden ratio by graphing the related function for the equation $x^2 - x - 1 = 0$. Now you can use the Quadratic Formula to find an exact value for the golden ratio.

3 EXAMPLE · Real-World 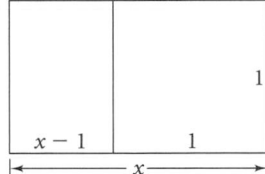 Connection

Art The golden ratio is the ratio of the longer side to the shorter side of a golden rectangle. Solve $x^2 - x - 1 = 0$ for x to find the exact value of the golden ratio.

$x^2 - x - 1 = 0$

$a = 1, b = -1, c = -1$ **Find the values of a, b, and c.**

$x = \dfrac{-b \pm \sqrt{b^2 - 4ac}}{2a}$ **Use the Quadratic Formula.**

$ = \dfrac{-(-1) \pm \sqrt{(-1)^2 - 4(1)(-1)}}{2(1)}$ **Substitute for a, b, and c.**

$ = \dfrac{1 \pm \sqrt{5}}{2}$ **Simplify.**

The golden ratio is $\dfrac{1 + \sqrt{5}}{2} : 1$, or simply $\dfrac{1 + \sqrt{5}}{2}$.

Check Is the answer reasonable? Since $\dfrac{1 - \sqrt{5}}{2}$ is a negative number, and a ratio of actual lengths cannot be negative, that answer is not reasonable. Since $\dfrac{1 + \sqrt{5}}{2} \approx 1.62$, which is the value for the golden ratio found in Lesson 5-5, that answer is reasonable.

 Check Understanding ⬤3 Use the Quadratic Formula to solve each equation. Find the exact solutions. Then approximate any radical solutions. Round to the nearest hundredth.

    a. $4x^2 = 8x - 3$ $\frac{1}{2}, \frac{3}{2}$ **b.** $x^2 + 4x = 41$ $-2 \pm 3\sqrt{5}$; $-8.71, 4.71$

OBJECTIVE
2 Using the Discriminant

Quadratic equations can have real or complex solutions. You can determine the type and number of solutions by finding the discriminant

🔑 **Key Concepts**

Definition	Discriminant of a Quadratic Equation

The **discriminant** of a quadratic equation in the form $ax^2 + bx + c = 0$ is the value of the expression $b^2 - 4ac$.

$$x = \dfrac{-b \pm \sqrt{\overset{\downarrow \, \textbf{discriminant}}{b^2 - 4ac}}}{2a}$$

The table on the next page shows the relationships among the value of the discriminant, the solutions of a quadratic equation, and the graph of the related function. These relationships are true for real number values of $a, b,$ and c.

Real-World 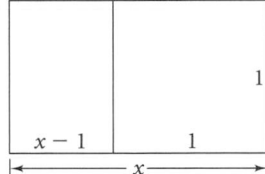 Connection

The golden ratio occurs in nature as well as in art. In sunflowers, the ratio of the number of clockwise spirals to the number of counterclockwise spirals approximates the golden ratio.

Lesson 5-8 The Quadratic Formula   **287**

📋 Additional Examples

❶ Use the Quadratic Formula to solve $3x^2 + 23x + 40 = 0$. $-5, -\frac{8}{3}$

❷ Solve $3x^2 + 2x = -4$. $-\frac{1}{3} \pm \frac{i\sqrt{11}}{3}$

❸ The longer leg of a right triangle is 1 unit longer than the shorter leg. The hypotenuse is 3 units long. What is the length of the shorter leg? $\frac{\sqrt{17} - 1}{2}$ units

OBJECTIVE
2 ⬇ Teaching Notes

❹ EXAMPLE Tactile Learners

Have an index card for each member of the class. On each card write a value for either a, b or c, for example $b = 5$. Randomly hand out the cards. Label three areas of the room as "two real solutions," "one real solution," and "two imaginary solutions." Direct student to arrange themselves in groups of three, each group containing values for a, b, and c. Then move as a group to the appropriate area in the room based on the value of "their" discriminant. Have students in each area compare their discriminants. Some students may incorrectly think that $\sqrt{b^2 - 4ac}$ is the discriminant instead of just $b^2 - 4ac$. Comparing answers will help these students correct their misconception.

Be sure students understand that they do not need to actually solve the equation. The type and number of solutions can be found from the discriminant. All they need to determine is if the discriminant is negative when the height is substituted into the equation. If so, there are no solutions, therefore the ball will not reach the given height.

Additional Examples

4 Determine the type and number of solutions of $x^2 + 5x + 10 = 0$. **two imaginary solutions**

5 A player throws a ball up and toward a wall that is 17 feet high. The height h in feet of the ball t seconds after it leaves the player's hand is modeled by $h = -16t^2 + 25t + 6$. If the ball makes it to where the wall is, will it go over the wall or hit the wall? **It will hit the wall.**

Closure

Have students explain what the discriminant is for a quadratic equation of the form $ax^2 + bx + c = 0$. Ask: *What are some of the things the discriminant is used for?* **The discriminant is the value of $b^2 - 4ac$. Answers may vary. Sample: This value can be used to determine how many roots there are and whether the roots are real or imaginary.**

pages 289–291 Exercises

1. 1, 3

2. −6, −2

3. $-\frac{7}{2}$, 1

4. $-1, \frac{1}{3}$

5. −5

6. $-\frac{5}{2}$, 1

7. $\frac{3 \pm \sqrt{5}}{2}$

8. $-3 \pm \sqrt{14}$

9. $\frac{2 \pm \sqrt{10}}{3}$

288

Value of the Discriminant	Type and Number of Solutions for $ax^2 + bx + c = 0$	Examples of Graphs of Related Functions $y = ax^2 + bx + c$
$b^2 - 4ac > 0$	two real solutions	two x-intercepts
$b^2 - 4ac = 0$	one real solution	one x-intercept
$b^2 - 4ac < 0$	no real solution; two imaginary solutions	no x-intercept

4 EXAMPLE Using the Discriminant

Determine the type and number of solutions of $x^2 + 6x + 8 = 0$.

$a = 1, b = 6, c = 8$ **Find the values of *a*, *b*, and *c*.**

$b^2 - 4ac = (6)^2 - 4(1)(8)$ **Evaluate the discriminant.**

$= 36 - 32$ **Simplify.**

$= 4$

● Since the discriminant is positive, $x^2 + 6x + 8 = 0$ has two real solutions.

✓ **Check Understanding 4** Determine the type and number of solutions of each equation.
a. $x^2 + 6x + 9 = 0$ **b.** $x^2 + 6x + 10 = 0$
   one real solution   **two imaginary solutions**

5 EXAMPLE Real-World Connection

Field Hockey Suppose a player makes a scoop that releases the ball with an upward velocity of 34 ft/s. The function $h = -16t^2 + 34t$ models the height h in feet of the ball at time t in seconds. Will the ball ever reach a height of 20 ft?

$h = -16t^2 + 34t$

$20 = -16t^2 + 34t$ **Substitute 20 for *h*.**

$0 = -16t^2 + 34t - 20$ **Write the equation in standard form.**

$a = -16, b = 34, c = -20$ **Find the values of *a*, *b*, and *c*.**

$b^2 - 4ac = (34)^2 - 4(-16)(-20)$ **Evaluate the discriminant.**

$= 1156 - 1280$ **Simplify.**

$= -124$

● Since the discriminant is negative, the equation $20 = -16t^2 + 34t$ has no real solutions. The ball will not reach a height of 20 ft.

✓ **Check Understanding 5** Will the ball in Example 5 ever reach a height of 15 ft? Explain.
Yes; the discriminant is positive.

Real-World Connection

A scoop is a field hockey pass that propels the ball from the ground into the air.

288 Chapter 5 Quadratic Equations and Functions

10. $-\frac{1}{2}, \frac{3}{4}$

11. 1, 4

12. $-\frac{5}{3}, \frac{1}{3}$

13. $3 \pm i\sqrt{2}$

14. $1 \pm 2i$

15. $-\frac{3}{2} \pm \frac{i\sqrt{11}}{2}$

16. $-2 \pm i\sqrt{2}$

17. $1 \pm i\sqrt{2}$

18. $-\frac{2}{3} \pm \frac{i\sqrt{26}}{3}$

19. $\frac{5}{2} \pm \frac{i\sqrt{3}}{2}$

20. $\frac{7}{4} \pm \frac{i\sqrt{15}}{4}$

You are now familiar with five methods of solving quadratic equations: finding square roots, factoring, graphing, completing the square, and using the Quadratic Formula. For $ax^2 = c$, finding square roots works best. The discriminant can help you decide how to solve equations that have an x-term.

 Key Concepts

Summary	Methods for Solving Quadratic Equations

Discriminant	Methods
positive square number	• factoring, graphing, Quadratic Formula, or completing the square
positive nonsquare number	• for approximate solutions: graphing, Quadratic Formula, or completing the square • for exact solutions: Quadratic Formula or completing the square
zero	• factoring, graphing, Quadratic Formula, or completing the square
negative	• Quadratic Formula or completing the square

EXERCISES

For more practice, see *Extra Practice*.

Practice and Problem Solving

A **Practice by Example**

Example 1
(page 286)

Solve each equation using the Quadratic Formula. 1–21. See margin pp. 288–289.

1. $x^2 - 4x + 3 = 0$
2. $x^2 + 8x + 12 = 0$
3. $2x^2 + 5x - 7 = 0$

4. $3x^2 + 2x - 1 = 0$
5. $x^2 + 10x = -25$
6. $2x^2 + 3x - 5 = 0$

7. $x^2 = 3x - 1$
8. $x^2 + 6x - 5 = 0$
9. $3x^2 - 4x - 2 = 0$

10. $8x^2 - 2x - 3 = 0$
11. $x(x - 5) = -4$
12. $9x^2 + 12x - 5 = 0$

Example 2
(page 286)

13. $x^2 - 6x + 11 = 0$
14. $x^2 = 2x - 5$
15. $x^2 + 3x + 5 = 0$

16. $2x^2 + 8x + 12 = 0$
17. $x^2 - 2x + 3 = 0$
18. $3x^2 + 4x + 10 = 0$

19. $-x^2 + 5x - 7 = 0$
20. $2x^2 = 7x - 8$
21. $15x^2 + 2x + 1 = 0$

Example 3
(page 287)

Solve each equation using the Quadratic Formula. Find the exact solutions. Then approximate any radical solutions. Round to the nearest hundredth.

22. $2x^2 - 5x - 3 = 0$
23. $3x^2 - 10x + 5 = 0$
24. $3x^2 + 4x - 3 = 0$

25. $6x^2 - 5x - 1 = 0$
26. $7x^2 - x - 12 = 0$
27. $5x^2 + 8x - 11 = 0$

28. $4x^2 + 4x = 22$
29. $2x^2 - 1 = 5x$
30. $2x^2 + x = \frac{1}{2}$
22–30. See margin.

Examples 4 and 5
(page 288)

Evaluate the discriminant of each equation. Tell how many solutions each equation has and whether the solutions are real or imaginary. 31–39. See margin.

31. $x^2 + 4x + 5 = 0$
32. $x^2 - 4x - 5 = 0$
33. $4x^2 + 20x + 25 = 0$

34. $2x^2 + x + 28 = 0$
35. $2x^2 + 7x - 15 = 0$
36. $6x^2 - 2x + 5 = 0$

37. $2x^2 + 7x = -6$
38. $x^2 - 12x + 36 = 0$
39. $x^2 = 8x - 16$

Lesson 5-8 The Quadratic Formula **289**

21. $-\frac{1}{15} \pm \frac{i\sqrt{14}}{15}$

22. $-\frac{1}{2}, 3$

23. $\frac{5}{3} \pm \frac{\sqrt{10}}{3}$; 0.61, 2.72

24. $-\frac{2}{3} \pm \frac{\sqrt{13}}{3}$; −1.87, 0.54

25. $-\frac{1}{6}, 1$

26. $\frac{1}{14} \pm \frac{\sqrt{337}}{14}$; −1.24, 1.38

27. $-\frac{4}{5} \pm \frac{\sqrt{71}}{5}$; −2.49, 0.89

28. $-\frac{1}{2} \pm \frac{\sqrt{23}}{2}$; −2.90, 1.90

29. $\frac{5}{4} \pm \frac{\sqrt{33}}{4}$; −0.19, 2.69

30. $-\frac{1}{4} \pm \frac{\sqrt{5}}{4}$; −0.81, 0.31

31. −4; two, imaginary

32. 36; two, real

33. 0; one, real

34. −223; two, imaginary

35. 169; two, real

36. −116; two, imaginary

37. 1; two, real

38. 0; one, real

39. 0; one, real

3. Practice

Assignment Guide

 **Objective**
A B Core 1–30, 41–54, 67
C Extension 69–71

 **Objective**
A B Core 31–40, 55–66, 68
C Extension 72–75

Standardized Test Prep 76–80

Mixed Review 81–87

Error Prevention

Exercises 31–39 Watch for students who describe the solutions as complex numbers rather than imaginary numbers. At this stage *all* numbers are complex numbers.

Enrichment 5-8
Reteaching 5-8
Practice 5-8

Practice 5-8 — The Quadratic Formula

Evaluate the discriminant of each equation. Tell how many solutions each equation has and whether the solutions are real or imaginary.

1. $y = x^2 + 10x - 25$ 2. $y = x^2 + 10x + 10$ 3. $y = 9x^2 - 24x$
4. $y = 4x^2 - 4x + 1$ 5. $y = 4x^2 - 5x + 1$ 6. $y = 4x^2 - 3x + 1$
7. $y = x^2 + 3x + 4$ 8. $y = x^2 + 7x - 3$ 9. $y = -2x^2 + 3x - 5$
10. $y = x^2 - 5x + 4$ 11. $y = x^2 + 12x + 36$ 12. $y = x^2 + 2x + 3$
13. $y = 2x^2 - 15x - 7$ 14. $y = -5x^2 + 6x - 4$ 15. $y = -4x^2 - 4x - 1$

Solve each equation using the Quadratic Formula.

16. $x^2 + 6x + 9 = 0$ 17. $x^2 - 15x + 56 = 0$ 18. $3x^2 - 5x + 2 = 0$
19. $2x^2 + 3x + 5 = 0$ 20. $10x^2 - 23x + 12 = 0$ 21. $4x^2 + x - 5 = 0$
22. $x^2 + 4x + 15 = 0$ 23. $3x^2 - 2x + 1 = 0$ 24. $x^2 + x + 5 = 0$
25. $x^2 - 4x - 12 = 0$ 26. $x^2 - 3x + 2 = 0$ 27. $2x^2 - 5x + 2 = 0$
28. $x^2 + 6x - 4 = 0$ 29. $x^2 - 2x - 5$ 30. $3x^2 + 7 - 6x$
31. $2x^2 + 6x + 3 = 0$ 32. $x^2 - 16x - 80$ 33. $x^2 + 9x - 13 = 0$
34. $x^2 - 8x + 25 = 0$ 35. $4x^2 + 13x = 12$ 36. $5x^2 - 5x - 12$
37. $3x^2 + 4x + 5 = 0$ 38. $2x^2 + 3x - 7$ 39. $5x^2 + 2x - 1 = 0$
40. $5x^2 + x + 3 = 0$ 41. $5x^2 + x + 3$ 42. $5x^2 - 2x + 7 = 0$
43. $x^2 - 2x + 3 = 0$ 44. $-2x^2 + 3x = 24$ 45. $4x^2 - 5x - 6$
46. $2x^2 + 6x + 5 = 0$ 47. $x^2 - 6x = -8$

Solve.
49. A model of the daily profits p of a gas station based on the price per gallon g is $p = -15,000g^2 + 34,500g - 16,800$. Use the discriminant to find whether the station can profit $4000 per day. Explain.

Solve each equation using the Quadratic Formula. Find the exact solutions. Then approximate any radical solutions. Round to the nearest hundredth.
50. $x^2 - 2x - 3 = 0$ 51. $x^2 + 5x + 4 = 0$ 52. $x^2 - 2x - 8 = 0$
53. $7x^2 - 12x + 3 = 0$ 54. $2x^2 + 5x - 1 = 0$ 55. $4x^2 + 5x + 1 = 0$
56. $6x^2 + 5x - 4 = 0$ 57. $x^2 + x = 6$ 58. $x^2 - 13x = 48$
59. $2x^2 + 5x = 0$ 60. $x^2 - 3x - 3 = 0$ 61. $2x^2 - 4x + 1 = 0$
62. $9x^2 - 6x - 7 = 0$ 63. $x^2 - 35 = 2x$ 64. $2x^2 + 7x + 10 = 0$

Algebra 2 Chapter 5   Lesson 5-8 Practice

Alternative Assessment

Have students work in groups of four. Each student writes three quadratic equations in standard form on separate slips of paper. Students mix the slips. Have groups exchange papers. Each student draws two slips and uses the quadratic formula to solve the quadratic equations written on the slips. Then students each draw one more slip and find the discriminant and determine the number of solutions. Students work in pairs to check each other's work.

40. Business The weekly revenue for a company is $R = -3p^2 + 60p + 1060$, where p is the price of the company's product. Use the discriminant to find whether there is a price for which the weekly revenue would be \$1500. **no**

Solve each equation using any method. When necessary, round real solutions to the nearest hundredth. For imaginary solutions, write exact solutions. **43–49. See margin.**

41. $x^2 = 11x - 10$ **1, 10**   **42.** $5x^2 = 210x$ **0, 42**   **43.** $4x^2 + 4x = 3$

44. $2x^2 + 4x = 10$ **45.** $x^2 - 2x + 2 = 0$ **46.** $x^2 - 3x - 8 = 0$

47. $-3x^2 + 147 = 0$ **48.** $x^2 + 8x = 4$ **49.** $x^2 = 6x - 11$

50. $4x^2 - 4x - 3 = 0$ $-\frac{1}{2}, \frac{3}{2}$ **51.** $\frac{x-3}{2} = \frac{6}{x-2}$ $-1, 6$ **52.** $\frac{x+2}{5} = \frac{3}{x+1}$ $-5.41, 2.41$

53a. $w(18 - w) = 36$

b. 2.29 in. by 15.71 in.

53. a. The area of a rectangle is 36 in.^{2}. The perimeter of the rectangle is 36 in. Write an equation using one variable to find the dimensions of the rectangle.
b. Find the dimensions of the rectangle to the nearest hundredth of an inch.

54. Matrices Find the value of n in the determinant at the right. $\begin{vmatrix} 2 & n & 4 \\ n & 2 & -1 \\ 4 & n & 7 \end{vmatrix} = -37$ **3 or** $-\frac{11}{3}$

55. Writing Summarize how to use the discriminant to analyze the types of solutions of a quadratic equation. **See margin.**

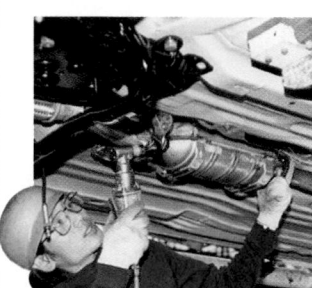

Real-World Connection

Automobiles are the primary source of carbon monoxide in the U.S. This worker is installing a catalytic converter, which decreases carbon monoxide emissions in cars.

56. Air Pollution The function $y = 0.0721x^2 - 2.8867x + 117.061$ models the emissions of carbon monoxide in the United States since 1985. In the function, y represents the amount of carbon monoxide released in a year in millions of tons, and $x = 0$ represents the year 1985. **a–b. See margin pp. 290–291.**
a. How can you use a graph to estimate the year in which less than 100 million tons of carbon monoxide were released into the air?
b. How can you use the Quadratic Formula to estimate the year in which less than 100 million tons of carbon monoxide were released into the air?
c. Which method do you prefer? Explain why. **Check students' work**

Without graphing, tell how many x-intercepts each function has.

57. $y = -2x^2 + 3x - 1$ **two**   **58.** $y = 0.25x^2 + 2x + 4$ **one**   **59.** $y = x^2 + 3x + 5$ **none**

60. $y = -x^2 + 3x + 10$ **two**   **61.** $y = 3x^2 - 10x + 6$ **two**   **62.** $y = 10x^2 + 13x - 3$ **two**

63. Critical Thinking Determine the value(s) of k for which $3x^2 + kx + 12 = 0$ has each type of solution. **a–c. See margin p. 291.**
a. exactly one real solution   **b.** two imaginary solutions   **c.** two real solutions

64. Open-Ended Find a value of k for which $x^2 + kx + 9 = 0$ has the given type of solution. **a–c. See margin p. 291.**
a. two imaginary solutions   **b.** two real solutions   **c.** one real solution

65. Error Analysis After analyzing a quadratic equation with real coefficients, a student says that the equation has exactly one imaginary solution. Explain how you know that the student is wrong. **See margin p. 291.**

66. Use the discriminant to match each function with its graph.
a. $f(x) = x^2 - 4x + 2$ **II**   **b.** $f(x) = x^2 - 4x + 4$ **III**   **c.** $f(x) = x^2 - 4x + 6$ **I**

I. 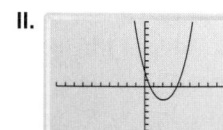   **II.**   **III.**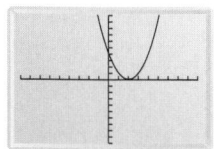

pages 289–291 Exercises

43. $-\frac{3}{2}, \frac{1}{2}$

44. $-3.45, 1.45$

45. $1 \pm i$

46. $-1.70, 4.70$

47. $-7, 7$

48. $-8.47, 0.47$

49. $3 \pm i\sqrt{2}$

55. Answers may vary. Sample: Assume the coefficients are real numbers. If the discriminant is negative, then there are 2 imaginary solutions. If the discriminant is 0, then there is 1 real solution. If the discriminant is positive, then there are 2 real solutions.

56a. Answers may vary. Sample: Graph $y = 0.0721x^2 - 2.8867x + 117.061$ and $y = 100$. Where they intersect is the year when 100 million tons were released in the

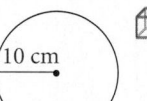

67. a. Geometry Write an equation to find the dimensions of a square that has the same area as the circle at the left. $x^2 = 100\pi$

 10 cm

b. Find the length of a side of the square, to the nearest hundredth centimeter. **17.72 cm**

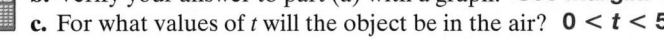

68. Physics The equation $h = 80t - 16t^2$ models the height h feet reached in t seconds by an object propelled straight up from the ground.

    a. Will the object ever reach a height of 90 ft? **yes**

    b. Verify your answer to part (a) with a graph. **See margin.**

    c. For what values of t will the object be in the air? **$0 < t < 5$**

Challenge

Write a quadratic equation with the given solutions. **69–71. See margin.**

69. $\dfrac{3 + \sqrt{5}}{2}, \dfrac{3 - \sqrt{5}}{2}$ **70.** $\dfrac{-5 + \sqrt{13}}{2}, \dfrac{-5 - \sqrt{13}}{2}$ **71.** $\dfrac{5 + i\sqrt{3}}{2}, \dfrac{5 - i\sqrt{3}}{2}$

Use the Quadratic Formula to solve each equation for x in terms of a.

72. $\dfrac{3 \pm i}{2a}$

72. $2a^2x^2 - 6ax = -5$ **73.** $5a^2x^2 - 10ax = 12$ **74.** $x^2 + 2ax = 25a^2$

73. $\dfrac{5 \pm \sqrt{85}}{5a}$

                                                                     $-a \pm a\sqrt{26}$

75. Use the Quadratic Formula to prove each statement. **a–b. See margin.**

    a. The sum of the solutions of the quadratic equation $ax^2 + bx + c = 0$ is $-\dfrac{b}{a}$.

    b. The product of the solutions of the quadratic equation $ax^2 + bx + c = 0$ is $\dfrac{c}{a}$.

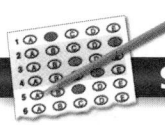

Standardized Test Prep

Multiple Choice

76. What is the discriminant of $qx^2 + rx + s = 0$? **C**
  A. $|a + b|$ **B.** $q^2 - 4rs$ **C.** $r^2 - 4qs$ **D.** $s^2 - 4qr$

77. How many different real solutions are there for $2x^2 - 3x + 5 = 0$? **F**
  F. 0   **G.** 1   **H.** 2   **I.** i

Take It to the NET
Online lesson quiz at
www.PHSchool.com
Web Code: aga-0508

78. Which equation has $-3 \pm 5i$ as its solutions? **A**
  A. $x^2 + 6x = -34$ **B.** $x^2 + 6x = -14$ **C.** $x^2 + 3x = 4$ **D.** $x^2 + 3x = 2$

Short Response

79. What is the discriminant of a quadratic equation, and what does its value tell you about the solution(s) of the equation? **See back of book.**

Extended Response

80. Explain how you can use the Quadratic Formula to solve $3x^2 + 5 = x + 9$. **See back of book.**

Mixed Review

Lesson 5-7

Solve by completing the square.

                                                                          $\dfrac{3 \pm \sqrt{41}}{2}$

81. $x^2 - 8x - 20 = 0$ **82.** $2y^2 = 4y - 1$ $\dfrac{2 \pm \sqrt{2}}{2}$ **83.** $x^2 - 3x - 8 = 0$
    −2, 10

Lesson 4-4

Each matrix represents vertices of a polygon. Translate each figure 3 units right and 2 units down. Express your answer as a matrix.

84. $\begin{bmatrix} 2 & 3 & -1 \\ -5 & 1 & 0 \end{bmatrix}$ $\begin{bmatrix} 5 & 6 & 2 \\ -7 & -1 & -2 \end{bmatrix}$ **85.** $\begin{bmatrix} 0 & -3 & 1 & -5 \\ 2 & -1 & 4 & -2 \end{bmatrix}$ $\begin{bmatrix} 3 & 0 & 4 & -2 \\ 0 & -3 & 2 & -4 \end{bmatrix}$

Lesson 4-3

Multiply.

86. $\begin{bmatrix} 0 & -3 \\ -3 & 1 \end{bmatrix}\begin{bmatrix} 4 & 0 \\ -9 & 1 \end{bmatrix}$ $\begin{bmatrix} 27 & -3 \\ -21 & 1 \end{bmatrix}$ **87.** $\begin{bmatrix} 3 & 10 \\ 1 & 5 \end{bmatrix}\begin{bmatrix} -2 & 4 \\ -1 & 4 \end{bmatrix}$ $\begin{bmatrix} -16 & 52 \\ -7 & 24 \end{bmatrix}$

air. Wherever $y = 0.0721x^2 - 2.8867x + 117.061$ is below $y = 100$ is where less than 100 million tons were released.

b. Answers may vary.
Sample: Where $y = 0.0721x^2 - 2.8867x + 117.061 < 100$ is the solution. Subtract 100 from both sides and you

get $y = 0.0721x^2 - 2.8867x + 117.061 < 0$. You then use the quadratic formula to solve.

 **Resources**
For additional practice with a variety of test item formats:
- Standardized Test Prep, p. 297
- Test-Taking Strategies, p. 292
- Test-Taking Strategies with Transparencies

Exercise 78 Tell students to ask themselves whether there might be a simple way to select the correct choice without completely solving the equations.

63a. 12 or −12
  b. k such that $|k| < 12$
  c. k such that $|k| > 12$
64a. k such that $|k| < 6$
  b. k such that $|k| > 6$
  c. 6, −6

65. Imaginary solutions always come in pairs because they are the positive and negative solution of the square root of a negative number.

68b.
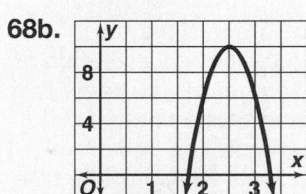

69. Answers may vary.
  Sample: $x^2 - 3x + 1 = 0$

70. Answers may vary.
  Sample: $x^2 + 5x + 3 = 0$

71. Answers may vary.
  Sample: $x^2 - 5x + 7 = 0$

75a. $\dfrac{-b + \sqrt{b^2 - 4ac}}{2a} + \dfrac{-b - \sqrt{b^2 - 4ac}}{2a}$
$= \dfrac{-2b}{2a} = \dfrac{-b}{a}$

  b. $\left(\dfrac{-b}{2a} + \dfrac{\sqrt{b^2 - 4ac}}{2a}\right) \times \left(\dfrac{-b}{2a} - \dfrac{\sqrt{b^2 - 4ac}}{2a}\right) =$
$\left(\dfrac{-b}{2a}\right)^2 - \left(\dfrac{\sqrt{b^2 - 4ac}}{2a}\right)^2 =$
$\dfrac{4ac}{4a^2} = \dfrac{c}{a}$

291

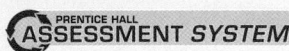

Using a Variable

Most word problems require you to define one or more variables and to write equations or inequalities to model the situations in the problems. This requires careful reading of the problem and careful thinking about how the quantities in the problem are related to one another.

Resources

ASSESSMENT SYSTEM
PRENTICE HALL

Test-Taking Strategies with Transparencies
• Transparency 5
• Practice sheet p. 29

Teaching Notes

Remember that when you are given the ratio of two quantities, the ratio tells you by what factor you can multiply one of the quantities to obtain the other.

When you are told that an unknown quantity is a solution of a certain equation, you know that substituting that quantity for the variable will give an equation that you can assume must be true.

Remind students that a diagram can often help to understand the relationship between the quantities in a problem.

Test-Taking Strategies with Transparencies

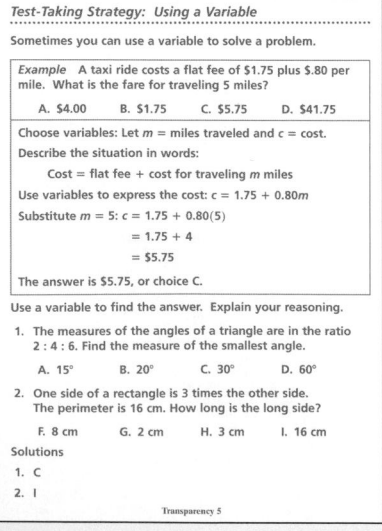

You can solve many problems by defining a variable to represent an unknown quantity. Use the variable to write and solve an equation or inequality.

EXAMPLE

The two nonzero roots of the quadratic equation $x^2 - 9x + k = 0$ are in the ratio $2:1$. Find the roots and the value of k.

Since the roots are in the ratio $2:1$, define one root as $2r$ and the other root as r. Substituting each expression into the equation yields a system of two equations in two unknowns.

$$x^2 - 9x + k = 0 \qquad\qquad x^2 - 9x + k = 0$$
$$(2r)^2 - 9(2r) + k = 0 \quad \textbf{Substitute.} \quad (r)^2 - 9(r) + k = 0$$
$$4r^2 - 18r + k = 0 \quad \textbf{Simplify.} \quad r^2 - 9r + k = 0$$
$$4r^2 - 18r + k - (r^2 - 9r + k) = 0 - 0 \quad \textbf{Subtract equations to solve by elimination.}$$
$$3r^2 - 9r = 0 \quad \textbf{Simplify.}$$
$$\frac{3r^2 - 9r}{r} = \frac{0}{r} \quad \textbf{Since } r \neq 0, \text{ you can divide each side by } r.$$
$$3r - 9 = 0 \quad \textbf{Simplify.}$$
$$3r = 9 \quad \textbf{Solve for } r.$$
$$r = 3$$
$$2r = 6 \quad \textbf{Find } 2r.$$

Now that you know r and $2r$, you can find k.

$$(3)^2 - 9(3) + k = 0 \quad \textbf{Substitute into the original equation.}$$
$$9 - 27 + k = 0 \quad \textbf{Simplify.}$$
$$k = 18 \quad \textbf{Solve for } k.$$

The nonzero roots of $x^2 - 9x + k = 0$ are 3 and 6, and $k = 18$.

EXERCISES

Write an equation to solve each problem. Clearly define the variables you use.

1. The nonzero roots of the equation $3x^2 - 4x + k = 0$ are in the ratio $3:1$. Find the roots and the value of k. **$1, \frac{1}{3}; k = 1$**

2. The roots of the equation $x^2 - 3x + k = 0$ differ by 2. Find the roots and the value of k. **$\frac{1}{2}, \frac{5}{2}; k = \frac{5}{4}$**

3. The perimeter of a rectangle is 21 cm. Its area is 20 cm². Find the dimensions of the rectangle. **2.5 cm by 8 cm**

4. The point $(0, 0)$ is on the parabola $y = 5x - x^2$. What other point on the parabola has x- and y-coordinates that are equal? **(4, 4)**

5. The length of the diagonal of a rectangle is 5 ft. The rectangle's perimeter is 13 ft. Find the rectangle's dimensions. Round your answers to the nearest tenth. **4.6 ft by 1.9 ft**

Chapter Review

Vocabulary

absolute value of a complex number (p. 271)	greatest common factor (GCF) of an expression (p. 255)	standard form of a quadratic equation (p. 263)
axis of symmetry (p. 235)	i (p. 270)	standard form of a quadratic function (p. 234)
completing the square (p. 278)	imaginary number (p. 270)	vertex form of a quadratic function (p. 248)
complex number (p. 271)	parabola (p. 235)	
complex number plane (p. 271)	perfect square trinomial (p. 258)	vertex of a parabola (p. 235)
difference of two squares (p. 259)	Quadratic Formula (p. 285)	zero of a function (p. 264)
discriminant (p. 287)	quadratic function (p. 234)	Zero Product Property (p. 263)
factoring (p. 255)		

Reading Math
Understanding Vocabulary

Take It to the NET
Online vocabulary quiz at www.PHSchool.com
Web Code: agj-0551

Choose the correct vocabulary term to complete each sentence.

1. The square of a binomial is a __?__. **perfect square trinomial**

2. Every quadratic equation can be solved with the __?__. **Quadratic Formula**

3. The __?__ reveals a translation of a parent quadratic function.
vertex form of a quadratic function

4. A __?__ is also an x-intercept of the graph of the function.
zero of a function

5. The __?__ completely determines the types of roots of a quadratic function.
discriminant

Skills and Concepts

5-1 Objectives

▼ To identify quadratic functions and graphs (p. 234)

▼ To model data with quadratic functions (p. 236)

The **standard form of a quadratic function** is $f(x) = ax^2 + bx + c$, where $a \neq 0$. The quadratic term is ax^2. The graph of a **quadratic function** is a **parabola**.

The **axis of symmetry** is a line that divides a parabola into two mirror images. The **vertex of a parabola** is the point at the intersection of the parabola and its axis of symmetry. Corresponding points on the parabola are the same distance from the axis of symmetry.

You can find a quadratic model for a set of data by solving a system of three equations for a, b, and c, or by using the quadratic regression feature of a graphing calculator.

Determine whether each function is linear or quadratic. Identify the quadratic, linear, and constant terms.

6. $y = (3 - x)(2x + 1)$
quadratic; $-2x^2$, $5x$, 3

7. $y = x - x^2 + 3$
quadratic; $-x^2$, x, 3

8. $y = 3 - 4x$
linear; none, $-4x$, 3

Identify the vertex, the axis of symmetry, and the points corresponding to P and Q.

9. $(0, -1)$, $x = 0$, $(2, 3)$ and $(-1, 0)$

10. $(-2, 1)$, $x = -2$, $(-2, 1)$ and $(-4, 0)$

11. $(1, -4)$, $x = 1$, $(3, -1)$ and $\left(2, -3\frac{1}{4}\right)$

9.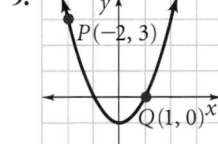

10.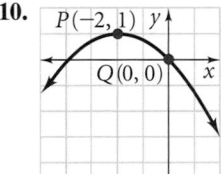

11.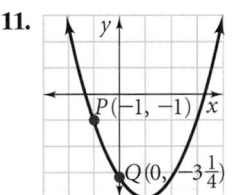

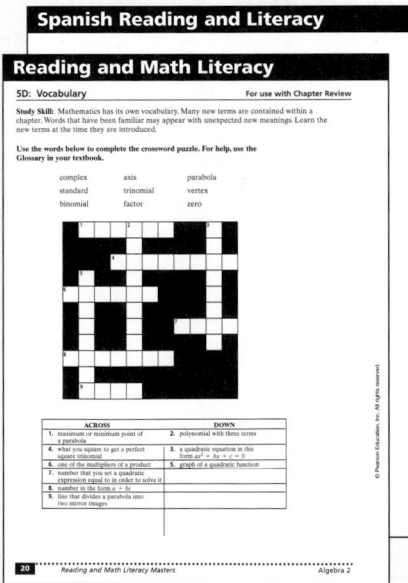

12a. $y = 614x^2 - 342x + 4962$, where $x = 0$ corresponds to 1995 and y is in thousands.

b. around 1999

c. $y = -25.5x^2 + 917.8x + 4776.7$

d. around 2007

e. $\approx 13{,}000{,}000$

13.

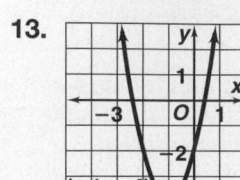

vertex $(-1, -4)$,
y-intercept: -2; $x = -1$

14.

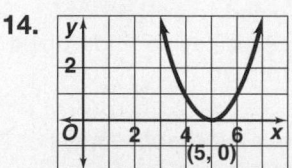

vertex $(5, 0)$,
y-intercept: 25; $x = 5$

15.

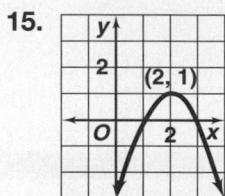

vertex $(2, 1)$,
y-intercept: -3; $x = 2$

16.

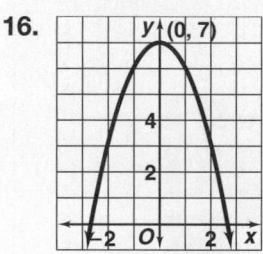

vertex $(0, 7)$,
y-intercept: 7; $x = 0$

17. $y = \left(x + \frac{1}{2}\right)^2 - 12\frac{1}{4}$;
minimum: $-12\frac{1}{4}$

18. $y = -(x - 1)^2 + 3$;
maximum: 3

19. $y = 2(x + 2)^2 - 11$;
minimum: -11

20. $y = -0.5(x - 0)^2 + 5$;
maximum: 5

21. $y = -\frac{1}{2}(x - 1)^2 + 2$;
maximum: 2

22. $y = \frac{4}{9}(x - 3)^2 - 1$;
minimum: -1

294

🌐 **12. a. Sports** Find a quadratic model for the attendance at college basketball games from 1995–1997 by solving three equations in a, b, and c.

b. Predict the year attendance will reach 12,000,000.

c. Use the quadratic regression feature of your calculator to find a model for all the data.

d. What does this regression model predict as the first year attendance will reach 12,000,000?

e. Find the maximum likely attendance.

a–e. See margin.

Year	Attendance (thousands)
1995	4962
1996	5234
1997	6734
1998	7387
1999	8010
2000	8698

Source: National Collegiate Athletic Association

5-2 and 5-3 Objectives

▼ To graph quadratic functions (p. 241)

▼ To find maximum and minimum values of quadratic functions (p. 243)

▼ To use the vertex form of a quadratic function (p. 248)

The constants a, b, and c characterize the graph of $y = ax^2 + bx + c$. The axis of symmetry is $x = -\frac{b}{2a}$, the vertex is at $\left(-\frac{b}{2a}, f\left(-\frac{b}{2a}\right)\right)$, and $f\left(-\frac{b}{2a}\right)$ is the maximum or minimum value. The **vertex form of a quadratic function** is $y = a(x - h)^2 + k$. The vertex is (h, k), the maximum or minimum value is k, and the axis of symmetry is the line $x = h$. If $a > 0$, the parabola opens up. If $a < 0$, it opens down.

Graph each function. Identify the vertex, y-intercept, and axis of symmetry.

13. $y = 2(x + 1)^2 - 4$ **14.** $y = (x - 5)^2$

15. $y = -(x - 2)^2 + 1$ **16.** $y = -x^2 + 7$

13–23. See margin.

Write each function in vertex form. Find its maximum or minimum value.

17. $y = x^2 + x - 12$ **18.** $y = -x^2 + 2x + 2$

19. $y = 2x^2 + 8x - 3$ **20.** $y = -0.5x^2 + 5$

21.
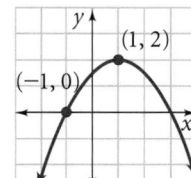

22.
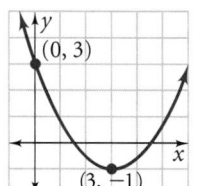

23.
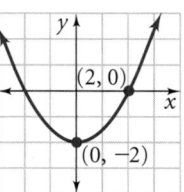

5-4 and 5-5 Objectives

▼ To find common and binomial factors of quadratic expressions (p. 255)

▼ To factor special quadratic expressions (p. 258)

▼ To solve quadratic equations by factoring and by finding square roots (p. 263)

▼ To solve quadratic equations by graphing (p. 264)

You can solve some quadratic equations by finding the square root of each side or by finding the zeros of the related function. You can solve some quadratic equations in the **standard form of a quadratic equation** $ax^2 + bx + c = 0$ by **factoring** if you can find two factors with product ac and sum b. Then use the **Zero Product Property**. For a **perfect square trinomial**, $ax^2 \pm 2abx + b^2 = (a \pm b)^2$. For the **difference of two squares**, $a^2 - b^2 = (a + b)(a - b)$. In all cases, first factor out the **greatest common factor (GCF)** of the expression.

24–38. See margin.

Solve by factoring, taking square roots, or, if necessary, by graphing. Give exact radical answers. For answers found by graphing, round to the nearest hundredth.

24. $x^2 - 7x = 0$ **25.** $x^2 + 2x - 8 = 0$ **26.** $(x + 3)^2 = 9$

27. $4(x - 2)^2 = 32$ **28.** $2x^2 - 6x - 8 = 0$ **29.** $x^2 - 5x - 5 = 0$

30. $3x^2 - 14x + 8 = 0$ **31.** $x^2 - 3x - 4 = 0$ **32.** $x^2 + 8x + 16 = 0$

33. $x^2 - 6x + 9 = 0$ **34.** $4x^2 - 12x + 9 = 0$ **35.** $x^2 - 9 = 0$

36. $6x^2 - 13x - 5 = 0$ **37.** $4x^2 + 3 = -8x$ **38.** $3x^2 + 4x - 10 = 0$

---

23. $y = \frac{1}{2}(x - 0)^2 - 2$;
minimum: -2

24. $0, 7$

25. $-4, 2$

26. $-6, 0$

27. $2 - 2\sqrt{2}, 2 + 2\sqrt{2}$

28. $-1, 4$

29. $-0.85, 5.85$ or $\frac{5 \pm 3\sqrt{5}}{2}$

30. $\frac{2}{3}, 4$

31. $-1, 4$

32. -4

33. 3

34. $\frac{3}{2}$

5-6 Objectives

▼ To identify and graph complex numbers (p. 270)

▼ To add, subtract, and multiply complex numbers (p. 272)

An **imaginary number** has the form $a + bi$, where $b \neq 0$. The imaginary number i is defined as $i^2 = -1$. A **complex number** has the form $a + bi$, where a and b are any real numbers. The **absolute value of a complex number** is its distance from the origin in the **complex number plane**. You graph $a + bi$ in the complex plane just as you graphed (a, b) in the coordinate plane. Complex numbers follow rules of operation like those of real numbers. Some quadratic equations have imaginary numbers as roots. Functions of complex numbers may be used to generate fractals.

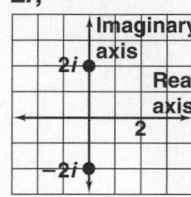

Simplify each expression.

39. $\sqrt{-25}$ **$5i$**
40. $\sqrt{-2} - 1$ **$-1 + i\sqrt{2}$**
41. $-4 - \sqrt{-1}$ **$-4 - i$**
42. $\sqrt{-27}$ **$3i\sqrt{3}$**

43. $2\sqrt{-32} + 4$ **$4 + 8i\sqrt{2}$**
44. $|3 - i|$ **$\sqrt{10}$**
45. $|-2 + 3i|$ **$\sqrt{13}$**
46. $|4i|$ **4**

47. $(3 + 4i) - (7 - 2i)$ **$-4 + 6i$**
48. $(5 - i)(9 + 6i)$ **$51 + 21i$**

49. $(3 + 8i) + (5 - 2i)$ **$8 + 6i$**
50. $(4 + 6i)(2 + i)$ **$2 + 16i$**

Find the additive inverse of each number. Graph the number and its inverse.

51. $2 - i$
52. $-4 + 3i$
53. $-7 - 4i$
54. $-2i$

51–54. See margin.

Solve each equation.

55. $x^2 + 2 = 0$ **$-i\sqrt{2}, i\sqrt{2}$**
56. $x^2 = -5$ **$-i\sqrt{5}, i\sqrt{5}$**

57. $3x^2 + 12 = 0$ **$-2i, 2i$**
58. $6x^2 + 4 = 0$ **$\frac{-i\sqrt{6}}{3}, \frac{i\sqrt{6}}{3}$**

Find the first three outputs of each fractal-generating function. Begin with $z = 0$.

59. $f(z) = z^2 - i$ **$-i, -1 - i, i$**
60. $f(z) = i - z^2$ **$i, 1 + i, -i$**

5-7 and 5-8 Objectives

▼ To solve equations by completing the square (p. 278)

▼ To rewrite functions in vertex form by completing the square (p. 280)

▼ To solve quadratic equations by using the Quadratic Formula (p. 285)

▼ To determine types of solutions by using the discriminant (p. 287)

Completing the square is based on the relationship $x^2 + bx + \left(\frac{b}{2}\right)^2 = \left(x + \frac{b}{2}\right)^2$. You can use it to write a quadratic function in vertex form. If the coefficient of the quadratic term is not 1, you must factor out the coefficient from the variable terms.

You can solve any quadratic equation by using the Quadratic Formula.

If $ax^2 + bx + c = 0$, then $x = \frac{-b \pm \sqrt{b^2 - 4ac}}{2a}$.

The discriminant $b^2 - 4ac$ determines the number and type of solutions of the equation. If $b^2 - 4ac > 0$, the equation has two real solutions. If $b^2 - 4ac = 0$, the equation has one real solution. If $b^2 - 4ac < 0$, the equation has no real solutions and two imaginary solutions.

Solve each equation by completing the square. 61–72. See margin.

61. $9x^2 + 6x + 1 = 4$
62. $x^2 + 3x = -25$
63. $x^2 - 2x + 4 = 0$

64. $-x^2 + x - 7 = 0$
65. $2x^2 + 3x = 8$
66. $4x^2 - x - 3 = 0$

Rewrite the equation in vertex form by completing the square. Find the vertex.

67. $y = x^2 + 3x - 1$
68. $y = 2x^2 - x - 1$
69. $y = x^2 + x + 2$

Determine the number and type of solutions. Solve using the Quadratic Formula.

70. $x^2 - 6x + 2 = 0$
71. $-2x^2 + 7x = 10$
72. $x^2 + 4 = 6x$

Chapter 5   Chapter Review   **295**

53. $7 + 4i$;

54. $2i$;

61. $-1, \frac{1}{3}$

62. $-\frac{3}{2} + \frac{i\sqrt{91}}{2}, -\frac{3}{2} - \frac{i\sqrt{91}}{2}$

63. $1 + i\sqrt{3}, 1 - i\sqrt{3}$

64. $\frac{1}{2} + \frac{3i\sqrt{3}}{2}, \frac{1}{2} - \frac{3i\sqrt{3}}{2}$

65. $-\frac{3}{4} + \frac{\sqrt{73}}{4}, -\frac{3}{4} - \frac{\sqrt{73}}{4}$

66. $-\frac{3}{4}, 1$

67. $y = \left(x + \frac{3}{2}\right)^2 - \frac{13}{4}$; $\left(-\frac{3}{2}, -\frac{13}{4}\right)$

68. $y = 2\left(x - \frac{1}{4}\right)^2 - \frac{9}{8}$; $\left(\frac{1}{4}, -\frac{9}{8}\right)$

69. $y = \left(x + \frac{1}{2}\right)^2 + \frac{7}{4}$; $\left(-\frac{1}{2}, \frac{7}{4}\right)$

70. 2 real solutions; $3 + \sqrt{7}, 3 - \sqrt{7}$

71. 2 imaginary solutions; $\frac{7}{4} + \frac{i\sqrt{31}}{4}, \frac{7}{4} - \frac{i\sqrt{31}}{4}$

72. 2 real solutions; $3 + \sqrt{5}, 3 - \sqrt{5}$

35. $-3, 3$

36. $-\frac{1}{3}, \frac{5}{2}$

37. $-\frac{3}{2}, -\frac{1}{2}$

38. $-2.61, 1.28$ or $\frac{-2 \pm \sqrt{34}}{3}$

51. $-2 + i$;

52. $4 - 3i$;

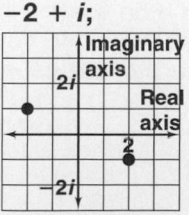

295

Chapter Test

Take It to the NET
Online chapter test at
www.PHSchool.com
····· Web Code: aga-0552

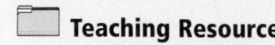

1. Write the equation of the parabola in standard form. Find the coordinates of the points corresponding to P, Q, and R. **See margin.**

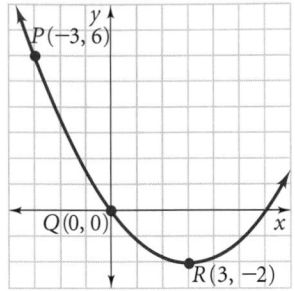

Sketch a graph of the parabola with the given vertex through the given point. 2–3. See back of book.

2. vertex $(0, 0)$, point $(-3, 3)$

3. vertex $(1, 5)$, point $(2, 11)$

4–7. See back of book for graphs.
Graph each quadratic function. Identify the axis of symmetry and the coordinates of the vertex.

4. $y = x^2 - 7$ **$x = 0$, $(0, -7)$**

5. $y = x^2 + 2x + 6$ **$x = -1$, $(-1, 5)$**

6. $y = -x^2 + 5x - 3$ **$x = 2.5$, $(2.5, 3.25)$**

7. $y = -\frac{1}{2}x^2 - 8$ **$x = 0$, $(0, -8)$**

Simplify each expression.

8. $\sqrt{-16}$ **$4i$**

9. $4\sqrt{-9} - 2$ **$-2 + 12i$**

10. $(4 - i) + (5 - 9i)$ **$9 - 10i$**

11. $(2 + 3i)(8 - 5i)$ **$31 + 14i$**

12. $(-3 + 2i) - (6 + i)$ **$-9 + i$**

13. $(7 - 4i)(10 - 2i)$ **$62 - 54i$**

14. **Physics** For a model rocket, the altitude h, in meters, as a function of time t, in seconds, is given by $h = 68t - 8t^2$. Find the maximum height of the rocket. How long does it take to reach the maximum height? **$h = 144.5$ m; $t = 4.25$ s**

Find the additive inverse of each number.

15. $3 - 7i$ **$-3 + 7i$**

16. $-2 + i$ **$2 - i$**

Graph each number on the complex plane. Then find its absolute value. 17–22. See back of book.

17. $7 - 2i$

18. $8i$

19. $4 + 8i$

20. 5

21. $6 - 4i$

22. $-2 + 3i$

23. **Writing** Compare graphing a number on the complex plane to graphing a point on the coordinate plane. How are they similar? How are they different? **See margin.**

Solve each quadratic equation. 24–32. See margin.

24. $x^2 - 25 = 0$

25. $x^2 + 5x - 24 = 0$

26. $x^2 + 8x - 9 = 0$

27. $3x^2 - 21x + 3 = 0$

28. $6x^2 = 9x$

29. $4x^2 + 4x + 4 = 0$

30. $5x^2 + x + 2 = 0$

31. $-3x^2 - 2x + 7 = 0$

32. $2x^2 + 6x + 12 = 0$

Write each function in vertex form. Sketch the graph of the function and label its vertex. 33–36. See back of book.

33. $y = x^2 - 6x + 5$

34. $y = -x^2 + 8x - 10$

35. $y = 2x^2 - 3x - 1$

36. $y = -\frac{1}{2}x^2 + 4x - 9$

Evaluate the discriminant of each equation. How many real and imaginary solutions does each have?

37. $x^2 + 6x - 7 = 0$ **64; 2 real solutions**

38. $3x^2 - x + 3 = 0$ **−35; 2 imaginary solutions**

39. $-2x^2 - 4x + 1 = 0$ **24; 2 real solutions**

40. $-x^2 + 6x - 9 = 0$ **0; 1 real solution**

41. **Open-Ended** Sketch the graph of a parabola that has no real solutions. **Check students' work.**

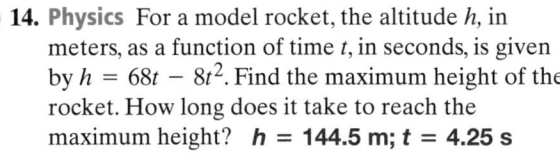
---

page 296   Chapter Test

1. $y = \frac{2}{9}x^2 - \frac{4}{3}x$; $(9, 6)$, $(6, 0)$, $(3, -2)$

23. **Answers may vary.**
Sample: In the coordinate plane you graph ordered pairs (a, b); in the complex plane you graph complex numbers $a + bi$. For both, you find a on the horizontal axis and you find b on the vertical axis.

24. $-5, 5$

25. $-8, 3$

26. $-9, 1$

27. $\dfrac{7 - 3\sqrt{5}}{2}, \dfrac{7 + 3\sqrt{5}}{2}$

28. $0, \dfrac{3}{2}$

29. $-\dfrac{1}{2} - \dfrac{i\sqrt{3}}{2}, -\dfrac{1}{2} + \dfrac{i\sqrt{3}}{2}$

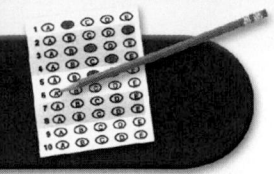

Standardized Test Prep

Reading Comprehension Read the passage below. Then answer the questions on the basis of what is *stated* or *implied* in the passage.

Dealing with Setbacks The boundary of a lot of land is called the property line. Many communities do not allow you to build up to the property line. Zoning laws may require a "setback" of several feet to ensure some distance between buildings and between a building and the property line.

Suppose the setback for a building is *s* feet on all four sides of a lot that has width 50 feet and length 60 feet. Then the maximum width of the building is (50 − 2*s*) feet, and the maximum length of the building is (60 − 2*s*) feet.

You can write and use functions in terms of *s* for the maximum area of the base of the building.

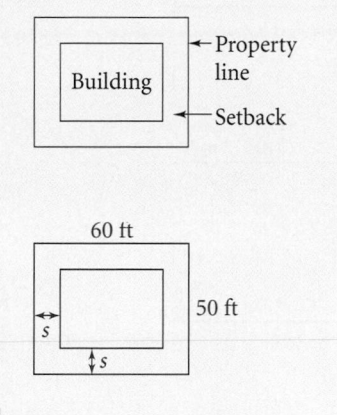

Students must be able to extract information from reading passages, answer multiple choice questions, and construct responses in order to be successful on current state and national assessments.

To answer the questions, students apply skills and concepts from this chapter and previous chapters.
Multiple Choice: Items 1–4, 11
Extended Response: Items 5–10

Resources

 **Teaching Resources**
Cumulative Review

Reaching All Students
Spanish Cumulative Review

 ASSESSMENT SYSTEM

Standardized Test Prep
• Ch. 5 Standardized Test Practice
Assessment Masters
• Cumulative Review
Computer Test Generator CD
• Standardized Test Practice

 **www.PHSchool.com**
• Standardized Test Practice
• Resources

Plus **iTEXT**

1. What is the area of the entire lot? **C**
   A. 220 ft
   B. 2576 ft²
   C. 3000 ft²
   D. (3000 − 4*s*²) ft²

2. Which function does NOT express the maximum area of the base of the building in terms of *s*? **I**
   F. $A(s) = (50 − 2s)(60 − 2s)$
   G. $A(s) = 3000 − 220s + 4s^2$
   H. $A(s) = 4s^2 − 220s + 3000$
   I. $A(s) = 2[(50 − 2s) + (60 − 2s)]$

3. What is the maximum area of the base of the building when *s* = 8 ft? **C**
   A. 64 ft²
   B. 156 ft
   C. 1496 ft²
   D. 2184 ft²

4. What is the minimum area that is NOT occupied by the base of the building when *s* = 6 ft? **F**
   F. 1176 ft²
   G. 1824 ft²
   H. 2376 ft²
   I. 2856 ft²

5. Suppose the building is set back five feet. Find the maximum area of the base of the building.
   2000 ft²

6. Suppose the maximum area of the base of the building is 2376 ft². What is the value of the setback? **3 ft**

7. Suppose the minimum area that is NOT occupied by the building is 1344 ft². What is the value of the setback? **7 ft**

8. Write a function for the perimeter of the base of the building in terms of *s*. $P(s) = 220 − 8s$

9. Suppose a lot is 30 feet by 90 feet. The setback is *s* feet. Write an expression for the maximum area of the base of the building.
   $A(s) = 2700 − 240s + 4s^2$

10. Suppose a lot has length ℓ, width *w*, and setback *s*.
    a. Write an expression for the maximum area of the base of the building. **a–b. See margin.**
    b. Write an expression for the maximum perimeter of the base of the building.

11. A lot is 22 ft by 58 ft, and the setback on each side is *s* ft. Which formula expresses the maximum area of the base of the building in terms of *s*? **A**
    A. $f(s) = 4s^2 − 160s + 1276$
    B. $f(s) = 1276 − 160s − 4s^2$
    C. $f(s) = (58 − s)(22 − s)$
    D. $f(s) = 1276 − s^2$

Chapter 5 Standardized Test Prep **297**

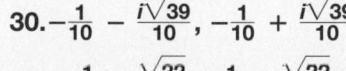

$$30.\ -\frac{1}{10} − \frac{i\sqrt{39}}{10},\ -\frac{1}{10} + \frac{i\sqrt{39}}{10}$$

$$31.\ -\frac{1}{3} − \frac{\sqrt{22}}{3},\ -\frac{1}{3} + \frac{\sqrt{22}}{3}$$

$$32.\ -\frac{3}{2} + \frac{i\sqrt{15}}{2},\ -\frac{3}{2} − \frac{i\sqrt{15}}{2}$$

page 297 Standardized Test Prep

10a. $A(s) = \ell w − 2\ell s − 2ws + 4s^2$

b. $P(s) = 2\ell + 2w − 8s$

Cumulative Review

Cumulative Review
Chapters 1–5

For Exercises 1–12, choose the correct letter.
1. Which line is perpendicular to $y = -\frac{2}{3}x + \frac{2}{3}$?
   A. $y = \frac{3}{2}x + 6$ B. $y = 3x − \frac{2}{3}$ C. $y = \frac{2}{3}x − \frac{1}{2}$ D. $y = \frac{3}{2}x + \frac{1}{2}$
2. What system describes this graph?
   A.   B.   C.   D.
3. Which of these is the standard form of $y = 8x + 12$?
   A. $y − 8x − 12 = 0$ B. $y − 8x = 12$
   C. $−8x + y = 12$ D. $8x − y = −12$
4. Find $4\begin{bmatrix} 5 & 0 & -6 \\ 2 & 3 & 0 \end{bmatrix}$
   A. $\begin{bmatrix} 20 & 0 & -24 \\ 8 & 3 & 0 \end{bmatrix}$ B. $\begin{bmatrix} 20 & 0 & -24 \\ 8 & 12 & 0 \end{bmatrix}$ C. $\begin{bmatrix} 9 & 4 & -2 \\ 6 & 7 & 4 \end{bmatrix}$ D. $\begin{bmatrix} 20 & 4 & -24 \\ 8 & 12 & 4 \end{bmatrix}$
5. Which number is irrational?
   A. $\sqrt{144}$ B. $\frac{27}{9}$ C. $\sqrt{2}$ D. $−0.5$
6. Which point lies on the graph of $2x − y + z = 0$?
   A. $(0, 4, -8)$ B. $(0, 2, 4)$ C. $(12, -6, 6)$ D. $(0, -5, -5)$
7. Which of these is the solution of $−7x > 4x + 33$?
   A. $x > 3$ B. $x < 3$ C. $x > -3$ D. $x < -3$
8. Simplify $(5 + 8i) + (2 − 3i)$.
   A. 4   B. $7 − 3i$ C. $7 + 3i$ D. $3 + 3i$
9. At which vertex is the objective function $C = 3x − 4y$ maximized?
   A. $(9, 0)$ B. $(-2, -20)$ C. $(-5, -2)$ D. $(0, -9)$
10. Which ordered triple is a solution to $\begin{cases} 3x + y + z = 7 \\ x + 3y − z = 13 \\ y = 2x − 1 \end{cases}$?
    A. $(2, 3, -2)$ B. $(2, -3, -20)$ C. $(-2, -5, 18)$ D. $(-2, 3, 10)$

Algebra 2 Chapter 5   Cumulative Review **37**

Polynomials and Polynomial Functions

Chapter at a Glance

 North Carolina Objectives

NCTM STANDARDS 2000

1 Number and Operations	6 Problem Solving
2 Algebra	7 Reasoning and Proof
3 Geometry	8 Communication
4 Measurement	9 Connections
5 Data Analysis and Probability	10 Representation

Pacing Options

This chart suggests pacing only for the lessons and their parts. It is provided as a possible guide. It will help you determine how much time you have in your schedule to cover other components, such as the features, Chapter Review, and Chapter Test.

Day	Traditional (45 min.)	Block (90 min.)
1	6-1 ▼	6-1 ▼ ▼
2	6-1 ▼	6-2 ▼
3	6-2 ▼	6-2 ▼
4	6-2 ▼ ▼	6-3 ▼ ▼
5	6-2 ▼	6-4 ▼
6	6-3 ▼	6-4 ▼
7	6-3 ▼ ▼	6-5 ▼
8	6-3 ▼	6-5 ▼
9	6-4 ▼	6-6 ▼
10	6-4 ▼	6-7 ▼
11	6-5 ▼	6-7 ▼
12	6-5 ▼ ▼	6-8 ▼
13	6-5 ▼	6-8 ▼
14	6-6 ▼	
15	6-7 ▼	
16	6-7 ▼	
17	6-8 ▼	
18	6-8 ▼	

NAEP Correlation (National Assessment of Educational Progress 2000 Mathematics Objectives)

6-1	6-2	6-3	6-4	6-5	6-6	6-7	6-8
N2d, D7, D6b	A9, N2c, N6d	N6c, N6e	A9, M4b, M5	N6e, A9	N6e, A9	D9	D9, A1d

N = Number Sense, Properties, and Operations; **M** = Measurement; **G** = Geometry and Spatial Sense;
D = Data Analysis, Statistics, and Probability; **A** = Algebra and Functions

Math Background

Chapter Overview

Students have already studied properties of linear and quadratic functions, the two simplest kinds of polynomial functions. Now they examine polynomial functions in general. They consider how to factor polynomials that have integer coefficients. They study the connection between zeros and linear factors. Students see how the Rational Roots Theorem and Factor Theorem can be used in solving many polynomial equations. The Factor Theorem and the Fundamental Theorem of Algebra lead to the conclusion that polynomial equations of degree n have exactly n complex solutions. Permutations and combinations are studied and then used to present the Binomial Theorem.

Polynomial Functions   6-1

Remind students that in a term involving only variables, such as x^5m^2, "1" is understood to be the coefficient. So $x^6 - x^5m^2 + 2\,x^5m^2 = x^6 + (-1)\,x^5m^2 + 2\,x^5m^2 = x^6 + (-1 + 2)x^5m^2 = x^6 + x^5m^2$. Students should be encouraged to write out this use of the Distributive Property if they have difficulty remembering this. Graphs help students see that the term of highest degree determines the behavior of a polynomial function for very large positive values and very small negative values of the variable.

Polynomials and Linear Factors   6-2

Linear factors of a polynomial are closely related to zeros of the related polynomial function. We find a *root of an equation* but a *zero of a function*. There are two distinct definitions for root and zero, but they are very closely related. A *zero* of a polynomial function $P(x)$ is also a *root* of the corresponding polynomial equation $P(x) = 0$. Often we refer simply to *roots of the polynomial $P(x)$*. The Factor theorem makes the connection explicit.

Dividing Polynomials   6-3

Polynomials may be divided by factors of the form $x - a$ by using long division and synthetic division. Students who have difficulty choosing r for synthetic division should observe that when $P(x) = (x - r) \cdot Q(x) = 0$, the equation $x - r = 0$, finds the root of the polynomial P, is an equivalent equation to $x = r$.

Solving Polynomial Equations   6-4

A wisely selected substitution can be made so a given equation becomes a quadratic equation and can be solved more easily. The difficulty lies in selecting a substitution that works. Here are examples to help students see how to select u.

1. $x^4 + 3x^2 - 4 = 0$ Let $u = x^2$. Then $u^2 = x^4$.
   Solve $u^2 + 3u - 4 = 0$.

2. $x - 6\sqrt{x} + 9 = 0$ Let $u = \sqrt{x}$. Then $u^2 = \sqrt{x}$.
   Solve $u^2 - 6u + 9 = 0$.

3. $(x + 4)^2 + (x + 4) - 2 = 0$ Let $u = (x + 4)$.
   Solve $u^2 + u - 2 = 0$.

Theorems about Roots of Polynomials   6-5

This is an excellent place for students to review the rules for divisibility of integers that they learned in arithmetic.

A number is divisible by

    2 if it ends in an even digit (0, 2, 4, 6, or 8).

    3 if the sum of its digits is divisible by 3.

    4 if the number formed by its last two digits is divisible by 4.

    5 if it ends in 5 or 0.

    6 if it is divisible by 2 and 3.

    8 if the number formed by its last three digits is divisible by 8.

    9 if the sum of its digits is divisible by 9.

  10 if it ends in 0.

  11 if, when $-$ and $+$ operations are alternated between its digits, the result is divisible by 11. (Try 33: $3 - 3 = 0$; or 54109: $5 - 4 + 1 - 0 + 9 = 11$; $33 = 11 \cdot 0$ and $54109 = 11 \cdot 4919$.)

any composite number if it is divisible by each of the powers of the primes in the factorization of the composite number. (For example, $60 = 2^2 \cdot 3 \cdot 5$, $45 = 3^2 \cdot 5$, and $12 = 2^2 \cdot 3$, so 60 is divisible by 12 since 2^2 and 3 are factors of 60, but 60 is not divisible by $45 = 3^2 \cdot 5$ since 3^2 is not a factor of 60.)

The rules for divisibility by 2, 5, and 10 are probably those with which the students feel most comfortable. There are rules for divisibility by 7 and 13 but they are complex.

The Fundamental Theorem of Algebra   6-6

Some students may have difficulty distinguishing between a conjugate and an opposite. Whether s is irrational or $s = \sqrt{-1}$, the opposite of $a + bs$ is $-a - bs$, while the conjugate is $a - bs$.

Permutations and Combinations   6-7

Three different notations are used for the number of combinations of n objects taken r at a time: ${}_nC_r$, $\binom{n}{r}$, and $C(n, r)$. The third form emphasizes that a combination is a function of n and r. Only two of these notations are used for the number of permutations of n objects taken r at time, ${}_nP_r$ and $P(n, r)$, but $\binom{n}{r}$ is the classic notation for the Binomial Theorem. Students should locate these functions, along with factorial, on their calculators and learn how to use them.

The Binomial Theorem   6-8

The binomial theorem offers an elegant connection between algebra and probability. The same binomial coefficients from the binomial expansion are used in the probability distribution called the Binomial Distribution, which is introduced in Lesson 12-6.

 # Ongoing Assessment and Intervention

Tools for Monitoring Student Progress

The Prentice Hall *Algebra 2* program provides you with many options for assessment in the Student Edition, the Teacher's Edition and the teaching resources. From these options you may choose instructional materials and techniques that are appropriate for your students and support your district's curriculum requirements.

Instant Check System™ in Chapter 6

Allows students to check their own learning before, during, and after each lesson.

Diagnosing Readiness before the chapter (p. 298)

Check Skills You'll Need exercises in each lesson (pp. 300, 307, 314, 321, 329, 335, 339, 347)

Check Understanding questions with each Example (pp. 301, 302, 303, 307, 308, 309, 310, 315, 316, 317, 321, 322, 323, 324, 330, 331, 332, 336, 337, 339, 340, 341, 348, 349)

Checkpoint Quiz (pp. 320, 345)

Test Prep in Chapter 6

Teaches students strategies and gives them practice with all the test item formats they will encounter on state tests and standardized national exams.

Standardized Test Prep exercises in each lesson (pp. 305, 313, 319, 326, 334, 338, 344, 351)

Test-Taking Strategies (p. 352)

Standardized Test Prep (p. 357)

All your assessment needs in one place!

Program Assessment

Assess student progress throughout the *Algebra 2* text with blackline masters and CD-ROM.

Assessment Resources

- Checkpoint Quizzes 1 & 2
- Chapter Test, Forms A & B
- Chapter Alternative Assessment

Spanish versions available.

 Computer Test Generator

- Unlimited questions of varying difficulty for every lesson objective.
- Create your own practice sheets, quizzes, and tests, or use the pre-made Chapter Tests.
- Diagnose readiness with questions on prerequisite skills.
- Prepare students by making tests based on standardized test objectives.
- Access Algebra 1, Geometry, and Algebra 2 content—all on one CD-ROM.

Test Preparation

A three-step approach to preparing students for high stakes, national, and state exams.

❶ **Diagnose & Prescribe**

Content Diagnostic Tests

- Diagnose strengths and weaknesses in content for national and state tests.
- Prescribe individualized reteaching opportunities.

❷ **Review & Reteach**

Skills and Concepts Review

- Provides reteaching worksheets with instruction and practice for each skill.
- Includes course prerequisite skills.

❸ **Practice & Assess**

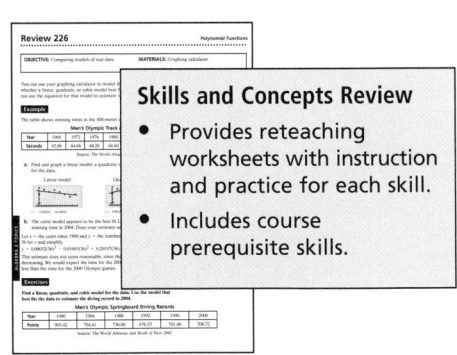

Test Preparation

- Features practice tests for End-of-Course and SAT/ACT exams.
- Includes standardized test practice by chapter for ongoing review.

Teacher's Guide with answers and correlations.

Test-Taking Strategies with Transparencies

- Support the Test-Taking Strategies pages in the Student Edition.
- Provide a teaching transparency and a practice worksheet for each strategy.

 # Reaching All Students

Support in the Student Text and Additional Resources

The textbook, the iText, and other technology components provide numerous opportunities to reach students of various ability levels and learning styles. Each Teacher's Edition lesson suggests how you can help *all* your students be successful and understand the mathematics in Chapter 6.

Below Level

Student Edition
- Diagnosing Readiness*: p. 298
- Check Skills You'll Need*: pp. 300, 307, 314, 321, 329, 335, 339, 347

Reteaching
Chapter 6 Support File: pp. 10–17

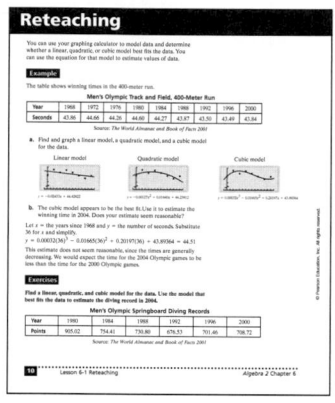

Advanced Learners

Student Edition
- Challenge exercises: pp. 305, 313, 319, 326, 334, 338, 344, 351
- Extension, pp. 306, 328

Enrichment
Chapter 6 Support File: pp. 18–25

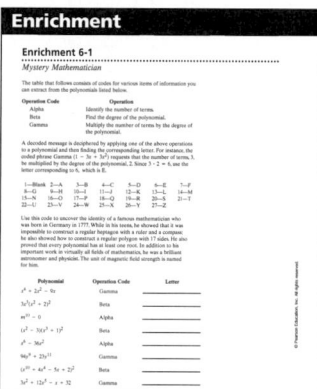

Connections to Precalculus Masters
Chapter 6 Enrichment Topic:
Approximate Factorizations

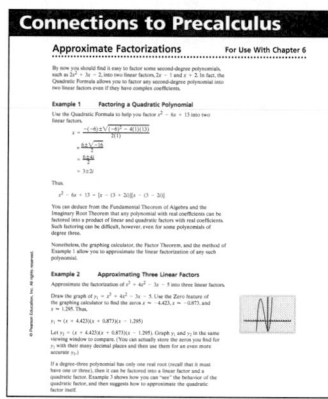

* Can be used with all ability levels to ensure mastery of prerequisite skills.

Reading and Math Literacy

Student Edition
- Vocabulary: pp. 299, 353, *plus* in every Lesson Preview
- Reading Math: pp. 301, 304, 310, 316, 325, 327, 329, 336
- Illustrated Glossary: pp. 871–913

Reading and Math Literacy Masters
Chapter 6: pp. 21–24

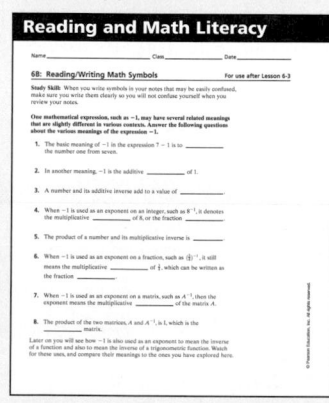

English Learners

Student Edition
- English/Spanish Illustrated Glossary: pp. 871–913

Workbook and Masters
Spanish Practice Workbook: pp. 2–9
Spanish Reading and Math Literacy Masters: pp. 21–24

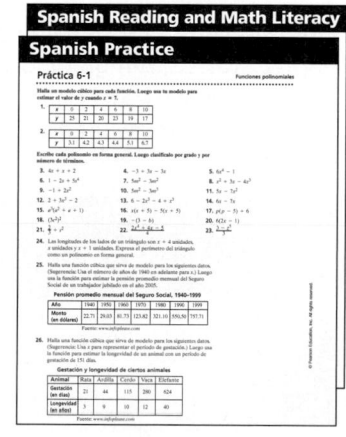

Learning Styles

Student Edition
- Investigation: pp. 300, 335, 346
- Technology: pp. 302, 321, 327, 339, 341
- Writing: pp. 304, 312, 319, 326, 334, 338, 343, 344, 346, 350, 356
- DK Activities: pp. 358–359

Activity Masters
Hands-On Activities: 43, 44

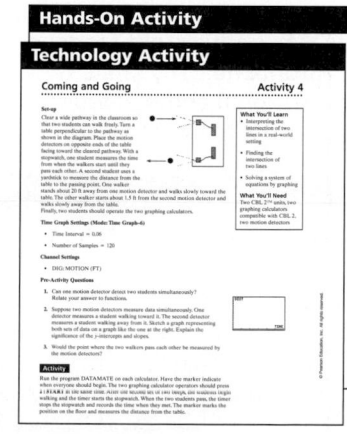

Program Resources

	Teaching Resources in Grab & Go™ Files				Resources for Reaching All Students			Spanish Resources			Transparencies				Presentation Assistant Plus!
	Practice	Reteach	Enrich	Checkpoint Quiz	Reading & Math Literacy	Technology Activities	Hands-On Activities	Practice	Reading & Math Literacy	Checkpoint Quiz	Skills Check	Additional Examples	Answers to Exercises	Lesson Quiz	Prentice Hall Presentation Pro CD-ROM
6-1	■	■	■		■			■			■	■	■	■	■
6-2	■	■	■					■			■	■	■	■	■
6-3	■	■	■	■	■		■	■	■	■	■	■	■	■	■
6-4	■	■	■					■			■	■	■	■	■
6-5	■	■	■				■	■			■	■	■	■	■
6-6	■	■	■					■			■	■	■	■	■
6-7	■	■	■	■	■			■	■	■	■	■	■	■	■
6-8	■	■	■					■			■	■	■	■	■
For the chapter	Chapter Tests, Alternative Assessment, Cumulative Review, Cumulative Assessment				Connections to Precalculus Masters			Spanish Chapter Tests, Alternative Assessment, Cumulative Review, Cumulative Assessment			Classroom Aid Transparencies				

Also available for use with the chapter:

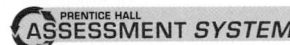 PRENTICE HALL ASSESSMENT SYSTEM *See page 298C.*

- Practice Workbook
- Solution Key

- For teacher support and access to student Web site materials, use Web Code agk-5500.
- For additional online and technology resources, see below.

Technology

 **Online and on CD-ROM**

Complete Interactive Student Text online and on CD-ROM—with instant feedback assessment, tutorial help, dynamic activities, instructional and real-world videos, audio, and additional practice.

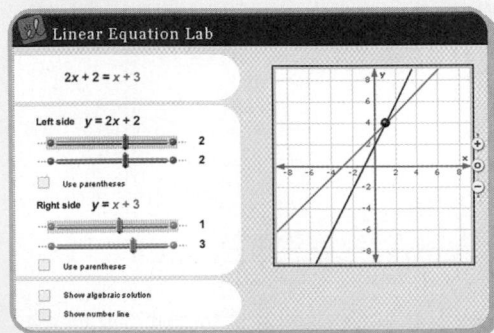

 www.PHSchool.com For Students

Use **Web Codes** for easy access to online activities, chapter projects, self-grading lesson quizzes and chapter tests, vocabulary quizzes, updated data sources, graphing calculator procedures, and more.

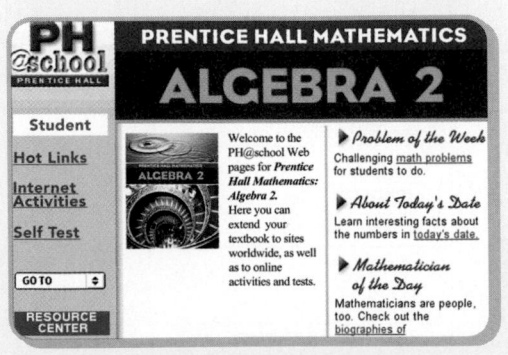

PH SuccessNet For Teachers

Online lesson planning with built-in state correlations, all the teaching resources, complete reference library, your own calendar and Teacher Web page, professional development, and more.

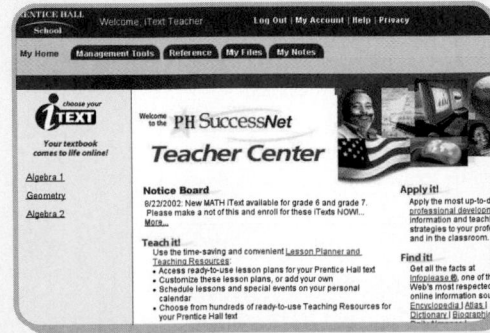

Presentation Assistant Plus!

The Prentice Hall *Presentation Assistant Plus!* provides you with the material you need to teach a lesson from beginning to end. Two easy-to-use formats—Transparencies and CD-ROM—allow you to present a lesson the way you are most comfortable.

Transparencies

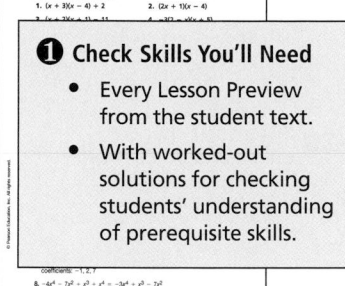

❶ Check Skills You'll Need
- Every Lesson Preview from the student text.
- With worked-out solutions for checking students' understanding of prerequisite skills.

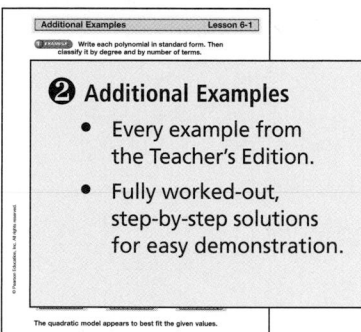

❷ Additional Examples
- Every example from the Teacher's Edition.
- Fully worked-out, step-by-step solutions for easy demonstration.

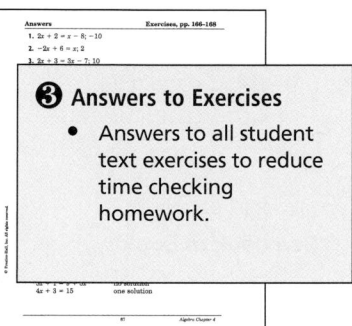

❸ Answers to Exercises
- Answers to all student text exercises to reduce time checking homework.

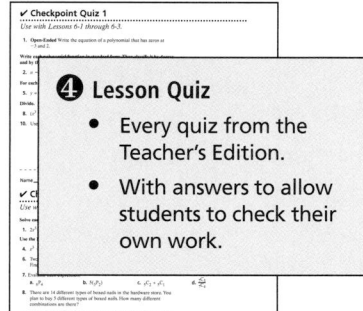

❹ Lesson Quiz
- Every quiz from the Teacher's Edition.
- With answers to allow students to check their own work.

Prentice Hall Presentation Pro CD-ROM

- Includes all Transparencies.
- Conveniently organized by lesson so you can easily ❶ Introduce, ❷ Teach, ❸ Check Homework, and ❹ Assess each lesson.
- Animated examples allow step-by-step instruction at your own pace.
- Easy to edit so you can create custom presentations.

Teaching Chapter 6 Using Presentation Assistant Plus!

	❶ Introduce	❷ Teach	❸ Check Homework	❹ Assess
	Check Skills You'll Need	Additional Examples	Student Edition Answers	Lesson Quiz
6-1	p. 36	pp. 113–114	✔	p. 126
6-2	p. 37	pp. 115–118	✔	p. 127
6-3	p. 38	pp. 118–121	✔	p. 127
6-4	p. 39	pp. 122–124	✔	p. 128
6-5	p. 40	pp. 125–128	✔	p. 128
6-6	p. 41	pp. 129–130	✔	p. 129
6-7	p. 42	pp. 131–132	✔	p. 129
6-8	p. 43	pp. 133–134	✔	p. 130

Throughout the Teacher's Edition, this symbol indicates material that is available on transparency in the Presentation Assistant Plus!

Prentice Hall Presentation Pro

CD-ROM with dynamic PowerPoint® presentations for every lesson. Helps you introduce and develop concepts, check homework, and assess progress. Part of Presentation Assistant Plus! *(See above.)*

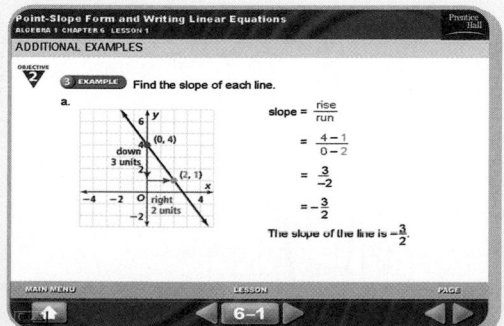

Computer Test Generator

CD-ROM to create practice sheets and tests for course objectives and standardized tests. Includes Instant Chapter Tests™, online testing, and student reports. Part of the PH Assessment System. *(See page 298C.)*

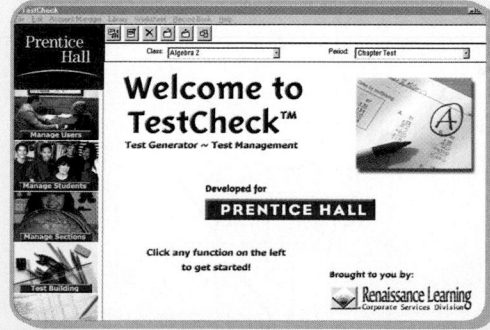

Resource Pro® with Planning Express®

CD-ROM with a lesson planning tool that allows you to import state and local objectives. Includes electronic versions of all the teaching resources.

Polynomials and Polynomial Functions

 Diagnosing Readiness

Students will find answers to these exercises in the back of their textbooks.

For intervention, direct students to:

Finding Models
Lesson 5-1: Example 3
Exercises 16–20
Extra Practice, p. 826

Graphing Functions
Lesson 2-2: Example 1
Exercises 1–8
Extra Practice, p. 823
Lesson 5-2: Example 1
Exercises 1–9
Extra Practice, p. 826

Solving Systems by Graphing
Lesson 5-5: Examples 4–5
Exercises 20–32
Extra Practice, p. 826

Solving Equations Algebraically
Lesson 5-5: Example 1
Exercises 1–6
Extra Practice, p. 826
Lesson 5-8: Examples 1–2
Exercises 1–21
Extra Practice, p. 826

Finding the Number and Type of Solutions
Lesson 5-8: Examples 4-5
Exercises 31–40
Extra Practice, p. 826

Finding Probability
Lesson 1-6: Example 1
Exercises 1–2
Extra Practice, p. 821

Where You've Been

- In Chapter 2, you learned to write and graph linear functions and to solve linear equations and inequalities.

- In Chapter 3, you learned to write, graph, and solve systems of linear equations and inequalities.

- In Chapter 5, you learned to write and graph quadratic functions and to solve quadratic equations.

 **iTEXT** Instant self-check online and on CD-ROM

 Diagnosing Readiness (For help, go to the Lesson in green.)

Finding models (Lesson 5-1)

Find a quadratic model for each set of values.

1. $(-1, 3), (0, 1), (2, 9)$
$y = 2x^2 + 1$

2. $(0, -1), (2, -2), (4, -5)$
$y = -\frac{1}{4}x^2 - 1$

3. $(-4, 75), (0, 3), (11, 300)$
$y = 3x^2 - 6x + 3$

Graphing functions (Lessons 2-2 and 5-2)

Graph each function. **4–5. See margin.**

4. $6x - 4y = -10$

5. $y = 3x^2 - 10x + 2$

6. $y = \frac{3}{4}(x^2 + 12) + 1$
See back of book.

Solving systems by graphing (Lesson 5-5)

Solve each equation by graphing. Round to the nearest hundredth.

7. $1 = 4x^2 - 3x$
$x = -0.25, 1$

8. $\frac{1}{2}x^2 + x - 14 = 0$
$x \approx -6.39, 4.39$

9. $5x^2 + 30x = 12$
$x \approx -6.38, 0.38$

Solving equations algebraically (Lessons 5-5 and 5-8)

Solve each equation algebraically.

10. $x^2 - 5x - 36 = 0$
$x = -4, 9$

11. $2x^2 - 13x + 21 = 0$
$x = 3, \frac{7}{2}$

12. $3x^2 - 4x = 3$
$x = \frac{2 \pm \sqrt{13}}{3}$

Finding the number and type of solutions (Lesson 5-8)

Evaluate the discriminant of each equation. Tell how many solutions each equation has and whether the solutions are real or imaginary.

13. $x^2 - 12x + 30 = 0$
24; 2 real solutions

14. $-4x^2 + 20x - 25 = 0$
0; 1 real solution

15. $2x^2 = 8x - 8$
0; 1 real solution

Finding probability (Lesson 1-6)

16. Suppose you select an integer from 100 to 200 at random. What is $P(\text{odd})$? $\frac{50}{101}$

page 298
Diagnosing
Readiness

4.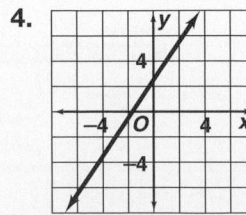

5.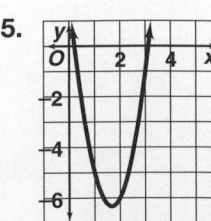

Polynomials and Polynomial Functions

Chapter 6

Where You're Going

- In Chapter 6, you will learn to write and graph polynomial functions and to solve polynomial equations.

- You will learn to use important theorems about the number of solutions to polynomial equations.

- You will learn to solve problems involving permutations, combinations, and binomial probability.

 **Real-World Snapshots** Applying what you learn, on pages 358–359 you will do activities involving soccer.

Key Vocabulary
- Binomial Theorem (p. 348)
- combination (p. 340)
- conjugates (p. 331)
- Factor Theorem (p. 309)
- Fundamental Theorem of Algebra (p. 335)
- Imaginary Root Theorem (p. 332)
- Irrational Root Theorem (p. 331)
- multiplicity (p. 310)
- Pascal's Triangle (p. 347)
- polynomial function (p. 309)
- Rational Root Theorem (p. 329)
- Remainder Theorem (p. 317)
- standard form of a polynomial (p. 301)
- synthetic division (p. 315)

Chapter 6 Overview

This chapter introduces students to polynomials and polynomial functions. Students begin by defining and identifying polynomial functions. They then learn how to find linear factors of polynomials, and how to divide polynomials. Next students learn how to solve polynomial equations. They also learn theorems about roots of polynomial equations, and the Fundamental Theorem of Algebra. Students then apply what they have learned to solve problems involving permutations and combinations, and then learn the binomial theorem.

Reading Math
Reading for Problem Solving, p. 327

Vocabulary
A complete list of terms, plus vocabulary exercises, appears in the Chapter Review, p. 353.

Illustrated Glossary
Examples for each vocabulary term, plus definitions in both English and Spanish, appear starting on p. 751.

Test-Taking Strategies
Drawing a Diagram, p. 352

Real-World Snapshots
See pages 358–359 for a real-world application of applying parabolas that utilizes Dorling Kindersley's (DK) unique graphic presentation.

Real-World Connections
Some of the applications you will find in this chapter are measurement (6-2), pet transportation (6-4), boating, literature, and government (6-7), and sports (6-8).

www.PHSchool.com
Internet support for this chapter includes:
- Self-grading Vocabulary and Chapter 6 Tests
- Chapter Project
- Chapter Planner
- Chapter 6 Resources

Plus

1. Plan

Lesson Preview

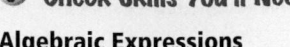 **Check Skills You'll Need**

Algebraic Expressions
Lesson 1-2: Example 4
Exercises 17–38
Extra Practice, p. 822

Lesson Resources

📁 **Teaching Resources**
Practice, Reteaching, Enrichment

👥 **Reaching All Students**
Practice Workbook 6-1
Spanish Practice Workbook 6-1
Reading and Math Literacy 6A
Spanish Reading & Literacy 6A

⏱ **Presentation Assistant Plus!**
Transparencies
• Check Skills You'll Need 6-1
• Additional Examples 6-1
• Student Edition Answers 6-1
• Lesson Quiz 6-1
PH Presentation Pro CD 6-1

 **ASSESSMENT SYSTEM**

Computer Test Generator CD

💿 **Technology**
Resource Pro® CD-ROM
Computer Test Generator CD
Prentice Hall Presentation Pro CD

💻 **www.PHSchool.com**
Student Site
• Teacher Web Code: agk-5500
• Updated Data
• Self-grading Lesson Quiz
Teacher Center
• Lesson Planner
• Resources

Plus **iTEXT**

6-1

Polynomial Functions

North Carolina Objectives — 2.04 Create and use best-fit models to solve problems.
2.06 Use cubic equations to model and solve problems. a) Solve using graphs.
b) Interpret constants and coefficients.

Lesson Preview

What You'll Learn

 OBJECTIVE 1 To classify polynomials

 OBJECTIVE 2 To model data using polynomial functions

. . . And Why

To model the world's gold production, as in Example 3

✓ Check Skills You'll Need   (For help, go to Lesson 1-2.)

Simplify each expression by combining like terms.

1. $3x + 5x - 7x$ x **2.** $-8xy^2 - 2x^2y + 5x^2y$ **3.** $-4x + 7x^2 + x$ $7x^2 - 3x$
$3x^2y - 8xy^2$

Find the number of terms in each expression.

4. $\frac{1}{2}bh$ **1 term**   **5.** $1 - x$ **2 terms**   **6.** $4x^3 - x^2 - 9$
3 terms

New Vocabulary • polynomial • polynomial function • degree
• standard form of a polynomial • degree of a polynomial

---

i TEXT Interactive lesson includes instant self-check, tutorials, and activities.

OBJECTIVE 1 **Exploring Polynomial Functions**

1. They are lines with the same slope.

3. Answers may vary. Sample: The ends of each graph extend away from each other in either Quadrants I and III or II and IV. The number of x-intercepts varies for each graph.

4a. for $y = x - 4$, 4; for $y = x^3$, 0; for $y = x^3 - 2x^2 - x + 2$, -1, 1, 2; for $y = x$, 0; for $y = -x^3 + 3x - 2$, -2, 1; for $y = x^2 - 3x + 3$, none; for $y = x^3 - 2x^2 - x - 4$, 2.8; for $y = -x^3 + 4x$, -2, 0, 2; for $y = x^2$, 0; for $y = -x^2 + 4x$, 0, 4

Investigation: Graphs of Polynomial Functions

• Use a graphing calculator to graph each equation listed at the right.

• Sketch each graph on a separate index card or sheet of paper. Label the graph with its equation.

• Sort the graphs into groups based on their shapes.

1. How are the graphs of the linear equations alike? **See left.**

2. How are the graphs of the quadratic equations alike? **They are all parabolas.**

3. How are the graphs of the remaining equations alike? How are they different? **See left.**

4. **a.** Estimate the x-intercept(s) of each graph. Write them on each card. **4a. See left.**

   b. **Make a Conjecture** Compare the number of x-intercepts of each graph and the greatest exponent found in its equation. What is the relationship? **The number of x-intercepts is less than or equal to the greatest exponent.**

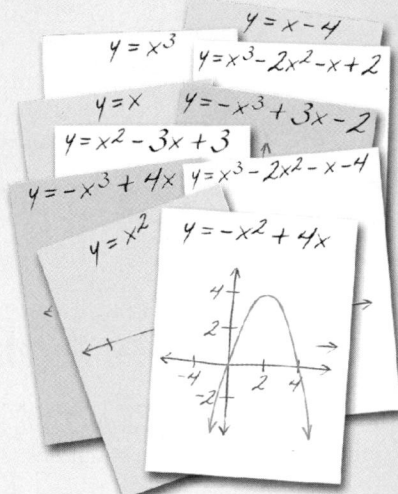

Ongoing Assessment and Intervention

Before the Lesson	**During the Lesson**	**After the Lesson**
Diagnose prerequisite skills using:	Monitor progress using:	Assess knowledge using:
• Check Skills You'll Need	• Check Understanding • Additional Examples • Standardized Test Prep	• Lesson Quiz • Computer Test Generator CD

A monomial is an expression that is either a real number, a variable, or a product of real numbers and variables with whole-number exponents. A **polynomial** is a monomial or the sum of monomials. For any polynomial, you can write the corresponding polynomial function, as shown below.

 Key Concepts

Definition	Polynomial Function

$P(x) = a_n x^n + a_{n-1}x^{n-1} + \ldots + a_1 x + a_0$ where n is a nonnegative integer and the coefficients $a_n, \ldots, a_0$ are real numbers.

 Reading Math

The prefix *poly* means "many."

The exponent of the variable in a term determines the **degree** of that term. The terms in the polynomial shown below are in *descending order* by degree. This order demonstrates the **standard form of a polynomial.** A one-variable polynomial in standard form has no two terms with the same degree, since all like terms have been combined.

$$P(x) = \boxed{2x^3 \quad - 5x^2 \quad - 2x \quad + 5} \leftarrow \text{Polynomial}$$

Leading coefficient   Cubic term   Quadratic term   Linear term   Constant term

You can classify a polynomial by the number of terms it contains. A polynomial of more than three terms does not usually have a special name. You can also classify a polynomial by its degree. The **degree of a polynomial** is the largest degree of any term of the polynomial. The name assigned to each degree is listed below.

Degree	Name Using Degree	Polynomial Example	Number of Terms	Name Using Number of Terms
0	constant	6	1	monomial
1	linear	$x + 3$	2	binomial
2	quadratic	$3x^2$	1	monomial
3	cubic	$2x^3 - 5x^2 - 2x$	3	trinomial
4	quartic	$x^4 + 3x^2$	2	binomial
5	quintic	$-2x^5 + 3x^2 - x + 4$	4	polynomial of 4 terms

1 EXAMPLE   **Classifying Polynomials**

Write each polynomial in standard form. Then classify it by degree and by number of terms.

a. $-7x + 5x^4$

$5x^4 - 7x$
The term with the largest degree is $5x^4$, so the polynomial is degree 4. It has two terms. The polynomial is a quartic binomial.

b. $x^2 - 4x + 3x^3 + 2x$

$3x^3 + x^2 - 2x$
The term with the largest degree is $3x^3$, so the polynomial is degree 3. It has three terms. The polynomial is a cubic trinomial.

1a. $-2x + 5$; linear binomial

b. $5x^3 + x^2 - 4x$; cubic trinomial

c. $-2x^5 + 6$; quintic binomial

✓ **Check Understanding**   **1** Write each polynomial in standard form. Then classify it by degree and by number of terms. **a–c. See left.**

a. $4x - 6x + 5$ **b.** $3x^3 + x^2 - 4x + 2x^3$ **c.** $6 - 2x^5$

Lesson 6-1   Polynomial Functions   **301**

2. Teach

 Professional Development

Math Background

The degree of a polynomial $P(x)$ determines the number of zeros of the related polynomial function. The end behavior of a polynomial function of even degree tends toward infinity, or negative infinity, at both the far left and the far right of the graph. For a polynomial function of odd degree, the end behavior tends toward infinity on one end and negative infinity on the other end.

OBJECTIVE
 Teaching Notes

Investigation (Optional)

Math Tip
Without using the terminology of polynomial functions, this investigation indicates that the shape of the graph of a polynomial function has a great deal to do with the degree of the related polynomial. It also suggests a connection between the degree of the related polynomial and the number of times the graph can touch or cross the *x*-axis.

1 EXAMPLE   **Connection to Geometry**

Students may wonder why, when the degree of a polynomial is 3, the polynomial is classified as cubic. Remind them that a cube has 3 dimensions: length, width, and height.

Additional Examples

1 Write each polynomial in standard form. Then classify it by degree and by number of terms.
a. $9 + x^3$ $x^3 + 9$, degree 3, cubic binomial
b. $x^3 - 2x^2 - 3x^4$
$-3x^4 + x^3 - 2x^2$, degree 4, quartic trinomial

 Reaching All Students

| **Below Level** Review with students the meanings of the words cubic, quartic, quintic, etc. | **Advanced Learners** Challenge students to explain why *quad*, meaning *four*, is the prefix in the word *quadratic* that describes a second-degree polynomial. | **English Learners** See note on page 302. **Inclusion** See note on page 302. |

Students who are visually impaired may need partners to help them make the comparison. The partner could say how many points each model passes through as it is graphed.

3 EXAMPLE English Learners

Explain that a *quartic* function is a polynomial function of degree 4. To remember the meaning of the word *quartic*, it may help students to think of related words such as *quadrilateral*.

Additional Examples

2 Using a graphing calculator, determine whether a linear, quadratic, or cubic model best fits the values in the table.

X	Y
0	2.8
2	5
4	6
6	5.5
8	4

quadratic

3 The table shows data on the number of employees that a small company had from 1975 to 2000. Find a cubic function to model the data. Use it to estimate the number of employees in 1998. Let 0 represent 1975.

Year	Number of Employees
1975	60
1980	65
1985	70
1990	60
1995	55
2000	64

$f(x) = 0.00963x^3 - 0.3754x^2 + 3.541x + 58.96$; about 59 employees

---

OBJECTIVE
2 **Modeling Data With a Polynomial Function**

You have already used lines and parabolas to model data. Sometimes you can fit data more closely by using a polynomial model of degree three or greater.

2 EXAMPLE Comparing Models

Using a graphing calculator, determine whether a linear model, a quadratic model, or a cubic model best fits the values in the table.

x	0	5	10	15	20
y	10.1	2.8	8.1	16.0	17.8

Enter the data. Use the LinReg, QuadReg, and CubicReg options of a graphing calculator to find the best-fitting model for each polynomial classification.

Graph each model and compare.

Linear model	**Quadratic model**	**Cubic model**
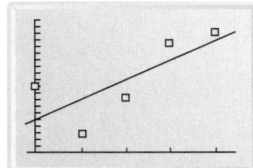	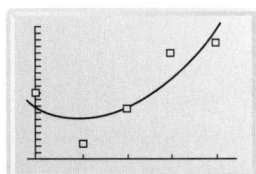	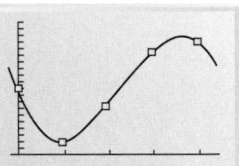

• The cubic model appears to best fit the given values.

2. Answers may vary. Sample: No; when $x = 25$ then, based on the cubic model, $y \approx 3.6$, but because of its turning points the cubic model is unreliable.

✓ **Check Understanding** **2** Can you use the model in Example 2 to predict the value of y for x = 25? Explain. **See left.**

Finding a close fit helps you estimate values between known data points.

3 EXAMPLE Real-World Connection

Gold The table below shows world gold production for several years. Find a quartic function to model the data. Use it to estimate production in 1988.

World Gold Production

Year	1975	1980	1985	1990	1995	2000
Production (millions of troy ounces)	38.5	39.2	49.3	70.2	71.8	82.6

SOURCES: *The World Almanac* and *World Gold*

Enter the data. Let 0 represent 1975. To find a quartic model, use the QuarticReg option of a graphing calculator. Graph the model.

Real-World Connection

The Federal Reserve stores gold in bars that weigh 400 troy ounces each.

```
QuarticReg
y=ax^4+bx^3+...+e
a=9.0333333E-4
b=-.0519296296
c=.9590277778
d=-3.898862434
↓e=38.85753968
```

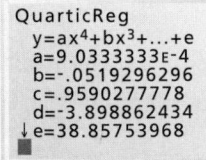

X	Y₁
7	42.915
8	46.157
9	49.519
10	52.875
11	56.12
12	59.168
13	61.959

X=13

Closure

Ask students how to determine the degree of a polynomial. **Write the polynomial in standard form. The degree of the polynomial is the largest degree** of any term of the polynomial. Describe a method for estimating values between known data points. **Graph the known data, choose an appropriate model to** fit the data, and use the model to estimate the values between the known data points.

The function $f(x) = 0.0009033x^4 - 0.05193x^3 + 0.959x^2 - 3.899x + 38.86$ is an approximate model for a quartic function.

To estimate gold production in 1988, you can use the Table option of a graphing calculator to find that $f(13) \approx 61.96$. According to the model, about 62 million troy ounces of gold were produced in 1988.

✓ **Check Understanding** ❸ Use the quartic model in Example 3 to estimate gold production in 1997.
75.9 million troy oz

EXERCISES

For more practice, see *Extra Practice*.

Practice and Problem Solving

Assign

❶ **Obje**
Ⓐ Ⓑ

Ⓒ **Extension** 60

❷ **Objective**
Ⓐ Ⓑ **Core** 13–23, 31–32, 59

Ⓒ **Extension** 61

Standardized Test Prep 62–65

Mixed Review 66–72

Ⓐ **Practice by Example**

Example 1
(page 301)

Write each polynomial in standard form. Then classify it by degree and by number of terms. 1–12. See margin.

1. $7x + 3x + 5$ **2.** $5 - 3x$ **3.** $2m^2 - 3 + 7m$

4. $-x^3 + x^4 + x$ **5.** $-4p + 3p + 2p^2$ **6.** $5a^2 + 3a^3 + 1$

7. $-x^5$ **8.** $3 + 12x^4$ **9.** $6x^3 - x^3$

10. $7x^3 - 10x^3 + x^3$ **11.** $4x + 5x^2 + 8$ **12.** $x^2 - x^4 + 2x^2$

Example 2
(page 302)

Find a cubic model for each set of values. 13–17. See back of book.

13. $(-2, -7), (-1, 0), (0, 1), (1, 2), (2, 9)$ **14.** $(0, -12), (1, 10), (2, 4), (3, 42)$

15. $(-1, 2.5), (0, 1), (1, 1.5), (2, 13)$ **16.** $(-3, 91), (-2, 84), (-1, 93), (0, 100)$

17. Vital Statistics The data at the right indicate that the life expectancy for residents of the United States has been increasing. Recall that in Chapter 3 you found a linear model for this data set.
  a. Find a quadratic model for the data set.
  b. Find a cubic model for the data set.
  c. Graph each model. Compare the quadratic and cubic models to determine which one is a better fit.

Life Expectancy (years)

Year of Birth	Males	Females
1970	67.1	74.7
1980	70.0	77.4
1990	71.8	78.8
2000	73.2	80.2
2010	74.5	81.3

SOURCE: U.S. Bureau of the Census.
Go to www.PHSchool.com for a data update.
Web Code: agg-2041

Example 3
(pages 302–303)

Find a cubic model for each function. Then use your model to estimate the value of y when $x = 17$. 18–23. See back of book.

18. $(-1, -3), (0, 0), (1, -1), (2, 0)$ **19.** $(10, 0), (11, 121), (12, 288), (13, 507)$

20. $(10, 500), (14, 588), (16, 512), (20, 0)$ **21.** $(1, 91), (10, 95), (20, 260), (30, 365)$

22.

x	0	3	5	6	9	11	12	14	16	18	20
y	42	31	26	21	17	15	19	22	28	30	29

23.

x	0	2	3	6	8	10	12	14	16	18	20
y	4.1	6	15.7	21.1	23.6	23.1	24.7	24.9	23.9	25.2	29.5

Ⓑ **Apply Your Skills**

24. Open-Ended Write a third-degree polynomial function. Make a table of values and a graph. Find the x- and y-intercepts. **Check students' work.**

Lesson 6-1   Polynomial Functions   **303**

Exercise 17 Challenge interested students to research why the life expectancies for males and females differ. Invite students to share their findings with the class.

Careers

Exercise 17 Insurance companies use vital statistics, such as life expectancies of males and females, and current age, to determine the cost of life insurance.

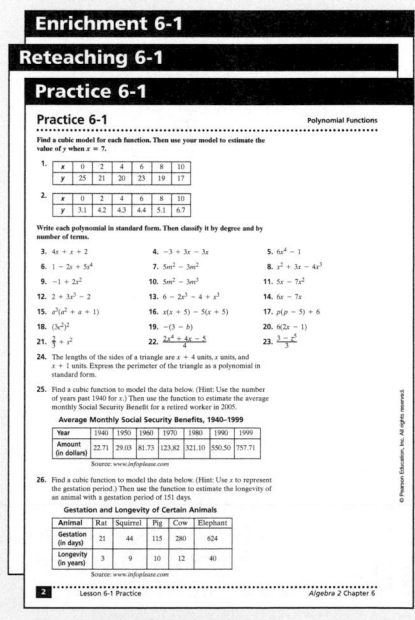

pages 303–305 Exercises

1. $10x + 5$; linear binomial

2. $-3x + 5$; linear binomial

3. $2m^2 + 7m - 3$; quadratic trinomial

4. $x^4 - x^3 + x$; quartic trinomial

5. $2p^2 - p$; quadratic binomial

6. $3a^3 + 5a^2 + 1$; cubic trinomial

7. $-x^5$; quintic monomial

8. $12x^4 + 3$; quartic binomial

9. $5x^3$; cubic monomial

10. $-2x^3$; cubic monomial

11. $5x^2 + 4x + 8$; quadratic trinomial

12. $-x^4 + 3x^3$; quartic binomial

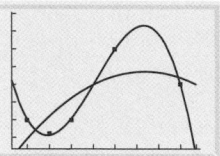

Lesson Quiz 6-1

Write each polynomial in standard form. Then classify it by degree and by number of terms.

1. $-x^2 + 2x + x^2$ **2x; degree 1, linear monomial**

2. $7x^2 + 10 + 4x^3$
   $4x^3 + 7x^2 + 10$; degree 3, cubic trinomial

3. $3x(4x) + x^2(2x^2)$
   $2x^4 + 12x^2$; degree 4, quartic binomial

4.

x	1	2	3	5	8
y	3	2.2	3	7	5

a. Find a cubic and a quadratic model for the table of values.

Xmin=0.3 Ymin=1.384
Xmax=8.7 Ymax=9
Xscl=1   Yscl=1

$y = -0.14401x^3 + 1.7805x^2 - 5.229x + 6.62$, $y = -0.1319x^2 + 1.682x + 0.37$

b. Which model appears to give the better fit? **the cubic model**

c. Using the model you selected in part b, estimate the value of y when x = 12. **−48.6**

Alternative Assessment

Organize students into groups of two. Have students search for data about sports, economics, science, or other topics of interest. Direct them to enter portions of the data on a graphing calculator to see if the data can be modeled in a reasonable way by a linear, quadratic, or cubic polynomial function. Students then record the equations for the models and sketch graphs of the data points and models. Have students classify their models by degree and number of terms.

304

31a. $V = 10\pi r^2$

b. $V = \frac{2}{3}\pi r^3$

c. $V = \frac{2}{3}\pi r^3 + 10\pi r^2$

Reading Math

To interpolate means to estimate a value inside the range of known values. To extrapolate means to estimate a value outside the range of known values.

46–58. See margin p. 305.

Write each polynomial in standard form. Then classify it by degree and by number of terms. 25–30. See margin.

25. $8x - 4x + x^3$ 26. $a^2 + a^3 - 4a^4$ 27. 7

28. $2x(3x)$ 29. $x^3(2 + x)$ 30. $\frac{3x^5 + 4x}{6}$

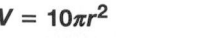 31. **Packaging Design** The diagram at the right shows a cologne bottle that consists of a cylindrical base and a hemispherical top.
   a. Write an expression for the cylinder's volume.
   b. Write an expression for the volume of the hemispherical top.
   c. Write a polynomial to represent the total volume.

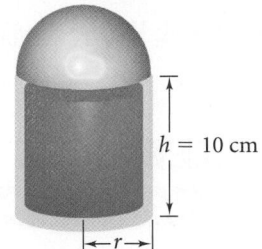

$h = 10$ cm

$\leftarrow r \rightarrow$

 32. **Writing** Explain why cubic functions are useful for interpolating between known data points. Why are they often not reliable for extrapolating data? **See margin.**

Simplify. Classify each result by number of terms. 33–45. See margin p. 305.

33. $(2c^2 + 9) - (3c^2 - 7)$ 34. $(-8d^3 - 7) + (-d^3 - 6)$

35. $(7x^2 + 8x - 5) + (9x^2 - 9x)$ 36. $(5x^3 - 6x + 8) - (3x^3 - 9)$

37. $(3a - 2b) + (6b - 2a)$ 38. $(4x - 5y) - (4x + 7y)$

39. $(3x^2 - 6y - 1) + (5x^2 + 1)$ 40. $(-a^2 - 3) - (3a - a^2 - 5)$

41. $(7x^3 + 9x^2 - 8x + 11) - (5x^3 - 13x - 16)$

42. $(-12x^3 + 5x - 23) - (4x^4 + 31 - 9x^3)$

43. $(30x^3 - 49x^2 + 7x) + (50x^3 - 75 - 60x^2)$

44. $(-3x^3 + 7x^2 - 8) - (-5x^3 + 9x^2 - 8x + 19)$

45. $(3a^2 - ab - 7) + (5a^2 + ab + 8) - (-2a^2 + 3ab - 9)$

Find each product. Classify the result by number of terms.

46. $x(2x)(4x + 1)$ 47. $5x^2(6x - 2)$ 48. $(2a - 5)(a^2 - 1)$

49. $b(b - 3)^2$ 50. $(x - 2)^3$ 51. $(x^2 + 1)^2$

52. $(2x + 5)^3 + 1$ 53. $(a - b)^2 (a + b)$ 54. $(a - 1)^4$

55. $(s + 3)(4s - 1)(3s + 7)$ 56. $(x + 1)(x - 1)(x + 2)$

57. $(2c - 3)(2c + 4)(2c - 1)$ 58. $(s + t)(s - t)(s + t)(s - t)$

59. The table shows U.S. energy production for a number of years.
   a. Find a linear model, a cubic model, and a quartic model for the data set. Let 0 represent 1960. **See margin p. 305.**
   b. Graph each model. Compare the three models to determine which fits best.
   c. Use your answer to part (b) to estimate U.S. energy production in 1997.

   b. See back of book.

   U.S. Energy Production

Year	1960	1965	1970	1975	1980	1985	1990	1995	1999
Production (×10¹⁵ Btu)	41.5	49.3	62.1	59.9	64.8	64.9	70.8	71.0	72.5

   SOURCE: *The World Almanac*   ≈72.2 × 10¹⁵ Btu

pages 303–305   Exercises

25. $x^3 + 4x$; cubic binomial

26. $-4a^4 + a^3 + a^2$; quartic trinomial

27. 7; constant monomial

28. $6x^2$; quadratic monomial

29. $x^4 + 2x^3$; quartic binomial

30. $\frac{1}{2}x^5 + \frac{2}{3}x$; quintic binomial

32. **Answers may vary. Sample: Cubic functions represent curvature in the data. Because of their turning points they can be unreliable for extrapolation.**

C Challenge **60. Geometry** Use the formula $V = \frac{\pi h}{3}(r^2 + rs + s^2)$ to find the volume of the truncated cone. Express your answer in scientific notation with the appropriate number of significant digits.

60. 2.5×10^8 cm^3

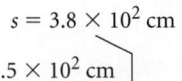

$s = 3.8 \times 10^2$ cm

$h = 3.5 \times 10^2$ cm

$r = 5.6 \times 10^2$ cm

 61. Critical Thinking Recall that each family of functions has a simplest function called the parent function.
   a. Compare the graphs of $y = x^3$ and $y = x^3 + 4$. Describe how the graph of $y = x^3 + 4$ relates to the graph of $y = x^3$. **up 4 units**
   b. Compare the graphs of $y = x^3$ and $y = 4x^3$. Describe how the graph of $y = 4x^3$ relates to the graph of $y = x^3$. **$y = 4x^3$ is more narrow.**
   c. Identify the parent function among the functions in parts (a) and (b). **$y = x^3$**

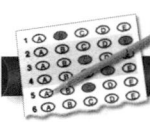

Standardized Test Prep

Quantitative Comparison

Compare the boxed quantity in Column A with the boxed quantity in Column B. Choose the best answer.
   A. The quantity in Column A is greater.
   B. The quantity in Column B is greater.
   C. The two quantities are equal.
   D. The relationship cannot be determined from the information given.

Take It to the NET
Online lesson quiz at
www.PHSchool.com
Web Code: agk-0601

Column A	Column B
62. B the degree of the quadratic term of a polynomial	the degree of the cubic term of a polynomial
63. A the degree of $-5x^2 + 1 + 2x^2$, written in standard form	the degree of $x^2 - 2x^2 + x^2 + 4$, written in standard form
64. A the leading coefficient of $3x + 1$	the constant term of $x^3 + 5x^2 - 3$

Short Response

65. Why is finding the degree of a polynomial simplified when the polynomial is written in standard form? **See back of book.**

Mixed Review

Lesson 5-8 Use the discriminant to find the number of real solutions.
   66. $3x^2 + x - 6 = 0$ **2**   **67.** $5x^2 - 9 = 0$ **2**   **68.** $-x^2 + 2x - 8 = 0$ **none**

Lesson 5-3 **69.** Graph $f(x) = 3x^2 - 1$. Translate the graph right five units and down two units. What is the vertex of the new graph? **See back of book.**

Lesson 4-4 Each matrix represents the vertices of a polygon. Translate each figure 3 units left and 2 units down. Express your answer as a matrix. **70–72. See back of book.**

70. $\begin{bmatrix} 4 & 0 & 4 & 8 \\ -6 & -1 & 2 & -1 \end{bmatrix}$ **71.** $\begin{bmatrix} 5 & 0 & -3 \\ 7 & 0 & 2 \end{bmatrix}$ **72.** $\begin{bmatrix} 1 & 2 & 1 & 2 \\ -1 & -1 & -2 & -2 \end{bmatrix}$

Lesson 6-1   Polynomial Functions   **305**

33. $-c^2 + 16$; binomial

34. $-9d^3 - 13$; binomial

35. $16x^2 - x - 5$; trinomial

36. $2x^3 - 6x + 17$; trinomial

37. $a + 4b$; binomial

38. $-12y$; monomial

39. $8x^2 - 6y$; binomial

40. $-3a + 2$; binomial

41. $2x^3 + 9x^2 + 5x + 27$; polynomial of 4 terms

42. $-4x^4 - 3x^3 + 5x - 54$; polynomial of 4 terms

43. $80x^3 - 109x^2 + 7x - 75$; polynomial of 4 terms

Standardized Test Prep

 **Resources**
For additional practice with a variety of test item formats:
• Standardized Test Prep, p. 357
• Test-Taking Strategies, p. 352
• Test-Taking Strategies with Transparencies

Error Prevention

Exercise 64 Tell students to read carefully. Exercises 62 and 63 compare the degree in each column. Exercise 64 compares the leading coefficient to the constant term.

44. $2x^3 - 2x^2 + 8x - 27$; polynomial of 4 terms

45. $10a^2 - 3ab + 10$; trinomial

46. $8x^3 + 2x^2$; binomial

47. $30x^3 - 10x^2$; binomial

48. $2a^3 - 5a^2 - 2a + 5$; polynomial of 4 terms

49. $b^3 - 6b^2 + 9b$; trinomial

50. $x^3 - 6x^2 + 12x - 8$; polynomial of 4 terms

51. $x^4 + 2x^2 + 1$; trinomial

52. $8x^3 + 60x^2 + 150x + 126$; polynomial of 4 terms

53. $a^3 - a^2b - b^2a + b^3$; polynomial of 4 terms

54. $a^4 - 4a^3 + 6a^2 - 4a + 1$; polynomial of 5 terms

55. $12s^3 + 61s^2 + 68s - 21$; polynomial of 4 terms

56. $x^3 + 2x^2 - x - 1$; trinomial

57. $8c^3 - 26c + 12$; trinomial

58. $s^4 - 2t^2s^2 + t^2$; trinomial

59a. $y = 0.7166x + 47.61$
$y = 0.0009365x^3 - 0.07442x^2 + 2.293x + 41.41$
$y = -0.00004789x^4 + 0.004666x^3 - 0.1647x^2 + 2.980x + 40.78$

305

End Behavior

Students learn to predict the behavior of the graph of a polynomial function by examining the term of highest degree and its coefficient. This will also help students check their graphs.

Resources

 Technology
Computer Test Generator CD-ROM, Chapter 0, Extension Topics

Teaching Notes

Inclusion

The arrow notation may be helpful for students who have difficulty describing the behavior with words.

Error Prevention

Students need to realize that it is the leading coefficient of a polynomial function *written in standard form* that should be inspected.

Auditory Learners

Stress the initial *o* in the words *odd* and *opposite* when describing the left behavior.

The end behavior of a graph describes the far left and the far right portions of the graph. The graphs of polynomial functions show four types of end behavior— *up and up*, *down and down*, *down and up*, and *up and down*.

Up and Up	Down and Down	Down and Up	Up and Down
(↖, ↗)	(↙, ↘)	(↙, ↗)	(↖, ↘)
Example	Example	Example	Example

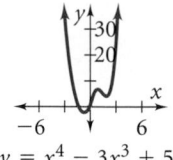 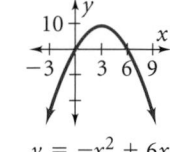 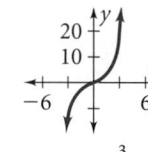 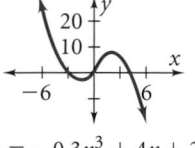

| $y = x^4 - 3x^3 + 5x$ | $y = -x^2 + 6x$ | $y = x^3$ | $y = -0.3x^3 + 4x + 2$ |

You can determine *by inspection* the end behavior of the graph of a polynomial function in standard form. Look at the coefficient and degree of the leading term.

Right If the leading coefficient is positive, then the graph rises to the right. If the leading coefficient is negative, then the graph falls to the right.

Left If the degree of the polynomial is even, then the left behavior is the same as the right behavior. If the degree of the polynomial is odd, then the left behavior is the opposite of the right behavior.

EXAMPLE **Describing End Behavior**

Determine by inspection the end behavior of the graph of each polynomial.

a. $y = 4x^3 - 3x$
The leading coefficient 4 is positive, so the graph rises to the right. The degree of the polynomial is 3, which is odd. The left behavior is opposite the right behavior, so the graph falls to the left. The end behavior is (↖, ↗).

b. $f(x) = -2x^4 + 8x^3 - 8x^2$
The leading coefficient –2 is negative, so the graph falls to the right. The degree of the polynomial is 4, which is even. The left behavior is the same as the right behavior, so the graph falls to the left. The end behavior is (↙, ↘).

EXERCISES

Determine by inspection the end behavior of the graph of each function.

1. $y = 3x + 2$ (↙,↗)

2. $y = 4x^3$ (↙,↗)

3. $g(t) = -t^2 + t$ (↙,↘)

4. $f(x) = 2x + x^5$ (↙,↗)

5. $g(x) = x^6$ (↖,↗)

6. $y = 3x^5 - 4x^4$ (↙,↗)

7. $y = -7x^8$ (↙,↘)

8. $f(x) = \frac{1}{2}x^4 - 2$ (↖,↗)

9. $y = -\frac{1}{2}x^3 + 4x^2 + x - 1$ (↖,↘)

10. $g(x) = x - x^3 + 5$ (↖,↘)

Polynomials and Linear Factors

North Carolina Objectives 1.03 Operate with algebraic expressions (polynomial, rational, complex fractions) to solve problems.

Lesson Preview

What You'll Learn

OBJECTIVE 1 To analyze the factored form of a polynomial

OBJECTIVE 2 To write a polynomial function from its zeros

. . . And Why

To find the dimensions of carry-on luggage, as in Example 3

 Check Skills You'll Need   (For help, go to Lessons 5-1 and 5-4.)

Factor each quadratic expression.

1. $x^2 + 7x + 12$
$(x + 4)(x + 3)$

2. $x^2 + 8x - 20$
$(x + 10)(x - 2)$

3. $x^2 - 14x + 24$
$(x - 12)(x - 2)$

Find each product.

4. $x(x + 4)$
$x^2 + 4x$

5. $(x + 1)^2$
$x^2 + 2x + 1$

6. $(x - 3)^2(x + 2)$
$x^3 - 4x^2 - 3x + 18$

New Vocabulary • relative maximum • relative minimum • Factor Theorem • multiple zero • multiplicity

1. Plan

Lesson Preview

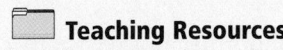 **Check Skills You'll Need**

Factoring Quadratic Expressions
Lesson 5-4: Examples 2–4
Exercises 7–24
Extra Practice, p. 826

Modeling Data With Quadratic Functions
Lesson 5-1: Example 1
Exercises 2–9
Extra Practice, p. 826

Lesson Resources

📁 **Teaching Resources**
Practice, Reteaching, Enrichment

👥 **Reaching All Students**
Practice Workbook 6-2
Spanish Practice Workbook 6-2

⏱ **Presentation Assistant Plus!**
Transparencies
• Check Skills You'll Need 6-2
• Additional Examples 6-2
• Student Edition Answers 6-2
• Lesson Quiz 6-2
PH Presentation Pro CD 6-2

PRENTICE HALL ASSESSMENT SYSTEM

Computer Test Generator CD

💿 **Technology**
Resource Pro® CD-ROM
Computer Test Generator CD
Prentice Hall Presentation Pro CD

💻 **www.PHSchool.com**
Student Site
• Teacher Web Code: agk-5500
• Self-grading Lesson Quiz
Teacher Center
• Lesson Planner
• Resources

Plus

OBJECTIVE

1 **The Factored Form of a Polynomial**

 Interactive lesson includes instant self-check, tutorials, and activities.

Just as you can rewrite a whole number as a product of its prime factors, you can write a polynomial as a product of its linear factors. Compare the factor trees for the whole number 6 and the quadratic expression $x^2 + 4x - 12$.

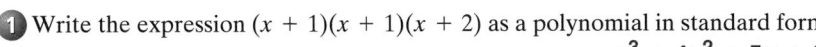

In the factor tree for the whole number 6, each branch ends with a prime number. Likewise, in the factor tree for the polynomial $x^2 + 4x - 12$, each branch ends with a "prime" linear factor. A linear factor is similar to a prime number in that it cannot be factored any further. Once a polynomial has been factored completely to its linear factors, it is in factored form.

1 **EXAMPLE**   **Writing a Polynomial in Standard Form**

Write the expression $(x + 1)(x + 2)(x + 3)$ as a polynomial in standard form.

$(x + 1)(x + 2)(x + 3) = (x + 1)(x^2 + 3x + 2x + 6)$ **Multiply $(x + 2)$ and $(x + 3)$.**

$= (x + 1)(x^2 + 5x + 6)$ **Simplify.**

$= x(x^2 + 5x + 6) + 1(x^2 + 5x + 6)$ **Distributive Property**

$= x^3 + 5x^2 + 6x + x^2 + 5x + 6$ **Multiply.**

$= x^3 + 6x^2 + 11x + 6$ **Simplify.**

● The expression $(x + 1)(x + 2)(x + 3)$ is the factored form of $x^3 + 6x^2 + 11x + 6$.

Need Help?
$a^n = a \cdot a \cdot a \cdot \ldots \cdot a$
   n factors of a
$a^m \cdot a^n = a^{m+n}$

✓ **Check Understanding** **1** Write the expression $(x + 1)(x + 1)(x + 2)$ as a polynomial in standard form.
$x^3 + 4x^2 + 5x + 2$

Ongoing Assessment and Intervention

Before the Lesson
Diagnose prerequisite skills using:
• Check Skills You'll Need

During the Lesson
Monitor progress using:
• Check Understanding
• Additional Examples
• Standardized Test Prep

After the Lesson
Assess knowledge using:
• Lesson Quiz
• Computer Test Generator CD

Math Background

There is a close connection between the problem of factoring a polynomial and the problem of finding its zeros. If $P(x)$ is a polynomial function, then $x - a$ is a linear factor of $P(x)$ if and only if $P(a) = 0$.

OBJECTIVE

① Teaching Notes

② EXAMPLE   Error Prevention

Some students may stop factoring after they find the GCF. Remind students that they must keep factoring as long as a polynomial is factorable.

③ EXAMPLE   Diversity

Some students may not have had the opportunity to fly in an airplane and, therefore, not understand what *carry-on* luggage is. Ask a student to explain the difference between *carry-on* luggage and *checked* luggage.

Additional Examples

① Write $(x - 1)(x + 3)(x + 4)$ as a polynomial in standard form. $x^3 + 6x^2 + 5x - 12$

② Write $3x^3 - 18x^2 + 24x$ in factored form. $3x(x - 2)(x - 4)$

> **Need Help?**
> The GCF is the greatest common factor.

You can sometimes use the GCF of the terms to help you factor a polynomial.

② EXAMPLE   Writing a Polynomial in Factored Form

Write $2x^3 + 10x^2 + 12x$ in factored form.

$$2x^3 + 10x^2 + 12x = 2x(x^2 + 5x + 6) \quad \text{Factor out the GCF, } 2x.$$
$$= 2x(x + 2)(x + 3) \quad \text{Factor } x^2 + 5x + 6.$$

Check $2x(x + 2)(x + 3) = 2x(x^2 + 5x + 6) \quad$ **Multiply** $(x + 2)(x + 3)$.
$$= 2x^3 + 10x^2 + 12x \checkmark \quad \text{Distributive Property}$$

✓ **Check Understanding** ② Write $3x^3 - 3x^2 - 36x$ in factored form. Check by multiplication.
$$3x(x - 4)(x + 3)$$

You can use polynomial functions to solve real-world problems. Consider the formula for volume: $V = \text{depth} \cdot \text{length} \cdot \text{width}$. Each dimension can represent a linear factor of a polynomial function.

③ EXAMPLE   Real-World Connection

Travel Several popular models of carry-on luggage have a length 10 in. greater than their depth. To comply with airline regulations, the sum of the length, width, and depth may not exceed 40 in.

a. Assume that the sum of the length, width, and depth is 40 in. Graph the function relating volume V to depth x. Find the x-intercepts. What do they represent?

Relate   Volume $=$ depth $\cdot$ length $\cdot$ width

Define   Let x $=$ depth. Then $x + 10$ $=$ length, and
$40 - (\text{depth} + \text{length})$ $=$ width.

Write $V(x) = x\,(x + 10)\,(40 - (x + x + 10))$
$$= x(x + 10)(30 - 2x)$$

Graph the function for volume. The x-intercepts of the function are $x = 0, x = -10$, and $x = 15$. These values of x produce a volume of zero.

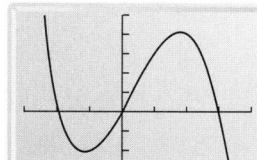

Xmin=–15
Xmax=20
Xscl=5
Ymin=–1500
Ymax=2500
Yscl=500

b. Describe a realistic domain.

The function has values over the set of all real numbers x. Since x represents the depth of the luggage, $x > 0$. Since the volume must be positive, $x < 15$. A realistic domain is $0 < x < 15$.

c. What is the maximum possible volume of a piece of luggage? What are the corresponding dimensions of the luggage?

Look for the greatest value of y that occurs within the domain $0 < x < 15$. Use the Maximum feature of a graphing calculator to find the maximum volume. A volume of approximately 2052 in.^{3} occurs for a depth of about 8.9 in. Then the length is about 18.9 in. and the width is about 12.2 in.

✓ **Check Understanding** ③ Suppose an airline raises the allowable sum of the luggage dimensions to 45 in. Find the maximum possible volume and the corresponding dimensions.
$V \approx 3014$ in.^{3}; depth 10.5 in., length 20.5 in., width 13.9 in.

Real-World Connection

Airlines regulate the size of carry-on luggage because space is limited in a plane's overhead compartments.

👥 Reaching All Students

Below Level Help students understand why odd functions have only relative minima and maxima whereas even functions have at least one absolute minimum or maximum.	**Advanced Learners** Have students write the polynomial equation of degree three that has roots 2, $3i$, and $-3i$, and check each other's work.	**Diversity** See note on page 308. **Error Prevention** See note on page 311.

The maximum value in Example 3 is the greatest value of the points in a region of the graph. It is called a **relative maximum**. Similarly, a **relative minimum** is the least y-value among nearby points on a graph.

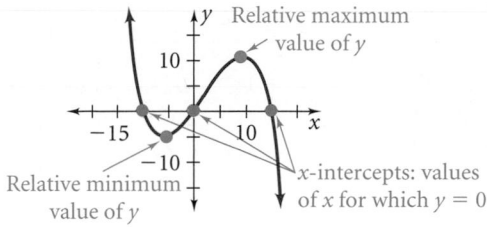

Recall that the x-intercepts of the graph of a function are called zeros because the value of the function is zero at each x-intercept.

OBJECTIVE

2 Factors and Zeros of a Polynomial Function

Need Help?

Zero Product Property
If a product equals zero, then at least one of its factors must equal zero.

If a polynomial is in factored form, you can use the Zero Product Property to find values that will make the polynomial equal zero.

4 EXAMPLE Finding Zeros of a Polynomial Function

Find the zeros of $y = (x - 2)(x + 1)(x + 3)$. Then graph the function.

Using the Zero Product Property, find a zero for each linear factor.

$x - 2 = 0$ or $x + 1 = 0$ or $x + 3 = 0$
    $x = 2$ $x = -1$ $x = -3$

The zeros of the function are 2, -1, and -3. Now graph the function.

4b.

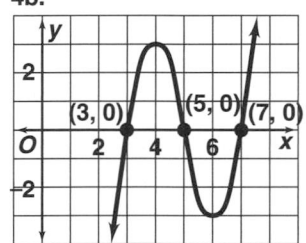

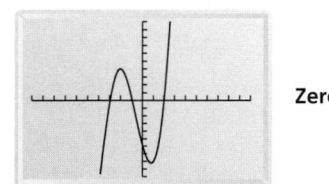

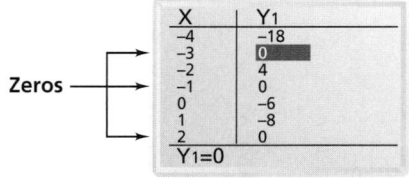

✔ **Check Understanding** 4 **a.** Find the zeros of the function $y = (x - 7)(x - 5)(x - 3)$. **7, 5, 3**
                         b. Graph the function and label the zeros.

You can reverse the process and write linear factors when you know the zeros. The relationship between the linear factors of a polynomial and the zeros of a polynomial is described by the Factor Theorem.

Key Concepts

Theorem	Factor Theorem
The expression $x - a$ is a linear factor of a polynomial if and only if the value a is a zero of the related polynomial function.	

---

3 Another airline has different carry-on luggage regulations. The sum of the length, width, and depth may not exceed 50 in.
a. Assume that the sum of the length, width, and depth is 50 in. and the length is 10 in. greater than the depth. Graph the function relating the volume V to depth x. Find the x-intercepts. What do they represent?
x-intercepts: 0, -10, and 20; These values of x produce a volume of zero.

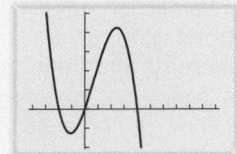

Xmin=-20 Ymin=-2000
Xmax=50   Ymax=5000
Xscl=5   Yscl=1000

b. Describe a realistic domain for $V(x)$. **$0 < x < 20$**
c. What is the maximum possible volume of the box? What are the corresponding dimensions of the box? **about 4225 in.^{3}; depth: about 12.2 in., length: about 22.2 in., width: about 15.6 in.**

OBJECTIVE

2 Teaching Notes

4 **EXAMPLE** Technology Tip

Students often think that graphing a function such as the one in this example requires them to multiply the binomials before entering the function on the Y= list. Actually, this is an unnecessary step. The function can be entered in exactly the form given.

Additional Examples

4 Find the zeros of $y = (x + 1)(x - 1)(x + 3)$. Then graph the function. **1, -1, -3**

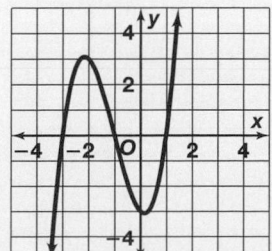

309

310

5 EXAMPLE   Math Tip

Point out that any constant multiple of $f(x)$ will also have two distinct zeros at -2 and 3. Other functions with these zeros can be obtained by using other powers of the linear factors.

6 EXAMPLE   Teaching Tip

Have students observe that if a polynomial function is written as a product of linear factors, they can use the factorization to identify multiple roots and their multiplicity. You may want to mention that if they do not see a way to write the polynomial in factored form, the graph may provide clues about multiple roots. Often, however, from mere visual inspection of the graph, there are no definitive answers to questions about multiple roots.

◢ Additional Examples

5 Write a polynomial function in standard form with zeros at 2, -3, and 0. **Answers may vary. Sample:** $f(x) = x^3 + x^2 - 6x$

6 Find any multiple zeros of $f(x) = x^5 - 6x^4 + 9x^3$ and state the multiplicity. **The number 0 is a zero with multiplicity 3, and 3 is a zero with multiplicity 2.**

Closure

Ask: *Suppose you are given a polynomial of degree greater than 1 and want to know whether $x - 2$ is a factor of the polynomial. How can you find out without dividing?* **Find the value of the polynomial for $x = 2$. If the value is 0, then $x - 2$ is a factor.**

5a. $y = x^3 + 5x^2 + 2x - 8$

b. $y = x^3 + 6x^2 + 8x$

c. **Answers may vary. Sample: The zero at 0 can be from $x = 0$, $x^2 = 0$, $x^3 = 0$, and so on. Each power will lead to a different answer.**

✓ **Check Understanding**

Reading Math

Distinct means "separate and different."

---

5 EXAMPLE   Writing a Polynomial Function From its Zeros

Write a polynomial function in standard form with zeros at $-2, 3,$ and 3.

$$\begin{array}{ccc} -2 & 3 & 3 \end{array} \qquad \text{zeros}$$
$$\downarrow \quad \downarrow \quad \downarrow$$

$f(x) = (x + 2)(x - 3)(x - 3)$ **Write a linear factor for each zero.**

$\quad = (x + 2)(x^2 - 6x + 9)$ **Multiply $(x - 3)$ and $(x - 3)$.**

$\quad = x(x^2 - 6x + 9) + 2(x^2 - 6x + 9)$ **Distributive Property**

$\quad = x^3 - 6x^2 + 9x + 2x^2 - 12x + 18$ **Distributive Property**

$\quad = x^3 - 4x^2 - 3x + 18$ **Simplify.**

● The function $f(x) = x^3 - 4x^2 - 3x + 18$ has zeros at $-2, 3,$ and 3.

5 **a.** Write a polynomial function in standard form with zeros at $-4, -2,$ and 1.
b. Write a polynomial function in standard form with zeros at $-4, -2,$ and 0.
c. Critical Thinking. Explain why the zero at 0 produces more than one possible answer to part (b).   **a–c. See left.**

While the polynomial function in Example 5 has three zeros, it has only two distinct zeros: -2 and 3. If a linear factor of a polynomial is repeated, then the zero is repeated. A repeated zero is called a **multiple zero.** A multiple zero has a **multiplicity** equal to the number of times the zero occurs. In Example 5, the zero 3 has a multiplicity of 2.

6 EXAMPLE   Finding the Multiplicity of a Zero

Find any multiple zeros of $f(x) = x^4 + 6x^3 + 8x^2$ and state the multiplicity.

$f(x) = x^4 + 6x^3 + 8x^2$

$f(x) = x^2(x^2 + 6x + 8)$ **Factor out the GCF, x^2.**

$f(x) = x^2(x + 4)(x + 2)$ **Factor $x^2 + 6x + 8$.**

Since you can rewrite x^2 as $(x - 0)(x - 0)$, or $(x - 0)^2$, the number 0 is a multiple zero of the function, with multiplicity 2.

✓ **Check Understanding**

6 For each function, find any multiple zeros and state the multiplicity.
a. $f(x) = (x - 2)(x + 1)(x + 1)^2$ **b.** $y = x^3 - 4x^2 + 4x$
-1, multiplicity of 3   **2, multiplicity of 2**

The Factor Theorem helps relate four key facts about a polynomial. These facts are equivalent—that is, if you know one of them, you know them all.

Key Concepts

Summary	Equivalent Statements about Polynomials

① -4 is a solution of $x^2 + 3x - 4 = 0$.
② -4 is an x-intercept of the graph of $y = x^2 + 3x - 4$.
③ -4 is a zero of $y = x^2 + 3x - 4$.
④ $x + 4$ is a factor of $x^2 + 3x - 4$.

---

pages 311–313   Exercises

1. $x^2 + x - 6$

2. $x^3 + 12x^2 + 47x + 60$

3. $x^3 - 7x^2 + 15x - 9$

7. $x(x - 6)(x + 6)$

8. $x(3x - 1)(3x + 3)$

9. $5x(2x^2 - 2x + 3)$

Practice and Problem Solving

 Practice by Example

Example 1
(page 307)

Write each expression as a polynomial in standard form. 1–3. See margin p. 310.

1. $(x + 3)(x - 2)$ **2.** $(x + 3)(x + 4)(x + 5)$ **3.** $(x - 3)^2 (x - 1)$

4. $x(x + 2)^2$ **5.** $x(x + 5)^2$ **6.** $x(x - 1)(x + 1)$
    $x^3 + 4x^2 + 4x$ $x^3 + 10x^2 + 25x$ $x^3 - x$

Example 2
(page 308)

7–9. See margin p. 310.

Write each polynomial in factored form. Check by multiplication.

7. $x^3 - 36x$ **8.** $9x^3 + 6x^2 - 3x$ **9.** $10x^3 - 10x^2 + 15x$

10. $x^3 + 7x^2 + 10x$ **11.** $x^3 + 8x^2 + 16x$ **12.** $x^3 - 7x^2 - 18x$
    $x(x + 5)(x + 2)$ $x(x + 4)^2$ $x(x - 9)(x + 2)$

Example 3
(pages 308–309)

Find the relative maximum, relative minimum, and zeros of each function.

13. $f(x) = x^3 + 4x^2 - 5x$ **14.** $f(x) = -x^3 + 16x^2 - 76x + 96$
   24.2, −1.4; 0, −5, 1   **5.0, −16.9; 2, 6, 8**

15. Metalwork A metalworker wants to make
an open box from a sheet of metal, by cutting
equal squares from each corner as shown.
  a. Write an expression for the length, width,
and height of the open box. **a–b. See margin.**
  b. Use your answer from part (a) to write a
function for volume. (*Hint*: Use factored form.)
  c. Graph the function. Find the maximum volume that can be
contained by the box and the size of the square cut that produces this volume.
See back of book.

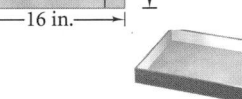

Example 4
(page 309)

Find the zeros of each function. Then graph the function.

16. $y = (x - 1)(x + 2)$ **17.** $y = (x - 2)(x + 9)$ **18.** $y = x(x + 5)(x - 8)$

19. $y = (x + 1)(x - 2)(x - 3)$ **20.** $y = (x + 1)(x - 1)(x - 2)$
16–20. See back of book.

Example 5
(page 310)

Write a polynomial function in standard form with the given zeros.
21–28. See margin.

21. $x = 5, 6, 7$ **22.** $x = -2, 0, 1$ **23.** $x = -5, -5, 1$ **24.** $x = 3, 3, 3$

25. $x = 1, -1, -2$ **26.** $x = -1, -2, -3$ **27.** $x = 0, 0, 2$ **28.** $x = -\frac{1}{2}, 0, 4$

Example 6
(page 310)

Find the zeros of each function. State the multiplicity of multiple zeros.
−1, 0, $\frac{1}{2}$

29. $y = (x + 3)^3$ **30.** $y = x(x - 1)^3$ **31.** $y = 2x^3 + x^2 - x$

29. −3 (mult. 3)

30. 0, 1 (mult. 3)

32. $y = 3x^3 - 3x$ **−1, 0, 1**   **33.** $y = (x - 4)^2$ **34.** $y = (x - 2)^2(x - 1)$
                      4 (mult. 2)   **1, 2 (mult. 2)**

35. $y = (2x + 3)(x - 1)^2$ **36.** $y = (x + 1)^2(x - 1)(x - 2)$
   $-\frac{3}{2}$, 1 (mult. 2)   **−1 (mult. 2), 1, 2**

 Apply Your Skills **37. Geometry** A box has length $2x + 1$ units, width $x + 4$ units, and height $x + 3$
units. To build the box using $x^3, x^2, x,$ and unit (1) blocks, how many of each will
you need? **2 x^3 blocks, 15 x^2 blocks, 31 x blocks, 12 unit blocks**

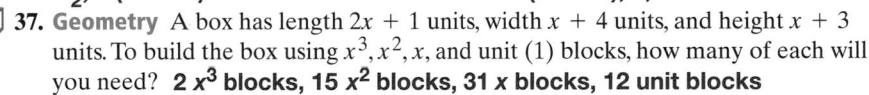

1 x x^2 x^3

15a. $h = x$, $\ell = 16 - 2x$,
    $w = 12 - 2x$

  b. $V = x(16 - 2x)$
    $(12 - 2x)$

21. $y = x^3 - 18x^2 + 107x$
    $- 210$

22. $y = x^3 + x^2 - 2x$

23. $y = x^3 + 9x^2 + 15x - 25$

24. $y = x^3 - 9x^2 + 27x - 27$

25. $y = x^3 + 2x^2 - x - 2$

26. $y = x^3 + 6x^2 + 11x + 6$

27. $y = x^3 - 2x^2$

28. $x^3 - \frac{7}{2}x^2 - 2x$

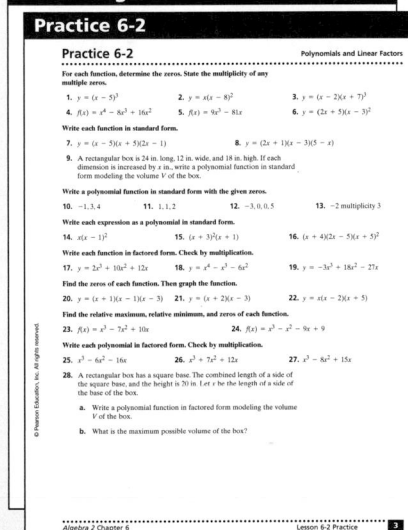

4. Assess

Alternative Assessment

Have each student write a linear
binomial on an index card. Direct
them to gather into groups of
three. Each group should write
the standard form of the
polynomial that has the binomials
of the group as its factors.
Students also find the zeros,
graph the function, and find the
relative maximum or minimum
values.

pages 311–313   Exercises

38a. $V = 2x^3 + 15x^2 + 31x$
$+ 12; 2x^3 + 7x^2 + 7x$
$+ 2$

b. $V = 8x^2 + 24x + 10$

40a. $h = x + 3; w = x$

b.
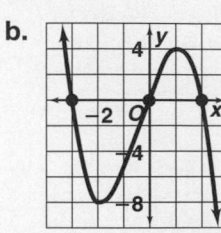

0, −3, 2; where the
volume is zero

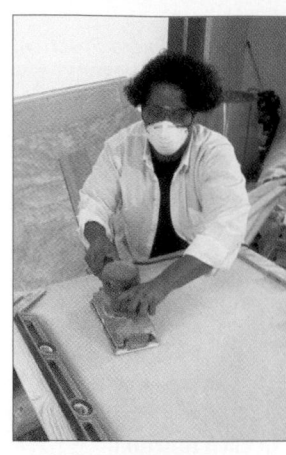

Real-World Connection

Careers Carpenters use
math to design and measure
components of buildings,
furniture, and art.

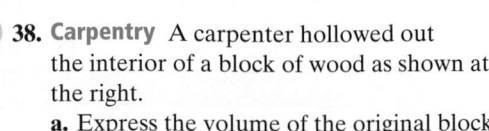

38. **Carpentry** A carpenter hollowed out
the interior of a block of wood as shown at
the right.
   a. Express the volume of the original block
   and the volume of the wood removed as
   polynomials in standard form.
   b. Write a polynomial for the volume
   of the wood remaining. **a–b. See margin.**

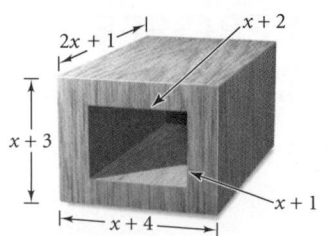

39. **Geometry** A rectangular box is $2x + 3$ units long, $2x - 3$ units wide, and
$3x$ units high. Express its volume as a polynomial. **$V = 12x^3 - 27x$**

40. **Measurement** The volume in cubic feet of a CD holder can be expressed
as $V(x) = -x^3 - x^2 + 6x$, or, when factored, as the product of its three
dimensions. The depth is expressed as $2 - x$. Assume that the height is greater
than the width. **a–b. See margin.**
   a. Factor the polynomial to find linear expressions for the height and the width.
   b. Graph the function. Find the x-intercepts. What do they represent?
   c. Describe a realistic domain for the function. **$0 < x < 2$**
   d. Find the maximum volume of the CD holder. **4.06 ft^3**

Write each function in standard form.

41. $y = (x + 1)(x - 4)(3 - 2x)$
$y = -2x^3 + 9x^2 - x - 12$

42. $y = (x + 7)(5x + 2)(x - 6)^2$
$y = 5x^4 - 23x^3 - 250x^2 +$

Write each function in factored form. Check by multiplication. $1164x + 504$

43. $y = 3x^3 - 27x^2 + 24x$
$y = 3x(x - 8)(x - 1)$

44. $y = -2x^3 - 2x^2 + 40x$
$y = -2x(x + 5)(x - 4)$

45. $y = x^4 + 3x^3 - 4x^2$
$y = x^2(x + 4)(x - 1)$

46. $y = \frac{1}{2}x^3 - \frac{1}{8}x$
$y = \frac{1}{2}x\left(x - \frac{1}{2}\right)\left(x + \frac{1}{2}\right)$

Find the relative maximum, relative minimum, and zeros of each function.

47. $y = 2x^3 - 23x^2 + 78x - 72$

48. $y = x^4 + 3x^3 - x^2 - 3x$

49. $y = 8x^3 - 10x^2 - x - 3$

50. $y = (x + 1)^4 - 1$

47–53. See margin pp. 312–313.

Write a polynomial function in standard form with the given zeros.

51. $5, -2, 0$

52. 7 multiplicity 3

53. $-2, -1, 3, 4$

For each function, determine the zeros. State the multiplicity of any multiple zeros.

54. $y = (x + 4)(x - 5)^3$
−4, 5 (mult. 3)

55. $f(x) = x^4 + 2x^3 + x^2$
0 (mult. 2), −1 (mult. 2)

56. $f(x) = x^3 - 36x$
0, 6, −6

57. **Critical Thinking** How can you find where the graph of a polynomial function
crosses the y-axis?

57. **Answers may vary.
Sample:** Write the
polynomial in
standard form. The
constant term is the
value of the
y-intercept.

58. A storage company needs to design a new storage box that has twice the
volume of its largest box. Its largest box is 5 ft long, 4 ft wide, and 3 ft high.
The new box must be formed by increasing each dimension by the same
amount. Find the increase in each dimension. **1 ft**

59. **Open-Ended** Write a polynomial function with the following features: it has
three distinct zeros; one of the zeros is 1; another zero has a multiplicity of 2.
See margin p. 313.

60. **Writing** Explain how the graph of a polynomial function can help you factor
the polynomial. **Answers may vary. Sample: The linear factors can be
determined by examining the x-intercepts of the graph.**

61. **Critical Thinking** A polynomial function has a zero at $x = -2a$. Find one
of its factors. **$x + 2a$**

47. $10.5, -7.1; \frac{3}{2}, 4, 6$

48. $0.9, -6.9, -1.4; 0, -3, -1, 1$

49. $2.98, -6.17; 1.5$

50. none, −1; −2, 0

51. **Answers may vary.
Sample:** $y = x^3 - 3x^2 - 10x$

52. $y = x^3 - 21x^2 + 147x - 343$

Challenge **62. Coordinate Geometry** The diagram at the right shows a rectangular region with one corner on the graph of $y = -x^2 + 2x + 4$.

62a. $A = -x^3 + 2x^2 + 4x$

    a. Write a polynomial in standard form for the area A of the rectangular region.

    b. Find the area of the rectangular region for $x = 2\frac{1}{2}$. $6\frac{7}{8}$ **square units**

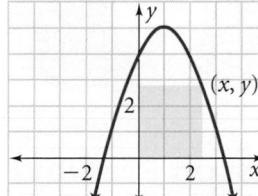

63. Find a fourth-degree polynomial function with zeros $1, -1, i,$ and $-i$. Write the function in both factored form and standard form. $y = (x - 1)(x + 1)(x - i)(x + i); y = x^4 - 1$

64a. Answers may vary. Sample: translation to the right 4 units

64. a. Compare the graphs of $y = (x + 1)(x + 2)(x + 3)$ and $y = (x - 1)(x - 2)(x - 3)$. What transformation could you use to describe the change from one graph to the other?

b. Compare the graphs of $y = (x + 1)(x + 3)(x + 7)$ and $y = (x - 1)(x - 3)(x - 7)$. Does the transformation that you chose in part (a) still hold true? Explain.

b. No; the second graph is not the result of a horizontal translation.

c. Make a Conjecture What transformation could you use to describe the effect of changing the signs of the zeros of a polynomial function?
Answers may vary. Sample: Rotation of 180° about the origin.

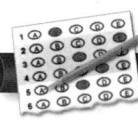

Resources
For additional practice with a variety of test item formats:
• Standardized Test Prep, p. 357
• Test-Taking Strategies, p. 352
• Test-Taking Strategies with Transparencies

Standardized Test Prep

Multiple Choice

65. Which expression is the factored form of $x^3 + 2x^2 - 5x - 6$? **C**
  A. $(x + 1)(x + 1)(x - 6)$ **B.** $(x + 2)(2x - 5)(x - 6)$
  C. $(x + 3)(x + 1)(x - 2)$ **D.** $(x - 3)(x - 1)(x + 2)$

Take It to the NET
Online lesson quiz at
www.PHSchool.com
Web Code: agk-0602

66. What are the zeros of the polynomial function $y = (x - 3)(2x + 1)(x - 1)$? **H**
  F. $\frac{1}{2}, 1, 3$ **G.** $-1, 1, 3$ **H.** $-\frac{1}{2}, 1, 3$ **I.** $-3, \frac{1}{2}, 1$

67. Which polynomial function has zeros at $-4, 3,$ and 5? **B**
  A. $f(x) = (x + 4)(x + 3)(x + 5)$ **B.** $g(x) = (x + 4)(x - 3)(x - 5)$
  C. $h(x) = (x - 4)(x - 3)(x - 5)$ **D.** $k(x) = (x - 4)(x + 3)(x + 5)$

Short Response

68. What is the factored form of $f(x) = x^4 + 8x^3 - 9x^2$? **See margin.**

Extended Response

69. What is the polynomial function, in standard form, whose zeros are $-2, 5,$ and 6, and whose leading coefficient is -2? Justify your reasoning.
See margin.

Mixed Review

Lesson 6-1

Write each polynomial in standard form. Then classify it by degree and by number of terms. **70–72. See margin.**

70. $x^2 - 1 - 3x^5 + 2x^2$ **71.** $-2x^3 - 7x^4 + x^3$ **72.** $6x + x^3 - 6x - 2$

Lesson 5-4

Factor each expression.

73. $x^2 + 5x + 4$ **74.** $x^2 - 2x - 15$ **75.** $x^2 - 12x + 36$
  $(x + 4)(x + 1)$ $(x - 5)(x + 3)$ $(x - 6)^2$

Lesson 4-5

Evaluate the determinant of each matrix.

76. $A = \begin{bmatrix} 1 & -4 \\ 2 & 0 \end{bmatrix}$ **8**   **77.** $B = \begin{bmatrix} 5 & 3 \\ 2 & -1 \end{bmatrix}$ **−11**   **78.** $C = \begin{bmatrix} 3 & -2 \\ 3 & -2 \end{bmatrix}$ **0**

53. $y = x^4 - 4x^3 - 7x^2 + 22x + 24$

59. Answers may vary. Sample: $y = x^4 - x^2$, **and zeros are** $0, \pm 1$.

68. [2] $f(x) = x^2(x + 9)(x - 1)$
  [1] **incomplete factoring** of $x^2 + 8x - 9$ **or other minor errors**

69. [4] **The student multiplies** $(x + 2)$, $(x - 5)$, $(x - 6)$ **and** -2 **to get** $y = -2x^3 + 18x^2 - 16x - 120$.

  [3] **appropriate methods but with one computational error**

  [2] **appropriate methods to find basic polynomial with given roots, but no multiplication of polynomial by** -2

  [1] **correct function, without work shown**

70. $-3x^5 + 3x^2 - 1$; **quintic trinomial**

71. $-7x^4 - x^3$; **quartic binomial**

72. $x^3 - 2$; **cubic binomial**

313

1. Plan

Lesson Preview

 **Check Skills You'll Need**

**Modeling Data With
Quadratic Functions**
Lesson 5-1: Example 1
Exercises 1–9
Extra Practice, p. 826

Polynomial Functions
Lesson 6-1: Example 1
Exercises 1–9
Extra Practice, p. 827

Lesson Resources

📁 **Teaching Resources**
Practice, Reteaching, Enrichment
Checkpoint Quiz 1

 **Reaching All Students**
Practice Workbook 6-3
Spanish Practice Workbook 6-3
Reading and Math Literacy 6B
Spanish Reading & Literacy 6B
Spanish Checkpoint Quiz 1
Hands-On Activities 43

🕐 **Presentation Assistant Plus!**
Transparencies
• Check Skills You'll Need 6-3
• Additional Examples 6-3
• Student Edition Answers 6-3
• Lesson Quiz 6-3
PH Presentation Pro CD 6-3

**PRENTICE HALL
ASSESSMENT SYSTEM**

Checkpoint Quiz 1
Computer Test Generator CD

 **Technology**
Resource Pro® CD-ROM
Computer Test Generator CD
Prentice Hall Presentation Pro CD

💻 **www.PHSchool.com**
Student Site
• Teacher Web Code: agk-5500
• Self-grading Lesson Quiz
Teacher Center
• Lesson Planner
• Resources

Plus **iTEXT**

314

Dividing Polynomials

North Carolina Objectives **1.03** Operate with algebraic expressions (polynomial, rational, complex fractions) to solve problems.

Lesson Preview

What You'll Learn

OBJECTIVE 1 To divide polynomials using long division

OBJECTIVE 2 To divide polynomials using synthetic division

...And Why

To find the dimensions of a sarcophagus, as in Example 4

✔ **Check Skills You'll Need** (For help, go to Lessons 5-1 and 6-1.)

Simplify each expression.

1. $(x + 3)(x - 4) + 2$ $x^2 - x - 10$ **2.** $(2x + 1)(x - 3)$ $2x^2 - 5x - 3$

3. $(x + 2)(x + 1) - 11$ $x^2 + 3x - 9$ **4.** $-3(2 - x)(x + 5)$
$3x^2 + 9x - 30$

Write each polynomial in standard form. Then list the coefficients. **5–8. See below left.**

5. $5x - 2x^2 + 9 + 4x^3$ **6.** $10 + 5x^3 - 9x^2$

7. $3x + x^2 - x + 7 - 2x^2$ **8.** $-4x^4 - 7x^2 + x^3 + x^4$

New Vocabulary • synthetic division • Remainder Theorem

OBJECTIVE
1 **Using Long Division**

 Interactive lesson includes instant self-check, tutorials, and activities.

You can use polynomial division to help find all the zeros of a polynomial function. Division of polynomials is similar to numerical division.

Recall that when a numerical division has a remainder of zero, as shown below, the divisor and quotient are both factors of the dividend.

$$\begin{array}{r} 7 \\ 8\overline{)56} \\ \underline{56} \\ 0 \end{array}$$ **7 and 8 are factors of 56.**

If numerical division leaves a remainder, as shown below, then neither the divisor nor the quotient is a factor of the dividend.

$$\begin{array}{r} 8 \\ 5\overline{)42} \\ \underline{40} \\ 2 \end{array}$$ **Neither 5 nor 8 is a factor of 42.**

Division serves as a test of whether one number is a factor of another.

The same is true for polynomial division. If you divide a polynomial by one of its factors, then you get another factor. When a polynomial division leaves no remainder, as shown below with monomials, you have factored the polynomial.

$$\begin{array}{r} 2x \\ x\overline{)2x^2} \\ \underline{2x^2} \\ 0 \end{array}$$ **x and $2x$ are factors of $2x^2$.**

To divide polynomials other than monomials, follow the same procedure you use to divide whole numbers.

? Need Help?

$$\begin{array}{r} 4 \leftarrow \textbf{Quotient} \\ 6\overline{)24} \leftarrow \textbf{Dividend} \\ \uparrow \\ \textbf{Divisor} \end{array}$$

5. $4x^3 - 2x^2 + 5x + 9$;
$4, -2, 5, 9$

6. $5x^3 - 9x^2 + 10$;
$5, -9, 0, 10$

7. $-x^2 + 2x + 7$;
$-1, 2, 7$

8. $-3x^4 + x^3 - 7x^2$;
$-3, 1, -7, 0, 0$

314 Chapter 6 Polynomials and Polynomial Functions

 Ongoing Assessment and Intervention

Before the Lesson
Diagnose prerequisite skills using:
• Check Skills You'll Need

During the Lesson
Monitor progress using:
• Check Understanding
• Additional Examples
• Standardized Test Prep

After the Lesson
Assess knowledge using:
• Lesson Quiz
• Computer Test Generator CD
• Chapter Checkpoint 1 (p. 320)

1 EXAMPLE Polynomial Long Division

Divide $x^2 + 3x - 12$ by $x - 3$.

$$
\begin{array}{r}
x \\
x - 3 \overline{\smash{)}\, x^2 + 3x - 12} \\
\underline{x^2 - 3x } \\
6x - 12
\end{array}
$$

Divide: $\frac{x^2}{x} = x$.

Multiply: $x(x - 3) = x^2 - 3x$.

Subtract: $x^2 + 3x - (x^2 - 3x) = 6x$. Bring down -12.

Repeat the process of dividing, multiplying, and subtracting.

$$
\begin{array}{r}
x + 6 \\
x - 3 \overline{\smash{)}\, x^2 + 3x - 12} \\
\underline{x^2 - 3x } \\
6x - 12 \\
\underline{6x - 18} \\
6
\end{array}
$$

Divide: $\frac{6x}{x} = 6$.

Multiply: $6(x - 3) = 6x - 18$.

Subtract: $6x - 12 - (6x - 18) = 6$.

The quotient is $x + 6$ with a remainder of 6, or simply $x + 6$, R 6.

Check Show that (divisor)(quotient) + remainder = dividend.

$$(x - 3)(x + 6) + 6 = (x^2 + 6x - 3x - 18) + 6 \quad \textbf{Multiply } (x - 3)(x + 6).$$
$$= x^2 + 3x - 12 \quad \textbf{Simplify.}$$

✓ **Check Understanding** ❶ Divide $x^2 - 3x + 1$ by $x - 4$. Check your answer. **x + 1, R 5**

You can use polynomial long division to find the factors of a polynomial.

2 EXAMPLE Checking Factors

Determine whether $x + 4$ is a factor of each polynomial.

a. $x^2 + 6x + 8$

$$
\begin{array}{r}
x + 2 \\
x + 4 \overline{\smash{)}\, x^2 + 6x + 8} \\
\underline{x^2 + 4x } \\
2x + 8 \\
\underline{2x + 8} \\
0
\end{array}
$$

Since the remainder is zero, $x + 4$ is a factor of $x^2 + 6x + 8$.

b. $x^3 + 3x^2 - 6x - 7$

$$
\begin{array}{r}
x^2 - x - 2 \\
x + 4 \overline{\smash{)}\, x^3 + 3x^2 - 6x - 7} \\
\underline{x^3 + 4x^2 } \\
-x^2 - 6x \\
\underline{-x^2 - 4x} \\
-2x - 7 \\
\underline{-2x - 8} \\
1
\end{array}
$$

Since the remainder $\neq 0$, $x + 4$ is not a factor of $x^3 + 3x^2 - 6x - 7$.

✓ **Check Understanding** ❷ Determine whether each divisor is a factor of each dividend.
a. $(2x^2 - 19x + 24) \div (x - 8)$ **yes**   **b.** $(x^3 - 4x^2 + 3x + 2) \div (x + 2)$ **no**

OBJECTIVE

2 Using Synthetic Division

To divide by a linear factor, you can use a simplified process that is known as **synthetic division.** In synthetic division, you omit all variables and exponents. By reversing the sign in the divisor, you can add throughout the process instead of subtracting.

Lesson 6-3 Dividing Polynomials   **315**

---

2. Teach

Professional Development

Math Background

The long division algorithm for polynomials is much like the long division algorithm for whole numbers. For polynomials, synthetic division shortens the process. This lesson concentrates on dividing by binomials of the form $x - a$. If you divide a polynomial $P(x)$ by $x - a$ and get a remainder of zero, then a is a zero of $P(x)$. Furthermore, the degree of the polynomial quotient $Q(x)$ will be one less than the degree of $P(x)$, and any zeros of $Q(x)$ will also be zeros of $P(x)$. We can often use these ideas to whittle away binomial factors until we have a complete factorization of $P(x)$.

OBJECTIVE

1 Teaching Notes

1 EXAMPLE Error Prevention

Watch for students who add $3x$ and $-3x$. Suggest they place $x^2 - 3x$ in parentheses, and write a minus sign in front of the parentheses.

Additional Examples

❶ Divide $x^2 + 2x - 30$ by $x - 5$.
x + 7, R 5

❷ Determine whether $x + 2$ is a factor of each polynomial.
a. $x^2 + 10x + 16$ **yes**
b. $x^3 + 7x^2 - 5x - 6$ **no**

👫 Reaching All Students

Below Level Make sure students understand that polynomial long division and synthetic division provide the same information.	**Advanced Learners** If $f(a)$ is zero, ask students what the Remainder Theorem implies about $(x - a)$. **(x − a) is a factor of f(x).**	**Visual Learners** See note on page 316. **Error Prevention** See note on page 315.

315

OBJECTIVE 2 Teaching Notes

3 EXAMPLE Visual Learners

Have two volunteers work the example on the board using long division and synthetic division. Have other volunteers point out the similarities between the two methods. They may want to circle or box these similarities. Help students see how synthetic division is a highly condensed form of the long division algorithm. Omitting the variables and exponents does not involve the loss of any essential data, because the position of a coefficient indicates the power associated with the coefficient.

4 EXAMPLE Connection to History

A sarcophagus is a coffin placed above the ground. They were usually made of stone, but sometimes wood or terra-cotta were used. The name means "flesh-eating" in Greek. The limestone used by the ancient Greeks allegedly consumed the whole body, except for teeth, within 40 days.

Reading Math

Synthetic division is sometimes called the method of detached coefficients.

3 EXAMPLE Using Synthetic Division

Use synthetic division to divide $3x^3 - 4x^2 + 2x - 1$ by $x + 1$.

Step 1 Reverse the sign of the constant term in the divisor. Write the coefficients of the polynomial in standard form.

$$\text{Write } \quad x + 1\overline{)3x^3 - 4x^2 + 2x - 1}$$

$$\text{as } \quad -1\,|\; 3 \quad -4 \quad 2 \quad -1.$$

Step 2 Bring down the first coefficient.

$$-1\,|\; 3 \quad -4 \quad 2 \quad -1 \quad \leftarrow \text{Bring down the 3. This begins the quotient.}$$

$$\underline{\qquad\qquad\qquad\qquad}$$

$$3$$

Step 3 Multiply the first coefficient by the new divisor. Write the result under the next coefficient. Add.

$$-1\,|\; 3 \quad -4 \quad 2 \quad -1 \quad \leftarrow \text{Multiply 3 by } -1. \text{ Write the result under } -4.$$

$$\times \qquad -3$$

$$\underline{\qquad\qquad\qquad\qquad}$$

$$3 \quad -7 \qquad\qquad \leftarrow \text{Add } -4 \text{ and } -3.$$

Step 4 Repeat the steps of multiplying and adding until the remainder is found.

$$-1\,|\; 3 \quad -4 \quad 2 \quad -1$$

$$\qquad\quad -3 \quad 7 \quad -9$$

$$\underline{\qquad\qquad\qquad\qquad}$$

$$3 \quad -7 \quad 9 \quad -10$$

$$\quad\downarrow \quad\;\; \downarrow \quad\; \downarrow \quad\;\; \downarrow$$

$$3x^2 - 7x + 9 \quad \text{Remainder}$$

● The quotient is $3x^2 - 7x + 9$, R -10.

✓ Check Understanding **3** Use synthetic division to divide $x^3 + 4x^2 + x - 6$ by $x + 1$.

$$x^2 + 3x - 2, \text{ R } -4$$

Real-World Connection

For the ancient Greeks, Romans, and Egyptians, a sarcophagus was a work of art created to honor a loved one. They decorated the stone tomb with elaborate inscriptions and ornaments.

4 EXAMPLE Real-World Connection

The volume in cubic feet of a sarcophagus (excluding the cover) can be expressed as the product of its three dimensions: $V(x) = x^3 - 13x + 12$. The length is $x + 4$.

a. Find linear expressions with integer coefficients for the other dimensions. Assume that the width is greater than the height.

$$-4\,|\; 1 \quad 0 \quad -13 \quad 12 \qquad \text{Divide. Use 0 as a place holder for any missing term.}$$

$$\qquad\quad -4 \quad 16 \quad -12$$

$$\underline{\qquad\qquad\qquad\qquad}$$

$$1 \quad -4 \quad 3 \quad 0$$

$$\downarrow \quad\;\; \downarrow \quad\; \downarrow \quad\; \downarrow$$

$$x^2 \quad -4x + 3 \quad \text{Remainder}$$

$$x^2 - 4x + 3 = (x - 1)(x - 3) \quad \text{Factor the quotient.}$$

The width and the height are $x - 1$ and $x - 3$, respectively.

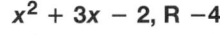

b. If the length of the sarcophagus is 10 ft, what are the other two dimensions?

$x + 4 = 10$ **Substitute 10 into the expression for length. Find x.**

$\qquad x = 6$

Since the width equals $x - 1$ and the height equals $x - 3$, the width is 5 ft and the height is 3 ft.

✓ **Check Understanding** **4 a.** Use synthetic division to divide $x^3 - 2x^2 - 5x + 6$ by $x + 2$. **$x^2 - 4x + 3$**

b. Use your answer from part (a) to completely factor $x^3 - 2x^2 - 5x + 6$.

$$(x + 2)(x - 3)(x - 1)$$

In Example 1, you saw that $x - 3$ is not a factor of $x^2 + 3x - 12$ because their quotient has a remainder of 6. If $x - 3$ were a factor of $x^2 + 3x - 12$, then 3 would be a zero of $P(x) = x^2 + 3x - 12$, and $P(3)$ would equal zero. You know that $P(3)$ does not equal zero, but what *does* it equal?

You can find $P(3)$ by substituting 3 for x.

$$P(x) = x^2 + 3x - 12$$
$$P(3) = (3)^2 + 3(3) - 12$$
$$\qquad = 6$$

$P(3)$ equals the remainder in Example 1, because

dividend = divisor × quotient + remainder.

$$P(x) = (x - 3)(x + 6) + 6$$
$$P(3) = (3 - 3)(3 + 6) + 6$$
$$\qquad = 0(3 + 6) + 6$$
$$\qquad = 6$$

This relationship is defined by the **Remainder Theorem**.

Key Concepts

Theorem	Remainder Theorem

If a polynomial $P(x)$ of degree $n \geq 1$ is divided by $(x - a)$, where a is a constant, then the remainder is $P(a)$.

You can use the Remainder Theorem to find values of $P(x)$.

5 EXAMPLE **Evaluating a Polynomial by Synthetic Division**

Use synthetic division to find $P(-4)$ for $P(x) = x^4 - 5x^2 + 4x + 12$.

By the Remainder Theorem, $P(-4)$ equals the remainder when $P(x)$ is divided by $x - (-4)$. $x + 4$

```
-4| 1    0    -5     4     12
        -4    16   -44    160
   ─────────────────────────
    1   -4    11   -40    172
```

The remainder is 172, so $P(-4) = 172$.

✓ **Check Understanding** **5** Use synthetic division to find $P(-1)$ for $P(x) = 2x^4 + 6x^3 - 5x^2 - 60$. **−69**

Lesson 6-3 Dividing Polynomials **317**

Math Tip

If $x - a$ is a factor of a polynomial $P(x)$, then $P(x) = Q(x)(x - a)$ for some polynomial $Q(x)$. Thus,

$$P(a) = Q(a)(a - a)$$
$$\qquad = Q(a) \cdot 0$$
$$\qquad = 0$$

So, a is a zero of $P(x)$.

5 EXAMPLE Alternative Method

To verify the truth of the Remainder Theorem, have students use a calculator to evaluate the polynomial for $x = -4$.

Additional Examples

3 Use synthetic division to divide $5x^3 - 6x^2 + 4x - 1$ by $x - 3$. **$5x^2 + 9x + 31$, R 92**

4 The volume in cubic feet of a shipping carton is $V(x) = x^3 - 6x^2 + 3x + 10$. The height is $x - 5$ feet.
a. Find linear expressions for the other dimensions. Assume that the length is greater than the width. **length $= x + 1$, width $= x - 2$**
b. If the width of the carton is 4 feet, what are the other two dimensions? **height $= 1$ ft, length $= 7$ ft**

5 Use synthetic division to find $P(3)$ for $P(x) = x^4 - 2x^3 + x - 9$. **21**

Closure

Say: *Suppose you use synthetic division to divide a polynomial of degree n (where n ≥ 1) by x − 5. What does the last number in the bottom line of the synthetic division represent?* **It is the remainder for the division problem. It is also the value of the polynomial when $x = 5$.**

317

3. Practice

Assignment Guide

1 Objective
Ⓐ Ⓑ Core 1–12, 34–47
Ⓒ Extension 56–57

2 Objective
Ⓐ Ⓑ Core 13–33, 48–55
Ⓒ Extension 58–60

Standardized Test Prep 61–64

Mixed Review 65–74

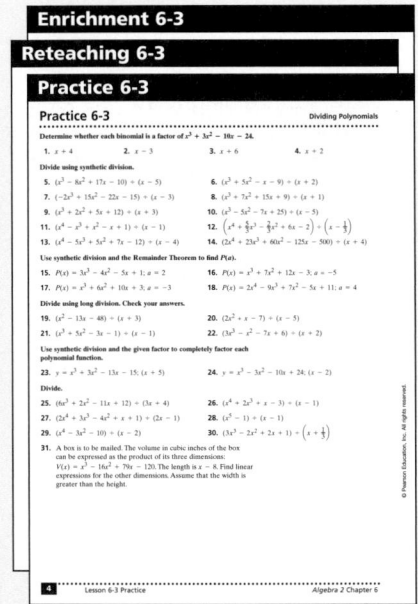

pages 318–320 Exercises

3. $x^2 + 4x + 3$, R 5

4. $2x^2 + 5x + 2$

5. $3x^2 - 7x + 2$

6. $9x - 12$, R -32

13. $x^2 + 4x + 3$

14. $x^2 - 2x + 2$

15. $x^2 - 11x + 37$, R -128

16. $x^2 + 2x + 5$

17. $x^2 - x - 6$

18. $-2x^2 + 9x - 19$, R 40

19. $x + 1$, R 4

20. $3x^2 + 8x - 3$

318

EXERCISES

For more practice, see *Extra Practice*.

Practice and Problem Solving

Ⓐ **Practice by Example**

Example 1
(page 315)

Divide using long division. Check your answers. 3–6. See margin.

1. $(x^2 - 3x - 40) \div (x + 5)$ **x − 8**

2. $(3x^2 + 7x - 20) \div (x + 4)$ **3x − 5**

3. $(x^3 + 3x^2 - x + 2) \div (x - 1)$

4. $(2x^3 - 3x^2 - 18x - 8) \div (x - 4)$

5. $(9x^3 - 18x^2 - x + 2) \div (3x + 1)$

6. $(9x^2 - 21x - 20) \div (x - 1)$

7. $(x^2 - 7x + 10) \div (x + 3)$
  x − 10, R 40

8. $(x^3 - 13x - 12) \div (x - 4)$
  x² + 4x + 3

Example 2
(page 315)

Determine whether each binomial is a factor of $x^3 + 4x^2 + x - 6$.

9. $x + 1$ **no**   **10.** $x + 2$ **yes**   **11.** $x + 3$ **yes**   **12.** $x - 3$ **no**

Example 3
(page 316)

Divide using synthetic division. 13–20. See margin.

13. $(x^3 + 3x^2 - x - 3) \div (x - 1)$

14. $(x^3 - 4x^2 + 6x - 4) \div (x - 2)$

15. $(x^3 - 7x^2 - 7x + 20) \div (x + 4)$

16. $(x^3 - 3x^2 - 5x - 25) \div (x - 5)$

17. $(x^3 - 2x^2 - 5x + 6) \div (x - 1)$

18. $(-2x^3 + 5x^2 - x + 2) \div (x + 2)$

19. $(x^2 + 3) \div (x - 1)$

20. $(3x^3 + 17x^2 + 21x - 9) \div (x + 3)$

21. $(x^3 + 27) \div (x + 3)$
  x² − 3x + 9

22. $(6x^2 - 8x - 2) \div (x - 1)$
  6x − 2, R −4

Example 4
(pages 316–317)

Use synthetic division and the given factor to completely factor each polynomial function.

23. $y = x^3 + 2x^2 - 5x - 6; (x + 1)$
  y = (x + 1)(x + 3)(x − 2)

24. $y = x^3 - 4x^2 - 9x + 36; (x + 3)$
  y = (x + 3)(x − 4)(x − 3)

📦 **25. Geometry** Refer to the diagram. The volume in cubic inches of the decorative box can be expressed as the product of the lengths of its sides as $V(x) = x^3 + x^2 - 6x$. Write linear expressions with integer coefficients for the locker's length and height. **ℓ = x + 3 and h = x**

width = x − 2

Example 5
(page 317)

Use synthetic division and the Remainder Theorem to find $P(a)$.

26. $P(x) = x^3 + 4x^2 - 8x - 6; a = -2$ **18**   **27.** $P(x) = x^3 + 4x^2 + 4x; a = -2$ **0**

28. $P(x) = x^3 - 7x^2 + 15x - 9; a = 3$ **0** **29.** $P(x) = x^3 + 7x^2 + 4x; a = -2$ **12**

30. $P(x) = 6x^3 - x^2 + 4x + 3; a = 3$ **168**   **31.** $P(x) = 2x^3 - x^2 + 10x + 5; a = \frac{1}{2}$ **10**

32. $P(x) = 2x^3 + 4x^2 - 10x - 9; a = 3$ **51**   **33.** $P(x) = 2x^4 + 6x^3 + 5x^2 - 45; a = -3$ **0**

Ⓑ **Apply Your Skills**

35. **x − 1 is not a factor of $x^3 - x^2 - 2x$ because it does not divide into $x^3 - x^2 - 2x$ evenly.**

34. Reasoning A polynomial $P(x)$ is divided by a binomial $x - a$. The remainder is zero. What conclusion can you draw? Explain. **P(a) = 0; x − a is a factor of P(x).**

35. Error Analysis A student represented the product of three linear factors as $x^3 - x^2 - 2x$. She used $x - 1$ as one of the factors. Use division to prove that the student made an error. **See left.**

318 Chapter 6 Polynomials and Polynomial Functions

---

52. $x^3 - x^2 + 1$

53. $x^3 - 2x^2 - 2x + 4$, R -35

54. $x^3 - 2x^2 - x + 6$

55. $x^3 - 4x^2 + x$

56a. $x + 1$
  b. $x^2 + x + 1$
  c. $x^3 + x^2 + x + 1$
  d. $(x - 1)(x^4 + x^3 + x^2 + x + 1)$

57a. $x^2 - x + 1$
  b. $x^4 - x^3 + x^2 - x + 1$
  c. $x^6 - x^5 + x^4 - x^3 + x^2 - x + 1$

36. Open-Ended Write a polynomial division that has a quotient of $x + 3$ and a remainder of 2. **Answers may vary. Sample: $(x^2 + x - 4) \div (x - 2)$**

Divide.

37. $x^2 + 4x + 5$

38. $x^3 - 3x^2 + 12x - 35$, R 109

39. $x^4 - x^3 + x^2 - x + 1$

37. $(2x^3 + 9x^2 + 14x + 5) \div (2x + 1)$ **38.** $(x^4 + 3x^2 + x + 4) \div (x + 3)$

39. $(x^5 + 1) \div (x + 1)$

40. $(x^4 + 4x^3 - x - 4) \div (x^3 - 1)$
$x + 4$

41. $(3x^4 - 5x^3 + 2x^2 + 3x - 2) \div (3x - 2)$
$x^3 - x^2 + 1$

Determine whether each binomial is a factor of $x^3 + x^2 - 16x - 16$.

42. $x + 2$ **no**   **43.** $x - 4$ **yes**   **44.** $x + 1$ **yes**

45. $x - 1$ **no**   **46.** $x - 2$ **no**   **47.** $x + 4$ **yes**

Use synthetic division to determine whether each binomial is a factor of $3x^3 + 10x^2 - x - 12$.

48. $x + 3$ **yes**   **49.** $x - 1$ **yes**   **50.** $x + 2$ **no**   **51.** $x - 4$ **no**

Divide using synthetic division. 52–55. See margin p. 318.

52. $(x^4 - 2x^3 + x^2 + x - 1) \div (x - 1)$ **53.** $(x^4 - 6x^2 - 27) \div (x + 2)$

54. $(x^4 - 5x^2 + 4x + 12) \div (x + 2)$ **55.** $\left(x^4 - \frac{9}{2}x^3 + 3x^2 - \frac{1}{2}x\right) \div \left(x - \frac{1}{2}\right)$

 Challenge

56. Reasoning Divide. Look for patterns in your answers. **a–d. See margin p. 318.**
 a. $(x^2 - 1) \div (x - 1)$ **b.** $(x^3 - 1) \div (x - 1)$ **c.** $(x^4 - 1) \div (x - 1)$
 d. Using the patterns, factor $x^5 - 1$.

57. Divide. Look for patterns in your answers. **a–d. See margin pp. 318–319.**
 a. $(x^3 + 1) \div (x + 1)$ **b.** $(x^5 + 1) \div (x + 1)$ **c.** $(x^7 + 1) \div (x + 1)$
 d. Using the patterns, factor $x^9 + 1$.

58. Critical Thinking Explain why a polynomial of degree n, divided by a polynomial of degree 1, yields a quotient of degree $n - 1$ and a remainder that is a constant. **See margin.**

59. Use synthetic division to find $(x^2 + 4) \div (x - 2i)$. **$x + 2i$**

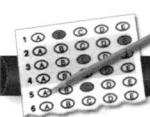 **60. Writing** Suppose 3, -1, and 4 are zeros of a cubic polynomial function. Sketch a graph of the function. Could there be more than one graph? Explain.
See margin.

Standardized Test Prep

Multiple Choice

61. What is the remainder when $x^2 - 5x + 7$ is divided by $x + 1$? **D**
 A. -13 **B.** -1 **C.** 1   **D.** 13

62. Which binomial is NOT a factor of $x^3 - x^2 - 17x - 15$? **I**
 F. $x - 5$ **G.** $x + 1$ **H.** $x + 3$ **I.** $x + 5$

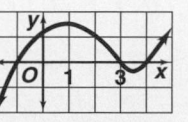
Take It to the NET
Online lesson quiz at
www.PHSchool.com
 Web Code: agk-0603

63. Which of the following, when multiplied by $x - 1$, results in a cubic polynomial whose standard form has three terms? **B**
 A. $(x - 1)^2$ **B.** $x^2 - x$ **C.** $x^2 - 1$ **D.** $x - 1$

64. One factor of $x^3 - 7x^2 - x + 7$ is $x - 1$. What are all the zeros of the related polynomial function? Show your work. **See back of book.**

d. $(x + 1)(x^8 - x^7 + x^6 - x^5 + x^4 - x^3 + x^2 - x + 1)$

58. By dividing it by a polynomial of degree 1, you are reducing the

degree-n polynomial by one, to $n - 1$. The remainder will be constant because it is not divisible by the variable.

60. Yes; the graph could rise to the right and fall to the left or it could fall to the right and rise to the left.

---

4. Assess

Lesson Quiz 6-3

1. a. Divide using long division.
$(9x^3 - 48x^2 + 13x + 3) \div (x - 5)$
$9x^2 - 3x - 2$, R -7
 b. Is $x - 5$ a factor of $9x^3 - 48x^2 + 13x + 3$? **no**

2. Divide using synthetic division.
$(6x^3 - 4x^2 + 14x - 8) \div (x + 2)$
$6x^2 - 16x + 46$, R -100

3. Use synthetic division and the given factor $x - 4$ to completely factor $x^3 - 37x + 84$.
$(x + 7)(x - 3)(x - 4)$

4. Use synthetic division and the Remainder Theorem to find $P(-2)$ when $P(x) = x^4 - 2x^3 + 4x^2 + x + 1$. **47**

Alternative Assessment

Group students in pairs. Have each group write two cubic polynomials and a polynomial of degree 4, all with integer coefficients. Each pair then works together using synthetic division to divide each polynomial by $x - 2$ and $x + 2$. Have them determine whether 2 and -2 are zeros of each polynomial.

Standardized Test Prep

Resources
For additional practice with a variety of test item formats:
• Standardized Test Prep, p. 357
• Test-Taking Strategies, p. 352
• Test-Taking Strategies with Transparencies

Technology Tip

Exercise 64 If graphing calculators are permitted, a quick way to answer a question like this is to use the **TABLE** function.

**To check understanding of
Lessons 6-1 to 6-3:**

Checkpoint Quiz 1 (p. 320)

📁 **Teaching Resources**
Checkpoint Quiz 1 (also in
 Prentice Hall Assessment
 System)

👥 **Reaching All Students**
Reading and Math Literacy 6B

Spanish versions available

pages 318–320   Exercises

65. $y = x^2 + 2x - 15$

66. $y = x^3 - 9x^2 + 8x$

67. $y = x^3 - 6x^2 + 3x + 10$

68. $y = x^4 - 4x^3 + 6x^2$
   $- 4x + 1$

72. $\begin{bmatrix} -0.5 & 0 & -1.5 \\ 0.5 & 1 & 1.5 \\ 0.5 & 0 & 0.5 \end{bmatrix}$

73. none exists

74. $\begin{bmatrix} 0 & 2 & 1 \\ 1 & -4 & -2 \\ 0.5 & -3.5 & -1.5 \end{bmatrix}$

Mixed Review

Lesson 6-2   Write a polynomial function in standard form with the given zeros.   **65–68. See margin.**

65. $3, -5$ **66.** $0, 1, 8$ **67.** $-1, 2, 5$ **68.** 1, multiplicity 4

Lesson 5-6   Simplify each expression.

69. $(-4i)(6i)$ **24**   **70.** $(2 + i)(2 - i)$ **5**   **71.** $(4 - 3i)(5 + i)$
                                                                                                 23 − 11i

Lesson 4-6   Find the inverse of each matrix, if it exists.   **72–74. See margin.**

72. $\begin{bmatrix} 1 & 0 & 3 \\ 1 & 1 & 0 \\ -1 & 0 & -1 \end{bmatrix}$ **73.** $\begin{bmatrix} 1 & 2 & 0 \\ 0 & 2 & -2 \\ 1 & 0 & 2 \end{bmatrix}$ **74.** $\begin{bmatrix} 2 & 1 & 0 \\ -1 & 1 & -2 \\ 3 & -2 & 4 \end{bmatrix}$

✓ Checkpoint Quiz 1   Lessons 6-1 through 6-3

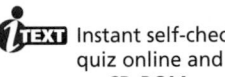 Instant self-check
quiz online and
on CD-ROM

1. Write a polynomial function with at least three zeros that are negative, one of which has multiplicity 2.   **Answers may vary. Sample:**
$y = (x + 1)^2(x + 2)(x + 3)$

Write each polynomial in standard form. Then classify it by degree and by number of terms.

2. $-3x^3 + 5x + 6$;
   degree 3, 3 terms

3. $x^4 - 3x^3 + \frac{3}{2}x$;
   degree 4, 3 terms

4. $3x^2 + 9x - 12$;
   degree 2, 3 terms

2. $-2x^3 + 6 - x^3 + 5x$ **3.** $\frac{1}{2}x + x^4 - 3x^2 + 2x$ **4.** $3(x - 1)(x + 4)$

For each function, determine the zeros and their multiplicity.

5. $y = (x - 2)^2(x - 1)$ **6.** $y = (2x + 1)(x - 4)$ **7.** $y = x^3(x - 3)(x + 1)^2$
   1, 2 (mult. 2)   **$-\frac{1}{2}$, 4**   **0 (mult. 3), 3, −1 (mult. 2)**

Divide.

8. $(x^3 + 3x^2 + 3x + 1) \div (x + 1)$ **9.** $(2x^3 - 7x^2 + 7x - 2) \div (x - 2)$
   $x^2 + 2x + 1$ **$2x^2 - 3x + 1$**

10. Use synthetic division to find $P(4)$ for $P(x) = 2x^4 - 3x^2 + 4x - 1$.
                                                                                479

Algebra at Work

••••••••••••••••••••••••••**Quality Control Engineer**

Quality control engineers establish procedures for assuring that products meet minimum standards of quality such as length or purity. Each product is sampled regularly. Data relating to each standard are collected and analyzed. All samples must fall within certain limiting parameters. Quality is further controlled by requiring that a significant portion of the samples fall within even stricter limiting parameters.

Take It to the NET For more information about quality control, go to **www.PHSchool.com**.
Web Code: agb-2031

Solving Polynomial Equations

1. Plan

North Carolina Objectives 1.03 Operate with algebraic expressions (polynomial, rational, complex fractions) to solve problems.

Lesson Preview

What You'll Learn

OBJECTIVE 1 To solve polynomial equations by graphing

OBJECTIVE 2 To solve polynomial equations by factoring

. . . And Why

To calculate the dimensions of a portable kennel, as in Example 2

✔ Check Skills You'll Need

(For help, go to Lessons 3-1 and 5-4.)

Graph each system. Find any points of intersection. 1–3. See back of book.

1. $\begin{cases} y = 3x + 1 \\ y = -2x + 6 \end{cases}$

2. $\begin{cases} -2x + 3y = 0 \\ x + 3y = 3 \end{cases}$

3. $\begin{cases} 2y = -x + 8 \\ x + 2y = -6 \end{cases}$

Factor each expression.

4. $x^2 - 2x - 15$
$(x - 5)(x + 3)$

5. $x^2 - 9x + 14$
$(x - 7)(x - 2)$

6. $x^2 + 6x + 5$
$(x + 5)(x + 1)$

New Vocabulary • sum of cubes • difference of cubes

Lesson Preview

✔ **Check Skills You'll Need**

Graphing Systems of Equations
Lesson 3-1: Example 1
Exercises 1–8
Extra Practice, p. 824

Factoring Quadratic Expressions
Lesson 5-4: Examples 2–4
Exercises 7–24
Extra Practice, p. 826

Lesson Resources

📁 **Teaching Resources**
Practice, Reteaching, Enrichment

Reaching All Students
Practice Workbook 6-4
Spanish Practice Workbook 6-4

⏱ **Presentation Assistant Plus!**
Transparencies
• Check Skills You'll Need 6-4
• Additional Examples 6-4
• Student Edition Answers 6-4
• Lesson Quiz 6-4
PH Presentation Pro CD 6-4

PRENTICE HALL ASSESSMENT SYSTEM

Computer Test Generator CD

💿 **Technology**
Resource Pro® CD-ROM
Computer Test Generator CD
Prentice Hall Presentation Pro CD

💻 **www.PHSchool.com**
Student Site
• Teacher Web Code: agk-5500
• Graphing Calculator, Procedure 27
• Self-grading Lesson Quiz
Teacher Center
• Lesson Planner
• Resources

Plus

OBJECTIVE 1 **Interactive lesson includes instant self-check, tutorials, and activities.**

Solving Equations by Graphing

You can solve a polynomial equation by graphing each side of the equation separately and finding the x values at the point(s) of intersection.

1 EXAMPLE Solving by Graphing

Solve $x^3 + 3x^2 = x + 3$ by graphing.

Step 1 Graph $y_1 = x^3 + 3x^2$ and $y_2 = x + 3$ on a graphing calculator.

Step 2 Use the Intersect feature to find the x values at the points of intersection.

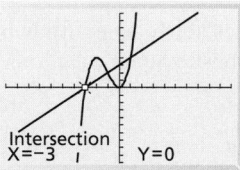 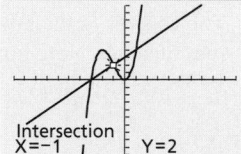 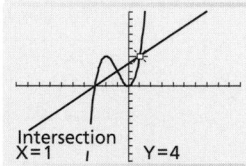

The solutions are -3, -1, and 1.

Check Show that each solution makes the original equation a true statement.

$$x^3 + 3x^2 = x + 3$$
$$(-3)^3 + 3(-3)^2 \stackrel{?}{=} -3 + 3$$
$$-27 + 27 \stackrel{?}{=} -3 + 3$$
$$0 = 0 ✓$$

$$x^3 + 3x^2 = x + 3$$
$$(-1)^3 + 3(-1)^2 \stackrel{?}{=} -1 + 3$$
$$-1 + 3 \stackrel{?}{=} -1 + 3$$
$$2 = 2 ✓$$

$$x^3 + 3x^2 = x + 3$$
$$(1)^3 + 3(1)^2 \stackrel{?}{=} 1 + 3$$
$$1 + 3 \stackrel{?}{=} 1 + 3$$
$$4 = 4 ✓$$

Graphing Calculator Hint

You can also solve the equation in Example 1 by graphing the related function $y = x^3 + 3x^2 - x - 3$ and finding its zeros.

1.
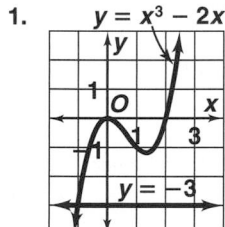
$y = x^3 - 2x^2$
$y = -3$

✔ **Check Understanding** **1** Graph and solve $x^3 - 2x^2 = -3$. Check your answers. **$x = -1$. See left for graph.**

Ongoing Assessment and Intervention

Before the Lesson
Diagnose prerequisite skills using:
• Check Skills You'll Need

During the Lesson
Monitor progress using:
• Check Understanding
• Additional Examples
• Standardized Test Prep

After the Lesson
Assess knowledge using:
• Lesson Quiz
• Computer Test Generator CD

Math Background

Mathematicians throughout history have looked for formulas, similar to the quadratic formula, for the solutions to higher degree equations. Such formulas exist for cubic and quartic equations but are not as straightforward as the quadratic formula. However, some higher degree equations can be solved with techniques already familiar to students.

OBJECTIVE
▼ 1 Teaching Notes

1 EXAMPLE Technology Tip

Have students use the method suggested in the Calculator Hint to the left of Example 1. If they use Zoom Decimal, they can use the Trace feature to find that the solutions are −3, −1, and 1. Students can also press [2nd] [TABLE] and find where the values in Y_1 and Y_2 are the same.

2 EXAMPLE Alternative Method

You do not need to multiply $(x + 7)x(x - 1)$. Have students enter y_2 in its factored form and note that the results are the same. Discuss the reasonable domain with the students. Since x is the width, the domain is positive, and it must be of a size that is manageable to carry.

Additional Examples

1 Graph and solve $x^3 - 19x = -2x^2 + 20$. **−5, −1, 4**

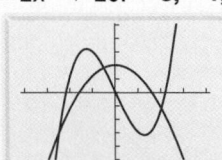

Xmin=−8 Ymin=−50
Xmax=8   Ymax=50
Xscl=2   Yscl=10

2 The dimensions in inches of the cubicle area inside a doghouse can be expressed as width x, length $x + 4$, and height $x - 3$. The volume is 15.9 ft³. Find the dimensions of the inside of the doghouse. **about 34 in. by 30 in. by 27 in.**

Real-World Connection

International regulations specify the allowable dimensions of pet transportation carriers.

You can write and solve a polynomial equation that models a real-world situation.

2 EXAMPLE Real-World Connection

Pet Transportation The dimensions in inches of a portable kennel can be expressed as width x, length $x + 7$, and height $x - 1$. The volume is 5.9 ft³. Find the portable kennel's dimensions.

$5.9 \text{ ft}^3 \cdot \dfrac{12^3 \text{ in.}^3}{\text{ft}^3} = 10{,}195.2 \text{ in.}^3$ — Convert the volume to cubic inches.

$V = \ell \cdot w \cdot h$ — Write the formula for volume.

$10{,}195.2 = (x + 7)x(x - 1)$ — Substitute.

Graph $y_1 = 10{,}195.2$ and $y_2 = (x + 7)x(x - 1)$. Use the Intersect option of the calculator. When $y = 10{,}195.2$, $x \approx 20$. So $x + 7 \approx 27$ and $x - 1 \approx 19$.

The dimensions of the portable kennel are about 27 in. by 20 in. by 19 in.

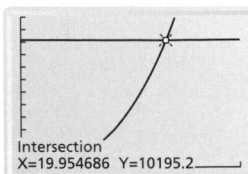

Intersection
X=19.954686 Y=10195.2

✓ **Check Understanding** **2** Find the dimensions of a carrier with volume 7 ft³, width x, length $x + 3$, and height $x - 2$. **22.7125 in., 25.7125 in., 20.7125 in.**

OBJECTIVE
▼ 2 Solving Equations by Factoring

Sometimes you can solve polynomial equations by factoring the polynomial and using the Factor Theorem. Recall that a quadratic expression that is the *difference of squares* has a special factoring pattern. Similarly, a cubic expression may be the **sum of cubes** or the **difference of cubes.**

Key Concepts

Properties	Sum and Difference of Cubes
	$a^3 + b^3 = (a + b)(a^2 - ab + b^2)$
	$a^3 - b^3 = (a - b)(a^2 + ab + b^2)$

You can verify the properties above by multiplying. Below are the steps for the sum of cubes. Note how opposite quadratic terms and linear terms drop out.

$(a + b)(a^2 - ab + b^2) = a(a^2 - ab + b^2) + b(a^2 - ab + b^2)$

$= a^3 - a^2b + ab^2 + a^2b - ab^2 + b^3$

$= a^3 + b^3$

3 EXAMPLE Factoring a Sum or Difference of Cubes

Factor $x^3 - 8$.

$x^3 - 8 = (x)^3 - (2)^3$ — Rewrite the expression as the difference of cubes.

$= (x - 2)(x^2 + 2x + (2)^2)$ — Factor.

$= (x - 2)(x^2 + 2x + 4)$ — Simplify.

✓ **Check Understanding** **3** Factor $8x^3 - 1$. **$(2x - 1)(4x^2 + 2x + 1)$**

Reaching All Students

Below Level Draw graphs and discuss with students why odd functions must have at least one real root while even functions may have only imaginary roots.	**Advanced Learners** Have students create polynomial equations by multiplying factors with both real and complex roots. Have pairs solve each other's equations.	**Error Prevention** See note on page 323. **Error Prevention** See note on page 324.

In Chapter 5, you found the complex roots of quadratic equations. You can do the same with polynomial equations of higher degree.

4 EXAMPLE Solving a Polynomial Equation

Solve $27x^3 + 1 = 0$. Find all complex roots.

$27x^3 + 1 = (3x)^3 + (1)^3$ **Rewrite the cubic expression as the sum of cubes.**

$\quad\quad\quad = (3x + 1)((3x)^2 - 3x + 1)$ **Factor.**

$\quad\quad\quad = (3x + 1)(9x^2 - 3x + 1)$ **Simplify.**

Since $3x + 1$ is a factor, $x = -\frac{1}{3}$ is a root.

The quadratic expression $9x^2 - 3x + 1$ cannot be factored, so use the Quadratic Formula to solve the related quadratic equation $9x^2 - 3x + 1 = 0$.

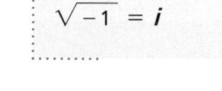

$x = \dfrac{-b \pm \sqrt{b^2 - 4ac}}{2a}$ **Quadratic Formula**

$\quad = \dfrac{-(-3) \pm \sqrt{(-3)^2 - 4(9)(1)}}{2(9)}$ **Substitute 9 for a, −3 for b, and 1 for c.**

$\quad = \dfrac{3 \pm \sqrt{-27}}{18}$ **Use the Order of Operations.**

$\quad = \dfrac{3 \pm 3i\sqrt{3}}{18}$ **Simplify.**

$\quad = \dfrac{1 \pm i\sqrt{3}}{6}$

● The roots are $-\frac{1}{3}$ and $\dfrac{1 \pm i\sqrt{3}}{6}$.

✓ Check Understanding **4** Solve each equation.

     a. $x^3 + 8 = 0$ **b.** $27x^3 - 1 = 0$

     $-2, 1 \pm i\sqrt{3}$ **$\frac{1}{3}, \frac{-1 \pm i\sqrt{3}}{6}$**

You can sometimes factor a polynomial of higher degree by using the techniques you have used in solving polynomials of lower degree.

5 EXAMPLE Factoring by Using a Quadratic Form

Factor $x^4 - 2x^2 - 8$.

Step 1 Since $x^4 - 2x^2 - 8$ has the form of a quadratic expression, you can factor it like one. Make a temporary substitution of variables.

     $x^4 - 2x^2 - 8 = (x^2)^2 - 2(x^2) - 8$ **Rewrite in the form of a quadratic expression.**

                  $= a^2 - 2a - 8$ **Substitute a for x^2.**

Step 2 Factor $a^2 - 2a - 8$.

     $a^2 - 2a - 8 = (a - 4)(a + 2)$

Step 3 Substitute back to the original variable.

     $(a - 4)(a + 2) = (x^2 - 4)(x^2 + 2)$ **Substitute x^2 for a.**

                    $= (x + 2)(x - 2)(x^2 + 2)$ **Factor completely.**

● The factored form of $x^4 - 2x^2 - 8$ is $(x + 2)(x - 2)(x^2 + 2)$.

✓ Check Understanding **5** Factor each expression.

     a. $x^4 + 7x^2 + 6$ **$(x^2 + 6)(x^2 + 1)$**   **b.** $x^4 - 3x^2 - 10$ **$(x^2 - 5)(x^2 + 2)$**

OBJECTIVE

▼2 Teaching Notes

3 EXAMPLE **Teaching Tip**

Point out that memorizing the factorization formulas for the sum and difference of two cubes makes it easy to factor quickly. Tell students that if they forget the formulas, they can use synthetic division to find the quadratic factor. To do so, they need to remember that $a^3 - b^3$ is divisible by $a - b$ and that $a^3 + b^3$ is divisible by $a + b$.

5 EXAMPLE **Error Prevention**

Students may forget that the substitution does not provide the solution for the original variable. Encourage them to highlight, circle, or underline the substituted variable as a reminder to resubstitute the original variable expression and solve to give solutions for the original variable.

Additional Examples

3 Factor $x^3 - 125$.
$(x - 5)(x^2 + 5x + 25)$

4 Solve $8x^3 + 125 = 0$. Find all complex roots. $-\frac{5}{2}, \dfrac{5 \pm 5i\sqrt{3}}{4}$

5 Factor $x^4 - 6x^2 - 27$.
$(x + 3)(x - 3)(x^2 + 3)$

6 Solve $x^4 - 4x^2 - 45 = 0$. **±3, ±$i\sqrt{5}$**

Closure

Have students describe two methods for solving polynomial equations that have a degree greater than two. **One method is to solve by graphing. To do this, graph both sides of the equation on a graphing calculator. Then use the Intersect feature to find the x-coordinates of the points where the graphs intersect. Another method is to write the equation in the form $P(x) = 0$. See if you can factor $P(x)$ into linear and quadratic factors. If you can, use the Zero Product Property to solve.**

? Need Help?

$\sqrt{-1} = i$

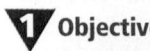

Assignment Guide

1 Objective
- Ⓐ Ⓑ Core 1–11, 33–41, 60–68
- Ⓒ Extension 70

2 Objective
- Ⓐ Ⓑ Core 12–32, 42–59
- Ⓒ Extension 69, 71

Standardized Test Prep 72–75

Mixed Review 76–82

Error Prevention

Exercises 24–29 Students may treat all the factors as linear expressions and only get two solutions (and those are generally not correct). Point out that some of the factors are not linear but quadratic.

Enrichment 6-4

Reteaching 6-4

Practice 6-4

---

6 EXAMPLE Solving a Higher-Degree Polynomial Equation

Solve $x^4 - x^2 = 12$.

$$x^4 - x^2 = 12$$

$x^4 - x^2 - 12 = 0$ Rewrite so one side of the equation is equal to zero.

$(x^2)^2 - (x^2) - 12 = 0$ Write in the form of a quadratic expression. Think of the expression as $a^2 - a - 12$, which factors as $(a - 4)(a + 3)$.

$(x^2 - 4)(x^2 + 3) = 0$

$(x - 2)(x + 2)(x^2 + 3) = 0$

$x = 2$ or $x = -2$ or $x^2 = -3$ Use the Factor Theorem.

$\qquad x = \pm 2$ or $x = \pm\sqrt{-3}$ Solve for x.

$\qquad x = \pm 2$ or $x = \pm i\sqrt{3}$ Simplify.

The solutions are $2, -2, i\sqrt{3}$, and $-i\sqrt{3}$.

✓ **Check Understanding** 6 Solve $x^4 + 11x^2 + 18 = 0$. **$3i, -3i, i\sqrt{2}, -i\sqrt{2}$**

EXERCISES

For more practice, see *Extra Practice*.

Practice and Problem Solving

Ⓐ **Practice by Example**

Examples 1 and 2
(pages 321 and 322)

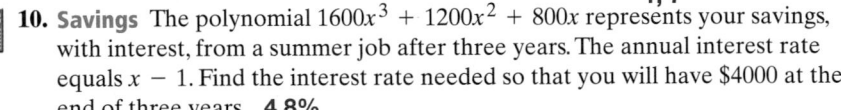 Solve each equation by graphing. Check your answers.

1. $x^3 - 4x^2 - 7x = -10$ **-2, 1, 5**
2. $3x^3 - 6x^2 - 9x = 0$ **-1, 0, 3**
3. $4x^3 - 8x^2 + 4x = 0$ **0, 1**

4. $6x^2 = 48x$ **0, 8**
5. $x^3 + 3x^2 + 2x = 0$
6. $2x^3 + 5x^2 = 7x$

5. 0, −1, −2
6. 0, −3.5, 1

7. $4x^3 = 4x^2 + 3x$ **0, −0.5, 1.5**
8. $2x^4 - 5x^3 - 3x^2 = 0$ **−0.5, 0, 3**
9. $x^2 - 8x + 7 = 0$ **1, 7**

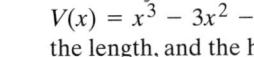 **10. Savings** The polynomial $1600x^3 + 1200x^2 + 800x$ represents your savings, with interest, from a summer job after three years. The annual interest rate equals $x - 1$. Find the interest rate needed so that you will have \$4000 at the end of three years. **4.8%**

11. Geometry The volume V of a container is modeled by the function $V(x) = x^3 - 3x^2 - 4x$. Let $x, x + 1$, and $x - 4$ represent the width, the length, and the height respectively. The container has a volume of 70 ft^3. Find the container's dimensions. **about 5.78 ft × 6.78 ft × 1.78 ft**

Example 3
(page 322)

Factor each expression. **12–14. See margin.**

12. $x^3 + 64$
13. $x^3 - 1000$
14. $125x^3 - 27$

Example 4
(page 323)

Solve each equation. **15–20. See margin.**

15. $x^3 - 27 = 0$
16. $x^3 + 64 = 0$
17. $x^3 - 125 = 0$

18. $2x^3 + 2 = 0$
19. $8x^3 - 1 = 0$
20. $64x^3 + 8 = 0$

Example 5
(page 323)

Factor each expression. **21–26. See margin.**

21. $x^4 - 8x^2 + 7$
22. $x^4 + 8x^2 - 20$
23. $x^4 - 7x^2 + 12$

24. $x^4 - 5x^2 + 4$
25. $x^4 - 1$
26. $4x^4 - 6x^2 + 2$

---

pages 324–326 **Exercises**

12. $(x + 4)(x^2 - 4x + 16)$

13. $(x - 10)(x^2 + 10x + 100)$

14. $(5x - 3)(25x^2 + 15x + 9)$

15. $3, \dfrac{-3 \pm 3i\sqrt{3}}{2}$

16. $-4, 2 \pm 2i\sqrt{3}$

17. $5, \dfrac{-5 \pm 5i\sqrt{3}}{2}$

18. $-1, \dfrac{1 \pm i\sqrt{3}}{2}$

19. $\dfrac{1}{2}, \dfrac{-1 \pm i\sqrt{3}}{4}$

20. $-\dfrac{1}{2}, \dfrac{1 \pm i\sqrt{3}}{4}$

21. $(x^2 - 7)(x - 1)(x + 1)$

22. $(x^2 + 10)(x^2 - 2)$

23. $(x^2 - 3)(x - 2)(x + 2)$

24. $(x - 2)(x + 2)(x - 1)(x + 1)$

25. $(x - 1)(x + 1)(x^2 + 1)$

26. $(2x^2 - 1)(x + 1)(x - 1)$

Example 6
(page 324)

Solve each equation. **27–29. See margin.**

27. $x^4 - 10x^2 + 9 = 0$ **28.** $x^4 - 8x^2 + 16 = 0$ **29.** $x^4 - 12x^2 - 64 = 0$

30. $x^4 + 7x^2 - 18 = 0$ **31.** $x^4 + 4x^2 - 12 = 0$ **32.** $x^4 + 8x^2 + 15 = 0$
$\pm 3i, \pm\sqrt{2}$ $\pm\sqrt{2}, \pm i\sqrt{6}$ $\pm i\sqrt{5}, \pm i\sqrt{3}$

 **B** **Apply Your Skills**

Solve each equation by graphing. Where necessary, round to the nearest hundredth.

33. −1, 3.24, −1.24

35. −2, −3, 1 2

36. 1.71, 0.83

33. $x^3 - x^2 - 6x - 4 = 0$ **34.** $2x^4 + 18x^3 = 0$ **−9, 0**

35. $x^4 + 2x^3 - 7x^2 - 8x = -12$ **36.** $x^4 + x^3 = 4x^2 + 4x - 5$

37. $x^3 + 13x = 10x^2$ **38.** $x^3 - 6x^2 + 6x = 0$ **39.** $12x^3 = 60x^2 + 75x$
0, 1.54, 8.46   **0, 1.27, 4.73**   **−1.04, 0, 6.04**

40. The product of three consecutive integers $n - 1, n$, and $n + 1$ is 210. Write and solve an equation to find the numbers. **$(n - 1)(n)(n + 1) = 210$; 5, 6, 7**

Real-World 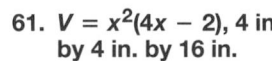 **Connection**

The vacuum bottle, or Dewar flask, was invented by the chemist James Dewar for storing liquefied gases.

41. Design The chamber in each container below consists of a cylinder on top of a hemisphere. Each chamber holds 500 cm³. Find the radius of each chamber.
about 3.58 cm, about 2.83 cm

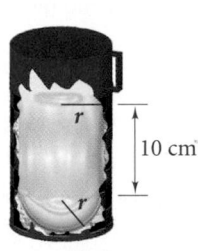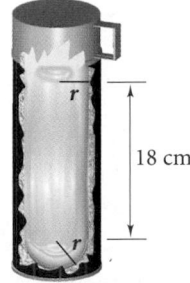

10 cm   18 cm

Solve each equation. **42–53. See margin.**

42. $125x^3 + 216 = 0$ **43.** $81x^3 - 192 = 0$ **44.** $x^4 - 64 = 0$

45. $-2x^4 + 46x^2 = -100$ **46.** $27 = -x^4 - 12x^2$ **47.** $x^5 - 5x^3 + 4x = 0$

48. $x^4 - 100 = 0$ **49.** $5x^3 = 5x^2 + 12x$ **50.** $64 - x^3 = 0$

51. $x^3 - 6x^2 + 6x = 0$ **52.** $2x^3 = 5x^2 + 12x$ **53.** $3x^4 + 12x^2 - 15 = 0$

54. $x^3 + 3x^2 - 4x - 12 = 0$ **−3, −2, 2** **55.** $x^3 - 5x^2 + 3x + 9 = 0$ **−1, 3, 3**

56. $4x^3 - 16x^2 + 12x = 0$ **0, 1, 3**   **57.** $2x^4 - 14x^3 + 12x^2 = 0$ **0, 0, 1, 6**

58. $4x^4 - 2x^2 - 4 = 2$ $\pm\sqrt{\frac{3}{2}}, \pm i$ **59.** $9x^4 - 9x^2 + 2 = 20$ $\pm\sqrt{2}, \pm i$

60. Open-Ended To solve a polynomial equation, you can use any combination of graphing, factoring, and the Quadratic Formula. Write and solve an equation to illustrate each method. **Check students' work.**

61. $V = x^2(4x - 2)$, **4 in. by 4 in. by 16 in.**

Reading Math

For help with reading and solving Exercise 61, see p. 327.

For Exercises 61 and 62, write a polynomial function to describe each volume. Then graph your function to solve each problem.

61. Geometry Suppose a 2-in. slice is cut from one face of the cheese block as shown. The remaining solid has a volume of 224 in.³. Find the dimensions of the original block.
See left.

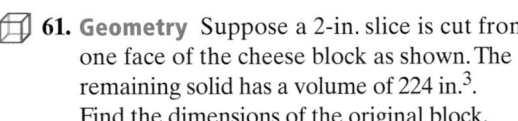

62. Geometry The width of a box is 2 m less than the length. The height is 1 m less than the length. The volume is 60 m³. Find the length of the box.
$x =$ length, $V = x(x - 1)(x - 2)$, 5 meters

Lesson 6-4 Solving Polynomial Equations **325**

27. $\pm 3, \pm 1$

28. ± 2

29. $\pm 4, \pm 2i$

42. $-\frac{6}{5}, \frac{3 \pm 3i\sqrt{3}}{5}$

43. $\frac{4}{3}, \frac{-2 \pm 2i\sqrt{3}}{3}$

44. $\pm 2\sqrt{2}, \pm 2i\sqrt{2}$

45. $\pm 5, \pm i\sqrt{2}$

46. $\pm 3i, \pm i\sqrt{3}$

47. $0, \pm 2, \pm 1$

48. $\pm\sqrt{10}, \pm i\sqrt{10}$

4. Assess

Lesson Quiz 6-4

1. Solve $x^3 - 2x^2 - 3 = x - 4$ by graphing. Where necessary, round to the nearest hundredth. **−0.80, 0.55, 2.25**

Factor each expression.

2. $216x^3 - 1$
   $(6x - 1)(36x^2 + 6x + 1)$

3. $8x^3 + 125$
   $(2x + 5)(4x^2 - 10x + 25)$

4. $x^4 - 5x^2 + 4$
   $(x + 1)(x - 1)(x + 2)(x - 2)$

Solve each equation.

5. $x^3 + 125 = 0$ **$-5, \frac{5 \pm 5i\sqrt{3}}{2}$**

6. $x^4 + 3x^2 - 28 = 0$
   $\pm 2, \pm i\sqrt{7}$

Alternative Assessment

Write one polynomial from each Exercise section on the board, one at a time. After you write each polynomial, instruct students to solve by graphing or factoring, whichever method they prefer. Students compare their solutions with others who chose the same method and a different method.

49. $0, \frac{1}{2} \pm \frac{\sqrt{265}}{10}$

50. $4, -2 \pm 2i\sqrt{3}$

51. $0, 3 \pm \sqrt{3}$

52. $-\frac{3}{2}, 0, 4$

53. $-1, 1, \pm i\sqrt{5}$

325

pages 324–326   Exercises

63. $-\frac{5}{2}, 1;$

   $y = (2x + 5)(x - 1)$

64. $\pm 3, \pm 1;$
   $y = (x - 1)(x + 1)$
   $(x - 3)(x + 3)$

65. $-1, 2, 2;$
   $y = (x + 1)(x - 2)^2$

66. $-2, 1, 3;$
   $y = (x + 2)(x - 1)(x - 3)$

67. $-4, -1, 3;$
   $y = (x + 4)(x + 1)(x - 3)$

69a. **Answers may vary.**
   Sample: $x^4 - 9 = 0,$
   $\pm \sqrt{3}, \pm i\sqrt{3}$

   b. **No; two of the roots are imaginary.**

70. **Answers may vary.**
   Sample: The pink block has volume $a^2(a - 3),$ **the orange block has volume** $9(a - 3),$ **the blue block has volume** $3a(a - 3),$ **and the purple block has volume 27.**
   Thus $a^3 - 27 =$
   $a^2(a - 3) + 3a(a - 3)$
   $+ 9(a - 3) =$
   $(a^2 + 3a + 9)(a - 3).$

74. **[2]** $\frac{a^3}{b^6} + \frac{1}{8} = \left(\frac{a}{b^2}\right)^3 + \left(\frac{1}{2}\right)^3$

   [1] attempts to write each of the terms as a cube

 Graph each function to find the zeros. Rewrite the function with the polynomial in factored form. 63–67. See margin.

63. $y = 2x^2 + 3x - 5$ 64. $y = x^4 - 10x^2 + 9$ 65. $y = x^3 - 3x^2 + 4$

66. $y = x^3 - 2x^2 - 5x + 6$ 67. $y = x^3 + 2x^2 - 11x - 12$

68. **Error Analysis** A student claims that 1, 2, 3, and 4 are the zeros of a cubic polynomial function. Explain why the student is mistaken. **A cubic can only have 3 zeros.**

C Challenge

69. a. **Open-Ended** Write and solve a fourth-degree polynomial equation that includes the difference of squares. **a–b. See margin.**
   b. **Critical Thinking** Are all the roots real numbers? Justify your answer.

 70. **Writing** From a large cube with edges a units long, you cut a smaller cube with edges three units long. Explain how the diagram at the right illustrates that $a^3 - 27 = (a - 3)(a^2 + 3a + 9).$ **See margin.**

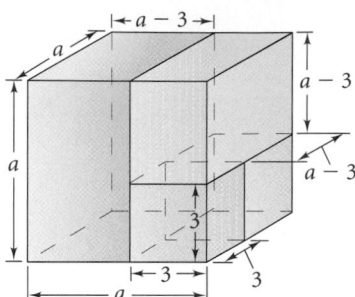

71. a. The sum of two positive numbers is 4 and the sum of their cubes is 28. What is the sum of their squares? **10**
   b. The product of two positive numbers is 96 and the sum of their squares is 208. What are the two numbers? **8 and 12**

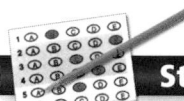

Standardized Test Prep

Multiple Choice

72. Which expression is a factor of $x^4 - 18x^2 + 81$? **A**
   A. $x^2 - 9$ **B.** $x^2 + 6x - 9$ **C.** $x^2 - 6x - 9$ **D.** $x^2 + 9$

73. Which value is NOT a solution of $x^4 - 3x^2 - 54 = 0$? **H**
   F. -3 **G.** 3   **H.** $-3i$ **I.** $-i\sqrt{6}$

Short Response

74. Show how you can rewrite $\frac{a^3}{b^6} + \frac{1}{8}$ as a sum of two cubes. **See margin.**

Extended Response

75. What are all the solutions to $8x^3 - 27 = 0$? Show your work.
   See back of book.

Mixed Review

Lesson 6-3

Divide.

76. $(x^3 - 2x^2 - 13x - 10) \div (x + 1)$ 77. $(2x^3 - 7x^2 - 7x + 14) \div (x - 4)$
   $x^2 - 3x - 10$ $2x^2 + x - 3,$ **R 2**

Lesson 5-5

Solve each equation by factoring or by taking square roots.

78. $n^2 - 4n = 12$ **$-2, 6$**   79. $n^2 + 1 = 37$ **± 6**   80. $2n^2 - 5n - 3 = 0$
   $-\frac{1}{2}, 3$

Lesson 4-7

Solve each matrix equation. If the coefficient matrix has no inverse, write *no unique solution.*

   no unique solution

81. $\begin{bmatrix} 2 & -1 \\ -3 & 2 \end{bmatrix}\begin{bmatrix} x \\ y \end{bmatrix} = \begin{bmatrix} 5 \\ -10 \end{bmatrix}$ $\begin{bmatrix} 0 \\ -5 \end{bmatrix}$ 82. $\begin{bmatrix} 1 & 4 \\ -2 & -8 \end{bmatrix}\begin{bmatrix} x \\ y \end{bmatrix} = \begin{bmatrix} 2 \\ -4 \end{bmatrix}$

Reading for Problem Solving

FOR USE WITH PAGE 325, EXERCISE 61

Read the problem below. Then follow along with Ian as he solves the problem. Check your understanding with the exercise at the bottom of the page.

Write a polynomial function to describe the volume. Then graph your function to solve the problem.

Geometry Suppose a 2-in. slice is cut from one face of the cheese block as shown. The remaining solid has a volume of 224 in.³. Find the dimensions of the original block.

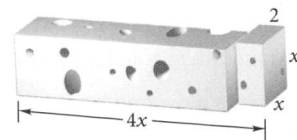

What Ian Thinks

From the diagram, it looks like the widths and heights of the two blocks are equal. I can subtract the amount cut off from the total length to find the length left.

The problem tells me that the volume of the leftover block is 224 in.³. I can write a relationship, substitute, and simplify.

The polynomial equation is a cubic, and the problem asks me to solve by graphing. I'll graph two equations and find their intersection.

I'll enter the equations as Y_1 and Y_2, and I'll change my window values to accommodate a y-value of 224.

Next, I'll use the INTERSECT feature. When $y = 224$, $x = 4$. OK! Now I know x.

I can use x to find the dimensions of the original block.

What Ian Writes

$$\text{length of leftover block} = 4x - \text{length of cut block}$$
$$= 4x - 2$$

$$\text{volume of leftover block} = \ell wh = 224$$
$$V = (4x - 2)(x)(x) = 224$$
$$(4x - 2)(x^2) = 224$$
$$4x^3 - 2x^2 = 224$$

$$Y1 = 4x^3 - 2x^2$$
$$Y2 = 224$$

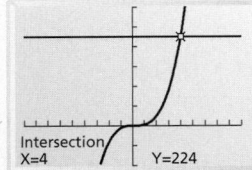

Xmin=−10
Xmax=10
Xscl=1
Ymin=−100
Ymax=100
Yscl=50

Intersection
X=4   Y=224

$$\text{Width} = \text{Height} = x = 4$$
$$\text{Length} = 4x = 4(4) = 16$$

The block of cheese measured 16 in. × 4 in. × 4 in.

EXERCISE

Slices of wood $\frac{1}{4}$-in. thick are cut from opposite sides of a cube of wood. The remaining solid has a volume of 151.25 in.³. Find the dimensions of the original block of wood. $5\frac{1}{2}$ in. × $5\frac{1}{2}$ in. × $5\frac{1}{2}$ in.

Reading For Problem Solving

Students solve a cubic polynomial to find the original dimensions of a block of cheese.

Teaching Notes

Point out to students that the width and the height of the block are both represented by x, so x gets substituted into the equation twice.

Technology

In order for students to see the line $y = 224$, the y range in the WINDOW menu must have a maximum greater than 224.

To use the INTERSECT feature, press [2nd] [CALC] 5. Students then must press [ENTER] three times to get the calculator to find the value.

Exercise

Remind students to clear the equations from the Y=list before they enter equations to solve the Check Understanding problem.

Descartes's Rule of Signs

Descartes's Rule of Signs

FOR USE WITH LESSON 6-4

Descartes's Rule of Signs is useful in determining the number of positive and negative real roots of a polynomial equation. Descartes published the rule in his book *La Géométrie* in 1637, but did not offer a proof of the rule. Many mathematicians supplied proofs and refined the rule from 1745–1828. (Source: www.und.nodak.edu)

Resources

Computer Test Generator CD-ROM, Chapter 0, Extension Topics

Teaching Notes

Math Tip

Students should always arrange the terms of the polynomial $P(x)$ according to descending powers of x before using Descartes's Rule of Signs. Explain that terms that have a coefficient of 0 can be ignored.

Visual Learners

To provide visual confirmation of Descartes's Rule of Signs, encourage students to use a graphing calculator to graph the polynomial functions for the equations in the exercises.

Error Prevention

Students should be careful with signs when they replace x with $-x$ in the polynomials. They should use $(-x)$, with parentheses, when they substitute. Then simplify the resulting expressions before counting sign changes.

René Descartes was a French mathematician, scientist, and philosopher. His many contributions to algebra include analytic geometry, which is the method of representing geometric figures with algebraic equations. He introduced the coordinate system we use, which is called the Cartesian system in his honor.

Descartes's Rule of Signs is a method for finding the number and sign of real roots of a polynomial equation in standard form.

The number of *positive* real roots of a polynomial equation $P(x) = 0$, with real coefficients, is equal to the number of sign changes (from positive to negative or vice versa) between the coefficients of the terms of $P(x)$, or is less than this number by a multiple of two.

The number of *negative* real roots of such a polynomial equation is equal to the number of sign changes between the coefficients of the terms of $P(-x)$, or is less than this number by a multiple of two.

EXAMPLE Using Descartes's Rule of Signs

Determine the possible number of positive and negative real roots of $x^4 - 4x^3 + 7x^2 - 6x - 18 = 0$.

Step 1 Count the number of sign changes of $P(x) = 0$.

$$P(x) = x^4 \quad - 4x^3 \quad + 7x^2 \quad - 6x \quad - 18$$

$+$ to $-$ to $+$ to $-$ $-$

From $+$ to $-$ is one sign change. There are three sign changes.

The number of positive real roots of $P(x) = 0$ is three or one.

Step 2 Count the number of sign changes of $P(-x) = 0$.

$$P(-x) = (-x)^4 - 4(-x)^3 + 7(-x)^2 - 6(-x) - 18$$
$$= x^4 \quad + 4x^3 \quad + 7x^2 \quad + 6x \quad - 18$$

$+$ $+$ $+$ $+$ to $-$

There is one sign change.

The number of negative real roots of $P(x) = 0$ is one.

EXERCISES

Determine the possible number of positive and negative real roots of each polynomial equation. 1–10. See margin.

1. $3x^3 + 10x^2 - x - 12 = 0$

2. $x^3 - 6x^2 + 11x - 6 = 0$

3. $x^3 - 12x - 16 = 0$

4. $3x^3 - 5x^2 - 4x + 4 = 0$

5. $x^4 + x^3 + x^2 - 9x - 10 = 0$

6. $-5x^4 + x^3 - 2x^2 + 4x + 7 = 0$

7. $x^4 - 3x^2 - 4 = 0$

8. $x^4 - 5x^2 + 4 = 0$

9. $x^5 - 3x^4 + 4x^3 - 8x^2 + 16 = 0$

10. $x^5 - 2x^4 - 3x^3 + 6x^2 - 4x + 8 = 0$

page 328 Extension

1. pos. real roots: 1
   neg. real roots: 2 or none

2. pos. real roots: 3 or 1
   neg. real roots: none

3. pos. real roots: 1
   neg. real roots: 2 or none

4. pos. real roots: 2 or none
   neg. real roots: 1

5. pos. real roots: 1
   neg. real roots: 3 or 1

6. pos. real roots: 3 or 1
   neg. real roots: 1

7. pos. real roots: 1
   neg. real roots: 1

8. pos. real roots: 2 or none
   neg. real roots: 2 or none

9. pos. real roots: 4, 2, or none
   neg. real roots: 1

10. pos. real roots: 4, 2, or none
    neg. real roots: 1

6-5 Theorems About Roots of Polynomial Equations

North Carolina Objectives
1.02 Define and compute with complex numbers.
1.03 Operate with algebraic expressions (polynomial, rational, complex fractions) to solve problems.

Lesson Preview

What You'll Learn

 OBJECTIVE 1
To solve equations using the Rational Root Theorem

OBJECTIVE 2
To use the Irrational Root Theorem and the Imaginary Root Theorem

. . . And Why

To find all the roots of a polynomial equation, as in Example 2

✓ Check Skills You'll Need

(For help, go to Lessons 1-1, 5-1, and 5-6.)

List all the integer factors of each number. 1–4. See margin p. 331.

1. 12 **2.** 24 **3.** 36 **4.** 48

Multiply.

5. $(x - 5)(x^2 + 7)$ $x^3 - 5x^2 + 7x - 35$ **6.** $(x + 2)(x + \sqrt{3})(x - \sqrt{3})$

6. $x^3 + 2x^2 - 3x - 6$

Define each set of numbers. 7–9. See margin p. 331.

7. rational **8.** irrational **9.** imaginary

New Vocabulary

- Rational Root Theorem
- Irrational Root Theorem
- Imaginary Root Theorem
- conjugates
- complex conjugates

Lesson Preview

 Check Skills You'll Need

Properties of Real Numbers
Lesson 1-1: Example 1
Practice Exercises 1–8
Extra Practice, p. 822

Complex Numbers
Lesson 5-6: Example 5
Practice Exercises 29–40
Extra Practice, p. 826

Lesson Resources

📁 **Teaching Resources**
Practice, Reteaching, Enrichment

👥 **Reaching All Students**
Practice Workbook 6-5
Spanish Practice Workbook 6-5
Hands-On Activities 44

⏱ **Presentation Assistant Plus!**
Transparencies
- Check Skills You'll Need 6-5
- Additional Examples 6-5
- Student Edition Answers 6-5
- Lesson Quiz 6-5
PH Presentation Pro CD 6-5

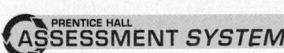

Computer Test Generator CD

💾 **Technology**
Resource Pro® CD-ROM
Computer Test Generator CD
Prentice Hall Presentation Pro CD

💻 **www.PHSchool.com**
Student Site
- Teacher Web Code: agk-5500
- Self-grading Lesson Quiz
Teacher Center
- Lesson Planner
- Resources

Plus

 **OBJECTIVE**

1 The Rational Root Theorem

 Reading Math

A polynomial equation has *roots*. A polynomial function has *zeros*.

You have learned several methods for finding the roots of a polynomial equation. Another method involves analyzing one or more integer coefficients of the polynomial in the equation.

Consider the equivalent equations $x^3 - 5x^2 - 2x + 24 = 0$ and $(x + 2)(x - 3)(x - 4) = 0$, which have $-2, 3$, and 4 as roots. The product of $2, 3$, and 4 is 24. Notice that all the roots are factors of the constant term, 24. In general, if the coefficients (including the constant term) in a polynomial equation are integers, then any integer root of the equation is a factor of the constant term.

A similar pattern applies to rational roots. Consider the equivalent equations $24x^3 - 22x^2 - 5x + 6 = 0$ and $\left(x + \frac{1}{2}\right)\left(x - \frac{2}{3}\right)\left(x - \frac{3}{4}\right) = 0$, which have $-\frac{1}{2}, \frac{2}{3}$, and $\frac{3}{4}$ as roots. The numerators $1, 2$, and 3 all are factors of the constant term, 6. The denominators $2, 3$, and 4 are factors of the leading coefficient, 24.

Both the constant term and the leading coefficient of a polynomial can play a key role in identifying the rational roots of the related polynomial equation. This role is expressed in the Rational Root Theorem.

 Key Concepts

Theorem	Rational Root Theorem

If $\frac{p}{q}$ is in simplest form and is a rational root of the polynomial equation $a_n x^n + a_{n-1} x^{n-1} + \ldots + a_1 x + a_0 = 0$ with integer coefficients, then p must be a factor of a_0 and q must be a factor of a_n.

 Ongoing Assessment and Intervention

Before the Lesson	During the Lesson	After the Lesson
Diagnose prerequisite skills using:	**Monitor progress using:**	**Assess knowledge using:**
• Check Skills You'll Need	• Check Understanding • Additional Examples • Standardized Test Prep	• Lesson Quiz • Computer Test Generator CD

2. Teach

Math Background

An interesting consequence of the rational root theorem is that $\sqrt{p}$ is irrational for p a prime number. If $\sqrt{p}$ were rational, the rational root theorem would guarantee that it is a factor of p since $\sqrt{p}$ is a root of $x^2 - p = 0$. Since p's only factors are one and itself, $\sqrt{p}$ must be irrational.

OBJECTIVE

1 Teaching Notes

1 **EXAMPLE** Alternative Method

A graphing calculator can quickly do the work for Step 2. Enter the possible rational roots in list L1. Enter $Y_1 = x^3 + x^2 - 3x - 3$ on the Y= list. On the home screen, type Y1(L1)→L2 and press ENTER. Then press STAT 1. The values of Y1 for the possible rational roots are displayed in L2.

2 **EXAMPLE** Teaching Tip

Point out that you could also use synthetic division to test roots. This will also be done in Lesson 6-6, Example 2.

Additional Examples

1 Find the rational roots of $3x^3 - x^2 - 15x + 5 = 0$. $\frac{1}{3}$

2 Find the roots of $5x^3 - 24x^2 + 41x - 20 = 0$. $\frac{4}{5}, 2 \pm i$

You can use the Rational Root Theorem to find any rational roots of a polynomial equation with integer coefficients.

1 **EXAMPLE** Finding Rational Roots

Find the rational roots of $x^3 + x^2 - 3x - 3 = 0$.

Step 1 List the possible rational roots.

The leading coefficient is 1. The constant term is -3. By the Rational Root Theorem, the only possible rational roots of the equation have the form $\frac{\text{factor of } -3}{\text{factor of } 1}$.

The factors of -3 are ± 1 and ± 3. The factors of 1 are ± 1. The only possible rational roots are ± 1 and ± 3.

Step 2 Test each possible rational root.

Test 1: $x^3 + x^2 - 3x - 3 = (1)^3 + (1)^2 - 3(1) - 3$
$$= -4 \neq 0$$

Test 3: $x^3 + x^2 - 3x - 3 = (3)^3 + (3)^2 - 3(3) - 3$
$$= 24 \neq 0$$

Test -1: $x^3 + x^2 - 3x - 3 = (-1)^3 + (-1)^2 - 3(-1) - 3$
$$= 0 \quad \text{So } -1 \text{ is a root.}$$

Test -3: $x^3 + x^2 - 3x - 3 = (-3)^3 + (-3)^2 - 3(-3) - 3$
$$= -12 \neq 0$$

● The only rational root of $x^3 + x^2 - 3x - 3 = 0$ is -1.

✓ **Check Understanding** **1** Find the rational roots of $x^3 - 4x^2 - 2x + 8 = 0$. **4**

You can often use the Rational Root Theorem to find all the roots of a polynomial equation.

2 **EXAMPLE** Using the Rational Root Theorem

Find the roots of $2x^3 - x^2 + 2x - 1 = 0$.

Step 1 List the possible rational roots.

The leading coefficient is 2. The constant term is -1. By the Rational Root Theorem, the only possible rational roots of the equation have the form $\frac{\text{factor of } -1}{\text{factor of } 2}$.

The factors of -1 are ± 1. The factors of 2 are ± 1 and ± 2. So the only possible rational roots are ± 1 and $\pm \frac{1}{2}$.

Step 2 Test each possible rational root until you find a root.

Test 1: $2x^3 - x^2 + 2x - 1 = 2(1)^3 - (1)^2 + 2(1) - 1$
$$= 2 \neq 0$$

Test $\frac{1}{2}$: $2x^3 - x^2 + 2x - 1 = 2\left(\frac{1}{2}\right)^3 - \left(\frac{1}{2}\right)^2 + 2\left(\frac{1}{2}\right) - 1$
$$= 0 \quad \text{So } \frac{1}{2} \text{ is a root.}$$

🧑‍🤝‍🧑 Reaching All Students

Below Level Have students multiply binomials of the form $ax + b$ together and then compare the known roots to the possible values of $\frac{p}{q}$.	**Advanced Learners** Have students create polynomial equations with imaginary and complex coefficients. Have them exchange their work and solve the equations.	**English Learners** See note on page 331. **Error Prevention** See note on page 332.

Step 3 Use synthetic division with the root you found in Step 2 to find the quotient.

$$\frac{1}{2} \begin{array}{|rrrr} 2 & -1 & 2 & -1 \\ & 1 & 0 & 1 \\ \hline 2 & 0 & 2 & 0 \end{array}$$

$$2x^2 \qquad +2 \qquad \text{Remainder}$$

Step 4 Find the roots of $2x^2 + 2 = 0$.

$$2x^2 + 2 = 0$$
$$2(x^2 + 1) = 0 \qquad \textbf{Factor out the GCF, 2.}$$
$$x^2 + 1 = 0$$
$$x^2 = -1$$
$$x = \pm i$$

2a. $\pm \sqrt{5}, 2$

b. $-1, \dfrac{1 \pm i\sqrt{2}}{3}$

● The roots of $2x^3 - x^2 + 2x - 1 = 0$ are $\frac{1}{2}$, i, and $-i$.

✓ **Check Understanding** ② Find the roots of each equation. **See left.**

a. $x^3 - 2x^2 - 5x + 10 = 0$ **b.** $3x^3 + x^2 - x + 1 = 0$

In Chapter 5 you learned to find irrational solutions to quadratic equations. For example, by the Quadratic Formula, the solutions of $x^2 - 4x - 1 = 0$ are $2 + \sqrt{5}$ and $2 - \sqrt{5}$. Number pairs of the form $a + \sqrt{b}$ and $a - \sqrt{b}$ are called **conjugates.**

You can often use conjugates to find the irrational roots of a polynomial equation.

🔑 **Key Concepts**

Theorem	**Irrational Root Theorem**

Let a and b be rational numbers and let $\sqrt{b}$ be an irrational number. If $a + \sqrt{b}$ is a root of a polynomial equation with rational coefficients, then the conjugate $a - \sqrt{b}$ also is a root.

3 EXAMPLE   **Finding Irrational Roots**

A polynomial equation with integer coefficients has the roots $1 + \sqrt{3}$ and $-\sqrt{11}$. Find two additional roots.

By the Irrational Root Theorem, if $1 + \sqrt{3}$ is a root, then its conjugate $1 - \sqrt{3}$ is also a root. If $-\sqrt{11}$ is a root, then its conjugate $\sqrt{11}$ also is a root.

● The additional roots are $1 - \sqrt{3}$ and $\sqrt{11}$.

✓ **Check Understanding** ③ **a.** A polynomial equation with rational coefficients has the roots $2 - \sqrt{7}$ and $\sqrt{5}$. Find two additional roots. $\mathbf{2 + \sqrt{7}, -\sqrt{5}}$

b. **Critical Thinking** One of the roots of a polynomial equation is $4 - \sqrt{2}$. Can you be certain that $4 + \sqrt{2}$ also is a root of the equation? Explain. **No; the Irrational Root Theorem does not apply unless you know that all of the coefficients of the polynomial are rational.**

Lesson 6-5   Theorems About Roots of Polynomial Equations   **331**

OBJECTIVE
2   **Teaching Notes**

3 EXAMPLE   **English Learners**

Help students just learning the English language relate the mathematical meaning of conjugate to the English language meaning of conjugate. Conjugate is an adjective used to describe two items having features in common but inverses or opposites in some aspect.

5 EXAMPLE   **Error Prevention**

Some students may write -3 as a root. Be sure students understand that if a is a nonzero real number root of a polynomial equation, $-a$ is not necessarily a root.

📄 **Additional Examples**

3 A polynomial equation with rational coefficients has the roots $2 - \sqrt{5}$ and $\sqrt{7}$. Find two additional roots. $\mathbf{2 + \sqrt{5}}$ **and** $\mathbf{-\sqrt{7}}$

4 A polynomial equation with real coefficients has the roots $2 + 9i$ and $7i$. Find two additional roots. $\mathbf{2 - 9i}$ **and** $\mathbf{-7i}$

5 Find a third degree polynomial equation with rational coefficients that has roots -2, and $2 - i$. $\mathbf{x^3 - 2x^2 - 3x + 10 = 0}$

Closure

Ask: *If a polynomial equation has integer coefficients, how can you find any rational roots the equation might have?* **Apply the Rational Root Theorem and test each possible root.** *If you find one irrational or imaginary root, how can you find another one?* **Write the conjugate.**

---

page 329   **Check Skills You'll Need**

1. $\pm 1, \pm 2, \pm 3, \pm 4, \pm 6, \pm 12$

2. $\pm 1, \pm 2, \pm 3, \pm 4, \pm 6, \pm 8, \pm 12, \pm 24$

3. $\pm 1, \pm 2, \pm 3, \pm 4, \pm 6, \pm 9, \pm 12, \pm 18, \pm 36$

4. $\pm 1, \pm 2, \pm 3, \pm 4, \pm 6, \pm 8, \pm 12, \pm 16, \pm 24, \pm 48$

7. A rational number can be written as the quotient of two integers, $\frac{a}{b}$ where $b \neq 0$.

8. Irrational numbers cannot be written as quotients of integers.

9. An imaginary number is a nonreal number of the form $a + bi$, where $b \neq 0$.

331

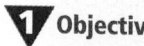

3. Practice

Assignment Guide

1 Objective
- Ⓐ Ⓑ Core 1–12, 25–31
- Ⓒ Extension 40

2 Objective
- Ⓐ Ⓑ Core 13–24, 32–39
- Ⓒ Extension 41–43

Standardized Test Prep 44–47

Mixed Review 48–56

Error Prevention

Exercises 1–12, 22–25 Students may recall the Rational Root Theorem incorrectly and check rational numbers $\frac{p}{q}$ for which p is a factor of the leading coefficient and q is a factor of the constant term. Suggest to students that they think about the solution $x = \frac{4}{3}$ of a linear equation like $9x - 12 = 0$. p (4 here) is a factor of the constant term and q (3 here) is a factor of the leading coefficient.

Enrichment 6-5
Reteaching 6-5
Practice 6-5

Practice 6-5   Theorems about Roots of Polynomial Equations

Number pairs of the form $a + bi$ and $a - bi$ are **complex conjugates.** You can use complex conjugates to find an equation's imaginary roots.

 **Key Concepts**

Theorem	**Imaginary Root Theorem**

If the imaginary number $a + bi$ is a root of a polynomial equation with real coefficients, then the conjugate $a - bi$ also is a root.

4 EXAMPLE **Finding Imaginary Roots**

A polynomial equation with integer coefficients has the roots $3 - i$ and $2i$. Find two additional roots.

By the Imaginary Root Theorem, if $3 - i$ is a root, then its complex conjugate $3 + i$ also is a root. If $2i$ is a root, then its complex conjugate $-2i$ also is a root.

● The additional roots are $3 + i$ and $2i$.

✓ **Check Understanding** **4** **a.** If a polynomial equation with real coefficients has $3i$ and $-2 + i$ among its roots, then what two other roots must it have? **$-3i$, $-2 - i$**
b. Critical Thinking Describe the degree of the equation. **4 or greater**

You can often use the Irrational Root Theorem and the Imaginary Root Theorem to write a polynomial equation if you know some of its roots.

5 EXAMPLE **Writing a Polynomial Equation from Its Roots**

Find a third-degree polynomial equation with rational coefficients that has roots 3 and $1 + i$.

Step 1 Find the other root using the Imaginary Root Theorem.

Since $1 + i$ is a root, then its complex conjugate $1 - i$ also is a root.

Step 2 Write the factored form of the polynomial using the Factor Theorem.

$(x - 3)(x - (1 + i))(x - (1 - i))$

Step 3 Multiply the factors.

$(x - 3)[x^2 - x(1 - i) - x(1 + i) + (1 + i)(1 - i)]$ Multiply $(x - (1 + i))$ $(x - (1 - i))$.

$(x - 3)(x^2 - x + ix - x - ix + 1 - i^2)$ **Simplify.**

$(x - 3)(x^2 - x - x + 1 + 1)$

$(x - 3)(x^2 - 2x + 2)$ **Multiply.**

$x^3 - 5x^2 + 8x - 6$

A third-degree polynomial equation with rational coefficients and roots 3 and $1 + i$ is $x^3 - 5x^2 + 8x - 6 = 0$.

✓ **Check Understanding** **5** **a.** Find a third-degree polynomial equation with rational coefficients that has roots -1 and $2 - i$. **$x^3 - 3x^2 + x + 5 = 0$**
b. Find a fourth-degree polynomial equation with rational coefficients that has roots i and $2i$. **$x^4 + 5x^2 + 4 = 0$**

332   Chapter 6   Polynomials and Polynomial Functions

---

pages 333–334 Exercises

1. $\pm1, \pm2$; 1

2. $\pm1, \pm2, \pm3, \pm6$; 1, $-2, -3$

3. $\pm1, \pm2, \pm4$; -1

4. $\pm\frac{1}{2}, \pm1, \pm2, \pm4, \pm8$; no rational roots

5. $\pm1, \pm2, \pm4, \pm8, \pm16$; -2

6. $\pm1, \pm3, \pm5, \pm15$; no rational roots

8. $5, \pm i\sqrt{7}$

9. $-3, 1, \frac{7}{2}$

10. $-5, \frac{1 \pm \sqrt{3}}{2}$

11. $\pm\frac{1}{2}, \pm3$

12. $1, -2, \frac{1 \pm \sqrt{7}}{3}$

332

EXERCISES

For more practice, see *Extra Practice*.

Practice and Problem Solving

 Practice by Example

Example 1
(page 330)

Use the Rational Root Theorem to list all possible rational roots for each polynomial equation. Then find any actual rational roots. **1–6. See margin p. 332.**

1. $x^3 - x^2 + 2x - 2 = 0$

2. $x^3 + 4x^2 + x - 6 = 0$

3. $x^3 + x^2 + 4x + 4 = 0$

4. $2x^3 - 9x^2 - 11x + 8 = 0$

5. $x^3 + 2x^2 - 8x - 16 = 0$

6. $x^4 + 2x^2 - 15 = 0$

Example 2
(pages 330–331)

Find the roots of each polynomial equation. **8–12. See margin p. 332.**

7. $x^3 - 2x^2 + 5x - 10 = 0$ **2, $\pm i\sqrt{5}$**

8. $x^3 - 5x^2 + 7x - 35 = 0$

9. $2x^4 - 5x^3 - 17x^2 + 41x - 21 = 0$

10. $4x^3 + 16x^2 - 22x - 10 = 0$

11. $4x^4 - 37x^2 + 9 = 0$

12. $9x^4 + 3x^3 - 30x^2 + 6x + 12 = 0$

Examples 3 and 4
(pages 331 and 332)

13. $-\sqrt{5}, \sqrt{13}$

A polynomial equation with rational coefficients has the given roots. Find two additional roots.

$$4 + \sqrt{6}, -\sqrt{3} \qquad 1 + \sqrt{10}, 2 - \sqrt{2}$$

13. $\sqrt{5}$ and $-\sqrt{13}$

14. $4 - \sqrt{6}$ and $\sqrt{3}$

15. $1 - \sqrt{10}$ and $2 + \sqrt{2}$

16. $1 + i$ and $-5i$
1 − i, 5i

17. $2 + 3i$ and $6i$
2 − 3i, −6i

18. $4 - i$ and $3 + 7i$
4 + i, 3 − 7i

Example 5
(page 332)

Find a third-degree polynomial equation with rational coefficients that has the given numbers as roots. **19–22. See margin.**

19. 1 and $3i$

20. -5 and $1 - i$

21. 2 and $-4i$

22. $3 + i$ and -3

23. $-2i$ and 6
$x^3 - 6x^2 + 4x - 24 = 0$

24. -1 and $i + 1$
$x^3 - x^2 + 2 = 0$

B **Apply Your Skills**

Use the Rational Root Theorem to list all possible rational roots for each polynomial equation. Then find any actual rational roots. **25–28. See margin.**

25. $12x^3 - 32x^2 + 25x - 6 = 0$

26. $10x^3 - 49x^2 + 68x - 20 = 0$

27. $6x^4 - 5x^3 - 65x^2 + 85x - 21 = 0$

28. $8x^3 - 28x^2 + 14x + 15 = 0$

Find a fourth-degree polynomial equation with integer coefficients that has the given numbers as roots.

29. $x^4 - 6x^3 + 14x^2 - 24x + 40 = 0$

30. $x^4 - 2x^3 - x^2 + 6x - 6 = 0$

31. $x^4 - 6x^3 + 2x^2 + 30x - 35 = 0$

29. $3 + i$ and $-2i$

30. $\sqrt{3}$ and $1 - i$

31. $3 + \sqrt{2}$ and $\sqrt{5}$

In each equation, r, s, and t represent integers. Indicate whether the statement is *sometimes*, *always*, or *never* true. Explain your answer. **33–36. See margin pp. 333–334.**

32. A root of the equation $3x^3 + rx^2 + sx + 8 = 0$ is 5.

32. Never true; 5 is not a factor of 8, so by the Rational Root Theorem, 5 is not a root of the equation.

33. A root of the equation $3x^3 + rx^2 + sx + 8 = 0$ is -2.

34. If a is a root of $x^3 + rx^2 + sx + t = 0$, then a is a factor of t.

35. $\sqrt{5}$ and $-\sqrt{5}$ are roots of $x^3 + rx^2 + sx + t = 0$.

36. $2 + i$ and $-2 - i$ are roots of $x^3 + rx^2 + sx + t = 0$.

38. Answers may vary. Sample:
$x^4 - x^2 - 2 = 0$;
roots are $\pm\sqrt{2}$ and $\pm i$.

37. Error Analysis A student claims that $2i$ is the only imaginary root of a polynomial equation that has real coefficients. Explain the student's mistake.
If 2i is a root, then so is −2i.

38. Open-Ended Write a fourth-degree polynomial equation with integer coefficients that has two irrational roots and two imaginary roots.

19. $x^3 - x^2 + 9x - 9 = 0$

20. $x^3 + 3x^2 - 8x + 10 = 0$

21. $x^3 - 2x^2 + 16x - 32 = 0$

22. $x^3 - 3x^2 - 8x + 30 = 0$

25. $\pm\frac{1}{12}, \pm\frac{1}{6}, \pm\frac{1}{4}, \pm\frac{1}{2}, \pm\frac{1}{3},$
$\pm\frac{2}{3}, \pm\frac{3}{4}, \pm 1, \pm\frac{3}{2}, \pm 2, \pm 3,$
$\pm 6; \frac{1}{2}, \frac{3}{2}, \frac{2}{3}$

26. $\pm\frac{1}{10}, \pm\frac{1}{5}, \pm\frac{2}{5}, \pm\frac{1}{2}, \pm\frac{4}{5}, \pm 1$
$\pm 2, \pm\frac{5}{2}, \pm 4, \pm 5, \pm 10,$
$\pm 20; 2, \frac{2}{5}, \frac{5}{2}$

333

Resources

For additional practice with a variety of test item formats:

- Standardized Test Prep, p. 357
- Test-Taking Strategies, p. 352
- Test-Taking Strategies with Transparencies

Exercise 44 The visual form of $2 + \sqrt{4}$ might tempt students to select choice B or to think that choices B and D are both correct. Remind students that the Irrational and Imaginary Root Theorems do not apply to rational numbers. $2 - \sqrt{4}$ equals $2 - 2$, or 0, a rational number.

pages 333–334   Exercises

34. **Always true; use the Rational Root Theorem with $p = a$ and $q = 1$.**

35. **Sometimes true; since $\sqrt{5}$ and $-\sqrt{5}$ are conjugates, they can be roots of a polynomial equation with integer coefficients.**

36. **Never true; since $2 + i$ and $-2 - i$ are not conjugates, they cannot be the only imaginary roots of a polynomial equation with integer roots. If their conjugates were also roots, there would be four roots and the equation would have to be of fourth degree.**

39. **If $\sqrt{b}$ of $a + \sqrt{b}$ were rational, then the sum would also be rational. Thus the roots would be rational, which is not always the case.**

40a. **2 real, 2 imaginary; 4 imaginary; 4 real**

b. **5 real; 3 real, 2 imaginary; 4 imaginary, 1 real**

c. **Answers may vary. Sample: It has an odd number of real solutions, but it must have at least one real solution.**

---

39. **Critical Thinking** Explain why the Irrational Root Theorem requires that $\sqrt{b}$ of $a + \sqrt{b}$ be an irrational number. **39–40. See margin.**

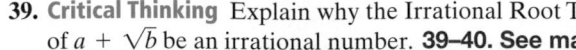

Challenge

40. **a.** Using *real* and *imaginary* as types of roots, list all possible combinations of root type for a fourth-degree polynomial equation.
   b. Repeat the process for a fifth-degree polynomial equation.
   c. **Make a Conjecture** Make a conjecture about the number of real roots of an odd-degree polynomial equation.

41. **Answers may vary. Sample: You cannot use the Irrational Root Theorem unless the equation has rational coefficients.**

41. **Writing** A student states that $2 + \sqrt{3}$ is a root of $x^2 - 2x - (3 + 2\sqrt{3}) = 0$. The student claims that $2 - \sqrt{3}$ is another root of the equation by the Irrational Root Theorem. Explain how you would respond to the student.

42. What polynomial equation with complex coefficients and no multiple roots has $-4i$ and $2 + 3i$ as its only roots? $x^2 + (-2 + i)x + 12 - 8i = 0$

43. **a.** Find a polynomial equation in which $1 + \sqrt{2}$ is the only root.
   b. Find a polynomial equation with root $1 + \sqrt{2}$ of multiplicity 2.
   c. Find c such that $1 + \sqrt{2}$ is a solution of $x^2 - 2x + c = 0$.
   a–c. Answers may vary. Samples:
   a. $x - 1 - \sqrt{2} = 0$ b. $x^2 - 2(1 + \sqrt{2})x + (1 + \sqrt{2})^2 = 0$ c. -1

Standardized Test Prep

Multiple Choice

44. Three roots of a polynomial equation with rational coefficients are $5 + \sqrt{3}$, -17, and $2 - \sqrt{4}$. Which number also is a root of the equation? **D**
   A. 17   B. $2 + \sqrt{4}$ C. $4 - \sqrt{2}$ D. $5 - \sqrt{3}$

Take It to the NET
Online lesson quiz at
www.PHSchool.com
Web Code: agk-0605

45. Two roots of a cubic polynomial equation with real coefficients are -3 and $-4i$. If the leading coefficient of the polynomial is 1, what is the equation?
   F. $x^3 - 3x^2 + 16x - 48 = 0$ G. $x^3 - 3x^2 - 16x + 48 = 0$ **H**
   H. $x^3 + 3x^2 + 16x + 48 = 0$ I. $x^3 + 3x^2 - 16x - 48 = 0$

Short Response

46. According to the Rational Root Theorem, what is the relationship between the polynomial equation $2x^4 - x^3 - 7x^2 + 3x + 3 = 0$ and rational roots of the form $\frac{p}{q}$, where $\frac{p}{q}$ is in simplest form?   **See margin.**

Extended Response

47. A third-degree polynomial equation with rational coefficients has roots -4 and $-4i$. If the leading coefficient of the equation is $\frac{3}{2}$, what is the equation? Show your work.   **See back of book.**

Mixed Review

Lesson 6-4

48. $-\frac{3}{2}, \frac{3 \pm 3i\sqrt{3}}{4}$

Solve each equation.

48. $8x^3 + 27 = 0$ 49. $x^4 - x^2 - 20 = 0$ 50. $2x^4 - 50 = 0$
                           $\pm\sqrt{5}, \pm 2i$ $\pm\sqrt{5}, \pm i\sqrt{5}$

Lesson 5-7

Solve each equation by completing the square.

51. $x^2 - 6x - 7 = 0$ 52. $p^2 + 4p = -8$ 53. $4x^2 - 11 = 12x$
   $-1, 7$ $-2 \pm 2i$ $\frac{3}{2} \pm \sqrt{5}$

Lesson 4-8

Use Cramer's Rule to solve each system.

54. $\begin{cases} -3x + y = -7 \\ 5x + 2y = -3 \end{cases}$ 55. $\begin{cases} x - 3y = -12 \\ 2x + 7y = 2 \end{cases}$ 56. $\begin{cases} 2x - 8y = 10 \\ -3x + y = -15 \end{cases}$

   $(1, -4)$ $(-6, 2)$ $(5, 0)$

46. **[2]** p is a factor of 3, so
   $p = \pm 1$ or ± 3
   q is a factor of 2, so
   $q = \pm 1$ or ± 2

   [1] relates p and q to the coefficients or the constant of the polynomial

6-6

The Fundamental Theorem of Algebra

 North Carolina Objectives
1.02   Define and compute with complex numbers.
1.03   Operate with algebraic expressions (polynomial, rational, complex fractions) to solve problems.

Lesson Preview

What You'll Learn

OBJECTIVE 1
To use the Fundamental Theorem of Algebra in solving polynomial equations with complex roots

. . . And Why

To find all the zeros of a polynomial function, as in Example 2

 Check Skills You'll Need   (For help, go to Lessons 5-8 and 6-1.)

Find the degree of each polynomial.

1. $3x^2 - x + 5$ **2**   2. $-x + 3 - x^3$ **3**   3. $-4x^5 + 1$ **5**

Solve each equation using the quadratic formula.

4. $x^2 + 16 = 0$ 5. $x^2 - 2x + 3 = 0$ 6. $2x^2 + 5x + 4 = 0$
   ±4i   **1 ± i√2**   **$\frac{-5 \pm i\sqrt{7}}{4}$**

New Vocabulary   • Fundamental Theorem of Algebra

OBJECTIVE

1   The Fundamental Theorem of Algebra

 Interactive lesson includes instant self-check, tutorials, and activities.

3. A fourth-degree polynomial function has 4 zeros regardless of type.

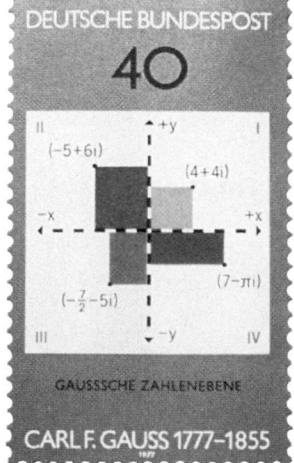

Real-World Connection

Germany issued this stamp in honor of the bicentennial of the birth of Gauss.

Investigation: Counting Zeros

In this activity you will find the solutions to polynomial equations, identify the types of solutions, and then count the number of solutions.

1. a. Find the solutions of $x^4 - 5x^2 + 4 = 0$. **−2, −1, 1, 2**
   b. Identify each solution as *real* or *imaginary*. **all real**
   c. How many solutions are there? **4**

2. a. Find the solutions of $x^4 + 7x^2 + 12 = 0$. **±i√3, ±2i**
   b. Identify each solution as *real* or *imaginary*. **all imaginary**
   c. How many solutions are there? **4**

3. Make a conjecture about the number of zeros of a fourth-degree polynomial function, regardless of the types of zeros. **See left.**

You have solved polynomial equations and found that their roots are included in the set of complex numbers. That is, the roots have been integers, rational numbers, irrational numbers, and imaginary numbers. But can all polynomial equations be solved using complex numbers?

In 1799, the German mathematician Carl Friedrich Gauss (1777–1855) proved that the answer to this question is yes. The roots of every polynomial equation, even those with imaginary coefficients, are complex numbers. The answer is so important that his theorem is called the **Fundamental Theorem of Algebra.**

A corollary to the Fundamental Theorem of Algebra describes the relationship between the degree of a polynomial and the number of zeros of the related polynomial function.

---

1. Plan

Lesson Preview

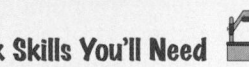 **Check Skills You'll Need**

The Quadratic Formula
Lesson 5-8: Examples 1 and 2
Practice Exercises 1–21
Extra Practice, p. 826

Polynomial Functions
Lesson 6-1: Example 1
Practice Exercises 1–9
Extra Practice, p. 827

Lesson Resources

Teaching Resources
Practice, Reteaching, Enrichment

Reaching All Students
Practice Workbook 6-6
Spanish Practice Workbook 6-6

Presentation Assistant Plus!
Transparencies
• Check Skills You'll Need 6-6
• Additional Examples 6-6
• Student Edition Answers 6-6
• Lesson Quiz 6-6
PH Presentation Pro CD 6-6

ASSESSMENT SYSTEM
Computer Test Generator CD

Technology
Resource Pro® CD-ROM
Computer Test Generator CD
Prentice Hall Presentation Pro CD

www.PHSchool.com
Student Site
• Teacher Web Code: agk-5500
• Self-grading Lesson Quiz
Teacher Center
• Lesson Planner
• Resources

Plus

Ongoing Assessment and Intervention

Before the Lesson
Diagnose prerequisite skills using:
• Check Skills You'll Need

During the Lesson
Monitor progress using:
• Check Understanding
• Additional Examples
• Standardized Test Prep

After the Lesson
Assess knowledge using:
• Lesson Quiz
• Computer Test Generator CD

2. Teach

Professional Development

Math Background

The Fundamental Theorem of Algebra guarantees the existence of a complex root, and as a consequence the number of roots, but does not provide a means for finding them. Students will need to combine the techniques learned in previous lessons to find all complex zeros of a polynomial function.

OBJECTIVE
① Teaching Notes

Investigation (Optional)

Each of these equations has four complex roots. In connection with Question 3, help students see that the Factor Theorem implies that a polynomial equation of degree n cannot have more than n zeros.

① EXAMPLE Teaching Tip

Suggest students review the Imaginary Root Theorem and the Rational Root Theorem before they begin this example.

② EXAMPLE Teaching Tip

Be sure students understand that "$x^2 - x + 1$ cannot be factored" means there are no linear factors that have only *real* coefficients.

Additional Examples

① For the equation $x^4 - 3x^3 + 4x + 1 = 0$, find the number of complex roots, the possible number of real roots, and the possible rational roots. **4; 0, 2, or 4; ±1**

② Find the number of complex zeros of $f(x) = x^5 + 3x^4 - x - 3$. Find all the zeros. **5 zeros; ±1, −3, ±i**

Closure

Ask: *How can you determine how many roots there are for a polynomial equation?* **Find the degree of the related polynomial. This degree gives the number of roots, including multiple roots.**

336

 **Key Concepts**

 Reading Math

A corollary is a deduction.

Theorem	**Fundamental Theorem of Algebra**

If $P(x)$ is a polynomial of degree $n \geq 1$ with complex coefficients, then $P(x) = 0$ has at least one complex root.

Corollary

Including imaginary roots and multiple roots, an nth degree polynomial equation has exactly n roots; the related polynomial function has exactly n zeros.

In other words, the corollary says that you can factor a polynomial of degree n into n linear factors. The number n includes multiple roots. For example, the equation $x^3 = 0$ should have three roots by the corollary to the Fundamental Theorem of Algebra. Since $x^3 = 0$ can be rewritten as $x \cdot x \cdot x = 0$ or $(x - 0)(x - 0)(x - 0) = 0$, the equation has three linear factors and three roots, all of which are zero.

① EXAMPLE Using the Fundamental Theorem of Algebra

For the equation $x^3 + 2x^2 - 4x - 6 = 0$, find the number of complex roots, the possible number of real roots, and the possible rational roots.

By the corollary to the Fundamental Theorem of Algebra, $x^3 + 2x^2 - 4x - 6 = 0$ has three complex roots.

By the Imaginary Root Theorem, the equation has either no imaginary roots or two imaginary roots (one conjugate pair). So the equation has either three real roots or one real root.

By the Rational Root Theorem, the possible rational roots of the equation are ±1, ±2, ±3, and ±6.

✓ Check Understanding ① For the equation $x^4 - 3x^3 + x^2 - x + 3 = 0$, find the number of complex roots, the possible number of real roots, and the possible rational roots.
4 complex roots, number of real roots: 0, 2, or 4, possible rational roots: ±1, ±3

You can often find all the zeros of a polynomial function by using some combination of graphing, the Factor Theorem, polynomial division, the Remainder Theorem, and the Quadratic Formula.

② EXAMPLE Finding All Zeros of a Polynomial Function

Find the number of complex zeros of $f(x) = x^3 + x^2 - x + 2$. Find all the zeros.

By the corollary to the Fundamental Theorem of Algebra, there are three complex zeros. You can use synthetic division to find a rational zero.

Step 1 Find a rational root from the possible roots of ±1 and ±2. Use synthetic division to test each possible root until you get a remainder of zero.

$$
\begin{array}{r|rrr}
-2 & 1 & 1 & -1 & 2 \\
   &   & -2 & 2 & -2 \\
\hline
   & 1 & -1 & 1 & 0 \\
   & \downarrow & \downarrow & \downarrow \\
   & 1x^2 & -1x & +1
\end{array}
$$

So -2 is one of the roots.

🌱 Reaching All Students

Below Level Make sure that students understand that the number of roots is equal to the number of factors, and that multiple roots are a result of identical factors.	**Advanced Learners** The equation $y = x^2 - 4x + 4$ has only 2 as a zero. Have students explain how this can be reconciled with the corollary to the Fundamental Theorem of Algebra.	**Error Prevention** See note on page 337.

Step 2 Since the expression $x^2 - x + 1$ cannot be factored, use the Quadratic Formula to solve the related quadratic equation $x^2 - x + 1 = 0$.

$$x = \frac{-b \pm \sqrt{b^2 - 4ac}}{2a}$$

$$x = \frac{-(-1) \pm \sqrt{(-1)^2 - 4(1)(1)}}{2(1)}$$

$$x = \frac{1 \pm \sqrt{-3}}{2}$$

$$x = \frac{1 \pm i\sqrt{3}}{2}$$

The polynomial function $f(x) = x^3 + x^2 - x + 2$ has one real zero of $x = -2$, and two complex zeros of $x = \frac{1 + i\sqrt{3}}{2}$ and $x = \frac{1 - i\sqrt{3}}{2}$.

✓ **Check Understanding** **2** **a.** Find all zeros of $y = x^3 - 2x^2 + 4x - 8$. **2, ±2*i***

b. Explain how you could use a graphing calculator to verify the zeros. **Graph the equation, and where the graph crosses the *x*-axis are the real zeros.**

EXERCISES

For more practice, see *Extra Practice*.

Practice and Problem Solving

(A) Practice by Example

Example 1
(page 336)

For each equation, state the number of complex roots, the possible number of real roots, and the possible rational roots. **1–8. See margin pp. 336–338.**

1. $x^3 + 4x^2 + 5x - 1 = 0$

2. $3x^2 - 7 = 0$

3. $-x^4 = 0$

4. $2x^5 - 4x^4 - 4x^2 + 5 = 0$

5. $x^7 - x^3 - 2x - 3 = 0$

6. $4x + 8 = 0$

7. $-2x^6 - x^2 + x - 7 = 0$

8. $x^{10} + x^8 - x^4 + 3x^2 - x + 1 = 0$

Example 2
(pages 336–337)

Find all the zeros of each function.

9. $y = 2x^3 + x^2 + 1$ **−1,** $\frac{1 \pm i\sqrt{7}}{4}$

10. $f(x) = x^3 - 3x^2 + x - 3$ **3, ±*i***

11. $g(x) = x^3 - 5x^2 + 5x - 4$ **4,** $\frac{1 \pm i\sqrt{3}}{2}$

12. $y = x^3 - 2x^2 - 3x + 6$ **2, ±√3**

13. $y = x^4 - 6x^2 + 8$ **±2, ±√2**

14. $f(x) = x^4 - 3x^2 - 4$ **±2, ±*i***

15. $y = x^3 - 3x^2 - 9x$ **0,** $\frac{3 \pm 3\sqrt{5}}{2}$

16. $y = x^3 + 6x^2 + x + 6$ **−6, ±*i***

(B) Apply Your Skills

For each equation, state the number of complex roots, the possible number of real roots, and the possible rational roots. **17–20. See back of book.**

17. $2x^4 - x^3 + 2x^2 + 5x - 26 = 0$

18. $x^5 - x^3 - 11x^2 + 9x + 18 = 0$

19. $-12 + x + 10x^2 + 3x^3 = 0$

20. $4x^6 - x^5 - 24 = 0$

Find all the zeros of each function.

21. $y = x^3 - 4x^2 + 9x - 36$ **4, ±3*i***

22. $f(x) = x^3 + 2x^2 - 5x - 10$ **−2, ±√5**

23. $y = 2x^3 + 14x^2 + 13x + 6$ **−6,** $\frac{-1 \pm i}{2}$

24. $y = 4x^3 + 9x^2 + 22x + 5$ **24.** $-\frac{1}{4}$**, −1 ± 2*i***

25. $g(x) = x^3 - \frac{1}{2}x^2 + 20x - 10$ **25.** $\frac{1}{2}$**, ±2*i*√5**

26. $y = 15x^3 - x^2 + 3x - 2$ **26.** $\frac{2}{5}$**,** $\frac{-1 \pm i\sqrt{11}}{6}$

27. Open-Ended Write a polynomial function that has four possible rational zeros but no actual rational zeros. **Answers may vary. Sample:** $y = x^4 + 3x^2 + 2$

Lesson 6-6 The Fundamental Theorem of Algebra **337**

pages 337–338 Exercises

1. 3 complex roots
number of real roots: 1 or 3
possible rational roots: ±1

2. 2 complex roots
number of real roots: 0 or 2
possible rational roots:

$\pm\frac{1}{3}, \pm\frac{7}{3}, \pm1, \pm7$

3. 4 complex roots
number of real roots: 0, 2, or 4
possible rational roots: 0

4. 5 complex roots number
of real roots: 1, 3, or 5
possible rational roots:
$\pm\frac{1}{2}, \pm1, \pm\frac{5}{2}, \pm5$

Assignment Guide

▼ Objective
Ⓐ Ⓑ **Core** 1–27
Ⓒ **Extension** 28–31

Standardized Test Prep 32–35

Mixed Review 36–41

Error Prevention

Exercise 3 Remind students to take the multiplicity of roots into account.

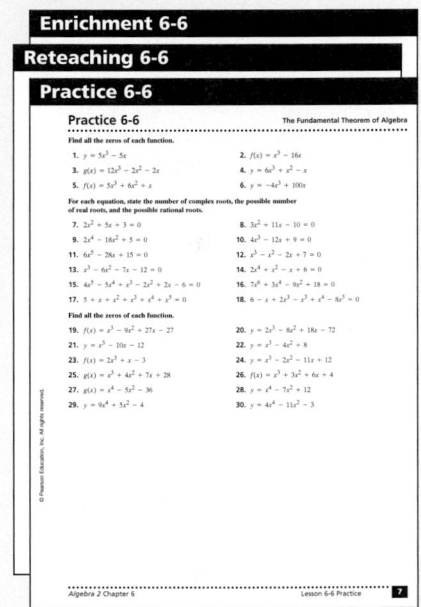

5. 7 complex roots
number of real roots: 1, 3, 5, or 7
possible rational roots:
±1, ±3

6. 1 complex root
number of real roots: 1
possible rational roots:
$\pm\frac{1}{4}, \pm\frac{1}{2}, \pm1, \pm2, \pm4, \pm8$

7. 6 complex roots
number of real roots: 0, 2, 4, or 6
possible rational roots:
$\pm\frac{1}{2}, \pm1, \pm\frac{7}{2}, \pm7$

8. 10 complex roots
number of real roots: 0, 2, 4, 6, 8, or 10
possible rational roots: ±1

337

Lesson Quiz 6-6

For each equation, state the number of complex roots, the possible number of real roots, and the possible rational roots.

1. $x^4 - 13x^3 + x^2 - 5 = 0$
   4; 0, 2, or 4; $\pm1, \pm5$

2. $x^7 - x^5 + x^2 - 3x + 3 = 0$
   7; 1, 3, 5, or 7; $\pm1, \pm3$

Find all the zeros of each function.

3. $x^3 - 3x^2 - 8x - 10 = 0$
   5, $-1\pm i$

4. $x^3 + 3x^2 - 2x - 6 = 0$ -3, $\pm\sqrt{2}$

5. $x^4 - 29x^2 + 100 = 0$ ±2, ±5

Alternative Assessment

Say: *Write an equation with integer coefficients that has 3 roots—one real root, and two imaginary roots.* Students trade equations to check. Repeat the process, but this time students write an equation with 4 roots—two rational roots and two imaginary roots.

Standardized Test Prep

Resources

For additional practice with a variety of test item formats:
- Standardized Test Prep, p. 357
- Test-Taking Strategies, p. 352
- Test-Taking Strategies with Transparencies

pages 337–338 Exercises

28. ±0.75

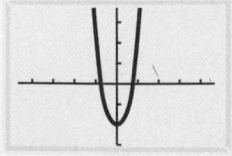

29. $-3.24, 1.24$

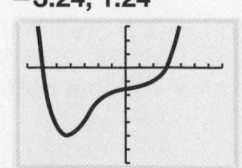

C Challenge

30. If you have no constant, then all terms have an x that can be factored out. The resulting expression will have a constant that can be used in the Rational Root Theorem.

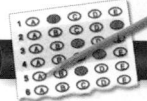

Graph each function. Approximate the real zeros to the nearest hundredth.

28. $f(x) = x^4 + 3x^2 - 2$

29. $f(x) = x^4 + 2x^3 - 2x^2 + 4x - 8$

28–29. See margin.

30. **Writing** Using the Rational Root Theorem, explain why the following statement is false: If a polynomial has no constant term, then the corresponding polynomial equation has only the number 0 as a possible rational root.

31. **Critical Thinking** Consider a polynomial with integer coefficients in which the leading coefficient is not equal to 1. Can the related polynomial equation have a rational root that is an integer? Explain. **Yes; for example, $2x^2 - 11x + 5$ has roots 0.5 and 5.**

Standardized Test Prep

Multiple Choice

32. Which number is a root of $f(x) = x^3 + 6x^2 + 9x$ that has multiplicity 1? **C**
    A. 3   B. 1   C. 0   D. -3

33. Three roots of a polynomial equation with real coefficients are 3, $5 - 3i$, and $-3i$. Which number(s) MUST also be roots of the equation? **C**

    I. -3 II. $5 + 3i$ III. $3i$

    A. II only   B. I and II only   C. II and III only   D. I, II, and III

Quantitative Comparison

Compare the boxed quantity in Column A with the boxed quantity in Column B. Choose the best answer.
   A. The quantity in Column A is greater.
   B. The quantity in Column B is greater.
   C. The two quantities are equal.
   D. The relationship cannot be determined from the information given.

Take It to the NET
Online lesson quiz at
www.PHSchool.com
Web Code: agk-0606

	Column A	Column B
34. A	the number of zeros of a degree four polynomial function	the number of zeros of the function $y = (2x - 5)(2x + 5)$
35. C	the degree of the polynomial $P(x) = (2x + 3)(x - 5)$	the degree of the quotient of $f(x) = 4x^5 + 3x^4 + x^2 - x + 1$ and $g(x) = 3x^3 - 2x^2 + x + 1$

Mixed Review

Lesson 6-5

36. Find a fourth-degree polynomial equation with integer coefficients that has $2i$ and $-3 + i$ as roots. $x^4 + 6x^3 + 14x^2 + 24x + 40 = 0$

Lesson 5-8

Solve each equation using the Quadratic Formula.

37. $x^2 - 6x + 9 = 0$
    3 (mult. 2)

38. $2x^2 + 5x = -9$
    $\dfrac{-5 \pm i\sqrt{47}}{4}$

39. $2(x^2 + 2) = 3x$
    $\dfrac{3 \pm i\sqrt{23}}{4}$

Lesson 5-1

Find a quadratic model for each function.

40. $f(-1) = 0, f(2) = 3, f(1) = 4$
    $f(x) = -x^2 + 2x + 3$

41. $f(-4) = 11, f(-5) = 5, f(-6) = 3$
    $f(x) = 2x^2 + 24x + 75$

6-7 Permutations and Combinations

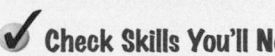 **6-7**

1. Plan

Lesson Preview

What You'll Learn

 OBJECTIVE 1 To count permutations

 OBJECTIVE 2 To count combinations

... And Why

To find the number of ways you can vote for candidates, as in Example 5

✓ Check Skills You'll Need

(For help, go to Lesson 1-2.)

Simplify each expression.

1. $10 \cdot 9 \cdot 8 \cdot 7 \cdot 6$ **30, 240**
2. $\frac{4 \cdot 3 \cdot 2}{6 \cdot 5}$ **$\frac{4}{5}$**
3. $\frac{7 \cdot 6 \cdot 5 \cdot 4 \cdot 3 \cdot 2 \cdot 1}{4 \cdot 3 \cdot 2 \cdot 1}$ **210**

Let $a * b = 2a(a + b)$. Evaluate each expression.

4. $3 * 4$ **42**
5. $2 * 7$ **36**
6. $5 * 1$ **60**
7. $6 * 10$ **192**

New Vocabulary • permutation • *n* factorial • combination

 Interactive lesson includes instant self-check, tutorials, and activities.

 **OBJECTIVE 1** **Permutations**

A **permutation** is an arrangement of items in a particular order. You can often find the number of permutations of some set of items by using the Multiplication Counting Principle or factorial notation.

You can use the Multiplication Counting Principle or factorial notation when you plan to choose all of the items of a particular set. Suppose you want to find the number of permutations for three items. There are three ways to choose the first item, two ways to choose the second item, and only one way to choose the third item. By the Multiplication Counting Principle, there are $3 \cdot 2 \cdot 1$ permutations. Using factorial notation, you can write $3 \cdot 2 \cdot 1$ as 3!, read "three factorial."

 Key Concepts

Definition	***n* Factorial**

For any positive integer $n, n! = n(n - 1) \cdot \ldots \cdot 3 \cdot 2 \cdot 1$.
For $n = 0, n! = 1$.

 Graphing Calculator Hint

To calculate factorials, press MATH and then choose the PRB menu and the ! option.

1 EXAMPLE **Finding Permutations**

In how many different orders can ten dogs line up to be groomed?

Since all ten dogs are being groomed, you are using all the items from the original set. You can use the Multiplication Counting Principle or factorial notation.

There are ten ways to select the first dog in line, nine ways to select the next dog, and so on. The total number of permutations is $10 \cdot 9 \cdot \ldots \cdot 2 \cdot 1 = 10!$.

$10! = 3,628,800$

● The ten dogs can line up in 3,628,800 different orders.

 ✓ Check Understanding ① In how many ways can you arrange six trophies on a shelf? **720**

 Teaching Resources
Practice, Reteaching, Enrichment
Checkpoint Quiz 2

 Reaching All Students
Practice Workbook 6-7
Spanish Practice Workbook 6-7
Reading and Math Literacy 6C
Spanish Reading & Literacy 6C
Spanish Checkpoint Quiz 2

Presentation Assistant Plus!
Transparencies
• Check Skills You'll Need 6-7
• Additional Examples 6-7
• Student Edition Answers 6-7
• Lesson Quiz 6-7
PH Presentation Pro CD 6-7

 **ASSESSMENT SYSTEM**

Checkpoint Quiz 2
Computer Test Generator CD

Technology
Resource Pro® CD-ROM
Computer Test Generator CD
Prentice Hall Presentation Pro CD

www.PHSchool.com
Student Site
• Teacher Web Code: agk-5500
• Self-grading Lesson Quiz
Teacher Center
• Lesson Planner
• Resources

Plus **iTEXT**

Lesson Preview

✓ Check Skills You'll Need

Algebraic Expressions
Lesson 1-2: Example 1
Practice Exercises 1–4
Extra Practice, p. 822

Lesson Resources

Lesson 6-7 Permutations and Combinations **339**

Ongoing Assessment and Intervention

Before the Lesson
Diagnose prerequisite skills using:
• Check Skills You'll Need

During the Lesson
Monitor progress using:
• Check Understanding
• Additional Examples
• Standardized Test Prep

After the Lesson
Assess knowledge using:
• Lesson Quiz
• Computer Test Generator CD
• Chapter Checkpoint 2 (p. 345)

Math Background

The branch of mathematics known as combinatorial analysis begins with questions of the form "In how many ways is it possible to arrange . . . ?" and "In how many ways is it possible to select . . . ?" Questions of the first type deal with permutations, and questions of the second type deal with combinations. Combinatorial analysis is important in algebra, probability, and many other branches of mathematics.

OBJECTIVE

 1 **Teaching Notes**

1 EXAMPLE **Tactile Learners**

Have students write the letters A, B, and C each on its own index card. Then lay the cards out from left to right. Have students arrange the cards in all possible orders and keep a list of the arrangements. Ask them what the value of 3! is. **6** Let students repeat the process for the letters A, B, C, and D and compare the result to 4!. **24** Ask: *Which would be easier to do, manually arrange cards representing 10 dogs or find 10!?* **find 10!**

2 EXAMPLE **Alternative Method**

One way to remember how to calculate permutations is using the phrase "possible choices times possible choices times possible choices." You say "possible choices" for each time there is a choice to make—three times for this example since there are three places awarded prizes.

Additional Examples

1 In how many orders can six people line up from left to right for a group photo?
720 orders

2 How many 4-letter codes can be made if no letter can be used twice? **358,800 codes**

340

Some permutations do not use all the items available in a set. You can still use the Multiplication Counting Principle or factorial notation. The relationship between permutations and factorials can be summarized with a formula.

 Key Concepts

Definition	Number of Permutations

The number of permutations of n items of a set arranged r items at a time is $_nP_r$.

$$_nP_r = \frac{n!}{(n-r)!} \text{ for } 0 \le r \le n$$

Example $\quad _{10}P_4 = \frac{10!}{(10-4)!} = \frac{10!}{6!} = 5040$

Real-World 🌐 **Connection**

In how many ways can these boats finish first, second, and third?

2 EXAMPLE **Real-World** 🌐 **Connection**

Boating Seven yachts enter a race. First, second, and third places will be given to the three fastest yachts. How many arrangements of first, second, and third places are possible with seven yachts?

Method 1 Use the Multiplication Counting Principle.
$$7 \cdot 6 \cdot 5 = 210$$

Method 2 Use the permutation formula. Since there are seven yachts arranged three at a time, $n = 7$ and $r = 3$.

$$_7P_3 = \frac{7!}{(7-3)!} = \frac{7!}{4!} = 210$$

There are 210 possible arrangements of first, second, and third places.

✓ **Check Understanding** **2** How many arrangements of first, second, and third places are possible with ten yachts? **720**

OBJECTIVE

 2 **Combinations**

In Example 2, you found the number of ways in which three of seven yachts can finish first, second, and third in a race. Each yacht would have a unique place. Consider a situation in which the three fastest yachts win the race with equal status, that is, without first, second, and third places. In that case, the *order* in which the three winning yachts cross the finish line does not matter. A selection in which order does not matter is a **combination.**

As with permutations, you can calculate the number of combinations of n items chosen r at a time by using a formula.

Key Concepts

Definition	Number of Combinations

The number of combinations of n items of a set chosen r items at a time is $_nC_r$.

$$_nC_r = \frac{n!}{r!(n-r)!} \text{ for } 0 \le r \le n$$

Example $\quad _5C_3 = \frac{5!}{3!(5-3)!} = \frac{5!}{3! \cdot 2!} = \frac{120}{6 \cdot 2} = 10$

340 Chapter 6 Polynomials and Polynomial Functions

👥 Reaching All Students

Below Level Tell students to think of a permutation as a way to award medals in the Olympics. The order in which the athletes finish races does affect the medal they are awarded.	**Advanced Learners** Have students explain how a tree diagram of probabilities reflects the Multiplication Counting Principle.	**English Learners** See note on page 341. **Tactile Learners** See note on page 340.

3 EXAMPLE Finding Combinations

Evaluate $_{12}C_3$.

$_{12}C_3 = \dfrac{12!}{3!(12-3)!}$ Use the formula $_nC_r = \dfrac{n!}{r!(n-r)!}$.

$= \dfrac{12!}{3! \cdot 9!}$ Simplify.

$= \dfrac{12 \cdot 11 \cdot 10 \cdot 9 \cdot 8 \cdot 7 \cdot 6 \cdot 5 \cdot 4 \cdot 3 \cdot 2 \cdot 1}{3 \cdot 2 \cdot 1 \cdot 9 \cdot 8 \cdot 7 \cdot 6 \cdot 5 \cdot 4 \cdot 3 \cdot 2 \cdot 1}$ Simplify each factorial.

$= \dfrac{12 \cdot 11 \cdot 10}{3 \cdot 2 \cdot 1}$

$= 220$

✓ **Check Understanding** **3** Evaluate each expression.

a. $_{10}C_5$ **252**   **b.** $_8C_2$ **28**   **c.** $_{25}C_7$ **480,700**

You can use a graphing calculator to find combinations.

4 EXAMPLE Real-World 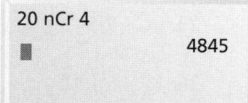 Connection

Literature A reading list for a course in world literature has 20 books on it. In how many ways can you choose four books to read?

Relate 20 books chosen 4 books at a time

Define Let n = total number of books.

Let r = number of books chosen at a time.

Write $_nC_r = {}_{20}C_4$

> 20 nCr 4
> ■   4845

Use the $_nC_r$ feature of your calculator.

● You can choose four books in 4845 different ways.

✓ **Check Understanding** **4** Of the 20 books, in how many ways can you choose seven books? Twelve books? **77,520; 125,970**

The National Association of Student Councils has more than 18,000 member schools.

5 EXAMPLE Real-World 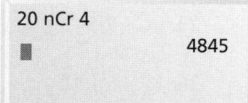 Connection

Government Ten candidates are running for three seats in the student government. You may vote for as many as three candidates. In how many ways can you vote for three or fewer candidates?

You may vote for   3 people,   2 people,   1 person,   or none.

$_{10}C_3$ $_{10}C_2$ $_{10}C_1$ $_{10}C_0$
120   45   10   1

The total number of ways to vote is $120 + 45 + 10 + 1 = 176$.

● There are 176 ways to cast your ballot.

✓ **Check Understanding** **5** In how many ways can you vote for five or fewer people? **638**

Graphing Calculator Hint

To find permutations and combinations, press MATH, and then choose the PRB menu.

Lesson 6-7   Permutations and Combinations   **341**

OBJECTIVE 2 Teaching Notes

4 EXAMPLE Technology Tip

Stress that the value of *n* must always be specified before selecting nCr from the PRB menu.

5 EXAMPLE English Learners

You may need to explain what *seats in the student government* means.

Additional Examples

3 Evaluate $_{10}C_4$. **210**

4 A disk jockey wants to select 5 songs from a new CD that contains 12 songs. How many 5-song selections are possible? **792 selections**

5 A pizza menu allows you to select 4 toppings at no extra charge from a list of 9 possible toppings. In how many ways can you select 4 or fewer toppings? **256 ways**

Closure

Ask: *How is a combination of n items chosen r at a time different from a permutation of n items chosen r at a time?* **In the combination, the only important thing is which items are selected. In the permutation, both the items and their order of selection are important.**

Assignment Guide

1 Objective

Ⓐ Ⓑ **Core** 1–20, 33–41, 46–47, 56–66, 68

Ⓒ **Extension** 71–72

2 Objective

Ⓐ Ⓑ **Core** 21–32, 42–45, 48–55, 67

Ⓒ **Extension** 69–70, 73

Standardized Test Prep 74–80

Mixed Review 81–94

Error Prevention

Exercises 7, 8 Students who use a graphing calculator to evaluate these expressions must remember to use parentheses around the entire denominator.

Exercise 9 Not all permutations are recommended for radial tires.

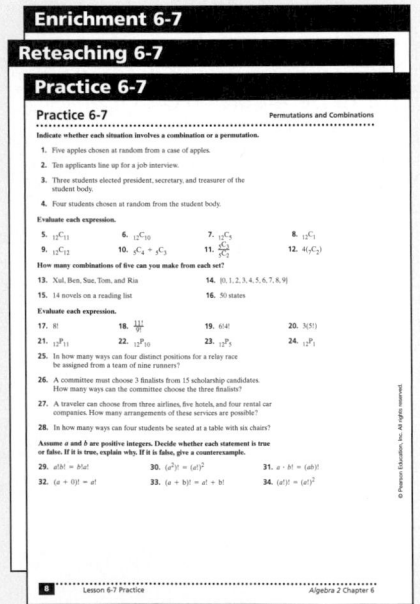

pages 342–345 Exercises

35. False; answers may vary.
Sample: $(3 + 2)! = 120$
and $3! + 2! = 8$

EXERCISES

For more practice, see *Extra Practice*.

Practice and Problem Solving

Ⓐ **Practice by Example**

Example 1
(page 339)

Evaluate each expression.

6,227,020,800

1. $5!$ **120** **2.** $10!$ **3,628,800** **3.** $13!$ **4.** $5!3!$ **720**

5. $\frac{12!}{6!}$ **665,280** **6.** $5(4!)$ **120** **7.** $\frac{10!}{7!3!}$ **120** **8.** $\frac{15!}{10!5!}$ **3003**

9. Automobiles Auto mechanics advise that tires on a car should be rotated every 6000 miles.
  a. In how many ways can four tires be arranged on a car? **24**
  b. If the spare tire is included, how many arrangements are possible? **120**

Example 2
(page 340)

Evaluate each expression.

10. $_8P_1$ **8** **11.** $_8P_2$ **56** **12.** $_8P_3$ **336** **13.** $_8P_4$ **1680**

14. $_3P_2$ **6** **15.** $_5P_4$ **120** **16.** $_9P_6$ **60,480** **17.** $_5P_3$ **60**

18. Fifteen students ask to visit the admissions representative from State University. Each visit includes one student. In how many ways can ten time slots be assigned? **10,897,286,400**

19. How many different nine-player batting orders can be chosen from a baseball squad of 16? **4,151,347,200**

20. The prom committee has four sites available for the banquet and three sites for the dance. How many arrangements are possible for the banquet and dance? **12**

Examples 3 and 4
(page 341)

Evaluate each expression.

21. $_6C_2$ **15** **22.** $_8C_5$ **56** **23.** $_4C_4$ **1** **24.** $_4C_3$ **4**

25. $_7C_3$ **35** **26.** $3(_5C_4)$ **15** **27.** $_6C_2 + _6C_3$ **35** **28.** $\frac{_7C_4}{_9C_4}$ $\frac{5}{18}$

29. Sports How many different teams of 11 players can be chosen from a soccer squad of 16? **4368**

30. Suppose you find seven articles related to the topic of your research paper. In how many ways can you choose five articles to read? **21**

Example 5
(page 341)

31. For a band camp, you can choose two or three roommates from a group of 25 friends. In how many ways can you choose? **2600**

32. A salad bar offers eight choices of toppings for lettuce. In how many ways can you choose four or five toppings? **126**

Ⓑ **Apply Your Skills**

33. true because of the Comm. Prop. of Add.

34. true because of the Assoc. Prop. of Mult.

Assume *a* and *b* are positive integers. Decide whether each statement is *true* or *false*. If it is true, explain why. If it is not true, give a counterexample. **35–38.**
See margin.

33. $a! + b! = b! + a!$ **34.** $a!(b!c!) = (a!b!)c!$ **35.** $(a + b)! = a! + b!$

36. $(ab)! = a!b!$ **37.** $(a!)! = (a!)^2$ **38.** $(a!)^b = a^{(b!)}$

39. Codes A car door lock has a five-button keypad. Each button has two numerals. How many different five-button patterns are possible? (*Hint:* You can use a button more than once.) **3125**

1/2 3/4 5/6 7/8 9/0

The entry code 21914 uses the same button sequence as the code 11023.

36. False; answers may vary.
Sample: $(3 \times 2)! = 720$
and $3! \times 2! = 12$

37. False; answers may vary. Sample: $(3!)! = 720$
and $(3!)^2 = 36$

38. False; answers may vary. Sample: $(3!)^2 = 36$
and $3^{(2!)} = 9$

Real-World Connection

Careers Consumer researchers use formulas to compare and rate products.

46. permutation

47. permutation

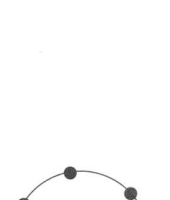

55c. Answers may vary. Sample: Each time you choose 3 of the 8 points to use as vertices of a △, the 5 remaining points could be used to form a pentagon.

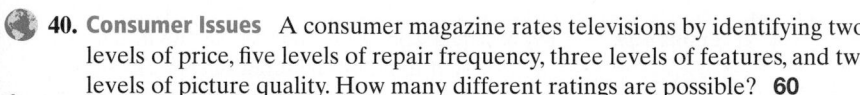

40. Consumer Issues A consumer magazine rates televisions by identifying two levels of price, five levels of repair frequency, three levels of features, and two levels of picture quality. How many different ratings are possible? **60**

41. Writing In how many ways is it possible to arrange the two numbers a and b in an ordered pair? Explain why such a pair is called an *ordered* pair.
2 ways, because order matters

Evaluate each expression.

42. $\dfrac{_{50}C_5}{_{50}C_{10}}$ $\dfrac{4}{19,393} \approx .000206$ **43.** $\dfrac{1}{3}(_{10}C_5)$ **84**   **44.** $\dfrac{_{25}C_2}{_{50}C_2}$ $\dfrac{12}{49}$ **45.** $\dfrac{_6C_2}{3}$ **5**

Indicate whether each situation involves a combination or a permutation.

46. 5 runners crossing the finish line   **47.** 12 books arranged on a shelf

48. 4 books pulled at random from a shelf **combination**

49. 3 flavors of juice selected from a variety pack **combination**

How many combinations of four can you make from each set? 50. 330,791,175

50. 300 people in a club   **51.** $\{0, 1, 2, 3, 4, 5, 6, 7, 8, 9\}$ **210**

52. 25 baseball cards **12,650 53.** a rose, a daisy, a peony, a daffodil, and a tulip **5**

54. Each line in the MODE screen of a graphing calculator shows two or more choices. In how many different ways can you set the mode of this calculator? **9504**

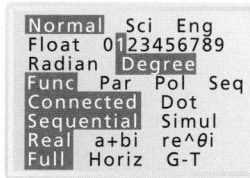

55. a. Geometry Eight points lie on a circle. How many triangles can you make using three of the points as vertices? **56**

    b. How many pentagons can you make using five points as vertices? **56**

    c. Reasoning Explain why your answers to parts (a) and (b) should be the same. **See left.**

How many four-letter permutations can you form from the letters of each word?

56. MODEL **120**   **57.** EQUATIONS **3024**   **58.** LINEAR **360**   **59.** REAL **24**

60. MATRICES **1680**   **61.** FORMULA **840**   **62.** CONJUGATES **5040**   **63.** SUM **0**

Open-Ended Write a problem that can be solved using each technique.
64–67. Check students' work.

64. the Multiplication Counting Principle   **65.** a single factorial

66. the permutation formula   **67.** the combination formula

68. a. Refer to the cartoon below. How many different sets of answers are possible if the test includes eleven true-or-false questions? **2048**

    b. Do you agree with the statement in the last frame? Justify your answer.
Answers may vary. Sample: No, because there are too many possible solutions.

A sheet of blank grids is available in Test-Taking Strategies with Transparencies booklet. Give this sheet to students for practice with filling in the grids.

 **Resources**

For additional practice with a variety of test item formats:
- Standardized Test Prep, p. 357
- Test-Taking Strategies, p. 352
- Test-Taking Strategies with Transparencies

Exercise 77 Be sure you follow the correct order of operations.

pages 342–345   Exercises

69a. The graph for $y = {}_xC_{x-2}$ is identical to the graph for $y = {}_xC_2$ because ${}_2C_{2-2} = {}_2C_2$, ${}_3C_{3-2} = {}_3C_2$, ${}_4C_{4-2} = {}_4C_2$, ${}_5C_{5-2} = {}_5C_2$, etc.

b. Answers may vary. Sample: The function is defined only at discrete whole-number values of x, and not over a smooth range of points as in a continuous function.

81. 3 complex roots
number of real roots: 1 or 3
possible rational roots: $\pm\frac{1}{12}, \pm\frac{1}{6}, \pm\frac{1}{4}, \pm\frac{1}{3}, \pm\frac{1}{2}, \pm\frac{2}{3}, \pm1, \pm2$

83. $-x^3 - 3x^2 + 6$; cubic trinomial

84. $2x^2 - 4x + 8$; quadratic trinomial

85. $5t^2 - 3t$; quadratic binomial

86. $x^4 - 100$; quartic binomial

87. $x^3 - 4x$; cubic binomial

88. $t^4 - 2t^3 + t^2$; quartic trinomial

C Challenge

70c. ${}_7C_3 = \frac{7!}{3!\,4!}$, so ${}_7C_3 \cdot 3! = \frac{7!}{4!}$, which is the permutation formula for ${}_7P_3$.

71a. All the terms contain the factors 2 and 5. Since multiplication is commutative, $2 \times 5 = 10$ and 10 times any integer ends in zero.

69. a. The graph at the right shows the function $y = {}_xC_2$. Use it to graph the function $y = {}_xC_{x-2}$.
b. Critical Thinking Explain why the graph consists of discrete points rather than a continuous curve.
a–b. See margin.

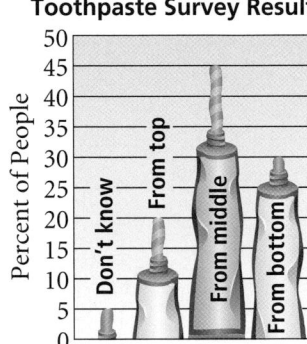

70. a. In how many ways can you choose three flags from a collection of seven different flags? **35**
b. Once you choose three flags, in how many different orders can you arrange them? **6**
c. Writing You want to arrange three flags from a group of seven. Explain how you can use ${}_7C_3 \cdot 3!$ to create the permutation formula. **See left.**

71. In the sequence $1!, 2!, 3!, 4!, 5!, 6!, \ldots$, the first term that ends with a zero is $5!$.
a. Explain why $5!$ and all the terms following $5!$ end with a zero. **See left.**
b. Find the number of zeros with which $100!$ ends. **24 zeros**

72. Find a number n for which entering $n!$ in your calculator causes overflow error. **Answers may vary. Sample: 99**

73. Data Analysis The bar graph at the right shows the results of 40 responses to a survey.
a. How many people said they squeeze the toothpaste from the middle of the tube? **18 people**
b. Use your answer to part (a). Find the number of possible combinations of five people who squeeze toothpaste from the middle of the tube. **8568**
c. Suppose five people are chosen at random from all the people who responded to the survey. How many combinations of five people are possible? **658,008**
d. Probability What is the probability that the five people selected at random all squeeze toothpaste from the middle of the tube? **0.013 or 1.3%**

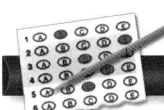

Toothpaste Survey Results

Squeezing Preference

Gridded Response

 Take It to the NET
Online lesson quiz at
www.PHSchool.com
Web Code: agk-0607

74. Find the value of $7!$. **5040**

75. What is the value of $\frac{5!}{8!}$? Write your answer as a fraction in simplest terms. $\frac{1}{336}$

76. What is the value of ${}_7C_2$? **21**

77. Find the value of $(3 + 2)! - (4 - 2)!$. **118**

78. How many ways are there to select 25 books from a collection of 27 books? **351**

79. What is the value of the sum $\frac{2!}{3!} + \frac{3!}{4!} + \frac{4!}{5!}$? Express your answer as a fraction in simplest terms. $\frac{47}{60}$

80. A box has 10 items, and you select 3 of them. What is the value of $P - C$, if P represents the number of permutations possible when selecting 3 of the items, and C is the number of combinations possible when selecting 3 of the items? **600**

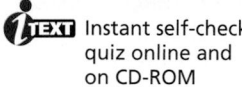

Chapter Checkpoint 2

To check understanding of Lessons 6-4 to 6-7:

Checkpoint Quiz 2 (p. 345)

📁 **Teaching Resources**
Checkpoint Quiz 2 (also in Prentice Hall Assessment System)

👥 **Reaching All Students**
Reading and Math Literacy 6C

Spanish versions available

Lesson 6-6

81. For the equation $12x^3 - 17x^2 + 3x + 2 = 0$, find the number of complex roots, the possible number of real roots, and the possible rational roots. **See margin p. 344.**

82. Find all the zeros of the function $f(x) = x^3 - 2x^2 + 6x - 12$. **2, $\pm i\sqrt{6}$**

Lesson 6-1

Write each polynomial in standard form. Then classify it by degree and by number of terms. **83–88. See margin p. 344.**

83. $-3x^2 + 6 - x^3$　　**84.** $2(x - 1)^2 + 6$　　**85.** $t^2 - 3t + 4t^2$

86. $-100 + x^4$　　　**87.** $x(x + 2)(x - 2)$　　**88.** $(t^2 - t)^2$

Lesson 5-4

Factor each expression completely.

89. $4x^2 - 8x + 4$　　**90.** $-x^2 - 6x - 9$　　**91.** $3x^2 - 75$
　　$4(x - 1)^2$　　　　$-(x + 3)^2$　　　$3(x - 5)(x + 5)$

Lesson 5-2

Determine whether the function has a maximum or minimum value. Then find the value.

92. $y = x^2 + 4x - 8$　　**93.** $y = -2x^2 + 5x + 1$　　**94.** $y = 4x^2 - 7$
　　minimum; −12　　　**maximum; 4.125**　　　**minimum; −7**

✓ **Checkpoint Quiz 2**　　　　　　　　　　**Lessons 6-4 through 6-7**

📱**TEXT** Instant self-check quiz online and on CD-ROM

Solve each equation.

1. $x^3 - 2x^2 = 5x - 6$　　**2.** $27x^3 - 1 = 0$　　**3.** $x^4 - 4x^2 - 45 = 0$
　　1, 3, −2　　　　　$\frac{1}{3}, \frac{-1 \pm i\sqrt{3}}{6}$　　　**$\pm 3, \pm i\sqrt{5}$**

Use the Rational Root Theorem to find all the roots of each equation.

4. $2x^3 + x^2 + x - 1 = 0$　$\frac{1}{2}, \frac{-1 \pm i\sqrt{3}}{2}$　　**5.** $3x^3 + 4x^2 - 12x - 16 = 0$
　　　　　　　　　　　　　　　　　　　$-2, 2, -\frac{4}{3}$

6. Two roots of a polynomial equation with real coefficients are $3 - 5i$ and $\sqrt{2}$.
　a. Find two additional roots. **$3 + 5i, -\sqrt{2}$**
　b. Describe the degree of the polynomial. **Degree must be ≥ 4.**

7. How many roots does a fifth-degree polynomial equation have? Explain.
　5; by the corollary to the Fundamental Theorem of Algebra

8. Evaluate each expression.
　a. $_4P_3 + {_6P_5}$ **744**　　　　　　**b.** $_4C_3 + {_6C_5}$ **10**

🌐 **9. Food Preparation** The students at a culinary arts school are learning to prepare seven different items. In how many ways can you choose each number of items?
　a. two items **21**　　**b.** three items **35**　　**c.** four items **35**　　**d.** five items **21**

🌐 **10. Advertising** Use the ad and the telephone keypad shown below. Find the last seven digits of this phone number. How many seven-number arrangements can be made with these digits? **5040**

Call 1-555-DIAL VSW
for information on
Video Sales Worldwide.

Pascal's Triangle

Students use a geometric pattern to develop Pascal's Triangle. Pascal's Triangle is used in Lesson 6-8 to expand binomials being raised to a power.

Resources

Grid paper, markers or colored pencils

Teaching Notes

The numbers at the middle of the triangle quickly become too large to conveniently count the number of paths on the grid. Students may become frustrated as the number of paths increases and the paths become more complex. Help students see that the total number of paths to a given corner in the grid is the sum of the number of paths to the corner directly above the given corner and the corner to the left of the given corner.

Error Prevention

Students may miscount the number of ways to move to different points because they fail to move right first and then down. Students may not realize that they can move right on the top line of the grid. Demonstrate on the board the different number of ways to reach points B3 and D2 from point A_1 to help students count properly.

Suppose you are standing at the corner of the grid shown below (point A1). You are allowed to travel down or to the right only.

The only way you can get to point A2 is by traveling down one unit. You can get to point B1 by traveling to the right one unit. The numbers of ways you can get to points A2, B1, and B2 are written next to these points.

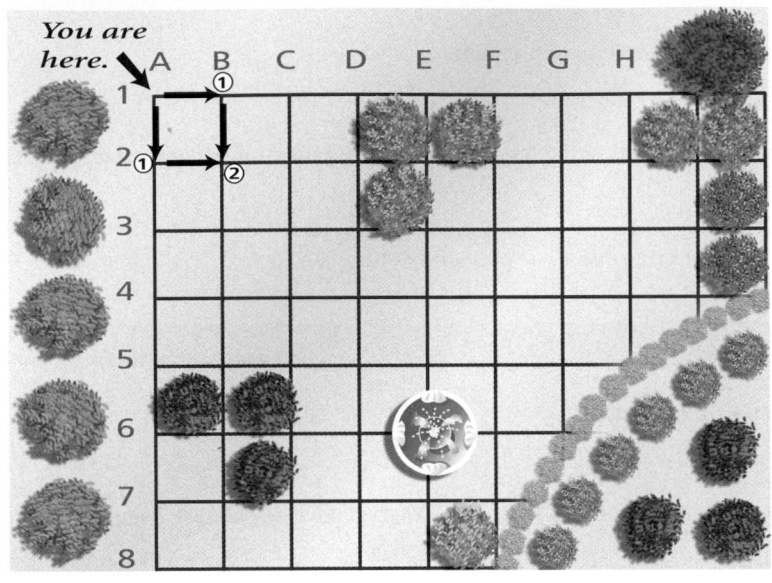

6. Answers may vary. Sample: The outer edges are all ones. Row 2 and Column B are consecutive positive integers. The number of paths counted at any point equals the sum of the paths counted at the points one unit above and one unit to the left.

1. The number 2 is written next to point B2. What are the two different ways you can get from point A1 to point B2? **From A1 to A2 to B2 or from A1 to B1 to B2**

2. Copy the grid. Travel only down or to the right. In how many ways can you get from point A1 to point A3? **1**

3. Use your copy of the grid from Exercise 2. In how many ways can you get from point A1 to point C2? **3**

4. In how many ways can you get to the fountain at point E6 from your starting point at A1? **126**

5. Mark the number of ways you can get to each point from point A1. **See back of book.**

6. **Reasoning** Describe any patterns you see in the numbers on the grid. **See above.**

7. **a.** Make a copy of your completed grid. Color the numbers that are multiples of 2. (You may need to extend the grid to see a pattern.) **a–b. See back of book.**
   b. The pattern you see in part (a) is called the Sierpinski triangle. Find another way to describe how to obtain this pattern.

 8. **Writing** The completed grid is called Pascal's Triangle. Turn your copy of the grid so that point A1 is at the top. Explain why the grid is called a triangle.
   Answers may vary. Sample: The numbers in the grid form a triangular shape.

The Binomial Theorem

North Carolina Objectives

1.03 Operate with algebraic expressions (polynomial, rational, complex fractions) to solve problems.

Lesson Preview

What You'll Learn

OBJECTIVE 1 To use Pascal's Triangle

OBJECTIVE 2 To use the Binomial Theorem

... And Why

To find probabilities associated with basketball, as in Example 4

✓ Check Skills You'll Need

(For help, go to Lessons 5-1 and 6-7.)

Multiply.

1. $(x + 2)^2$ 2. $(2x + 3)^2$ 3. $(x - 3)^3$ 4. $(a + b)^4$
   $x^2 + 4x + 4$ $4x^2 + 12x + 9$ $x^3 - 9x^2 + 27x - 27$

Evaluate.

5. $_5C_0$ **1**   6. $_5C_1$ **5**   7. $_5C_2$ **10**   8. $_5C_3$ **10**   9. $_5C_4$ **5**

New Vocabulary • expand • Pascal's Triangle • Binomial Theorem

4. $a^4 + 4a^3b + 6a^2b^2 + 4ab^3 + b^4$

 Interactive lesson includes instant self-check, tutorials, and activities.

OBJECTIVE

1 Binomial Expansion and Pascal's Triangle

You have learned to multiply binomials using the FOIL method and the Distributive Property. If you are raising a *single* binomial to a power, you have another option for finding the product.

Consider the expansion of several binomials. To **expand** a binomial being raised to a power, first multiply; then write the result as a polynomial in standard form.

$$(a + b)^2 = (a + b)(a + b) = a^2 + 2ab + b^2$$

$$(a + b)^3 = (a + b)(a + b)(a + b) = a^3 + 3a^2b + 3ab^2 + b^3$$

In the first case, the coefficients of the product are 1, 2, 1. In the second case, they are 1, 3, 3, 1. Notice that each set of coefficients matches a row of **Pascal's Triangle** below. Pascal's Triangle is a triangular array of numbers formed by first lining the border with 1's, and then placing the sum of two adjacent numbers within a row between and underneath the two original numbers.

Coefficients of an Expansion (Pasca 's Triang e)

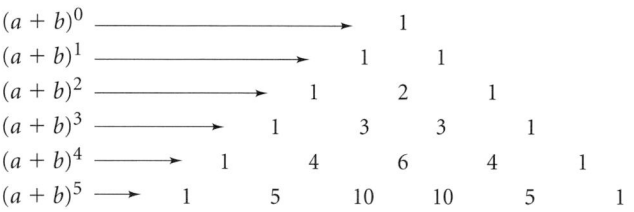

$(a + b)^0$ ⟶ 1
$(a + b)^1$ ⟶ 1   1
$(a + b)^2$ ⟶ 1   2   1
$(a + b)^3$ ⟶ 1   3   3   1
$(a + b)^4$ ⟶ 1   4   6   4   1
$(a + b)^5$ ⟶ 1   5   10   10   5   1

The earliest known version of Pascal's Triangle was developed between 300 and 200 B.C. by the Indian mathematician Halayudha. Although other cultures were aware of the triangle, it has been named for Blaise Pascal (1623–1662), a French mathematician.

Each row of Pascal's Triangle contains coefficients for the expansion of $(a + b)^n$. For example, when $n = 6$, you can find the coefficients for the expansion of $(a + b)^6$ in the row that begins $1, 6, 15, \ldots$

Real-World Connection

In addition to his famous triangle, Pascal made many contributions to math, physics, and philosophy. In 1642 he built the first mechanical digital calculating machine.

Ongoing Assessment and Intervention

Before the Lesson
Diagnose prerequisite skills using:
• Check Skills You'll Need

During the Lesson
Monitor progress using:
• Check Understanding
• Additional Examples
• Standardized Test Prep

After the Lesson
Assess knowledge using:
• Lesson Quiz
• Computer Test Generator CD

---

1. Plan

Lesson Preview

✓ Check Skills You'll Need

Permutations and Combinations
Lesson 6-7: Example 3
Practice Exercises 21–28
Extra Practice, p. 827

Lesson Resources

📁 **Teaching Resources**
Practice, Reteaching, Enrichment

👥 **Reaching All Students**
Practice Workbook 6-8
Spanish Practice Workbook 6-8

⏱ **Presentation Assistant Plus!**
Transparencies
• Check Skills You'll Need 6-8
• Additional Examples 6-8
• Student Edition Answers 6-8
• Lesson Quiz 6-8
PH Presentation Pro CD 6-8

PRENTICE HALL ASSESSMENT SYSTEM

Computer Test Generator CD

Technology
Resource Pro® CD-ROM
Computer Test Generator CD
Prentice Hall Presentation Pro CD

💻 **www.PHSchool.com**
Student Site
• Teacher Web Code: agk-5500
• Self-grading Lesson Quiz
Teacher Center
• Lesson Planner
• Resources

Plus

Professional Development

Math Background

The expansion of $(a + b)^n$ is given by adding together multiples of all possible terms of the form $a^{n-k}b^k$, for any integer k where $0 \le k \le n$. The coefficient of each term is given by $_nC_k$. This is also the number of ways of getting a term of the form $a^{n-k}b^k$.

OBJECTIVE
1 Teaching Notes

1 EXAMPLE Teaching Tip

Point out the symmetry in the string of coefficients. When the exponents of a and b are interchanged, the coefficients remain the same.

Additional Examples

1 Use Pascal's Triangle to expand $(a + b)^5$. $a^5 + 5a^4b + 10a^3b^2 + 10a^2b^3 + 5ab^4 + b^5$

2 Use Pascal's Triangle to expand $(x - 3)^4$.
$x^4 - 12x^3 + 54x^2 - 108x + 81$

OBJECTIVE
2 Teaching Notes

3 EXAMPLE Technology Tip

To calculate the coefficients quickly without referring to Pascal's Triangle, enter Y1= 4 nCr X on the Y= list. Press [2nd] [TBLSET], use TblStart = 0 and △Tbl = 1. Then press [2nd] [TABLE].

Additional Examples

3 Use the Binomial Theorem to expand $(x - y)^9$. $x^9 - 9x^8y + 36x^7y^2 - 84x^6y^3 + 126x^5y^4 - 126x^4y^5 + 84x^3y^6 - 36x^2y^7 + 9xy^8 - y^9$

4 Refer to Example 4. Find the probability that Dawn Staley makes exactly 7 out of 12 consecutive free throws. about 0.38%

Closure

Ask: *What is the coefficient of* $a^{n-k}b^k$ *in the binomial expansion of* $(a + b)^n$? $_nC_k$

Pascal's Triangle

```
                1
              1   1
            1   2   1
          1   3   3   1
        1   4   6   4   1
      1   5  10  10   5   1
    1   6  15  20  15   6   1
  1   7  21  35  35  21   7   1
1   8  28  56  70  56  28   8   1
```

1 EXAMPLE **Using Pascal's Triangle**

Use Pascal's Triangle to expand $(a + b)^6$.

Use the row that has 6 as its second number.

The exponents for a begin with 6 and decrease.
$$1a^6b^0 + 6a^5b^1 + 15a^4b^2 + 20a^3b^3 + 15a^2b^4 + 6a^1b^5 + 1a^0b^6$$
The exponents for b begin with 0 and increase.

In simplest form, the expansion is
$a^6 + 6a^5b + 15a^4b^2 + 20a^3b^3 + 15a^2b^4 + 6ab^5 + b^6$.

✓ **Check Understanding** **1** Use Pascal's Triangle to expand $(a + b)^8$.

$a^8 + 8a^7b + 28a^6b^2 + 56a^5b^3 + 70a^4b^4 + 56a^3b^5 + 28a^2b^6 + 8ab^7 + b^8$

Sometimes the terms of the binomial have coefficients other than 1. You can still base the expansion to standard form on the pattern for $(a + b)^n$.

2 EXAMPLE **Expanding a Binomial**

Use Pascal's Triangle to expand $(x - 2)^3$.

First write the pattern for raising a binomial to the third power.

$$\begin{array}{cccc} 1 & 3 & 3 & 1 \end{array} \quad \text{coefficients from Pascal's Triangle}$$
$$(a + b)^3 = a^3 + 3a^2b + 3ab^2 + b^3$$

Since $(x - 2)^3 = (x + (-2))^3$, substitute x for a and -2 for b.

$$(x + (-2))^3 = x^3 + 3x^2(-2) + 3x(-2)^2 + (-2)^3$$
$$= x^3 - 6x^2 + 12x - 8$$

The expansion of $(x - 2)^3$ is $x^3 - 6x^2 + 12x - 8$.

✓ **Check Understanding** **2** Use Pascal's Triangle to expand $(x - 2)^4$. $x^4 - 8x^3 + 24x^2 - 32x + 16$

OBJECTIVE
2 **The Binomial Theorem**

You can also use combinations to help find the terms of a binomial expansion. For example, if you evaluate the combinations $_4C_0, _4C_1, _4C_2, _4C_3,$ and $_4C_4$, you can see a pattern. The results, 1, 4, 6, 4, and 1 match the row of Pascal's Triangle that you would use to expand $(a + b)^4$. You can use the **Binomial Theorem** as a general formula for expanding a binomial.

Key Concepts

Theorem	Binomial Theorem
For every positive integer n, $(a + b)^n =$ $_nC_0a^n + {}_nC_1a^{n-1}b + {}_nC_2a^{n-2}b^2 + \ldots + {}_nC_{n-1}ab^{n-1} + {}_nC_nb^n$	

Notice that the sequence of exponents decreases for a while it increases for b.

👥 Reaching All Students

| **Below Level** Combination notation is not essential to the Binomial Theorem. Have students check that the fifth row of Pascal's Triangle corresponds to $_5C_0$, $_5C_1$, and so on. | **Advanced Learners** Have students use the binomial theorem to write the seventh entry in the tenth row of Pascal's triangle. | **Tactile Learners** See note on page 352. **Error Prevention** See note on page 349. |

Graphing Calculator Hint

To evaluate a combination, use the **MATH** feature, the PRB menu, and the $_nC_r$ option.

---

3 EXAMPLE Using the Binomial Theorem

Use the Binomial Theorem to expand $(g + h)^4$.

Write the pattern for raising a binomial to the fourth power.
$$(a + b)^4 = {}_4C_0a^4 + {}_4C_1a^3b + {}_4C_2a^2b^2 + {}_4C_3ab^3 + {}_4C_4b^4$$

Substitute g for a and h for b. Evaluate each combination.
$$(g + h)^4 = {}_4C_0g^4 + {}_4C_1g^3h + {}_4C_2g^2h^2 + {}_4C_3gh^3 + {}_4C_4h^4$$
$$= g^4 + 4g^3h + 6g^2h^2 + 4gh^3 + h^4$$

The expansion of $(g + h)^4$ is $g^4 + 4g^3h + 6g^2h^2 + 4gh^3 + h^4$.

✓ **Check Understanding** 3 Use the Binomial Theorem to expand each binomial.

a. $(v + w)^9$ **b.** $(c - 2)^5$ $c^5 - 10c^4 + 40c^3 - 80c^2 + 80c - 32$

3a. $v^9 + 9v^8w + 36v^7w^2$
$+ 84v^6w^3 + 126v^5w^4$
$+ 126v^4w^5 + 84v^3w^6$
$+ 36v^2w^7 + 9vw^8$
$+ w^9$

You can use the Binomial Theorem to solve probability problems. Suppose an event has a probability of success p and a probability of failure q. Each term in the expansion of $(p + q)^n$ represents a probability. For example, $_{10}C_2\,p^8q^2$ represents the probability of eight successes in ten trials.

Real-World Connection

WNBA star Dawn Staley makes about 90% of the free throws she attempts.

4 EXAMPLE Real-World Connection

Sports Refer to the photo. Assume that Dawn's probability of success on any single shot is the same as her cumulative record to date. Find the probability that she will make exactly 6 out of 10 consecutive free throws.

Since you want 6 successes (and 4 failures), use the term containing p^6q^4. This term has the coefficient $_{10}C_4$.

Probability (6 out of 10) $= {}_{10}C_4\,p^6q^4$
$$= \frac{10!}{4! \cdot 6!} \cdot (0.9)^6(0.1)^4 \qquad \text{The probability } p \text{ of success = 90\%, or 0.9.}$$
$$= 0.011160261 \qquad \text{Simplify.}$$

Dawn Staley has about a 1% chance of making exactly 6 out of 10 consecutive free throws.

✓ **Check Understanding** 4 **a.** Find the probability that Dawn Staley will make exactly 9 out of 10 consecutive free throw attempts. **about 0.387**

b. Find the probability that she will make exactly 10 out of 10 attempts. **about 0.349**

EXERCISES

For more practice, see *Extra Practice*.

Practice and Problem Solving

A Practice by Example

Examples 1 and 2 (page 348)

3–6. See back of book. 7–12. See margin.

Use Pascal's Triangle to expand each binomial.

1. $(a + b)^3$ $a^3 + 3a^2b + 3ab^2 + b^3$ **2.** $(x - y)^2$ $x^2 - 2xy + y^2$ **3.** $(a + b)^4$

4. $(x - y)^5$ **5.** $(a - b)^6$ **6.** $(x - y)^7$

7. $(x + y)^8$ **8.** $(d + e)^9$ **9.** $(x - 3)^3$

10. $(a + 3b)^4$ **11.** $(x - 2)^6$ **12.** $(x - 4)^8$

Lesson 6-8 The Binomial Theorem   **349**

---

3. Practice

Assignment Guide

1 Objective
- **Ⓐ Ⓑ Core** 1–12, 23–42, 59
- **Ⓒ Extension** 65–66

2 Objective
- **Ⓐ Ⓑ Core** 13–22, 43–58, 60–64
- **Ⓒ Extension** 67–68

Standardized Test Prep 69–74

Mixed Review 75–85

Error Prevention

Exercises 2–12 Suggest students make sure each binomial is written in the form $(a + b)$ before using Pascal's Triangle to write the expansion.

---

pages 349–351   Exercises

7. $x^8 + 8x^7y + 28x^6y^2$
$+ 56x^5y^3 + 70x^4y^4$
$+ 56x^3y^5 + 28x^2y^6$
$+ 8xy^7 + y^8$

8. $d^9 + 9d^8e + 36d^7e^2$
$+ 84d^6e^3 + 126d^5e^4$
$+ 126d^4e^5 + 84d^3e^6$
$+ 36d^2e^7 + 9de^8 + e^9$

9. $x^3 - 9x^2 + 27x - 27$

10. $a^4 + 12a^3b + 54a^2b^2$
$+ 108ab^3 + 81b^4$

11. $x^6 - 12x^5 + 60x^4 - 160x^3$
$+ 240x^2 - 192x + 64$

12. $x^8 - 32x^7 + 448x^6$
$- 3584x^5 + 17,920x^4$
$- 57,344x^3 + 114,688x^2$
$- 131,072x + 65,536$

349

Alternative Assessment

Have students work in groups of three or four. A student names two whole numbers greater than 2 and less than 10. Suppose the numbers are h and k. All students in the group find the coefficient of a^hb^k in the expansion of $(a + b)^{h + k}$. Students check one another's work and correct errors, if any. Another student picks a different pair of whole numbers, and the activity continues as before, until each student has had two turns selecting a pair of whole numbers for the group to use.

pages 349–351   Exercises

13. $x^4 + 4x^3y + 6x^2y^2 + 4xy^3$
    $+ y^4$

14. $w^5 + 5w^4 + 10w^3 + 10w^2$
    $+ 5w + 1$

15. $s^2 - 2st + t^2$

16. $x^6 - 6x^5 + 15x^4 - 20x^3$
    $+ 15x^2 - 6x + 1$

17. $x^4 - 4x^3y + 6x^2y^2 - 4xy^3$
    $+ y^4$

18. $p^7 + 7p^6q + 21p^5q^2$
    $+ 35p^4q^3 + 35p^3q^4$
    $+ 21p^2q^5 + 7pq^6 + q^7$

19. $x^5 - 15x^4 + 90x^3 - 270x^2$
    $+ 405x - 243$

20. $64 - 48x + 12x^2 - x^3$

Example 3
(page 349)

Use the Binomial Theorem to expand each binomial. 13–20. See margin.

13. $(x + y)^4$ 14. $(w + 1)^5$ 15. $(s - t)^2$ 16. $(x - 1)^6$

17. $(x - y)^4$ 18. $(p + q)^7$ 19. $(x - 3)^5$ 20. $(4 - x)^3$

Example 4
(page 349)

21. **Probability** A coin is tossed ten times. The probability of heads on each toss is 0.5. Evaluate each probability.
   a. exactly 5 heads   b. exactly 6 heads   c. exactly 7 heads
       about 25%   **about 21%**   **about 12%**

22. A calculator contains four batteries. With normal use, each battery has a 90% chance of lasting for one year. Find the probability that all four batteries will last a year. **about 66%**

B **Apply Your Skills**

Expand each binomial. 23–42. See margin pp. 350–351.

23. $(x + y)^7$ 24. $(x - 5y)^8$ 25. $(3x - y)^4$ 26. $(x - 4y)^5$

27. $(7 - 2x)^6$ 28. $(2x + 3y)^3$ 29. $(x^2 + y^2)^2$ 30. $(x^2 - 2y)^3$

31. $(x + 1)^6$ 32. $(x - 1)^6$ 33. $(x + 2)^5$ 34. $(x - 2)^5$

35. $(2x + 3y)^4$ 36. $(3x + 5y)^3$ 37. $(2x + 2y)^6$ 38. $(3x + 2y)^4$

39. $(2x + y)^5$ 40. $(3x + y)^7$ 41. $(x + 3y)^6$ 42. $(x + 5y)^3$

43. **Genetics** A family has five children. Assume that the probability of having a boy is 0.5. Write the term in the expansion of $(b + g)^5$ for each outcome described. Then evaluate each probability.
   a. exactly 3 boys   b. exactly 4 boys   c. exactly 4 girls
       about 31%   **about 16%**   **about 16%**

44. In the expansion of $(m + n)^9$, one of the terms contains m^3.
   a. What is the exponent of n in this term? **6**
   b. What is the coefficient of this term? **84**

45. Suppose $_8C_3x^5y^3$ is a term of a binomial expansion. Write the next term. $_8C_4x^4y^4$

46. The term $126c^4d^5$ appears in the expansion of $(c + d)^n$. Find n. **9**

47. The coefficient of the second term in the expansion of $(r + s)^n$ is 7. Find the value of n, and write the complete term. **7, $7r^6s$**

Find the specified term of each binomial expansion.

48. Third term of $(x + 3)^{12}$ $594x^{10}$ 49. Fourth term of $(x + 2)^5$ $80x^2$

50. Second term of $(x + 3)^9$ $27x^8$ 51. Third term of $(x - 2)^{12}$ $264x^{10}$

52. Twelfth term of $(2 + x)^{11}$ x^{11} 53. Seventh term of $(x - 2y)^6$ $64y^6$

54. Eighth term of $(x - 2y)^{15}$ 55. Third term of $(3x - 2)^9$

56. Seventh term of $(x^2 - 2y)^{11}$ 57. Eighth term of $(x^2 + y^2)^{13}$

54. $-823,680x^8y^7$

55. $314,928x^7$

56. $29,568x^{10}y^6$

57. $1716x^{12}y^{14}$

✏️ 58. **Writing** Explain why the terms of $(a - 4)^6$ have alternating positive and negative signs. **See margin p. 351.**

📦 59. **Geometry** A cube has sides of length s. Suppose each of the dimensions of the cube is increased by 0.5.
   a. Write a binomial expression for the volume of the new cube. **$(s + 0.5)^3$**
   b. Expand the binomial. **$s^3 + 1.5s^2 + 0.75s + 0.125$**

60. The exponent of q should be 5 because the exponent of q should be the degree (7) minus the exponent of p.

60. **Error Analysis** A student claims that $_7C_5p^2q^4$ is a term in a binomial expansion. Explain the student's error.

350   Chapter 6   Polynomials and Polynomial Functions

23. $x^7 + 7x^6y + 21x^5y^2$
    $+ 35x^4y^3 + 35x^3y^4$
    $+ 21x^2y^5 + 7xy^6 + y^7$

24. $x^8 - 40x^7y + 700x^6y^2$
    $- 7000x^5y^3 + 43,750x^4y^4$
    $- 175,000x^3y^5 + 437,500x^2y^6$
    $- 625,000xy^7 + 390,625y^8$

25. $81x^4 - 108x^3y + 54x^2y^2$
    $- 12xy^3 + y^4$

26. $x^5 - 20x^4y + 160x^3y^2$
    $- 640x^2y^3 + 1280xy^4$
    $- 1024y^5$

State the number of terms in each expansion and give the first two terms.

61. $(d + e)^{12}$ **62.** $(x - y)^{15}$ **63.** $(2a + b)^5$ **64.** $(x - 3y)^7$

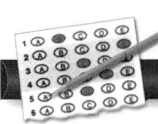 **Challenge**

61. 13, d^{12}, $12d^{11}e$

62. 16, x^{15}, $-15x^{14}y$

63. 6, $32a^5$, $80a^4b$

64. 8, x^7, $-21x^6y$

65. a. Expand $(1 + i)^4$.   **−4**
    b. Verify that $1 - i$ is a fourth root of -4 by repeating the process in part (a)
    for $(1 - i)^4$. $(1 - i)^4 = 1 - 4i - 6 + 4i + 1 = -4$ ✓
                                           See margin.

66. Verify that $-1 + \sqrt{3}i$ is a cube root of 8 by expanding $(-1 + \sqrt{3}i)^3$.

67. Open-Ended Write a probability problem for which $_5C_3(0.5)^2(0.5)^3$ is
the solution. **See back of book.**

68. a. Show that $(k + 1)! = (k + 1) \cdot k!$.   **a–c. See back of book.**
    b. Show that $_nC_k + {_nC_{k+1}} = {_{n+1}C_{k+1}}$.
    c. Suppose $n = 4$ and $k = 2$. What entries in Pascal's Triangle are represented
    by $_nC_k$, $_nC_{k+1}$, and $_{n+1}C_{k+1}$? Verify that the equation in part (b) is true
    for these entries.

Standardized Test Prep

Multiple Choice

69. What is the expanded form of $(a - b)^3$?   **D**
  A. $a^3 + a^2b + ab^2 + b^3$ **B.** $a^3 + 3a^2b + 3ab^2 + b^3$
  C. $a^3 - a^2b + ab^2 - b^3$ **D.** $a^3 - 3a^2b + 3ab^2 - b^3$

70. What is the third term in the expansion of $(a - b)^7$?   **I**
  F. $-21a^5b^2$ **G.** $-7a^6b$ **H.** $7a^6b$ **I.** $21a^5b^2$

Take It to the NET
Online lesson quiz at
www.PHSchool.com
Web Code: agk-0608

71. What is the coefficient of the third term in the expansion of $(2a - b)^5$?   **D**
  A. -80 **B.** 32   **C.** 40   **D.** 80

72. Which term in the expansion of $(2a - 3b)^6$ has coefficient 2160?   **G**
  F. second term   **G.** third term
  H. fourth term   **I.** fifth term

Short Response

73. One term of a binomial expansion is $_7C_2x^5y^2$. What is the term just before
that term? **See back of book.**

Extended Response

74. Explain how you can use the Binomial Theorem to find the sixth term in
the expansion of $(2x - 3y)^7$. **See back of book.**

Mixed Review

Lesson 6-7   **Simplify each expression.**

75. $_5P_2$ **20**   **76.** $4!$ **24**   **77.** $_7C_3$ **35**

78. $11!$ **39,916,800**   **79.** $\dfrac{7!}{3!(7 - 3)!}$ **35**   **80.** $_5C_2 + {_5C_3}$ **20**

Lesson 6-2   **Find the relative maximum, relative minimum, and zeros of each function.**

81. $f(x) = x^3 - 2x^2 - 11x + 12$ **82.** $f(x) = -x^3 - x^2 + 25x + 25$
     20.75; −12.60; −3, 1, 4   **65.67; −32.49; −5, −1, 5**

Lesson 5-3   **Write each function in vertex form.**

83. $y = x^2 - 6x + 2$ **84.** $y = x^2 + 7x - 1$ **85.** $y = -4x^2 + 9$
     $y = (x - 3)^2 - 7$ $y = (x + 3.5)^2 - 13.25$ $y = -4(x - 0)^2 + 9$

Lesson 6-8   The Binomial Theorem   **351**

27. $117,649 - 201,684x$
$+ 144,060x^2 - 54,880x^3$
$+ 11,760x^4 - 1344x^5 + 64x^6$

28. $8x^3 + 36x^2y + 54xy^2 + 27y^3$

29. $x^4 + 2x^2y^2 + y^4$

30. $x^6 - 6x^4y + 12x^2y^2 - 8y^3$

31. $x^6 + 6x^5 + 15x^4 + 20x^3$
$+ 15x^2 + 6x + 1$

32. $x^6 - 6x^5 + 15x^4 - 20x^3$
$+ 15x^2 - 6x + 1$

33. $x^5 + 10x^4 + 40x^3 + 80x^2$
$+ 80x + 32$

34. $x^5 - 10x^4 + 40x^3$
$- 80x^2 + 80x - 32$

Standardized Test Prep

📁 **Resources**

For additional practice with a
variety of test item formats:
- Standardized Test Prep, p. 357
- Test-Taking Strategies, p. 352
- Test-Taking Strategies with
  Transparencies

Teaching Tip

Exercise 70 Point out that b has
an even exponent in the third
term and the term will be
positive.

35. $16x^4 + 96x^3y + 216x^2y^2$
$+ 216xy^3 + 81y^4$

36. $27x^3 + 135x^2y + 225xy^2$
$+ 125y^3$

37. $64x^6 + 384x^5y + 960x^4y^2$
$+ 1280x^3y^3 + 960x^2y^4$
$+ 384xy^5 + 64y^6$

38. $81x^4 + 216x^3y + 216x^2y^2$
$+ 96xy^3 + 16y^4$

39. $32x^5 + 80x^4y + 80x^3y^2 +$
$40x^2y^3 + 10xy^4 + y^5$

40. $2187x^7 + 5103x^6y$
$+ 5103x^5y^2 + 2835x^4y^3$
$+ 945x^3y^4 + 189x^2y^5$
$+ 21xy^6 + y^7$

41. $x^6 + 18x^5y + 135x^4y^2$
$+ 540x^3y^3 + 1215x^2y^4$
$+ 1458xy^5 + 729y^6$

42. $x^3 + 15x^2y + 75xy^2$
$+ 125y^3$

58. **Answers may vary.**
Sample: Since one of the
terms is negative and it is
alternately raised to odd
and even powers, the
term is negative when
raised to an odd power
and positive when raised
to an even power.

66. $(-1 + \sqrt{3} \cdot i)^3 = -1$
$+ 3i\sqrt{3} + 9 - 3i\sqrt{3} =$
8 ✓

Drawing a Diagram

This feature demonstrates to students how drawing a diagram can help them solve problems that would otherwise be very complex.

Resources

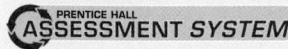

Test-Taking Strategies with Transparencies
- Transparency 6
- Practice sheet p. 30

Teaching Notes

1 EXAMPLE

Students may be tempted to use the INTERSECT function of the graphing calculator to find the real solution to this problem. They only need to know the *number* of real and complex solutions.

Tactile Learners

Suggest students use manipulatives as an alternative to drawing diagrams for Example 2. Students could use one color of beads to represent the people, and a second color of bead to indicate whether the person is president or vice-president.

Test-Taking Strategies with Transparencies

Test-Taking Strategy: Drawing a Diagram

If a test problem does not already have a diagram, you can draw one.

$A(-1, 3)$, $B(3, 3)$, $C(3, -2)$, and $D(-1, -2)$ are the vertices of rectangle $ABCD$. What is the area of this rectangle?

It is difficult to compute the side lengths of this rectangle because some of the coordinates are negative. Draw a diagram of rectangle $ABCD$ on a coordinate grid to find the side lengths.

With the diagram, it is easy to see that the width of the rectangle is 5 and the length is 4. Since $A = \ell w$, the area is 5×4 or 20 square units.

Practice drawing diagrams to solve these problems.

1. $Q(-2, -3)$, $R(1, 1)$, and $S(3, -3)$ are the vertices of triangle QRS. What is the area of this triangle?

2. If $X(-2, -3)$ is the center of a circle that has a radius of 3, which of these points lies on the circle?

   A. (1, 0)   B. (0, 1)   C. (-1, 4)   D. (-8, 1)

Solutions

1. 10 square units

2. B

Transparency 6

352

A picture or a graph can help you solve a problem. If a test problem does not already have a diagram, you can draw one.

1 EXAMPLE

How many real and how many imaginary solutions does the equation $x^5 = x + 5$ have?

The question asks for the number of solutions, not the solutions themselves. Graph $y_1 = x^5$ and $y_2 = x + 5$. There is just one point of intersection. So the equation has just one real solution. Since the related function $y = x^5 - x - 5$ is a fifth-degree function with five zeros, the other four solutions must be imaginary.

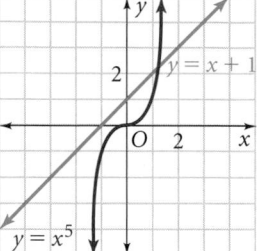

● The equation $x^5 = x + 5$ has one real and four imaginary solutions.

2 EXAMPLE

In how many ways can the titles president, vice-president, and treasurer be assigned to 5 people?

Method 1   Assign titles to people. Draw 5 spaces to represent the 5 people. Assign president (P) to the first person. Then you can assign vice-president (V) to any of the remaining 4, and treasurer (T) to any of the remaining 3. There are $4 \cdot 3$, or 12, ways to assign the titles V and T, if the first person is president. Since P can be assigned to 5 people, there are $5 \cdot 12$ ways to assign the titles.

$$P(\_\ \_\ \_\ \_)$$
$$P\ V(\_\ \_\ \_)$$
$$P\ V\ T\ \_\ \_$$

The answer is 60 ways.

Method 2   Assign people to titles. Draw 3 spaces to represent the 3 titles. Five people can be assigned to the first title, 4 to the second title, and 3 to the third title. There are $5 \cdot 4 \cdot 3$ ways to assign people to titles.

$$\underline{5}\ \_\ \_$$
$$\underline{5}\ \underline{4}\ \_$$
$$\underline{5}\ \underline{4}\ \underline{3}$$

● Again, the answer is 60 ways.

EXERCISES

Find the number of real solutions.

1. $x + 3 = (x - 5)^2$ **2**

2. $x^4 = x - 10$ **0**

3. $x^3 = 5 - x$ **1**

4. In how many ways can two cars be assigned to six people, if no car can be assigned to more than one person, and no person can be assigned to more than one car? **30 ways**

5. Is it easier to draw a diagram that assigns 3 jobs to 100 people, or to draw a diagram that assigns 100 people to 3 jobs? Explain. **100 people to 3 jobs; it requires that only 3 spaces be drawn, rather than 100.**

Chapter Review

Vocabulary

Binomial Theorem (p. 348)
combination (p. 340)
complex conjugates (p. 332)
conjugates (p. 331)
degree (p. 301)
degree of a polynomial (p. 301)
difference of cubes (p. 322)
expand (p. 347)
Factor Theorem (p. 309)

Fundamental Theorem of Algebra
(p. 335)
Imaginary Root Theorem (p. 332)
Irrational Root Theorem (p. 331)
multiple zero (p. 310)
multiplicity (p. 310)
n factorial (p. 339)
Pascal's Triangle (p. 347)
permutation (p. 339)
polynomial (p. 301)

polynomial function (p. 301)
Rational Root Theorem (p. 329)
relative maximum (p. 309)
relative minimum (p. 309)
Remainder Theorem (p. 317)
standard form of a polynomial (p. 301)
sum of cubes (p. 322)
synthetic division (p. 315)

Reading Math
Understanding
Vocabulary

Take It to the NET
Online vocabulary quiz
at www.PHSchool.com
Web Code: agj-0651

Choose the correct vocabulary word or phrase to complete each sentence.

1. The exponent of the variable in a term determines its ___?___. **degree**

2. The ___?___ has terms written in descending order by degree. **standard form of a polynomial**

3. The number of appearances of a zero of a polynomial function describes the ___?___ of that zero. **multiplicity**

4. The numbers $a + bi$ and $a - bi$ are called ___?___. **complex conjugates**

5. Order is not important when counting ___?___. **combinations**

Skills and Concepts

6-1 Objectives

▼ To classify polynomials (p. 300)

▼ To model data using polynomial functions (p. 302)

6. $3p^3 - 2p$; cubic binomial

7. $-5x^9 + 3$; degree 9, binomial

8. $-x^5 - x^3 + x$; quintic trinomial

9. $4x^3 + 2x^2 + 2x$; cubic trinomial

10. $x^7 + x^4 - x^2 + x + 5$; degree 7, 5 terms

A **polynomial** is a monomial or a sum of monomials with whole-number exponents. The exponent of the variable in a term is the **degree** of that term. The **degree of a polynomial** is the largest degree of any term of the polynomial. When the terms of a polynomial are in descending order by degree, the polynomial is in standard form. You can classify a polynomial by the number of terms it contains or by its degree. A **polynomial function** in one variable can be written in the form $P(x) = a_n x^n + a_{n-1} x^{n-1} + \ldots + a_1 x + a_0$, where $n \geq 0$ and the coefficients $a_n, \ldots, a_0$ are complex numbers.

You can use a calculator to find cubic or quartic polynomial functions to model data, just as you have done with linear and quadratic polynomial functions.

Write each polynomial in standard form. Then classify it by degree and by number of terms. **6–10. See left.**

6. $p^3 - 2p + 2p^3$ 7. $3 - 5x^9$ 8. $x - x^3 - x^5$

9. $3x + 2x^2 - x + 4x^3$ 10. $5 + x + x^4 - x^2 + x^7$ **11.** s

s; linear monomial

12. Find both a cubic and a quartic model for the set of values. Graph each model. Compare the two models to determine which is a better fit. **See margin.**

x	1.2	1.4	1.6	1.8	2.0	2.2
y	3.1	−4.2	4.1	7.5	−8.9	10

pages 353–355   Chapter Review

12. cubic: $y = 62.2685x^3 - 303.194x^2 + 481.8148x - 248.522$;
quartic: $y = 984.375x^4 - 6631.481x^3 + 16{,}498.68x^2 - 17{,}954.685x + 7208.88$;

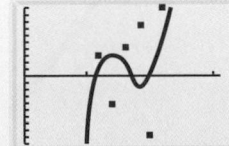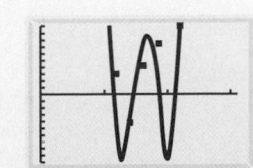

The quartic model better fits the data.

Resources

Student Edition
Extra Practice for Ch. 6, p. 827
English/Spanish Glossary, p. 871
Properties and Formulas, p. 865
Table of Symbols, p. 860

 Reaching All Students
Reading and Math Literacy 6D
Spanish Reading and Math
Literacy 6D

 PRENTICE HALL
ASSESSMENT *SYSTEM*

Standardized Test Prep
• Ch. 6 practice in standardized test formats

 www.PHSchool.com
Student Site
• Self-grading Vocabulary Test
Teacher Center
• Resources

Plus

Spanish Reading and Math Literacy

Reading and Math Literacy

20. $x^2 + 5x + 8$, R 12; check
students' work.

21. $x^3 - x^2 + x - 2$, R 4;
check students' work.

34. $(x - 2)(x^2 + 2x + 4)$; 2,
$-1 \pm i\sqrt{3}$

35. $t^4(2t - 1)(2t + 1)$;
$0, \frac{1}{2}, -\frac{1}{2}$

36. $(2x + 1)(4x^2 - 2x + 1)$;
$-\frac{1}{2}, \frac{1 \pm i\sqrt{3}}{4}$

37. $x(x - 4)(x - 1)$; 0, 1, 4

38. $x(x^2 - 2x - 5)$;
$0, 1 \pm \sqrt{6}$

39. $(x + 2)^2(x^2 - 2x + 4)^2$;
$-2, 1 \pm i\sqrt{3}$

6-2 and 6-3 Objectives

▼ To analyze the factored
form of a polynomial
(p. 307)

▼ To write a polynomial
function from its zeros
(p. 309)

▼ To divide polynomials
using long division
(p. 314)

▼ To divide polynomials
using synthetic division
(p. 315)

13. $f(x) = x(x - 4)(x + 3)$;
$-3, 0, 4$; rel. max. =
12.60, rel. min. =
-20.75

14. $g(x) = (2 - x)(2 + x)$;
$-2, 2$; rel. max. = 4;
no rel. min.

15. $y = x^3(x + 2)^4$; 0 (mult.
3), -2 (mult. 4); rel.
max. = 0, rel. min. =
-1.07

16. $f(x) = x^4 + 3x^3 - 4x^2$
$- 12x$

17. $f(x) = x^3 - 4x^2 + 5x$
$- 2$

18. $f(x) = x^4 + 2x^3 - 3x^2$

19. $f(x) = x^3 + 6x^2 + 12x$
$+ 8$

A polynomial can be factored into linear factors. The **Factor Theorem** states that
the expression $x - a$ is a linear factor of a polynomial if and only if a is a zero of
the related polynomial function. Then a is an x-intercept of the polynomial
function and is a solution of the related polynomial equation.

If the zeros of a polynomial function are known, a polynomial function can be
determined by finding the product of the corresponding linear factors. If $x - a$ is
repeated as a factor k times, then a is a **multiple zero** of the polynomial—a zero of
multiplicity k.

When you consider only neighboring points on a graph, the greatest y-value occurs
at a **relative maximum** and the least y-value occurs at a **relative minimum.**

You can divide a polynomial by one of its factors to find another factor. When you
divide by a linear factor, you can simplify this division by writing only the
coefficients of each term. This process is called **synthetic division.** The **Remainder
Theorem** guarantees that $P(a)$ is the remainder when $P(x)$ is divided by $x - a$.

**Write each polynomial function in factored form. List the zeros of the function,
and their multiplicity. Find any relative maximum or relative minimum values.
Round to the nearest hundredth if necessary.**

13. $f(x) = x^3 - x^2 - 12x$ **14.** $g(x) = 4 - x^2$ **15.** $y = x^3(x + 2)^4$

Write a polynomial function in standard form with the given zeros.

16. $-3, -2, 0, 2$ **17.** $1, 1, 2$ **18.** $-3, 0, 0, 1$ **19.** $-2, -2, -2$

Divide. Use both long division and synthetic division. Show your work.

20. $(x^3 + 3x^2 - 2x - 4) \div (x - 2)$ **21.** $(x^4 - x + 2) \div (x + 1)$
20–21. See margin.

Use synthetic division and the given factor to completely factor each polynomial.

22. $x^3 - 3x^2 - x + 3; x + 1$ **23.** $x^3 - 4x^2 - 3x + 18; x - 3$
$\quad (x + 1)(x - 3)(x - 1)$ $\quad (x - 3)^2(x + 2)$

Use synthetic division and the Remainder Theorem to find $P(a)$.

24. $P(x) = x^4 + x^3 - x^2 - 2x; a = 3$ 93 **25.** $P(x) = 4 - x - x^5; a = 2$ -30

26. $P(x) = 5x^4 - x^2 + 1; a = -2$ 77 **27.** $P(x) = x^3 - 8x^2 + 5x - 7; a = 1$
$\quad -9$

6-4 Objectives

▼ To solve polynomial
equations by graphing
(p. 321)

▼ To solve polynomial
equations by factoring
(p. 322)

28. $-1, 1.38, 3.62$

29. -1.78

30. 0

You can solve polynomial equations by graphing or by factoring. The **sum of cubes**
and the **difference of cubes** have factor formulas. Sometimes you can use the
Quadratic Formula to factor polynomial expressions of higher degree.

Solve each equation by graphing. If necessary, round to the nearest hundredth.

28. $x^3 - 4x^2 + 5 = 0$ **29.** $x - 3 = 4 - x^2 + x^3$ **30.** $x^3 + x = 3x^2 - 3x^3$

31. $x^3 + x + 5 = 0$ **32.** $-5 = 2 - x^2 + x^3$ **33.** $x^3 + 4 = x^3 - 3x^2$
$\quad -1.52$ $\quad -1.63$ $\quad$ no real solution

Factor the expression on the left side of each equation. Then solve each equation.

34. $x^3 - 8 = 0$ **35.** $4t^6 - t^4 = 0$ **36.** $8x^3 + 1 = 0$

37. $x^3 - 5x^2 + 4x = 0$ **38.** $x^3 - 2x^2 - 5x = 0$ **39.** $x^6 + 16x^3 + 64 = 0$
34–39. See margin.

6-5 and 6-6 Objectives

▼ To solve equations using the Rational Root Theorem (p. 329)

▼ To use the Irrational Root Theorem and the Imaginary Root Theorem (p. 331)

▼ To use the Fundamental Theorem of Algebra (p. 335)

▼ To solve polynomial equations with complex zeros (p. 336)

The **Rational Root Theorem** identifies all possible rational roots of a polynomial equation with integer coefficients. A rational root of a polynomial equation is the quotient of a factor of the constant term and a factor of the leading coefficient.

Number pairs of the form $a + \sqrt{b}$ and $a - \sqrt{b}$ are called **conjugates,** while those of the form $a + bi$ and $a - bi$ are called **complex conjugates.** The **Irrational Root Theorem** states that irrational roots of a polynomial equation with rational coefficients occur in conjugate pairs. Similarly, the **Imaginary Root Theorem** states that imaginary roots of a polynomial equation with real coefficients occur in complex conjugate pairs.

The **Fundamental Theorem of Algebra** and its corollary assert that an nth degree polynomial equation, where $n \geq 1$, has exactly n complex roots.

For each equation, state the number of complex roots, the possible number of real roots, and the possible rational roots. Then find all the roots. 40–45. See margin.

40. $x^3 - 6x^2 + 11x - 6 = 0$ **41.** $10x^4 - 13x^3 - 21x^2 + 10x + 8 = 0$

42. $x^4 - 6x^2 + 7 = 0$ **43.** $x^4 + 6x^3 + 13x^2 + 12x + 4 = 0$

44. $x^3 - 3x^2 + x + 5 = 0$ **45.** $x^4 - 2x^3 - 7x^2 + 18x - 18 = 0$

Write a polynomial equation of least possible degree, with integer coefficients, that has the given numbers as roots.

46. $2, i, -i$
$x^3 - 2x^2 + x - 2 = 0$

47. $4 + \sqrt{2}, 4 - \sqrt{3}$
$x^4 - 16x^3 + 91x^2 - 216x + 182 = 0$

48. $3 + i, 2 - i$
$x^4 - 10x^3 + 39x^2 - 70x + 50 = 0$

49. $0, -2i, 3 + \sqrt{2}$
$x^5 - 6x^4 + 11x^3 - 24x^2 + 28x = 0$

50. $1 + 2i, 3 - \sqrt{3}$
$x^4 - 8x^3 + 23x^2 - 42x + 30 = 0$

51. $\sqrt{5}, -\sqrt{7}$
$x^4 - 12x^2 + 35 = 0$

6-7 and 6-8 Objectives

▼ To count permutations (p. 339)

▼ To count combinations (p. 340)

▼ To use Pascal's Triangle (p. 347)

▼ To use the Binomial Theorem (p. 348)

The notation $n!$, read "*n* **factorial,**" means $n(n - 1)(n - 2) \cdot \ldots \cdot 3 \cdot 2 \cdot 1$, and $0! = 1$.

A **permutation** is an arrangement of items in a particular order. You can count permutations using the Multiplication Counting Principle or factorial notation. To compute the number of permutations of n objects chosen r at a time, you can also use the formula $_nP_r = \frac{n!}{(n - r)!}$, for $0 \leq r \leq n$.

A selection in which order does not matter is a **combination.** The number of combinations of n objects chosen r at a time is $_nC_r = \frac{n!}{r!(n - r)!}$, for $0 \leq r \leq n$.

Use the **Binomial Theorem** to **expand** a binomial raised to a power. For $n \geq 0$, $(a + b)^n = {_nC_0}a^n + {_nC_1}a^{n-1}b + {_nC_2}a^{n-2}b^2 + \ldots + {_nC_{n-1}}ab^{n-1} + {_nC_n}b^n$. The coefficients in the expansion of $(a + b)^n$ are found in **Pascal's Triangle.** You can also use the Binomial Theorem to find probabilities when an event has only two possible outcomes.

Evaluate each expression.

52. $3(4!)$ **72**   **53.** $_4P_3$ **24**   **54.** $_7C_4$ **35**   **55.** $_5P_2 + {_5C_3}$ **30**   **56.** $\frac{_6C_3}{_5C_3}$ **2**

57. In how many ways can you arrange 5 different canisters in a row on a shelf? **120**

58. Find the fourth term in the binomial expansion of $(2x + 3y)^6$. **$4320x^3y^3$**

59. A coin is tossed seven times. Find the probability of getting exactly four heads. **about 27%**

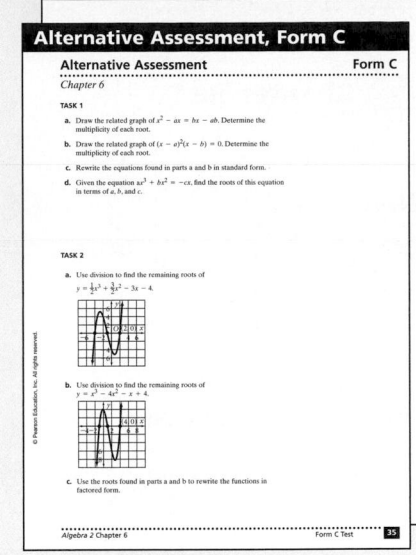

40. 3 complex roots;
number of real roots: 3 or 1;
possible rational roots: $\pm 1, \pm 2, \pm 3, \pm 6$;
roots: 1, 2, 3

41. 4 complex roots;
number of real roots: 4, 2, or 0;
possible rational roots: $\pm 1, \pm 2, \pm 4, \pm 8, \pm \frac{1}{2}, \pm \frac{1}{5}, \pm \frac{2}{5}, \pm \frac{4}{5}, \pm \frac{8}{5}, \pm \frac{1}{10}$;
roots: $-1, -\frac{1}{2}, \frac{4}{5}, 2$

42. 4 complex roots;
number of real roots: 4, 2, or 0;
possible rational roots: $\pm 1, \pm 7$;
roots: $\pm 1.26, \pm 2.10$

43. 4 complex roots;
number of real roots: 4, 2, or 0;
possible rational roots: $\pm 1, \pm 2, \pm 4$;
roots: $-1, -2$

44. 3 complex roots;
number of real roots: 3 or 1;
possible rational roots: $\pm 1, \pm 5$;
roots: $-1, 2 \pm i$

45. 4 complex roots;
number of real roots: 4, 2, or 0;
possible rational roots: $\pm 1, \pm 2, \pm 3, \pm 6, \pm 9, \pm 18$;
roots: $\pm 3, 1 \pm i$

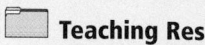

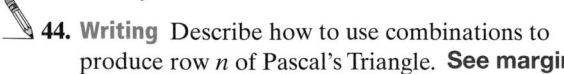
Take It to the NET
Online chapter test at
www.PHSchool.com
Web Code: aga-0652

Resources

 **Teaching Resources**
Ch. 6 Test, Forms A & B
Ch. 6 Alternative Assessment,
Form C

 Reaching All Students
Spanish Ch. 6 Test, Forms A & B
Spanish Ch. 6 Alternative
Assessment, Form C

 PRENTICE HALL
ASSESSMENT SYSTEM

Assessment Masters
- Ch. 6 Test, Forms A & B
- Ch. 6 Alternative Assessment,
  Form C
Computer Test Generator
- Ch. 6 pre-made Test
- Make your own Ch. 6 test

www.PHSchool.com
Student Site
- Self-grading Chapter 6 Test
Teacher Center
- Resources

Plus **iTEXT**

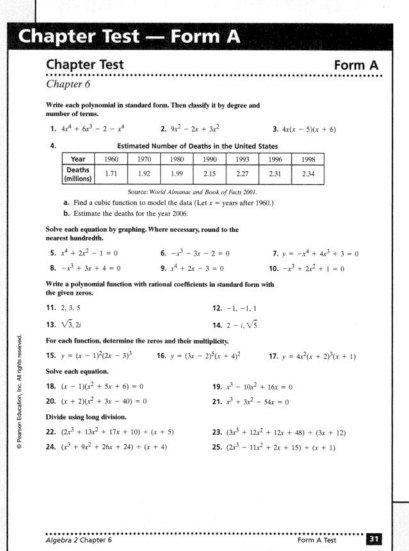

Write each polynomial in standard form. Then classify it by degree and by number of terms. 1–2. See margin.

1. $3x^2 - 7x^4 + 9 - x^4$

2. $11x^2 + \frac{3}{8}x - 3x^2$

3. $2x(x - 3)(x + 2)$ **$2x^3 - 2x^2 - 12x$; cubic trinomial**

4. $(t - 2)(t + 1)(t + 1)$
   $t^3 - 3t - 2$; cubic trinomial

Graph each function. Approximate the real zeros to the nearest hundredth. 5–9. See back of book.

5. $P(x) = -x^3 - x^2 + x$

6. $P(x) = (x + 1)(x + 2)(x^2 + 4x - 5)$

7. $f(x) = x^4 + 3x^3 - 1$

8. $g(x) = -x^6 - x^3 + 2$

9. $f(x) = x^3 - 3x^2 + 2$

Write a polynomial function with rational coefficients in standard form with the given zeros.

10. $x = 1, 2, \frac{3}{5}$ **$y = x^3 - \frac{18}{5}x^2 + \frac{19}{5}x - \frac{6}{5}$**

11. $x = -2, 0, \sqrt{3}$ **$y = x^4 + 2x^3 - 3x^2 - 6x$**

12. $x = -4, -4, -4$ **$y = x^3 + 12x^2 + 48x + 64$**

13. $x = -1, 1, 1$ **$y = x^3 - x^2 - x + 1$**

14. $x = \sqrt{2}, -i$ **$y = x^4 - x^2 - 2$**

15. $x = 3 + i, 1 - \sqrt{5}$
    $y = x^4 - 8x^3 + 18x^2 + 4x - 40$

16. **Open-Ended** Write a polynomial function with real coefficients that has an imaginary zero and an irrational zero. **See margin.**

Solve each equation. $-2, -\frac{2}{3}, \frac{7}{8}, \frac{3}{2}$

17. $(2x - 3)(3x + 2)(x + 2)(x + 2)\left(x - \frac{7}{8}\right) = 0$

18. $(x^2 - 3)(x^2 + 3x - 4) = 0$ **$\pm\sqrt{3}, -4, 1$**

19. $\left(x + \frac{2}{3}\right)(x^2 + 5x + 1) = 0$ **$-\frac{2}{3}, \frac{-5 \pm \sqrt{21}}{2}$**

20. $x^3 - 2x^2 + x = 0$ **0, 1**

21. $x^3 + 3x^2 - 5x - 4 = 0$ **$\frac{1 \pm \sqrt{5}}{2}, -4$**

Divide using long division.

22. $(x^2 + 3x - 4) \div (x - 1)$ **$x + 4$**

23. $(x^3 + 7x^2 - 5x - 6) \div (x + 2)$
    $x^2 + 5x - 15$, R 24

Divide using synthetic division.

24. $(3x^2 - 3x + 4) \div (x + 1)$ **$3x - 6$, R 10**

25. $(x^3 + x^2 + x - 14) \div (x + 2)$ **$x^2 - x + 3$, R −20**

Use synthetic division and the Remainder Theorem to find $P(a)$.

26. $P(x) = 6x^4 + 19x^3 - 2x^2 - 44x - 24; a = \frac{-2}{3}$ **0**

27. $P(x) = -x^3 - x^2 + x; a = 0$ **0**

28. $P(x) = 2x^3 - 2x^2 - 12x; a = 3$ **0**

29. $P(x) = x^4 + 3x^3 - 7x^2 - 9x + 12; a = 3$ **84**

30. $P(x) = x^3 + 3x^2 - 5x - 4; a = -1$ **3**

Evaluate each expression.   35. 19,958,400

31. $6!$ **720**   32. $\frac{6!}{4!2!}$ **15**

33. $_7C_3$ **35**   34. $_5P_2$ **20**

35. $_{11}P_9$ 36. $_9C_8$ **9**

37. $2(_5C_4) - {_3C_2}$ **7**

Indicate whether each situation involves a combination or a permutation. Then solve.

38. How many ways are there to select five actors from a troupe of nine to improvise a scene?
    combination, 126

39. How many different three-student study groups can be formed from a class of 15? **combination, 455**

40. You are looking for a new apartment. There are five apartments available. In how many ways can you inspect the apartments? **permutation, 120**

Use the Binomial Theorem to expand each binomial.

41. $(x + z)^5$ **See margin.**   42. $(1 - 2t)^2$
    $1 - 4t + 4t^2$

43. A weighted coin has $P(\text{heads}) = \frac{2}{5}$. The coin is tossed seven times. Find the probability of getting exactly six heads. **1.7%**

44. **Writing** Describe how to use combinations to produce row n of Pascal's Triangle. **See margin.**

45. **Geometry** The volume V of a prism is modeled by $V = 2\ell^3 - 2\ell$, where ℓ is the length of the prism. The width of the prism equals $\ell - 1$. Find the height of the prism. **$2\ell + 2$**

---

page 356   Chapter Test

1. $-8x^4 + 3x^2 + 9$; quartic trinomial

2. $8x^2 + \frac{3}{8}x$; quadratic binomial

16. Answers may vary.
    Sample: Using $\pm i$ and $\pm\sqrt{2}, y = x^4 - x^2 - 2$.

41. $x^5 + 5x^4z + 10x^3z^2 + 10x^2z^3 + 5xz^4 + z^5$

44. Combinations can be used by starting with $_nC_0$ for the first term. Then the second term would be $_nC_1$, the third $_nC_2$,

and so forth until you reach $_nC_{n-1}$, and finally $_nC_n$.

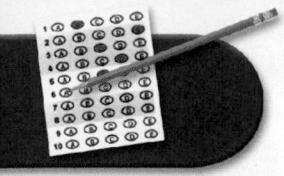

Standardized Test Prep

Multiple Choice

For Exercises 1–10, choose the correct letter.

1. For which function is 5 a zero? **A**
 A. $y = (x - 5)^2$ **B.** $y = (x + 5)^2$
 C. $y = (x - 1)^2 + 5$ **D.** $y = (x + 1)^2 - 5$

2. The graph of which line is perpendicular to the graph of $y = 2x + 1$? **G**
 F. $y = \frac{1}{2}x + 7$ **G.** $x + 2y = 4$
 H. $y = -2x - 5$ **I.** $x - 2y = 10$

3. What is the equation of the function $y = x^2$ translated 3 units up and 4 units left? **B**
 A. $y = (x - 3)^2 - 4$ **B.** $y = (x + 4)^2 + 3$
 C. $y = (x - 4)^2 + 3$ **D.** $y = (x + 3)^2 - 4$

4. What is the axis of symmetry of the graph of a quadratic function with vertex at $(5, -1)$? **F**
 F. $x = 5$ **G.** $x = -5$
 H. $y = -1$ **I.** $y = 1$

5. What is the solution of the matrix equation? **B**
$$\begin{bmatrix} 1 & 0 & 2 \\ 3 & 1 & 1 \\ -5 & 4 & 0 \end{bmatrix} X = \begin{bmatrix} 0 & -1 & 20 \\ -2 & 2 & 27 \\ 22 & -5 & -22 \end{bmatrix}$$

 A. $\begin{bmatrix} 1 & 3 & -2 \\ -1 & 0 & 1 \\ 7 & 2 & 6 \end{bmatrix}$ **B.** $\begin{bmatrix} -2 & 1 & 6 \\ 3 & 0 & 2 \\ 1 & -1 & 7 \end{bmatrix}$

 C. $\begin{bmatrix} -2 & 3 & 1 \\ 1 & 0 & 1 \\ 6 & 2 & 7 \end{bmatrix}$ **D.** $\begin{bmatrix} -2 & 0 & 7 \\ 3 & 1 & -1 \\ 1 & 2 & 6 \end{bmatrix}$

6. Which relation is NOT a function? **H**
 F. $y = 3\sqrt{x} - 1$ **G.** $y = |x - 7|$
 H. $y = \pm 3x$ **I.** $y = 1 - x^3$

7. Which is a factor of $x^4 + 2x^3 - 3x^2 - 4x + 4$?
 I. $x + 2$ **II.** $x - 1$ **III.** $x + 1$ **C**
 A. I only **B.** II only
 C. I and II **D.** II and III

8. Which ordered pair is a solution of this system? **I**
$$\begin{cases} y \le 2x + 3 \\ y > |x + 1| \\ y < -x + 4 \end{cases}$$
 I. $(0, 2)$ **II.** $(1, -3)$ **III.** $(-1, 4)$
 F. II and III **G.** II only
 H. I and II **I.** I only

9. At which point is the cost function $C = 3x + y$ minimized for the restrictions $x + y \ge 1$, $x \ge 0$, and $y \ge 0$? **C**
 A. $(3, 1)$ **B.** $(1, 0)$ **C.** $(0, 1)$ **D.** $(0, 0)$

10. What are the solutions of $x^3 + 4x^2 + x - 6 = 0$?
 F. $-1, -2, 3$ **G.** $-1, 2, -3$ **H**
 H. $1, -2, 3$ **I.** $-1, 2, 3$

Quantitative Comparison

Compare the boxed quantity in Column A with the boxed quantity in Column B. Choose the best answer.

 A. The quantity in Column A is greater.
 B. The quantity in Column B is greater.
 C. The two quantities are equal.
 D. The relationship cannot be determined from the information given.

	Column A	Column B
11. B	$_8C_2$	$_8P_2$
12. C	$[3 - (2 - x)]$	$1 + x$
13. B	sum of the roots of $x^2 + 4x + 3 = 0$	degree of $2x^4 - 3x^2$

Gridded Response

14. Find $7!$. **5040**

15. Find $_3P_2 - _3C_2$. **3**

16. What is the coefficient of a^2b^3 in the expansion of $(a + b)^5$? **10**

Short Response **17–18. See back of book.**

17. An employer is selecting 4 out of 30 workers as employees of the month.
 a. Does this situation involve a combination or a permutation? Explain.
 b. How many different selections are possible?

Extended Response

18. Open-Ended Graph a polygon. Use matrices to find the image of the polygon after a reflection in the x-axis followed by a rotation of 90° counterclockwise. Show your work.

Resources

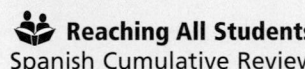
📁 **Teaching Resources**
Cumulative Review

Reaching All Students
Spanish Cumulative Review

ASSESSMENT SYSTEM
Standardized Test Prep
• Ch 6 Standardized Test Practice
Assessment Masters
• Cumulative Review
Computer Test Bank CD-ROM
• Standardized Test Practice

www.PHSchool.com
• Standardized Test Practice
• Resources

Plus **iTEXT**

Item	1	2	3	4	5	6	7	8	9	10	11	12	13	14	15	16	17	18
Lesson	6-1	2-2	5-3	5-2	4-3	2-1	6-2	3-3	3-4	6-4	6-7	1-2	5-5	1-6	6-7	6-8	6-7	4-4

As the Ball Flies

In these activities students apply their knowledge of parabolas and quadratic equations.

Connecting to Prior Knowledge

Have students share what they know about the game of soccer, and famous soccer players. Have volunteers describe the rules and objectives of the game of soccer, including various kinds of kicks and what the various objectives for each kind of kick might be.

Teaching Notes

Have a volunteer read the introductory paragraph. Ask: *If you were not ignoring the effects of wind and air resistance, what difference might these factors make in how a player plans a kick?*

Teaching Tip

Ask a volunteer to review, perhaps using a simple drawing on the board, what a vector represents and how vectors can show the result of two forces acting on one object.

Tactile Learners

Have a soccer ball in the classroom to pass around, and ask students to demonstrate how to kick the ball at different angles, without actually kicking the ball. If time and space allows, have students go outside and experiment kicking the ball at different angles.

Connection to Science

Have students research information about the gravitational constant, including comparing the force of gravity on Earth and on the moon.

358

Real-World Snapshots

As the Ball Flies

Applying Quadratic Functions Have you ever wondered how far a soccer player can kick a ball? Ignoring wind and air resistance, you can use a linear function and a quadratic function to describe the path of a soccer ball. These functions depend on two factors that are within the soccer player's control: velocity of the kick (v_k) and angle of the kick (θ). A good high-school soccer player can kick the ball at speeds ranging from 50 to 60 mi/h. A strong professional player can kick the ball at nearly 80 mi/h.

Activity 1

a. Use the information in the diagram on the facing page to calculate the horizontal and vertical velocities of a ball kicked at a 35° angle with an initial velocity of 60 mi/h. Convert the velocities to ft/s.

b. The equations $x(t) = v_x t$ and $y(t) = v_y t + 0.5gt^2$ describe the x- and y-coordinates of a soccer ball as a function of time. (The gravitational constant g is described on the facing page.) Use the second equation to calculate the time the ball will take to complete its path.

c. Use the first equation to calculate how far the ball will travel horizontally from its original position.

The Soccer Ball
The easily recognized form of a soccer ball is due to its unique combination of pentagons and hexagons.

Men's Soccer
Jurgen Klinsmann is one of Germany's most successful strikers. He led his team to the 1996 European Championship.

pages 357–359
Real-World Snapshots

Activity 1

a. $v_x \approx 72.1$ ft/s, $v_y \approx 50.5$ ft/s

b. about 3.15 s

c. about 227.4 ft

In practice, air resistance and wind play a role in determining the ball's path, but these factors make the equations more complex.

A ball in flight follows a parabolic path.

y

θ

x

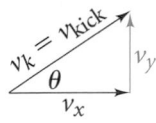

$v_k = v_{kick}$

v_y

θ

v_x

Vectors

The vectors at the left describe the initial velocity of the soccer ball as the combination of a vertical and a horizontal velocity.

$v_x = v_k \cos \theta$
$v_y = v_k \sin \theta$

Gravity

The constant g represents the acceleration of any object as a result of Earth's gravity. The value of g near the surface of Earth is about -32 ft/s^2.

Activity 2

a. Use the technique developed in Activity 1 to calculate the horizontal distance of the kick for angles in 5° increments from 5° to 90°. (You may find a spreadsheet helpful for making these calculations.)

b. Graph the horizontal distance of the kick as a function of the angle of the kick. Which angle gives the greatest distance?

Activity 3

Suppose you played soccer on the moon, where the gravitational acceleration is about one sixth of its value on Earth. What are the maximum height and maximum horizontal distance you could kick the ball by giving it an initial velocity of 48 mi/h?

The Women's World Cup

Cindy Parlow of the U.S. women's soccer team avoids a tackle in the 1999 final against China.

Take It to the NET For more information about soccer, go to **www.PHSchool.com**.
Web Code: age-0653

Teaching Tip
Before students begin the activity, discuss the illustrations and their captions. Have each team read through the activities before beginning to work. Have students work in pairs or in small groups to complete the activities. If time is limited, after all teams have completed Activity 1, have some teams go on to Activity 2 and others do one or both of the Additional Activities.

Activity 1

Materials: paper and pencil

Inclusion

Help students organize their work by estimating the form and units for each of the answers in Activity 1.

Activity 2

Materials: paper and pencil, graph paper, spreadsheet (optional)

Teaching Tip

If a spreadsheet program is not available, divide the calculations among various members of the team, or among teams and then have them combine the results.

Scoring Rubric

This scoring rubric can be used for evaluating student work on each activity. Share this scoring rubric with students before they begin work.

4 Equations and calculations (and graphs, if required) are correct.
Steps are neat, accurate, and clearly show the mathematics. Responses are clearly indicated and give the appropriate units.

3 Equations, calculations, and graphs are mostly correct, with some minor errors. Steps are neat and mostly accurate. Units are not completely accurate.

2 Equations, calculations, and graphs contain both major and minor errors.

1 Correct answer, but no work is shown.

Activity 2

a.

Angle	Distance	Angle	Distance	Angle	Distance
5	42.02	35	227.41	65	185.38
10	82.77	40	238.32	70	155.55
15	121.00	45	242.00	75	121.00
20	155.55	50	238.32	80	82.77
25	185.38	55	227.41	85	42.02
30	209.58	60	209.58	90	0.00

b.

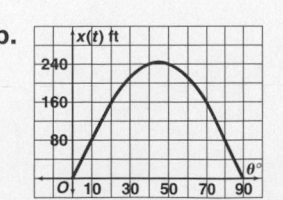

45°

Activity 3

max. height: about 232 ft;
max. distance: about 465 ft

Chapter 7

Radical Functions and Rational Exponents

Chapter at a Glance

North Carolina Objectives

7-1 Roots and Radical Expressions — 1.01
NCTM 1, 2, 7, 10
▼ Roots and Radical Expressions

7-2 Multiplying and Dividing Radical Expressions — 1.01
NCTM 1, 2, 10
▼ Multiplying Radical Expressions
▽ Dividing Radical Expressions

7-3 Binomial Radical Expressions — 1.01
NCTM 1, 2, 7, 10
▼ Adding and Subtracting Radical Expressions
▽ Multiplying and Dividing Binomial Radical Expressions

7-4 Rational Exponents — 1.01
NCTM 1, 2, 7
▼ Simplifying Expressions With Rational Exponents

7-5 Solving Radical Equations — 2.07a
NCTM 1, 2, 6
▼ Solving Radical Equations

7-6 Function Operations — 2.01
NCTM 2, 6, 10
▼ Operations With Functions
▽ Composition of Functions

7-7 Inverse Relations and Functions — 2.01
NCTM 1, 2, 7
▼ The Inverse of a Function

7-8 Graphing Radical Functions — 2.07a, b
NCTM 2, 6, 9
▼ Radical Functions

NCTM STANDARDS 2000

1 Number and Operations
2 Algebra
3 Geometry
4 Measurement
5 Data Analysis and Probability
6 Problem Solving
7 Reasoning and Proof
8 Communication
9 Connections
10 Representation

Pacing Options

This chart suggests pacing only for the lessons and their parts. It is provided as a possible guide. It will help you determine how much time you have in your schedule to cover other components, such as the features, Chapter Review, and Chapter Test.

Day	Traditional (45 min.)	Block (90 min.)
1	7-1 ▼	7-1 ▼
2	7-2 ▼	7-2 ▼
3	7-2 ▼ ▽	7-2 ▽
4	7-2 ▽	7-3 ▼
5	7-3 ▼	7-3 ▽
6	7-3 ▽	7-4 ▼
7	7-3 ▽	7-4 ▼
8	7-4 ▼	7-5 ▼
9	7-4 ▼	7-6 ▼
10	7-4 ▼	7-6 ▽
11	7-5 ▼	7-7 ▼
12	7-5 ▼	7-8 ▼
13	7-6 ▼	7-8 ▼
14	7-6 ▽	7-8 ▼
15	7-7 ▼	
16	7-8 ▼	
17	7-8 ▼	

NAEP Correlation (National Assessment of Educational Progress 2000 Mathematics Objectives)

7-1	7-2	7-3	7-4	7-5	7-6	7-7	7-8
N2e, M7c, A5a	N3a, A5a	N3a, M4a, A5a	N3a, M10, A5a	N3a, M5, A5a	N5e, A5b, A11	M5, A5b, A11	A3d, A12

N = Number Sense, Properties, and Operations; **M** = Measurement; **G** = Geometry and Spatial Sense;
D = Data Analysis, Statistics, and Probability; **A** = Algebra and Functions

Math Background

Chapter Overview

Chapter 7 introduces nth roots of real numbers and relates them to nth powers and rational exponents. Students learn to perform operations on radical expressions, simplify radical expressions, and solve radical equations.

Operations on functions are examined, including function composition. Next, inverse relations and inverse functions are discussed. Finally, students graph radical functions and see how to sketch translations of parent graphs.

Roots and Radical Expressions   7-1

It is important to remember that $\sqrt[n]{x}$ where x is positive has two values when n is a positive even number but only one value when n is odd. To help students see that $\sqrt{x^2}$ is equal to $|x|$ rather than to x, you can ask students to graph $y = \sqrt{x^2}$, $y = |x|$, and $y = x$ and compare the graphs. They will see that the graphs of $y = \sqrt{x^2}$ and $y = |x|$ are the same.

Multiplying and Dividing Radical Expressions   7-2

Help students understand why restrictions on the values of variables are necessary for many equations. For example, the equation $\sqrt[n]{a} \cdot \sqrt[n]{b} = \sqrt[n]{ab}$ must have the specification that $\sqrt[n]{a}$ and $\sqrt[n]{b}$ are real numbers because $\sqrt[n]{a}$ and $\sqrt[n]{b}$ would be complex if either a or b were negative.

Binomial Radical Expressions   7-3

Most of the work in this lesson involves straightforward applications of earlier skills. Rationalizing the denominator in expressions such as $\dfrac{3}{1 + \sqrt{2}}$ or $\dfrac{7}{\sqrt{5} - \sqrt{3}}$ is not difficult after one or two examples. Some students need help recognizing that different types of denominators require different multipliers; the point is to eliminate radicals in denominators.

Rational Exponents   7-4

Point out to students that the definitions for rational exponents are designed to be consistent with the earlier definitions and rules for integer exponents.

Solving Radical Equations   7-5

As in solving an equation for a variable, solving a radical equation involves isolating a radical on one side of the equation. The process of squaring both sides of the equation might produce extraneous roots, so students must check possible solutions in the original equation. Also, students can be encouraged to recognize equations that will have no solution, such as $\sqrt{x + 2} = -5$.

Function Operations   7-6

The notation $f \circ g$ for the composition of function f with function g looks similar to the notation for the product of f and g. Point out that the operations are quite different. Also point out that function multiplication is commutative, but function composition is not.

Inverse Relations and Functions   7-7

Students may have difficulty understanding why saying "the inverse of the function f is f^{-1}," is not the same as saying "f and f^{-1} are inverse functions." The first statement should be interpreted in light of the fact that f can have an inverse relation that is denoted by f^{-1}. The second statement is true only if this inverse relation f^{-1} also happens to be a function. It may help students to recall that the graph of a relation and its inverse are reflections of each other in $y = x$. The inverse relation f^{-1} must satisfy the vertical line test before one can call it an inverse function. A corresponding horizontal line test can be used to test whether a function has an inverse that is also a function.

> Horizontal Line Test: If it is possible for a horizontal line to intersect a graph at more than one point, then the graph of the *inverse* is not the graph of a function.

So, if a graph of a function passes the horizontal line test, then the graph of the *inverse* passes the vertical line test and is also the graph of a function.

You may wish to show students that, in all cases, there is a connection between the inverse relationship and the identity for the relation. For example, $a \cdot \dfrac{1}{a} = 1$ means the product of a number and its multiplicative inverse is the multiplicative identity. The composition of a function and its inverse is the identity function $i = f \circ f^{-1} = f^{-1} \circ f$ that maps an element to itself.

Graphing Radical Functions   7-8

The procedures for graphing radical functions and translations of graphs of parent functions are similar to those for other functions. Students can use graphing calculators to examine the graphs of radical functions for the solutions to problems.

Ongoing Assessment and Intervention

Tools for Monitoring Student Progress

The Prentice Hall *Algebra 2* program provides you with many options for assessment in the Student Edition, the Teacher's Edition and the teaching resources. From these options you may choose instructional materials and techniques that are appropriate for your students and support your district's curriculum requirements.

 Instant Check System™ in Chapter 7

Allows students to check their own learning before, during, and after each lesson.

Diagnosing Readiness before the chapter (p. 360)

Check Skills You'll Need exercises in each lesson (pp. 363, 368, 374, 379, 385, 392, 400, 408)

Check Understanding questions with each Example (pp. 364, 365, 368, 369, 370, 371, 374, 375, 376, 379, 380, 381, 382, 385, 386, 387, 392, 393, 394, 401, 402, 403, 409, 410, 411)

Checkpoint Quiz (pp. 378, 398)

 Test Prep in Chapter 7

Teaches students strategies and gives them practice with all the test item formats they will encounter on state tests and standardized national exams.

Standardized Test Prep exercises in each lesson (pp. 367, 373, 378, 384, 390, 397, 405, 413)

Test-Taking Strategies (p. 414)

Standardized Test Prep (p. 419)

All your assessment needs in one place!

Program Assessment

Assess student progress throughout the *Algebra 2* text with blackline masters and CD-ROM.

Assessment Resources
- Checkpoint Quizzes 1 & 2
- Chapter Test, Forms A & B
- Chapter Alternative Assessment

Spanish versions available.

 Computer Test Generator

- Unlimited questions of varying difficulty for every lesson objective.
- Create your own practice sheets, quizzes, and tests, or use the pre-made Chapter Tests.
- Diagnose readiness with questions on prerequisite skills.
- Prepare students by making tests based on standardized test objectives.
- Access Algebra 1, Geometry, and Algebra 2 content—all on one CD-ROM.

Test Preparation

A three-step approach to preparing students for high stakes, national, and state exams.

❶ **Diagnose & Prescribe**

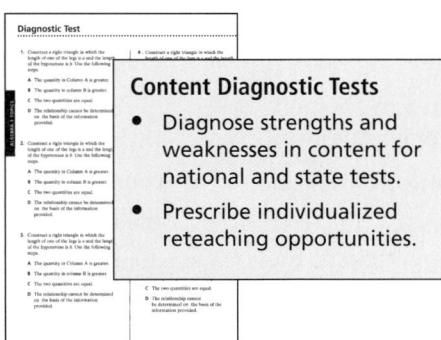

Content Diagnostic Tests
- Diagnose strengths and weaknesses in content for national and state tests.
- Prescribe individualized reteaching opportunities.

❷ **Review & Reteach**

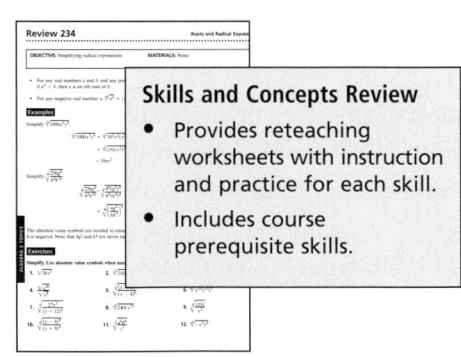

Skills and Concepts Review
- Provides reteaching worksheets with instruction and practice for each skill.
- Includes course prerequisite skills.

❸ **Practice & Assess**

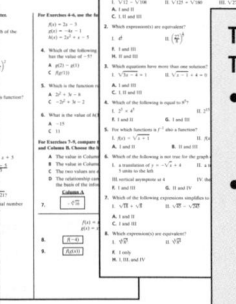

Test Preparation
- Features practice tests for End-of-Course and SAT/ACT exams.
- Includes standardized test practice by chapter for ongoing review.

Teacher's Guide with answers and correlations.

Test-Taking Strategies with Transparencies
- Support the Test-Taking Strategies pages in the Student Edition.
- Provide a teaching transparency and a practice worksheet for each strategy.

🔖 Reaching All Students

Support in the Student Text and Additional Resources

The textbook, the iText, and other technology components provide numerous opportunities to reach students of various ability levels and learning styles. Each Teacher's Edition lesson suggests how you can help *all* your students be successful and understand the mathematics in Chapter 7.

Below Level

Student Edition
- Diagnosing Readiness*: p. 360
- Check Skills You'll Need*: pp. 363, 368, 374, 379, 385, 392, 400, 408

Reteaching
Chapter 7 Support File: pp. 10–17

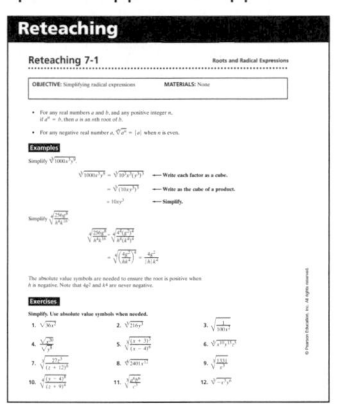

Advanced Learners

Student Edition
- Challenge exercises: pp. 367, 372, 377, 383, 384, 390, 397, 405, 412, 413

Enrichment
Chapter 7 Support File: pp. 18–25

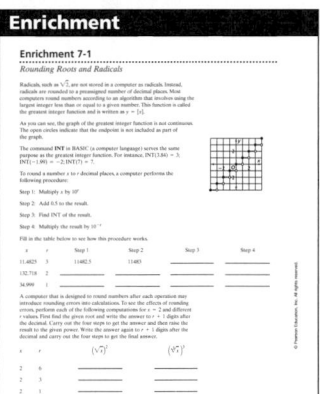

Connections to Precalculus Masters
Chapter 7 Enrichment Topic: Complex Numbers

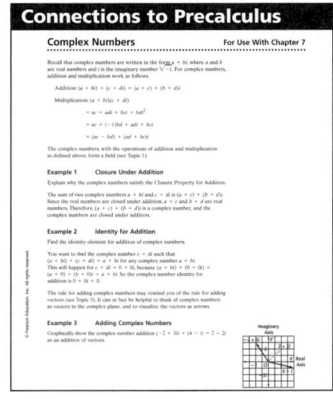

* Can be used with all ability levels to ensure mastery of prerequisite skills.

📖 Reading and Math Literacy

Student Edition
- Vocabulary: pp. 361, 415, *plus* in every Lesson Preview
- Reading Math: pp. 363, 364, 369, 379, 393, 396, 399, 402
- Illustrated Glossary: pp. 871–913

Reading and Math Literacy Masters
Chapter 7: pp. 25–28

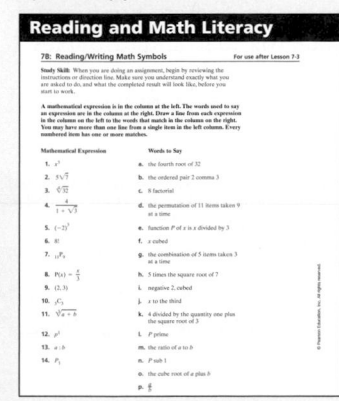

English Learners

Student Edition
- English/Spanish Illustrated Glossary: pp. 871–913

Workbook and Masters
Spanish Practice Workbook: pp. 2–9
Spanish Reading and Math Literacy Masters: pp. 25–28

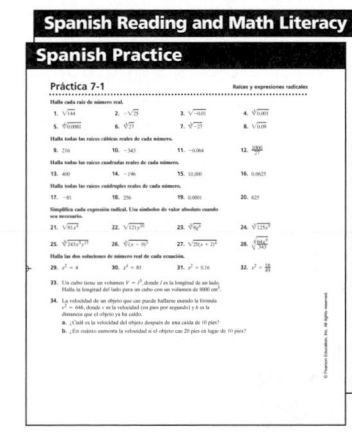

Learning Styles

Student Edition
- Investigation: pp. 388, 400
- Technology: pp. 380, 407
- Writing: pp. 362, 367, 372, 377, 383, 389, 396, 397, 405, 412, 418

Activity Masters
Hands-On Activities: 45, 46
Technology Activities: 31

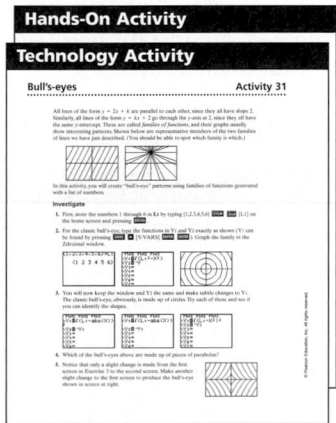

Program Resources

Lesson	Teaching Resources in Grab & Go™ Files				Resources for Reaching All Students			Spanish Resources			Transparencies				Prentice Hall Presentation Pro CD-ROM
	Practice	Reteach	Enrich	Checkpoint Quiz	Reading & Math Literacy	Technology Activities	Hands-On Activities	Practice	Reading & Math Literacy	Checkpoint Quiz	Skills Check	Additional Examples	Answers to Exercises	Lesson Quiz	
7-1	■	■	■		■		■	■	■		■	■	■	■	■
7-2	■	■	■					■			■	■	■	■	■
7-3	■	■	■	■	■			■	■	■	■	■	■	■	■
7-4	■	■	■					■			■	■	■	■	■
7-5	■	■	■				■	■			■	■	■	■	■
7-6	■	■	■	■	■			■		■	■	■	■	■	■
7-7	■	■	■					■			■	■	■	■	■
7-8	■	■	■			■		■			■	■	■	■	■
For the chapter	Chapter Tests, Alternative Assessment, Cumulative Review, Cumulative Assessment				Connections to Precalculus Masters			Spanish Chapter Tests, Alternative Assessment, Cumulative Review, Cumulative Assessment			Classroom Aid Transparencies				

Also available for use with the chapter:

 *See page 360C.*

- Practice Workbook
- Solution Key

- For teacher support and access to student Web site materials, use Web Code agk-5500.
- For additional online and technology resources, see below.

 ## Technology

 Online and on CD-ROM

Complete Interactive Student Text online and on CD-ROM—with instant feedback assessment, tutorial help, dynamic activities, instructional and real-world videos, audio, and additional practice.

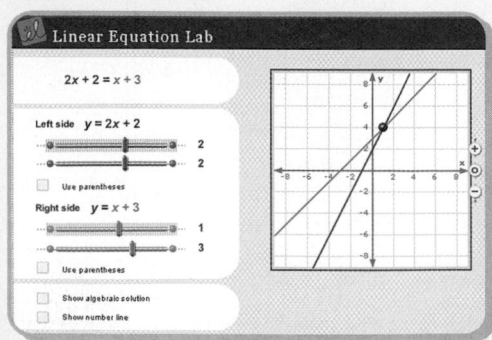

www.PHSchool.com For Students

Use **Web Codes** for easy access to online activities, chapter projects, self-grading lesson quizzes and chapter tests, vocabulary quizzes, updated data sources, graphing calculator procedures, and more.

PH SuccessNet For Teachers

Online lesson planning with built-in state correlations, all the teaching resources, complete reference library, your own calendar and Teacher Web page, professional development, and more.

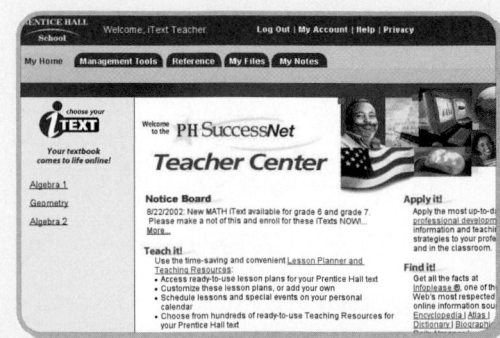

Presentation Assistant Plus!

The Prentice Hall *Presentation Assistant Plus!* provides you with the material you need to teach a lesson from beginning to end. Two easy-to-use formats—Transparencies and CD-ROM—allow you to present a lesson the way you are most comfortable.

Transparencies

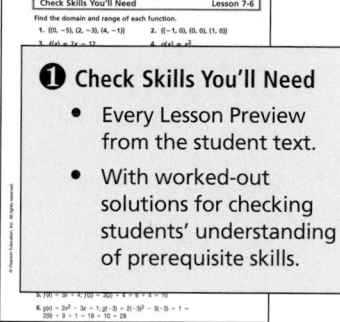

❶ Check Skills You'll Need
- Every Lesson Preview from the student text.
- With worked-out solutions for checking students' understanding of prerequisite skills.

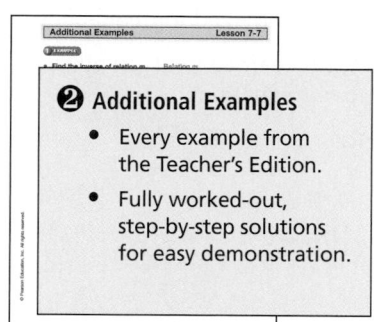

❷ Additional Examples
- Every example from the Teacher's Edition.
- Fully worked-out, step-by-step solutions for easy demonstration.

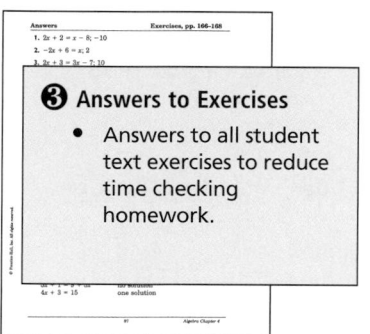

❸ Answers to Exercises
- Answers to all student text exercises to reduce time checking homework.

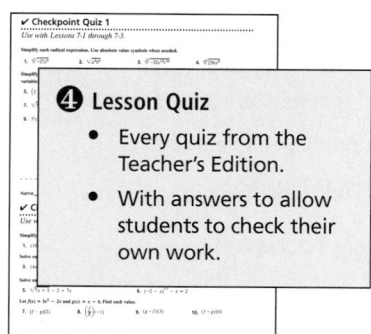

❹ Lesson Quiz
- Every quiz from the Teacher's Edition.
- With answers to allow students to check their own work.

 Throughout the Teacher's Edition, this symbol indicates material that is available on transparency in the Presentation Assistant Plus!

Prentice Hall Presentation Pro CD-ROM

- Includes all Transparencies.
- Conveniently organized by lesson so you can easily ❶ Introduce, ❷ Teach, ❸ Check Homework, and ❹ Assess each lesson.
- Animated examples allow step-by-step instruction at your own pace.
- Easy to edit so you can create custom presentations.

Teaching Chapter 7 Using Presentation Assistant Plus!

	❶ Introduce	❷ Teach	❸ Check Homework	❹ Assess
	Check Skills You'll Need	Additional Examples	Student Edition Answers	Lesson Quiz
7-1	p. 44	pp. 135–137	✔	p. 131
7-2	p. 45	pp. 138–140	✔	p. 132
7-3	p. 46	pp. 140–141	✔	p. 133
7-4	p. 47	pp. 142–144	✔	p. 134
7-5	p. 48	pp. 144–147	✔	p. 135
7-6	p. 49	pp. 148–149	✔	p. 136
7-7	p. 50	pp. 150–153	✔	p. 137
7-8	p. 51	pp. 154–155	✔	p. 138

Prentice Hall Presentation Pro

CD-ROM with dynamic PowerPoint® presentations for every lesson. Helps you introduce and develop concepts, check homework, and assess progress. Part of Presentation Assistant Plus! *(See above.)*

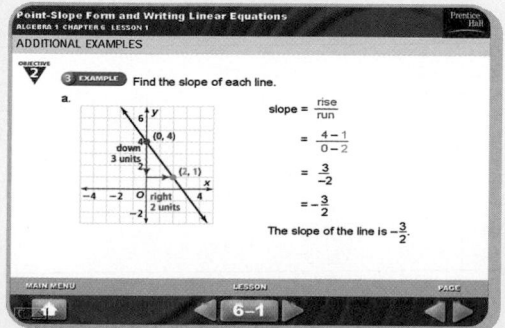

Computer Test Generator

CD-ROM to create practice sheets and tests for course objectives and standardized tests. Includes Instant Chapter Tests™, online testing, and student reports. Part of the PH Assessment System. *(See page 360C.)*

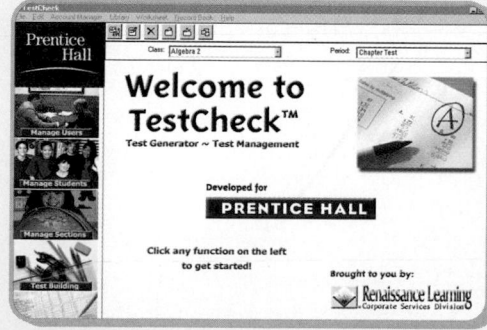

Resource Pro® with Planning Express®

CD-ROM with a lesson planning tool that allows you to import state and local objectives. Includes electronic versions of all the teaching resources.

Radical Functions and Rational Expressions

 Diagnosing Readiness

Students will find answers to these exercises in the back of their textbooks.

For intervention, direct students to:

Multiplying Binomials
Lesson 6-2: Example 1, Exercises 1–6. Extra Practice, p. 827.

Simplifying Exponential Expressions
Skills Handbook: page 852, Examples 2–4, Exercises 5–32

Solve by Factoring
Lesson 5-5: Example 1, Exercises 1–6. Extra Practice, p. 826. Lesson 6-4: Example 5, Exercises 21–23. Extra Practice, p. 827.

Finding the Domain and Range of Functions
Lesson 2-1: Example 2, Exercises 5–7. Extra Practice, p. 823.

Graphing Quadratic Functions
Lesson 5-3: Example 1, Exercises 1–12. Extra Practice, p. 826.

page 360   Diagnosing Readiness

15. domain {1, 2, 3, 4}, range {2, 3, 4, 5}

16. domain {1, 2, 3, 4}, range {2}

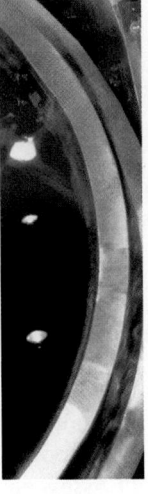

Where You've Been

- In Chapter 2, you learned about relations and functions and their domains and ranges. You also learned to draw graphs of relations and functions on the coordinate plane.

- In Chapter 5, you reviewed square roots and the multiplication and division of square roots. Then you used these skills in graphing and solving quadratic equations.

- In Chapter 6, you learned to graph polynomial functions and solve polynomial equations.

TEXT Instant self-check online and on CD-ROM

 **Diagnosing Readiness**   (For help, go to the Lesson in green.)

Multiplying Binomials (Lesson 6-2)

Multiply.

1. $(3y - 2)(y - 4)$
$3y^2 - 14y + 8$

2. $(7a + 10)(7a - 10)$
$49a^2 - 100$

3. $(x - 3)(x + 6)(x + 1)$
$x^3 + 4x^2 - 15x - 18$

Simplifying Exponential Expressions (Skills Handbook p. 852)

Simplify each expression. Use only positive integers.

4. $(3x^3)^2$ $9x^6$

5. $(2b^{-2})(4b^5)$ $8b^3$

6. $(xy^{-3})^2$ $\dfrac{x^2}{y^6}$

7. $\dfrac{18a^2}{3a^{-4}}$ $6a^6$

8. $\dfrac{4ab^{-3}}{6a^2b^3}$ $\dfrac{2}{3ab^6}$

Solving by Factoring (Lessons 5-5 and 6-4)

Solve each equation by factoring.

9. $x^2 - 5x - 14 = 0$ **−2, 7**

10. $2x^2 - 11x + 15 = 0$ $\frac{5}{2}$**, 3**

11. $3x^2 + 10x - 8 = 0$ **−4,** $\frac{2}{3}$

12. $12x^2 - 12x + 3 = 0$ $\frac{1}{2}$

13. $8x^2 - 98 = 0$ $\pm\frac{7}{2}$

14. $x^4 - 14x^2 + 49 = 0$ **±2.65**

Finding the Domain and Range of Functions (Lesson 2-1)

Find the domain and range of each function. **15–16. See margin.**

15. {(1, 2), (2, 3), (3, 4), (4, 5)}

16. {(1, 2), (2, 2), (3, 2), (4, 2)}

17. $f(x) = -x - 1$ **domain** $\{x \mid x \in \mathbf{R}\}$**, range** $\{y \mid y \in \mathbf{R}\}$

18. $f(x) = 2x^2 + 3$ **domain** $\{x \mid x \in \mathbf{R}\}$**, range** $\{y \mid y \in \mathbf{R} \text{ and } y \geq 3\}$

Graphing Quadratic Functions (Lesson 5-3)

Graph each function. **19–24. See back of book.**

19. $y = 2x^2 - 4$

20. $y = -3(x^2 + 1)$

21. $y = \frac{1}{2}(x - 3)^2 + 1$

22. $y = -(x + 4)^2 - 5$

23. $y = \frac{1}{4}(x + 2)^2 - 1$

24. $y = 7 - (5 - x)^2$

Radical Functions and Rational Exponents

Where You're Going

- In Chapter 7, you will extend your knowledge of roots to include cube roots, fourth roots, fifth roots, and so on.

- You will learn to add, subtract, multiply, and divide radical expressions, including binomial radical expressions.

- You will solve radical equations, and graph translations of radical functions and their inverses.

 Real-World Connection Applying what you learn, on page 380 you will solve a problem involving space travel.

LESSONS

Key Vocabulary

Chapter 7 Overview

Students begin the chapter with an introduction to roots and radical expressions. Next students learn how to multiply and divide radical expressions. Students then study binomial radical expressions and rational exponents. Subsequently, students learn how to solve radical equations, and are introduced to function operations. The chapter concludes with lessons on inverse relations and functions, and graphing radical functions.

 Reading Math
Reading for Mathematical Symbols, p. 399

 Vocabulary
A complete list of terms, plus vocabulary exercises, appears in the Chapter Review, p. 415.

 Illustrated Glossary
Examples for each vocabulary term, plus definitions in both English and Spanish, appear starting on p. 871.

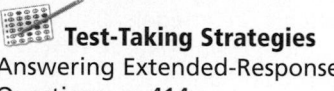 **Test-Taking Strategies**
Answering Extended-Response Questions, p. 414

 Real-World Connections
Some of the applications you will find in this chapter are Einstein's Theory (7-2), Space (7-4), Solar Energy (7-5), and Accident Investigation (7-7).

 www.PHSchool.com
Internet support for this chapter includes:
- Self-grading Vocabulary and Chapter 7 Tests
- Chapter Project
- Chapter Planner
- Chapter 7 Resources

Plus **iTEXT**

361

Properties of Exponents

Students will find it helpful to review simplifying expressions with integer exponents before they study rational exponents in Lesson 7-4.

Resources

Technology

Computer Test Generator CD-ROM, Chapter 0, Integer, Decimal, and Fraction Operations

Teaching Notes

EXAMPLE

Remind students that all the properties used to simplify expressions with whole number exponents apply when the exponents are integers. Be sure students understand that for $a \neq 0$ and any integer exponent n, $a^{-n} = \frac{1}{a^n}$.

Error Prevention

Make sure students understand that to write expressions in simplified form, they must be sure that all exponents are positive.

page 362   Algebra 1 Review

25. Answers may vary.
    Sample:
    $15^0 = 1$
    $\frac{4^5}{4^3} = 4^{5-3} = 4^2 = 16$
    $(2 \cdot 5)^2 = 2^2 \cdot 5^2 =$
      $4 \cdot 25 = 100$
    $\left(\frac{2}{3}\right)^5 = \frac{2^5}{3^5}$
    $2^3 \cdot 2^5 = 2^{3+5} = 2^8$
    $4^{-3} = \frac{1}{4^3} = \frac{1}{64}$
    $(3^2)^3 = 3^{2\cdot3} = 3^6 = 729$
    In $(ab)^m = a^m b^m$ and
    $\left(\frac{a}{b}\right)^m = \frac{a^m}{b^m}$ the exponent
    is distributed to both
    factors and to both the
    numerator and the
    denominator.

362

Exponents are used to indicate powers. Their properties are listed below. Assume throughout your work that no denominator is equal to zero and that m and n are positive integers.

- $a^0 = 1, a \neq 0$
- $a^m \cdot a^n = a^{m+n}$
- $(ab)^n = a^n b^n$
- $(a^m)^n = a^{mn}$
- $a^{-n} = \frac{1}{a^n}$
- $\frac{a^m}{a^n} = a^{m-n}$
- $\left(\frac{a}{b}\right)^n = \frac{a^n}{b^n}$

EXAMPLE

Simplify and rewrite each expression using only positive exponents.

a. $(7a^2)(-2a^{-5})$

$(7a^2)(-2a^{-5})$

$= 7(-2)a^{2+(-5)}$

$= -14a^{-3}$

$= \frac{-14}{a^3}$, or $-\frac{14}{a^3}$

b. $(-2x^{-1}y^2)^3$

$(-2x^{-1}y^2)^3$

$= (-2)^3(x^{-1})^3(y^2)^3$

$= -8x^{-3}y^6$

$= \frac{-8y^6}{x^3}$, or $-\frac{8y^6}{x^3}$

c. $\frac{2ab^5c^2}{a^3bc^2}$

$\frac{2ab^5c^2}{a^3bc^2}$

$= 2a^{1-3}b^{5-1}c^{2-2}$

$= 2a^{-2}b^4c^0$

$= \frac{2b^4}{a^2}$

EXERCISES

Simplify each expression. Use only positive exponents.

1. $(3a^2)(4a^6)$ **$12a^8$**

2. $(-4x^2)(-2x^{-2})$ **8**

3. $(4x^3y^5)^2$ **$16x^6y^{10}$**

4. $(2x^{-5}y^4)^3$ **$\frac{8y^{12}}{x^{15}}$**

5. $\frac{8a^5}{2a^2}$ **$4a^3$**

6. $\frac{6x^7y^5}{3x^{-1}}$ **$2x^8y^5$**

7. $\frac{(4x^2)^0}{2xy^5}$ **$\frac{1}{2xy^5}$**

8. $\left(\frac{3x^2}{2}\right)^2$ **$\frac{9x^4}{4}$**

9. $(-6m^2n^2)(3mn)$ **$-18m^3n^3$**

10. $(3x^4y^5)^{-3}$ **$\frac{1}{27x^{12}y^{15}}$**

11. $\frac{(2r^{-1}s^2t^0)^{-2}}{2rs}$ **$\frac{r}{8s^5}$**

12. $x^5(2x)^3$ **$8x^8$**

13. $\frac{x^4x^{-2}}{x^{-5}}$ **x^7**

14. $\frac{(12x^2y^6)^2}{8x^4y^7}$ **$18y^5$**

15. $(4p^2q)(p^2q^3)$ **$4p^4q^4$**

16. $\frac{4x^3}{2x}$ **$2x^2$**

17. $(p^2)^{-2}$ **$\frac{1}{p^4}$**

18. $\frac{-15x^4}{3x}$ **$-5x^3$**

19. $\frac{r^2s^3t^4}{r^2s^4t^{-4}}$ **$\frac{t^8}{s}$**

20. $\frac{xy^2}{2} \cdot \frac{6x}{y^2}$ **$3x^2$**

21. $(s^2t)^3(st)$ **s^7t^4**

22. $(3x^{-3}y^{-2})^{-2}$ **$\frac{x^6y^4}{9}$**

23. $(h^4k^5)^0$ **1**

24. $\frac{s^2t^3}{r} \cdot \frac{sr^3}{t}$ **$r^2s^3t^2$**

 25. Writing Write a numerical example for each property of exponents shown above. Which properties could be called distributive properties for exponents? Explain. **See margin.**

  North Carolina Objectives   1.01   Simplify and perform operations with rational exponents and logarithms (common and natural) to solve problems.

Lesson Preview

What You'll Learn

OBJECTIVE 1   To simplify *n*th roots

. . . And Why

To solve a packaging problem, as in Example 4

 Check Skills You'll Need   (For help, go to Lesson 5-4.)

Write each number as a square of a number.

1. 25 5^2 2. 0.09 0.3^2 3. $\frac{4}{49}$ $\left(\frac{2}{7}\right)^2$

Write each expression as a square of an expression.

4. x^{10} $(x^5)^2$ 5. x^4y^2 $(x^2y)^2$ 6. $169x^6y^{12}$ $(13x^3y^6)^2$

New Vocabulary   • *n*th root   • radicand   • index   • principal root

---

OBJECTIVE 1   **Roots and Radical Expressions**

   Interactive lesson includes instant self-check, tutorials, and activities.

Since $5^2 = 25, 5$ is a square root of 25.

Since $5^3 = 125, 5$ is a cube root of 125.

Since $5^4 = 625, 5$ is a fourth root of 625.

Since $5^5 = 3125, 5$ is a fifth root of 3125.

This pattern leads to the definition of *n*th root.

 Key Concepts

Definition	*n*th Root
For any real numbers a and b, and any positive integer n, if $a^n = b$, then a is an **n*th root** of b.	

 Reading Math

The term *root* is used in two ways in mathematics:
    root of an equation
    root of a number.

The roots of the equation $y^4 = 16$ are the fourth roots of 16.

Since $2^4 = 16$ and $(-2)^4 = 16$, both 2 and -2 are fourth roots of 16.

Since there is no real number x such that $x^4 = -16, -16$ has no real fourth root.

Since -5 is the only real number whose cube is $-125, -5$ is the only real cube root of -125.

Some roots, such as the square roots of 10, are irrational numbers. Nevertheless, there is a positive square root and a negative square root of 10.

Here is a summary of the number of possible real roots of a real number.

Type of Number	Number of Real *n*th Roots When *n* Is Even	Number of Real *n*th Roots When *n* Is Odd
positive	2	1
0	1	1
negative	none	1

 **Ongoing Assessment and Intervention**

Before the Lesson	**During the Lesson**	**After the Lesson**
Diagnose prerequisite skills using:	**Monitor progress using:**	**Assess knowledge using:**
• Check Skills You'll Need	• Check Understanding	• Lesson Quiz
	• Additional Examples	• Computer Test Generator CD
	• Standardized Test Prep	

Lesson Preview

 **Check Skills You'll Need**

Factoring Quadratic Expressions
Lesson 5-4: Example 7
Exercises 37–45
Extra Practice, p. 86

Lesson Resources

📁 **Teaching Resources**
Practice, Reteaching, Enrichment

👥 **Reaching All Students**
Practice Workbook 7-1
Spanish Practice Workbook 7-1
Reading and Math Literacy 7A
Spanish Reading & Literacy 7A
Hands-On Activities 45

⏱ **Presentation Assistant Plus!**
Transparencies
• Check Skills You'll Need 7-1
• Additional Examples 7-1
• Student Edition Answers 7-1
• Lesson Quiz 7-1
PH Presentation Pro CD 7-1

PRENTICE HALL ASSESSMENT SYSTEM

Computer Test Generator CD

💿 **Technology**
Resource Pro® CD-ROM
Computer Test Generator CD
Prentice Hall Presentation Pro CD

💻 **www.PHSchool.com**
Student Site
• Teacher Web Code: agk-5500
• Self-grading Lesson Quiz
Teacher Center
• Lesson Planner
• Resources

Plus 🔲**TEXT**

363

Professional Development

Math Background

The real number a is an nth root of the real number b if and only if $a^n = b$, and n is a positive integer greater than or equal to 2. Every real number b has exactly one nth root if n is odd. In cases where n is even, the situation is more complicated. If b is positive, then b has a positive and a negative nth root. If b is 0, then 0 is the only nth root of b. If b is negative, then the nth roots are imaginary. In this chapter, we consider only real nth roots.

OBJECTIVE

 1 Teaching Notes

2 EXAMPLE Teaching Tip

Have students practice identifying the index, radicand, and principle root for each question in the example.

3 EXAMPLE Alternative Method

If students do not understand why absolute value signs must be used for some roots, give them the following example. Ask them to evaluate each side of the equation $\sqrt{x^6} = x^3$ for $x = -2$. This results in the false statement $8 = -8$ since $\sqrt{(-2)^6} = \sqrt{64} = 8$ and $(-2)^3 = -8$. Even though 64 has two square roots, -8 and 8, the radical sign signifies the principal square root, which is always positive. Therefore we must write $\sqrt{x^6} = |x^3|$. The absolute value sign ensures that the equation is true.

---

1 EXAMPLE Finding All Real Roots

Find all the real roots.

a. the cube roots of 0.008, -1000, and $\frac{1}{27}$

Since $(0.2)^3 = 0.008$, 0.2 is the cube root of 0.008.
Since $(-10)^3 = -1000$, -10 is the cube root of -1000.
Since $\left(\frac{1}{3}\right)^3 = \frac{1}{27}$, $\frac{1}{3}$ is the cube root of $\frac{1}{27}$.

b. the fourth roots of 1, -0.0001, and $\frac{16}{81}$

Since $1^4 = 1$ and $(-1)^4 = 1$, 1 and -1 are fourth roots of 1.
There is no real number with a fourth power of -0.0001.
Since $\left(\frac{2}{3}\right)^4 = \frac{16}{81}$ and $\left(-\frac{2}{3}\right)^4 = \frac{16}{81}$, $\frac{2}{3}$ and $-\frac{2}{3}$ are fourth roots of $\frac{16}{81}$.

✓ **Check Understanding** **1 a.** Find all the real fifth roots of 0, -1, and 32. **0; −1; 2**
b. Find all the real square roots of 0.0001, -1, and $\frac{36}{121}$.
0.01 and −0.01, no real square root, $\frac{6}{11}$ and $-\frac{6}{11}$

 Reading Math

Like the word *radish*, *radical* comes from the Latin word for root.

A radical sign is used to indicate a root. The number under the radical sign is the **radicand**. The **index** gives the degree of the root.

When a number has two real roots, the positive root is called the **principal root** and the radical sign indicates the principal root. The principal fourth root of 16 is written as $\sqrt[4]{16}$.

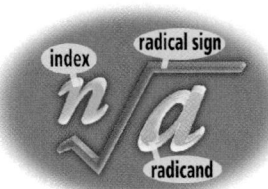

The principal fourth root of 16 is 2 because $\sqrt[4]{16}$ equals $\sqrt[4]{2^4}$. The other fourth root of 16 is written as $-\sqrt[4]{16}$, which equals -2.

2 EXAMPLE Finding Roots

Find each real-number root.

a. $\sqrt[3]{-8}$
$\sqrt[3]{-8} = \sqrt[3]{(-2)^3}$ Rewrite -8 as the third power of a number.
$= -2$ Simplify.

b. $\sqrt{-100}$
There is no real number whose square is -100.

✓ **Check Understanding** **2** Find each real-number root.

a. $\sqrt[3]{-27}$ **−3**   **b.** $\sqrt[4]{81}$ **3**   **c.** $\sqrt{49}$ **7**

Notice that when $x = 5$, $\sqrt{x^2} = \sqrt{5^2} = \sqrt{25} = 5 = x$,
and when $x = -5$, $\sqrt{x^2} = \sqrt{(-5)^2} = \sqrt{25} = 5 \neq x$.

 Key Concepts

Property	**nth Root of a^n, $a < 0$**
For any negative real number a, $\sqrt[n]{a^n} = |a|$ when n is even.	

👥 Reaching All Students

Below Level Ask students to square and then to cube 2, −2, 3, and −3. Discuss the need for absolute value notation when taking the square roots and cube roots of the results.	**Advanced Learners** The equation for the period of a simple pendulum is $T = 2\pi\sqrt{\frac{\ell}{g}}$. Ask students to find several more formulas involving radicals.	**Alternative Method** See note on page 364. **Error Prevention** See note on page 366.

3 EXAMPLE Simplifying Radical Expressions

Simplify each radical expression.

a. $\sqrt{4x^6}$

$$\sqrt{4x^6} = \sqrt{2^2(x^3)^2} = \sqrt{(2x^3)^2} = 2|x^3|$$

Absolute value symbols ensure that the root is positive when x is negative.

b. $\sqrt[3]{a^3b^6}$

$$\sqrt[3]{a^3b^6} = \sqrt[3]{a^3(b^2)^3} = \sqrt[3]{(ab^2)^3} = ab^2$$

Absolute value symbols must not be used here. If a is negative, then the radicand is negative and the root must also be negative.

c. $\sqrt[4]{x^4y^8}$

$$\sqrt[4]{x^4y^8} = \sqrt[4]{x^4(y^2)^4} = \sqrt[4]{(xy^2)^4} = |x|y^2$$

Absolute value symbols ensure that the root is positive when x is negative. They are not needed for y because y^2 is never negative.

Need Help?

$(a^m)^n = a^{mn}$

✓ **Check Understanding** 3 Simplify each radical expression. Use absolute value symbols when needed.
a. $\sqrt{4x^2y^4}$ **$2|x|y^2$**   **b.** $\sqrt[3]{-27c^6}$ **$-3c^2$**   **c.** $\sqrt[4]{x^8y^{12}}$ **$x^2|y^3|$**

4 EXAMPLE Real-World Connection

Packaging A citrus grower wants to ship a select grade of oranges that weigh from 8 to 9 ounces in gift cartons. Each carton will hold three dozen oranges, in 3 layers of 3 oranges by 4 oranges.

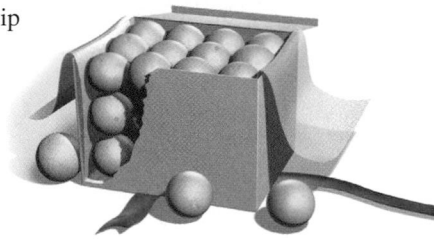

The weight of an orange is related to its diameter by the formula $w = \dfrac{d^3}{4}$, where d is the diameter in inches and w is the weight in ounces. Cartons can be ordered in whole-inch dimensions. What size cartons should the grower order?

Find the diameters of the oranges.

$8 \le$	w	≤ 9	**Write an inequality.**
$8 \le$	$\dfrac{d^3}{4}$	≤ 9	**Substitute for w in terms of d.**
$32 \le$	d^3	≤ 36	**Multiply by 4.**
$\sqrt[3]{32} \le$	$\sqrt[3]{d^3}$	$\le \sqrt[3]{36}$	**Take cube roots.**
$3.17 \le$	d	≤ 3.30	**The diameters range from 3.17 in. to 3.30 in.**

The length of a row of 4 of the largest oranges is 4(3.30 in.) = 13.2 in. The length of a row of 3 of the largest oranges is 3(3.30 in.) = 9.90 in. The grower should order cartons that are 14 in. long by 10 in. wide by 10 in. high to accommodate three dozen of the largest oranges.

Graphing Calculator Hint

Use the $\sqrt[3]{}$ feature in the MATH menu to find cube roots. For other roots, type the index first and then select the $\sqrt[x]{}$ feature.

✓ **Check Understanding** 4 Use the formula in Example 4 to find the diameter of each orange.
a. 3 oz **2.29 in.**   **b.** 5.5 oz **2.8 in.**   **c.** 6.25 oz **2.92 in.**

Additional Examples

1 Find all the real roots.
a. the cube roots of 0.027, -125, and $\frac{1}{64}$ **0.3, -5, $\frac{1}{4}$**
b. the fourth roots of 625, -0.0016, and $\frac{81}{625}$ **± 5, none, $\pm\frac{3}{5}$**

2 Find each real-number root.
a. $\sqrt[3]{-1000}$ **-10**
b. $\sqrt{-81}$ **none**

3 Simplify each radical expression.
a. $\sqrt{9x^{10}}$ **$3|x^5|$**
b. $\sqrt[3]{a^3b^3}$ **ab**
c. $\sqrt[4]{x^{16}y^4}$ **$x^4|y|$**

4 A cheese manufacturer wants to ship cheese balls that weigh from 10 to 11 ounces in cartons that will have 3 layers of 3 cheese balls by 4 cheese balls. The weight of a cheese ball is related to its diameter by the formula $w = \frac{d^3}{5}$, where d is the diameter in inches and w is the weight in ounces. What size cartons should be used? Assume whole-inch dimensions. **16 in. long by 12 in. wide by 12 in. high**

Closure

Ask students to explain what is meant by the nth root of a number, where n is a positive integer and $n \ge 2$. Have them explain under what conditions it is necessary to use absolute value in simplifying expressions involving nth roots. **A real number a is an nth root of a nonnegative real number b if $a^n = b$. If n is even and a can have negative values then $\sqrt[n]{a^n}$ must be simplified to $|a|$.**

3. Practice

pages 366–367   Exercises

22. $0.5|x^3|$

23. $x^4|y^9|$

24. $8b^{24}$

44. $3xy^2\sqrt{3}$

45. $12y^2z^2x\sqrt{xz}$

46. y^4

47. $-y^4$

48. k^3

366

EXERCISES

For more practice, see *Extra Practice*.

Practice and Problem Solving

Ⓐ **Practice by Example**

Example 1
(page 364)

Find all the real square roots of each number.

1. 225 **15, −15**   **2.** 0.0049 **0.07, −0.07**   **3.** $-\frac{1}{121}$ **none**   **4.** $\frac{64}{169}$ $\frac{8}{13}, -\frac{8}{13}$

Find all the real cube roots of each number.

5. −64 **−4**   **6.** 0.125 **0.5**   **7.** $-\frac{27}{216}$ $-\frac{1}{2}$ **8.** 0.000343 **0.07**

Find all the real fourth roots of each number.

9. 16 **2, −2**   **10.** −16 **none**   **11.** 0.0081 **0.3, −0.3**   **12.** $\frac{10,000}{81}$ $\frac{10}{3}, -\frac{10}{3}$

Example 2
(page 364)

Find each real-number root.

13. $\sqrt{36}$ **6**   **14.** $-\sqrt{36}$ **−6**   **15.** $\sqrt{-36}$ **no real root**   **16.** $\sqrt{0.36}$ **0.6**

17. $-\sqrt[3]{64}$ **−4**   **18.** $\sqrt[3]{-64}$ **−4**   **19.** $-\sqrt[4]{81}$ **−3**   **20.** $\sqrt[4]{-81}$ **no real root**

Example 3
(page 365)

Simplify each radical expression. Use absolute value symbols when needed.

22–24. See margin.

21. $\sqrt{16x^2}$ **4|x|**   **22.** $\sqrt{0.25x^6}$ **23.** $\sqrt{x^8y^{18}}$ **24.** $\sqrt{64b^{48}}$

25. $\sqrt[3]{-64a^3}$ **−4a**   **26.** $\sqrt[3]{27y^6}$ **3y²**   **27.** $\sqrt[4]{x^8y^{12}}$ **x²|y³|**   **28.** $\sqrt[5]{32y^{10}}$ **2y²**

Example 4
(page 365)

Geometry The formula for the volume of a sphere is $V = \frac{4}{3}\pi r^3$. Find the radius to the nearest hundredth of a sphere with each volume.

29. 10 in.³ **1.34 in.**   **30.** 20 ft³ **1.68 ft**   **31.** 0.45 cm³ **0.48 cm**   **32.** 0.002 mm³ **0.08 mm**

Ⓑ **Apply Your Skills**

Find the two real-number solutions of each equation.

33. $x^2 = 100$ **10, −10**   **34.** $x^4 = 1$ **1, −1**   **35.** $x^2 = 0.25$ **0.5, −0.5**   **36.** $x^4 = \frac{16}{81}$ $\frac{2}{3}, -\frac{2}{3}$

37. Arrange the numbers $\sqrt[3]{-64}$, $-\sqrt[3]{-64}$, $\sqrt{64}$, and $\sqrt[6]{64}$ in order from least to greatest. $\sqrt[3]{-64}, \sqrt[6]{64}, -\sqrt[3]{-64}, \sqrt{64}$

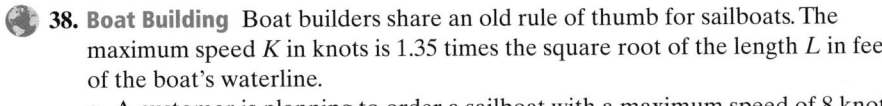

38. Boat Building Boat builders share an old rule of thumb for sailboats. The maximum speed K in knots is 1.35 times the square root of the length L in feet of the boat's waterline.
   a. A customer is planning to order a sailboat with a maximum speed of 8 knots. How long should the waterline be? **≈35 ft**
   b. How much longer would the waterline have to be to achieve a maximum speed of 10 knots? **≈20 ft longer**

44–50. See margin.
Simplify each radical expression. Use absolute value symbols when needed.

39. $\sqrt[3]{0.125}$ **0.5**   **40.** $\sqrt[3]{\frac{8}{216}}$ $\frac{1}{3}$ **41.** $\sqrt[4]{0.0016}$ **0.2**   **42.** $\sqrt[4]{\frac{1}{256}}$ $\frac{1}{4}$

43. $\sqrt[4]{16c^4}$ **2|c|**   **44.** $\sqrt[3]{81x^3y^6}$ **45.** $\sqrt{144x^3y^4z^5}$ **46.** $\sqrt[5]{y^{20}}$

47. $\sqrt[5]{-y^{20}}$ **48.** $\sqrt[5]{k^{15}}$ **49.** $\sqrt[5]{-k^{15}}$ **50.** $\sqrt{(x+3)^2}$

51. $\sqrt{(x+1)^4}$ **(x + 1)²**   **52.** $\sqrt[2n]{x^{2n}}$ **x**   **53.** $\sqrt[2n]{x^{4n}}$ **x²**   **54.** $\sqrt[2n]{x^{6n}}$ **x³**

55. Open-Ended Find three radical expressions that simplify to $-2x^2$. **See margin.**

---

49. $-k^3$

50. $|x + 3|$

55. **Answers may vary.**
   Sample: $\sqrt[3]{-8x^6}$, $-\sqrt[4]{16x^8}$, $\sqrt[5]{-32x^{10}}$

366

56a. for all positive integers

b. for all odd positive integers

56. Critical Thinking For what positive integers n is each of the statements true?
a. If $x^n = b$, then x is an nth root of b.   **b.** If $x^n = b$, then $x = \sqrt[n]{b}$.

 **57. Writing** Is 10 a first root of 10? Explain. **Yes, because 10 is really 10^1.**

Tell whether each equation is true for *all*, *some*, or *no values* of the variable.
Explain your answers.   **58–61. See margin.**

58. $\sqrt{x^4} = x^2$ **59.** $\sqrt{x^6} = x^3$ **60.** $\sqrt[3]{x^8} = x^2$ **61.** $\sqrt[3]{x^3} = |x|$

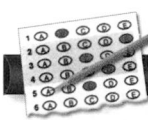 **Challenge**

Simplify each rational expression. *n* is an even number.

62. $\sqrt[n]{m^n}$ $|m|$ **63.** $\sqrt[n]{m^{2n}}$ m^2 **64.** $\sqrt[n]{m^{3n}}$ $|m^3|$ **65.** $\sqrt[n]{m^{4n}}$ m^4

Simplify each rational expression. *n* is an odd number.

66. $\sqrt[n]{m^n}$ m **67.** $\sqrt[n]{m^{2n}}$ m^2 **68.** $\sqrt[n]{m^{3n}}$ m^3 **69.** $\sqrt[n]{m^{4n}}$ m^4

Standardized Test Prep

Multiple Choice

70. Which equation has more than one real-number solution? **B**
    A. $x^2 = 0$ **B.** $x^2 = 1$ **C.** $x^2 = -1$ **D.** $x^3 = -1$

71. Which number is greatest? **I**
    F. $\sqrt{0.5}$ **G.** $\sqrt[3]{0.5}$ **H.** $\sqrt[4]{0.5}$ **I.** $\sqrt[5]{0.5}$

72. Which statement is NOT true? **B**
    A. $-3 = -\sqrt{9}$ **B.** $-3 = -\sqrt{-9}$
    C. $-3 = \sqrt[3]{-27}$ **D.** $-3 = -\sqrt[4]{81}$

Take It to the NET
Online lesson quiz at
www.PHSchool.com
Web Code: aga-0701

73. Absolute value symbols are needed when you simplify some of these expressions. Which ones are they? **H**

    I. $\sqrt[3]{-x^3y^6}$ **II.** $\sqrt{x^2y^4}$ **III.** $\sqrt[4]{x^8y^{12}}$ **IV.** $\sqrt{x^4y^6}$

    F. II and III only   **G.** II and IV only
    H. II, III and IV only   **I.** I, II, III and IV

Short Response

74. For what values of x and y does $\sqrt{x^2y^4}$ equal $\sqrt[3]{x^3y^6}$? Explain your answer.
                                                     See back of book.

Mixed Review

Lesson 6-8

Expand each binomial.   **75–78. See margin.**

75. $(x + y)^5$ **76.** $(2 - 3y)^4$ **77.** $(3x - 5)^6$ **78.** $(2a - b)^7$

Lesson 6-2

Write each function in factored form. Check by multiplying.

79. $y = x(2x - 7)(2x + 7)$
79. $y = 4x^3 - 49x$ **80.** $y = 81x^2 + 36x + 4$

80. $y = (9x + 2)^2$
81. $y = 4x^3 + 8x^2 + 4x$ **82.** $y = 12x^3 + 14x^2 + 2x$
        $y = 4x(x + 1)^2$ $y = 2x(6x + 1)(x + 1)$

Lesson 5-3

Rewrite each equation in vertex form.

85. $y = \frac{1}{4}(x + 4)^2 - 5$
83. $y = 3x^2 - 7$ **84.** $y = -2x^2 + x - 10$ **85.** $y = \frac{x^2}{4} + 2x - 1$
        $y = 3(x - 0)^2 - 7$ $y = -2\left(x - \frac{1}{4}\right)^2 - \frac{79}{8}$

                        Lesson 7-1   Roots and Radical Expressions   **367**

58. All; x^2 is always positive.

59. Some; they are equal for $x \geq 0$.

60. Some; they are equal for $x = -1, 0, 1$.

61. Some; they are equal for $x \geq 0$.

75. $x^5 + 5x^4y + 10x^3y^2 + 10x^2y^3 + 5xy^4 + y^5$

76. $16 - 96y + 216y^2 - 216y^3 + 81y^4$

77. $729x^6 - 7290x^5 + 30{,}375x^4 - 67{,}500x^3 + 84{,}375x^2 - 56{,}250x + 15{,}625$

78. $128a^7 - 448a^6b + 672a^5b^2 - 560a^4b^3 + 280a^3b^4 - 84a^2b^5 + 14ab^6 - b^7$

Lesson Quiz 7-1

1. Find all the real square roots of each number.
   a. 121 ± 11 **b.** -49 **none**
   c. 64 ± 8 **d.** $-\frac{1}{25}$ **none**

2. Find all the real cube roots of each number.
   a. -8000 -20
   b. $\frac{1}{216}$ $\frac{1}{6}$

3. Find each real-number root.
   a. $\sqrt{0.49}$ 0.7
   b. $\sqrt[3]{125}$ 5
   c. $-\sqrt{81}$ -9
   d. $\sqrt[4]{-625}$ **none**

4. Simplify each radical expression.
   a. $\sqrt[3]{-8x^3}$ $-2x$
   b. $\sqrt{16y^4}$ $4y^2$
   c. $\sqrt{36x^{14}}$ $6|x^7|$

5. The formula for the volume of a cone with a base of radius r and height r is $V = \frac{1}{3}\pi r^3$. Find the radius to the nearest hundredth of a centimeter if the volume is 40 cm^3. **about 3.37 cm**

Alternative Assessment

Ask students to write three radical expressions that simplify to $3x$, three that simplify to $-2x$, three that simplify to $2|x|$, and three that simplify to $x|y|$. Some of the expressions should use radicals with even indices and some should use radicals with odd indices. Have students share their expressions with the class.

Standardized Test Prep

 **Resources**

For additional practice with a variety of test item formats:
- Standardized Test Prep, p. 419
- Test-Taking Strategies, p. 414
- Test-Taking Strategies with Transparencies

1. Plan

Lesson Preview

 Check Skills You'll Need

Finding Factors
Algebra 1 Review: Page 362,
Exercises 1–9

Lesson Resources

 Teaching Resources
Practice, Reteaching, Enrichment

 Reaching All Students
Practice Workbook 7-2
Spanish Practice Workbook 7-2

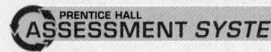 **Presentation Assistant Plus!**
Transparencies
• Check Skills You'll Need 7-2
• Additional Examples 7-2
• Student Edition Answers 7-2
• Lesson Quiz 7-2
PH Presentation Pro CD 7-2

 PRENTICE HALL
ASSESSMENT SYSTEM

Computer Test Generator CD

 Technology
Resource Pro® CD-ROM
Computer Test Generator CD
Prentice Hall Presentation Pro CD

 **www.PHSchool.com**
Student Site
• Teacher Web Code: agk-5500
• Self-grading Lesson Quiz
Teacher Center
• Lesson Planner
• Resources

Plus **iTEXT**

368

7-2

Multiplying and Dividing Radical Expressions

North Carolina Objectives

1.01 Simplify and perform operations with rational exponents and logarithms (common and natural) to solve problems.

Lesson Preview

What You'll Learn

 OBJECTIVE 1
To multiply radical expressions

 OBJECTIVE 2
To divide radical expressions

...Any Why

To transform a famous formula, as in Example 6

 Check Skills You'll Need   (For help, go to page 362.)

Find each missing factor.

1. $150 = 5^2(\blacksquare)$ **6**

2. $54 = (\blacksquare)^3(2)$ **3**

3. $48 = 4^2(\blacksquare)$ **3**

4. $x^5 = (\blacksquare)^2(x)$ x^2

5. $3a^3b^4 = (\blacksquare)^3(3b)$ ab

6. $75a^7b^8 = (\blacksquare)^2(3a)$ $5a^3b^4$

New Vocabulary • rationalize the denominator

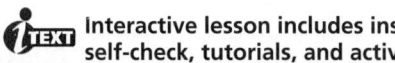 **iTEXT** Interactive lesson includes instant self-check, tutorials, and activities.

OBJECTIVE
1 **Multiplying Radical Expressions**

To multiply radicals consider the following.

$\sqrt{16} \cdot \sqrt{9} = 4 \cdot 3 = 12$ and $\sqrt{16 \cdot 9} = \sqrt{144} = 12$.
So $\sqrt{16} \cdot \sqrt{9} = \sqrt{16 \cdot 9}$.

$\sqrt[3]{-8} \cdot \sqrt[3]{27} = -2 \cdot 3 = -6$ and $\sqrt[3]{-8 \cdot 27} = \sqrt[3]{-216} = -6$.
So $\sqrt[3]{-8} \cdot \sqrt[3]{27} = \sqrt[3]{-8 \cdot 27}$.

In general, the product of the principal nth roots of two numbers equals the principal nth root of their product.

Key Concepts

Property	**Multiplying Radical Expressions**
If $\sqrt[n]{a}$ and $\sqrt[n]{b}$ are real numbers, then $\sqrt[n]{a} \cdot \sqrt[n]{b} = \sqrt[n]{ab}$.	

1 EXAMPLE **Multiplying Radicals**

Multiply. Simplify if possible.

a. $\sqrt{2} \cdot \sqrt{8}$

$\sqrt{2} \cdot \sqrt{8} = \sqrt{2 \cdot 8} = \sqrt{16} = 4$

b. $\sqrt[3]{-5} \cdot \sqrt[3]{25}$

$\sqrt[3]{-5} \cdot \sqrt[3]{25} = \sqrt[3]{-125} = \sqrt[3]{(-5)^3} = -5$

c. $\sqrt{-2} \cdot \sqrt{8}$

The property for multiplying radicals does *not* apply. $\sqrt{-2}$ is not a real number.

 Check Understanding **1** Multiply. Simplify if possible.

a. $\sqrt{3} \cdot \sqrt{12}$ **6**   **b.** $\sqrt[3]{3} \cdot \sqrt[3]{-9}$ **−3**   **not possible**
c. $\sqrt[4]{4} \cdot \sqrt[4]{-4}$

INSTANT CHECK SYSTEM **Ongoing Assessment and Intervention**

Before the Lesson **Diagnose prerequisite skills using:**	**During the Lesson** **Monitor progress using:**	**After the Lesson** **Assess knowledge using:**
• Check Skills You'll Need	• Check Understanding • Additional Examples • Standardized Test Prep	• Lesson Quiz • Computer Test Generator CD

$2\sqrt[3]{3}$ is considered to be a simplified form of $\sqrt[3]{24}$. You can use the property for multiplying radical expressions to simplify some radical expressions.

2 EXAMPLE Simplifying Radical Expressions

Simplify each expression. Assume that all variables are positive. Then absolute value symbols are never needed in the simplified expression.

Reading Math

The phrase *all variables are positive* is a short way of saying that the domain of the variables is the set of positive numbers.

a. $\sqrt{72x^3}$

$$\sqrt{72x^3} = \sqrt{6^2 \cdot 2 \cdot x^2 \cdot x} \qquad \text{Factor into perfect squares.}$$
$$= \sqrt{6^2x^2} \cdot \sqrt{2x} \qquad \sqrt[n]{a} \cdot \sqrt[n]{b} = \sqrt[n]{ab}$$
$$= 6x\sqrt{2x} \qquad \text{Simplify.}$$

b. $\sqrt[3]{80n^5}$

$$\sqrt[3]{80n^5} = \sqrt[3]{2^3 \cdot 10 \cdot n^3 \cdot n^2} \qquad \text{Factor into perfect cubes.}$$
$$= \sqrt[3]{2^3n^3} \cdot \sqrt[3]{10n^2} \qquad \sqrt[n]{a} \cdot \sqrt[n]{b} = \sqrt[n]{ab}$$
$$= 2n\sqrt[3]{10n^2} \qquad \text{Simplify.}$$

✓ **Check Understanding** **2** Simplify $\sqrt{50x^4}$ and $\sqrt[3]{18x^4}$. Assume that x is positive.
$$5x^2\sqrt{2}; \; x\sqrt[3]{18x}$$

Simplify the products of radicals as much as possible.

3 EXAMPLE Multiplying Radical Expressions

Multiply and simplify $\sqrt[3]{54x^2y^3} \cdot \sqrt[3]{5x^3y^4}$. Assume that all variables are positive.

$$\sqrt[3]{54x^2y^3} \cdot \sqrt[3]{5x^3y^4} = \sqrt[3]{54x^2y^3 \cdot 5x^3y^4} \qquad \sqrt[n]{a} \cdot \sqrt[n]{b} = \sqrt[n]{ab}$$
$$= \sqrt[3]{3^3x^3(y^2)^3 \cdot 10x^2y} \qquad \text{Factor into perfect cubes.}$$
$$= \sqrt[3]{3^3x^3(y^2)^3} \cdot \sqrt[3]{10x^2y} \qquad \sqrt[n]{a} \cdot \sqrt[n]{b} = \sqrt[n]{ab}$$
$$= 3xy^2\sqrt[3]{10x^2y} \qquad \text{Simplify.}$$

✓ **Check Understanding** **3** Multiply and simplify $3\sqrt{7x^3} \cdot 2\sqrt{21x^3y^2}$. Assume that all variables are positive.
$$42x^3y\sqrt{3}$$

OBJECTIVE 2 Dividing Radical Expressions

To divide radicals, consider the following.

$$\frac{\sqrt{36}}{\sqrt{25}} = \frac{6}{5} \text{ and } \sqrt{\frac{36}{25}} = \sqrt{\left(\frac{6}{5}\right)^2} = \frac{6}{5}. \text{ So } \frac{\sqrt{36}}{\sqrt{25}} = \sqrt{\frac{36}{25}}.$$

In general, the quotient of the principal nth roots of two numbers equals the principal nth root of their quotient.

🔑 **Key Concepts**

Property	Dividing Radical Expressions
If $\sqrt[n]{a}$ and $\sqrt[n]{b}$ are real numbers and $b \neq 0$, then $\dfrac{\sqrt[n]{a}}{\sqrt[n]{b}} = \sqrt[n]{\dfrac{a}{b}}$.	

---

2. Teach

Professional Development

Math Background

The properties for multiplying and dividing radicals, presented in this lesson, both actually hold under less restrictive conditions on $\sqrt[n]{a}$ and $\sqrt[n]{b}$, but more restrictive conditions on n. Students can investigate these conditions using their knowledge of imaginary numbers from Chapter 5. Both properties aid in simplifying radical expressions. To simplify radical expressions that involve fractions, write the expressions so that no denominator contains a radical and no radicand contains a fraction.

OBJECTIVE 1 Teaching Notes

2 EXAMPLE Math Tip

Point out that to simplify an nth root, you need to look for nth powers that are factors of the radicand. For example, if $n = 2$, then look for factors of the radicand that are perfect squares.

Additional Examples

1 Multiply. Simplify if possible.
a. $\sqrt{3} \cdot \sqrt{12}$ **6**
b. $\sqrt[3]{-16} \cdot \sqrt[3]{4}$ **−4**
c. $\sqrt{-4} \cdot \sqrt{16}$ **The Property for Multiplying Radicals does not apply.**

2 Simplify each expression. Assume all variables are positive.
a. $\sqrt{50x^5}$ **$5x^2\sqrt{2x}$**
b. $\sqrt[3]{54n^8}$ **$3n^2\sqrt[3]{2n^2}$**

3 Multiply and simplify $\sqrt[3]{25xy^8} \cdot \sqrt[3]{5x^4y^3}$. Assume all variables are positive. **$5xy^3\sqrt[3]{x^2y^2}$**

👥 Reaching All Students

Below Level Have students write out the properties for multiplying and dividing radical expressions using several different numerical examples.	**Advanced Learners** Point out to students that rationalizing a denominator is a necessary algebraic skill in some higher mathematics.	**Alternative Method** See note on page 370. **Error Prevention** See note on page 371.

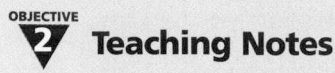
The expression in part b is simplified using Method II. However, the expression can also be simplified with Method I by rewriting the expression as the square root of a fraction.

Additional Examples

4 Divide and simplify. Assume all variables are positive.

a. $\dfrac{\sqrt[3]{-81}}{\sqrt[3]{3}}$ -3

b. $\dfrac{\sqrt[3]{192x^8}}{\sqrt[3]{3x}}$ $4x^2\sqrt[3]{x}$

5 Rationalize the denominator of each expression. Assume all variables are positive.

a. $\dfrac{\sqrt{3}}{\sqrt{5}}$ $\dfrac{\sqrt{15}}{5}$

b. $\dfrac{\sqrt{x^5}}{\sqrt{3x^2y}}$ $\dfrac{x\sqrt{3xy}}{3y}$

c. $\sqrt[3]{\dfrac{5}{4y}}$ $\dfrac{\sqrt[3]{10y^2}}{2y}$

6 The distance d in meters that an object will fall in t seconds is given by $d = 4.9t^2$. Express t in terms of d and rationalize the denominator. $t = \dfrac{\sqrt{10d}}{7}$

Closure

Ask students to describe how to multiply and divide two nth roots, both of which are real numbers. **To multiply the nth roots, take the nth root of the product of the radicands. To divide the nth roots, take the nth root of the quotient of the radicands.**

---

4 EXAMPLE Dividing Radicals

Divide and simplify. Assume that all variables are positive.

a. $\dfrac{\sqrt[3]{32}}{\sqrt[3]{-4}}$

$\dfrac{\sqrt[3]{32}}{\sqrt[3]{-4}} = \sqrt[3]{\dfrac{32}{-4}} = \sqrt[3]{-8} = -2$

b. $\dfrac{\sqrt[3]{162x^5}}{\sqrt[3]{3x^2}}$

$\dfrac{\sqrt[3]{162x^5}}{\sqrt[3]{3x^2}} = \sqrt[3]{\dfrac{162x^5}{3x^2}} = \sqrt[3]{54x^3} = \sqrt[3]{3^3x^3 \cdot 2} = \sqrt[3]{3^3x^3} \cdot \sqrt[3]{2} = 3x\sqrt[3]{2}$

✓ **Check Understanding** **4** Divide and simplify. Assume that all variables are positive.

a. $\dfrac{\sqrt{243}}{\sqrt{27}}$ 3

b. $\dfrac{\sqrt{12x^4}}{\sqrt{3x}}$ $2x\sqrt{x}$

c. $\dfrac{\sqrt[4]{1024x^{15}}}{\sqrt[4]{4x}}$ $4x^3\sqrt[4]{x^2}$

To **rationalize the denominator** of an expression, rewrite it so there are no radicals in any denominator and no denominators in any radical.

Rationalizing the denominator of a numerical expression makes it easier to calculate its decimal approximation. For example, $\dfrac{1}{\sqrt{2}} = \dfrac{\sqrt{2}}{2}$ and it is easier to divide by 2 than by $\sqrt{2}$.

5 EXAMPLE Rationalizing the Denominator

Rationalize the denominator of each expression. Assume that all variables are positive.

a. $\dfrac{\sqrt{2}}{\sqrt{3}}$

Method 1

$\dfrac{\sqrt{2}}{\sqrt{3}} = \sqrt{\dfrac{2}{3}} = \sqrt{\dfrac{2 \cdot 3}{3 \cdot 3}} = \sqrt{\dfrac{6}{3^2}} = \dfrac{\sqrt{6}}{\sqrt{3^2}} = \dfrac{\sqrt{6}}{3}$ 　Rewrite as a square root of a fraction. Then make the denominator a perfect square.

Method 2

$\dfrac{\sqrt{2}}{\sqrt{3}} = \dfrac{\sqrt{2} \cdot \sqrt{3}}{\sqrt{3} \cdot \sqrt{3}} = \dfrac{\sqrt{6}}{3}$ 　Multiply the numerator and denominator by $\sqrt{3}$ so the denominator becomes a whole number.

b. $\dfrac{\sqrt{x^3}}{\sqrt{5xy}}$

$\dfrac{\sqrt{x^3}}{\sqrt{5xy}} = \dfrac{\sqrt{x^3} \cdot \sqrt{5xy}}{\sqrt{5xy} \cdot \sqrt{5xy}} = \dfrac{\sqrt{5x^4y}}{5xy} = \dfrac{x^2\sqrt{5y}}{5xy} = \dfrac{x\sqrt{5y}}{5y}$

c. $\sqrt[3]{\dfrac{2}{3x}}$

$\sqrt[3]{\dfrac{2}{3x}} = \sqrt[3]{\dfrac{2 \cdot 3^2x^2}{3x \cdot 3^2x^2}} = \sqrt[3]{\dfrac{18x^2}{3^3x^3}} = \dfrac{\sqrt[3]{18x^2}}{3x}$ 　Rewrite the fraction so the denominator is a perfect cube.

✓ **Check Understanding** **5** Rationalize the denominator of each expression. Assume that the variables are positive.

a. $\sqrt{\dfrac{7}{5}}$ $\dfrac{\sqrt{35}}{5}$

b. $\dfrac{\sqrt{2x^3}}{\sqrt{10xy}}$ $\dfrac{x\sqrt{5y}}{5y}$

c. $\dfrac{\sqrt[3]{4}}{\sqrt[3]{6x}}$ $\dfrac{\sqrt[3]{18x^2}}{3x}$

6 **EXAMPLE** Real-World Connection

Einstein's famous formula $E = mc^2$ relates energy E, mass m, and the speed of light c. Express c in terms of E and m and rationalize the denominator.

$$E = mc^2$$

$$c^2 = \frac{E}{m}$$

$$c = \sqrt{\frac{E}{m}} = \sqrt{\frac{Em}{m^2}} = \frac{\sqrt{Em}}{\sqrt{m^2}} = \frac{\sqrt{Em}}{m}$$

 Check Understanding **6** The formula $a = \frac{d}{t^2}$ relates the acceleration a of a moving object to the distance d it moves in the time t. Solve the formula for t and rationalize the denominator.

$$t = \frac{\sqrt{da}}{a}$$

EXERCISES

For more practice, see *Extra Practice*.

Practice and Problem Solving

A **Practice by Example**

Example 1
(page 368)

Multiply, if possible. Then simplify.

1. $\sqrt{8} \cdot \sqrt{32}$ **16**
2. $\sqrt[3]{4} \cdot \sqrt[3]{16}$ **4**
3. $\sqrt[3]{9} \cdot \sqrt[3]{-81}$ **−9**
4. $\sqrt[4]{8} \cdot \sqrt[4]{32}$ **4**
5. $\sqrt{-5} \cdot \sqrt{5}$ **not possible**
6. $\sqrt[3]{-5} \cdot \sqrt[3]{-25}$ **5**
7. $\sqrt[3]{9} \cdot \sqrt[3]{-24}$ **−6**
8. $\sqrt[3]{-12} \cdot \sqrt[3]{-18}$ **6**

Example 2
(page 369)

Simplify. Assume that all variables are positive. **9–12. See margin.**

9. $\sqrt{20x^3}$
10. $\sqrt[3]{81x^2}$
11. $\sqrt{50x^5}$
12. $\sqrt[3]{32a^5}$
13. $\sqrt[3]{54y^{10}}$ **$3y^3\sqrt[3]{2y}$**
14. $\sqrt{200a^6b^7}$ **$10a^3b^3\sqrt{2b}$**
15. $\sqrt[3]{-250x^6y^5}$ **$-5x^2y\sqrt[3]{2y^2}$**
16. $\sqrt[4]{64x^3y^6}$ **$2y\sqrt[4]{4x^3y^2}$**

Example 3
(page 369)

Multiply and simplify. Assume that all variables are positive.

17. $\sqrt[3]{6} \cdot \sqrt[3]{16}$ **$2\sqrt[3]{12}$**
18. $\sqrt{8y^5} \cdot \sqrt{40y^2}$ **$8y^3\sqrt{5y}$**
19. $\sqrt{7x^5} \cdot \sqrt{42xy^9}$ **$7x^3y^4\sqrt{6y}$**
20. $4\sqrt{2x} \cdot 5\sqrt{6xy^2}$ **$40xy\sqrt{3}$**
21. $3\sqrt[3]{5y^3} \cdot 2\sqrt[3]{50y^4}$ **$30y^2\sqrt[3]{2y}$**
22. $-\sqrt[3]{2x^2y^2} \cdot 2\sqrt[3]{15x^5y}$ **$-2x^2y\sqrt[3]{30x}$**

Example 4
(page 370)

Divide and simplify. Assume that all variables are positive.

23. $\dfrac{\sqrt{500}}{\sqrt{5}}$ **10**
24. $\dfrac{\sqrt{48x^3}}{\sqrt{3xy^2}}$ **$\dfrac{4x}{y}$**
25. $\dfrac{\sqrt{56x^5y^5}}{\sqrt{7xy}}$ **$2x^2y^2\sqrt{2}$**
26. $\dfrac{\sqrt[3]{250x^7y^3}}{\sqrt[3]{2x^2y}}$ **$5x\sqrt[3]{x^2y^2}$**

Example 5
(page 370)

Rationalize the denominator of each expression. Assume that all variables are positive. **30–34. See margin.**

27. $\dfrac{\sqrt{x}}{\sqrt{2}}$ **$\dfrac{\sqrt{2x}}{2}$**
28. $\dfrac{\sqrt{5}}{\sqrt{8x}}$ **$\dfrac{\sqrt{10x}}{4x}$**
29. $\dfrac{\sqrt[3]{x}}{\sqrt[3]{2}}$ **$\dfrac{\sqrt[3]{4x}}{2}$**
30. $\sqrt[3]{\dfrac{5}{3x}}$
31. $\dfrac{\sqrt[4]{2}}{\sqrt[4]{5}}$
32. $\dfrac{15\sqrt{60x^5}}{3\sqrt{12x}}$
33. $\dfrac{\sqrt{3xy^2}}{\sqrt{5xy^3}}$
34. $\dfrac{\sqrt{5x^4y}}{\sqrt{2x^2y^3}}$

Example 6
(page 371)

35. **Physics** The formula $F = \dfrac{Gm_1m_2}{r^2}$ relates the gravitational force F between an object of mass m_1 and an object of mass m_2 separated by distance r. G is a constant known as the constant of gravitation. Solve the formula for r. Rationalize the denominator. **$r = \dfrac{\sqrt{Gm_1m_2F}}{F}$**

Lesson 7-2 Multiplying and Dividing Radical Expressions **371**

3. Practice

Assignment Guide

1 **Objective**
Ⓐ Ⓑ **Core** 1–22, 37–45, 56–58, 59
Ⓒ **Extension** 61–63, 68

2 **Objective**
Ⓐ Ⓑ **Core** 23–36, 46–54, 55, 60
Ⓒ **Extension** 64–67

Standardized Test Prep 69–75

Mixed Review 76–95

Error Prevention

Exercises 9–16 Remind students that they do not need to use absolute value signs since the variables are positive.

Connection to Physics

Exercise 35 You may wish to point out that the distance r is the distance between the centers of the objects.

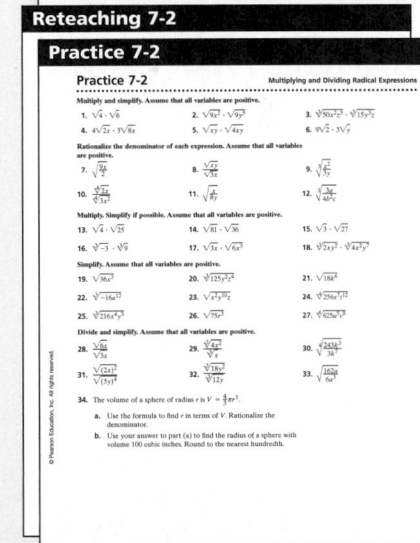

---

9. $2x\sqrt{5x}$
10. $3\sqrt[3]{3x^2}$
11. $5x^2\sqrt{2x}$
12. $2a\sqrt[3]{4a^2}$
30. $\dfrac{\sqrt[3]{45x^2}}{3x}$
31. $\dfrac{\sqrt[4]{250}}{5}$
32. $5x^2\sqrt{5}$
33. $\dfrac{\sqrt{15y}}{5y}$
34. $\dfrac{x\sqrt{10}}{2y}$

4. Assess

36. a. Simplify $\frac{\sqrt{2} + \sqrt{3}}{\sqrt{75}}$ by multiplying the numerator and denominator by $\sqrt{75}$.

b. Simplify the expression in (a) by multiplying by $\sqrt{3}$ instead of $\sqrt{75}$.

c. Explain how you would simplify $\frac{\sqrt{2} + \sqrt{3}}{\sqrt{98}}$. **a–c. See margin.**

Simplify each expression. Rationalize all denominators. Assume that all variables are positive.

37. $\sqrt{5} \cdot \sqrt{40}$ **10$\sqrt{2}$** **38.** $\sqrt[3]{4} \cdot \sqrt[3]{80}$ **4$\sqrt[3]{5}$** **39.** $\sqrt{x^5 y^5} \cdot 3\sqrt{2x^7 y^6}$ **$3x^6 y^5 \sqrt{2y}$**

40. $5\sqrt{2xy^6} \cdot 2\sqrt{2x^3 y}$ **41.** $\sqrt{2}(\sqrt{50} + 7)$ **42.** $3(5 + \sqrt{21})$

43. $\sqrt{5}(\sqrt{5} + \sqrt{15})$ **44.** $\sqrt[3]{2x} \cdot \sqrt[3]{4} \cdot \sqrt[3]{2x^2}$ **45.** $\sqrt[3]{3x^2} \cdot \sqrt[3]{x^2} \cdot \sqrt[3]{9x^3}$

46. $\frac{\sqrt{5x^4}}{\sqrt{2x^2 y^3}}$ **$\frac{x\sqrt{10y}}{2y^2}$** **47.** $\frac{5\sqrt{2}}{3\sqrt{7x}}$ **$\frac{5\sqrt{14x}}{21x}$** **48.** $\frac{1}{\sqrt[3]{9x}}$ **$\frac{\sqrt[3]{3x^2}}{3x}$**

49. $\frac{10}{\sqrt[3]{5x^2}}$ **$\frac{2\sqrt[3]{25x}}{x}$** **50.** $\frac{\sqrt[3]{14}}{\sqrt[3]{7x^2 y}}$ **$\frac{\sqrt[3]{2xy^2}}{xy}$** **51.** $\frac{3\sqrt{11x^3 y}}{-2\sqrt{12x^4 y}}$ **$\frac{\sqrt{33x}}{-4x}$**

52. $-2(\sqrt[3]{32} + \sqrt[3]{54})$ **$-4\sqrt[3]{4} - \sqrt[3]{2}$** **53.** $\frac{3 + \sqrt{5}}{\sqrt{5}}$ **$\frac{3\sqrt{5} + 5}{5}$** **54.** $\frac{\sqrt{3} - \sqrt{2}}{\sqrt{8}}$ **$\frac{\sqrt{6} - 2}{4}$**

55. Satellites The circular velocity v, in miles per hour, of a satellite orbiting Earth is given by the formula $v = \sqrt{\frac{1.24 \times 10^{12}}{r}}$, where r is the distance in miles from the satellite to the center of Earth. How much greater is the velocity of a satellite orbiting at an altitude of 100 mi than one orbiting at an altitude of 200 mi? (The radius of Earth is 3950 mi.) **212 mi/h greater**

56. Geometry A rectangular shelf is $\sqrt{440}$ cm by $\sqrt{20}$ cm. Find its area.

57. Error Analysis Explain the error in this simplification of radical expressions.
$\sqrt{-2} \cdot \sqrt{-8} = \sqrt{-2(-8)} = \sqrt{16} = 4$ **56–57. See margin.**

58. Physics A freely falling object hit the ground in $\sqrt{18a^5}$ seconds. It fell h feet. Use the formula $h = 16t^2$ to find h in terms of a. **288 a^5 ft**

Real-World  **Connection**

A satellite being launched from the cargo bay of the space shuttle

59. Writing Does $\sqrt{x^3} = \sqrt[3]{x^2}$ for all, some, or no values of x? Explain. **See margin.**

60. Open-Ended Of the equivalent expressions $\sqrt{\frac{2}{3}}$, $\frac{\sqrt{2}}{\sqrt{3}}$, and $\frac{\sqrt{6}}{3}$, which do you prefer to use for finding a decimal approximation with a calculator? Justify your reasoning. **Check students' work.**

C Challenge

Simplify each expression. Rationalize all denominators. Assume that all variables are positive.

61. $\sqrt{\sqrt{16x^4 y^4}}$ **2xy** **62.** $\sqrt[3]{\sqrt{64x^6 y^{12}}}$ **2xy^2** **63.** $\sqrt{\sqrt[3]{8000}}$ **2$\sqrt{5}$**

64. $\sqrt[3]{x^{-1} y^{-2}}$ **$\frac{\sqrt[3]{x^2 y}}{xy}$** **65.** $\sqrt[5]{x^{-4} y}$ **$\frac{\sqrt[5]{yx}}{x}$** **66.** $\sqrt[6]{\frac{y^{-3}}{x^{-4}}}$ **$\frac{\sqrt[6]{x^4 y^3}}{y}$**

67. $a = -2c, b = -6d$

67. Critical Thinking When $\sqrt{x^a y^b}$ is simplified, the result is $\frac{1}{x^c y^{3d}}$, where c and d are positive integers. Express a in terms of c, and b in terms of d.

68. Critical Thinking In Example 3 you saw that $\sqrt[3]{54x^2 y^3} \cdot \sqrt[3]{5x^3 y^4}$ simplifies to $3xy^2 \sqrt[3]{10x^2 y}$, if you assume that all the variables are positive. Now assume that the variables represent any real numbers. What changes must be made in the answer? Explain. **See margin.**

(Left margin)

Assume that all variables are positive.

1. Multiply. Simplify if possible.
 a. $\sqrt{5} \cdot \sqrt{45}$ **15**
 b. $\sqrt[3]{4} \cdot \sqrt[3]{2000}$ **20**

2. Simplify.
 a. $\sqrt{8x^5}$ **$2x^2\sqrt{2x}$**
 b. $\sqrt[3]{-243x^3 y^{10}}$ **$-3xy^3 \sqrt[3]{9y}$**

3. Multiply and simplify.
 a. $\sqrt{18x^3} \cdot \sqrt{2x^2 y^3}$
 $6x^2 y\sqrt{xy}$
 b. $\sqrt[3]{10x^2 y^4} \cdot \sqrt[3]{4x^2 y}$
 $2xy\sqrt[3]{5xy^2}$

4. Divide and simplify.
 a. $\frac{\sqrt{128x^3}}{\sqrt{2xy}}$ **$\frac{8x\sqrt{y}}{y}$**
 b. $\frac{\sqrt[3]{270x}}{\sqrt[3]{10xy^2}}$ **$\frac{3\sqrt[3]{y}}{y}$**

5. Rationalize the denominator of each expression.
 a. $\frac{\sqrt{7x}}{\sqrt{3}}$ **$\frac{\sqrt{21x}}{3}$**
 b. $\frac{\sqrt[3]{x^2}}{\sqrt[3]{4}}$ **$\frac{\sqrt[3]{2x^2}}{2}$**

Alternative Assessment

Have students work in pairs. Each student should make up a problem similar to those in each of Examples 1–5. Then have students work each other's problems and check each other's work.

pages 371–373 Exercises

36a. $\frac{\sqrt{6} + 3}{15}$

 b. $\frac{\sqrt{6} + 3}{15}$

 c. Answers may vary. Sample: First simplify the denominator. Since $\sqrt{98} = \sqrt{2 \cdot 49} = 7\sqrt{2}$, to rationalize the denominator, multiply the fraction by $\frac{\sqrt{2}}{\sqrt{2}}$. This yields $\frac{\sqrt{2 \cdot 2} + \sqrt{3 \cdot 2}}{7\sqrt{2 \cdot 2}} = \frac{2 + \sqrt{6}}{14}$.

372

(Bottom answers)

40. $20x^2 y^3 \sqrt{y}$

41. $10 + 7\sqrt{2}$

42. $15 + 3\sqrt{21}$

43. $5 + 5\sqrt{3}$

44. $2x\sqrt[3]{2}$

45. $3x^2\sqrt[3]{x}$

56. $20\sqrt{22}$ cm^3

57. A product of two square roots can be simplified in this way only if the square roots are real numbers. $\sqrt{-2}$ and $\sqrt{-8}$ are not.

59. For some values, it is easy to see that the equation is true if $x = 0$ or $x = 1$. But when $x < 0$, $\sqrt{x^3}$ is not a real number, although $\sqrt[3]{x^2}$ is.

68. No changes need to be made; since they are both odd roots, there is no need for absolute value symbols.

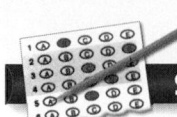

Multiple Choice

69. Which expression does NOT simplify to -10? **C**

A. $-\sqrt[3]{1000}$

B. $\sqrt{25} \cdot \sqrt[3]{-8}$

C. $-\sqrt{25} \cdot \sqrt[5]{-32}$

D. $\sqrt[3]{-125} \cdot \sqrt[4]{16}$

70. How can you write $\sqrt[3]{\dfrac{5}{2xy}}$ with a rationalized denominator? **H**

F. $\dfrac{\sqrt[3]{5}}{2xy}$

G. $\dfrac{\sqrt[3]{20}}{2xy}$

H. $\dfrac{\sqrt[3]{20x^2y^2}}{2xy}$

I. $\dfrac{\sqrt[3]{4x^2y^2}}{2xy}$

Take It to the NET
Online lesson quiz at
www.PHSchool.com
Web Code: aga-0702

71. What is the simplified form of $\dfrac{3 - \sqrt{5}}{\sqrt{5}}$? **A**

A. $\dfrac{3\sqrt{5} - 5}{5}$

B. $\dfrac{5\sqrt{3} - 5}{5}$

C. $\dfrac{3\sqrt{3} - \sqrt{15}}{5}$

D. $\dfrac{14 - 6\sqrt{5}}{5}$

72. To rationalize the denominator of $\sqrt[3]{\dfrac{2}{9}}$, by what number would you multiply the numerator and denominator of the fraction? **G**

F. 2

G. 3

H. 6

I. 9

73. Which of the following expressions is in simplest form? **D**

A. $\sqrt{20x^3}$

B. $\sqrt[3]{81x}$

C. $\sqrt{\dfrac{6}{2}}$

D. $\dfrac{\sqrt{2}}{5}$

Short Response

74. For what values of x is $\sqrt{x} \cdot \sqrt{-x}$ a real number? Explain. 74–75. See margin.

Extended Response

75. Rationalize the denominator of $\sqrt[3]{\dfrac{3}{2x}}$. Explain your steps.

Mixed Review

Lesson 7-1

Simplify each radical expression. Use absolute value symbols as needed.

76. $\sqrt{121a^{90}}$ $11|a^{45}|$

77. $-\sqrt{81c^{48}d^{64}}$ $-9c^{24}d^{32}$

78. $\sqrt[3]{-64a^{81}}$ $-4a^{27}$

79. $\sqrt[5]{32y^{25}}$ $2y^5$

80. $\sqrt{0.25x^6}$ $0.5|x^3|$

81. $\sqrt[7]{x^{14}y^{35}}$ x^2y^5

82. $\sqrt[4]{16x^{36}y^{96}}$ $2|x^9|y^{24}$

83. $\sqrt{0.0064x^{40}}$ $0.08x^{20}$

Lesson 6-3

Divide. Tell whether each divisor is a factor of the dividend.

84. $(y^3 - 64) \div (y + 4)$

85. $(x^3 + 27) \div (x + 3)$

86. $(6a^3 + a^2 - a + 4) \div (2a + 1)$

87. $(2x^4 - 3x^3 - 4x + 10) \div (x - 2)$

84–87. See margin.

Lesson 5-7

Complete the square.

88. $x^2 + 10x + \blacksquare$ 25

89. $x^2 - 10x + \blacksquare$ 25

90. $x^2 + 11x + \blacksquare$ $\dfrac{121}{4}$

91. $x^2 - 11x + \blacksquare$ $\dfrac{121}{4}$

92. $x^2 - \dfrac{x}{3} + \blacksquare$ $\dfrac{1}{36}$

93. $x^2 + 0.3x + \blacksquare$ 0.0225

94. $x^2 - \dfrac{3}{4}x + \blacksquare$ $\dfrac{9}{64}$

95. $x^2 + \dfrac{3}{5}x + \blacksquare$ $\dfrac{9}{100}$

Standardized Test Prep

Resources
For additional practice with a variety of test item formats:
- Standardized Test Prep, p. 419
- Test-Taking Strategies, p. 414
- Test-Taking Strategies with Transparencies

Exercise 69 Tell students to carefully examine all of the answer choices, paying close attention to the signs.

74. [2] $\sqrt{x}$ is a real number if $x \geq 0$ and $\sqrt{-x}$ is a real number if $x \leq 0$. So the only value that makes $\sqrt{x} \cdot \sqrt{-x}$ a real number is $x = 0$.

[1] answer only OR error describing value(s) of variables

75. [4] You should multiply $\sqrt[3]{\dfrac{3}{2x}}$ by $\dfrac{\sqrt[3]{4x^2}}{\sqrt[3]{4x^2}}$ because

$$\sqrt[3]{\dfrac{3}{2x}} \cdot \dfrac{\sqrt[3]{4x^2}}{\sqrt[3]{4x^2}} =$$

$$\dfrac{\sqrt[3]{3}}{\sqrt[3]{2x}} \cdot \dfrac{\sqrt[3]{4x^2}}{\sqrt[3]{4x^2}} =$$

$$\dfrac{\sqrt[3]{12x^2}}{\sqrt[3]{8x^2}} = \dfrac{\sqrt[3]{12x^2}}{2x},$$

which has a denominator without a radical.

[3] appropriate methods, but with one minor error

[2] major error, but subsequent steps consistent with that error

[1] correct final expression, but no work shown

84. $y^2 - 4y + 16$, R -128, not a factor

85. $x^2 - 3x + 9$, a factor

86. $3a^2 - 8a - 2$, R 6, not a factor

87. $2x^3 + x^2 + 2x$, R 10, not a factor

 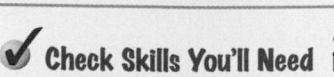
North Carolina Objectives

1.01 Simplify and perform operations with rational exponents and logarithms (common and natural) to solve problems.

Lesson Preview

What You'll Learn

OBJECTIVE 1 To add and subtract radical expressions

OBJECTIVE 2 To multiply and divide binomial radical expressions

. . . And Why

To find the dimensions of a window design, as in Example 2

✓ **Check Skills You'll Need**   (For help, go to Lesson 5-1 or Skills Handbook page 853.)

Multiply.

1. $(5x + 4)(3x - 2)$ $15x^2 + 2x - 8$

2. $(-8x + 5)(3x - 7)$ $-24x^2 + 71x - 35$

3. $(x + 4)(x - 4)$ $x^2 - 16$

4. $(4x + 5)(4x - 5)$ $16x^2 - 25$

5. $(x + 5)^2$ $x^2 + 10x + 25$

6. $(2x - 9)^2$ $4x^2 - 36x + 81$

New Vocabulary   • like radicals

OBJECTIVE 1

 Interactive lesson includes instant self-check, tutorials, and activities.

Adding and Subtracting Radical Expressions

Like radicals are radical expressions that have the same index and the same radicand. To add or subtract like radicals, use the Distributive Property.

1 EXAMPLE   Adding and Subtracting Radical Expressions

Add or subtract if possible.

a. $5\sqrt[3]{x} - 3\sqrt[3]{x}$

$5\sqrt[3]{x} - 3\sqrt[3]{x} = (5 - 3)\sqrt[3]{x}$ **Distributive Property**

$= 2\sqrt[3]{x}$ **Subtract.**

b. $4\sqrt{2} + 5\sqrt{3}$

The radicals are not like radicals. They cannot be combined.

✓ **Check Understanding** ❶ Add or subtract if possible.

a. $2\sqrt{7} + 3\sqrt{7}$ $5\sqrt{7}$ **b.** $7\sqrt[4]{5} - 2\sqrt[3]{5}$ **cannot combine**   **c.** $4\sqrt{xy} + 5\sqrt{xy}$ $9\sqrt{xy}$

2 EXAMPLE   Real-World 🌐 Connection

Art This is a design for a stained glass window. Each small square is 5 in. on a side. Express the dimensions of the window and its perimeter in simplest radical form.

The diagonal of a square with side length s is $s\sqrt{2}$. So the window's height is $2(5\sqrt{2})$ in., or $10\sqrt{2}$ in. The length is $4(5\sqrt{2})$ in., or $20\sqrt{2}$ in. The perimeter is $2(10\sqrt{2} + 20\sqrt{2})$ in., or $60\sqrt{2}$ in.

2. $72\sqrt{2}$ in. or about 101.8 in.

✓ **Check Understanding** ❷ Find the perimeter of the window if each small square is 6 in. on a side. **See left.**

✓ Ongoing Assessment and Intervention

Before the Lesson
Diagnose prerequisite skills using:
• Check Skills You'll Need

During the Lesson
Monitor progress using:
• Check Understanding
• Additional Examples
• Standardized Test Prep

After the Lesson
Assess knowledge using:
• Lesson Quiz
• Computer Test Generator CD
• Chapter Checkpoint 1 (p. 378)

Simplify radicals before adding or subtracting so you can find all the like radicals.

3 EXAMPLE Simplifying Before Adding or Subtracting

Simplify $6\sqrt{18} + 4\sqrt{8} - 3\sqrt{72}$.

$$6\sqrt{18} + 4\sqrt{8} - 3\sqrt{72} = 6\sqrt{3^2 \cdot 2} + 4\sqrt{2^2 \cdot 2} - 3\sqrt{6^2 \cdot 2}$$ **Factor each radicand.**

$$= 6 \cdot 3\sqrt{2} + 4 \cdot 2\sqrt{2} - 3 \cdot 6\sqrt{2}$$ **Simplify each radical.**

$$= 18\sqrt{2} + 8\sqrt{2} - 18\sqrt{2}$$ **Multiply.**

$$= (18 + 8 - 18)\sqrt{2}$$ **Distributive Property**

$$= 8\sqrt{2}$$

✓ **Check Understanding** ③ Simplify $\sqrt{50} + 3\sqrt{32} - 5\sqrt{18}$. **$2\sqrt{2}$**

OBJECTIVE

2 Multiplying and Dividing Binomial Radical Expressions

Multiply radical expressions that are in the form of binomials by using FOIL.

4 EXAMPLE Multiplying Binomial Radical Expressions

Multiply $(3 + 2\sqrt{5})(2 + 4\sqrt{5})$.

$$(3 + 2\sqrt{5})(2 + 4\sqrt{5}) = 3 \cdot 2 + 3 \cdot 4\sqrt{5} + 2 \cdot 2\sqrt{5} + 2\sqrt{5} \cdot 4\sqrt{5}$$ **Use FOIL.**

$$= 6 + 12\sqrt{5} + 4\sqrt{5} + 40$$ **Multiply.**

$$= 6 + (12 + 4)\sqrt{5} + 40$$ **Combine like radicals.**

$$= 46 + 16\sqrt{5}$$

✓ **Check Understanding** ④ Multiply $(\sqrt{2} - \sqrt{3})^2$. **$5 - 2\sqrt{6}$**

Need Help?

To review conjugates, go to Lesson 6-5.

Conjugates are expressions, such as $\sqrt{a} + \sqrt{b}$ and $\sqrt{a} - \sqrt{b}$, that differ only in the sign of the second terms. If a and b are rational numbers, then the product of these conjugates is a rational number.

Let a and b represent rational numbers.

$$(\sqrt{a} + \sqrt{b})(\sqrt{a} - \sqrt{b}) = (\sqrt{a})^2 - (\sqrt{b})^2$$ **The product is the difference of squares.**

$$= a - b$$ **Simplify.**

The difference of the rational numbers a and b is a rational number. So the product of the conjugates is a rational number.

5 EXAMPLE Multiplying Conjugates

Multiply $(2 + \sqrt{3})(2 - \sqrt{3})$.

$$(2 + \sqrt{3})(2 - \sqrt{3}) = 2^2 - (\sqrt{3})^2$$ $(a + b)(a - b) = a^2 - b^2$

$$= 4 - 3$$

$$= 1$$

✓ **Check Understanding** ⑤ Multiply $(\sqrt{5} + \sqrt{2})(\sqrt{5} - \sqrt{2})$. **3**

Reaching All Students

| **Below Level** Remind students of the meaning of the terms "index" and "radicand." Ask them to give examples of like and unlike radicals. | **Advanced Learners** Ask students to rationalize $\frac{1}{\sqrt[3]{7}}$ and $\frac{1}{\sqrt[4]{2}}$. Discuss whether $\frac{1}{1 - \sqrt[3]{7}}$ can be rationalized. | **Visual Learners** See note on page 376. **Error Prevention** See note on page 376. |

2. Teach

Math Background

Radical expressions play an important role in many applications. Learning how to simplify radical expressions is a key tool in expressing answers exactly.

OBJECTIVE

1 Teaching Notes

Additional Examples

① Add or subtract if possible.

a. $7\sqrt{xy} + 3\sqrt{xy}$ **$10\sqrt{xy}$**

b. $2\sqrt[3]{x} - 2\sqrt[3]{5}$ **not possible**

② The rectangular window shown below is made up of three equilateral triangles and two right triangles. The equilateral triangles have sides of length 4 feet. What is the perimeter of the window? **$16 + 4\sqrt{3}$ ft, or about 22.9 ft**

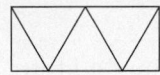

③ Simplify $3\sqrt{20} - \sqrt{45} + 4\sqrt{80}$. **$19\sqrt{5}$**

OBJECTIVE

2 Teaching Notes

Additional Examples

④ Multiply $(2 + 4\sqrt{3})(1 - 5\sqrt{3})$. **$-58 - 6\sqrt{3}$**

⑤ Multiply $(3 + \sqrt{7})(3 - \sqrt{7})$. **2**

⑥ Rationalize the denominator of $\frac{2 - \sqrt{3}}{4 + \sqrt{3}}$. **$\frac{11 - 6\sqrt{3}}{13}$**

Closure

Ask students what must be true of radical expressions in order to add them, but not to multiply them. **They must be like to add them, but not to multiply them.**

375

Assignment Guide

1 **Objective**
Ⓐ Ⓑ **Core** 1–12, 27–32, 46, 48
Ⓒ **Extension** 51–53

2 **Objective**
Ⓐ Ⓑ **Core** 13–26, 33–45, 47, 49–50
Ⓒ **Extension** 54–55

Standardized Test Prep 56–62

Mixed Review 63–76

Error Prevention
Exercises 7–12 Remind students to first simplify the radical expressions they want to add or subtract. Otherwise, they will not always find all the like terms.

Visual Learners
Exercise 47 Suggest that students sketch a diagram for this exercise.

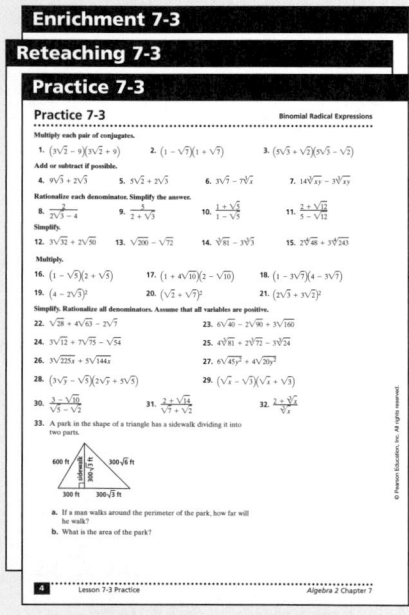

Sometimes you need to rationalize the denominator of a fraction when the denominator is a binomial radical expression. Multiply the numerator and denominator of the fraction by the conjugate of the denominator.

6 **EXAMPLE** **Rationalizing Binomial Radical Denominators**

Rationalize the denominator of $\frac{3 + \sqrt{5}}{1 - \sqrt{5}}$.

$\frac{3 + \sqrt{5}}{1 - \sqrt{5}} = \frac{3 + \sqrt{5}}{1 - \sqrt{5}} \cdot \frac{1 + \sqrt{5}}{1 + \sqrt{5}}$ **1 + $\sqrt{5}$ is the conjugate of 1 − $\sqrt{5}$.**

$= \frac{(3 + \sqrt{5})(1 + \sqrt{5})}{(1 - \sqrt{5})(1 + \sqrt{5})}$ **Multiply.**

$= \frac{3 + 3\sqrt{5} + \sqrt{5} + (\sqrt{5})^2}{1^2 - (\sqrt{5})^2}$ **Simplify.**

$= \frac{8 + 4\sqrt{5}}{-4}$

$= \frac{8}{-4} + \frac{4\sqrt{5}}{-4}$

$= -2 - \sqrt{5}$

✓ **Check Understanding** **6** Rationalize the denominator of $\frac{6 + \sqrt{15}}{4 - \sqrt{15}}$. **39 + 10$\sqrt{15}$**

EXERCISES

For more practice, see *Extra Practice*.

Practice and Problem Solving

Ⓐ **Practice by Example**

Examples 1 and 2
(page 374)

Add or subtract if possible.   **cannot combine**

1. $5\sqrt{6} + \sqrt{6}$ **6$\sqrt{6}$**   **2.** $6\sqrt[3]{3} - 2\sqrt[3]{3}$ **4$\sqrt[3]{3}$**   **3.** $4\sqrt{3} + 4\sqrt[3]{3}$

4. $3\sqrt{x} - 5\sqrt{x}$ **−2$\sqrt{x}$**   **5.** $14\sqrt{x} + 3\sqrt{y}$ **cannot combine**   **6.** $7\sqrt[3]{x^2} - 2\sqrt[3]{x^2}$ **5$\sqrt[3]{x^2}$**

Example 3
(page 375)

Simplify.

7. $6\sqrt{18} + 3\sqrt{50}$ **33$\sqrt{2}$**   **8.** $14\sqrt{20} - 3\sqrt{125}$ **13$\sqrt{5}$**   **9.** $\sqrt{18} + \sqrt{32}$ **7$\sqrt{2}$**

10. $\sqrt[3]{54} + \sqrt[3]{16}$ **5$\sqrt[3]{2}$**   **11.** $3\sqrt[3]{81} - 2\sqrt[3]{54}$ **9$\sqrt[3]{3}$ − 6$\sqrt[3]{2}$**   **12.** $\sqrt[4]{32} + \sqrt[4]{48}$ **2$\sqrt[4]{2}$ + 2$\sqrt[4]{3}$**

Example 4
(page 375)

Multiply.

13. $(3 + \sqrt{5})(1 + \sqrt{5})$ **8 + 4$\sqrt{5}$**   **14.** $(2 + \sqrt{7})(1 + 3\sqrt{7})$ **23 + 7$\sqrt{7}$**

15. $(3 - 4\sqrt{2})(5 - 6\sqrt{2})$ **63 − 38$\sqrt{2}$**   **16.** $(\sqrt{3} + \sqrt{5})^2$ **8 + 2$\sqrt{15}$**

17. $(\sqrt{13} + 6)^2$ **49 + 12$\sqrt{13}$**   **18.** $(2\sqrt{5} + 3\sqrt{2})^2$ **38 + 12$\sqrt{10}$**

Example 5
(page 375)

Multiply each pair of conjugates.

19. $(5 - \sqrt{11})(5 + \sqrt{11})$ **14**   **20.** $(4 - 2\sqrt{3})(4 + 2\sqrt{3})$ **4**

21. $(2\sqrt{6} + 8)(2\sqrt{6} - 8)$ **−40**   **22.** $(\sqrt{3} + \sqrt{5})(\sqrt{3} - \sqrt{5})$ **−2**

Example 6
(page 376)

Rationalize each denominator. Simplify the answer. **23–26. See margin.**

23. $\frac{4}{1 + \sqrt{3}}$ **24.** $\frac{4}{3\sqrt{3} - 2}$ **25.** $\frac{5 + \sqrt{3}}{2 - \sqrt{3}}$ **26.** $\frac{3 + \sqrt{8}}{2 - 2\sqrt{8}}$

376 Chapter 7 Radical Functions and Rational Exponents

pages 376–378 **Exercises**

23. $-2 + 2\sqrt{3}$ **25.** $13 + 7\sqrt{3}$

24. $\frac{12\sqrt{3} + 8}{23}$ **26.** $\frac{11 + 8\sqrt{2}}{-14}$

B Apply Your Skills

30–38. See margin.

Simplify. Rationalize all denominators. Assume that all the variables are positive.

27. $\sqrt{72} + \sqrt{32} + \sqrt{18}$ $13\sqrt{2}$

28. $\sqrt{75} + 2\sqrt{48} - 5\sqrt{3}$ $8\sqrt{3}$

29. $5\sqrt{32x} + 4\sqrt{98x}$ $48\sqrt{2x}$

30. $\sqrt{75} - 4\sqrt{18} + 2\sqrt{32}$

31. $4\sqrt{216y^2} + 3\sqrt{54y^2}$

32. $3\sqrt[3]{16} - 4\sqrt[3]{54} + \sqrt[3]{128}$

33. $(\sqrt{3} - \sqrt{7})(\sqrt{3} + 2\sqrt{7})$

34. $(2\sqrt{5} + 3\sqrt{2})(5\sqrt{5} - 7\sqrt{2})$

35. $(1 + \sqrt{72})(5 + \sqrt{2})$

36. $(2 - \sqrt{98})(3 + \sqrt{18})$

37. $(\sqrt{x} + \sqrt{3})(\sqrt{x} + 2\sqrt{3})$

38. $(2\sqrt{y} - 3\sqrt{2})(4\sqrt{y} - 5\sqrt{2})$

39. $\frac{4 + \sqrt{27}}{2 - 3\sqrt{27}}$ $\frac{89 + 42\sqrt{3}}{-239}$

40. $\frac{4 + \sqrt{6}}{\sqrt{2} + \sqrt{3}}$ $2\sqrt{3} - \sqrt{2}$

Real-World Connection

The Golden Ratio is found in the growth patterns of many plants. $\frac{AC}{CD} = \frac{BC}{BD} = \frac{1 + \sqrt{5}}{2}$

41. $\frac{5 - \sqrt{21}}{\sqrt{3} - \sqrt{7}}$ $\frac{\sqrt{3} - \sqrt{7}}{2}$

42. $\frac{3 + \sqrt[3]{2}}{\sqrt[3]{2}}$ $\frac{2 + 3\sqrt[3]{4}}{2}$

43. $\frac{5 + \sqrt[4]{x}}{\sqrt[4]{x}}$ $\frac{x + 5\sqrt[4]{x^3}}{x}$

44. $\frac{4 - 2\sqrt[3]{6}}{\sqrt[3]{4}}$ $2\sqrt[3]{2} - \sqrt[3]{12}$

45. The Golden Ratio is $\frac{1 + \sqrt{5}}{2}$. Find the reciprocal of the Golden Ratio and compare it with the number that is 1 less than the Golden Ratio. **See margin.**

46. Critical Thinking Describe the possible values of a such that $\sqrt{72} + \sqrt{a}$ can be simplified to a single term. **a must be twice a perfect square.**

47. Geometry A rectangular walk is $\sqrt{7}$ m wide and $6\sqrt{7}$ m long. What is the perimeter of the walk?   **$14\sqrt{7}$ m**

48. Writing Discuss the advantages and disadvantages of first simplifying $\sqrt{72} + \sqrt{32} + \sqrt{18}$ in order to estimate its decimal value. **See margin.**

49. Open-Ended Find two pairs of conjugates with a product of 3. **See margin.**

50. Physics An object is moving at a speed of $(3 + \sqrt{2})$ ft/s. How long will it take the object to travel 20 ft?   **$\frac{60 - 20\sqrt{2}}{7}$ s, or about 4.53 s**

C Challenge

Add or subtract.

51. $\frac{1}{1 - \sqrt{5}} + \frac{1}{1 + \sqrt{5}}$ $-\frac{1}{2}$

52. $\frac{4}{\sqrt{5} - \sqrt{3}} - \frac{4}{\sqrt{5} + \sqrt{3}}$ $4\sqrt{3}$

53. For what values of a and b does $\sqrt{a} + \sqrt{b} = \sqrt{a + b}$? **($a = 0$ and $b \geq 0$) or ($b = 0$ and $a \geq 0$).**

54. Error Analysis A student used the steps shown below to simplify an expression. Find the student's error and explain why the step is incorrect.

$\frac{1}{(1 - \sqrt{2})^2} = (1 - \sqrt{2})^{-2}$

$= 1^{-2} - (\sqrt{2})^{-2}$

$= \frac{1}{1^2} - \frac{1}{(\sqrt{2^2})}$

$= \frac{1}{1} - \frac{1}{2}$

$= \frac{1}{2}$

In the second step the exponent was incorrectly distributed: $(a - b)^x \neq a^x - b^x$.

55a. m and n can be any positive integers.

   b. m must be even or n must be odd.

55. In the expression $\sqrt[n]{x^m}$, m and n are positive integers and x is a real number. The expression can be simplified.
   a. If $x > 0$, what are the possible values for m and n?
   b. If $x < 0$, what are the possible values for m and n?
   c. If $x < 0$ and an absolute value symbol is needed in the simplified expression, what are the possible values of m and n? **m must be even, and n can be any positive integer.**

Lesson 7-3   Binomial Radical Expressions   **377**

30. $5\sqrt{3} - 4\sqrt{2}$

31. $33y\sqrt{6}$

32. $-2\sqrt[3]{2}$

33. $-11 + \sqrt{21}$

34. $8 + \sqrt{10}$

35. $17 + 31\sqrt{2}$

36. $-36 - 15\sqrt{2}$

37. $x + 3\sqrt{3x} + 6$

38. $8y - 22\sqrt{2y} + 30$

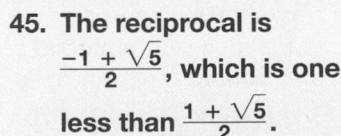 **Lesson Quiz 7-3**

Simplify.

1. $6\sqrt{10} - 4\sqrt{10}$ $2\sqrt{10}$

2. $8\sqrt[3]{x} + 5\sqrt[3]{x}$ $13\sqrt[3]{x}$

3. $2\sqrt{27} + \sqrt{48}$ $10\sqrt{3}$

4. $\sqrt[3]{128} - \sqrt[3]{54}$ $\sqrt[3]{2}$

5. Multiply $(7 + 2\sqrt{3})(5 - \sqrt{3})$.
   $29 + 3\sqrt{3}$

6. Rationalize the denominator in $\frac{3 - 2\sqrt{7}}{10 - \sqrt{7}}$. $\frac{16 - 17\sqrt{7}}{93}$

Alternative Assessment

Have students write two addition problems and two subtraction problems that involve radicals and that have an answer of $3\sqrt{5}$. Then have them write a multiplication problem and a division problem, each involving two binomial radical expressions that have an answer of $2 + \sqrt{5}$. Have students share their problems with another student to check their work.

45. The reciprocal is $\frac{-1 + \sqrt{5}}{2}$, which is one less than $\frac{1 + \sqrt{5}}{2}$.

48. Answers may vary. Sample: Without simplifying first, you must estimate three separate square roots, and then add the estimates. If they are first simplified, then they can be combined as $13\sqrt{2}$. Then only one square root need be estimated.

49. Answers may vary. Sample: $(\sqrt{7} + 2)(\sqrt{7} - 2)$ $(2\sqrt{2} + \sqrt{5})(2\sqrt{2} - \sqrt{5})$

Resources

For additional practice with a variety of test item formats:
- Standardized Test Prep, p. 419
- Test-Taking Strategies, p. 414
- Test-Taking Strategies with Transparencies

Exercise 58 Point out to students that the products are products of conjugates. They should be able to eliminate incorrect choices without actually finding all terms of the products.

To check understanding of Lessons 7-1 to 7-3:

Checkpoint Quiz 1 (p. 378)

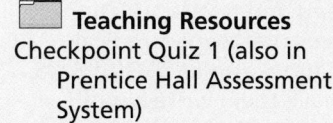

Teaching Resources
Checkpoint Quiz 1 (also in Prentice Hall Assessment System)

Reaching All Students
Reading and Math Literacy 7B

Spanish versions available

---

pages 376–378 Exercises

61. [2] $(1 - \sqrt[3]{8})(1 + \sqrt[3]{8}) =$
    $(1 - 2)(1 + 2) =$
    $1 - 4 = -3$, which is rational.

    [1] the value -3 only OR yes only OR minor error in calculation

62. [4] $\dfrac{2}{5 + 2\sqrt{2}} - \dfrac{3}{5 - 2\sqrt{2}} =$

    $\dfrac{2}{5 + 2\sqrt{2}} \cdot \dfrac{5 - 2\sqrt{2}}{5 - 2\sqrt{2}} -$

    $\dfrac{3}{5 - 2\sqrt{2}} \cdot \dfrac{5 + 2\sqrt{2}}{5 + 2\sqrt{2}}$

    $= \dfrac{10 - 4\sqrt{2}}{25 - 4 \cdot 2} - \dfrac{15 + 6\sqrt{2}}{25 - 4 \cdot 2}$

    $= \dfrac{10 - 4\sqrt{2}}{17} - \dfrac{15 + 6\sqrt{2}}{17}$

    $= \dfrac{10 - 4\sqrt{2} - 15 - 6\sqrt{2}}{17}$

    $= \dfrac{-5 - 10\sqrt{2}}{17}$

    [3] minor error, but appropriate method

378

Standardized Test Prep

Multiple Choice

56. Which expression does NOT simplify to one term? **B**
    A. $-4\sqrt{8} + \sqrt{18}$
    B. $\sqrt{27} - \sqrt{8}$
    C. $\sqrt{32} + 3\sqrt{8}$
    D. $\sqrt{12} - \sqrt{75}$

57. What is an expression for $\sqrt{20} - \sqrt{80} + \sqrt{125}$? **I**
    F. $\sqrt{65}$
    G. $13\sqrt{5}$
    H. $11\sqrt{5}$
    I. $3\sqrt{5}$

Take It to the NET
Online lesson quiz at
www.PHSchool.com
Web Code: aga-0703

58. Which expression is NOT equal to 13? **D**
    A. $(4 + \sqrt{3})(4 - \sqrt{3})$
    B. $(5 - 2\sqrt{3})(5 + 2\sqrt{3})$
    C. $(6 + \sqrt{23})(6 - \sqrt{23})$
    D. $(7 - \sqrt{6})(7 + \sqrt{6})$

59. How can you write $\dfrac{1 + \sqrt{3}}{5 - \sqrt{3}}$ with a rationalized denominator? **I**
    F. -1
    G. $-2 - 3\sqrt{3}$
    H. $4 + 3\sqrt{3}$
    I. $\dfrac{4 + 3\sqrt{3}}{11}$

60. Which of the following is equivalent to $(2 + 3\sqrt{5})(3 + 3\sqrt{5})$? **D**
    A. 51
    B. $6 + 9\sqrt{5}$
    C. $6 + 24\sqrt{5}$
    D. $51 + 15\sqrt{5}$

Short Response

61. Is the product $\left(1 - \sqrt[3]{8}\right)\left(1 + \sqrt[3]{8}\right)$ a rational number? Explain. **See margin.**

Extended Response

62. What is the value of $\dfrac{2}{5 + 2\sqrt{2}} - \dfrac{3}{5 - 2\sqrt{2}}$? Show your work. **See margin.**

Mixed Review

Lesson 7-2

Simplify each expression. Rationalize all denominators. Assume that all variables are positive.

63. $\sqrt[3]{3} \cdot \sqrt[3]{18}$ $3\sqrt[3]{2}$
64. $\sqrt{3x} \cdot \sqrt{5x}$ $x\sqrt{15}$
65. $\dfrac{\sqrt{32}}{\sqrt{2}}$ 4
66. $\dfrac{\sqrt{62}}{\sqrt{6}}$ $\dfrac{\sqrt{93}}{3}$

67. $\sqrt[3]{2x^2} \cdot \sqrt[3]{4x}$ $2x$
68. $\sqrt{7x} \cdot \sqrt{14x^3}$ $7x^2\sqrt{2}$
69. $\dfrac{\sqrt{6m}}{\sqrt{2mn}}$ $\dfrac{\sqrt{3n}}{n}$
70. $\sqrt[3]{\dfrac{4}{5x}}$ $\dfrac{\sqrt[3]{100x^2}}{5x}$

Lesson 6-4

Solve each equation.

71. $2x^3 - 16 = 0$ $2, -1 \pm i\sqrt{3}$
72. $x^3 + 1000 = 0$ $-10, 5 \pm 5i\sqrt{3}$
73. $125x^3 - 1 = 0$ $\dfrac{1}{5}, \dfrac{-1 \pm i\sqrt{3}}{10}$

74. $x^4 - 14x^2 + 49 = 0$ $\pm\sqrt{7}$
75. $25x^4 - 40x^2 + 16 = 0$ $\dfrac{\pm 2\sqrt{5}}{5}$
76. $81x^4 - 1 = 0$ $\pm\dfrac{i}{3}, \pm\dfrac{1}{3}$

Checkpoint Quiz 1   Lessons 7-1 through 7-3

Instant self-check quiz online and on CD-ROM

Simplify each radical expression. Use absolute value symbols when needed.

1. $\sqrt[4]{b^4c^8}$ $|b|c^2$
2. $\sqrt[5]{x^5y^{10}}$ xy^2
3. $\sqrt[3]{-a^3}$ $-a$
4. $\sqrt[5]{-y^{10}}$ $-y^2$

Simplify each expression. Rationalize all denominators. Assume that all variables are positive.

5. $\sqrt{8}(\sqrt{24} + 3\sqrt{8})$ $8\sqrt{3} + 24$
6. $2\sqrt{5x^3} \cdot 3\sqrt{28x^3y^2}$ $12x^3y\sqrt{35}$

7. $4\sqrt[3]{81} - 3\sqrt[3]{54}$ $12\sqrt[3]{3} - 9\sqrt[3]{2}$
8. $\dfrac{4\sqrt{2xy}}{9\sqrt{5x^2y}}$ $\dfrac{4\sqrt{10x}}{45x}$

9. $(\sqrt{5} + 2\sqrt{3})(\sqrt{5} - 2\sqrt{3})$ -7
10. $\dfrac{5}{4\sqrt{7} + 5}$ $\dfrac{20\sqrt{7} - 25}{87}$

[2] correct method, but finds $\dfrac{10 - 4\sqrt{2}}{17} +$

$\dfrac{15 + 6\sqrt{2}}{17}$ and gets

$\dfrac{25 + 2\sqrt{2}}{17}$

[1] answer only, no work shown

Rational Exponents

 North Carolina Objectives

1.01 Simplify and perform operations with rational exponents and logarithms (common and natural) to solve problems.

Lesson Preview

What You'll Learn

OBJECTIVE 1 To simplify expressions with rational exponents

...And Why

To model simulated gravity in a spacecraft, as in Example 3

✓ Check Skills You'll Need

(For help, go to page 362.)

Simplify.

1. 2^{-4} $\frac{1}{16}$

2. $(3x)^{-2}$ $\frac{1}{9x^2}$

3. $(5x^2y)^{-3}$ $\frac{1}{125x^6y^3}$

4. $2^{-2} + 4^{-1}$ $\frac{1}{2}$

5. $(2a^{-2}b^3)^4$ $\frac{16b^{12}}{a^8}$

6. $(4a^3b^{-1})^{-2}$ $\frac{b^2}{16a^6}$

New Vocabulary • rational exponent

---

1. Plan

Lesson Preview

✓ Check Skills You'll Need

Integer Exponents
Algebra 1 Review: Page 362, Exercises 10–17

Lesson Resources

📁 **Teaching Resources**
Practice, Reteaching, Enrichment

👥 **Reaching All Students**
Practice Workbook 7-4
Spanish Practice Workbook 7-4

⏱ **Presentation Assistant Plus!**
Transparencies
• Check Skills You'll Need 7-4
• Additional Examples 7-4
• Student Edition Answers 7-4
• Lesson Quiz 7-4
PH Presentation Pro CD 7-4

ASSESSMENT SYSTEM
Computer Test Generator CD

🔧 **Technology**
Resource Pro® CD-ROM
Computer Test Generator CD
Prentice Hall Presentation Pro CD

💻 **www.PHSchool.com**
Student Site
• Teacher Web Code: agk-5500
• Self-grading Lesson Quiz
Teacher Center
• Lesson Planner
• Resources

Plus

OBJECTIVE

1 Simplifying Expressions With Rational Exponents

🔲 **Interactive lesson** includes instant self-check, tutorials, and activities.

Another way to write a radical expression is to use a **rational exponent.** See the examples at the right.

 Reading Math

Exponent comes from the Latin word meaning "place outside."

Like the radical form, the exponent form always indicates the principal root.

Radical form		Exponent form
$\sqrt{25}$	=	$25^{\frac{1}{2}}$
$\sqrt[3]{27}$	=	$27^{\frac{1}{3}}$
$\sqrt[4]{16}$	=	$16^{\frac{1}{4}}$

1 EXAMPLE Simplifying Expressions With Rational Exponents

Simplify each expression.

a. $125^{\frac{1}{3}}$

$125^{\frac{1}{3}} = \sqrt[3]{125}$ **Rewrite as a radical.**

$= \sqrt[3]{5^3}$ **Rewrite 125 as a cube.**

$= 5$ **Simplify.**

b. $5^{\frac{1}{2}} \cdot 5^{\frac{1}{2}}$

$5^{\frac{1}{2}} \cdot 5^{\frac{1}{2}} = \sqrt{5} \cdot \sqrt{5}$ **Rewrite as radicals.**

$= 5$ **By definition, $\sqrt{5}$ is the number whose square is 5.**

c. $10^{\frac{1}{3}} \cdot 100^{\frac{1}{3}}$

$10^{\frac{1}{3}} \cdot 100^{\frac{1}{3}} = \sqrt[3]{10} \cdot \sqrt[3]{100}$ **Rewrite as radicals.**

$= \sqrt[3]{10 \cdot 100}$ **Property for multiplying radical expressions**

$= \sqrt[3]{10^3}$ **Rewrite the radicand as a cube.**

$= 10$ **Simplify.**

✓ **Check Understanding** ① Simplify each expression.

a. $16^{\frac{1}{4}}$ **2**

b. $2^{\frac{1}{2}} \cdot 2^{\frac{1}{2}}$ **2**

c. $2^{\frac{1}{2}} \cdot 8^{\frac{1}{2}}$ **4**

Ongoing Assessment and Intervention

Before the Lesson
Diagnose prerequisite skills using:
• Check Skills You'll Need

During the Lesson
Monitor progress using:
• Check Understanding
• Additional Examples
• Standardized Test Prep

After the Lesson
Assess knowledge using:
• Lesson Quiz
• Computer Test Generator CD

2. Teach

Math Background

Recall that the use of an integer exponent represents repeated multiplication, such as
$2^3 = 2 \cdot 2 \cdot 2 = 8$ or
$2^{-3} = \frac{1}{2} \cdot \frac{1}{2} \cdot \frac{1}{2} = \frac{1}{8}$. The use of a positive or negative rational exponent of the form $\frac{1}{n}$, represents the nth root of the base or the nth root of the multiplicative inverse of the base, respectively. These ideas can be combined to understand rational exponents of the form $\frac{m}{n}$, where m and n are integers.

OBJECTIVE

 1 **Teaching Notes**

1 EXAMPLE **Auditory Learners**

Students may find it helpful to say to themselves in words what is shown symbolically in the equations. For example, in part a, they can say, "125 to the one-third power is equal to the cube root of 125." Hearing the words helps reinforce the concept.

2 EXAMPLE **Math Tip**

Remind students that terminating or repeating decimals are rational numbers. To write the expression $y^{-2.5}$ in radical form, first rewrite the exponent as a fraction.

3 EXAMPLE **English Learners**

Make sure students understand terms such as *apparatus, rate of rotation, artificial acceleration,* and *gravitational acceleration.* Even if students understand the math involved in the problem, they must also understand the vocabulary.

4 EXAMPLE **Math Tip**

In part a, students may wonder if they could find $(-32)^{\frac{3}{5}}$ by first finding $(-32)^3$ and then raising the result to the one-fifth power. The expression can be simplified in this way, but a calculator is necessary. The method in the textbook requires only pencil and paper.

380

A rational exponent may have a numerator other than 1. The property $(a^m)^n = a^{mn}$ shows how to rewrite an expression with an exponent that is an improper fraction.

$$25^{\frac{3}{2}} = 25^{\left(3 \cdot \frac{1}{2}\right)} = (25^3)^{\frac{1}{2}} = \sqrt{25^3} \qquad \text{or} \qquad 25^{\frac{3}{2}} = 25^{\left(\frac{1}{2} \cdot 3\right)} = \left(25^{\frac{1}{2}}\right)^3 = (\sqrt{25})^3$$

Key Concepts

Definition	Rational Exponents

If the nth root of a is a real number and m is an integer, then

$$a^{\frac{1}{n}} = \sqrt[n]{a} \quad \text{and} \quad a^{\frac{m}{n}} = \sqrt[n]{a^m} = \left(\sqrt[n]{a}\right)^m. \qquad \text{If } m \text{ is negative, } a \neq 0.$$

2c. If m is negative,
$a^{\frac{m}{n}} = \frac{1}{\left(\sqrt[n]{a}\right)^m}$, **and if**
$a = 0$, **then the denominator of the fraction would be zero. Since this cannot happen,**
$a \neq 0$.

2 EXAMPLE **Converting to and From Radical Form**

a. Write the exponential expressions $x^{\frac{3}{5}}$ and $y^{-2.5}$ in radical form.

$$x^{\frac{3}{5}} = \sqrt[5]{x^3} \text{ or } \left(\sqrt[5]{x}\right)^3 \qquad\qquad y^{-2.5} = y^{-\frac{5}{2}} = \frac{1}{\sqrt{y^5}} \text{ or } \frac{1}{(\sqrt{y})^5}$$

b. Write the radical expressions $\sqrt{a^3}$ and $\left(\sqrt[5]{b}\right)^2$ in exponential form.

$$\sqrt{a^3} = a^{\frac{3}{2}} \qquad\qquad \left(\sqrt[5]{b}\right)^2 = b^{\frac{2}{5}}$$

✓ **Check Understanding** **2 a.** Write the expressions $y^{-\frac{3}{8}}$ and $z^{0.4}$ in radical form. $\frac{1}{\sqrt[8]{y^3}}$, $\sqrt[5]{z^2}$

b. Write the expressions $\sqrt[3]{x^2}$ and $\left(\sqrt{y}\right)^3$ in exponential form. $x^{\frac{2}{3}}$, $y^{\frac{3}{2}}$

c. **Critical Thinking** Refer to the definition of rational exponents. Explain the need for the following restriction: If m is negative, $a \neq 0$. **See left.**

3 EXAMPLE **Real-World**  **Connection**

Space Travel Bone loss for astronauts on lengthy space voyages may be prevented with a bedlike apparatus that rotates to simulate the effect of gravity. In the formula $N = \frac{a^{0.5}}{2\pi r^{0.5}}$, N is the rate of rotation in revolutions per second, a is the simulated acceleration in m/s^2, and r is the radius of the apparatus in meters. How fast would an apparatus with a radius of 1.7 m have to rotate to simulate the acceleration of 9.8 m/s^2 that is due to Earth's gravity?

Graphing Calculator Hint

Use the ⋀ key to enter an exponent. If the exponent is a fraction, enclose it in parentheses. For example, $729^{\frac{2}{3}}$ is entered as
729 ⋀ (2 ÷ 3).

$$N = \frac{a^{0.5}}{2\pi r^{0.5}} \qquad \text{Write the formula.}$$

$$= \frac{9.8^{0.5}}{2\pi(1.7)^{0.5}} \qquad \text{Substitute for } a \text{ and } r.$$

$$\approx 0.382 \qquad \text{Use a calculator.}$$

3. about 0.270 revolutions per second, or about 16 revolutions per minute

The apparatus would have to rotate about 0.382 revolutions per second, or about 23 revolutions per minute.

✓ **Check Understanding** **3** Calculate the rate of rotation needed for the apparatus in Example 3 to simulate a gravitational acceleration half as strong as Earth's. **See left.**

👥 Reaching All Students

Below Level Review the properties of exponents and provide students with more examples of when to add or subtract exponents and when to multiply them.	**Advanced Learners** Have students approximate $2^{\frac{7\pi}{11}}$, then compare their approximation with their calculator answer.	**English Learners** See note on page 380. **Auditory Learners** See note on page 380.

All of the properties of integer exponents also apply to rational exponents. Here is a summary.

Key Concepts

Need Help?

Refer to the properties of integer exponents on p. 362.

Summary	Properties of Rational Exponents

Let m and n represent rational numbers. Assume that no denominator equals 0.

Property	Example
$a^m \cdot a^n = a^{m+n}$	$8^{\frac{1}{3}} \cdot 8^{\frac{2}{3}} = 8^{\frac{1}{3}+\frac{2}{3}} = 8^1 = 8$
$(a^m)^n = a^{mn}$	$\left(5^{\frac{1}{2}}\right)^4 = 5^{\frac{1}{2} \cdot 4} = 5^2 = 25$
$(ab)^m = a^m b^m$	$(4 \cdot 5)^{\frac{1}{2}} = 4^{\frac{1}{2}} \cdot 5^{\frac{1}{2}} = 2 \cdot 5^{\frac{1}{2}}$
$a^{-m} = \dfrac{1}{a^m}$	$9^{-\frac{1}{2}} = \dfrac{1}{9^{\frac{1}{2}}} = \dfrac{1}{3}$
$\dfrac{a^m}{a^n} = a^{m-n}$	$\dfrac{\pi^{\frac{3}{2}}}{\pi^{\frac{1}{2}}} = \pi^{\frac{3}{2}-\frac{1}{2}} = \pi^1 = \pi$
$\left(\dfrac{a}{b}\right)^m = \dfrac{a^m}{b^m}$	$\left(\dfrac{5}{27}\right)^{\frac{1}{3}} = \dfrac{5^{\frac{1}{3}}}{27^{\frac{1}{3}}} = \dfrac{5^{\frac{1}{3}}}{3}$

You can simplify a number with a rational exponent by using the properties of exponents or by converting the expression to a radical expression.

4 EXAMPLE Simplifying Numbers With Rational Exponents

Simplify each number.

a. $(-32)^{\frac{3}{5}}$

Method 1

$(-32)^{\frac{3}{5}} = \left((-2)^5\right)^{\frac{3}{5}}$

$= (-2)^{5 \cdot \frac{3}{5}}$

$= (-2)^3$

$= -8$

Method 2

$(-32)^{\frac{3}{5}} = \left(\sqrt[5]{-32}\right)^3$

$= \left(\sqrt[5]{(-2)^5}\right)^3$

$= (-2)^3$

$= -8$

b. $4^{-3.5}$

Method 1

$4^{-3.5} = 4^{-\frac{7}{2}}$

$= (2^2)^{-\frac{7}{2}}$

$= 2^{2 \cdot -\frac{7}{2}}$

$= 2^{-7}$

$= \dfrac{1}{2^7}$

$= \dfrac{1}{128}$

Method 2

$4^{-3.5} = 4^{-\frac{7}{2}}$

$= \dfrac{1}{4^{\frac{7}{2}}}$

$= \dfrac{1}{(\sqrt{4})^7}$

$= \dfrac{1}{2^7}$

$= \dfrac{1}{128}$

✔ **Check Understanding** **4** Simplify each number.

a. $25^{-\frac{3}{2}}$ $\dfrac{1}{125}$ **b.** $32^{\frac{3}{5}}$ **8** **c.** $(-32)^{\frac{4}{5}}$ **16**

Additional Examples

1 Simplify each expression.
a. $64^{\frac{1}{3}}$ **4** **b.** $7^{\frac{1}{2}} \cdot 7^{\frac{1}{2}}$ **7**
c. $5^{\frac{1}{3}} \cdot 25^{\frac{1}{3}}$ **5**

2 a. Write the exponential expression $x^{\frac{2}{7}}$ and $y^{-0.4}$ in radical form. $\sqrt[7]{x^2}$ or $\left(\sqrt[7]{x}\right)^2$, $\dfrac{1}{\sqrt[5]{y^2}}$ or $\dfrac{1}{\left(\sqrt[5]{y}\right)^2}$
b. Write the radical expressions $\sqrt[4]{c^3}$ and $\left(\sqrt[3]{b}\right)^5$ in exponential form. $c^{\frac{3}{4}}, b^{\frac{5}{3}}$

3 The time t in hours needed to cook a pot roast that weighs p pounds can be approximated by using the equation $t = 0.89p^{0.6}$. To the nearest hundredth of an hour, how long would it take to cook a pot roast that weighs 13 lb? **4.15 h**

4 Simplify each number.
a. $(-27)^{\frac{2}{3}}$ **9** **b.** $25^{-2.5}$ $\dfrac{1}{3125}$

5 Write $\left(243a^{-10}\right)^{\frac{2}{5}}$ in simplest form. $\dfrac{9}{a^4}$

Closure

Have students use a radical expression to explain the meaning of $a^{\frac{m}{n}}$, where, m and n are integers, the nth root of a is a real number, and $a \ne 0$ if m is negative.
$a^{\frac{m}{n}}$ means $\sqrt[n]{a^m}$ or $\left(\sqrt[n]{a}\right)^m$.

381

3. Practice

Assignment Guide

▼ **Objective**
- Ⓐ Ⓑ **Core** 1–80
- Ⓒ **Extension** 81–87

Standardized Test Prep 88–94

Mixed Review 95–106

Error Prevention

Exercises 18–21 Be sure students recall that the index for a square root expression is 2.

Exercises 65–76 You may need to remind students that the expressions in each final answer should contain only positive exponents.

To write an expression with rational exponents in simplest form, write every exponent as a positive number.

5 EXAMPLE **Writing Expressions in Simplest Form**

Write $(16y^{-8})^{-\frac{3}{4}}$ in simplest form.

$$(16y^{-8})^{-\frac{3}{4}} = (2^4 y^{-8})^{-\frac{3}{4}}$$
$$= 2^{4\cdot(-\frac{3}{4})} \cdot y^{-8\cdot(-\frac{3}{4})}$$
$$= 2^{-3} y^6$$
$$= \frac{y^6}{2^3}$$
$$= \frac{y^6}{8}$$

✔ **Check Understanding** **5** Write $(8x^{15})^{-\frac{1}{3}}$ in simplest form. $\frac{1}{2x^5}$

EXERCISES

For more practice, see *Extra Practice*.

Practice and Problem Solving

Ⓐ **Practice by Example**

Example 1
(page 379)

Simplify each expression.

1. $36^{\frac{1}{2}}$ **6**
2. $27^{\frac{1}{3}}$ **3**
3. $49^{\frac{1}{2}}$ **7**
4. $10^{\frac{1}{2}} \cdot 10^{\frac{1}{2}}$ **10**
5. $(-3)^{\frac{1}{3}} \cdot (-3)^{\frac{1}{3}} \cdot (-3)^{\frac{1}{3}}$ **−3**
6. $3^{\frac{1}{2}} \cdot 12^{\frac{1}{2}}$ **6**
7. $2^{\frac{1}{2}} \cdot 32^{\frac{1}{2}}$ **8**
8. $3^{\frac{1}{3}} \cdot 9^{\frac{1}{3}}$ **3**
9. $3^{\frac{1}{4}} \cdot 27^{\frac{1}{4}}$ **3**

Example 2
(page 380)

Write each expression in radical form.

10. $x^{\frac{1}{6}}$ $\sqrt[6]{x}$
11. $x^{\frac{1}{5}}$ $\sqrt[5]{x}$
12. $x^{\frac{2}{7}}$ $\sqrt[7]{x^2}$ or $(\sqrt[7]{x})^2$
13. $y^{\frac{2}{5}}$ $\sqrt[5]{y^2}$ or $(\sqrt[5]{y})^2$
14. $y^{-\frac{9}{8}}$ $\frac{1}{\sqrt[8]{y^9}}$ or $\frac{1}{(\sqrt[8]{y})^9}$
15. $t^{-\frac{3}{4}}$ $\frac{1}{\sqrt[4]{t^3}}$ or $\frac{1}{(\sqrt[4]{t})^3}$
16. $x^{1.5}$ $\sqrt{x^3}$ or $(\sqrt{x})^3$
17. $y^{1.2}$
17. $y^{\frac{6}{5}}$ $\sqrt[5]{y^6}$ or $(\sqrt[5]{y})^6$

Write each expression in exponential form.

18. $\sqrt{-10}$ $(-10)^{\frac{1}{2}}$
19. $\sqrt{7x^3}$ $7^{\frac{1}{2}} x^{\frac{3}{2}}$
20. $\sqrt{(7x)^3}$ $(7x)^{\frac{3}{2}}$
21. $(\sqrt{7x})^3$ $(7x)^{\frac{3}{2}}$
22. $\sqrt[3]{a^2}$ $a^{\frac{2}{3}}$
23. $(\sqrt[3]{a})^2$ $a^{\frac{2}{3}}$
24. $\sqrt[4]{c^2}$ $c^{\frac{1}{2}}$
25. $\sqrt[3]{(5xy)^6}$ $25x^2y^2$

Example 3
(page 380)

The optimal height h of the letters of a message printed on pavement is given by the formula $h = \frac{0.00252d^{2.27}}{e}$. Here d is the distance of the driver from the letters and e is the height of the driver's eye above the pavement. All of the distances are in meters. Find h for the given values of d and e.

26. $d = 100$ m, $e = 1.2$ m $\approx$ **72.8 m**
27. $d = 50$ m, $e = 1.2$ m $\approx$ **15.1 m**
28. $d = 50$ m, $e = 2.3$ m $\approx$ **7.9 m**
29. $d = 25$ m, $e = 2.3$ m $\approx$ **1.6 m**

Example 4
(page 381)

Simplify each number.

30. $8^{\frac{2}{3}}$ **4**
31. $64^{\frac{2}{3}}$ **16**
32. $(-8)^{\frac{2}{3}}$ **4**
33. $(-32)^{\frac{6}{5}}$ **64**
34. $(32)^{-\frac{4}{5}}$ $\frac{1}{16}$
35. $4^{1.5}$ **8**
36. $16^{1.5}$ **64**
37. $10,000^{0.75}$ **1000**

Example 5
(page 382)

40. $\frac{1}{3x^{\frac{2}{3}}}$

41. $\frac{5}{x^{\frac{2}{3}}}$

45. $x^4 \sqrt[3]{x}$

Write each expression in simplest form. Assume that all variables are positive.

38. $\left(x^{\frac{2}{3}}\right)^{-3}$ $\frac{1}{x^2}$

39. $\left(x^{-\frac{4}{7}}\right)^7$ $\frac{1}{x^4}$

40. $\left(3x^{\frac{2}{3}}\right)^{-1}$

41. $5\left(x^{\frac{2}{3}}\right)^{-1}$

42. $\left(-27x^{-9}\right)^{\frac{1}{3}}$ $-\frac{3}{x^3}$

43. $\left(-32y^{15}\right)^{\frac{1}{5}}$ $-2y^3$

44. $\left(\frac{x^3}{x^{-1}}\right)^{-\frac{1}{4}}$ $\frac{1}{x}$

45. $\left(\frac{x^2}{x^{-11}}\right)^{\frac{1}{3}}$

46. $\left(x^{\frac{1}{2}}y^{-\frac{2}{3}}\right)^{-6}$ $\frac{y^4}{x^3}$

47. $\left(x^{\frac{2}{3}}y^{-\frac{1}{6}}\right)^{-12}$ $\frac{y^2}{x^8}$

48. $\left(\frac{x^{\frac{1}{4}}}{y^{-\frac{3}{4}}}\right)^{12}$ x^3y^9

49. $\left(\frac{x^{-\frac{2}{3}}}{y^{-\frac{1}{3}}}\right)^{15}$ $\frac{y^5}{x^{10}}$

B **Apply Your Skills**

Simplify each number.

50. $(-343)^{\frac{1}{3}}$ -7

51. $(-243)^{\frac{1}{5}}$ -3

52. $32^{1.2}$ 64

53. $243^{1.2}$ 729

54. $64^{3.5}$ $2{,}097{,}152$

55. $100^{4.5}$ $1{,}000{,}000{,}000$ or 10^9

56. $32^{-0.4}$ $\frac{1}{4}$

57. $64^{-0.5}$ $\frac{1}{8}$

58. $(-216)^{-\frac{2}{3}}$ $\frac{1}{36}$

59. $2(16)^{\frac{3}{4}}$ 16

60. $-(-27)^{-\frac{4}{3}}$ $-\frac{1}{81}$

61. $\frac{1000^{\frac{4}{3}}}{100^{\frac{1}{2}}}$ 10

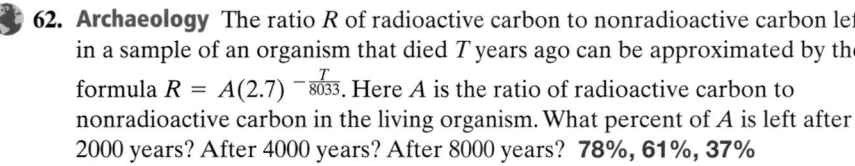

62. **Archaeology** The ratio R of radioactive carbon to nonradioactive carbon left in a sample of an organism that died T years ago can be approximated by the formula $R = A(2.7)^{-\frac{T}{8033}}$. Here A is the ratio of radioactive carbon to nonradioactive carbon in the living organism. What percent of A is left after 2000 years? After 4000 years? After 8000 years?   **78%, 61%, 37%**

63. **Biology** The expression $0.036m^{\frac{3}{4}}$ is used in the study of fluids. Evaluate the expression for $m = 46 \times 10^4$.   **635.87**

64. **Physics** In the expression $PV^{\frac{7}{5}}$, P represents the pressure and V represents the volume of a sample of a gas. Evaluate the expression for $P = 6$ and $V = 32$.   **768**

Simplify each expression. Assume that all variables are positive.

65. $x^{\frac{2}{7}} \cdot x^{\frac{3}{14}}$ $x^{\frac{1}{2}}$

66. $y^{\frac{1}{2}} \cdot y^{\frac{3}{10}}$ $y^{\frac{4}{5}}$

67. $x^{\frac{3}{5}} \div x^{\frac{1}{10}}$ $x^{\frac{1}{2}}$

68. $y^{\frac{5}{7}} \div y^{\frac{3}{14}}$ $y^{\frac{1}{2}}$

73. $\frac{1}{x^{\frac{13}{16}}}$

74. $\frac{1}{x^{\frac{7}{24}}}$

75. $\frac{1}{x^{\frac{1}{3}}}$

76. $\frac{1}{(xy)^{\frac{1}{2}}}$

79a. **Answers may vary.**
   Sample: $4 - 5^{\frac{1}{2}}$,
   $2\left(4 - 5^{\frac{1}{2}}\right), \frac{4 - 5^{\frac{1}{2}}}{2}$

69. $\frac{x^{\frac{3}{2}}y^{-\frac{1}{4}}}{x^{\frac{1}{2}}y^{-\frac{1}{2}}}$ $x^{\frac{1}{6}}y^{\frac{1}{4}}$

70. $\frac{x^{\frac{1}{2}}y^{-\frac{1}{3}}}{x^{\frac{3}{4}}y^{\frac{1}{2}}}$ $\frac{1}{x^{\frac{1}{4}}y^{\frac{5}{6}}}$

71. $\left(\frac{16x^{14}}{81y^{18}}\right)^{\frac{1}{2}}$ $\frac{4x^7}{9y^9}$

72. $\left(\frac{81y^{16}}{16x^{12}}\right)^{\frac{1}{2}}$ $\frac{9y^8}{4x^6}$

73. $\left(x^{\frac{1}{2}} \cdot x^{\frac{5}{12}}\right)^{\frac{1}{3}} \div x^{\frac{2}{3}}$

74. $\left(x^{\frac{3}{4}} \div x^{\frac{7}{8}}\right) \cdot x^{-\frac{1}{6}}$

75. $\left[\left(x^{-\frac{1}{2}}\right)^2\right]^{\frac{1}{3}}$

76. $\left[\left(\sqrt{x^3y^3}\right)^{\frac{1}{3}}\right]^{-1}$

77. **Writing** Explain why $(-64)^{\frac{1}{3}} = -64^{\frac{1}{3}}$ and $(-64)^{\frac{1}{2}} \neq -64^{\frac{1}{2}}$.   **See margin.**

78. **Error Analysis** Explain why the following simplification is incorrect.
   $5\left(4 - 5^{\frac{1}{2}}\right) = 5(4) - 5\left(5^{\frac{1}{2}}\right) = 20 - 25^{\frac{1}{2}} = 15$ **See margin.**

79. a. **Open-Ended** Find three numbers a such that $a\left(4 + 5^{\frac{1}{2}}\right)$ is a rational number.
   b. **Critical Thinking** Are there any rational numbers a such that $a\left(4 + 5^{\frac{1}{2}}\right)$ is a rational number?   **no**

80. a. **Reasoning** Show that $\sqrt[4]{x^2} = \sqrt{x}$ by using the definition of fourth root.
   b. **Reasoning** Show that $\sqrt[4]{x^2} = \sqrt{x}$ by rewriting $\sqrt[4]{x^2}$ in exponential form.   **a–b. See margin.**

C **Challenge**

Exponents that are irrational numbers can be defined so that all the properties of rational exponents are also true for irrational exponents. Use those properties to simplify each expression.

81. $\left(7^{\sqrt{2}}\right)^{\sqrt{2}}$ **49**

82. $\frac{3^{3+\sqrt{5}}}{3^{1+\sqrt{5}}}$ **9**

83. $\frac{x^{4\pi}}{x^{2\pi}}$ $x^{2\pi}$

84. $5^{2\sqrt{3}} \cdot 25^{-\sqrt{3}}$ **1**

85. $9^{\frac{1}{\sqrt{2}}}$ $3^{\sqrt{2}}$

86. $\left(3^{2+\sqrt{2}}\right)^{2-\sqrt{2}}$ **9**

---

pages 382–384   Exercises

77. The cube root of -64 is -4, which equals $-(64)^{\frac{1}{3}}$. The square root of -64 is not a real number, but $-(64)^{\frac{1}{2}} = -\sqrt{64} = -8$.

78. The exponent $\frac{1}{2}$ applies only to the 5, not to the 25.

80a. $\sqrt{x} \cdot \sqrt{x} \cdot \sqrt{x} \cdot \sqrt{x} = x \cdot x$
   $= x^2$, so $\sqrt[4]{x^2} = \sqrt{x}$
   b. $\sqrt[4]{x^2} = (x^2)^{\frac{1}{4}} = x^{\frac{2}{4}} =$
   $x^{\frac{1}{2}} = \sqrt{x}$

Resources

For additional practice with a variety of test item formats:
- Standardized Test Prep, p. 419
- Test-Taking Strategies, p. 414
- Test-Taking Strategies with Transparencies

Exercises 88, 89 It may help to write each expression in simplest form with fractional exponents.

pages 382–384   Exercises

98. $15 - 4\sqrt{14}$

99. $\dfrac{4 + 6\sqrt{5} + 2\sqrt{10} + 15\sqrt{2}}{-41}$

100. $\dfrac{10 - 8\sqrt{2}}{7}$

101. $4x(x^2 - 2x + 4)$

102. $(x + 2)^2$

103. $(x - 9)^2$

104. $(4a - 3b)(4a + 3b)$

105. $(5x - 4y)^2$

106. $(3x + 8)^2$

---

 87. Weather Using data for the effect of temperature and wind on an exposed face, the National Weather Service uses the following formula.

$$\text{Wind Chill Index} = 35.74 + 0.6215T - 35.75V^{0.16} + 0.4275TV^{0.16}$$

T is the temperature in degrees Fahrenheit and V is the velocity of the wind in miles per hour. Frostbite occurs in about 15 minutes when the wind chill index is about -20. Find the wind speed that produces a wind chill index of -20 when the temperature is 5°F. **33.13 mph**

Standardized Test Prep

Multiple Choice

88. Which expression is NOT equivalent to $\sqrt[4]{4n^2}$? **B**

   A. $(4n^2)^{\frac{1}{4}}$ **B.** $2n^{\frac{1}{2}}$ **C.** $(2n)^{\frac{1}{2}}$ **D.** $\sqrt{2n}$

89. Which expression is NOT equivalent to $\sqrt[6]{81x^4y^8}$? **H**

   F. $(3xy^2)^{\frac{2}{3}}$ **G.** $(3x)^{\frac{2}{3}}y^{\frac{4}{3}}$ **H.** $(3x^2y^4)^{\frac{1}{3}}$ **I.** $\sqrt[3]{9x^2y^4}$

Short Response

90. What is the value of x if $32^{0.8}x = 1$? Simplify the answer. **See left.**

Quantitative Comparison

Compare the boxed quantity in Column A with the boxed quantity in Column B. Choose the best answer.

   A. The quantity in Column A is greater.
   B. The quantity in Column B is greater.
   C. The two quantities are equal.
   D. The relationship cannot be determined from the information given.

90. [2] $x = \frac{1}{16}$
   [1] minor error

	Column A	Column B
91. B	$14^{\frac{2}{3}}$	$14^{\frac{3}{2}}$
92. A	$5^{-\frac{3}{4}}$	$5^{-\frac{4}{3}}$
93. C	$16^{-\frac{3}{4}}$	$32^{-\frac{3}{5}}$
94. A	$(-17)^{100}$	$(-17)^{101}$

Take It to the NET
Online lesson quiz at
www.PHSchool.com
Web Code: aga-0704

Mixed Review

Lesson 7-3

Simplify. Rationalize all denominators.

                                                  $1 + 3\sqrt{5}$

95. $6\sqrt[3]{3} - 2\sqrt[3]{3}$ $4\sqrt[3]{3}$ **96.** $3\sqrt{18} + 2\sqrt{72}$ $21\sqrt{2}$ **97.** $(\sqrt{5} - 1)(\sqrt{5} + 4)$

98. $(\sqrt{8} - \sqrt{7})^2$ **99.** $\dfrac{2 + \sqrt{10}}{2 - 3\sqrt{5}}$ **100.** $\dfrac{-2 + \sqrt{8}}{-3 - \sqrt{2}}$

Lesson 5-4

Factor each expression. 98–106. See margin.

101. $4x^3 - 8x^2 + 16x$ **102.** $x^2 + 4x + 4$ **103.** $x^2 - 18x + 81$

104. $16a^2 - 9b^2$ **105.** $25x^2 - 40xy + 16y^2$ **106.** $9x^2 + 48x + 64$

Solving Radical Equations

 North Carolina Objectives 2.07 Use equations with radical expressions to model and solve problems; justify results. a) Solve using tables, graphs, and algebraic properties.

Lesson Preview

What You'll Learn

OBJECTIVE 1 To solve radical equations

. . . And Why

To find the radius of a circular solar cell, as in Example 3

✓ **Check Skills You'll Need** (For help, go to Lesson 5-4.)

Solve by factoring.

1. $x^2 = -x + 6$ **-3, 2**
2. $x^2 = 5x + 14$ **-2, 7**
3. $2x^2 + x = 3$ **1, $-\frac{3}{2}$**
4. $3x^2 - 2 = 5x$ **$-\frac{1}{3}$, 2**
5. $4x^2 = -8x + 5$ **$-\frac{5}{2}, \frac{1}{2}$**
6. $6x^2 = 5x + 6$ **$-\frac{2}{3}, \frac{3}{2}$**

New Vocabulary • radical equation

OBJECTIVE

1 **Solving Radical Equations**

 Interactive lesson includes instant self-check, tutorials, and activities.

A **radical equation** is an equation that has a variable in a radicand or has a variable with a rational exponent.

$3 + \sqrt{x} = 10$ radical equation

$(x - 2)^{\frac{2}{3}} = 25$ radical equation

$\sqrt{3} + x = 10$ not a radical equation

To solve a radical equation, isolate the radical on one side of the equation and then raise both sides of the equation to the same power.

If $\sqrt[n]{x} = k$, then $(\sqrt[n]{x})^n = k^n$ and $x = k^n$.

1 EXAMPLE Solving Radical Equations With Index 2

Solve $2 + \sqrt{3x - 2} = 6$.

$2 + \sqrt{3x - 2} = 6$

$\sqrt{3x - 2} = 4$ **Isolate the radical.**

$(\sqrt{3x - 2})^2 = 4^2$ **Square each side.**

$3x - 2 = 16$

$3x = 18$

$x = 6$

Check $2 + \sqrt{3x - 2} = 6$

$2 + \sqrt{3(6) - 2} \stackrel{?}{=} 6$

$2 + \sqrt{16} \stackrel{?}{=} 6$

$2 + 4 \stackrel{?}{=} 6$

$6 = 6$ ✓

✓ **Check Understanding** **1** Solve $\sqrt{5x + 1} - 6 = 0$. **7**

 ## Ongoing Assessment and Intervention

Before the Lesson	**During the Lesson**	**After the Lesson**
Diagnose prerequisite skills using:	**Monitor progress using:**	**Assess knowledge using:**
• Check Skills You'll Need	• Check Understanding	• Lesson Quiz
	• Additional Examples	• Computer Test Generator CD
	• Standardized Test Prep	

1. Plan

Lesson Preview

✓ **Check Skills You'll Need**

Quadratic Equations
Lesson 5-5: Example 1
Exercises 1–6
Extra Practice, p. 826

Lesson Resources

 Teaching Resources
Practice, Reteaching, Enrichment

Reaching All Students
Practice Workbook 7-5
Spanish Practice Workbook 7-5
Hands-On Activities 46

Presentation Assistant Plus!
Transparencies
• Check Skills You'll Need 7-5
• Additional Examples 7-5
• Student Edition Answers 7-5
• Lesson Quiz 7-5
PH Presentation Pro CD 7-5

 **ASSESSMENT SYSTEM**

Computer Test Generator CD

 Technology
Resource Pro® CD-ROM
Computer Test Generator CD
Prentice Hall Presentation Pro CD

 www.PHSchool.com
Student Site
• Teacher Web Code: agk-5500
• Self-grading Lesson Quiz
Teacher Center
• Lesson Planner
• Resources

Plus

2. Teach

Professional Development

Math Background

Equations of the form $x^{\frac{m}{n}} = k$ can be solved by raising each side of the equation to the $\frac{n}{m}$ power since $\left(x^{\frac{m}{n}}\right)^{\frac{n}{m}} = x^{\frac{mn}{nm}} = x^1 = x$. Raising both sides of an equation to a power may introduce extraneous solutions. For instance, if we square both sides of $x^3 = -8$ we find $x^6 = 64$. The original equation has $x = -2$ as its only solution, whereas the second equation has $x = \pm 2$ as solutions. Thus, checking solutions is important. This may be done by direct substitution or by graphing both sides of the original equation and finding all intersection points.

OBJECTIVE

1 Teaching Notes

1 EXAMPLE Alternative Method

You may want to have students use a graphing calculator to graph $Y_1 = 2 + \sqrt{3x - 2}$ and $Y_2 = 6$. The x-coordinate of the point of intersection of the graphs is the solution of the given equation.

3 EXAMPLE English Learners

You may need to explain the terms *solar cell*, *watts*, and *minimum radius* so that students understand the problem.

4 EXAMPLE Teaching Tip

Point out that if you start with $x = 4$ and square both sides to get $x^2 = 16$, you go from an equation with one solution, 4, to one with two solutions, -4 and 4. Since the original equation only had one possible solution, an extraneous solution has been added.

Investigation (Optional)
This investigation shows how graphing can help you determine how many solutions a radical equation has. It helps eliminate extraneous solutions.

You can solve equations of the form $x^{\frac{m}{n}} = k$ by raising each side of the equation to the power $\frac{n}{m}$, the reciprocal of $\frac{m}{n}$. If n is even, then $\left(x^{\frac{m}{n}}\right)^{\frac{n}{m}} = |x|$. If n is odd, then $\left(x^{\frac{m}{n}}\right)^{\frac{n}{m}} = x$.

2 EXAMPLE Solving Radical Equations With Rational Exponents

Solve $2(x - 2)^{\frac{2}{3}} = 50$.

$$2(x - 2)^{\frac{2}{3}} = 50$$

$$(x - 2)^{\frac{2}{3}} = 25 \qquad \text{Divide each side by 2.}$$

$$\left((x - 2)^{\frac{2}{3}}\right)^{\frac{3}{2}} = 25^{\frac{3}{2}} \qquad \text{Raise each side to the } \tfrac{3}{2} \text{ power.}$$

$$|x - 2|^1 = 25^{\frac{3}{2}} \qquad \text{Multiply exponents. Use absolute value when taking an even root.}$$

$$x - 2 = \pm 125 \qquad \text{Simplify.}$$

$$x = 127 \text{ or } x = -123$$

Check

$$2(x - 2)^{\frac{2}{3}} = 50 \qquad\qquad 2(x - 2)^{\frac{2}{3}} = 50$$
$$2(127 - 2)^{\frac{2}{3}} \stackrel{?}{=} 50 \qquad\qquad 2(-123 - 2)^{\frac{2}{3}} \stackrel{?}{=} 50$$
$$2(5^3)^{\frac{2}{3}} \stackrel{?}{=} 50 \qquad\qquad 2(-125)^{\frac{2}{3}} \stackrel{?}{=} 50$$
$$2(5)^2 \stackrel{?}{=} 50 \qquad\qquad 2(-5)^2 \stackrel{?}{=} 50$$
$$50 = 50 \checkmark \qquad\qquad 50 = 50 \checkmark$$

✓ **Check Understanding** ② Solve $2(x + 3)^{\frac{3}{2}} = 54$ **6**

3 EXAMPLE Real-World Connection

Solar Energy A company manufactures solar cells that produce 0.02 watts of power per square centimeter of surface area. A circular solar cell needs to produce at least 10 watts. What is its minimum radius?

Relate | area of cell | · | power per square centimeter | ≥ | total power |

Define Let $r =$ the radius in centimeters.

Write $\pi r^2 \qquad \cdot \qquad 0.02 \qquad \geq \qquad 10$

$$\pi r^2 \cdot 0.02 \geq 10$$
$$r^2 \geq \frac{10}{0.02\pi}$$
$$r^2 \geq \frac{1000}{2\pi}$$
$$r^2 \geq \frac{500}{\pi}$$
$$(r^2)^{\frac{1}{2}} \geq \left(\frac{500}{\pi}\right)^{\frac{1}{2}}$$
$$r \geq 12.62 \qquad \text{Use a calculator.}$$

The minimum radius is about 12.62 cm.

Real-World Connection

Solar cells convert sunlight directly into electricity. They power calculators, emergency road signs, satellites, and experimental vehicles.

✓ **Check Understanding** ③ Find the minimum radius of a circular solar cell that will produce 20 watts of power. **about 17.84 cm**

👥 Reaching All Students

| **Below Level** Review the products of reciprocals. In Example 5, students may need to convert the decimal exponents to fractions. | **Advanced Learners** Challenge students to solve $\sqrt{x + 1} + \sqrt{2x} = \sqrt{5x + 3}$. **1** | **English Learners** See note on page 386. **English Learners** See note on page 388. |

Extraneous solutions can be introduced when you raise both sides of an equation to a power. So check all possible solutions in the original equation.

Need Help?

To review extraneous solutions, go to Lesson 1-5.

4 EXAMPLE Checking for Extraneous Solutions

Solve $\sqrt{x-3} + 5 = x$. Check for extraneous solutions.

$$\sqrt{x-3} + 5 = x$$

$\sqrt{x-3} = x - 5$	Isolate the radical.
$(\sqrt{x-3})^2 = (x-5)^2$	Square each side.
$x - 3 = x^2 - 10x + 25$	Simplify.
$0 = x^2 - 11x + 28$	Combine like terms.
$0 = (x-4)(x-7)$	Factor.
$x - 4 = 0$ or $x - 7 = 0$	Factor Theorem
$x = 4$ or $x = 7$	

Check

$\sqrt{x-3} + 5 = x$ $\sqrt{x-3} + 5 = x$

$\sqrt{4-3} + 5 \overset{?}{=} 4$ $\sqrt{7-3} + 5 \overset{?}{=} 7$

$\sqrt{1} + 5 \overset{?}{=} 4$ $\sqrt{4} + 5 \overset{?}{=} 7$

$6 \neq 4$ $7 = 7$

● The only solution is 7.

✓ Check Understanding 4 Solve $\sqrt{5x-1} + 3 = x$. Check for extraneous solutions. **10**

If an equation contains two radical expressions (or two terms with rational exponents), isolate one of the radicals (or one of the terms).

5 EXAMPLE Solving Equations With Two Rational Exponents

Solve $(2x+1)^{0.5} - (3x+4)^{0.25} = 0$. Check for extraneous solutions.

$$(2x+1)^{0.5} - (3x+4)^{0.25} = 0$$

$(2x+1)^{0.5} = (3x+4)^{0.25}$	
$((2x+1)^{0.5})^4 = ((3x+4)^{0.25})^4$	Raise each side to the 4th power.
$(2x+1)^2 = 3x+4$	Simplify exponents.
$4x^2 + 4x + 1 = 3x + 4$	Simplify.
$4x^2 + x - 3 = 0$	Combine like terms.
$(4x-3)(x+1) = 0$	Factor.
$x = \frac{3}{4}$ or $x = -1$	Factor Theorem

Check $(2x+1)^{0.5} - (3x+4)^{0.25} = 0$ $(2x+1)^{0.5} - (3x+4)^{0.25} = 0$

$\left(2 \cdot \frac{3}{4} + 1\right)^{0.5} - \left(3 \cdot \frac{3}{4} + 4\right)^{0.25} \overset{?}{=} 0$ $(2(-1)+1)^{0.5} - (3(-1)+4)^{0.25} \overset{?}{=} 0$

$\left(\frac{5}{2}\right)^{0.5} - \left(\frac{25}{4}\right)^{0.25} \overset{?}{=} 0$ $(-1)^{0.5} - (1)^{0.25} \overset{?}{=} 0$

$\left(\frac{5}{2}\right)^{0.5} - \left(\left(\frac{5}{2}\right)^2\right)^{0.25} \overset{?}{=} 0$ $(-1)^{0.5}$ is not a real number.

$\left(\frac{5}{2}\right)^{0.5} - \left(\frac{5}{2}\right)^{0.5} = 0$

● The only solution is $\frac{3}{4}$.

✓ Check Understanding 5 Solve $\sqrt{3x+2} - \sqrt{2x+7} = 0$. Check for extraneous solutions. **5**

Lesson 7-5 Solving Radical Equations   **387**

5 EXAMPLE Technology Tip

To check the solutions quickly, you can press 3 ÷ 4 STO► X,T,θ,n ENTER to store the value $\frac{3}{4}$ (0.75) as the value of x. Next, type the expression on the left side of the equation and press ENTER. The calculator will display 0 as the value of the expression for $x = \frac{3}{4}$. If you repeat this process and use -1 as the value of x, the calculator will give you an error message telling you that the result is not real.

Additional Examples

1 Solve $-10 + \sqrt{2x+1} = -5$. **12**

2 Solve $3(x+1)^{\frac{3}{5}} = 24$. **31**

3 An artist wants to make a plastic sphere for a sculpture. The plastic weighs 0.8 ounce per cubic inch. The maximum weight of the sphere is to be 80 pounds. The formula for the volume V of a sphere is $V = \frac{4}{3}\pi r^3$, where r is the radius of the sphere. What is the maximum radius the sphere can have? **about 2.88 in.**

4 Solve $\sqrt{x+2} - 3 = 2x$. Check for extraneous solutions. **−1**

5 Solve $(x+1)^{\frac{2}{3}} - (9x+1)^{\frac{1}{3}} = 0$. Check for extraneous solutions. **0, 7**

Closure

Have students describe the procedure for solving a radical equation. **Answers may vary. Sample: Isolate a radical expression on one side of the equation. Next, raise both sides to the power that is the index of this radical. Simplify. Repeat for any remaining radical. Solve the final polynomial equation, and check for extraneous solutions.**

387

3. Practice

Assignment Guide

1 Objective

Ⓐ Ⓑ **Core** 1–53
Ⓒ **Extension** 54–58

Standardized Test Prep 59–64

Mixed Review 65–90

English Learners

Exercises 15–20 Remind students that *extraneous* solutions are *extra* solutions. When substituted into the equation they do not make the statement true.

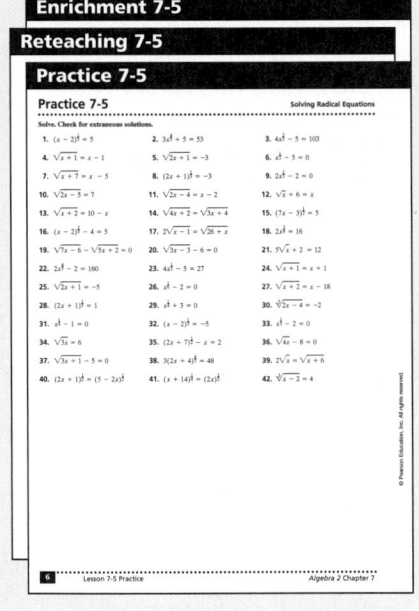

Investigation: Checking for Extraneous Solutions

You can use a graphing calculator to check for extraneous solutions.

1. a. Solve $x = \sqrt{x + 7} + 5$. How many apparent solutions do you get? **2**

b. Any or all of the apparent solutions may be extraneous. One way to find out is to let y_1 equal the left side of the equation and let y_2 equal the right side. Graph the two equations. In how many points do they intersect? **1**

1c. 2 is extraneous.

c. The x-values of the points of intersection are solutions of the original equation. Are any of the apparent solutions extraneous?

d. Substitute the apparent solutions in the original equation. Does this algebraic check agree with the calculator check? **yes**

2. Use a graphing calculator to determine the number of solutions of each equation.

a. $\sqrt{x} = x - 2$ **1**   **b.** $\sqrt{x^2 + 3} = 2x - 1$ **1**   **c.** $x + 8 = 4\sqrt{x + 5}$ **2**

EXERCISES

For more practice, see *Extra Practice*.

Practice and Problem Solving

Ⓐ **Practice by Example**

Example 1
(page 385)

Solve.

1. $3\sqrt{x} + 3 = 15$ **16**

2. $4\sqrt{x} - 1 = 3$ **1**

3. $\sqrt{x + 3} = 5$ **22**

4. $\sqrt{3x + 4} = 4$ **4**

5. $\sqrt{2x + 3} - 7 = 0$ **23**

6. $\sqrt{6 - 3x} - 2 = 0$ **$\frac{2}{3}$**

Example 2
(page 386)

Solve.

7. $(x + 5)^{\frac{2}{3}} = 4$ **3, −13**

8. $(x - 2)^{\frac{2}{3}} = 9$ **29, −25**

9. $3(x - 2)^{\frac{3}{4}} = 24$ **18**

10. $3(x + 3)^{\frac{3}{4}} = 81$ **78**

11. $(x + 1)^{\frac{3}{2}} - 2 = 25$ **8**

12. $3 + (4 - x)^{\frac{3}{2}} = 11$ **0**

Example 3
(page 386)

13. Volume. A spherical water tank holds 15,000 ft³ of water. Find the diameter of the tank. (*Hint:* $V = \frac{\pi}{6}d^3$) **30.6 ft**

14. Hydraulics The maximum flow of water in a pipe is modeled by the formula $Q = Av$, where A is the cross-sectional area of the pipe and v is the velocity of the water. Find the diameter of a pipe that allows a maximum flow of 50 ft³/min of water flowing at a velocity of 600 ft/min. Round your answer to the nearest inch. **2 in.**

Example 4
(page 387)

Solve. Check for extraneous solutions.

15. $\sqrt{11x + 3} - 2x = 0$ **3**

16. $(5x + 4)^{\frac{1}{2}} - 3x = 0$ **1**

17. $\sqrt{3x + 13} - 5 = x$ **−3, −4**

18. $\sqrt{x + 7} + 5 = x$ **9**

19. $(x + 3)^{\frac{1}{2}} - 1 = x$ **1**

20. $(5 - x)^{\frac{1}{2}} = x + 1$ **1**

Example 5
(page 387)

Solve. Check for extraneous solutions.

21. $\sqrt{3x} = \sqrt{x + 6}$ **3**

22. $(x + 5)^{\frac{1}{2}} - (5 - 2x)^{\frac{1}{4}} = 0$ **-2**

23. $(7x + 6)^{\frac{1}{2}} = (9 + 4x)^{\frac{1}{2}}$ **1**

24. $\sqrt{3x + 7} = x - 1$ **6**

25. $\sqrt{x + 7} - x = 1$ **2**

26. $\sqrt{-3x - 5} = x + 3$ **-2**

27. $(3x + 2)^{\frac{1}{2}} - (2x + 7)^{\frac{1}{2}} = 0$ **5**

28. $x + 8 = (x^2 + 16)^{\frac{1}{2}}$ **-3**

29. $(2x)^{\frac{1}{2}} = (x + 5)^{\frac{1}{2}}$ **5**

30. $1 = (3 + x)^{\frac{1}{2}}$ **-2**

B **Apply Your Skills** **31. Geometry** The formula for the area A of a square whose side is s units long is $A = s^2$. Solve the formula for s. Find the length of the side of a square that has an area of 32 m². **$s = \sqrt{A}$; $4\sqrt{2}$ m, or about 5.7 m**

32. a. Package Design The formula for the area A of a hexagon with a side s units long is $A = \frac{3s^2\sqrt{3}}{2}$. See the figure below. Solve the formula for s and rationalize the denominator. **$s = \frac{\sqrt{2\sqrt{3}A}}{3}$**

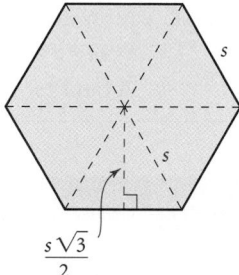 

$\frac{s\sqrt{3}}{2}$

b. A package designer wants the hexagonal base of a hat box to have an area of about 200 in.² About how long is each side? **about 8.8 in.**

c. What is the distance between opposite sides of the hat box? **about 15.2 in.**

33. a. Form a pair of simultaneous equations by letting y_1 equal the left side and y_2 equal the right side of $\sqrt{5} - x = 1$. Graph the equations. **a–d. See margin.**

b. Repeat part (a) with the equivalent equation $\sqrt{5} = x + 1$.

c. Repeat part (a) with the equivalent equation $\sqrt{5} - x - 1 = 0$.

✏️ **d. Writing** Describe the similarities and differences among the graphs of the three sets of simultaneous equations.

Solve. Check for extraneous solutions.

34. $3\sqrt{2x} - 3 = 9$ **8**

35. $2(2x)^{\frac{1}{3}} + 1 = 5$ **4**

36. $\sqrt{2x - 1} - 3 = 0$ **5**

37. $(2x + 3)^{\frac{1}{2}} - 7 = 0$ **23**

38. $\sqrt{x^2 + 3} = x + 1$ **1**

39. $\sqrt{x - 5} - \sqrt{x} = -2$ **5.0625**

40. $(2x + 3)^{\frac{3}{4}} - 3 = 5$ **6.5**

41. $2(x - 1)^{\frac{4}{3}} + 4 = 36$ **9, -7**

42. $x^{\frac{1}{2}} - (x - 5)^{\frac{1}{2}} = 2$ **$\frac{81}{16}$**

43. $\sqrt{x} = \sqrt{x - 8} + 2$ **9**

44. $\sqrt{5x + 1} - \sqrt{4x + 3} = 0$ **2**

45. $\sqrt{x + 10} + \sqrt{3 - x} = 5$ **-1, -6**

46. $(3x + 2)^{\frac{1}{2}} = 8(3x + 2)^{-\frac{1}{2}}$ **2**

47. $\sqrt{4x - 10} = 3\sqrt{x - 5}$ **7**

48. $(x - 9)^{\frac{1}{2}} + 1 = x^{\frac{1}{2}}$ **25**

49. $\sqrt{10x} - 2\sqrt{5x - 25} = 0$ **10**

50. $(2x + 1)^{\frac{1}{3}} = (2 + 3x)^{\frac{1}{3}}$ **-1**

51. $(2x - 1)^{\frac{1}{3}} = (x + 1)^{\frac{1}{6}}$ **$\frac{5}{4}$**

Lesson 7-5 Solving Radical Equations **389**

Alternative Assessment

Ask students to select a whole number and then *work backward* to write two radical equations that have that whole number as a solution. One equation should involve square roots and the other cube roots. Students may need to experiment to find a whole number for which they can most easily write radical equations. Have students share their equations within small groups and solve each equation.

d. The graph of each pair consists of two straight lines, one of which is horizontal. They intersect at different points, but these points have the same x-value, about 1.236.

389

pages 388–390 Exercises

33a.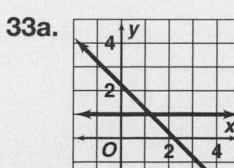

b.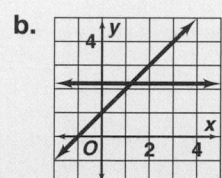

c.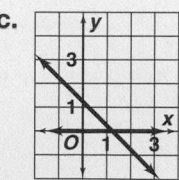

Standardized Test Prep

A sheet of blank grids is available in the Test-Taking Strategies with Transparencies booklet. Give this sheet to students for practice with filling in the grids.

📁 Resources

For additional practice with a variety of test item formats:
- Standardized Test Prep p. 419
- Test-Taking Strategies, p. 414
- Test-Taking Strategies with Transparencies

Error Prevention

Exercise 61 It is important to move one of the radical expressions to the right side of the equation before raising both sides to a power.

pages 388–390 Exercises

57. Plan 1: Use a calculator to evaluate $\sqrt{2}$ and record it. Add 2, take the square root, and record it. Add 2, take the square root, and record it. Continue this procedure about seven times until it becomes clear that the values are approaching 2. **Plan 2:** The given equation is equivalent to $x = \sqrt{2 + x}$. Solve this equation to find that $x = 2$.

85. 3, 4

86. 3, 5

87. −5, −4

88. $-2, -\frac{2}{3}$

89. $-\frac{1}{3}, -\frac{4}{3}$

90. $-2, -\frac{3}{4}$

---

 52. Physics The velocity v of an object dropped from a tall building is given by the formula $v = \sqrt{64d}$, where d is the distance the object has dropped. Solve the formula for d. $\quad d = \frac{v^2}{64}$

53. Open-Ended Write an equation that has two radical expressions and no real roots. **Answers may vary. Sample:** $\sqrt{x - 3} = \sqrt{3x + 5}$

⦿ Challenge **Solve. Check for extraneous solutions.**

54. $\sqrt{x + 1} + \sqrt{2x} = \sqrt{5x + 3}$ **1**

55. $\sqrt{x} + \sqrt{2x} = 2$ **2**

56. $\sqrt{\sqrt{x + 25}} = \sqrt{x + 5}$ **0**

57. Critical Thinking Devise a plan to find the value of x. **See margin.**
$$x = \sqrt{2 + \sqrt{2 + \sqrt{2 + \ldots}}}$$

58. Critical Thinking You have solved equations containing square roots by squaring both sides. You were using the property that if $a = b$ then $a^2 = b^2$. Show that the following statements are *not* true for all real numbers.
a. If $a^2 = b^2$ then $a = b$. **a. A counterexample is $a = 3$, $b = -3$.**
b. If $a < b$ then $a^2 < b^2$. **b. A counterexample is $a = -5$, $b = 3$.**

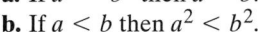
Standardized Test Prep

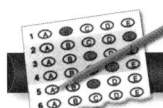

Gridded Response

59. Solve $\sqrt{4x - 23} - 3 = 2$. **12**

60. Solve $(x + 2)^{\frac{3}{4}} = 27$. **79**

 Take It to the NET
Online lesson quiz at
www.PHSchool.com
········ Web Code: aga-0705

61. Solve $\sqrt{2x + 1} - \sqrt[4]{x + 11} = 0$. $\frac{5}{4}$

62. Solve $5\sqrt{x} + 7 = 8$. $\frac{1}{25}$

63. Solve $-\sqrt[3]{x} + 3 = 0$. **27**

64. Solve $\sqrt{x + 2} = x$. **2**

Mixed Review

Lesson 7-4 **Simplify each expression.**

65. $64^{\frac{2}{3}}$ **16** **66.** $25^{1.5}$ **125** **67.** $6^{\frac{1}{2}} \cdot 12^{\frac{1}{2}}$ **$6\sqrt{2}$** **68.** $8^{\frac{1}{2}} \cdot 40^{\frac{1}{2}}$ **$8\sqrt{5}$** **69.** $3^{\frac{1}{3}} \cdot 18^{\frac{1}{3}}$ **$3\sqrt[3]{2}$**

70. $81^{-0.25}$ $\frac{1}{3}$ **71.** $4^{3.5}$ **128** **72.** $125 \cdot 125^{-\frac{1}{3}}$ **25** **73.** $32 \cdot 256^{-\frac{1}{2}}$ **2** **74.** $100^{-\frac{3}{2}} \cdot 0.01^{\frac{3}{2}}$ $\frac{1}{10^6}$

Lesson 6-7 **Evaluate each expression.**

75. $_7P_1$ **7** **76.** $_7P_3$ **210** **77.** $_5P_3$ **60** **78.** $_8P_4$ **1680** **79.** $_4P_4$ **24**

80. $_5C_2$ **10** **81.** $_7C_5$ **21** **82.** $_5C_5$ **1** **83.** $_6C_5$ **6** **84.** $_7C_1$ **7**

Lesson 5-5 **Solve each equation by factoring. 85–90. See margin.**

85. $x^2 - 7x + 12 = 0$ **86.** $x^2 - 8x + 15 = 0$ **87.** $x^2 + 9x + 20 = 0$

88. $3x^2 + 8x + 4 = 0$ **89.** $9x^2 + 15x + 4 = 0$ **90.** $4x^2 + 11x + 6 = 0$

Radical Expressions in Formulas

FOR USE WITH LESSON 7-5

You frequently need to use radical expressions in geometry formulas.

EXAMPLE

The cube at the right fits in (is inscribed in) the sphere. How much more than the cube does the sphere hold?

A. 25% more   **B.** 50% more   **C.** 100% more   **D.** 150% more

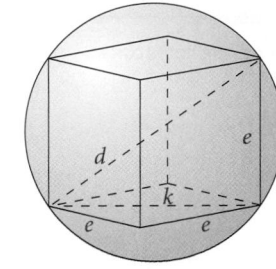

Step 1 Find k.

k is the diagonal of the square that is the base of the cube. Use the Pythagorean Theorem.

$$k^2 = e^2 + e^2$$
$$= 2e^2$$
$$k = e\sqrt{2}$$

Step 2 Find the radius of the sphere.

The diameter d of the sphere is also the diagonal of the cube and the hypotenuse of a right triangle with legs k and e.

$$d^2 = k^2 + e^2$$
$$= (e\sqrt{2})^2 + e^2$$
$$= 2e^2 + e^2$$
$$= 3e^2$$
$$d = e\sqrt{3}.$$

So the radius of the sphere is $\frac{d}{2}$ or $\frac{e\sqrt{3}}{2}$.

Step 3 Find the ratio of the volume of the sphere to the volume of the cube.

The volume of a sphere is $V = \frac{4}{3}\pi r^3$.

The volume of the cube is e^3.

$$\frac{\text{volume of sphere}}{\text{volume of cube}} = \frac{\frac{4}{3}\pi\left(\frac{e\sqrt{3}}{2}\right)^3}{e^3}$$
$$= \frac{4\pi \cdot 3e^3\sqrt{3}}{3 \cdot 8 \cdot e^3}$$
$$= \frac{\pi\sqrt{3}}{2} \approx 2.7$$

The sphere holds about 2.7 times as much as the cube, so it holds 1.7 times more, or 170% more than the cube. If you chose answer D, you are a very good estimator!

EXERCISES

1. **a.** The cube at the right is inscribed in a cylinder. Estimate the percent by which the volume of the cylinder exceeds the volume of the cube. Then compute the percent. (The formula for the volume of a cylinder is $V = \pi r^2 h$.) **about 57% more volume**

   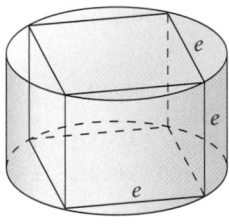

   b. Estimate the percent by which the surface area of the cylinder exceeds the surface area of the cube. Then compute the percent. (The formula for the surface area of a cylinder is S.A. $= 2\pi r^2 + 2\pi rh$.) **about 26% more surface area**

2. Estimate the percent by which the surface area of a sphere exceeds the surface area of its inscribed cube. Then compute the percent. (The formula for the surface area of a sphere is S.A. $= 4\pi r^2$.) **about 57% more surface area**

3. Estimate the percent by which the area and circumference of a circle exceed the area and perimeter of its inscribed square. Then compute the percents. **See margin.**

Using Radical Expressions in Formulas

This review will give students insight into the important role that radical expressions play in the study of geometric figures.

Resources

Technology
Computer Test Generator CD-ROM, Chapter 0, Geometry and Measurement

Teaching Notes

1 **EXAMPLE** **Teaching Tip**

Urge students to read the question carefully. It asks how *much more* the sphere holds than the cube. This is quite different from asking how *many times more* the sphere holds than the cube. They should also note that the choices make it clear that an estimate is desired, not an exact answer.

Error Prevention

Exercise 2 Students should be careful to use the correct formula for the surface area of the cube, S.A. $= 6e^2$.

page 391   Geometry Review

3. **The area of the circle exceeds the area of the square by about 57%. The circumference of the circle exceeds the perimeter of the square by about 11%.**

7-6

1. Plan

Lesson Preview

 Check Skills You'll Need

Relations and Functions
Lesson 2-1: Examples 2 and 6
Exercises 5–7, 20–23
Extra Practice, p. 823

Lesson Resources

 Teaching Resources
Practice, Reteaching, Enrichment
Checkpoint Quiz 2

 Reaching All Students
Practice Workbook 7-6
Spanish Practice Workbook 7-6
Reading and Math Literacy 7C
Spanish Reading & Literacy 7C
Spanish Checkpoint Quiz 2

 Presentation Assistant Plus!
Transparencies
• Check Skills You'll Need 7-6
• Additional Examples 7-6
• Student Edition Answers 7-6
• Lesson Quiz 7-6
PH Presentation Pro CD 7-6

 PRENTICE HALL
ASSESSMENT SYSTEM

Checkpoint Quiz 2
Computer Test Generator CD

 Technology
Resource Pro® CD-ROM
Computer Test Generator CD
Prentice Hall Presentation Pro CD

 www.PHSchool.com
Student Site
• Teacher Web Code: agk-5500
• Self-grading Lesson Quiz
Teacher Center
• Lesson Planner
• Resources

Plus

392

Function Operations

North Carolina Objectives

2.01 Use the composition and inverse of functions to model and solve problems; justify results.

Lesson Preview

What You'll Learn

 OBJECTIVE **1**
To add, subtract, multiply, and divide functions

 OBJECTIVE **2**
To find the composite of two functions

. . . And Why

To find successive discounts, as in Example 4

 Check Skills You'll Need (For help, go to Lesson 2-1.)

Find the domain and range of each function. 1–4. See back of book.

1. $\{(0, -5), (2, -3), (4, -1)\}$ **2.** $\{(-1, 0), (0, 0), (1, 0)\}$

3. $f(x) = 2x - 12$ **4.** $g(x) = x^2$

Evaluate each function for the given value of x.

5. Let $f(x) = 3x + 4$. Find $f(2)$. **10**   **6.** Let $g(x) = 2x^2 - 3x + 1$. Find $g(-3)$.
                                                                28

New Vocabulary • composite function

---

 iTEXT Interactive lesson includes instant self-check, tutorials, and activities.

OBJECTIVE

1 **Operations With Functions**

If an airplane has an airspeed of 415 mi/h, then $f(x) = 415x$ represents the distance traveled by the plane in still air in x hours. If the wind speed is 30 mi/h, then $g(x) = 30x$ represents the motion of the wind, and $f(x) + g(x) = 415x + 30x$ represents the distance traveled by the airplane flying with the wind.

You can add, subtract, multiply, and divide functions.

🔑 **Key Concepts**

1. $f + g = 5x^2 + x + 1$, domain: all real numbers; $f - g = 5x^2 - 9x - 1$, domain: all real numbers

Definition	Function Operations
Addition	$(f + g)(x) = f(x) + g(x)$
Multiplication	$(f \cdot g)(x) = f(x) \cdot g(x)$
Subtraction	$(f - g)(x) = f(x) - g(x)$
Division	$\left(\dfrac{f}{g}\right)(x) = \dfrac{f(x)}{g(x)}, g(x) \neq 0$

❓ **Need Help?**
The domain of a function is the set of all possible inputs of the function.
The range of a function is the set of all possible outputs of the function.

The domains of the sum, difference, product, and quotient functions consist of the x-values that are in the domains of both f and g. However, the domain of a quotient function does not contain any x-value for which $g(x) = 0$.

1 **EXAMPLE** **Adding and Subtracting Functions**

Let $f(x) = 3x + 8$ and $g(x) = 2x - 12$. Find $f + g$ and $f - g$ and their domains.

$(f + g)(x) = f(x) + g(x) = (3x + 8) + (2x - 12) = 5x - 4$

$(f - g)(x) = f(x) - g(x) = (3x + 8) - (2x - 12) = x + 20$

• The domains of $f + g$ and $f - g$ are the set of real numbers.

✓ **Check Understanding** **1** Let $f(x) = 5x^2 - 4x$ and $g(x) = 5x + 1$. Find $f + g$ and $f - g$ and their domains.
See above left.

392 Chapter 7 Radical Functions and Rational Exponents

 Ongoing Assessment and Intervention

Before the Lesson	During the Lesson	After the Lesson
Diagnose prerequisite skills using:	**Monitor progress using:**	**Assess knowledge using:**
• Check Skills You'll Need	• Check Understanding	• Lesson Quiz
	• Additional Examples	• Computer Test Generator CD
	• Standardized Test Prep	• Chapter Checkpoint 2 (p. 398)

2 EXAMPLE Multiplying and Dividing Functions

Let $f(x) = x^2 - 1$ and $g(x) = x + 1$. Find $f \cdot g$ and $\frac{f}{g}$ and their domains.

$$(f \cdot g)(x) = f(x) \cdot g(x) = (x^2 - 1)(x + 1) = x^3 + x^2 - x - 1$$

$$\left(\frac{f}{g}\right)(x) = \frac{f(x)}{g(x)} = \frac{x^2 - 1}{x + 1} = \frac{(x + 1)(x - 1)}{x + 1} = x - 1,\ x \neq -1$$

The domains of f and g are the set of real numbers, so the domain of $f \cdot g$ is also.

● The domain of $\frac{f}{g}$ does not include -1 because $g(-1) = 0$.

2. $f \cdot g = 12x^3 + 8x^2 - 17x + 5$, domain: all real numbers; $\frac{f}{g} = 3x + 5$, domain: all real numbers except $\frac{1}{2}$

✓ **Check Understanding** **2** Let $f(x) = 6x^2 + 7x - 5$ and $g(x) = 2x - 1$. Find $f \cdot g$ and $\frac{f}{g}$ and their domains.
See left.

OBJECTIVE
2 Composition of Functions

The diagram below shows what happens when you apply one function $g(x)$ after another function $f(x)$.

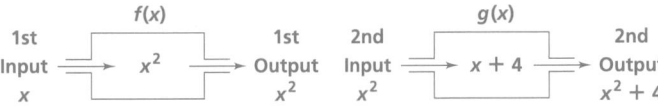

The output from the first function becomes the input for the second function. When you combine two functions as in the diagram above, you form a **composite function.**

Reading Math

Composite means "put together."

🔑 **Key Concepts**

Definition	Composition of Functions

The composition of function g with function f is written as $g \circ f$ and is defined as $(g \circ f)(x) = g(f(x))$, where the domain of $g \circ f$ consists of the values a in the domain of f such that $f(a)$ is in the domain of g.

$$(g \circ f)(x) = g(f(x))$$

① Evaluate the inner function $f(x)$ first.

② Then use your answer as the input of the outer function $g(x)$.

3 EXAMPLE Composition of Functions

Let $f(x) = x - 2$ and $g(x) = x^2$. Find $(g \circ f)(-5)$.

3b. No; the order in which operations are performed changes between $(f \circ g)$ and $(g \circ f)$, which changes what each composition equals.

Method 1
$(g \circ f)(x) = g(f(x)) = g(x - 2) = (x - 2)^2$
$(g \circ f)(-5) = (-5 - 2)^2$
$\qquad = (-7)^2$
$\qquad = 49$

Method 2
$(g \circ f)(x) = g(f(x))$
$g(f(-5)) = g(-5 - 2)$
$\qquad = g(-7)$
$\qquad = (-7)^2 = 49$

✓ **Check Understanding** **3 a.** Find $(f \circ g)(x)$ and evaluate $(f \circ g)(-5)$ for the functions f and g defined in Example 3. **$(f \circ g)(x) = x^2 - 2$, $(f \circ g)(-5) = 23$**
b. Critical Thinking Is a composition of functions commutative? Explain.
See left.

Lesson 7-6 Function Operations **393**

👥 **Reaching All Students**

Below Level Remind students to read $f(x)$ as 'f of x.' The notation for composition of functions also resembles multiplication. Make sure students understand that $(g \circ f)(x) \neq g(x) \cdot f(x)$.	**Advanced Learners** Have students investigate and report on the connection between composition of functions, fractal geometry, and the Mandelbrot Set.	**Auditory Learners** See note on page 393. **Error Prevention** See note on page 395.

393

Additional Examples

3 Let $f(x) = x^3$ and $g(x) = x^2 + 7$. Find $(g \circ f)(2)$. **71**

4 A store offers a 20% discount on all items. You have a coupon worth $3.

a. Use functions to model discounting an item by 20% and to model applying the coupon. $f(x) = 0.8x$, $g(x) = x - 3$

b. Use a composition of your two functions to model how much you would pay for an item if the clerk applies the discount first and then the coupon. $(g \circ f)(x) = 0.8x - 3$

c. Use a composition of your two functions to model how much you would pay for an item if the clerk applies the coupon first and then the discount. $(f \circ g)(x) = 0.8x - 2.4$

d. How much more is any item if the clerk applies the discount first? **$.60**

Closure

Have students assume that $f(x)$ and $g(x)$ are two functions. Ask them to explain how to find the value of $f + g$, $f - g$, $f \cdot g$, $\frac{f}{g}$, and $g \circ f$ when $x = 5$, given that the domain of each of the functions is the set of all real numbers. **Answers may vary. Sample: First find $f(5)$ and $g(5)$. Suppose these values are a and b respectively, and $b \neq 0$. The values of $f + g$, $f - g$, $f \cdot g$, and $\frac{f}{g}$ for $x = 5$ are $a + b$, $a - b$, $a \cdot b$, and $\frac{a}{b}$, respectively. To find the value of $(g \circ f)$ when $x = 5$, find the value of $g(a)$.**

pages 394–398 **Exercises**

13. $2x^2 + 2x - 4$; domain: all real numbers

14. $-2x^2 + 2$; domain: all real numbers

15. $2x^2 - 2$; domain: all real numbers

16. $2x^3 - x^2 - 4x + 3$; domain: all real numbers

17. $2x + 3$; domain: all real numbers except 1

4 **EXAMPLE** **Real-World** **Connection**

Consumer Issues Suppose you are shopping in the store in the photo. You have a coupon worth $5 off any item.

a. Use functions to model discounting an item by 20% and to model applying the coupon.

Let $x =$ the original price.

Cost with 20% discount:
$$f(x) = x - 0.2x = 0.8x$$

Cost with a coupon for $5:
$$g(x) = x - 5$$

b. Use a composition of your two functions to model how much you would pay for an item if the clerk applies the discount first and then the coupon.

$(g \circ f)(x) = g(f(x))$ **applying the discount first**
$ = g(0.8x)$
$ = 0.8x - 5$

c. Use a composition of your two functions to model how much you would pay for an item if the clerk applies the coupon first and then the discount.

$(f \circ g)(x) = f(g(x))$ **applying the coupon first**
$ = f(x - 5)$
$ = 0.8(x - 5)$
$ = 0.8x - 4$

d. How much more is any item if the clerk applies the coupon first?
$(f \circ g)(x) - (g \circ f)(x) = (0.8x - 4) - (0.8x - 5)$ **Subtract the functions.**
$ = 1$

Any item will cost $1 more.

4a. Let $f(x) = 0.9x$ and $g(x) = 0.75x$. Then $(g \circ f)(x) = g(0.9x) = 0.75(0.9x)$.

b. $(f \circ g)(x) = f(0.75x) = 0.9(0.75)x$.

✓ **Check Understanding** **4** A store is offering a 10% discount on all items. In addition, employees get a 25% discount. **a–b. See left.**
a. Write a composite function to model taking the 10% discount first.
b. Write a composite function to model taking the 25% discount first.
c. Suppose you are an employee. Which discount would you prefer to take first? **It makes no difference.**

EXERCISES

For more practice, see *Extra Practice*.

Practice and Problem Solving

A **Practice by Example**

Examples 1 and 2
(pages 392 and 393)

Let $f(x) = 3x + 5$ and $g(x) = x^2$. Perform each function operation.

1. $f(x) + g(x)$ $x^2 + 3x + 5$ **2.** $g(x) - f(x)$ $x^2 - 3x - 5$ **3.** $f(x) - g(x)$ $-x^2 + 3x + 5$

4. $f(x) \cdot g(x)$ $3x^3 + 5x^2$ **5.** $\dfrac{f(x)}{g(x)}$ $\dfrac{3x + 5}{x^2}$ **6.** $\dfrac{g(x)}{f(x)}$ $\dfrac{x^2}{3x + 5}$

7. $(f + g)(x)$ $x^2 + 3x + 5$ **8.** $(f - g)(x)$ $-x^2 + 3x + 5$ **9.** $(g - f)(x)$ $x^2 - 3x - 5$

10. $(f \cdot g)(x)$ $3x^3 + 5x^2$ **11.** $\left(\dfrac{f}{g}\right)(x)$ $\dfrac{3x + 5}{x^2}$ **12.** $\left(\dfrac{g}{f}\right)(x)$ $\dfrac{x^2}{3x + 5}$

18. $\frac{1}{2x + 3}$; domain: all real numbers except $-\frac{3}{2}$ and 1

19. $27x$, domain: all real numbers; 3, domain: all real numbers except 0

Let $f(x) = 2x^2 + x - 3$ and $g(x) = x - 1$. Perform each function operation and then find the domain.   **13–19. See margin.**

13. $f(x) + g(x)$

14. $g(x) - f(x)$

15. $f(x) - g(x)$

16. $f(x) \cdot g(x)$

17. $\dfrac{f(x)}{g(x)}$

18. $\dfrac{g(x)}{f(x)}$

19. Let $f(x) = 9x$ and $g(x) = 3x$. Find $(f \cdot g)(x)$ and $\left(\dfrac{f}{g}\right)(x)$ and their domains.

Example 3
(page 393)

Use each diagram to find $(g \circ f)(x)$. Then evaluate $(g \circ f)(3)$ and $(g \circ f)(-2)$.

20.

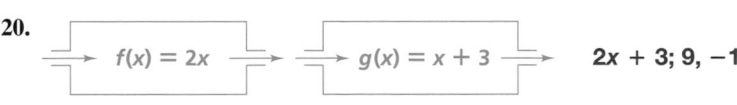

$f(x) = 2x \longrightarrow g(x) = x + 3 \longrightarrow$ $2x + 3$; 9, -1

21.

$f(x) = x^2 \longrightarrow g(x) = |x + 5| \longrightarrow$ $x^2 + 5$; 14, 9

Let $g(x) = 2x$ and $h(x) = x^2 + 4$. Evaluate each expression.

22. $(h \circ g)(1)$ **8**

23. $(h \circ g)(-5)$ **104**

24. $(h \circ g)(-2)$ **20**

25. $(g \circ h)(-2)$ **16**

26. $(g \circ h)(0)$ **8**

27. $(g \circ h)(-1)$ **10**

28. $(g \circ g)(3)$ **12**

29. $(h \circ h)(2)$ **68**

30. $(h \circ h)(-4)$ **404**

Let $f(x) = x^2$ and $g(x) = x - 3$. Find each value or expression.

31. $(g \circ f)(-2)$ **1**

32. $(f \circ g)(-2)$ **25**

33. $(g \circ f)(0)$ **-3**

34. $(f \circ g)(0)$ **9**

35. $(g \circ f)(3.5)$ **9.25**

36. $(f \circ g)(3.5)$ **0.25**

37. $(f \circ g)\left(\frac{1}{2}\right)$ **6.25**

38. $(g \circ f)\left(\frac{1}{2}\right)$ **-2.75**

39. $(f \circ g)(c)$ **$c^2 - 6c + 9$**

40. $(g \circ f)(c)$ **$c^2 - 3$**

41. $(f \circ g)(-a)$ **$a^2 + 6a + 9$**

42. $(g \circ f)(-a)$ **$a^2 - 3$**

Example 4
(page 394)

43. Sales A car dealer offers a 10% discount off the list price x for any car on the lot. At the same time, the manufacturer offers a $2000 rebate for each purchase of a car.
  a. Write a function $f(x)$ to represent the price after the discount. **$f(x) = 0.9x$**

43b. $g(x) = x - 2000$

  b. Write a function $g(x)$ to represent the price after the $2000 rebate.
  c. Suppose the list price of a car is $18,000. Use a composite function to find the price of the car if the discount is applied before the rebate. **$14,200**
  d. Suppose the list price of a car is $18,000. Use a composite function to find the price of the car if the rebate is applied before the discount. **$14,400**

Real-World 🌐 Connection

International companies must often compute their costs in many currencies.

44. Economics Suppose the function $f(x) = 0.12x$ represents the number of U.S. dollars equivalent to x Chinese yuan and the function $g(x) = 9.14x$ represents the number of Mexican pesos equivalent to x U.S. dollars.
  a. Write a composite function that represents the number of Mexican pesos equivalent to x Chinese yuan. **$(g \circ f)(x) = 1.0968x$**
  b. Find the value in Mexican pesos of an item that costs 15 Chinese yuan.
    16.45 pesos

Error Prevention

Exercises 31–42 Some students may assume that exercises such as Exercises 31 and 32 have the same answer. Caution students that composition of functions is not a commutative operation.

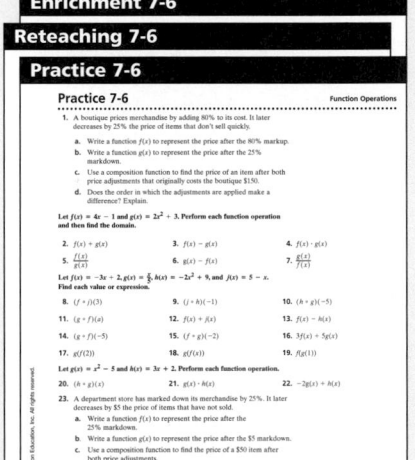

Connection to Geometry

Exercise 62 If you draw a diagram representing the circles at 2 s and at 4 s, you would be drawing *concentric circles*. Concentric circles are in the same plane and have the same center.

In the function $r(x)$, the input for x is in seconds. In the function $A(x)$, the input is in inches. Students may be confused about the seemingly dual use of x in $(A \circ r)(x)$. You can draw a diagram like the one on page 393 for a composition of functions. The input x for the function r is x seconds. The output, $12.5x$, is in inches and this is the input for the function A. The output from the second function, $(12.5x)^2$, is in square inches. In the notation $(A \circ r)(x)$, x refers to the first input which is in seconds.

pages 394–398   Exercises

51. $-3x^2 + 2x + 16$, domain: all real numbers

52. $3x^2 - 12$, domain: all real numbers

53. $3x^3 + 8x^2 - 4x + 16$, domain: all real numbers

54. $-9x^3 - 24x^2 + 12x + 48$, domain: all real numbers

55. $3x - 4$, domain: all real numbers except -2

56. $15x - 20$, domain: all real numbers except -2

57. 7; answers may vary. **Sample:** First evaluate $f(3)$ since the expression is $(g \circ f)(3)$, and that means $g(f(3))$. Then evaluate $g(6)$.

69a. Answers may vary. **Sample:** $g(x) = 0.12x$

b. $f(x) = 9.50x$

c. $(g \circ f)(x) = 1.14x$; your savings will be $1.14 for each hour you work.

72a. $g(x)$ is the bonus earned when x is the amount of sales over $5000. $h(x)$ is the excess of x sales over $5000.

396

 **B Apply Your Skills**

45. $x^2 - x + 7$

47. $x^2 - 5x - 3$

 Reading Math

For help with reading and solving Exercise 62a, see p. 399.

62a. ≈1963; the area after 2 seconds is about 1963 in.².

65. $12x^2 + 2$, $6x^2 + 4$

66. $x - 3$, $x - 6$

67. $-4x - 7$, $-4x - 28$

68. $\frac{x^2 + 5}{2}$, $\frac{x^2 + 10x + 25}{4}$

Let $f(x) = 2x + 5$ and $g(x) = x^2 - 3x + 2$. Perform each function operation.

45. $f(x) + g(x)$ 46. $3f(x) - 2$ **$6x + 13$**   47. $g(x) - f(x)$

48. $-2g(x) + f(x)$ 49. $f(x) - g(x) + 10$ 50. $4f(x) + 2g(x)$
    $-2x^2 + 8x + 1$ **$-x^2 + 5x + 13$**   **$2x^2 + 2x + 24$**

Let $f(x) = 3x^2 + 2x - 8$ and $g(x) = x + 2$. Perform each function operation and then find the domain. **51–56. See margin.**

51. $-f(x) + 4g(x)$ 52. $f(x) - 2g(x)$ 53. $f(x) \cdot g(x)$

54. $-3f(x) \cdot g(x)$ 55. $\dfrac{f(x)}{g(x)}$ 56. $\dfrac{5f(x)}{g(x)}$

 57. **Writing** Evaluate $(g \circ f)(3)$, when $f(x) = 2x$ and $g(x) = x + 1$. Explain what you do first and why. **See margin.**

Let $g(x) = 3x + 2$ and $f(x) = \frac{x-2}{3}$. Find each value.

58. $f(g(1))$ **1**   59. $g(f(-4))$ **−4**   60. $f(g(0))$ **0**   61. $g(f(2))$ **2**

62. **Geometry** You toss a pebble into a pool of water and watch the circular ripples radiate outward. You find that the function $r(x) = 12.5x$ describes the radius r in inches of a circle x seconds after it was formed. The function $A(x) = \pi x^2$ describes the area A of a circle with radius x.
   a. Find $(A \circ r)(x)$ when $x = 2$. Interpret your answer. **See left.**
   b. Find the area of a circle 4 seconds after it was formed. **≈7854 in.²**

For each pair of functions, find $f(g(x))$ and $g(f(x))$.

63. $f(x) = 3x, g(x) = x^2$ **$3x^2$, $9x^2$**   64. $f(x) = x + 3, g(x) = x - 5$ **$x - 2, x - 2$**

65. $f(x) = 3x^2 + 2, g(x) = 2x$ 66. $f(x) = \frac{x-3}{2}, g(x) = 2x - 3$

67. $f(x) = -x - 7, g(x) = 4x$ 68. $f(x) = \frac{x+5}{2}, g(x) = x^2$

69. **Open-Ended** Write a function rule that approximates each value.
   a. The amount you save is a percent of what you earn. (You choose the percent.)
   b. The amount you earn depends on how many hours you work. (You choose the hourly wage.) **a–c. See margin.**
   c. Write and simplify a composite function that expresses your savings as a function of the number of hours you work. Interpret your results.

70. a. **Technology** Suppose $f(x) = 3x$ and $g(x) = x^2 + 3$. In the spreadsheet, values for x are in Column A. What do the formulas in B and C represent?
   $f(x)$ and $g(x)$

	A	B	C	D	E
1		=3*A1	=A1^2+3	■	■
2	0	■	■	■	■
3	5	■	■	■	■
4	10	■	■	■	■

   b. If the formulas in columns B and C are copied down the columns, what numbers will appear? **0, 15, 30; 3, 28, 103**
   c. Find $(f \circ g)(x)$. **$3x^2 + 9$**
   d. Complete column D for $(f \circ g)(x)$. **3*A1^2 + 9, 9, 84, 309**
   e. Find $(g \circ f)(x)$. **$9x^2 + 3$**
   f. Complete column E for $(g \circ f)(x)$. **9*A1^2 + 3, 3, 228, 903**

396   Chapter 7   Radical Functions and Rational Exponents

---

b. $(g \circ h)(x)$ because you first need to find the excess sales over $5000 to calculate bonus.

73. $(f + g)(x)$
   $= f(x) + g(x)$ Def. of Function Add.
   $= 3x - 2 + (x^2 + 1)$ Substitution
   $= x^2 + 3x - 2 + 1$ Comm. Prop.
   $= x^2 + 3x - 1$ Arithmetic

Real-World Connection

Careers A craftsman and business owner uses math to find profit.

71. Profit A craftsman makes and sells violins. The function $C(x) = 1000 + 700x$ represents his cost in dollars to produce x violins. The function $I(x) = 5995x$ represents the income in dollars from selling x violins.
  a. Write and simplify a function $P(x) = I(x) - C(x)$. **P(x) = 5295x − 1000**
  b. Find $P(30)$, the profit earned when he makes and sells 30 violins.
      $158,750

72. Writing A salesperson earns a 3% bonus on weekly sales over $5000.

$$g(x) = 0.03x$$
$$h(x) = x - 5000$$

  a. Explain what each function above represents. **a–b. See margin p. 396.**
  b. Which composition, $(h \circ g)(x)$ or $(g \circ h)(x)$, represents the weekly bonus? Explain.

Let $f(x) = 3x - 2$ and $g(x) = x^2 + 1$. **Perform each function operation and use the properties of real numbers to justify each step in simplifying your answer.**

73. $(f + g)(x)$ **74.** $(f - g)(x)$ **75.** $(f \circ g)(x)$
73–75. See margin pp. 396–397.

76. Grades Suppose your teacher offers to give the whole class a bonus if everyone passes the next math test. The teacher says she will (1) give everyone a 10-point bonus and (2) increase everyone's grade by 9% of their score.
  a. Let x represent the original test scores. Write statements (1) and (2) as the functions $f(x)$ and $g(x)$, respectively. **a–c. See margin p. 398.**
  b. Explain the meaning of $f(g(x))$. Evaluate $f(g(75))$.
  c. Explain the meaning of $g(f(x))$. Evaluate $g(f(75))$.
  d. Does $g(f(x)) = f(g(x))$? **no**

C Challenge

Let $f(x) = x^4 + 2x^3 - 5x^2 - 10x$ and $g(x) = x^3 - 3x^2 - 5x + 15$. **Perform each function operation and simplify, and then find the domain.** **77–79. See margin p. 398.**

77. $f(x) \cdot g(x)$ **78.** $\dfrac{f(x)}{g(x)}$ **79.** $\dfrac{g(x)}{f(x)}$

Find each composition of functions. Simplify your answer.

80. Let $f(x) = \frac{1}{x}$. Find $f(f(x))$. **x**

81. Let $f(x) = \frac{1}{x}$. Find $f(f(f(x)))$. **$\frac{1}{x}$**

82. Let $f(x) = 1 - \frac{x}{2}$. Find $f(f(f(x)))$. **$\frac{6 - x}{8}$**

83. Let $f(x) = 2x - 3$. Find $\dfrac{f(1 + h) - f(1)}{h}, h \neq 0$. **2**

84. Let $f(x) = 4x - 1$. Find $\dfrac{f(a + h) - f(a)}{h}, h \neq 0$. **4**

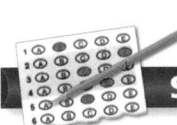

Standardized Test Prep

Multiple Choice

85. Let $f(x) = -4x + 1$ and $g(x) = 2x - 6$. Find $(g - f)(x)$. **B**
  A. $6x - 5$ **B.** $6x - 7$ **C.** $-6x + 5$ **D.** $-6x + 7$

86. If $f(x) = 2x^2$ and $g(x) = 3x$, what is $(g \circ f)(x)$? **F**
  F. $6x^2$ **G.** $9x^2$ **H.** $18x^2$ **I.** $8x^4$

Short Response

87. If $f(x) = 3x - 4$ and $g(x) = x + 3$, what does $(f \cdot g)(x)$ mean? What is the value of $(f \cdot g)(x)$? Simplify the answer. **See margin p. 398.**

74. $(f - g)(x) = f(x) - g(x)$ **Def. of Function subtraction**
$= 3x - 2 - (x^2 + 1)$ **Substitution**
$= 3x - 2 - x^2 - 1$ **Opp. of Sum Prop.**
$= -x^2 + 3x - 2 - 1$ **Comm. Prop.**
$= -x^2 + 3x - 3$ **Arithmetic**

75. $(f \circ g)(x)$
$= f(g(x))$ **Def. of Comp. Functions**
$= f(x^2 + 1)$ **Substitution**
$= 3(x^2 + 1) - 2$ **Substitution**
$= 3x^2 + 3 - 2$ **Dist. Prop.**
$= 3x^2 + 1$ **Arithmetic**

Alternative Assessment

Have students work individually. Ask them to write a linear function $f(x)$ and a quadratic function $g(x)$. They should then find $f(x) + g(x)$, $f(x) - g(x)$, $f(x) \cdot g(x)$, $\dfrac{f(x)}{g(x)}$, and $(f \circ g)(x)$. Finally, they should state the domain of each function.

Standardized Test Prep

Resources

For additional practice with a variety of test item formats:
• Standardized Test Prep, 419
• Test-Taking Strategies, p. 414
• Test-Taking Strategies with Transparencies

397

Chapter Checkpoint 2

To check understanding of Lessons 7-4 to 7-6:

Checkpoint Quiz 2 (p. 398)

📁 Teaching Resources
Checkpoint Quiz 2 (also in Prentice Hall Assessment System)

👥 Reaching All Students
Reading and Math Literacy 7C

Spanish versions available

---

pages 394–398   Exercises

76a. $f(x) = x + 10$;
$g(x) = 1.09x$

  b. **Each grade is increased 9% before adding the 10-point bonus; 91.75.**

  c. **Add the 10-point bonus and then increase the sum by 9%; 92.65.**

77. $x^7 - x^6 - 16x^5 + 10x^4 + 85x^3 - 25x^2 - 150x$; **domain: all real numbers**

78. $\frac{x^2 + 2x}{x - 3}$; **domain: all real numbers except 3, $\sqrt{5}$, and $-\sqrt{5}$**

79. $\frac{x - 3}{x^2 + 2x}$; **domain: all real numbers except 0, −2, $\sqrt{5}$, and $-\sqrt{5}$**

87. **[2]** $(f \cdot g)(x)$ means $f(x)$ times $g(x)$ or in this case $(3x - 4)(x + 3)$. The value of $(f \cdot g)(x)$ is $3x^2 + 5x - 12$.

  [1] only $3x^2 + 5x - 12$ OR minor error in explanation

98. $x^8 + 32x^7 + 448x^6 + 3584x^5 + 17{,}920x^4 + 57{,}344x^3 + 114{,}688x^2 + 131{,}072x + 65{,}536$

99. $x^6 + 6x^5y + 15x^4y^2 + 20x^3y^3 + 15x^2y^4 + 6xy^5 + y^6$

398

Quantitative Comparison

For problems 88–91, use $f(x) = 2x^2$, $g(x) = 3x - 5$, and $h(x) = \frac{1}{x}$. Compare the boxed quantity in Column A with the boxed quantity in Column B. Choose the best answer.

  A. The quantity in Column A is greater.
  B. The quantity in Column B is greater.
  C. The two quantities are equal.
  D. The relationship cannot be determined from the information given.

💻 Take It to the NET
Online lesson quiz at
www.PHSchool.com
Web Code: aga-0706

	Column A	Column B
88. A	$(f \circ g)(5)$	$(g \circ f)(5)$
89. C	$(h \cdot f)(x)$	$(f \cdot h)(x)$
90. B	$(h \circ f)(1)$	$(f \circ h)(1)$
91. D	$(g \cdot h)(x)$	$(h \cdot g)(x)$

Mixed Review

Lesson 7-5   **Solve. Check for extraneous solutions.**

92. $\sqrt{x^2 + 3} = x + 1$ **1**   93. $x + 8 = (x^2 + 16)^{\frac{1}{2}}$ **−3**   94. $\sqrt{x^2 + 9} = x + 1$ **4**

95. $(x^2 - 9)^{\frac{1}{2}} - x = -3$ **3**   96. $\sqrt{x^2 + 12} - 2 = x$ **2**   97. $(3x)^{\frac{1}{2}} = (x + 6)^{\frac{1}{2}}$ **3**

Lesson 6-8   **Expand each binomial.   98–105. See margin.**

98. $(x + 4)^8$ 99. $(x + y)^6$ 100. $(2x - y)^4$ 101. $(2x - 3y)^7$

102. $(9 - 2x)^5$ 103. $(4x - y)^5$ 104. $(x^2 + x)^4$ 105. $(x^2 + 2y^3)^6$

Lesson 5-6   **Simplify each expression.**

106. $(2 - 3\sqrt{-4}) + (4 + 2\sqrt{-16})$ **6 + 2i**

107. $3\sqrt{-50} - (2 - \sqrt{-32})$ **−2 + 19i$\sqrt{2}$**

108. $(6 + \sqrt{-20}) - (-7 - \sqrt{-45})$ **13 + 5i$\sqrt{5}$**

109. $(5 - \sqrt{-9})(2 - \sqrt{-36})$ **−8 − 36i**

✓ Checkpoint Quiz 2   Lessons 7-4 through 7-6

📱 iTEXT Instant self-check quiz online and on CD-ROM

Simplify each expression.

1. $(-27x^3)^{\frac{4}{3}}$ **81x⁴**   2. $(32y^5)^{-0.4}$ **$\frac{1}{4y^2}$**

Solve each equation.

3. $\sqrt{3x + 1} - 4 = 0$ **5**   4. $(5x + 2)^{\frac{2}{3}} = 9$ **5, $-\frac{29}{5}$**

Solve each equation. Check for extraneous solutions.

5. $\sqrt{3x + 3} - 3 = 3x$ **$-\frac{2}{3}$, −1**   6. $(2 - x)^{0.5} - x = 4$ **−2**

Let $f(x) = 2x + 3$ and $g(x) = x^2 - x$. Find each value.

7. $(f + g)\left(\frac{1}{2}\right)$ **$\frac{15}{4}$**   8. $(f \cdot g)(1)$ **0**   9. $\left(\frac{f}{g}\right)(2)$ **$\frac{7}{2}$**   10. $(f \circ g)(5)$ **43**

---

100. $16x^4 - 32x^3y + 24x^2y^2 - 8xy^3 + y^4$

101. $128x^7 - 1344x^6y + 6048x^5y^2 - 15{,}120x^4y^3 + 22{,}680x^3y^4 - 20{,}412x^2y^5 + 10{,}206xy^6 - 2187y^7$

102. $59{,}049 - 65{,}610x + 29{,}160x^2 - 6480x^3 + 720x^4 - 32x^5$

103. $1024x^5 - 1280x^4y + 640x^3y^2 - 160x^2y^3 + 20xy^4 - y^5$

104. $x^8 + 4x^7 + 6x^6 + 4x^5 + x^4$

105. $x^{12} + 12x^{10}y^3 + 60x^8y^6 + 160x^6y^9 + 240x^4y^{12} + 192x^2y^{15} + 64y^{18}$

Read the problem below. Then read how function notation is used. Check your understanding with the exercise at the bottom of the page.

Geometry You toss a pebble into a pool of water and watch the circular ripples radiate outward. You find that the function $r(x) = 12.5x$ describes the radius r in inches of a circle x seconds after it was formed. The function $A(x) = \pi x^2$ describes the area A of a circle with radius x.

a. Find $(A \circ r)(x)$ when $x = 2$. Interpret your answer.

The problem uses function notation. Here is the way to read function notation.

Write	$f(x)$	$f(g(x))$	$(f \circ g)(x) = f(g(x))$
Read	f of x	f of g of x	The composition of f with g equals f of g of x.

Examples   For $f(x) = x^2$, find $f(3)$.

$f(3) = 3^2 = 9$ **Substitute the value 3 for x and simplify.**

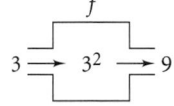

$3 \longrightarrow 3^2 \longrightarrow 9$

For $f(x) = x^2$ and $g(x) = 2x$, find $(f \circ g)(5)$.

$(f \circ g)(5) = f(g(5))$

$g(x) = 2 \cdot 5 = 10$ **Find $g(5)$ first.**

$f(10) = 10^2 = 100$ **Use the output $g(5) = 10$ as the input for $f(x)$.**

$5 \longrightarrow 2(5) \longrightarrow 10 \longrightarrow 10^2 \longrightarrow 100$

Now find $(A \circ r)(x)$ when $x = 2$. Recall that $r(x) = 12.5x$ and $A(x) = \pi x^2$.

$(A \circ r)(2) = A(r(2))$

$r(2) = 12.5(2) = 25$ **Find $r(2)$ first.**

$A(25) = \pi(25)^2$ **Use the output $r(2) = 25$ as the input for $A(x)$.**

$= 625\pi \approx 1963$

To interpret your answer is to explain what your answer means in terms of the problem. The problem tells you that $A(x)$ is the area of a circle with radius x and that $r(x)$ is the radius of a circle x seconds after it was formed.

So $(A \circ r)(2)$ is the area of a circle after 2 seconds. The area is about 1963 in.^{2}.

75π; 3 seconds after it is formed a ripple will have a circumference of 75π in.

EXERCISE

You toss a pebble into a pool of water and watch the circular ripples radiate outward. You find that the function $r(x) = 12.5x$ describes the radius of the first circle r in inches after x seconds. The function $C(x) = 2\pi x$ describes the circumference C of a circle with radius x. Find $(C \circ r)(x)$ when $x = 3$. Interpret your answer.

Reading Math

Reading Mathematical Symbols

Students learn how to read and interpret the symbols and parentheses in function notation. Students use what they have learned to solve a problem in function notation.

Teaching Notes

You may want to write several more examples of function notation on the chalkboard or overhead projector and have students practice reading them aloud.

Work through the example in which students find $(A \circ r)(x)$ until students understand that $(A \circ r)(x)$ is equivalent to $A(r(x))$.

Tell students to look back at the original problem when they are trying to interpret the answer. The explanation of the answer is often a restatement of the question in the original problem.

Auditory Learners

Place students in pairs. Have one student write several functions ($f(x) = 3x$ for example) and then say the functions aloud. The other student then records the functions and compares them to the original functions written by the first student.

Exercise

Remind students that the circumference of a circle is different from the area, which was the quantity they were asked to find in the example.

Lesson Preview

 Check Skills You'll Need

Relations and Functions
Lesson 3-1: Example 1
Exercises 1–4
Extra Practice, p. 823

Lesson Resources

 Teaching Resources
Practice, Reteaching, Enrichment

 Reaching All Students
Practice Workbook 7-7
Spanish Practice Workbook 7-7

 Presentation Assistant Plus!
Transparencies
• Check Skills You'll Need 7-7
• Additional Examples 7-7
• Student Edition Answers 7-7
• Lesson Quiz 7-7
PH Presentation Pro CD 7-7

Computer Test Generator CD

 Technology
Resource Pro® CD-ROM
Computer Test Generator CD
Prentice Hall Presentation Pro CD

 www.PHSchool.com
Student Site
• Teacher Web Code: agk-5500
• Self-grading Lesson Quiz
Teacher Center
• Lesson Planner
• Resources

Plus

400

 # Inverse Relations and Functions

North Carolina Objectives   2.01 Use the composition and inverse of functions to model and solve problems; justify results.

Lesson Preview

What You'll Learn

OBJECTIVE 1 To find the inverse of a relation or function

. . . And Why

To estimate the speed of a car, as in Example 5

✓ **Check Skills You'll Need** (For help, go to Lesson 3-1)

Graph each pair of functions on a single coordinate plane. **1–6. See back of book.**

1. $y = x - 6$
$y = x + 6$

2. $y = \frac{x - 7}{2}$
$y = 2x + 7$

3. $y = 3x - 1$
$y = \frac{x + 1}{3}$

4. $y = 0.5x + 1$
$y = 2x - 2$

5. $y = -x + 4$
$y = \frac{-x + 4}{-1}$

6. $y = \frac{x + 4}{5}$
$y = 5x - 4$

New Vocabulary • inverse relation • inverse functions

 Interactive lesson includes instant self-check, tutorials, and activities.

OBJECTIVE

1 **The Inverse of a Function**

Investigation: Inverses

• Function f doubles the input and then subtracts 8. $f(x) = 2x - 8$
• Function g adds 8 to the input and then divides by 2. $g(x) = \frac{x + 8}{2}$

$$10 \longrightarrow \boxed{\; f(x) \;\;\; 2x - 8 \;} \longrightarrow \boxed{\; g(x) \;\;\; \frac{x + 8}{2} \;} \longrightarrow ?$$

1. a. Find $f(10)$ and $g(f(10))$. **12, 10**
  b. Find $f(0)$ and $g(f(0))$. **−8, 0**
  c. Find $f(-7)$ and $g(f(-7))$. **−22, −7**
  d. Without computing, use the pattern in parts (a)–(c) to find $g(f(-1496))$. **−1496**

$$6 \longrightarrow \boxed{\; g(x) \;\;\; \frac{x + 8}{2} \;} \longrightarrow \boxed{\; f(x) \;\;\; 2x - 8 \;} \longrightarrow ?$$

2. a. Find $g(6)$ and $f(g(6))$. **7, 6**
  b. Find $g(0)$ and $f(g(0))$. **4, 0**
  c. Find $g(-32)$ and $f(g(-32))$. **−12, −32**
  d. Without computing, use the pattern in parts (a)–(c) to find $f(g(\pi))$. **π**

3. a. Interchange the x and y variables in $y = 2x - 8$ and solve for y.
  b. Graph your two equations in part (a) on the same coordinate axes. Fold your graph paper so the two lines coincide. How are the two graphs related? **a–b. See left.**

3a. $y = \frac{x + 8}{2}$

b.

They are reflections of each other in the line $y = x$.

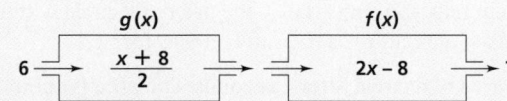 **Ongoing Assessment and Intervention**

Before the Lesson	**During the Lesson**	**After the Lesson**
Diagnose prerequisite skills using:	**Monitor progress using:**	**Assess knowledge using:**
• Check Skills You'll Need	• Check Understanding	• Lesson Quiz
	• Additional Examples	• Computer Test Generator CD
	• Standardized Test Prep	

Need Help?

Both relations and functions are sets of ordered pairs.

When each element of the domain is associated with only one element of the range, the relation is a function.

If a relation maps element *a* of its domain to element *b* of its range, the **inverse relation** "undoes" the relation and maps *b* back to *a*. So, if (a, b) is an ordered pair of a relation, then (b, a) is an ordered pair of its inverse.

This diagram shows a relation *r* and its inverse.

The range of the relation is the domain of the inverse, and the domain of the relation is the range of the inverse.

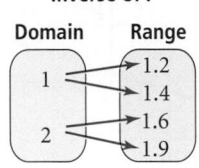

1 EXAMPLE Finding the Inverse of a Relation

a. Find the inverse of relation *s*.

Relation *s*

x	−1	0	1	1
y	1	2	3	4

Interchange the *x* and *y* values to get the inverse.

Inverse of Relation *s*

x	1	2	3	4
y	−1	0	1	1

1a. The line $y = x$ is the perpendicular bisector of each segment connecting a point in *s* to the corresponding point in the inverse of *s*. The graph of the inverse of *s* is a reflection in the line $y = x$ of the graph of *s*.

b. Graph *s* and its inverse.

Relation *s*   Reversing the Ordered Pairs   Inverse of *s*

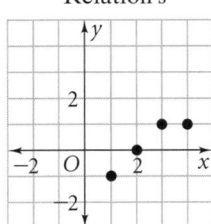 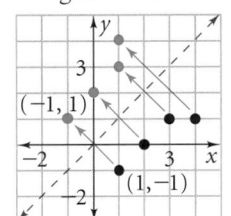 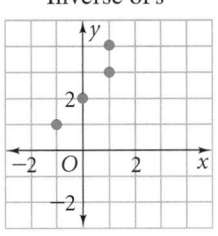

✓ **Check Understanding** **1 a.** Describe how the line $y = x$ is related to the graphs of *s* and its inverse.
b. In Example 1, is relation *s* a function? Is the inverse of *s* a function?
yes; no

As shown in Example 1, the graph of the inverse of a relation is the reflection in the line $y = x$ of the graph of the relation. If a relation or function is described by an equation in *x* and *y*, you can interchange *x* and *y* to get the inverse.

2a. Yes; no; for every *x*-value except 3 in the domain of the inverse there are two *y*-values.

b. $y = \frac{1}{3}x + \frac{10}{3}$; it is a function because for each value of *x* there is only one *y*-value.

2 EXAMPLE Interchanging *x* and *y*

Find the inverse of $y = x^2 + 3$.

$$y = x^2 + 3$$
$$x = y^2 + 3 \quad \text{Interchange } x \text{ and } y.$$
$$x - 3 = y^2 \quad \text{Solve for } y.$$
$$\pm\sqrt{x - 3} = y \quad \text{Find the square root of each side.}$$

✓ **Check Understanding** **2 a.** Does $y = x^2 + 3$ define a function? Is its inverse a function? Explain.
b. Find the inverse of $y = 3x - 10$. Is the inverse a function? Explain.

Lesson 7-7 Inverse Relations and Functions **401**

---

2. Teach

Professional Development

Math Background

The function $g(x) = x$ is the identity function over the real numbers. That is, given any real number *a* it maps *a* onto itself, $g(a) = a$. If functions *f* and *g* are inverses, then their compositions give the identity function. In other words, $(g \circ f)(x) = (f \circ g)(x) = x$. Thus, if *f* acts on *a* and takes it to *b*, or $f(a) = b$, then *g* acts on *b* and maps it to *a*, or $g(b) = a$, and vice versa. Hence, the domain of *f* equals the range of *g* and the range of *f* equals the domain of *g*.

OBJECTIVE

1 Teaching Notes

Investigation (Optional)
The functions *f* and *g* in this investigation undo one another in the sense that $g(f(x)) = x$ and $f(g(x)) = x$. After discovering this property of the functions, students discover that the graphs of the functions are reflection images of one another with respect to the line $y = x$.

1 EXAMPLE Tactile Learners

Provide students with a greatly enlarged grid. Have students place small objects such as dimes or number cubes at the points for the relation and its inverse.

👥 **Reaching All Students**

Below Level Review the definition of a function, display graphs of functions and non functions, and review the vertical line test.	**Advanced Learners** Discuss with students why, if a function's inverse is a function, the composition of the function and its inverse is always commutative.	**Tactile Learners** See note on page 401. **Error Prevention** See note on page 404.

402

3 EXAMPLE Math Tip

You may want to point out that $y = \pm\sqrt{x - 3}$ represents two equations. The graph of $y = \pm\sqrt{x - 3}$ is not the graph of a single function but of two functions.

4 EXAMPLE Math Tip

Be sure that students understand that the graph of $f(x) = \sqrt{x + 1}$ is half a parabola. The graph of the equation $y = x^2 - 1$ is a full parabola. It is therefore important to discuss the statements in part c about the domains and ranges of f and f^{-1}.

5 EXAMPLE Careers

You may want to mention that police departments, highway patrol departments, and insurance companies often have employees who are specially trained in accident investigation. These employees usually have additional duties as well.

Additional Examples

1   **Relation m**

x	−1	0	1	2
y	−2	−1	−1	−2

a. Find the inverse of relation m.

x	−2	−1	−1	−2
y	−1	0	1	2

b. Graph m and its inverse on the same graph.

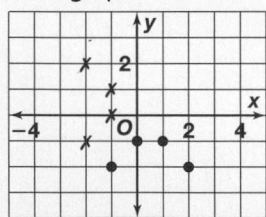

2 Find the inverse of $y = x^2 - 2$.
$y = \pm\sqrt{x + 2}$

3.

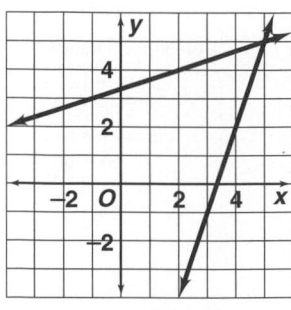

✓ **Check Understanding** **3** Graph $y = 3x - 10$ and its inverse.   **See left.**

---

3 EXAMPLE Graphing a Relation and Its Inverse

Graph $y = x^2 + 3$ and its inverse, $y = \pm\sqrt{x - 3}$.

The graph of $y = x^2 + 3$ is a parabola that opens upward with vertex $(0, 3)$. The reflection of the parabola in the line $y = x$ is the graph of the inverse.

You can also find points on the graph of the inverse by reversing the coordinates of points on $y = x^2 + 3$.

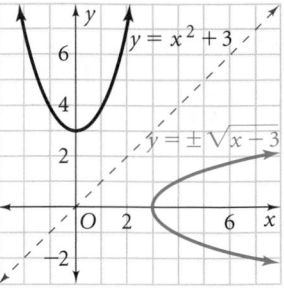

Reading Math

For a number x, x^{-1} is the multiplicative inverse of x, or $\frac{1}{x}$.

For a function f, f^{-1} is the relation that is the inverse of f.

The inverse of function f is denoted by f^{-1}. Read f^{-1} as "the inverse of f" or as "f inverse." The notation $f(x)$ is used for functions, but $f^{-1}(x)$ may be a relation that is *not* a function.

4 EXAMPLE Finding an Inverse Function

Consider the function $f(x) = \sqrt{x + 1}$.

a. Find the domain and range of f.

Since the radicand cannot be negative, the domain is the set of numbers greater than or equal to −1. Since the principal square root is nonnegative, the range is the set of nonnegative numbers.

b. Find f^{-1}.

$$f(x) = \sqrt{x + 1}$$
$$y = \sqrt{x + 1} \qquad \text{Rewrite the equation using } y.$$
$$x = \sqrt{y + 1} \qquad \text{Interchange } x \text{ and } y. \text{ Since } x \text{ equals a principal square root, } x \geq 0.$$
$$x^2 = y + 1 \qquad \text{Square both sides.}$$
$$y = x^2 - 1 \qquad \text{Solve for } y.$$

So, $f^{-1}(x) = x^2 - 1$, $x \geq 0$.

c. Find the domain and range of f^{-1}.

The domain of f^{-1} equals the range of f, which is the set of nonnegative numbers. Since $x^2 \geq 0$, $x^2 - 1 \geq -1$. Thus the range of f^{-1} is the set of numbers greater than or equal to −1. Note that the range of f^{-1} is the same as the domain of f.

d. Is f^{-1} a function? Explain.

For each x in the domain of f^{-1}, there is only one value of $f^{-1}(x)$. So f^{-1} is a function.

✓ **Check Understanding** **4** Let $f(x) = 10 - 3x$. Find each of the following.   **a–c. See margin p. 403.**
   a. the domain and range of f **b.** f^{-1}
   c. the domain and range of f^{-1} **d.** $f^{-1}(f(3))$ **3**
   e. $f(f^{-1}(2))$ **2**

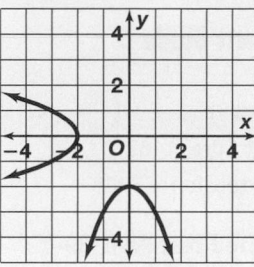
Functions that model real-life situations are frequently expressed as formulas with letters that remind you of the variables they represent. When finding the inverse of a formula, it would be very confusing to interchange the letters. Keep the letters the same and just solve the formula for the other variable.

5 EXAMPLE **Real-World**  **Connection**

Physics The function $d = \frac{r^2}{24}$ is a model for the distance d in feet that a car with locked brakes skids in coming to a complete stop from a speed of r mi/h. Find the inverse of the function. Use the inverse to estimate the speed of a car that made skid marks 114 feet long.

$d = \frac{r^2}{24}$

$r^2 = 24d$ **Solve for r. Do not interchange the variables.**

$r = \sqrt{24d}$ **Rate of speed must be positive.**

$= \sqrt{24 \cdot 114}$ **Substitute 114 for d.**

≈ 52 **Use a calculator.**

• The car was traveling about 52 mi/h.

Real-World  **Connection**

Many safe driving programs include experience with braking distance.

✓ **Check Understanding** **5** The function $d = \frac{v^2}{64}$ is a model relating the distance a stone has fallen in feet to its velocity in feet per second (ft/s). Find the inverse of the function and use it to find the velocity of a stone that has fallen 30 ft. **≈44 ft/s**

If f and f^{-1} are both functions, and if f pairs a with b, then f^{-1} must pair b with a.

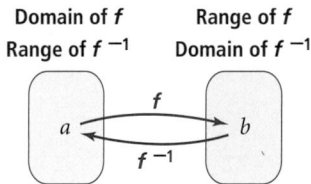

Domain of f Range of f
Range of f^{-1} Domain of f^{-1}

If f and f^{-1} are functions, they are called **inverse functions.** For inverse functions, $f^{-1}(f(x)) = x$ and $f(f^{-1}(x)) = x$.

🔧 **Key Concepts**

Property	**Composition of Inverse Functions**
If f and f^{-1} are inverse functions, then	
$(f^{-1} \circ f)(x) = x$ and $(f \circ f^{-1})(x) = x.$	

6 EXAMPLE **Composition of Inverse Functions**

For the function $f(x) = \frac{x-7}{6}$, find $(f^{-1} \circ f)(374)$ and $(f \circ f^{-1})(-99\pi)$.

Since f is a linear function, so is f^{-1}. Therefore f^{-1} is a function.

• So $(f^{-1} \circ f)(374) = 374$ and $(f \circ f^{-1})(-99\pi) = -99\pi$.

✓ **Check Understanding** **6** For $f(x) = 5x + 11$, find $(f^{-1} \circ f)(777)$ and $(f \circ f^{-1})(-5802)$. **777, -5802**

❸ Graph $y = -x^2 - 2$ and its inverse $y = \pm\sqrt{-x-2}$.

❹ Consider the function $f(x) = \sqrt{2x + 2}$.
a. Find the domain and range of f. **domain: all numbers greater than or equal to -1; range: all nonnegative numbers**
b. Find f^{-1}. $f^{-1}(x) = \frac{x^2 - 2}{2}, x \geq 0$
c. Find the domain and range of f^{-1}. **domain: all nonnegative numbers; range: all numbers greater than or equal to -1**
d. Is f^{-1} a function? Explain. **Yes; for each x in the domain of f^{-1}, there is only one value of $f^{-1}(x)$.**

❺ The function $d = 16t^2$ models the distance d in feet that an object falls in t seconds. Find the inverse of the function. Use the inverse to estimate the time it takes an object to fall 50 ft. $t = \frac{1}{4}\sqrt{d}$; **about 1.77 s**

❻ For the function $f(x) = \frac{1}{2}x + 5$, find $(f^{-1} \circ f)(652)$ and $(f \circ f^{-1})(-\sqrt{86})$. **652, $-\sqrt{86}$**

Closure

Ask students how they can find an equation that models the inverse of a relation or function if they have an equation in x and y for the original relation or function. **Interchange the variables x and y in the original equation. Solve the resulting equation for y.**

Lesson 7-7   Inverse Relations and Functions   **403**

page 403   **Check Understanding**

4a. D: all real numbers, R: all real numbers

b. $f^{-1}(x) = \frac{-x + 10}{3}$

c. D: all real numbers, R: all real numbers

Assignment Guide

1 Objective

Ⓐ Ⓑ **Core** 1–62

Ⓒ **Extension** 63–68

Standardized Test Prep 69–73

Mixed Review 74–93

Error Prevention

Exercises 1–4 Check that the graphs of the relation and its inverse are reflections over the line $y = x$.

Enrichment 7-7

Reteaching 7-7

Practice 7-7

(Practice 7-7 worksheet thumbnail)

EXERCISES

For more practice, see *Extra Practice*.

Practice and Problem Solving

Ⓐ **Practice by Example**

Example 1 (page 401)

Find the inverse of each relation. Graph the given relation and its inverse.

1.

x	1	2	3	4
y	0	1	0	2

1–4. See back of book.

2.

x	1	2	3	4
y	0	1	2	3

3.

x	0	1	2	3
y	0	1	4	9

4.

x	−3	−2	−1	0
y	2	2	2	2

Example 2 (page 401)

$X = 3y + 1$

$\dfrac{x - 1}{3} = y$

Find the inverse of each function. Is the inverse a function? 5–13. See margin.

5. $y = 3x + 1$

6. $y = 2x - 1$

7. $y = 4 - 3x$

8. $y = 5 - 2x^2$

9. $y = x^2 + 4$

10. $y = 3x^2 - 5$

11. $y = (x + 1)^2$

12. $y = (3x - 4)^2$

13. $y = (1 - 2x)^2 + 5$

Example 3 (page 402)

Graph each relation and its inverse. 14–22. See back of book.

14. $y = 2x - 3$

15. $y = 3 - 7x$

16. $y = -x$

17. $y = 3x^2$

18. $y = -x^2$

19. $y = 4x^2 - 2$

20. $y = (x - 1)^2$

21. $y = (2 - x)^2$

22. $y = (3 - 2x)^2 - 1$

Example 4 (page 402)

For each function f, find f^{-1} and the domain and range of f and f^{-1}. Determine whether f^{-1} is a function. 23–28. See back of book.

23. $f(x) = 3x + 4$

24. $f(x) = \sqrt{x - 5}$

25. $f(x) = \sqrt{x + 7}$

26. $f(x) = \sqrt{-2x + 3}$

27. $f(x) = 2x^2 + 2$

28. $f(x) = -x^2 + 1$

Example 5 (page 403)

29. The formula for converting from Celsius to Fahrenheit temperatures is $C = \frac{9}{5}F + 32$.

a. $F = \frac{5}{9}(C - 32)$; yes

a. Find the inverse of the formula. Is the inverse a function?

b. Use the inverse to find the Fahrenheit temperature that corresponds to 25°C.
−3.89°F

30. Geometry The formula for the volume of a sphere is $V = \frac{4}{3}\pi r^3$.

a. Find the inverse of the formula. Is the inverse a function? $r = \sqrt[3]{\dfrac{3V}{4\pi}}$; yes

b. Use the inverse to find the radius of a sphere that has a volume of 35,000 ft^3.
20.29 ft

Example 6 (page 403)

For Exercises 31–34, $f(x) = 10x - 10$. Find each value.

31. $(f^{-1} \circ f)(10)$ **10**

32. $(f \circ f^{-1})(-10)$ **−10**

33. $(f^{-1} \circ f)(0.2)$ **0.2**

34. $(f \circ f^{-1})(d)$ **d**

Ⓑ **Apply Your Skills**

Find the inverse of each function. Is the inverse a function? 35–43. See margin.

35. $f(x) = 1.5x^2 - 4$

36. $f(x) = \dfrac{3x^2}{4}$

37. $f(x) = \sqrt{2x - 1} + 3$

38. $f(x) = (x + 1)^2$

39. $f(x) = (2x - 1)^2$

40. $f(x) = (x + 1)^2 - 1$

41. $f(x) = x^3$

42. $f(x) = x^4$

43. $f(x) = \dfrac{2x^2}{5} + 1$

---

pages 404–406 Exercises

5. $y = \frac{1}{3}x - \frac{1}{3}$; yes

6. $y = \frac{1}{2}x + \frac{1}{2}$; yes

7. $y = -\frac{1}{3}x + \frac{4}{3}$; yes

8. $y = \pm\sqrt{\dfrac{5 - x}{2}}$; no

9. $y = \pm\sqrt{x - 4}$; no

10. $y = \pm\sqrt{\dfrac{x + 5}{3}}$; no

11. $y = \sqrt{x - 1}$; no

12. $y = \dfrac{\sqrt{x} + 4}{3}$; no

13. $y = -\dfrac{\sqrt{x - 5} - 1}{2}$; no

35. $f^{-1}(x) = \pm\sqrt{\dfrac{2x + 8}{3}}$; no

36. $f^{-1}(x) = \pm 2\sqrt{\dfrac{x}{3}}$; no

37. $f^{-1}(x) = \dfrac{x^2 - 6x + 10}{2}$; yes

38. $f^{-1}(x) = \pm\sqrt{x} - 1$; no

39. $f^{-1}(x) = \dfrac{1 \pm \sqrt{x}}{2}$; no

40. $f^{-1}(x) = -1 \pm \sqrt{x + 1}$; no

41. $f^{-1}(x) = \sqrt[3]{x}$; yes

42. $f^{-1}(x) = \pm\sqrt[4]{x}$; no

43. $f^{-1}(x) = \pm\sqrt{\dfrac{5x - 5}{2}}$; no

404

Real-World  Connection

Water towers are tall because each foot of height provides 0.43 lb/in.² of pressure. A typical tower holds about a one-day supply for users.

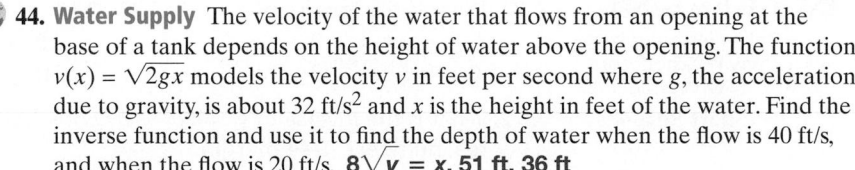

🌐 **44. Water Supply** The velocity of the water that flows from an opening at the base of a tank depends on the height of water above the opening. The function $v(x) = \sqrt{2gx}$ models the velocity v in feet per second where g, the acceleration due to gravity, is about 32 ft/s² and x is the height in feet of the water. Find the inverse function and use it to find the depth of water when the flow is 40 ft/s, and when the flow is 20 ft/s. **$8\sqrt{v} = x$, 51 ft, 36 ft**

✏️ **45. Writing** Explain how you can find the range of the inverse of $f(x) = \sqrt{x-1}$ without finding the inverse itself. **The range of the inverse is the domain of f, which is $x \geq 1$.**

46. A function consists of the pairs $(2, 3)$, $(x, 4)$ and $(5, 6)$. What values, if any, may x not assume? **2 and 5**

For each function f, find f^{-1}, the domain and range of f and f^{-1}, and determine whether f^{-1} is a function. **47–58. See back of book.**

47. $f(x) = -\sqrt{x}$

48. $f(x) = \sqrt{x} + 3$

49. $f(x) = \sqrt{-x+3}$

50. $f(x) = \sqrt{x+2}$

51. $f(x) = \frac{x^2}{2}$

52. $f(x) = \frac{1}{x^2}$

53. $f(x) = (x-4)^2$

54. $f(x) = (7-x)^2$

55. $f(x) = \frac{1}{(x+1)^2}$

56. $f(x) = 4 - 2\sqrt{x}$

57. $f(x) = \frac{3}{\sqrt{x}}$

58. $f(x) = \frac{1}{\sqrt{-2x}}$

59. a. Copy the mapping diagram at the right. Complete it by writing members of the domain and range and connecting them with arrows so that r is a function and r^{-1} is not a function. **a–b. See margin.**
   b. Repeat part (a) so that r is not a function and r^{-1} is a function.

Relation r
Domain   Range
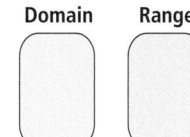

60. Critical Thinking Relation r has one element in its domain and two elements in its range. Is r a function? Is the inverse of r a function? Explain. **See margin.**

61. $n = s\sqrt{2}$; $3\sqrt{2}$ in. ≈ 4.2 in.

🔷 **61. Geometry** Write a function that gives the length of the hypotenuse of an isosceles right triangle with side length s. Evaluate the inverse of the function to find the side length of an isosceles right triangle with a hypotenuse of 6 in.

62. Open-Ended Write a function f such that the graph of f^{-1} lies in Quadrants III and IV. **Check students' work.**

Ⓒ Challenge

Find the inverse of each function. Is the inverse a function? **63–65. See margin.**

63. $f(x) = \frac{1}{5}x^3$

64. $f(x) = \sqrt[3]{x-5}$

65. $f(x) = \frac{\sqrt[3]{x}}{3}$

66. $f(x) = (x-2)^3$
$f^{-1}(x) = 2 + \sqrt[3]{x}$; yes

67. $f(x) = \sqrt[4]{x}$
$f^{-1}(x) = x^4$; yes

68. $f(x) = 1.2x^4$
$f^{-1}(x) = \pm\sqrt[4]{\frac{5x}{6}}$; no

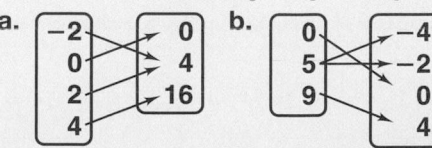

Standardized Test Prep

Multiple Choice

69. What is the inverse of $y = 5x - 1$? **B**

   A. $y = 5x + 1$ **B.** $y = \frac{x+1}{5}$ **C.** $y = \frac{x}{5} + 1$ **D.** $y = \frac{x}{5} - 1$

70. If $f(x) = 4x - 3$, what is $(f^{-1} \circ f)(10)$? **G**
   F. $\frac{13}{4}$ **G.** 10   **H.** 37   **I.** $\frac{481}{4}$

59a-b. Answers may vary. Sample:
a.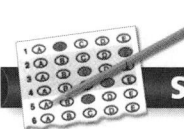
−2	→ 0
0	→ 4
2	→ 16
4	
b.
0	→ −4
5	→ −2
9	→ 0
	4

60. r is not a function because there are two y-values for one x-value. r^{-1} is a function because each of its x-values has one y-value.

63. $f^{-1}(x) = \sqrt[3]{5x}$; yes
64. $f^{-1}(x) = x^3 + 5$; yes
65. $f^{-1}(x) = 27x^3$; yes

---

4. Assess

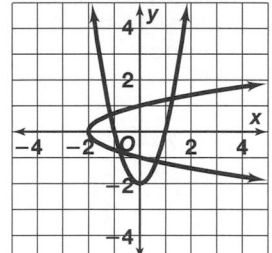

Lesson Quiz 7-7

1. Find the inverse of the function $y = 4x - 7$. Is the inverse a function?
$y = \frac{x+7}{4}$; **yes**

2. Find the inverse of $y = \sqrt{x} + 9$. Is the inverse a function? $y = x^2 - 9$; **yes**

3. Graph the relation $y = 2x^2 - 2$ and its inverse.

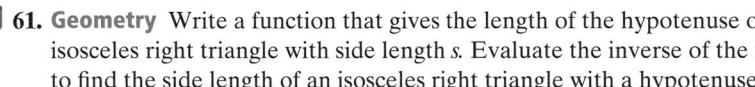

4. For the function $f(x) = 2x^2 - 1$, find f^{-1}, and the domain and range of f and f^{-1}. Determine whether f^{-1} is a function.
$f^{-1}(x) = \pm\frac{1}{2}\sqrt{2x+2}$; **domain of f: all numbers, range of f: all numbers greater than or equal to −1, domain of f^{-1}: all numbers greater than or equal to −1, range of f^{-1}: all numbers; not a function**

5. If $f(x) = 5x + 8$, find $(f^{-1} \circ f)(59)$ and $(f \circ f^{-1})(3001)$. **59, 3001**

6. A right triangle has a leg of length x and a hypotenuse of length $2x$. Write an equation to find the length s of the other leg, and use it to estimate s when the hypotenuse has a length of 5 cm. $s = x\sqrt{3}$; **about 4.33 cm**

Alternative Assessment

Ask a volunteer for a function in the form $f(x) = ax + b$. Have the students write its inverse and compare answers. Discuss aloud any discrepancies. Repeat for functions in the form of $f(x) = ax^2 + b$, and $f(x) = \sqrt{ax + b}$, with $a \neq 0$. Instruct students to graph the functions and their inverses.

405

📁 **Resources**

For additional practice with a variety of test item formats:
- Standardized Test Prep, p. 419
- Test-Taking Strategies, p. 414
- Test-Taking Strategies with Transparencies

pages 404–406   Exercises

72. [2] $y^2 = \frac{x-5}{4}$, and

$y = \pm \frac{\sqrt{x-5}}{2}$.

The inverse has values that are real numbers when $x \geq 5$.

[1] $y = \pm \frac{\sqrt{x-5}}{2}$ OR

$x \geq 5$ OR minor error

73. [4] $x = y^2 - 2y + 1$ or $x = (y-1)^2$. Then

$y - 1 = \pm\sqrt{x}$ or

$y = \pm\sqrt{x} + 1$. It is not a function because each positive value of x gives two values of y.

[3] minor error in finding inverse

[2] attempt to find inverse and a statement that the inverse is not a function

[1] attempt to find inverse OR a statement that the inverse is not a function

88. $\pm 1, \pm 2, \pm 3, \pm 4, \pm 6, \pm 12,$ $\pm\frac{1}{2}, \pm\frac{3}{2};$ roots are $-\frac{3}{2}$, ± 2.

89. $\pm 1, \pm 2, \pm 4, \pm\frac{1}{3}, \pm\frac{2}{3}, \pm\frac{4}{3};$ roots are $\frac{2}{3}$, 2, −1.

90. $\pm 1, \pm 2, \pm 3, \pm 4, \pm 6, \pm 12,$ $\pm\frac{1}{3}, \pm\frac{2}{3}, \pm\frac{4}{3};$ roots are 1, $-\frac{4}{3}$, −3.

91. $\pm 1, \pm 2, \pm 3, \pm 5, \pm 6, \pm 10,$ $\pm 15, \pm 30, \pm\frac{1}{2}, \pm\frac{3}{2}, \pm\frac{5}{2},$ $\pm\frac{15}{2};$ roots are 5, $-\frac{3}{2}$, 2.

92. $\pm 1, \pm 2, \pm 3, \pm 6;$ roots are 1, 2, 3.

93. $\pm 1, \pm 2, \pm 3, \pm 4, \pm 6, \pm 12;$ roots are −2, 2, −3.

Take It to the NET
Online lesson quiz at
www.PHSchool.com
Web Code: aga-0707

Short Response

Extended Response

71. What is the inverse of $y = x^2 - 3$? **C**
   A. $y = \pm\sqrt{x} + 3$
   B. $y = \pm\sqrt{x} - 3$
   C. $y = \pm\sqrt{x+3}$
   D. $y = \pm\sqrt{x-3}$

72. What is the inverse of $y = 4x^2 + 5$? For what values of x is the inverse a real number? **See margin.**

73. What is the inverse of $y = x^2 - 2x + 1$? Is the inverse a function? Explain.
   See margin.

Mixed Review

Lesson 7-6   Let $f(x) = 4x$, $g(x) = \frac{1}{2}x + 7$, and $h(x) = |-2x + 4|$. Simplify each function.

74. $(f \circ g)(x)$ **2x + 28**   **75.** $(g \circ f)(x)$ **2x + 7**   **76.** $(h \circ g)(x)$ **|−x − 10|**

77. $g(x) + g(x)$ **x + 14**   **78.** $(h \circ (g \circ f))(x)$
   |−4x − 10|

79. $(f \circ g)(x) + h(x)$
   2x + 28 + |−2x + 4|

Lesson 7-1   Find each indicated root if it is a real number.

80. $\sqrt[4]{16}$ **2**   **81.** $-\sqrt[4]{16}$ **−2**   **82.** $\sqrt[4]{-16}$ **not a real number**   **83.** $\sqrt[5]{243}$ **3**

84. $-\sqrt[5]{243}$ **−3**   **85.** $\sqrt[5]{-243}$ **−3**   **86.** $\sqrt[3]{0.064}$ **0.4**   **87.** $\sqrt[4]{810,000}$ **30**

Lesson 6-5   List all possible rational roots for each equation. Then use the Rational Root Theorem to find each root. **88–93. See margin.**

88. $2x^3 + 3x^2 - 8x - 12 = 0$ **89.** $3x^3 - 5x^2 - 4x + 4 = 0$

90. $3x^3 + 10x^2 - x - 12 = 0$ **91.** $2x^3 - 11x^2 - x + 30 = 0$

92. $x^3 - 6x^2 + 11x - 6 = 0$ **93.** $x^3 + 3x^2 - 4x - 12 = 0$

Algebra at Work

·····················Demographer

Demographers study human populations. They collect, analyze, and present data relating to the basic life cycle: birth, marriage, divorce, family formation, employment, aging, migration, and death. Demographers draw on the related disciplines of sociology, economics, political science, anthropology, psychology, public health, and ecology.

Demography is also concerned with the broader nature of social and economic change and its impact on the natural environment. It includes studying family structure, the role of women, and the value of children, as well as the social, cultural, and institutional context of demographic change. Demography is an essential component of many activities, such as planning government policies and market research.

Take It to the NET For more information about demography, go to **www.PHSchool.com**.
Web Code: agb-2031

Graphing Inverses

FOR USE WITH LESSON 7-7

Technology

Graphing Inverses

Students use a graphing calculator to explore two ways of graphing a function and its inverse.

Resources

Students may use any graphing calculator that has a DrawInv feature and parametric graphing capabilities.

Teaching Notes

Using the DrawInv feature to display the graph of the inverse is faster than using parametric equations. However, it has the disadvantage that you cannot use Trace to trace the graph of the inverse.

Error Prevention

Students should press **WINDOW** to check the window settings. Be sure students understand how the Tmin, Tmax, and Tstep values can affect the graph display. If students have little or no experience with parametric graphing, you may want to allow some extra time for experimenting with different settings.

page 407   Technology

You can graph inverses of functions on a graphing calculator by using the DrawInv feature or by using parametric equations. It takes more keystrokes to set up parametric equations, but once you do you can easily change from one function to another and quickly see graphs of a function and its inverse.

EXAMPLE

Graph $y = 0.3x^2 + 1$ and its inverse.

Method 1 Use the DrawInv feature.

Step 1 Press **Y=** and enter the equation. Press **ZOOM** 5 to see a graph of the function with equal x- and y-intervals.

Step 2 Press **DRAW** 8. You will see **DrawInv** followed by a flashing cursor. Select equation Y_1 by pressing **VARS** ▶ 1 1. Press **ENTER** to see the graph of the function and its inverse.

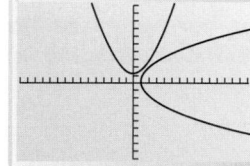

Method 2 Use parametric equations.

Step 1 Set to parametric mode. Press **MODE**, select **Par**, and press **QUIT**.

Step 2 Enter the given equation in parametric form. Press **Y=** and enter the equations $X_{1T} = T$ and $Y_{1T} = .3T^2 + 1$.

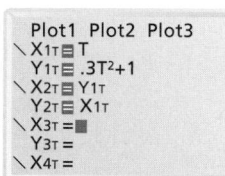
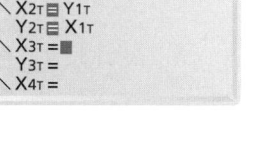

Step 3 Now use $X_{2T} = Y_{1T}$ and $Y_{2T} = X_{1T}$ to interchange the x- and y-values of the first parametric equation. Press **Y=** and move the cursor to follow $X_{2T} =$. Select Y_{1T} by pressing **VARS** ▶ 2 2. Enter the equation $Y_{2T} = X_{1T}$ in a similar fashion.

Step 4 Press **ZOOM** 5. Adjust the Window so that Tmin and Tmax approximately agree with Xmin and Xmax. Press **GRAPH** to see the graph of the function and its inverse.

5. The third graph would be the same as the first. Interchanging the pairs twice restores the original pairs.

EXERCISES

Graph each function and its inverse with a graphing calculator. Then sketch the graphs. 1. See back of book. 2–4. See margin.

1. $y = x^2 - 5$ **2.** $y = (x - 3)^2$ **3.** $y = 0.01x^4$ **4.** $y = 0.5x^3 - 3$

5. Critical Thinking In Method 2, suppose you added a third pair of parametric equations that interchanged the x- and y-values of the second pair ($X_{3T} = Y_{2T}$ and $Y_{3T} = X_{2T}$). What would be the effect on the graphs? Explain.   **See above.**

6. Writing Change the parametric equation $X_{2T} = Y_{1T}$ in Method 2, Step 3 to $X_{2T} = -Y_{1T}$. Describe the graph that results. **The graph is the reflection of the first graph in the x-axis.**

2.
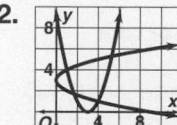

3.
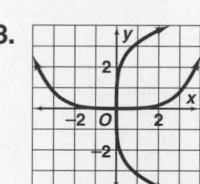

4.
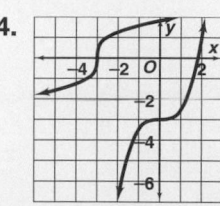

407

1. Plan

Graphing Radical Functions

2.07 Use equations with radical expressions to model and solve problems. a) Solve using graphs. b) Interpret the degree, constants, and coefficients in the context of the problem.

North Carolina Objectives

Lesson Preview

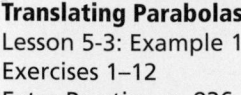
✓ Check Skills You'll Need

Translating Parabolas
Lesson 5-3: Example 1
Exercises 1–12
Extra Practice, p. 826

What You'll Learn

OBJECTIVE **1** To graph radical functions

. . . And Why

To estimate the mass of a giraffe, as in Example 5

✓ Check Skills You'll Need

(For help, go to Lesson 5-3.)

Graph each equation. 1–6. See back of book.

1. $y = (x + 2)^2$ **2.** $y = (x - 3)^2$ **3.** $y = -(x + 4)^2$

4. $y = -x^2 - 1$ **5.** $y = -(x + 1)^2 + 1$ **6.** $y = 3x^2 + 3$

New Vocabulary • radical function

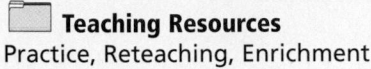
Lesson Resources

📁 **Teaching Resources**
Practice, Reteaching, Enrichment

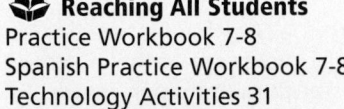
👥 **Reaching All Students**
Practice Workbook 7-8
Spanish Practice Workbook 7-8
Technology Activities 31

⏱ **Presentation Assistant Plus!**
Transparencies
• Check Skills You'll Need 7-8
• Additional Examples 7-8
• Student Edition Answers 7-8
• Lesson Quiz 7-8
PH Presentation Pro CD 7-8

PRENTICE HALL
ASSESSMENT SYSTEM

Computer Test Generator CD

💿 **Technology**
Resource Pro® CD-ROM
Computer Test Generator CD
Prentice Hall Presentation Pro CD

🖥 **www.PHSchool.com**
Student Site
• Teacher Web Code: agk-5500
• Self-grading Lesson Quiz
Teacher Center
• Lesson Planner
• Resources

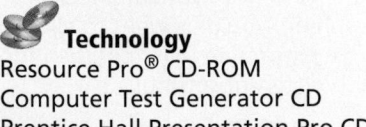
Plus **iTEXT**

iTEXT Interactive lesson includes instant self-check, tutorials, and activities.

OBJECTIVE **1** **Radical Functions**

A horizontal line can intersect the graph of $f(x) = x^2$ in two points. For example, $f(-2) = f(2)$. Therefore, a vertical line can intersect the graph of the inverse of $f(x) = x^2$ in two points, and f^{-1} is *not* a function.

❓ **Need Help?**

To review the vertical line test, go to Lesson 2-1.

$f(x) = x^2$ $f^{-1}(x) = \pm\sqrt{x}$

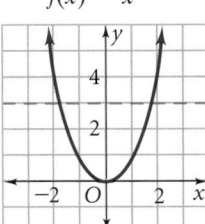 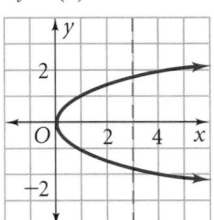

You can restrict the domain of f so that its inverse is a function.

$f(x) = x^2, x \geq 0$ $f^{-1}(x) = \sqrt{x}$

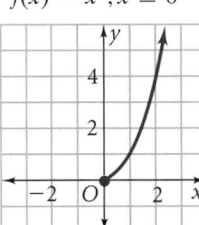 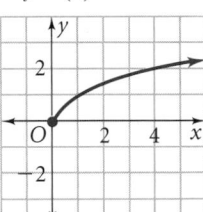

The inverse of $g(x) = x^3$ is a function.

$g(x) = x^3$ $g^{-1}(x) = \sqrt[3]{x}$

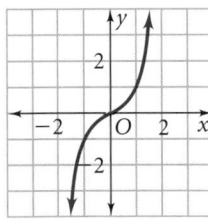 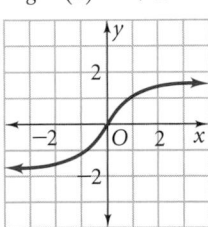

408 Chapter 7 Radical Functions and Rational Exponents

✓ Ongoing Assessment and Intervention

Before the Lesson
Diagnose prerequisite skills using:
• Check Skills You'll Need

During the Lesson
Monitor progress using:
• Check Understanding
• Additional Examples
• Standardized Test Prep

After the Lesson
Assess knowledge using:
• Lesson Quiz
• Computer Test Generator CD

A radical equation defines a **radical function.** The graph of the radical function $y = \sqrt{x} + k$ is a translation of the graph of $y = \sqrt{x}$. If k is positive, the graph is translated k units up. If k is negative, the graph is translated $|k|$ units down.

1 EXAMPLE Translating Square Root Functions Vertically

Graph $y = \sqrt{x} + 2$ and $y = \sqrt{x} - 1$.

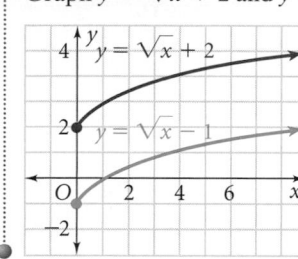

The graph of $y = \sqrt{x} + 2$ is the graph of $y = \sqrt{x}$ shifted up 2 units. The graph of $y = \sqrt{x} - 1$ is the graph of $y = \sqrt{x}$ shifted down 1 unit.

The domains of both functions are the set of nonnegative numbers, but their ranges differ.

1.
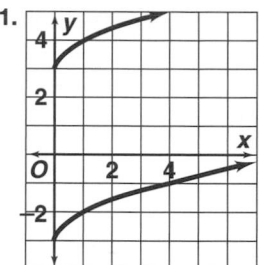

✓ **Check Understanding** ❶ Graph $y = \sqrt{x} - 3$ and $y = \sqrt{x} + 3$. **See left.**

The graph of $y = \sqrt{x - h}$ is a translation of $y = \sqrt{x}$. If h is positive, the graph is translated h units right. If h is negative, the graph is translated $|h|$ units left.

2 EXAMPLE Translating Square Root Functions Horizontally

Graph $y = \sqrt{x + 3}$ and $y = \sqrt{x - 2}$.

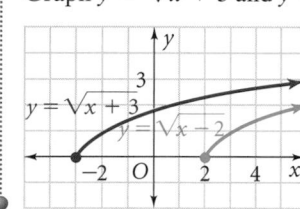

The graph of $y = \sqrt{x + 3}$ is the graph of $y = \sqrt{x}$ shifted left 3 units. The graph of $y = \sqrt{x - 2}$ is the graph of $y = \sqrt{x}$ shifted right 2 units.

The ranges of both functions are the set of nonnegative numbers, but their domains differ.

2.
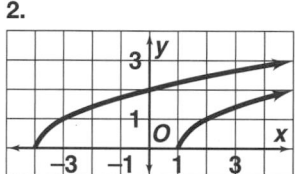

✓ **Check Understanding** ❷ Graph $y = \sqrt{x - 1}$ and $y = \sqrt{x + 4}$. **See left.**

The graph of $y = a\sqrt{x}$ is a vertical stretch or compression of the graph of $y = \sqrt{x}$ by a factor of $|a|$. If $a < 0$, the graph is a reflection across the x-axis.

3 EXAMPLE Graphing Square Root Functions

Graph $y = \sqrt{x}$, $y = 0.5\sqrt{x}$, and $y = 2\sqrt{x}$.

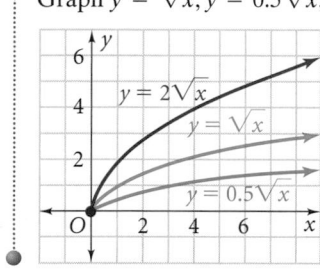

Each y-value of $y = 2\sqrt{x}$ is four times the corresponding y-value of $y = 0.5\sqrt{x}$.

The domains and ranges of all three functions are the set of nonnegative numbers.

3.
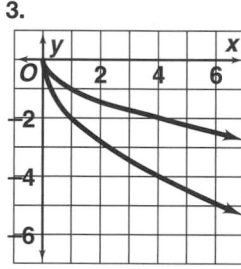

✓ **Check Understanding** ❸ Graph $y = -\sqrt{x}$ and $y = -2\sqrt{x}$. **See left.**

Lesson 7-8 Graphing Radical Functions **409**

2. Teach

Professional Development

Math Background

Graphs whose equations have the form $y = a(x - h)^2 + k$ are translations h units horizontally and k units vertically of the graph of $y = ax^2$, as seen in Lesson 5-3. The same holds true for functions of the form $y = a\sqrt[n]{x - h} + k$; the graphs are translations of the graph of the parent function $y = a\sqrt[n]{x}$.

OBJECTIVE

1 Teaching Notes

3 EXAMPLE Inclusion

For students who have difficulty reading small type, you may want to enlarge the graphs on a copier.

Additional Examples

❶ Graph $y = \sqrt{x} + 5$ and $y = \sqrt{x} - 7$.

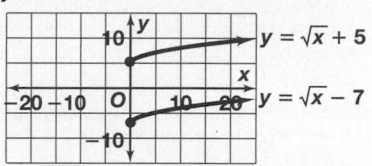

❷ Graph $y = \sqrt{x + 7}$ and $y = \sqrt{x - 5}$.

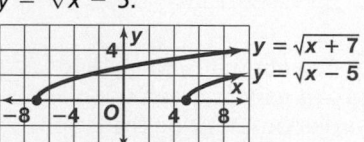

❸ Graph $y = -\sqrt{x}$, $y = -2\sqrt{x}$, and $y = -1.5\sqrt{x}$.

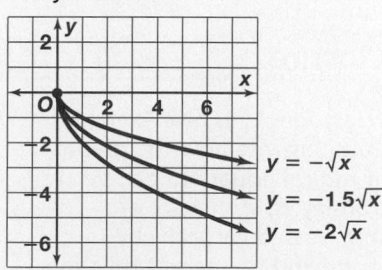

👥 **Reaching All Students**

| **Below Level** Graph $f(x) = x^2 - 4$ using a graphing calculator. Use the DRAW function to draw the inverse and observe that the inverse is not a function. | **Advanced Learners** Ask students to use a graphing calculator to graph the function $y - \sqrt[3]{x} - 4$ and find the root of the equation. Discuss the domain and range of the function. | **English Learners** See note on page 411. **Inclusion** See note on page 409. |

409

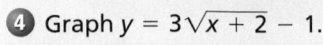

4 Graph $y = 3\sqrt{x + 2} - 1$.

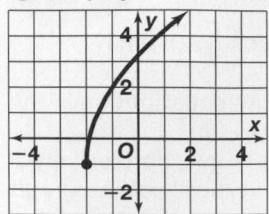

5 The function $h(x) = 0.5\sqrt[3]{x}$ models the height h in meters of one group of male giraffes with a body mass of x kilograms. Graph the model with a graphing calculator. Use the graph to estimate the body mass of a young male giraffe with a height of 3 meters. **216 kg**

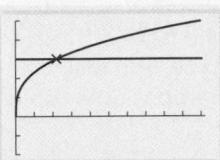

Intersection
X=216   Y=3

6 Graph $y = 2\sqrt[3]{x + 2} - 2$.

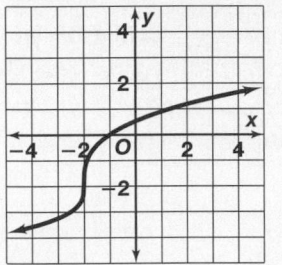

7 Rewrite $y = \sqrt{9x + 18}$ to make it easy to graph using a translation. Describe the graph.
$y = 3\sqrt{x + 2}$; The graph of $y = 3\sqrt{x + 2}$ is the graph of $y = 3\sqrt{x}$ translated 2 units left.

Closure

Ask students to give examples that illustrate how the graphs of radical equations can be translated, stretched, or compressed vertically by modifying the parent functions $y = \sqrt{x}$ and $y = \sqrt[3]{x}$. **Check students' work.**

4.

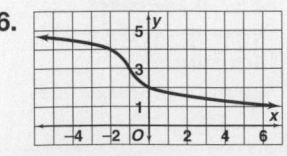

✓ **Check Understanding** **4** Graph $y = \frac{1}{4}\sqrt{x - 2} - 4$. **See left.**

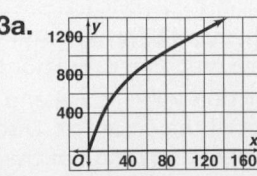

2.5 m

✓ **Check Understanding**

In general, the graph of $y = a\sqrt{x - h} + k$ is a translation h units horizontally and k units vertically of $y = a\sqrt{x}$. The vertical stretch or compression is determined by a.

4 EXAMPLE Graphing Square Root Functions

Graph $y = -2\sqrt{x + 1} - 3$.

$y = -2\sqrt{x - (-1)} + (-3)$, so translate the graph of $y = -2\sqrt{x}$ left 1 unit and down 3 units.

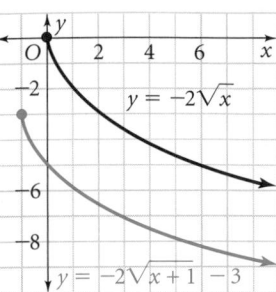

5 EXAMPLE Real-World Connection

Zoology The function $h(x) = 0.4\sqrt[3]{x}$ models the height h in meters of a female giraffe that has a mass of x kilograms. Graph the model with a graphing calculator. Use the graph to estimate the mass of the young giraffe in the photograph.

The height of the young giraffe is 2.5 m. Graph $y = 0.4\sqrt[3]{x}$ and $y = 2.5$. Adjust the window so the graphs intersect. Use the Intersect feature to find that $x \approx 244$ when $y = 2.5$.

The giraffe has a mass of about 244 kilograms.

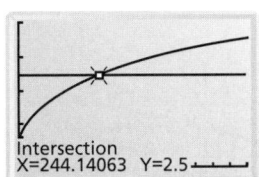

Intersection
X=244.14063 Y=2.5

✓ **Check Understanding** **5** Use a graphing calculator to estimate the mass of a 3.2-meter female giraffe. **512 kg**

The pattern for graphing square root functions applies to other radical functions. For example, the graph of $y = a\sqrt[3]{x} - h + k$ is a translation h units horizontally and k units vertically of $y = a\sqrt[3]{x}$.

6 EXAMPLE Graphing Cube Root Functions

Graph $y = 2\sqrt[3]{x + 3} - 1$.

The graph of $y = 2\sqrt[3]{x + 3} - 1$ is the graph of $y = 2\sqrt[3]{x}$ translated 3 units left and 1 unit down.

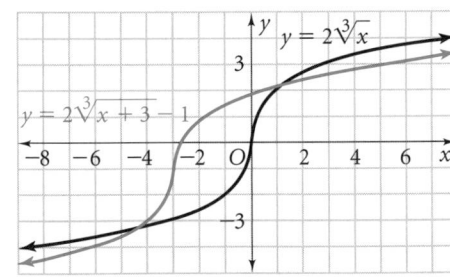

✓ **Check Understanding** **6** Graph $y = 3 - \sqrt[3]{x + 1}$. **See margin.**

410 Chapter 7 Radical Functions and Rational Exponents

pages 409–411 **Check Understanding**

6.

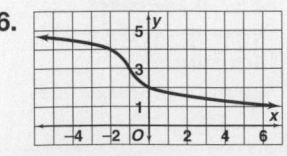

pages 411–413 **Exercises**

23a.

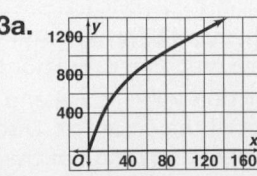

30. $y = 3\sqrt{x - 1}$; the graph is the graph of $y = 3\sqrt{x}$ translated 1 unit to the right.

Sometimes you have to rewrite a radical equation so you can graph it using a translation.

7 EXAMPLE **Transforming Radical Equations.**

Rewrite $y = \sqrt{4x - 12}$ to make it easy to graph using a translation. Describe the graph.

$$y = \sqrt{4x - 12} = \sqrt{4(x - 3)} = 2\sqrt{x - (3)}$$

The graph of $y = \sqrt{4x - 12}$ is the graph of $y = 2\sqrt{x}$ translated 3 units right.

 Check Understanding **7** Rewrite $y = \sqrt[3]{8x - 24} + 3$ to make it easy to graph using a translation. Describe the graph. **$y = 2\sqrt[3]{x - 3} + 3$; the graph is the graph of $y = 2\sqrt[3]{x}$ translated 3 units right and 3 units up.**

EXERCISES

For more practice, see *Extra Practice*.

Practice and Problem Solving

A **Practice by Example**

Examples 1 and 2
(page 409)

Graph each function. 1–8. See back of book.

1. $y = \sqrt{x} + 1$ **2.** $y = \sqrt{x} - 2$ **3.** $y = \sqrt{x} - 4$ **4.** $y = \sqrt{x} + 5$

5. $y = \sqrt{x - 3}$ **6.** $y = \sqrt{x + 1}$ **7.** $y = \sqrt{x + 6}$ **8.** $y = \sqrt{x - 4}$

Example 3
(page 409)

Graph each function. 9–16. See back of book.

9. $y = 3\sqrt{x}$ **10.** $y = -0.25\sqrt{x}$ **11.** $y = \frac{1}{3}\sqrt{x}$ **12.** $y = -4\sqrt{x}$

13. $y = \frac{2}{5}\sqrt{x}$ **14.** $y = -5\sqrt{x}$ **15.** $y = -0.75\sqrt{x}$ **16.** $y = -0.5\sqrt{x}$

Examples 4 and 5
(page 410)

Graph each function. 17–22. See back of book.

17. $y = -\sqrt{x - 1}$

18. $y = 3\sqrt{x + 1} + 4$

19. $y = -2\sqrt{x + 4} - 5$

20. $y = -\sqrt{x - 3} + 2$

21. $y = \frac{1}{4}\sqrt{x + 2} - 1$

22. $y = -0.4\sqrt{x - 6} + 7$

23. Agriculture A center-pivot irrigation system can water from 1 to 130 acres of crop land. The length ℓ in feet of rotating pipe needed to irrigate A acres is given by the function $\ell = 117.75\sqrt{A}$. **a. See margin p. 410.**
a. Graph the equation on your calculator. Make a sketch of the graph.
b. Find the lengths of pipe needed to irrigate 40, 80, and 130 acres.
≈745 ft, ≈1053 ft, ≈1343 ft

Example 6
(page 410)

Graph each function. 24–29. See back of book.

24. $y = \sqrt[3]{x} + 5$ **25.** $y = \sqrt[3]{x} - 4$ **26.** $y = \sqrt[3]{x + 2} - 7$

27. $y = -\sqrt[3]{x + 3} - 1$ **28.** $y = 2\sqrt[3]{x - 6} - 9$ **29.** $y = \frac{1}{2}\sqrt[3]{x - 1} + 3$

Example 7
(page 411)

Rewrite each function to make it easy to graph using a translation. Describe the graph. 30–35. See margin pp. 410–411.

30. $y = \sqrt{9x - 9}$ **31.** $y = -\sqrt{16x + 32}$ **32.** $y = -2\sqrt{49x + 49}$

33. $y = \sqrt[3]{64x + 128}$ **34.** $y = \sqrt{64x - 128} - 3$ **35.** $y = \sqrt[3]{27x - 54} + 1$

Lesson 7-8   Graphing Radical Functions   **411**

31. $y = -4\sqrt{x + 2}$; the graph is the graph of $y = -4\sqrt{x}$ translated 2 units to the left.

32. $y = -14\sqrt{x + 1}$; the graph is the graph of $y = -14\sqrt{x}$ translated 1 unit to the left.

33. $y = 4\sqrt[3]{x + 2}$; the graph is the graph of $y = 4\sqrt[3]{x}$ translated 2 units to the left.

3. Practice

Assignment Guide

1 Objective
   A B Core 1–63
   C Extension 64–69

Standardized Test Prep 70–75

Mixed Review 76–91

Error Prevention

Exercises 17–22 Students may want to use a graphing calculator to help sketch the graph. Caution them to be careful to enclose the expression under the radical sign in parentheses.

English Learners

Exercises 23 You may need to explain the meaning of *center-pivot irrigation* and *acres*.

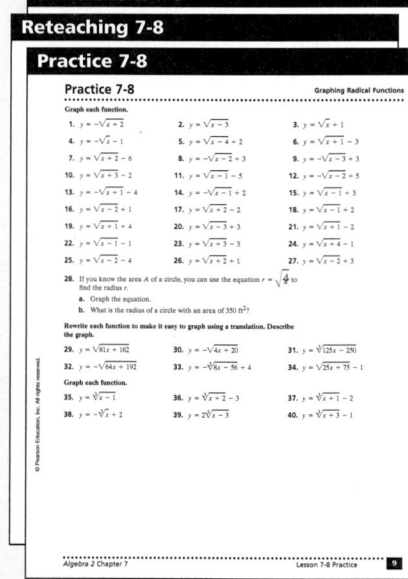

34. $y = 8\sqrt{x - 2} - 3$; the graph is the graph of $y = 8\sqrt{x}$ translated 2 units to the right and 3 units down.

35. $y = 3\sqrt[3]{x - 2} + 1$; the graph is the graph of $y = 3\sqrt[3]{x}$ translated 2 units to the right and 1 unit up.

411

Lesson Quiz 7-8

Lesson Quiz 7-8

Graph each function on the same graph.

1. $y = \sqrt{x} - 6$

2. $y = \sqrt{x} + 8$

3. $y = \frac{2}{3}\sqrt{x}$

4. $y = \sqrt[3]{x - 2} + 5$

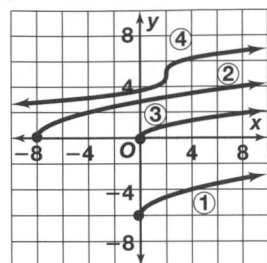

5. The formula $t = 2\pi\sqrt{\frac{L}{9.8}}$ can be used to estimate the number of seconds t it takes a pendulum of length L meters to make one complete swing. Graph the equation on a graphing calculator. Then use the graph to estimate the values of t for pendulums of lengths 1.5 meters and 2.5 meters. **about 2.46 s, about 3.17 s**

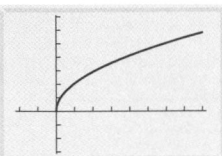

6. Rewrite $y = 2\sqrt{9x - 27}$ to make it easy to graph using a translation. $y = 6\sqrt{x - 3}$

Alternative Assessment

Have students work individually. For each of the parent functions $y = \sqrt{x}$ and $y = \sqrt[3]{x}$, have students write an equation for a vertical translation, a horizontal translation, and a stretch or compression of the graph of the parent function. Then have them use a graphing calculator to help sketch the graph of each function.

412

B Apply Your Skills

36–50. See back of book.

Graph. Find the domain and the range of each function.

36. $y = \sqrt{x} + 7$

37. $y = \sqrt{x} - 6$

38. $y = \sqrt{x - 6}$

39. $y = -3\sqrt{x} + 2$

40. $y = -\frac{4}{5}\sqrt{x}$

41. $y = 7 - \sqrt{2x - 1}$

42. $y = 4\sqrt[3]{x - 2} + 1$

43. $y = \frac{1}{2}\sqrt{x - 1} + 3$

44. $y = -3\sqrt[3]{x - 4} - 3$

45. $y = -\sqrt{x + \frac{1}{2}}$

46. $y = -\sqrt[3]{8x} + 5$

47. $y = -2\sqrt[3]{x - 4}$

48. $y = -1 - \sqrt{4x + 20}$

49. $y = 4 - \sqrt[3]{x + 2.5}$

50. $y = -3\sqrt{x - \frac{3}{4}} + 7$

 51. **Circus** The time t in seconds for a trapeze to complete one full cycle is given by the function $t = 1.11\sqrt{\ell}$, where ℓ is the length of the trapeze in feet.
   a. Graph the equation on your calculator. Make a sketch of the graph.
   b. How long is a full cycle if the trapeze is 15 ft. long? 30 ft. long?
   a–b. See margin.

52. a. Graph $y = \sqrt{x - 2} - 2$. **a, d. See margin.**
   b. Find the domain and the range. **D: $x \geq 2$, R: $y \geq -2$**
   c. At what coordinate point does the graph start? **(2, -2)**
   d. **Critical Thinking** What is the relationship of the point at which the graph starts to the domain and the range?

53. a. The graph of $y = \sqrt{x}$ is translated five units to the right and two units down. Write an equation of the translated function. $y = \sqrt{x - 5} - 2$
   b. The translated graph from part (a) is again translated, this time four units left and three units down. Write an equation of the translated funtion.
   $y = \sqrt{x - 1} - 5$

54. a. Graph $y = \sqrt{x - 2} + 1$ and $y = -\sqrt{x - 2} + 1$.
   b. Find the domain and the range of each function.
   a–b. See back of book.

Rewrite each function to make it easy to graph using a translation. Describe the graph. 55–60. See back of book.

55. $y = \sqrt{25x - 100} - 1$

56. $y = \sqrt{36x + 108} + 4$

57. $y = -\sqrt[3]{8x - 2}$

58. $y = \sqrt{\frac{x - 1}{4}} - 2$

59. $y = 10 - \sqrt[3]{\frac{x + 3}{27}}$

60. $y = \sqrt{\frac{x}{9} + 1} + 5$

61. **Open-Ended** Write a cube root function in which the vertical translation of $y = \sqrt[3]{x}$ is twice the horizontal translation.

 62. **Electronics** The size of a television screen is the length of the screen's diagonal d in inches. The equation $d = \sqrt{2A}$ models the length of a diagonal of a television screen with area A.
   a. Graph the equation on your calculator. **See margin p. 413.**
   b. Suppose you want to buy a new television that has twice the area of your old television. Your old television has an area of 100 in.^{2}. What size screen should you buy? **14 in.**

63. **Writing** Explain the effect that a has on the graph of $y = a\sqrt{x}$.
   See back of book.

C Challenge

Rewrite each function to make it easy to graph using a translation. Describe the graph. Find the domain and the range of each function.

64. $y = -\sqrt{2x + 8}$

65. $y = -\sqrt{2(4x - 3)}$

66. $y = \sqrt{3x - 5} + 6$

67. $y = -3 - \sqrt{12x + 18}$

64–67. See back of book.

Real-World **Connection**

The length of the pendulum formed by an aerialist on a trapeze depends on how far he hangs below the bar.

412 Chapter 7 Radical Functions and Rational Exponents

---

pages 411–413 Exercises

51a.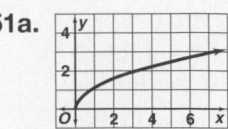

b. ≈4.3 s; ≈6.1 s

52a.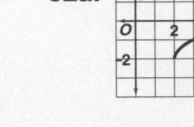

d. **The domain is based on the x-coordinate of that point, and the range is based on the y-coordinate.**

61. **Answers may vary.**
   Sample:
   $y = \sqrt[3]{x - 2} + 4$

68. a. Graph $y = \sqrt{-x}$, $y = \sqrt{1-x}$, and $y = \sqrt{2-x}$.
   b. Make a Conjecture How does the graph of $y = \sqrt{h-x}$ differ from the graph of $y = \sqrt{x-h}$?   **a–b. See back of book.**

69. For what positive integers n are the domain and range of $y = \sqrt[n]{x}$ the set of real numbers? Assume that x is a real number.   **for all odd positive integers**

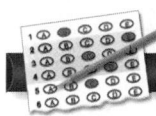
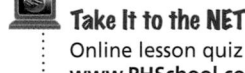
Multiple Choice

70. How is the graph of $y = \sqrt{x} + 7$ translated from the graph of $y = \sqrt{x}$? **A**
  A. shifted 7 units left   **B.** shifted 7 units right
  C. shifted 7 units up   **D.** shifted 7 units down

71. How is the graph of $y = \sqrt{x} - 5$ translated from the graph of $y = \sqrt{x}$? **I**
  F. shifted 5 units left   **G.** shifted 5 units right
  H. shifted 5 units up   **I.** shifted 5 units down

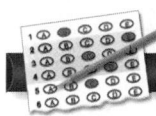
Take It to the NET
Online lesson quiz at
www.PHSchool.com
Web Code: aga-0708

72. The graph of $y = -\sqrt{x}$ is shifted 4 units up and 3 units right. Which equation represents the new graph? **B**
  A. $y = -\sqrt{x-4} + 3$ **B.** $y = -\sqrt{x-3} + 4$
  C. $y = -\sqrt{x+3} + 4$ **D.** $y = -\sqrt{x+4} + 3$

73. Which equation shows $y + 3 = \sqrt{\frac{x}{16} + 2}$ rewritten in the form $y = a\sqrt{x-h} + k$? **H**
  F. $y = \frac{3}{4}\sqrt{x - (-2)}$ **G.** $y = \frac{1}{4}\sqrt{x - (-2)} + (-3)$
  H. $y = \frac{1}{4}\sqrt{x - (-32)} + (-3)$ **I.** $y = \frac{1}{8}\sqrt{x + 32} + (-3)$

Short Response

74. At the right is the graph of $y = \sqrt{x}$. How are the graphs of $f(x) = \sqrt{x-1}$ and $g(x) = \sqrt{x} - 1$ like that graph, and how are they different?

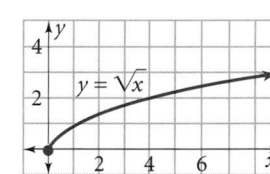

Extended Response

75. What are the differences in the domains and ranges of functions $f(x)$ and $g(x)$ from Exercise 74?
74–75. See margin.

Lesson 7-7

Find the inverse of each function. Is the inverse a function?   **76–81. See margin.**
  76. $f(x) = 4x - 1$ **77.** $f(x) = \frac{2}{3}x - 3$ **78.** $f(x) = 2.4x^2 + 1$
  79. $f(x) = \sqrt{x+3} - 4$ **80.** $f(x) = (2x+1)^2$ **81.** $f(x) = 2x^3$

Lesson 7-2

Rationalize the denominator of each expression. Assume that all variables are positive.   **82–85. See margin.**
  82. $\frac{\sqrt{36x^3}}{\sqrt{12x}}$ **83.** $\sqrt[3]{\frac{3x}{2y}}$ **84.** $\frac{\sqrt[3]{x}}{\sqrt[3]{3y}}$ **85.** $\sqrt[5]{\frac{3x^3}{2y}}$

Lesson 5-8

Solve using the Quadratic Formula.   **86–91. See margin.**
  86. $5x^2 + x = 3$ **87.** $3x^2 + 9x = 27$ **88.** $x^2 - 9x + 15 = 0$
  89. $x^2 + 10x + 11 = 0$ **90.** $x^2 - 12x + 25 = 0$ **91.** $8x^2 + 2x - 15 = 0$

Lesson 7-8   Graphing Radical Functions   **413**

62a.

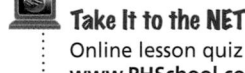

74. **[2]** Both graphs have the same shape as the graph of $y = \sqrt{x}$. The graph of $f(x) = \sqrt{x-1}$ is the graph of $y = \sqrt{x}$ moved 1 unit to the right, and the graph of $g(x) = \sqrt{x} - 1$ is the graph of $y = \sqrt{x}$ moved 1 unit down.

[1] minor error in either direction

Standardized Test Prep

  Resources

For additional practice with a variety of test item formats:
- Standardized Test Prep, p. 419
- Test-Taking Strategies, p. 414
- Test-Taking Strategies with Transparencies

75. **[4]** For $f(x) = \sqrt{x-1}$ the domain is $x \geq 1$ and the range is $y \geq 0$. For $g(x) = \sqrt{x} - 1$ the domain is $x \geq 0$ and the range is $y \geq -1$.

[3] minor error in one of the descriptions of domains or ranges

[2] correct domains or ranges

[1] some attempt to describe the domains

76. $y = \frac{x+1}{4}$; yes

77. $y = \frac{3(x+3)}{2}$; yes

78. $y = \pm\sqrt{\frac{x-1}{2.4}}$; no

79. $y = (x+4)^2 - 3$; yes

80. $y = \frac{-1 \pm \sqrt{x}}{2}$; no

81. $y = \sqrt[3]{\frac{x}{2}}$; yes

82. $x\sqrt{3}$

83. $\frac{\sqrt[3]{12xy^2}}{2y}$

84. $\frac{\sqrt[3]{9xy^2}}{3y}$

85. $\frac{\sqrt[5]{48x^3y^4}}{2y}$

86. $\frac{-1 \pm \sqrt{61}}{10}$

87. $\frac{-3 \pm 3\sqrt{5}}{2}$

88. $\frac{9 \pm \sqrt{21}}{2}$

89. $-5 \pm \sqrt{14}$

90. $6 \pm \sqrt{11}$

91. $\frac{5}{4}, -\frac{3}{2}$

Finding Multiple Correct Answers

This feature introduces students to the fact that in some types of multiple choice questions, more than one answer might be correct.

Resources

ASSESSMENT SYSTEM

Test-Taking Strategies with Transparencies
- Transparency 7
- Practice sheet p. 31

Teaching Notes

1 EXAMPLE

The main difference between these types of problems and standard multiple-choice problems is the fact that there are multiple expressions to evaluate. Only when students have evaluated all three expressions (I, II, and III) should they investigate the answer choices.

2 EXAMPLE

Suggest that students circle, highlight, or otherwise mark the expressions that are correct as they evaluate them. This makes choosing the correct answer choice easier.

Test-Taking Strategies with Transparencies

Test-Taking Strategy: Finding Multiple Correct Answers

Examine each choice to see which one(s) are true.

Example Which of the following are true about the graph of the line $y = -4x - 5$?

   I. The slope is 4.
   II. The y-intercept is -5.
   III. The point $(1, -9)$ is on the line.

   A. None   B. II only   C. III only   D. II and III only

The line is in slope-intercept form: $y = mx + b$, so its slope is -4 and its y-intercept is -5.

So, choice I is false, and choice II is true.

Notice, $-9 = -4(1) - 5$, so choice III is true.

The answer is II and III only are true, or choice D.

Find the answer. Explain your reasoning.

1. If $3x + 4 < 5$, which of the following are true?
   I. $6x + 8 < 10$ II. $-6x - 8 < -10$ III. $-3x > -1$
   A. None   B. I only   C. III only   D. I and III only

2. Use the data: 3, 5, 7, 10, 15. Which of the following are true?
   I. The mean is 8.   II. The median is 7.   III. The range is 12.
   F. None   G. I and II only   H. II only   I. All

Solutions

1. D

2. I

Transparency 7

414

In some multiple-choice questions, there may be several correct answers.

1 EXAMPLE

Which of the following are true for all values of x?

   I. $\sqrt[3]{2^x} = \left(\sqrt[3]{2}\right)^x$ **II.** $\sqrt{x^2} = \sqrt[3]{x^3}$ **III.** $\sqrt{x^2 + 1} = |x| + 1$

   A. I only   **B.** I and II only   **C.** I and III only   **D.** II and III only

Determine whether each statement is true for all values of x.

Equation I $\sqrt[3]{2^x} = (2^x)^{\frac{1}{3}} = \left(2^{\frac{1}{3}}\right)^x = \left(\sqrt[3]{2}\right)^x$ *True*

Equation II $\sqrt{x^2} = |x| \neq x = \sqrt[3]{x^3}$ *False*

Equation III   Square each side to get
$x^2 + 1 = x^2 + 2|x| + 1,$
or $0 = 2|x|$, which is true only for $x = 0$.   *False*

● Only statement I is true for all values of x. The answer is A.

2 EXAMPLE

Which of the following are equal to x for all nonzero values of x?

   I. $\sqrt{x^2}$ **II.** $\sqrt[3]{x^3}$ **III.** $\dfrac{\sqrt[3]{x^4}}{\sqrt[3]{x}}$

   A. I only   **B.** II only   **C.** II and III only   **D.** I, II and III

Rewrite each statement.

Expression I $\sqrt{x^2} = x$ only when x is positive.

Expression II $\sqrt[3]{x^3} = x$ for all values of x.

Expression III $\dfrac{\sqrt[3]{x^4}}{\sqrt[3]{x}} = \dfrac{x^{\frac{4}{3}}}{x^{\frac{1}{3}}} = x^{\frac{4}{3} - \frac{1}{3}} = x$ when $x \neq 0$.

● Expressions II and III are correct choices. The answer is C.

2. All equations are true for $x = 0$. Only statements I and II are true for $x = 1$.

EXERCISES

1. Test each equation in Example 1 with $x = 2$ and $x = -2$. What do your results show about each of the three equations? **Only statement I is true.**

2. **Critical Thinking** Test each equation in Example 1 with $x = 0$ and $x = 1$. Explain why these values do not help you choose the true equations. **See above.**

3. Which of the following equations are true? **A**

   I. $\left(\sqrt[4]{\sqrt{3}}\right)^8 = 3$ **II.** $\left(\sqrt[4]{\sqrt{3}}\right)^6 = 3$ **III.** $\dfrac{1}{\left(\frac{3}{5}\right)^{-1}} = \dfrac{5}{3}$

   A. I only   **B.** I and II only   **C.** I and III only   **D.** II and III only

Chapter Review

Vocabulary

composite function (p. 393)
index (p. 364)
inverse functions (p. 403)
inverse relation (p. 401)

like radicals (p. 374)
*n*th root (p. 363)
principal root (p. 364)
radical equation (p. 385)

radical function (p. 409)
radicand (p. 364)
rational exponent (p. 379)
rationalize the denominator (p. 370)

 **Reading Math**
Understanding
Vocabulary

Choose the correct vocabulary term to complete each sentence.

1. In the expression $\sqrt[3]{8}$, 8 is called the *(principal root, radicand)*. **radicand**

2. In the expression $\sqrt[3]{8}$, 3 is called the *(principal root, index)*. **index**

3. When you rewrite an expression so there are no radicals in any denominator and no denominators in any radical, you *(rationalize the denominator, compose two functions)*. **rationalize the denominator**

4. The expressions $\sqrt{x}$ and $\sqrt[5]{x}$ *(are, are not)* examples of like radicals.
   are not

5. The definition of *(rational exponents, inverse functions)* allows us to write $7^{\frac{2}{3}} = \sqrt[3]{7^2}$. **rational exponents**

6. If $g(x) = x - 4$ and $h(x) = x^2$, $(g \circ h)(x) = x^2 - 4$ is a *(radical function, composite function)*. **composite function**

   rational exponents
7. To multiply expressions you sometimes add *(radicands, rational exponents)*.

8. If f and f^{-1} are *(composite functions, inverse functions)*, then $(f \circ f^{-1})(x) = x$ and $(f^{-1} \circ f)(x) = x$. **inverse functions**

9. $(x - 7)^{\frac{1}{2}} + 2 = x$ is an example of *(a radical equation, an inverse relation)*.
   a radical equation
10. The positive even root of a number is called the *(principal root, rational exponent)*. **principal root**

Take It to the NET
Online vocabulary quiz
at www.PHSchool.com
Web Code: agj-0751

Skills and Concepts

7-1 and 7-2 Objectives

▼ To simplify *n*th roots (p. 363)

▼ To multiply radical expressions (p. 368)

▼ To divide radical expressions (p. 369)

For any real numbers a and b, and any positive integer n, if $a^n = b$, then a is an nth root of b. The **principal root** of a number with two real roots is the positive root. The principal nth root of b is written as $\sqrt[n]{b}$. b is the **radicand** and n is the **index** of the radical.

For any negative real number a, $\sqrt[n]{a^n} = |a|$ when n is even.

If $\sqrt[n]{a}$ and $\sqrt[n]{b}$ are real numbers, then $\sqrt[n]{a} \cdot \sqrt[n]{b} = \sqrt[n]{ab}$, and, if $b \neq 0$, then $\dfrac{\sqrt[n]{a}}{\sqrt[n]{b}} = \sqrt[n]{\dfrac{a}{b}}$.

To **rationalize the denominator** of an expression, rewrite it so there are no radicals in any denominator and no denominators in any radical.

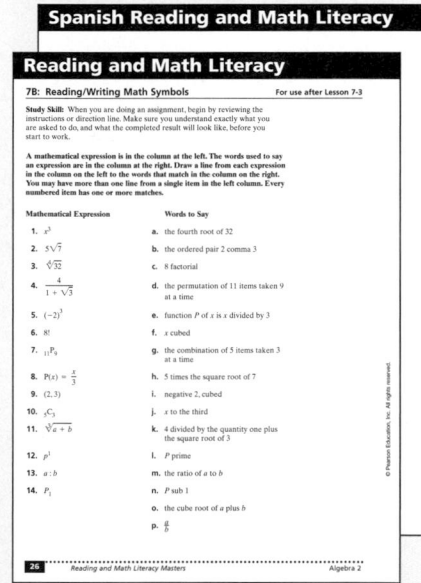

Resources

Student Edition
Extra Practice, Ch. 7, p. 828
English/Spanish Glossary, p. 871
Properties and Formulas, p. 865
Table of Symbols, p. 861

Reaching All Students
Reading and Math Literacy 7D
Spanish Reading and Math
   Literacy 7D

PRENTICE HALL
ASSESSMENT SYSTEM

Standardized Test Prep
● Ch. 7 practice in standardized test formats

www.PHSchool.com
Student Site
● Self-grading Vocabulary Test
Teacher Center
● Resources

Plus **iTEXT**

Find each indicated root if it is a real number.

11. $\sqrt{144}$ **12** **12.** $\sqrt[3]{-0.064}$ **13.** $\sqrt[4]{7^4}$ **7**   **14.** $\sqrt{0.25}$ **0.5** **15.** $-\sqrt[3]{27}$ **-3**
$\qquad\qquad\qquad\qquad$ **-0.4**

Simplify each radical expression. Use absolute value symbols as needed.

16. $\sqrt{49x^2y^{10}}$ **7$|xy^5|$** $\qquad$ **17.** $\sqrt[3]{-64y^9}$ **$-4y^3$** $\qquad$ **18.** $\sqrt{(a-1)^4}$ **$(a-1)^2$**

19. $\sqrt[5]{243x^{15}}$ **$3x^3$** $\qquad$ **20.** $\sqrt[3]{(y+3)^6}$ **$(y+3)^2$** $\qquad$ **21.** $\sqrt{32x^9y^5}$ **$4x^4y^2\sqrt{2xy}$**

Simplify each expression. Assume that all variables are positive.

24. $10x^2y\sqrt[3]{12y^2}$

25. $7x^2\sqrt{2}$

26. $15x^3y^2\sqrt{x}$

27. $6xy\sqrt[4]{2y}$

31. $6xy\sqrt{3x}$

32. $3a^2b\sqrt[3]{b}$

37. $\dfrac{y\sqrt[3]{150x}}{10x^2}$

22. $\sqrt{10}\cdot\sqrt{40}$ **20** $\qquad$ **23.** $\sqrt[3]{12}\cdot\sqrt[3]{36}$ **$6\sqrt[3]{2}$** $\qquad$ **24.** $2\sqrt[3]{2x^2y}\cdot5\sqrt[3]{6x^4y^4}$

25. $\sqrt{7x^3}\cdot\sqrt{14x}$ $\qquad$ **26.** $\sqrt{5x^4y^3}\cdot\sqrt{45x^3y}$ $\qquad$ **27.** $3\sqrt[4]{4x^3}\cdot\sqrt[4]{8xy^5}$

28. $\dfrac{\sqrt{128}}{\sqrt{8}}$ **4** $\qquad$ **29.** $\dfrac{\sqrt[3]{56y^5}}{\sqrt[3]{7y}}$ **$2y\sqrt[3]{y}$** $\qquad$ **30.** $\dfrac{\sqrt{75x^3}}{\sqrt{3x}}$ **$5x$** $\qquad$ **31.** $\dfrac{\sqrt{216x^3y^2}}{\sqrt{2}}$ $\qquad$ **32.** $\dfrac{\sqrt[3]{81a^8b^5}}{\sqrt[3]{3a^2b}}$

Simplify each expression. Rationalize all denominators. Assume that all variables are positive.

33. $\dfrac{\sqrt{8}}{\sqrt{6}}$ **$\dfrac{2\sqrt{3}}{3}$** $\qquad$ **34.** $\dfrac{\sqrt{3x^5}}{\sqrt{8x^2}}$ **$\dfrac{x\sqrt{6x}}{4}$** $\qquad$ **35.** $\dfrac{\sqrt[3]{5}}{\sqrt[3]{x^4}}$ **$\dfrac{\sqrt[3]{5x^2}}{x^2}$** $\qquad$ **36.** $\dfrac{\sqrt{2a^7b^2}}{\sqrt{32b^3}}$ $\qquad$ **37.** $\dfrac{\sqrt[3]{6x^2y^4}}{2\sqrt[3]{5x^7y}}$
$\qquad\qquad\qquad\qquad\qquad\qquad\qquad\qquad\qquad\qquad\qquad\qquad\qquad\qquad\qquad\qquad$ **$\dfrac{a^3\sqrt{ab}}{4b}$**

7-3 and 7-4 Objectives

▼ To add and subtract radical expressions (p. 374)

▼ To multiply and divide binomial radical expressions (p. 375)

▼ To simplify expressions with rational exponents (p. 379)

Like radicals have the same index and the same radicand. Use the distributive property to add or subtract them. Simplify radicals to find all the like radicals.

Use FOIL to multiply binomial radical expressions.

Binomials such as $a+b$ and $a-b$ are called conjugate expressions.

If the denominator of a fraction is a binomial radical expression, multiply both the numerator and denominator of the fraction by the conjugate of the denominator to rationalize the denominator.

The definition of **rational exponents** states that if the nth root of a is a real number and m is an integer, then $a^{\frac{1}{n}}=\sqrt[n]{a}$ and $a^{\frac{m}{n}}=\sqrt[n]{a^m}=\left(\sqrt[n]{a}\right)^m$. If m is negative, $a\neq0$. The usual properties of exponents hold for rational exponents.

Simplify each expression.

38. $\sqrt{27}+\sqrt{75}-\sqrt{12}$ $\qquad$ **39.** $(5+\sqrt{3})(2-\sqrt{3})$ $\qquad$ **40.** $(7-\sqrt{6})(7+\sqrt{6})$
$\qquad\qquad$ **$6\sqrt{3}$** $\qquad\qquad\qquad\qquad\qquad$ **$7-3\sqrt{3}$** $\qquad\qquad\qquad\qquad\qquad\qquad$ **43**

Simplify each expression. Rationalize all denominators. Assume that all variables are positive.

41. $\sqrt{2x}-\sqrt{8x}+\sqrt{18x}$ $\qquad$ **42.** $\dfrac{6}{7+2\sqrt{3}}$ **$\dfrac{42-12\sqrt{3}}{37}$** $\qquad$ **43.** $\dfrac{\sqrt{2}}{1-\sqrt{5}}$ **$-\dfrac{\sqrt{2}+\sqrt{10}}{4}$**
$\qquad\qquad$ **$2\sqrt{2x}$**

Write each expression in radical form.

44. $3^{\frac{1}{5}}$ **$\sqrt[5]{3}$** $\qquad$ **45.** $x^{\frac{2}{3}}$ **$\sqrt[3]{x^2}$** $\qquad$ **46.** $2^{-\frac{3}{4}}$ **$\sqrt[4]{\dfrac{1}{8}}$** $\qquad$ **47.** $3^{0.2}$ **$\sqrt[5]{3}$** $\qquad$ **48.** $p^{-2.25}$ **$\sqrt[4]{\dfrac{1}{p^9}}$**

Simplify each expression. Assume that all variables are positive.

53. $\dfrac{y^4}{x^6}$

49. $(243)^{\frac{4}{5}}$ **81** $\qquad$ **50.** $36^{\frac{3}{2}}$ **216** $\qquad$ **51.** $\left(x^{\frac{3}{4}}\right)^{\frac{4}{3}}$ **x** $\qquad$ **52.** $x^{\frac{1}{6}}\cdot x^{\frac{2}{3}}$ **$x^{\frac{5}{6}}$** $\qquad$ **53.** $\left(x^{-\frac{3}{8}}y^{\frac{1}{4}}\right)^{16}$

7-5 Objective

▼ To solve radical equations (p. 385)

To solve a **radical equation,** isolate a radical or a term with a rational exponent on one side of the equation. Then raise both sides of the equation to the same power. Check all possible solutions in the original equation to eliminate extraneous solutions.

Solve each equation. Check for extraneous solutions.

54. $\sqrt[3]{3x + 1} = -5$ **55.** $\sqrt{x + 7} = x + 1$ **56.** $x^{\frac{1}{2}} - 3 = 8$

      −42   2   121

7-6 and 7-7 Objectives

▼ To add, subtract, multiply, and divide functions (p. 392)

▼ To find the composite of two functions (p. 393)

▼ To find the inverse of a relation or function (p. 400)

The following are definitions of function operations.

Addition $(f + g)(x) = f(x) + g(x)$ Subtraction $(f - g)(x) = f(x) - g(x)$

Multiplication $(f \cdot g)(x) = f(x) \cdot g(x)$ Division $\left(\dfrac{f}{g}\right)(x) = \dfrac{f(x)}{g(x)}, g(x) \neq 0$

The composition of function g with function f is written as $g \circ f$ and is defined as $(g \circ f)(x) = g(f(x))$. The domain of the **composite function** $g \circ f$ consists of the values a in the domain of f such that $f(a)$ is in the domain of g.

If (a, b) is an ordered pair of a relation, then (b, a) is an ordered pair of its **inverse relation.** If a relation or function is described by an equation in x and y, you can interchange x and y to get the inverse. The inverse of a function is denoted by f^{-1}.

If f and f^{-1} are both functions, they are called **inverse functions,** and $(f^{-1} \circ f)(x) = x$ and $(f \circ f^{-1})(x) = x$.

Let $f(x) = 2x + 5$ and $g(x) = x^2 - 3x + 2$. Perform each function operation.

57. $(f + g)(x)$ **58.** $f(x) - g(x)$ **59.** $g(x) \cdot f(x)$ **60.** $(g - f)(x)$ **61.** $\dfrac{g(x)}{f(x)}$

57. $x^2 - x + 7$

58. $-x^2 + 5x + 3$

59. $2x^3 - x^2 - 11x + 10$

60. $x^2 - 5x - 3$

61. $\dfrac{x^2 - 3x + 2}{2x + 5}, x \neq -\dfrac{5}{2}$

Let $f(x) = x^2$ and $g(x) = x - 3$. Evaluate each expression.

62. $(g \circ f)(-2)$ **63.** $(f \circ g)(-2)$ **64.** $(f \circ g)(0)$ **65.** $(g \circ g)(7)$ **66.** $(f \circ g)(c)$

    1   25   9   1 $c^2 - 6c + 9$

Find the inverse of each function. Is the inverse a function?

67. $y = 6x + 2$ **68.** $y = 2x^3 + 1$ **69.** $y = (x - 2)^4$ **70.** $y = \sqrt{x + 2}$

67–70. See margin.

Let $f(x) = 3x + 1$. Find each value.

71. $(f^{-1} \circ f)(5)$ **72.** $(f^{-1} \circ f)(-5)$ **73.** $(f^{-1} \circ f)(6)$ **74.** $(f^{-1} \circ f)(t)$

    5   −5   6 t

7-8 Objective

▼ To graph radical functions (p. 408)

A **radical function** such as $y = \sqrt{x}$ has a restricted domain. For $y = \sqrt{x}$, the domain is the set of nonnegative real numbers.

The graph of $y = a\sqrt{x - h} + k$ is a translation h units horizontally and k units vertically of $y = a\sqrt{x}$.

Graph each function. 75–78. See margin.

75. $y = \sqrt{x} + 3$ **76.** $y = \sqrt{x - 1}$

77. $y = -3\sqrt{x} + 6$ **78.** $y = \sqrt{x + 7} - 2$

Chapter 7   Chapter Review   **417**

pages 415–417   Chapter Review

67. $y = \frac{1}{6}x - \frac{1}{3}$; yes

68. $y = \left(\frac{x - 1}{2}\right)^{\frac{1}{3}}$; yes

69. $y = \pm\sqrt[4]{x} + 2$; no

70. $y = x^2 - 2$; yes

75.

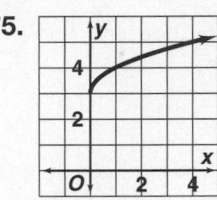

76.

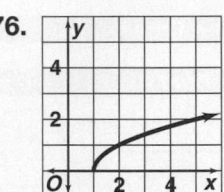

77.

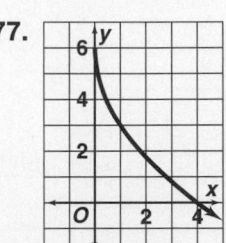

78.

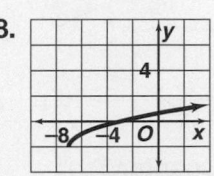

Resources

Chapter Test

Chapter **7**

Take It to the NET
Online chapter test at
www.PHSchool.com
Web Code: aga-0752

Simplify each radical expression. Use absolute value symbols when they are needed.

1. $\sqrt[3]{-0.027}$ **-0.3**

2. $\sqrt{54x^3y^5}$ **$3|x|y^2\sqrt{6xy}$**

3. $\sqrt[5]{-64x^{14}y^{20}}$ **$-2x^2y^4\sqrt[5]{2x^4}$**

4. $\sqrt{(x-2)^4}$ **$(x-2)^2$**

Simplify each expression. Rationalize all denominators. Assume that all variables are positive.

5. $\sqrt{7x^3} \cdot \sqrt{14x}$ **$7x^2\sqrt{2}$**

6. $\sqrt{3y^3} \cdot \sqrt{4xy^4} \cdot \sqrt{6x^5y^2}$ **$6x^3y^4\sqrt[4]{2y}$**

7. $\dfrac{\sqrt{7x^4y}}{\sqrt{63xy^2}}$ **$\dfrac{x\sqrt{xy}}{3y}$**

8. $\dfrac{1-\sqrt{3x}}{\sqrt{6x}}$ **$\dfrac{\sqrt{6x}-3x\sqrt{2}}{6x}$**

9. $\sqrt{48} + 2\sqrt{75} + 5\sqrt{12}$ **$24\sqrt{3}$**

10. $\sqrt{98} + \sqrt{50} - \sqrt{5}$ **$12\sqrt{2} - \sqrt{5}$**

11. $(3 + 2\sqrt{5})(1 - \sqrt{20})$ **$-17 - 4\sqrt{5}$**

12. $(7 + \sqrt{3})(3 + 5\sqrt{3})$ **$36 + 38\sqrt{3}$**

13. $\dfrac{5}{3 - 2\sqrt{6}}$ **$-1 - \dfrac{2}{3}\sqrt{6}$**

14. $\dfrac{1+\sqrt{3}}{\sqrt{3}-\sqrt{2}}$ **$3 + \sqrt{2} + \sqrt{3} + \sqrt{6}$**

Simplify each expression. Assume that all variables are positive.

15. $(125)^{-\frac{2}{3}}$ **$\dfrac{1}{25}$**

16. $x^{\frac{1}{6}} \cdot x^{\frac{1}{3}}$ **$x^{\frac{1}{2}}$**

17. $\left(\dfrac{8x^9y^3}{27x^2y^{12}}\right)^{\frac{2}{3}}$ **$\dfrac{4x^4\sqrt[3]{x^2}}{9y^6}$**

Solve each equation. Check for extraneous solutions.

18. $\sqrt{x-3} = x - 5$ **7**

19. $\sqrt{x+4} = \sqrt{3x}$ **2**

20. $(3x+4)^{\frac{1}{3}} = -5$ **-43**

21. $x - 6 = (x-4)^{\frac{1}{2}}$ **8**

Let $f(x) = x - 2$ and $g(x) = x^2 - 3x + 2$. **Perform each function operation and then find the domain.**
22–27. See margin.

22. $g(x) - f(x)$

23. $-2g(x) + f(x)$

24. $\dfrac{g(x)}{f(x)}$

25. $-f(x) \cdot g(x)$

For each pair of functions, find $f(g(x))$ and $g(f(x))$.

26. $f(x) = x^2 - 2, g(x) = 4x + 1$

27. $f(x) = 2x^2 + x - 7, g(x) = -3x - 1$

28. Writing Explain why -108 has no real 6th roots. **See margin.**

29. Discounts While purchasing a pair of shoes on sale for 50% off, you noticed that the price on the cash register was only 25% off. The cashier then took another 25% off that price. **b, d. See margin.**
   a. Write a function $f(x)$ to represent the 50%-off price of the shoes. **$f(x) = 0.5x$**
   b. Write a function $g(x)$ to represent the price the cash register rang up the first time.
   c. Write a composite function to represent the price of the shoes after the cashier's solution to the problem. **$g(g(x)) = 0.5625x$**
   d. Compare the result of the cashier's solution to the correct price of the shoes.

Rewrite each function to make it easy to graph using a translation. Describe the graph. 30–31. See margin.

30. $y = \sqrt{16x + 80} - 1$

31. $y = \sqrt{9x + 3}$

Graph. Find the domain and range of each function.

32. $y = 2\sqrt{x} + 3$

33. $y = \sqrt{2x + 3}$

34. $y = -\dfrac{1}{2}\sqrt{x - 4}$

35. $y = \sqrt{x + 3} - 4$

32–35. See back of book.

Let $f(x) = x^3 + 1$ and $g(x) = 7x - 4$. **Find each value.**

36. $f(g(-2))$ **-5831**

37. $g(f(3))$ **192**

38. $f(g(0))$ **-63**

Find the inverse of each function. Is the inverse a function? 39–42. See margin p. 419.

39. $f(x) = 3x^3 - 2$

40. $g(x) = \sqrt{x + 3} - 1$

41. $g(x) = \sqrt{2x + 1}$

42. $f(x) = \dfrac{1}{4}x^4$

43. a. Geometry For a sphere, $V = \dfrac{4}{3}\pi r^3$. Find the volume of a sphere with radius 4 in.
   b. Solve the formula in part (a) for r.
   c. Find to the nearest hundredth the radius of a sphere of volume 100 in.^{3}. **a–c. See margin p. 419.**

44. Open-Ended Write a relation rule that is not a function, but whose inverse is a function. **Check students' work.**

45. Measurement The time t in seconds for a swinging pendulum to complete one full cycle is given by the function $t = 0.2\sqrt{\ell}$, where ℓ is the length of the pendulum in cm. How long is a full cycle if the pendulum is 10 cm long? 20 cm long? **≈0.6 seconds; ≈0.9 seconds**

---

page 418 Chapter Test

22. $x^2 - 4x + 4$;
domain: all real numbers

23. $-2x^2 + 7x - 6$;
domain: all real numbers

24. $x - 1$,
domain: $\{x \mid x \neq 2\}$

25. $-x^3 + 5x^2 - 8x + 4$,
domain: all real numbers

26. $16x^2 + 8x - 1, 4x^2 - 7$

27. $18x^2 + 9x - 6$,
$-6x^2 - 3x + 20$

28. The sixth power of a real number is always nonnegative.

29b. $g(x) = 0.75x$

d. The cashier's solution is too high by 6.25% of the original price.

30. $y = 4\sqrt{x + 5} - 1$;
$y = 4\sqrt{x}$ translated 5 units left and 1 unit down

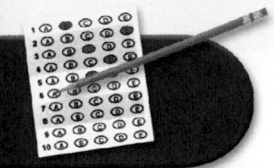

Standardized Test Prep

Reading Comprehension Read the passage below. Then answer the questions on the basis of what is *stated* or *implied* in the passage.

Boxing Match You can make an open box from a piece of flat cardboard. First, cut congruent squares from the four corners of the cardboard. Then, fold and tape the sides.

Let *x* equal the side of each congruent square. As *x* increases, so does the depth of the box. The usable area of cardboard decreases as *x* increases, and so do the length and width of the box.

What happens to the volume of the box? Does it increase or decrease as *x* increases? Would the answer *both* surprise you?

What size squares should you cut from the corners to maximize the volume of your box?

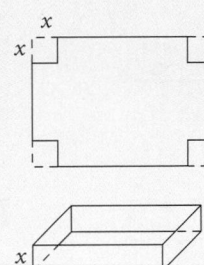

For Questions 1–6, consider a box made from a piece of cardboard that is 80 centimeters by 54 centimeters.

1. What are the dimensions of the box in centimeters? **C**
   A. $80 - x$, $54 - x$, x
   B. $80 - 2x$, $54 - 2x$, $2x$
   C. $80 - 2x$, $54 - 2x$, x
   D. $x - 80$, $x - 54$, x

2. Which function models the area of the cardboard after the corners are cut away? **H**
   F. $A(x) = (80 - 2x)(54 - 2x)$
   G. $A(x) = (80 - 2x)(54 - 2x) + 4x^2$
   H. $A(x) = 4320 - 4x^2$
   I. $A(x) = 4320 - 4(2x)^2$

3. By how much does the area of the cardboard decrease when *x* changes from 8 cm to 9 cm? **B**
   A. 145 cm^2 B. 68 cm^2
   C. 26 cm^2 D. 17 cm^2

4. Which function models the volume of the box? **H**
   F. $V(x) = (80 - x)(54 - x)x$
   G. $V(x) = (80 - x)(54 - x) + x$
   H. $V(x) = (80 - 2x)(54 - 2x)x$
   I. $V(x) = (80 - 2x) + (54 - 2x) + x$

5. What is a reasonable domain for *x*? **A**
   A. $0 \le x \le 27$
   B. $0 \le x \le 40$
   C. $0 \le x \le 54$
   D. all real numbers

6. Which is the best value for the maximum volume of the box? **G**
   F. about 20,440 cm^2
   G. about 20,444 cm^2
   H. about 20,450 cm^2
   I. about 20,452 cm^2

For Questions 7–9, consider a box made from a piece of cardboard that is 18 inches square.

7. Write a function that models the volume of the box. $V(x) = (18 - 2x)^2 x$

8. What is a reasonable domain for *x*? $0 \le x \le 9$

9. Find the maximum volume. Is this the maximum of the volume function? Explain. **See margin.**

10. **Open-Ended** Find the dimensions of three different rectangular pieces of cardboard you could use to make a box with volume 432 unit^3. **Check students' work.**

To answer the questions, students apply skills and concepts from this chapter and previous chapters.
Multiple Choice: Items 1–6
Extended Response: Items 7–10

Resources

Teaching Resources
Cumulative Review
Quarter 2 Test, Forms A & B
Mid-Course Test, Forms A & B

Reaching All Students
Spanish Cumulative Review
Spanish Quarter 2 Tests
Spanish Mid-Course Tests

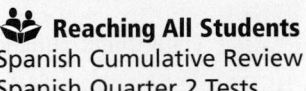
PRENTICE HALL ASSESSMENT SYSTEM

Standardized Test Prep
• Ch. 7 Standardized Test Practice
Assessment Masters
• Cumulative Review
• Quarter 2 Test, Forms A & B
• Mid-Course Test, Forms A & B
Computer Test Generator CD
• Standardized Test Practice

www.PHSchool.com
• Standardized Test Practice
• Resources

Plus  **i TEXT**

Cumulative Review

Cumulative Review
Chapters 1–7

For Exercises 1–12, choose the correct letters.

1. What is an equation for this graph?
   A. $y = (x + 3)^2 + 1$ B. $y = (x - 3)^2 + 1$
   C. $y = (x - 1)^2 - 3$ D. $y = (x - 1)^2 + 3$

2. Simplify $4^{\frac{3}{2}}$.
   A. 24   B. $\frac{9}{2}$ C. 6   D. 8

3. Which of the following represents three letters arranged in six permutations?
   I. $3 \cdot 2 \cdot 1$ II. $_3P_6$ III. $3!$ IV. $3(3 + 1)$
   A. I and II   B. III and IV   C. I and III   D. II and IV

4. Which of the following polynomials has roots 0, 1, and 2?
   A. $p(x) = x^2 + x + 2$ B. $p(x) = x^3 - 3x^2 + 2x$
   C. $p(x) = x^3 - 2x + 1$ D. $p(x) = x^2 + 2x$

5. Which expression represents a number of permutations equal to 720?
   A. $_7P_3$ B. $_{10}P_3$ C. $_9P_4$ D. $_6P_3$

6. Let $f(x) = x^2 + 5x - 2$ and $h(x) = x^2 - 2x - 6$. Which is the function rule for $h(x) + f(x)$?
   A. $2x^2 + 3x - 8$ B. $4x^2 + x - 8$ C. $-2x^2 + 3x - 2$ D. $2x^2 + x - 8$

7. Use a calculator to simplify $\frac{12!}{6!}$.
   A. 3!   B. 831,600   C. 19,958,400   D. 6

8. Which is the solution to $x^2 - 5x + 1 = 0$?

Algebra 2 Chapter 7   *Cumulative Review*   **37**

---

31. $y = 3\sqrt{x + \frac{1}{3}}$; $y = 3\sqrt{x}$
    translated $\frac{1}{3}$ unit left

39. $y = \sqrt[3]{\frac{x + 2}{3}}$; yes

40. $y = (x + 1)^2 - 3$;
    $x \ge -1$; yes

41. $y = \frac{x^2 - 1}{2}$, $x \ge 0$; yes

42. $y = \pm\sqrt[4]{4x}$, $x \ge 0$; no

43. a. $V = \frac{256\pi}{3} \approx 268.08$
    b. $r = \left(\frac{3V}{4\pi}\right)^{\frac{1}{3}}$
    c. $r \approx 2.88$ in.

page 419   Standardized Test Prep

9. 432 in.^{2}; no; as *x* gets bigger, $(18 - 2x)$ becomes a larger negative, so $(18 - 2x)^2 x$ is a large positive number.

Exponential and Logarithmic Functions

Chapter at a Glance

North Carolina Objectives

8-1
Exploring Exponential Models   2.03, 2.04

NCTM
1, 2, 7
▼ Exponential Growth
▼ Exponential Decay

8-2
Properties of Exponential Functions   2.03a, b

NCTM
1, 2
▼ Comparing Graphs
▼ The Number *e*

8-3
Logarithmic Functions as Inverses   1.01, 2.01

NCTM
1, 2, 7
▼ Writing and Evaluating Logarithmic Expressions
▼ Graphing Logarithmic Functions

8-4
Properties of Logarithms   1.01

NCTM
1, 2, 9
▼ Using the Properties of Logarithms

8-5
Exponential and Logarithmic Equations   1.01, 2.01

NCTM
1, 2, 6
▼ Solving Exponential Equations
▼ Solving Logarithmic Equations

8-6
Natural Logarithms   1.01, 2.01

NCTM
1, 2, 9,
10
▼ Natural Logarithms
▼ Natural Logarithmic and Exponential Equations

NCTM STANDARDS 2000

1 Number and Operations	6 Problem Solving
2 Algebra	7 Reasoning and Proof
3 Geometry	8 Communication
4 Measurement	9 Connections
5 Data Analysis and Probability	10 Representation

Pacing Options

This chart suggests pacing only for the lessons and their parts. It is provided as a possible guide. It will help you determine how much time you have in your schedule to cover other components, such as the features, Chapter Review, and Chapter Test.

Day	Traditional (45 min.)	Block (90 min.)
1	8-1 ▼	8-1 ▼
2	8-1 ▼	8-1 ▼ ▼
3	8-2 ▼	8-2 ▼ ▼
4	8-2 ▼	8-3 ▼ ▼
5	8-3 ▼	8-4 ▼
6	8-3 ▼	8-5 ▼ ▼
7	8-4 ▼	8-6 ▼ ▼
8	8-5 ▼	
9	8-5 ▼	
10	8-6 ▼	
11	8-6 ▼	

NAEP Correlation (National Assessment of Educational Progress 2000 Mathematics Objectives)

8-1	8-2	8-3	8-4	8-5	8-6
A5a, N5d, A3a	A5a, N5d, A3d	A5a, A3d, N5a	A5a, N3d, N4a	A5a, A6a, N4a	A5a, M5, N3d

N = Number Sense, Properties, and Operations; **M** = Measurement; **G** = Geometry and Spatial Sense;
D = Data Analysis, Statistics, and Probability; **A** = Algebra and Functions

Math Background

Chapter Overview

Most of the functions studied so far have involved a variable quantity raised to a power, as in $y = x^2$, $y = 4x^3$, or $y = x^{\frac{2}{3}}$. For such functions, there is a variable base and an exponent that is a constant. For *exponential functions*, these roles are reversed: the base is a constant and the exponent varies, as in $y = 2^x$. The most basic exponential functions have the form $y = b^x$, where $b > 0$ and $b \neq 1$. Inverses of such functions are also functions and are called *logarithmic functions*.

Important applications of exponential functions include population growth, depreciation, compound interest, and radioactive decay. Logarithmic functions are useful in describing the loudness of sounds and pH levels in chemistry.

Exploring Exponential Models   8-1

Exponential functions have the form $y = ab^x$, where $a \neq 0$, $b > 0$, and $b \neq 1$. In Lesson 7-4, positive and negative rational exponents were defined. Now the meaning of exponent is extended further to include irrational exponents, so that any exponential expression a^x, where $a > 0$, is defined for all real numbers x. This allows for the definition of *exponential function*. In Lesson 8-3, a *logarithmic function* is defined as the inverse of an exponential function. Important applications of exponential functions include population growth, radioactive decay, depreciation, and compound interest.

Properties of Exponential Functions   8-2

The irrational number e is defined as the limit of $\left(1 + \frac{1}{x}\right)^x$ as the value of x increases without bound. This limit is called e in honor of Swiss mathematician Leonhard Euler (1707–1783), who established it. (Incidentally, Euler's approval of the Greek letter π—another irrational number—for the ratio of the circumference to the diameter of a circle led to its conventional use.) Students can experiment with the definition of e by computing values for larger and larger values of x.

Logarithmic Functions as Inverses   8-3

Since the exponential function passes the horizontal line test, it is clear that its inverse is a function. A logarithmic function $y = \log_b x$ is defined as the inverse of an exponential function of the form $y = b^x$, where $b > 0$ and $b \neq 1$. The equations $y = b^x$

and $\log_b y = x$ are equivalent. Logarithms were discovered by John Napier (1550–1617) in response to the need to simplify complicated, time-consuming calculations that arose in astronomy and navigation. With graphing calculators, the user no longer has to be concerned with the complexities of the calculations, but the calculator itself uses logarithms to perform many of its internal calculations. Logarithms also remain of great importance because of their mathematical properties and the role they play in modeling real-world situations. Logarithmic scales are used to measure pH levels, decibel levels of sounds, and brightness of stars.

Properties of Logarithms   8-4

Students may be helped to a deeper understanding of the relationships between exponents and logarithms by discussing the table below.

Properties of Logarithms	Properties of Exponents
$\log_a (x \cdot y) = \log_a x + \log_a y$	$a^m \cdot a^n = a^{m+n}$
$\log_a \frac{x}{y} = \log_a x - \log_a y$	$\dfrac{a^m}{a^n} = a^{m-n}$
$\log_a x^p = p \cdot \log_a x$	$(a^m)^n = a^{m \cdot n}$

Exponential and Logarithmic Equations   8-5

A function is called a *one-to-one* function if it has an inverse that is also a function. The strategies of "taking the log of" both sides of an exponential equation and "exponentiating" both sides of a logarithmic equation are justified by the one-to-oneness of the logarithmic and exponential functions. It is true that:

> For any positive real numbers a, x, and y, with $a \neq 1$, $x = y$ is true iff $\log_a x = \log_a y$ or iff $a^x = a^y$.

Natural Logarithms   8-6

Natural logarithms often represent natural phenomena better than base 10 logarithms. The mathematical importance of natural logarithms will become much clearer to those students who go on to study calculus.

Ongoing Assessment and Intervention

Tools for Monitoring Student Progress

The Prentice Hall *Algebra 2* program provides you with many options for assessment in the Student Edition, the Teacher's Edition and the teaching resources. From these options you may choose instructional materials and techniques that are appropriate for your students and support your district's curriculum requirements.

Instant Check System™ in Chapter 8

Allows students to check their own learning before, during, and after each lesson.

Diagnosing Readiness before the chapter (p. 420)

Check Skills You'll Need exercises in each lesson (pp. 422, 431, 438, 446, 453, 462)

Check Understanding questions with each Example (pp. 422, 423, 424, 425, 426, 431, 432, 433, 434, 438, 439, 440, 441, 447, 448, 453, 454, 455, 456, 462, 463, 464)

Checkpoint Quiz (pp. 437, 460)

Test Prep in Chapter 8

Teaches students strategies and gives them practice with all the test item formats they will encounter on state tests and standardized national exams.

Standardized Test Prep exercises in each lesson (pp. 429, 436, 444, 451, 459, 466)

Test-Taking Strategies (p. 468)

Standardized Test Prep (p. 473)

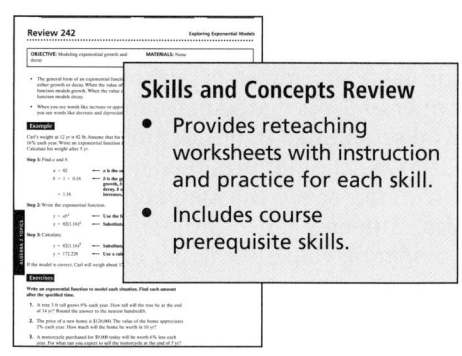

All your assessment needs in one place!

Program Assessment

Assess student progress throughout the *Algebra 2* text with blackline masters and CD-ROM.

Assessment Resources

- Checkpoint Quizzes 1 & 2
- Chapter Test, Forms A & B
- Chapter Alternative Assessment

Spanish versions available.

Computer Test Generator

- Unlimited questions of varying difficulty for every lesson objective.
- Create your own practice sheets, quizzes, and tests, or use the pre-made Chapter Tests.
- Diagnose readiness with questions on prerequisite skills.
- Prepare students by making tests based on standardized test objectives.
- Access Algebra 1, Geometry, and Algebra 2 content—all on one CD-ROM.

Test Preparation

A three-step approach to preparing students for high stakes, national, and state exams.

❶ Diagnose & Prescribe

Content Diagnostic Tests

- Diagnose strengths and weaknesses in content for national and state tests.
- Prescribe individualized reteaching opportunities.

❷ Review & Reteach

Skills and Concepts Review

- Provides reteaching worksheets with instruction and practice for each skill.
- Includes course prerequisite skills.

❸ Practice & Assess

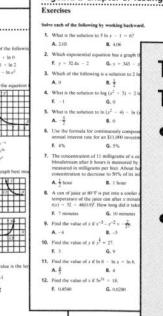

Test Preparation

- Features practice tests for End-of-Course and SAT/ACT exams.
- Includes standardized test practice by chapter for ongoing review.

Teacher's Guide with answers and correlations.

Test-Taking Strategies with Transparencies

- Support the Test-Taking Strategies pages in the Student Edition.
- Provide a teaching transparency and a practice worksheet for each strategy.

👥 Reaching All Students

Support in the Student Text and Additional Resources

The textbook, the iText, and other technology components provide numerous opportunities to reach students of various ability levels and learning styles. Each Teacher's Edition lesson suggests how you can help *all* your students be successful and understand the mathematics in Chapter 8.

Below Level

Student Edition
- Diagnosing Readiness*: p. 420
- Check Skills You'll Need*: pp. 422, 431, 438, 446, 453, 462

Reteaching
Chapter 8 Support File: pp. 8–13

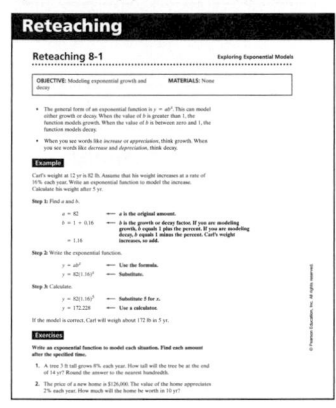

Advanced Learners

Student Edition
- Challenge exercises: pp. 428, 436, 443, 451, 459, 466
- Extension, p. 461

Enrichment
Chapter 8 Support File: pp. 14–19

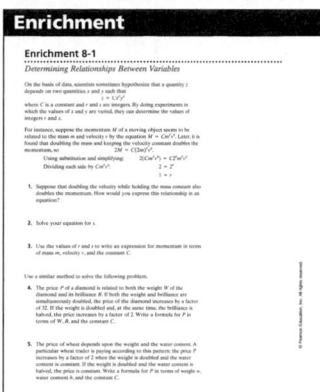

Connections to Precalculus Masters

Chapter 8 Enrichment Topic:
   Identity and Inverse Functions

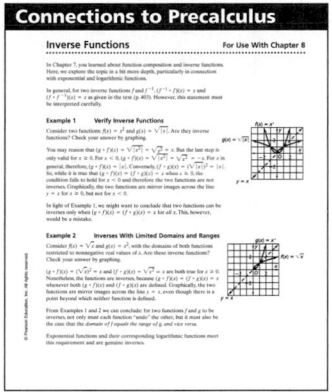

* Can be used with all ability levels to ensure mastery of prerequisite skills.

📖 Reading and Math Literacy

Student Edition
- Vocabulary: pp. 421, 469, *plus* in every Lesson Preview
- Reading Math: pp. 425, 426, 435, 439, 442, 445, 447, 462
- Illustrated Glossary: pp. 871–913

Reading and Math Literacy Masters
Chapter 8: pp. 29–32

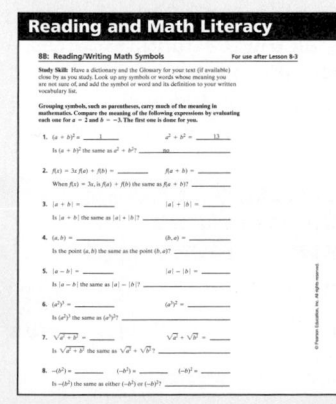

English Learners

Student Edition
- English/Spanish Illustrated Glossary: pp. 871–913

Workbook and Masters
Spanish Practice Workbook: pp. 2–7
Spanish Reading and Math Literacy Masters: pp. 29–32

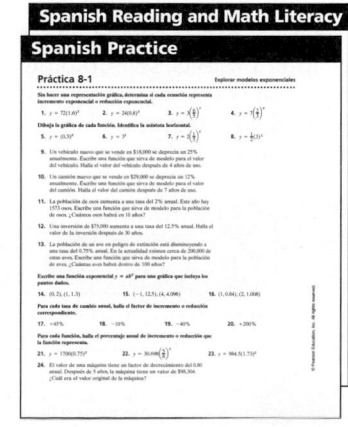

Learning Styles

Student Edition
- Investigation: pp. 424, 446
- Technology: pp. 430, 442, 452, 461, 464
- Writing: pp. 429, 430, 435, 442, 450, 457, 460, 461, 466, 472
- DK Activities: pp. 474–475

Activity Masters
Hands-On Activities: 47, 48
Technology Activities: 8, 11, 12, 30, 32

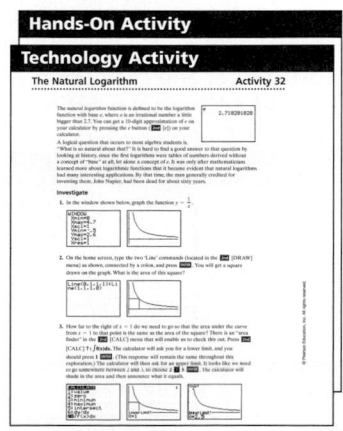

Program Resources

	Teaching Resources in Grab & Go™ Files				Resources for Reaching All Students			Spanish Resources			Transparencies				Presentation Assistant Plus!
	Practice	Reteach	Enrich	Checkpoint Quiz	Reading & Math Literacy	Technology Activities	Hands-On Activities	Practice	Reading & Math Literacy	Checkpoint Quiz	Skills Check	Additional Examples	Answers to Exercises	Lesson Quiz	Prentice Hall Presentation Pro CD-ROM
8-1	■	■	■		■			■	■		■	■	■	■	■
8-2	■	■	■	■	■	■		■		■	■	■	■	■	■
8-3	■	■	■					■			■	■	■	■	■
8-4	■	■	■					■			■	■	■	■	■
8-5	■	■	■	■	■	■	■	■		■	■	■	■	■	■
8-6	■	■	■			■					■	■	■	■	■
For the chapter	Chapter Tests, Alternative Assessment, Cumulative Review, Cumulative Assessment				Connections to Precalculus Masters			Spanish Chapter Tests, Alternative Assessment, Cumulative Review, Cumulative Assessment			Classroom Aid Transparencies				

Also available for use with the chapter:

 *See page 420C.*

- Practice Workbook
- Solution Key

- For teacher support and access to student Web site materials, use Web Code agk-5500.
- For additional online and technology resources, see below.

Technology

 **Online and on CD-ROM**

Complete Interactive Student Text online and on CD-ROM—with instant feedback assessment, tutorial help, dynamic activities, instructional and real-world videos, audio, and additional practice.

 www.PHSchool.com For Students

Use **Web Codes** for easy access to online activities, chapter projects, self-grading lesson quizzes and chapter tests, vocabulary quizzes, updated data sources, graphing calculator procedures, and more.

PH SuccessNet **For Teachers**

Online lesson planning with built-in state correlations, all the teaching resources, complete reference library, your own calendar and Teacher Web page, professional development, and more.

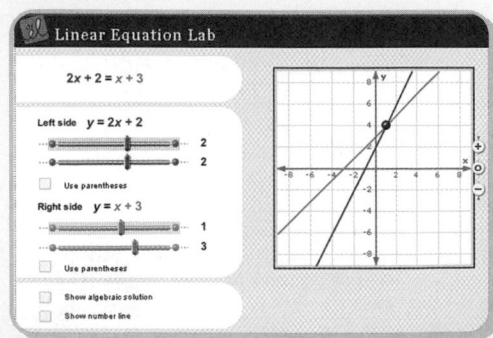

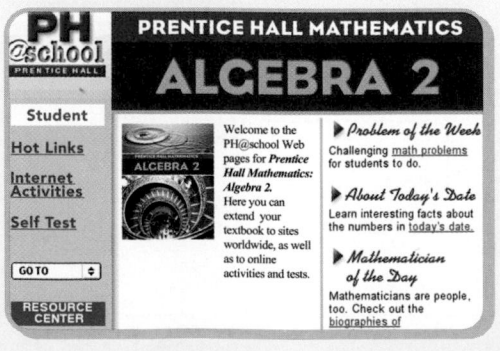

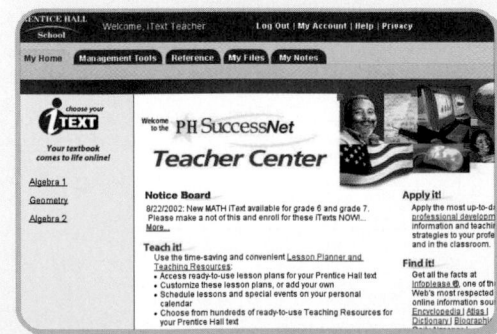

Presentation Assistant Plus!

The Prentice Hall *Presentation Assistant Plus!* provides you with the material you need to teach a lesson from beginning to end. Two easy-to-use formats—Transparencies and CD-ROM—allow you to present a lesson the way you are most comfortable.

Transparencies

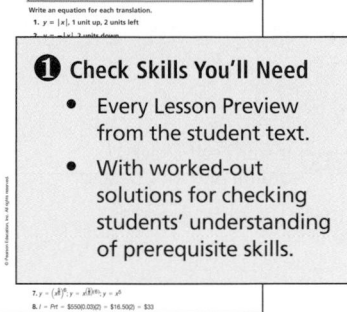

❶ Check Skills You'll Need
- Every Lesson Preview from the student text.
- With worked-out solutions for checking students' understanding of prerequisite skills.

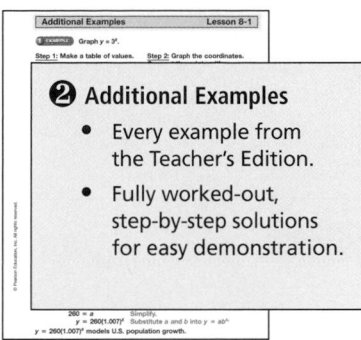

❷ Additional Examples
- Every example from the Teacher's Edition.
- Fully worked-out, step-by-step solutions for easy demonstration.

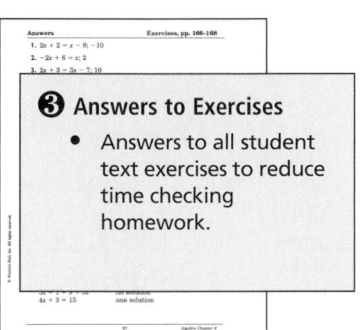

❸ Answers to Exercises
- Answers to all student text exercises to reduce time checking homework.

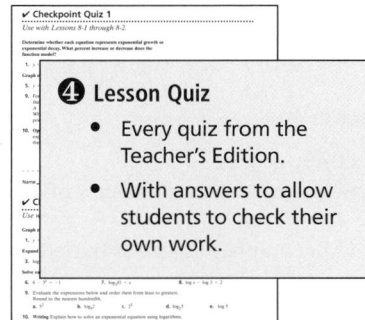

❹ Lesson Quiz
- Every quiz from the Teacher's Edition.
- With answers to allow students to check their own work.

Prentice Hall Presentation Pro CD-ROM

- Includes all Transparencies.
- Conveniently organized by lesson so you can easily ❶ Introduce, ❷ Teach, ❸ Check Homework, and ❹ Assess each lesson.
- Animated examples allow step-by-step instruction at your own pace.
- Easy to edit so you can create custom presentations.

Teaching Chapter 8 Using Presentation Assistant Plus!

	❶ Introduce	❷ Teach	❸ Check Homework	❹ Assess
	Check Skills You'll Need	Additional Examples	Student Edition Answers	Lesson Quiz
8-1	p. 52	pp. 156–159	✔	p. 139
8-2	p. 53	pp. 160–162	✔	p. 140
8-3	p. 54	pp. 163–165	✔	p. 141
8-4	p. 55	pp. 166–167	✔	p. 141
8-5	p. 56	pp. 168–171	✔	p. 142
8-6	p. 57	pp. 172–173	✔	p. 142

Throughout the Teacher's Edition, this symbol indicates material that is available on transparency in the Presentation Assistant Plus!

Prentice Hall Presentation Pro

CD-ROM with dynamic PowerPoint® presentations for every lesson. Helps you introduce and develop concepts, check homework, and assess progress. Part of Presentation Assistant Plus! *(See above.)*

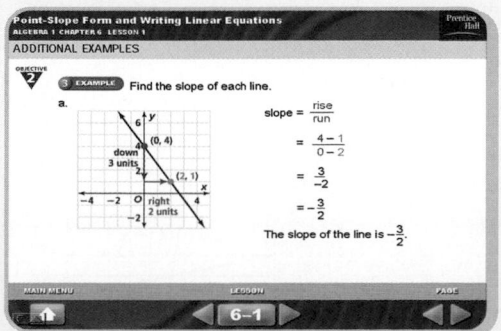

Computer Test Generator

CD-ROM to create practice sheets and tests for course objectives and standardized tests. Includes Instant Chapter Tests™, online testing, and student reports. Part of the PH Assessment System. *(See page 420C.)*

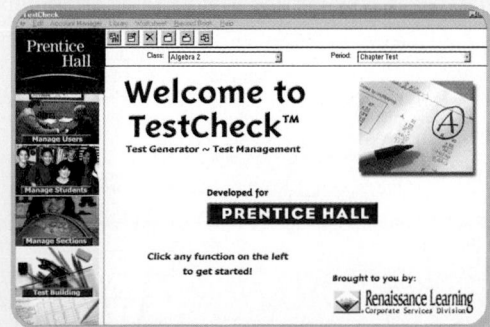

Resource Pro® with Planning Express®

CD-ROM with a lesson planning tool that allows you to import state and local objectives. Includes electronic versions of all the teaching resources.

Chapter 8

Exponential and Logarithmic Functions

✓ **Diagnosing Readiness**

Students will find answers to these exercises in the back of their textbooks.

For intervention, direct students to:

Evaluating Expressions
Lesson 1-2: Example 2
Exercises 1–8
Extra Practice, p. 822

Using Linear Models
Lesson 2-4: Example 1
Exercises 1–4
Extra Practice, p. 823

Using Quadratic Models
Lesson 5-1: Example 3
Exercises 16–20
Extra Practice, p. 826

Graphic Translations
Lesson 5-3: Example 4
Exercises 27–35
Extra Practice, p. 826

Graphing Inverse Functions
Lesson 7-7: Example 3
Exercises 11–16
Extra Practice, p. 828

page 420   Diagnosing Readiness

5. $y = x^2 - 4x$

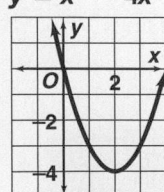

6. $y = 3x^2 - 2x + 7$

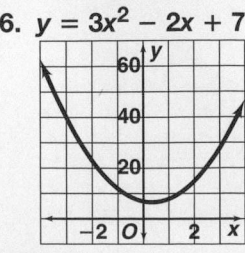

420

Where You've Been

- In Chapters 1 and 2, you learned to model linear functions and to solve linear equations.

- In Chapter 5, you learned to model quadratic functions and to solve quadratic equations.

- In Chapter 6, you learned to model polynomial functions and to solve polynomial equations.

- In Chapter 7, you learned to find and graph the inverse of a function.

 **Diagnosing Readiness**

i TEXT Instant self-check online and on CD-ROM

(For help, go to the Lesson in green.)

Evaluating Expressions (Lesson 1-2)

Evaluate each expression for $x = -2, -1, 0, 1,$ and 2.

1. 10^{x+1} **0.1, 1, 10, 100, 1000**   **2.** $\left(\frac{3}{2}\right)^x$ **$\frac{4}{9}, \frac{2}{3}, 1, \frac{3}{2}, \frac{9}{4}$**   **3.** $x^4 - x^2$ **12, 0, 0, 0, 12**

Using Linear Models (Lesson 2-4)

4a. $n = 3d$

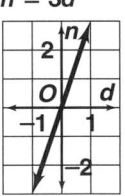

4. Each day, a squirrel buries three acorns.
   a. Write and graph a function to model the number n of acorns the squirrel buries in d days.
   b. Use your function to find the number of acorns buried in four weeks. **b. 84 acorns**
   c. Suppose the squirrel had started out with nine acorns already buried. Explain how this would change your function and its graph. **The function would be $n = 9 + 3d$ and the graph would shift 9 units upward.**

Using Quadratic Models (Lesson 5-1)

Find a quadratic function to model each set of values. Then graph the function.

5. $\{(0, 0), (2, -4), (3, -3)\}$ **6.** $\{(0, 7), (2, 15), (5, 72)\}$
   5–6. See margin.

Graphing Translations (Lesson 5-3)

Identify the parent function of each equation. Graph each equation as a translation of its parent function. **7–11. See margin pp. 420–421.**

7. $y = -(x - 1)^2 + 4$ **8.** $y = 3(x + 2)^2 - 1$

Graphing Inverse Functions (Lesson 7-7)

Graph each function and its inverse on a coordinate plane.

9. $y = -5x$ **10.** $y = \sqrt{5x + 12}$ **11.** $y = 2x^3$

7. $y = -x^2$

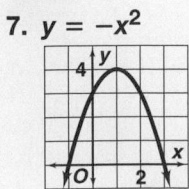

8. $y = 3x^2$

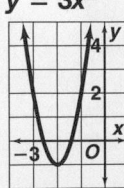

9.

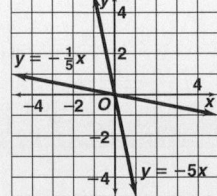

Exponential and Logarithmic Functions

LESSONS

Key Vocabulary

- asymptote (p. 425)
- Change of Base Formula (p. 453)
- common logarithm (p. 439)
- continuously compounded interest formula (p. 433)
- decay factor (p. 425)
- exponential equation (p. 453)
- exponential function (p. 422)
- growth factor (p. 422)
- logarithm (p. 439)
- logarithmic equation (p. 455)
- logarithmic function (p. 440)
- natural logarithmic function (p. 462)

Where You're Going

- In Chapter 8, you will learn to use exponential functions to model real-world data.

- You will learn to graph exponential functions and their inverses, logarithmic functions.

- You will learn to solve exponential and logarithmic equations.

Real-World Snapshots Applying what you learn, on pages 692–693 you will do activities involving world population.

Chapter 8 Overview

Students begin the chapter by exploring exponential models and properties of exponential functions. These lessons are followed by logarithmic functions as inverses, and properties of logarithms. Students continue in the chapter by learning about exponential and logarithmic equations, and conclude with a lesson on natural logarithms.

📖 **Reading Math**
Reading Data, p. 445

📖 **Vocabulary**
A complete list of terms, plus vocabulary exercises, appears in the Chapter Review, p. 469.

📖 **Illustrated Glossary**
Examples for each vocabulary term, plus definitions in both English and Spanish, appear starting on p. 871.

Real-World Snapshots
See pages 474–475 for a real-world application of exponential functions that utilizes Dorling Kindersley's (DK) unique graphic presentation.

Test-Taking Strategies
Working Backward, p. 468

🌐 **Real-World Connections**
Some of the applications you will find in this chapter are social studies (8-1), chemistry (8-3), noise control (8-4), and zoology (8-5).

💻 **www.PHSchool.com**
Internet support for this chapter includes:
- Self-grading Vocabulary and Chapter 8 Tests
- Chapter Project
- Chapter Planner
- Chapter 8 Resources

Plus 🔲**TEXT**

421

10.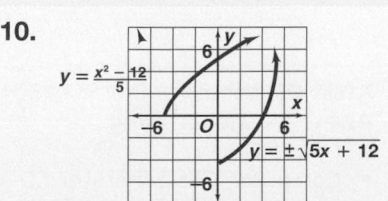
$$y = \frac{x^2 - 12}{5}$$
$$y = \pm\sqrt{5x + 12}$$

11.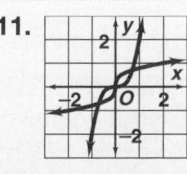

1. Plan

Lesson Preview

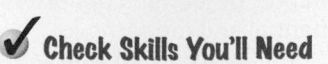 **Check Skills You'll Need**

Algebraic Expressions
Lesson 1-2: Examples 1, 2
Exercises 1–8
Extra Practice, p. 823

Lesson Resources

 **Teaching Resources**
Practice, Reteaching, Enrichment

Reaching All Students
Practice Workbook 8-1
Spanish Practice Workbook 8-1
Reading and Math Literacy 8A
Spanish Reading & Literacy 8A
Technology Activities 8, 11
Hands-On Activities 47

Presentation Assistant Plus!
Transparencies
• Check Skills You'll Need 8-1
• Additional Examples 8-1
• Student Edition Answers 8-1
• Lesson Quiz 8-1
PH Presentation Pro CD 8-1

 **ASSESSMENT SYSTEM**

Computer Test Generator CD

Technology
Resource Pro® CD-ROM
Computer Test Generator CD
Prentice Hall Presentation Pro CD

www.PHSchool.com
Updated Data
Student Site
• Teacher Web Code: agk-5500
• Graphing Calculator,
  Procedure 17
• Self-grading Lesson Quiz
Teacher Center
• Lesson Planner
• Resources

Plus iTEXT

 **8-1**

Exploring Exponential Models

2.03 Use exponential functions to model and solve problems.
2.04 Create and use best-fit mathematical models of exponential functions to solve problems involving sets of data.

Lesson Preview

What You'll Learn

OBJECTIVE **1** To model exponential growth

OBJECTIVE **2** To model exponential decay

. . . And Why

To model a car's depreciation, as in Example 6

 Check Skills You'll Need *(For help, go to Lesson 1-2.)*

Evaluate each expression for the given value of x.

1. 2^x for $x = 3$ **8**
2. 4^{x+1} for $x = 1$ **16**
3. 2^{3x+4} for $x = -1$ **2**
4. $3^x 3^{x-2}$ for $x = 2$ **9**
5. $\left(\frac{1}{2}\right)^x$ for $x = 0$ **1**
6. 2^x for $x = -2$ **$\frac{1}{4}$**

New Vocabulary
• exponential function • growth factor
• decay factor • asymptote

OBJECTIVE **1** **Exponential Growth**

Need Help?

If the value of a function depends on the value of x, then x is the independent variable.

For some data, the best model is a function that uses the independent variable as an exponent. An **exponential function** is a function with the general form $y = ab^x$, where x is a real number, $a \neq 0$, $b > 0$, and $b \neq 1$.

You can use an exponential function to model growth when $b > 1$. When $b > 1$, b is the **growth factor.**

Exponential Growth

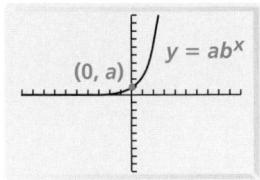

Growth factor $b > 1$

1a.
b.

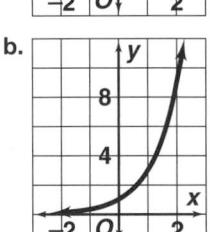

1 EXAMPLE **Graphing Exponential Growth**

Graph $y = 2^x$.

Step 1 Make a table of values.

x	2^x	y
−3	2^{-3}	$\frac{1}{8} = 0.125$
−2	2^{-2}	$\frac{1}{4} = 0.25$
−1	2^{-1}	$\frac{1}{2} = 0.5$
0	2^0	1
1	2^1	2
2	2^2	4
3	2^3	8

Step 2 Graph the coordinates. Connect the points with a smooth curve.

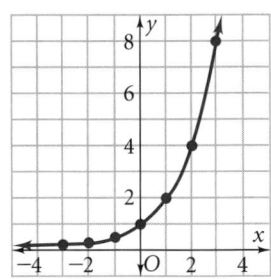

✓ **Check Understanding** **1** Graph each function. **a–b. See left.**

a. $y = 4(2)^x$
b. $y = 3^x$

422 Chapter 8 Exponential and Logarithmic Functions

Ongoing Assessment and Intervention

Before the Lesson
Diagnose prerequisite skills using:
• Check Skills You'll Need

During the Lesson
Monitor progress using:
• Check Understanding
• Additional Examples
• Standardized Test Prep

After the Lesson
Assess knowledge using:
• Lesson Quiz
• Computer Test Generator CD

You can use an exponential function to model population growth. If you know the rate of increase r, you can find the growth factor by using the equation $b = 1 + r$.

2 EXAMPLE   Real-World 🌐 Connection

Population Refer to the graph. In 2000, the annual rate of increase in the U.S. population was about 1.24%.
a. Find the growth factor for the U.S. population.
b. Suppose the rate of increase continues to be 1.24%. Write a function to model U.S. population growth.

Real-World 🌐 Connection

The United States counts its population every 10 years.

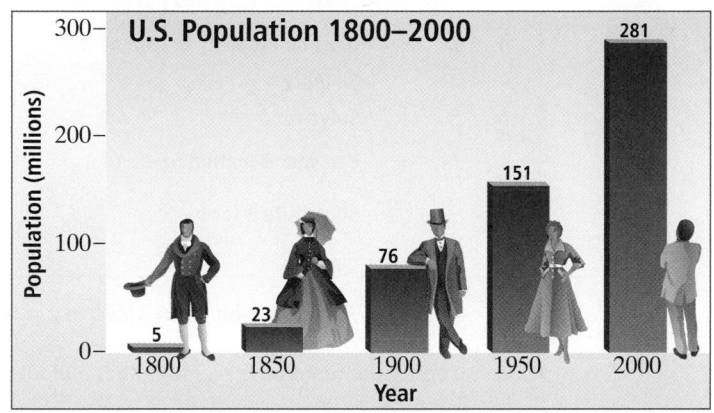

U.S. Population 1800–2000

SOURCE: U.S. Census Bureau. Go to **www.PHSchool.com** for a data update. Web Code: agg-2041

a. Find the growth factor.

$b = 1 + r$

$\quad = 1 + 0.0124$ **Substitute 1.24%, or 0.0124, for r.**

$\quad = 1.0124$ **Simplify.**

b. Write a function.

Relate The population increases exponentially, so use the general form of an exponential function, $y = ab^x$.

Define Let $\boxed{x}$ = number of years after 2000.

Let $\boxed{y}$ = the population in millions.

Write $\boxed{y} = a(1.0124)^x$

$281 = a(1.0124)^0$ **To find a, substitute the 2000 values: $y = 281$, $x = 0$.**

$281 = a \cdot 1$ **Any number to the zero power equals 1.**

$281 = a$ **Simplify.**

$y = 281(1.0124)^x$ **Substitute a and b into $y = ab^x$.**

● The function $y = 281(1.0124)^x$ models U.S. population growth.

✓ Check Understanding **2 a.** Predict U.S. population in 2015 to the nearest million. **about 338 million**
b. **Critical Thinking** Explain why the model and your prediction may not be valid for 2015. **The growth factor may change.**
c. Suppose the rate of population increase changes to 1.4%. Write a function to model population growth and use it to predict the 2015 population to the nearest million. $y = 281 (1.014)^x$; **about 346 million**

2. Teach

Professional Development

Math Background

Exponential functions model data that have a constant percent increase or a constant percent decrease. This should not be confused with a constant rate of change, which linear functions have. Informally, a constant percent increase or decrease guarantees that the data grow or decay rapidly.

OBJECTIVE
1 ▼ Teaching Notes

1 EXAMPLE **Alternative Method**

Rather than having students sketch the graph, ask them to use a graphing calculator to graph the function. Then ask them to draw on graph paper what they see in the viewing window. They can use the TABLE feature to find points on the curve.

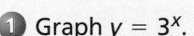 **Additional Examples**

❶ Graph $y = 3^x$.

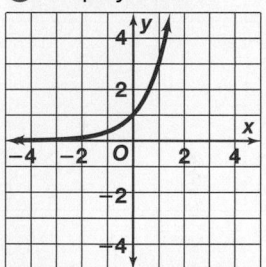

❷ The population of the United States in 1994 was about 260 million with an average annual rate of increase of about 0.7%.
a. Find the growth factor for that year. **1.007**
b. Suppose the rate of growth had continued to be 0.7%. Write a function to model this population growth. $y = 260(1.007)^x$ **(in millions)**

👥 Reaching All Students

Below Level Have students use their graphing calculators to graph $y = 2^x$ and $y = \left(\frac{1}{2}\right)^x$. How do these graphs compare? Are they inverses of each other? Discuss growth and decay factors.	**Advanced Learners** Some futurists predict that information growth will become so rapid no one can keep up. Students may be interested in researching this idea.	**English Learners** See note on page 425. **Error Prevention** See note on page 427.

 **EXAMPLE** **Math Tip**

Ask a student volunteer to remind the class of the Division Property of Exponents.

Additional Example

❸ Write an exponential function $y = ab^x$ for a graph that includes (1, 6) and (0, 2). $y = 2 \cdot 3^x$

Investigation (Optional)
Make sure students understand that two teams compete in each game. Also tell students that only teams that win go on to play in the following round. In other words, 64 teams pair off to play 32 games in the first round. Then 32 teams pair off to play the second round. This pattern repeats. There must be a winner for each game, so there are no ties.

page 424 Investigation

2a.

After Round x	Number of Teams Left in Tournament (y)
0	64
1	32
2	16
3	8
4	4
5	2
6	1

b.

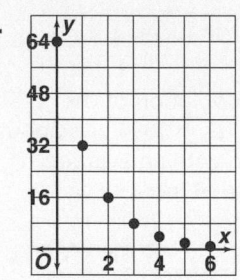

You can write an exponential function from two points on the function's graph.

❸ **EXAMPLE** **Writing an Exponential Function**

Write an exponential function $y = ab^x$ for a graph that includes (2, 2) and (3, 4).

$y = ab^x$	Use the general form.
$2 = a \cdot b^2$	Substitute for x and y using (2, 2).
$\frac{2}{b^2} = a$	Solve for a.
$y = ab^x$	Use the general form.
$4 = \frac{2}{b^2} b^3$	Substitute for x and y using (3, 4) and for a using $\frac{2}{b^2}$.
$4 = 2b^{3-2}$	Division Property of Exponents
$4 = 2b$	Simplify.
$b = 2$	Solve for b.
$a = \frac{2}{b^2}$	Use your equation for a.
$a = \frac{2}{2^2}$	Substitute 2 for b.
$a = \frac{1}{2}$	Simplify.
$y = \frac{1}{2} \cdot 2^x$	Substitute $\frac{1}{2}$ for a and 2 for b in $y = ab^x$.

The exponential function for a graph that includes (2, 2) and (3, 4) is $y = \frac{1}{2} \cdot 2^x$.

✔ **Check Understanding** ❸ Write an exponential function $y = ab^x$ for a graph that includes (2, 4) and (3, 16). $y = 0.25(4)^x$

OBJECTIVE
2 **Exponential Decay**

Real-World 🌐 Connection

On a day in March, the NCAA announces the selection of 64 teams for its annual tournament.

4. No; the change from one point to the next is not constant.

Investigation: Tournament Play

The National Collegiate Athletic Association (NCAA) holds an annual basketball tournament. The top 64 teams in Division I are invited to play each spring. When a team loses, it is out of the tournament.

1. How many teams are left in the tournament after the first round of basketball games? **32 teams**

2. a. Copy, complete, and extend the table until only one team is left. **a–b. See margin.**
   b. Graph the points from your table on graph paper.

After Round x	Number of Teams Left in Tournament (y)
0	64
1	■
2	■

3. How many rounds are played in the tournament? **6 rounds**

4. Does the graph represent a linear function? Explain.

5. How does the number of teams left in each round compare to the number of teams in the previous round? **There are half as many teams as in the previous round.**

An exponential function can be used to model decay when $0 < b < 1$. When $b < 1$, b is a **decay factor**.

Exponential Decay

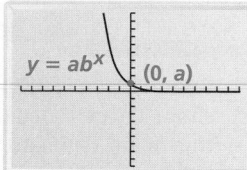

Decay factor $b < 1$

4 EXAMPLE — Analyzing a Function

4 EXAMPLE — Analyzing a Function

Without graphing, determine whether the function $y = 14(0.95)^x$ represents exponential growth or exponential decay.

In $y = 14(0.95)^x$, $b = 0.95$. Since $b < 1$, the function represents exponential decay.

 Check Understanding 4 Without graphing, determine whether each function represents exponential growth or exponential decay.

a. $y = 100(0.12)^x$ **b.** $y = 0.2(5)^x$ **c.** $y = 16\left(\frac{1}{2}\right)^x$

exponential decay   **exponential growth**   **exponential decay**

An **asymptote** is a line that a graph approaches as x or y increases in absolute value.

> **Reading Math**
>
> In the word asymptote, *asym* means "not together."

5 EXAMPLE — Graphing Exponential Decay

Graph $y = 24\left(\frac{1}{2}\right)^x$. Identify the horizontal asymptote.

Step 1 Make a table of values.

x	−3	−2	−1	0	1	2	3
y	192	96	48	24	12	6	3

Step 2 Graph the coordinates. Connect the points with a smooth curve.

5a.

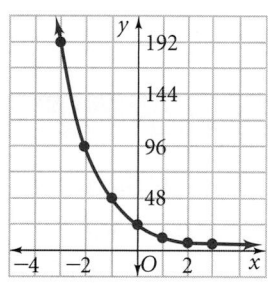

As x increases, y approaches 0.

The asymptote is the x-axis, $y = 0$.

Check Understanding 5 Graph each decay function. Identify the horizontal asymptote. **For graphs, see left.**

a. $y = 24\left(\frac{1}{3}\right)^x$ **y = 0**   **b.** $y = 100(0.1)^x$ **y = 0**

Lesson 8-1 Exploring Exponential Models   **425**

4 EXAMPLE — English Learners

Direct students to a dictionary or thesaurus to look up synonyms for *decay* (samples: decline, decrease, rot). Explain that the mathematical meaning of this word—decrease—is the opposite of growth.

5 EXAMPLE — Teaching Tip

Discuss the fact that as the y-values decrease, the graph approaches the asymptote without ever touching it. Have students substitute 0 for y to get $0 = 24\left(\frac{1}{4}\right)^x$. The next step in solving for x is to divide 0 by 24, resulting in $0 = \left(\frac{1}{4}\right)^x$. Ask students what power of $\frac{1}{4}$ equals 0. **No power of $\frac{1}{4}$ equals 0.** Thus, y cannot equal 0, and the graph will never intercept the x-axis.

Additional Examples

4 Without graphing, determine whether the function $y = 3\left(\frac{2}{3}\right)^x$ represents exponential growth or exponential decay. **decay**

5 Graph $y = 36(0.5)^x$. Identify the horizontal asymptote. **y = 0**

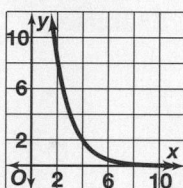

425

 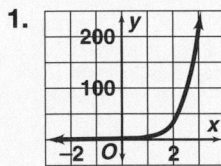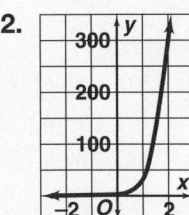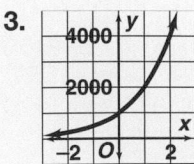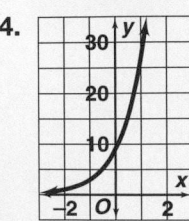
Reading Math

Depreciate comes from a prefix meaning "lower" and a root meaning "price."

Depreciation is the decline in an item's value resulting from age or wear. When an item loses about the same percent of its value each year, you can use an exponential function to model the depreciation.

6 **EXAMPLE**   **Real-World 🌐 Connection**

Depreciation The exponential decay graph shows the expected depreciation for a car over four years. Estimate the value of the car after six years.

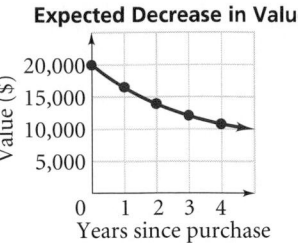
Expected Decrease in Value

The decay factor b equals $1 + r$, where r is the annual rate of decrease. The initial value of the car is $20,000. After one year the value of the car is about $17,000.

$r = \dfrac{\text{final value} - \text{initial value}}{\text{initial value}}$ **Write an equation for r.**

$= \dfrac{17,000 - 20,000}{20,000}$ **Substitute.**

$= -0.15$ **Simplify.**

$b = 1 + r$ **Use r to find b.**

$= 1 + (-0.15) = 0.85$ **Simplify.**

Write a function, and then evaluate it for $x = 6$.

Relate The value of the car decreases exponentially; $b = 0.85$.

Define Let x = number of years. Let y = value of the car.

Write $y = ab^x$

$20,000 = a(0.85)^0$ **Substitute using (0, 20,000).**

$20,000 = a$ **Solve for a.**

$y = 20,000(0.85)^x$ **Substitute a and b into $y = ab^x$.**

$y = 20,000(0.85)^6$ **Evaluate for $x = 6$.**

≈ 7542.99 **Simplify.**

The car's value after six years will be about $7540.

✔ **Check Understanding** **6** Estimate the value of the car after 10 years. **about $3900**

EXERCISES

For more practice, see *Extra Practice.*

Practice and Problem Solving

A **Practice by Example**

Graph each function. **1–8. See margin.**

Example 1
(page 422)

1. $y = 6^x$ **2.** $y = 3(10)^x$ **3.** $y = 1000(2)^x$ **4.** $y = 9(3)^x$

5. $f(x) = 2(3)^x$ **6.** $s(t) = 1.5^t$ **7.** $y = 8(5)^x$ **8.** $y = 2^{2x}$

Example 2
(page 423)

9. Population The world population in 2000 was approximately 6.08 billion. The annual rate of increase was about 1.26%.
  a. Find the growth factor for the world population. **1.0126**
  b. Suppose the rate of increase continues to be 1.26%. Write a function to model world population growth. **$y = 6.08(1.0126)^x$, where $x = 0$ corresponds to 2000**

5.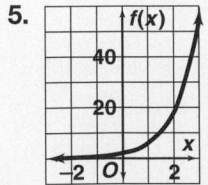

6.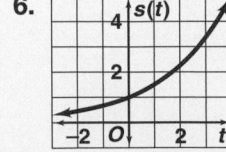

7.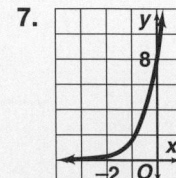

8.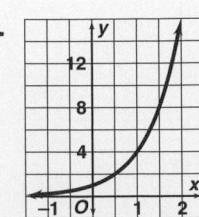

Example 3
(page 424)

Write an exponential function $y = ab^x$ for a graph that includes the given points.

10. $(4, 8), (6, 32)$ $y = 0.5(2)^x$ 11. $(2, 122.5), (3, 857.5)$ $y = 8(1.5)^x$ 12. $(2, 18), (5, 60.75)$
$y = 2.5(7)^x$

13. $\left(-1, 8\frac{1}{3}\right), (2, 1.8)$ 14. $(-3, 24), (-2, 12)$ 15. $(0, 24), \left(3, \frac{8}{9}\right)$
$y = 5(0.6)^x$ $y = 3(0.5)^x$ $y = 24\left(\frac{1}{3}\right)^x$

Example 4
(page 425)

Without graphing, determine whether each function represents exponential growth or exponential decay.   16–23. See below left.

16. $y = 129(1.63)^x$ 17. $f(x) = 2(0.65)^x$ 18. $y = 12\left(\frac{17}{10}\right)^x$ 19. $y = 0.8\left(\frac{1}{8}\right)^x$

20. $f(x) = 4\left(\frac{5}{6}\right)^x$ 21. $y = 0.45 \cdot 3^x$ 22. $y = \frac{1}{100}\left(\frac{4}{3}\right)^x$ 23. $f(x) = 2^{-x}$

Example 5
(page 425)

Graph each function. Identify the horizontal asymptote.   24–31. See back of book.

24. $y = (0.75)^x$ 25. $y = 2(0.5)^x$ 26. $y = (0.25)^x$ 27. $g(x) = 5(0.2)^x$

28. $f(x) = \left(\frac{1}{5}\right)^x$ 29. $y = 81\left(\frac{1}{3}\right)^x$ 30. $s(t) = \left(\frac{1}{10}\right)^t$ 31. $y = \frac{1}{2}\left(\frac{1}{2}\right)^x$

Example 6
(page 426)

Write an exponential function for each graph. Evaluate the function for $x = 6$.

16.   exponential growth

17.   exponential decay

18.   exponential growth

19.   exponential decay

20.   exponential decay

21.   exponential growth

22.   exponential growth

23.   exponential decay

32.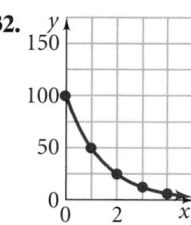

33.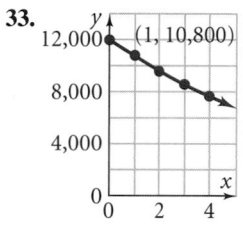

34.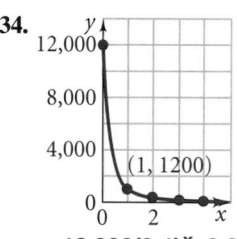

$y = 100(0.5)^x$; 1.5625 $y = 12,000(0.9)^x$; 6377 $y = 12,000(0.1)^x$; 0.012

35. **Business** A computer valued at $6500 depreciates at the rate of 14.3% per year.
   a. Write a function that models the value of the computer. $y = 6500(0.857)^x$
   b. Find the value of the computer after three years. $4091.25

B Apply Your Skills 36. **Social Studies** The table below shows information about the population of the four largest cities in the world in 2000.

World's Largest Cities

Rank in 2000	City	2000 Population	Projected Average Annual Growth
1	Tokyo, Japan	26,444,000	0.00%
2	Mexico City, Mexico	18,131,000	0.39%
3	Bombay, India	18,066,000	2.51%
4	São Paulo, Brazil	17,755,000	0.94%

SOURCE: *The World Almanac*

36a. Tokyo: 26,444,000, Mexico City: 18,850,649, Bombay: 23,148,579, São Paulo: 19,496,367

   a. Using the appropriate projected growth rate, project the population of each city for the year 2010.   **See left.**
   b. According to your prediction, does the order of the cities' ranks change by 2010? If so, rank the cities in order.   **yes; Tokyo, Bombay, São Paulo, Mexico City**

For each function, find the annual percent increase or decrease that the function models.   37–42. See margin.

37. $y = 1298(1.63)^x$ 38. $y = 0.65(1.3)^x$ 39. $f(x) = 2(0.65)^x$

40. $y = 12\left(\frac{17}{10}\right)^x$ 41. $y = 0.8\left(\frac{1}{8}\right)^x$ 42. $y = 16\left(\frac{1}{4}\right)^x$

Lesson 8-1 Exploring Exponential Models   **427**

37. 63% increase   40. 70% increase

38. 30% increase   41. 87.5% decrease

39. 35% decrease   42. 75% decrease

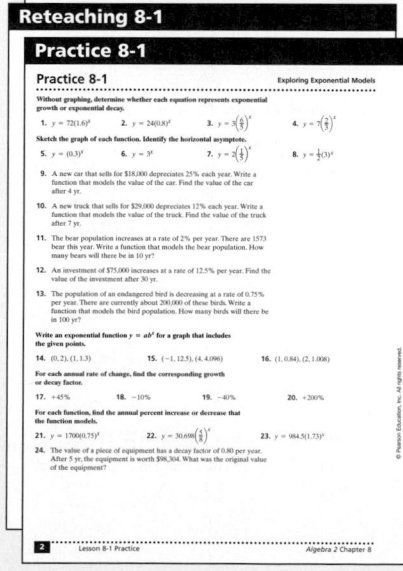

Sketch the graph of each function. Identify the horizontal asymptote.

1. $y = (0.8)^x$ $y = 0$

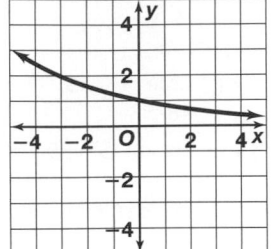

2. $y = \left(\frac{1}{4}\right)^x$ $y = 0$

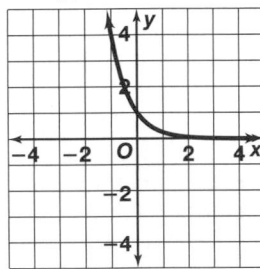

Without graphing, determine whether each equation represents exponential growth or decay.

3. $y = 15(7)^x$ **growth**

4. $y = 1285(0.5)^x$ **decay**

Write an exponential function for a graph that includes the given points.

5. $(0, 0.5), (1, 3)$ $y = 0.5(6)^x$

6. $(-1, 5), (0.5, 40)$ $y = 20(4)^x$

Alternative Assessment

List various growth and decay functions. Instruct each student to write down whether the function is for growth or decay, and then sketch the function. Let students compare answers. Repeat.

pages 426–429 Exercises

59a. A negative growth rate would be represented by adding the negative rate to 1.

Real-World 🌐 Connection

Careers Oceanographers model conditions on the ocean floor, interactions between plant and animal life, and the impact of pollution on seawater.

44. $y = 30,000(0.7)^x$ for car 1, $y = 15,000(0.8)^x$ for car 2; car 2 will be worth more.

45a. $y = 80(0.965)^x$

b.

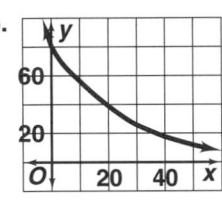

about 47 years

54. $y = 34(1.26)^x$, where x represents the number of years since 1995.

ⓒ Challenge

43. Oceanography The function $y = 20 \cdot 0.975^x$ models the intensity of sunlight beneath the surface of the ocean. The output y represents the percent of surface sunlight intensity that reaches a depth of x feet. The model is accurate from about 20 feet to about 600 feet beneath the surface. **5.6%**
  a. Find the percent of sunlight 50 feet beneath the surface of the ocean.
  b. Find the percent of sunlight at a depth of 370 ft. **0.0017%**

🌐 44. a. Depreciation Each graph below shows the expected decrease in a car's value over the next five years. Write a function to model each car's depreciation. Determine which car will be worth more after 10 years.
See below left.

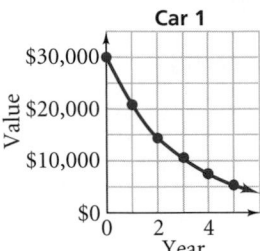
Car 1

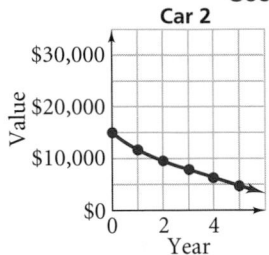
Car 2

  b. Data Collection Find the initial value and the expected decrease in value of your favorite type of car. Write an exponential function to model the car's depreciation. **Check students' work.**

45. The population of a certain animal species decreases at a rate of 3.5% per year. You have counted 80 of the animals in the habitat you are studying. **a–b. See left.**
  a. Write a function that models the change in the animal population.
  b. Graph the function. Estimate the number of years until the population first drops below 15 animals.

For each annual rate of change, find the corresponding growth or decay factor.

46. $+70\%$ **1.70**   **47.** $+500\%$ **6**   **48.** -75% **0.25**   **49.** -55% **0.45**

50. $+12.5\%$ **1.125** **51.** -0.1% **0.999** **52.** $+0.1\%$ **1.001** **53.** $+100\%$ **2**

🌐 54. Communications Cellular phone usage grew about 26% each year from 1995 (about 34 million) to 1999. Write a function to model U.S. cellular phone usage over that time period. **See left.**

55. Open-Ended Write a problem that could be modeled with $y = 20(1.1)^x$. **Check students' work.**

56. The value of an industrial machine has a decay factor of 0.75 per year. After six years, the machine is worth $7500. What was the original value of the machine?
about $42,140

🌐 57. Zoology Determine which situation best matches the graph.
  A. A population of 120 cougars decreases 98.75% yearly.
  B. A population of 125 cougars increases 1.25% yearly.
  C. A population of 115 cougars decreases 1.25% yearly.
  D. A population of 200 cougars decreases 50% yearly.
C

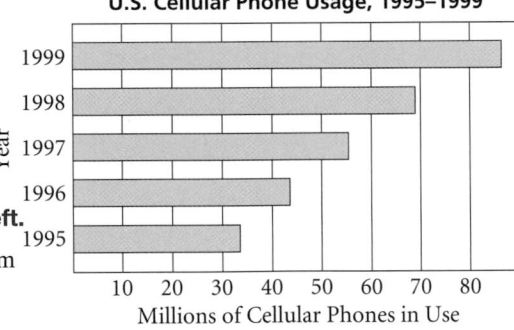
U.S. Cellular Phone Usage, 1995–1999

SOURCE: The CTIA Semi-Annual Wireless Survey

b. Armenia: $y = 9.2(1.06)^x$,
Canada: $y = 688.3(1.03)^x$,
Oman: $y = 18.6(0.915)^x$,
Paraguay: $y = 19.8(0.995)^x$.

x in each equation represents the number of years since 1998.

c. Armenia: $13.8 billion,
Canada: $846.5 billion,
Oman: $10.0 billion,
Paraguay: $19.1 billion.

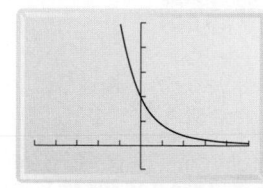

58. Critical Thinking Analyze the graph at the left to determine which function the graph represents. Explain your reasoning. **See left.**

A. $y = \left(\frac{1}{3}\right)2^x$ **B.** $y = 2\left(\frac{1}{3}\right)^x$ **C.** $y = -2\left(\frac{1}{3}\right)^x$

58. B; the graph shows a decreasing function, which eliminates A. The y-values are all positive, which eliminates C.

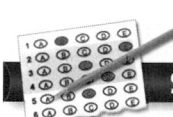 **59. Economics** The table gives the 1998 gross domestic product and the real growth rate for several countries.

 a. Writing Explain how a negative growth rate affects the equation for an exponential model.

b. Write a function for each country to model the GDP.

c. Suppose the given real growth rates continue. Predict the gross domestic product for each country in 2005.
a–c. See margin p. 428.

Domestic Product Growth Rates

Country	1998 Gross Domestic Product (billions)	1998 Real Growth Rate
Armenia	$9.2	6%
Canada	$688.3	3%
Oman	$18.6	−8.5%
Paraguay	$19.8	−0.5%

SOURCE: *Time Almanac*

Standardized Test Prep

Multiple Choice

60. Which function represents exponential growth? **C**
A. $y = 35x^{1.35}$ **B.** $y = 35 \cdot (0.35)^x$
C. $y = 35 \cdot (1.35)^x$ **D.** $y = 35 \div (1.35)^x$

Take It to the NET
Online lesson quiz at
www.PHSchool.com
······· Web Code: aga-0801

61. Which function represents the value after x years of a delivery van that was purchased new for $17,500 and depreciates 11% each year? **H**
F. $y = -11(17,500)^x$ **G.** $y = 17,500(0.11)^x$
H. $y = 17,500(0.89)^x$ **I.** $y = 17,500(1.11)^x$

62. What is the equation of the asymptote of $y = 15 \cdot \left(\frac{1}{3}\right)^x$? **B**
A. $y = 1$ **B.** $y = 0$ **C.** $y = x$ **D.** $y = \frac{1}{3}$

Short Response

63. Sketch the graph of the function $y = 2 \cdot \left(\frac{1}{4}\right)^x$. **See back of book.**

Extended Response

64. Write an exponential equation in the form $y = ab^x$ for a graph that includes $(2, 54)$ and $\left(\frac{1}{2}, 2\right)$. Show your work. **See back of book.**

Mixed Review

Lesson 7-8 Graph each function. **65–67. See margin.**
65. $y = \sqrt{x + 2}$ **66.** $y = -2\sqrt[3]{x} + 4$ **67.** $y = \sqrt{9x - 153} - 5$

Lesson 7-2 Simplify each expression.
68. $\sqrt{180n^5}$ **69.** $3\sqrt[3]{72r^5} \cdot 2\sqrt[3]{343r^3}$ **70.** $\frac{\sqrt{64x^4}}{\sqrt{144x^5}}$ $\frac{2\sqrt{x}}{3x}$
$6n^2\sqrt{5n}$ $84r^2\sqrt[3]{9r^2}$

Lesson 6-2 Construct a polynomial function with the given zeros. **Answers may vary. Samples are given.**
71. $x = 0, 1, 4$ **72.** $x = -2, -1, 3$ **73.** $x = 5, 0, 2$
$y = x^3 - 5x^2 + 4x$ $y = x^3 - 7x - 6$ $y = x^3 - 7x^2 + 10x$

Lesson 5-2 Each point lies on a parabola with vertex $(0, 2)$. Write the equation of the parabola.

74–81. See margin.
74. $(1, 3)$ **75.** $(1, -3)$ **76.** $(-1, 4)$ **77.** $(2, 42)$
78. $(-2, 8)$ **79.** $(-1, 5)$ **80.** $(2, 0)$ **81.** $(2, -2)$

Standardized Test Prep

Resources
For additional practice with a variety of test item formats:
• Standardized Test Prep, p. 473
• Test-Taking Strategies, p. 468
• Test-Taking Strategies with Transparencies

Error Prevention

Exercise 61 It can save time to find one part of the answer choices that is unique to each one, then use just that part to help find the correct choice. You must be sure that the part you are comparing can "stand alone," or is not affected by other parts of the answer choice. Since all of the decay factors are different and are not affected by other parts of the equation, find the one that represents $100\% - 11\%$.

65.
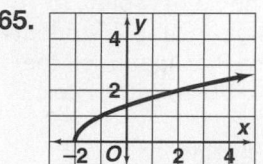

66.
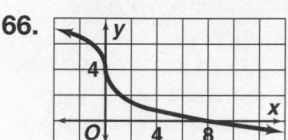

67.
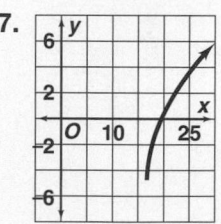

74. $y = x^2 + 2$
75. $y = -5x^2 + 2$
76. $y = 2x^2 + 2$
77. $y = 10x^2 + 2$
78. $y = \frac{3}{2}x^2 + 2$
79. $y = 3x^2 + 2$
80. $y = -\frac{1}{2}x^2 + 2$
81. $y = -x^2 + 2$

Technology

Fitting Exponential Curves to Data

Students use a graphing calculator to find the exponential function that best fits a given set of data points.

Resources

Students may use any graphing calculator.

Teaching Notes

Technology Tip

Remind students to clear the lists before starting a new plot. To plot the points in Step 2, students must turn on Plot 1, and tell the calculator to use a scatter plot.

Error Prevention

Have students work with a partner. After each step, such as entering a list, or plotting points, encourage partners to compare windows to make sure that they have not made an error.

page 430 Technology

1. $y = 6.25(0.5)^x$

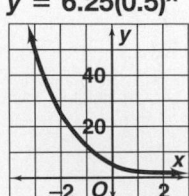

2. $y = 2.0(1.2)^x$

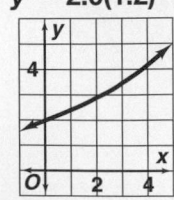

430

Technology | **Fitting Exponential Curves to Data**

FOR USE WITH LESSON 8-1

You can use your graphing calculator to fit an exponential curve to data and find the exponential function.

Take It to the NET
Graphing Calculator procedures online at **www.PHSchool.com**
Web Code: age-2123

EXAMPLE

The table at the right shows the number of degrees above room temperature for a cup of coffee after x minutes of cooling. Graph the data. Find the best-fitting exponential function.

Step 1 Press [STAT] [ENTER] to enter the data in lists.

Step 2 Use the **STAT PLOT** feature to plot the points.

Step 3 Find the equation for the best-fitting exponential function. Press [STAT] [▶] 0 [ENTER] to use the **ExpReg** feature. The line of best fit can be approximated by $f(x) = 133.458 (0.942)^x$.

```
ExpReg
 y=a*b^x
 a=133.4584506
 b=.942405561
 r=-.9997925841
```

Step 4 Graph the function. Press [Y=] [CLEAR] [VARS] 5 [▶] [▶] [ENTER] to enter the **ExpReg** results. Press [GRAPH] to display the data and the function together. Press [ZOOM] 9 to automatically adjust the window.

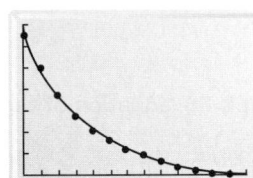

Cooling Coffee

Time (min)	°F Above Room Temperature
0	135
5	100
10	74
15	55
20	41
25	30
30	22
35	17
40	12
45	9
50	7
55	5
60	4

EXERCISES

Use a graphing calculator to find the exponential function that best fits each set of data. Graph each function. Sketch your graph.   **1–4. See margin.**

1.

x	−3	−2	−1	0	1	2
y	50	25	12.5	6.25	3.13	1.56

2.

x	0	1	2	3	4	5
y	2	2.4	2.88	3.46	4.15	5

3.

x	1	2	3	4	5	6
y	1.2	4.8	19.2	76.8	307.2	1228.8

4.

x	−10	−9	−8	−7	−6	−5
y	0.03	0.07	0.14	0.27	0.55	1.09

5. As the temperature of the coffee approaches the temperature of the room, the room temperature ceases to affect the coffee temperature.

6. Find the linear and exponential regression equations and see which value of *r* is closer to 1.

 5. Writing In the example above, the function appears to level off. Explain why this happens.   **See right.**

6. Explain how you could decide whether an exponential model is a better fit than a linear model.   **See right.**

430 Technology   Fitting Exponential Curves to Data

3. $y = 0.3(4)^x$

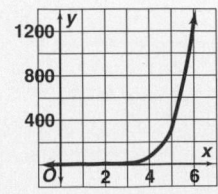

4. $y = 38.7(2.0)^x$

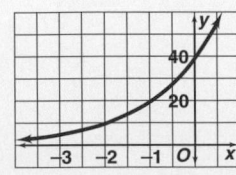

Properties of Exponential Functions

North Carolina Objectives

2.03 Use exponential functions to model and solve problems. a) Solve using tables, graphs, and algebraic properties. b) Interpret the constants, coefficients, and bases in the context of the problem.

Lesson Preview

What You'll Learn

 OBJECTIVE 1
To identify the role of constants in $y = ab^{cx}$

 OBJECTIVE 2
To use e as a base

. . . And Why

To model the half-life of a radioactive substance, as in Example 3

✓ **Check Skills You'll Need** (For help, go to Lessons 2-6, 5-3, and 7-4.)

Write an equation for each translation. **1–4. See below.**

1. $y = |x|$, 1 unit up, 2 units left

2. $y = -|x|$, 2 units down

3. $y = x^2$, 2 units down, 1 unit right

4. $y = -x^2$, 3 units up, 1 unit left

Write each equation in simplest form. Assume that all variables are positive.

5. $y = \left(x^{-\frac{5}{4}}\right)^4$ $y = \frac{1}{x^5}$

6. $y = \left(x^{-\frac{1}{7}}\right)^{-7}$ $y = x$

7. $y = \left(x^{\frac{5}{6}}\right)^6$ $y = x^5$

8. Use the formula for simple interest $I = Prt$. Find the interest for a principal of $550 at a rate of 3% for 2 years. **$33**

New Vocabulary • continuously compounded interest formula

1. $y = |x + 2| + 1$ **2.** $y = -|x| - 2$
3. $y = (x - 1)^2 - 2$ **4.** $y = -(x + 1)^2 + 3$ Interactive lesson includes instant self-check, tutorials, and activities.

OBJECTIVE

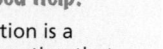 **1** **Comparing Graphs**

 Need Help?
A reflection is a transformation that creates symmetry on the coordinate plane.

So far you have graphed functions of the form $y = ab^x$ for values of a greater than zero. When $a < 0$, the graph of $y = ab^x$ is a reflection of $y = |a|b^x$ over the x-axis.

1 EXAMPLE **Graphing $y = ab^x$ When $a < 0$**

Graph $y = \frac{1}{2} \cdot 2^x$ and $y = -\frac{1}{2} \cdot 2^x$. Label the asymptote of each graph.

Step 1 Make a table of values.

x	$y = \frac{1}{2} \cdot 2^x$	$y = -\frac{1}{2} \cdot 2^x$
-2	$\frac{1}{8}$	$-\frac{1}{8}$
-1	$\frac{1}{4}$	$-\frac{1}{4}$
0	$\frac{1}{2}$	$-\frac{1}{2}$
1	1	-1
2	2	-2
3	4	-4

Step 2 Graph the functions.

The y-intercept is a, or $\frac{1}{2}$.

The asymptote is $y = 0$ for both graphs.

The y-intercept is a, or $-\frac{1}{2}$.

1a.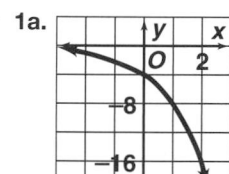

b.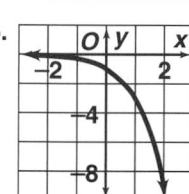

✓ **Check Understanding** **1** Graph each function. **See left.**

a. $y = -4(2)^x$

b. $y = -3^x$

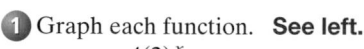 **Ongoing Assessment and Intervention**

Before the Lesson
Diagnose prerequisite skills using:
• Check Skills You'll Need

During the Lesson
Monitor progress using:
• Check Understanding
• Additional Examples
• Standardized Test Prep

After the Lesson
Assess knowledge using:
• Lesson Quiz
• Computer Test Generator CD
• Chapter Checkpoint 1 (p. 437)

Lesson Preview

 ✓ **Check Skills You'll Need**

Translations
Lesson 2-6: Example 8
Exercises 27–30
Extra Practice, p. 823

Translating Parabolas
Lesson 5-3: Example 2
Exercises 13–20
Extra Practice, p. 826

Rational Exponents
Lesson 7-4: Example 5
Exercises 37–44
Extra Practice, p. 828

Lesson Resources

📁 **Teaching Resources**
Practice, Reteaching, Enrichment
Checkpoint Quiz 1

👥 **Reaching All Students**
Practice Workbook 8-2
Spanish Practice Workbook 8-2
Reading and Math Literacy 8B
Spanish Reading & Literacy 8B
Spanish Checkpoint Quiz 1
Technology Activities 30

⏰ **Presentation Assistant Plus!**
Transparencies
• Check Skills You'll Need 8-2
• Additional Examples 8-2
• Student Edition Answers 8-2
• Lesson Quiz 8-2
PH Presentation Pro CD 8-2

 **ASSESSMENT SYSTEM**

Checkpoint Quiz 1
Computer Test Generator CD

 **Technology**
Resource Pro® CD-ROM
Computer Test Generator CD
Prentice Hall Presentation Pro CD

 **www.PHSchool.com**
Student Site
• Teacher Web Code: agk-5500
• Self-grading Lesson Quiz
Teacher Center
• Lesson Planner
• Resources

Plus 🔲**TEXT**

431

Professional Development

Math Background

The number e plays an important role in modeling exponential functions with continuous growth or decay. It is an irrational number whose value is given by the limiting value of $y = \left(1 + \frac{1}{x}\right)^x$ as x increases without bound. It is also a transcendental number—like π, e is not the root of any polynomial with rational coefficients.

OBJECTIVE

① Teaching Notes

② EXAMPLE Auditory Learning

Have a student explain informally the effect of h on the graph. Have another student explain the effect of k on the graph. Help students associate h with *horizontal* movement.

③ EXAMPLE Tactile Learning

Demonstrate exponential decay and half-life by having all students move to one side of the room. If there is an odd number of students, you may participate in the activity. Then direct one half to move to their seats. Continue by asking one half of the remaining group also to move to their seats, taking part yourself or not, as needed for an even number. Repeat until fewer than four persons remain.

Additional Examples

① Graph $y = 3 \cdot 2^x$ and $y = -3 \cdot 2^x$. Label the asymptote of each.

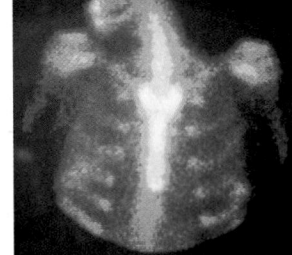

② Graph $y = 6\left(\frac{1}{2}\right)^x$ and $y = 6\left(\frac{1}{2}\right)^{x-3} - 2$. **See back of book.**

You can graph many exponential functions as translations of the parent function $y = ab^x$. The graph of $y = ab^{x-h} + k$ is the graph of $y = ab^x$ translated h units horizontally and k units vertically.

② EXAMPLE Translating $y = ab^x$

Graph $y = 8\left(\frac{1}{2}\right)^x$ and $y = 8\left(\frac{1}{2}\right)^{x+2} + 3$.

Step 1 Graph $y = 8\left(\frac{1}{2}\right)^x$. The horizontal asymptote is $y = 0$.

Step 2 For $y = 8\left(\frac{1}{2}\right)^{x+2} + 3$, $h = -2$ and $k = 3$. So shift the graph of the parent function 2 units left and 3 units up. The horizontal asymptote is $y = 3$.

✓ **Check Understanding** ② Graph each function as a translation of $y = 9(3)^x$.
   a. $y = 9(3)^{x+1}$ **a–c. See back**
   b. $y = 9(3)^x - 4$ **of book.**
   c. $y = 9(3)^{x-3} - 1$

Some exponential functions are of the form $y = ab^{cx}$, where c is a nonzero constant.

③ EXAMPLE Real-World 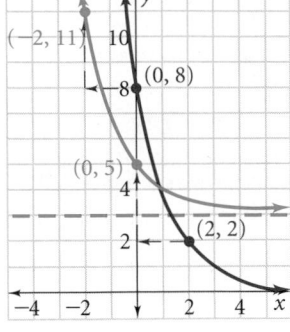 Connection

Real-World Connection

As technetium-99m decays, it emits low-energy gamma rays. The rays are detected by a gamma camera to produce images like the one above.

Medicine The half-life of a radioactive substance is the time it takes for half of the material to decay. A hospital prepares a 100-mg supply of technetium-99m, which has a half-life of 6 hours. Make a table showing the amount of technetium-99m that remains at the end of each 6-hour interval for 36 hours. Then write an exponential function to find the amount of technetium-99m that remains after 75 hours.

The amount of technetium-99m is reduced by one half each 6 hours.

Number of 6-h Intervals	0	1	2	3	4	5	6
Number of Hours Elapsed	0	6	12	18	24	30	36
Technetium-99m (mg)	100	50	25	12.5	6.25	3.13	1.56

Relate The amount of technetium-99m is an exponential function of the number of half-lives. The initial amount is 100 mg. The decay factor is $\frac{1}{2}$. One half-life equals 6 h.

Define Let y = the amount of technetium-99m.

Let x = the number of hours elapsed. Then $\frac{1}{6}x$ = the number of half-lives.

Write $y = 100\left(\frac{1}{2}\right)^{\frac{1}{6}x}$

$y = 100\left(\frac{1}{2}\right)^{\frac{1}{6} \cdot 75}$ **Substitute 75 for x.**

$= 100\left(\frac{1}{2}\right)^{12.5}$ **Simplify.**

≈ 0.017 **Use a calculator.**

After 75 hours, about 0.017 mg of technetium-99m remains.

👥 Reaching All Students

Below Level Review the translation forms when $x - h$ is substituted for x and $y - k$ is substituted for y.	**Advanced Learners** Have students graph the function $y = \left(1 + \frac{1}{x}\right)^x$. Challenge them to describe the asymptotes they find and explain why those asymptotes exist.	**English Learners** See note on page 435. **Tactile Learners** See note on page 432.

✓ **Check Understanding** ❸ Arsenic-74 is used to locate brain tumors. It has a half-life of 17.5 days. Write an exponential decay function for a 90-mg sample. Use the function to find the amount remaining after 6 days. $y = 90\left(\frac{1}{2}\right)^{\frac{2}{35}x}$; **about 71 mg**

OBJECTIVE

2 The Number e

At the right is part of the graph of the function $y = \left(1 + \frac{1}{x}\right)^x$. One of the graph's asymptotes is $y = e$, where e is an irrational number approximately equal to 2.71828.

Exponential functions with a base of e are useful for describing continuous growth or decay. Your graphing calculator has a key for e^x.

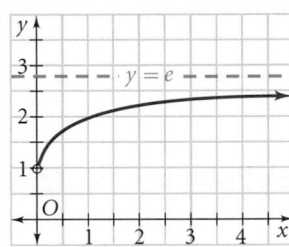

❹ **EXAMPLE** Evaluating e^x

Graph $y = e^x$. Evaluate e^2 to four decimal places.

Step 1 Graph $y = e^x$.

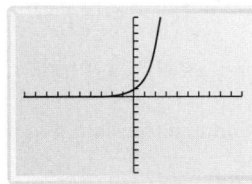

Step 2 Find y when $x = 2$.

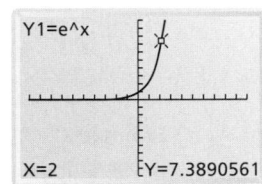

Y1=e^x

X=2   Y=7.3890561

● The value of e^2 is about 7.3891.

✓ **Check Understanding** ❹ Use the graph of $y = e^x$ to evaluate each expression to four decimal places.

a. e^4 **54.5982**   **b.** e^{-3} **0.0498**   **c.** $e^{\frac{1}{2}}$ **1.6487**

In previous courses, you have studied simple interest and compound interest. The more frequently interest is compounded, the more quickly the amount in an account increases. The formula for *continuously* compounded interest uses the number e.

 Key Concepts

Definition	Continuously Compounded Interest Formula

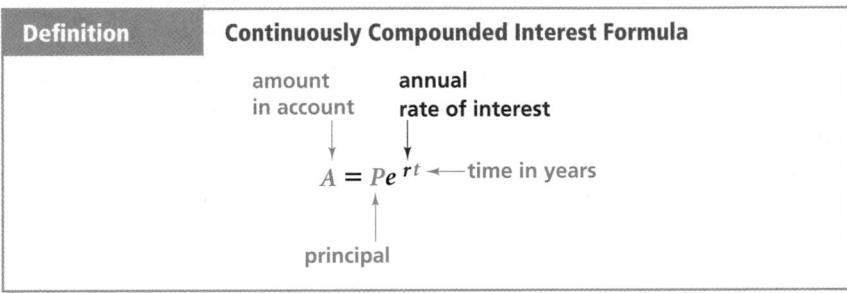

amount
in account

annual
rate of interest

$A = Pe^{rt}$ ← time in years

principal

Graphing Calculator Hint

After graphing e^x, press TRACE 2 ENTER to find y for $x = 2$.

---

❹ **EXAMPLE** **Connection to Analysis**

The number e occurs also in this very famous equation: $e^{i\pi} + 1 = 0$. This equation is sometimes called Euler's Equation or The Famous Five because it contains the basic five constants of mathematics.

Additional Examples

❹ Use the graph of $y = e^x$ to evaluate e^3 to four decimal places. **20.0855**

❺ Suppose you invest $100 at an annual interest rate of 4.8% compounded continuously. How much will you have in the account after three years? **about $115**

Closure

Ask students to explain how h and k in $y = e^{x-h} + k$ affect the graph of the exponential function $y = e^x$. **h translates the graph horizontally, and k translates the graph vertically.** Also ask how you can find the approximate value of e^6. **Answers may vary. Sample: To find e^6, graph $y = e^x$. Then, press CALC, set x equal to 6 and press ENTER.**

Lesson 8-2 Properties of Exponential Functions **433**

3. Practice

Assignment Guide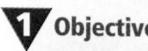

1 Objective
- **A B Core** 1–17, 27–29, 31–35, 39
- **C Extension** 48, 50

2 Objective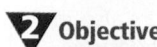
- **A B Core** 18–26, 30, 36–38, 40–47
- **C Extension** 49

Standardized Test Prep 51–55

Mixed Review 56–81

Error Prevention
Exercises 11–14 Suggest that students circle the operation sign in the exponent to help them remember that the horizontal translation is the direction opposite to this sign.

Enrichment 8-2
Reteaching 8-2
Practice 8-2

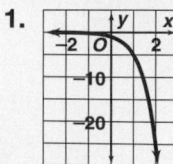

---

pages 434–437 Exercises

1–8. Asymptote is $y = 0$.

1.

---

5 EXAMPLE   Real-World Connection

Investments Suppose you invest \$1050 at an annual interest rate of 5.5% compounded continuously. How much will you have in the account after five years?

$A = Pe^{rt}$

$= 1050 \cdot e^{0.055(5)}$ **Substitute 1050 for *P*, 0.055 for *r*, and 5 for *t*.**

$= 1050 \cdot e^{0.275}$ **Simplify.**

$\approx 1050(1.316531)$ **Evaluate $e^{0.275}$.**

≈ 1382.36 **Simplify.**

You will have about \$1382 in the account after five years.

✓ Check Understanding **5** Suppose you invest \$1300 at an annual interest rate of 4.3% compounded continuously. Find the amount you will have in the account after three years.
\$1479.00

EXERCISES

For more practice, see *Extra Practice*.

Practice and Problem Solving

A **Practice by Example**

Example 1 (page 431)

Graph each function. Label the asymptote of each graph. **1–8. See margin pp. 434–435.**

1. $y = -5^x$ **2.** $y = -\left(\frac{1}{2}\right)^x$ **3.** $y = -2(4)^x$ **4.** $y = -9(3)^x$

5. $y = -3(2)^x$ **6.** $y = -24\left(\frac{1}{2}\right)^x$ **7.** $y = -4^x$ **8.** $y = -\left(\frac{1}{3}\right)^x$

Example 2 (page 432)

Graph each function as a translation of its parent function. **9–14. See back of book.**

9. $y = 8^x + 5$ **10.** $y = 15\left(\frac{4}{3}\right)^x - 8$ **11.** $y = -(0.3)^{x-2}$

12. $y = -2(5)^{x+3}$ **13.** $y = 52\left(\frac{2}{13}\right)^{x-1} + 26$ **14.** $y = 9\left(\frac{1}{3}\right)^{x+7} - 3$

Example 3 (page 432)

15. Botany Phosphorus-32 is used to study a plant's use of fertilizer. It has a half-life of 14.3 days. Write the exponential decay function for a 50-mg sample. Find the amount of phosporus-32 remaining after 84 days. $y = 50\left(\frac{1}{2}\right)^{\frac{1}{14.3}x}$; **0.85 mg**

16. Public Works Iodine-131 is used to find leaks in water pipes. It has a half-life of 8.14 days. Write the exponential decay function for a 200-mg sample. Find the amount of iodine-131 remaining after 72 days. $y = 200\left(\frac{1}{2}\right)^{\frac{1}{8.14}x}$; **0.43 mg**

17. Archaeology Carbon-14 is used to determine the age of artifacts in carbon dating. It has a half-life of 5730 years. Write the exponential decay function for a 24-mg sample. Find the amount of carbon-14 remaining after 30 millennia (1 millennium = 1000 years). $y = 24\left(\frac{1}{2}\right)^{\frac{1}{5730}x}$; **0.64 mg**

Example 4 (page 433)

Use the graph of $y = e^x$ to evaluate each expression to four decimal places.

18. e^3 **20.0855**   **19.** e^6 **403.4288**   **20.** e^{-2} **0.1353**   **21.** e^0 **1**   **22.** $e^{\frac{5}{2}}$ **12.1825**   **23.** e^e **15.1543**

Example 5 (page 434)

Find the amount in a continuously compounded account for the given conditions.

24. principal: \$2000   **25.** principal: \$400   **26.** principal: \$950
annual interest 5.1%   annual interest 7.6%   annual interest 6.5%
time: 3 yr **\$2330.65**   time: 1.5 yr **\$448.30**   time: 10 yr **\$1819.76**

434   Chapter 8   Exponential and Logarithmic Functions

---

2. 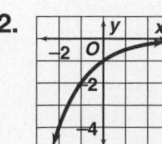   **3.**   **4.** 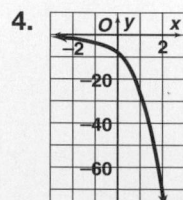   **5.**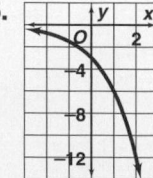

434

B **Apply Your Skills**

27. Find the value of a for which the graph of $y = ab^x$ is a horizontal line. **0**

28. Find the value of b for which the graph of $y = ab^x$ is a horizontal line. **1**

29. Assume that a and b are positive. Describe the effects of $c < 0, c = 0,$ and $c > 0$ on the graph of the function $y = ab^{cx}$. **See margin.**

 30. Savings A student wants to save $8000 for college in five years. How much should be put into an account that earns 5.2% annual interest compounded continuously? **$6168.41**

31. When $a < 0$ and $b > 1$, $y = ab^x$ models negative exponential growth.
   a. Open-Ended Write an exponential function that models negative growth.
   b. Give an example of a situation that could be modeled by your function.
   c. Critical Thinking Explain one difference between negative exponential growth and exponential decay. **a–c. See margin.**

The parent function for each graph below is of the form $y = ab^x$. Write the parent function. Then write a function for the translation indicated.

32.

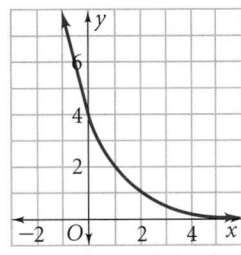

translation: left 4 units, up 3 units

33.

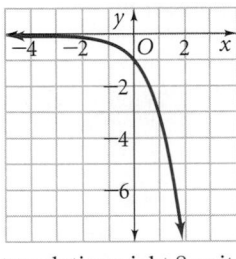

translation: right 8 units, up 2 units

34.

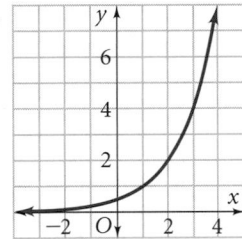

translation: right 6 units, down 7 units

35.

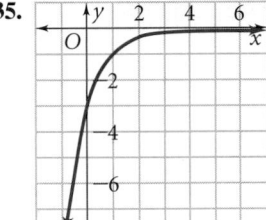

translation: left 5 units, down 1 unit

36. Physics At a constant temperature, the atmospheric pressure p in pascals is given by the formula $p = 101.3e^{-0.001h}$, where h is the altitude in meters. Find p at an altitude of 300 m. **75.0 pascals**

37. Investment How long would it take to double your principal at an annual interest rate of 8% compounded continuously? **8.7 yr**

38. Writing Like a debt, a deficit is a negative amount of money. Explain how you would model a deficit that is growing exponentially. In $y = ab^{cx}$, would the values of a and c be positive or negative? Would the value of b be greater than 1 or less than 1?

39. Economics The gross domestic product, or GDP, of the United States was about 8.511 trillion in 1998. **a–c. See margin.**
   a. Assume that GDP grows 3.8% each year. Write an exponential function to describe such growth.
   b. Describe the GDP growth that occurs over 18 years.
   c. Describe the growth in half that time.

Real-World  Connection

A savings plan can be an important part of preparing for college.

32. $y = 4\left(\frac{1}{2}\right)^x$;
   $y = 4\left(\frac{1}{2}\right)^{x+4} + 3$

33. $y = -3^x$;
   $y = -3^{x-8} + 2$

34. $y = \frac{1}{2}(2)^x$;
   $y = \frac{1}{2}(2)^{x-6} - 7$

35. $y = -3\left(\frac{1}{3}\right)^x$;
   $y = -3\left(\frac{1}{3}\right)^{x+5} - 1$

38. A deficit that is growing exponentially is modeled by $y = ab^{cx}$, where $a < 0$, and either $b > 1$ and $c > 0$ or $0 < b < 1$ and $c < 0$.

---

29. If $c < 0$, the graph models exponential decay. If $c = 0$, the graph is a horizontal line. If $c > 0$, the graph models exponential growth.

31a. Answers may vary. Sample: $y = -2(1.3)^x$

   b. Answers may vary. Sample: I am in debt for $2 and my debt is growing at a rate of 30% per year.

   c. The graph of exponential decay approaches the asymptote $y = 0$ as x increases. The graph of negative exponential growth approaches the asymptote $y = 0$ as x decreases.

39a. GDP $= 8.511(1.038)^t$ where $t = 0$ corresponds to 1998 and 8.511 is trillions.

   b. It almost doubles. (about 195.7%)

   c. In 9 years, the growth is about 40%.

6.

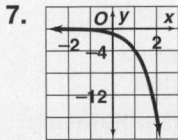

7.

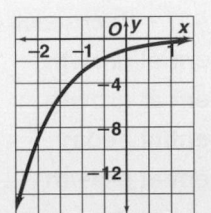

8.

4. Assess

Lesson Quiz 8-2

Describe how the graph of each function relates to its parent function. Then graph the function.

1. $y = -5^x - 1$ **reflected over the x-axis and translated down 1**

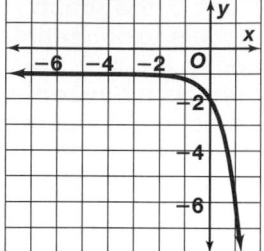

2. $y = 3(5)^{x-2} + 1$ **rises more steeply, is translated 2 to the right and up 1**

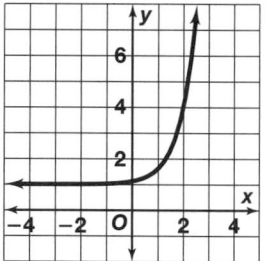

3. Use the formula $A = Pe^{rt}$ to find the amount in a continuously compounded account where the principal is $2000 at an annual interest rate of 5% for 3 years. **about $2324**

4. Use the graph of $y = e^x$ to evaluate $e^{\frac{1}{3}}$ to four decimal places. **1.3956**

Alternative Assessment

Give each student a laminated coordinate plane and a pipe cleaner. Write $y = 2^x$ on the board. Ask the students to model its graph using the pipe cleaner. Now make changes to the function that reflect and/or translate the graph. Instruct students to move the pipe cleaner to match the changes to the function. Walk around the classroom during the whole process to assess student success.

436

Need Help?

The compound interest formula is

$A = P\left(1 + \frac{r}{n}\right)^{nt}$,

where n is the number of times per year the interest is compounded.

Challenge

48a. 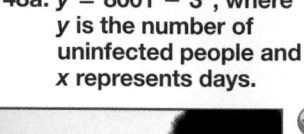 $y = 8001 - 3^x$, where y is the number of uninfected people and x represents days.

Real-World 🌐 Connection

Careers Psychologists use models to evaluate and predict learning rates.

---

40. Suppose you invest $2000 at an annual interest rate of 4.5%, compounded quarterly.
  a. How much will you have in the account after five years? **$2501.50**
  b. Determine how much more you would have if the interest were compounded continuously. **$3.15 more**

41. An investor withdraws all $525 from an account that was neglected for 8 years. It earned 3.4% annual interest, compounded continuously. How much was the initial deposit? **$399.97**

Without graphing, determine whether each equation represents exponential growth or exponential decay. 42–47. See margin.

42. $s(t) = 5e^t$ **43.** $y = \frac{1}{6}e^x$ **44.** $y = \left(\frac{1}{e}\right)^x$

45. $y = \frac{7}{5}\left(\frac{e}{2}\right)^x$ **46.** $f(x) = \left(\frac{e}{3.7}\right)^x$ **47.** $y = -70e^t$

48. Biology A new flu virus is introduced when a stranger visits an isolated village of 8000 people. Every infected person infects two more each day.
  a. Write an exponential function to model the number of *uninfected* people.
  b. Determine how many people remain uninfected after one week. **5814 people**
  c. After how many days will the entire population be infected? **about 9 days**

49. Psychology Psychologists use an exponential model of the learning process, $f(t) = c(1 - e^{-kt})$, where c is the total number of tasks to be learned, k is the rate of learning, t is time, and $f(t)$ is the number of tasks learned.
  a. Suppose you move to a new school, and you want to learn the names of 30 classmates in your homeroom. If your learning rate for new tasks is 20% per day, how many complete names will you know after 2 days? After 8 days?
  b. Graph the function on your graphing calculator. How many days will it take to learn everyone's name? Explain. **a–c. See margin.**
  c. Open-Ended Does this function seem to describe your own learning rate? If not, how could you adapt it to reflect your learning rate?

50. Work begins on digging a moat on the perimeter of a property. After the first weekend, the first worker recruits a friend to help. After every succeeding weekend, each moat-digger recruits another friend. One person can dig 15 m³ of dirt per weekend. The moat should be 4 m wide and 3 m deep, and it must lie entirely within the 60 m-by-70 m property. **2928 m³**
  a. Geometry Determine the volume of dirt that must be removed for the moat.
  b. Write an exponential function to model the volume of dirt remaining to be shoveled after x weekends. $V = 2928 - 15(2^{x-1})$
  c. On which weekend will the moat be completed? **ninth weekend**

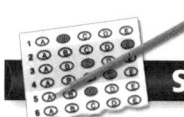

Standardized Test Prep

Multiple Choice

Take It to the NET
Online lesson quiz at
www.PHSchool.com
Web Code: aga-0802

51. How is the graph of $y = 4 \cdot \left(\frac{1}{2}\right)^{x-3}$ translated from the graph of $y = 4 \cdot \left(\frac{1}{2}\right)^x$? **A**
  A. 3 units right   **B.** 3 units left   **C.** 3 units down   **D.** 3 units up

52. How is the graph of $y = 4 \cdot \left(\frac{1}{2}\right)^x + 3$ translated from the graph of $y = 4 \cdot \left(\frac{1}{2}\right)^x$? **I**
  F. 3 units right   **G.** 3 units left   **H.** 3 units down   **I.** 3 units up

---

pages 434–437 Exercises

42. exponential growth

43. exponential growth

44. exponential decay

45. exponential growth

46. exponential decay

47. exponential growth

49a. about 10 names; about 24 names
  b. Graphically, it will never happen; the graph has $y = 30$ as an asymptote. (In reality, you would be close to knowing all the names in about 21 days.)
  c. Answers may vary. Sample: I learn names pretty quickly; my learning rate might be 0.4.

53. A savings account earns 4.62% annual interest, compounded continuously. After approximately how many years will a principal of $500 double? **C**
   A. 2 years   **B.** 10 years   **C.** 15 years   **D.** 44 years

54. Sodium-24 has a half-life of 15 hours. How much sodium-24 will you have after 60 hours if your original sample is 64 mg? **F**
   F. 4 mg   **G.** 16 mg   **H.** 32 mg   **I.** 64 mg

Short Response   **55.** How much should you invest in a continuously compounded account at an annual interest rate of 6% if you want exactly $8000 after four years? Show how you got your answer. **See margin.**

Standardized Test Prep

 Resources

For additional practice with a variety of test item formats:
- Standardized Test Prep, p. 473
- Test-Taking Strategies, p. 468
- Test-Taking Strategies with Transparencies

Mixed Review

Lesson 8-1   **Write an exponential equation $y = ab^x$ for a graph that includes the given points.**

57. $y = -2(4)^x$ **56.** $(0, 1), (1, 3)$ $y = 3^x$ **57.** $(1, -8), (2, -32)$ **58.** $(0, -5), (2, -20)$

58. $y = -5(2)^x$ **59.** $(-1, 16), (3, 1)$ **60.** $(-3, 0.07), (-1, 7)$ **61.** $(2, 6400), (4, 4096)$
                              $y = 8(0.5)^x$ $y = 70(10)^x$ $y = 10,000(0.8)^x$

Lesson 7-3   **Simplify each expression.**

62. $6\sqrt{5}$ **62.** $5\sqrt{5} + \sqrt{5}$ **63.** $\sqrt[3]{4} - 2\sqrt[3]{4}$ $-\sqrt[3]{4}$ **64.** $\sqrt{75} + \sqrt{125}$ **65.** $\sqrt[4]{32} + \sqrt[4]{128}$

65. $2(\sqrt[4]{2} + \sqrt[4]{8})$ **66.** $5\sqrt{3} - 2\sqrt{12}$ $\sqrt{3}$ **67.** $3\sqrt{63} + \sqrt{28}$ $11\sqrt{7}$ **68.** $(3 - \sqrt{6})^2$ $15 - 6\sqrt{6}$ **69.** $\dfrac{-2 - 2\sqrt{5}}{1 - \sqrt{5}}$ $\dfrac{5(\sqrt{3} + \sqrt{5})}{3 + \sqrt{5}}$

Lesson 6-3   **Divide using either long division or synthetic division.**

71. $x^2 - x - 6$ **70.** $(x^2 - 3x - 1) \div x$ $x - 3$ R -1 **71.** $(x^3 - 2x^2 - 5x + 6) \div (x - 1)$

72. $x^2 - 1$ **72.** $(x^3 + 4x^2 - x - 4) \div (x + 4)$ **73.** $(x^3 - 4x^2 - 4x - 5) \div (x - 5)$

73. $x^2 + x + 1$ **74.** $(13x^2 - 51x - 4) \div (x - 4)$ $13x + 1$ **75.** $(9x^3 - 18x^2 - x + 2) \div (3x + 1)$ $3x^2 - 7x + 2$

Lesson 3-5   **Find the equations of the traces of each graph.**

76. $x - y + z = 5$ **77.** $x + y + 4z = -2$ **78.** $3x + 3y - 6z = 24$

79. $x - y + 2z = 8$ **80.** $3x + y + 9z = -18$ **81.** $-2x + y - 5z = 10$
76–81. See margin.

✓ Checkpoint Quiz 1   Lessons 8-1 through 8-2

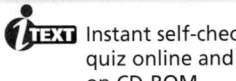 Instant self-check quiz online and on CD-ROM

Identify each function as modeling either exponential growth or exponential decay. What percent of increase or decrease does the function model? 1–4. See margin.

1. $y = 15(1.45)^x$ **2.** $y = 0.32(0.99)^x$ **3.** $y = 0.1(1.7)^x$ **4.** $y = 7.3(0.8)^x$

Graph each function. 5–7. See margin. 8. See back of book.

5. $y = 3^x$ **6.** $y = 2^x + 1$ **7.** $y = (0.25)^x$ **8.** $y = 4^x - 5$

9. Open-Ended Describe a real-world problem that you could model with an exponential growth function. **See back of book.**

🌐 **10. Chemistry** An element has a half-life of 30 hours. Write the exponential decay function for a 100-mg sample. Use the function to find the amount of the element remaining after 100 hours. $y = 100\left(\frac{1}{2}\right)^{\frac{1}{30}x}$; **about 9.9 mg**

Lesson 8-2 Properties of Exponential Functions   **437**

✓ Chapter Checkpoint 1

To check understanding of Lessons 8-1 to 8-2:

Checkpoint Quiz 1 (p. 437)

 Teaching Resources
Checkpoint Quiz 1 (also in Prentice Hall Assessment System)

👥 **Reaching All Students**
Reading and Math Literacy 8B

Spanish versions available

---

page 437 Checkpoint Quiz 1

1. exponential growth; 45% increase

2. exponential decay; 1% decrease

3. exponential growth; 70% increase

4. exponential decay; 20% decrease

5.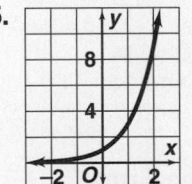

6.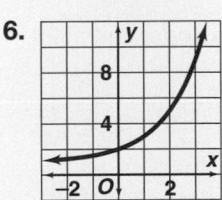

7.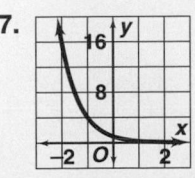

---

55. [2] $A = Pe^{rt}$
   $8000 = Pe^{(0.06)(4)}$
   $\dfrac{8000}{e^{(0.06)(4)}} = P$
   $P = \$6293.02$
   [1] **answer only, without work shown**

76. $x - y = 5, x + z = 5,$
   $-y + z = 5$

77. $x + y = -2, x + 4z = -2,$
   $y + 4z = -2$

78. $x + y = 8,$
   $x - 2z = 8,$
   $y - 2z = 8$

79. $x - y = 8, x + 2z = 8,$
   $-y + 2z = 8$

80. $3x + y = -18,$
   $x + 3z = -6,$
   $y + 9z = -18$

81. $-2x + y = 10, -2x - 5z = 10, y - 5z = 10$

1. Plan

Lesson Preview

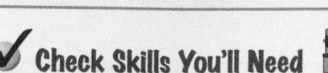 **Check Skills You'll Need**

Roots and Radical Expressions
Lesson 7-1: Example 3
Exercises 21–28
Extra Practice, p. 828

Multiplying Special Cases
Lesson 7-7: Example 3
Exercises 11–16
Extra Practice, p. 828

Lesson Resources

 **Teaching Resources**
Practice, Reteaching, Enrichment

Reaching All Students
Practice Workbook 8-3
Spanish Practice Workbook 8-3

 **Presentation Assistant Plus!**
Transparencies
• Check Skills You'll Need 8-3
• Additional Examples 8-3
• Student Edition Answers 8-3
• Lesson Quiz 8-3
PH Presentation Pro CD 8-3

ASSESSMENT SYSTEM

Computer Test Generator CD

Technology
Resource Pro® CD-ROM
Computer Test Generator CD
Prentice Hall Presentation Pro CD

 **www.PHSchool.com**
Student Site
• Teacher Web Code: agk-5500
• Graphing Calculator,
  Procedure 18
• Self-grading Lesson Quiz
Teacher Center
• Lesson Planner
• Resources

Plus **iTEXT**

 **8-3**

Logarithmic Functions as Inverses

North Carolina Objectives

1.01 Simplify and perform operations with rational exponents and logarithms (common and natural) to solve problems.
2.01 Use the inverse of functions to model and solve problems.

Lesson Preview

What You'll Learn

 OBJECTIVE 1
To write and evaluate logarithmic expressions

 OBJECTIVE 2
To graph logarithmic functions

... And Why

To compare the acidities of milk and lemon juice, as in Example 4

✓ Check Skills You'll Need

(For help, go to Lessons 7-1 and 7-7.)

Solve each equation.

1. $8 = x^3$ **2**   **2.** $x^{\frac{1}{4}} = 2$ **16**   **3.** $27 = 3^x$ **3**   **4.** $4^6 = 4^{3x}$ **2**

Graph each relation and its inverse on a coordinate plane.

5. $y = 5x$ **6.** $y = 2x^2$ **7.** $y = -x^3$ **8.** $y = \frac{1}{2}x$
5–8. See back of book.

New Vocabulary • logarithm • common logarithm • logarithmic function

---

OBJECTIVE 1

Writing and Evaluating Logarithmic Expressions

 Interactive lesson includes instant self-check, tutorials, and activities.

The magnitude of an earthquake is a measure of the amount of energy released at its source. The Richter scale is an exponential measure of earthquake magnitude. An earthquake of magnitude 5 releases about 30 times as much energy as an earthquake of magnitude 4.

The Richter Scale

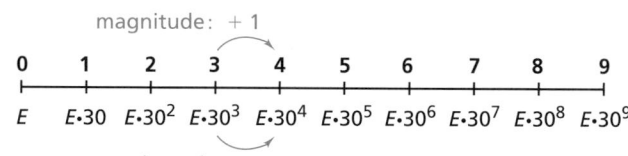

Real-World Connection

The earthquake that struck Washington in 2001 measured 6.8 on the Richter scale.

1 EXAMPLE   Real-World Connection

Seismology In 1995, an earthquake in Mexico registered 8.0 on the Richter scale. In 2001, an earthquake of magnitude 6.8 shook Washington state. Compare the amounts of energy released in the two earthquakes.

$\dfrac{E \cdot 30^{8.0}}{E \cdot 30^{6.8}}$ **Write a ratio.**

$= \dfrac{30^{8.0}}{30^{6.8}}$ **Simplify.**

$= 30^{8.0 - 6.8}$ **Division Property of Exponents**

$= 30^{1.2}$ **Simplify.**

≈ 59.2 **Use a calculator.**

The earthquake in Mexico released about 59 times as much energy as the earthquake in Washington.

✓ Check Understanding **1** In 1997, an earthquake in Alabama registered 4.9 on the Richter scale. In 1999, one in California registered 7.0. Compare the energy released in the two quakes.
See back of book.

Ongoing Assessment and Intervention

Before the Lesson
Diagnose prerequisite skills using:
• Check Skills You'll Need

During the Lesson
Monitor progress using:
• Check Understanding
• Additional Examples
• Standardized Test Prep

After the Lesson
Assess knowledge using:
• Lesson Quiz
• Computer Test Generator CD

The exponents used by the Richter scale shown in Example 1 are called logarithms, or logs.

 Key Concepts

Definition	Logarithm

The **logarithm** to the base b of a positive number y is defined as follows:

If $y = b^x$, then $\log_b y = x$.

 Reading Math

Read $\log_b y$ as "log base b of y."

The exponent x in the exponential expression b^x is the logarithm in the equation $\log_b y = x$. The base b in b^x is the same as the base b in the logarithm. In both cases, $b \neq 1$ and $b > 0$.

A positive number b raised to any power x cannot equal a number y less than or equal to zero. Therefore, the logarithm of a negative number or zero is undefined.

2 EXAMPLE Writing in Logarithmic Form

Write $25 = 5^2$ in logarithmic form.

If $y = b^x$, then $\log_b y = x$. **Write the definition.**

If $25 = 5^2$, then $\log_5 25 = 2$. **Substitute.**

● The logarithmic form of $25 = 5^2$ is $\log_5 25 = 2$.

✓ **Check Understanding** ❷ Write each equation in logarithmic form.
a. $729 = 3^6$ $\log_3 729 = 6$ **b.** $\left(\frac{1}{2}\right)^3 = \frac{1}{8}$ $3 = \log_{\frac{1}{2}} \left(\frac{1}{8}\right)$ **c.** $10^0 = 1$ $0 = \log_{10} 1$

To evaluate logarithms, you can write them in exponential form.

3 EXAMPLE Evaluating Logarithms

Evaluate $\log_8 16$.

$\log_8 16 = x$ **Write an equation in logarithmic form.**
$16 = 8^x$ **Convert to exponential form.**
$2^4 = (2^3)^x$ **Write each side using base 2.**
$2^4 = 2^{3x}$ **Power Property of Exponents**
$4 = 3x$ **Set the exponents equal to each other.**
$\frac{4}{3} = x$ **Solve for x.**

● So $\log_8 16 = \frac{4}{3}$.

✓ **Check Understanding** ❸ Evaluate each logarithm.
a. $\log_{64} \frac{1}{32}$ $-\frac{5}{6}$ **b.** $\log_9 27$ $\frac{3}{2}$ **c.** $\log_{10} 100$ 2

A **common logarithm** is a logarithm that uses base 10. You can write the common logarithm $\log_{10} y$ as $\log y$.

Lesson 8-3 Logarithmic Functions as Inverses **439**

---

2. Teach

Professional Development

Math Background

Functions of the form $f(x) = b^x$ are one-to-one. This means that each y-value on the graph of $f(x) = b^x$ has a unique x-value. This is useful when solving equations such as $2^4 = 2^{3x}$. It allows us to conclude that $4 = 3x$.

OBJECTIVE
❶ Teaching Notes

❷ EXAMPLE Tactile Learners

Have students write the equation components y, b, x, log and $=$ on different colored pieces of paper. Direct students to arrange the papers to form the equation $y = b^x$. Then have them rearrange the papers to form $x = \log_b y$.

❸ EXAMPLE Teaching Tip

Show students how to use estimation to check their answers. Tell students to first ask themselves, *What power of 8 is equal to 16?* They can use the powers they know for the estimation. For example, they know that 8 to the power of 1 is 8. Also, 8 to the power of 2 is 64. Sixteen is between 8 and 64 so students can expect the power to be a value between 1 and 2.

Additional Examples

❶ Compare the amount of energy released in an earthquake that registered 6 on the Richter scale with one that registers 3. **The first released about 27,000 times as much energy as the second.**

❷ Write $32 = 2^5$ in logarithmic form. **$\log_2 32 = 5$**

❸ Evaluate $\log_3 81$. **4**

 Reaching All Students

Below Level Have students use their calculators to graph $y = 10^x$, then use the Draw Inv function to plot the inverse. Next, graph the function $y = \log(x)$. Discuss how the graphs compare.	**Advanced Learners** Ask students to find out about several other scientific quantities typically measured on a logarithmic scale and discuss why this might be helpful.	**Tactile Learners** See note on page 439. **Visual Learners** See note on page 440.

439

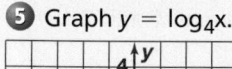
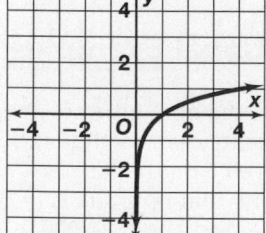
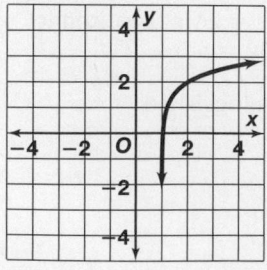
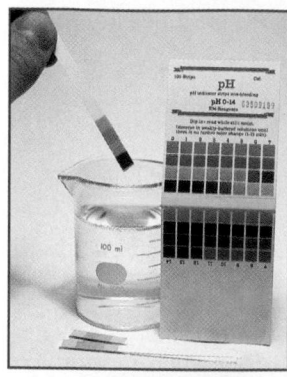

Real-World Connection

You can use pH strips to measure the acidity of a water solution. The pH scale ranges from 0 to 14.

Scientists use common logarithms to measure acidity, which increases as the concentration of hydrogen ions in a substance increases. The pH of a substance equals $-\log[\text{H}^+]$, where $[\text{H}^+]$ is the concentration of hydrogen ions.

4 **EXAMPLE** **Real-World Connection**

Chemistry The pH of lemon juice is 2.3, while the pH of milk is 6.6. Find the concentration of hydrogen ions in each substance. Which substance is more acidic?

Lemon juice	Milk
$\text{pH} = -\log[\text{H}^+]$	$\text{pH} = -\log[\text{H}^+]$
$2.3 = -\log[\text{H}^+]$	$6.6 = -\log[\text{H}^+]$
$\log[\text{H}^+] = -2.3$	$\log[\text{H}^+] = -6.6$
$[\text{H}^+] = 10^{-2.3}$	$[\text{H}^+] = 10^{-6.6}$
$\approx 5.0 \times 10^{-3}$	$\approx 2.5 \times 10^{-7}$

The $[\text{H}^+]$ of lemon juice is about 5.0×10^{-3}. The $[\text{H}^+]$ of milk is about 2.5×10^{-7}. Lemon juice has a higher concentration of hydrogen ions, so it is more acidic.

✓ **Check Understanding** **4** Find the concentration of hydrogen ions in seawater of pH 8.5. **3.2×10^{-9}**

OBJECTIVE
2 **Graphing Logarithmic Functions**

A **logarithmic function** is the inverse of an exponential function. The graph shows $y = 10^x$ and $y = \log x$. Note that $(0, 1)$ and $(1, 10)$ lie on the graph of $y = 10^x$, and that $(1, 0)$, and $(10, 1)$ lie on the graph of $y = \log x$.

Recall that the graph of a function is symmetric to the graph of its inverse over the line $y = x$. You can graph $y = \log_b x$ as the inverse of $y = b^x$.

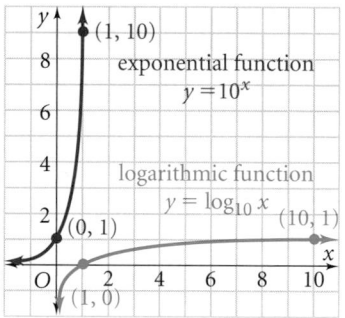

5 **EXAMPLE** **Graphing a Logarithmic Function**

Graph $y = \log_2 x$.

By the definition of logarithm, $y = \log_2 x$ is the inverse of $y = 2^x$.

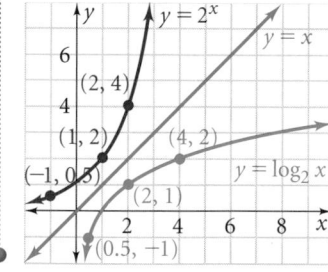
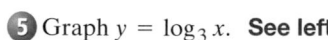

Step 1 Graph $y = 2^x$.

Step 2 Draw $y = x$.

Step 3 Choose a few points on $y = 2^x$. Reverse the coordinates and plot the points of $y = \log_2 x$.

5.
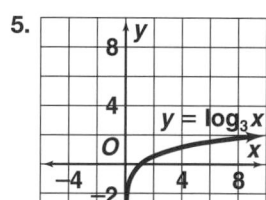

✓ **Check Understanding** **5** Graph $y = \log_3 x$. **See left.**

Closure

Ask: *What is the relationship between a logarithm and an exponent? What does the graph of $y = \log_{10} x$ look like?* **A logarithm is an exponent. The** graph of $y = \log_{10} x$ is the graph of $y = 10^x$ reflected over $y = x$.

The function $y = \log_b x$ is the inverse of $y = b^x$. Since $(0, 1)$ and $(1, b)$ are points on the graph of $y = b^x$, $(1, 0)$ and $(b, 1)$ are points on the graph of $y = \log_b x$. Since the x-axis is an asymptote of the graph of $y = b^x$, the y-axis is an asymptote of the graph of $y = \log_b x$. Using these facts, you can sketch graphs of $y = \log_b x$.

You can graph $y = \log_b (x - h) + k$ as the translation h units horizontally and k units vertically of $y = \log_b x$.

 **Key Concepts**

	Summary	Translations of Logarithmic Functions

Characteristic	$y = \log_b x$	$y = \log_b (x - h) + k$
Asymptote	$x = 0$	$x - h = 0$, or $x = h$
Domain	$x > 0$	$x > h$
Range	All real numbers	All real numbers

6 EXAMPLE Translating $y = \log_b x$

Graph $y = \log_6 (x - 2) + 3$.

Step 1 Make a table of values for the parent function.

x	$\log_6 x$	y
6	$\log_6 6 = 1$	1
1	$\log_6 1 = 0$	0
$\frac{1}{6}$	$\log_6 \frac{1}{6} = -1$	-1
$\frac{1}{36}$	$\log_6 \frac{1}{36} = -2$	-2
$\frac{1}{216}$	$\log_6 \frac{1}{216} = -3$	-3

Step 2 Graph the function by shifting the points from the table to the right 2 units and up 3 units.

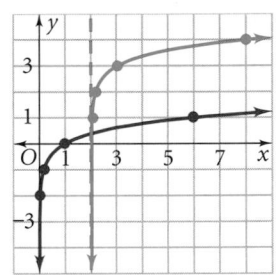

? Need Help?

A parent function is the simplest function in a family of functions.

✓ **Check Understanding** 6 Graph $y = \log_3 (x + 3)$.

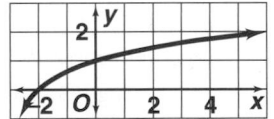

EXERCISES

For more practice, see *Extra Practice*.

Practice and Problem Solving

A Practice by Example

Example 1 (page 438)

Seismology In 1812, an earthquake of magnitude 7.9 shook New Madrid, Missouri. Compare the amount of energy released by that earthquake to the amount of energy released by each earthquake below. **1–5. See margin.**

1. magnitude 7.7 in San Francisco, California, in 1906

2. magnitude 9.5 in Valdivia, Chile, in 1960

3. magnitude 3.2 in Charlottesville, Virginia, in 2001

4. magnitude 6.9 in Kobe, Japan, in 1995

5. magnitude 9.2 in Prince William Sound, Alaska, in 1964

Lesson 8-3 Logarithmic Functions as Inverses **441**

pages 441–444 Exercises

1. The earthquake in Missouri released about 1.97 times more energy.

2. The earthquake in Chile released about 231 times more energy.

3. The earthquake in Missouri released about 8,759,310 times more energy.

4. The earthquake in Missouri released about 30 times more energy.

5. The earthquake in Alaska released about 83 times more energy.

3. Practice

Assignment Guide

▼1 **Objective**

Ⓐ Ⓑ **Core** 1–34, 41–51, 53–62

Ⓒ **Extension** 84–88

▼2 **Objective**

Ⓐ Ⓑ **Core** 35–40, 52, 63–83

Ⓒ **Extension** 89–90

Standardized Test Prep 91–96

Mixed Review 97–109

Connection to Geology

Exercises 1–5 An earthquake is caused by rapid movement of the Earth's outer layer. This happens when energy that is usually stored within the Earth in the form of stress in rocks, suddenly releases. This energy is transmitted to the surface of the Earth by earthquake waves. Several hundred earthquakes occur every day around the world. Very large earthquakes, such as the Alaskan one in Exercise 1, occur once every few years. Moderate earthquakes occur about 20 times a year worldwide.

Enrichment 8-3

Reteaching 8-3

Practice 8-3

Practice 8-3	Logarithmic Functions as Inverses

Write each equation in exponential form.

1. $\log_4 256 = 4$ 2. $\log_5 1 = 0$ 3. $\log_2 32 = 5$ 4. $\log 10 = 1$

5. $\log_6 5 = 1$ 6. $\log_{11} \frac{1}{11} = -2$ 7. $\log_6 59,049 = 5$ 8. $\log_{17} 289 = 2$

9. $\log_{25} 1 = 0$ 10. $\log_{12} \frac{1}{144} = -2$ 11. $\log_{10} \frac{1}{10,000} = -10$ 12. $\log_9 6561 = 8$

Write each equation in logarithmic form.

13. $9^2 = 81$ 14. $25^2 = 625$ 15. $8^3 = 512$ 16. $13^2 = 169$

17. $2^9 = 512$ 18. $4^5 = 1024$ 19. $5^4 = 625$ 20. $10^{-3} = 0.001$

21. $4^{-3} = \frac{1}{64}$ 22. $5^{-2} = \frac{1}{25}$ 23. $8^{-1} = \frac{1}{8}$ 24. $11^0 = 1$

25. $6^1 = 6$ 26. $6^{-3} = \frac{1}{216}$ 27. $17^0 = 1$ 28. $17^1 = 17$

29. A single-celled bacterium divides every hour. The number N of bacteria after t hours is given by the formula $\log_2 N = t$. After how many hours will there be 32 bacteria?

Evaluate each logarithm.

30. $\log_{13} 16$ 31. $\log_5 8$ 32. $\log_4 4$ 33. $\log_2 2$

34. $\log_2 1$ 35. $\log_2 \frac{1}{2}$ 36. $\log_4 \frac{1}{4}$ 37. $\log_3 \frac{1}{3}$

38. $\log_{16} 16$ 39. $\log_5 125$ 40. $\log_{11} 121$ 41. $\log 0.1$

42. $\log 1$ 43. $\log_3 1$ 44. $\log_{16} 216$ 45. $\log_{12} 12$

46. $\log_{10} 30$ 47. $\log 100,000$ 48. $\log_9 \frac{1}{9}$ 49. $\log_2 \frac{1}{27}$

50. $\log \frac{1}{100}$ 51. $\log_4 32$ 52. $\log_3 \frac{1}{27}$ 53. $\log_{81} 9$

For each pH given, find the concentration of hydrogen ions $[H^+]$. Use the formula pH $= -\log[H^+]$.

54. 7.2   55. 7.3   56. 8.2   57. 6.2

58. 5.6   59. 4.6   60. 7.0   61. 2.9

Graph each logarithmic function.

62. $y = \log x$ 63. $y = \log_2 x$ 64. $y = \log_5 x$

65. $y = \log_3 x$ 66. $y = \log_3(x + 1)$ 67. $y = \log_2 x - 3$

68. $y = \log_3(x + 2)$ 69. $y = \log_2(x - 4) + 1$ 70. $y = \log_3(x - 3) + 1$

4   Lesson 8-3 Practice   Algebra 2 Chapter 8

441

Exercise 49 Different soils have different pH levels, and different plants need different pH levels to thrive. Landscape architects must know what types of plants prefer which pH levels. Areas with high rainfall usually have acidic soil, while arid regions usually have alkaline soil. The architects can modify the pH level by adding limestone (to decrease acidity) or sulfur (to increase acidity).

pages 441–444   Exercises

6. $\log_7 49 = 2$

7. $3 = \log 1000$

8. $\log_5 625 = 4$

9. $\log \frac{1}{10} = -1$

26. 6.3×10^{-6}

27. 6.3×10^{-3}

28. 1.0×10^{-8}

29. 7.9×10^{-4}

30. 5.0×10^{-7}

31. 1.3×10^{-5}

35.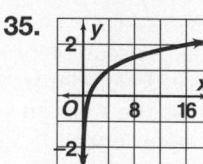

36.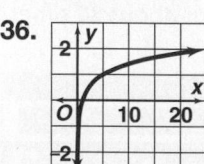

37.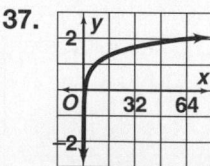

38.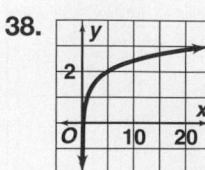

39.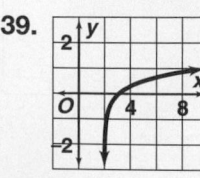

Example 2
(page 439)

Write each equation in logarithmic form.   6–9. See margin.

6. $49 = 7^2$ 7. $10^3 = 1000$ 8. $625 = 5^4$ 9. $\frac{1}{10} = 10^{-1}$

10. $8^2 = 64$ 11. $4 = \left(\frac{1}{2}\right)^{-2}$ 12. $\left(\frac{1}{3}\right)^3 = \frac{1}{27}$ 13. $10^{-2} = 0.01$
    $2 = \log_8 64$ $-2 = \log_{\frac{1}{2}} 4$ $3 = \log_{\frac{1}{3}}\left(\frac{1}{27}\right)$ $-2 = \log 0.01$

Example 3
(page 439)

Evaluate each logarithm.

14. $\log_2 16$ **4**   15. $\log_4 2$ $\frac{1}{2}$ 16. $\log_8 8$ **1**   17. $\log_4 8$ $\frac{3}{2}$

20. **undefined**

18. $\log_2 8$ **3**   19. $\log_{49} 7$ $\frac{1}{2}$ 20. $\log_5 (-25)$ 21. $\log_3 9$ **2**

22. $\log_2 2^5$ **5**   23. $\log_{\frac{1}{2}} \frac{1}{2}$ **1**   24. $\log 10{,}000$ **4**   25. $\log_5 125$ **3**

Example 4
(page 440)

The pH of each food is given. Find the concentration of hydrogen ions $[H^+]$.

26–31. See margin.

26. maple syrup, 5.2   27. lime juice, 2.2   28. egg white, 8.0

29. cider vinegar, 3.1   30. condensed milk, 6.3   31. soy sauce, 4.9

32. tomato juice, 4.0   33. watermelon, 5.4   34. mustard, 3.6
    1.0×10^{-4} 4.0×10^{-6} 2.5×10^{-4}

Examples 5 and 6
(pages 440 and 441)

Graph each logarithmic function.   35–40. See margin.

35. $y = \log_4 x$ 36. $y = \log_5 x$ 37. $y = \log_8 x$

38. $y = \log_5 x + 1$ 39. $y = \log_7 (x - 2)$ 40. $y = \log_3 (x - 5) + 3$

B Apply Your Skills

41. 0.6990; 0

42. −4.2147; −5

43. −1.0969; −2

Use your calculator to evaluate each logarithm to four decimal places. Then find the largest integer that is less than the value of the logarithm.

2.3010; 2

41. $\log 5$ 42. $\log (6.1 \times 10^{-5})$ 43. $\log 0.08$ 44. $\log 200$

45. $\log \frac{1}{6}$ 46. $\log 17.52$ 47. $\log (1.3 \times 10^7)$ 48. $\log \frac{13}{4}$
    −0.7782; −1   1.2435; 1   7.1139; 7   0.5119; 0

Reading Math

For help with reading and solving Exercise 49, see p. 445.

49. **Chemistry** The pH scale ranges from 0 to 14. A pH level of 7 is neutral. A level greater than 7 is basic, and a level less than 7 is acidic. The table shows the hydrogen ion concentration $[H^+]$ for selected foods. Find the pH of each item. Determine whether it is basic or acidic.
    See margin.

Approximate [H⁺] of Foods

Food	$[H^+]$
Apple juice	3.2×10^{-4}
Buttermilk	2.5×10^{-5}
Cream	2.5×10^{-7}
Ketchup	1.3×10^{-4}
Shrimp sauce	7.9×10^{-8}
Strained peas	1.0×10^{-6}

50. **Error Analysis** Find the error in the following evaluation of $\log_{27} 3$. Then evaluate the logarithm correctly.

$\log_{27} 3 = x$
$27 = x^3$ **The error is in the**
$3 = x$ **second line. It should**
        read $3 = 27^x$; the
$\log_{27} 3 = 3$ **correct answer is $\frac{1}{3}$.**

51. First rewrite $y = \log_1 x$ as $1^y = x$. For any real number $y, x = 1$.

51. **Writing** Explain why the base b in $y = \log_b x$ cannot equal 1.

52. **Open-Ended** Write a logarithmic function of the form $y = \log_b x$. Find its inverse function. Graph both functions on one set of axes. **See margin p. 443.**

Write each equation in exponential form.

0.0001 = 10⁻⁴   16,807 = 7⁵

53. $\log_2 128 = 7$ **$128 = 2^7$** 54. $\log 0.0001 = -4$ 55. $\log_7 16{,}807 = 5$

56. $\log_6 6 = 1$ **$6 = 6^1$**   57. $\log_4 1 = 0$ **$1 = 4^0$**   58. $\log_3 \frac{1}{9} = -2$ **$\frac{1}{9} = 3^{-2}$**

59. $\log_2 \frac{1}{2} = -1$ 60. $\log 10 = 1$ **$10 = 10^1$**   61. $\log_2 8192 = 13$
    $\frac{1}{2} = 2^{-1}$ **$8192 = 2^{13}$**

40.

49. apple juice: 3.5, acidic;
buttermilk: 4.6, acidic;
cream: 6.6, acidic;
ketchup: 3.9, acidic;
shrimp sauce: 7.1, basic;
strained peas: 6, acidic

Real-World  **Connection**

Samples are loaded into a linear accelerator for carbon dating.

67. $y = 10^x - 1$

68. $y = 10^{x-1}$

62. Archaeology One method of dating artifacts is radiocarbon dating. The artifacts in the table were found at a dig site near Kit Carson, Colorado. An artifact's age t in years is $t = 1.904 \times 10^4 \cdot \log\left(\frac{13.7}{R}\right)$, where R is the number of beta radiation emissions per minute per gram of carbon in the artifact.

Beta Emissions of Artifacts

Object	Mass of Carbon (g)	Beta Emissions per Minute
Buffalo bone	400	1640 ± 30
Bone fragment	15	61.5 ± 1.5
Pottery shard	25	342 ± 7
Charcoal	10	41.0 ± 1.3
Spear shaft	250	1020 ± 30

  a. For each artifact, use the range of beta emissions to find the artifact's maximum and minimum ages. **a–b. See margin.**

  b. Critical Thinking Which artifact is significantly different in age from the others? Give two possible explanations for the difference.

Find the inverse of each function.

63. $y = \log_4 x$ $y = 4^x$ **64.** $y = \log_{0.5} x$ $y = 0.5^x$ **65.** $y = \log_{10} x$ $y = 10^x$

66. $y = \log_2 2x$ $y = 2^{x-1}$ **67.** $y = \log(x+1)$ **68.** $y = \log 10x$

69. $y = \log(x-2)$ **70.** $y = \log_5 x^2$ $y = 5^{\frac{x}{2}}$ **71.** $y = \log_x 3$ $y = 3^{\frac{1}{x}}$
  $y = 10^x + 2$

Graph each logarithmic function.   **72–83. See margin p. 444.**

72. $y = \log 2x$ **73.** $y = 2\log_2 x$ **74.** $y = \log_4(2x+3)$

Find the domain and the range of the graph of each function.

75. $y = \log_5 x$ **76.** $y = 3\log x$ **77.** $y = \log_2(x-3)$

78. $y = 1 + \log x$ **79.** $y = \log(x-2)+1$ **80.** $y = \log_6(x+1)$

81. $y = \log_8 x - 2$ **82.** $y = \log_2 x + \frac{1}{3}$ **83.** $y = \log(x-t)$

C **Challenge** 🌐 **Sound** The loudness in decibels (dB) of a sound is defined as $10\log\frac{I}{I_0}$. I is the intensity of the sound. I_0 is 10^{-12}, the intensity of a barely audible sound. Complete the table.

Loudness of Sounds

	Type of Sound	Intensity (W/m²)	Loudness (dB)	
	Pain-producing	1	120	
84.	Jackhammer	10^{-2}	▦	**100**
85.	Busy street	10^{-5}	▦	**70**
86.	Conversation	10^{-6}	▦	**60**
87.	Whisper	10^{-10}	▦	**20**
88.	Rustle of leaves	10^{-11}	▦	**10**
	Barely audible sound	10^{-12}	0	

89. Match each function with its inverse.
  a. $y = \log_{\frac{1}{4}} x$ **III**   **b.** $y = \log_4 x$ **I**   **c.** $y = -\log_4 x$ **IV**   **d.** $y = -\log_{\frac{1}{4}} x$ **II**
  I. $y = 4^x$ **II.** $y = \left(\frac{1}{4}\right)^{-x}$ **III.** $y = \left(\frac{1}{4}\right)^x$ **IV.** $y = 4^{-x}$

Lesson 8-3 Logarithmic Functions as Inverses   **443**

52. Answers may vary.
Sample: $y = \log_3 x$;
$y = 3^x$

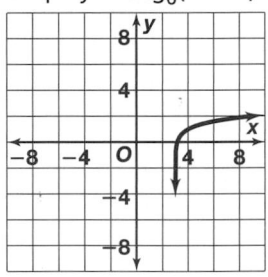

62a. buffalo bone: 9826 to 10,128 years old, bone fragment: 9776 to 10,180 years old, pottery shard: 0 to 183 years old, charcoal: 9718

4. Assess

📖 **Lesson Quiz 8-3**

Evaluate each logarithm.

1. $\log_2 32$ **5**

2. $\log_{10}(-100)$ **undefined**

3. $\log_5 \frac{1}{25}$ **−2**

Write each equation in exponential form.

4. $\log 0.01 = -2$ **$10^{-2} = 0.01$**

5. $\log_3 27 = 3$ **$3^3 = 27$**

6. Graph $y = \log_6(x-3)+1$.

Alternative Assessment

Organize students into groups of four. Have each student write a logarithmic function in the form of $y = \log_b x$. Direct students to pass their papers to the right. This student makes a table of x- and y-values and passes the paper to the right. This student graphs the function, and then rewrites the function to include a translation before passing the paper to the right. The last student graphs the translation. Have students pick 2 of their group's functions to review together to make sure all is correct. If there is time, let groups review all of their functions.

to 10,242 years old, spear shaft: 9776 to 10,263 years old

b. The pottery shard; answers may vary. Samples: the pottery may be from a later civilization, or the mass or the beta radiation emissions may have been measured incorrectly.

443

Standardized Test Prep

 **Resources**

For additional practice with a variety of test item formats:
- Standardized Test Prep, p. 473
- Test-Taking Strategies, p. 468
- Test-Taking Strategies with Transparencies

Exercises 93–96 It is usually best to simplify each value before carefully making an answer choice.

pages 441–444 Exercises

72.
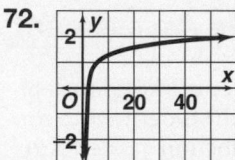

73.
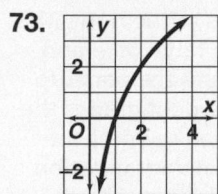

74.
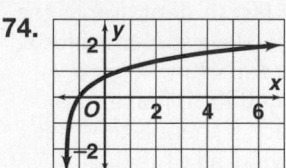

75. domain $\{x \mid x > 0\}$, range: all reals

76. domain $\{x \mid x > 0\}$, range: all reals

77. domain $\{x \mid x > 3\}$, range: all reals

78. domain $\{x \mid x > 0\}$, range: all reals

79. domain $\{x \mid x > 2\}$, range: all reals

80. domain $\{x \mid x > -1\}$, range: all reals

444

81. domain $\{x \mid x > 0\}$, range: all reals

82. domain $\{x \mid x > 0\}$, range: all reals

83. domain $\{x \mid x > t\}$, range: all reals

---

90. Match each function with the graph of its inverse.

a. $y = \log_3 x$ **II**   b. $y = \log_2 4x$ **III**   c. $y = \log_{\frac{1}{2}} x$ **I**

I. 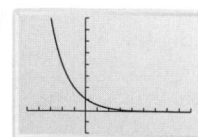   **II.** 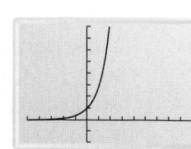   **III.**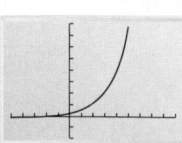

Standardized Test Prep

Multiple Choice

91. What is the ratio of $(65 \cdot 3^{17})$ to $(65 \cdot 3^{14})$? **D**
A. 17 to 14   B. 3 to 1   C. 9 to 1   D. 27 to 1

92. What is the logarithmic form of the exponential equation $2^4 = 16$? **I**
F. $\log_{16} 2 = 4$ G. $\log_{16} 4 = 2$ H. $\log_4 16 = 2$ I. $\log_2 16 = 4$

Quantitative Comparison

Take It to the NET
Online lesson quiz at
www.PHSchool.com
Web Code: aga-0803

Compare the boxed quantity in Column A with the boxed quantity in Column B. Choose the best answer.
A. The quantity in Column A is greater.
B. The quantity in Column B is greater.
C. The two quantities are equal.
D. The relationship cannot be determined from the information given.

	Column A	Column B
93. C	the value of x if $4^x = 64$	the value of y if $y = \log_5 125$
94. A	$\log_4 1$	$\log_4 \frac{1}{16}$
95. B	the value of x if $\log_x 36 = 2$	the value of y if $\log_{10} y = 2$
96. C	$\log_{16} 4$	$\log_{81} 9$

Mixed Review

Lesson 8-2   **Sketch the graph of each function. Then locate the asymptote of the curve.**

97. $y = 5^x - 100$ **98.** $y = -10(4)^{x+2}$ **99.** $y = -27(3)^{x-1} + 9$
97–99. See margin pp. 444–445.

Lesson 7-4   **Write each expression in radical form.**

100. $t^{\frac{2}{3}}$ $\sqrt[3]{t^2}$ **101.** $(16w^3)^{\frac{1}{2}}$ $4\sqrt{w^3}$ **102.** $z^{\frac{8}{5}}$ $\sqrt[5]{z^8}$ **103.** $x^{\frac{p}{n}}$ $\sqrt[n]{x^p}$

Lesson 6-4   **Solve each equation by graphing. If necessary, round to the nearest thousandth.**

104. $3x^2 + 18x + 24 = 0$ **105.** $1 - x = x^2 - 7x$ **106.** $x^4 = 7x^3 + 10x^2$
−2, −4   **−0.162, 6.162**   **−1.217, 0, 8.217**

Lesson 5-4   **Factor each expression.**

107. $4x^2 - 8x + 3$ **108.** $\frac{1}{4}b^2 - 4$ **109.** $5x^2 + 13x - 6$
$(2x - 3)(2x - 1)$ **$\left(\frac{1}{2}b - 2\right)\left(\frac{1}{2}b + 2\right)$**   **$(5x - 2)(x + 3)$**

97. 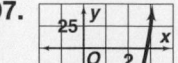  $y = -100$

98. 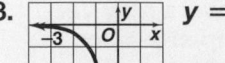 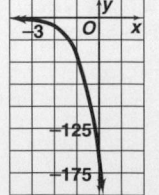 $y = 0$

Reading Data

FOR USE WITH PAGE 442, EXERCISE 49

Read the problem below to see how a table of values represents data. Check your understanding with the exercise at the bottom of the page.

Chemistry The pH scale ranges from 0 to 14. A pH level of 7 is neutral. A level greater than 7 is basic, and a level less than 7 is acidic. The table shows the hydrogen ion concentration [H+] for selected foods. Find the pH of each item. Determine whether it is basic or acidic.

Approximate [H+] of Selected Foods

Food	[H+]
Apple Juice	3.2×10^{-4}
Buttermilk	2.5×10^{-5}
Cream	2.5×10^{-7}
Ketchup	1.3×10^{-4}
Shrimp Sauce	7.9×10^{-8}
Strained Peas	1.0×10^{-6}

A table is a tool for organizing data.

The title of the table indicates the type of data represented. →

Approximate [H+] of Selected Foods

Food	[H+]
Apple Juice	3.2×10^{-4}
Buttermilk	2.5×10^{-5}

← Each row represents a different item. Row 1 contains data for apple juice.

Each column represents a different category of data. Column 2 lists the [H+] of each food.

Now you can use the table.

$$pH = -\log [H^+]$$ Refer to page 440 for the formula for pH.
$$pH \text{ of apple juice} = -\log ([H^+] \text{ of apple juice})$$ Use the formula.
$$= -\log (3.2 \times 10^{-4})$$ Substitute.
$$\approx 3.49$$ Simplify.

Since the pH of apple juice is less than 7, it is acidic.

The problem asks you to find the pH and whether the item is basic or acidic. To organize the information, you can add two columns to the table.

Food	[H+]	pH	Acid or Base
Apple Juice	3.2×10^{-4}	3.49	Acid

EXERCISE

Copy and complete the table below.

	[H+]	pH	Acid or Base	
7.34	4.6×10^{-8}	▪	▪	base
2.43	3.7×10^{-3}	▪	▪	acid
3.74	1.8×10^{-4}	▪	▪	acid

Reading Data

Students learn how to read and interpret data from a table of values. Once students understand the given information, students then use the data to perform calculations to solve problems.

Teaching Notes

Point out to students that the hydrogen ion concentration [H+] *is not* the same as the pH. Students must use the [H+] values listed in the table to find the pH for each food, and then they can determine whether the food is acidic or basic.

Foods that are acidic usually have a sour taste and foods that are basic usually have a bitter taste.

Because pH values are always positive and hydrogen ion concentrations are almost always fractional, it is very important for students to remember to find the negative log of the hydrogen ion concentration when finding pH.

Visual Learners

Suggest that students use the data in the table to create a graph that has [H+] ion concentration on one axis, and pH on another axis. Have students draw conclusions about the relationship between [H+] ion concentration and pH based on the graph

Exercise

The question asks students to fill in the pH and corresponding acidity. Remind students that the acidity depends on the pH value.

99. 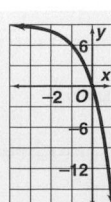 $y = 9$

1. Plan

Lesson Preview

✓ **Check Skills You'll Need**

Logarithmic Functions as Inverses
Lesson 8-3: Example 3
Exercises 7–12
Extra Practice, p. 329

Algebraic Expressions
Lesson 1-2: Examples 1, 2
Exercises 1–8
Extra Practice, p. 321

Lesson Resources

📁 **Teaching Resources**
Practice, Reteaching, Enrichment

👫 **Reaching All Students**
Practice Workbook 8-4
Spanish Practice Workbook 8-4

⏰ **Presentation Assistant Plus!**
Transparencies
• Check Skills You'll Need 8-4
• Additional Examples 8-4
• Student Edition Answers 8-4
• Lesson Quiz 8-4
PH Presentation Pro CD 8-4

PRENTICE HALL ASSESSMENT *SYSTEM*

Computer Test Generator CD

💿 **Technology**
Resource Pro® CD-ROM
Computer Test Generator CD
Prentice Hall Presentation Pro CD

💻 **www.PHSchool.com**
Student Site
• Teacher Web Code: agk-5500
• Self-grading Lesson Quiz
Teacher Center
• Lesson Planner
• Resources

Plus 🄸**TEXT**

8-4

Properties of Logarithms

 North Carolina Objectives

1.01 Simplify and perform operations with rational exponents and logarithms (common and natural) to solve problems.

Lesson Preview

What You'll Learn

OBJECTIVE **▼1** To use the properties of logarithms

. . . And Why

To relate sound intensity and decibel level, as in Example 4

✓ **Check Skills You'll Need**   (For help, go to Lessons 8-3 and 1-2.)

Simplify each expression.

1. $\log_2 4 + \log_2 8$ **5**   **2.** $\log_3 9 - \log_3 27$ **−1**   **3.** $\log_2 16 \div \log_2 64$ $\frac{2}{3}$

Evaluate each expression for $x = 3$.

4. $x^3 - x$ **24**   **5.** $x^5 \cdot x^2$ **2187**   **6.** $\frac{x^6}{x^9}$ $\frac{1}{27}$ **7.** $x^3 + x^2$ **36**

 **Interactive lesson includes instant self-check, tutorials, and activities.**

OBJECTIVE **1**
Using the Properties of Logarithms

1. 0, 0.301, 0.477, 0.602, 0.699, 0.778, 0.845, 0.903, 0.954, 1, 1.176, 1.301

2. The sum of the logarithms equals the log of the product.

> ### Investigation: Properties of Logarithms
>
> **1.** Complete the table. Round to the nearest thousandth.
>
> | x | 1 | 2 | 3 | 4 | 5 | 6 | 7 | 8 | 9 | 10 | 15 | 20 |
> |---|---|---|---|---|---|---|---|---|---|----|----|----|
> | log x | ▪ | ▪ | ▪ | ▪ | ▪ | ▪ | ▪ | ▪ | ▪ | ▪ | ▪ | ▪ |
>
> **2.** Complete each pair of statements. What do you notice? **See left.**
> **a.** log 3 + log 5 = ▪ and log (3 · 5) = ▪   **1.176, 1.176**
> **b.** log 1 + log 7 = ▪ and log (1 · 7) = ▪   **0.845, 0.845**
> **c.** log 2 + log 4 = ▪ and log (2 · 4) = ▪   **0.903, 0.903**
> **d.** log 10 + log 2 = ▪ and log (10 · 2) = ▪   **1.301, 1.301**
>
> **3.** Complete the statement: log M + log N = ▪.   **log (MN)**
>
> **4. a.** **Make a Conjecture** How could you rewrite the expression $\log \frac{M}{N}$ using the expressions log M and log N? $\log \frac{M}{N} = \log M - \log N$
> **b.** Use your calculator to verify your conjecture for several values of M and N.   **Check students' work.**

The properties of logarithms are summarized below.

🔧 **Key Concepts**

Properties	**Properties of Logarithms**
For any positive numbers, M, N, and b, $b \neq 1$,	
$\log_b MN = \log_b M + \log_b N$	**Product Property**
$\log_b \frac{M}{N} = \log_b M - \log_b N$	**Quotient Property**
$\log_b M^x = x \log_b M$	**Power Property**

 Ongoing Assessment and Intervention

Before the Lesson	**During the Lesson**	**After the Lesson**
Diagnose prerequisite skills using:	**Monitor progress using:**	**Assess knowledge using:**
• Check Skills You'll Need	• Check Understanding	• Lesson Quiz
	• Additional Examples	• Computer Test Generator CD
	• Standardized Test Prep	

You can use the properties of logarithms to rewrite logarithmic expressions.

1 EXAMPLE **Identifying the Properties of Logarithms**

State the property or properties used to rewrite each expression.

a. $\log_2 8 - \log_2 4 = \log_2 2$

Quotient Property: $\log_2 8 - \log_2 4 = \log_2 \frac{8}{4} = \log_2 2$

b. $\log_b x^3 y = 3 \log_b x + \log_b y$

Product Property: $\log_b x^3 y = \log_b x^3 + \log_b y$

Power Property: $\log_b x^3 + \log_b y = 3 \log_b x + \log_b y$

✓ **Check Understanding** **1** State the property or properties used to rewrite each expression.
a. $\log_5 2 + \log_5 6 = \log_5 12$ **Product Property**
b. $3 \log_b 4 - 3 \log_b 2 = \log_b 8$ **Power Property, Quotient Property**

You can write the sum or difference of logarithms with the same base as a single logarithm.

2 EXAMPLE **Simplifying Logarithms**

Write each logarithmic expression as a single logarithm.

a. $\log_3 20 - \log_3 4$

$\log_3 20 - \log_3 4 = \log_3 \frac{20}{4}$ **Quotient Property**

$= \log_3 5$ **Simplify.**

b. $3 \log_2 x + \log_2 y$

$3 \log_2 x + \log_2 y = \log_2 x^3 + \log_2 y$ **Power Property**

$= \log_2 \left(x^3 y \right)$ **Product Property**

So $\log_3 20 - \log_3 4 = \log_3 5$, and $3 \log_2 x + \log_2 y = \log_2 \left(x^3 y \right)$.

✓ **Check Understanding** **2 a.** Write $3 \log 2 + \log 4 - \log 16$ as a single logarithm. **log 2**

3a. $\log_2 7 + \log_2 b$

b. $2 \log y - 2 \log 3$

c. $3 \log_7 a + 4 \log_7 b$

b. Critical Thinking Can you write $3 \log_2 9 - \log_6 9$ as a single logarithm? Explain. **No; they do not have the same base.**

You can sometimes write a single logarithm as a sum or difference of two or more logarithms.

Reading Math

In mathematics, to expand means "to show the full form of."

3 EXAMPLE **Expanding Logarithms**

Expand each logarithm.

a. $\log_5 \frac{x}{y}$

$= \log_5 x - \log_5 y$ **Quotient Property**

b. $\log 3r^4$

$= \log 3 + \log r^4$ **Product Property**

$= \log 3 + 4 \log r$ **Power Property**

✓ **Check Understanding** **3** Expand each logarithm. **See above left.**
a. $\log_2 7b$ **b.** $\log \left(\frac{y}{3} \right)^2$ **c.** $\log_7 a^3 b^4$

👥 **Reaching All Students**

Below Level Have students state the Properties of Logarithms in words. Give illustrations using those words. Discuss whether these agree with the Property chosen.	**Advanced Learners** Ask students to explain how the properties of Logarithms on page 446 are similar to and how they are different from the properties of exponents.	**Inclusion** See note on page 448. **Error Prevention** See note on page 448.

---

2. Teach

Professional Development

Math Background

Many students want to believe that $\log_b (M + N) = \log_b M + \log_b N$. However, this would be equivalent to adding the exponents in expressions such as $x^2 + x^3$, which cannot be done. Thus, it is reasonable that there is *no* property for the logarithm of a sum. Do not confuse this with the valid property for a logarithm of a product, $\log_b (MN) = \log_b M + \log_b N$.

OBJECTIVE
1 ▼ **Teaching Notes**

Investigation (Optional)
Teaching Tip

Remind students that a logarithm is an exponent. Therefore, it seems reasonable that there are properties for operations with logarithms that are similar to the properties for operations with exponents.

2 EXAMPLE **Math Tip**

Point out to students that the bases are the same within each expression in part (a) and within each expression in part (b). The properties for logarithms do not apply unless the bases are the same.

Additional Examples

1 State the property or properties used to rewrite each expression.

a. $\log 6 = \log 2 + \log 3$
Product Property

b. $\log_b \frac{x^2}{y} = 2 \log_b x - \log_b y$

Quotient Property and Power Property

2 Write each expression as a single logarithm.
a. $\log_4 64 - \log_4 16$ **$\log_4 4$ or 1**
b. $6 \log_5 x + \log_5 y$ **$\log_5 (x^6 y)$**

Logarithms are used to model sound. The intensity of a sound is a measure of the energy carried by the sound wave. The greater the intensity of a sound, the louder it seems. This apparent loudness L is measured in decibels. You can use the formula $L = 10 \log \frac{I}{I_0}$, where I is the intensity of the sound in watts per square meter (W/m^2). I_0 is the lowest-intensity sound that the average human ear can detect.

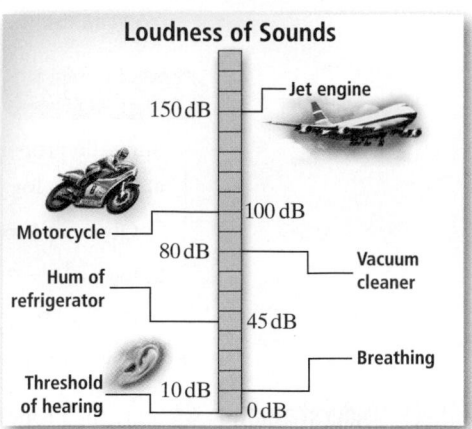

Loudness of Sounds

150 dB — Jet engine
100 dB
Motorcycle
80 dB — Vacuum cleaner
Hum of refrigerator
45 dB
Breathing
Threshold of hearing   10 dB
0 dB

4 EXAMPLE Real-World Connection

Real-World Connection

The workers who direct planes at airports must wear ear protection.

Noise Control A shipping company has started flying cargo planes out of the city airport. Residents in a nearby neighborhood have complained that the cargo planes are too loud. Suppose the shipping company hires you to design a way to reduce the intensity of the sound by half. By how many decibels would the loudness of the sound be decreased?

Relate The reduced intensity is one half of the present intensity.

Define Let $I_1 =$ present intensity.
Let $I_2 =$ reduced intensity.
Let $L_1 =$ present loudness.
Let $L_2 =$ reduced loudness.

Write $I_2 = 0.5 I_1$

$$L_1 = 10 \log \frac{I_1}{I_0}$$

$$L_2 = 10 \log \frac{I_2}{I_0}$$

$$L_1 - L_2 = 10 \log \frac{I_1}{I_0} - 10 \log \frac{I_2}{I_0}$$ Find the decrease in loudness $L_1 - L_2$.

$$= 10 \log \frac{I_1}{I_0} - 10 \log \frac{0.5 I_1}{I_0}$$ Substitute $I_2 = 0.5 I_1$.

$$= 10 \log \frac{I_1}{I_0} - 10 \log \left(0.5 \cdot \frac{I_1}{I_0}\right)$$

$$= 10 \log \frac{I_1}{I_0} - 10 \left(\log 0.5 + \log \frac{I_1}{I_0}\right)$$ Product Property

$$= 10 \log \frac{I_1}{I_0} - 10 \log 0.5 - 10 \log \frac{I_1}{I_0}$$ Distributive Property

$$= -10 \log 0.5$$ Combine like terms.

$$\approx 3.0$$ Use a calculator.

4. about 6 decibels

The decrease in loudness would be about three decibels.

✓ **Check Understanding** **4** Suppose the shipping company wants you to reduce the sound intensity to 25% of the original intensity. By how many decibels would the loudness be reduced?

pages 449–451 Exercises

1. Product Property
2. Quotient Property
3. Power Property
4. Power Property
5. Power Property, Quotient Property
6. Power Property
7. Power Property, Quotient Property
8. Power Property, Product Property
9. Power Property, Quotient Property
10. Power Property, Product Property

EXERCISES

For more practice, see *Extra Practice*.

Practice and Problem Solving

Ⓐ Practice by Example

Example 1
(page 447)

1–10. See margin p. 448.

State the property or properties used to rewrite each expression.

1. $\log 4 + \log 5 = \log 20$

2. $\log_3 32 - \log_3 8 = \log_3 4$

3. $\log z^2 = 2 \log z$

4. $\log_6 \sqrt[n]{x^p} = \frac{p}{n} \log_6 x$

5. $8 \log 2 - 2 \log 8 = \log 4$

6. $\log \sqrt[3]{3x} = \frac{1}{3} \log 3x$

7. $3 \log_4 5 - 3 \log_4 3 = \log_4 \left(\frac{5}{3}\right)^3$

8. $2 \log w + 4 \log z = \log w^2 z^4$

9. $2 \log_2 m - 4 \log_2 n = \log_2 \frac{m^2}{n^4}$

10. $\log_b \frac{1}{8} + 3 \log_b 4 = \log_b 8$

Example 2
(page 447)

Write each logarithmic expression as a single logarithm.

11. $\log 7 + \log 2$ **log 14**

12. $\log_2 9 - \log_2 3$ **$\log_2 3$**

13. $5 \log 3 + \log 4$ **log 972**

14. $\log 8 - 2 \log 6 + \log 3$ **$\log \frac{2}{3}$**

15. $4 \log m - \log n$ **$\log \frac{m^4}{n}$**

16. $\log 5 - k \log 2$ **$\log \frac{5}{2^k}$**

17. $\log_6 5 + \log_6 x$ **$\log_6 5x$**

18. $\log_7 x + \log_7 y - \log_7 z$ **$\log_7 \frac{xy}{z}$**

Example 3
(page 447)

Expand each logarithm. **19–30. See margin.**

19. $\log x^3 y^5$

20. $\log_7 22xyz$

21. $\log_4 5\sqrt{x}$

22. $\log 3m^4 n^{-2}$

23. $\log_5 \frac{r}{s}$

24. $\log_3 (2x)^2$

25. $\log_3 7(2x - 3)^2$

26. $\log \frac{a^2 b^3}{c^4}$

27. $\log \sqrt{\frac{2x}{y}}$

28. $\log_8 8\sqrt{3a^5}$

29. $\log \frac{s\sqrt{7}}{t^2}$

30. $\log_b \frac{1}{x}$

Example 4
(page 448)

31. One brand of ear plugs claims to block the sound of snoring as loud as 22 dB. A second brand claims to block snoring that is eight times as intense. If the claims are true, for how many more decibels is the second brand effective? **9 dB**

32. A sound barrier along a highway reduced the intensity of the noise reaching a community by 95%. By how many decibels was the noise reduced? **13 dB**

Ⓑ Apply Your Skills

Use the properties of logarithms to evaluate each expression.

33. $\log_2 4 - \log_2 16$ **−2**

34. $3 \log_2 2 - \log_2 4$ **1**

35. $\log_3 3 + 5 \log_3 3$ **6**

36. $\log 1 + \log 100$ **2**

37. $\log_6 4 + \log_6 9$ **2**

38. $2 \log_8 4 - \frac{1}{3} \log_8 8$ **1**

39. $2 \log_3 3 - \log_3 3$ **1**

40. $\frac{1}{2} \log_5 1 - 2 \log_5 5$ **−2**

41. $\log_9 \frac{1}{3} + 3 \log_9 3$ **1**

42. The coefficient $\frac{1}{2}$ is missing in $\log_4 s$; $\log_4 \sqrt{\frac{t}{s}} = \frac{1}{2} \log_4 \frac{t}{s} = \frac{1}{2}(\log_4 t - \log_4 s) = \frac{1}{2} \log_4 t - \frac{1}{2} \log_4 s$.

42. Error Analysis Explain why the expansion below of $\log_4 \sqrt{\frac{t}{s}}$ is incorrect. Then do the expansion correctly. **See left.**

$$\log_4 \sqrt{\frac{t}{s}} = \frac{1}{2} \log_4 \frac{t}{s}$$
$$= \frac{1}{2} \log_4 t - \log_4 s$$

43. Open-Ended Write log 150 as a sum or difference of two logarithms.
Answers may vary. Sample: log 150 = log 15 + log 10.

19. $3 \log x + 5 \log y$

20. $\log_7 22 + \log_7 x + \log_7 y + \log_7 z$

21. $\log_4 5 + \frac{1}{2} \log_4 x$

22. $\log 3 + 4 \log m - 2 \log n$

23. $\log_5 r - \log_5 s$

24. $2 \log_3 2 + 2 \log_3 x$

25. $\log_3 7 + 2 \log (2x - 3)$

26. $2 \log a + 3 \log b - 4 \log c$

27. $\frac{1}{2} \log 2 + \frac{1}{2} \log x - \frac{1}{2} \log y$

28. $1 + \frac{1}{2} \log_8 3 + \frac{5}{2} \log_8 a$

29. $\log s + \frac{1}{2} \log 7 - 2 \log t$

30. $-\log_b x$

Assignment Guide

1 Objective

Ⓐ Ⓑ Core 1–87
Ⓒ Extension 88–90

Standardized Test Prep 91–95

Mixed Review 96–108

Diversity

Exercise 32 Some students may not know what a sound barrier along a highway looks like. Ask students to bring pictures, draw a sketch, or tell where one can be seen nearby. Discuss the fact that highway sound barriers are often built to prevent highway noise from affecting neighborhoods.

Enrichment 8-4
Reteaching 8-4
Practice 8-4

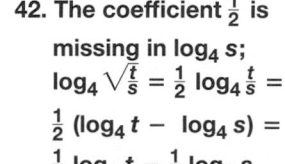

Alternative Assessment

Have students work in small groups to prepare an informal proof of an expanded logarithm from Exercises 79–87. They should justify each step, using the Properties of Logarithms. Then ask each group to present their proof at the board, and encourage class discussion of the proof.

71. No; the expression $(2x + 1)$ is a sum, so it is not covered by the Product, Quotient, or Power properties.

73. $\log_3 \sqrt[4]{2x}$

74. $\log_x \frac{2\sqrt{y}}{z^3}$

75. $\log \frac{27}{2}$

76. $\log_4 \frac{m^x n^{\frac{1}{y}}}{p}$

77. $\log_b \frac{\sqrt[3]{x^2}\sqrt[4]{y^3}}{z^5}$

78. $\log \frac{\sqrt[4]{z}}{\sqrt[4]{3}\sqrt{x^5}}$

pages 449–451 Exercises

58. True; $\log_2 4 = 2$ and $\log_2 8 = 3$.

59. False; $\frac{1}{2}\log_3 3 = \log_3 3^{\frac{1}{2}}$, not $\log_3 \frac{3}{2}$.

60. True; it is an example of the Power Property since $8 = 2^3$.

61. False; the two logs have different bases.

Real-World Connection

Decibel meters are used to measure sound levels.

Assume that $\log 4 \approx 0.6021$, $\log 5 \approx 0.6990$, and $\log 6 \approx 0.7782$. Use the properties of logarithms to evaluate each expression. Do not use your calculator.

44. $\log 24$ **1.3803**
45. $\log 30$ **1.4772**
46. $\log 16$ **1.2042**
47. $\log 125$ **2.097**
48. $\log 1.5$ **0.1761**
49. $\log 0.8$ **−0.0969**
50. $\log \frac{1}{4}$ **−0.6021**
51. $\log \frac{1}{25}$ **−1.398**
52. $\log 25$ **1.398**
53. $\log \frac{1}{6}$ **−0.7782**
54. $\log 36$ **1.5564**
55. $\log \sqrt{5}$ **0.3495**

56. **Noise Control** New components reduce the sound intensity of a certain model of vacuum cleaner from 10^{-4} W/m² to 6.31×10^{-6} W/m². By how many decibels do these new components reduce the vacuum cleaner's loudness? **12 dB**

57. **Reasoning** If $\log x = 5$, what is the value of $\frac{1}{x}$? **0.00001**

Write *true* or *false* for each statement. Justify your answer. **58–67. See margin.**

58. $\log_2 4 + \log_2 8 = 5$
59. $\log_3 \frac{3}{2} = \frac{1}{2}\log_3 3$
60. $\log_3 8 = 3 \log_3 2$
61. $\log_5 16 - \log 2 = \log_5 8$
62. $\log (x - 2) = \frac{\log x}{\log 2}$
63. $\frac{\log_b x}{\log_b y} = \log_b \frac{x}{y}$
64. $(\log x)^2 = \log x^2$
65. $\log_4 7 - \log_4 3 = \log_4 4$
66. $\log x + \log(x^2 + 2) = \log(x^3 + 2x)$
67. $\log_2 3 + \log_3 2 = \log_6 6$
68. $\log_2 x - 4 \log_2 y = \log_2 \frac{x}{y^4}$
68–69. See margin p. 451.
69. $\log_b \frac{1}{8} + 3 \log_b 4 = \log_b 8$

70. **Construction** Suppose you are the supervisor on a road construction job. Your team is blasting rock to make way for a roadbed. One explosion has an intensity of 1.65×10^{-2} W/m². What is the loudness of the sound in decibels? (Use $I_0 = 10^{-12}$ W/m².) **102 dB**

71. **Critical Thinking** Can you expand $\log_3 (2x + 1)$? Explain.

72. **Writing** Explain why $\log (5 \cdot 2) \neq \log 5 \cdot \log 2$. **See margin p. 451.**

Write each logarithmic expression as a single logarithm. **73–78. See left.**

73. $\frac{1}{4}\log_3 2 + \frac{1}{4}\log_3 x$
74. $\frac{1}{2}(\log_x 4 + \log_x y) - 3 \log_x z$
75. $2 \log 3 - \frac{1}{2}\log 4 + \frac{1}{2}\log 9$
76. $x \log_4 m + \frac{1}{y}\log_4 n - \log_4 p$
77. $\left(\frac{2 \log_b x}{3} + \frac{3 \log_b y}{4}\right) - 5 \log_b z$
78. $\frac{\log z - \log 3}{4} - 5 \frac{\log x}{2}$

Expand each logarithm. **79–87. See back of book.**

79. $\log \left(\frac{2\sqrt{x}}{5}\right)^3$
80. $\log \frac{m^3}{n^4 p^{-2}}$
81. $\log 2 \sqrt{\frac{4r}{s^2}}$
82. $\log_b \frac{\sqrt{x}\sqrt[3]{y^2}}{\sqrt[5]{z^2}}$
83. $\log_4 \frac{\sqrt{x^5 y^7}}{zw^4}$
84. $\log \frac{\sqrt{x^2 - 4}}{(x + 3)^2}$
85. $\log \sqrt{\frac{x\sqrt{2}}{y^2}}$
86. $\log_3 \left[(xy)^{\frac{1}{3}} \div z^2\right]^3$
87. $\log_7 \frac{\sqrt{r + 9}}{s^2 t^{\frac{1}{3}}}$

62. False; this is not an example of the Quotient Property. $\log(x - 2) \neq \log x - \log 2$.

63. False; $\log_b \frac{x}{y} = \log_b x - \log_b y$.

64. False; the exponent on the left means $\log x$, quantity squared, not the log of x^2.

65. False; $\log_4 7 - \log_4 3 = \log_4 \frac{7}{3}$, not $\log_4 4$.

66. True; $\log x + \log (x^2 + 2) = \log x(x^2 + 2)$, which equals $\log (x^3 + 2x)$.

67. False; the three logs have different bases.

C **Challenge**

88. Let $u = \log_b M$, and let $v = \log_b N$. Prove the Product Property of Logarithms by completing the equations below.

88. $v = \log_b N$
$b^v = N$
$MN = b^u \cdot b^v =$
b^{u+v}

$\log_b MN = u + v$
$\log_b MN = \log_b M$
$+ \log_b N$

Statement	Reason
$u = \log_b M$	Given
$b^u = M$	Rewrite in exponential form.
$v = \blacksquare$	Given
$b^v = \blacksquare$	Rewrite in exponential form.
$MN = b^u b^v = b^{\blacksquare}$	Apply the Product Property of Exponents.
$\log_b MN = \blacksquare$	Take the logarithm of each side.
$\log_b MN = \log_b \blacksquare + \log_b \blacksquare$	Substitute $\log_b M$ for u and $\log_b N$ for v.

89. Let $u = \log_b M$. Prove the Power Property of logarithms. **See margin.**

90. Let $u = \log_b M$ and $v = \log_b N$. Prove the Quotient Property of logarithms.
See margin.

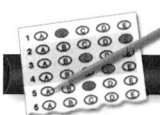

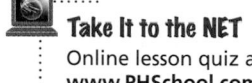
Standardized Test Prep

Multiple Choice

91. Which statement is NOT correct? **B**
  A. $\log_2 25 = 2 \cdot \log_2 5$ **B.** $\log_3 16 = 2 \cdot \log_3 8$
  C. $\log_5 27 = 3 \cdot \log_5 3$ **D.** $\log_8 10{,}000 = 4 \cdot \log_8 10$

Take It to the NET
Online lesson quiz at
www.PHSchool.com
Web Code: aga-0804

92. Which expression is equal to $\log_7 5 + \log_7 3$? **G**
  F. $\log_7 8$ **G.** $\log_7 15$ **H.** $\log_7 125$ **I.** $\log_{49} 15$

93. Which expression is equal to $\log_5 x + 4 \cdot \log_5 y - 2 \cdot \log_5 z$? **D**
  A. $\log_5 (-8xyz)$ **B.** $-\log_5 \frac{4xy}{2z}$ **C.** $\log_5 \frac{(xy)^4}{z^2}$ **D.** $\log_5 \frac{xy^4}{z^2}$

Short Response

94. $\log_5 10 \approx 1.4307$ and $\log_5 20 \approx 1.8614$. Find the value of $\log_5 \left(\frac{1}{2}\right)$ without using a calculator. Explain how you found the value. **See margin.**

Extended Response

95. Use the properties of logarithms to write log 12 in four different ways. Name each property you use. **See back of book.**

Mixed Review

Lesson 8-3
Write each equation in logarithmic form.
$-3 = \log_5 \frac{1}{125}$

96. $49 = 7^2$ **97.** $5^3 = 125$ **98.** $\frac{1}{4} = 8^{-\frac{2}{3}}$ **99.** $5^{-3} = \frac{1}{125}$
$\log_7 49 = 2$ $3 = \log_5 125$ $\log_8 \frac{1}{4} = -\frac{2}{3}$

Lesson 7-5
Solve each equation. Check for extraneous solutions.

100. $\sqrt[3]{y^4} = 16$ **8, −8**   **101.** $\sqrt[3]{7x} - 4 = 0$ $\frac{64}{7}$ **102.** $2\sqrt{w - 1} = \sqrt{w + 2}$ **2**

Lesson 6-5
A polynomial equation with integer coefficients has the given roots. What additional roots can you identify?

103. $\sqrt{3}, -\sqrt{5}$ $-\sqrt{3}, \sqrt{5}$ **104.** $-i, 4i$ $i, -4i$ **105.** $2i, -4 + i$ $-2i, -4 - i$

106. $\sqrt{2}, i - 1$ **107.** $-\sqrt{7}, -\sqrt{11}$ $\sqrt{7}, \sqrt{11}$ **108.** $-2i + 3, i$ $2i + 3, -i$
$-\sqrt{2}, -i - 1$

68. True; the power and quotient properties are used correctly.

69. True; the left side equals $\log_b \left(\frac{1}{8} \cdot 4^3\right)$, which equals $\log_b 8$.

72. The log of a product is equal to the sum of the logs. $\log (MN) = \log M + \log N$. So $\log (5 \cdot 2) = \log 10 = 1$, $\log 5 \cdot \log 2 \approx (0.7)(0.3) = 0.21$, which is not equal to 1.

Standardized Test Prep

📁 **Resources**
For additional practice with a variety of test item formats:
- Standardized Test Prep, p. 473
- Test-Taking Strategies, p. 468
- Test-Taking Strategies with Transparencies

Exercise 94 If some students are not sure how to begin working on this problem, suggest that they look for a way to rewrite $\frac{1}{2}$ using 10 and 20, and then use the properties of logarithms.

89. 1. $u = \log_b M$ (given)
2. $b^u = M^b$ (Rewrite in exponential form.)
3. $(b^u)^x = M^x$ (Raise each side to x power.)
4. $b^{ux} = M^x$ (Power Property of exponents)
5. $\log_b b^{ux} = \log_b M^x$ (Take the log of each side.)
6. $ux = \log_b M^x$ (Simplify.)
7. $\log_b M^x = x \cdot \log_b M$ (substitution)

90. 1. $u = \log_b M$ (given)
2. $b^u = M$ (Rewrite in exponential form.)
3. $v = \log_b N$ (given)
4. $b^v = N$ (Rewrite in exponential form.)
5. $\frac{M}{N} = \frac{b^u}{b^v} = b^{u-v}$ (Quotient Property of Exponents)
6. $\log_b \frac{M}{N} = \log_b b^{u-v}$ (Take the log of each side.)
7. $\log_b \frac{M}{N} = u - v$ (Simplify.)
8. $\log_b \frac{M}{N} = \log_b M - \log_b N$ (substitution)

94. [2] By the Quotient Property, $\log_5 \left(\frac{1}{2}\right) = \log_5 \left(\frac{10}{20}\right) \approx 1.4307 - 1.8614 = -0.4307$.
[1] correct answer, without work shown

451

Verifying Properties of Logarithms

Students use a graphing calculator to verify an instance of each logarithm property. They do this by graphing each side of the property equation and showing that these graphs are the same.

Resources

Students may use any graphing calculator.

Teaching Notes

Technology Tip

In Step 3, remind students to use the negative key (rather than the key for subtraction) to enter the Xmin and Ymin of −2 for the window.

Teaching Tip

Make sure students understand that they are only verifying these properties for one specific example. To prove the properties, students need to show that they hold in general. This can be done by using the definition of a logarithm and the properties of exponents.

page 452 Technology

3. Since the graphs are equivalent it is an identity; therefore the expressions are equal for all values of x > 1.

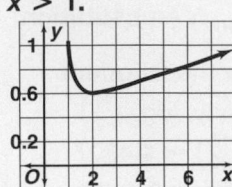

4.

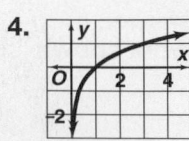

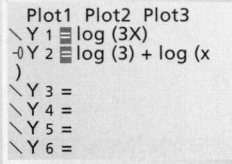

Technology **Verifying Properties of Logarithms**

FOR USE WITH LESSON 8-4

You can verify the properties of logarithms by graphing two equations simultaneously.

Take It to the NET
Graphing Calculator procedures online at www.PHSchool.com
Web Code: age-2117

EXAMPLE

Verify the Product Property for logarithms, $\log_b MN = \log_b M + \log_b N$, by graphing equations of the form $y = \log_b MN$ and $y = \log_b M + \log_b N$.

Step 1 Enter $Y_1 = \log(3x)$ and $Y_2 = \log(3) + \log(x)$. Don't forget to enter a closing parenthesis in Y_2.

Step 2 Place the cursor to the left of Y_2 and press ENTER four times. This changes the "path style" so that the second graph can be seen as drawn over the first graph.

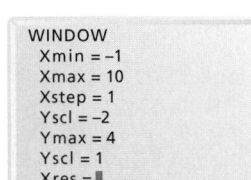

Step 3 Adjust the viewing window.

Step 4 Graph the equations. The moving circular cursor shows that the equations have the same graph.

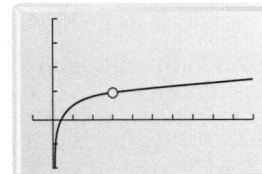

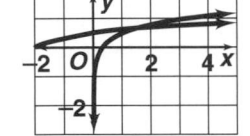

EXERCISES

1. Verify each property. **a–b. Check students' work.**
   a. Quotient Property   **b.** Power Property

2. a. Two expressions form an identity if they are always equal, regardless of the values of the variables. Substitute $M = 3$ and $N = x$ to show whether $\log(M + N) = \log M + \log N$ is an identity. Sketch the graph.
   b. For what values of x are the expressions equal? **1.5**

2a.
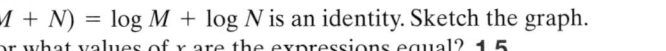

3. Show whether $\log\left(\frac{x}{x-1} + x\right) = \log\frac{x}{x-1} + \log x$ is an identity. Sketch the graph. For what values of x are the expressions equal? **See margin.**

4. A graphing calculator cannot directly graph logarithmic functions that are not common logarithms or natural logarithms. You can graph equations such as $y = \log_3 x$ by using the Change of Base Formula, $\log_b M = \frac{\log_c M}{\log_c b}$. Graph $y = \log_3 x$ using the Change of Base Formula. Use common logarithms in Y_1 and natural logarithms in Y_2. Sketch your graph. **See margin.**

5. Use your calculator to graph each equation. Sketch your graph. **a–c. See margin.**
   a. $y = \log_6 x$ **b.** $y = \log_8 x$ **c.** $y = \log_{16} x$

5a.
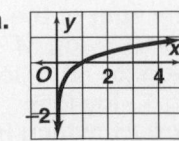

b.
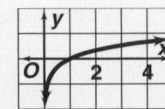

c.
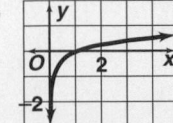

Exponential and Logarithmic Equations

 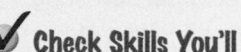

1.01 Simplify and perform operations with rational exponents and logarithms (common and natural) to solve problems.
2.01 Use the inverse of functions to model and solve problems.

Lesson Preview

What You'll Learn

 OBJECTIVE 1 To solve exponential equations

 OBJECTIVE 2 To solve logarithmic equations

. . . And Why

To model animal populations, as in Example 5

 Check Skills You'll Need (For help, go to Lessons 8-3 and 7-4.)

Evaluate each logarithm.

1. $\log_9 81 \cdot \log_9 3$ **1**　　**2.** $\log 10 \cdot \log_3 9$ **2**　　**3.** $\log_2 16 \div \log_2 8$ **$\frac{4}{3}$**

4. Simplify $125^{-\frac{2}{3}}$. **$\frac{1}{25}$**

New Vocabulary • exponential equation • Change of Base Formula
• logarithmic equation

Lesson Preview

 **Check Skills You'll Need**

Logarithmic Functions as Inverses
Lesson 8-3: Example 3
Exercises 7–12
Extra Practice, p. 829

Rational Exponents
Lesson 7-4: Example 4
Exercises 29–36
Extra Practice, p. 828

Lesson Resources

Teaching Resources
Practice, Reteaching, Enrichment
Checkpoint Quiz 2

 Reaching All Students
Practice Workbook 8-5
Spanish Practice Workbook 8-5
Reading and Math Literacy 8C
Spanish Reading & Literacy 8C
Spanish Checkpoint Quiz 2
Technology Activities 12
Hands-On Activities 48

Presentation Assistant Plus!
Transparencies
• Check Skills You'll Need 8-5
• Additional Examples 8-5
• Student Edition Answers 8-5
• Lesson Quiz 8-5
PH Presentation Pro CD 8-5

ASSESSMENT SYSTEM
Checkpoint Quiz 2
Computer Test Generator CD

Technology
Resource Pro® CD-ROM
Computer Test Generator CD
Prentice Hall Presentation Pro CD

www.PHSchool.com
Updated Data
Student Site
• Teacher Web Code: agk-5500
• Self-grading Lesson Quiz
Teacher Center
• Lesson Planner
• Resources

Plus

 OBJECTIVE 1 **Solving Exponential Equations**

 Need Help?

In a general form of an equation, c refers to a constant.

 Interactive lesson includes instant self-check, tutorials, and activities.

An equation of the form $b^{cx} = a$, where the exponent includes a variable, is an **exponential equation**. If m and n are positive and $m = n$, then $\log m = \log n$. You can therefore solve an exponential equation by taking the logarithm of each side of the equation.

1 EXAMPLE **Solving an Exponential Equation**

Solve $7^{3x} = 20$.

$$7^{3x} = 20$$

$\log 7^{3x} = \log 20$ — Take the common logarithm of each side.

$3x \log 7 = \log 20$ — Use the power property of logarithms.

$x = \dfrac{\log 20}{3 \log 7}$ — Divide each side by 3 log 7.

≈ 0.5132 — Use a calculator.

Check $7^{3x} = 20$

$7^{3(0.5132)} \approx 20.00382 \approx 20$ ✓

 Check Understanding **1** Solve each equation. Round to the nearest ten-thousandth. Check your answers.
a. $3^x = 4$ **1.2619**　　**b.** $6^{2x} = 21$ **0.8496**　　**c.** $3^{x+4} = 101$ **0.2009**

To evaluate a logarithm with any base, you can use the **Change of Base Formula**.

Key Concepts

Property	**Change of Base Formula**

For any positive numbers, M, b, and c, with $b \neq 1$ and $c \neq 1$,

$$\log_b M = \frac{\log_c M}{\log_c b}$$

 Ongoing Assessment and Intervention

Before the Lesson	**During the Lesson**	**After the Lesson**
Diagnose prerequisite skills using:	**Monitor progress using:**	**Assess knowledge using:**
• Check Skills You'll Need	• Check Understanding	• Lesson Quiz
	• Additional Examples	• Computer Test Generator CD
	• Standardized Test Prep	• Chapter Checkpoint 2 (p. 460)

Math Background

The Change of Base Formula allows you to rewrite any logarithm in terms of a logarithm to any desired base. Rewriting logarithms using base 10 or base e (discussed in Lesson 8-6) is important since most calculators can only compute logarithms with these two bases. Using the Change of Base Formula, students can write programs for their calculators that will compute logarithms whose bases are neither 10 nor e.

OBJECTIVE

1 Teaching Notes

1 EXAMPLE Math Tip

Point out that you can take the common logarithm (using base 10) of both sides of the equation no matter what base occurs in the equation. This means that you can use the feature of a calculator that finds the common logarithm.

3 EXAMPLE Auditory Learners

To help students see the meaning of $\log_2 2^{3x}$, have them say: *What power of 2 gives you 2 to the 3x?*

4 EXAMPLE Error Prevention

When you enter $y = 6^{2x}$, be sure to use parentheses to enter it as 6^(2x).

5 EXAMPLE Connection to Biology

Although the mathematical model may indicate a population in the single digits, the reality of living creatures will not fit the mathematical model exactly. There is a minimum population level below which an endangered species will probably not be able to survive.

---

2 EXAMPLE Using the Change of Base Formula

Use the Change of Base Formula to evaluate $\log_3 15$. Then convert $\log_3 15$ to a logarithm in base 2.

$$\log_3 15 = \frac{\log 15}{\log 3}$$ Use the Change of Base Formula.

$$\approx 2.4650$$ Use a calculator.

$$\log_3 15 = \log_2 x$$ Write an equation.

$$2.4650 \approx \log_2 x$$ Substitute $\log_3 15 = 2.465$.

$$2.4650 \approx \frac{\log x}{\log 2}$$ Use the Change of Base Formula.

$$2.4650 \cdot \log 2 \approx \log x$$ Multiply each side by log 2.

$$0.7420 \approx \log x$$ Simplify.

$$x \approx 10^{0.7420}$$ Write in exponential form.

$$\approx 5.5208$$ Use a calculator.

The expression $\log_3 15$ is approximately equal to 2.4650, or $\log_2 5.5208$.

✔ **Check Understanding** **2** **a.** Evaluate $\log_5 400$ and convert it to a logarithm in base 8. **3.7227, $\log_8 2301$**
   b. Critical Thinking Consider the equation $2.465 \approx \log_2 x$ from Example 2. How could you solve the equation without using the Change of Base Formula?
   Answers may vary. Sample: Use a calculator to raise 2 to the 2.465 power.

You can use the Change of Base Formula to solve an exponential equation. Take the logarithm of each side using the base of the exponent as the base for the logarithm. Then use the Change of Base Formula.

? Need Help?
If $y = b^x$, then $\log_b y = x$.

3 EXAMPLE Solving an Exponential Equation by Changing Bases

Solve $2^{3x} = 172$.

$$2^{3x} = 172$$

$$\log_2 2^{3x} = \log_2 172$$ Take the base-2 logarithm of each side.

$$3x = \log_2 172$$ Simplify.

$$3x = \frac{\log 172}{\log 2}$$ Use the Change of Base Formula.

$$x \approx 2.4754$$ Use a calculator to solve for x.

✔ **Check Understanding** **3** Use the Change of Base Formula to solve $7^{5x} = 3000$. Check your answer.
   0.8229

You can also solve exponential equations by graphing.

4 EXAMPLE Solving an Exponential Equation by Graphing

Solve $6^{2x} = 1500$.

Graph the equations $y = 6^{2x}$ and $y = 1500$. Find the point of intersection.

Intersection
X=2.040793   Y=1500

The solution is $x \approx 2.0408$.

🧑‍🤝‍🧑 Reaching All Students

Below Level When solving an exponential equation by taking the logarithm of both sides, the Power Property of Logarithms is used to solve for the variable. Review the Power Property.	**Advanced Learners** Have students research what form of radioactive dating is most useful for charcoal that is less than 50,000 years old.	**English Learners** See note on page 457. **Auditory Learners** See note on page 454.

✓ **Check Understanding** ④ Solve $11^{6x} = 786$ by graphing. **0.4634**

⑤ **EXAMPLE** <u>Real-World</u> 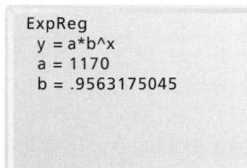 **Connection**

Zoology Refer to the photo. Write an exponential equation to model the decline in the population. If the decay rate remains constant, in what year might only five peninsular bighorn sheep remain in the United States?

Step 1 Enter the data into your calculator. Let 0 represent the initial year, 1971.

Step 2 Use the **ExpReg** feature to find the exponential function that fits the data.

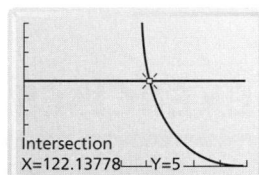
```
ExpReg
y = a*b^x
a = 1170
b = .9563175045
```

Real-World 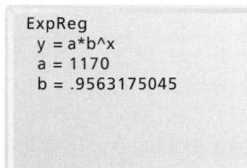 **Connection**

The U.S. population of peninsular bighorn sheep was 1170 in 1971. By 1999, only 335 remained.

Step 3 Graph the function and the line $y = 5$.

Step 4 Find the point of intersection.

The solution is $x \approx 122$, and $1971 + 122 = 2093$, so there may be only five peninsular bighorn sheep in 2093.

```
          ⨯
Intersection
X=122.13778   Y=5
```

✓ **Check Understanding** ⑤ The population of peninsular bighorn sheep in Mexico was approximately 6200 in 1971. By 1999, about 2300 remained. Determine the year by which only 200 peninsular bighorn sheep might remain in Mexico. **2068**

OBJECTIVE
2
Solving Logarithmic Equations

An equation that includes a logarithmic expression is called a **logarithmic equation.**

⑥ **EXAMPLE** **Solving a Logarithmic Equation**

Solve $\log (3x + 1) = 5$.

$\log (3x + 1) = 5$

$\quad 3x + 1 = 10^5$ **Write in exponential form.**

$\quad 3x + 1 = 100{,}000$

$\quad\quad\quad x = 33{,}333$ **Solve for x.**

Check $\log (3x + 1) = 5$

$\quad\quad \log (3 \cdot 33{,}333 + 1) \stackrel{?}{=} 5$

$\quad\quad\quad\quad \log 100{,}000 \stackrel{?}{=} 5$

$\quad\quad\quad\quad\quad \log 10^5 = 5 \checkmark$

✓ **Check Understanding** ⑥ Solve $\log (7 - 2x) = -1$. Check your answer. **3.45**

In some cases, you must use the properties of logarithms to simplify expressions before solving the equation.

Lesson 8-5 Exponential and Logarithmic Equations   **455**

Additional Examples

① Solve $5^{2x} = 16$. **about 0.861**

② Use the Change of Base Formula to evaluate $\log_6 12$. Then convert $\log_6 12$ to a logarithm in base 3. **about 1.387; about $\log_3 4.589$**

③ Solve $5^{2x} = 120$. **about 1.487**

④ Solve $4^{3x} = 1100$ by graphing. $x \approx 1.684$

⑤ The population of trout in a certain stretch of the Platte River is shown for five consecutive years in the table, where 0 represents the year 1997. If the decay rate remains constant, in the beginning of which year might at most 100 trout remain in this stretch of river? **2015**

Time t	0	1	2	3	4
Pop. $P(t)$	5000	4000	3201	2561	2049

OBJECTIVE
2 **Teaching Notes**

⑦ **EXAMPLE** **Teaching Tip**

Ask a volunteer to explain why the logarithm of a negative number must be undefined.

Additional Examples

⑥ Solve $\log (2x - 2) = 4$. **5001**

⑦ Solve $3 \log x - \log 2 = 5$. **about 58.48**

Closure

Ask students to give examples of equations that can be solved by using the properties of exponents and logarithms.

Assignment Guide

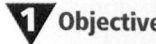 **Objective**

Ⓐ Ⓑ **Core** 1–32, 48–54, 61–63, 79–81

Ⓒ **Extension** 98–99, 104–105

 **Objective**

Ⓐ Ⓑ **Core** 33–47, 55–60, 64–78, 82–96

Ⓒ **Extension** 97, 100–103

Standardized Test Prep 107–113

Mixed Review 114–127

Enrichment 8-5

Reteaching 8-5

Practice 8-5

⑦ EXAMPLE Using Logarithmic Properties to Solve an Equation

Solve $2 \log x - \log 3 = 2$.

$2 \log x - \log 3 = 2$

$\log \left(\frac{x^2}{3}\right) = 2$ **Write as a single logarithm.**

$\frac{x^2}{3} = 10^2$ **Write in exponential form.**

$x^2 = 3(100)$ **Multiply each side by 3.**

$x = \pm 10\sqrt{3}$, or about ± 17.32

Since the logarithm of a negative number is undefined, the only solution is $10\sqrt{3}$, or about 17.32.

✓ **Check Understanding** ⑦ Solve $\log 6 - \log 3x = -2$. **200**

EXERCISES

For more practice, see *Extra Practice.*

Practice and Problem Solving

Ⓐ **Practice by Example**

Example 1
(page 453)

Solve each equation. Round to the nearest ten-thousandth. Check your answers.

1. $2^x = 3$ **1.5850**   **2.** $4^x = 19$ **2.1240**   **3.** $5^x = 81.2$ **2.7320**   **4.** $3^x = 27.3$ **3.0101**

5. $8 + 10^x = 1008$ **3**   **6.** $5 - 3^x = -40$ **3.4650**   **7.** $9^{2y} = 66$ **0.9534**

8. $14^{x+1} = 36$ **0.3579**   **9.** $12^{y-2} = 20$ **3.2056**   **10.** $25^{2x+1} = 144$ **0.2720**

Example 2
(page 454)

Use the Change of Base Formula to evaluate each expression. Then convert it to a logarithm in base 8.   **11–18. See margin.**

11. $\log_2 9$ **12.** $\log_4 8$ **13.** $\log_3 54$ **14.** $\log_5 62$

15. $\log_3 33$ **16.** $\log_2 7$ **17.** $\log_5 510$ **18.** $\log_4 1.116$

Example 3
(page 454)

Use the Change of Base Formula to solve each equation.   **19–22. See margin.**

19. $2^x = 5$ **20.** $6^{2x} = 21$ **21.** $7^{x+2} = 54$ **22.** $3^x = 27.3$

23. $4^{2x} = 17$ **1.0219**   **24.** $5^{x+1} = 24$ **0.9746**   **25.** $3^{x+4} = 101$ **0.2009**   **26.** $4^{x-2} = 89$ **5.2379**

Examples 4 and 5
(pages 454 and 455)

Solve by graphing.

27. $4^{7x} = 250$ **0.5690**   **28.** $5^{3x} = 500$ **1.2871**   **29.** $6^x = 4565$ **4.7027**   **30.** $1.5^x = 356$ **14.4894**

31. An investment of $2000 earns 5.75% interest, which is compounded quarterly. After approximately how many years will the investment be worth $3000? **about 7.1 years**

32. The equation $y = 281(1.0124)^x$ models the U.S. population y, in millions of people, x years after the year 2000. Graph the function on your graphing calculator. Estimate when the U.S. population will reach 350 million. **about 2018**

Example 6
(page 455)

Solve each equation. Check your answers.

33. $\log 2x = -1$ **0.05**   **34.** $2 \log x = -1$ **34.** $\frac{\sqrt{10}}{10}$ or about 0.3162

35. $\log (3x + 1) = 2$ **33**

36. $\log x + 4 = 8$ **10,000**   **37.** $\log 6x - 3 = -4$ **37.** $\frac{1}{60}$, or ≈0.0167

38. $\log (x - 2) = 1$ **12**

39. $3 \log x = 1.5$ $\sqrt{10}$, or about 3.1623   **40.** $2 \log (x + 1) = 5$ **40.** $100\sqrt{10} - 1$, or ≈ 315.2

41. $\log (5 - 2x) = 0$ **2**

pages 456–460 Exercises

11. 3.1699; $\log_8 729$

12. 1.5; $\log_8 22.627$

13. 3.6309; $\log_8 1901.3$

14. 2.5643; $\log_8 206.93$

15. 3.1827; $\log_8 748.56$

16. 2.8074; $\log_8 343$

17. 3.8737; $\log_8 3149.6$

18. 0.0792; $\log_8 1.1790$

19. 2.3219

20. 0.8496

21. 0.0499

22. 3.0101

Example 7
(page 456)

Solve each equation.

42. $\log x - \log 3 = 8$ **3×10^8**

43. $\log 2x + \log x = 11$ **$100{,}000\sqrt{5}$, or about 223,606.8**

44. $2 \log x + \log 4 = 2$ **5**

45. $\log 5 - \log 2x = 1$ **$\frac{1}{4}$**

46. $3 \log x - \log 6 + \log 2.4 = 9$ **1357.2**

47. $\log (7x + 1) = \log (x - 2) + 1$ **7**

B **Apply Your Skills**

48. Consider the equation $2^{\frac{x}{3}} = 80$. **a–c. See margin.**
  a. Solve the equation by taking the logarithm in base 10 of each side.
  b. Solve the equation by taking the logarithm in base 2 of each side.
  c. Writing Compare your result in parts (a) and (b). What are the advantages of either method? Explain.

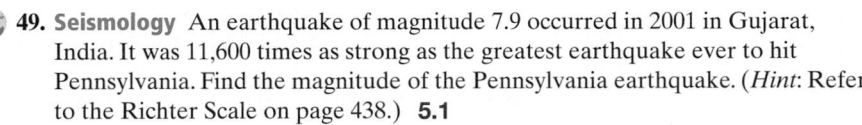

49. Seismology An earthquake of magnitude 7.9 occurred in 2001 in Gujarat, India. It was 11,600 times as strong as the greatest earthquake ever to hit Pennsylvania. Find the magnitude of the Pennsylvania earthquake. (*Hint*: Refer to the Richter Scale on page 438.) **5.1**

Write an equation. Then solve the equation without graphing.

50. A parent raises a child's allowance by 20% each year. If the allowance is $8 now, when will it reach $20? **$20 = 8(1.2)^x$, 5 years**

51. Protactinium-234*m*, a toxic radioactive metal with no known use, has a half-life of 1.17 minutes. How long does it take for a 10-mg sample to decay to 2 mg? **See margin.**

52. As a town gets smaller, the population of its high school decreases by 12% each year. The student body numbers 125 students now. In how many years will it number about 75 students? **$75 = 125(0.88)^x$, 4 years**

Real-World **Connection**

Careers Seismologists use models to determine the source, nature, and size of seismic events.

Mental Math Solve each equation.

53. $2^x = \frac{1}{2}$ **−1**

54. $3^x = 27$ **3**

55. $\log_9 3 = x$ **$\frac{1}{2}$**

56. $\log_4 64 = x$ **3**

57. $\log_8 2 = x$ **$\frac{1}{3}$**

58. $10^x = \frac{1}{100}$ **−2**

59. $\log_7 343 = x$ **3**

60. $25^x = \frac{1}{5}$ **$-\frac{1}{2}$**

Population The table below shows information about the population of the four most populous states in the United States in 2000. Use it for Exercises 61–63.

Largest States

Rank in 2000	State	2000 Population	Average Annual Percentage Increase Since 1990
1	California	33,871,648	1.30%
2	Texas	20,851,820	2.08%
3	New York	18,976,457	0.54%
4	Florida	15,982,378	2.13%

SOURCE: U.S. Census Bureau. Go to **www.PHSchool.com** for a data update. Web Code: agg-2041

61a. Florida growth factor = 1.0213, $y = 15{,}982{,}378 \cdot (1.0213)^x$; New York growth factor = 1.0054, $y = 18{,}976{,}457 \cdot (1.0054)^x$

b. 2011

62a. Texas growth factor = 1.0208, $y = 20{,}851{,}820 \cdot (1.0208)^x$; California growth factor = 1.013, $y = 33{,}871{,}648 \cdot (1.013)^x$

61. a. Determine the growth factors for Florida and New York. Then write an equation to model each state's population growth. **a–b. See left.**
  b. Estimate when Florida's population might exceed New York's population.

62. a. Determine the growth factors for Texas and California. Then write an equation to model each state's population growth.
  b. Estimate when Texas's population might exceed California's population. **2063**

63. Critical Thinking Is it likely that Florida's population will exceed that of Texas? Explain your reasoning. **See margin.**

48a. 18.9658

  b. 18.9658

c. Answers may vary. Sample: You don't have to use the change of base formula with the base-10 method, but there are fewer steps with the base-2 method.

51. $2 = 10\left(\frac{1}{2}\right)^{\frac{x}{1.17}}$, 2.7 min

English Learners
Exercise 51 Ask a volunteer student to explain the meaning of *toxic*. Discuss the pronunciation of *protactinium*, with help from the chemistry teacher or a dictionary if needed. **prō´ tak tin´ ē əm**

Alternative Method
Exercise 53 Organize students in groups of 3. Have each student in the group try a different method: making a table to show successive values, graphing, or solving without graphing. Then have them discuss the relative merits of each method.

63. Since Florida's growth rate is larger than Texas's growth rate, in theory, given constant conditions, Florida would exceed Texas in about 543 years. However, since no state has unlimited capacity for growth, it is unrealistic to predict over a long period of time.

457

pages 456–460   Exercises

65. Answers may vary.
Sample: $\log x = 1.6$
$10^{1.6} = x$, $x \approx 39.81$

66. Answers may vary.
Sample: A possible model is
$y = 1465(1.0838)^x$ where
$x = 0$ represents 1991; the growth is probably exponential and
$1465(1.0838)^{10} \approx 3276$; using this model, there will be 10,000 manatees in about 2015.

67a. $x = \dfrac{\log b}{\log a}$

b. $x = \log_a b = \dfrac{\log b}{\log a}$

c. Substituting the result from part (a) into the results from part (b), or vice versa, yields $\log_a b = \dfrac{\log b}{\log a}$. This justifies the Change of Base Formula for $c = 10$.

77a. top up: 10^{-5} W/m^2, top down: $10^{-2.5}$ W/m^2

b. 99.68%

Real-World 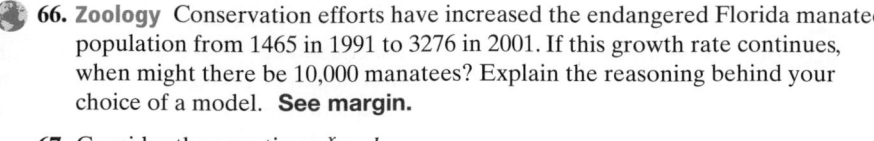 **Connection**

Many Florida manatees die after collisions with motorboats.

75. $\dfrac{\log (x + 1)}{\log x}$

---

64. Error Analysis What is wrong with the "proof" below that $2 = 1$?

$$2 = \tfrac{2}{1} = \frac{\log 10^2}{\log 10^1} = \log 10^{2-1} = \log 10^1 = 1 \qquad \frac{\log 10^2}{\log 10^1} \neq \log 10^{2-1}$$

65. Open-Ended Write and solve a logarithmic equation. **See margin.**

66. Zoology Conservation efforts have increased the endangered Florida manatee population from 1465 in 1991 to 3276 in 2001. If this growth rate continues, when might there be 10,000 manatees? Explain the reasoning behind your choice of a model. **See margin.**

67. Consider the equation $a^x = b$.
   a. Solve the equation by using log base 10. **a–c. See margin.**
   b. Solve the equation by using log base a.
   c. Use your results in parts (a) and (b) to justify the Change of Base Formula.

Write each logarithm as the quotient of two common logarithms. Do not simplify the quotient.

68. $\log_7 2$ $\dfrac{\log 2}{\log 7}$ **69.** $\log_3 8$ $\dfrac{\log 8}{\log 3}$ **70.** $\log_5 140$ $\dfrac{\log 140}{\log 5}$ **71.** $\log_9 3.3$ $\dfrac{\log 3.3}{\log 9}$

72. $\log_4 3x$ $\dfrac{\log 3x}{\log 4}$ **73.** $\log_6 (1 - x)$ $\dfrac{\log (1 - x)}{\log 6}$ **74.** $\log_x 5$ $\dfrac{\log 5}{\log x}$ **75.** $\log_x (x + 1)$
   See left.

Acoustics In Exercises 76–78, the loudness measured in decibels (dB) is defined by loudness $= 10 \log \dfrac{I}{I_0}$, where I is the intensity and $I_0 = 10^{-12}$ W/m^2.

76. The human threshold for pain is 120 dB. Instant perforation of the eardrum occurs at 160 dB.
   a. Find the intensity of each sound. 10^0 (or 1) W/m^2, 10^4 W/m^2
   b. How many times as intense is the noise that will perforate an eardrum as the noise that causes pain? **10,000 times more intense**

77. The noise level inside a convertible driving along the freeway with its top up is 70 dB. With the top down, the noise level is 95 dB. **a–b. See margin.**
   a. Find the intensity of the sound with the top up and with the top down.
   b. By what percent does leaving the top up reduce the intensity of the sound?

78. A screaming child can reach 90 dB. A launch of the space shuttle produces sound of 180 dB at the launch pad.
   a. Find the intensity of each sound. 10^{-3} W/m^2, 10^6 W/m^2
   b. How many times as intense as the noise from a screaming child is the noise from a shuttle launch? 10^9 **times more intense**

Solve each equation. If necessary, round to the nearest ten-thousandth.

79. $8^x = 444$ **2.9315**   **80.** $14^{9x} = 146$ **0.2098**

81. $3^{7x} = 120$ **0.6225**   **82.** $\tfrac{1}{2} \log x + \log 4 = 2$ **625**

83. $4 \log_3 2 - 2 \log_3 x = 1$ **2.3094**   **84.** $\log x^2 = 2$ **10**

85. $9^{2x} = 42$ **0.8505**   **86.** $\log_8 (2x - 1) = \tfrac{1}{3}$ **1.5**

87. $1.3^x = 7$ **7.4168**   **88.** $\log (5x - 4) = 3$ **200.8**

89. $2.1^x = 9$ **2.9615**   **90.** $12^{4-x} = 20$ **2.7944**

91. $5^{3x} = 125$ **1**   **92.** $\log 4 + 2 \log x = 6$ **500**

93. $4^{3x} = 77.2$ **1.0451**   **94.** $\log_7 3x = 3$ **114.$\overline{3}$**

95. $3^x + 0.7 = 4.9$ **1.3063**   **96.** $7^x - 1 = 371$ **3.0417**

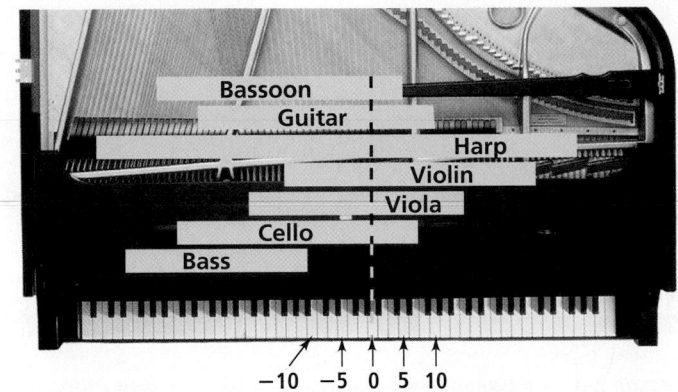

Lesson Quiz 8-5

Use mental math to solve each equation.

1. $2^x = \frac{1}{8}$ **−3**
2. $\log_4 2 = x$ **$\frac{1}{2}$**
3. $10^{6x} = 1$ **0**
4. Solve $5^{2x} = 125.$ **$\frac{3}{2}$**

C Challenge

97a. bassoon, guitar, harp, violin, viola, cello

b. bassoon, guitar, harp, cello, bass

c. harp, violin

d. harp, violin

97. Music The pitch, or frequency, of a piano note is related to its position on the keyboard by the function $F(n) = 440 \cdot 2^{\frac{n}{12}}$, where F is the frequency of the sound wave in cycles per second and n is the number of piano keys above or below Concert A, as shown above. If $n = 0$ at Concert A, which of the instruments shown in the diagram can sound notes of the given frequency?

a. 590　　　　**b.** 120　　　　**c.** 1440　　　　**d.** 2093

98. Astronomy The brightness of an astronomical object is called its magnitude. A decrease of five magnitudes increases the brightness exactly 100 times. The sun is magnitude -26.7, and the full moon is magnitude -12.5. The sun is about how many times brighter than the moon?　**478,630 times**

99. Archaeology A scientist carbon-dates a piece of fossilized tree trunk that is thought to be over 5000 years old. The scientist determines that the sample contains 65% of the original amount of carbon-14. The half-life of carbon-14 is 5730 years. Is the reputed age of the tree correct? Explain.　**No; solving $0.65 = (0.5)^{\frac{x}{5730}}$ for x, the age in years of the sample, yields an age of about 3561 yr.**

Solve each equation.

104. 20,031 m above sea level

100. $\log_7 (2x - 3)^2 = 2$　**5**

101. $\log_2 (x^2 + 2x) = 3$　**−4, 2**

102. $\log_4 (x^2 - 17) = 3$　**−9, 9**

103. $\frac{3}{2} \log_2 4 - \frac{1}{2} \log_2 x = 3$　**1**

104. In the formula $P = P_0 (\frac{1}{2})^{\frac{h}{4795}}$, P is the atmospheric pressure in millimeters of mercury at elevation h meters above sea level. P_0 is the atmospheric pressure at sea level. If P_0 equals 760 mm, at what elevation is the pressure 42 mm?

105b. 0.928 mg or 1.061 mg

c. Estimate in hours is more accurate; the days have a larger rounding error.

105. Chemistry A technician found 12 mg of a radon isotope in a soil sample. After 24 hours, another measurement revealed 10 mg of the isotope.

　a. Estimate the length of the isotope's half-life to the nearest hour and to the nearest day.　**91 hours or 4 days**

　b. For each estimate, determine the amount of the isotope after two weeks.

　c. Compare your answers to part (b). Which is more accurate? Explain.

Alternative Assessment

Have a class discussion. Ask students to talk about which aspect of solving exponential and logarithmic equations they found most confusing or difficult, citing specific examples from the lesson. Have other students give tips and explanations to help clarify the topics. Be sure each student contributes to the discussion.

Standardized Test Prep

A sheet of blank grids is available in the Test-Taking Strategies with Transparencies booklet. Give this sheet to students for practice with filling in the grids.

Resources

For additional practice with a variety of test item formats:
- Standardized Test Prep, p. 473
- Test-Taking Strategies, p. 468
- Test-Taking Strategies with Transparencies

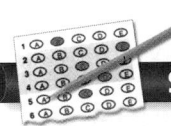

Standardized Test Prep

Gridded Response　Use a calculator to solve each equation. Enter each answer to the nearest hundredth.

106. $7^{2x} = 75$　**1.11**　　　**107.** $11^{x-5} = 250$　**7.30**　　　**108.** $1080 = 15^{3x-4}$　**2.19**

To check understanding of Lessons 8-3 to 8-5:

Checkpoint Quiz 2 (p. 460)

📁 **Teaching Resources**
Checkpoint Quiz 2 (also in Prentice Hall Assessment System)

👥 **Reaching All Students**
Reading and Math Literacy 8C

Spanish versions available

---

pages 456–460   Exercises

113. $\log 2 + 3 \log x - 2 \log y$

114. $\log_3 x - \log_3 y$

115. $3 \log_2 3 + 3 \log_2 x$

116. $\log_3 7 + 2 \log_3 (2x - 3)$

117. $\log_4 5 + \frac{1}{2} \log_4 x$

118. $\log_2 5 + \log_2 a - 2 \log_2 b$

page 460   Checkpoint Quiz 2

1.
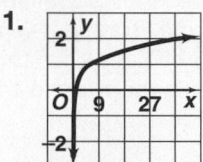

2.
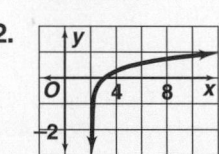

4. $2 \log_6 3 + 2 \log_6 x + 2 \log_6 y$

5. $\log_6 4 + \frac{1}{2} \log_6 x$

10. Rewrite $\log_2 10$ as $\frac{\log 10}{\log 2}$ and evaluate it to get ≈ 3.322. Then set $3.322 = \log_3 x$. Rewrite to get $3.322 = \frac{\log x}{\log 3}$ and solve. Convert $\log x = 1.585$ to $10^{1.585} = x$ or $x \approx 38.46$. So $\log_2 10 \approx \log_3 38.46$.

Gridded Response

Take It to the NET
Online lesson quiz at
www.PHSchool.com
Web Code: aga-0805

Use the Change of Base Formula to solve each equation. Enter the answer to the nearest tenth.

109. $\log_5 x = \log_3 29$ **138.8**

110. $\log_9 x = \log_6 15$ **27.7**

Solve each equation.

111. $\log (2 + 4x) = 3$ **249.5**

112. $\log (x - 3) = 2$ **103**

Mixed Review

Lesson 8-4 **Expand each logarithm. 113–118. See margin.**

113. $\log 2x^3 y^{-2}$

114. $\log_3 \frac{x}{y}$

115. $\log_2 (3x)^3$

116. $\log_3 7(2x - 3)^2$

117. $\log_4 5\sqrt{x}$

118. $\log_2 \left(\frac{5a}{b^2} \right)$

Lesson 7-6 **Evaluate each expression for $f(x) = 3x$ and $g(x) = x^2 - 1$.**

119. $(f + g)(x)$
$x^2 + 3x - 1$

120. $(g - f)(x)$
$x^2 - 3x - 1$

121. $(f \cdot g)(x)$
$3x^3 - 3x$

Lesson 6-6 **Find all the zeros of each function.**

122. $y = x^3 - x^2 + x - 1$ **1, ± i**

123. $f(x) = x^4 - 16$ **±2, ±2i**

124. $f(x) = x^4 - 5x^2 + 6$ **±√2, ±√3**

125. $y = 3x^3 - 21x - 18$ **−2, −1, 3**

Lesson 1-3 **Write an equation to solve each problem.**

126. A customer at a hardware store mentions that he is buying fencing for a vegetable garden that is 12 ft longer than it is wide. He buys 128 ft of fencing. What is the width of the garden? **2(x) + 2(x + 12) = 128; 26 ft**

127. A bowler has an average of 133. In a set of games one night, her scores are 135, 127, 119, 142, and 156. What score must she bowl in the sixth game to maintain her average? **$\frac{679 + x}{6} = 133$; 119**

✓ Checkpoint Quiz 2   Lessons 8-3 through 8-5

 Instant self-check quiz online and on CD-ROM

Graph each logarithmic function. 1–2. See margin.

1. $y = \log_6 x$

2. $y = \log (x - 2)$

Expand each logarithm. 4–5. See margin.

3. $\log \frac{s^3}{r^5}$ **3 log s − 5 log r**

4. $\log_6 (3xy)^2$

5. $\log_6 4\sqrt{x}$

Solve each equation.

6. $7 - 2^x = -1$ **3**

7. $\log 5x = 2$ **20**

8. $3 \log x = 9$ **1000**

9. $\log 2 = 0.3010$,
$\log_3 2 = 0.6309$,
$\log_2 3 = 1.5850$,
$2^3 = 8$,
$3^2 = 9$

9. Evaluate the expressions below and order them from least to greatest.
2^3 $\log_2 3$ $\log_3 2$ 3^2 $\log 2$

✏️ 10. **Writing** Explain how to use the Change of Base Formula to rewrite $\log_2 10$ as a logarithmic expression with base 3. **See margin.**

Linear and Exponential Models

FOR USE WITH LESSON 8-5

You can transform an exponential function into a linear function by taking the logarithm of each side. Since linear models are easy to recognize, you can then determine whether an exponential function is a good model for a set of values.

 Take It to the NET
Graphing Calculator procedures online at **www.PHSchool.com**
Web Code: age-2117

$y = ab^x$	Write the general form of an exponential function.
$\log y = \log ab^x$	Take the logarithm of each side.
$\log y = \log a + x(\log b)$	Product Property and Power Property
$\log y = (\log b)x + \log a$	Rewrite.

If $\log b$ and $\log a$ are constants, then $\log y = (\log b)x + \log a$ is a linear equation in slope-intercept form. To confirm that $\log b$ is a constant, check that the graph of $\log y = (\log b)x + \log a$ is a line.

EXAMPLE

Determine whether an exponential function is a good model for the values in the table.

x	0	2	4	6	8	10
y	3.0	5.1	8.6	14.5	24.5	41.4

Step 1 Enter the values into STAT lists L_1 and L_2. To enter the values of $\log y$, place the cursor in the heading of L_3 and press LOG L_2 ENTER.

Step 2 To graph $\log y$, access the **STAT PLOT** feature and press 1. Then enter L_3 next to Ylist:. Then press ZOOM 9.

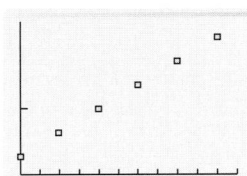

L1	L2	L3	1
0	3	0.47712	
2	5.1	0.70757	
4	8.6	0.9345	
6	14.5	1.1614	
8	24.5	1.3892	
10	41.4	1.617	

L1(1) = 0

Since the graph of $\log y = (\log b)x + \log a$ is linear, the slope $\log b$ is constant, and b also is constant. An exponential function therefore is a suitable model.

Step 3 Press STAT ▶ 0 ENTER to find the exponential function: $y = 3(1.3)^x$.

EXERCISES

For each set of values, determine whether an exponential function is a good model. If so, find the function.

1.

x	1	3	5	7	9
y	6	22	54	102	145

not a good model

2.

x	−1	0	1	2	3
y	40.2	19.8	9.9	5.1	2.5

$y = 20.0(0.50)^x$

3. Writing Explain how you could determine whether a logarithmic function is a good model for a set of values. **Answers may vary. Sample: Use Change of Base Formula to get $\log x = \frac{\log b}{a} y$. Let $L_1 = x$, $L_2 = y$, and $L_3 = \log x$. Graph L_2 and L_3. If it is linear, then the equation is logarithmic.**

Linear Models of Exponential Behavior

Students use a graphing calculator to transform an exponential function into a linear function. The linear form makes it easier to recognize whether the function is a good model for a given set of data points.

Resources

Technology
Computer Test Generator CD-ROM, Chapter 0, Cubic Functions

Teaching Notes

Error Prevention

Students may get frustrated when they get an error message and can't find what they are doing incorrectly. Suggest that students work with a partner and compare their work at each step.

Remind students to clear all lists before they begin each exercise.

8-6

1. Plan

Lesson Preview

 Check Skills You'll Need

Properties of Exponential Functions
Lesson 8-2: Example 4
Exercises 17–20
Extra Practice, p. 329

Exponential and Logarithmic Equations
Lesson 8-5: Example 6
Exercises 21–24
Extra Practice, p. 329

Lesson Resources

📁 Teaching Resources
Practice, Reteaching, Enrichment

👥 Reaching All Students
Practice Workbook 8-6
Spanish Practice Workbook 8-6
Technology Activities 32

⏰ Presentation Assistant Plus!
Transparencies
- Check Skills You'll Need 8-6
- Additional Examples 8-6
- Student Edition Answers 8-6
- Lesson Quiz 8-6
PH Presentation Pro CD 8-4

ASSESSMENT SYSTEM
Computer Test Generator CD

💿 Technology
Resource Pro® CD-ROM
Computer Test Generator CD
Prentice Hall Presentation Pro CD

💻 www.PHSchool.com
Student Site
- Teacher Web Code: agk-5500
- Self-grading Lesson Quiz
Teacher Center
- Lesson Planner
- Resources

Plus

462

8-6

Natural Logarithms

1.01 Simplify and perform operations with rational exponents and logarithms (common and natural) to solve problems.
2.01 Use the inverse of functions to model and solve problems.

Lesson Preview

What You'll Learn

 OBJECTIVE 1 To evaluate natural logarithmic expressions

 OBJECTIVE 2 To solve equations using natural logarithms

. . . And Why

To model the velocity of a rocket, as in Example 2

✓ Check Skills You'll Need

(For help, go to Lessons 8-2 and 8-5.)

Use your calculator to evaluate each expression to the nearest thousandth.

1. e^5 **148.413** **2.** $2e^3$ **40.171** **3.** e^{-2} **0.135** **4.** $\frac{1}{e}$ **0.368** **5.** $4.2e$ **11.417**

Solve.

6. $\log_3 x = 4$ **81** **7.** $\log_{16} 4 = x$ $\frac{1}{2}$ **8.** $\log_{16} x = 4$ **65,536**

New Vocabulary • natural logarithmic function

 Interactive lesson includes instant self-check, tutorials, and activities.

OBJECTIVE

1 Natural Logarithms

In Lesson 8-2, you learned that the number $e \approx 2.71828$ can be used as a base for exponents. The function $y = e^x$ has an inverse, the **natural logarithmic function.**

🔑 Key Concepts

Definition	Natural Logarithmic Function

If $y = e^x$, then $\log_e y = x$, which is commonly written as $\ln y = x$.

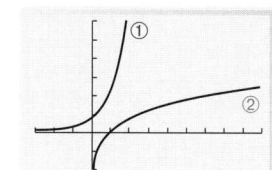

① $y = e^x$
② $y = \ln x$

The properties of common logarithms apply to natural logarithms also.

📖 Reading Math

ln y means "the natural logarithm of y." The l stands for "logarithm" and the n stands for "natural."

1 EXAMPLE Simplifying Natural Logarithms

Write $3 \ln 6 - \ln 8$ as a single natural logarithm.

$$3 \ln 6 - \ln 8 = \ln 6^3 - \ln 8 \quad \text{Power Property}$$
$$= \ln \frac{6^3}{8} \quad \text{Quotient Property}$$
$$= \ln 27 \quad \text{Simplify.}$$

✓ Check Understanding Write each expression as a single natural logarithm.

a. $5 \ln 2 - \ln 4$ **ln 8** **b.** $3 \ln x + \ln y$ **ln x^3y** **c.** $\frac{1}{4} \ln 3 + \frac{1}{4} \ln x$

ln $\sqrt[4]{3x}$

462 Chapter 8 Exponential and Logarithmic Functions

Before the Lesson
Diagnose prerequisite skills using:
- Check Skills You'll Need

During the Lesson
Monitor progress using:
- Check Understanding
- Additional Examples
- Standardized Test Prep

After the Lesson
Assess knowledge using:
- Lesson Quiz
- Computer Test Generator CD

Natural logarithms are useful because they help express many relationships in the physical world.

2 EXAMPLE Real-World Connection

Space A spacecraft can attain a stable orbit 300 km above Earth if it reaches a velocity of 7.7 km/s. The formula for a rocket's maximum velocity v in kilometers per second is $v = -0.0098t + c \ln R$. The booster rocket fires for t seconds and the velocity of the exhaust is c km/s. The ratio of the mass of the rocket with fuel to its mass without fuel is R. Suppose a rocket used to propel a spacecraft has a mass ratio of 25, an exhaust velocity of 2.8 km/s, and a firing time of 100 s. Can the spacecraft attain a stable orbit 300 km above Earth?

Let $R = 25$, $c = 2.8$, and $t = 100$. Find v.

$v = -0.0098t + c \ln R$	Use the formula.
$= -0.0098(100) + 2.8 \ln 25$	Substitute.
$\approx -0.98 + 2.8(3.219)$	Use a calculator.
≈ 8.0	Simplify.

The maximum velocity of 8.0 km/s is greater than the 7.7 km/s needed for a stable orbit. Therefore, the spacecraft can attain a stable orbit 300 km above Earth.

Real-World Connection

The space shuttle is launched into orbit.

✓ **Check Understanding** **2 a.** A booster rocket for a spacecraft has a mass ratio of about 15, an exhaust velocity of 2.1 km/s, and a firing time of 30 s. Find the velocity of the spacecraft. Can the spacecraft achieve a stable orbit 300 km above Earth? **≈5.4 km/s; no**

b. Critical Thinking Suppose a rocket, as designed, cannot provide enough velocity to achieve a stable orbit. Look at the variables in the velocity formula. What alterations could be made to the rocket so that a stable orbit could be achieved? **One could increase its mass ratio or its exhaust velocity.**

OBJECTIVE

2 Natural Logarithmic and Exponential Equations

You can use the properties of logarithms to solve natural logarithmic equations.

3 EXAMPLE Solving a Natural Logarithmic Equation

Solve $\ln (3x + 5)^2 = 4$.

$\ln (3x + 5)^2 = 4$	
$(3x + 5)^2 = e^4$	Rewrite in exponential form.
$(3x + 5)^2 \approx 54.60$	Use a calculator.
$3x + 5 \approx \pm \sqrt{54.60}$	Take the square root of each side.
$3x + 5 \approx 7.39$ or -7.39	Use a calculator.
$x \approx 0.797$ or -4.130	Solve for x.

Check $\ln (3 \cdot 0.797 + 5)^2 \overset{?}{=} 4$ $\qquad$ $\ln (3 \cdot (-4.130) + 5)^2 \overset{?}{=} 4$

$\ln 54.6 \overset{?}{=} 4$ $\qquad\qquad\qquad$ $\ln 54.6 \overset{?}{=} 4$

$4 \approx 4$ ✓ $\qquad\qquad\qquad\qquad$ $4 \approx 4$ ✓

✓ **Check Understanding** **3** Solve each equation. Check your answers.

a. $\ln x = 0.1$ **1.105** $\qquad$ **b.** $\ln (3x - 9) = 21$ **439,605,247.8** $\qquad$ **c.** $\ln \left(\frac{x + 2}{3}\right) = 12$ **488,262.4**

Lesson 8-6 Natural Logarithms **463**

Reaching All Students

Below Level Review the general formula for growth or decay, $N = N_0 e^{kt}$ and the formula for continuously compounded interest, $A = Pe^{rt}$. Compare the meanings of corresponding variables.	**Advanced Learners** Ask students to solve $3 \cdot 7^{2x} + 3 = 14$ by taking logs to the base 7 and using the change of base formula.	**Error Prevention** See note on page 463. **Alternative Method** See note on page 465.

Additional Examples

③ Solve $\ln (2x - 4)^3 = 6$.
about 5.695

④ Use natural logarithms to solve $4e^{3x} + 1.2 = 14$. **about 0.388**

⑤ An initial investment of $200 is now valued at $254.25. The interest rate is 6%, compounded continuously. How long has the money been invested?
about 4 years

④ EXAMPLE **Technology Tip**

Have students check to see if their calculator has separate keys for LOG and LN.

Closure

Ask students to compare and contrast natural and common logarithms. **Answers may vary. Sample: They are both exponents; they both obey the same properties of exponents and logarithms; they use a different base. The base for common logarithms is the rational number 10; for natural logarithms, it is the irrational number e.**

You can use natural logarithms to solve exponential equations.

④ EXAMPLE **Solving an Exponential Equation**

Use natural logarithms to solve $7e^{2x} + 2.5 = 20$.

$$7e^{2x} + 2.5 = 20$$

Need Help?

If $y = e^x$, then $\ln y = x$.

$7e^{2x} = 17.5$	Subtract 2.5 from each side.
$e^{2x} = 2.5$	Divide each side by 7.
$\ln e^{2x} = \ln 2.5$	Take the natural logarithm of each side.
$2x = \ln 2.5$	Simplify.
$x = \frac{\ln 2.5}{2}$	Solve for x.
$x = 0.458$	Use a calculator.

✔ **Check Understanding** ④ Use natural logarithms to solve each equation.
    a. $e^{x+1} = 30$ **2.401**   **b.** $e^{\frac{2x}{5}} + 7.2 = 9.1$ **1.605**

⑤ EXAMPLE **Real-World Connection**

Investing An initial investment of $100 is now valued at $149.18. The interest rate is 8%, compounded continuously. How long has the money been invested?

$A = Pe^{rt}$	Continuously compounded interest formula
$149.18 = 100e^{0.08t}$	Substitute 149.18 for A, 100 for P, and 0.08 for r.
$1.4918 = e^{0.08t}$	Divide each side by 100.
$\ln 1.4918 = \ln e^{0.08t}$	Take the natural logarithm of each side.
$\ln 1.4918 = 0.08t$	Simplify.
$\frac{\ln 1.4918}{0.08} = t$	Solve for t.
$5 \approx t$	Use a calculator.

The money has been invested for about five years.

✔ **Check Understanding** ⑤ An initial investment of $200 is worth $315.24 after seven years of continuous compounding. Find the interest rate. **6.5%**

EXERCISES

For more practice, see *Extra Practice*.

Practice and Problem Solving

Ⓐ **Practice by Example**

Example 1
(page 462)

Write each expression as a single natural logarithm.

1. $3 \ln 5$ **ln 125**   **2.** $\ln 9 + \ln 2$ **ln 18**   **3.** $\ln 24 - \ln 6$ **ln 4**

4. $4 \ln 8 + \ln 10$ **ln 40,960** **5.** $\ln 3 - 5 \ln 3$ **ln $\frac{1}{81}$**   **6.** $2 \ln 8 - 3 \ln 4$ **ln 1**

7. $5 \ln m - 3 \ln n$ **ln $\frac{m^5}{n^3}$** **8.** $\frac{1}{3}(\ln x + \ln y) - 4 \ln z$ **9.** $\ln a - 2 \ln b + \frac{1}{2} \ln c$

                                    ln $\frac{\sqrt[3]{xy}}{z^4}$ **ln $\frac{a\sqrt{c}}{b^2}$**

Example 2
(page 463)

Find the value of y for the given value of x.

10. $y = 15 + 3 \ln x$, for $x = 7.2$ **20.92**   **11.** $y = 0.05 - 10 \ln x$, for $x = 0.09$
                                                                      24.13

For Exercises 12 and 13, use $v = -0.0098t + c \ln R$.

12. **Space** Find the velocity of a spacecraft whose booster rocket has a mass ratio of 20, an exhaust velocity of 2.7 km/s, and a firing time of 30 s. Can the spacecraft achieve a stable orbit 300 km above Earth? **7.79 km/s; yes**

13. A rocket has a mass ratio of 24 and an exhaust velocity of 2.5 km/s. Determine the minimum firing time for a stable orbit 300 km above Earth. **25 s**

Example 3
(page 463)

Solve each equation. Check your answers.

14. $\ln 3x = 6$ **134.476**   15. $\ln x = -2$ **0.135**   16. $\ln(4x - 1) = 36$ **1.078×10^{15}**

17. **1488.979**   17. $\ln(2m + 3) = 8$ 18. $\ln(t - 1)^2 = 3$ **5.482, −3.482**   19. $1.1 + \ln x^2 = 6$ **±11.588**

20. $\ln \frac{x-1}{2} = 4$ **110.196**   21. $\ln 4r^2 = 3$ **±2.241**   22. $2 \ln 2x^2 = 1$ **±0.908**

Example 4
(page 464)

Use natural logarithms to solve each equation.

23. $e^x = 18$ **2.890**   24. $e^{2x} = 10$ **1.151**   25. $e^{x+1} = 30$ **2.401**

26. $e^{\frac{x}{5}} + 4 = 7$ **5.493**   27. $e^{2x} = 12$ **1.242**   28. $e^{\frac{x}{9}} - 8 = 6$ **23.752**

Example 5
(page 464)

29. **Investing** An initial deposit of $200 is now worth $331.07. The account earns 8.4% interest, compounded continuously. Determine how long the money has been in the account. **6 years**

30. An investor sold 100 shares of stock valued at $34.50 per share. The stock was purchased at $7.25 per share two years ago. Find the rate of continuously compounded interest that would be necessary in a banking account for the investor to make the same profit. **78%**

B **Apply Your Skills**

Mental Math Simplify each expression.

31. $\ln e$ **1**   32. $\ln e^2$ **2**   33. $\ln e^{10}$ **10**   34. $10 \ln e$ **10**

35. $\ln 1$ **0**   36. $\frac{\ln e}{4}$ **$\frac{1}{4}$**   37. $\frac{\ln e^2}{2}$ **1**   38. $\ln e^{83}$ **83**

 39. **Space** Use the formula for maximum velocity $v = -0.0098t + c \ln R$. Find the mass ratio of a rocket with an exhaust velocity of 3.1 km/s, a firing time of 50 s, and a maximum shuttle velocity of 6.9 km/s. **10.8**

 40. **Power** The battery power available to run a satellite is given by the formula $P = 50e^{-\frac{t}{250}}$, where P is power in watts and t is time in days. How long can the satellite run if it requires 15 watts? 45 watts? **301 days; 26 days**

41. **sometimes**
42. **never**
43. **always**

Determine whether each statement is _always_ true, _sometimes_ true, or _never_ true.

41. $\ln e^x > 1$ 42. $\ln e^x = \ln e^x + 1$ 43. $\ln t = \log_e t$

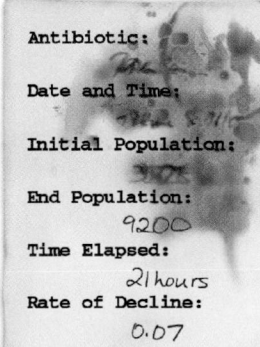

 **Biology For Exercises 44–46, use the formula $H = \left(\frac{1}{r}\right)(\ln P - \ln A)$. H is the number of hours, r is the rate of decline, P is the initial bacteria population, and A is the reduced bacteria population.**

about 5.8% per hour

44. A scientist determines that an antibiotic reduces a population of 20,000 bacteria to 5000 in 24 hours. Find the rate of decline caused by the antibiotic.

45. A laboratory assistant tests an antibiotic that causes a rate of decline of 0.14. How long should it take for a population of 8000 bacteria to shrink to 500? **about 19.8 h**

46. A scientist spilled coffee on the lab report shown at the left. Determine the initial population of the bacteria. **about 40,000 bacteria**

Assignment Guide

1 Objective
- **Ⓐ Ⓑ Core** 1–13, 31–38
- **Ⓒ Extension** 63

2 Objective
- **Ⓐ Ⓑ Core** 14–30, 39–62
- **Ⓒ Extension** 64–66

Standardized Test Prep 67–70

Mixed Review 71–80

Alternative Method

Exercises 31–38 Suggest that students ask themselves the question in a different form. For example, for Exercise 32 ask: _What power of the base e gives me the number e^2?_

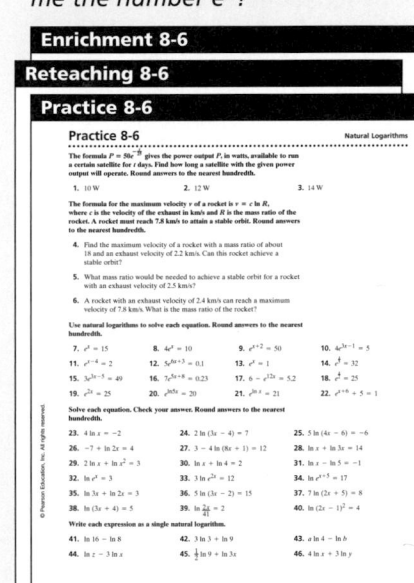

4. Assess

Lesson Quiz 8-6

1. Write $4 \ln 6 - 2 \ln 3$ as a single natural logarithm. **ln 144**

2. Solve $e^{3x} = 15$. **about 0.903**

3. Simplify $\ln e^7$. **7**

Alternative Assessment

Ask students to discuss with a partner the differences in the procedures and answers for solving these two equations: $\ln x - \ln (x - 1) = 2$ and $\log x - \log (x - 1) = 2$. Then have each pair write a paragraph that summarizes their discussion. **The procedures are the same. If b is the base for the logarithm, then the answer for both equations is $b^2 \div (b^2 - 1)$. However, for the first equation, $b = e$ and for the second equation, $b = 10$. The answers are about 1.157 and about 1.010.**

pages 464–467 Exercises

63. **No; using the Change of Base Formula would result in one of the log expressions being written as a quotient of logs, which couldn't then be combined with the other expression to form a single logarithm.**

64d. $t = \dfrac{\ln\left(\dfrac{y}{300}\right)}{0.241}$, **where y is the number of Internet users in millions and t is time in years.**

e. **Substitute the number of users found in (b) and (c) into the equation in (d). Determine whether your answers in years are the same as t for each.**

58. 81.286

59. 1.2639

60. no solution

Savings Suppose you invest $500 at 5% interest compounded continuously. Copy and complete the table to find how long it will take to reach each amount.

	Amount (A)	Time (years)		
47.	$600	■	**47.**	**3.6**
48.	$700	■	**48.**	**6.7**
49.	$800	■	**49.**	**9.4**
50.	$900	■	**50.**	**11.8**
51.	$1000	■	**51.**	**13.9**
52.	$1100	■	**52.**	**15.8**
53.	$1200	■	**53.**	**17.5**
54.	$1300	■	**54.**	**19.1**

Solve each equation.

55. $\ln x - 3 \ln 3 = 3$ **542.31**   56. $\ln (2x - 1) = 0$ **1**   57. $4e^{x+2} = 32$ **0.0794**

58. $\ln (5x - 3)^{\frac{1}{3}} = 2$ 59. $2e^{3x-2} + 4 = 16$ 60. $2e^{x-2} = e^x + 7$

61. $\frac{1}{3} \ln x + \ln 2 - \ln 3 = 3$ **27,347.9**   62. $\ln (x + 2) - \ln 4 = 3$ **78.342**

C Challenge

63. **Critical Thinking** Can $\ln 5 + \log_2 10$ be written as a single logarithm? Explain. **See margin.**

64. In 2000, there were about 300 million Internet users. That number is projected to grow to 1 billion in 2005. $y = 300e^{0.241t}$

a. Let t represent the time, in years, since 2000. Write a function of the form $y = ae^{ct}$ that models the expected growth in the population of Internet users.

b. In what year might there be 500 million Internet users? **2002**

c. In what year might there be 1.5 billion Internet users? **2006**

d. Solve your equation for t. **d–e. See margin.**

e. **Writing** Explain how you can use your equation from part (d) to verify your answers to parts (b) and (c).

65. **Physics** The function $T(t) = T_r + (T_i - T_r)e^{kt}$ models Newton's Law of Cooling. $T(t)$ is the temperature of a heated substance t minutes after it has been removed from a heat (or cooling) source. T_i is the substance's initial temperature, k is a constant for that substance, and T_r is room temperature.

a. The initial surface temperature of a beef roast is 236°F and room temperature is 72°F. If $k = -0.041$, how long will it take for this roast to cool to 100°F?

b. Write and graph an equation that you can use to check your answer to part (a). Use your graph to complete the table below. **a–b. See margin.**

Temperature (°F)	225	200	175	150	125	100	75
Minutes Later	■	■	■	■	■	■	■
	1.7	6.0	11.3	18.1	27.6	43.1	97.6

66. **Open-Ended** Write a real-world problem that you can answer using Newton's Law of Cooling. Then answer it. **Check students' work.**

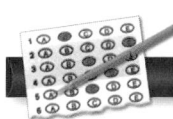

Standardized Test Prep

Multiple Choice

67. Which expression is equal to $3 \ln 4 - 5 \ln 2$? **C**

   A. $\ln (-18)$ **B.** $\ln \left(\frac{6}{5}\right)$ **C.** $\ln 2$ **D.** $\ln 32$

466 Chapter 8 Exponential and Logarithmic Functions

65a. **about 43 min**

b. $t = \dfrac{-1}{0.041} \ln\left(\dfrac{T - 72}{164}\right)$

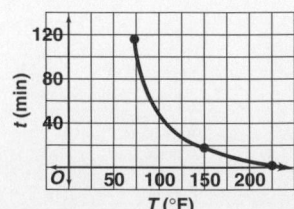

Take It to the NET
Online lesson quiz at
www.PHSchool.com
Web Code: aga-0806

68. What is the value of x if $17e^{4x} = 85$? **H**

   F. $\frac{5}{4}$ **G.** $\frac{\ln 85}{17 \cdot \ln 4}$ **H.** $\frac{\ln 5}{4}$ **I.** $\frac{\ln 85 - \ln 17}{\ln 4}$

69. An investment of $750 will be worth $1500 after 12 years of continuous compounding at a fixed interest rate. What is that interest rate? **B**

   A. 2.00%   **B.** 5.78%   **C.** 6.93%   **D.** 200%

Extended Response

70. The table shows the values of an investment after the given number of years of continuously compounded interest.

Years	0	1	2	3	4
Value	$500.00	$541.64	$586.76	$635.62	$688.56

   a. What is the rate of interest? **a–c. See margin.**
   b. Write an equation to model the growth of the investment.
   c. To the nearest year, when will the investment be worth $1800?

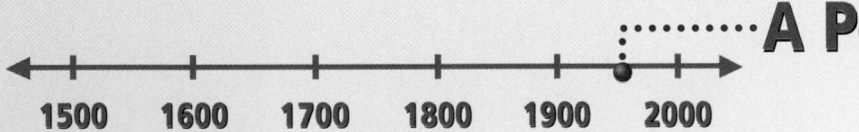

Mixed Review

Lesson 8-5   **Solve each equation.**

71. $3^{2x} = 6561$ **4**   **72.** $7^x - 2 = 252$ **2.846**   **73.** $25^{2x+1} = 144$ **0.272**

74. $\log 3x = 4$ **3333.$\overline{3}$**   **75.** $\log 5x + 3 = 3.7$ **1.002**   **76.** $\log 9 - \log x + 1 = 6$
                                                                 9.0 × 10^{-5}

Lesson 7-7   **Find the inverse of each function. Is the inverse a function?** **77–79. See margin.**

77. $y = 5x + 7$ **78.** $y = 2x^3 + 10$ **79.** $y = -x^2 + 5$

Lesson 6-7   **80.** The Nut Shop carries 30 different types of nuts. The shop special is the Triple Play, a made-to-order mixture of any three different types of nuts. How many different Triple Plays are possible? **4060 possible combinations**

A P●int in Time

1500   1600   1700   1800   1900   2000

The first manned moon landing on July 20, 1969, gave scientists a unique opportunity to test their theories about the moon's geologic history.

A logarithmic function was used to date lunar rocks. Radioactive rubidium-87 decays into stable strontium-87 at a fixed rate. The ratio r of the two isotopes in a sample can be measured and used in the equation $T = -h\frac{\ln(r + 1)}{\ln 0.5}$, where T is the age in years and h is the half-life of rubidium-87, 4.7×10^{10} years. For the lunar sample, r was measured at 0.0588, giving an approximate age of 3.87 billion years.

Take It to the NET For more information about space exploration, go to **www.PHSchool.com**.
Web Code: age-2032

Standardized Test Prep

 **Resources**

For additional practice with a variety of test item formats:
- Standardized Test Prep, p. 473
- Test-Taking Strategies, p. 468
- Test-Taking Strategies with Transparencies

70.[4]   **a.** 8%

   b. $A = Pe^{rt} =$
       $500\, e^{0.08t}$

   c. $1800 = 500\, e^{0.08t}$
       $3.6 = e^{0.08t}$
       $\ln 3.6 = 0.08t$
       $\frac{\ln 3.6}{0.08} = t$
       $16 \approx t$

       about 16 years

  [3] correct model, computation error in (b) or (c)

  [2] incorrect model, solved correctly

  [1] correct model, but without work shown in (c)

77. $y = \frac{x - 7}{5}$; **yes**

78. $y = \sqrt[3]{\frac{x - 10}{2}}$; **yes**

79. $y = \pm\sqrt{5 - x}$; **no**

Testing Multiple Choices

Many assessment tests include multiple-choice problems. Sometimes testing each answer choice in the problem can be an efficient way to make a selection.

Resources

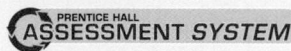
PRENTICE HALL
ASSESSMENT *SYSTEM*

Test-Taking Strategies with Transparencies
• Transparency 8
• Practice sheet p. 32

Teaching Notes

Use the transparency for more instruction on working backward.

Assign the worksheet to give students more practice with working backward to find the correct answer choice.

Inclusion

Exercise 3 Everyone processes information in their own way. Suggest that students learn and practice strategies such as working backwards, and experiment with other strategies to find the ones that best fit their way of thinking.

Test-Taking Strategies with Transparencies

Test-Taking Strategy: Testing Multiple Choices

When you take a multiple-choice test, one of the answer choices is always correct. You can solve a problem by testing the answer choices to find the correct one.

Solve $5^x + 12 = 637$.

  A. 2   B. 3   C. 4   D. 5

Work backward by substituting each answer choice for x.

$5^2 + 12 = ?$
$25 + 12 = 37$ not correct

$5^3 + 12 = ?$
$125 + 12 = 137$ not correct

$5^4 + 12 = ?$
$625 + 12 = 637$ correct

You do not have to continue substituting answer choices once you find the correct choice.

The answer is C, 4.

Solve these problems by working backward.

1. Solve $4^x - 7 = 4089$.

  A. 5   B. 6   C. 7   D. 8

2. Solve $y^4 - 24 = 57$.

  A. 7   B. 5   C. 3   D. 1

Solutions

1. B
2. C

Transparency 8

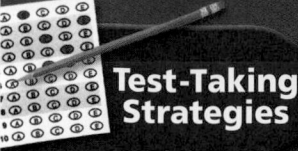
One advantage of multiple-choice tests is that the correct answer is among the choices. A frequently useful strategy is to test a choice in the original problem.

EXAMPLE

What number is the solution to $\left(\frac{1}{4}\right)^x = 8$?

  A. -2 **B.** $-\frac{3}{2}$ **C.** 0   **D.** 16

You can answer the question without solving the equation. Substitute each answer choice into the equation until you find the right one.

If $x = -2$, then $\left(\frac{1}{4}\right)^x = \left(\frac{1}{4}\right)^{-2} = 4^2 = 16$. Since $16 \neq 8$, answer A is wrong.

If $x = -\frac{3}{2}$, then $\left(\frac{1}{4}\right)^x = \left(\frac{1}{4}\right)^{-\frac{3}{2}} = 4^{\frac{3}{2}} = 8$. Since $8 = 8$, the correct answer is B.

You don't have to test the two other choices.

When answering a multiple-choice question that involves solving a difficult equation, you often can save time and effort by working backward from the answers to the question.

EXERCISES 1–2. See right.

1. Refer to the Example. Explain why you can eliminate choices C and D even before trying A and B.

2. Algebraically solve the equation in the Example to show that B is the correct answer.

Answer each question by testing the choices. Then solve each equation algebraically.

3. What is the solution to $\log_x (3x + 2) = x + 1$? **B**
  A. 0   **B.** 2   **C.** 6   **D.** 10

4. What is the solution to $2^{x+1} + 2x + 1 = 0$? **I**
  F. 2   **G.** 0   **H.** $-\frac{1}{2}$ **I.** -1

5. What is the solution to $\ln \sqrt{x + 2} + \ln \sqrt{3x + 4} = \ln 15$? **D**
  A. -1 **B.** 0   **C.** 1   **D.** 7

6. What is the solution to $\log (\log (3x - 2)) = 0$? **H**
  F. $\frac{2}{3}$ **G.** 1   **H.** 4   **I.** 34

7. Use the formula for continuously compounded interest, $A = Pe^{rt}$, to find the annual interest rate for an \$8000 investment that earns \$410.17 in one year. **C**
  A. 7%   **B.** 6%   **C.** 5%   **D.** 4%

1. Answers may vary.
Sample: $a^0 = 1$ for every nonzero a, so $x \neq 0$.
$\left(\frac{1}{4}\right)^x < 1$ for all $x > 0$, so $x \neq 16$.

2. $\log \left(\frac{1}{4}\right)^x = \log 8$
$x = \dfrac{\log 8}{\log \left(\frac{1}{4}\right)} =$
$-1.5 = -\frac{3}{2}$

Chapter Review

Vocabulary

asymptote (p. 425)
Change of Base Formula (p. 453)
common logarithm (p. 439)
continuously compounded interest
  formula (p. 433)

decay factor (p. 425)
exponential equation (p. 453)
exponential function (p. 422)
growth factor (p. 422)
logarithm (p. 439)

logarithmic equation (p. 455)
logarithmic function (p. 440)
natural logarithmic function (p. 462)

Reading Math
Understanding
Vocabulary

Take It to the NET
Online vocabulary quiz
at www.PHSchool.com
Web Code: agj-0851

Choose the correct term to complete each sentence.

1. In the exponential function $y = ab^x$, when $b > 1$, b is the __?__. **growth factor**

2. A __?__ is a logarithm that uses base 10. **common logarithm**

3. The line $x = 2$ is a(n) __?__ of the function $f(x) = \frac{2}{x-2}$. **asymptote**

4. The Change of Base Formula can be used to evaluate a __?__ with any base.
logarithm

5. An __?__ can be solved by taking the logarithm of each side of the equation.
exponential equation

Skills and Concepts

8-1 Objectives

▼ To model exponential
growth (p. 422)

▼ To model exponential
decay (p. 424)

The general form of an **exponential function** is $y = ab^x$, where x is a real number, $a \neq 0, b > 0,$ and $b \neq 1$. When $b > 1$, the function models exponential growth, and b is the **growth factor**. When $0 < b < 1$, the function models exponential decay, and b is the **decay factor**.

Determine whether each equation represents exponential growth or exponential decay. Find the rate of increase or decrease for each model. Graph each equation.

6. $y = 5^x$ **7.** $y = 2(4)^x$ **8.** $y = 0.2(3.8)^x$ **9.** $y = 3(0.25)^x$

6–9. See margin.

Write an exponential equation whose graph passes through the given points.

10. $y = \frac{25}{7}\left(\frac{7}{5}\right)^x$

11. $y = 0.0015(10)^x$

12. $y = 2.25\left(\frac{1}{3}\right)^x$

13. $y = \left(\frac{1}{3}\right)^x$

10. $(1, 5), (2, 7)$ **11.** $(3, 1.5), (4, 15)$ **12.** $\left(-1, 6\frac{3}{4}\right), \left(2, \frac{1}{4}\right)$ **13.** $(-2, 9), (0, 1)$

Write an exponential function to model each situation. Find the value of each function after five years, to the nearest dollar.

14. A \$12,500 car depreciates 9% each year. $y = 12{,}500(0.91)^x$; \$7800

15. A baseball card bought for \$50 increases 3% in value each year.
$y = 50(1.03)^x$; \$58

Write an exponential equation for each graph. Evaluate the equation for $x = 4$.

16.
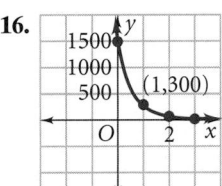

$y = 1500(0.2)^x$; 2.4

17.
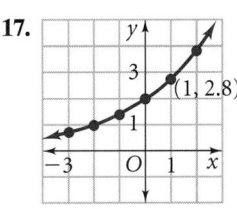

$y = 2(1.4)^x$; 7.6832

Resources

Student Edition
Extra Practice, Ch. 8, p. 329
English/Spanish Glossary, p. 871
Properties and Formulas, p. 865
Table of Symbols, p. 861

Reaching All Students
Reading and Math Literacy 8D
Spanish Reading and Math
  Literacy 8D

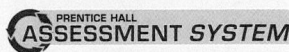**ASSESSMENT SYSTEM**

Standardized Test Prep
• Ch. 8 practice in standardized
  test formats

www.PHSchool.com
Student Site
• Self-grading Vocabulary Test
Teacher Center
• Resources

Plus

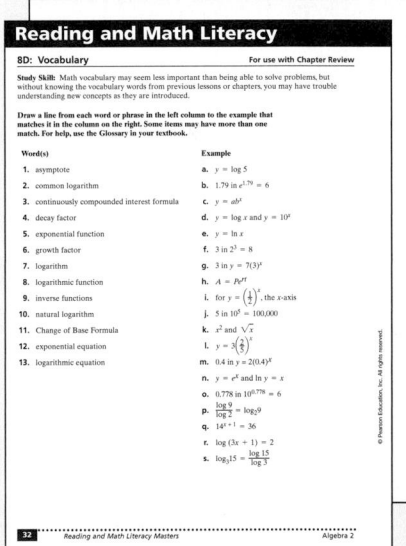

**6. exponential
growth; 400%**
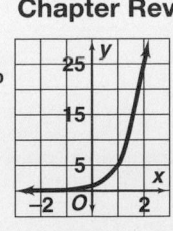

7. exponential growth; 300%
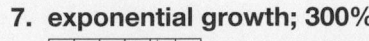

8. exponential growth; 280%

9. exponential decay; −75%
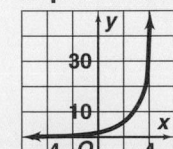
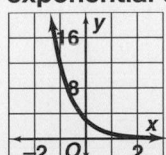

pages 469–471   Chapter Review

18. $y = 3^x$ reflected over the x-axis and translated up 1 unit

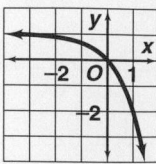

19. $y = 8^x$ translated down 1 unit

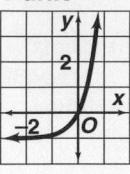

20. $y = 2(2)^x$ translated left 1 unit and up 3 units

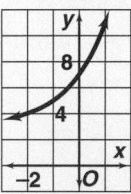

21. $y = 2\left(\frac{1}{3}\right)^x$ reflected over the x-axis and translated right 2 units

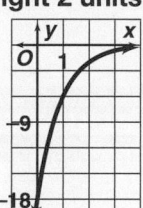

40.

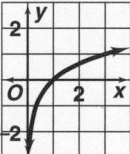

41.

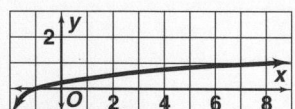

42.

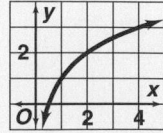

43.

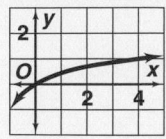

470

8-2 Objectives

▼ To identify the role of constants in $y = ab^{cx}$ (p. 431)

▼ To use e as a base (p. 433)

Exponential functions can be translated and reflected. The graph of $y = ab^{x-h} + k$ is the graph of $y = ab^x$ translated h units horizontally and k units vertically.

The **continuously compounded interest** formula is $A = Pe^{rt}$, where P is the principal, r is the annual rate, and t is time in years.

Describe how the graph of each function relates to the graph of its parent function. Then graph each function.   18–21. See margin.

18. $y = -3^x + 1$ **19.** $y = 8^x - 1$

20. $y = 2(2)^{x+1} + 3$ **21.** $y = -2\left(\frac{1}{3}\right)^{x-2}$

Find the amount in a continuously compounded account for the given conditions.

22. principal: $1000, annual interest rate: 4.8%, time: 2 yr   **$1100.76**

23. principal: $250, annual interest rate: 6.2%, time: 2.5 yr   **$291.91**

24. principal: $500, annual interest rate: 8.5%, time: 3 yr   **$645.23**

Evaluate to four decimal places.

25. e^1 **2.7183**   **26.** e^{-1} **0.3679**   **27.** e^5 **148.4132**   **28.** $e^{-\frac{1}{2}}$ **0.6065**

 29. Physics Radium has a half-life of 1620 years. Write the decay function for a 3-mg sample. Find the amount of radium remaining after 50 years.
$$y = 3\left(\tfrac{1}{2}\right)^{\frac{x}{1620}}; \approx\textbf{2.937 mg}$$

8-3 Objectives

▼ To write and evaluate logarithmic expressions (p. 438)

▼ To graph logarithmic functions (p. 440)

If $y = b^x$, then $\log_b y = x$. The **logarithmic function** is the inverse of the exponential function, so the graphs of the functions are reflections of one another over the line $y = x$. Logarithmic functions can be translated and reflected.

When $b = 10$, the logarithm is called a **common logarithm**, which you can write as $\log y$.

 30. Chemistry The pH of a substance equals $-\log[\text{H}^+]$, where $[\text{H}^+]$ is the concentration of hydrogen ions. A sample of well water has a pH of 5.7. Find the concentration of hydrogen ions in the sample.   **2.0×10^{-6}**

31. The concentration of hydrogen ions in water is 10^{-7}. Find the pH of water.   **7**

Write each equation in logarithmic form.

32. $6^2 = 36$ **$2 = \log_6 36$**   **33.** $2^{-3} = 0.125$ **$-3 = \log_2 0.125$**

34. $3^3 = 27$ **$3 = \log_3 27$**   **35.** $10^{-3} = 0.001$ **$-3 = \log 0.001$**

Evaluate each logarithm.

36. $\log_2 64$ **6**   **37.** $\log_3 \frac{1}{9}$ **-2**

38. $\log 0.00001$ **-5**   **39.** $\log_2 1$ **0**

Graph each logarithmic function.   40–43. See margin.

40. $y = \log_3 x$ **41.** $y = \log(x + 2)$

42. $y = \log_2 2x$ **43.** $y = \log_5(x + 1)$

470   Chapter 8   Chapter Review

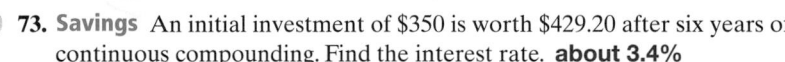

8-4 Objective

▼ To use the properties of logarithms (p. 446)

For any positive numbers, M, N, and $b, b \neq 1$, each of the following statements is true. Each can be used to rewrite a logarithmic expression.

- $\log_b MN = \log_b M + \log_b N$, by the Product Property
- $\log_b \frac{M}{N} = \log_b M - \log_b N$, by the Quotient Property
- $\log_b M^x = x \log_b M$, by the Power Property

Write each logarithmic expression as a single logarithm.

48. $2 \log_4 x + 3 \log_4 y$; Product and Power Properties

49. $\log 4 + 4 \log S + \log t$; Product and Power Properties

50. $\log_3 2 - \log_3 x$; Quotient Property

51. $2 \log (x + 3)$; Power Property

44. $\log 8 + \log 3$ **log 24**

45. $\log_2 5 - \log_2 3$ $\log_2 \frac{5}{3}$

46. $4 \log_3 x + \log_3 7$ $\log_3 7x^4$

47. $\log z - \log y$ $\log \frac{z}{y}$

Expand each logarithm. State the properties of logarithms that you use.

48. $\log_4 x^2 y^3$ **49.** $\log 4s^4 t$ **50.** $\log_3 \frac{2}{x}$ **51.** $\log (x + 3)^2$

52. Use the formula $L = 10 \log \frac{I}{I_0}$. Suppose the sound intensity of a fan must be reduced by one third. By how many decibels would the loudness be decreased? **about 1.76 dB**

8-5 Objectives

▼ To solve exponential equations (p. 453)

▼ To solve logarithmic equations (p. 455)

An equation in the form $b^{cx} = a$, where the exponent includes a variable, is called an **exponential equation**. You can solve exponential equations by taking the logarithm of each side of the equation. An equation that includes a logarithmic expression is called a **logarithmic equation**.

Solve each equation. Round your answers to the nearest hundredth.

53. $4^x = 27$ **2.38**   **54.** $3^x = 36$ **3.26**   **55.** $7^{x-3} = 25$ **4.65** **56.** $5^x = 9$ **1.37**

Solve by graphing.

57. $5^{2x} = 25$ **1**   **58.** $3^{7x} = 160$ **≈0.66**   **59.** $6^{3x+1} = 215$ **≈0.67**   **60.** $0.5^x = 0.12$ **≈3.06**

Solve each logarithmic equation. Leave your answer in exact form.

61. $\log 3x = 1$ $\frac{10}{3}$

62. $\log_2 4x = 5$ **8**

63. $\log x = \log 2x^2 - 2$ **50**

64. $2 \log_3 x = 54$ **7,625,597,484,987**

65. Convert $\log_2 7$ to a logarithm in base 5. $\log_5$ **91.68**

 66. Biology A culture of 10 bacteria is started, and the number of bacteria will double every hour. In about how many hours will there be 3,000,000 bacteria? **about 18.2 h**

8-6 Objectives

▼ To evaluate natural logarithmic expressions (p. 462)

▼ To solve equations using natural logarithms (p. 463)

The inverse of $y = e^x$ is the **natural logarithmic function** $y = \log_e x = \ln x$. You solve natural logarithm equations in the same way as common logarithm equations.

Solve each equation.

67. $e^{3x} = 12$ **0.83**

68. $\ln x + \ln(x + 1) = 2$ **2.26**

69. $2 \ln x + 3 \ln 2 = 5$ **4.31**

70. $\ln 4 - \ln x = 10$ **0.00018**

71. $4e^{(x - 1)} = 64$ **3.77**

72. $3 \ln x + \ln 5 = 7$ **6.03**

 73. Savings An initial investment of $350 is worth $429.20 after six years of continuous compounding. Find the interest rate. **about 3.4%**

Chapter 8

Chapter Test

Take It to the NET
Online chapter test at
www.PHSchool.com
Web Code: aga-0852

Resources

📁 **Teaching Resources**
Ch. 8 Test, Forms A & B
Ch. 8 Alternative Assessment,
Form C

👥 **Reaching All Students**
Spanish Ch. 8 Test, Forms A & B
Spanish Ch. 8 Alternative
Assessment, Form C

PRENTICE HALL
ASSESSMENT SYSTEM

Assessment Masters
• Ch. 8 Test, Forms A & B
• Ch. 8 Alternative Assessment,
Form C
Computer Test Generator CD
• Ch. 8 pre-made Test
• Make your own Ch. 8 test

 www.PHSchool.com
Student Site
• Self-grading Chapter 8 Test
Teacher Center
• Resources

Plus

Evaluate each function to the nearest hundredth for for $x = 0, 1, 2, 3, 4, 5$. Graph each function.

1. $y = 3(0.25)^x$

2. $f(x) = -(6)^x$

3. $y = 0.1(10)^x$

4. $f(x) = 100(2)^x$

1–4. See back of book.

5. Open-Ended Give an example of an exponential function that models exponential growth and an example of an exponential function that models exponential decay. **See margin.**

Write an exponential function of the form $y = ab^x$ that has a graph through the given points.

6. $(1, 1), (2, 3)$ $y = \frac{1}{3}(3)^x$

7. $\left(-2, \frac{2}{25}\right), (1, 10)$ $y = 2(5)^x$

8. $\left(-3, \frac{1}{16}\right), (-1, 1)$ $y = 4(4)^x$

🌐 **9. Investment** You put $1500 into an account earning 7% annual interest compounded continuously. How long will it be until you have $2000 in your account? **4.11 years**

Describe how the graph of each function is related to the graph of its parent function.

10. $y = 3^x + 2$ $y = 3^x$ translated up 2 units

11. $y = 3\left(\frac{1}{2}\right)^{x+1}$ $y = 3\left(\frac{1}{2}\right)^x$ translated left 1 unit

12. $y = 5^{x-2} - 1$

13. $y = -(2)^{x+2}$ **12–13. See margin.**

Evaluate each logarithm.

14. $\log_2 8$ **3**

15. $\log_7 7$ **1**

16. $\log_5 25$ **2**

17. $\log_3 27$ **3**

18. $\log_{11} 1$ **0**

19. $\log_4 256$ **4**

Graph each logarithmic function.

20. $y = \log_9 x$ **20–23. See back of book.**

21. $y = \log_3 (x - 1)$

22. $y = \frac{1}{2} \log_3 (x + 2)$

23. $y = 1 - \log_2 x$

Use the properties of logarithms to rewrite each logarithmic expression. 24–27. See margin.

24. $\log_2 4 + 3 \log_2 9$

25. $3 \log a - 2 \log b$

26. $\log_7 \frac{a}{b}$

27. $\log 3x^3 y^2$

Use the properties of logarithms to evaluate each expression.

28. $\log_3 27 - \log_3 9$ **1**

29. $2 \log_2 64 + \log_2 2$ **13**

30. $-\log_4 \frac{1}{16} - \log_4 64$ **−1**

31. $2 \log 5 + \log 40$ **3**

✏️ **32. Writing** Show that solving the equation $3^{2x} = 4$ by taking common logarithms of both sides is equivalent to solving it by taking logarithms to the base 3 of both sides.
See back of book.

Solve each equation.

33. $\left(\frac{3}{4}\right)^x = 81$ **−15.28**

34. $3^{x-1} = 24$ **3.89**

35. $\log 4x = 3$ **250**

36. $2 \log x = -4$ **0.01**

Use the Change of Base Formula to rewrite each expression using common logarithms.

37. $\log_3 16$ $\frac{\log 16}{\log 3}$

38. $\log_2 10$ $\frac{1}{\log 2}$

39. $\log_7 8$ $\frac{\log 8}{\log 7}$

Use the properties of logarithms to simplify each equation and solve it. Round to thousandths.

40. $\ln 2 + \ln x = 1$ **1.359**

41. $\ln (x + 1) + \ln (x - 1) = 4$ **7.456**

42. $\ln (2x - 1)^2 = 7$ **17.058, −16.058**

43. $3 \ln x - \ln 2 = 4$ **4.780**

🌐 **44. Physics** Seawater absorbs light. In some instances, this relationship is modeled by $\ln I = \ln I_0 - 0.014d$. I_0 is the intensity of the light at the surface of the water, and I is the intensity at a depth of d cm. At what depth will the intensity of the light in the water be 25% of the surface intensity? **about 99 cm**

page 472   Chapter Test

5. Answers may vary. Both answers should be of the form $y = ab^x$. For the growth model, $b > 1$. For the decay model, $0 < b < 1$.

12. $y = 5^x$ translated right 2 units and down 1 unit

13. $y = 2^x$ translated left 2 units and reflected over the x-axis

24. $\log_2 2916$

25. $\log \frac{a^3}{b^2}$

26. $\log_7 a - \log_7 b$

27. $\log 3 + 3 \log x + 2 \log y$

Multiple Choice

For Exercises 1–7, choose the correct letter.

1. What can you tell about the roots of $3x^2 + 4x - 1 = 0$ from the discriminant? **A**
   A. There are two real roots.
   B. There are two imaginary roots.
   C. There is one real and one imaginary root.
   D. There are no roots.

2. Which expressions are equivalent to $\log a - 3\log b$? **G**

   I. $\log ab^3$ II. $\log \frac{a}{b^3}$
   III. $\log a - \log b^3$ IV. $\log (ab)^3$

   F. I and II   G. II and III
   H. III and IV   I. I and IV

3. What is the factored form of $2x^3 + 5x^2 - 12x$? **A**
   A. $x(2x - 3)(x + 4)$
   B. $(2x^2 - 3)(x + 4)$
   C. $x(2x + 4)(x - 3)$
   D. $(2x - 4)(x + 3)$

4. Which is NOT a solution of the system? **I**
   $$\begin{cases} 2x - y > 3 \\ 2x + y \geq 5 \end{cases}$$
   F. $(3, 0)$ G. $(4, -1)$
   H. $(6, 1)$ I. $(0, -3)$

5. How is the graph of $y = (x - 4)^2 + 1$ translated from the graph of $y = x^2$? **D**
   A. left 1, up 4   B. left 4, down 1
   C. right 1, down 4   D. right 4, up 1

6. What is the inverse of $\begin{bmatrix} 3 & -5 \\ 1 & 4 \end{bmatrix}$? **I**

   F. $\begin{bmatrix} 4 & 5 \\ -1 & 3 \end{bmatrix}$ G. $\begin{bmatrix} -2 & 5 \\ -1 & -3 \end{bmatrix}$

   H. $\begin{bmatrix} -3 & 5 \\ -1 & -4 \end{bmatrix}$ I. $\frac{1}{17}\begin{bmatrix} 4 & 5 \\ -1 & 3 \end{bmatrix}$

7. Solve the system. $\begin{cases} 2x + 3y - z = -2 \\ x - 4y + 2z = 18 \\ 5x + 2y - 6z = 8 \end{cases}$ **C**
   A. $x = 3, y = 1, z = 2$
   B. $x = -3, y = 2, z = -1$
   C. $x = 4, y = -3, z = 1$
   D. $x = -1, y = 3, z = 2$

Quantitative Comparison

Compare the boxed quantity in Column A with the boxed quantity in Column B. Choose the best answer.

   A. The quantity in Column A is greater.
   B. The quantity in Column B is greater.
   C. The two quantities are equal.
   D. The relationship cannot be determined from the information given.

	Column A	Column B
8. **A**	e^2	$2 \ln e$
9. **B**	$\log_3 2$	$\log_2 3$
10. **A**	$\log_a a$	$\log_a 1$

Gridded Response

11. Solve $3^x = 7$. Round your answer to the nearest hundredth. **1.77**

12. What is the discriminant of $2x^2 - 8x + 8 = 0$? **0**

13. Evaluate $\log_4 8$. $\frac{3}{2}$ **or 1.5**

Short Response 14–15. See margin.

14. Write $\log \frac{x^2 y^3}{z^6}$ in expanded form.

15. Solve $5^{2x + 1} = 62$. Round your answer to the nearest hundredth. Show your work.

16. Graph the function $y = 10^{x + 1} - 3$ as a translation of its parent function.
    See back of book.

Extended Response

17. Suppose you put $1000 in an account earning 5.5% interest compounded continuously. How much will be in the account after one year? After four years? **See back of book.**

18. What is the determinant of $\begin{bmatrix} 1 & 2 & 3 \\ 2 & 1 & 3 \\ 2 & 3 & 1 \end{bmatrix}$?
    Show your work. **See back of book.**

Resources

📁 **Teaching Resources**
Cumulative Review

 Reaching All Students
Spanish Cumulative Review

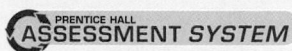 PRENTICE HALL
ASSESSMENT SYSTEM

Standardized Test Prep
• Ch. 8 Standardized Test Practice
Assessment Masters
• Cumulative Review
Computer Test Generator CD
• Standardized Test Practice

 www.PHSchool.com
• Standardized Test Practice
• Resources

Plus

Cumulative Review

Cumulative Review
Chapters 1–8

Item	Lesson	Item	Lesson
1	5-8	10	8-4
2	8-4	11	8-5
3	6-2	12	5-8
4	3-3	13	8-4
5	5-3	14	8-4
6	4-5	15	8-5
7	3-6	16	8-1
8	8-6	17	8-1
9	8-4	18	4-6

page 473   Standardized Test Prep

14. [2] $2 \log x + 3 \log y - 6 \log z$

   [1] **fails to complete one part of the expansion**

15. [2] $(2x + 1) \log 5 = \log 62$

   $2x + 1 = \frac{\log 62}{\log 5}$

   $x = \frac{1}{2}\left[\frac{\log 62}{\log 5} - 1\right]$

   $x \approx .78$

   [1] **answer only, without work shown**

A Crowded House

In this activity students apply their knowledge of exponential functions, graphs, and lines of best fit, as well as logarithms.

Connecting to Prior Knowledge

Ask students to describe what must be true for a given population to have a zero growth rate or a negative growth rate. Have students compare and give examples of linear growth and exponential growth.

Teaching Notes

Have a volunteer read the introductory paragraph. Have them discuss some of the consequences for a country, and for the world, of zero, negative, linear, and exponential population growth rates.

Teaching Tip

Suggest that students gather information about the population growth rate for their town or state over the last 100 years.

Connection to Demographics

Have students use the Internet to research recent population growth rates for various countries around the world, and color groups of countries on a world map to show the various rates. Ask them to form conjectures about possible patterns on this map.

English Learners

Ask a volunteer to explain the meaning of *population density*. Make sure that all students understand the meaning of *doubled* and *tripled*.

474

 **Real-World Snapshots**

A Crowded House

Applying Exponential Functions The number of people in the world has more than tripled since 1900—from less than 2 billion to more than 6 billion. In 2000, an average of about 360,000 babies were born each day. That means that there were four babies born every second.

Old South Meeting House

Historical Site

Old South Meeting House, in Boston, Massachusetts, (left about 1903, right in 2002), was built in 1730. At the time, it was the tallest building in Boston. Note that the time on the clock is 1:43 in both photos.

Proportional Populations

These maps of China, the United States, and Australia are drawn so that their sizes are proportional to their populations.

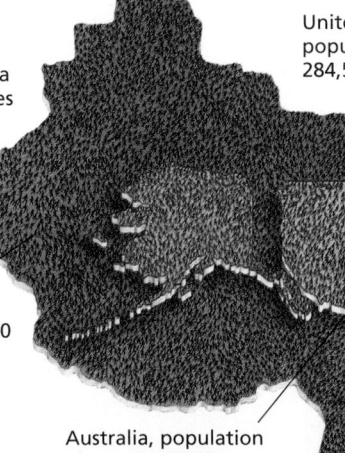

United States, population about 284,500,000

China, population about 1,273,300,000

Australia, population about 19,400,000

About one of every five people in the world lives in China.

474   All photographs © Dorling Kindersley Limited unless otherwise credited on acknowledgments page

---

pages 474–475   Real-World Snapshots

Activity

a. $P(n) = 2515k^n$
$$\ln (P(n)) = \ln (2515k^n)$$
$$= \ln (2515) + \ln (k^n)$$
$$= \ln (2515) + n\ln (k)$$

b.

n	P(n)	ln P(n)
0	2,515,000,000	21.65
10	3,019,000,000	21.83
20	3,698,000,000	22.03
30	4,450,000,000	22.22
40	5,284,000,000	22.39
50	6,080,000,000	22.53

c–d.

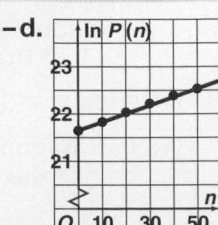

Teaching Tip

Before students begin the activity, discuss the illustrations and their captions. Have students work in pairs or in small groups to complete the activity. Have them read it before beginning.

Population Densities

All cities are crowded, but some are more crowded than others. Hong Kong Island is so closely packed that if it were divided into tennis courts, there would be 25 people on each court. London would have only one person on each court.

London: 1 person in an area the size of a tennis court

Hong Kong Island: 25 people in an area the size of a tennis court. A tennis court covers 2,808 sq ft. (261 sq m)

Activity

The population graph shows that population growth since 1950 has been exponential. You can use the data to write the equation $P(n) = 2515k^n$, where n = the number of years since 1950, k = the growth factor, and $P(n)$ is the population in millions. You will use this equation to estimate population.

a. Show that taking the natural log of each side of the equation yields the equation $\ln(P(n)) = \ln 2515 + n \ln k$.

b. Use the population graph. Make a table of the data for n and $P(n)$. Add a third column to the table to show $\ln(P(n))$.

c. Examine the structure of the equation in part (a). If you think of the parts in black as constants and the parts in red as variables, then this is the slope-intercept form of a linear equation relating $\ln(P(n))$ to n. Graph these two variables on a coordinate plane.

d. Draw a line of best fit and calculate the slope of the line.

e. Look closely at the slope-intercept equation in part (a). Which quantity represents the slope of the line?

f. Use the slope to determine the approximate growth factor k of the world's population since 1950.

g. Use your growth factor to write an exponential equation that models the population growth.

h. Estimate the population in the years 2005 and 2010.

Take It to the NET For more information about population growth, go to **www.PHSchool.com**.
Web Code: age-0853

World population in 2000: 6,080,000,000

World population in 1990: 5,284,000,000

World population in 1980: 4,450,000,000

World population in 1970: 3,698,000,000

World population in 1960: 3,019,000,000

World population in 1950: 2,515,000,000

World population in 1900: 1,633,000,000

World population in 1850: 1,094,000,000

World population in 1800: 954,000,000

World population in 1700: 679,000,000

World population in 1600: 579,000,000

1500 1600 1700 1800 1900 2000

475

Activity

Materials: paper and pencil, ruler, graph paper

Connection to Social Studies

Have students research and report on current population density of a number of different states in the United States of America. Ask them to compare density in various areas, for example, on the coasts and for inland western states.

Scoring Rubric

This scoring rubric can be used for evaluating student work on both activities. Share this scoring rubric with students before they begin work.

4 Equations, calculations, and graphs are correct.
   Steps are neat, accurate, and clearly show the mathematics. Responses are clearly indicated and give the appropriate units.

3 Equations, calculations, and graphs are mostly correct, with some minor errors. Steps are neat and mostly accurate. Units are not completely accurate.

2 Equations, calculations, and graphs contain both major and minor errors.

1 Correct answer, but no work is shown.

e. $\ln k$

f–h. **Answers may vary. Samples are given.**

f. about 1.02

g. $P(n) = 2515(1.02^n)$

h. 2005: $\approx 7,474,000,000$
   2010: $\approx 8,252,000,000$

Chapter 9

Rational Functions

Chapter at a Glance

North Carolina Objectives

NCTM STANDARDS 2000

1	Number and Operations	6	Problem Solving
2	Algebra	7	Reasoning and Proof
3	Geometry	8	Communication
4	Measurement	9	Connections
5	Data Analysis and Probability	10	Representation

Pacing Options

This chart suggests pacing only for the lessons and their parts. It is provided as a possible guide. It will help you determine how much time you have in your schedule to cover other components, such as the features, Chapter Review, and Chapter Test.

Day	Traditional (45 min.)	Block (90 min.)
1	9-1 ▼	9-1 ▼ ▼
2	9-1 ▼	9-2 ▼ ▼
3	9-2 ▼ ▼	9-3 ▼ ▼
4	9-3 ▼	9-4 ▼ ▼
5	9-3 ▼	9-5 ▼ ▼
6	9-4 ▼ ▼	9-6 ▼ ▼
7	9-5 ▼	9-7 ▼ ▼
8	9-5 ▼	
9	9-6 ▼	
10	9-6 ▼	
11	9-7 ▼	
12	9-7 ▼	

NAEP Correlation (National Assessment of Educational Progress 2000 Mathematics Objectives)

9-1	9-2	9-3	9-4	9-5	9-6	9-7
M10, A5c	A3a, A3d	A3a, A9	N3a, M5, A9	N3a, N6c, A5a	N3a, M10, A5a	D11b, D11c

N = Number Sense, Properties, and Operations; **M** = Measurement; **G** = Geometry and Spatial Sense;
D = Data Analysis, Statistics, and Probability; **A** = Algebra and Functions

Math Background

Chapter Overview

A rational function is a function that can be written in the form $y = \frac{P(x)}{Q(x)}$, where $P(x)$ and $Q(x)$ are polynomials and $Q(x) \neq 0$. If $Q(x)$ is a nonzero constant, then the function is also a polynomial function. Since students have already studied polynomial functions, this chapter concentrates on rational functions that are not polynomial functions.

The simplest rational functions are inverse variations, which have the form $y = \frac{k}{x}$, where k is a nonzero constant. Graphs of inverse variations have the x- and y-axes as asymptotes. Students see that graphs of more complicated rational functions may have many asymptotes. They may also have holes, where a single point is missing. Students learn how to find such points of discontinuity and how to use asymptotes in sketching graphs.

Students see that simplifying rational expressions and performing operations on them are similar in many ways to the corresponding processes for ordinary fractions in arithmetic. They learn to solve rational equations and check for extraneous solutions.

The chapter concludes with another look at probability. This time students calculate probabilities of multiple events.

Inverse Variation   9-1

Students learned about direct variation in Chapter 2. Inverse variation is similar to direct variation in that in both, the value of one variable changes in relation to the other. However, with inverse variation, the constant of variation is the product of the x and y values.

Graphing Inverse Variations   9-2

The graphs of inverse variations are hyperbolas, though they are not identified as such. The asymptotes are the x- and y-axes. Students may be helped by a discussion of the meaning of having no y-intercept. For instance, in Example 4, if a pipe has no length, it clearly will produce no sound.

Rational Functions and Their Graphs   9-3

When working with rational functions, we assume that the denominator cannot equal zero because the function would then be undefined. In addition to horizontal and vertical asymptotes, students may enjoy using polynomial division to find the non-horizontal linear asymptotes that occur in graphing rational functions whose numerator is one degree greater than its denominator.

Rational Expressions   9-4

Have students look over the exercises and discuss which of the exercises can be more easily simplified by multiplying numerator and denominator by the LCD and which are more easily simplified by multiplying the numerator by the reciprocal of the denominator.

Adding and Subtracting Rational Expressions   9-5

Students can use the formula $\frac{a}{b} \pm \frac{c}{d} = \frac{ad \pm bc}{bd}$ to add or subtract rational expressions. While this technique will always provide an answer, students should be aware of the following two shortcomings:

- If more than two fractions are to be added or subtracted, it is tiresome to have to apply this formula over and over again.

- When the formula is applied to rational expressions whose denominators have a common factor, it sometimes becomes difficult for students to write a solution in simplest form.

Solving Rational Equations   9-6

No extraneous solutions can be introduced when solving an equation using the addition property of equality because both of the following are true for all numbers:

$$\text{If } a = b, \text{ then } a + c = b + c.$$
$$\text{If } a + c = b + c, \text{ then } a = b.$$

However, extraneous solutions can be introduced when solving an equation using the multiplication property of equality.

$$\text{If } a = b, \text{ then } ac = bc \text{ is true for all numbers } a, b, \text{ and } c.$$
$$\text{But if } ac = bc, \text{ then } a = b \text{ may not be true if } c = 0.$$

This means that solutions of the derived equation may not be solutions of the original equation.

It is essential to check solutions to equations that are solved using the multiplication property because the procedure can introduce extraneous (wrong) answers.

Probability of Multiple Events   9-7

This lesson defines independent, dependent, and mutually exclusive events. Students may have an intuitive grasp of independent events, but you may wish to point out to them that the algebraic definition is sometimes the only guarantee of independence. Students will continue their study of probability in Chapter 12.

Ongoing Assessment and Intervention

Tools for Monitoring Student Progress

The Prentice Hall *Algebra 2* program provides you with many options for assessment in the Student Edition, the Teacher's Edition and the teaching resources. From these options you may choose instructional materials and techniques that are appropriate for your students and support your district's curriculum requirements.

 Instant Check System™ in Chapter 9

Allows students to check their own learning before, during, and after each lesson.

Diagnosing Readiness before the chapter (p. 476)

Check Skills You'll Need exercises in each lesson (pp. 478, 485, 491, 499, 504, 512, 519)

Check Understanding questions with each Example (pp. 479, 480, 485, 486, 487, 488, 492, 493, 494, 495, 499, 500, 501, 505, 506, 507, 512, 513, 514, 520, 521, 522)

Checkpoint Quiz (pp. 498, 510)

 **Test Prep in Chapter 9**

Teaches students strategies and gives them practice with all the test item formats they will encounter on state tests and standardized national exams.

Standardized Test Prep exercises in each lesson (pp. 483, 490, 497, 498, 503, 509, 510, 517, 525)

Test-Taking Strategies (p. 526)

Standardized Test Prep (p. 531)

All your assessment needs in one place!

Program Assessment

Assess student progress throughout the *Algebra 2* text with blackline masters and CD-ROM.

Assessment Resources

- Checkpoint Quizzes 1 & 2
- Chapter Test, Forms A & B
- Chapter Alternative Assessment

Spanish versions available.

 Computer Test Generator

- Unlimited questions of varying difficulty for every lesson objective.
- Create your own practice sheets, quizzes, and tests, or use the pre-made Chapter Tests.
- Diagnose readiness with questions on prerequisite skills.
- Prepare students by making tests based on standardized test objectives.
- Access Algebra 1, Geometry, and Algebra 2 content—all on one CD-ROM.

Test Preparation

A three-step approach to preparing students for high stakes, national, and state exams.

❶ **Diagnose & Prescribe**

Content Diagnostic Tests
- Diagnose strengths and weaknesses in content for national and state tests.
- Prescribe individualized reteaching opportunities.

❷ **Review & Reteach**

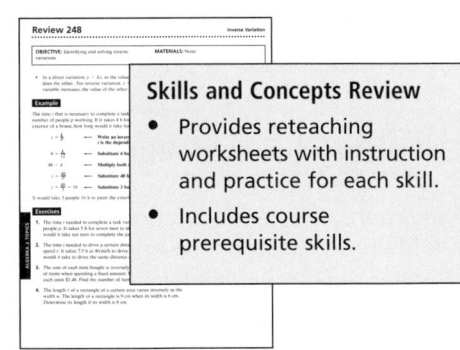

Skills and Concepts Review
- Provides reteaching worksheets with instruction and practice for each skill.
- Includes course prerequisite skills.

❸ **Practice & Assess**

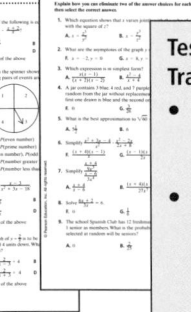

Test Preparation
- Features practice tests for End-of-Course and SAT/ACT exams.
- Includes standardized test practice by chapter for ongoing review.

Teacher's Guide with answers and correlations.

Test-Taking Strategies with Transparencies
- Support the Test-Taking Strategies pages in the Student Edition.
- Provide a teaching transparency and a practice worksheet for each strategy.

Reaching All Students

Support in the Student Text and Additional Resources

The textbook, the iText, and other technology components provide numerous opportunities to reach students of various ability levels and learning styles. Each Teacher's Edition lesson suggests how you can help *all* your students be successful and understand the mathematics in Chapter 9.

Below Level

Student Edition
- Diagnosing Readiness*: p. 476
- Check Skills You'll Need*: pp. 478, 485, 491, 499, 504, 512, 519

Reteaching
Chapter 9 Support File: pp. 8–14

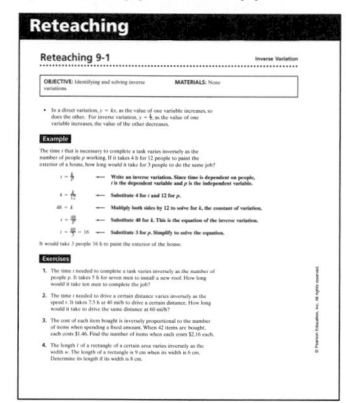

Advanced Learners

Student Edition
- Challenge exercises: pp. 482, 483, 489, 490, 497, 502, 503, 509, 517, 524

Enrichment
Chapter 9 Support File: pp. 15–21

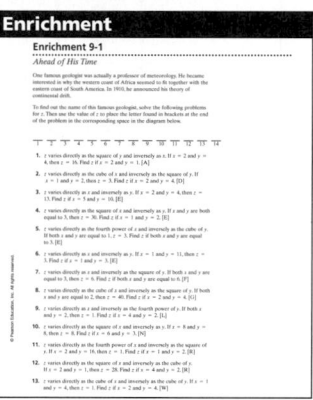

Connections to Precalculus Masters
Chapter 9 Enrichment Topic:
Function Domains

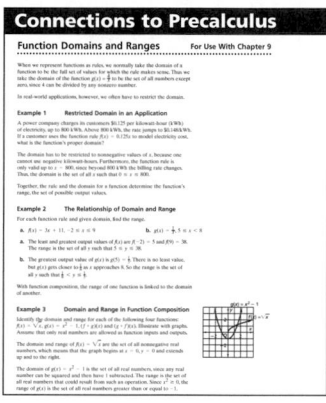

* Can be used with all ability levels to ensure mastery of prerequisite skills.

Reading and Math Literacy

Student Edition
- Vocabulary: pp. 477, 527, *plus* in every Lesson Preview
- Reading Math: pp. 479, 480, 485, 491, 515, 518, 521
- Illustrated Glossary: pp. 871–913

Reading and Math Literacy Masters
Chapter 9: pp. 33–36

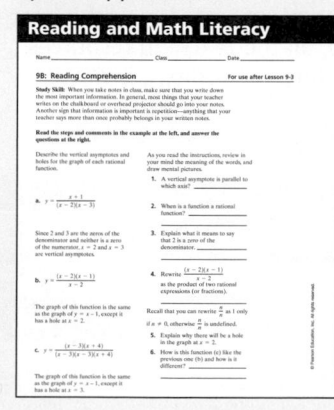

English Learners

Student Edition
- English/Spanish Illustrated Glossary: pp. 871–913

Workbook and Masters
Spanish Practice Workbook: pp. 1–7
Spanish Reading and Math Literacy
Masters: pp. 33–36

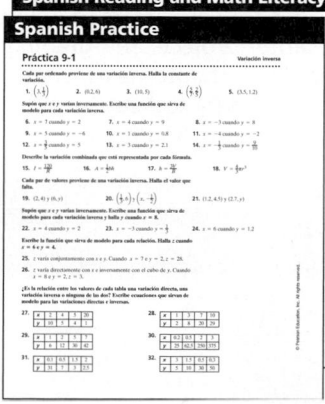

Learning Styles

Student Edition
- Investigation: pp. 504, 511, 519
- Technology: pp. 484, 486, 492
- Writing: pp. 482, 487, 489, 496, 502, 508, 516, 530

Activity Masters
Hands-On Activities: 49, 50
Technology Activities: 33

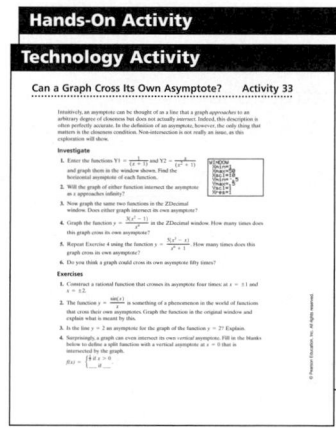

Program Resources

	Teaching Resources in Grab & Go™ Files				Resources for Reaching All Students			Spanish Resources			Transparencies				Presentation Assistant Plus!
	Practice	Reteach	Enrich	Checkpoint Quiz	Reading & Math Literacy	Technology Activities	Hands-On Activities	Practice	Reading & Math Literacy	Checkpoint Quiz	Skills Check	Additional Examples	Answers to Exercises	Lesson Quiz	Prentice Hall Presentation Pro CD-ROM
9-1	■	■	■		■			■			■	■	■	■	■
9-2	■	■	■				■	■			■	■	■	■	■
9-3	■	■	■	■	■	■		■		■	■	■	■	■	■
9-4	■	■	■				■	■			■	■	■	■	■
9-5	■	■	■	■	■			■		■	■	■	■	■	■
9-6	■	■	■					■			■	■	■	■	■
9-7	■	■	■					■			■	■	■	■	■
For the chapter	Chapter Tests, Alternative Assessment, Cumulative Review, Cumulative Assessment				Connections to Precalculus Masters			Spanish Chapter Tests, Alternative Assessment, Cumulative Review, Cumulative Assessment			Classroom Aid Transparencies				

Also available for use with the chapter:

 PRENTICE HALL ASSESSMENT SYSTEM *See page 476C.*

- Practice Workbook
- Solution Key

- For teacher support and access to student Web site materials, use Web Code agk-5500.
- For additional online and technology resources, see below.

Technology

iTEXT — Online and on CD-ROM

Complete Interactive Student Text online and on CD-ROM—with instant feedback assessment, tutorial help, dynamic activities, instructional and real-world videos, audio, and additional practice.

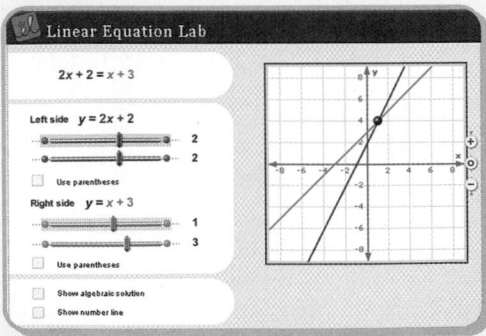

www.PHSchool.com — For Students

Use **Web Codes** for easy access to online activities, chapter projects, self-grading lesson quizzes and chapter tests, vocabulary quizzes, updated data sources, graphing calculator procedures, and more.

PH SuccessNet — For Teachers

Online lesson planning with built-in state correlations, all the teaching resources, complete reference library, your own calendar and Teacher Web page, professional development, and more.

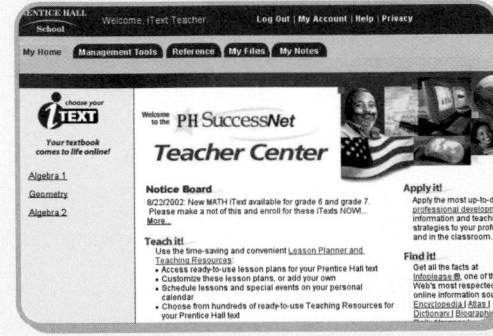

Presentation Assistant Plus!

The Prentice Hall *Presentation Assistant Plus!* provides you with the material you need to teach a lesson from beginning to end. Two easy-to-use formats—Transparencies and CD-ROM—allow you to present a lesson the way you are most comfortable.

 ## Transparencies

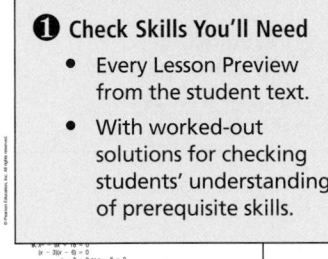

❶ Check Skills You'll Need
- Every Lesson Preview from the student text.
- With worked-out solutions for checking students' understanding of prerequisite skills.

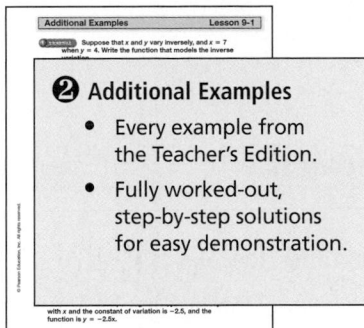

❷ Additional Examples
- Every example from the Teacher's Edition.
- Fully worked-out, step-by-step solutions for easy demonstration.

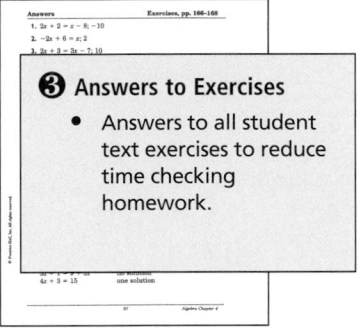

❸ Answers to Exercises
- Answers to all student text exercises to reduce time checking homework.

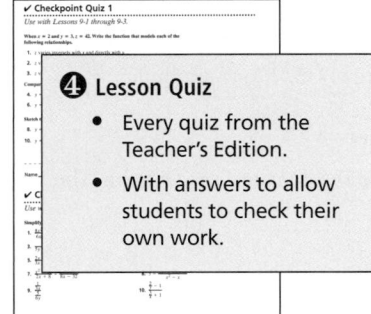

❹ Lesson Quiz
- Every quiz from the Teacher's Edition.
- With answers to allow students to check their own work.

 Throughout the Teacher's Edition, this symbol indicates material that is available on transparency in the Presentation Assistant Plus!

 ## Prentice Hall Presentation Pro CD-ROM

- Includes all Transparencies.
- Conveniently organized by lesson so you can easily ❶ Introduce, ❷ Teach, ❸ Check Homework, and ❹ Assess each lesson.
- Animated examples allow step-by-step instruction at your own pace.
- Easy to edit so you can create custom presentations.

Teaching Chapter 9 Using Presentation Assistant Plus!

	❶ Introduce	❷ Teach	❸ Check Homework	❹ Assess
	Check Skills You'll Need	Additional Examples	Student Edition Answers	Lesson Quiz
9-1	p. 58	pp. 174–176	✔	p. 143
9-2	p. 59	pp. 176–177	✔	p. 144
9-3	p. 60	pp. 178–179	✔	p. 145
9-4	p. 61	pp. 179–184	✔	p. 146
9-5	p. 62	pp. 185–187	✔	p. 147
9-6	p. 63	p. 188	✔	p. 148
9-7	p. 64	pp. 189–191	✔	p. 149

 ### Prentice Hall Presentation Pro

CD-ROM with dynamic PowerPoint® presentations for every lesson. Helps you introduce and develop concepts, check homework, and assess progress. Part of Presentation Assistant Plus! *(See above.)*

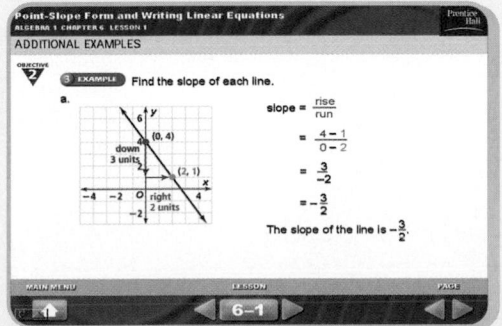

 ### Computer Test Generator

CD-ROM to create practice sheets and tests for course objectives and standardized tests. Includes Instant Chapter Tests™, online testing, and student reports. Part of the PH Assessment System. *(See page 476C.)*

 ### Resource Pro® with Planning Express®

CD-ROM with a lesson planning tool that allows you to import state and local objectives. Includes electronic versions of all the teaching resources.

Chapter **9**

Rational Functions

 Diagnosing Readiness

Students will find answers to these exercises in the back of their textbooks.

For intervention, direct students to:

Finding Theoretical Properties
Lesson 1-6: Example 3
Exercises 6–18
Extra Practice, p. 822

Using Direct Variation
Lesson 2-3: Example 2
Exercises 9–16
Extra Practice, p. 823

Factoring Quadratic Expressions
Lesson 5-4: Example 1
Exercises 1–6
Extra Practice, p. 826

Solving Quadratic Equations
Lesson 5-5: Example 1
Exercises 1–6
Extra Practice, p. 826

Where You've Been

- In Chapter 1, you learned to find theoretical probabilities for random events.

- In Chapter 2, you learned to write and interpret direct variation equations to solve real-world problems.

- In Chapter 5, you learned to factor quadratic expressions and to solve quadratic equations.

 **Diagnosing Readiness**   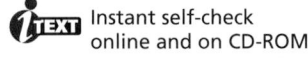 Instant self-check online and on CD-ROM

(For help, go to the Lesson in green.)

Finding Theoretical Probabilities (Lesson 1-6)

A bookshelf contains 18 math books, 27 science books, 21 history books, and 15 grammar books. You pick one book at random from the shelf. Find each theoretical probability.

1. P(history) $\frac{7}{27}$ **2.** P(science) $\frac{1}{3}$ **3.** P(math or science) $\frac{5}{9}$

4. P(math or science or history) **5.** P(not grammar) $\frac{22}{27}$ **6.** P(not math and not science) $\frac{12}{27}$
     $\frac{22}{27}$

Using Direct Variation (Lesson 2-3)

For each direct variation, find the constant of variation. Then find the value of y when $x = -3$.

7. $y = 4$ when $x = 3$ $\frac{4}{3}$; **−4**   **8.** $y = 1$ when $x = -1.5$ $-\frac{2}{3}$; **2**

9. $y = -5$ when $x = \frac{3}{2}$ $-\frac{10}{3}$; **10**   **10.** $y = -16$ when $x = 7$ $-\frac{16}{7}$; $\frac{48}{7}$

Factoring Quadratic Expressions (Lesson 5-4)

Factor each expression.

11. $x^2 + x - 6$ **(x + 3)(x − 2)**   **12.** $4x^2 + 17x + 15$ **(4x + 5)(x + 3)**   **13.** $9x^2 - 25$ **(3x − 5)(3x + 5)**

14. $x^2 - 12x + 36$ **(x − 6)²**   **15.** $3x^2 + 10x + 8$ **(3x + 4)(x + 2)**   **16.** $x^2 - 5x + 6$ **(x − 3)(x − 2)**

Solving Quadratic Equations (Lesson 5-5)

Solve each equation.

17. $x^2 + 7x - 8 = 0$ **1, −8**   **18.** $\frac{1}{4}x^2 + \frac{7}{2}x = -12$ **−6, −8**   **19.** $3x^2 = 18x - 24$ **4, 2**

20. $9x^2 + 6x = 0$ **0, $-\frac{2}{3}$**   **21.** $4x^2 + 16 = 34x$ **8, $\frac{1}{2}$**   **22.** $x^2 - 13x - 30 = 0$ **15, −2**

Rational Functions

Where You're Going

- In Chapter 9, you will learn to use inverse variation and the graphs of inverse variations to solve real-world problems.

- You will learn to identify properties of rational functions.

- You will learn to simplify rational expressions and to solve rational equations.

Real-World Connection Applying what you learn, on page 505 you will solve a problem involving photography.

Key Vocabulary

- branch (p. 485)
- combined variation (p. 480)
- complex fraction (p. 506)
- dependent events (p. 519)
- independent events (p. 519)
- inverse variation (p. 478)
- mutually exclusive events (p. 521)
- point of discontinuity (p. 491)
- rational function (p. 491)
- simplest form (p. 499)

Chapter 9 Overview

Students begin the chapter by exploring the concept of inverse variation, and learning how to graph inverse variations. Students then study rational functions and their graphs. Students then study how to multiply, divide, add, and subtract rational expressions. They then study how to solve rational equations. Students conclude the chapter by exploring finding the probability of multiple events.

📖 **Reading Math**
Reading for Problem Solving, p. 518

📖 **Vocabulary**
A complete list of terms, plus vocabulary exercises, appears in the Chapter Review, p. 527.

📖 **Illustrated Glossary**
Examples for each vocabulary term, plus definitions in both English and Spanish, appear starting on p. 871.

Test-Taking Strategies
Eliminating Answers, p. 526

🌐 **Real-World Connections**
Some of the applications you will find in this chapter are physics (9-1), music (9-2), business (9-3), industrial design (9-4), aerodynamics (9-6), and radio (9-7).

💻 **www.PHSchool.com**
Internet support for this chapter includes:
- Self-grading Vocabulary and Chapter 9 Tests
- Chapter Project
- Chapter Planner
- Chapter 9 Resources

Plus **i TEXT**

477

✔ Check Skills You'll Need

Direct Variation
Lesson 2-3: Example 4
Exercises 24–27
Extra Practice, p. 823

Lesson Resources

📁 Teaching Resources
Practice, Reteaching, Enrichment

🌱 Reaching All Students
Practice Workbook 9-1
Spanish Practice Workbook 9-1
Reading and Math Literacy 9A
Spanish Reading & Literacy 9A

⏱ Presentation Assistant Plus!
Transparencies
• Check Skills You'll Need 9-1
• Additional Examples 9-1
• Student Edition Answers 9-1
• Lesson Quiz 9-1
PH Presentation Pro CD 9-1

PRENTICE HALL ASSESSMENT SYSTEM

Computer Test Generator CD

💿 Technology
Resource Pro® CD-ROM
Computer Test Generator CD
Prentice Hall Presentation Pro CD

🖥 www.PHSchool.com
Student Site
• Teacher Web Code: agk-5500
• Self-grading Lesson Quiz
Teacher Center
• Lesson Planner
• Resources

Plus 📘 **TEXT**

9-1

Inverse Variation

1.05   Model and solve problems using direct, inverse, combined and joint variation.

North Carolina Objectives

Lesson Preview

What You'll Learn

OBJECTIVE 1 To use inverse variation

OBJECTIVE 2 To use combined variation

. . . And Why

To find the life spans of mammals, as in Example 3

✔ Check Skills You'll Need

(For help, go to Lesson 2-3.)

In Exercises 1–3, y varies directly with x.

1. Given that $x = 2$ when $y = 4$, find y when $x = 5$.   **10**
2. Given that $x = 1$ when $y = 5$, find y when $x = 3$.   **15**
3. Given that $x = 10$ when $y = 3$, find y when $x = 4$.   **1.2**

New Vocabulary   • inverse variation · • combined variation

📘 **TEXT**   Interactive lesson includes instant self-check, tutorials, and activities.

Using Inverse Variation

In Chapter 2, you studied direct variation. A direct variation is a linear function of the form $y = kx$, where k is the nonzero constant of variation. A function of the form $y = \frac{k}{x}$ or $xy = k$, where $k \neq 0$, is an **inverse variation.**

The table and graph below show the time needed to bike 24 miles pedaling at different rates.

Rate (mi/h)	Time (h)
3	8
6	4
12	2
24	1

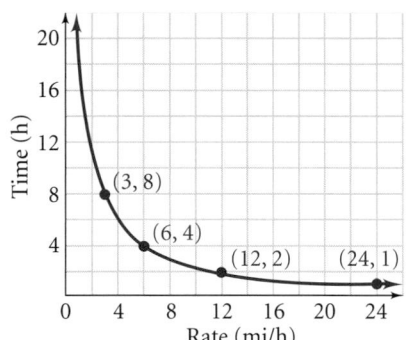

Notice that as the rate increases, the time decreases. Doubling the rate halves the time. The inverse variation $t = \frac{24}{r}$ models this situation.

1 EXAMPLE   Modeling Inverse Variation

Suppose that x and y vary inversely, and $x = 3$ when $y = -5$. Write the function that models the inverse variation.

$y = \frac{k}{x}$ *x and y vary inversely.*

$-5 = \frac{k}{3}$ **Substitute the given values of x and y.**

$-15 = k$ **Find k.**

$y = \frac{-15}{x}$ **Use the value of k to write the function.**

⚡ Ongoing Assessment and Intervention

Before the Lesson	**During the Lesson**	**After the Lesson**
Diagnose prerequisite skills using:	Monitor progress using:	Assess knowledge using:
• Check Skills You'll Need	• Check Understanding • Additional Examples • Standardized Test Prep	• Lesson Quiz • Computer Test Generator CD

✓ **Check Understanding** ① Suppose that x and y vary inversely, and $x = 0.3$ when $y = 1.4$. Write the function that models the inverse variation. $y = \frac{0.42}{x}$

② **EXAMPLE** **Identifying Direct and Inverse Variations**

Is the relationship between the variables in each table a direct variation, an inverse variation, or neither? Write functions to model the direct and inverse variations.

a.

x	0.5	2	6
y	1.5	6	18

As x increases, y increases. Since each y-value is 3 times the corresponding x-value, y varies directly with x, the constant of variation is 3, and the function is $y = 3x$.

b.

x	0.2	0.6	1.2
y	12	4	2

As x increases, y decreases. The product of each pair of x- and y-values is 2.4. y varies inversely with x and the constant of variation is 2.4. So $xy = 2.4$ and the function is $y = \frac{2.4}{x}$.

c.

x	1	2	3
y	2	1	0.5

As x increases, y decreases, but this is not an inverse variation. Not all the products of x and y are the same $(2 \cdot 1 \neq 3 \cdot 0.5)$. This is neither a direct variation nor an inverse variation.

Reading Math

You can describe an inverse variation as "y varies inversely as x" or as "y is inversely proportional to x."

✓ **Check Understanding** ② Is the relationship between the values in each table a direct variation, an inverse variation, or neither? Write functions to model the direct and inverse variations.

a.

x	0.8	0.6	0.4
y	0.9	1.2	1.8

b.

x	2	4	6
y	3.2	1.6	1.1

c.

x	1.2	1.4	1.6
y	18	21	24

2a. inverse; $y = \frac{0.72}{x}$

b. neither

c. direct; $y = 15x$

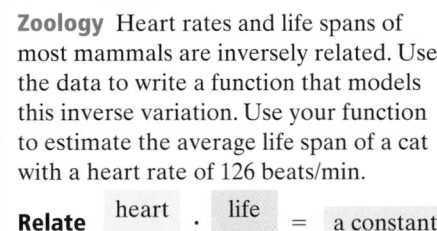

Real-World Connection

Horses have a life span of about 30 years.

③ **EXAMPLE** **Real-World Connection**

Zoology Heart rates and life spans of most mammals are inversely related. Use the data to write a function that models this inverse variation. Use your function to estimate the average life span of a cat with a heart rate of 126 beats/min.

Relate $\boxed{\text{heart rate}} \cdot \boxed{\text{life span}} = \boxed{\text{a constant}}$

Define Let $\boxed{r}$ = heart rate (beats/min).

Let $\boxed{s}$ = life span (min).

Let $\boxed{k}$ = constant of variation (beats in a life span).

Write $\boxed{r} \; \boxed{s} = \boxed{k}$

Heart Rate and Life Span

Mammal	Heart rate (beats/min)	Life span (min)
Mouse	634	1,576,800
Rabbit	158	6,307,200
Lion	76	13,140,000
Horse	63	15,768,000

SOURCE: *The Handy Science Answer Book*

For each of the four mammals in the table, $rs \approx 1,000,000,000$.

$rs = 1,000,000,000$ **Substitute 1,000,000,000 for k.**

$126s = 1,000,000,000$ **Substitute 126 for r.**

$s \approx 8,000,000$

A cat's life span is about 8 million minutes, or about 15.2 years.

3a. about 5,000,000 min, or about 10 yr

✓ **Check Understanding** ③ **a.** A squirrel's heart rate is 190 beats per minute. Estimate its life span.
b. An elephant's life span is about 70 years. Estimate its average heart rate.
about 27 beats per min

Lesson 9-1 Inverse Variation **479**

Math Background

In Chapter 2, students learned that in a direct variation $y = kx$, $(k > 0)$, the y-values increase as the x-values increase. The opposite is true for an indirect variation, $y = \frac{k}{x}$. The y-values decrease as the x-values increase. Students will learn later that the graph is a hyperbola.

OBJECTIVE
① **Teaching Notes**

① **EXAMPLE** **Math Tip**

Point out that in any inverse variation function, the values of x and y are never zero. Ask students why. **The definition of an inverse variation says $k \neq 0$. So, if $xy = k$, neither x nor y can be 0.**

③ **EXAMPLE** **English Learners**

Explain the terms *zoology, heart rate, life span,* and *mammal,* or have a student find their definitions.

Additional Examples

① Suppose that x and y vary inversely, and $x = 7$ when $y = 4$. Write the function that models the inverse variation. $y = \frac{28}{x}$

② Is the relationship between the variables in each table a direct variation, an inverse variation, or neither? Write functions to model the direct and inverse variations.

a.

x	2	4	14
y	0.7	0.35	0.1

inverse variation; $y = \frac{1.4}{x}$

b.

x	-2	-1.3	7
y	6	5	-4

neither

c.

x	-2	4	6
y	5	-10	-15

direct variation; $y = -2.5x$

👥 **Reaching All Students**

| **Below Level** If students are unsure whether a function is a direct variation or indirect variation, suggest that they consider substituting in both $y = kx$ and $y = \frac{k}{x}$. | **Advanced Learners** If the temperature of an enclosed gas is held constant, the pressure and volume vary inversely. Discuss the volume if the pressure is doubled or halved. | **English Learners** See note on page 479. **Auditory Learners** See note on page 481. |

Pressure (lb/in.^{2})	Volume (in.^{3})
3	32
5	19.2
8	12

OBJECTIVE 2 Teaching Notes

4 EXAMPLE | Connection to Physics

You may want to tell students that the constant G has a value of about 6.672×10^{-11} N $\frac{m^2}{kg^2}$, where N stands for the unit of force called the *newton*.

Additional Examples

4 The mass m of a moving object is related to its kinetic energy k and its velocity v by the formula $m = \frac{2k}{v^2}$. Describe the relationship as a combined variation. **m varies directly as the kinetic energy k and inversely as the square of the velocity v.**

5 The area of an equilateral triangle varies directly as the square of the radius r of its circumscribed circle. The area of an equilateral triangle for which $r = 2$ is $3\sqrt{3}$. Find the formula for the area A of an equilateral triangle in terms of r. **$A = \frac{3\sqrt{3}}{4}r^2$**

Closure

Ask students to write an equation that shows what it means for a quantity w to vary jointly as x and y and inversely as z. **$w = \frac{kxy}{z}$, where k is a nonzero constant**

OBJECTIVE 2 Using Combined Variation

A **combined variation** combines direct and inverse variations in more complicated relationships.

Examples of Combined Variations

Combined Variation	Equation Form
y varies directly with the square of x.	$y = kx^2$
y varies inversely with the cube of x.	$y = \frac{k}{x^3}$
z varies jointly with x and y.	$z = kxy$
z varies jointly with x and y and inversely with w.	$z = \frac{kxy}{w}$
z varies directly with x and inversely with the product of w and y.	$z = \frac{kx}{wy}$

Reading Math

You can write "z varies jointly with x and y" as "z varies directly with the product of x and y."

4 EXAMPLE Real-World Connection

Physics Newton's Law of Universal Gravitation is modeled by the formula $F = \frac{Gm_1m_2}{d^2}$. F is the gravitational force between two objects with masses m_1 and m_2, and d is the distance between the objects. G is the gravitational constant. Describe Newton's law as a combined variation.

$F = \frac{Gm_1m_2}{d^2}$ ← F varies jointly with the masses m_1 and m_2, and
  ← F varies inversely with the square of the distance d.

✔ **Check Understanding** **4 Geometry** The formula for the area of a trapezoid is $A = \frac{1}{2}h(b_1 + b_2)$. Describe this relationship as a combined variation.   **A varies jointly with the height and the sum of the bases.**

5 EXAMPLE Finding a Formula

Geometry The volume of a regular tetrahedron varies directly as the cube of the length of an edge. The volume of a regular tetrahedron with edge length 3 is $\frac{9\sqrt{2}}{4}$. Find the formula for the volume of a regular tetrahedron.

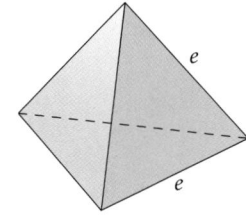

$V = ke^3$ V varies directly as the cube of e.

$\frac{9\sqrt{2}}{4} = k(3)^3$ Substitute the values for V and e.

$\frac{\sqrt{2}}{12} = k$ Solve for k.

$V = \frac{\sqrt{2}}{12}e^3$ Substitute the value for k.

✔ **Check Understanding** **5** The volume of a square pyramid with congruent edges varies directly as the cube of the length of an edge. The volume of a square pyramid with edge length 4 is $\frac{32\sqrt{2}}{3}$. Find the formula for the volume of a square pyramid with congruent edges.

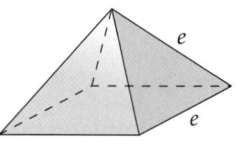

$V = \frac{\sqrt{2}}{6}e^3$

EXERCISES

For more practice, see *Extra Practice*.

Practice and Problem Solving

Ⓐ Practice by Example

Suppose that x and y vary inversely. Write a function that models each inverse variation.

Example 1
(page 478)

$y = \frac{11}{x}$ $y = \frac{-1300}{x}$ $y = \frac{1}{x}$

1. $x = 1$ when $y = 11$ **2.** $x = -13$ when $y = 100$ **3.** $x = 1$ when $y = 1$

$y = -\frac{56}{x}$ $y = \frac{3.6}{x}$ $y = \frac{250}{x}$

4. $x = 28$ when $y = -2$ **5.** $x = 1.2$ when $y = 3$ **6.** $x = 2.5$ when $y = 100$

Example 2
(page 479)

Is the relationship between the values in each table a direct variation, an inverse variation, or neither? Write equations to model the direct and inverse variations.

7.

x	3	8	10	22
y	15	40	50	110

7. direct; $y = 5x$

8.

x	3	5	7	10.5
y	14	8.4	6	4

8. inverse; $y = \frac{42}{x}$

9.

x	0.5	2.1	3.5	11
y	1	4.2	7	22

9. direct; $y = 2x$

10.

x	0.1	3	6	24
y	3	0.1	0.05	0.0125

10. inverse; $y = \frac{0.3}{x}$

11.

x	7	3	1	$\frac{1}{5}$
y	$\frac{1}{7}$	$\frac{1}{3}$	1	5

inverse; $y = \frac{1}{x}$

12.

x	10	12	20	23
y	2	$2\frac{2}{5}$	4	$5\frac{3}{5}$

neither

Example 3
(page 479)

Suppose that x and y vary inversely. Write a function that models each inverse variation and find y when $x = 10$.

13. $x = 20$ when $y = 5$ **14.** $x = 20$ when $y = -4$ **15.** $x = 5$ when $y = -\frac{1}{3}$

$y = \frac{100}{x}$; 10 $y = -\frac{80}{x}$; −8 $y = -\frac{5}{3x}$; −$\frac{1}{6}$

Example 4
(page 480)

Describe the combined variation that is modeled by each formula.

16. $A = \pi r^2$ **17.** $A = 0.5bh$ **18.** $h = \frac{2A}{b}$ **19.** $V = \frac{Bh}{3}$

20. $V = \pi r^2 h$ **21.** $h = \frac{V}{\pi r^2}$ **22.** $V = \ell w h$ **23.** $\ell = \frac{V}{wh}$

16–23. See margin.

Example 5
(page 480)

Write the function that models each relationship. Find z when $x = 4$ and $y = 9$.

24. z varies directly with x and inversely with y. When $x = 6$ and $y = 2$, $z = 15$.

$z = \frac{5x}{y}$; $\frac{20}{9}$

25. $z = 10xy$; 360

25. z varies jointly with x and y. When $x = 2$ and $y = 3$, $z = 60$.

26. z varies directly with the square of x and inversely with y. When $x = 2$ and $y = 4$, $z = 3$. $z = \frac{3x^2}{y}$; $\frac{16}{3}$

27. $z = \frac{4}{xy}$; $\frac{1}{9}$

27. z varies inversely with the product of x and y. When $x = 2$ and $y = 4$, $z = 0.5$.

Ⓑ Apply Your Skills

28. a. The spreadsheet shows data that could be modeled by an equation of the form $PV = k$. Estimate the value of k. **14,000**

b. Estimate P when $V = 62$. **226**

Each ordered pair is from an inverse variation. Find the constant of variation.

29. $(6, 3)$ **18**   **30.** $(0.9, 4)$ **3.6**   **31.** $\left(\frac{3}{8}, \frac{2}{3}\right)$ $\frac{1}{4}$

32. $\left(\sqrt{2}, \sqrt{18}\right)$ **6**   **33.** $\left(\sqrt{3}, \sqrt{27}\right)$ **9**   **34.** $\left(\sqrt{8}, \sqrt{32}\right)$ **16**

	A	B
1	P	V
2	140.00	100
3	147.30	95
4	155.60	90
5	164.70	85
6	175.00	80
7	186.70	75

Lesson 9-1 Inverse Variation **481**

---

pages 481–483   **Exercises**

16. *A* varies directly with the square of *r*.

17. *A* varies jointly with *b* and *h*.

18. *h* varies directly with *A* and inversely with *b*.

19. *V* varies jointly with *B* and *h*.

20. *V* varies jointly with *h* and the square of *r*.

21. *h* varies directly with *V* and inversely with the square of *r*.

22. *V* varies jointly with *ℓ*, *w*, and *h*.

23. *ℓ* varies directly with *V* and inversely with the product of *w* and *h*.

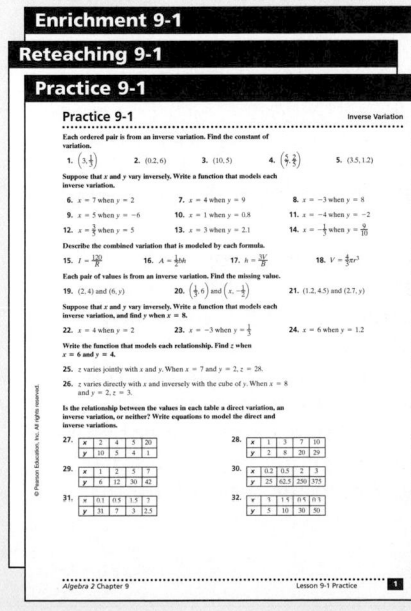
481

1. Suppose x and y vary inversely, and $x = 5$ when $y = 1.6$.
   a. Write a function that models the inverse variation. $y = \frac{8}{x}$
   b. Find y when $x = 32$. **0.25**

Tell whether the relationship between the variables in each table is a direct variation, an inverse variation, or neither. Write functions to model the direct and inverse variations.

2.

x	0.1	1.5	4
y	3	2	1.6

neither

3.

x	48	−4	8
y	2	−24	12

inverse variation; $y = \frac{96}{x}$

4.

x	3	7	−10
y	21	49	−70

direct variation; $y = 7x$

5. Describe the combined variation modeled by the formula $V = \frac{1}{3}\pi r^2 h$.
   V varies jointly as the square of r and h.

6. Suppose z varies directly as x and inversely as the square of y. When $x = 35$ and $y = 7$, the value of z is 50. Write the function that models the relationship and find z when $x = 5$ and $y = 10$. $z = \frac{70x}{y^2}$, **3.5**

Alternative Assessment

Have students work in pairs. Each student should create a table of values in which y and x vary directly, one in which y and x vary inversely, and one in which z varies jointly as x and y. Students trade tables. Each student writes an equation that models the variation for each table.

482

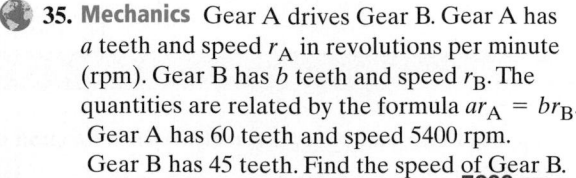

35. **Mechanics** Gear A drives Gear B. Gear A has a teeth and speed r_A in revolutions per minute (rpm). Gear B has b teeth and speed r_B. The quantities are related by the formula $ar_A = br_B$. Gear A has 60 teeth and speed 5400 rpm. Gear B has 45 teeth. Find the speed of Gear B. **7200 rpm**

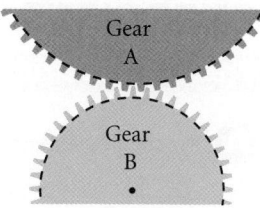

36. **Physics** The force F of gravity on a rocket varies directly with its mass m and inversely with the square of its distance d from Earth. Write a model for this combined variation. $F = k\frac{m}{d^2}$

Each pair of values is from a direct variation. Find the missing value.

37. $(3, 7), (8, y)$ $18\frac{2}{3}$ 38. $(2, 5), (4, y)$ **10**   39. $(4, 6), (x, 3)$ **2**

40. $(9, 5), (x, 3)$ **5.4**   41. $(8.3, 7.1), (5, y)$ **4.277**   42. $(2.6, 4.5), (x, 6.3)$ **3.64**

Each pair of values is from an inverse variation. Find the missing value.

43. $(3, 7), (8, y)$ **2.625**   44. $(2, 5), (4, y)$ **2.5**   45. $(4, 6), (x, 3)$ **8**

46. $(9, 5), (x, 3)$ **15**   47. $(8.3, 7.1), (5, y)$ **11.786**   48. $(2.6, 4.5), (x, 6.3)$ **1.857**

49. Suppose that y varies inversely with the square of x, and $y = 50$ when $x = 4$. Find y when $x = 5$. **32**

50. Suppose that c varies jointly with d and the square of g, and $c = 30$ when $d = 15$ and $g = 2$. Find d when $c = 6$ and $g = 8$. $\frac{3}{16}$

51. Suppose that d varies jointly with r and t, and $d = 110$ when $r = 55$ and $t = 2$. Find r when $d = 40$ and $t = 3$. $\frac{40}{3}$

Exercise 52

52. **Construction** A concrete supplier sells premixed concrete in 300-ft³ truckloads. The area A that the concrete will cover is inversely proportional to the depth d of the concrete.
   a. Write a model for the relationship between the area and the depth of a truckload of poured concrete. $A = \frac{300}{d}$
   b. What area will the concrete cover if it is poured to a depth of 0.5 ft? A depth of 1 ft? A depth of 1.5 ft? **600 ft²; 300 ft²; 200 ft²**
   c. When the concrete is poured into a circular area, the depth of the concrete is inversely proportional to the square of the radius r. Write a model for this relationship. $d = \frac{300}{\pi r^2}$

53. Suppose that y varies directly with x and inversely with z^2, and $x = 48$ when $y = 8$ and $z = 3$. Find x when $y = 12$ and $z = 2$. **32**

54. Suppose that t varies directly with s and inversely with the square of r. How is the value of t changed when the value of s is doubled? Is tripled? **doubled; tripled**

55. Suppose that x varies directly with the square of y and inversely with z. How is the value of x changed if the value of y is halved? Is quartered? **quartered; divided by 16**

C Challenge

56. **Writing** Explain why 0 cannot be in the domain of an inverse variation. **Division by zero is undefined.**

57. **Critical Thinking** Suppose that (x_1, y_1) and (x_2, y_2) are values from an inverse variation. Show that $\frac{x_1}{x_2} = \frac{y_2}{y_1}$. **See margin.**

58. **Open-Ended** The height h of a cylinder varies directly with its volume V and inversely with the square of its radius r. Find at least four ways to change the volume and radius of a cylinder so that its height is quadrupled. **See margin.**

482 Chapter 9 Rational Functions

pages 481–483 Exercises

57. $x_1 y_1 = k$ and $x_2 y_2 = k$
   def. of inverse variation
   $x_1 y_1 = x_2 y_2$ transitivity
   $\frac{x_1}{x_2} = \frac{y_2}{y_1}$ Divide both sides by $x_2 y_1$.

58. **Answers may vary.**
   Sample: Quadruple the volume and leave the radius constant, halve the radius and leave the volume constant, multiply the volume by 16 and double the radius, and multiply the volume and radius by $\frac{1}{4}$.

59. Health Health care professionals use the body mass index (BMI) to establish guidelines for determining any possible risks of their patients and for planning any useful preventative programs. The BMI varies directly with weight and inversely with the square of height. Use this portion of the BMI chart to determine the BMI formula. $BMI \approx \frac{705\,w}{h^2}$

Weights and Body Mass Index (BMI)

Height	Range of Weight (pounds)			
	BMI 19–24.9	BMI 25–29.9	BMI 30–39.9	BMI ≥ 40
5'6"	118–154	155–185	186–246	≥247
5'7"	121–158	159–190	191–254	≥255
5'8"	125–163	164–196	197–261	≥262
5'9"	128–168	169–202	203–269	≥270
5'10"	132–173	174–208	209–277	≥278
5'11"	136–178	179–214	215–285	≥286
6'0"	140–183	184–220	221–293	≥294

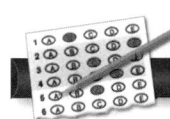

 **Standardized Test Prep**

Multiple Choice

60. Which equation does NOT represent inverse variation between x and z? **B**

  A. $x = \frac{y}{z}$ **B.** $x = \frac{-15z}{y}$

  C. $z = \frac{-15y}{x}$ **D.** $xz = 5y$

61. If p and q vary inversely, and $p = 10$ when $q = -4$, what is q when $p = -2$? **F**

  F. 20   **G.** $\frac{4}{5}$ **H.** $-\frac{4}{5}$ **I.** -20

Take It to the NET
Online lesson quiz at
www.PHSchool.com
Web Code: aga-0901

62. Which equation shows that z varies directly with the square of x and inversely with the cube of y? **A**

  A. $z = \frac{x^2}{y^3}$ **B.** $z = \frac{x^3}{y^2}$ **C.** $z = \frac{y^2}{x^3}$ **D.** $z = \frac{y^3}{x^2}$

Short Response

63. Describe how the variables A and r vary in the formula for the area of a circle, $A = \pi r^2$.   **See margin.**

Extended Response

64. Which data set shows inverse variation: (24.4, 4.8) and (9.6, 12.2), or (24.0, 4.5) and (18.0, 6.5)? Explain.   **See margin.**

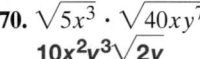 **Mixed Review**

Lesson 8-6   Solve each equation.

65. $\ln 4 + \ln x = 5$ **66.** $\ln x - \ln 3 = 4$ **67.** $2 \ln x + 3 \ln 4 = 4$
  $\frac{e^5}{4} \approx 37.1$ $3e^4 \approx 163.79$ $\frac{e^2}{8} \approx 0.92$

Lesson 7-2   Multiply and simplify. Assume that all variables are positive.

68. $-5\sqrt{6x} \cdot 3\sqrt{6x^2}$ **69.** $3\sqrt[3]{4x^2} \cdot 7\sqrt[3]{12x^4}$ **70.** $\sqrt{5x^3} \cdot \sqrt{40xy^7}$
  $-90x\sqrt{x}$ $42x^2\sqrt[3]{6}$ $10x^2y^3\sqrt{2y}$

Lesson 7-1   Simplify each radical expression. Use absolute value bars where they are needed.

71. $\sqrt{x^{10}y^{100}}$ **72.** $\sqrt[3]{-64a^3b^6}$ **73.** $\sqrt[4]{64m^8n^4}$ **74.** $\sqrt[n]{x^n}$ $|x|$
  $|x^5|y^{50}$ $-4ab^2$ $2m^2|n|\sqrt[4]{4}$

Resources
For additional practice with a variety of test item formats:
• Standardized Test Prep, p. 531
• Test-Taking Strategies, p. 526
• Test-Taking Strategies with Transparencies

Exercise 60 It may help to solve the equations in answer choices C and D for the variable x.

63. [2] *A* varies directly with the square of *r* OR *r* varies directly with the square root of *A*.

  [1] incomplete answer

64. [4] (24.4, 4.8) and (9.6, 12.2); in both pairs the product is 117.12, so *k* is the same for both. In the other 2 pairs *k* is not equal.

  [3] appropriate methods, but one computational error

  [2] incomplete explanation

  [1] answer only, with no explanation

Technology

Graphing Rational Functions

Students use a graphing calculator to explore graphs of rational functions.

Resources

Students may use any graphing calculator for this activity.

Teaching Notes

Technology Tip

Graphing calculators often display a graph that mistakenly includes vertical asymptotes. Using Dot mode is one way to get around this difficulty. The window settings can have a significant effect on the appearance of the graph of a rational function. You may want students to experiment with different settings.

Error Prevention

Caution students to be careful with the use of parentheses when they enter the functions on the Y= list. Except for Exercise 1, the entire denominator of each fraction should be in parentheses.

page 484   Technology

13a.

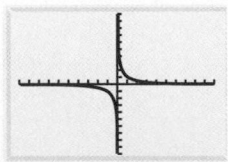

b. If x is negative and approaches 0, the y values approach −∞. If x is positive and approaches 0, the y values approach +∞.

c. As x increases, the y values approach 0; as x decreases, the y values approach 0.

484

You can use your graphing calculator to graph rational functions. It is sometimes preferable to use the Dot plotting mode rather than the Connected plotting mode. The Connected mode can join branches of a graph that should be separated. Try both modes to get the best graph.

EXAMPLE

Graph $y = \frac{4}{x - 3} - 1.5$.

Step 1 Press the MODE key. Scroll down to highlight the word **Dot**. Then press ENTER.

Step 2 Enter the function. Use parentheses to enter the denominator accurately.

Step 3 Graph the function.

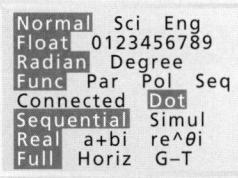

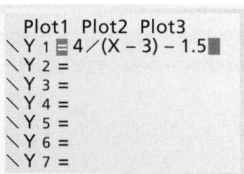

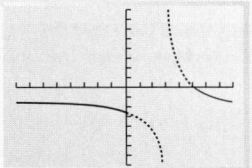

EXERCISES

Use a graphing calculator to graph each function. Then sketch the graph.   **1–12. See back of book.**

1. $y = \frac{7}{x}$

2. $y = \frac{3}{x + 4} - 2$

3. $y = \frac{x + 2}{(x + 1)(x + 3)}$

4. $y = \frac{4x + 1}{x - 3}$

5. $y = \frac{2}{x - 2}$

6. $y = \frac{1}{x + 2} + 3$

7. $y = \frac{2x}{x + 3}$

8. $y = \frac{x^2}{x^2 - 5}$

9. $y = \frac{20}{x^2 + 5}$

10. $y = \frac{1}{x - 3} - 6$

11. $y = \frac{10}{x^2 - 5x - 10}$

12. $y = \frac{x}{x^2 - 1}$

13. a. Graph $y = \frac{1}{x}$. Sketch the graph.   **a–c. See margin.**

    b. Examine both negative and positive values of x. Describe what happens to the y-values as x approaches zero.

    c. What happens to the y-values as x increases? As x decreases?

14. a. Change the mode on your graphing calculator to **Connected**. Graph the function from the example. Sketch the graph.   **a–c. See margin.**

    b. Press the TRACE key and trace the function. What happens between $x \approx 2.9$ and $x \approx 3.2$?

    c. Critical Thinking How does your graph differ from the graph in the example? Explain the differences.

14a.

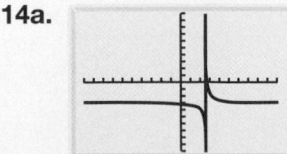

b. Answers may vary. Sample: The y values change from very large negative values to very large positive values.

c. In connected mode, the calculator will try to connect the values for x ≈ 2.9 and x ≈ 3.2.

Graphing Inverse Variations

 North Carolina Objectives

Lesson Preview

1.05 Model and solve problems using inverse variation.
2.05 Use rational equations to solve problems. c) Identify the asymptotes and intercepts graphically and algebraically.

What You'll Learn

 OBJECTIVE 1 To graph inverse variations

 OBJECTIVE 2 To graph translations of inverse variations

... And Why

To analyze musical pitch and the size of the instrument, as in Example 4

✓ Check Skills You'll Need

(For help, go to Lesson 2-6.)

Each of the following equations is a translation of $y = |x|$. Describe each translation.

1. $y = |x| + 2$ **2 units up**
2. $y = |x + 2|$ **2 units left**
3. $y = |x| - 3$ **3 units down**
4. $y = |x - 3|$ **3 units right**
5. $y = |x + 4| - 5$
   4 units left and 5 units down
6. $y = |x - 10| + 7$
   10 units right and 7 units up

New Vocabulary • branch

Lesson Preview

✓ Check Skills You'll Need

Vertical and Horizontal Translations
Lesson 2-6: Example 7
Exercises 21–26
Extra Practice, p. 823

Lesson Resources

📁 **Teaching Resources**
Practice, Reteaching, Enrichment

👥 **Reaching All Students**
Practice Workbook 9-2
Spanish Practice Workbook 9-2
Hands-On Activities 49

⏱ **Presentation Assistant Plus!**
Transparencies
• Check Skills You'll Need 9-2
• Additional Examples 9-2
• Student Edition Answers 9-2
• Lesson Quiz 9-2
PH Presentation Pro CD 9-2

ASSESSMENT SYSTEM
Computer Test Generator CD

💿 **Technology**
Resource Pro® CD-ROM
Computer Test Generator CD
Prentice Hall Presentation Pro CD

💻 **www.PHSchool.com**
Student Site
• Teacher Web Code: agk-5500
• Self-grading Lesson Quiz
Teacher Center
• Lesson Planner
• Resources

Plus

iTEXT Interactive lesson includes instant self-check, tutorials, and activities.

OBJECTIVE 1
Graphing Inverse Variations

The graphs of inverse variations have two parts.

1 EXAMPLE **Graphing an Inverse Variation**

Draw a graph of $y = \frac{6}{x}$.

Make a table of values that includes positive and negative values of x. Notice that x cannot be 0.

1.
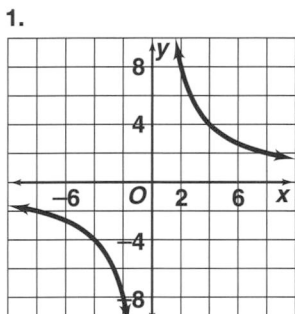

x	-12	-6	-3	-2	-1	$-\frac{1}{2}$	$\frac{1}{2}$	1	2	3	6	12
y	$-\frac{1}{2}$	-1	-2	-3	-6	-12	12	6	3	2	1	$\frac{1}{2}$

Graph the points and connect them with a smooth curve.

The graph has two parts. Each part is called a **branch.**

The x-axis is a horizontal asymptote.

● The y-axis is a vertical asymptote.

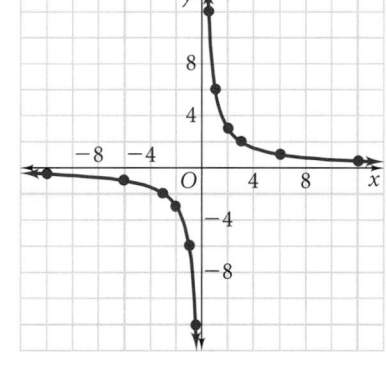

📖 Reading Math

In a graph, a branch is a distinct part of a curve, just as, in nature, a branch is a distinct part of a river.

✓ Check Understanding

① Draw a graph of $y = \frac{16}{x}$. **See left.**

A function must be defined for all values of its domain. Since $\frac{k}{x}$ is not defined for $x = 0$, zero is not included in the domain of an inverse variation $y = \frac{k}{x}$. The domain is all nonzero real numbers.

Lesson 9-2 Graphing Inverse Variations **485**

⚡ Ongoing Assessment and Intervention

Before the Lesson
Diagnose prerequisite skills using:
• Check Skills You'll Need

During the Lesson
Monitor progress using:
• Check Understanding
• Additional Examples
• Standardized Test Prep

After the Lesson
Assess knowledge using:
• Lesson Quiz
• Computer Test Generator CD

Math Background

Professional Development

Graphs of inverse variations have two parts. However, many real-world applications are represented by only one of these parts, such as Example 4 on page 486. Students should be careful to consider the domain relative to each problem situation.

OBJECTIVE

1 **Teaching Notes**

3 EXAMPLE Visual Learners

Students can draw their own graphs of these functions, trace one graph on tracing paper, and rotate the tracing by 90°.

4 EXAMPLE Diversity

Point out that a wide variety of Andean panpipe music is available in libraries and record stores. The craftspeople that build such instruments understand the relationship between the length of a pipe and its pitch.

Additional Examples

1 Draw a graph of $y = \frac{0.5}{x}$.

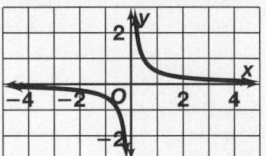

2 Compare the graphs of $y = \frac{1}{x}$ and $y = \frac{0.25}{x}$ shown below. What points on the graphs are closest to the origin?

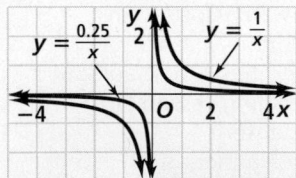

The axes are asymptotes for both; both are symmetric with respect to $y = x$ and to $y = -x$. The graph of the second function is closest to the axes. The points $(1, 1)$, $(-1, -1)$, $(0.5, 0.5)$, and $(-0.5, -0.5)$ are closest to the origin.

Need Help?

Quadrant II	Quadrant I
Quadrant III	Quadrant IV

3. The axes are asymptotes for both graphs. Both graphs are symmetric with respect to $y = x$ and $y = -x$. Each graph is a 90° rotation about the origin of the other graph.

✓ **Check Understanding**

When k is positive, the branches of $y = \frac{k}{x}$ are in Quadrants I and III.

2 EXAMPLE Comparing Graphs of Inverse Variations

Compare the graphs of $y = \frac{4}{x}$ and $y = \frac{9}{x}$ shown at the right. What points on the graphs are closest to the origin?

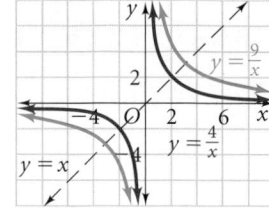

The axes are asymptotes for both graphs. Both graphs are symmetric with respect to $y = x$ and $y = -x$. The branches of $y = \frac{4}{x}$ are closer to the axes than are the branches of $y = \frac{9}{x}$. The intersections of the graphs with $y = x$ are $(\sqrt{k}, \sqrt{k})$ and $(-\sqrt{k}, -\sqrt{k})$, where k is the constant of variation.
These points, $(2, 2)$, $(-2, -2)$, $(3, 3)$, and $(-3, -3)$, are closest to the origin.

✓ **Check Understanding** **2** Use a graphing calculator. Draw and compare the graphs of $y = \frac{25}{x}$ and $y = \frac{100}{x}$. Compare their intersections with the graph of $y = x$. **See margin p. 487.**

When k is negative, the branches of $y = \frac{k}{x}$ are in Quadrants II and IV.

3 EXAMPLE Comparing Graphs of Inverse Variations

Compare the graphs of $y = \frac{1}{x}$ and $y = -\frac{1}{x}$ shown at the right.

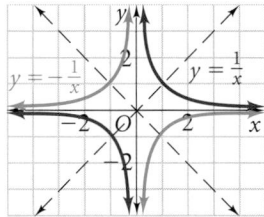

The axes are asymptotes for both graphs. Both graphs are symmetric with respect to $y = x$ and $y = -x$. The x-and y-axes are lines of reflection of the two graphs.

✓ **Check Understanding** **3** Use a graphing calculator. Compare the graphs of $y = \frac{5}{x}$ and $y = -\frac{5}{x}$. **See left.**

4 EXAMPLE Real-World Connection

Real-World Connection

The length, not the diameter, of a panpipe or organ pipe determines its pitch.

Music A musical pitch is determined by the frequency of vibration of the sound waves reaching the ear. The greater the frequency, the higher is the pitch. Frequency is measured in vibrations per second, or hertz (Hz).

The pitch y produced by a panpipe varies inversely with the length x of the pipe. The function $y = \frac{564}{x}$ models the inverse variation where x is the length in feet. Find the length of the pipe that produces a pitch of 277 Hz.

Graph the functions $y = \frac{564}{x}$ and $y = 277$. Use the **Intersect** feature.

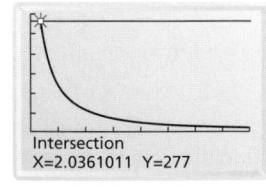

Xmin=0   Ymin=−75
Xmax=40   Ymax=300
Xscl=5   Yscl=50

Intersection
X=2.0361011 Y=277

The pipe should be about 2.0 ft long.

Reaching All Students

Below Level Review why certain values are excluded from the domain of a function. Discuss how asymptotes help you graph a function.	**Advanced Learners** Have students compute the distance from the graph of Example 5 to the point $(2, -3)$ (the translated origin), and compare their methods.	**Visual Learners** See note on page 486. **Diversity** See note on page 486.

4 a. Pitches of 247 Hz, 311 Hz, and 370 Hz form a musical chord. Find the length of pipe that will produce each pitch. **2.28 ft, 1.81 ft, 1.52 ft**

b. Writing The asymptotes of $y = \frac{564}{x}$ are $x = 0$ and $y = 0$. Explain why this makes sense in terms of the panpipe. **As the pipe becomes very short, the pitch becomes very high (great frequency). As the pipe becomes very long, the pitch becomes low (frequency near 0).**

2 **Graphing Translations of Inverse Variations**

The graphs at the right show the parent function $y = \frac{4}{x}$ and two of its translations, $y = \frac{4}{x-2}$ and $y = \frac{4}{x+4}$.

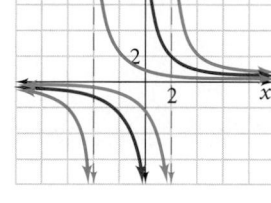

The vertical asymptotes of the graphs are $x = 0$, $x = 2$, and $x = -4$.

The graphs at the right show the parent function $y = \frac{4}{x}$ and two of its translations, $y = \frac{4}{x} + 2$ and $y = \frac{4}{x} - 4$.

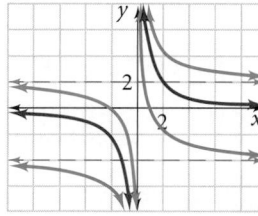

The horizontal asymptotes of the graphs are $y = 0$, $y = 2$, and $y = -4$.

🔧 **Key Concepts**

Properties	Translations of Inverse Variations

The graph of $y = \frac{k}{x-b} + c$ is a translation of $y = \frac{k}{x}$ by b units horizontally and c units vertically. The vertical asymptote is $x = b$. The horizontal asymptote is $y = c$.

You can use asymptotes to graph translations of inverse variations.

5 EXAMPLE **Graphing a Translation**

Sketch the graph of $y = \frac{1}{x-2} - 3$.

Step 1 Draw the asymptotes.
For $y = \frac{1}{x-2} + (-3)$, $b = 2$ and $c = -3$.
The vertical asymptote is $x = 2$. The horizontal asymptote is $y = -3$.

Step 2 Translate $y = \frac{1}{x}$.
The graph of $y = \frac{1}{x}$ includes $(1, 1)$ and $(-1, -1)$. Translate these points 2 units to the right and 3 units down to $(3, -2)$ and $(1, -4)$. Draw the branches through these points.

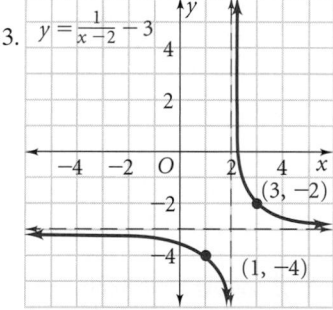

✓ **Check Understanding** **5** Find the asymptotes and sketch the graph of $y = -\frac{1}{x+7} - 3$. **See back of book.**

page 487
Check Understanding

2.

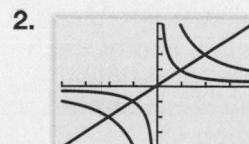

The axes are asymptotes for both graphs. Both graphs are symmetric with respect to $y = x$ and $y = -x$. The branches of $y = \frac{25}{x}$ are closer to the axes than are the branches of $y = \frac{100}{x}$; the intersections of $y = \frac{25}{x}$ and $y = x$ are closer to the origin than those of $y = \frac{100}{x}$.

3 Compare the graphs of $y = \frac{2}{x}$ and $y = -\frac{2}{x}$. **The axes are asymptotes for both graphs. The y-axis is a line of reflection. Both graphs are symmetric with respect to $y = x$ and to $y = -x$.**

4 The frequency f in hertz of a sound wave varies inversely with its wavelength w. The function $f = \frac{343}{w}$ models the relationship between f and w for a wave with a velocity of 343 m/s. Find the wavelength of a sound wave with a frequency of 440 Hz. **about 0.78 m**

📘 **Additional Examples**

5 Sketch the graph of $y = \frac{1}{x+2} + 2$.

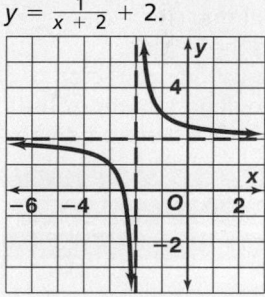

6 Write an equation for the translation of $y = -\frac{7}{x}$ that has asymptotes at $x = 8$ and $y = -4$. $y = -\frac{7}{x-8} - 4$

Closure

Ask students to describe the graph of an inverse variation $y = \frac{k}{x}$. Ask them to write an equation for a translation of the graph a units to the right and b units up. Finally, ask them to write equations for the asymptotes of the translated graph. **Answers may vary. Sample: The graph will be in Quadrants I and III or else in Quadrants II and IV, depending on the sign of k. It will be symmetric with respect to $y = x$ and $y = -x$ and will have the axes as asymptotes; $y = \frac{k}{x-a} + b$; $x = a$, $y = b$**

487

Assignment Guide

▼ **1 Objective**
Ⓐ Ⓑ **Core** 1–13, 25, 27–38
Ⓒ **Extension** 48–51

▼ **2 Objective**
Ⓐ Ⓑ **Core** 14–24, 26, 39–47
Ⓒ **Extension** 52

Standardized Test Prep 53–59

Mixed Review 60–72

Error Prevention

Exercises 23, 24 Students may use the wrong operation sign in the denominator of their equation. Remind them that the *x*-value determining the vertical asymptote must be subtracted from *x* in the denominator of the equation for the translated graph.

pages 488–490 Exercises

4. The graph of $y = \frac{3}{x}$ is closer to the *x*- and *y*-axes than the graph of $y = \frac{5}{x}$.

5. The graph of $y = \frac{1}{x}$ is closer to the axes.

6. The graph of $y = \frac{0.2}{x}$ is closer to the axes.

488

If you know the translations or asymptotes of the graph of an inverse variation, you can write its equation.

6 EXAMPLE Writing the Equation of a Translation

Write an equation for the translation of $y = \frac{5}{x}$ that has asymptotes at $x = -2$ and $y = 3$.

$y = \dfrac{5}{x - b} + c$ Use the general form of a translation.

$\quad = \dfrac{5}{x - (-2)} + 3$ Substitute -2 for *b* and 3 for *c*.

$\quad = \dfrac{5}{x + 2} + 3$ Simplify.

● An equation for the translation is $y = \dfrac{5}{x + 2} + 3$.

✓ **Check Understanding** **6 a.** Write an equation for the translation of $y = -\frac{1}{x}$ that is 4 units left and 5 units up.
b. Check your work by graphing your solution to part (a).
a. $y = -\dfrac{1}{x + 4} + 5$
b. See back of book.

EXERCISES

For more practice, see *Extra Practice*.

Ⓐ **Practice by Example**

Example 1
(page 485)

Draw a graph of each inverse variation. **1–3. See back of book.**

1. $y = \frac{2}{x}$ **2.** $y = \frac{10}{x}$ **3.** $y = -\frac{10}{x}$

Example 2 and 3
(page 486)

Compare the graphs of the inverse variations. **4–9. See margin.**

4. $y = \frac{3}{x}$ and $y = \frac{5}{x}$ **5.** $y = \frac{1}{x}$ and $y = \frac{100}{x}$ **6.** $y = \frac{0.2}{x}$ and $y = \frac{0.5}{x}$

7. $y = \frac{8}{x}$ and $y = -\frac{8}{x}$ **8.** $y = -\frac{2}{x}$ and $y = -\frac{3}{x}$ **9.** $y = \frac{12}{x}$ and $y = -\frac{12}{x}$

Example 4
(page 486)

The weight *P* in pounds that a beam can safely carry is inversely proportional to the distance *D* in feet between the supports of the beam. For a certain type of wooden beam, $P = \frac{9200}{D}$. Use a graphing calculator and the Intersect feature to find the distance between supports that is needed to carry each given weight.

10. 500 lb **18.4 ft**   **11.** 1200 lb **7.67 ft**   **12.** 2400 lb **3.83 ft**   **13.** 5000 lb **1.84 ft**

Example 5
(page 487)

Sketch the asymptotes and the graph of each equation. **14–21. See back of book.**

14. $y = \frac{1}{x} - 3$ **15.** $y = \frac{-2}{x} - 3$ **16.** $y = \frac{1}{x - 2} + 5$ **17.** $y = \frac{1}{x - 3} + 4$

18. $y = \frac{2}{x + 6} - 1$ **19.** $y = \frac{-10}{x + 1} - 8$ **20.** $y = \frac{1}{x} + 2$ **21.** $y = \frac{-8}{x + 5} - 6$

Example 6
(page 488)

Write an equation for the translation of $y = \frac{2}{x}$ that has the given asymptotes.

22. $x = 0$ and $y = 4$ **23.** $x = -2$ and $y = 3$ **24.** $x = 4$ and $y = -8$
$\quad\;\; y = \frac{2}{x} + 4$ $y = \frac{2}{x + 2} + 3$ $y = \frac{2}{x - 4} - 8$

Ⓑ **Apply Your Skills** **25. a.** **Budgeting** A high school spends $750 each year on student academic achievement awards. The amount spent per award depends on how many awards are given. Write and graph a function of the number *a* of awards given and the cost *c* of each award. Find the asymptotes.
b. Explain how the asymptotes are related to the given facts.
a–b. See back of book.

---

7. The branches of $y = \frac{8}{x}$ are in Quadrants I and III. The branches of $y = -\frac{8}{x}$ are in Quadrants II and IV. Each graph is a 90° rotation about the origin of the other graph.

8. The graphs of both equations are in Quadrants II and IV. The graph of $y = -\frac{2}{x}$ is closer to the axes.

9. The branches of $y = \frac{12}{x}$ are in Quadrants I and III. The branches of $y = -\frac{12}{x}$ are in Quadrants II and IV. Each graph is a 90° rotation about the origin of the other graph.

26. Open-Ended Write an equation for a horizontal translation of $y = \frac{2}{x}$. Then write an equation for a vertical translation of $y = \frac{2}{x}$. Identify the horizontal and vertical asymptotes of the graph of each function. **Check students' work.**

Write each equation in the form $y = \frac{k}{x}$.

27. $y = \frac{1}{2x}$ $y = \frac{0.5}{x}$ **28.** $y = \frac{3}{4x}$ $y = \frac{0.75}{x}$ **29.** $y = -\frac{25}{3x}$ $y = -\frac{8.3}{x}$

30. $xy = -0.01$ $y = -\frac{0.01}{x}$ **31.** $3xy = 12$ $y = \frac{4}{x}$ **32.** $-7 = 5xy$ $y = -\frac{1.4}{x}$

Sketch the graph of each function.   **33–38. See back of book.**

33. $xy = 3$ **34.** $xy + 5 = 0$ **35.** $3xy = 1$

36. $5xy = 2$ **37.** $10xy = -4$ **38.** $3xy = -17$

39. Writing Explain how knowing the asymptotes of a translation of $y = \frac{k}{x}$ can help you graph the function. Include an example. **See left.**

39. Answers may vary. Sample: The graph of the translation looks similar to the graph of $y = \frac{k}{x}$, so knowing the asymptotes helps to position the translation; check students' work.

40. Meteorology The function $p = \frac{69.1}{a + 2.3}$ relates atmospheric pressure p in inches of mercury to altitude a in miles.   **a–b. See margin.**
  a. Graph the function.
  b. The photo shows various altitudes on Earth. Find the atmospheric pressure at each altitude.
  c. Is there an altitude at which the atmospheric pressure is 0 in. of mercury? Use your graph to justify your reasoning.
  No; $p = 0$ is an asymptote.

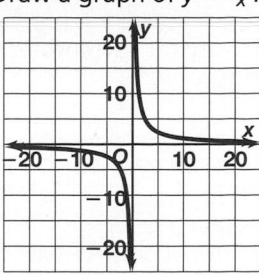
Sahara Desert average alt. 1500 ft
Kalahari Desert average alt. 3100 ft
Mt. Kilimanjaro alt. 19,340 ft
Vinson Massif alt. 16,860 ft

Need Help?
1 mi = 5280 ft

Graph each pair of functions. Find the approximate point(s) of intersection.
41–46. See back of book.

41. $y = \frac{6}{x - 2}, y = 6$ **42.** $y = -\frac{1}{x - 3} - 6, y = 6.2$

43. $y = \frac{3}{x + 1}, y = -4$ **44.** $y = -\frac{2}{x^2}, y = -10$

45. $y = -\frac{1}{x - 4}, y = 4.2$ **46.** $y = \frac{4}{x^2} + 2, y = 9$

47a–b. See back of book.

47. a. Gasoline Mileage Suppose you drive an average of 10,000 miles each year. Your gasoline mileage (mi/gal) varies inversely with the number of gallons of gasoline you use each year. Write and graph a model for your average mileage m in terms of the gallons g of gasoline used.
  b. After you begin driving on the highway more often, you use 50 gal less per year. Write and graph a new model to include this information.
  c. Calculate your old and new mileage assuming that you originally used 400 gal of gasoline per year.   **25 mi/gal, 28.57 mi/gal**

C Challenge

Critical Thinking Compare each pair of graphs and find any points of intersection.

48–50. See back of book.

48. $y = \frac{1}{x}$ and $y = \left|\frac{1}{x}\right|$ **49.** $y = \frac{1}{x}$ and $y = \frac{1}{x^2}$ **50.** $y = \left|\frac{1}{x}\right|$ and $y = \frac{1}{x^2}$

51. Find the equations for two inverse variations such that the minimum distance from the origin to the graph of each inverse variation is $4\sqrt{2}$. $y = \frac{16}{x}, y = -\frac{16}{x}$

40a.
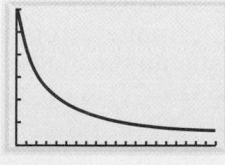

```
WINDOW FORMAT
Xmin=0
Xmax=20
Xscl=1
Ymin=0
Ymax=30
Yscl=5
```

b. Sahara Desert: 26.74 in., Kalahari Desert: 29.93 in., Mt. Kilimanjaro: 11.59 in., Vinson Massif: 12.58 in.

Lesson Quiz 9-2

1. Draw a graph of $y = \frac{12}{x}$.

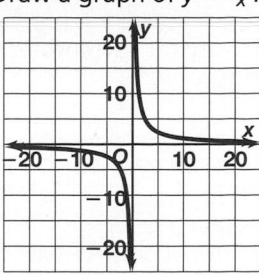

2. Compare the graphs of $y = \frac{6}{x}$ and $y = \frac{12}{x}$. **Answers may vary. Sample: Both graphs lie in Quadrants I and III. Both have the axes as asymptotes. Both are symmetric with respect to $y = x$ and $y = -x$.**

3. A group of college students rents a large two-story house. The amount of rent in dollars that each student pays per month is inversely proportional to the number of students. The rent r per month for one student is related to the number of students n by the equation $r = \frac{1200}{n}$. Find the monthly rent each student pays if there are 8 students in the house. **$150**

4. Sketch the asymptotes and the graph of $y = -\frac{0.5}{x + 2} - \frac{1}{2}$.

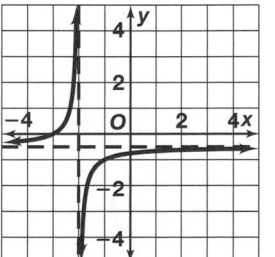

5. Write an equation for the translation of $y = \frac{13}{x}$ that has asymptotes at $x = 5$ and $y = -8$. $y = \frac{13}{x - 5} - 8$

489

Alternative Assessment

Have students work individually and roll a number cube to determine three numbers a, b, and c. Have them sketch the graphs of $y = \frac{a}{x}$, $y = -\frac{a}{x}$, $y = \frac{a}{x + b} + c$, and $y = -\frac{a}{x - b} - c$ and identify the asymptotes of each graph.

Standardized Test Prep

Resources

For additional practice with a variety of test item formats:
- Standardized Test Prep, p. 531
- Test-Taking Strategies, p. 526
- Test-Taking Strategies with Transparencies

pages 488–490   Exercises

52a. $y = \frac{0.6}{x - 2}$

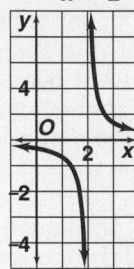

b. $y = -\frac{0.25}{x - 0.5}$

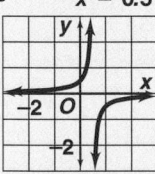

c. $y = \frac{1}{x} - 2$

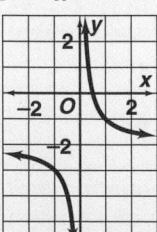

d. $y = \frac{1}{x - 1}$

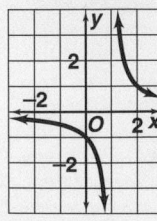

490

---

52. Write each equation in the form $y = \frac{k}{x - b} + c$, and sketch the graph. **a–d. See back of book.**

a. $y = \frac{2}{3x - 6}$

b. $y = \frac{1}{2 - 4x}$

c. $xy + 2x = 1$

d. $xy - y = 1$

Standardized Test Prep

Multiple Choice

53. Which point is NOT on the graph of $y = -\frac{2}{x}$? **D**

A. $\left(-\frac{1}{2}, 4\right)$

B. $(-1, 2)$

C. $(2, -1)$

D. $\left(8, -\frac{1}{16}\right)$

54. Which equation is a line of symmetry for $xy = -7$ and does NOT intersect the branches of the graph? **H**

F. $x = 0$

G. $y = 0$

H. $y = x$

I. $y = -x$

55. What are the asymptotes of the graph of $y = \frac{10}{x - 5}$? **B**

A. $x = 0$, $y = 5$

B. $x = 5$, $y = 0$

C. $x = 5$, $y = 10$

D. $x = 10$, $y = 5$

56. What are the asymptotes of the graph of $y = \frac{10}{x} + 5$? **F**

F. $x = 0$, $y = 5$

G. $x = 5$, $y = 5$

H. $x = 5$, $y = 10$

I. $x = 10$, $y = 5$

57. What is an equation for the translation of $y = \frac{2}{x}$ that has asymptotes at $x = 3$ and $y = -5$? **A**

A. $y = \frac{2}{x - 3} - 5$

B. $y = \frac{2}{x + 3} + 5$

C. $y = \frac{2}{x + 5} - 3$

D. $y = \frac{2}{x - 5} + 3$

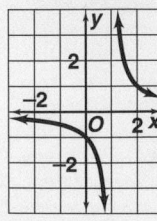

Take It to the NET

Online lesson quiz at
www.PHSchool.com
······ Web Code: aga-0902

Short Response

58. Explain how to find the asymptotes of $y = -\frac{3}{x - 2} + 11$. **See back of book.**

Extended Response

59. Explain how to find an equation for the translation of $y = \frac{-3}{x}$ that has asymptotes at $x = -5$ and $y = -13$. **See margin.**

Mixed Review

Lesson 9-1   Describe the combined variation that is modeled by each formula.

60. $V = \frac{s^2 h}{3}$ **61.** $h = \frac{3V}{s^2}$ **62.** $B = \frac{3V}{h}$ **63.** $w = \frac{V}{\ell h}$ **64.** $b = \frac{2A}{h}$

60–64. See back of book.

Lesson 8-1   Identify each function as exponential growth or decay, and find the growth or decay factor.

65. $y = 3 \cdot 4^x$ **66.** $y = 0.1 \cdot 2^x$ **67.** $y = 5 \cdot (0.8)^x$ **68.** $y = 3 \cdot \left(\frac{1}{2}\right)^x$
    growth, 4   growth, 2   decay, 0.8   decay, 0.5

Lesson 7-3   Multiply.

69. $\left(5\sqrt{3} - 2\right)^2$ **79 − 20√3**   **70.** $\left(\sqrt{3} + \sqrt{5}\right)\left(\sqrt{3} - \sqrt{5}\right)$ **−2**

71. $\left(3\sqrt{5} + 2\sqrt{10}\right)\left(2\sqrt{5} + \sqrt{10}\right)$ **72.** $\left(4 + 2\sqrt{3}\right)\left(6 - 3\sqrt{3}\right)$ **6**
    50 + 35√2

59. [4] The general form of a translation of $y = \frac{-3}{x}$ is $y = \frac{-3}{x - b} + c$.
For asymptotes at $x = -5$ and $y = -13$, $b = -5$ and $c = -13$.

Substituting, $y = \frac{-3}{x - (-5)} - 13$, or $y = \frac{-3}{x + 5} - 13$.

[3] minor error, such as a sign error

[2] several errors OR major error, such as writing $y = \frac{-3}{x - 13} + (-5)$

[1] answer only, with no explanation

Rational Functions and Their Graphs

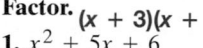 North Carolina Objectives   2.05 Use rational equations to solve problems. b) Interpret the constants and coefficients in the context of the problem. c) Identify the asymptotes and intercepts graphically and algebraically.

Lesson Preview

What You'll Learn

 OBJECTIVE 1 To identify properties of rational functions

 OBJECTIVE 2 To graph rational functions

. . . And Why

To find the average cost of producing CD-ROMs, as in Example 5

 Check Skills You'll Need   (For help, go to Lessons 5-4 and 5-5.)

Factor.

1. $x^2 + 5x + 6$ (x + 3)(x + 2)
2. $x^2 - 6x + 8$ (x − 4)(x − 2)
3. $x^2 - 12x + 27$ (x − 3)(x − 9)
4. $2x^2 + x - 28$ (2x − 7)(x + 4)
5. $2x^2 - 11x + 15$ (2x − 5)(x − 3)
6. $2x^2 - 19x + 24$ (2x − 3)(x − 8)

Solve.

7. $x^2 + x - 12 = 0$ 3, −4
8. $x^2 - 3x - 28 = 0$ −4, 7
9. $x^2 - 9x + 18 = 0$ 3, 6

New Vocabulary • rational function • point of discontinuity

OBJECTIVE 1

Properties of Rational Functions

iTEXT Interactive lesson includes instant self-check, tutorials, and activities.

An inverse variation is an example of a rational function.

 Key Concepts

Definition	Rational Function

A **rational function** $f(x)$ is a function that can be written as

$$f(x) = \frac{P(x)}{Q(x)},$$

where $P(x)$ and $Q(x)$ are polynomial functions and $Q(x) \neq 0$.

 Reading Math

A rational function is a ratio of functions, just as a rational number is a ratio of numbers.

The graphs of the rational functions $y = \frac{-2x}{x^2 + 1}$, $y = \frac{1}{x^2 - 4}$, and $y = \frac{(x + 2)(x - 1)}{x + 1}$ are shown below.

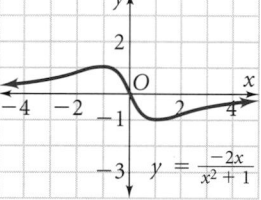
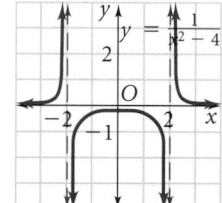
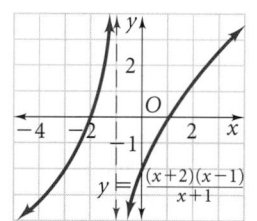

In the first rational function, there is no value of x that makes the denominator 0. The graph is continuous because it has no jumps, breaks, or holes in it. It can be drawn with a pencil that never leaves the paper.

In the second rational function, x cannot be 2 or −2. In the third, x cannot be −1. The last two graphs are discontinuous.

If a is a real number for which the denominator of a rational function f is zero, then a is not in the domain of f. The graph of f is not continuous at $x = a$ and the function has a **point of discontinuity** at $x = a$.

Lesson 9-3 Rational Functions and Their Graphs **491**

---

1. Plan

Lesson Preview

 Check Skills You'll Need

Factoring Quadratic Expressions
Lesson 5-4: Examples 2–6
Exercises 7–36
Extra Practice, p. 826

Quadratic Equations
Lesson 5-5: Example 1
Exercises 1–6
Extra Practice, p. 826

Lesson Resources

 Teaching Resources
Practice, Reteaching, Enrichment
Checkpoint Quiz 1

 **Reaching All Students**
Practice Workbook 9-3
Spanish Practice Workbook 9-3
Reading and Math Literacy 9B
Spanish Reading & Literacy 9B
Spanish Checkpoint Quiz 1
Technology Activities 33

 Presentation Assistant Plus!
Transparencies
• Check Skills You'll Need 9-3
• Additional Examples 9-3
• Student Edition Answers 9-3
• Lesson Quiz 9-3
PH Presentation Pro CD 9-3

 **ASSESSMENT SYSTEM**

Checkpoint Quiz 1
Computer Test Generator CD

 Technology
Resource Pro® CD-ROM
Computer Test Generator CD
Prentice Hall Presentation Pro CD

 **www.PHSchool.com**
Student Site
• Teacher Web Code: agk-5500
• Updated Data
• Self-grading Lesson Quiz
Teacher Center
• Lesson Planner
• Resources

Plus

Ongoing Assessment and Intervention

Before the Lesson
Diagnose prerequisite skills using:
• Check Skills You'll Need

During the Lesson
Monitor progress using:
• Check Understanding
• Additional Examples
• Standardized Test Prep

After the Lesson
Assess knowledge using:
• Lesson Quiz
• Computer Test Generator CD
• Chapter Checkpoint 1 (p. 498)

491

2. Teach

Professional Development

Math Background

Rational is related to *ratio*. A rational expression is the ratio of two polynomials. Students will draw on all they know about polynomials.

OBJECTIVE

1 Teaching Notes

1 EXAMPLE Math Tip

In part (b), there is another way to see that the function is defined for all real numbers. The value of x^2 is always greater than or equal to 0. Therefore, $x^2 + 1$ is always positive. You may want to have students graph the functions in both parts of the example on a graphing calculator to analyze the behavior of the graphs in more detail.

2 EXAMPLE Teaching Tip

In part (c), note the common factor $x + 4$ in the numerator and denominator. So there is a hole at $x = -4$. The factor $x - 3$ occurs once in the numerator but twice in the denominator. So it follows that $x = 3$ is an asymptote.

To find points of discontinuity, find the values of x that make the denominator 0.

1 EXAMPLE Finding Points of Discontinuity

For each rational function, find any points of discontinuity.

a. $y = \dfrac{1}{x^2 + 2x + 1}$

The function is undefined at value(s) of x for which $x^2 + 2x + 1 = 0$.

$x^2 + 2x + 1 = 0$ **Set the denominator equal to zero.**

$(x + 1)(x + 1) = 0$ **Solve by factoring or using the Quadratic Formula.**

$x + 1 = 0$ **Zero Product Property**

$x = -1$ **Solve for x.**

There is a point of discontinuity at $x = -1$.

b. $y = \dfrac{-x + 1}{x^2 + 1}$

The function is undefined at value(s) of x for which $x^2 + 1 = 0$.

$x^2 + 1 = 0$ **Set the denominator equal to zero.**

$x^2 = -1$ **Solve for x.**

$x = \pm \sqrt{-1}$

Since $\sqrt{-1}$ is not a real number, there is no real value for x for which the function $y = \dfrac{-x + 1}{x^2 + 1}$ is undefined. There is no point of discontinuity.

✓ **Check Understanding** ❶ For each rational function, find any points of discontinuity.

a. $y = \dfrac{1}{x^2 - 16}$ **−4, 4**   **b.** $y = \dfrac{x^2 - 1}{x^2 + 3}$ **none**   **c.** $y = \dfrac{x + 1}{x^2 + 2x - 8}$ **−4, 2**

The graph of $y = \dfrac{x + 1}{(x - 1)(x + 2)}$ is shown at the right. The zeros of the denominator are 1 and −2. The graph has vertical asymptotes at those points.

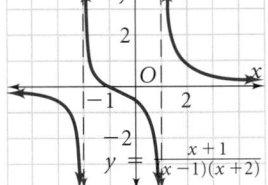

Graphing Calculator Hint

A hole in a graph is not displayed on a graphing calculator.

2 is a zero of both the numerator and the denominator of the rational function $y = \dfrac{(x - 2)(x + 1)}{x - 2}$. The graph of this function is the same as the graph of $y = x + 1$, except it has a hole at $x = 2$.

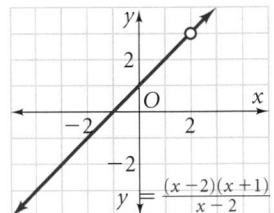

2 is a zero of both the numerator and the denominator of the rational function $y = \dfrac{x - 2}{(x - 2)(x - 1)}$. The graph of this function is the same as the graph of $y = \dfrac{1}{x - 1}$, except it has a hole at $x = 2$.

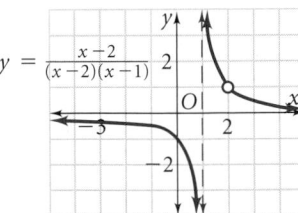

👥 Reaching All Students

| **Below Level** Rational functions can be written as the ratio of two polynomial functions. Point out that it is not necessary to simplify rational functions in order to graph them. | **Advanced Learners** Have students investigate the behavior of an expression such as $y = a^x$. Does it have any horizontal or vertical asymptotes? | **Alternative Method** See note on page 493. **Error Prevention** See note on page 495. |

2 is a zero of both the numerator and the denominator of the rational function $y = \frac{x-2}{(x-2)^2}$.

The graph of this function is exactly the same as the graph of $y = \frac{1}{x-2}$. The vertical asymptote is $x = 2$ and there is no hole.

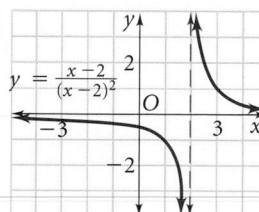

$$y = \frac{x-2}{(x-2)^2}$$

 Key Concepts

Properties	**Vertical Asymptotes**

The rational function $f(x) = \frac{P(x)}{Q(x)}$ has a point of discontinuity for each real zero of $Q(x)$.

If $P(x)$ and $Q(x)$ have no common real zeros, then the graph of $f(x)$ has a vertical asymptote at each real zero of $Q(x)$.

If $P(x)$ and $Q(x)$ have a common real zero a, then there is a hole in the graph or a vertical asymptote at $x = a$.

2a. Since 1 and −3 are the zeroes of the denominator and neither is a zero of the numerator, $x = 1$ and $x = -3$ are vertical asymptotes.
b. The graph of this function is the same as the graph of $y = \frac{1}{x+3}$, except that it has a hole at $x = 2$. The vertical asymptote is $x = -3$.
c. The graph of this function is the same as the graph of $y = x - 1$, except that it has a hole at $x = -1$.

2 **EXAMPLE** **Finding Vertical Asymptotes**

Describe the vertical asymptotes and holes for the graph of each rational function.

a. $y = \frac{x+1}{(x-2)(x-3)}$

Since 2 and 3 are the zeros of the denominator and neither is a zero of the numerator, $x = 2$ and $x = 3$ are vertical asymptotes.

b. $y = \frac{(x-2)(x-1)}{x-2}$

The graph of this function is the same as the graph of $y = x - 1$, except it has a hole at $x = 2$.

c. $y = \frac{(x-3)(x+4)}{(x-3)(x-3)(x+4)}$

The graph of this function is the same as the graph of $y = \frac{1}{x-3}$, except it has a hole at $x = -4$. The vertical asymptote is $x = 3$.

✓ **Check Understanding** **2** Describe the vertical asymptotes and holes for the graph of each rational function.

a. $y = \frac{x-2}{(x-1)(x+3)}$ **b.** $y = \frac{x-2}{(x-2)(x+3)}$ **c.** $y = \frac{x^2-1}{x+1}$

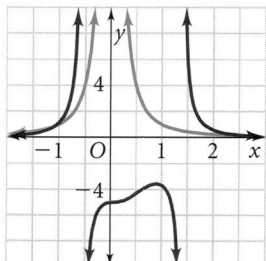

For the graphs of rational functions such as $y = \frac{1}{x}$ and $y = \frac{1}{x^2}$, the horizontal asymptote is $y = 0$. As shown at the left, when the absolute value of x is large, the graph of $y = \frac{2x^2 - x + 10}{5x^4 - 7x^3 + x^2 - 2}$ is very close to the graph of $y = \frac{1}{x^2}$. So $y = 0$ is the horizontal asymptote of both graphs.

In fact, $y = 0$ is the horizontal asymptote of the graph of any rational function, if the degree of the denominator is greater than the degree of the numerator.

If the degree of the numerator equals the degree of the denominator, then the horizontal asymptote can be found as shown in Example 3.

---

3 EXAMPLE **Alternative Method**

Another way to see that there is a horizontal asymptote at $y = 3$ is to think about the end behavior of $y = \frac{11}{x-2} + 3$. The greater the absolute value of x, the closer the value of $\frac{11}{x-2}$ is to 0. Therefore, the greater the absolute value of x, the closer the points on the graph of $y = \frac{11}{x-2} + 3$ will be to the horizontal line $y = 3$.

Additional Examples

1 For each rational function, find any points of discontinuity.
a. $y = \frac{3}{x^2 - x - 12}$ points of discontinuity at $x = -3$, $x = 4$

b. $y = \frac{2x}{3x^2 + 4}$ none

2 Describe the vertical asymptotes and holes for the graph of each rational function.

a. $y = \frac{x-7}{(x+1)(x+5)}$ vertical asymptotes $x = -1$, $x = -5$

b. $y = \frac{x(x+3)}{x+3}$ hole at $x = -3$

c. $y = \frac{(x-6)(x+9)}{(x+9)(x+9)(x-6)}$ hole at $x = 6$, vertical asymptote at $x = -9$

Additional Example

③ Find the horizontal asymptote of $y = \frac{-4x + 3}{2x + 1}$. **$y = -2$**

OBJECTIVE
2 Teaching Notes

4 EXAMPLE Teaching Tip

Pick a value for x, such as $x = 2$. Have students state the sign of each binomial in the equation for the function. Then ask them whether the value of the function will be positive, negative, or zero for $x = 2$. Repeat the process with other x-values.

 Additional Examples

④ Sketch the graph of $y = \frac{x + 1}{(x - 3)(x + 2)}$

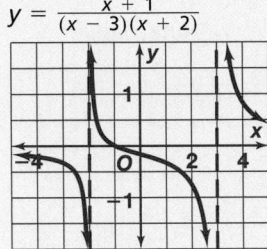

⑤ A vat contains 20 gallons of cleaning solution that is 15% bleach. A second vat has a solution that is 50% bleach. A few gallons from the second vat will be added to the first vat to get a solution that is more than 15% bleach.
a. Write a function for the percent bleach in the new solution if x gallons from the second vat are added to the first vat. Graph the function.
$y = \frac{3 + 0.5x}{20 + x}$

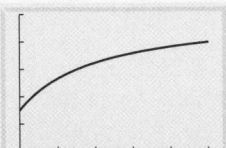

Xmin=0   Ymin=0
Xmax=50   Ymas=.5
Xscl=10   Yscl=.1
b. What percent bleach will the new solution be if 10 gallons from the second vat are used? If 17 gallons are used? **about 27%; about 31%**

494

---

③ **EXAMPLE** Finding Horizontal Asymptotes

Find the horizontal asymptote of $y = \frac{3x + 5}{x - 2}$.

Divide the numerator by the denominator as shown at the right. The function $y = \frac{3x + 5}{x - 2}$ can be written as $y = \frac{11}{x - 2} + 3$. Its graph is a translation of $y = \frac{11}{x}$. The horizontal asymptote of the graph of $y = \frac{3x + 5}{x - 2}$ is $y = 3$.

$$\begin{array}{r} 3 \\ x - 2 \overline{)3x + 5} \\ \underline{3x - 6} \\ 11 \end{array}$$

✓ **Check Understanding** ③ Find the horizontal asymptote of the graph of each rational function.
a. $y = \frac{-2x + 6}{x - 1}$ **$y = -2$**   **b.** $y = \frac{2x^2 + 5}{x^2 + 1}$ **$y = 2$**

Key Concepts

Properties	**Horizontal Asymptotes**

The graph of a rational function has at most one horizontal asymptote.

The graph of a rational function has a horizontal asymptote at $y = 0$ if the degree of the denominator is greater than the degree of the numerator.

If the degrees of the numerator and the denominator are equal, then the graph has a horizontal asymptote at $y = \frac{a}{b}$. a is the coefficient of the term of highest degree in the numerator and b is the coefficient of the term of highest degree in the denominator.

If the degree of the numerator is greater than the degree of the denominator, then the graph has no horizontal asymptote.

OBJECTIVE
2 Graphing Rational Functions

You can use asymptotes to sketch the graphs of rational functions.

④ **EXAMPLE** Sketching Graphs of Rational Functions

Sketch the graph of $y = \frac{x + 2}{(x + 3)(x - 4)}$.

The degree of the denominator is greater than the degree of the numerator, so the y-axis is the horizontal asymptote. When $x > 4$, y is positive. So as x increases, the graph approaches the y-axis from above. When $x < -3$, y is negative. So as x decreases, the graph approaches the y-axis from below.

Since -2 is the zero of the numerator, the x-intercept is at -2. Since -3 and 4 are the zeros of the denominator, the vertical asymptotes are at $x = -3$ and $x = 4$.

Calculate the values of y for values of x near the asymptotes. Plot those points and sketch the graph.

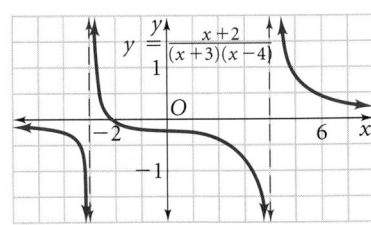

✓ **Check Understanding** ④ Sketch the graph of $y = \frac{x + 3}{(x - 1)(x - 5)}$. **See back of book.**

494 Chapter 9 Rational Functions

Closure

Ask students how factoring the numerator and denominator of a rational function can help in deciding whether the graph of the function has holes or asymptotes. **Answers may vary. Sample: If a number makes a factor of the denominator zero, there will be a hole or an asymptote. Comparing the zeros of the numerator and the denominator can help you tell which kind of discontinuity there will be.**

 **5 EXAMPLE** **Real-World** 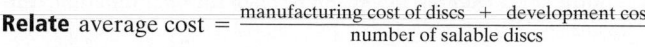 **Connection**

Business The CD-ROMs for a computer game can be manufactured for $.25 each. The development cost is $124,000. The first 100 discs are samples and will not be sold.

a. Write a function for the average cost of a salable disc. Graph the function.

Relate average cost = $\dfrac{\text{manufacturing cost of discs} + \text{development cost}}{\text{number of salable discs}}$

Define Let x = number of CD-ROMs produced.
Let y = average cost of one saleable disc.

Write $y = \dfrac{0.25x + 124,000}{x - 100}$

Graph the function. Adjust the viewing window.

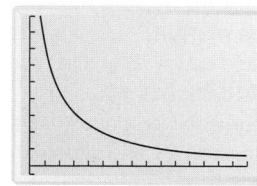

Xmin=0   Ymin=−10
Xmax=15000 Ymax=100
Xscl=1000   Yscl=10

b. What is the average cost if 2000 discs are produced? If 12,800 discs are produced?

Use the **CALC** feature to evaluate the function at $x = 2000$ and at $x = 12,800$. If 2000 discs are produced, the average cost will be about $65.53. If 12,800 discs are produced, the average cost will be about $10.02.

✓ Check Understanding **5 a. Critical Thinking** How could you find the number of discs that must be produced to bring the average cost under $8? **See back of book.**

b. What is the vertical asymptote of the graph of the function in Example 5? What is the horizontal asymptote? $x = 100; y = 0.25$

c. Describe how the asymptotes are related to the information given in Example 5. **See margin.**

EXERCISES

For more practice, see *Extra Practice*.

Practice and Problem Solving

 **Practice by Example**

Example 1
(page 492)

Find any points of discontinuity for each rational function. 1–18. See margin.

1. $y = \dfrac{2x^2 + 5}{x^2 - 2x}$ **2.** $y = \dfrac{x^2 + 2x}{x^2 + 2}$ **3.** $y = \dfrac{3x - 3}{x^2 - 1}$

4. $y = \dfrac{6 - 3x}{x^2 - 5x + 6}$ **5.** $y = \dfrac{x^2 + 5x + 6}{x^2 + 6x + 9}$ **6.** $y = \dfrac{x^2 + 4x + 3}{2x^2 + 5x - 7}$

7. $y = \dfrac{x^3 - 8}{x^3 - 8}$ **8.** $y = \dfrac{x^2}{x^2 + 1}$ **9.** $y = \dfrac{1}{2x^2 + 3x - 7}$

Example 2
(page 493)

Describe the vertical asymptotes and holes for the graph of each rational function.

10. $y = \dfrac{3}{x + 2}$ **11.** $y = \dfrac{x + 5}{x + 5}$ **12.** $y = \dfrac{x + 3}{(2x + 3)(x - 1)}$

13. $y = \dfrac{(x + 3)(x - 2)}{(x - 2)(x + 1)}$ **14.** $y = \dfrac{x^2 - 4}{x + 2}$ **15.** $y = \dfrac{x + 5}{x^2 + 9}$

16. $y = \dfrac{9 - x^2}{x^2 - 9}$ **17.** $y = \dfrac{2x^2}{2x^2 + 2}$ **18.** $y = \dfrac{6x^2 + x - 2}{3x^2 + 17x + 10}$

Lesson 9-3 Rational Functions and Their Graphs   **495**

Right margin

3. Practice

Assignment Guide

 **Objective**
A B Core 1–24, 41–43
C Extension 44

 **Objective**
A B Core 25–40
C Extension 45

Standardized Test Prep 46–50

Mixed Review 51–59

Error Prevention

Exercise 14 Students may not factor the numerator of the fraction. This will lead them to think that $x = -2$ is a vertical asymptote. Remind students that a common factor in the numerator and denominator can signal a hole.

Enrichment 9-3
Reteaching 9-3
Practice 9-3

13. vertical asymptote at $x = -1$, hole at $x = 2$

14. hole at $x = -2$

15. none

16. holes at $x = \pm 3$

17. none

18. vertical asymptote at $x = -5$, hole at $x = -\frac{2}{3}$

Bottom

pages 495–498   Exercises

1. $x = 0, x = 2$

2. none

3. $x = 1, x = -1$

4. $x = 2, x = 3$

5. $x = -3$

6. $x = -\frac{7}{2}, x = 1$

7. $x = 2$

8. none

9. $x = -2.77, x = 1.277$

10. vertical asymptote at $x = -2$

11. hole at $x = -5$

12. vertical asymptotes at $x = -\frac{3}{2}$ and $x = 1$

495

Careers

Exercise 45 Point out that knowledge of changes in wages and labor resources is important for people who work in the field of economics. Economists frequently use mathematical models for planning.

pages 495–498   Exercises

25.

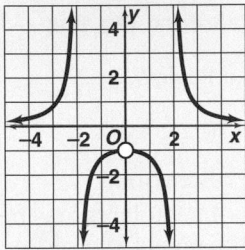

26.

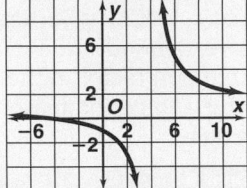

27.

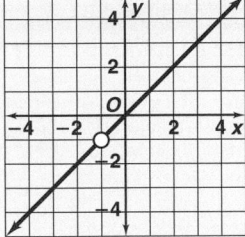

28.

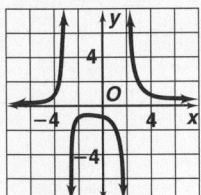

29.

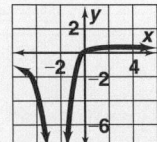

30.

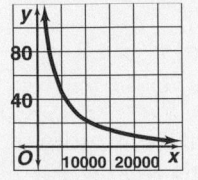

31a. $y = \dfrac{0.19x + 210{,}000}{x - 500}$

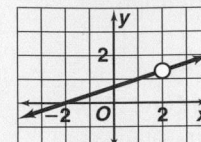

Example 3
(page 494)

Find the horizontal asymptote of the graph of each rational function.

19. $y = \dfrac{5}{x + 6}$ **y = 0**

20. $y = \dfrac{x + 2}{2x^2 - 4}$ **y = 0**

21. $y = \dfrac{x + 1}{x + 5}$ **y = 1**

22. $y = \dfrac{x^2 + 2}{2x^2 - 1}$ **y = ½**

23. $y = \dfrac{5x^3 + 2x}{2x^5 - 4x^3}$ **y = 0**

24. $y = \dfrac{3x - 4}{4x + 1}$ **y = ¾**

Example 4
(page 494)

Sketch the graph of each rational function.   25–30. See margin.

25. $y = \dfrac{x^2 - 4}{3x - 6}$

26. $y = \dfrac{4x}{x^3 - 4x}$

27. $y = \dfrac{x + 4}{x - 4}$

28. $y = \dfrac{x(x + 1)}{x + 1}$

29. $y = \dfrac{x + 6}{(x - 2)(x + 3)}$

30. $y = \dfrac{3x}{(x + 2)^2}$

Example 5
(page 495)

31. Business CDs can be manufactured for \$.19 each. The development cost is \$210,000. The first 500 discs are samples and will not be sold.
   a. Write a function for the average cost of a salable disc. Graph the function. **See margin.**
   b. What is the average cost if 5000 discs are produced? If 15,000 discs are produced? **\$46.88; \$14.68**
   c. How many discs must be produced to bring the average cost under \$10? **more than 21,916 discs**
   d. What are the vertical and horizontal asymptotes of the graph of the function? **x = 500, y = 0.19**

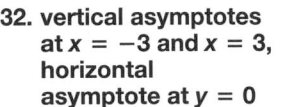 **Apply Your Skills**

Find the vertical and horizontal asymptotes, if any, of the graph of each rational function.

32. vertical asymptotes at $x = -3$ and $x = 3$, horizontal asymptote at $y = 0$

33. vertical asymptote at $x = -2$

34. horizontal asymptote at $y = 0$

32. **33.** **34.**

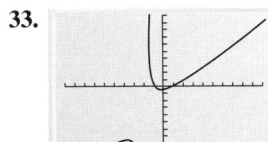

Sketch the graph of each rational function.   35–40. See back of book.

35. $y = \dfrac{2x + 3}{x - 5}$

36. $y = \dfrac{x^2 + 6x + 9}{x + 3}$

37. $y = \dfrac{4x^2 - 100}{2x^2 + x - 15}$

38. $y = -\dfrac{x}{(x - 1)^2}$

39. $y = \dfrac{2x}{3x - 1}$

40. $y = \dfrac{2}{x^2 - 4}$

41. Answers may vary. Sample: There is no value of x for which the denominator equals 0.

41. Writing Describe the conditions that will produce a rational function with a graph that has no vertical asymptotes.

42. Basketball A basketball player has made 21 of her last 30 free throws—an average of 70%. To model the player's rate of success if she makes x more consecutive free throws, use the function $y = \dfrac{21 + x}{30 + x}$.
   a. Graph the function. **See margin.**
   b. Use the graph to find the number of consecutive free throws the player needs to raise her success rate to 75%. **6 free throws**

43. Data Analysis The president of XYZ Company earns \$200,000 a year. Each of the other x employees earns \$20,000 a year.
   a. Write and graph a function that models the average salary of all employees of XYZ. **See back of book.**
   b. What is the average salary if there are three employees? If there are 30 employees? **\$65,000; \$25,806.45**
   c. Critical Thinking Is the average salary the best measure of the workers' pay? Explain. What other measure could you use?
   Answers may vary. Sample: No; the president's salary throws off the average; the median or mode would be a better measure.

42a.

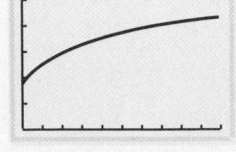

```
WINDOW FORMAT
Xmin=0
Xmax=100
Xscl=10
Ymin=.5
Ymax=1
Yscl=.1
```

C Challenge   **44. Reasoning** Look for a pattern in the sequence of shells below.

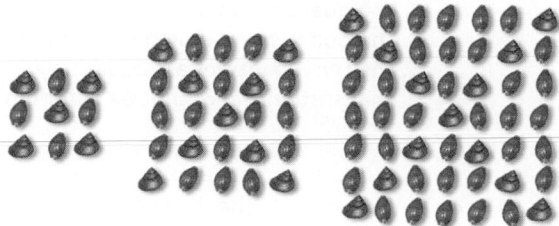

44a. $P(n) = 4n^2$

b. $R(n) = 4n + 1$

c. $y = \frac{4n^2}{4n + 1}; \frac{64}{17};$
**check students'
work.**

a. Write a model for the number of purple shells $P(n)$ at each step n.
b. Write a model for the number of red shells $R(n)$ at each step n.
c. Write a model for the ratio of $P(n)$ to $R(n)$. Use it to predict the ratio of purple shells to red shells in the next figure. Verify your answer.

🌐 **45. Wage Policy** The graph below compares the average hourly wage for production workers and the minimum hourly wage from 1950 to 2000.

History of the Minimum Wage

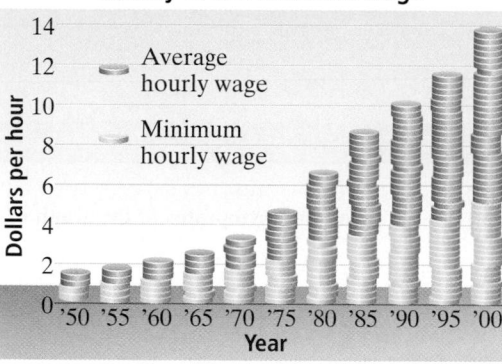

Source: Bureau of Labor Statistics.
Go to **www.PHSchool.com** for a data update.
Web Code: agg-2041

**45a. The increase in
production
workers' average
hourly wage is
greater.**

c. $R(x) = \frac{M(x)}{A(x)}$

a. How has the comparison of the minimum wage to the production workers' wage changed over the years?
b. If the minimum wage and the production workers' wage are modeled by polynomials, what type of function would model their ratio? **rational**
c. The quadratic function $M(x) = 0.00081x^2 + 0.049x + 0.68$ models the minimum wage, where x is the number of years since 1950. The quadratic function $A(x) = 0.0043x^2 + 0.04x + 1.21$ models the average wage. Write a model for the ratio of these two functions.
d. Graph your model. If the present trends continue, when will the minimum wage decrease to 25% of the average wage? **See back of book.**

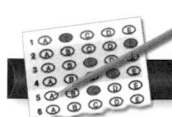

Standardized Test Prep

Multiple Choice   **46.** What are the points of discontinuity for $y = \frac{(2x + 3)(x - 5)}{(x + 5)(2x - 1)}$? **C**

      A. $-5, 1$ **B.** $-\frac{3}{2}, 5$ **C.** $-5, \frac{1}{2}$ **D.** $5, -\frac{1}{2}$

Short Response   **47.** Find the horizontal asymptote of $y = \frac{5x + 7}{x + 3}$ by dividing the numerator by the denominator. Explain your steps. **See margin.**

47. [2]

$$\begin{array}{r} 5 \\ x + 3 \overline{)5x + 7} \\ \underline{5x + 15} \\ -8 \end{array}$$

So $y = \frac{5x + 7}{x + 3}$ can be

written as $y = \frac{-8}{x + 3} + 5.$
**As x becomes larger, the
fraction approaches 0
and y approaches the
asymptote at 5.**

**[1] answer only, with no
explanation**

📋 **Lesson Quiz 9-3**

1. Find any points of discontinuity for the rational function $y = \frac{x + 7}{x^2 + 5x - 14}$.
$x = 2, x = -7$

2. Describe the vertical asymptotes and holes for the graph of $y = \frac{x + 5}{(x - 3)(x + 5)}$.
**vertical asymptote at $x = 3$;
hole at $x = -5$**

3. Find the horizontal asymptote of $y = \frac{x^2 - 9}{3x^2 + 5}$.
$y = \frac{1}{3}$

4. Sketch the graph of $y = \frac{x^2 - 9}{x(x^2 + 2x - 15)}$.

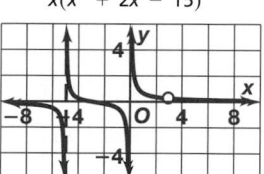

5. The cost in dollars of publishing x copies of a certain book is modeled by $30,000 + 10x + 0.0001x^2$.
a. Write a function for the average cost per book. Graph the function.
$f(x) = \frac{30,000 + 10x + 0.0001x^2}{x}$

Xmin=0   Ymin=0
Xmax=50000   Ymas=30
Xscl=5000   Yscl=5

b. What is the average cost per book if 12,000 copies are published? if 15,000 copies are published?
$13.70; $13.50

Alternative Assessment

Ask each student to write three rational functions with the numerator and denominator in factored form: one with two vertical asymptotes and no horizontal asymptote; another with one vertical asymptote, one hole, and no horizontal asymptote; and the third with both vertical and horizontal asymptotes. Students check one another's work.

Standardized Test Prep

 **Resources**

For additional practice with a variety of test item formats:
- Standardized Test Prep, p. 531
- Test-Taking Strategies, p. 526
- Test-Taking Strategies with Transparencies

✓ Chapter Checkpoint 1

To check understanding of Lessons 9-1 to 9-3:

Checkpoint Quiz 1 (p. 498)

📁 **Teaching Resources**
Checkpoint Quiz 1 (also in Prentice Hall Assessment System)

👥 **Reaching All Students**
Reading and Math Literacy 9B

Spanish versions available

---

pages 495–498   Exercises

51. vertical: $x = 0$, horizontal: $y = 4$

52. vertical: $x = -3$, horizontal: $y = 0$

53. vertical: $x = -1$, horizontal: $y = 1$

54. vertical: $x = 7$, horizontal: $y = -3$

55. vertical: $x = 2$, horizontal: $y = 0$

56. vertical: $x = 5$, horizontal: $y = -6$

page 498   Checkpoint Quiz 1

4. Answers may vary. Sample: Both have vertical asymptote $x = 0$ and horizontal asymptote $y = 0$. $y = \frac{4}{x}$ is closer to the axes.

5. Answers may vary. Sample: $y = \frac{1}{x} + 5$ is a vertical translation of $y = \frac{1}{x}$ up 5 units.

6. Answers may vary. Sample: $y = \frac{1}{x - 1} + 2$ as vertical asymptote $x = 1$ and horizontal asymptote $y = 2$. $y = \frac{1}{x + 1} - 2$ has vertical asymptote $x = -1$ and horizontal asymptote $y = -2$.

498

Quantitative Comparison

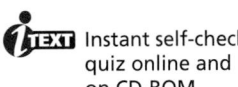 **Take It to the NET**
Online lesson quiz at
www.PHSchool.com
Web Code: aga-0903

Compare the boxed quantity in Column A with the boxed quantity in Column B. Choose the best answer.
- **A.** The quantity in Column A is greater.
- **B.** The quantity in Column B is greater.
- **C.** The two quantities are equal.
- **D.** The relationship cannot be determined from the information given.

	Column A	Column B
48. B	the value of the discontinuity of $y = \frac{2x}{3x + 7}$	the value of the discontinuity of $y = \frac{5}{2x}$
49. A	the number of points of discontinuity of $y = \frac{2x}{x^2 - 1}$	the number of points of discontinuity of $y = \frac{2x}{x^2 + 1}$
50. C	the number of vertical asymptotes of $y = \frac{(x - 3)(x - 5)(x - 4)}{(x - 2)(x - 6)}$	the number of points of discontinuity of $y = \frac{(x - 3)(x - 5)(x - 4)}{(x - 2)(x - 6)}$

Mixed Review

Lesson 9-2   **Find the asymptotes of the graph of each equation. 51–56. See margin.**

51. $y = \frac{3}{x} + 4$ **52.** $y = \frac{2}{x + 3}$ **53.** $y = \frac{-1}{x + 1} + 1$

54. $y = \frac{5}{x - 7} - 3$ **55.** $y = \frac{5}{2 - x}$ **56.** $y = \frac{-2}{5 - x} - 6$

Lesson 8-2   **Describe how the graph of each function relates to the graph of $y = 4(0.8)^x$.**

57. $y = 4(0.8)^{x-1}$
1 unit right

58. $y = 4(0.8)^x + 3$
3 units up

59. $y = 4(0.8)^{x+1} - 5$
1 unit left and 5 units down

✓ Checkpoint Quiz 1   Lessons 9-1 through 9-3

🖥 Instant self-check quiz online and on CD-ROM

If $z = 30$ when $x = 3$ and $y = 2$, write the function that models each relationship.

1. z varies jointly with x and y. **$z = 5xy$**

2. z varies directly with x and inversely with y. **$z = \frac{20x}{y}$**

3. z varies inversely with the product of x and y. **$z = \frac{180}{xy}$**

Compare the graphs of the inverse variations. 4–6. See margin.

4. $y = \frac{4}{x}$ and $y = \frac{9}{x}$

5. $y = \frac{1}{x}$ and $y = \frac{1}{x} + 5$

6. $y = \frac{1}{x - 1} + 2$ and $y = \frac{1}{x + 1} - 2$

Sketch the graph of each rational function. 7–8, 10. See margin.

7. $y = \frac{x^2 - 9}{2x + 6}$ **8.** $y = \frac{3x}{x^3 - x}$ **9.** $y = \frac{x + 3}{x - 3}$ **10.** $y = \frac{x^2 - 2x}{x - 2}$

See back of book.

7.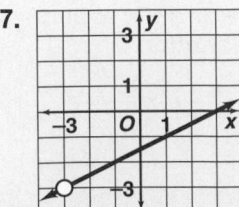

8.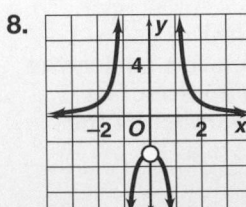

10.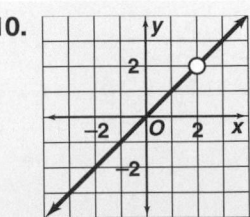

Rational Expressions

North Carolina Objectives 1.03 Operate with algebraic expressions (polynomial, rational, complex fractions) to solve problems.

Lesson Preview

What You'll Learn

OBJECTIVE 1 To simplify rational expressions

OBJECTIVE 2 To multiply and divide rational expressions

... And Why

To compute ratios of volume to surface area, as in Example 2

✓ **Check Skills You'll Need** (For help, go to Lesson 5-4 and Skills Handbook page 843.)

Factor.

1. $2x^2 - 3x + 1$ **(2x − 1)(x − 1)**

2. $4x^2 - 9$ **(2x + 3)(2x − 3)**

3. $5x^2 + 6x + 1$ **(5x + 1)(x + 1)**

4. $10x^2 - 10$ **10(x + 1)(x − 1)**

Multiply or divide.

5. $\frac{3}{8} \cdot \frac{5}{6}$ **$\frac{5}{16}$**

6. $\frac{1}{2} \cdot \frac{4}{6}$ **$\frac{1}{3}$**

7. $\frac{8}{3} \cdot \frac{2}{16}$ **$\frac{1}{3}$**

8. $\frac{2}{5} \cdot \frac{3}{7}$ **$\frac{6}{35}$**

9. $\frac{5}{8} \div 4$ **$\frac{5}{32}$**

10. $\frac{3}{4} \div \frac{1}{2}$ **$\frac{3}{2}$**

11. $\frac{9}{16} \div \frac{3}{4}$ **$\frac{3}{4}$**

12. $\frac{5}{4} \div \frac{15}{8}$ **$\frac{2}{3}$**

New Vocabulary • simplest form

OBJECTIVE

1 Simplifying Rational Expressions

 Interactive lesson includes instant self-check, tutorials, and activities.

A rational expression is in **simplest form** when its numerator and denominator are polynomials that have no common divisors.

In simplest form	Not in simplest form
$\frac{x}{x-1}$ $\frac{2}{x^2+3}$	$\frac{x}{x^2}$ $\frac{\frac{1}{x}}{x+1}$ $\frac{2(x-3)}{3(x-3)}$

Need Help?

Restrictions on the variables may be needed to prevent division by 0.

You can simplify some expressions by dividing out common factors.

1 EXAMPLE **Simplifying Rational Expressions**

Simplify $\frac{x^2 + 10x + 25}{x^2 + 9x + 20}$. State any restrictions on the variable.

$$\frac{x^2 + 10x + 25}{x^2 + 9x + 20} = \frac{(x + 5)(x + 5)}{(x + 4)(x + 5)}$$ **Factor the polynomials. Notice that $x \neq -4$ or -5.**

$$= \frac{(x + 5)(x + 5)}{(x + 4)(x + 5)}$$ **Divide out common factors.**

$$= \frac{x + 5}{x + 4}$$

The simplified expression is $\frac{x + 5}{x + 4}$ for $x \neq -4$ or -5. The restrictions on x are needed to prevent the denominator of the original expression from being zero.

1a. $-\frac{3}{x}; x \neq 0, y \neq 0$

b. $\frac{-3(x + 2)}{(x - 2)(x - 4)};$ $x \neq 2$ or 4

c. $\frac{2x + 1}{x - 3}; x \neq 2$ or 3

✓ **Check Understanding** **1** **1.** Simplify each expression. State any restrictions on the variables.

a. $\frac{-27x^3y}{9x^4y}$

b. $\frac{-6 - 3x}{x^2 - 6x + 8}$

c. $\frac{2x^2 - 3x - 2}{x^2 - 5x + 6}$

Lesson 9-4 Rational Expressions **499**

---

1. Plan

Lesson Preview

✓ **Check Skills You'll Need**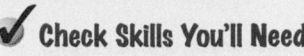

Factoring Quadratic Expressions
Lesson 5-4: Example 6
Exercises 31–36
Extra Practice, p. 826

Lesson Resources

📁 **Teaching Resources**
Practice, Reteaching, Enrichment

👥 **Reaching All Students**
Practice Workbook 9-4
Spanish Practice Workbook 9-4
Hands-On Activities 50

⏱ **Presentation Assistant Plus!**
Transparencies
• Check Skills You'll Need 9-4
• Additional Examples 9-4
• Student Edition Answers 9-4
• Lesson Quiz 9-4
PH Presentation Pro CD 9-4

PRENTICE HALL ASSESSMENT SYSTEM

Computer Test Generator CD

💿 **Technology**
Resource Pro® CD-ROM
Computer Test Generator CD
Prentice Hall Presentation Pro CD

💻 **www.PHSchool.com**
Student Site
• Teacher Web Code: agk-5500
• Self-grading Lesson Quiz
Teacher Center
• Lesson Planner
• Resources

Plus

 **Ongoing Assessment and Intervention**

Before the Lesson	**During the Lesson**	**After the Lesson**
Diagnose prerequisite skills using:	Monitor progress using:	Assess knowledge using:
• Check Skills You'll Need	• Check Understanding	• Lesson Quiz
	• Additional Examples	• Computer Test Generator CD
	• Standardized Test Prep	

Math Background

Simplifying a rational expression depends on factoring polynomials.

 1 **Teaching Notes**

Additional Examples

1 Simplify $\frac{x^2 - 6x - 16}{x^2 + 5x + 6}$. State any restrictions on the variable. $\frac{x - 8}{x + 3}$; $x \neq -2, -3$

2 Compare the ratio of the volume to surface area of a sphere with radius r with the ratio of volume to surface area of a sphere with radius $2r$. **The first ratio is $\frac{r}{3}$; the second ratio is $\frac{2r}{3}$. The second ratio is twice the first.**

OBJECTIVE

 2 **Teaching Notes**

Additional Examples

3 Multiply $\frac{3x^2 + 5x - 2}{x - 5}$ and $\frac{x^2 - 25}{3x^2 - 7x + 2}$. State any restrictions on the variable. $\frac{x^2 + 7x + 10}{x - 2}$; $x \neq \frac{1}{3}, 2, 5$

4 Divide $\frac{3 - y}{(2x - 1)(x + 5)}$ by $\frac{6(y - 3)}{(2x - 1)(x - 7)}$. State any restrictions on the variables. $\frac{-x + 7}{6x + 30}$; $x \neq -5, \frac{1}{2}, 7, y \neq 3$

Closure

Ask students to explain how to simplify, multiply, and divide rational expressions. **To simplify a rational expression, divide the numerator and denominator by their common factors. To multiply, divide out common factors of the numerators and denominators of both expressions. To divide, multiply by the reciprocal of the divisor, then divide out common factors.**

500

Real-World Connection

Crystal Bridge botanical gardens in Oklahoma City

2 EXAMPLE **Real-World Connection**

Architecture One factor in designing a structure is the need to maximize the volume (space for working) for a given surface area (material needed for construction). Compare the ratio of the volume to surface area of a cylinder with radius r and height r to a cylinder with radius r and height $2r$.

Use the formulas for volume and surface area of a cylinder.

$$\text{Volume } (V) = \pi r^2 h$$
$$\text{Surface Area (S.A.)} = 2\pi rh + 2\pi r^2$$

Cylinder with height r Cylinder with height $2r$

$\dfrac{V}{\text{S.A.}} = \dfrac{\pi r^2 h}{2\pi rh + 2\pi r^2}$	$\dfrac{V}{\text{S.A.}} = \dfrac{\pi r^2 h}{2\pi rh + 2\pi r^2}$ Write a ratio.
$= \dfrac{\pi r^2 (r)}{2\pi r(r) + 2\pi r^2}$	$= \dfrac{\pi r^2 (2r)}{2\pi r(2r) + 2\pi r^2}$ Substitute for h.
$= \dfrac{\pi r^3}{2\pi r^2 + 2\pi r^2}$	$= \dfrac{2\pi r^3}{4\pi r^2 + 2\pi r^2}$ Simplify.
$= \dfrac{\pi r^3}{4\pi r^2}$	$= \dfrac{2\pi r^3}{6\pi r^2}$ Combine like terms.
$= \dfrac{r}{4}$	$= \dfrac{r}{3}$ Simplify.

For a given radius, the ratio of volume to surface area is greater for the cylinder with a height of $2r$.

✓ Check Understanding **2 a.** Find the ratio of volume to surface area of a cylinder whose height is $4r$. $\frac{2r}{5}$
    b. Critical Thinking Let mr be the height of a cylinder of radius r, with m a positive number. Describe how the ratio of volume to surface area changes as m changes. **As m gets larger, the ratio gets larger.**

OBJECTIVE

2 Multiplying and Dividing Rational Expressions

You can use what you know about simplifying rational expressions when you multiply and divide them.

3 EXAMPLE **Multiplying Rational Expressions**

Multiply $\frac{2x^2 + 7x + 3}{x - 4}$ and $\frac{x^2 - 16}{x^2 + 8x + 15}$. State any restrictions on the variable.

$$\frac{2x^2 + 7x + 3}{x - 4} \cdot \frac{x^2 - 16}{x^2 + 8x + 15} = \frac{(2x + 1)(x + 3)}{x - 4} \cdot \frac{(x - 4)(x + 4)}{(x + 3)(x + 5)} \quad \text{Factor.}$$

$$= \frac{(2x + 1)(x + 3)}{x - 4} \cdot \frac{(x - 4)(x + 4)}{(x + 3)(x + 5)} \quad \begin{array}{l}\text{Divide out}\\\text{common factors.}\end{array}$$

$$= \frac{(2x + 1)(x + 4)}{x + 5}$$

3. $\frac{a - 2}{a(a - 1)}$;
  $a \neq 0, 1, -1, \text{ or } -2$

The product is $\frac{(2x + 1)(x + 4)}{x + 5}$ for $x \neq 4, -3, \text{ or } -5$.

✓ Check Understanding **3** Multiply $\frac{a^2 - 4}{a^2 - 1}$ and $\frac{a + 1}{a^2 + 2a}$. State any restrictions on the variable. **See left.**

500   Chapter 9   Rational Functions

 Reaching All Students

Below Level Compare simplifying, multiplying, and dividing rational expressions to the same operations with rational numbers.	**Advanced Learners** In Example 1, challenge students to explain why $x \neq -5$ in the original expression, though $x = 5$ is not a restriction in the derived expression.	**Error Prevention** See note on page 501.

To divide rational expressions, remember to multiply by the reciprocal of the divisor, just as you did when dividing rational numbers.

Need Help?

For practice in dividing fractions, go to p. 843.

4 EXAMPLE Dividing Rational Expressions

Divide $\dfrac{4 - x}{(3x + 2)(x - 2)}$ by $\dfrac{5(x - 4)}{(x - 2)(7y - 5)}$. State any restrictions on the variables.

$$\dfrac{4 - x}{(3x + 2)(x - 2)} \div \dfrac{5(x - 4)}{(x - 2)(7y - 5)}$$

$$= \dfrac{4 - x}{(3x + 2)(x - 2)} \cdot \dfrac{(x - 2)(7y - 5)}{5(x - 4)} \qquad \text{Multiply by the reciprocal.}$$

$$= \dfrac{\overset{1}{-(x - 4)}}{(3x + 2)(x - 2)} \cdot \dfrac{(x - 2)(7y - 5)}{5(x - 4)} \qquad \text{Divide out common factors.}$$

$$= \dfrac{-1}{3x + 2} \cdot \dfrac{7y - 5}{5} \qquad \text{Rewrite the expression.}$$

$$= \dfrac{-(7y - 5)}{5(3x + 2)} \qquad \text{Multiply.}$$

The quotient is $\dfrac{-(7y + 5)}{5(3x + 2)}$ for $x \neq -\frac{2}{3}, 2,$ or 4, and $y \neq \frac{5}{7}$.

✓ **Check Understanding** 4 Divide $\dfrac{a^2 + 2a - 15}{a^2 - 16}$ by $\dfrac{a + 1}{3a - 12}$. State any restrictions on the variable.
$$\dfrac{3(a + 5)(a - 3)}{(a + 1)(a + 4)}; a \neq -1, -4, \text{ or } 4$$

EXERCISES

For more practice, see *Extra Practice*.

Practice and Problem Solving

A Practice by Example

Examples 1 and 2
(pages 499–500)

Simplify each rational expression. State any restrictions on the variable.

1. $\dfrac{2x}{4x^2 - 2x}$ $\dfrac{1}{2x - 1}; x \neq 0$ or $\frac{1}{2}$

2. $\dfrac{6c^2 + 9c}{3c}$ $2c + 3; c \neq 0$

3. $\dfrac{b^2 - 1}{b - 1}$ $b + 1; b \neq 1$

4. $\dfrac{z^2 - 49}{z + 7}$ $z - 7; z \neq -7$

5. $\dfrac{2x + 10}{x^2 + 10x + 25}$ $\dfrac{2}{x + 5}; x \neq -5$

6. $\dfrac{x^2 + 8x + 16}{x^2 - 2x - 24}$ $\dfrac{x + 4}{x - 6}; x \neq 6$ or -4

Example 3
(page 500)

Multiply. State any restrictions on the variables.

7. $\dfrac{4x^2}{5y} \cdot \dfrac{7y}{12x^4}$ $\dfrac{7}{15x^2}; x \neq 0, y \neq 0$

8. $\dfrac{2x^4}{10y^2} \cdot \dfrac{5y^3}{4x^3}$ $\dfrac{xy}{4}; x \neq 0, y \neq 0$

10. $\dfrac{4(x + 6)}{3(3x + 8)}; x \neq 3$ or $-\frac{8}{3}$

9. $\dfrac{8y - 4}{10y - 5} \cdot \dfrac{5y - 15}{3y - 9}$ $\dfrac{4}{3}; y \neq \frac{1}{2}$ or 3

10. $\dfrac{2x + 12}{3x - 9} \cdot \dfrac{2x - 6}{3x + 8}$

12. $1; x \neq -2, -1, 2,$ or 3

11. $\dfrac{x^2 - 4}{x^2 - 1} \cdot \dfrac{x + 1}{x^2 + 2x}$ $\dfrac{x - 2}{x(x - 1)}; x \neq 0, 1, -1,$ or -2

12. $\dfrac{x^2 - 5x + 6}{x^2 - 4} \cdot \dfrac{x^2 + 3x + 2}{x^2 - 2x - 3}$

Example 4
(page 501)

Divide. State any restrictions on the variables. 16–18. See margin.

13. $\dfrac{7x}{4y^3} \div \dfrac{21x^3}{8y}$ $\dfrac{2}{3x^2y^2}; x \neq 0, y \neq 0$

14. $\dfrac{3x^3}{5y^2} \div \dfrac{6x^5}{5y^3}$ $\dfrac{y}{2x^2}; x \neq 0, y \neq 0$

15. $\dfrac{6x + 6y}{x - y} \div \dfrac{18}{5x - 5y}$ $\dfrac{5(x + y)}{3}; x \neq y$

16. $\dfrac{3y - 12}{2y + 4} \div \dfrac{6y - 24}{4y + 8}$

17. $\dfrac{x^2}{x^2 + 2x + 1} \div \dfrac{3x}{x^2 - 1}$

18. $\dfrac{y^2 - 5y + 6}{y^3} \div \dfrac{y^2 + 3y - 10}{4y^2}$

3. Practice

Assignment Guide

1 Objective

Ⓐ Ⓑ Core 1–6, 19–21, 23–26, 33–35, 37

Ⓒ Extension 38

2 Objective

Ⓐ Ⓑ Core 7–18, 22, 27–32, 36

Ⓒ Extension 39–41

Standardized Test Prep 42–47

Mixed Review 48–56

Error Prevention

Exercises 13–18 When students state restrictions on the variables, they may forget that values that make the numerator of the divisor equal to 0 must also be excluded. Remind them that any value that makes a factor of the numerator or the denominator of the divisor equal to 0 must be excluded.

pages 501–503 Exercises

16. $1; y \neq -2$ or 4

17. $\dfrac{x(x - 1)}{3(x + 1)}; x \neq -1, 1,$ or 0

18. $\dfrac{4(y - 3)}{y(y + 5)}; y \neq 2, -5,$ or 0

501

Lesson Quiz 9-4

Simplify. State any restrictions on the variable.

1. $\dfrac{x^2 + x - 6}{x^2 + 3x} \cdot \dfrac{x - 2}{x}$; $x \neq -3, 0$

2. $\dfrac{4x^2 - 25}{2x^2 + 3x - 20} \cdot \dfrac{2x + 5}{x + 4}$, $x \neq -4, \frac{5}{2}$

3. Multiply. State any restrictions on the variable.
$\dfrac{x^2 + 6x - 7}{x^2 + 5x} \cdot \dfrac{3x^2 + 16x + 5}{2x^2 + 7x - 9}$
$\dfrac{3x^2 + 22x + 7}{2x^2 + 9x}$; $x \neq -5, -\frac{9}{2}$, $0, 1$

4. Divide. State any restrictions on the variable.
$\dfrac{y^2 + 5y + 4}{y^2 - 49} \div \dfrac{2y^2 + 5y - 12}{y^2 + 9y + 14}$
$\dfrac{y^2 + 3y + 2}{2y^2 - 17y + 21}$; $y \neq -7, -4$, $-2, \frac{3}{2}, 7$

Alternative Assessment

Have students work in pairs. Ask one student to write three problems using Exercises 1, 12, and 17 as models. Ask the other student to write three problems using Exercises 3, 11, and 18 as models. Have each student work the problems written by the other. Then have students check one another's work.

Connection to Physics

Exercise 37 Be sure students understand the distinction between velocity and acceleration. Velocity is the rate of change of distance with respect to time. Acceleration is the rate of change of velocity with respect to time.

pages 501–503 Exercises

23. The student is not correct; $x = 2$ will make the denominator of $\frac{x}{x - 2}$ equal 0, so $x = 2$ is not a solution.

25. The numerator and the denominator have no common factors; check students' work.

B Apply Your Skills

19. $\dfrac{(x - 8)}{(x - 10)}$; $x \neq -3$ or 10

20. $\dfrac{(y + 6)}{(y - 2)}$; $y \neq 2$

21. $\dfrac{y(y + 3)}{12(y + 4)}$; $x \neq 0$, $y \neq -4$ or 3

24. Check students' work.

Exercise 26

27–35. See margin pp. 502–503.

C Challenge

Simplify each rational expression. State any restrictions on the variables.

19. $\dfrac{x^2 - 5x - 24}{x^2 - 7x - 30}$

20. $\dfrac{2y^2 + 8y - 24}{2y^2 - 8y + 8}$

21. $\dfrac{xy^3 - 9xy}{12xy^2 + 12xy - 144x}$

22. Write an expression for the area of the rectangle at the right. $\dfrac{6(a + 1)}{a - 3}$

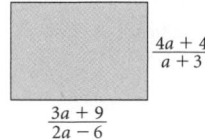
$\frac{4a + 4}{a + 3}$
$\frac{3a + 9}{2a - 6}$

23. **Error Analysis** A student claims that $x = 2$ is the only solution of the equation $\frac{x}{x - 2} = \frac{1}{2} + \frac{2}{x - 2}$. Is the student correct? Explain. **See margin.**

24. **Open-Ended** Write three rational expressions that simplify to $\frac{x}{x + 1}$.

25. **Writing** How can you tell whether a rational expression is in simplest form? Include an example with your explanation. **See margin.**

26. **Industrial Design** A storage tank will have a circular base of radius r and a height of r. The tank can be either cylindrical or hemispherical (half a sphere).
   a. Write and simplify an expression for the ratio of the volume of the hemispherical tank to its surface area (including the base). For a sphere, $V = \frac{4}{3}\pi r^3$ and S.A. $= 4\pi r^2$. **a–d. See margin.**
   b. Write and simplify an expression for the ratio of the volume of the cylindrical tank to its surface area (including the bases).
   c. Compare the ratios of volume to surface area for the two tanks.
   d. Compare the volumes of the two tanks.

Multiply or divide. State any restrictions on the variable.

27. $\dfrac{a + 3}{a^2 + a - 12} \div \dfrac{a^2 - 9}{a^2 + 7a + 12}$

28. $\dfrac{b^2 - 25}{(b + 5)^2} \div \dfrac{2b + 10}{4b + 20}$

29. $\dfrac{6x^3 - 6x^2}{x^4 + 5x^3} \div \dfrac{3x^2 - 15x + 12}{2x^2 + 2x - 40}$

30. $\dfrac{2x^2 - 6x}{x^2 + 18x + 81} \cdot \dfrac{9x + 81}{x^2 - 9}$

31. $\dfrac{x^2 - x - 2}{2x^2 - 5x + 2} \div \dfrac{x^2 - x - 12}{2x^2 + 5x - 3}$

32. $\dfrac{2x^2 + 5x + 2}{4x^2 - 1} \cdot \dfrac{2x^2 + x - 1}{x^2 + x - 2}$

Simplify. State any restrictions on the variables.

33. $\dfrac{(x^2 - x)^2}{x(x - 1)^{-2}(x^2 + 3x - 4)}$

34. $\dfrac{2x + 6}{(x - 1)^{-1}(x^2 + 2x - 3)}$

35. $\dfrac{54x^3 y^{-1}}{3x^{-2}y}$

36. The width of the rectangle at the right is $\frac{a + 10}{3a + 24} \cdot \frac{2(a + 8)}{2a + 5}$. Write an expression for the length of the rectangle.

$A = \frac{2a + 20}{6a + 15}$

37. **Physics** The acceleration of an object is a measure of how much its velocity changes in a given period of time.

acceleration $= \dfrac{\text{final velocity} - \text{initial velocity}}{\text{time}}$

Suppose you are riding a bicycle at 6 m/s. You step hard on the pedals and increase your speed to 12 m/s in about 5 s.
   a. Find your acceleration in m/s^2. **1.2 m/s^2**
   b. A sedan can go from 0 to 60 mi/h in about 10 s. What is the acceleration in m/s^2? (*Hints:* 1 mi $\approx$ 1609 m; 1 h $=$ 3600 s.) **2.68 m/s^2**

38. a. **Critical Thinking** Simplify $\frac{(2x^n)^2 - 1}{2x^n - 1}$, where x is an integer and n is a positive integer. (*Hint:* Factor the numerator.) **$2x^n + 1$**
   b. Use the result from part (a) to show that the value of the given expression is always an odd integer. **2 is a factor of $2x^n$, so $2x^n$ is even, and $2x^n + 1$ is odd.**

26a. $\dfrac{\frac{2}{3}\pi r^3}{2\pi r^2 + \pi r^2} = \dfrac{2r}{9}$

b. $\dfrac{\pi r^2(r)}{2\pi r^2 + 2\pi r(r)} = \dfrac{r}{4}$

c. The ratio for the cylindrical tank is always larger.

d. For a given value of r, the cylindrical tank will have a larger volume.

27. $\dfrac{a + 3}{(a - 3)(a - 3)}$; $a \neq -4$, -3, or 3

Use the fact that $\dfrac{\frac{a}{b}}{\frac{c}{d}} = \dfrac{a}{b} \div \dfrac{c}{d}$ to simplify each rational expression. State any restrictions on the variables.

39. $\dfrac{\frac{8x^2y}{x+1}}{\frac{6xy^2}{x+1}}$

$\dfrac{4x}{3y}; x \neq 0 \text{ or } -1, y \neq 0$

40. $\dfrac{\frac{3a^3b^3}{a-b}}{\frac{4ab}{b-a}}$

$-\dfrac{3a^2b^2}{4}; a \neq 0 \text{ or } b, b \neq 0$

41. $\dfrac{\frac{9m+6n}{m^2n^2}}{\frac{12m+8n}{5m^2}}$

$\dfrac{15}{4n^2}; m \neq 0 \text{ or } -\frac{2}{3}n, n \neq 0$

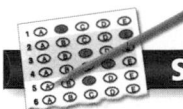

Standardized Test Prep

Multiple Choice

42. Which expression can be simplified to $\dfrac{x-1}{x-3}$? **D**

A. $\dfrac{x^2 - x - 6}{x^2 - x - 2}$

B. $\dfrac{x^2 - 2x + 1}{x^2 + 2x - 3}$

C. $\dfrac{x^2 - 3x - 4}{x^2 - 7x + 12}$

D. $\dfrac{x^2 - 4x + 3}{x^2 - 6x + 9}$

43. Which expression is in simplest form? **G**

F. $\dfrac{x^2 - x}{x^2 - 1}$

G. $\dfrac{x^2 - 1}{x^2 + 1}$

H. $\dfrac{x^2 - 1}{x + 1}$

I. $\dfrac{x + 3}{x^2 + 4x + 3}$

44. What is the product of $\dfrac{4x^2 - 1}{2x^2 - 5x - 3}$ and $\dfrac{x^2 - 6x + 9}{2x^2 + 5x - 3}$? **D**

A. 1

B. $x - 3$

C. $x + 3$

D. $\dfrac{x - 3}{x + 3}$

45. What are the restrictions on x when $\dfrac{x^2 - x - 2}{x^2 - 9}$ is divided by $\dfrac{x - 8}{x^2 + 10x + 25}$? **H**

F. $x \neq -3$ or -5

G. $x \neq 3, -3,$ or -5

H. $x \neq 3, -3, -5,$ or 8

I. $x \neq 2, 9, 8,$ or -25

Short Response

46. Let $f(x), g(x), h(x),$ and $k(x)$ be rational expressions. Explain how to find all the restrictions for $\dfrac{f(x)}{g(x)} \div \dfrac{h(x)}{k(x)}$. **See margin.**

Take It to the NET
Online lesson quiz at
www.PHSchool.com
········ Web Code: aga-0904

47. The product of $\dfrac{x^2 - 11x + 28}{x^2 - 2x - 35}$ and a second rational expression $\dfrac{f(x)}{g(x)}$ is $\dfrac{x + 4}{x + 5}$. What is the second rational expression? Show each step of your work. **See margin.**

Mixed Review

Lesson 9-3 | Describe the vertical asymptotes and holes for the graph of each rational function.

50. hole at $x = 4$, vertical asymptote at $x = -3$

48. $y = \dfrac{x - 3}{x - 3}$
hole at $x = 3$

49. $y = \dfrac{x - 1}{(3x + 2)(x + 1)}$
vertical asymptotes at $x = -\frac{2}{3}$ and $x = -1$

50. $y = \dfrac{(x - 4)(x + 5)}{(x + 3)(x - 4)}$

Lesson 8-3 | Evaluate each logarithm.

51. $\log_4 64$ **3**

52. $\log_2 \frac{1}{32}$ **−5**

53. $\log_5 5\sqrt{5}$ $\frac{3}{2}$

54. $\log_{16} 8$ $\frac{3}{4}$

Lesson 7-5 | Solve each equation.

55. $\sqrt{x + 3} - 1 = 4$ **$x = 22$**

56. $\sqrt{7x + 1} - \sqrt{6x + 7} = 0$ **$x = 6$**

Standardized Test Prep

Resources
For additional practice with a variety of test item formats:
• Standardized Test Prep, p. 531
• Test-Taking Strategies, p. 526
• Test-Taking Strategies with Transparencies

Exercise 47 It is all right to give an answer in simplified form or non-simplified form.

28. $\dfrac{2(b - 5)}{b + 5}; b \neq -5$

29. $\dfrac{4}{x}; x \neq 0, -5, 4,$ or 1

30. $\dfrac{18x}{(x + 9)(x + 3)}; x \neq -9, -3,$ or 3

31. $\dfrac{x + 1}{x - 4}; x \neq -3, \frac{1}{2}, 2,$ or 4

32. $\dfrac{x + 1}{x - 1}; x \neq -\frac{1}{2}, \frac{1}{2}, 1,$ or −2

33. $\dfrac{x(x - 1)^3}{(x + 4)}, x \neq -4, 0, 1$

34. $2, x \neq -3, 1$

35. $\dfrac{18x^5}{y^2}, y \neq 0$

46. [2] $\dfrac{f(x)}{g(x)} \div \dfrac{h(x)}{k(x)} = \dfrac{f(x)}{g(x)} \cdot \dfrac{k(x)}{h(x)}$

The restrictions are all the values of x that make any denominator equal zero, so the restrictions are that $g(x) \neq 0, k(x) \neq 0,$ and $h(x) \neq 0$.

[1] incomplete answer

47. [2]
$\dfrac{x^2 - 11x + 28}{x^2 - 2x - 35} \cdot \dfrac{f(x)}{g(x)} = \dfrac{x + 4}{x + 5}$

$\dfrac{f(x)}{g(x)} = \dfrac{x + 4}{x + 5} \div \dfrac{x^2 - 11x + 28}{x^2 - 2x - 35}$

$= \dfrac{x + 4}{x + 5} \cdot \dfrac{x^2 - 2x - 35}{x^2 - 11x + 28}$

$= \dfrac{x + 4}{x + 5} \cdot \dfrac{(x - 7)(x + 5)}{(x - 7)(x - 4)}$

$= \dfrac{x + 4}{x - 4}$

[1] answer only, with no work shown OR one mistake, such as in factoring

1. Plan

Lesson Preview

✓ **Check Skills You'll Need**

Operations with Fractions
Skills Handbook: page 843,
Examples 1, 2, Exercises 1–10

Lesson Resources

📁 **Teaching Resources**
Practice, Reteaching, Enrichment
Checkpoint Quiz 2

👥 **Reaching All Students**
Practice Workbook 9-5
Spanish Practice Workbook 9-5
Reading and Math Literacy 9C
Spanish Reading & Literacy 9C
Spanish Checkpoint Quiz 2

⏱ **Presentation Assistant Plus!**
Transparencies
• Check Skills You'll Need 9-5
• Additional Examples 9-5
• Student Edition Answers 9-5
• Lesson Quiz 9-5
PH Presentation Pro CD 9-5

ⓟ ASSESSMENT SYSTEM

Checkpoint Quiz 2
Computer Test Generator CD

💻 **Technology**
Resource Pro® CD-ROM
Computer Test Generator CD
Prentice Hall Presentation Pro CD

🖥 **www.PHSchool.com**
Student Site
• Teacher Web Code: agk-5500
• Self-grading Lesson Quiz
Teacher Center
• Lesson Planner
• Resources

Plus

9-5 Adding and Subtracting Rational Expressions

North Carolina Objectives

1.03 Operate with algebraic expressions (polynomial, rational, complex fractions) to solve problems.

Lesson Preview

What You'll Learn

OBJECTIVE 1 To add and subtract rational expressions

OBJECTIVE 2 To simplify complex fractions

. . . And Why

To find the focal length of a camera lens, as in Example 1

New Vocabulary • complex fraction

✓ **Check Skills You'll Need** (For help, go to Skills Handbook page 843.)

Find the least common multiple of the two numbers.

1. 7, 21 **21** **2.** 6, 10 **30** **3.** 11, 17 **187** **4.** 30, 105 **210**

Add or subtract.

5. $\frac{5}{19} + \frac{7}{38}$ **$\frac{17}{38}$** **6.** $\frac{2}{15} + \frac{3}{25}$ **$\frac{19}{75}$** **7.** $\frac{7}{24} - \frac{5}{36}$ **$\frac{11}{72}$** **8.** $\frac{11}{12} - \frac{7}{45}$ **$\frac{137}{180}$**

OBJECTIVE 1

📱 Interactive lesson includes instant self-check, tutorials, and activities.

Adding and Subtracting Rational Expressions

> **Investigation: Graphs of Inverse Variations**
>
> **1.** Add. Simplify where possible.
>
> **a.** $\frac{2}{x} + \frac{3}{x}$ $\frac{5}{x}$ **b.** $\frac{4}{3x} + \frac{2}{3x}$ $\frac{2}{x}$ **c.** $\frac{3c}{2c-1} + \frac{5c+1}{2c-1}$ $\frac{8c+1}{2c-1}$
>
> **2.** Explain the steps you followed in Question 1.
>
> **3.** How is adding rational expressions similar to adding fractions?
>
> **2–3. See back of book.**

To produce a clear photograph, light rays must be focused on the film. The focal length of a camera lens is the distance from the lens to the point where parallel rays of light are focused.

When you focus a camera, you change the distance from the lens to the film.

The lens equation is $\frac{1}{f} = \frac{1}{d_i} + \frac{1}{d_o}$.

f = focal length of the lens

d_i = distance from the lens to the film

d_o = distance from the lens to the object

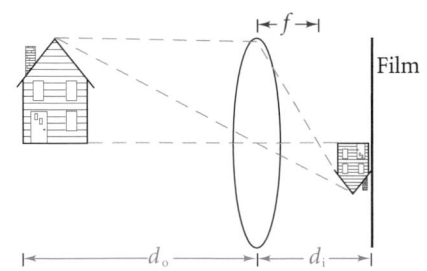

🔄 Ongoing Assessment and Intervention

Before the Lesson	**During the Lesson**	**After the Lesson**
Diagnose prerequisite skills using:	**Monitor progress using:**	**Assess knowledge using:**
• Check Skills You'll Need	• Check Understanding • Additional Examples • Standardized Test Prep	• Lesson Quiz • Computer Test Generator CD • Chapter Checkpoint 2 (p. 510)

1 EXAMPLE Real-World Connection

Photography An object is 15 cm from a camera lens. The object is in focus on the film when the lens is 10 cm from the film. Find the focal length of the lens.

$\frac{1}{f} = \frac{1}{d_i} + \frac{1}{d_o}$ **Use the lens equation.**

$\frac{1}{f} = \frac{1}{10} + \frac{1}{15}$ **Substitute.**

$= \frac{3}{30} + \frac{2}{30}$ **Write equivalent fractions with the LCD.**

$= \frac{5}{30} = \frac{1}{6}$ **Add and simplify.**

Since $\frac{1}{f} = \frac{1}{6}$, the focal length of the lens is 6 cm.

✓ **Check Understanding** ❶ Suppose an object is 20 cm from a camera lens. When the object is properly focused, the lens is 5 cm from the film. Find the focal length of the lens. **4 cm**

Need Help?

For practice in adding and subtracting fractions, go to p. 843.

To add or subtract rational expressions with different denominators, you must write all the expressions with a common denominator. It is easiest to use the least common denominator (LCD). To do this, find the least common multiple of the denominators.

2 EXAMPLE Finding Least Common Multiples

Find the least common multiple of $4x^2 - 36$ and $6x^2 + 36x + 54$.

Step 1 Find the prime factors of each expression.

$4x^2 - 36 = 4(x^2 - 9) = (2)(2)(x - 3)(x + 3)$

$6x^2 + 36x + 54 = 6(x^2 + 6x + 9) = (2)(3)(x + 3)(x + 3)$

Step 2 Write each prime factor the greatest number of times it appears in either expression. Simplify where possible.

$(2)(2)(3)(x - 3)(x + 3)(x + 3) = 12(x - 3)(x + 3)^2$

The least common multiple is $12(x - 3)(x + 3)^2$.

✓ **Check Understanding** ❷ Find the least common multiple of each pair of expressions.
a. $3x^2 - 9x - 30$ and $6x + 30$ **b.** $5x^2 + 15x + 10$ and $2x^2 - 8$
    $6(x - 5)(x + 5)(x + 2)$ $10(x + 2)(x - 2)(x + 1)$

3 EXAMPLE Adding Rational Expressions

Simplify $\dfrac{1}{x^2 + 5x + 4} + \dfrac{5x}{3x + 3}$.

$\dfrac{1}{x^2 + 5x + 4} + \dfrac{5x}{3x + 3} = \dfrac{1}{(x + 1)(x + 4)} + \dfrac{5x}{3(x + 1)}$ **Factor the denominators.**

$= \dfrac{1}{(x + 1)(x + 4)} \cdot \dfrac{3}{3} + \dfrac{5x}{3(x + 1)} \cdot \dfrac{x + 4}{x + 4}$ **identity for multiplication**

$= \dfrac{3}{3(x + 1)(x + 4)} + \dfrac{5x(x + 4)}{3(x + 1)(x + 4)}$ **Multiply.**

$= \dfrac{3 + 5x(x + 4)}{3(x + 1)(x + 4)}$ **Add.**

$= \dfrac{5x^2 + 20x + 3}{3(x + 1)(x + 4)}$ **Simplify the numerator.**

Lesson 9-5 Adding and Subtracting Rational Expressions   **505**

---

2. Teach

Professional Development

Math Background

Addition and subtraction of rational expressions is much like addition and subtraction of rational numbers. First find the least common denominator for the rational expressions. Next, rewrite both expressions using this common denominator. Finally, add or subtract the fractions and simplify the result.

OBJECTIVE

❶ **Teaching Notes**

Investigation
Teaching Tip
For each part of Question 1, point out that both expressions have the same denominator. Ask students to make a conjecture about how they might add rational expressions with different denominators.

3 EXAMPLE Teaching Tip

Write $\frac{2}{3} + \frac{3}{4}$ on the board. Invite a volunteer to write the steps for adding the fractions on the board. Have the student explain the work. Help students understand that the steps in Example 3 are the same as the steps on the board.

Additional Examples

❶ An object is 24 cm from a camera lens. The object is in focus on the film when the lens is 12 cm from the film. Find the focal length of the lens. **8 cm**

❷ Find the least common multiple of $2x^2 - 8x + 8$ and $15x^2 - 60$. **$30(x + 2)(x - 2)^2$**

❸ Simplify

$\dfrac{1}{3x^2 + 21x + 30} + \dfrac{4x}{3x + 15}$.

$\dfrac{4x^2 + 8x + 1}{3(x + 2)(x + 5)}$

🧑‍🤝‍🧑 Reaching All Students

Below Level Review the definitions of least common multiple (LCM) and least common denominator (LCD).	**Advanced Learners** Challenge students to find the values of A and B if $\frac{A}{x + 1} + \frac{B}{x + 4} = \frac{5x + 11}{(x + 1)(x + 4)}$.	**English Learners** See note on page 508. **Error Prevention** See note on page 508.

505

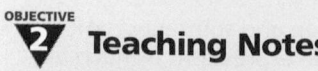

Additional Examples

4 Simplify $\dfrac{2x}{x^2 - 2x - 3} - \dfrac{3}{4x + 4}$.

$\dfrac{5x + 9}{4(x + 1)(x - 3)}$

5 EXAMPLE Alternative Method

You can combine ideas from Methods I and II. Consider Method II. After simplifying the numerator and the denominator of the original complex fraction to get $\dfrac{\frac{1 + 3x}{x}}{\frac{5 + 4y}{y}}$, multiply both numerator and denominator by their common denominator xy. Simplifying the numerator and denominator of the resulting complex fraction yields $\dfrac{(1 + 3x)y}{(5 + 4y)x}$ or $\dfrac{y + 3xy}{5x + 4xy}$.

Additional Examples

5 Simplify $\dfrac{\frac{1}{x} + \frac{1}{y}}{\frac{2}{y} - \frac{1}{x}}$. $\dfrac{x + y}{2x - y}$

Closure

Ask students to explain how they add or subtract two rational expressions. Then ask them to explain how they simplify a complex fraction. **Answers may vary. Sample: To add or subtract two rational expressions, write them so that they have a common denominator. Add or subtract the numerators, and keep the same common denominator. Then simplify. To simplify a complex fraction, perform any operations indicated in the numerator and denominator. Then divide the numerator of the resulting complex fraction by the denominator.**

✓ **Check Understanding** **3** Simplify $\dfrac{1}{x^2 - 4x - 12} + \dfrac{3x}{4x + 8}$. $\dfrac{3x^2 - 18x + 4}{4(x - 6)(x + 2)}$

4 EXAMPLE Subtracting Rational Expressions

Simplify $\dfrac{7y}{5y^2 - 125} - \dfrac{4}{3y + 15}$.

$\dfrac{7y}{5y^2 - 125} - \dfrac{4}{3y + 15} = \dfrac{7y}{5(y + 5)(y - 5)} - \dfrac{4}{3(y + 5)}$ Factor the denominators.

$= \dfrac{7y}{5(y + 5)(y - 5)} \cdot \dfrac{3}{3} - \dfrac{4}{3(y + 5)} \cdot \dfrac{5(y - 5)}{5(y - 5)}$ identity for multiplication

$= \dfrac{(3)(7y)}{(3)(5)(y + 5)(y - 5)} - \dfrac{(4)(5)(y - 5)}{(3)(5)(y + 5)(y - 5)}$ Multiply.

$= \dfrac{(3)(7y) - (4)(5)(y - 5)}{(3)(5)(y + 5)(y - 5)}$ Simplify.

$= \dfrac{y + 100}{15(y + 5)(y - 5)}$ Simplify.

✓ **Check Understanding** **4** Simplify each expression.

a. $\dfrac{-2}{3x^2 + 36x + 105} - \dfrac{3x}{6x + 30}$

$\dfrac{-3x^2 - 21x - 4}{6(x + 5)(x + 7)}$

b. $\dfrac{x}{3x^2 - 9x + 6} - \dfrac{2x + 1}{3x^2 + 3x - 6}$

$\dfrac{-x^2 + 5x + 2}{3(x - 1)(x - 2)(x + 2)}$

OBJECTIVE

2 Simplifying Complex Fractions

Need Help?

Note that the complex fractions below are *not* equivalent.

$\dfrac{\frac{a}{b}}{c}$ $\dfrac{a}{\frac{b}{c}}$

A **complex fraction** is a fraction that has a fraction in its numerator or denominator or in both its numerator and denominator. Here are some examples.

$\dfrac{\frac{1}{x}}{y}$ $\dfrac{3}{1 - \frac{1}{2y}}$ $\dfrac{\frac{x - 2}{x} - \frac{2}{x + 1}}{\frac{3}{x - 1} - \frac{1}{x + 1}}$

To simplify a complex fraction such as $\dfrac{\frac{a}{b}}{\frac{c}{d}}$ you can multiply the numerator $\frac{a}{b}$ and denominator $\frac{c}{d}$ by their LCD bd. Or you can divide the numerator $\frac{a}{b}$ by the denominator $\frac{c}{d}$.

5 EXAMPLE Simplifying Complex Fractions

Simplify $\dfrac{\frac{1}{x} + 3}{\frac{5}{y} + 4}$.

Method I First find the LCD of all the rational expressions.

$\dfrac{\frac{1}{x} + 3}{\frac{5}{y} + 4} = \dfrac{\left(\frac{1}{x} + 3\right) \cdot xy}{\left(\frac{5}{y} + 4\right) \cdot xy}$ The LCD is *xy*. Multiply the numerator and denominator by *xy*.

$= \dfrac{\frac{1}{x} \cdot xy + 3 \cdot xy}{\frac{5}{y} \cdot xy + 4 \cdot xy}$ Use the Distributive Property.

$= \dfrac{y + 3xy}{5x + 4xy}$ Simplify.

Method 2 First simplify the numerator and denominator.

$$\frac{\frac{1}{x}+3}{\frac{5}{y}+4} = \frac{\frac{1}{x}+\frac{3x}{x}}{\frac{5}{y}+\frac{4y}{y}}$$ Write equivalent expressions with common denominators.

$$= \frac{\frac{1+3x}{x}}{\frac{5+4y}{y}}$$ Add.

$$= \frac{1+3x}{x} \div \frac{5+4y}{y}$$ Divide the numerator fraction by the denominator fraction.

$$= \frac{1+3x}{x} \cdot \frac{y}{5+4y}$$ Multiply by the reciprocal.

$$= \frac{(1+3x)y}{x(5+4y)}$$

$$= \frac{y+3xy}{5x+4xy}$$

✓ **Check Understanding** ⑤ Simplify each complex fraction.

a. $\dfrac{\frac{1}{x}}{\frac{1}{y}}$ $\frac{1}{xy}$

b. $\dfrac{3}{1-\frac{1}{2y}}$ $\frac{6y}{2y-1}$

c. $\dfrac{\frac{x-2}{x}-\frac{2}{x+1}}{\frac{3}{x-1}-\frac{1}{x+1}}$

$\frac{x^3-4x+x+2}{2x^3+4x}$

EXERCISES

For more practice, see *Extra Practice*.

Practice and Problem Solving

Ⓐ **Practice by Example**

The focal length f of a camera lens is 2 in. The lens equation is $\frac{1}{f} = \frac{1}{d_i} + \frac{1}{d_o}$, where d_i is the distance between the lens and the film and d_o is the distance between the lens and the object.

Example 1
(page 505)

1. The object to be photographed is 10 ft away. How far should the lens be from the film? $\frac{120}{59} \approx 2.03$ in.

2. The object to be photographed is 20 ft away. How far should the lens be from the film? $\frac{240}{119} \approx 2.02$ in.

3. Critical Thinking Explain why one setting on the camera is used for photographing all objects that are more than 10 ft from the camera.
For distances greater than 10 ft, d_i is nearly constant.

Example 2
(page 505)

Find the least common multiple of each pair of polynomials. **4–7. See margin.**

4. $9(x+2)(2x-1)$ and $3(x+2)$

5. x^2-1 and x^2+2x+1

6. $(x-2)(x+3)$ and $10(x+3)^2$

7. $12x^2-6x-126$ and $18x-63$

8. $5y^2-80$ and $y+4$
$5(y+4)(y-4)$

9. $x^2-32x-10$ and $2x+10$
$2(x+5)(x^2-32x-10)$

Example 3
(page 505)

Simplify each sum.

10. $\dfrac{1}{2x}+\dfrac{1}{2x}$ $\frac{1}{x}$

11. $\dfrac{d-3}{2d+1}+\dfrac{d-1}{2d+1}$ $\frac{2(d-2)}{2d+1}$

13. $\dfrac{7x^2+20x-18}{(x-3)(x+3)(x+4)}$

12. $\dfrac{5y+2}{xy^2}+\dfrac{2x-4}{4xy}$ $\frac{xy+8y+4}{2xy^2}$

13. $\dfrac{5x}{x^2-9}+\dfrac{2}{x+4}$

15. $\dfrac{5x^2+14x-12}{(x-3)(x+2)^2}$

14. $\dfrac{-3x}{x^2-9}+\dfrac{4}{2x-6}$ $\frac{-x+6}{(x-3)(x+3)}$

15. $\dfrac{5x}{x^2-x-6}+\dfrac{4}{x^2+4x+4}$

3. Practice

Assignment Guide

▼**1** Objective
　Ⓐ Ⓑ **Core** 1–21, 31–43

▼**2** Objective
　Ⓐ Ⓑ **Core** 22–30, 44–53
　Ⓒ **Extension** 54, 55

Standardized Test Prep 56–61

Mixed Review 62–74

Exercises 4–9 Remind students to begin by writing each polynomial in factored form.

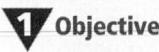

Enrichment 9-5

Reteaching 9-5

Practice 9-5

pages 507–510   Exercises

4. $9(x+2)(2x-1)$

5. $(x-1)(x+1)(x+1)$

6. $10(x-2)(x+3)^2$

7. $18(2x-7)(x+3)$

Example 4
(page 506)

Simplify each difference.

16. $\dfrac{-2}{x} - \dfrac{1}{x}$ $-\dfrac{3}{x}$

17. $\dfrac{-5y}{2y - 1} - \dfrac{y + 3}{2y - 1}$ $\dfrac{-3(2y + 1)}{2y - 1}$

18. $\dfrac{y}{2y + 4} - \dfrac{3}{y + 2}$ $\dfrac{y - 6}{2(y + 2)}$

19. $\dfrac{x}{3x + 9} - \dfrac{8}{x^2 + 3x}$ $\dfrac{x^2 - 24}{3x(x + 3)}$

20. $\dfrac{3y}{y^2 - 25} - \dfrac{8}{y - 5}$ $\dfrac{-5(y + 8)}{(y - 5)(y + 5)}$

21. $\dfrac{2x}{x^2 - x - 2} - \dfrac{4x}{x^2 - 3x + 2}$
$\dfrac{-2x(x + 3)}{(x - 2)(x - 1)(x + 1)}$

Example 5
(page 506)

Simplify each complex fraction.

22. $\dfrac{\frac{1}{x}}{\frac{2}{y}}$ $\dfrac{y}{2x}$

23. $\dfrac{1 - \frac{1}{4}}{2 - \frac{3}{5}}$ $\dfrac{15}{28}$

24. $\dfrac{\frac{2}{x + y}}{3}$ $\dfrac{2}{3(x + y)}$

25. $\dfrac{\frac{1}{3}}{\frac{3}{b}}$ $\dfrac{b}{9}$

26. $\dfrac{1}{1 + \frac{x}{y}}$ $\dfrac{y}{x + y}$

27. $\dfrac{3}{\frac{2}{x} + y}$ $\dfrac{3x}{2 + xy}$

28. $\dfrac{\frac{2}{x + y}}{\frac{5}{x + y}}$ $\dfrac{2}{5}$

29. $\dfrac{\frac{3}{x - 4}}{1 - \frac{2}{x - 4}}$ $\dfrac{3}{x - 6}$

30. $\dfrac{-3}{\frac{5}{x} + y}$ $\dfrac{-3x}{5 + xy}$

Ⓑ Apply Your Skills

Add or subtract. Simplify where possible.

31. $\dfrac{3}{4x} - \dfrac{2}{x^2}$ $\dfrac{3x - 8}{4x^2}$

32. $\dfrac{3}{x + 1} + \dfrac{x}{x - 1}$ $\dfrac{x^2 + 4x - 3}{(x + 1)(x - 1)}$

33. $\dfrac{2x}{x^2 - 1} - \dfrac{1}{x^2}$ $\dfrac{2x^3 - x^2 + 1}{x^2(x + 1)(x - 1)}$

34. $\dfrac{4}{x^2 - 9} + \dfrac{7}{x + 3}$ $\dfrac{7x - 17}{(x - 3)(x + 3)}$

35. $\dfrac{x + 2}{x - 1} - \dfrac{x - 3}{2x + 1}$ $\dfrac{x^2 + 9x - 1}{(x - 1)(2x + 1)}$

36. $\dfrac{x}{2x^2 - x} + \dfrac{1}{2x}$ $\dfrac{4x - 1}{2x(2x - 1)}$

37. $\dfrac{5x^2 + 6x + 12}{(x - 3)(x + 2)^2}$

37. $\dfrac{5x}{x^2 - x - 6} - \dfrac{4}{x^2 + 4x + 4}$

38. $3x + \dfrac{x^2 + 5x}{x^2 - 2}$ $\dfrac{x(3x^2 + x - 1)}{x^2 - 2}$

39. $4y - \dfrac{y + 2}{y^2 + 3y}$ $\dfrac{4y^3 + 12y^2 - y - 2}{y(y + 3)}$

40. $\dfrac{5y}{y^2 - 7y} - \dfrac{4}{2y - 14} + \dfrac{9}{y}$ $\dfrac{3(4y - 21)}{y(y - 7)}$

41. Open-Ended Write two rational expressions whose sum is $\dfrac{x - 2}{x + 4}$.
Check students' work.

42. Factoring is used to determine the least common multiple of the denominators; check students' work.

42. Writing Explain how factoring is used when adding or subtracting rational expressions. Include an example in your explanation.

43. Error Analysis How would you convince a student that $\dfrac{7x + 25}{x^2 - 9}$ is *not* the sum of $\dfrac{4}{x^2 - 9}$ and $\dfrac{7}{x + 3}$?

43. Answers may vary. Sample: Substitute 0 for *x* in the three expressions, and show that $\dfrac{4}{-9} + \dfrac{7}{3} \neq \dfrac{25}{-9}$.

Simplify each complex fraction.

44. $\dfrac{\frac{2}{x} + \frac{3}{y}}{\frac{-5}{x} + \frac{7}{y}}$ $\dfrac{3x + 2y}{7x - 5y}$

45. $\dfrac{\frac{5}{x} - \frac{2}{y}}{\frac{-4}{x} - \frac{6}{y}}$ $\dfrac{2x - 5y}{2(3x + 2y)}$

46. $\dfrac{1 + \frac{2}{x}}{2 + \frac{3}{2x}}$ $\dfrac{2(x + 2)}{4x + 3}$

47. $\dfrac{\frac{1}{xy} - \frac{1}{y^2}}{\frac{1}{x^2y} - \frac{1}{xy^2}}$ x

48. $\dfrac{\frac{2}{x + 4} + 2}{1 + \frac{3}{x + 4}}$ $\dfrac{2(x + 5)}{x + 7}$

49. $\dfrac{\frac{3}{x - 2} - 5}{2 - \frac{4}{x - 2}}$ $\dfrac{-5x + 13}{2(x - 4)}$

50. Open-Ended Write two different complex fractions that simplify to $\dfrac{x - 2}{x + 4}$.
Check students' work.

51. Critical Thinking What real numbers are not in the domain of function f? Explain.
$f(x) = \dfrac{\frac{x + 1}{x + 2}}{\frac{x + 3}{x + 4}}$ **$x \neq -2, -3, -4$; those values result in division by 0, which is undefined.**

Real-World  **Connection**

Shortening a guitar string to $\frac{1}{2}$ or $\frac{2}{3}$ its original length produces a sound in harmony with its original pitch.

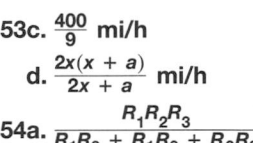

C **Challenge**

53c. $\frac{400}{9}$ mi/h

d. $\frac{2x(x + a)}{2x + a}$ mi/h

54a. $\frac{R_1 R_2 R_3}{R_1 R_2 + R_1 R_3 + R_2 R_3}$

52. Music Another kind of average is the harmonic mean. The harmonic mean of two numbers a and b equals $\dfrac{2}{\frac{1}{a} + \frac{1}{b}}$. As you vary the length of a violin or guitar string, its pitch changes. If a full-length string is 1 unit long, then many lengths that are simple fractions produce pitches that harmonize, or sound pleasing together. The harmonic mean relates three lengths that produce harmonious sounds. For example, $\frac{1}{3}$ is the harmonic mean of $\frac{1}{2}$ and $\frac{1}{4}$, and strings of these lengths produce harmonious sounds. Find the harmonic mean for strings of lengths 1 and $\frac{1}{2}$, $\frac{3}{4}$ and $\frac{1}{2}$, and $\frac{3}{4}$ and $\frac{3}{5}$. **$\frac{2}{3}, \frac{3}{5}, \frac{2}{3}$**

53. a. If you jog 12 mi at an average rate of 4 mi/h and walk the same route back at an average rate of 3 mi/h, you have traveled 24 mi in 7 h and your overall rate is $\frac{24}{7}$ mi/h. What is your overall average rate if you travel d mi at 3 mi/h and d mi at 4 mi/h? **$\frac{24}{7}$ mi/h**

   b. Harmonic Mean Find the harmonic mean (see Exercise 52) of 3 and 4. **$\frac{24}{7}$**

   c. If you travel any distance at x mi/h and the same distance at y mi/h then your average rate for the trip is the harmonic mean of x and y. Find the average rate of speed if you travel to a distant city at 50 mi/h and return at 40 mi/h.

   d. You travel to a city at x mi/h and the return trip is a mi/h faster. Express your average rate in terms of x and a.

54. Electricity The total resistance R for a parallel circuit with three bulbs is $R = \dfrac{1}{\frac{1}{R_1} + \frac{1}{R_2} + \frac{1}{R_3}}$.

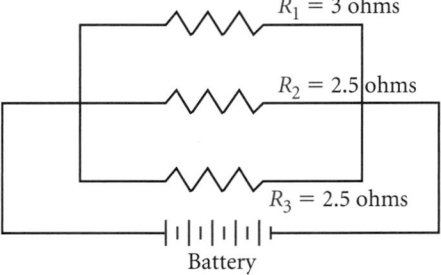

$R_1 = 3$ ohms

$R_2 = 2.5$ ohms

$R_3 = 2.5$ ohms

Battery

   a. Simplify the right side of the equation.

   b. Find the total resistance R of a parallel circuit with bulbs that have resistances of 3 ohms, 2.5 ohms, and 2.5 ohms. **0.88 ohms**

55. Physics Use the camera lens equation $\frac{1}{f} = \frac{1}{d_i} + \frac{1}{d_o}$, where d_i is the distance from the lens to the film and d_o is the distance from the lens to an object.

   a. Solve the lens equation for f by taking the reciprocal of each side of the equation. Simplify the equation so it contains no complex fraction.

   b. When an object is in focus, a lens is x cm from the object and $(2x + 1)$ cm from the film. Find the focal length of the lens.

   a. $f = \dfrac{d_i d_o}{d_i + d_o}$ **b.** $\dfrac{x(2x + 1)}{3x + 1} = f$

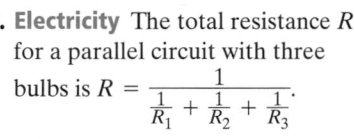

Standardized Test Prep

Multiple Choice

56. Find the least common multiple of $x^2 - 1$ and $x^2 - x$. **B**
   A. $x - 1$
   B. $x(x - 1)(x + 1)$
   C. $x(x - 1)^2(x + 1)$
   D. $(x - 1)^2(x + 1)^2 x^2$

57. Which expression equals $\dfrac{1}{x^2 - 2x - 3} + \dfrac{1}{x^2 - 4x + 3}$? **H**

   F. $\dfrac{2x - 1}{(x - 1)(x + 3)(x + 1)}$ **G.** $\dfrac{2x + 1}{(x - 1)(x + 1)(x - 3)}$

   H. $\dfrac{2x}{(x - 1)(x + 1)(x - 3)}$ **I.** $\dfrac{2x}{(x + 3)(x - 1)(x + 1)}$

Lesson 9-5 Adding and Subtracting Rational Expressions   **509**

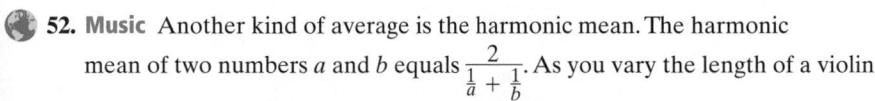

Lesson Quiz 9-5

1. The lens equation for a camera is $\frac{1}{f} = \frac{1}{d_i} + \frac{1}{d_o}$, where f is the focal length of the lens, d_i is the distance between the lens and the film, and d_o is the distance between the lens and the object. For a certain camera, an object that is 18 cm from the lens is in focus when the lens is 9 cm from the film. What is the focal length of the lens? **6 cm**

2. Find the least common multiple of $x(x^2 - 5x + 6)$ and $x^3(x^2 + 4x - 21)$. **$x^3(x - 2)(x - 3)(x + 7)$**

Simplify.

3. $\dfrac{x}{x^2 - 4} + \dfrac{7}{3x + 6}$ $\dfrac{10x - 14}{3x^2 - 12}$

4. $\dfrac{m}{m + 3} - \dfrac{6m}{m^2 - 9}$ $\dfrac{m^2 - 9m}{m^2 - 9}$

5. $\dfrac{\frac{2y}{2y + 1} - 1}{1 - \frac{2y}{2y - 1}}$ $\dfrac{2y - 1}{2y + 1}$

Alternative Assessment

Have students work individually. Each student writes two rational expressions with binomial numerators. One rational expression should have $x^2 - 4$ as its denominator, and the other should have $x + 2$ as its denominator. They find the sum and difference of their expressions. Then have each student write a complex fraction that has the original expressions as numerator and denominator. The student then simplifies the complex fraction.

Standardized Test Prep

Resources

For additional practice with a variety of test item formats:
- Standardized Test Prep, p. 531
- Test-Taking Strategies, p. 526
- Test-Taking Strategies with Transparencies

509

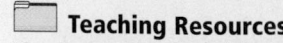
To check understanding of Lessons 9-4 to 9-5:

Checkpoint Quiz 2 (p. 510)

📁 **Teaching Resources**
Checkpoint Quiz 2 (also in Prentice Hall Assessment System)

👥 **Reaching All Students**
Reading and Math Literacy 9C

Spanish versions available

---

pages 507–510 Exercises

60. [2] First factor both denominators:
$x^2 - 5x - 6$
$= (x - 6)(x + 1)$
$x^2 - 12x + 36$
$= (x - 6)^2$. The least common denominator would have to include the factors $(x - 6)$, $(x + 1)$ and $(x - 6)^2$, so the LCD is
$(x - 6)^2(x + 1)$
$= x^3 - 11x^2 + 24x + 36$.

[1] answer only, no work shown

61. [4] $\dfrac{2 - \frac{15}{x}}{\frac{3}{x}} = 9$

$\dfrac{\frac{2x}{x} - \frac{15}{x}}{\frac{3}{x}} = 9$

Find a common denominator for the numerator.
$\dfrac{\frac{2x - 15}{x}}{\frac{3}{x}} = 9$

Combine the numerators.
$\dfrac{2x - 15}{x} \cdot \dfrac{x}{3} = 9$

Multiply the numerator by the reciprocal of the denominator.
$\dfrac{2x - 15}{3} = 9$

Solve for x.
$2x - 15 = 27$
$2x = 42$
$x = 21$

[3] one calculation error

510

---

58. Which expression equals $\dfrac{5x}{x^2 - 9} - \dfrac{4x}{x^2 + 5x + 6}$? **C**

A. $\dfrac{7x}{(x - 3)(x + 3)(x + 2)}$ **B.** $\dfrac{x^2 - 2x}{(x - 3)(x + 3)(x + 2)}$

C. $\dfrac{x^2 + 22x}{(x - 3)(x + 3)(x + 2)}$ **D.** $\dfrac{9x^2 - 2x}{(x - 3)(x + 3)(x + 2)}$

 Take It to the NET
Online lesson quiz at
www.PHSchool.com
Web Code: aga-0905

59. Simplify $\dfrac{\frac{2}{x} - 5}{\frac{6}{x} - 3}$. **F**

F. $\dfrac{2 - 5x}{6 - 3x}$ **G.** $\dfrac{2 + 5x}{6 - 3x}$ **H.** $\dfrac{2x - 5}{6x + 3}$ **I.** $\dfrac{6 + 3x}{2 - 5x}$

Short Response

60. Find the least common denominator for the rational expressions $\dfrac{1}{x^2 - 5x - 6}$ and $\dfrac{1}{x^2 - 12x + 36}$. Show your work. **See margin.**

61. Solve the equation $\dfrac{2 - \frac{15}{x}}{\frac{3}{x}} = 9$. Show your work. **See margin.**

Mixed Review

Lesson 9-4

Divide. State any restrictions on the variables.

63. $\dfrac{1}{4xy}$; $a \ne 0, b \ne 0,$ $x \ne 0, y \ne 0$

65. $\dfrac{12x}{x + 3}$; $x \ne -3, 2,$ or 3

66. $\dfrac{3(x - 2)}{4(x - 3)}$; $x \ne -2, 2,$ or 3

67. $\dfrac{3(x + 1)}{2(x + 3)}$; $x \ne 1, -1,$ or -3

62. $\dfrac{4x^3}{3y^4} \div \dfrac{16x^2}{9y^2}$ $\dfrac{3x}{4y^2}$; $x \ne 0, y \ne 0$

63. $\dfrac{7ax^3}{8by^2} \div \dfrac{14ax^4}{4by}$

64. $\dfrac{6x^2}{y} \div \dfrac{12x^4}{y^3} \cdot \dfrac{y^2}{2x}$; $x \ne 0, y \ne 0$

65. $\dfrac{3x^2 - 9x}{x - 2} \div \dfrac{x^2 - 9}{4x - 8}$

66. $\dfrac{3x - 6}{12x + 24} \div \dfrac{x^2 - 5x + 6}{3x^2 - 12}$

67. $\dfrac{5x + 15}{10x - 10} \div \dfrac{x^2 + 6x + 9}{3x^2 - 3}$

Lesson 8-4

Write each expression as a single logarithm.

68. $\log_3 y + 4 \log_3 t$ **69.** $7 \log_{10} p + \log_{10} q$ **70.** $\log_5 x - \frac{1}{5} \log_5 y$
$\log_3 t^4 y$ $\log_{10} p^7 q$ $\log_5 \frac{x}{\sqrt[5]{y}}$

Lesson 7-6

Let $f(x) = x^2 + 1$ and $g(x) = 3x$. Find each value.

71. $(g \circ f)(-3)$ **72.** $(f \circ g)(-3)$ **73.** $(g \circ f)\left(\frac{1}{2}\right)$ **74.** $(f \circ f)(3)$
30   82 $\frac{15}{4}$ 101

✓ Checkpoint Quiz 2   **Lessons 9-4 through 9-5**

TEXT Instant self-check quiz online and on CD-ROM

Simplify each expression.

1. $\dfrac{3x - 6}{5x - 20} \cdot \dfrac{x - 8}{5x - 10}$ $\dfrac{3(x - 8)}{25(x - 4)}$

2. $\dfrac{14x + 7}{4x - 6} \cdot \dfrac{8x - 12}{42x + 21}$ $\dfrac{2}{3}$

3. $\dfrac{y^2 - 25}{(y + 5)^2} \div \dfrac{2y - 10}{4y + 20}$ 2

4. $\dfrac{y^2 - 25}{y^2 - 16} \div \dfrac{2y + 10}{y^2 - 4y}$ $\dfrac{y(y - 5)}{2(y + 4)}$

5. $\dfrac{8}{3x^3y} + \dfrac{4}{9xy^3}$ $\dfrac{4(6y^2 + x^2)}{9x^3y^3}$

6. $\dfrac{7}{5y + 25} + \dfrac{4}{3y + 15}$ $\dfrac{41}{15(y + 5)}$

7. $\dfrac{5x}{2y + 4} - \dfrac{6}{y^2 + 2y}$ $\dfrac{5xy - 12}{2y(y + 2)}$

8. $3x - \dfrac{x^2 + 5x}{x^2 - 2}$ $\dfrac{3x^3 - x^2 - 11x}{x^2 - 2}$

9. $\dfrac{\frac{3}{2y}}{\frac{6}{8x}}$ $\dfrac{2x}{y}$

10. $\dfrac{\frac{1}{x} + 3}{4 + \frac{5}{y}}$ $\dfrac{y(3x + 1)}{x(4y + 5)}$

510 Chapter 9   Rational Functions

[2] one process error, such as an error in simplifying the numerator

[1] answer only, no work shown

Extraneous Solutions

Since division by zero is undefined, strange and illogical things can happen when division by zero sneaks unnoticed into algebraic procedures.

Does $2 = 1$? Study the proof below.

①	$a = b$
②	$a^2 = ab$
③	$a^2 - b^2 = ab - b^2$
④	$(a - b)(a + b) = b(a - b)$
⑤	$\dfrac{(a - b)(a + b)}{a - b} = \dfrac{b(a - b)}{a - b}$
⑥	$a + b = b$
⑦	$b + b = b$
⑧	$2b = b$
⑨	$2 = 1$

1a. ① **given**
② **Multiply both sides by a.**
③ **Subtract b^2 from both sides.**
④ **Factor.**
⑤ **Divide both sides by $a - b$.**
⑥ **division property**
⑦ **Substitute b for a.**
⑧ **Combine like terms.**
⑨ **Divide both sides by b.**

1. a. Describe each step of the proof.
  b. Check equation ① by replacing a and b with a number such as 3. Do the same for each of the other equations. Which equations are true? **①, ②, ③, and ④**
  c. Equation ⑤ seems to be derived by using the Division Property of Equality: If $a = b$ and $c \neq 0$, then $\frac{a}{c} = \frac{b}{c}$. Explain why the property is not used correctly. **See margin.**

2. a. Justify each step of the solution to $\frac{1}{x^2} = \frac{2}{x}$.

①	$\dfrac{1}{x^2} = \dfrac{2}{x}$
②	$2x^2 = x$
③	$2x^2 - x = 0$
④	$x(2x - 1) = 0$
⑤	$x = 0$ or $x = \dfrac{1}{2}$

① **given**
② **Multiplication Property of Equality**
③ **Subtract x from both sides.**
④ **Factor.**
⑤ **Use the Zero-Product Property.**

  b. Check the solution $x = \frac{1}{2}$ in equations ④, ③, ②, and ①. **It checks in all four equations.**
  c. Check the solution $x = 0$ in equations ④, ③, ②, and ①. **It checks in ④, ③, and ②.**
  d. How are the checks different? Explain. **See margin.**
  e. If equations ④ and ① have the same solutions, then you can work backward to derive equation ① from ④. What goes wrong when you try? **You divide by 0.**
  f. Critical Thinking Explain why equation ③ can be derived from ②, and ② from ③, thereby ensuring that they have the same solutions. **See margin.**
  g. Equation ② is derived from equation ① using the Multiplication Property of Equality: If $a = b$ then $ac = bc$. Both sides of equation ① are multiplied by x^3 to obtain equation ②. Is there anything wrong with this step? **no**
  h. Critical Thinking Explain why equation ② can be derived from ①, but ① cannot be derived from ②. **② can be derived from ① using the Multiplication Property of Equality. ① cannot be derived from ② because the Division Property of Equality does not allow division by 0.**

Extraneous Solutions

This investigation will help students in Lesson 9-6 as they solve rational equations.

Resources

None

Teaching Notes

Teaching Tip
Relate the work in this investigation to Example 1 in Lesson 9-4. Be sure students understand that when they simplify a fraction by dividing out a common factor from numerator and denominator, the common factor cannot have the value 0.

Error Prevention

Exercise 1c Students may confuse the variables used to state the Division Property of Equality with the variables in the 9-step "proof" that $2 = 1$. If so, it may help to restate the Division Property of Equality using other variables.

page 511 Exploration

1c. If $a = b$, then $a - b = 0$. The Division Property of Equality does not allow division by 0.

2d. $x = 0$ does not check in ① since division by 0 is undefined.

f. ③ can be derived from ② using the Subtraction Property of Equality. ② can be derived from ③ using the Addition Property of Equality.

1. Plan

Lesson Preview

 Check Skills You'll Need

Operations with Fractions
Skills Handbook: p. 843,
Examples 1, 2, Exercises 1–10

Lesson Resources

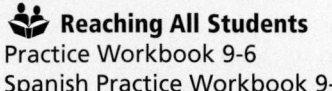

📁 **Teaching Resources**
Practice, Reteaching, Enrichment

👥 **Reaching All Students**
Practice Workbook 9-6
Spanish Practice Workbook 9-6

⏰ **Presentation Assistant Plus!**
Transparencies
• Check Skills You'll Need 9-6
• Additional Examples 9-6
• Student Edition Answers 9-6
• Lesson Quiz 9-6
PH Presentation Pro CD 9-6

 ASSESSMENT SYSTEM

Computer Test Generator CD

 Technology
Resource Pro® CD-ROM
Computer Test Generator CD
Prentice Hall Presentation Pro CD

 **www.PHSchool.com**
Student Site
• Teacher Web Code: agk-5500
• Self-grading Lesson Quiz
Teacher Center
• Lesson Planner
• Resources

Plus **iTEXT**

512

9-6

Solving Rational Equations

 **North Carolina Objectives**

2.05 Use rational equations to model and solve problems. a) Solve using tables, graphs, and algebraic properties. b) Interpret the constants and coefficients in the context of the problem.

Lesson Preview

What You'll Learn

 OBJECTIVE 1
To solve rational equations

 OBJECTIVE 2
To use rational equations in solving problems

. . . And Why

To find the average speed of a bicycle trip, as in Example 3

✔ **Check Skills You'll Need** (For help, go to Skills Handbook page 843.)

Find the LCD of each pair of fractions.

1. $\frac{1}{3t}, \frac{1}{5t^2}$ $15t^2$

2. $\frac{x}{2}, \frac{3x}{8}$ 8

3. $\frac{4}{3h^2}, \frac{2h}{h^3}$ $3h^3$

4. $\frac{4}{y+2}, \frac{3}{y-1}$ $(y+2)(y-1)$

5. $\frac{z}{2z+1}, \frac{1}{z}$ $z(2z+1)$

6. $\frac{1}{k+2}, \frac{3k}{k^2-4}$ $(k+2)(k-2)$

OBJECTIVE 1 **Solving Rational Equations**

iTEXT Interactive lesson includes instant self-check, tutorials, and activities.

Extraneous solutions can be introduced when you multiply both sides of an equation by the same algebraic expression. An extraneous solution is a solution of the derived equation, but not of the original equation.

You must check all solutions of the derived equation in the original equation to find whether any of them are not solutions of the original equation.

1 EXAMPLE **Solving Rational Equations**

Solve $\frac{5}{2x-2} = \frac{15}{x^2-1}$. Check each solution.

$$\frac{5}{2x-2} = \frac{15}{x^2-1}$$

$5(x^2-1) = 15(2x-2)$	Write the cross products.
$5x^2 - 5 = 30x - 30$	Distributive Property
$5x^2 - 30x + 25 = 0$	Write in standard form.
$x^2 - 6x + 5 = 0$	Divide each side by 5.
$(x-1)(x-5) = 0$	Factor.
$x = 1$ or $x = 5$	Zero-Product Property

Check When $x = 1$, both denominators in the original equation are zero. The original equation is undefined at $x = 1$. So $x = 1$ is not a solution.

When 5 is substituted for x in the original equation, both sides equal $\frac{5}{8}$.

● The solution is $x = 5$.

 Need Help?

In a proportion, the cross products are equal.
If $\frac{a}{b} = \frac{c}{d}$, then $ad = cb$
$(b \neq 0, d \neq 0)$.

✔ **Check Understanding** 1 Solve each equation. Check each solution.

a. $\frac{-4}{5(x+2)} = \frac{3}{x+2}$ **no solution**

b. $\frac{-2}{x^2-2} = \frac{2}{x-4}$ **−3, 2**

Ongoing Assessment and Intervention

Before the Lesson
Diagnose prerequisite skills using:
• Check Skills You'll Need

During the Lesson
Monitor progress using:
• Check Understanding
• Additional Examples
• Standardized Test Prep

After the Lesson
Assess knowledge using:
• Lesson Quiz
• Computer Test Generator CD

When an equation has a sum or difference of two rational expressions, you can use the least common denominator (LCD) to simplify the equation.

2 EXAMPLE Solving Rational Equations

Solve $\frac{1}{2x} - \frac{2}{5x} = \frac{1}{2}$.

$$\frac{1}{2x} - \frac{2}{5x} = \frac{1}{2}$$

$10x\left(\frac{1}{2x} - \frac{2}{5x}\right) = 10x\left(\frac{1}{2}\right)$ **Multiply each side by the LCD, 10x.**

$\dfrac{10x}{2x} - \dfrac{10x(2)}{5x} = \dfrac{10x}{2}$ **Distributive Property**

$5 - 4 = 5x$ **Simplify.**

$x = \dfrac{1}{5}$

Since $\frac{1}{5}$ makes the original equation true, the solution is $x = \frac{1}{5}$.

✓ **Check Understanding** ② Solve $\frac{4}{x} - \frac{3}{x+1} = 1$. Check your solution. **2, −2**

OBJECTIVE
2 Using Rational Equations

3 EXAMPLE Real-World Connection

Real-World Connection

This high-performance bicycle has the aerodynamic design of a custom racing bicycle, but is practical enough for everyday riding.

Aerodynamics The aerodynamic covering on this bicycle increases a cyclist's average speed by 10 mi/h. The time for a 75-mi trip is reduced by 2 h. What is the average speed for the trip using the aerodynamic covering?

Relate   speed with aerodynamic covering = speed without covering + 10

Define

	Distance (mi)	Rate (mi/h)	Time (h)
Without Covering	75	$\dfrac{75}{t}$	t
With Covering	75	$\dfrac{75}{t-2}$	$t - 2$

Write $\dfrac{75}{t-2} = \dfrac{75}{t} + 10$

$\dfrac{75}{t-2} = \dfrac{75}{t} + 10$

$t(t-2)\left(\dfrac{75}{t-2}\right) = t(t-2)\left(\dfrac{75}{t}\right) + t(t-2)(10)$ **Multiply by the LCD, $t(t-2)$.**

$t(75) = (t-2)(75) + 10t(t-2)$ **Simplify.**

$75t = 75t - 150 + 10t^2 - 20t$ **Distributive Property**

$0 = 10t^2 - 20t - 150$ **Simplify.**

$0 = t^2 - 2t - 15$ **Divide each side by 10.**

$0 = (t-5)(t+3)$ **Factor.**

$t = 5$ or $t = -3$ The time must be positive, so $\dfrac{75}{t-2} = \dfrac{75}{5-2} = 25$.

3. 10 mi/h downhill, 6 mi/h uphill

The average speed with the aerodynamic covering is 25 mi/h.

✓ **Check Understanding** ③ Rosa can jog 5 mi downhill in the same time it takes her to jog 3 mi uphill. She jogs downhill 4 mi/h faster than she jogs uphill. Find her jogging rate each way.

Professional Development

Math Background

To solve some rational equations, you can multiply each side by the LCD. To solve others that are proportions, you can use cross products. Remind students that cross multiplying is simply an efficient method, equivalent to solving a proportion by multiplying each side by the LCD.

OBJECTIVE
▼ 1 Teaching Notes

2 EXAMPLE Technology Tip

After students have studied the algebraic solution, you may want to have them use a graphing calculator to solve the equation. Have them enter the equations $Y_1 = \frac{1}{2x} - \frac{2}{5x}$ and $Y_2 = \frac{1}{2}$ on the Y= list, and then find the x-coordinate of the intersection point. Caution them to use parentheses around the denominators in the first equation. Good settings for the graphing window are Xmin=−3, Xmax=3, Ymin=−1.5, Ymax=1.5.

Additional Examples

① Solve $\frac{1}{x-3} = \frac{6x}{x^2-9}$. Check each solution. $\frac{3}{5}$

② Solve $\frac{3}{5x} - \frac{4}{3x} = \frac{1}{3}$. $-\frac{11}{5}$

OBJECTIVE
2 Teaching Notes

Additional Examples

③ Josefina can row 4 miles upstream in a river in the same time it takes her to row 6 miles downstream. Her rate of rowing in still water is 2 miles per hour. Find the speed of the river current. **0.4 mi/h**

👥 **Reaching All Students**

Below Level Remind students that they can only cross multiply if an equation is a proportion. Other equations require simplifying one or both sides before cross-multiplying.	**Advanced Learners** Have students explore at least 2 ways of using graphing calculators to solve rational equations.	**English Learners** See note on page 515. **Error Prevention** See note on page 515.

4 Jim and Alberto have to paint 6000 square feet of hallway in an office building. Alberto works twice as fast as Jim. Working together, they can complete the job in 15 hours. How long would it take each of them working alone? **Alberto: 22.5 h, Jim: 45 h**

Closure

Ask students to describe what they must do to find the solutions of a rational equation. **Answers may vary. Sample: First, clear the equation of fractions. One way to do this is to simplify both sides and then multiply both sides of the resulting equation by the least common denominator of all expressions. The result will be a polynomial equation. Solve this equation. Check the solutions in the original equation to eliminate extraneous solutions.**

---

4 EXAMPLE Real-World Connection

Volunteerism Tim can stuff envelopes three times as fast as his daughter Georgia. They have to stuff 5000 envelopes for a fund-raiser. Working together, Tim and Georgia can complete the job in four hours. How long would it take each of them working alone?

Relate   Tim's rate + Georgia's rate = combined rate

Define

	Time (hr)	Rate (envelopes per hour)
Tim	x	$\dfrac{5000}{x}$
Georgia	$3x$	$\dfrac{5000}{3x}$
Combined	4	$\dfrac{5000}{4} = 1250$

Write $\dfrac{5000}{x} + \dfrac{5000}{3x} = 1250$

$$\frac{5000}{x} + \frac{5000}{3x} = 1250$$

$$3x\left(\frac{5000}{x} + \frac{5000}{3x}\right) = 3x(1250) \quad \text{Multiply by the LCD, } 3x.$$

$$\frac{3x(5000)}{x} + \frac{3x(5000)}{3x} = 3x(1250) \quad \text{Distributive Property.}$$

$$15{,}000 + 5000 = 3750x \quad \text{Simplify.}$$

$$20{,}000 = 3750x \quad \text{Simplify.}$$

$$5.33 \approx x \quad \text{Solve for } x.$$

Tim could stuff 5000 envelopes in about 5.33 hours.

● Georgia could stuff 5000 envelopes in 3(5.33) hours, or about 16 hours.

✓**Check Understanding** **4 a.** Suppose Maria can stuff envelopes twice as fast as her friend Paco. Together, they can stuff 6750 envelopes in 4.5 hours. How long would it take each of them working alone? **Maria: 6.75 h, Paco: 13.5 h**

b. Suppose Adrian can weed the garden twice as fast as his son Phillip. Together they can weed the garden in 3 hours. How long would it take each of them working alone? **Adrian: 4.5 h, Phillip: 9 h**

EXERCISES

For more practice, see *Extra Practice*.

Practice and Problem Solving

 Practice by Example

Example 1
(page 512)

Solve each equation. Check each solution.

1. $\dfrac{x}{5} = \dfrac{x+3}{8}$ **5**

2. $\dfrac{1}{5x} = \dfrac{1}{9x}$ **no solution**

3. $\dfrac{4}{3x+3} = \dfrac{12}{x^2-1}$ **10**

4. $\dfrac{2}{x-1} = \dfrac{x+4}{3}$ **2 or −5**

5. $\dfrac{3}{x+1} = \dfrac{1}{x^2-1}$ **$\frac{4}{3}$**

6. $\dfrac{4}{2x-3} = \dfrac{x}{5}$ **$-\frac{5}{2}$ or 4**

7. $\dfrac{3}{x} = \dfrac{12}{x+7}$ **$\frac{7}{3}$**

8. $\dfrac{10}{6x+7} = \dfrac{6}{2x+9}$ **3**

9. $\dfrac{2}{3x-5} = \dfrac{4}{x-15}$ **−1**

Example 2
(page 513)

Solve each equation. Check each solution.

10. $\frac{1}{4} - x = \frac{x}{8}$ $\frac{2}{9}$ **11.** $\frac{y}{5} + \frac{y}{2} = 7$ **10**   **12.** $\frac{2x}{3} - \frac{1}{2} = \frac{2x + 5}{6}$ **4**

13. $\frac{3x - 2}{12} - \frac{1}{6} = \frac{1}{6}$ **2**   **14.** $\frac{1}{x} + \frac{x}{2} = \frac{x + 4}{2x}$ **−1 or 2**   **15.** $\frac{11}{3x} - \frac{1}{3} = \frac{-4}{x^2}$ **−1 or 12**

16. $\frac{3}{2x} - \frac{5}{3x} = 2$ $-\frac{1}{12}$ **17.** $\frac{5x}{4} - \frac{3}{x} = \frac{1}{4}$ **18.** $\frac{2}{y} + \frac{1}{2} = \frac{5}{2y}$ **1**
 **−1.45 or 1.65**

19. $x + \frac{6}{x} = -5$ **−3, −2**   **20.** $\frac{1}{4x} - \frac{3}{4} = \frac{7}{x}$ **−9**   **21.** $\frac{5}{2x} - \frac{2}{3} = \frac{1}{x} + \frac{5}{6}$ **1**

Examples 3 and 4
(pages 513 and 514)

22. Carlos can travel 40 mi on his motorbike in the same time it takes Paul to travel 15 mi on his bicycle. If Paul rides his bike 20 mi/h slower than Carlos rides his motorbike, find the speed for each bike.   **Carlos: 32 mi/h, Paul: 12 mi/h**

23. A passenger train travels 392 mi in the same time that it takes a freight train to travel 322 mi. If the passenger train travels 20 mi/h faster than the freight train, find the speed of each train.   **passenger train: 112 mi/h, freight train: 92 mi/h**

24. Shelley can paint a fence in 8 hours. Karen can do it in 4 hours. How long will it take them to do the job if they work together? $2\frac{2}{3}$ **h**

25. One pump can fill a tank with oil in 4 hours. A second pump can fill the same tank in 3 hours. If both pumps are used at the same time, how long will they take to fill the tank? $1\frac{5}{7}$ **h**

B **Apply Your Skills**

Solve each equation for the given variable.   **27–31. See margin.**

26. $m = \frac{2E}{V^2}; E$ $\boldsymbol{E = \frac{mV^2}{2}}$ **27.** $\frac{c}{E} - \frac{1}{mc} = 0; E$ **28.** $\frac{m}{F} = \frac{1}{a}; F$

29. $\frac{1}{c} - \frac{c}{a^2 - b^2} = 0; c$ **30.** $\frac{\ell}{T^2} = \frac{g}{4\pi^2}; T$ **31.** $\frac{q}{m} = \frac{2V}{B^2 r^2}; B$

Reading Math

For help with reading and solving Exercise 32, see page 518.

32. Anita and Fran have volunteered to contact every member of their organization by phone to inform them of an upcoming event. Fran can complete the calls in six days if she works alone. Anita can complete them in four days. How long will they take to complete the calls working together? $2\frac{2}{5}$ **days**

 33. **Test Scores** On the first four tests of the term your average is 84%. You think you can score 96% on each of the remaining tests. How many consecutive test scores of 96% would you need to bring your average up to 90% for the term?   **4**

34. You are planning a school field trip to a local theater. It costs $60 to rent the bus. Each theater ticket costs $5.50. $c(x) = \frac{5.50x + 60}{x}$
a. Write a function $c(x)$ to represent the cost per student if x students sign up.
b. How many students must sign up if the cost is to be no more than $10 per student?   **14 students**

35a. $L = \frac{24(R - r)}{T}$
b. 32 in., 28.24 in., 25.26 in.

 35. **Woodworking** A tapered cylinder is made by decreasing the radius of a rod continuously as you move from one end to the other. The speed at which it tapers is the taper per foot. You can calculate the taper per foot using the formula $T = \frac{24(R - r)}{L}$. The lengths R, r, and L are measured in inches.

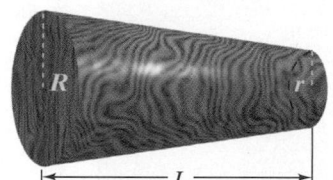

a. Solve this equation for L.
b. Find L if $R = 4$ in.; $r = 3$ in.; and $T = 0.75, 0.85,$ and 0.95.

Assignment Guide

1 Objective
Ⓐ Ⓑ Core 1–21, 26–31, 39–52
Ⓒ Extension 56

2 Objective
Ⓐ Ⓑ Core 22–25, 32–38, 53–55
Ⓒ Extension 57, 58

Standardized Test Prep 59–64

Mixed Review 65–74

Error Prevention

Exercises 10–21, 39–52 Students may forget to check for extraneous solutions. Stress that this is an essential step when solving rational equations.

English Learners

Exercise 35 You may need to explain the terms *tapered cylinder* and *continuously*.

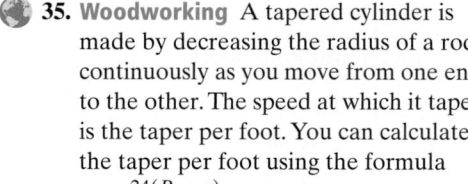

---

pages 514–517   Exercises

27. $E = mc^2$

28. $F = ma$

29. $c = \sqrt{a^2 - b^2}$

30. $T = \sqrt{\dfrac{4\pi^2 \ell}{g}}$

31. $B = \sqrt{\dfrac{2Vm}{r^2 q}}$

515

36b. $\frac{15,000}{24 + x}(1.60)$

c. $1000 - \frac{15,000}{24 + x}(1.60)$

37. Check students' work.

49. no solution

Real-World **Connection**

Careers Masons build patterns with brick or stone.

 36. Fuel Economy Suppose you drive an average of 15,000 miles per year, and your car gets 24 miles per gallon. Suppose gasoline costs $1.60 a gallon.
   a. How much money do you spend each year on gasoline? **$1000**
   b. You plan to trade in your car for one that gets x more miles per gallon. Write an expression to represent the new yearly cost of gasoline.
   c. Write an expression to represent your savings on gasoline.
   d. Suppose you save $200 a year with the new car. How many miles per gallon does the new car get? **30 mi/gal**

37. Open-Ended Write a rational equation that has the same solution as the question in the cartoon.

The Family Circus by Bil Keane

4-25

"What's 129 divided by 4?"

 38. Industry The average hourly wage $H(x)$ of workers in an industry is modeled by the function $H(x) = \frac{16.24x}{0.062x + 39.42}$, where x represents the number of years since 1970. **about 2037**
   a. In what year does the model predict that wages will be $25/h?
   b. **Critical Thinking** Is the prediction reasonable? Explain. **Check students' work.**

Solve each equation. Check each solution.

39. $\frac{15}{x} + \frac{9x - 7}{x + 2} = 9$ **3**

40. $\frac{2}{x + 2} - \frac{1}{x} = \frac{-4}{x(x + 2)}$ **no solution**

41. $\frac{1}{b + 1} + \frac{1}{b - 1} = \frac{2}{b^2 - 1}$ **no solution**

42. $c - \frac{c}{3} + \frac{c}{5} = 26$ **30**

43. $\frac{2}{x - 3} - \frac{4}{x + 3} = \frac{8}{x^2 - 9}$ **5**

44. $\frac{1}{8} + \frac{5x}{x + 2} = \frac{5}{2}$ $\frac{38}{21}$

45. $\frac{1}{x - 5} = \frac{x}{x^2 - 25}$ **no solution**

46. $\frac{k}{k + 1} + \frac{k}{k - 2} = 2$ **−4**

47. $\frac{3}{x + 5} + \frac{2}{5 - x} = \frac{-4}{x^2 - 25}$ **21**

48. $\frac{5}{x + 2} = \frac{-1}{x^2 + 7x + 10} + \frac{3}{-x - 5}$ **−4**

49. $\frac{5}{x^2 - 7x + 12} - \frac{2}{3 - x} = \frac{5}{x - 4}$

50. $\frac{10}{2y + 8} - \frac{7y + 8}{y^2 - 16} = \frac{-8}{2y - 8}$ **−4**

51. $\frac{7x + 3}{x^2 - 8x + 15} + \frac{3x}{x - 5} = \frac{1}{3 - x}$ $1, -\frac{2}{3}$

52. $\frac{2}{x + 3} - \frac{3}{4 - x} = \frac{2x - 2}{x^2 - x - 12}$ **−1**

 53. Landscape Design Suppose you want to double the area of the patio shown at the right. Find the increase x of both the length and width of the patio. $x \approx$ **4.5 ft**

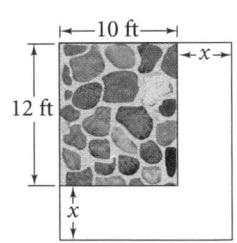

54. Writing Write and solve a problem that can be modeled by a rational equation. **Check students' work.**

55. Transportation A plane flies from New York to Chicago (about 700 miles) at a speed of 360 mi/h.
   a. The speed s of the plane is given by $s = \frac{d}{t}$. $t = \frac{d}{s}$ d represents the distance and t is the time. Solve the equation for t.
   b. Find the time for the trip. $\frac{35}{18}$ **h**
   c. On the return trip from Chicago to New York, a tail wind helps the plane move faster. Write an expression for the speed of the plane on the return trip. Let x represent the speed of the tail wind. $\frac{d}{t} + x$
   d. The total flying time for the round trip is 3.5 h. Write a rational equation for the sum of the flying times. Find the speed x of the tail wind. $\frac{700}{360} + \frac{700}{360 + x} = 3.5$; **90 mi/h**

C Challenge

56a–c. Check students' work.

56. **Open-Ended** Write a rational equation that has the following.
   a. one solution   **b.** two solutions   **c.** no real solution

57. A salesman drove from his home to a nearby city at an average speed of 40 mi/h. He returned home at an average speed of 50 mi/h. What was his average speed for the entire trip? **44.44 mi/h**

58. An automatic pitching machine can pitch all its baseballs in $1\frac{1}{4}$ hours. One attendant can retrieve all the baseballs pitched by one machine in $3\frac{1}{2}$ hours. At least how many attendants working at the same rate should be hired so that the baseballs from 10 machines are all retrieved in less than 8 hours? **5 attendants**

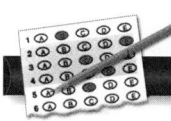

Standardized Test Prep

Multiple Choice

59. Which value of x would NOT make the equation $\frac{5}{2x-1} = \frac{7x}{x^2-25}$ undefined? **B**
   A. -5 **B.** 0   **C.** $\frac{1}{2}$ **D.** 5

60. What is the solution of $x + \frac{1}{x} = -2$? **I**
   F. 1 or -1 **G.** 0 only   **H.** $-\frac{1}{2}$ only   **I.** -1 only

61. Which equation has 2 as an extraneous solution? **D**
   A. $\frac{x+1}{17} = \frac{x+3}{15}$ **B.** $\frac{3}{3x+6} = \frac{4}{x^2-4}$
   C. $\frac{3x+1}{3x} = \frac{5x}{5x+3}$ **D.** $\frac{4}{2x-4} = \frac{1}{x-2}$

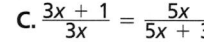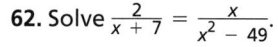

Take It to the NET
Online lesson quiz at
www.PHSchool.com
········ Web Code: aga-0906

62. Solve $\frac{2}{x+7} = \frac{x}{x^2-49}$. **F**
   F. 14 only   **G.** 7 only   **H.** 7 or -7 **I.** -7 only

Short Response

63. A large snowplow can clear a parking lot in 4 hours. A small snowplow needs more time to clear the lot. Working together, they can clear the lot in 3 hours. How long would it take the small plow to clear the lot by itself? Show your work. **See margin.**

Extended Response

64. Solve and check the equation $\frac{x}{3x+9} = \frac{x+2}{x+3}$. Show your work. **See margin.**

Mixed Review

Lesson 9-5

Simplify each difference. **65–67. See margin.**

65. $\frac{3y+1}{4y+4} - \frac{2y+7}{2y+2}$ 66. $\frac{5x}{2y+4} - \frac{6}{y^2+2y}$ 67. $\frac{x+1}{2x-2} - \frac{2x}{x^2+2x-3}$

Lesson 8-5

Solve each equation.

68. $\log_{10} 0.001 = x$ **x = -3**   69. $\log_3 27 = 3x + 6$ **x = -1**

70. $\log_{0.1}(x+1) = 3$ **x = -0.999**   71. $\log_3 \frac{1}{9} = \frac{x}{3}$ **x = -6**

Lesson 7-7

Find the inverse of each function. Is the inverse a function?

72. $y = 5 - 2x$
   $y = \frac{5-x}{2}$; **yes**

73. $y = x^2 + 1$
   $y = \pm\sqrt{x-1}$; **no**

74. $y = x^3 - 4$
   $y = \sqrt[3]{x+4}$; **yes**

Lesson 9-6 Solving Rational Equations   **517**

Standardized Test Prep

📁 **Resources**

For additional practice with a variety of test item formats:
- Standardized Test Prep, p. 531
- Test-Taking Strategies, p. 526
- Test-Taking Strategies with Transparencies

pages 514–517   Exercises

63. [2] $\frac{1}{4} + \frac{1}{x} = \frac{1}{3}$
   $12x(\frac{1}{4} + \frac{1}{x}) = 12x(\frac{1}{3})$
   $\frac{12x}{4} + \frac{12x}{x} = \frac{12x}{3}$
   $3x + 12 = 4x$
   $12 = x$
   It would take the small plow 12 hours to clear the lot by itself.

   [1] answer only, with no work shown

64. [4] $\frac{x}{3x+9} = \frac{x+2}{x+3}$
   $\frac{x}{3(x+3)} = \frac{x+2}{x+3}$
   $x(x+3) = 3(x+3)$
   $\qquad\qquad (x+2)$
   $x = 3(x+2)$
   $x = 3x + 6$
   $-2x = 6$
   $x = -3$
   However, $x = -3$ makes the denominators in the original equation equal 0, which is undefined. So, the equation has no solution.

   [3] one computational error

   [2] gets $x = -3$, but does not state that the equation has no solution

   [1] answer only, with no work shown

65. $\frac{-y-13}{4(y+1)}$

66. $\frac{5xy-12}{2y(y+2)}$

67. $\frac{x^2+3}{(2x-2)(x+3)}$

517

Reading for Problem Solving

Students solve a rational equation by working through an annotated sample problem. In addition to the worked out problem, students are also given notes about each step in the solution process.

Teaching Notes

Point out that Fran's rate is total work over 6 because she can make the calls in 6 days, and Anita's rate is total work over 4 because she can make the calls in 4 days.

Auditory Learners

Place students in pairs or small groups. Have students take turns working through the steps to solve a problem similar to the one in the example. After each step is completed, the student who did the work explains aloud to the other students what he or she did.

Exercise

Make sure students label their answers. The rate will not make sense without a label. Tell students to be mindful of the units. The time units in the example problem was days, and the Exercise problem is in minutes.

Reading for Problem Solving

Read the problem below. Then follow along with Ahmed as he solves the problem. Check your understanding with the exercise at the bottom of the page.

Anita and Fran have volunteered to contact every member of their organization by phone to inform them of an upcoming event. Fran can complete the calls in six days if she works alone. Anita can complete them in four days. How long will they take to complete the calls working together?

What Ahmed Thinks

I'll write the information in my own words.

Work problems involve rates. Even though I don't know the number of calls Fran and Anita are making, maybe I can just consider the entire job, or total amount of work, being done.

I'll define variables, t for time and w for work.

Now I can write an equation.

The variable w is going to cancel out of the equation, so I can just solve for t.

I can write my answer in a sentence now.

What Ahmed Writes

Fran can complete the work in 6 days.
Anita can complete the work in 4 days.

$$\text{rate} = \frac{\text{work being done}}{\text{time}}$$

$$\text{Fran's rate} = \frac{\text{work being done}}{\text{time}} = \frac{\text{total work}}{6}$$

$$\text{Anita's rate} = \frac{\text{work being done}}{\text{time}} = \frac{\text{total work}}{4}$$

$w = $ total work
$t = $ time working together

$$\text{Fran's rate} + \text{Anita's rate} = \text{combined rate}$$

$$\frac{\text{total work}}{6} + \frac{\text{total work}}{4} = \frac{\text{total work}}{\text{time together}}$$

$$\frac{w}{6} + \frac{w}{4} = \frac{w}{t}$$

$$\frac{1}{6} + \frac{1}{4} = \frac{1}{t}$$

$$2t + 3t = 12$$

$$5t = \frac{12}{5} = 2\frac{2}{5}$$

It will take Anita and Fran, working together, $2\frac{2}{5}$ days to complete all the calls.

EXERCISE

Charlene and Robert are washing cars for a fund-raiser. Charlene can wash a car in 15 minutes, and Robert can wash the same size car in 12 minutes. How long will it take them to wash a car if they work together? $6\frac{2}{3}$ **min**

Probability of Multiple Events

Lesson Preview

What You'll Learn

 OBJECTIVE 1 To find the probabilities of events *A* and *B*

 OBJECTIVE 2 To find the probabilities of events *A* or *B*

... And Why

To solve problems involving radio call-in shows, as in Example 2

✓ **Check Skills You'll Need** (For help, go to Lesson 1-6.)

A bag contains 24 green marbles, 22 blue marbles, 14 yellow marbles, and 12 red marbles. Suppose you pick one marble at random. Find each probability.

1. P(yellow) $\frac{7}{36}$ **2.** P(not blue) $\frac{25}{36}$ **3.** P(green or red) $\frac{1}{2}$

4. Of 300 senior students at Taft High, 150 have taken physics, 192 have taken chemistry, and 30 have taken neither physics nor chemistry. How many students have taken both physics and chemistry? **72**

New Vocabulary • **dependent events** • **independent events** • **mutually exclusive events**

---

1. Plan

Lesson Preview

✓ **Check Skills You'll Need**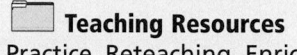

Probability
Lesson 1-6: Example 3
Exercises 6–18
Extra Practice, p. 822

Lesson Resources

📁 **Teaching Resources**
Practice, Reteaching, Enrichment

👥 **Reaching All Students**
Practice Workbook 9-7
Spanish Practice Workbook 9-7

⏱ **Presentation Assistant Plus!**
Transparencies
• Check Skills You'll Need 9-7
• Additional Examples 9-7
• Student Edition Answers 9-7
• Lesson Quiz 9-7
PH Presentation Pro CD 9-7

ASSESSMENT SYSTEM

Computer Test Generator CD

💿 **Technology**
Resource Pro® CD-ROM
Computer Test Generator CD
Prentice Hall Presentation Pro CD

🖥 **www.PHSchool.com**
Student Site
• Teacher Web Code: agk-5500
• Updated Data
• Self-grading Lesson Quiz
Teacher Center
• Lesson Planner
• Resources

Plus **iTEXT**

OBJECTIVE 1 Finding *P*(*A* and *B*)

 Interactive lesson includes instant self-check, tutorials, and activities.

> ### Investigation: Multiple Events
>
> • Work with a partner to analyze the game Primarily Odd.
>
> • **Partner A:** Roll two standard number cubes. If the sum is either odd *or* a prime number, score a point.
>
> • **Partner B:** Roll two standard number cubes. If the sum is both odd *and* a prime number, score a point.
>
> • Alternate turns rolling the number cubes.
>
> **1. a.** List all the possible outcomes of rolling two number cubes. **See margin p. 521.**
> **b.** How many outcomes result in an odd sum? Calculate the probability of getting an odd sum. **18; $\frac{1}{2}$**
> **c.** How many outcomes result in a prime sum? Calculate the probability of getting a prime sum. **15; $\frac{5}{12}$**
>
> **2.** Predict which partner is more likely to score points in Primarily Odd. Justify your reasoning. **See left.**
>
> **3.** Play the game with your partner. Take 10 turns each. Keep track of each player's score. How do your results compare with the prediction you made in Question 2? **Check students' work.**

2. Partner A is more likely to score points, since that player has more rolls that result in points.

When the outcome of one event affects the outcome of a second event, the two events are **dependent events.** When the outcome of one event does *not* affect the outcome of a second event, the two events are **independent events.**

⚡ Ongoing Assessment and Intervention

Before the Lesson	**During the Lesson**	**After the Lesson**
Diagnose prerequisite skills using:	**Monitor progress using:**	**Assess knowledge using:**
• Check Skills You'll Need	• Check Understanding	• Lesson Quiz
	• Additional Examples	• Computer Test Generator CD
	• Standardized Test Prep	

Math Background

The use of the word "or" in mathematics is inclusive. If something is in *A or B* it can be in *A* and not *B*, *B* and not *A*, or both *A* and *B*. In general, to find $P(A \text{ or } B)$ we calculate $P(A) + P(B) - P(A \text{ and } B)$, subtracting $P(A \text{ and } B)$ so it is not counted twice. If *A* and *B* are mutually exclusive, then $P(A \text{ and } B) = 0$. $P(A \text{ given } B)$, or the probability that *A* happens given that *B* is considered the sample space, is just $\frac{P(A \text{ and } B)}{P(B)}$, that is, the ratio of the portion of *A* in *B* to *B*. Thus, $P(A \text{ and } B) = P(B) \cdot P(A \text{ given } B)$. If *A* and *B* are independent, then $P(A \text{ given } B) = P(A)$.

OBJECTIVE 1 Teaching Notes

Investigation (Optional)
In this investigation, students explore a situation that illustrates the concepts of dependent and independent events. For Questions 1b and 1c, have students count the number of times the event occurs. Then divide by the number of possible outcomes determined in part (a). Tell students to write their probabilities as fractions.

Additional Examples

1 Classify each pair of events as *dependent* or *independent*.
a. Spin a spinner. Then, select a marble from a bag that contains marbles of different colors. **independent**
b. Select a marble from a bag that contains marbles of two colors. Put the marble aside, and select a second marble from the bag. **dependent**

2 A box contains 20 red marbles and 30 blue marbles. A second box contains 10 white marbles and 47 black marbles. If you choose one marble from each box without looking, what is the probability that you get a blue marble and a black marble? $\frac{47}{95}$

520

---

1 EXAMPLE Classifying Events

Classify each pair of events as *dependent* or *independent*.

a. Roll a number cube. Then toss a coin.
Since the two events do not affect each other, they are independent.

b. Pick a flower from a garden. Then pick another flower from the same garden.
Picking the first flower affects the possible outcomes of picking the second flower. So the events are dependent.

✓ **Check Understanding** ❶ Suppose you select a marble from a bag of marbles. You replace the marble and then select again. Are your selections dependent or independent events? Explain. **Independent; the number of marbles is the same after the marble is replaced.**

You can find the probability that two independent events will both occur by multiplying probabilities.

Key Concepts

Property	Probability of *A* and *B*

If *A* and *B* are independent events, then $P(A \text{ and } B) = P(A) \cdot P(B)$.

Example: If $P(A) = \frac{1}{2}$ and $P(B) = \frac{1}{3}$, then $P(A \text{ and } B) = \frac{1}{2} \cdot \frac{1}{3} = \frac{1}{6}$.

2 EXAMPLE Real-World Connection

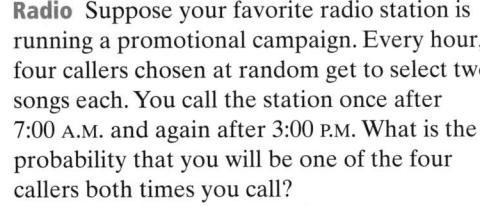

Real-World Connection

Careers Radio broadcasters try to increase the size of their listening audience so they can increase their advertising rates.

Radio Suppose your favorite radio station is running a promotional campaign. Every hour, four callers chosen at random get to select two songs each. You call the station once after 7:00 A.M. and again after 3:00 P.M. What is the probability that you will be one of the four callers both times you call?

WKW Radio Statistics

Hour	Calls Received That Hour
7:00 A.M.	125
3:00 P.M.	200

Relate probability of both events is probability of first event times probability of second event

Define Event A = you are one of the four callers after 7:00 A.M. Then $P(A) = \frac{4}{125}$.

Event B = you are one of the four callers after 3:00 P.M. Then $P(B) = \frac{4}{200}$.

Write $P(A \text{ and } B) = P(A) \cdot P(B)$

$$P(A \text{ and } B) = \frac{4}{125} \cdot \frac{4}{200}$$

$$= \frac{16}{25,000} \qquad \textbf{Multiply.}$$

$$= \frac{2}{3125} \qquad \textbf{Simplify.}$$

The probability of being one of the four callers selected at random both times you call is $\frac{2}{3125}$, or 0.064%.

✓ **Check Understanding** ❷ Suppose the radio station changes the promotional campaign. Now it chooses five callers at random each hour. **a–b. See margin p. 521.**
a. What is the probability of being one of the five callers after 7 A.M? After 3 P.M.?
b. Find the probability of being one of the five callers both times you call.

Reaching All Students

Below Level Use a bag of marbles similar to the one described. Have students select marbles from the bag and discuss the probabilities involved.	**Advanced Learners** Have students research how meteorologists determine probabilities of precipitation.	**Error Prevention** See note on page 523.

When two events cannot happen at the same time, the events are **mutually exclusive events.** If *A* and *B* are mutually exclusive events, then $P(A \text{ and } B) = 0$.

Reading Math

Events that are not mutually exclusive are sometimes called inclusive events, or non-mutually exclusive events.

3a. Not mutually exclusive since 2 is both even and prime.

3 EXAMPLE Mutually Exclusive Events

Are the events mutually exclusive? Explain.

a. rolling a 2 or a 3 on a number cube

Since you cannot roll a 2 and a 3 at the same time, the events are mutually exclusive.

b. rolling an even number or a multiple of 3 on a number cube

By rolling a 6, you can roll an even number and a multiple of 3 at the same time. So the events are not mutually exclusive.

✓ **Check Understanding** **3** Are the events mutually exclusive? Explain.
a. rolling an even number and rolling a prime number on a number cube
b. rolling an even number and rolling a number less than 2 on a number cube
Mutually exclusive since no number is both even and less than 2.

You need to determine whether events *A* and *B* are mutually exclusive before you can find the probability of (*A* or *B*).

Key Concepts

Property	Probability of *A* or *B*
If *A* and *B* are mutually exclusive events, then $P(A \text{ or } B) = P(A) + P(B)$. If *A* and *B* are not mutually exclusive events, then $P(A \text{ or } B) = P(A) + P(B) - P(A \text{ and } B)$.	

Many statistical measures are based on probabilities of the form *P(A or B)*.

4 EXAMPLE Real-World 🌐 Connection

College Enrollment About 53% of U.S. college students are under 25 years old. About 21% of U.S. college students are over 34 years old. What is the probability that a U.S. college student chosen at random is under 25 or over 34?

Since a student cannot be under 25 and over 34, the events are mutually exclusive.

4a. about 0.26 or about 26%

b. about 0.47 or about 47%

c. about 0.79 or about 79%

$P(\text{under 25 or over 34}) = P(\text{under 25}) + P(\text{over 34})$ Use the *P(A or B)* formula for mutually exclusive events.

$= 0.53 + 0.21$

$= 0.74$

The probability that a U.S. college student chosen at random is under 25 or over 34 is about 0.74, or about 74%.

✓ **Check Understanding** **4** A U.S. college student is chosen at random. Find the probability for each age range of the student.
a. 25–34   **b.** 25–34 or over 34   **c.** under 34

Lesson 9-7   Probability of Multiple Events   **521**

page 519   Investigation

1a. 1, 1), (1, 2), (1, 3),
(1, 4), (1, 5), (1, 6),
(2, 1), (2, 2), (2, 3),
(2, 4), (2, 5), (2, 6),
(3, 1), (3, 2), (3, 3),
(3, 4), (3, 5), (3, 6),

(4, 1), (4, 2), (4, 3),
(4, 4), (4, 5), (4, 6),
(5, 1), (5, 2), (5, 3),
(5, 4), (5, 5), (5, 6),
(6, 1), (6, 2), (6, 3),
(6, 4), (6, 5), (6, 6)

page 520
Check Understanding

2a. $\frac{1}{25}$ or 4%; $\frac{1}{40}$ or 2.5%

b. $\frac{1}{1000}$ or 0.1%

OBJECTIVE
2 Teaching Notes

3 EXAMPLE Math Tip

When you discuss this example, remind students that *independent* and *mutually exclusive* do not mean the same thing.

4 EXAMPLE Teaching Tip

Point out that the equation $P(A \text{ or } B) = P(A) + P(B) - P(A \text{ and } B)$ also works. Since the events *A* (under 25) and *B* (over 34) are mutually exclusive, $P(A \text{ and } B) = 0$.

Additional Examples

3 Are the events mutually exclusive? Explain.
a. rolling an even number and rolling a number greater than 5 on a number cube **no; 6 is even and also greater than 5**
b. rolling a prime number or a multiple of 6 on a number cube **yes; no prime number is a multiple of 6**

4 At a restaurant, customers get to choose one of four vegetables with any main course. About 33% of the customers choose green beans, and about 28% choose spinach. What is the probability that a customer will choose beans or spinach? **0.61**

5 A spinner has twenty equal-size sections numbered from 1 to 20. If you spin the spinner, what is the probability that the number you spin will be a multiple of 2 or a multiple of 3? $\frac{13}{20}$

Closure

Ask students to explain how they decide whether two events, *A* and *B*, are independent or mutually exclusive. Ask them how to find *P(A and B)* if *A* and *B* are independent and if *A* and *B* are mutually exclusive. Finally, ask them how to calculate *P(A or B)*. **Events A and B are independent if the outcomes of A do not affect the outcomes of B. The events are mutually exclusive if A and B cannot occur at the same time. For independent events, $P(A \text{ and } B) = P(A) \cdot P(B)$. For mutually exclusive events, $P(A \text{ and } B) = 0$. For any events, $P(A \text{ or } B) = P(A) + P(B) - P(A \text{ and } B)$.**

521

3. Practice

Assignment Guide

1 Objective

A B Core 1–9, 36–40, 45

C Extension 48–50

2 Objective

A B Core 10–35, 41–44, 46, 47

C Extension 51, 52

Standardized Test Prep 53–58

Mixed Review 59–70

Exercise 9 Urge students to read the exercise carefully. The crucial point to note is that the book is put back in the bag.

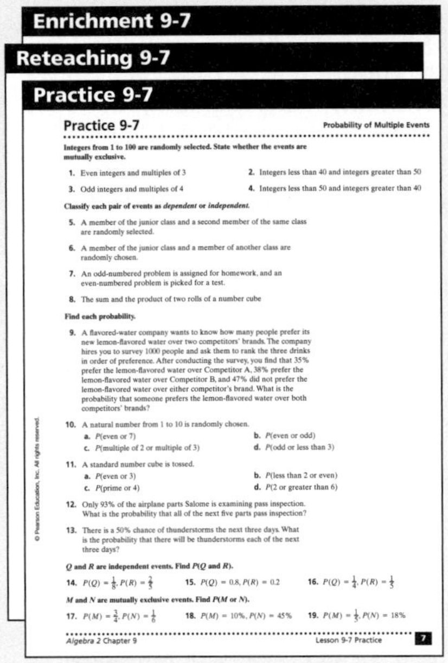
Enrichment 9-7

Reteaching 9-7

Practice 9-7

Practice 9-7 — Probability of Multiple Events

Integers from 1 to 100 are randomly selected. State whether the events are mutually exclusive.

1. Even integers and multiples of 3
2. Integers less than 40 and integers greater than 50
3. Odd integers and multiples of 4
4. Integers less than 50 and integers greater than 40

Classify each pair of events as *dependent* or *independent*.

5. A member of the junior class and a second member of the same class are randomly selected.
6. A member of the junior class and a member of another class are randomly chosen.
7. An odd-numbered problem is assigned for homework, and an even-numbered problem is picked for a test.
8. The sum and the product of two rolls of a number cube

Find each probability.

9. A flavored-water company wants to know how many people prefer its new lemon-flavored water over two competitors' brands. The company hires you to survey 1000 people and ask them to rank the three drinks in order of preference. After conducting the survey, you find that 35% prefer the lemon-flavored water over Competitor A, 38% prefer the lemon-flavored water over Competitor B, and 47% did not prefer the lemon-flavored water over either competitor's brand. What is the probability that someone prefers the lemon-flavored water over both competitors' brands?
10. A natural number from 1 to 10 is randomly chosen.
    a. P(even or 7) b. P(even or odd)
    c. P(multiple of 2 or multiple of 3) d. P(odd or less than 3)
11. A standard number cube is tossed.
    a. P(even or 3) b. P(less than 2 or even)
    c. P(prime or 4) d. P(2 or greater than 6)
12. Only 93% of the airplane parts Salome is examining pass inspection. What is the probability that all of the next five parts pass inspection?
13. There is a 50% chance of thunderstorms the next three days. What is the probability that there will be thunderstorms each of the next three days?

Q and R are independent events. Find $P(Q \text{ and } R)$.

14. $P(Q) = \frac{1}{8}, P(R) = \frac{2}{5}$ 15. $P(Q) = 0.8, P(R) = 0.2$ 16. $P(Q) = \frac{1}{4}, P(R) = \frac{1}{5}$

M and N are mutually exclusive events. Find $P(M \text{ or } N)$.

17. $P(M) = \frac{3}{4}, P(N) = \frac{1}{6}$ 18. $P(M) = 10\%, P(N) = 45\%$ 19. $P(M) = \frac{1}{5}, P(N) = 18\%$

Algebra 2 Chapter 9 Lesson 9-7 Practice 7

pages 522–525 Exercises

10. Not mutually exclusive since 2 is a prime number and less than 4.

11. Mutually exclusive since if the numbers are equal, then the sum is even.

12. Not mutually exclusive since $6 \cdot 4 = 24$, which is greater than 20 and a multiple of 3.

When two events are *not* mutually exclusive, you need to subtract the probability of the common outcomes.

5 EXAMPLE Probabilities of Events

Food Suppose you reach into the fruit bowl at the left and select a piece of fruit at random. What is the probability that the piece of fruit is an apple or green?

$$P(\text{apple or green}) = P(\text{apple}) + P(\text{green}) - P(\text{apple and green})$$
$$= \frac{5}{9} + \frac{3}{9} - \frac{2}{9}$$
$$= \frac{6}{9}$$

The probability of picking a piece of fruit that is an apple or green is $\frac{6}{9}$, or $\frac{2}{3}$.

✓ Check Understanding 5 Find each probability.

a. P(apple or red) $\frac{5}{9}$ b. P(green or citrus fruit) $\frac{2}{3}$

EXERCISES

For more practice, see *Extra Practice*.

Practice and Problem Solving

A Practice by Example

Example 1 (page 520)

Classify each pair of events as *dependent* or *independent*.

1. A month is selected at random; a number from 1 to 30 is selected at random. **independent**
2. A month is selected at random; a day of that month is selected at random. **dependent**
3. A letter of the alphabet is selected at random; one of the remaining letters is selected at random. **dependent**
4. The color of a car is selected at random; the type of transmission is selected at random. **independent**

Example 2 (page 520)

Q and R are independent events. Find $P(Q \text{ and } R)$.

5. $P(Q) = \frac{1}{4}, P(R) = \frac{2}{3}$ $\frac{1}{6}$
6. $P(Q) = \frac{12}{17}, P(R) = \frac{3}{8}$ $\frac{9}{34}$
7. $P(Q) = 0.6, P(R) = 0.9$ **0.54**
8. $P(Q) = \frac{1}{3}, P(R) = \frac{6}{x}$ $\frac{2}{x}$
9. Suppose you have five books in your book bag. Three are novels, one is a biography, and one is a poetry book. Today you grab one book out of your bag without looking, and return it later. Tomorrow you do the same thing. What is the probability that you grab a novel both days? $\frac{9}{25}$

Example 3 (page 521)

Two standard number cubes are tossed. State whether the events are mutually exclusive. Explain your reasoning. **10–12. See margin.**

10. The sum is a prime number; the sum is less than 4.
11. The numbers are equal; the sum is odd.
12. The product is greater than 20; the product is a multiple of 3.

Example 4 (page 521)

13. **Population** About 30% of the U.S. population is under 20 years old. About 17% of the population is over 60. What is the probability that a person chosen at random is under 20 or over 60? **47%**

Error Prevention

Exercises 18–25 You may need to remind students that after they add the probabilities, they must subtract $P(A \text{ and } B)$.

S and *T* are mutually exclusive events. Find $P(S \text{ or } T)$.

14. $P(S) = \frac{5}{8}, P(T) = \frac{1}{8}$ $\frac{3}{4}$

15. $P(S) = \frac{3}{5}, P(T) = \frac{1}{3}$ $\frac{14}{15}$

16. $P(S) = 12\%, P(T) = 27\%$ **39%**

17. $P(S) = \frac{1}{7}, P(T) = 60\%$ $\frac{26}{35}$

Example 5
(page 522)

A standard number cube is tossed. Find each probability.

18. $P(3 \text{ or odd})$ $\frac{1}{2}$

19. $P(4 \text{ or even})$ $\frac{1}{2}$

20. $P(\text{even or less than 4})$ $\frac{5}{6}$

21. $P(\text{odd or greater than 2})$ $\frac{5}{6}$

22. $P(\text{odd or prime})$ $\frac{2}{3}$

23. $P(\text{even or prime})$ $\frac{5}{6}$

24. $P(4 \text{ or less than 6})$ $\frac{5}{6}$

25. $P(\text{greater than 1 or less than 5})$ **1**

 **Apply Your Skills**

C and *D* are not mutually exclusive events. Copy and complete the table below to find each missing probability.

	$P(C)$	$P(D)$	$P(C \text{ and } D)$	$P(C \text{ or } D)$	
26.	$\frac{4}{9}$	$\frac{4}{9}$	■	$\frac{5}{9}$	$\frac{1}{3}$
27.	$\frac{1}{2}$	$\frac{1}{3}$	$\frac{1}{4}$	■	$\frac{7}{12}$
28.	$\frac{2}{3}$	$\frac{3}{5}$	■	$\frac{13}{15}$	$\frac{2}{5}$
29.	$\frac{3}{7}$	$\frac{1}{4}$	$\frac{1}{8}$	■	$\frac{31}{56}$

30a. $\frac{1}{5}; \frac{1}{4}$; no; 20 is a multiple of both 4 and 5.

30. Suppose a number from 1 to 100 is selected at random.
 a. What is the probability that a multiple of 5 is chosen? That a multiple of 4 is chosen? Are these two events mutually exclusive? Explain.
 b. What is the probability that a multiple of both 5 and 4 is chosen? $\frac{1}{20}$

Real-World Connection

Careers Support personnel keep business and industry running smoothly.

🌐 **Statistics** The graph at the right shows the types of jobs held by people in the United States. Find each probability.

31. A person is in a service occupation. **13%**

32. A person is in service or support. **42%**

33. A person is not in farming, fishing, or forestry. **98%**

34. A person is neither an operator nor a laborer, nor in precision production. **75%**

35. A person is neither in service nor in support. **58%**

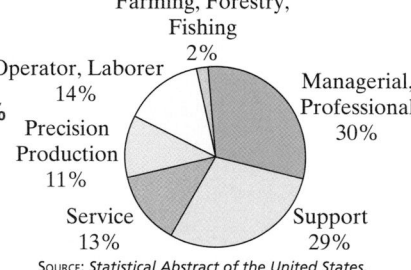

U.S. Employment, by Occupation

Farming, Forestry, Fishing 2%
Operator, Laborer 14%
Managerial, Professional 30%
Precision Production 11%
Service 13%
Support 29%

Source: *Statistical Abstract of the United States.*
Go to **www.PHSchool.com** for a data update.
Web Code: agg-2041

A jar contains four blue marbles and two red marbles. Suppose you choose a marble at random, and do not replace it. Then you choose a second marble. Find the probability of each event.

36. You select a blue marble and then a red marble. $\frac{4}{15}$

37. You select a red marble and then a blue marble. $\frac{4}{15}$

38. One of the marbles you select is blue and the other is red. $\frac{8}{15}$

39. Both of the marbles you select are red. $\frac{1}{15}$

40. You select two red marbles or two blue marbles. $\frac{7}{15}$

Lesson Quiz 9-7

1. Classify each pair of events as dependent or independent.
   a. Flip a quarter. Then flip a penny. **independent**
   b. Choose a time for a Monday dental appointment. Then choose a time for that same Monday to meet a friend. **dependent**

2. M and N are independent events. If $P(M) = \frac{1}{6}$ and $P(N) = \frac{3}{10}$, find $P(M \text{ and } N)$. $\frac{1}{20}$

3. Two standard number cubes are tossed. State whether the events are mutually exclusive.
   a. The product is greater than 6; the sum is less than 7. **no**
   b. The sum is odd; the product is odd. **yes**

4. A spinner has ten equal-size sections numbered from 1 to 10. Find the probability of each event when you spin the spinner.
   a. $P(\text{even or multiple of 5})$ $\frac{3}{5}$
   b. $P(\text{multiple of 3 or multiple of 4})$ $\frac{1}{2}$

Alternative Assessment

Have students work individually. Tell students to imagine that they have two spinners. One spinner has five equal-size sections numbered 1 to 5. The other spinner has seven equal-size sections labeled A through G. Ask students to give two examples of independent events X and Y and two examples of mutually exclusive events R and Q that are based on this situation. Then ask them to calculate $P(X \text{ and } Y)$ and $P(R \text{ or } Q)$ for the events in their examples.

H and J are not mutually exclusive events. Copy and complete the table below to find each missing probability.

	$P(H)$	$P(J)$	$P(H \text{ and } J)$	$P(H \text{ or } J)$	
41.	$\frac{7}{11}$	$\frac{3}{11}$	■	$\frac{9}{11}$	$\frac{1}{11}$
42.	$\frac{1}{2}$	■	$\frac{1}{4}$	$\frac{2}{3}$	$\frac{5}{12}$
43.	■	$\frac{2}{5}$	$\frac{1}{5}$	$\frac{2}{3}$	$\frac{7}{15}$
44.	$\frac{2}{x}$	$\frac{3}{2x}$	$\frac{1}{x}$	■	$\frac{5}{2x}$

 45. **Tests** A multiple-choice test has four choices for each answer.
   a. What is the probability that a random guess on a question will yield the correct answer? $\frac{1}{4}$
   b. Suppose you need to make a random guess on three of the ten test questions. What is the probability that you will answer all three correctly? $\frac{1}{64}$

46. **Open-Ended** Describe two events that are not mutually exclusive. Estimate the probability of both events occurring. **Check students' work.**

47. **Error Analysis** Events F and G are mutually exclusive independent events. A student says that $P(F \text{ and } G)$ is greater than $P(F \text{ or } G)$. Explain how you can tell that the student is wrong. $P(F \text{ or } G) = P(F) + P(G)$ **and** $P(F \text{ and } G)$ $= P(F) \cdot P(G)$. **Since** $0 \leq P(F)$ **and** $P(G) \leq 1$, $P(F \text{ or } G) \geq P(F \text{ and } G)$.

C **Challenge**

Use the tables below for Exercises 48–50. One student from each school is chosen at random to be on a committee. Find each probability.

School A

Freshman	Sophomore	Junior	Senior
30%	27%	25%	18%

School B

Freshman	Sophomore	Junior	Senior
28%	28%	24%	20%

48. a junior from School A and a senior from School B **5%**

49. two juniors **6%**

50. a freshman or sophomore from School A and a senior from School B **11.4%**

51. Two number cubes are rolled. What is the probability that the sum is greater than 9 or less than 6? $\frac{4}{9}$

52. **Critical Thinking** Tatyana has $x + 2$ pens in the pocket of her backpack. Samuel has $2x - 1$ pens in the pocket of his backpack.
   a. Tatyana has 2 blue pens. Find the probability that she pulls out a blue pen at random.
   b. Samuel has $x - 3$ blue pens. Find the probability that he pulls out a blue pen at random.
   c. Find the probability that both Tatyana and Samuel pull out blue pens at random.
   d. Find the probability that either Tatyana or Samuel pulls out a blue pen at random.

52a. $\frac{2}{x + 2}$
   b. $\frac{x - 3}{2x - 1}$
   c. $\frac{2(x - 3)}{(x + 2)(2x - 1)}$
   d. $\frac{x^2 + 3x - 8}{(x + 2)(2x - 1)}$

Standardized Test Prep

A blank sheet of grids is available in the Test-Taking Strategies with Transparencies booklet. Give this sheet to students for practice with filling in the grids.

📁 **Resources**

For additional practice with a variety of test item formats:
- Standardized Test Prep, p. 531
- Test-Taking Strategies, p. 526
- Test-Taking Strategies with Transparencies

Exercises 53–58 Stress that the word *or* is used in nearly all of these exercises.

Use this information for Exercises 53–58.

Bag 1 contains 7 red marbles, 5 blue marbles, 3 yellow marbles, and 4 green marbles. Bag 2 contains 1 red pencil, 6 red pens, 2 blue pencils, and 10 blue pens.

Gridded Response

53. One marble is drawn from bag 1. What is the probability that the marble is red or yellow? $\frac{10}{19}$

54. One marble is drawn from bag 1. What is the probability that the marble is blue or not green? $\frac{15}{19}$

55. One marble is drawn from bag 1. What is the probability that it is blue or yellow or green? $\frac{12}{19}$

56. One item is drawn from bag 2. What is the probability that it is red? $\frac{7}{19}$

57. One item is drawn from bag 2. What is the probability that it is a pen or a red pencil? $\frac{17}{19}$

58. One item is drawn from bag 2. What is the probability that it is blue or a pencil? $\frac{13}{19}$

💻 **Take It to the NET**
Online lesson quiz at
www.PHSchool.com
Web Code: aga-0907

Mixed Review

Lesson 9-6

Solve each equation. Check your answer.

59. $\frac{1}{2} - x = \frac{x}{6}$ $\frac{3}{7}$

60. $\frac{2}{2x - 1} = \frac{x}{3} - \frac{3}{2}$ or 2

61. $\frac{3}{2x} - \frac{2}{3x} = 5$ $\frac{1}{6}$

Lesson 8-6

Solve each equation.

62. $\ln 2x = 3$ $\frac{e^3}{2} \approx 10.04$

63. $\ln x + \ln 2 = 6$ $\frac{e^6}{2} \approx 201.71$

64. $\ln x - \ln 4 = 5$ $4e^5 \approx 593.65$

65. $\ln x^2 + 1 = 5$ $\pm e^2 \approx \pm 7.39$

66. $\ln x^2 + \ln x = 6$ $e^2 \approx 7.39$

67. $e^x = 12$ $\ln 12 \approx 2.48$

68. $e^{x+1} = 8$ $3 \cdot \ln(2) - 1 \approx 1.08$

69. $e^{x^2} = 3$ $\pm \sqrt{1.1}$

70. $2e^{2x} + 1 = 5$ 0.3466

Algebra at Work

·· **Economist**

 Economists study the relationship between the supply of a product and public demand for it. A supply curve shows that the number of units a manufacturer produces will increase as the price of the item increases. A demand curve shows that the number of units sold will decrease as the price increases. The curves cross at a point that establishes a stable equilibrium price.

💻 **Take It to the NET** For more information about economists, go to **www.PHSchool.com**.
Web Code: agb-2031

Eliminating Answers

Many standardized tests are timed, and students cannot spend too much time on one question. It is often possible to save time by looking for easy ways to eliminate some of the choices in multiple choice items.

Resources

Test-Taking Strategies with Transparencies
• Transparency 9
• Practice sheet 33

Teaching Notes

Math Tip

For Example 1, you might ask for the approximate value of $\frac{3}{2 - \sqrt{27}}$. Help students see that since $\sqrt{27}$ is close to 5, the denominator is close to -3. Therefore, the value of the fraction is close to -1.

For Exercise 4, help students see that if the answer were 0, getting a red chip and a green chip would be impossible. But that possibility clearly does exist. Likewise, if 1 were the answer, getting a red and a green chip would be unavoidable. That is clearly not the case either.

Test-Taking Strategies with Transparencies

Test-Taking Strategy: Eliminating Answers

The easiest way to narrow down the answer choices in a multiple-choice item is to eliminate obviously wrong answers.

Solve $\frac{|2x + 16|}{x - 8} = 10$.

A. –4   B. 8   C. 10   D. 12

Look at each answer choice to see if it can be eliminated.

–4 If –4 is substituted then the denominator would be negative which would make the quotient negative. The given quotient is positive, so this answer choice can be eliminated.

8   If 8 is substituted, the denominator would be zero and division by zero is undefined. This answer choice can be eliminated.

The answer choice is either C or D. Substitute these choices for x to select the correct one. D is correct.

Solve these problems by eliminating answer choices.

1. Solve $\frac{625}{y} = -125$.

A. –25   B. –5   C. 5   D. 25

2. Solve $\frac{1295}{b} = 259$.

A. 5   B. 8   C. 10   D. 12

Solutions

1. B

2. A

Transparency 9

Before you try to find the answer to a problem, you may be able to eliminate some answer choices. Cross out the answers you eliminate in the test booklet, NOT on the answer sheet.

1 EXAMPLE

What is the best approximation to $\sqrt{105} - \frac{3}{2 - \sqrt{27}}$?

A. −5.1   **B.** 8.3   **C.** 11.2   **D.** 28.3

The denominator of $\frac{3}{2 - \sqrt{27}}$ is a negative number, so $\sqrt{105} - \frac{3}{2 - \sqrt{27}}$ is a positive number. Therefore, you can eliminate A.

Since $\sqrt{105}$ is close to 10, and $-\frac{3}{2 - \sqrt{27}}$ is a small positive number, $\sqrt{105} - \frac{3}{2 - \sqrt{27}}$ is a little larger than 10. You can eliminate B and D.

The correct answer must be C.

2 EXAMPLE

Solve $\frac{2x}{x + 2} = 1 + \frac{x}{x - 2}$.

A. $x = \frac{2}{3}, x = -2$, or $x = 2$

B. $x = \frac{2}{3}$

C. $x = 2$ or $x = -2$

D. $x = \frac{3}{2}$

The equation has denominators $x + 2$ and $x - 2$. Since the denominators cannot equal zero, you know that x cannot equal -2 or 2. You can eliminate A and C.

EXERCISES

1. What is the correct answer to Example 2? **B**

Explain how you can eliminate two of the answer choices for each problem.   2–4. See margin.

2. Solve $\frac{x}{x - 4} + 2 = \frac{3x}{x + 1}$.

A. $x = \frac{8}{7}$ **B.** $x = 4, x = \frac{8}{7}$ **C.** $x = \frac{7}{8}, x = -1$ **D.** $x = \frac{7}{8}$

3. What is the best approximation to $\sqrt{50} + \frac{1}{\sqrt{5} - 3}$?

A. 5.66   **B.** 5.76   **C.** 7.66   **D.** 7.67

4. A jar contains 3 red, 3 green, and 3 yellow chips. Two chips are drawn at random from the jar, without replacement. What is the probability that one chip is red and the other is green?

A. 0   **B.** $\frac{1}{9}$ **C.** $\frac{1}{4}$ **D.** 1

page 526   Test-Taking Strategies

2. The equation has denominators $x - 4$ and $x + 1$. Since the denominators cannot equal zero, you know that $x \neq 4$ or -1. You can eliminate B and C.

3. $\frac{1}{\sqrt{5} - 3}$ is a small negative number, and $\sqrt{50}$ is close to 7. So $\sqrt{50} + \frac{1}{\sqrt{5} - 3}$ is a little smaller than 7. You can eliminate C and D.

4. Since there are red and green chips, you know the probability cannot be 0. Since there are also yellow chips, you know the probability cannot be 1. You can eliminate A and D.

Chapter Review

Vocabulary

branch (p. 485)
combined variation (p. 480)
complex fraction (p. 506)
dependent events (p. 519)

independent events (p. 519)
inverse variation (p. 478)
mutually exclusive events (p. 521)
point of discontinuity (p. 491)

rational function (p. 491)
simplest form (p. 499)

 **Reading Math**
Understanding
Vocabulary

Take It to the NET
Online vocabulary quiz
at www.PHSchool.com
Web Code: agj-0951

Choose the correct vocabulary term to complete each sentence.

1. Two events are _?_ if they cannot happen at the same time. **mutually exclusive**

2. When the numerator and denominator of a rational expression are polynomials with no common divisors, the rational expression is in _?_. **simplest form**

3. When the outcome of one event does not affect the outcome of a second event, the two events are _?_. **independent events**

4. A part of the graph of an inverse variation is called a(n) _?_. **branch**

5. If a is a zero of the denominator of a function, the function has a(n) _?_ at $x = a$. **point of discontinuity**

Skills and Concepts

9-1 Objectives

▼ To use inverse variation (p. 478)

▼ To use combined variation (p. 480)

An equation in two variables of the form $y = \frac{k}{x}$ or $xy = k$, where $k \neq 0$, is an **inverse variation. Combined variation** is an extension of direct and inverse variation to more complicated relationships.

Suppose that x and y vary inversely. Write a function that models each inverse variation. Find y when $x = 5$.

6. $x = 10$ when $y = 15$
$y = \frac{150}{x}$; 30

7. $x = 30$ when $y = 2$
$y = \frac{60}{x}$; 12

8. $x = 6$ when $y = 30$
$y = \frac{180}{x}$; 36

If possible, write direct or inverse variation equations to model each relation.

9.

x	3	4	8
y	24	18	9

$y = \frac{72}{x}$

10.

x	11	13	15
y	15	13	11

not possible

11.

x	5	7	9
y	30	42	54

$y = -2x$

Write the function that models each relationship. Find z when $x = 4$ and $y = 8$.

12. z varies jointly with x and y. When $x = 2$ and $y = 2$, $z = 7$. $z = \frac{7}{4}xy$; 56

13. z varies directly with x and inversely with y. When $x = 5$ and $y = 2$, $z = 10$.
$13. z = \frac{4x}{y}$; 2

14. z varies directly with the cube of x and inversely with y. When $x = 3$ and $y = 3$, $z = 9$. $z = \frac{x^3}{y}$; 8

Describe the combined variation modeled by each equation.

15. $R = kmn^2$
R varies jointly with k, m and the square of n.

16. $W = \frac{k}{d^2}$
W varies inversely with the square of d.

17. $P = \frac{kx}{y^2z}$

17. P varies directly with x and inversely with the product of z and the square of y.

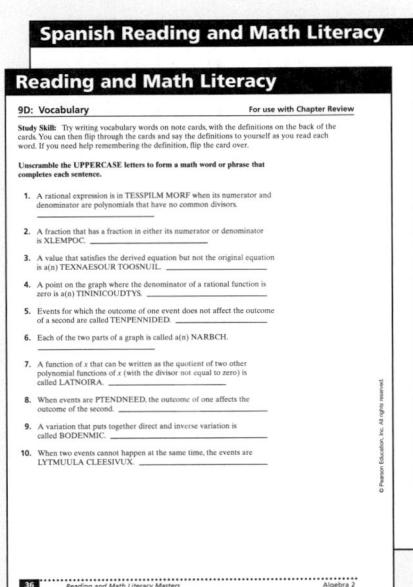

18.

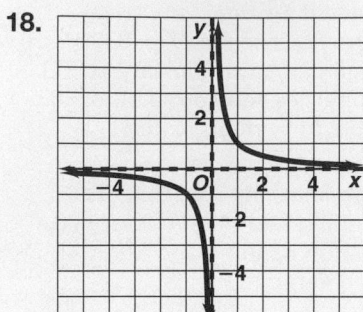

19.

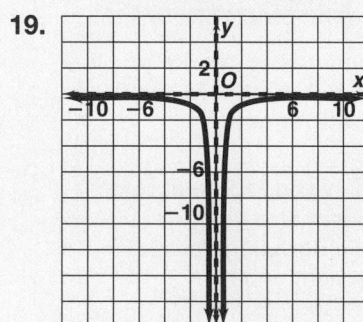

20.

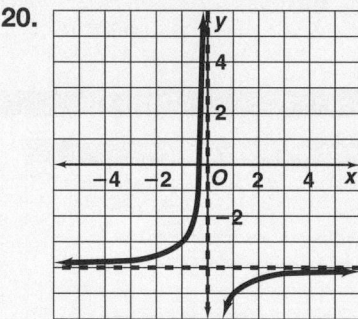

21.

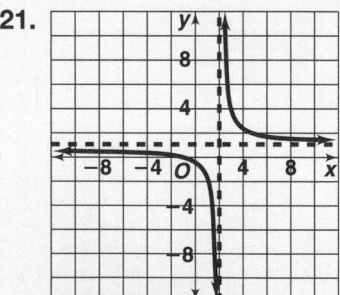

25.

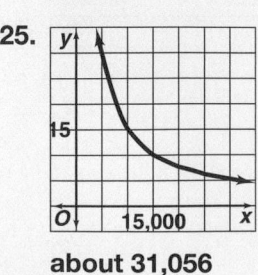

about 31,056 headsets

9-2 Objectives

▼ To graph inverse variations (p. 485)

▼ To graph translations of inverse variations (p. 487)

The graph of an inverse variation has two parts called **branches**. The graph of $y = \frac{k}{x - b} + c$ is a translation of $y = \frac{k}{x}$ by b units horizontally and c units vertically. It has a vertical asymptote at $x = b$ and a horizontal asymptote at $y = c$.

Sketch the graph of each equation. 18–21. See margin.

18. $y = \frac{1}{x}$

19. $y = \frac{-2}{x^2}$

20. $y = \frac{-1}{x} - 4$

21. $y = \frac{3}{x - 2} + 1$

Write an equation for the translation of $xy = 4$ that has the given asymptotes.

22. $x = 0, y = 3$
$y = \frac{4}{x} + 3$

23. $x = 2, y = 2$
$y = \frac{4}{x - 2} + 2$

24. $x = -3, y = -4$
$y = \frac{4}{x + 3} - 4$

9-3 Objectives

▼ To identify properties of rational functions (p. 491)

▼ To graph rational functions (p. 494)

The rational function $f(x) = \frac{P(x)}{Q(x)}$ has a **point of discontinuity** for each real zero of $Q(x)$. If $P(x)$ and $Q(x)$ have no common factors, then the graph of $f(x)$ has a vertical asymptote when $Q(x) = 0$. If $P(x)$ and $Q(x)$ have a common real zero a, then there is a hole or a vertical asymptote at $x = a$.

If the degree of $Q(x)$ is greater than the degree of $P(x)$, then the graph of $f(x)$ has a horizontal asymptote at $y = 0$.

If $P(x)$ and $Q(x)$ have equal degrees, then there is a horizontal asymptote at $y = \frac{a}{b}$, where a and b are the coefficients of the terms of greatest degree in $P(x)$ and $Q(x)$.

If the degree of $P(x)$ is greater than the degree of $Q(x)$, then there is no horizontal asymptote.

25. A headset can be manufactured for \$.17. The development cost is \$150,000. Graph the function that represents the average cost of a headset. About how many must be manufactured to result in a cost of less than \$5 per headset?
See margin.

30. $\frac{(x - 1)(x + 1)}{x + 3}$;
$x \neq -4, -3, \text{ or } 6$

31. $\frac{(2x - 1)(x + 1)}{x + 4}$;
$x \neq -4, -1, \text{ or } 0$

Find any points of discontinuity for each rational function. Sketch the graph. Describe any vertical or horizontal asymptotes and any holes. 26–29. See margin pp. 528–529.

26. $y = \frac{2.5}{x + 7}$

27. $y = \frac{x - 1}{(x + 2)(x - 1)}$

28. $y = \frac{x^3 - 1}{x^2 - 1}$

29. $y = \frac{2x^2 + 3}{x^2 + 2}$

9-4 and 9-5 Objectives

▼ To simplify rational expressions (p. 499)

▼ To multiply and divide rational expressions (p. 500)

▼ To add and subtract rational expressions (p. 504)

▼ To simplify complex fractions (p. 506)

A rational expression is in **simplest form** when its numerator and denominator are polynomials that have no common divisors. To add or subtract rational expressions with different denominators, write each expression with the least common denominator.

A fraction that has a fraction in its numerator or denominator or in both is called a **complex fraction**. You can simplify a complex fraction by multiplying the numerator and denominator by the LCD of all the rational expressions.

30–31. See above left.
Simplify each rational expression. State any restrictions on the variable.

30. $\frac{x^2 - 2x - 24}{x^2 + 7x + 12} \cdot \frac{x^2 - 1}{x - 6}$

31. $\frac{4x^2 - 2x}{x^2 + 5x + 4} \div \frac{2x}{x^2 + 2x + 1}$

---

26. −7

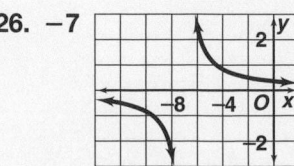

vertical asymptote $x = -7$, horizontal asymptote $y = 0$

27. −2, 1

vertical asymptote $x = -2$, horizontal asymptote $y = 0$, hole at $x = 1$

32. What is the ratio of the volume of a sphere to its surface area? $\frac{r}{3}$

33. A camera's focal length is 4 cm. If the lens is 6 cm from the film, what is the distance from the lens to an object that is in focus? **12 cm**

Simplify each expression.

34. $\dfrac{3x}{x^2 - 4} + \dfrac{6}{x + 2}$
$\dfrac{3(3x - 4)}{(x - 2)(x + 2)}$

35. $\dfrac{1}{x^2 - 1} - \dfrac{2}{x^2 + 3x}$
$\dfrac{-x^2 + 3x + 2}{x(x + 1)(x - 1)(x + 3)}$

36. $\dfrac{2 - \frac{2}{3}}{3 - \frac{1}{2}}$
$\dfrac{8}{15}$

37. $\dfrac{\frac{1}{x + y}}{4}$
$\dfrac{1}{4(x + y)}$

9-6 Objectives

▼ To solve rational equations (p. 512)

▼ To use rational equations in solving problems (p. 513)

Solving a rational equation often requires multiplying both sides by an algebraic expression. This may introduce an extraneous solution—a solution of a derived equation but not of the original equation. Check all possible solutions in the original equation.

Solve each equation. Check each solution.

38. $\dfrac{1}{x} = \dfrac{5}{x - 4}$ **−1**

39. $\dfrac{2}{x + 3} - \dfrac{1}{x} = \dfrac{-6}{x(x + 3)}$ **no solution**

40. $\dfrac{1}{2} + \dfrac{x}{6} = \dfrac{18}{x}$ **−12, 9**

41. One pump can fill a water cistern twice as fast as a second pump. Working together, the two pumps can fill the cistern in 5 hours. Find how long it takes each pump to fill the cistern when working alone. **7.5 h, 15 h**

9-7 Objectives

▼ To find the probabilities of events A and B (p. 519)

▼ To find the probabilities of events A or B (p. 521)

When the occurrence of one event affects the probability of another event, the two events are **dependent events**. When the occurrence of one event does not affect the probability of another event, the two events are **independent events**. When two events cannot happen at the same time, the events are **mutually exclusive events.**

If A and B are independent, then $P(A \text{ and } B) = P(A) \cdot P(B)$.

If A and B are mutually exclusive, then $P(A \text{ and } B) = 0$.

If A and B are mutually exclusive, then $P(A \text{ or } B) = P(A) + P(B)$.

If A and B are not mutually exclusive, then
$P(A \text{ or } B) = P(A) + P(B) - P(A \text{ and } B)$.

Classify each pair of events as *dependent* **or** *independent*.

42. A student in your algebra class is selected at random. One of the remaining students is selected at random. **dependent**

43. A number 1 through 6 is chosen by tossing a standard number cube. The same number cube is tossed again to select a number 1 through 6. **independent**

Two standard number cubes are tossed. State whether the events are mutually exclusive. **not mutually exclusive**

44. One of the numbers is 1 less than the other. The sum is odd.

45. The sum is greater than 10. Six is one of the numbers.
not mutually exclusive

A standard number cube is tossed. Find each probability.

46. a 5 or a 6 $\frac{1}{3}$

47. an even number or a number greater than 4 $\frac{2}{3}$

48. an odd number or a number less than or equal to 5 $\frac{5}{6}$

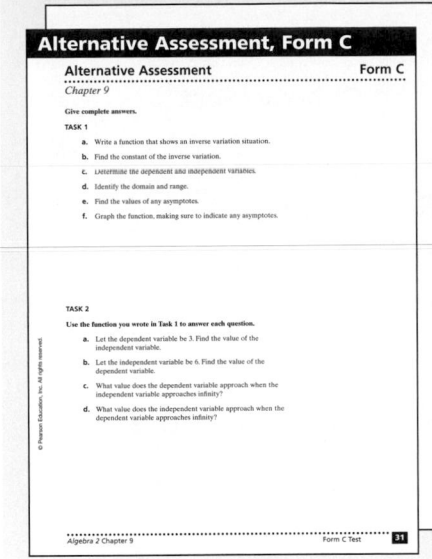
28. **1, −1**

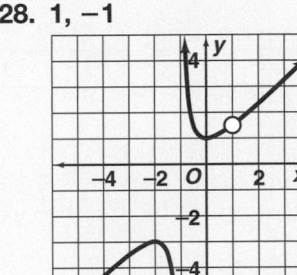

vertical asymptote
$x = -1$, **hole at** $x = 1$

29. **no points of discontinuity**

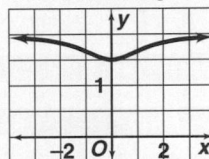

horizontal asymptote
$y = 2$

Chapter Test — Form B

Chapter Test — Form A

Chapter Test   Form A

Chapter 9

page 530   Chapter Test

9. **vertical asymptote** $x = 1$,
   horizontal asymptote
   $y = 1$

10. **hole at** $x = -3$

530

**Chapter
9**

Chapter Test

 ⋯⋯⋯
Take It to the NET
Online chapter test at
www.PHSchool.com
Web Code: aga-0952

Write a function that models each variation. $y = \frac{-16}{x}$

1. $x = 2$ when $y = -8$. y varies inversely with x.

2. $x = 0.2$ and $y = 3$ when $z = 2$. z varies jointly with
   x and y. $z = \frac{10}{3}xy$

3. $x = \frac{1}{3}, y = \frac{1}{5}$, and $r = 3$ when $z = \frac{1}{2}$. z varies
   directly with x and inversely with the product of
   r^2 and y. $z = \frac{2.7x}{r^2 y}$

**Is the relationship between the values in each table a
direct variation, an inverse variation, or neither? Write
an equation to model any direct or inverse variation.**

4.

x	3	5	7	9
y	6	8	10	12

neither

5.

x	4	6	8	10
y	10	8	6	4

neither

6.

x	4	8	16	32
y	32	16	8	4

inverse variation; $y = \frac{128}{x}$

Graph the translation of $y = \frac{7}{x}$ **with the given
asymptotes. Write the equation of the translation.**

7. $x = 1; y = 2$ 8. $x = -3; y = -2$
7–8. See back of book.

**For each rational function, identify any holes, or
horizontal or vertical asymptotes of its graph.**

9. $y = \frac{x + 1}{x - 1}$ 10. $y = \frac{x + 3}{x + 3}$

11. $y = \frac{x - 2}{(x + 1)(x - 2)}$ 12. $y = \frac{2x^2}{x^2 - 4x}$

13. $y = \frac{1}{x + 2} - 3$ 14. $y = \frac{5}{x - 2} + 1$

15. $y = \frac{x^2 + 5}{x - 5}$ 16. $y = \frac{x + 2}{(x + 2)(x - 3)}$

9–16. See margin.

**Simplify each rational expression. State any restrictions
on the variable.**

17. $\frac{x^2 + 7x + 12}{x^2 - 9}$ $\frac{x + 4}{x - 3}; x \neq -3$ or 3

18. $\frac{(x + 3)(2x - 1)}{x(x + 4)} \div \frac{(-x - 3)(2x + 1)}{x}$ **See back
of book.**

---

19. **Open-Ended** Write a function whose graph has
    a vertical asymptote, a horizontal asymptote,
    and a hole. **Check students' work.**

**Find the least common multiple of each pair
of polynomials.**

20. $3x + 5$ and $9x^2 - 25$ $9x^2 - 25$

21. $5(x + 3)(x + 1)$ and $2(x + 1)(x - 3)$
    $10(x + 3)(x + 1)(x - 3)$

Simplify each sum or difference.

22. $\frac{x + 2}{(x - 3)(x + 1)} + \frac{(x - 1)(x + 2)}{x - 3}$ $\frac{x^2(x + 2)}{(x - 3)(x + 1)}$

23. $\frac{x^2 - 1}{(x - 2)(3x - 1)} - \frac{x + 1}{x + 3}$ $\frac{(x + 1)(2x^2 - 9x + 5)}{(x - 2)(3x - 1)(x + 3)}$

24. $\frac{x(x + 4)}{x - 2} + \frac{x - 1}{x^2 - 4}$ $\frac{x^3 + 6x^2 + 9x - 1}{x^2 - 4}$

Simplify each complex fraction.

25. $\frac{\frac{2}{x}}{1 - \frac{1}{y}}$ $\frac{2y}{x(y - 1)}$ 26. $\frac{3 - \frac{3}{4}}{\frac{1}{2} - \frac{1}{4}}$ 9

Solve each equation. Check each solution.

27. $\frac{x}{2} = \frac{x + 1}{4}$ 1 28. $\frac{3}{x - 1} = \frac{4}{3x + 2}$ -2

29. $\frac{3x}{x + 1} = 0$ 0 30. $\frac{3}{x + 1} = \frac{1}{x^2 - 1}$ $\frac{4}{3}$

31. $\frac{1}{x} + \frac{1}{3} = \frac{6}{x^2}$ -6 or 3 32. $\frac{1}{x} + \frac{x}{x + 2} = 1$ 2

33. Almir can seal a driveway in 4 hours. Working
    together, he and Louis can seal it in 2.3 hours. How
    long would it take Louis to seal it working alone?
    ≈ 5.4 h

**Two standard number cubes are tossed. State whether
the events are mutually exclusive. Then find $P(A$ or $B)$.**

34. A means their sum is 12; B means both are odd
    mutually exclusive; $\frac{1}{9}$

35. A means they are equal; B means their sum is a
    multiple of 3 **not mutually exclusive;** $\frac{4}{9}$

36. a. **Writing** Suppose you select a number at random
       from the set $\{90, 91, 92, \ldots, 99\}$. Event A is
       selecting a multiple of 3. Event B is selecting a
       multiple of 4. Are these two events mutually
       exclusive? Explain.
    b. Find $P(A$ and $B)$. $\frac{1}{10}$
    c. Find $P(A$ or $B)$. $\frac{1}{2}$

    a. No; 96 is a
    multiple of both
    3 and 4.

---

11. hole at $x = 2$, vertical
    asymptote $x = -1$,
    horizontal asymptote $y = 0$

12. hole at $x = 0$, vertical
    asymptote $x = 4$, horizontal
    asymptote $y = 2$

13. vertical asymptote $x = -2$,
    horizontal asymptote
    $y = -3$

14. vertical asymptote $x = 2$,
    horizontal asymptote
    $y = 1$

15. vertical asymptote $x = 5$

16. hole at $x = -2$, vertical
    asymptote $x = 3$;
    horizontal asymptote at
    $y = 0$

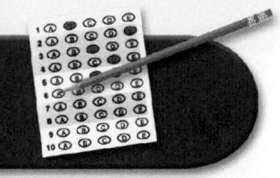

Standardized Test Prep

Reading Comprehension Read the passage below. Then answer the questions on the basis of what is *stated* or *implied* in the passage.

Payback Buying a house is the biggest investment most people ever make. So it's important to know how mortgage loans work.

Suppose you borrow $80,000 for a 30-year mortgage with an annual interest rate of 7.8%. The bank calculates a *monthly* interest rate (7.8% ÷ 12 = 0.0065) and uses it to calculate a monthly payment of $575.90. Each month, the bank adds the monthly interest to the current principal to get the balance, and then subtracts the payment to get the new principal.

End of Month	Current Principal	Amount of Interest	Balance	Payment	New Principal
1	80,000.00	520.00	80,520.00	575.90	79,944.10
2	79,944.10	519.64	80,463.74	575.90	79,887.84
3	79,887.84	519.27	80,407.11	575.90	79,831.21

You can calculate the monthly payment for any mortgage with the formula $P = \dfrac{A \cdot m(1 + m)^{12y}}{(1 + m)^{12y} - 1}$. P is the monthly payment, A is the amount borrowed, m is the monthly interest rate, and y is the length of the mortgage in years.

If you know the monthly payment you want to make, you can use the formula $A = \dfrac{P\left[(1 + m)^{12y} - 1\right]}{m(1 + m)^{12y}}$ to find the total amount you can borrow.

---

1. For the mortgage loan described above, what will be the 4th month's balance after the interest is added to the principal? **D**
   A. $518.90 B. $575.90
   C. $79,744.21 D. $80,350.11

2. If the annual interest for a loan is 8.55%, what is the monthly interest rate? **I**
   F. 8.8375% G. 7.125
   H. 0.07125% I. 0.007125

3. Consider a 15-year mortgage for $65,000 with an annual interest rate of 6%. Rewrite the formula $P = \dfrac{A \cdot m(1 + m)^{12y}}{(1 + m)^{12y} - 1}$ by substituting values for A, m, and y. **See margin.**

4. To the nearest cent, what is the monthly payment for a 15-year mortgage loan of $65,000 with an annual interest rate of 6%? **$591.53**

5. To the nearest cent, what is the monthly payment for a 15-year mortgage loan of $65,000 with an annual interest rate of 7.5%? **$659.27**

6. Suppose you want to make a monthly mortgage payment of $675.00. To the nearest hundred dollars, what is the most you can borrow for a 25-yr mortgage with an annual interest rate of 7.2%? **$82,900**

7. Show how to derive the formula $A = \dfrac{P\left[(1 + m)^{12y} - 1\right]}{m(1 + m)^{12y}}$ from the formula $P = \dfrac{A \cdot m(1 + m)^{12y}}{(1 + m)^{12y} - 1}$. **See margin.**

Students must be able to extract information from reading passages, answer multiple choice questions, and construct responses in order to be successful on current state and national assessments.

To answer the questions, students apply skills and concepts from this chapter and previous chapters.
Multiple Choice: Items 1–2
Extended Response: Items 3–7

Resources

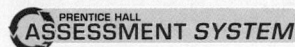 **Teaching Resources**
Cumulative Review

 **Reaching All Students**
Spanish Cumulative Review

 **ASSESSMENT SYSTEM**

Standardized Test Prep
• Ch. 9 Standardized Test Practice
Assessment Masters
• Cumulative Review
Computer Test Generator CD
• Standardized Test Practice

www.PHSchool.com
• Standardized Test Practice
• Resources

Plus **iTEXT**

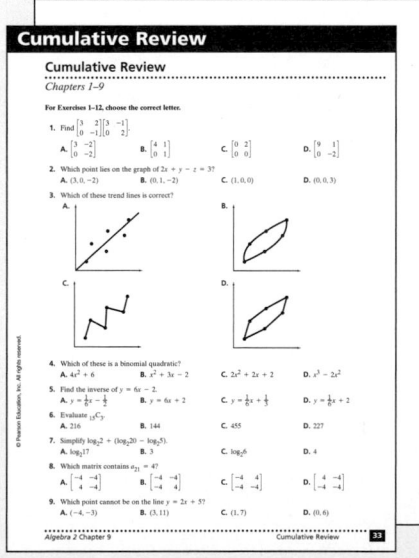

---

page 531 Standardized Test Prep

3. $P = \dfrac{65{,}000 \cdot 0.005 \, (1.005)^{180}}{(1.005)^{180} - 1}$

7. $P = \dfrac{A \cdot m \, (1 + m)^{12y}}{(1 + m)^{12y} - 1}$

$P\left[(1 + m)^{12y} - 1\right] = A \cdot m \, (1 + m)^{12y}$

$\dfrac{P\left[(1 + m)^{12y} - 1\right]}{m(1 + m)^{12y}} = A$

Quadratic Relations

Chapter at a Glance  North Carolina Objectives

10-1	Exploring Conic Sections	2.09a, b
NCTM 2, 3, 10	▽ Graphing Equations of Conic Sections ▽ Identifying Conic Sections	

10-2	Parabolas	2.09a, b
NCTM 2, 3, 6	▽ Writing the Equation of a Parabola ▽ Graphing Parabolas	

10-3	Circles	2.09a, b
NCTM 2, 3, 6	▽ Writing the Equation of a Circle ▽ Using the Center and Radius of a Circle	

10-4	Ellipses	
NCTM 2, 3, 6	▽ Writing the Equation of an Ellipse ▽ Finding and Using the Foci of an Ellipse	

10-5	Hyperbolas	
NCTM 2, 3, 6	▽ Graphing Hyperbolas Centered at the Origin ▽ Using the Foci of a Hyperbola	

10-6	Translating Conic Sections	2.09a, b
NCTM 2, 3, 6	▽ Writing Equations of Translated Conic Section ▽ Identifying Translated Conic Sections	

NCTM STANDARDS 2000

1	Number and Operations	6	Problem Solving
2	Algebra	7	Reasoning and Proof
3	Geometry	8	Communication
4	Measurement	9	Connections
5	Data Analysis and Probability	10	Representation

Pacing Options

This chart suggests pacing only for the lessons and their parts. It is provided as a possible guide. It will help you determine how much time you have in your schedule to cover other components, such as the features, Chapter Review, and Chapter Test.

Day	Traditional (45 min.)	Block (90 min.)
1	10-1 ▽	10-1 ▽ ▽
2	10-1 ▽	10-2 ▽ ▽
3	10-2 ▽ ▽	10-3 ▽ ▽
4	10-3 ▽	10-4 ▽ ▽
5	10-3 ▽	10-5 ▽ ▽
6	10-4 ▽	10-6 ▽ ▽
7	10-4 ▽	
8	10-5 ▽	
9	10-5 ▽	
10	10-6 ▽ ▽	

NAEP Correlation (National Assessment of Educational Progress 2000 Mathematics Objectives)

10-1	10-2	10-3	10-4	10-5	10-6
G4b, G9b	G9b	G9b, G63	G9b	G9b	G9b, G3b

N = Number Sense, Properties, and Operations; **M** = Measurement; **G** = Geometry and Spatial Sense;
D = Data Analysis, Statistics, and Probability; **A** = Algebra and Functions

Math Background

Chapter Overview

The ancient Greeks defined a conic section as the intersection of a plane and a double cone. Much later, it was shown how to give simple definitions using loci and two-dimensional coordinate geometry. The definitions used in most present-day textbooks are analytic geometry definitions thanks to the work of Germinal Pierre Dandelin, a 19th century French mathematician who studied the connections between the three-dimensional and two-dimensional approaches.

Conic sections are extremely important in astronomy and in many parts of physics and technology. A number of interesting applications of conic sections are presented in the chapter.

Exploring Conic Sections   10-1

A plane that contains the vertex of a double cone will intersect the cone in a pair of intersecting lines (a degenerate hyperbola), a single line (a degenerate parabola), or a single point (the vertex of the cone, a degenerate ellipse). Other planes will intersect the cone in a parabola, an ellipse (which may be a circle), or a hyperbola. Students explore these curves by graphing equations that describe them.

Parabolas   10-2

Students have learned that the graph of a quadratic function is a parabola. Here the standard locus definition is presented. The first example shows how the locus definition yields a quadratic function. Students must become familiar with the terms focus and directrix and relate these terms to equations and graphs.

Circles and Ellipses   10-3, 10-4

A locus definition of an ellipse is presented. Again, students must become familiar with the terms foci, major axis, minor axis, vertices, and co-vertices of an ellipse.

You may wish to suggest that interested students use the distance formula to show how to obtain the standard-form equation for the ellipse with center at the origin and foci at $(-4, 0)$ and $(4, 0)$,
given that the sum of the distances from a point on the ellipse to the foci is 10.

A circle is a special case of an ellipse in which the major axis and the minor axis have the same length. So, $a = b$ and $c = 0$, and the foci of a circle centered at the origin are at the origin, which is also the center of the circle. The radius a or b is usually called r.

Hyperbolas   10-5

The work with hyperbolas parallels that for ellipses. Emphasize to students the importance of drawing the asymptotes to help sketch a graph.

To make a connection between the equation of a rectangular hyperbola and an equation in standard form, consider the hyperbola $xy = 1$. Its center is at $(0, 0)$ and one vertex is at $(1, 1)$. Explain to students that, in future courses, they will learn to use trigonometric functions to re-orient (rotate) such a hyperbola, so that its equation can then be written in a standard form with $a = b = \sqrt{2}$. Note that this is the distance from the origin to the vertex in either form.

Translating Conic Sections   10-6

It can be shown that the graphs of second-degree equations of the form $Ax^2 + Bxy + Cy^2 + Dx + Ey + F = 0$ (A and C not both 0) are either conics, degenerate conics, two parallel lines, or the null set. The determining fact is the value of $B^2 - 4AC$. Suppose A, B, and C are not all 0 and the graph is not degenerate. (Note B is the coefficient of xy, not of y^2 as in the lesson.)

- If $B^2 - 4AC < 0$, then the graph is a circle or an ellipse. (For a circle, $A = C$ and $B = 0$.)

- If $B^2 - 4AC = 0$, then the graph is a parabola.

- If $B^2 - 4AC > 0$, then the graph is hyperbola.

Some students may observe that in this text, it is always true that $B = 0$. Assure them that later work using trigonometry to rotate graphs will convince them that this causes no loss of generality.

 # Ongoing Assessment and Intervention

Tools for Monitoring Student Progress

The Prentice Hall *Algebra 2* program provides you with many options for assessment in the Student Edition, the Teacher's Edition and the teaching resources. From these options you may choose instructional materials and techniques that are appropriate for your students and support your district's curriculum requirements.

Instant Check System™ in Chapter 10

Allows students to check their own learning before, during, and after each lesson.

Diagnosing Readiness before the chapter (p. 532)

Check Skills You'll Need exercises in each lesson (pp. 535, 543, 549, 556, 562, 570)

Check Understanding questions with each Example (pp. 536, 537, 538, 544, 545, 546, 550, 551, 552, 557, 558, 564, 565, 569, 571, 572, 573)

Checkpoint Quiz (pp. 554, 568)

Test Prep in Chapter 10

Teaches students strategies and gives them practice with all the test item formats they will encounter on state tests and standardized national exams.

Standardized Test Prep exercises in each lesson (pp. 540, 548, 554, 561, 567, 576)

Test-Taking Strategies (p. 578)

Standardized Test Prep (p. 583)

All your assessment needs in one place!

Program Assessment

Assess student progress throughout the *Algebra 2* text with blackline masters and CD-ROM.

Assessment Resources

- Checkpoint Quizzes 1 & 2
- Chapter Test, Forms A & B
- Chapter Alternative Assessment

Spanish versions available.

Computer Test Generator

- Unlimited questions of varying difficulty for every lesson objective.
- Create your own practice sheets, quizzes, and tests, or use the pre-made Chapter Tests.
- Diagnose readiness with questions on prerequisite skills.
- Prepare students by making tests based on standardized test objectives.
- Access Algebra 1, Geometry, and Algebra 2 content—all on one CD-ROM.

Test Preparation

A three-step approach to preparing students for high stakes, national, and state exams.

❶ **Diagnose & Prescribe**

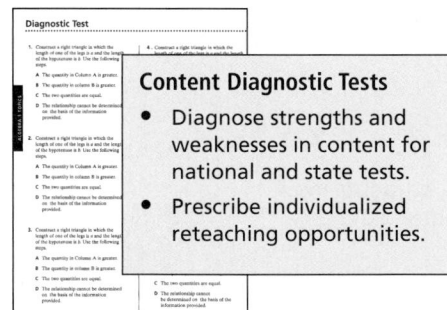

Content Diagnostic Tests

- Diagnose strengths and weaknesses in content for national and state tests.
- Prescribe individualized reteaching opportunities.

❷ **Review & Reteach**

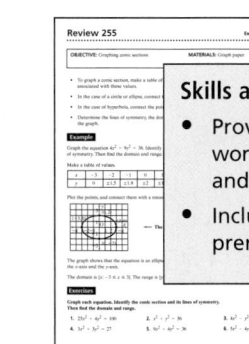

Skills and Concepts Review

- Provides reteaching worksheets with instruction and practice for each skill.
- Includes course prerequisite skills.

❸ **Practice & Assess**

Test Preparation

- Features practice tests for End-of-Course and SAT/ACT exams.
- Includes standardized test practice by chapter for ongoing review.

Teacher's Guide with answers and correlations.

Test-Taking Strategies with Transparencies

- Support the Test-Taking Strategies pages in the Student Edition.
- Provide a teaching transparency and a practice worksheet for each strategy.

👥 Reaching All Students

Support in the Student Text and Additional Resources

The textbook, the iText, and other technology components provide numerous opportunities to reach students of various ability levels and learning styles. Each Teacher's Edition lesson suggests how you can help *all* your students be successful and understand the mathematics in Chapter 10.

Below Level

Student Edition
- Diagnosing Readiness*: p. 532
- Check Skills You'll Need*: pp. 535, 543, 549, 556, 562, 570

Reteaching
Chapter 10 Support File: pp. 8–13

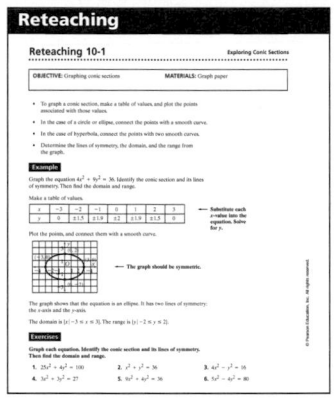

Advanced Learners

Student Edition
- Challenge exercises: pp. 540, 548, 553, 554, 560, 561, 567, 575, 576
- Extension, pp. 555, 557

Enrichment
Chapter 10 Support File: pp. 14–19

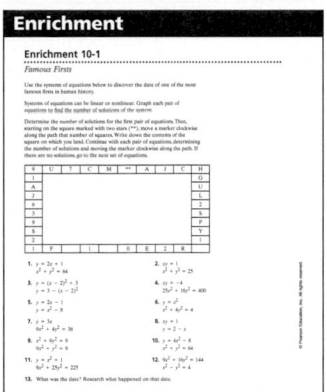

Connections to Precalculus Masters
Chapter 10 Enrichment Topic:
Polar Coordinates

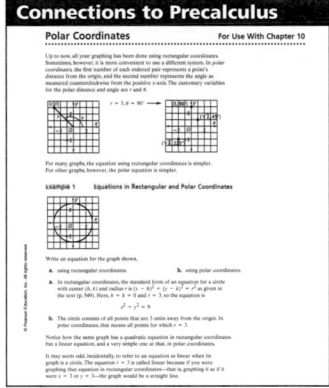

* Can be used with all ability levels to ensure mastery of prerequisite skills.

📖 Reading and Math Literacy

Student Edition
- Vocabulary: pp. 533, 579, *plus* in every Lesson Preview
- Reading Math: pp. 538, 540, 556, 559, 562, 566, 569
- Illustrated Glossary: pp. 871–913

Reading and Math Literacy Masters
Chapter 10: pp. 37–40

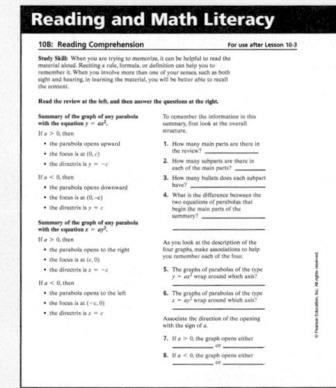

English Learners

Student Edition
- English/Spanish Illustrated Glossary: pp. 871–913

Workbook and Masters
Spanish Practice Workbook: pp. 2–7
Spanish Reading and Math Literacy Masters: pp. 37–40

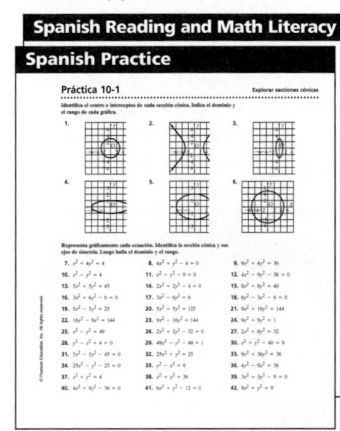

Learning Styles

Student Edition
- Investigation: pp. 534, 562, 570
- Technology: pp. 542, 550, 555
- Writing: pp. 539, 542, 547, 553, 555, 560, 566, 574, 577, 582
- DK Activities: pp. 584–585

Activity Masters
Hands-On Activities: 51, 52
Technology Activities: 13, 29, 34, 38

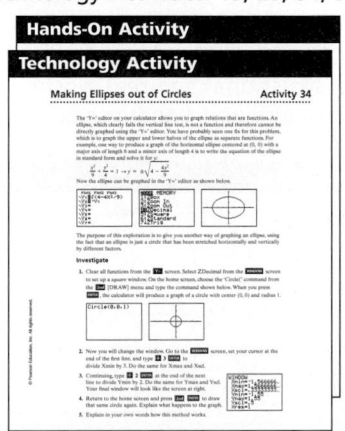

Program Resources

	Teaching Resources in Grab & Go™ Files				Resources for Reaching All Students			Spanish Resources			Transparencies (Presentation Assistant Plus!)				Prentice Hall Presentation Pro CD-ROM
	Practice	Reteach	Enrich	Checkpoint Quiz	Reading & Math Literacy	Technology Activities	Hands-On Activities	Practice	Reading & Math Literacy	Checkpoint Quiz	Skills Check	Additional Examples	Answers to Exercises	Lesson Quiz	
10-1	■	■	■		■	■		■	■		■	■	■	■	■
10-2	■	■	■			■		■				■	■	■	■
10-3	■	■	■	■	■			■	■	■	■	■	■	■	■
10-4	■	■	■			■	■	■			■	■		■	■
10-5	■	■	■	■	■		■	■		■	■	■	■	■	■
10-6	■	■	■			■		■			■	■	■	■	■
For the chapter	Chapter Tests, Alternative Assessment, Cumulative Review, Cumulative Assessment				Connections to Precalculus Masters			Spanish Chapter Tests, Alternative Assessment, Cumulative Review, Cumulative Assessment			Classroom Aid Transparencies				

Also available for use with the chapter:

 PRENTICE HALL ASSESSMENT *SYSTEM* *See page 532C.*

- Practice Workbook
- Solution Key

- For teacher support and access to student Web site materials, use Web Code agk-5500.
- For additional online and technology resources, see below.

Technology

 iTEXT Online and on CD-ROM

Complete Interactive Student Text online and on CD-ROM—with instant feedback assessment, tutorial help, dynamic activities, instructional and real-world videos, audio, and additional practice.

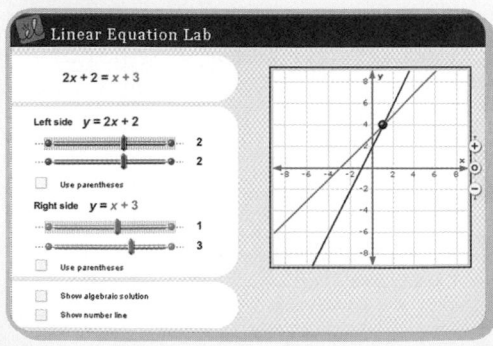

www.PHSchool.com For Students

Use **Web Codes** for easy access to online activities, chapter projects, self-grading lesson quizzes and chapter tests, vocabulary quizzes, updated data sources, graphing calculator procedures, and more.

PH SuccessNet For Teachers

Online lesson planning with built-in state correlations, all the teaching resources, complete reference library, your own calendar and Teacher Web page, professional development, and more.

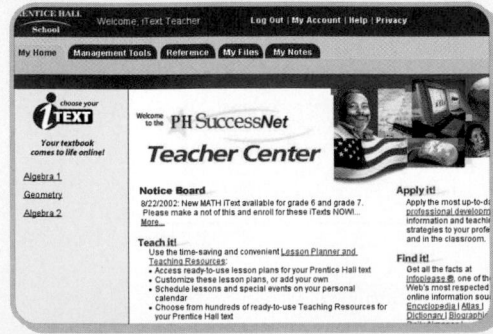

Presentation Assistant Plus!

The Prentice Hall *Presentation Assistant Plus!* provides you with the material you need to teach a lesson from beginning to end. Two easy-to-use formats—Transparencies and CD-ROM—allow you to present a lesson the way you are most comfortable.

Transparencies

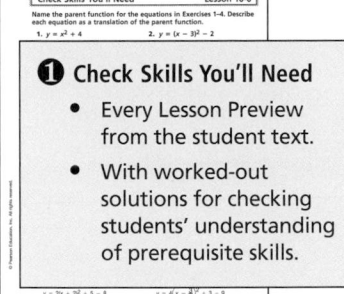

❶ Check Skills You'll Need
- Every Lesson Preview from the student text.
- With worked-out solutions for checking students' understanding of prerequisite skills.

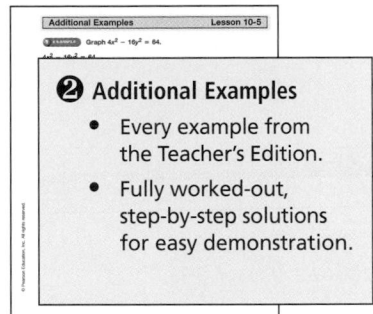

❷ Additional Examples
- Every example from the Teacher's Edition.
- Fully worked-out, step-by-step solutions for easy demonstration.

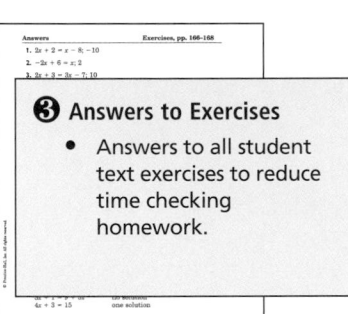

❸ Answers to Exercises
- Answers to all student text exercises to reduce time checking homework.

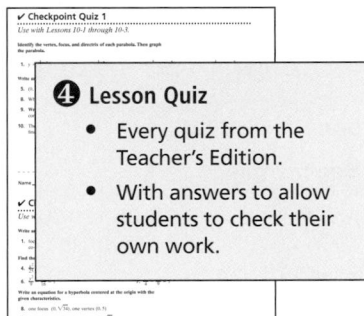

❹ Lesson Quiz
- Every quiz from the Teacher's Edition.
- With answers to allow students to check their own work.

 Throughout the Teacher's Edition, this symbol indicates material that is available on transparency in the Presentation Assistant Plus!

Prentice Hall Presentation Pro CD-ROM

- Includes all Transparencies.
- Conveniently organized by lesson so you can easily ❶ Introduce, ❷ Teach, ❸ Check Homework, and ❹ Assess each lesson.
- Animated examples allow step-by-step instruction at your own pace.
- Easy to edit so you can create custom presentations.

Teaching Chapter 10 Using Presentation Assistant Plus!

	❶ Introduce	❷ Teach	❸ Check Homework	❹ Assess
	Check Skills You'll Need	Additional Examples	Student Edition Answers	Lesson Quiz
10-1	p. 65	pp. 192–195	✔	p. 150
10-2	p. 66	pp. 196–199	✔	p. 151
10-3	p. 67	pp. 200–201	✔	p. 151
10-4	p. 68	pp. 202–203	✔	p. 152
10-5	p. 69	pp. 204–206	✔	p. 152
10-6	p. 70	pp. 207–210	✔	p. 153

Prentice Hall Presentation Pro

CD-ROM with dynamic PowerPoint® presentations for every lesson. Helps you introduce and develop concepts, check homework, and assess progress. Part of Presentation Assistant Plus! *(See above.)*

Computer Test Generator

CD-ROM to create practice sheets and tests for course objectives and standardized tests. Includes Instant Chapter Tests™, online testing, and student reports. Part of the PH Assessment System. *(See page 532C.)*

Resource Pro® with Planning Express®

CD-ROM with a lesson planning tool that allows you to import state and local objectives. Includes electronic versions of all the teaching resources.

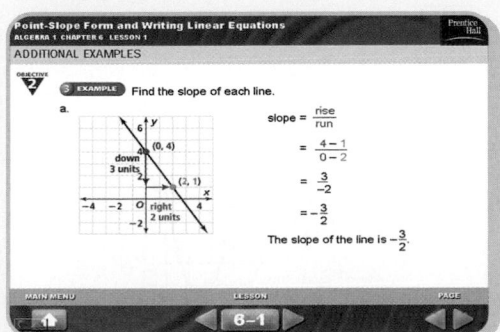

Chapter 10

Quadratic Relations

 Diagnosing Readiness

Students will find answers to these exercises in the back of their textbooks.

For intervention, direct students to:

Modeling Data with Quadratic Functions
Lesson 5-1: Example 1
Exercises 1–9
Extra Practice, p. 826

Properties of Parabolas
Lesson 5-2: Examples 1 and 2
Exercises 1–21
Extra Practice, p. 826

Completing the Square
Lesson 5-7: Examples 2 and 6
Exercises 7–12, 28–33
Extra Practice, p. 826

Theorems About Roots of Polynomial Equations
Lesson 6-5: Example 2
Exercises 7–12
Extra Practice, p. 827

Exploring Exponential Models
Lesson 8-1: Example 5
Exercises 24–31
Extra Practice, p. 829

---

page 532   Diagnosing Readiness

1. quadratic; $-x^2$, $6x$, 1

2. linear; none, $-12x$, -18

3. linear; none, x, $-\frac{13}{2}$

4. quadratic; $-8x^2$, $28x$, none

5. quadratic; $-2x^2$, $-3x$, 6

6. linear; none, $-x$, -10

7.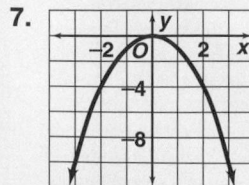

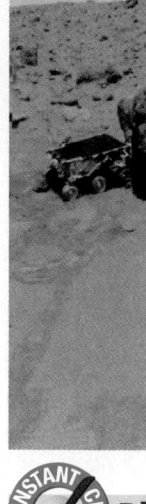

Where You've Been

- In Chapter 5, you learned to write and graph the equation of a parabola.

- In Chapter 5, you also learned to rewrite a quadratic equation by completing the square.

- In Chapter 8, you learned to locate the asymptote of the graph of an exponential function.

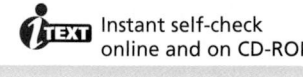 Instant self-check online and on CD-ROM

 **Diagnosing Readiness**   (For help, go to the Lesson in green.)

Identifying Quadratic Functions (Lesson 5-1)

Determine whether each function is linear or quadratic. Identify the quadratic, linear, and constant terms. **1–6. See margin.**

1. $y = 6x - x^2 + 1$ **2.** $f(x) = -2(3 + x)^2 + 2x^2$ **3.** $y = 2x - y - 13$

4. $y = 4x(7 - 2x)$ **5.** $g(x) = -2x^2 - 3(x - 2)$ **6.** $y = x - 2(x + 5)$

Graphing Quadratic Functions (Lesson 5-2)

Graph each function. **7–10. See margin.**

7. $y = -x^2$ **8.** $y = \frac{1}{3}x^2$ **9.** $y = 2x^2 + 5$ **10.** $y = x^2 + 6x + 8$

Completing the Square (Lesson 5-7)

Complete the square.

11. $x^2 + 8x + \blacksquare$ **16**   **12.** $x^2 - 5x + \blacksquare$ **$\frac{25}{4}$**   **13.** $x^2 + 14x + \blacksquare$ **49**

Rewrite each function in vertex form. Then graph the function. **14–16. See margin p. 533 for graphs.**

14. $y = x^2 + 6x + 7$
   $y = (x + 3)^2 - 2$

15. $y = 2x^2 - 4x + 10$
   $y = 2(x - 1)^2 + 8$

16. $y = -3x^2 + x$
   $y = -3\left(x - \frac{1}{6}\right)^2 + \frac{1}{12}$

Solving Polynomial Equations (Lesson 6-5)

Find all the roots of each polynomial equation.

17. $2x^3 - x^2 + 10x - 5 = 0$ $\frac{1}{2} \pm i\sqrt{5}$ **18.** $2x^3 - 5x^2 + 4x - 1 = 0$ $\frac{1}{2} \pm i\sqrt{5}$, **1**

Graphing Exponential Decay (Lesson 8-1)   **19–21. See back of book.**

Sketch the graph for each decay function. Label the asymptote.

19. $y = 8\left(\frac{1}{2}\right)^x$ **20.** $y = 2(0.4)^x$ **21.** $y = \left(\frac{3}{4}\right)^x$

8.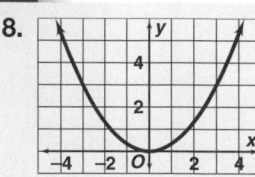

9.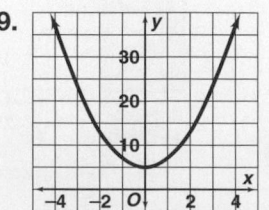

10.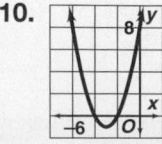

Quadratic Relations

LESSONS

Key Vocabulary

- center (p. 549)
- circle (p. 549)
- conic section (p. 535)
- co-vertices (p. 556)
- directrix (p. 543)
- ellipse (p. 556)
- focus of a parabola (p. 543)
- focus of an ellipse (p. 556)
- focus of a hyperbola (p. 563)
- hyperbola (p. 563)
- major axis (p. 556)
- minor axis (p. 556)
- radius (p. 549)
- standard form of an equation of a circle (p. 549)
- transverse axis (p. 563)
- vertices of an ellipse (p. 556)
- vertices of a hyperbola (p. 563)

Chapter 10 Overview

In this chapter, students learn that conic sections are curves that can be formed by intersecting a plane with a double cone. They learn how to graph parabolas, circles, ellipses, and hyperbolas, as well as how to identify the different conic sections from their equations. Students also learn to apply the same techniques that they used to translate parabolas in Lesson 5-3 to translate circles, ellipses, and hyperbolas.

Reading Math
Reading for Problem Solving, p. 569

Vocabulary
A complete list of terms, plus vocabulary exercises, appears in the Chapter Review, p. 579

Illustrated Glossary
Examples for each vocabulary term, plus definitions in both English and Spanish, appear starting on p. 871

Real-World Snapshots
See pages 584–585 for a real-world application of Conic Sections that utilizes Dorling Kindersley's (DK) unique graphic presentation.

Real-World Connections
Some of the applications you will find in this chapter are sound (10-1), solar energy (10-2), architecture (10-4), astronomy (10-4), air traffic control (10-5), and navigation (10-6)

www.PHSchool.com
Internet support for this chapter includes:
- Self-grading Vocabulary and Chapter 10 Tests
- Chapter Project
- Chapter Planner
- Ch. 10 Resources

Plus iTEXT

Where You're Going

- In Chapter 10, you will learn to use conic sections to model real-world problems.

- You will learn to graph parabolas, circles, ellipses, and hyperbolas.

- You will learn to identify the equation of a specific conic section by completing the square.

 Applying what you learn, on pages 584–585 you will do activities involving planetary exploration.

14.
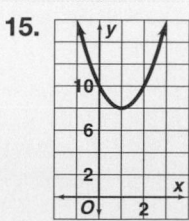

15.

16.
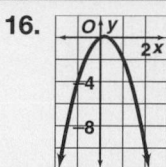

 **Investigation**

Conic Sections

Students learn that conic sections are curves that lie in a plane and are formed by intersecting a plane with a double cone. The templates and models created in this investigation will provide students with a visual for each of the conic sections studied in the rest of the chapter.

Resources

Students use paper, tape, scissors, and compasses to form cones and templates of conic sections.

Teaching Notes

Connection to History of Mathematics

An early study of conic sections is credited to the Greek Menaechmus in 350 B.C. In 225 B.C., Appollonius of Perga showed that conic sections could be formed by varying the inclination of a cutting plane to a double cone.

Tactile Learners

Extend the idea in the Investigation by challenging students to form the conic sections by cutting foam cones that they may obtain at a craft store. Have students slice the cones and paint the inside surfaces to show the shape of a parabola, an ellipse, and a circle. Students can hold the sections of the cones together by long pins. They may be able to pin two cones together to demonstrate the hyperbola. These sliced cones make excellent class models.

Investigation

Conic Sections

FOR USE WITH LESSON 10-1

A conic section is a special curve formed by the intersection of a cone and a plane. You can use paper cutouts to investigate conic sections.

Step 1 Draw two circular areas, each one measuring four inches in diameter. Cut out each circular area, and then cut it in half. Roll each half into a cone and secure it with tape.

Step 2 Trace the three templates below onto a sheet of paper. Cut out the parts corresponding to the white areas. The remaining parts corresponding to the blue areas are the templates. Label each one.

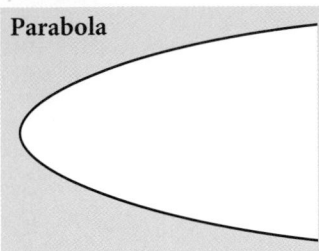

Parabola

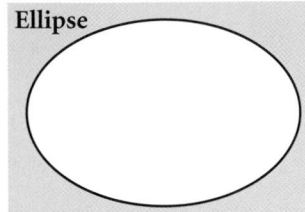

Ellipse

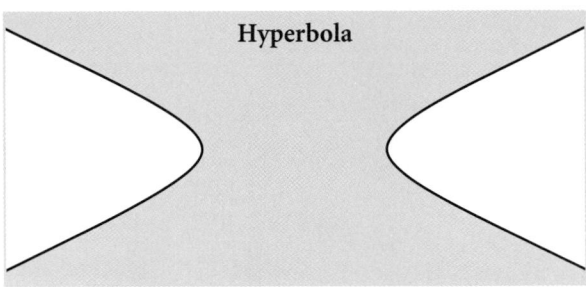

Hyperbola

Step 3 Make a fourth template for a circle. Use a compass or a coin of any size to draw the circle.

Step 4 Fit each template around the cones so that the template stays flat, like a plane. The ellipse is shown at the right. Sketch each result.

1a. Answers may vary. Sample: The individual cones must touch at their vertices, and the axes of the individual cones must align.

b. Answers may vary. Sample: Yes; the other three templates can fit around either of the two cones that form the double cone.

2a. 2 ways for the ellipse, 1 way for the parabola, 2 ways for the hyperbola, infinitely many ways for the circle

b. ellipse: 2 axes of symmetry; parabola: 1 axis of symmetry; hyperbola: 2 axes of symmetry; circle: infinitely many axes of symmetry

EXERCISES

1. a. The template for a hyperbola has two parts. Explain how you must position the cones to use this template as a model of a hyperbola.
b. Suppose you tried to fit your other three templates around a double cone. Would the results change? Explain.

2. a. Fold the template for each curve so that two halves coincide. In how many ways can you do this for each of the four templates?
b. How many axes of symmetry does each template have?

Exploring Conic Sections

North Carolina Objectives

2.09 Use the equations of parabolas and circles to model and solve problems. a) Solve using tables, graphs, and algebraic properties. b) Interpret the constants and coefficients in the context of the problem.

Lesson Preview

What You'll Learn

OBJECTIVE 1
To graph conic sections

OBJECTIVE 2
To identify conic sections

. . . And Why

To analyze Moiré patterns, as in Example 5

✔ Check Skills You'll Need

(For help, go to Lessons 2-2, 5-2, and 5-5.)

Find the x- and y-intercepts of the graph of each function.

1. $y = 3x + 6$ **−2, 6**   2. $2y = -x - 3$ **−3, −1.5**

3. $3x - 4y = -12$ **−4, 3**   4. $y = x^2 - 4$ **±2, −4**

5. $y = (x - 3)^2$ **3, 9**   6. $y = -4x^2 + 1$ **±0.5, 1**

New Vocabulary   • conic section

 Interactive lesson includes instant self-check, tutorials, and activities.

OBJECTIVE 1

Graphing Equations of Conic Sections

A **conic section** is a curve formed by the intersection of a plane and a double cone. By changing the inclination of the plane, you can create a circle, a parabola, an ellipse, or a hyperbola. You can use lines of symmetry to graph a conic section.

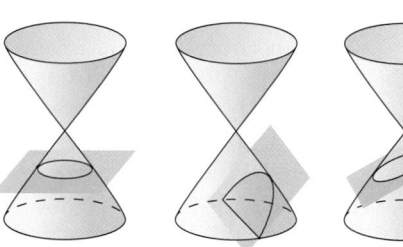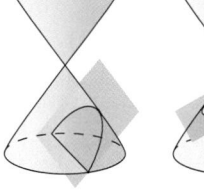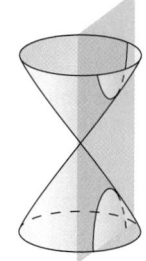

1 EXAMPLE   Graphing a Circle

Graph the equation $x^2 + y^2 = 25$. Describe the graph and its lines of symmetry. Then find the domain and range.

Make a table of values.

x	−5	−4	−3	0	3	4	5
y	0	±3	±4	±5	±4	±3	0

Plot the points and connect them with a smooth curve.

The graph is a circle of radius 5. Its center is at the origin. Every line through the center is a line of symmetry.

Recall from Chapter 2 that you can use set notation to describe a domain or a range. In this example, the domain is $\{x \mid -5 \le x \le 5\}$. The range is $\{y \mid -5 \le y \le 5\}$.

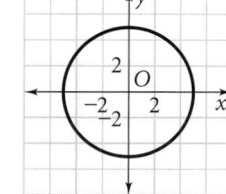

The photograph shows a double cone of illuminated smoke being intersected by a laser to produce a circle.

Lesson Preview

✔ Check Skills You'll Need

Linear Equations
Lesson 2-2: Example 2
Exercises 9–10
Extra Practice, p. 823

Properties of Parabolas
Lesson 5-2: Examples 1, 2
Exercises 1–21
Extra Practice, p. 826

Quadratic Equations
Lesson 5-5: Example 2
Exercises 7–12
Extra Practice, p. 826

Lesson Resources

📁 **Teaching Resources**
Practice, Reteaching, Enrichment

👥 **Reaching All Students**
Practice Workbook 10-1
Spanish Practice Workbook 10-1
Reading and Math Literacy 10A
Spanish Reading & Literacy 10A
Technology Activities 38

⏱ **Presentation Assistant Plus!**
Transparencies
• Check Skills You'll Need 10-1
• Additional Examples 10-1
• Student Edition Answers 10-1
• Lesson Quiz 10-1
PH Presentation Pro CD 10-1

PRENTICE HALL ASSESSMENT SYSTEM
Computer Test Generator CD

💿 **Technology**
Resource Pro® CD-ROM
Computer Test Generator CD
Prentice Hall Presentation Pro CD

💻 **www.PHSchool.com**
Student Site
• Teacher Web Code: agk-5500
• Graphing Calculator, Procedure 10
• Self-grading Lesson Quiz
Teacher Center
• Lesson Planner
• Resources

Plus

Before the Lesson
Diagnose prerequisite skills using:
• Check Skills You'll Need

During the Lesson
Monitor progress using:
• Check Understanding
• Additional Examples
• Standardized Test Prep

After the Lesson
Assess knowledge using:
• Lesson Quiz
• Computer Test Generator CD

Math Background

Conic sections are formed by the intersection of a plane and a double cone. An interesting topic for students to investigate is Dandelin spheres. Dandelin spheres help connect the 2- and 3-dimensional descriptions of conics.

OBJECTIVE

1 **Teaching Notes**

1 EXAMPLE **Math Tip**

Clarify that the graph is just the circular boundary. Points in the interior of the circle are not part of the graph. Have students pick any point in the interior of the circle, such as (2, 2), and, by substituting the point into the equation, demonstrate that the point does not satisfy the equation.

2 EXAMPLE **Auditory Learners**

Ask students to describe how the equation of a circle is different from the equation of an ellipse.

3 EXAMPLE **Teaching Tip**

Students may have difficulty writing the domain because of the gap between the two branches of the hyperbola. Students must take this gap into consideration when they write the domain. Hint that they can use absolute values to describe the domain.

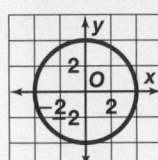 **Additional Examples**

1 Graph the equation $x^2 + y^2 = 16$. Describe the graph and its lines of symmetry. Then find the domain and range.

The graph is a circle of radius 4 with center (0, 0). Every line through the center is a line of symmetry;
domain: $\{x \mid -4 \le x \le 4\}$,
range: $\{y \mid -4 \le y \le 4\}$

536

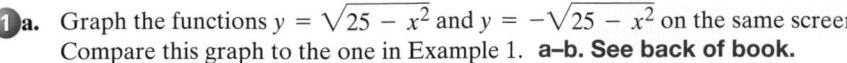

✔ **Check Understanding** **1** **a.** Graph the functions $y = \sqrt{25 - x^2}$ and $y = -\sqrt{25 - x^2}$ on the same screen. Compare this graph to the one in Example 1. **a–b. See back of book.**
 b. Explain how you can get the equations in part (a) from $x^2 + y^2 = 25$.
 c. **Critical Thinking** Why is there no point on the graph of Example 1 with an x-coordinate of 6? **When $x = 6$, $25 - x^2 = -11$. $\sqrt{-11}$ is not a real number.**

An ellipse is similar to a circle, but it has only two lines of symmetry.

2 EXAMPLE **Graphing an Ellipse**

Graph the equation $9x^2 + 16y^2 = 144$. Describe the graph and the lines of symmetry. Then find the domain and range.

Make a table of values.

x	−4	−3	0	3	4
y	0	±2.0	±3	±2.0	0

Plot the points and connect them with a smooth curve.

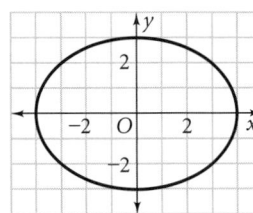

The graph is an ellipse. The center is at the origin. It has two lines of symmetry, the x-axis and the y-axis.

The domain is $\{x \mid -4 \le x \le 4\}$.
The range is $\{y \mid -3 \le y \le 3\}$.

✔ **Check Understanding** **2** **a.** How far are the x-intercepts from the center of the ellipse? How far are the y-intercepts from the center? Describe how an ellipse differs from a circle.
 b. The point (1, 2.9) is an approximation of a point on the graph of Example 2. Use symmetry to find three other approximate points on the ellipse.
 c. Graph the equation $2x^2 + y^2 = 18$. Describe the graph and give the coordinates of the x- and y-intercepts. **See back of book.**

2a. 4 units; 3 units; an ellipse is oblong instead of round. It has 2 axes of symmetry rather than infinitely many.

b. (1, −2.9), (−1, 2.9), (−1, −2.9)

Not all conic sections consist of one smooth curve. Note the unique shape of the hyperbola.

3 EXAMPLE **Graphing a Hyperbola**

Graph the equation $x^2 - y^2 = 9$. Describe the graph and its lines of symmetry. Then find the domain and range.

Make a table of values.

x	−5	−4	−3	−2	−1	0	1	2	3	4	5
y	±4	±2.6	0	−	−	−	−	−	0	±2.6	±4

Plot the points and connect them with smooth curves.

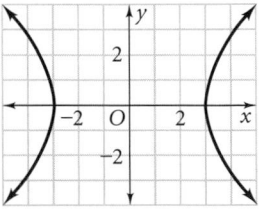

The graph is a hyperbola that consists of two branches. Its center is at the origin. It has two lines of symmetry, the x-axis and the y-axis.

The domain is $\{x \mid x \le -3 \text{ or } x \ge 3\}$. The range is all real numbers.

Here the laser intersects the smoke to produce an ellipse.

Here the laser intersects the smoke to produce a hyperbola.

536 Chapter 10 Quadratic Relations

👥 Reaching All Students

Below Level Remind students that among the conic sections, only parabolas may be functions.	**Advanced Learners** Have students research which types of conic sections are represented by orbits of astronomical objects.	**Inclusion** See note on page 537. **Auditory Learners** See note on page 536.

✓ **Check Understanding** **3** **a.** Does the graph in Example 3 represent a function? Explain.
b. In the table in Example 3, why is the *y*-value undefined when
$x = -2, -1, 0, 1,$ or 2? **a–b. See back of book.**
c. Critical Thinking What two lines does each branch of this hyperbola get
very close to? What are these lines called? **$y = x$ and $y = -x$; asymptotes**

OBJECTIVE

2 Identifying Conic Sections

The center and the intercepts are important points to identify on the graph of
some conic sections.

4 EXAMPLE Identifying Graphs of Conic Sections

Identify the center and intercepts of each conic section. Then find the domain and
range. In part (b), each interval on the graph represents one unit.

a.

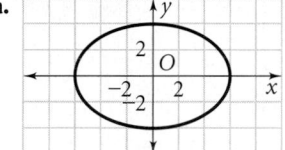

The center of the ellipse is $(0, 0)$. The *x*-intercepts are $(-6, 0)$ and $(6, 0)$, and
the *y*-intercepts are $(0, -4)$ and $(0, 4)$. The domain is $\{x \mid -6 \leq x \leq 6\}$, and the
range is $\{y \mid -4 \leq y \leq 4\}$.

b.

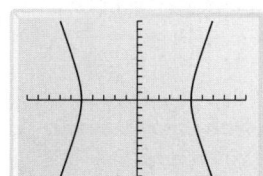

The center of the hyperbola is $(0, 0)$. The *x*-intercepts are $(-5, 0)$ and $(5, 0)$, and
there are no *y*-intercepts. The domain is $\{x \mid x \geq 5 \text{ and } x \leq -5\}$, and the range is
all real numbers.

✓ **Check Understanding** **4** Identify the center and intercepts of the conic section. Then find the domain and
range. Each interval represents one unit.   **center: (0, 0); no *x*-intercepts,**
y-intercepts: −4, 4; domain: all
real numbers, range: all *y* such that
$y \geq 4$ or $y \leq -4$

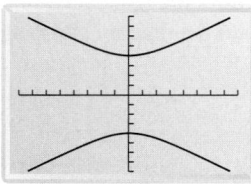

You will study each conic section in detail later in this chapter. Even before you
learn the details of the equations of conic sections, you can match the equations
with their graphs.

Lesson 10-1 Exploring Conic Sections   **537**

---

2 Graph the equation
$9x^2 + 4y^2 = 36$. Describe the
graph and the lines of symmetry.
Then find the domain and range.

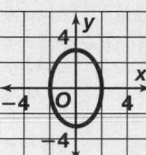

The graph is an
ellipse with center
(0, 0); there are
two lines of
symmetry, the
x-axis and
the *y*-axis. The domain is
$\{x \mid -2 \leq x \leq 2\}$. The range is
$\{y \mid -3 \leq y \leq 3\}$.

3 Graph the equation
$x^2 - y^2 = 4$. Describe the graph
and its lines of symmetry. Then
find the domain and range.

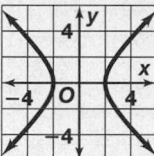

The graph is a
hyperbola that
consists of two
branches. Its
center is at the
origin. The lines
of symmetry are the *x*-axis and
the *y*-axis. The domain is
$\{x \mid x \leq -2 \text{ or } x \geq 2\}$. The range is
all real numbers.

OBJECTIVE

2 Teaching Notes

5 EXAMPLE Inclusion

Help visually impaired students
understand the patterns by
having other students describe
each pattern that is overlapped.
Then, guide the visually impaired
students' fingers over the shapes
of the overlapping patterns and
the unintended pattern.

Additional Examples

4 Identify the center and
intercepts of the conic section.

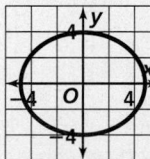

center: (0, 0); *x*-int: (±5, 0),
y-int: (0, ±4)

5 Determine whether each
equation models a circle, an
ellipse, or a hyperbola.
a. $25x^2 + 4y^2 = 100$ **ellipse**
b. $x^2 + y^2 = 4$ **circle**
c. $2x^2 - y^2 = 16$ **hyperbola**

Closure

Ask students to give an example
of an equation that models a
circle, an ellipse, and a hyperbola.
Then, ask students to explain how
they can identify each conic

section from its equation.
Answers may vary. Sample:
$x^2 + y^2 = 1, 4x^2 + y^2 = 4,$
$x^2 - y^2 = 1.$ **For conic sections**
centered at the origin students
should indicate that they can
be written in the form

$ax^2 + by^2 = c$, where $a = b > 0$
and $c > 0$ for a circle, $a \neq b$ and
$a, b, c > 0$ for an ellipse, and a
and b are of opposite signs with
$c > 0$ for a hyperbola.

537

Assignment Guide

 **Objective**

A B Core 1–16, 29–32, 35–40

C Extension 46, 48

 **Objective**

A B Core 17–28, 33, 34, 41–45

C Extension 47, 49

Standardized Test Prep 50–55

Mixed Review 56–73

Error Prevention

Exercises 1, 4 These equations describe hyperbolas with vertices on the *y*-axis, not the *x*-axis.

Diversity

Exercise 45 Students vary in their ability to visualize in three dimensions. Encourage students to work in pairs to discuss the figures they visualize. Students can increase their visualization skills with practice.

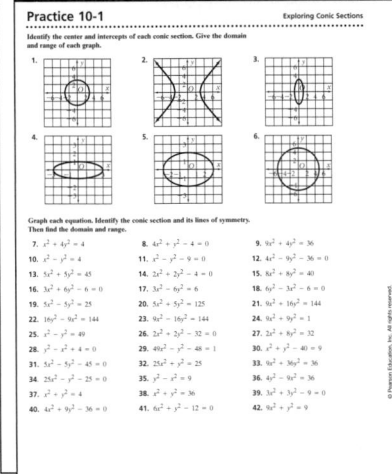

---

5 EXAMPLE **Real-World Connection**

 **Reading Math**

Moiré is a French word meaning "watered" or "wavy."

Design Moiré patterns are formed when two patterns, such as arrays of dots or lines, overlap to produce a third, unintended pattern. Moiré patterns cause problems for printers and video technicians. Describe each unintended pattern. Match it with one of these possible equations: $x^2 - y^2 = 1$, $x^2 + y^2 = 16$, or $9x^2 + 25y^2 = 225$.

a.

b.
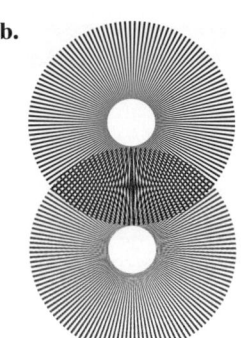

c.
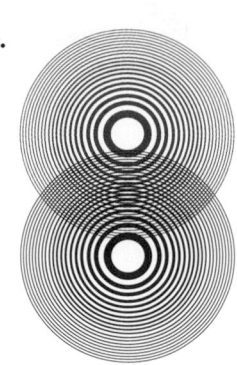

a. Ellipse: The equation $9x^2 + 25y^2 = 225$ represents a conic section with two sets of intercepts, $(\pm5, 0)$ and $(0, \pm3)$. Since the intercepts are not equidistant from the center, the equation models an ellipse.

b. Hyperbola: The equation $x^2 - y^2 = 1$ represents a conic section with one set of intercepts, $(\pm1, 0)$, so the equation must model a hyperbola.

c. Circle: The equation $x^2 + y^2 = 16$ represents a conic section with two sets of intercepts, $(\pm4, 0)$ and $(0, \pm4)$. Since each intercept is 4 units from the center, the equation models a circle.

✓ **Check Understanding** **a. Critical Thinking** What similarities do you notice among the three equations in Example 5? **a–b. See back of book.**
b. What differences do you notice?

EXERCISES

For more practice, see *Extra Practice*.

Practice and Problem Solving

A **Practice by Example**

Examples 1, 2, and 3
(pages 535 and 536)

Graph each equation. Identify the conic section and describe the graph and its lines of symmetry. Then find the domain and range. 1–16. See back of book.

1. $3y^2 - x^2 = 25$

2. $2x^2 + y^2 = 36$

3. $x^2 + y^2 = 16$

4. $3y^2 - x^2 = 9$

5. $4x^2 + 25y^2 = 100$

6. $x^2 + y^2 = 49$

7. $x^2 - y^2 + 1 = 0$

8. $x^2 - 2y^2 = 4$

9. $6x^2 + 6y^2 = 600$

10. $x^2 + y^2 - 4 = 0$

11. $6x^2 + 24y^2 - 96 = 0$

12. $4x^2 + 4y^2 - 20 = 0$

13. $x^2 + 9y^2 = 1$

14. $4x^2 - 36y^2 = 144$

15. $4y^2 - 36x^2 = 1$

16. $36x^2 + 4y^2 = 144$

538 Chapter 10 Quadratic Relations

---

pages 538–541 Exercises

17. center (0, 0), *x*-intercepts at ±3, *y*-intercepts at ±2; domain: −3 ≤ *x* ≤ 3, range: −2 ≤ *y* ≤ 2

18. center (0, 0), no *x*-intercepts, *y*-intercepts at ±2; domain: all real numbers, range: *y* ≤ −2 or *y* ≥ 2

19. center (0, 0), *x*-intercepts at ±3, no *y*-intercepts; domain: *x* ≤ −3 or *x* ≥ 3, range: all real numbers

Identify the center and intercepts of each conic section. Give the domain and range of each graph. On graphing calculator screens, each interval represents one unit.

17.
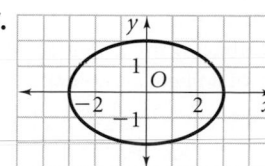

18.
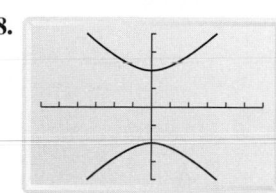

19.
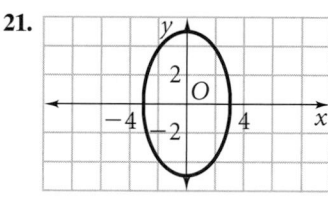

20.
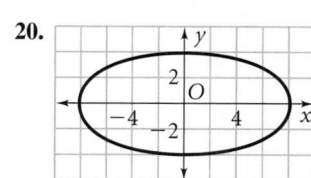

21.

22.
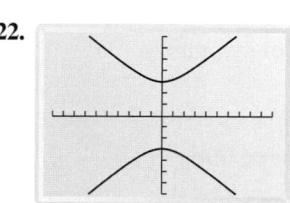

Example 5
(page 538)

Match each equation with a graph in Exercises 17–22.

23. $x^2 - y^2 = 9$ **19**

24. $4x^2 + 9y^2 = 36$ **17**

25. $y^2 - x^2 = 4$ **18**

26. $x^2 + 4y^2 = 64$ **20**

27. $25x^2 + 9y^2 = 225$ **21**

28. $y^2 - x^2 = 9$ **22**

B Apply Your Skills

Graph each equation. Describe the graph and its lines of symmetry. Then find the domain and range. 29–32. See margin.

29. $9x^2 - y^2 = 144$

30. $11x^2 + 11y^2 = 44$

31. $-8x^2 + 32y^2 - 128 = 0$

32. $25x^2 + 16y^2 - 320 = 0$

33. **a. Writing** Describe the relationship between the center of a circle and the axes of symmetry of the circle. **a–b. See back of book.**

   b. Make a Conjecture Where is the center of an ellipse or a hyperbola located in relation to the axes of symmetry? Verify your conjectures with examples.

34. **Light** The light emitted from a lamp with a shade forms a shadow on the wall. Explain how you could turn the lamp in relation to the wall so that the shadow cast by the shade forms each conic section. **a–d. See back of book.**

   a. hyperbola   **b.** parabola   **c.** ellipse   **d.** circle

Mental Math Each given point is on the graph of the given equation. Use symmetry to find at least one more point on the graph.

35–40. Answers may vary. Samples are given.

35. $(2, -4), y^2 = 8x$ **(2, 4)**

36. $(-\sqrt{2}, 1), x^2 + y^2 = 3$ **($\sqrt{2}$, 1)**

37. $(2, 2\sqrt{2}), x^2 + 4y^2 = 36$ **(−2, 2$\sqrt{2}$)**

38. $(-2, 0), 9x^2 + 9y^2 - 36 = 0$ **(2, 0)**

39. $(-3, -\sqrt{51}), 6y^2 - 9x^2 - 225 = 0$ **(−3, $\sqrt{51}$)**

40. $(0, \sqrt{7}), x^2 + 2y^2 = 14$ **(0, −$\sqrt{7}$)**

29.
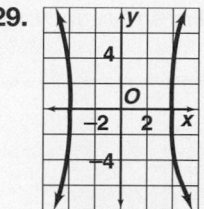

Hyperbola: center (0, 0), x-intercepts ±4, the lines of symmetry are the x- and y-axes; domain: $x \le -4$ or $x \ge 4$, range: all real numbers.

30.
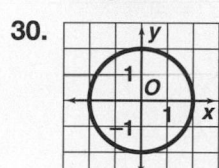

Circle: center (0, 0), radius 2, x- and y-intercepts at ±2, there are infinitely many lines of symmetry; domain: $-2 \le x \le 2$, range: $-2 \le y \le 2$.

31.
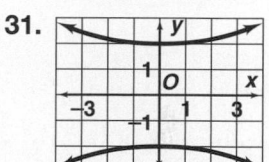

Hyperbola: center (0, 0), y-intercepts at ±2, the lines of symmetry are the x- and y-axes; domain: all real numbers, range: $y \le -2$ or $y \ge 2$.

32.
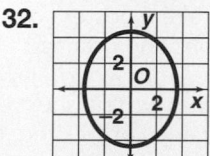

Ellipse: center (0, 0), x-intercepts at $\pm\frac{8\sqrt{5}}{5}$, y-intercepts at $\pm 2\sqrt{5}$, the lines of symmetry are the x- and y-axes; domain: $-\frac{8\sqrt{5}}{5} \le x \le \frac{8\sqrt{5}}{5}$, range: $-2\sqrt{5} \le y \le 2\sqrt{5}$.

20. **center (0, 0), x-intercepts at ±8, y-intercepts at ±4; domain: $-8 \le x \le 8$, range: $-4 \le y \le 4$**

21. **center (0, 0), x-intercepts at ±3, y-intercepts at ±5; domain: $-3 \le x \le 3$, range: $-5 \le y \le 5$**

22. **center (0, 0), no x-intercepts, y-intercepts at ±3; domain: all real numbers; range: $y \le -3$ or $y \ge 3$**

539

41. radius 6   **42.** radius $\frac{1}{2}$ **43.** diameter 8   **44.** diameter 2.5
41–44. See back of book.

45. Open-Ended Describe any other figures you can imagine that can be formed by the intersection of a plane and other shapes. **Check students' work.**

46. a. Graph the equation $xy = 16$. Use both positive and negative values for x.
    b. Which conic section does the equation appear to model? **hyperbola**
    c. Identify any intercepts and lines of symmetry.
    d. Does your graph represent a function? If so, rewrite the equation using function notation. **yes; $f(x) = \frac{16}{x}$**

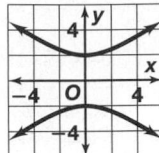

Lesson Quiz 10-1

Graph each equation.
Identify the conic section and determine its intercepts. Then, give the domain and range of each graph.

1. $2y^2 - x^2 = 8$

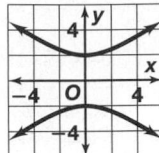

hyperbola, $(0, \pm 2)$;
domain: all real numbers,
range: $\{y \mid -\infty < y \le -2$ or $2 \le y < \infty\}$

2. $16x^2 + 25y^2 = 400$

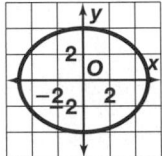

ellipse, x-int: $(\pm 5, 0)$,
y-int: $(0, \pm 4)$;
domain: $\{x \mid -5 \le x \le 5\}$,
range: $\{y \mid -4 \le y \le 4\}$

3. $2x^2 + 2y^2 = 50$

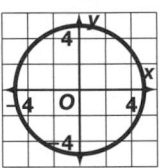

circle, x-int: $(\pm 5, 0)$,
y-int: $(0, \pm 5)$;
domain: $\{x \mid -5 \le x \le 5\}$,
range: $\{y \mid -5 \le y \le 5\}$

C Challenge

46a.

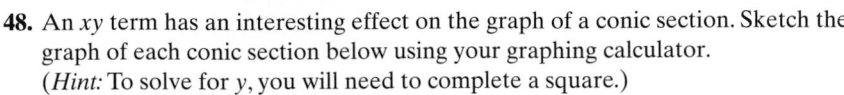

c. No intercepts, but $y = x$ and $y = -x$ are lines of symmetry.

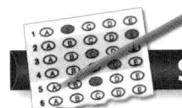

Reading Math

Cone comes from the Indo-European word for "sharpen." Section comes from the word for "cut."

47. The sharpened portion of the pencil at the right meets each painted side in a curved path. Describe the curve and justify your reasoning. **See margin.**

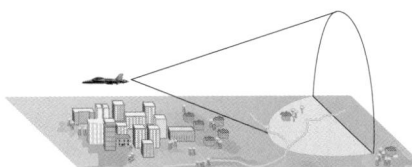

48. An xy term has an interesting effect on the graph of a conic section. Sketch the graph of each conic section below using your graphing calculator. (*Hint:* To solve for y, you will need to complete a square.)
    a. $4x^2 + 2xy + y^2 = 9$ **a–b. See margin.**
    b. $4x^2 + 2xy - y^2 = 9$

49. Sound An airplane flying faster than the speed of sound creates a cone-shaped pressure disturbance in the air. This is heard by people on the ground as a sonic boom. What is the shape of the path on the ground? **a parabola, or part of a hyperbola**

Alternative Assessment

Have students make a poster showing equations and graphs of a circle, ellipse, and hyperbola. Then have students write a short essay comparing and contrasting the conic sections and their equations.

Standardized Test Prep

Multiple Choice

50. The graph of which equation of a circle contains all the points in the table below? **D**

x	-3	0	3
y	0	± 3	0

A. $x^2 + y^2 - 4 = 0$ **B.** $x^2 + y^2 = 25$
C. $x^2 + y^2 = 36$ **D.** $6x^2 + 6y^2 = 54$

51. The graph of which ellipse contains all the points in the table below? **F**

x	-4	-2	0	2	4
y	0	$\pm\sqrt{3}$	± 2	$\pm\sqrt{3}$	0

F. $x^2 + 4y^2 = 16$ **G.** $4x^2 + 16y^2 = 144$
H. $4x^2 + 25y^2 = 64$ **I.** $9x^2 + y^2 = 81$

52. Which point is NOT on the graph of $4x^2 - y^2 = 4$? **D**
    A. $(-2, -2\sqrt{3})$ **B.** $(-1, 0)$ **C.** $(1, 0)$ **D.** $(2, 2)$

53. Which equation does NOT represent a line of symmetry for the circle with equation $x^2 + y^2 = 100$? **I**
    F. $x = 0$ **G.** $y = \frac{1}{2}x$ **H.** $y = x$ **I.** $y = x + 1$

pages 538–541 Exercises

47. The curve is a small piece of a hyperbola. Each side of the unsharpened pencil is a portion of a plane parallel to the line

540

represented by the lead in the pencil. The plane would intersect both parts of the cone if the pencil were a double cone.

48a.

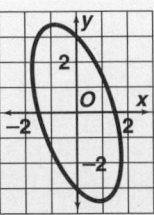

b.

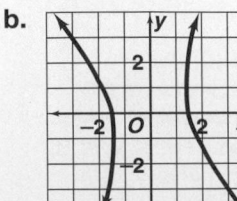

54. Which equation represents a line of symmetry for the ellipse with equation $x^2 + 9y^2 = 9$? **B**

   A. $y = -x$ **B.** $y = 0$ **C.** $y = x$ **D.** $xy = 1$

Short Response   **55.** The graph of the equation $x^2 + y^2 = 121$ is a circle. Describe the graph and its lines of symmetry. Find the domain and the range. **See margin.**

Mixed Review

Lesson 9-7   **A standard number cube is tossed. Find each probability.**

56. P(5 or greater than 3) $\frac{1}{2}$ **57.** P(even or 6) $\frac{1}{2}$

58. P(even or 7) $\frac{1}{2}$ **59.** P(prime or 2) $\frac{1}{2}$

Lesson 9-1   **Suppose z varies jointly with x and y. Write a function that models each relationship. Find the value of z when $x = -2$ and $y = 3$. 60–63. See margin.**

60. $z = -5$ when $x = -1$ and $y = -1$ **61.** $z = 72$ when $x = 3$ and $y = -6$

62. $z = 32$ when $x = 0.1$ and $y = 8$ **63.** $z = 5$ when $x = -4$ and $y = 2.5$

Lesson 8-1   **Write an exponential equation $y = ab^x$ whose graph passes through the given points. 64–73. See margin.**

64. $(-1, 2)$ and $(3, 32)$ **65.** $\left(0, \frac{1}{2}\right)$ and $(2, 8)$ **66.** $(1, 6)$ and $(2, 12)$

67. $\left(0, \frac{1}{3}\right)$ and $(2, 3)$ **68.** $\left(-1, \frac{2}{3}\right)$ and $(2, 18)$ **69.** $\left(-1, \frac{1}{8}\right)$ and $(4, 4)$

Lesson 6-8   **Expand each binomial.**

70. $(x - y)^3$ **71.** $(p + q)^6$ **72.** $(x - 2)^4$ **73.** $(3 - x)^5$

········ A Point in Time

Titanic was the largest passenger liner that had yet been built. On its maiden voyage in 1912, it struck an iceberg and sank. More than 1500 people died.

In 1985 a French and American team searched for *Titanic*. Research vessels combed the area with sonar. Transmitters aboard each ship sent out powerful spherical sound waves. Each wave reflected off any object in a half-mile-wide strip of ocean floor and returned to a receiver. The receiver then converted the echo to a picture of the object and calculated its depth. Two months after the search began, *Titanic* was discovered lying in two sections at a depth of some 13,000 feet.

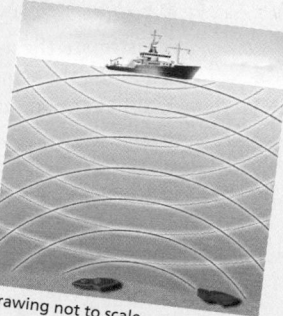

Drawing not to scale

Take It to the NET For more information about *Titanic*, go to **www.PHSchool.com**.
········ Web Code: age-2032

Lesson 10-1 Exploring Conic Sections   **541**

Standardized Test Prep

📁 **Resources**

For additional practice with a variety of test item formats:
- Standardized Test Prep, p. 583
- Test-Taking Strategies, p. 578
- Test-Taking Strategies with Transparencies

Exercises 50–51 Encourage students to begin by substituting 0 for x into each equation.

55. **[2] It is a circle with center at (0, 0) and a radius of 11. The x- and y-intercepts are at ±11. The lines of symmetry are all lines through the origin. The domain is $-11 \le x \le 11$ and the range is $-11 \le y \le 11$.**

  [1] includes either description OR domain and range, but not both

60. $z = -5xy$; 30

61. $z = -4xy$; 24

62. $z = 40xy$; −240

63. $z = -\frac{1}{2}xy$; 3

64. $y = 4(2)^x$

65. $y = \frac{1}{2}(4)^x$

66. $y = 3(2)^x$

67. $y = \frac{1}{3}(3)^x$

68. $y = 2(3)^x$

69. $y = \frac{1}{4}(2)^x$

70. $x^3 - 3x^2y + 3xy^2 - y^3$

71. $p^6 + 6p^5q + 15p^4q^2 + 20p^3q^3 + 15p^2q^4 + 6pq^5 + q^6$

72. $x^4 - 8x^3 + 24x^2 - 32x + 16$

73. $243 - 405x + 270x^2 - 90x^3 + 15x^4 - x^5$

Graphing Conic Sections

Students learn how to use their graphing calculators to graph conic sections. In additon to being able to check their work throughout the chapter, students will find these techniques helpful in Lesson 10-6 when learning how to translate conic sections.

Resources

Students may use any graphing calculator to graph conic sections.

Teaching Notes

Technology Tip

Remind students that they can press ZOOM 5 to have their calculators graph the conic section in the default square viewing window. Then, if the figure is too small, they can change the window.

Technology Tip

Exercise 11 Remind students that $y - 3 = x$ or $y - 3 = -x$. Then, have students solve each equation for y. Help students realize that each equation must be graphed separately. Remind them that the domain is $\{x \mid x \geq 0\}$. To graph only for $x \geq 0$, students must surround the entire equation with parentheses. After entering the equation, enter the domain in parentheses. (To get $\geq$, press 2nd [TEST] 4).

page 542   Technology

7a.

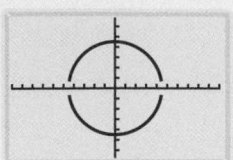

b. *x*-intercepts at ± 4.5, *y*-intercepts at ± 4.5

542

 **Technology   Graphing Conic Sections**

You can use your graphing calculator to graph relations that are not functions.

 Take It to the NET
Graphing Calculator procedures online at **www.PHSchool.com**
Web Code: age-2110

EXAMPLE

Graph the ellipse $\frac{x^2}{16} + \frac{y^2}{9} = 1$.

Step 1 Solve the equation for y.

$$\frac{x^2}{16} + \frac{y^2}{9} = 1$$

$$\frac{y^2}{9} = 1 - \frac{x^2}{16}$$

$$y^2 = 9\left(1 - \frac{x^2}{16}\right)$$

$$y = \pm 3\sqrt{1 - \frac{x^2}{16}}$$

Step 2 Enter the equations as Y_1 and Y_2.

Step 3 Select a square window.

Step 4 Graph.

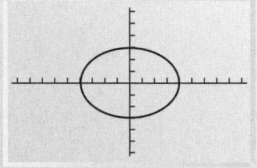

```
Plot1 Plot2 Plot3
\Y1 ▤ 3√(1–(X²/16))
\Y2 ▤ –3√(1–(X²/16))
\Y3 = ■
\Y4 =
\Y5 =
```

```
WINDOW
Xmin = –9.4
Xmax = 9.4
Xscl = 1
Ymin = –6.2
Ymax = 6.2
Yscl = 1
Xres = 1■
```

EXERCISES

Graph each conic section.   1–6. See back of book.

1. $x^2 + y^2 = 25$

2. $4x^2 + y^2 = 16$

3. $9x^2 - 16y^2 = 144$

4. $x^2 - y^2 = 3$

5. $\frac{x^2}{4} - \frac{y^2}{9} = 1$

6. $x^2 + \frac{y^2}{4} = 16$

7. a. Graph the functions $y = \sqrt{\frac{81}{4} - x^2}$ and $y = -\sqrt{\frac{81}{4} - x^2}$.   **a–b. See margin.**

   b. Estimate the x-intercepts and find the y-intercepts.

   c. Adjust the window to $-9.3 \leq x \leq 9.5$. Verify the x-intercepts.   **Check students' work.**

   d. What conic section does the graph represent?   **circle with center (0, 0) and radius 4.5**

Graph each conic section. Find the x- and y-intercepts.   8–10. See margin for graphs.

8. $4x^2 + y^2 = 25$ $\pm 2.5, \pm 5$

9. $x^2 + y^2 = 30$ $\pm \sqrt{30}, \pm \sqrt{30}$

10. $9x^2 - 4y^2 = 72$ $\pm 2\sqrt{2}$, **none**

 11. Writing Explain how to use a graphing calculator to graph the relation $x = |y - 3|$. **Answers may vary. Sample: Graph $y = (3 - x)$ where $x \geq 0$ and $y = (3 + x)$ where $x \geq 0$, on the same screen.**

8.

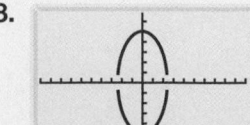

9.

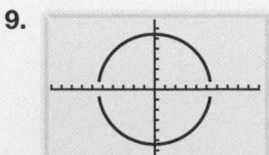

10.

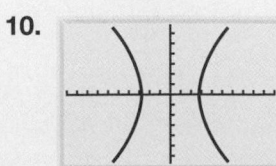

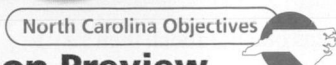

Parabolas

 **North Carolina Objectives**

2.09 Use the equations of parabolas and circles to model and solve problems. a) Solve using tables, graphs, and algebraic properties. b) Interpret the constants and coefficients in the context of the problem.

Lesson Preview

What You'll Learn

 OBJECTIVE 1
To write the equation of a parabola

 OBJECTIVE 2
To graph parabolas

. . . And Why

To model a solar collector, as in Example 3

✔ Check Skills You'll Need

(For help, go to Skills Handbook pages 844 and 856.)

Solve for c.

1. $\frac{1}{8} = \frac{1}{c}$ **8**
2. $\frac{1}{8} = \frac{1}{2c}$ **4**
3. $\frac{1}{12} = \frac{1}{4c}$ **3**
4. $2 = \frac{1}{4c}$ $\frac{1}{8}$

Find the distance between the given points.

5. $(2, 3)$ and $(4, 1)$ $2\sqrt{2}$
6. $(4, 6)$ and $(3, -2)$ $\sqrt{65}$
7. $(-1, 5)$ and $(2, -3)$ $\sqrt{73}$

New Vocabulary
• focus of a parabola • directrix

Lesson Preview

✔ **Check Skills You'll Need**

Ratios and Proportions
Skills Handbook: p. 844,
Example 3, Exercises 6–15

Distance Formula
Skills Handbook: p. 856,
Example 2, Exercises 10–21

Lesson Resources

📁 **Teaching Resources**
Practice, Reteaching, Enrichment

👥 **Reaching All Students**
Practice Workbook 10-2
Spanish Practice Workbook 10-2
Technology Activities 29

⏲ **Presentation Assistant Plus!**
Transparencies
• Check Skills You'll Need 10-2
• Additional Examples 10-2
• Student Edition Answers 10-2
• Lesson Quiz 10-2
PH Presentation Pro CD 10-2

PRENTICE HALL ASSESSMENT SYSTEM
Computer Test Generator CD

💰 **Technology**
Resource Pro® CD-ROM
Computer Test Generator CD
Prentice Hall Presentation Pro CD

💻 **www.PHSchool.com**
Student Site
• Teacher Web Code: agk-5500
• Self-grading Lesson Quiz
Teacher Center
• Lesson Planner
• Resources

Plus **iTEXT**

iTEXT Interactive lesson includes instant self-check, tutorials, and activities.

Writing the Equation of a Parabola

In Chapter 5 you learned that a parabola is the graph of a quadratic equation. By definition, a parabola is the set of all points in a plane that are the same distance from a fixed line and a fixed point not on the line. The fixed point is the **focus of a parabola.** The fixed line is the **directrix.** The line through the focus and perpendicular to the directrix is the axis of symmetry.

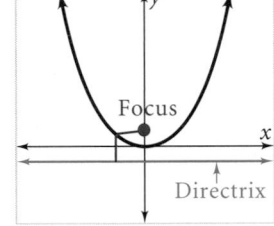

1 EXAMPLE Using the Definition of a Parabola

Write an equation for a graph that is the set of all points in the plane that are equidistant from the point $F(0, 3)$ and the line $y = -3$.

You need to find all points $P(x, y)$ such that FP and the distance from P to the given line are equal.

$$FP = PQ$$
$$\sqrt{(x - 0)^2 + (y - 3)^2} =$$
$$\sqrt{(x - x)^2 + (y - (-3))^2}$$
$$x^2 + (y - 3)^2 = 0^2 + (y + 3)^2$$
$$x^2 + y^2 - 6y + 9 = y^2 + 6y + 9$$
$$x^2 = 12y$$
$$y = \frac{1}{12}x^2$$

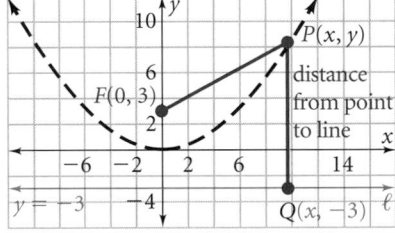

Need Help?
The distance between $P_1(x_1, y_1)$ and $P_2(x_2, y_2)$ is
$\sqrt{(x_2 - x_1)^2 + (y_2 - y_1)^2}$.

An equation of the set of all points equidistant from $F(0, 3)$ and $y = -3$ is $y = \frac{1}{12}x^2$.

✔ **Check Understanding** 1 Write an equation for a graph that is the set of all points in the plane that are equidistant from the point $F(2, 0)$ and the line $x = -2$. $x = \frac{1}{8}y^2$

INSTANT CHECK SYSTEM

🗹 Ongoing Assessment and Intervention

Before the Lesson
Diagnose prerequisite skills using:
• Check Skills You'll Need

During the Lesson
Monitor progress using:
• Check Understanding
• Additional Examples
• Standardized Test Prep

After the Lesson
Assess knowledge using:
• Lesson Quiz
• Computer Test Generator CD

Professional Development

Math Background

Parabolas play an important role in many applications. In this lesson, students learn how to model solar collectors. In physics, students learn that light beams, which approach a parabolic surface parallel to the axis of symmetry are reflected to the focus of the parabola. These facts are used in the construction of objects such as solar collectors and flashlights.

OBJECTIVE

1 Teaching Notes

1 EXAMPLE   Auditory Learners

Encourage students to say, *"A point is on a parabola if its distances from the focus and directrix are equal."* Have students use this sentence along with the graph in Example 1 to write $FP = PQ$.

3 EXAMPLE   Visual Learners

Bend a sheet of paper into a trough to model the solar collectors in this example. Clarify that you can only see the parabola when you look at a cross section. Point out that this parabolic shape does not extend upward indefinitely.

Additional Examples

1 Write an equation for a graph that is the set of all points in the plane that are equidistant from the point $F(0, 1)$ and the line $y = -1$. $y = \frac{1}{4}x^2$

2 Write an equation of a parabola with a vertex at the origin and a focus at $(0, -7)$.
$y = -\frac{1}{28}x^2$

In Chapter 5 you learned about the special relationship between the value of a and the graph of a quadratic function in the form $y = ax^2$. Now you will learn about the relationship between the value of a and the graph of a quadratic relation in the form $y = ax^2$ or $x = ay^2$.

If c is the distance from the vertex to the focus of a parabola, then $|a| = \frac{1}{4c}$.

Consider any parabola with equation $y = ax^2$.

If $a > 0$, then
• the parabola opens upward
• the focus is at $(0, c)$
• the directrix is $y = -c$

If $a < 0$, then
• the parabola opens downward
• the focus is at $(0, -c)$
• the directrix is at $y = c$

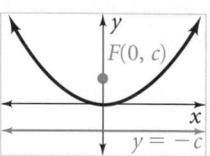

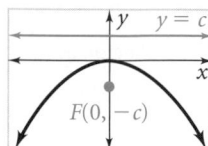

Consider any parabola with equation $x = ay^2$.

If $a > 0$, then
• the parabola opens to the right
• the focus is at $(c, 0)$
• the directrix is at $x = -c$

If $a < 0$, then
• the parabola opens to the left
• the focus is at $(-c, 0)$
• the directrix is at $x = c$

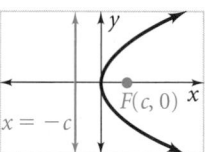

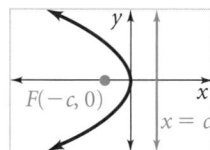

You can use the information above to write an equation of a parabola.

2 EXAMPLE   Writing the Equation of a Parabola

Write an equation of a parabola with a vertex at the origin and a focus at $(-5, 0)$.

Step 1 Determine the orientation of the parabola. Make a sketch. Since the focus is located to the left of the vertex, the parabola must open to the left. Use $x = ay^2$.

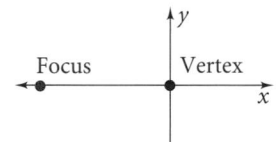

Step 2 Find a.

$$|a| = \frac{1}{4c}$$
$$= \frac{1}{4(5)}$$ **Since the focus is a distance of 5 units from the vertex, $c = 5$.**
$$= \frac{1}{20}$$

Since the parabola opens to the left, a is negative. So $a = -\frac{1}{20}$.

An equation for the parabola is $x = -\frac{1}{20}y^2$.

✓ Check Understanding 2 Write an equation of a parabola with a vertex at the origin and a focus at $\left(\frac{1}{2}, 0\right)$.

$x = \frac{1}{2}y^2$

👥 Reaching All Students

Below Level Review the distance formula, and discuss how to find the distance from a line to a point not on it. Also review completing the square.	**Advanced Learners** Have students explore the definitions of an ellipse and a hyperbola in terms of foci and directrices, and share their results with the class.	**English Learners** See note on page 545. **Visual Learners** See note on page 544.

You can find the equation of a parabola that models a real-world situation.

3 EXAMPLE **Real-World** **Connection**

Solar Energy In some solar collectors, a mirror with a parabolic cross section is used to concentrate sunlight on a pipe, which is located at the focus of the mirror.

a. Suppose the pipe is located 6 in. from the vertex of the mirror. Write an equation of the parabola that models the cross section of the mirror.

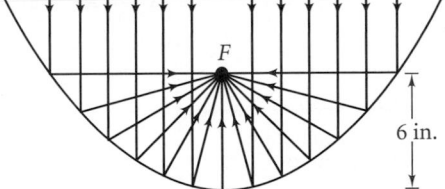

b. The amount of light collected by the mirror is directly proportional to its width. Using this mirror, the pipe receives 30^2, or 900, times more sunlight than it would without the mirror. Suppose the diameter of the pipe is 1 in. What must be the width of the mirror?

a. The distance from the vertex to the focus is 6 in., so $c = 6$. Find the value of a.

$a = \frac{1}{4c}$

$\quad = \frac{1}{4(6)}$

$\quad = \frac{1}{24}$ **Since the parabola opens upward, a is positive.**

The equation of the parabola is $y = \frac{1}{24}x^2$.

b. The width of the mirror must be 30 times the diameter of the pipe, or 30 in.

 Check Understanding **3** Suppose the pipe is located 8.25 in. from the vertex of the mirror. Write an equation of the parabola to model the cross section of the mirror. **$y = \frac{1}{33}x^2$**

OBJECTIVE
2 **Graphing Parabolas**

You can use the value of a to identify the focus and directrix of a parabola.

4 EXAMPLE **Identifying Focus and Directrix**

Identify the focus and the directrix of the graph of the equation $y = -\frac{1}{16}x^2$.

The parabola is of the form $y = ax^2$, so the vertex is at the origin and the parabola has a vertical axis of symmetry. Since $a < 0$, the parabola opens downward.

$|a| = \frac{1}{4c}$

$\left|-\frac{1}{16}\right| = \frac{1}{4c}$ **Substitute $-\frac{1}{16}$ for a.**

$4c = 16$ **Solve for c.**

$c = 4$

The focus is at $(0, -4)$. The equation of the directrix is $y = 4$.

Check Understanding **4** Identify the focus and the directrix of the graph of the equation $y = \frac{1}{12}x^2$.
(0, 3), y = −3

Additional Example

3 A parabolic mirror has a focus that is located 4 in. above the vertex of the mirror. Write an equation of the parabola that models the cross section of the mirror. $y = \frac{1}{16}x^2$

OBJECTIVE
2 **Teaching Notes**

4 EXAMPLE **English Learners**

To help students learn the terms *vertex*, *focus*, and *directrix*, have them copy one of the figures that is before Example 2. Encourage students to label the figure with the terms. Stress to students that the directrix is a line and must be given as an equation of a line.

Additional Examples

4 Identify the focus and directrix of the graph of the equation $x = -\frac{1}{8}y^2$. **(−2, 0), x = 2**

5 Identify the vertex, the focus, and the directrix of the graph of the equation $x^2 + 4x + 8y - 4 = 0$. Then graph the parabola. **(−2, 1), (−2, −1), y = 3;**

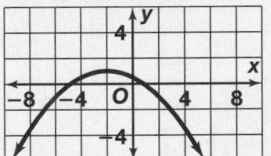

Closure

Ask students to explain how to write the equation of a parabola and how to graph a parabola. **An equation of a parabola is determined by the set of all points that are equidistant from a fixed line called a directrix and a fixed point not on the line called a focus. The graph can be determined from the vertex and two other points.**

Assignment Guide

1 Objective

Ⓐ Ⓑ **Core** 1–15, 36–41, 43–45, 52–56

Ⓒ **Extension** 57, 59

2 Objective

Ⓐ Ⓑ **Core** 16–35, 42, 46–51

Ⓒ **Extension** 58, 60

Standardized Test Prep 61–66

Mixed Review 67–76

Error Prevention

Exercises 1–6 Encourage students to begin by determining whether the graphs open upward, downward, right, or left. Have them verify their findings with their equations.

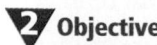

Enrichment 10-2

Reteaching 10-2

Practice 10-2

You can use the focus and directrix to graph the equation of a parabola.

5 EXAMPLE Graphing the Equation of a Parabola

Identify the vertex, the focus, and the directrix of the graph of the equation $y^2 - 4x - 4y + 16 = 0$. Then graph the parabola.

$y^2 - 4x - 4y + 16 = 0$

$4x = y^2 - 4y + 16$ **Solve for x, since x is in only one term.**

$4x = (y^2 - 4y + 4) + 16 - 4$ **Complete the square in y.**

$x = \frac{1}{4}(y^2 - 4y + 4) + 4 - 1$ **Divide both sides of the equation by 4.**

$x = \frac{1}{4}(y - 2)^2 + 3$ **vertex form**

The parabola is of the form $x = a(y - k)^2 + h$, so the vertex is at $(3, 2)$ and the parabola has a horizontal axis of symmetry. Since $a > 0$, the parabola opens to the right.

$|a| = \frac{1}{4c}$

$\left|\frac{1}{4}\right| = \frac{1}{4c}$ **Substitute $\frac{1}{4}$ for a.**

$4c = 4$ **Solve for c.**

$c = 1$

The vertex is at $(3, 2)$ and the focus is at $(4, 2)$. The equation of the directrix is $x = 2$.

Locate one or more points on the parabola. Select a value for y, such as 4. The point on the parabola with a y-value of 4 is $(4, 4)$. Use the symmetric nature of a parabola to find the corresponding point, $(4, 0)$.

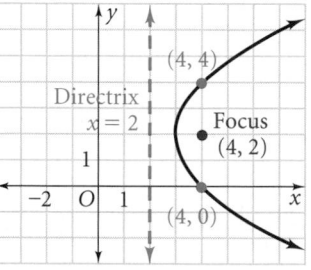

Need Help?

To review completing the square, go to Lesson 5-7.

5. $(-3, -1), (-3, -1.75),$ $y = -\frac{1}{4}$

✓ **Check Understanding**   **5** Identify the vertex, the focus, and the directrix of the graph of $x^2 + 6x + 3y + 12 = 0$. Then graph the equation. **See left.**

EXERCISES

For more practice, see *Extra Practice.*

Practice and Problem Solving

Ⓐ **Practice by Example**

Example 1 (page 543)

Write an equation for a graph that is the set of all points in the plane that are equidistant from the given point and the given line. **1–9. See margin.**

1. $F(0, 2), y = -2$ **2.** $F(0, -1), y = 1$ **3.** $F(-3, 0), x = 3$

4. $F(0, -8), y = 8$ **5.** $F(0, 4), y = 0$ **6.** $F\left(\frac{1}{2}, 0\right), x = -\frac{1}{2}$

Example 2 (page 544)

Write an equation of a parabola with a vertex at the origin and the given focus.

7. focus at $(6, 0)$ **8.** focus at $(0, -4)$ **9.** focus at $(0, 7)$

10. focus at $(-1, 0)$ **11.** focus at $(2, 0)$ **12.** focus at $(0, -5)$
     $x = -\frac{1}{4}y^2$ $x = \frac{1}{8}y^2$ $y = -\frac{1}{20}x^2$

Example 3 (page 545)

Write an equation of a parabola opening upward with a vertex at the origin.

13. focus 1.5 units from vertex   **14.** focus $\frac{1}{8}$ of a unit from vertex
     $y = \frac{1}{6}x^2$ $y = 2x^2$

546   Chapter 10   Quadratic Relations

pages 546–548 Exercises

1. $y = \frac{1}{8}x^2$

2. $y = -\frac{1}{4}x^2$

3. $x = -\frac{1}{12}y^2$

4. $y = -\frac{1}{32}x^2$

5. $y = \frac{1}{8}x^2 + 2$

6. $x = \frac{1}{2}y^2$

7. $x = \frac{1}{24}y^2$

8. $y = -\frac{1}{16}x^2$

9. $y = \frac{1}{28}x^2$

15a. Answers may vary. Sample: $y = x^2$

    b. The light produced by the bulb will reflect off the parabolic mirror and will be emitted in parallel rays.

15. Optics A cross section of a flashlight reflector is a parabola. The bulb is located at the focus. Suppose the bulb is located $\frac{1}{4}$ in. from the vertex of the reflector. You can model the reflector with a parabola that opens upward and has a vertex at the origin. **a–b. See margin p. 546.**
    a. Write an equation of the parabola to model the cross section of the reflector.
    b. Reasoning Use the properties of parabolas to explain the advantages of this design.

16–23.

Example 4
(page 545)

Identify the focus and the directrix of the graph of each equation. See margin.

16. $y = \frac{1}{4}x^2$ 17. $y = x^2$ 18. $y = -\frac{1}{8}x^2$ 19. $x = \frac{1}{2}y^2$

20. $y = \frac{1}{2}x^2$ 21. $x = \frac{1}{36}y^2$ 22. $x = -\frac{1}{18}y^2$ 23. $y = -2x^2$

Example 5
(page 546)

Identify the vertex, the focus, and the directrix of the graph of each equation. Then sketch the graph. 24–35. See back of book.

24. $x = \frac{1}{24}y^2$ 25. $y = -\frac{1}{4}x^2$ 26. $x = \frac{1}{12}y^2$

36. $x = \frac{1}{12}y^2$

37. $y = \frac{1}{400}x^2$

38. $y = -\frac{1}{20}x^2$

27. $y^2 - 25x = 0$ 28. $x^2 = 4y$ 29. $x^2 = -4y$

30. $(x - 2)^2 = 4y$ 31. $-8x = y^2$ 32. $(x + 2)^2 = y - 4$

33. $y^2 - 6x = 18$ 34. $x^2 + 24y - 8x = -16$ 35. $y^2 - 12x + 2y = -37$

B **Apply Your Skills**

Write an equation of a parabola with a vertex at the origin. 36–38. See left.

36. directrix $x = -3$ 37. focus at $(0, 100)$ 38. directrix $y = 5$

39. focus at $(-7, 0)$ 40. directrix $x = 9$ 41. directrix $y = 2.8$
     $x = -\frac{1}{28}y^2$ $x = -\frac{1}{36}y^2$ $y = -\frac{5}{56}x^2$

42. Earth Science The equation $d = \frac{1}{10}s^2$ relates the depth d (in meters) of the ocean to the speed s (in meters per second) at which tsunamis travel. Graph the equation. **See margin.**

Use the information in each graph to write the equation for the graph.

43.

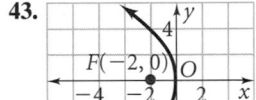

$x = -\frac{1}{8}y^2$

44.

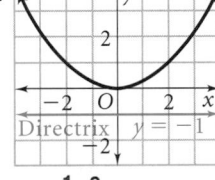

$y = \frac{1}{4}x^2$

45.

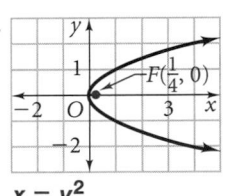

$x = y^2$

Graph each equation.

46. $y^2 - 8x = 0$ 47. $y^2 - 8y + 8x = -16$ 48. $2x^2 - y + 20x = -53$

49. $x^2 = 12y$ 50. $y = 4(x - 3)^2 - 2$ 51. $(y - 2)^2 = 4(x + 3)$
46–51. See back of book.

Write an equation of a parabola with a vertex at $(1, 1)$.

52. $y = \frac{1}{6}(x - 1)^2 + 1$

53. $x = -\frac{1}{2}(y - 1)^2 + 1$

54. $y = -\frac{1}{4}(x - 1)^2 + 1$

52. directrix $y = -\frac{1}{2}$ 53. directrix $x = \frac{3}{2}$ 54. focus at $(1, 0)$

55. Open-Ended Write an equation for a parabola that opens to the left. Give the focus and directrix of the parabola. **Check students' work.**

 56. Writing Explain how to find the distance from the focus to the directrix of the parabola $x = 2y^2$. **See margin.**

Real-World  **Connection**

Tsunamis are ocean waves that result from an undersea earthquake. As the waves approach shallow water, their height increases and their speed decreases.

16. $(0, 1), y = -1$
17. $\left(0, \frac{1}{4}\right), y = -\frac{1}{4}$
18. $(0, -2), y = 2$
19. $\left(\frac{1}{2}, 0\right), x = -\frac{1}{2}$

20. $\left(0, \frac{1}{2}\right), y = -\frac{1}{2}$
21. $(9, 0), x = -9$
22. $\left(-\frac{9}{2}, 0\right), x = \frac{9}{2}$
23. $\left(0, -\frac{1}{8}\right), y = \frac{1}{8}$

42.

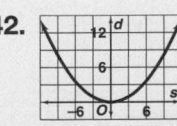

---

4. Assess

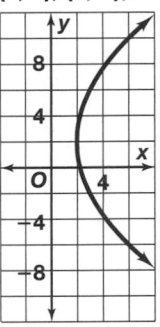

Lesson Quiz 10-2

1. Write an equation for a graph that is the set of all points in the plane equidistant from the point $F\left(-\frac{1}{8}, 0\right)$ and the line $x = \frac{1}{8}$. $x = -2y^2$

2. Write an equation of a parabola with a vertex at the origin and a focus at $(0, -3)$. $y = -\frac{1}{12}x^2$

3. Identify the vertex, the focus, and the directrix of the equation $y^2 - 4y - 16x + 36 = 0$. Then, graph the parabola. **(2, 2), (6, 2), x = -2;**

Alternative Assessment

On four large pieces of paper, make quick sketches of each of the four parabolas at the top of page 544. Tack one paper at each of the four corners of your classroom. Explain that you will say a fact about a parabola. Students are to move to the parabola or parabolas for which the fact is true. Name facts such as the parabola opens downward, $a > 0$, the directrix is parallel to the y-axis, the focus is on the x-axis, the equation has the form $y = ax^2$, and so on.

56. Answers may vary. Sample: Write the equation in the form $x = \frac{1}{4\left(\frac{1}{8}\right)}y^2$. The distance from the focus to the directrix is $2\left(\frac{1}{8}\right)$, or $\frac{1}{4}$.

547

Resources

For additional practice with a variety of test item formats:
- Standardized Test Prep, p. 583
- Test-Taking Strategies, p. 578
- Test-Taking Strategies with Transparencies

pages 546–548 Exercises

57. The directrix will have equation $y = k - c$. A point (x, y) is on the parabola if and only if the distance from (x, y) to the directrix is equal to the distance from (x, y) to the focus. So (x, y) is on the parabola if and only if $|y - (k - c)| = \sqrt{(x - h)^2 + (y - k - c)^2}$ Square and simplify to get the equivalent equation $4cy - 4kc = (x - h)^2$, or $(x - h)^2 = 4c(y - k)$.

58.

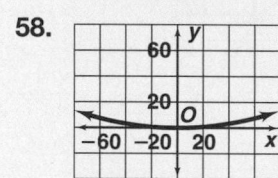

65. [2] $|a| = \frac{1}{4c}$

$|a| = \frac{1}{4 \cdot 4}$

$|a| = \frac{1}{16}$

so since the focus is at $(0, 4)$ and the directrix is $y = -4$, a is positive. The equation is $y = \frac{1}{16}x^2$.

[1] answer correct, without work shown

66. [2] $|a| = \frac{1}{4c}$

$|\frac{1}{36}| = \frac{1}{4c}$

$36 = 4c$

$c = 9$

so the focus is at $(0, 9)$ since $a > 0$ and the equation of the directrix is $y = -9$.

[1] answer correct, without work shown

67.

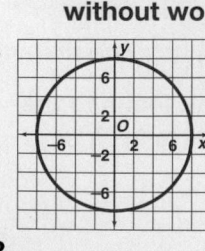

548

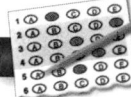 **Challenge**

59a. the bottom half of the parabola $y^2 = x$

b. domain: all non-negative real numbers, range: all non-positive real numbers

60a. The vertex moves up, and the parabola widens.

b. The vertex moves down, and the parabola narrows.

---

57. **Critical Thinking** Use the definition of a parabola to show that the parabola with vertex (h, k) and focus $(h, k + c)$ has the equation $(x - h)^2 = 4c(y - k)$. **57–58. See margin.**

58. **Modeling** Draw a cross section of a parabolic mirror modeled by the equation $y = 0.002323x^2$.

59. **a.** What part of a parabola is modeled by the function $y = -\sqrt{x}$?
    b. State the domain and range for the function in part (a).

60. The directrix of a parabola is the line $y = -2$. The focus is the point $(0, 2)$.
    a. Suppose the directrix remains fixed, but the focus is shifted along the y-axis farther away from the directrix. Explain what happens to the vertex and the shape of the parabola.
    b. Suppose the focus moves along the y-axis toward the directrix. Explain what happens to the vertex and the shape of the parabola.
    c. What would happen if the focus moved down all the way to the directrix? **The parabola would degenerate into the ray with endpoint $(0, -2)$ that passes through the origin.**

Standardized Test Prep

Multiple Choice

61. What is the distance from $P(2, -5)$ to the line $y = -8$? **B**
    A. -6 B. 3   C. 5   D. 10

62. Which point is equidistant from $F(0, 5)$ and the line $y = -5$? **F**
    F. $(-10, 5)$ G. $(-5, 0)$ H. $(0, 1)$ I. $(10, 10)$

Take It to the NET
Online lesson quiz at
www.PHSchool.com
Web Code: aga-1002

63. Which equation represents a parabola that opens to the left? **A**
    A. $x = -2y^2$ B. $x = 2y^2$ C. $y = -2x^2$ D. $y = 2x^2$

64. Which equation represents a parabola that opens downward? **H**
    F. $x = -2y^2$ G. $x = 2y^2$ H. $y = -2x^2$ I. $y = 2x^2$

Short Response

65. What is the equation of a parabola that is the set of all points that are equidistant from $F(0, 4)$ and the line $y = -4$? **See margin.**

66. Find the focus and the directrix of the parabola with equation $y = \frac{1}{36}x^2$. **See margin.**

Mixed Review

Lesson 10-1   Graph each equation.   **67–69. See margin.**

67. $x^2 + y^2 = 64$ 68. $x^2 + 9y^2 = 9$ 69. $4x^2 - 9y^2 = 36$

Lesson 9-2   Find the asymptotes of the graph of each equation.   **70–75. See margin.**

70. $y = \frac{3}{x}$ 71. $y = \frac{1}{x} + 4$ 72. $y = \frac{4}{x + 1}$

73. $y = -\frac{1}{x - 1}$ 74. $y = \frac{5}{x + 5} + 2$ 75. $y = \frac{2}{x - 3} - 1$

Lesson 8-2 76. **Investing** Suppose you have a continuously compounding account with a beginning principal of $3,800 and an interest rate of 8.1%. What is the balance after 4 years? **$5254.06**

68.

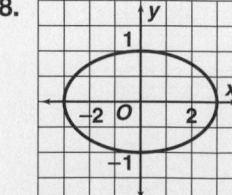

69.

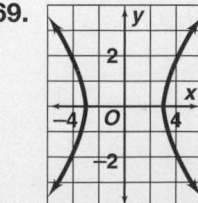

70. the x- and y-axes
71. $x = 0$ and $y = 4$
72. $x = -1$ and $y = 0$
73. $x = 1$ and $y = 0$
74. $x = -5$ and $y = 2$
75. $x = 3$ and $y = -1$

Circles

1. Plan

 North Carolina Objectives

Lesson Preview

2.09 Use the equations of parabolas and circles to model and solve problems. a) Solve using tables, graphs, and algebraic properties. b) Interpret the constants and coefficients in the context of the problem.

What You'll Learn

 OBJECTIVE 1
To write and graph the equation of a circle

OBJECTIVE 2
To find the center and radius of a circle and use it to graph the circle

. . . And Why

To model gears in machinery, as in Example 3

✓ **Check Skills You'll Need** (For help, go to Lesson 5-7 and Skills Handbook page 855.)

Simplify.

1. $\sqrt{16}$ 4   2. $\sqrt{49}$ 7   3. $\sqrt{20}$ $2\sqrt{5}$ 4. $\sqrt{48}$ $4\sqrt{3}$ 5. $\sqrt{72}$ $6\sqrt{2}$

Find the missing value to complete the square.

6. $x^2 - 2x + \blacksquare$ 1   7. $x^2 + 4x + \blacksquare$ 4   8. $x^2 - 6x + \blacksquare$ 9

New Vocabulary • circle • center • radius
• standard form of an equation of a circle

Lesson Preview

✓ **Check Skills You'll Need**

Operations with Radicals
Skills Handbook: p. 855,
Example 1, Exercises 1–7

Completing the Square
Lesson 5-7: Example 2
Exercises 7–12
Extra Practice, p. 826

 Interactive lesson includes instant self-check, tutorials, and activities.

OBJECTIVE

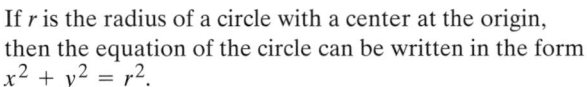 **1 Writing the Equation of a Circle**

Real-World 🌐 Connection

People of many cultures use circular dwellings, like those shown above in Mali, to maximize volume for a given surface area.

A **circle** is the set of all points in a plane that are a distance r from a given point, called the **center.** The distance r is the **radius** of the circle.

If r is the radius of a circle with a center at the origin, then the equation of the circle can be written in the form $x^2 + y^2 = r^2$.

Not every circle has its center at the origin. You can use the distance formula to find an equation of a circle with a radius r and a center at the point (h, k).

Let (x, y) be any point on the circle. The distance from (h, k) to (x, y) is the radius.

$d = \sqrt{(x_2 - x_2)^2 + (y_2 - y_1)^2}$ **Distance Formula**

$r = \sqrt{(x - h)^2 + (y - k)^2}$ **Substitute r for d, (h, k) for (x_1, y_1), and (x, y) for (x_2, y_2).**

$r^2 = (x - h)^2 + (y - k)^2$ **Square each side.**

The above proof leads to a definition.

 Key Concepts

Definition **Standard Form of an Equation of a Circle**
The standard form of an equation of a circle with center (h, k) and radius r is $$(x - h)^2 + (y - k)^2 = r^2.$$

Lesson Resources

📁 **Teaching Resources**
Practice, Reteaching, Enrichment
Checkpoint Quiz 1

👥 **Reaching All Students**
Practice Workbook 10-3
Spanish Practice Workbook 10-3
Reading and Math Literacy 10B
Spanish Reading & Literacy 10B
Spanish Checkpoint Quiz 1

⏱ **Presentation Assistant Plus!**
Transparencies
• Check Skills You'll Need 10-3
• Additional Examples 10-3
• Student Edition Answers 10-3
• Lesson Quiz 10-3
PH Presentation Pro CD 10-3

ASSESSMENT SYSTEM
Checkpoint Quiz 1
Computer Test Generator CD

💿 **Technology**
Resource Pro® CD-ROM
Computer Test Generator CD
Prentice Hall Presentation Pro CD

🖥 **www.PHSchool.com**
Student Site
• Teacher Web Code: agk-5500
• Self-grading Lesson Quiz
Teacher Center
• Lesson Planner
• Resources

Plus

Lesson 10-3 Circles **549**

 **Ongoing Assessment and Intervention**

Before the Lesson
Diagnose prerequisite skills using:
• Check Skills You'll Need

During the Lesson
Monitor progress using:
• Check Understanding
• Additional Examples
• Standardized Test Prep

After the Lesson
Assess knowledge using:
• Lesson Quiz
• Computer Test Generator CD
• Chapter Checkpoint 1 (p. 554)

Math Background

Techniques learned in this lesson will be useful for modeling applications involving circles, and in graphing three-dimensional surfaces in future courses.

OBJECTIVE

1 **Teaching Notes**

1 EXAMPLE **Alternative Method**

Begin by having students sketch the circle. Have them label the center and a point (x, y) on the circle. Then, have students find the distance from (x, y) to the center.

2 EXAMPLE **Math Tip**

Point out that they only need to find the equation of the circle with center $(-4, 3)$ with the same radius.

3 EXAMPLE **Tactile Learners**

To help students understand that the radius of Gear A must be 8 times the radius of Gear B, point out that one rotation of a gear travels a distance equal to the circumference of the circle. Have students use compasses to draw a circle with radius 6 cm and a circle with radius 2 cm, representing two gears. Then, have students cut pieces of string to the size of the circumference of each circle. Have students determine the number of pieces of the small string required to make up the large string. **3** This number represents the number of rotations of the small gear for one rotation of the large gear. It is equal to the ratio of the circumference of the large gear to the circumference of the small gear, or equivalently the ratio of the radius of the large gear to the radius of the small gear.

550

You can use the center and the radius of a circle to write an equation for a circle.

1 EXAMPLE **Writing the Equation of a Circle**

Write an equation of a circle with center $(-4, 3)$ and radius 4.

$(x - h)^2 + (y - k)^2 = r^2$ Use the standard form of the equation of a circle.

$(x - (-4))^2 + (y - 3)^2 = 4^2$ Substitute -4 for h, 3 for k, and 4 for r.

$(x + 4)^2 + (y - 3)^2 = 16$ Simplify.

An equation for the circle is $(x + 4)^2 + (y - 3)^2 = 16$.

Graphing Calculator Hint

When graphing a conic section, press ZOOM 5 to select a square window. The standard window makes a circle look like an ellipse.

Check   Solve the equation for y and enter both functions into your graphing calculator.

$(x + 4)^2 + (y - 3)^2 = 16$

$(y - 3)^2 = 16 - (x + 4)^2$

$y - 3 = \pm \sqrt{16 - (x + 4)^2}$

$y = 3 \pm \sqrt{16 - (x + 4)^2}$

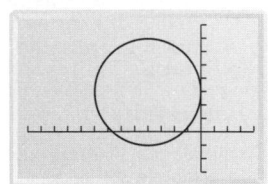

✓ **Check Understanding** **1** Write an equation for a circle with center at $(5, -2)$ and radius 8. Check your answer. $(x - 5)^2 + (y + 2)^2 = 64$

The graph of the equation $(x - h)^2 + (y - k)^2 = r^2$ is the graph of $x^2 + y^2 = r^2$ translated h units horizontally and k units vertically. When h is positive the graph shifts right; when h is negative the graph shifts left. When k is positive the graph shifts up; when k is negative the graph shifts down.

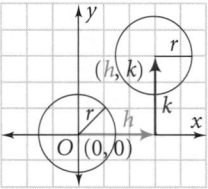

You can use translations to write an equation of a circle.

2 EXAMPLE **Using Translations to Write an Equation**

Write an equation for the translation of $x^2 + y^2 = 9$ four units left and three units up. Then graph the translation.

$(x - h)^2 + (y - k)^2 = r^2$ Use standard form.

$(x - (-4))^2 + (y - 3)^2 = 9$ Substitute -4 for h, 3 for k, and 9 for r^2.

$(x + 4)^2 + (y - 3)^2 = 9$ Simplify.

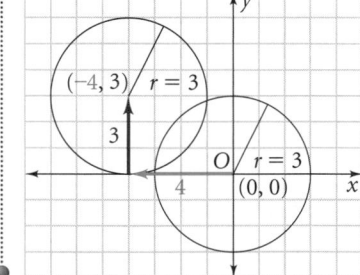

✓ **Check Understanding** **2** Write an equation for each translation.

   a. $x^2 + y^2 = 1$; left 5 and down 3   **b.** $x^2 + y^2 = 9$; right 2 and up 3

     $(x + 5)^2 + (y + 3)^2 = 1$ $(x - 2)^2 + (y - 3)^2 = 9$

🧑‍🤝‍🧑 Reaching All Students

| **Below Level** Students may use a graphing calculator to graph the equation of a circle, if they solve the equation for y as in Example 1. | **Advanced Learners** Have students verify that the standard form of a circle given in the chapter is equivalent to the general form. | **Tactile Learners** See note on page 550. **Error Prevention** See note on page 552. |

You can write an equation of a circle to model a real-world situation.

3 **EXAMPLE** Real-World Connection

Machinery The diagram below shows four gears in a motor assembly. Gear *B* rotates 8 times for each rotation of gear *A*. Gears *B* and *C* share the same shaft, with centers at the origin. The radius of gear *C* is 6 times the radius of gear *B*. The radius of gear *D* is $\frac{1}{3}$ the radius of gear *C*. Write the equation of the circle that represents each gear.

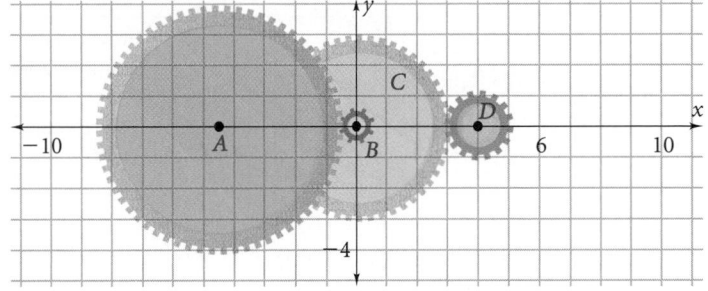

Make a table. Let the radius of gear $B = \frac{1}{2}$. The radius of gear *A* must be 8 times the radius of gear *B*, or 4.

Gear	(h, k)	r	Equation
A	$\left(-4\frac{1}{2}, 0\right)$	4	$\left(x + \frac{9}{2}\right)^2 + y^2 = 16$
B	$(0, 0)$	$\frac{1}{2}$	$x^2 + y^2 = \frac{1}{4}$
C	$(0, 0)$	3	$x^2 + y^2 = 9$
D	$(4, 0)$	1	$(x - 4)^2 + y^2 = 1$

✓ **Check Understanding** **3** Write the equation of a circle for a gear that is the same size as gear *D* and has center $(0, -4)$. $x^2 + (y + 4)^2 = 1$

OBJECTIVE
2 **Using the Center and Radius of a Circle**

You can find the center and radius of a circle by rewriting the equation in the standard form of a circle.

4 **EXAMPLE** Finding the Center and Radius

Find the center and radius of the circle with equation $(x - 16)^2 + (y + 9)^2 = 144$.

$(x - h)^2 + (y - k)^2 = r^2$ **Write the standard form.**

$(x - 16)^2 + (y + 9)^2 = 144$ **Write the equation.**

$(x - 16)^2 + (y - (-9))^2 = 12^2$ **Rewrite the equation in standard form.**

$h = 16 \quad k = -9 \quad r = 12$ **Find h, k, and r.**

The center of the circle is $(16, -9)$. The radius is 12.

✓ **Check Understanding** **4** Find the center and radius of the circle with equation $(x + 8)^2 + (y + 3)^2 = 121$.
$(-8, -3), 11$

Lesson 10-3 Circles   **551**

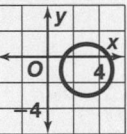

Error Prevention

Exercises 1–8 To help avoid sign errors, suggest students place parentheses around the values that they are substituting for h and k.

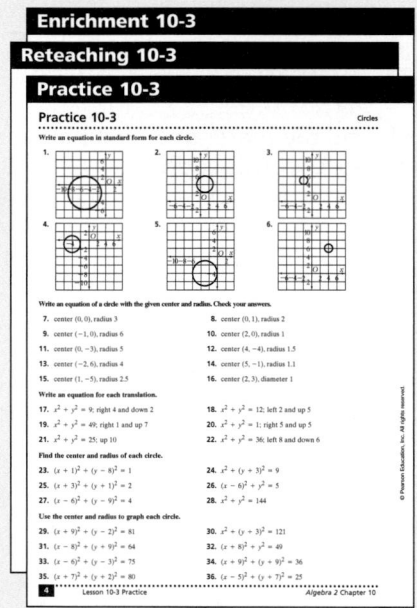

You can use the center and the radius to graph a circle.

5 EXAMPLE **Graphing a Circle Using Center and Radius**

Graph $(x + 1)^2 + (y - 3)^2 = 25$.

$(x - h)^2 + (y - k)^2 = r^2$ **Find the center and the radius of the circle.**
$(x - (-1))^2 + (y - 3)^2 = 25$
$h = -1 \qquad k = 3 \qquad r^2 = 25, \text{ or } r = 5$

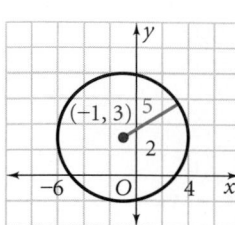

Draw the center $(-1, 3)$ and radius 5. Draw a smooth curve.

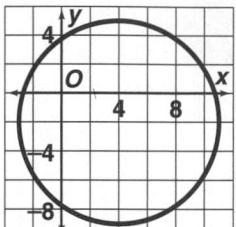

✓ **Check Understanding** ⑤ Graph $(x - 4)^2 + (y + 2)^2 = 49$.

EXERCISES

For more practice, see *Extra Practice*.

Practice and Problem Solving

Ⓐ **Practice by Example**

Example 1
(page 550)

Write an equation of a circle with the given center and radius. Check your answers.

1. $(0, 0), 10$ 2. $(-4, -6), 7$ 3. $(2, 3), 4.5$ 4. $(-6, 10), 1$
5. $(1, -3), 10$ 6. $(-5, -1), 6$ 7. $(-3, 0), 8$ 8. $(-1.5, -3), 2$
1–8. See margin.

Example 2
(page 550)

Write an equation for each translation. **9–14. See margin.**

9. $x^2 + y^2 = 9$; down 1 10. $x^2 + y^2 = 1$; left 1

11. $x^2 + y^2 = 25$; right 2 and down 4 12. $x^2 + y^2 = 81$; left 1 and up 3

13. $x^2 + y^2 = 100$; down 5 14. $x^2 + y^2 = 49$; right 3 and up 2

15. $x^2 + y^2 = 20$; left 6 and up 1 16. $x^2 + y^2 = 50$; right 5
$(x + 6)^2 + (y - 1)^2 = 20$ $(x - 5)^2 + y^2 = 50$

Example 3
(page 551)

Write an equation for each circle. Each interval represents one unit.

17.  18.

$(x + 3)^2 + (y - 4)^2 = 9$ $(x - 2)^2 + (y + 6)^2 = 16$

Example 4
(page 551)

For each equation, find the center and radius of the circle.

19. $(x - 1)^2 + (y - 1)^2 = 1$ **(1, 1), 1** 20. $(x + 2)^2 + (y - 10)^2 = 4$

20. **(−2, 10), 2**

21. $(x - 3)^2 + (y + 1)^2 = 36$ **(3, −1), 6** 22. $(x + 3)^2 + (y - 5)^2 = 81$

22. **(−3, 5), 9**

23. $x^2 + (y + 3)^2 = 25$ **(0, −3), 5** 24. $(x + 6)^2 + y^2 = 121$ **(−6, 0), 11**

25. **(−2, −4), 16**

25. $(x + 2)^2 + (y + 4)^2 = 256$ 26. $(x - 3)^2 + (y - 7)^2 = 96$

26. **(3, 7), 4√6**

552 Chapter 10 Quadratic Relations

pages 552–554 Exercises

1. $x^2 + y^2 = 100$
2. $(x + 4)^2 + (y + 6)^2 = 49$
3. $(x - 2)^2 + (y - 3)^2 = 20.25$
4. $(x + 6)^2 + (y - 10)^2 = 1$

5. $(x - 1)^2 + (y + 3)^2 = 100$
6. $(x + 5)^2 + (y + 1)^2 = 36$
7. $(x + 3)^2 + y^2 = 64$
8. $(x + 1.5)^2 + (y + 3)^2 = 4$
9. $x^2 + (y + 1)^2 = 9$

10. $(x + 1)^2 + y^2 = 1$
11. $(x - 2)^2 + (y + 4)^2 = 25$
12. $(x + 1)^2 + (y - 3)^2 = 81$
13. $x^2 + (y + 5)^2 = 100$
14. $(x - 3)^2 + (y - 2)^2 = 49$

Example 5
(page 552)

Use the center and the radius to graph each circle.

27. $(x + 9)^2 + (y + 2)^2 = 100$

28. $(x + 4)^2 + (y - 4)^2 = 4$

29. $(x - 6)^2 + y^2 = 64$

30. $(x - 1)^2 + (y + 3)^2 = 16$

31. $x^2 + y^2 = 9$

32. $(x + 3)^2 + (y - 9)^2 = 49$

33. $(x - 7)^2 + (y - 1)^2 = 100$

34. $x^2 + (y + 4)^2 = 144$

27–34. See back of book.

B **Apply Your Skills**

Write the equation of the circle that passes through the given point and has a center at the origin. (*Hint:* You can use the distance formula to find the radius.)

35. $x^2 + y^2 = 16$ 35. $(0, 4)$ 36. $(0, -3)$ 37. $(-5, 0)$ 38. $(\sqrt{3}, 0)$ 39. $(4, -3)$

36. $x^2 + y^2 = 9$ 40. $(-5, -12)$ 41. $(12, -5)$ 42. $(-2, 3)$ 43. $(1, -5)$ 44. $(-6, -4)$

37. $x^2 + y^2 = 25$

38. $x^2 + y^2 = 3$

39. $x^2 + y^2 = 25$ Use the given information to write an equation of the circle. 45–52. See margin.

40. $x^2 + y^2 = 169$ 45. radius 7, center $(-6, 13)$ 46. area 78.54, center $(5, -3)$

41. $x^2 + y^2 = 169$ 47. center $(-2, 7.5)$, circumference 3π 48. center $(1, -2)$, through $(0, 1)$

42. $x^2 + y^2 = 13$ 49. center $(2, 1)$, through $(6, 4)$ 50. center $(6, 4)$, through $(2, 1)$

43. $x^2 + y^2 = 26$ 51. translation of $(x - 1)^2 + (y + 3)^2 = 36$, 2 units left and 4 units down

44. $x^2 + y^2 = 52$

52. **Recreation** Write the equation of the circular fountain at the right.

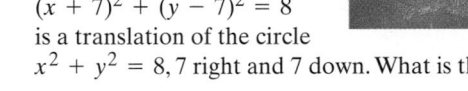

10   C(24, 22)

53. Check students' work.

53. **Open-Ended** Write two functions that together represent a circle.

54. **Error Analysis** A student claims that the circle $(x + 7)^2 + (y - 7)^2 = 8$ is a translation of the circle $x^2 + y^2 = 8$, 7 right and 7 down. What is the student's mistake? **See margin.**

Find the center and the radius of each circle.

55. $x^2 + y^2 = 2$ **(0, 0), $\sqrt{2}$**   56. $x^2 + (y + 1)^2 = 5$ **(0, -1), $\sqrt{5}$**

57. $x^2 + y^2 = 14$ **(0, 0), $\sqrt{14}$**   58. $x^2 + (y - 4)^2 = 11$ **(0, 4), $\sqrt{11}$**

60. $(-2, -4), 5\sqrt{2}$ 59. $(x + 5)^2 + y^2 = 18$ **(-5, 0), $3\sqrt{2}$**   60. $(x + 2)^2 + (y + 4)^2 = 50$

61. $(-3, 5), \sqrt{38}$ 61. $(x + 3)^2 + (y - 5)^2 = 38$ 62. $x^2 + 2x + 1 + y^2 = 4$ **(-1, 0), 2**

63. $(3, 1), \sqrt{6}$ 63. $x^2 + y^2 - 6x - 2y + 4 = 0$ 64. $x^2 + y^2 - 4y - 16 = 0$

64. $(0, 2), 2\sqrt{5}$

Graph each pair of equations. Identify the conic section represented by the graph. Then write the equation of the conic section. 65–66. See margin.

65. $y = 3 + \sqrt{16 - (x - 4)^2}$ 66. $y = -2 + \sqrt{x - 3}$
     $y = 3 - \sqrt{16 - (x - 4)^2}$ $y = -2 - \sqrt{x - 3}$

C **Challenge**

67. **Reasoning** Let $P(x, y)$ be any point on the circle with center $(0, 0)$ and radius r. Choose a method for proving that $x^2 + y^2 = r^2$. **See back of book.**

68. **a. Writing** Explain why $x^2 + y^2 = 0$ does not represent a circle.
    b. Critical Thinking What does the equation represent? **point (0, 0)**

68a. The radius would have length 0.

Lesson 10-3 Circles   **553**

45. $(x + 6)^2 + (y - 13)^2 = 49$ 49. $(x - 2)^2 + (y - 1)^2 = 25$

46. $(x - 5)^2 + (y + 3)^2 = 25$ 50. $(x - 6)^2 + (y - 4)^2 = 25$

47. $(x + 2)^2 + (y - 7.5)^2 = 2.25$ 51. $(x + 1)^2 + (y + 7)^2 = 36$

48. $(x - 1)^2 + (y + 2)^2 = 10$ 52. $(x - 24)^2 + (y - 22)^2 = 100$

54. Replacing x with $x + 7$ and y with $y - 7$ has the effect of translating the circle 7 units left and 7 units up.

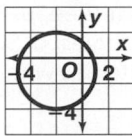
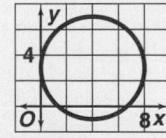
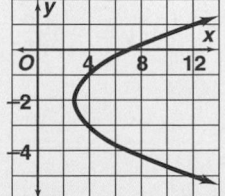

A sheet of blank grids is available in the Test-Taking Strategies with Transparencies booklet. Give this sheet to students for practice with filling in the grids.

 **Resources**

For additional practice with a variety of test item formats:
* Standardized Test Prep, p. 583
* Test-Taking Strategies, p. 578
* Test-Taking Strategies with Transparencies

Error Prevention

Exercise 73 Some students may be tempted to use 169 as the diameter of Circle A rather than 26. Remind students that 169 is the square of the radius of Circle A, not twice the radius.

 **Chapter Checkpoint 1**

To check understanding of Lessons 10-1 to 10-3:

Checkpoint Quiz 1 (p. 554)

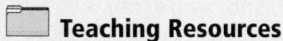 **Teaching Resources**
Checkpoint Quiz 1 (also in Prentice Hall Assessment System)

Reaching All Students
Reading and Math Literacy 10B

Spanish versions available

---

69. The table gives the diameters of four planets.
  a. Use a center of $(0, 0)$ to graph a circle that represents the size of each planet. **a–b. See back of book.**
  b. Write an equation representing the circular cross section through the center of each planet.

Planet	Diameter (miles)
Pluto	1430
Mercury	3031
Mars	4222
Earth	7926

70a. $(x - 3)^2 + (y - 4)^2 = 25$
  b. $y = -\frac{1}{3}x^2 + \frac{10}{3}x$

70. a. A circle contains $(0, 0)$, $(6, 8)$, and $(7, 7)$. Find its equation by solving a system of three equations.
  b. Several parabolas contain the three points of part (a), but only one is described by a quadratic function. Find that function.

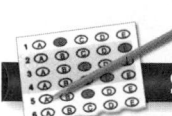

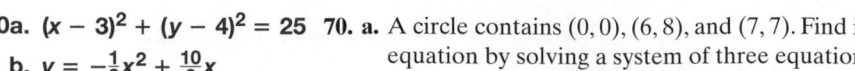
Standardized Test Prep

Gridded Response

71. What is the radius of the circle with equation $(x + 5)^2 + (y - 3)^2 = 144$? **12**

72. What is the radius of the circle with equation $(x - 2)^2 + 3 + (y + 1)^2 = 7$? **2**

73. Circle A has equation $(x + 5)^2 + y^2 = 169$. The diameter of circle B is one fourth as long as the diameter of circle A. What is the radius of circle B? **3.25**

74. What is the distance between $T(9, -5)$ and the center of the circle with equation $(x - 6)^2 + (y + 1)^2 = 10$? **5**

75. Find the distance between the centers of the circles with equations $(x - 5)^2 + (y - 1)^2 = 16$ and $(x + 1)^2 + (y - 9)^2 = 49$. **10**

76. What is the area of the circle whose equation is $(x + 1)^2 + (y + 1)^2 = 1$? Round your answer to the nearest hundredth. **3.14**

Take It to the NET
Online lesson quiz at
www.PHSchool.com
Web Code: aga-1003

Mixed Review

Lesson 10-2

77. Write an equation of a parabola opening left with vertex $(0, 0)$ and focus $(-3, 0)$.
$$x = -\frac{1}{12}y^2$$

Lesson 9-3

For each rational function, find any points of discontinuity.

78. $y = \frac{2}{x + 1}$
$x = -1$

79. $y = \frac{1}{x^2 - 5x + 6}$
$x = 2, x = 3$

80. $y = \frac{2x - 1}{x^2 + 4}$
no discontinuities

Lesson 8-3

Evaluate each logarithm.

81. $\log_2 16$ **4**

82. $\log_5 25$ **2**

83. $\log_3 \frac{1}{27}$ **−3**

84. $\log 10,000$ **4**

85. $\log_3 81$ **4**

86. $\log_{36} 6$ **$\frac{1}{2}$**

87. $\log_4 256$ **4**

88. $\log_2 \frac{1}{4}$ **−2**

89. $\log_{100} 100$ **1**

 Checkpoint Quiz 1   **Lessons 10-1 through 10-3**

TEXT Instant self-check quiz online and on CD-ROM

Identify the vertex, focus, and directrix of each parabola. Then graph the parabola.

1. $y = 3x^2$

2. $x = 4(y + 2)^2$

3. $y + 1 = (x - 3)^2$

1–3. See margin.

4. $(x + 6)^2 + (y - 3)^2 = 64$

4. Write an equation in standard form of the circle with center $(-6, 3)$ and radius 8.

5. What translation of $x^2 + y^2 = 18$ results in $(x + 4)^2 + (y - 6)^2 = 18$?
4 units left and 6 units up

---

page 554   Checkpoint Quiz 1

1. $(0, 0)$, $\left(0, \frac{1}{12}\right)$, $y = -\frac{1}{12}$;

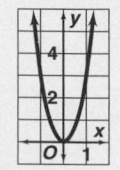

554

2. $(0, -2)$, $\left(\frac{1}{16}, -2\right)$, $x = -\frac{1}{16}$;

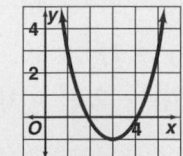

3. $(3, -1)$, $\left(3, -\frac{3}{4}\right)$, $y = -\frac{5}{4}$;

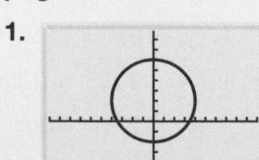

page 555   Extension

1.

Using Parametric Form

FOR USE WITH LESSON 10-3

The graphing calculator program below uses parametric forms to graph a circle. To enter the program, use the PRGM NEW menu. Name your program **CIRCLE**.

Note that you find the **Disp**, **Prompt**, and **DispGraph** features in the PRGM I/O menu, and X_{1T} and Y_{1T} in the VARS Y-Vars Parametric menu. You can find **Par** and **Radian** under MODE, and **Tmin**, **Tmax**, and **Tstep** in the VARS Window T/θ menu.

Use ALPHA keys to enter words, quotation marks, and variables $H, K, R,$ and T.

```
PROGRAM:CIRCLE
:Disp "CENTER (H,K)"
:Disp "RADIUS R"
:Prompt H,K,R
:"Rcos(T)+H"→X₁T
■
```

```
PROGRAM:CIRCLE
:"Rsin(T)+K"→Y₁T
:Param
:Radian
:0→Tmin
:2π→Tmax
:.05→Tstep
:DispGraph■
```

The next screens show the program being run for a circle with a center at $(-2, 3)$ and a radius of 5. Enter appropriate square-window values with the calculator in function mode. Then choose the program from the PRGM EXEC menu.

```
WINDOW
Xmin=-12
Xmax=12
Xscl=1
Ymin=-8
Ymax=8
Yscl=1
Xres=1■
```

```
prgmCIRCLE
CENTER (H,K)
RADIUS R
H=?-2
K=?3
R=?5■
```

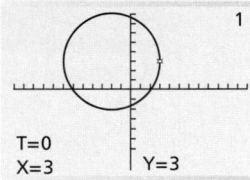

Note that you can trace to find the coordinates of points on the circle.

EXERCISES

Use your program to graph each circle. Use an appropriate square window for each graph. 1–6. See margin pp. 554–555. 7–8. See back of book.

1. center $(0, 2)$, radius 4

2. center $(5, -2)$, radius 5

3. center $(-1, 3)$, radius 8

4. $(x - 2)^2 + (y + 1)^2 = 25$

5. $(x + 4)^2 + (y - 3)^2 = 100$

6. $x^2 + (y + 2)^2 = 49$

7. $(x - 1)^2 + (y + 2)^2 = 36$

8. $(x - 6)^2 + y^2 = 100$

9. Open-Ended Use TRACE to find four points in Quadrant III that lie on the circle described by the equation $(x + 5)^2 + (y - 2)^2 = 16$. **Check students' work.**

10. Writing Describe how to change your program to work in degrees and plot a point every 5° of rotation. **In the program, change radian to degree, change $2\pi \to T_{max}$ to $360 \to T_{max}$, and change $0.05 \to T_{step}$ to $5 \to T_{step}$.**

Students learn how to write a program for their calculators that will graph a circle when the center and radius are given. This program uses the same information that students needed to graph a circle by hand.

Resources

Technology
Computer Test Generator CD-ROM, Chapter 0, Extension Topics

Teaching Notes

Teaching Tip
Students may wish to revisit the Technology Extension for Lesson 3-2 for a review of parametric equations.

Error Prevention
Exercise 10 Students having difficulty should be encouraged to examine the program and identify the instruction lines that use, or refer to, angles or radians. Students should explain how to rewrite these lines so that they refer to degrees instead of radians.

5.

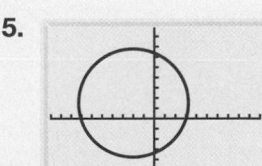

6.

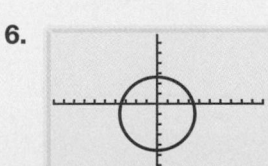

2.

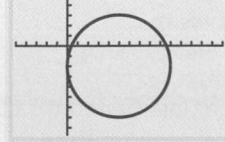

3.

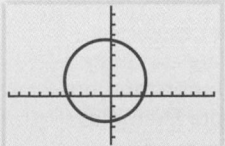

4.

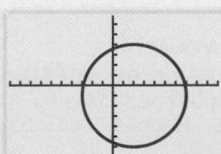

Ellipses

Lesson Preview

Lesson Preview

What You'll Learn

OBJECTIVE 1 To write the equation of an ellipse

OBJECTIVE 2 To find the foci of an ellipse and to graph an ellipse

... And Why

To model NASA's Transonic Tunnel, as in Example 2

✓ Check Skills You'll Need (For help, go to Lesson 5-5 and Skills Handbook page 846.)

Solve each equation.

1. $27 = x^2 + 11$ **±4**   **2.** $x^2 = 48$ **±4$\sqrt{3}$**   **3.** $84 = 120 - x^2$ **±6**

Evaluate each expression for $a = 3$ and $b = 5$.

4. $a^2 + b^2$ **34**   **5.** $a^2 - b^2$ **−16**   **6.** $b^2 - 2a^2$ **7**

New Vocabulary • ellipse • focus of an ellipse • major axis • vertices of an ellipse • minor axis • co-vertices

---

🅸TEXT **Interactive lesson includes instant self-check, tutorials, and activities.**

OBJECTIVE 1

Writing the Equation of an Ellipse

Ellipses play an important role in science. For example, the planets follow elliptical, not circular, orbits around the sun.

🔑 **Key Concepts**

Definition	**Ellipse**

An **ellipse** is a set of points P in a plane such that the sum of the distances from P to two fixed points F_1 and F_2 is a given constant k.

$$PF_1 + PF_2 = k, \text{ where } k > F_1F_2$$

📖 **Reading Math**

Ellipse comes from a Greek word for "smaller." The cutting plane of an ellipse makes a smaller angle with the base than does the side of the cone. See p. 535.

Each fixed point F is a **focus of an ellipse** (plural: foci). The **major axis** is the segment that contains the foci and has its endpoints on the ellipse. The endpoints of the major axis are **vertices of an ellipse.** The midpoint of the major axis is the center of the ellipse. The **minor axis** is perpendicular to the major axis at the center. The endpoints of the minor axis are **co-vertices.**

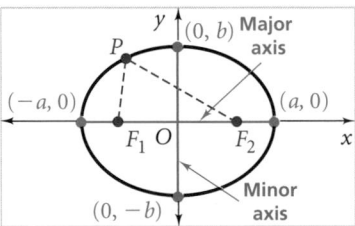

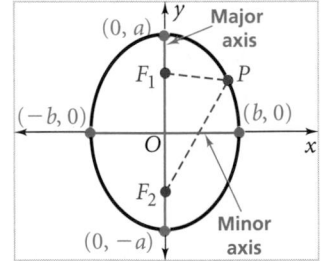

$$\frac{x^2}{a^2} + \frac{y^2}{b^2} = 1$$
← standard forms of an equation of an ellipse, with center at the origin and $a > b > 0$ →
$$\frac{x^2}{b^2} + \frac{y^2}{a^2} = 1$$

major axis: horizontal
vertices: $(\pm a, 0)$
co-vertices: $(0, \pm b)$

major axis: vertical
vertices: $(0, \pm a)$
co-vertices: $(\pm b, 0)$

You can write the equation of an ellipse with a center at the origin if you know an *x*-intercept and a *y*-intercept.

1 EXAMPLE Writing the Equation of an Ellipse

Write an equation in standard form of an ellipse that has a vertex at $(0, 5)$, a co-vertex at $(2, 0)$, and a center at the origin.

Since $(0, 5)$ is a vertex of the ellipse, the other vertex is at $(0, -5)$, and the major axis is vertical. Since $(2, 0)$ is a co-vertex, the other co-vertex is at $(-2, 0)$, and the minor axis is horizontal. So $a = 5, b = 2, a^2 = 25$, and $b^2 = 4$.

$\dfrac{x^2}{b^2} + \dfrac{y^2}{a^2} = 1$ **standard form of an equation of an ellipse with a vertical major axis**

$\dfrac{x^2}{4} + \dfrac{y^2}{25} = 1$ **Substitute 4 for b^2 and 25 for a^2.**

● An equation of the ellipse is $\dfrac{x^2}{4} + \dfrac{y^2}{25} = 1$.

✓ Check Understanding ❶ Write an equation in standard form for an ellipse that has a vertex at $(0, -6)$, a co-vertex at $(3, 0)$, and a center at the origin. $\dfrac{x^2}{9} + \dfrac{y^2}{36} = 1$

You can write an equation for an ellipse with a center at the origin if you know the length of both axes.

2 EXAMPLE Real-World Connection

Architecture The Transonic Tunnel at NASA Langley Research Center, Virginia, is used to study the dynamics of air flow. The elliptical opening of the Transonic Tunnel is 82 ft wide and 58 ft high. Find an equation of the ellipse.

Imagine a large coordinate grid placed over the elliptical opening. Since the widest part of the ellipse is horizontal and the width is 82 ft, place the vertices at $(\pm 41, 0)$. Place the co-vertices at $(0, \pm 29)$.

So $a = 41, b = 29, a^2 = 1681$, and $b^2 = 841$.

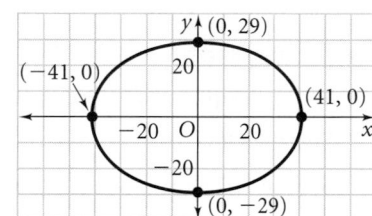

$\dfrac{x^2}{a^2} + \dfrac{y^2}{b^2} = 1$ **standard form for an ellipse with a horizontal major axis**

$\dfrac{x^2}{1681} + \dfrac{y^2}{841} = 1$ **Substitute 1681 for a^2 and 841 for b^2.**

● An equation of the ellipse is $\dfrac{x^2}{1681} + \dfrac{y^2}{841} = 1$.

✓ Check Understanding ❷ Find an equation of an ellipse centered at the origin that is 12 units wide and 30 units high. $\dfrac{x^2}{36} + \dfrac{y^2}{225} = 1$

esson 10-4 Ellipses **557**

Real-World Connection

The guide vanes in the elliptical opening of the Transonic Tunnel allow a smooth flow of air through the passageway.

👥 Reaching All Students

Below Level Show students how to draw an ellipse using two push pins and a piece of string. Ask them to explain how this construction technique relates to the definition of an ellipse.	**Advanced Learners** Students with an interest in astronomy can look up Kepler's three laws of planetary motion. Have students report their findings to the class.	**Tactile Learners** See note on page 557. **English Learners** See note on page 559.

---

2. Teach

Professional Development

Math Background

Students build on their knowledge of circles to help them develop the techniques necessary to write the equation of an ellipse and graph an ellipse. An interesting application of ellipses is based on the property that when a light or sound wave is emitted at one focus it passes through the other focus. This property is typically studied in science, geometry, and calculus courses. Also, note that a circle is an ellipse whose two foci are coincident.

OBJECTIVE
▼ 1 Teaching Notes

Definition of an Ellipse
Tactile Learners
Go outside and organize students into groups of three. Give each group a piece of string about 15 ft long and at least 20 colored counters. Have two students stand about 10 ft apart and each hold an end of the string. The third student takes the counters and the middle of the string and walks a few paces until the string is taut. A counter is placed at this spot. Now the student walks around the other two students, sliding the string between the fingers, but always keeping it taut. The student places counters on the ground every couple of paces. Students should see that the counters are forming an ellipse. Students acting as foci may need to duck so that the string does not get caught around their bodies.

📓 Additional Examples

❶ Write an equation in standard form of an ellipse that has a vertex at $(0, -4)$, a co-vertex at $(3, 0)$, and is centered at the origin.
$\dfrac{x^2}{9} + \dfrac{y^2}{16} = 1$

❷ Find an equation of an ellipse centered at the origin that is 20 units wide and 10 units high.
$\dfrac{x^2}{100} + \dfrac{y^2}{25} = 1$

557

Connection to Geometry

3 EXAMPLE

Students may not see how the relationship for a, b, and c is related to the Pythagorean Theorem. Ask: *Which variables represent the legs?* **b and c** *Which variable represents the hypotenuse?* **a** Write $b^2 + c^2 = a^2$ on the board. Then use the Subtraction Property of Equality to write $c^2 = a^2 - b^2$.

Technology Tip

4 EXAMPLE

Students may wish to graph this ellipse and verify their graphs from Example 3 by using their graphing calculators. They can either apply the technique used in Lesson 10-3 Example 1 or modify the circle program created in the Extension for Lesson 10-3. To modify the program, students need to change "Prompt H, K, R" to "Prompt H, K, A, B", "Rcos T + H" to "Acos T + H", and "Rsin T + K" to "Bsin T + K", where (H, K) is the center of the ellipse, A is the distance from the center to a vertex, and B is the distance from the center to a co-vertex.

Additional Examples

3 Find the foci of the ellipse with the equation $9x^2 + y^2 = 36$. Graph the ellipse. **(0, ±4√2)**

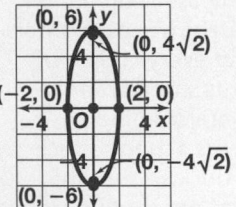

4 Write an equation of the ellipse with foci at (0, ±4) and co-vertices at (±2, 0).
$$\frac{x^2}{4} + \frac{y^2}{20} = 1$$

Closure

Have students explain the process for writing the equation of an ellipse, graphing an ellipse, and determining the foci of an ellipse. Assume that the ellipse is centered at the origin.

558

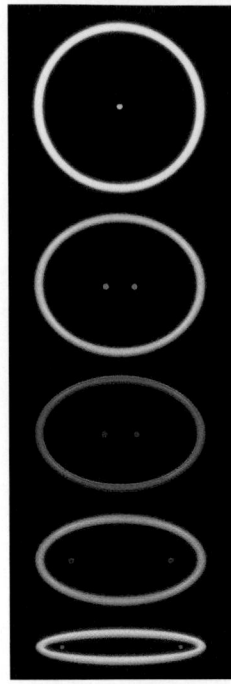

The figure above shows the relationship between the center of a circle and the foci of an ellipse.

✓ **Check Understanding**

3. $(2\sqrt{2}, 0), (-2\sqrt{2}, 0);$

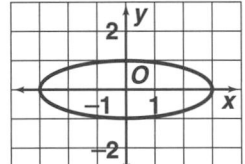

✓ **Check Understanding**

The foci are important points in an ellipse. For example, the sun is at a focus, not at the center, of Earth's orbit around the sun.

The foci of an ellipse are always on the major axis at c units from the center.

There is an important and useful relationship among a, b, and c:
$c^2 = a^2 - b^2$.

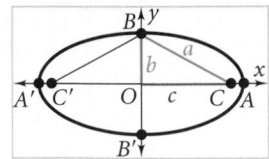

You can use the relationship to find the foci of an ellipse.

3 EXAMPLE Finding the Foci of an Ellipse

Find the foci of the ellipse with the equation $25x^2 + 9y^2 = 225$. Graph the ellipse.

$25x^2 + 9y^2 = 225$

$\quad \frac{x^2}{9} + \frac{y^2}{25} = 1$ **Write in standard form.**

Since $25 > 9$ and 25 is with y^2, the major axis is vertical, $a^2 = 25$, and $b^2 = 9$.

$c^2 = a^2 - b^2$ **Find c.**

$\quad = 25 - 9$ **Substitute 25 for a^2 and 9 for b^2.**

$\quad = 16$

$c = 4$

The major axis is vertical, so the coordinates of the foci are $(0, \pm c)$. The foci are $(0, 4)$ and $(0, -4)$.

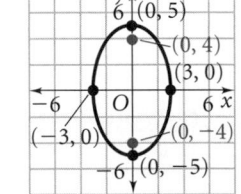

The vertices are $(0, \pm 5)$. The co-vertices are $(\pm 3, 0)$.

3 Find the foci of the ellipse with the equation $x^2 + 9y^2 = 9$. Graph the ellipse.
See left.

You can use the relationship among a, b, and c to write the equation of an ellipse.

4 EXAMPLE Using the Foci of an Ellipse

Write an equation of the ellipse with foci at $(\pm 7, 0)$ and co-vertices at $(0, \pm 6)$.

Since the foci have coordinates $(\pm 7, 0)$, the major axis is horizontal.

Since $c = 7$ and $b = 6$, $c^2 = 49$ and $b^2 = 36$.

$c^2 = a^2 - b^2$ **Use the equation to find a^2.**

$49 = a^2 - 36$ **Substitute 49 for c^2 and 36 for b^2.**

$a^2 = 85$ **Simplify.**

$\frac{x^2}{85} + \frac{y^2}{36} = 1$ **Substitute 85 for a^2 and 36 for b^2.**

An equation of the ellipse is $\frac{x^2}{85} + \frac{y^2}{36} = 1$.

4 Write an equation of the ellipse with foci at $\left(0, \pm\sqrt{17}\right)$ and co-vertices at $(\pm 8, 0)$. $\frac{x^2}{64} + \frac{y^2}{81} = 1$

Determine the vertices, co-vertices, and major and minor axes. The equation has the form $\frac{x^2}{a^2} + \frac{y^2}{b^2} = 1$ or $\frac{x^2}{b^2} + \frac{y^2}{a^2} = 1$, where a is the distance from the center to a vertex and b is the

distance from the center to a co-vertex. Use this information to graph the equation. The foci lie on the major axis and are $(\pm c, 0)$ or $(0, \pm c)$, where $c^2 = a^2 - b^2$.

EXERCISES

Practice and Problem Solving

For more practice, see *Extra Practice*.

Ⓐ **Practice by Example**

Example 1
(page 557)

Write an equation of an ellipse in standard form with center at the origin and with the given vertex and co-vertex.   1–8. See margin.

1. $(4, 0), (0, 3)$ **2.** $(0, 1), (2, 0)$ **3.** $(3, 0), (0, -1)$ **4.** $(0, 6), (1, 0)$

5. $(0, -7), (4, 0)$ **6.** $(-6, 0), (0, 5)$ **7.** $(-9, 0), (0, -2)$ **8.** $(0, 5), (-3, 0)$

Example 2
(page 557)

Find an equation of an ellipse for each given height and width. Assume that the center of the ellipse is $(0, 0)$.   9–17. See back of book.

9. $h = 1$ m, $w = 3$ m   **10.** $h = 32$ ft, $w = 16$ ft   **11.** $h = 20$ ft, $w = 12$ ft

12. $h = 10$ cm, $w = 7$ cm   **13.** $h = 14$ yd, $w = 28$ yd   **14.** $h = 8$ ft, $w = 2$ ft

15. $h = 15$ ft, $w = 32$ ft   **16.** $h = 40$ mi, $w = 60$ mi   **17.** $h = 5$ m, $w = 2$ m

Example 3
(page 558)

Find the foci for each equation of an ellipse. Then graph the ellipse.

18. $\frac{x^2}{4} + \frac{y^2}{9} = 1$ **19.** $\frac{x^2}{9} + \frac{y^2}{25} = 1$ **20.** $\frac{x^2}{81} + \frac{y^2}{49} = 1$

21. $\frac{x^2}{100} + \frac{y^2}{36} = 1$ **22.** $\frac{x^2}{64} + \frac{y^2}{100} = 1$ **23.** $3x^2 + y^2 = 9$

24. $x^2 + 4y^2 = 16$ **25.** $\frac{x^2}{225} + \frac{y^2}{144} = 1$ **26.** $\frac{x^2}{256} + \frac{y^2}{121} = 1$

18–26. See back of book.

Example 4
(page 558)

Write an equation of an ellipse for the given foci and co-vertices.

27. foci $(\pm 6, 0)$, co-vertices $(0, \pm 8)$ **28.** foci $(0, \pm 8)$, co-vertices $(\pm 8, 0)$

29. foci $(\pm 5, 0)$, co-vertices $(0, \pm 8)$ **30.** foci $(0, \pm 4)$, co-vertices $(\pm 2, 0)$

31. foci $(\pm 14, 0)$, co-vertices $(0, \pm 7)$ **32.** foci $(\pm 17, 0)$, co-vertices $(0, \pm 15)$

27–32. See margin.

Ⓑ **Apply Your Skills**

Find the foci for each equation of an ellipse.   33–40. See below left.

33. $4x^2 + 9y^2 = 36$ **34.** $16x^2 + 4y^2 = 64$ **35.** $36x^2 + 4y^2 = 144$

36. $25x^2 + 4y^2 = 100$ **37.** $36x^2 + 8y^2 = 288$ **38.** $25x^2 + 24y^2 = 600$

39. $25x^2 + 16y^2 + 150x = 160y - 225$ **40.** $2x^2 + 8x + y^2 + 4 = 0$

Reading Math

Eccentric means "out of center."

41. The eccentricity of an ellipse is a measure of how nearly circular it is. Eccentricity is defined as $\frac{c}{a}$, where c is the distance from the center to a focus and a is the distance from the center to a vertex.
   a. Find the eccentricity of an ellipse with foci $(\pm 9, 0)$ and vertices $(\pm 10, 0)$. Sketch the graph.   **a–d. See back of book.**
   b. Find the eccentricity of an ellipse with foci $(\pm 1, 0)$ and vertices $(\pm 10, 0)$. Sketch the graph.
   c. Describe the shape of an ellipse that has an eccentricity close to 0.
   d. Describe the shape of an ellipse that has an eccentricity close to 1.

42. Find the equation of the ellipse with foci on the x-axis, major axis 9 units long, minor axis 4 units long, and center at the origin. $\frac{x^2}{20.25} + \frac{y^2}{4} = 1$

43. a. Critical Thinking Suppose the foci of an ellipse are near the center of the ellipse. Will the shape of the ellipse be nearly a circle? Explain.
   b. Is a circle also an ellipse? Explain.   **a–b. See back of book.**

33. $(\sqrt{5}, 0), (-\sqrt{5}, 0)$

34. $(0, 2\sqrt{3}), (0, -2\sqrt{3})$

35. $(0, 4\sqrt{2}), (0, -4\sqrt{2})$

36. $(0, \sqrt{21}), (0, -\sqrt{21})$

37. $(0, 2\sqrt{7}), (0, -2\sqrt{7})$

38. $(0, 1), (0, -1)$

39. $(-3, 8), (-3, 2)$

40. $(-2, \sqrt{2}), (-2, -\sqrt{2})$

English Learners

Exercise 41 Have students look up the word *eccentric* in a dictionary or thesaurus. Suggest additional meanings such as *irregular* or *abnormal* to help students further understand the mathematical meaning of the word.

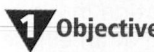

Enrichment 10-4

Reteaching 10-4

Practice 10-4

---

pages 559–561   Exercises

1. $\frac{x^2}{16} + \frac{y^2}{9} = 1$

2. $\frac{x^2}{4} + y^2 = 1$

3. $\frac{x^2}{9} + y^2 = 1$

4. $x^2 + \frac{y^2}{36} = 1$

5. $\frac{x^2}{16} + \frac{y^2}{49} = 1$

6. $\frac{x^2}{36} + \frac{y^2}{25} = 1$

7. $\frac{x^2}{81} + \frac{y^2}{4} = 1$

8. $\frac{x^2}{9} + \frac{y^2}{25} = 1$

27. $\frac{x^2}{100} + \frac{y^2}{64} = 1$

28. $\frac{x^2}{64} + \frac{y^2}{128} = 1$

29. $\frac{x^2}{89} + \frac{y^2}{64} = 1$

30. $\frac{x^2}{4} + \frac{y^2}{20} = 1$

31. $\frac{x^2}{245} + \frac{y^2}{49} = 1$

32. $\frac{x^2}{514} + \frac{y^2}{225} = 1$

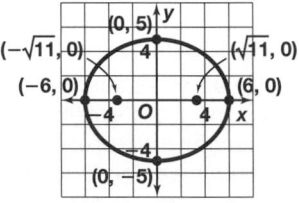
44. $\frac{x^2}{9} + \frac{y^2}{4} = 1$

45. $\frac{x^2}{16} + y^2 = 1$

46. $x^2 + \frac{y^2}{9} = 1$

47. $\frac{x^2}{4} + \frac{y^2}{16} = 1$

50. $\frac{x^2}{4} + \frac{y^2}{3} = 1$

51. $\frac{x^2}{25} + \frac{y^2}{4} = 1$

52. $\frac{x^2}{121} + \frac{y^2}{81} = 1$

53. $\frac{x^2}{702.25} + \frac{y^2}{210.25} = 1$

54. $\frac{x^2}{169} + \frac{y^2}{144} = 1$

55. $\frac{x^2}{256} + \frac{y^2}{324} = 1$

56. $\frac{x^2}{72.25} + \frac{y^2}{90.25} = 1$

57. $\frac{x^2}{400} + \frac{y^2}{100} = 1$

58. $\frac{x^2}{16} + \frac{y^2}{12} = 1$

59. $\frac{x^2}{16} + \frac{y^2}{25} = 1$

60. $\frac{x^2}{39} + \frac{y^2}{64} = 1$

61. $\frac{x^2}{36} + \frac{y^2}{27} = 1$

62. $\frac{x^2}{4} + \frac{y^2}{9} = 1$

63. $\frac{x^2}{18} + \frac{y^2}{20} = 1$

Write an equation for each ellipse.

44.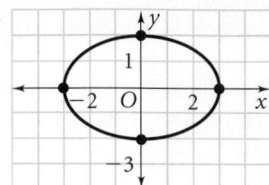

45.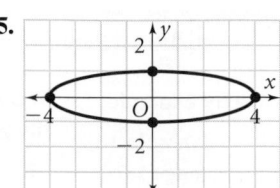

46.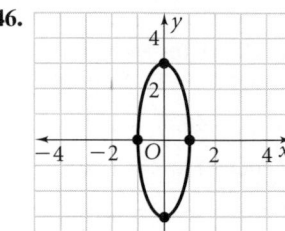

47.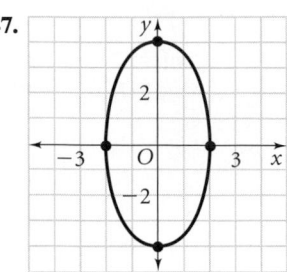

48. **Error Analysis** A student claims that an ellipse has vertices at $(\pm 3, 0)$ and co-vertices at $(0, \pm 7)$. What is the student's error? **See back of book.**

49. **Open-Ended** Find a real-world design that uses ellipses. Place a coordinate grid over the design and write an equation of the ellipse. **Check students' work.**

Write an equation of an ellipse in standard form with center at the origin and with the given characteristics.

50. focus $(1, 0)$, width 4

51. $a = 5$, $b = 2$, width 10

52. vertex $(-11, 0)$, co-vertex $(0, 9)$

53. height 29, width 53

54. focus $(-5, 0)$, co-vertex $(0, -12)$

55. $c^2 = 68$, vertex $(0, -18)$

56. focus $(0, 3\sqrt{2})$, height 19

57. focus $(10\sqrt{3}, 0)$, width 40

58. focus $(2, 0)$, x-intercept 4

59. focus $(0, 3)$, y-intercept 5

60. focus $(0, -5)$, y-intercept 8

61. focus $(3, 0)$, x-intercept -6

62. $a = 3$, $b = 2$, width 4

63. $a = 2\sqrt{5}$, $b = 3\sqrt{2}$, width $6\sqrt{2}$

64. Draw an ellipse by placing two tacks in a piece of graph paper laid over a piece of cardboard. Place a loop of string around the tacks. With your pencil keeping the string taut, draw around the tacks. Mark the center of your ellipse $(0, 0)$ and draw the x- and y-axes. **a–c. See back of book.**
    a. Where are the vertices and co-vertices of your ellipse?
    b. Where are the foci?
    c. Write the equation of your ellipse.

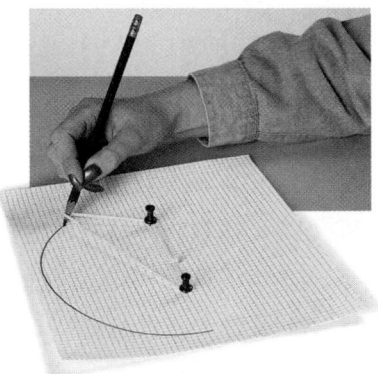

C Challenge  65. **Writing** The area of a circle is πr^2. The area of an ellipse is πab. Explain the connection. **See back of book.**

66a. 3×10^6 mi

b. about 0.016

c. $\dfrac{x^2}{8.649 \times 10^{15}} + \dfrac{y^2}{8.64675 \times 10^{15}} = 1$

66. Astronomy The sun is at a focus of Earth's elliptical orbit.
   a. Find the distance from the sun to the other focus.
   b. Refer to Exercise 41 for the definition of eccentricity. What is the eccentricity of the orbit?
   c. Write an equation of Earth's orbit. Assume that the major axis is horizontal.

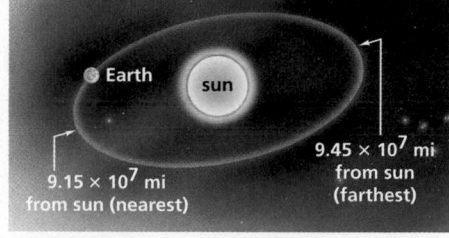

Earth   sun

9.15×10^7 mi from sun (nearest)

9.45×10^7 mi from sun (farthest)

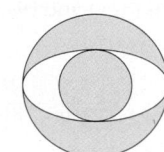

67. An ellipse and two circles share a center. The major axis of the ellipse is twice as long as its minor axis. The diameter of the larger circle is the same length as the major axis of the ellipse. The diameter of the smaller circle is the same length as the minor axis of the ellipse. The area of an ellipse is πab. Compare the areas of the blue and white regions at the left. **area of blue region = 3(area of white region)**

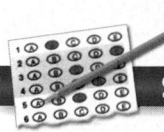 **68. Acoustics** In "whispering galleries" a sound made at one focus can be clearly heard at the other focus, even though very little can be heard by someone in between. Suppose an elliptical room measures 320 ft long and 150 ft wide. How far would the listener have to be from the source of the sound in order to hear it? **$10\sqrt{799}$ or about 282.7 ft**

Standardized Test Prep

Multiple Choice

69. The point $A(-10, 0)$ is on the ellipse with equation $\dfrac{x^2}{100} + \dfrac{y^2}{64} = 1$. What is the sum of the distances $AF_1 + AF_2$, where F_1 and F_2 are the foci? **D**
   A. 10   **B.** 12   **C.** 14   **D.** 20

Take It to the NET
Online lesson quiz at
www.PHSchool.com
Web Code: aga-1004

70. What is the length of the major axis on the graph of $\dfrac{x^2}{100} + \dfrac{y^2}{64} = 1$? **I**
   F. 12   **G.** $2\sqrt{41}$ **H.** 16   **I.** 20

71. What is the length of the minor axis of the graph of $\dfrac{x^2}{100} + \dfrac{y^2}{64} = 1$? **C**
   A. 12   **B.** $2\sqrt{41}$ **C.** 16   **D.** 20

Short Response

72. Explain how to find an equation for the ellipse, centered at the origin, that is 50 units wide and 40 units high. **See back of book.**

Mixed Review

Lesson 10-3

Write an equation of a circle with the given center and radius.

73. center $(2, -3)$, radius 6
$(x - 2)^2 + (y + 3)^2 = 36$

74. center $(-4, 7)$, radius 11
$(x + 4)^2 + (y - 7)^2 = 121$

Lesson 9-4

Simplify each expression. What are the restrictions on the variables?

75–77. See back of book. **75.** $\dfrac{3x}{6x^2 - 9x^5}$ **76.** $\dfrac{x^2 - 36}{x^2 + 5x - 6}$ **77.** $\dfrac{x^2 - 3x - 10}{x^3 + 8}$

Lesson 8-4

Write each logarithmic expression as a single logarithm.

78. $\log 3 + \log 5$ **log 15**   **79.** $\log_3 12 - \log_3 2$ **$\log_3 6$**   **80.** $3 \log 2 - \log 4$ **log 2**

81. $5 \log 2 + \log 10$ **log 320**   **82.** $\log x - \log y$ **$\log \frac{x}{y}$**   **83.** $k \log 5 - \log 4$ **$\log \frac{5^k}{4}$**

Standardized Test Prep

Resources

For additional practice with a variety of test item formats:
- Standardized Test Prep, p. 583
- Test-Taking Strategies, p. 578
- Test-Taking Strategies with Transparencies

Error Prevention

Exercise 72 Caution students that they are given the lengths of the axes not the distance from the center of the ellipse to a vertex or co-vertex.

Lesson Preview

 **Check Skills You'll Need**

Linear Equations
Lesson 2-2: Examples 4–6
Exercises 20–37
Extra Practice, p. 823

Lesson Resources

📁 **Teaching Resources**
Practice, Reteaching, Enrichment
Checkpoint Quiz 2

👥 **Reaching All Students**
Practice Workbook 10-5
Spanish Practice Workbook 10-5
Reading and Math Literacy 10C
Spanish Reading & Literacy 10C
Spanish Checkpoint Quiz 2
Hands-On Activities 52

⏱ **Presentation Assistant Plus!**
Transparencies
• Check Skills You'll Need 10-5
• Additional Examples 10-5
• Student Edition Answers 10-5
• Lesson Quiz 10-5
PH Presentation Pro CD 10-5

 **ASSESSMENT SYSTEM**

Checkpoint Quiz 2
Computer Test Generator CD

💿 **Technology**
Resource Pro® CD-ROM
Computer Test Generator CD
Prentice Hall Presentation Pro CD

🖥 **www.PHSchool.com**
Student Site
• Teacher Web Code: agk-5500
• Self-grading Lesson Quiz
Teacher Center
• Lesson Planner
• Resources

Plus

 **10-5**

Hyperbolas

Lesson Preview

What You'll Learn

OBJECTIVE 1 To graph hyperbolas

OBJECTIVE 2 To find and use the foci of a hyperbola

. . . And Why

To write an equation that models the path of Voyager 2 around Saturn, as in Example 3

✓ **Check Skills You'll Need** (For help, go to Lesson 2-2 and Skills Handbook page 846.)

Write an equation of a line in slope-intercept form using the given information.

1. rise -5, run 2, through the origin   **2.** through $(3, 1)$ and $(9, 3)$

Solve each equation for *y*.   1–5. See margin p. 563.

3. $\frac{x^2}{4} - \frac{y^2}{16} = 1$ **4.** $\frac{y^2}{9} - \frac{x^2}{25} = 1$ **5.** $\frac{x^2}{36} - \frac{y^2}{81} = 1$

New Vocabulary • hyperbola • transverse axis • focus of a hyperbola • vertices of a hyperbola

---

OBJECTIVE 1

*i*TEXT Interactive lesson includes instant self-check, tutorials, and activities.

Graphing Hyperbolas Centered at the Origin

📖 **Reading Math**

Hyperbola comes from a Greek word for "greater." The cutting plane of a hyperbola makes a greater angle with the base than does the side of the cone. See p. 535.

1. column 1: 60, 27, 33
   column 2: 20, 53, 33
   column 3: 48, 14, 34
   column 4: 8, 43, 35
   column 5: 41, 7, 34
   column 6: 20, 54, 34
   column 7: 63, 30, 33

Investigation: Analyzing Hyperbolas

1. The diagram below shows the shape of a hyperbola. Measure the distances to the nearest millimeter to complete the table. **See left.**

2. **Make a Conjecture** What is the relationship between the distances from the points F_1 and F_2 to any point on the hyperbola? $|PF_1 - PF_2|$ **is constant.**

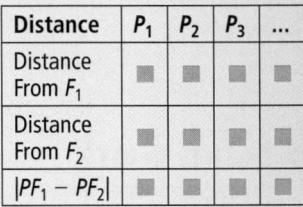

Distance	P_1	P_2	P_3	...
Distance From F_1	■	■	■	■
Distance From F_2	■	■	■	■
$\|PF_1 - PF_2\|$	■	■	■	■

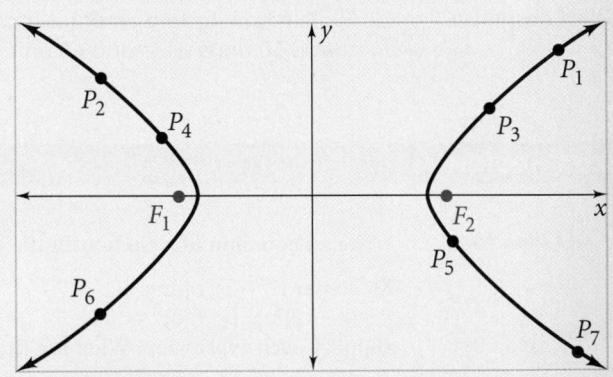

Hyperbolas play an important role in science and navigation. Some comets follow hyperbolic paths.

⚡ **Ongoing Assessment and Intervention**

Before the Lesson
Diagnose prerequisite skills using:
• Check Skills You'll Need

During the Lesson
Monitor progress using:
• Check Understanding
• Additional Examples
• Standardized Test Prep

After the Lesson
Assess knowledge using:
• Lesson Quiz
• Computer Test Generator CD
• Chapter Checkpoint 2 (p. 568)

Key Concepts

Definition	Hyperbola

A **hyperbola** is a set of points P in a plane such that the difference between the distances from P to two fixed points F_1 and F_2 is a given constant k.

$$|PF_1 - PF_2| = k, \text{ where } k < F_1F_2$$

Each fixed point F is a **focus of a hyperbola.** The segment that lies on the line containing the foci and has endpoints on a hyperbola is the **transverse axis.** The endpoints are the **vertices of a hyperbola.** The midpoint of the segment is the center of a hyperbola.

Below are the standard forms of the equation of a hyperbola centered at $(0, 0)$.

$$\frac{x^2}{a^2} - \frac{y^2}{b^2} = 1$$

standard form of an equation of a hyperbola with a horizontal transverse axis

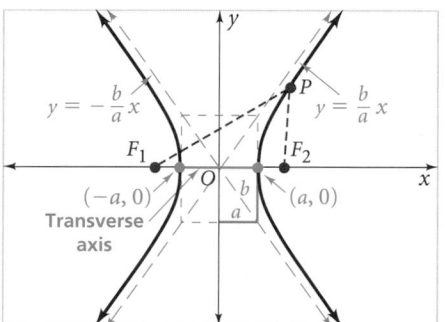

foci: F_1, F_2

vertices: $(\pm a, 0)$

asymptotes: $y = \pm \frac{b}{a}x$

x-intercepts: $\pm a$

y-intercepts: none

Need Help?

An asymptote is a line that a graph approaches.

$$\frac{y^2}{a^2} - \frac{x^2}{b^2} = 1$$

standard form of an equation of a hyperbola with a vertical transverse axis

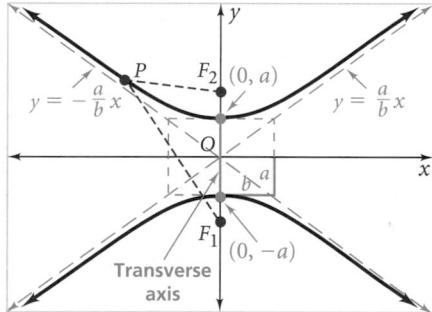

foci: F_1, F_2

vertices: $(0, \pm a)$

asymptotes: $y = \pm \frac{a}{b}x$

x-intercepts: none

y-intercepts: $\pm a$

To graph a hyperbola, use the standard form of the equation to find the values of a and b. You can use a and b to find and graph the vertices and to draw a central rectangle that is used to guide the graph.

Draw the asymptotes through the diagonals of the central rectangle. Then draw the branches of the hyperbola through the vertices so they approach the asymptotes.

Lesson 10-5 Hyperbolas **563**

Reaching All Students

Below Level Point out to students that the hyperbola is the only conic section with asymptotes. While a parabola may appear to have asymptotes, it does not.	**Advanced Learners** Have students research Boyle's law and graph $PV = 36$. What are the asymptotes?	**Tactile Learners** See note on page 563. **English Learners** See note on page 564.

Math Background

Students learn that the definition of a hyperbola closely resembles that of an ellipse in that it depends on the distances between a set of points in a plane to two fixed points called foci. Students will revisit graphing hyperbolas in calculus courses as the graphs lend themselves well to the study of limits.

OBJECTIVE 1 Teaching Notes

Investigation (Optional)

Tactile Learners

Once students have made all the measurements from the diagram, have them reproduce the diagram on the classroom floor. Challenge a team of students to choose a scale for the model and then convert the distances in the diagram to distances for the floor. They can use different colors of tape or chalk for the axes, the rectangle, and the asymptotes, string for the hyperbola, and different colored counters for the foci and vertices.

Key Concepts

Teaching Tip

The amount of information presented in the diagrams may overwhelm students. Rather than presenting all the facts at once, draw each hyperbola on the board. Then step by step add the details to your diagram. At each step, introduce the facts and formulas one by one. Before you introduce each new fact, ask students questions about the fact you presented.

page 562 Check Skills You'll Need

1. $y = -\frac{5}{2}x$

2. $y = \frac{1}{3}x$

3. $y = \pm 2\sqrt{x^2 - 4}$

4. $y = \pm \frac{3}{5}\sqrt{x^2 + 25}$

5. $y = \pm \frac{3}{2}\sqrt{x^2 - 36}$

563

Stress that the transverse axis is not always the *x*-axis or *y*-axis. In fact, it is not necessarily horizontal or vertical. *Transverse* means to cut across. Suggest students think of the transverse axis as crossing from one vertex of a hyperbola to the other. Students will see hyperbolas in Lesson 10-6 whose transverse axes are horizontal or vertical, but not the *x*-axis or *y*-axis.

Additional Example

① Graph $4x^2 - 16y^2 = 64$.

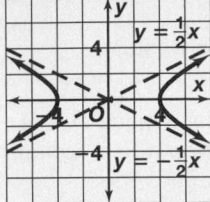

OBJECTIVE
2 Teaching Notes

② EXAMPLE Technology Tip

Graphs may be verified using the graphing calculator. Solve the equation for *y* to get $y = \pm\frac{1}{3}\sqrt{x^2 - 36}$ and enter both functions into the graphing calculator. Also enter $y = \pm\frac{1}{3}x$, the equations of the asymptotes, as two separate functions. You may also wish to point out that a^2 is not necessarily the larger of the two denominators in the standard form of an equation of a hyperbola as it was for an ellipse. Rather, determining which denominator is a^2 is based on which term is added in the formula.

③ EXAMPLE Alternative Method

Some students may feel overwhelmed by the large numbers in this example. Solve a simplified version of this example using $a = 3$ and $c = 5$. Once students understand this example have them use it as a guide for solving Example 3.

564

---

① **EXAMPLE** Graphing a Hyperbola

Graph $9x^2 - 25y^2 = 225$.

$9x^2 - 25y^2 = 225$

$\frac{x^2}{25} - \frac{y^2}{9} = 1$ **Rewrite the equation in standard form.**

The equation is of the form $\frac{x^2}{a^2} - \frac{y^2}{b^2} = 1$, so the transverse axis is horizontal. Since $a^2 = 25$ and $b^2 = 9$, $a = 5$ and $b = 3$.

Step 1 Graph the vertices. Since the transverse axis is horizontal, the vertices lie on the *x*-axis. The coordinates are $(\pm a, 0)$, or $(\pm 5, 0)$.

Step 2 Use the values of *a* and *b* to draw the central rectangle. The lengths of its sides are $2a$ and $2b$, or 10 and 6.

Step 3 Draw the asymptotes. The equations of the asymptotes are $y = \pm\frac{b}{a}x$ or $y = \pm\frac{3}{5}x$. The asymptotes contain the diagonals of the central rectangle.

Step 4 Sketch the branches of the hyperbola through the vertices so they approach the asymptotes.

1.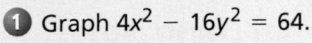

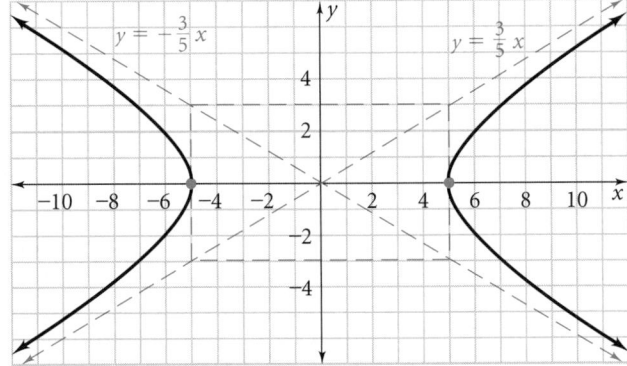

✓ **Check Understanding** ① Graph the hyperbola with equation $\frac{y^2}{16} - \frac{x^2}{9} = 1$. **See left.**

OBJECTIVE
2 Using the Foci of a Hyperbola

Use $(\pm c, 0)$ for the coordinates of the foci if the transverse axis is horizontal or $(0, \pm c)$ if it is vertical.

The distance between the foci, $2c$, is also the length of the diagonal of the central rectangle.

You can find the value of *c* using the Pythagorean Theorem.
$$c^2 = a^2 + b^2$$

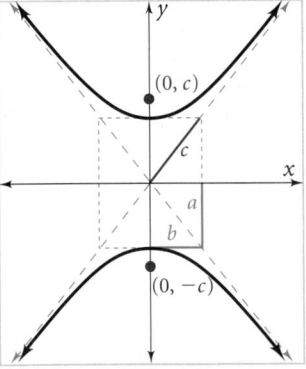

564 Chapter 10 Quadratic Relations

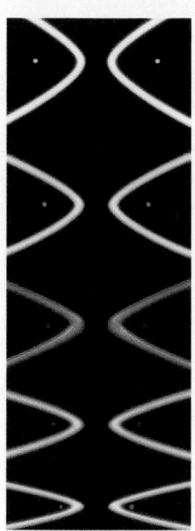

The figures above show how the shape of a hyperbola changes with decreased distances between the foci and the vertices.

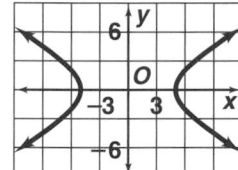

✓ **Check Understanding**

2. $(\sqrt{34}, 0), (-\sqrt{34}, 0)$;

2 EXAMPLE Finding the Foci of a Hyperbola

Find the foci of the graph $\frac{x^2}{36} - \frac{y^2}{4} = 1$. Draw the graph.

The equation is in the form $\frac{x^2}{a^2} - \frac{y^2}{b^2} = 1$, so the transverse axis is horizontal; $a^2 = 36$ and $b^2 = 4$.

$$c^2 = a^2 + b^2 \quad \text{Use the Pythagorean Theorem.}$$
$$= 36 + 4 \quad \text{Substitute 36 for } a^2 \text{ and 4 for } b^2.$$
$$c = \sqrt{40} \approx 6.3 \quad \text{Find the square root of each side of the equation.}$$

The foci $(\pm c, 0)$ are approximately $(-6.3, 0)$ and $(6.3, 0)$. The vertices $(\pm a, 0)$ are $(6, 0)$ and $(-6, 0)$. The asymptotes are the lines $y = \pm\frac{b}{a}x$, or $y = \pm\frac{1}{3}x$.

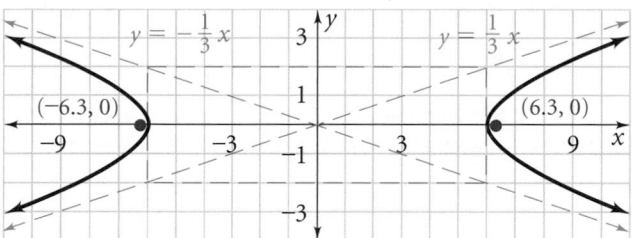

✓ **Check Understanding** ② Find the foci of $\frac{x^2}{25} - \frac{y^2}{9} = 1$. Draw the graph. **See left.**

You can use the value of c to write the equation of a hyperbola.

3 EXAMPLE Real-World 🌐 Connection

Space As a spacecraft approaches a planet, the gravitational pull of the planet changes the spacecraft's path to a hyperbola that diverges from its asymptote. Find an equation that models the path of Voyager 2 around Saturn, given that $a = 332,965$ km and $c = 492,788.2$ km.

Assume that the center of the hyperbola is at the origin and that the transverse axis is horizontal. The equation will be in the form $\frac{x^2}{a^2} - \frac{y^2}{b^2} = 1$.

$$c^2 = a^2 + b^2 \quad \text{Use the Pythagorean Theorem.}$$
$$(492,788.2)^2 = (332,965)^2 + b^2 \quad \text{Substitute.}$$
$$2.428 \times 10^{11} = 1.109 \times 10^{11} + b^2 \quad \text{Use a calculator.}$$
$$b^2 = 2.428 \times 10^{11} - 1.109 \times 10^{11} \quad \text{Solve for } b^2.$$
$$= 1.320 \times 10^{11}$$

$$\frac{x^2}{1.109 \times 10^{11}} - \frac{y^2}{1.320 \times 10^{11}} = 1 \quad \text{Substitute } a^2 \text{ and } b^2.$$

The path of Voyager 2 around Saturn can be modeled by

$$\frac{x^2}{1.109 \times 10^{11}} - \frac{y^2}{1.320 \times 10^{11}} = 1.$$

✓ **Check Understanding** ③ Find an equation that models the path of Voyager 2 around Jupiter, given that $a = 2,184,140$ km and $c = 2,904,906.2$ km.

$$\frac{x^2}{4.770 \times 10^{12}} - \frac{y^2}{3.668 \times 10^{12}} = 1$$

② Find the foci of the graph $\frac{y^2}{4} - \frac{x^2}{9} = 1$. Draw the graph. $(0, \pm\sqrt{13})$

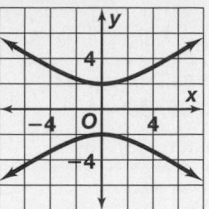

③ As a spacecraft approaches a planet, the gravitational pull of the planet changes the spacecraft's path to a hyperbola that diverges from its asymptote. Find an equation that models the path of the spacecraft around the planet given that $a = 300,765$ km and $c = 424,650$ km. Assume that the center of the hyperbola is at the origin and that the transverse axis is horizontal.

$$\frac{x^2}{9.046 \times 10^{10}} - \frac{y^2}{8.987 \times 10^{10}} = 1$$

Closure

Ask students to explain how to graph a hyperbola and how to find its foci. Also, explain how the foci can be used to write the equation of a hyperbola. **To graph a hyperbola, use the standard form of the equation to determine the values of a and b. Use a and b to find the vertices and asymptotes. Draw the corresponding central rectangle and use it to guide the graph. The foci can be determined using the formula $c^2 = a^2 + b^2$, where c represents the distance that a focus is from the center of the hyperbola. Thus, given any two values among a, b, and c, this relationship can be used to find the missing value. Then, the equation of the hyperbola can be written using the values of a and b.**

Lesson 10-5 Hyperbolas **565**

Assignment Guide

 **Objective**

A B Core 1–9, 27–31, 33–35, 39–44

C Extension 45, 46

 **Objective**

A B Core 10–26, 32, 36–38

C Extension 47, 48

Standardized Test Prep 49–53

Mixed Review 54–62

Error Prevention

Exercise 1–18 Suggest students check their results using graphing calculators.

Teaching Tip

Exercise 30–32 Encourage students to ask themselves these questions as they work through each problem:
- What do I know?
- What do I need to know?
- What new information can I find with what I have?

Enrichment 10-5

Reteaching 10-5

Practice 10-5

EXERCISES

For more practice, see *Extra Practice*.

Practice and Problem Solving

A Practice by Example

Example 1
(page 564)

Graph each equation. **1–18. See back of book.**

1. $\frac{x^2}{16} - \frac{y^2}{4} = 1$

2. $\frac{y^2}{169} - \frac{x^2}{16} = 1$

3. $\frac{x^2}{25} - \frac{y^2}{36} = 1$

4. $x^2 - 4y^2 = 4$

5. $36y^2 - 9x^2 = 324$

6. $25x^2 - 16y^2 = 400$

7. $9x^2 - 49y^2 = 441$

8. $25x^2 - 35y^2 = 875$

9. $81y^2 - 9x^2 = 729$

Example 2
(page 565)

Find the foci of each hyperbola. Then draw the graph.

10. $\frac{y^2}{81} - \frac{x^2}{16} = 1$

11. $\frac{y^2}{49} - \frac{x^2}{64} = 1$

12. $\frac{x^2}{121} - \frac{y^2}{144} = 1$

13. $\frac{x^2}{64} - \frac{y^2}{36} = 1$

14. $\frac{y^2}{25} - \frac{x^2}{100} = 1$

15. $\frac{x^2}{36} - \frac{y^2}{169} = 1$

16. $4y^2 - 25x^2 = 100$

17. $36x^2 - 8y^2 = 288$

18. $14y^2 - 28x^2 = 448$

Example 3
(page 565)

For Exercises 19–21, find the equation of a hyperbola with the given values. Assume that the transverse axis is horizontal. **19–26. See margin.**

19. $a = 263, c = 407$

20. $b = 100, c = 500$

21. $a = 13{,}872, c = 19{,}043$

22. Find an equation that models the path of Voyager 2 around Jupiter, given that $a = 1{,}362{,}450$ km and $c = 1{,}543{,}781$ km.

B Apply Your Skills

Write the equation of a hyperbola with the given foci and vertices.

23. foci $(\pm 5, 0)$, vertices $(\pm 3, 0)$

24. foci $(0, \pm 13)$, vertices $(0, \pm 5)$

25. foci $(0, \pm 2)$, vertices $(0, \pm 1)$

26. foci $(\pm\sqrt{5}, 0)$, vertices $(\pm 2, 0)$

Graph each equation. **27–32. See back of book.**

27. $5x^2 - 12y^2 = 120$

28. $16x^2 - 20y^2 = 560$

29. $\frac{y^2}{20} - \frac{x^2}{5} = 1$

Write the equation of a hyperbola from the given information. Graph the equation. Place the center of each hyperbola at the origin of the coordinate plane.

30. Transverse axis is vertical and is 9 units; central rectangle is 9 units by 4 units.

31. Perimeter of central rectangle is 16 units; vertices are at $(0, 3)$ and $(0, -3)$.

32. (Distance from the center of a hyperbola to a focus)$^2 = 96$; endpoints of the transverse axis are at $\left(-\sqrt{32}, 0\right)$ and $\left(\sqrt{32}, 0\right)$.

Reading Math

For help with reading and solving Exercise 32, see p. 569.

Solve each equation for *y*. Graph each relation on your graphing calculator. Use the TRACE feature to locate the vertices. **33–35. See back of book.**

33. $x^2 - 2y^2 = 4$

34. $x^2 - y^2 = 1$

35. $3x^2 - y^2 = 2$

36. Open-Ended Choose two points on an axis to be the vertices of a hyperbola. Choose two other points on the same axis to be the foci. Write the equation of your hyperbola and draw its graph. **Check students' work.**

38. Answers may vary. Sample: axes of symmetry, vertices, asymptotes

37. Writing Describe the similarities and differences between hyperbolas and ellipses. **See back of book.**

38. List all the properties of a hyperbola that allow you to sketch its graph.

20. $\frac{x^2}{240{,}000} - \frac{y^2}{10{,}000} = 1$

21. $\frac{x^2}{192{,}432{,}384} - \frac{y^2}{170{,}203{,}465} = 1$

22. $\frac{x^2}{1.856 \times 10^{12}} - \frac{y^2}{5.270 \times 10^{11}} = 1$

23. $\frac{x^2}{9} - \frac{y^2}{16} = 1$

24. $\frac{y^2}{25} - \frac{x^2}{144} = 1$

25. $y^2 - \frac{x^2}{3} = 1$

26. $\frac{x^2}{4} - y^2 = 1$

39. $(0, \pm 1), y = \pm x$

40. $(\pm 1, 0), y = \pm\frac{1}{3}x$

41. $(0, \pm 8), y = \pm 2x$

42. $(\pm 5, 0), y = \pm\frac{4}{5}x$

43. $(0, \pm 4), y = \pm 2x$

pages 566–568 Exercises

19. $\frac{x^2}{69{,}169} - \frac{y^2}{96{,}480} = 1$

Find the vertices and the asymptotes of each hyperbola.

39. $y^2 - x^2 = 1$ **40.** $x^2 - 9y^2 = 1$ **41.** $y^2 - 4x^2 = 64$

42. $16x^2 - 25y^2 = 400$ **43.** $9y^2 - 36x^2 = 144$ **44.** $25x^2 - 49y^2 = 1225$

39–45. See margin pp. 566–567.

 Challenge

45. Recall what you have learned about translating graphs. Rewrite the equation $4x^2 - 9y^2 = 36$ in standard form for a translation right 3 units and down 5 units.

46. Air Traffic Control Suppose you are an air traffic controller directing the pilot of a plane on a hyperbolic flight path. You and another air traffic controller from a different airport send radio signals to the pilot simultaneously. The two airports are 48 km apart. The pilot's instrument panel tells him that the signal from your airport always arrives 100 μs (microseconds) before the signal from the other airport.

  a. To which airport is the plane closer? **your airport**

  b. If the signals travel at a rate of 300 m/μs, what is the difference in distances from the plane to the two airports? **30 km**

  c. Write the equation of the flight path. (*Hint:* $k = 2a$) $\dfrac{x^2}{225} - \dfrac{y^2}{351} = 1$

  d. Draw the hyperbola. Which branch represents the flight path? **See margin.**

Real-World  **Connection**

Careers Air traffic controllers coordinate the flow of air traffic by the use of radar and visual observation.

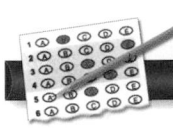

47. The function $y = \sqrt{x^2 - 9}$ represents part of a hyperbola. The tables at the right show the coordinates of several points on the graph.

  a. Explain why ERROR appears for some entries. **a–d. See back of book.**

  b. Describe the relationship between the x- and y-coordinates as x gets larger.

  c. Critical Thinking Do you think that the x- and y-coordinates will ever be equal? Explain.

  d. Make a Conjecture What are the equations of the asymptotes of this hyperbola? Verify your answer by drawing the complete graph.

X	Y1
0	ERROR
1	ERROR
2	ERROR
3	0
4	2.6458
5	4
6	5.1962
X=0	

X	Y1
10	9.5394
20	19.774
30	29.85
40	39.887
50	49.91
60	59.925
70	69.936
X=10	

48. a. Prove that the hyperbola $\dfrac{y^2}{a^2} - \dfrac{x^2}{b^2} = 1$ never intersects its asymptotes.

  b. Is $\dfrac{y^2}{16} - \dfrac{x^2}{9} = 4$ a hyperbola? Is $\dfrac{y^2}{16} - \dfrac{x^2}{9} = -1$ a hyperbola? Explain.

  a–b. See back of book.

 Standardized Test Prep

Multiple Choice

49. Which hyperbola has $(\pm 6, 0)$ as its x-intercepts? **D**

  A. $y^2 - x^2 = 36$ **B.** $\dfrac{y^2}{36} - \dfrac{x^2}{49} = 1$ **C.** $\dfrac{x^2}{25} - \dfrac{y^2}{36} = 1$ **D.** $\dfrac{x^2}{36} - \dfrac{y^2}{4} = 1$

50. Which hyperbola does NOT have $(0, \pm 4)$ as its y-intercepts? **H**

  F. $y^2 - x^2 = 16$ **G.** $4y^2 - 16x^2 = 64$

  H. $\dfrac{x^2}{25} - \dfrac{y^2}{16} = 1$ **I.** $\dfrac{y^2}{16} - \dfrac{x^2}{9} = 1$

51. What are the x-intercepts of $\dfrac{y^2}{25} - \dfrac{x^2}{49} = 1$? **D**

  A. $(\pm 7, 0)$ **B.** $(\pm 5, 0)$ **C.** $(0, \pm 5)$ **D.** none

Short Response

52. What is the standard form of an equation of a hyperbola? Explain how to rewrite $25x^2 - 49y^2 = 1225$ in standard form. **See back of book.**

Lesson 10-5 Hyperbolas   **567**

44. $(\pm 7, 0)$, $y = \pm\dfrac{5}{7}x$

45. Replace x with $x - 3$ and y with $y + 5$ and rewrite to obtain

$\dfrac{(x-3)^2}{9} - \dfrac{(y+5)^2}{4} = 1$.

46d.

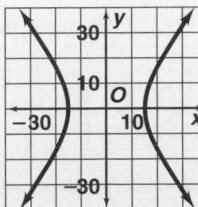

the branch that contains the vertex closest to your airport

Lesson Quiz 10-5

1. Graph $16y^2 - 9x^2 = 144$.

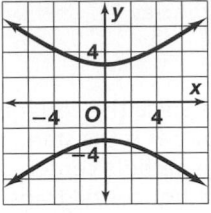

2. Find the foci of the graph $\dfrac{x^2}{4} - \dfrac{y^2}{36} = 1$. Draw the graph. $(\pm 2\sqrt{10}, 0)$

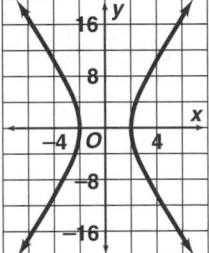

3. Find the equation of a hyperbola that has one focus located at $(4, 0)$ and one vertex located at $(-2, 0)$. Assume that the center of the hyperbola is at the origin. $\dfrac{x^2}{4} - \dfrac{y^2}{12} = 1$

Alternative Assessment

Have students work in pairs. On a sheet of paper, each group writes the equations of two hyperbolas centered at the origin, one with a horizontal transverse axis and one with a vertical transverse axis. They both have the same asymptotes and a and b are both integers between 1 and 5 inclusive (or other appropriate integers based on the size of the Geoboards). Students fold the piece of paper and leave it on the desk. Using a Geoboard and rubber bands, each group creates a coordinate system and graphs the asymptotes of their hyperbolas. Groups then switch stations and must write the equations of the two hyperbolas from the asymptotes on the Geoboards. They verify their equations with those written on the piece of paper on the desk.

📁 **Resources**

For additional practice with a variety of test item formats:
- Standardized Test Prep, p. 583
- Test-Taking Strategies, p. 578
- Test-Taking Strategies with Transparencies

Math Tip

Exercise 50 Since the equation in answer choice H is the standard form of a hyperbola centered at (0, 0) with a horizontal transverse axis, students should immediately be able to see that the graph of this equation has no *y*-intercepts.

✓ **Chapter Checkpoint 2**

To check understanding of Lessons 10-4 to 10-5:

Checkpoint Quiz 2 (p. 568)

📁 **Teaching Resources**
Checkpoint Quiz 2 (also in Prentice Hall Assessment System)

👥 **Reaching All Students**
Reading and Math Literacy 10C

Spanish versions available

---

pages 566–568   Exercises

57. $\frac{3}{10x}$

58. $\frac{2x^2 - x - 7}{x^3 + x^2 - 9x - 9}$

59. $\frac{x + 3}{x - 3}$

page 568   Checkpoint Quiz 2

4. $(\sqrt{65}, 0), (-\sqrt{65}, 0)$

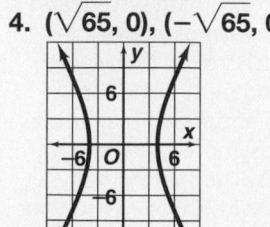

568

Reading Comprehension

53a.
$$\frac{x^2}{1.19 \times 10^{12}} - \frac{y^2}{8.86 \times 10^{11}} = 1$$

b.
$$\frac{x^2}{2.76 \times 10^{10}} - \frac{y^2}{2.05 \times 10^{10}} = 1$$

💻 **Take It to the NET**
Online lesson quiz at
www.PHSchool.com
Web Code: aga-1005

53. Read the article below. Then complete the exercises.

Jupiter Bound: Voyager on its Way . . .

Voyager 1 explored the outer planets of our solar system. Its path was a hyperbola that depended on the planet that was closest. The table below gives the distance *c* from each planet to the center of the hyperbola and the distance *a* from the vertex of the hyperbola to the center of the hyperbola. At each vertex, Voyager 1's path was directly between a planet and the center of the hyperbola.

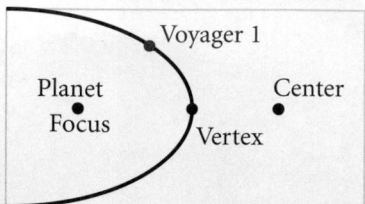

	Jupiter	Saturn
a	1,092,356 km	166,152 km
c	1,441,909.92 km	219,320.64 km

a. Write an equation of the path taken by Voyager 1 around Jupiter.
b. Write an equation of the path taken by Voyager 1 around Saturn.

Mixed Review

Lesson 10-4   Find the vertices and co-vertices of each ellipse.

54. $\frac{x^2}{34} + \frac{y^2}{25} = 1$
$(\pm\sqrt{34}, 0), (0, \pm5)$

55. $3x^2 + 2y^2 = 6$
$(0, \pm\sqrt{3}), (\pm\sqrt{2}, 0)$

56. $25x^2 + 16y^2 = 1600$
$(0, \pm 10), (\pm8, 0)$

Lesson 9-5   Simplify each expression. 57–59. See margin.

57. $\frac{1}{5x} + \frac{1}{10x}$

58. $\frac{2x}{x^2 - 2x - 3} - \frac{7}{x^2 - 9}$

59. $\frac{4}{2x - 6} + \frac{x + 1}{x - 3}$

Lesson 8-5   Solve each equation.

60. $8^{2x} = 4$ $\frac{1}{3}$

61. $\log 8x = 3$ **125**

62. $2\log_3 x - \log_3 4 = 2$ **6**

✓ Checkpoint Quiz 2   Lessons 10-4 through 10-5

📱 **TEXT** Instant self-check quiz online and on CD-ROM

1. $\frac{x^2}{25} + \frac{y^2}{16} = 1$

2. $\frac{x^2}{25} + \frac{y^2}{29} = 1$

3. $\frac{x^2}{100} + \frac{y^2}{149} = 1$

10. $\frac{y^2}{64} - \frac{x^2}{12.25} = 1$

Write an equation for each ellipse with the given foci and co-vertices. See left.

1. foci $(\pm3, 0)$
co-vertices $(0, \pm4)$

2. foci $(0, \pm2)$
co-vertices $(\pm5, 0)$

3. foci $(0, \pm7)$
co-vertices $(\pm10, 0)$

Find the foci for each conic section. Then draw the graph.   4–7. See margin.

4. $\frac{x^2}{16} - \frac{y^2}{49} = 1$

5. $\frac{y^2}{100} - \frac{x^2}{36} = 1$

6. $\frac{x^2}{4} - \frac{y^2}{81} = 1$

7. $\frac{y^2}{25} - \frac{x^2}{64} = 1$

Write an equation for a hyperbola centered at the origin with the given characteristics.

8. horizontal transverse axis, $a = 11, c = 15$ $\frac{x^2}{121} - \frac{y^2}{104} = 1$

9. vertices $(\pm4, 0)$, perimeter of central rectangle 28 units $\frac{x^2}{16} - \frac{y^2}{9} = 1$

10. Transverse axis is vertical, 16 units long; central rectangle is 16 units by 7 units.

---

5. $(0, 2\sqrt{34}), (0, -2\sqrt{34})$

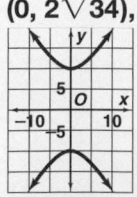

6. $(\sqrt{85}, 0), (-\sqrt{85}, 0)$

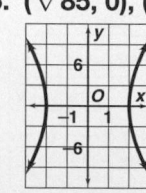

7. $(0, \sqrt{89}), (0, -\sqrt{89})$

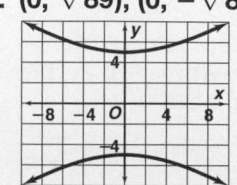

Reading for Problem Solving

Read the problem below. Then follow along with Michelle as she solves the problem. Check your understanding with the exercise at the bottom of the page.

Write the equation of a hyperbola from the given information. Graph the equation. Place the center of the hyperbola at the origin of the coordinate plane.

32. (Distance from the center of a hyperbola to a focus)^2 = 96; endpoints of the transverse axis are at $\left(-\sqrt{32}, 0\right)$ and $\left(\sqrt{32}, 0\right)$.

What Michelle Thinks

There is a lot of information here. I'll start with the second part. The endpoints of the transverse axis of a hyperbola are its vertices.

I know that the hyperbola opens horizontally, because the transverse axis lies on the x-axis. The vertices are at $(-a, 0)$ and $(a, 0)$, so I know the value of a^2.

Now I'll work on the first part of the given information. The distance from the center to the focus is c, which is also half the length of the diagonal of the central rectangle. I'll draw what I know so far.

Knowing c will help me find b! I can use the Pythagorean Theorem.

I'm ready to fill in the rest of the standard form of the equation for the hyperbola. Then I'll graph the hyperbola.

What Michelle Writes

Vertices: $\left(-\sqrt{32}, 0\right)$ and $\left(\sqrt{32}, 0\right)$

The transverse axis is horizontal, so the equation will look like $\frac{x^2}{a^2} - \frac{y^2}{b^2} = 1$.

$a = \sqrt{32}$, so $a^2 = 32$.

c = distance from center to focus
  = half length of diagonal

$c^2 = 96$, so $c = \sqrt{96}$

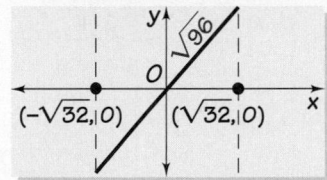

$b^2 = c^2 - a^2 = 96 - 32 = 64$

Equation:
$\frac{x^2}{32} - \frac{y^2}{64} = 1$

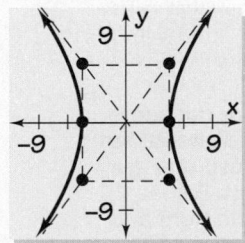

EXERCISE

Write the equation of a hyperbola from the given information. Graph the equation. Place the center of the hyperbola at the origin of the coordinate plane.

(Distance from the center of a hyperbola to a focus)^2 = 40; endpoints of the transverse axis are at $(-4, 0)$ and $(4, 0)$.

$\frac{x^2}{16} - \frac{y^2}{24} = 1$
See margin for graph.

Reading for Problem Solving

Students read an example problem in which the equation of a hyperbola is written from given information. Along with the worked-out problem are explanations for each step of the work.

Teaching Notes

Have students explain some of the assumptions in the problem that are not otherwise explained. For example, Michelle states that she knows the transverse axis is the x-axis. Ask students to explain why. **The endpoints of the transverse axis both lie on the x-axis.**

Technology

Suggest that students use their graphing calculators to graph the hyperbola to check their work.

Exercise

Have students place a piece of blank paper over the "What Michelle Writes" column of the example problem. Then have students work out the Check Understanding problem on this piece of paper, using the clues in the "What Michelle Thinks" column as a guide.

page 569   Exercise

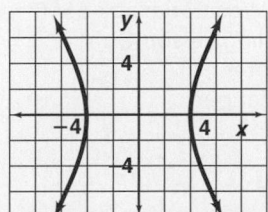

Translating Conic Sections

North Carolina Objectives

2.09 Use the equations of parabolas and circles to model and solve problems. a) Solve using tables, graphs, and algebraic properties. b) Interpret the constants and coefficients in the context of the problem.

Lesson Preview

 Check Skills You'll Need

Translating Parabolas
Lesson 5-3: Examples 1 and 4
Exercises 1–12, 27–35
Extra Practice, p. 826

Lesson Resources

 Teaching Resources
Practice, Reteaching, Enrichment

Reaching All Students
Practice Workbook 10-6
Spanish Practice Workbook 10-6
Technology Activities 13

 Presentation Assistant Plus!
Transparencies
• Check Skills You'll Need 10-6
• Additional Examples 10-6
• Student Edition Answers 10-6
• Lesson Quiz 10-6
PH Presentation Pro CD 10-6

PRENTICE HALL ASSESSMENT SYSTEM

Computer Test Generator CD

 Technology
Resource Pro® CD-ROM
Computer Test Generator CD
Prentice Hall Presentation Pro CD

www.PHSchool.com
Student Site
• Teacher Web Code: agk-5500
• Self-grading Lesson Quiz
Teacher Center
• Lesson Planner
• Resources

Plus **iTEXT**

Lesson Preview

What You'll Learn

 OBJECTIVE 1
To write the equation of a translated conic section

 OBJECTIVE 2
To identify the equation of a translated conic section

. . . Any Why

To explore the LORAN navigation system, as in Example 3

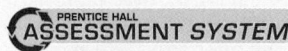

✓ **Check Skills You'll Need** (For help, go to Lesson 5-3.)

Name the parent function for the equations in Exercises 1–4. Describe each equation as a translation of the parent function. 2, 4. See below.

1. $y = x^2 + 4$ $y = x^2$; 4 units up
2. $y = (x - 3)^2 - 2$
3. $y - 1 = x^2$ $y = x^2$; 1 unit up
4. $y = (x + 5)^2 + 6$

Rewrite each equation in vertex form.
5. $y = x^2 - 6x + 1$ $y = (x - 3)^2 - 8$
6. $y = x^2 + 10x - 7$ $y = (x + 5)^2 - 32$
7. $y = 2x^2 + 8x + 5$ $y = 2(x + 2)^2 - 3$
8. $y = 4x^2 - 12x + 3$ $y = 4\left(x - \frac{3}{2}\right)^2 - 6$

---

2. $y = x^2$; 3 units right and 2 units down
4. $y = x^2$; 5 units left, 6 units up

 Interactive lesson includes instant self-check, tutorials, and activities.

OBJECTIVE 1

Writing Equations of Translated Conic Sections

? Need Help?

A translation is an operation that shifts a graph horizontally, vertically, or both.

1. They are the same size and shape, but their positions are different. Ellipse 2 is 2 units right and 3 units down from ellipse 1.

2. $\dfrac{(x - 2)^2}{36} + \dfrac{(y + 3)^2}{16} = 1$

3. $\dfrac{(x + 4)^2}{9} - \dfrac{(y - 1)^2}{4} = 1$

Investigation: Translating Conic Sections

1. Examine the calculator screen at the right. Describe the relationship between the two ellipses. How are they similar? How are they different?

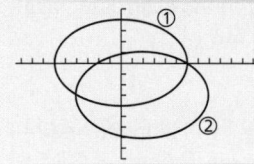

Xmin=-9   Ymin=-9
Xmax=12   Ymax=5
Xscl=1   Yscl=1

2. The equation of ellipse ① is $\dfrac{x^2}{36} + \dfrac{y^2}{16} = 1$. Use what you know about translations to write the equation of ellipse ②.

3. The graph at the right shows the hyperbola with equation $\dfrac{x^2}{9} - \dfrac{y^2}{4} = 1$. Write the equation of the hyperbola that has been shifted four units left and one unit up.

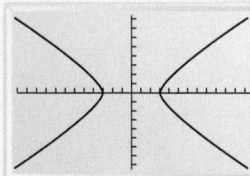

Xmin=-12   Ymin=-8
Xmax=12   Ymax=8
Xscl=1   Yscl=1

Just as you have translated parabolas in Chapter 5 and circles in Lesson 10-2, you can also translate ellipses and hyperbolas. A translated ellipse or hyperbola has center (h, k).

570 Chapter 10 Quadratic Relations

Ongoing Assessment and Intervention

Before the Lesson	During the Lesson	After the Lesson
Diagnose prerequisite skills using:	**Monitor progress using:**	**Assess knowledge using:**
• Check Skills You'll Need	• Check Understanding	• Lesson Quiz
	• Additional Examples	• Computer Test Generator CD
	• Standardized Test Prep	

Summary	**Equations of Conic Sections**	
Conic Section	**Standard Form of Equation**	
Parabola	Vertex $(0,0)$ $y = ax^2$ $x = ay^2$	Vertex (h, k) $y - k = a(x - h)^2$ or $y = a(x - h)^2 + k$ $x - h = a(y - k)^2$ or $x = a(y - k)^2 + h$
Circle	Center $(0,0)$ $x^2 + y^2 = r^2$	Center (h, k) $(x - h)^2 + (y - k)^2 = r^2$
Ellipse	Center $(0,0)$ $\dfrac{x^2}{a^2} + \dfrac{y^2}{b^2} = 1$ $\dfrac{x^2}{b^2} + \dfrac{y^2}{a^2} = 1$	Center (h, k) $\dfrac{(x - h)^2}{a^2} + \dfrac{(y - k)^2}{b^2} = 1$ $\dfrac{(x - h)^2}{b^2} + \dfrac{(y - k)^2}{a^2} = 1$
Hyperbola	Center $(0,0)$ $\dfrac{x^2}{a^2} - \dfrac{y^2}{b^2} = 1$ $\dfrac{y^2}{a^2} - \dfrac{x^2}{b^2} = 1$	Center (h, k) $\dfrac{(x - h)^2}{a^2} - \dfrac{(y - k)^2}{b^2} = 1$ $\dfrac{(y - k)^2}{a^2} - \dfrac{(x - h)^2}{b^2} = 1$

1 EXAMPLE **Writing the Equation of a Translated Ellipse**

Write an equation of an ellipse with center $(-3, -2)$, vertical major axis of length 8, and minor axis of length 6.

The length of the major axis is $2a$. So $2a = 8$ and $a = 4$. The length of the minor axis is $2b$. So $2b = 6$ and $b = 3$. Since the center is $(-3, -2)$, $h = -3$ and $k = -2$.

The major axis is vertical, so the equation has the form $\dfrac{(x - h)^2}{b^2} + \dfrac{(y - k)^2}{a^2} = 1$.

$\dfrac{(x - (-3))^2}{3^2} + \dfrac{(y - (-2))^2}{4^2} = 1$ **Substitute −3 for h and −2 for k.**

The equation of the ellipse is $\dfrac{(x + 3)^2}{9} + \dfrac{(y + 2)^2}{16} = 1$.

Check Solve the equation for y and graph both equations.

$$\dfrac{(x + 3)^2}{9} + \dfrac{(y + 2)^2}{16} = 1$$
$$16(x + 3)^2 + 9(y + 2)^2 = 144$$
$$9(y + 2)^2 = 144 - 16(x + 3)^2$$
$$(y + 2)^2 = \tfrac{1}{9}(144 - 16(x + 3)^2)$$
$$y + 2 = \pm\sqrt{\tfrac{1}{9}(144 - 16(x + 3)^2)}$$
$$y = -2 \pm \tfrac{1}{3}\sqrt{144 - 16(x + 3)^2}$$

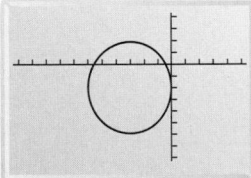

1. $\dfrac{(x - 1)^2}{25} + \dfrac{(y + 4)^2}{4} = 1$

✓ **Check Understanding** ① Write an equation of an ellipse with center $(1, -4)$, horizontal major axis of length 10, and minor axis of length 4. Check your answer.

---

2. Teach

Professional Development

Math Background

The techniques used to translate ellipses and hyperbolas are analogous to those used to translate parabolas and circles. In future courses, students will learn that these techniques can also be applied to three-dimensional surfaces.

OBJECTIVE
① Teaching Notes

Investigation (Optional)
Teaching Tip

Tell students to think about how they translated parabolas and circles. Tell them to apply these methods to the equations of the ellipse and hyperbola.

1 EXAMPLE **Alternative Method**

You may wish to reinforce ideas that students developed in the Investigation or previously. Encourage them to begin by writing the equation of an ellipse with center $(0, 0)$, vertical major axis of length 8, and minor axis of length 6. Then, have students translate this ellipse so that its center is at $(-3, -2)$.

Additional Examples

① Write an equation of an ellipse with center $(-2, 4)$, vertical major axis of length 10, and minor axis of length 8.
$\dfrac{(x + 2)^2}{16} + \dfrac{(y - 4)^2}{25} = 1$

👥 **Reaching All Students**

Below Level Be sure students understand that if there are squared terms in both x and y, they must complete the square for each variable.	**Advanced Learners** Ask students to research how navigation systems other than LORAN use mathematics, and report their findings to the class.	**Error Prevention** See note on page 574. **Error Prevention** See note on page 577.

571

Additional Examples

2 Write an equation of a hyperbola with vertices $(-1, 2)$ and $(3, 2)$, and foci $(-3, 2)$ and $(5, 2)$. $\dfrac{(x-1)^2}{4} - \dfrac{(y-2)^2}{12} = 1$

3 Use the information from Example 3. Find the equation of the hyperbola if the transmitters are 80 mi apart located at $(0,0)$ and $(80, 0)$, and all points on the hyperbola are 30 mi closer to one transmitter than the other. $\dfrac{(x-40)^2}{225} - \dfrac{y^2}{1375} = 1$

OBJECTIVE

2 Teaching Notes

4 EXAMPLE Math Tip

Remind students that the coefficients of x^2 and y^2 must be 1 to complete the square.

Additional Examples

4 Identify the conic section with equation $9x^2 - 4y^2 + 18x = 27$. If it is a parabola, give the vertex. If it is a circle, give the center and radius. If it is an ellipse or a hyperbola, give the center and foci. Sketch the graph.
hyperbola; center: $(-1, 0)$, foci: $(-1 - \sqrt{13}, 0)$ and $(-1 + \sqrt{13}, 0)$

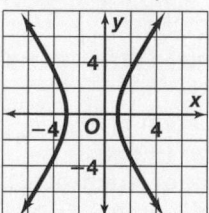

Closure

Ask: *Explain the process for writing the equation of a translated ellipse or hyperbola with center (h, k).* **Use the standard form of the conic section with center at (0, 0). Then, replace x with (x − h) and y with (y − k).** *Explain how to identify the equation of a translated conic section from the general equation for all conic sections.* **Rewrite the general equation as an equation in standard form. This may require completing the square.**

572

Need Help?

The midpoint of the segment joining (x_1, y_1) and (x_2, y_2) is $\left(\dfrac{x_1 + x_2}{2}, \dfrac{y_1 + y_2}{2}\right)$.

2. $\dfrac{(y-3)^2}{16} - \dfrac{(x-2)^2}{33} = 1$

✓ **Check Understanding**

Real-World Connection

LORAN stands for *long range navigation.* It uses simultaneously broadcast radio signals from three transmitters to locate the ship's position at the intersection of the red and the blue hyperbolas.

---

2 EXAMPLE Writing the Equation of a Translated Hyperbola

Write an equation of a hyperbola with vertices $(0, 1)$ and $(6, 1)$, and foci $(-1, 1)$ and $(7, 1)$.

Draw a sketch. The center is the midpoint of the line joining the vertices. Its coordinates are $(3, 1)$.

The distance between the vertices is $2a$ and the distance between the foci is $2c$. $2a = 6$, so $a = 3$; $2c = 8$, so $c = 4$.

Find b^2 using the Pythagorean Theorem.
$$c^2 = a^2 + b^2$$
$$16 = 9 + b^2$$
$$b^2 = 7$$

The transverse axis is horizontal. The equation has form $\dfrac{(x-h)^2}{a^2} - \dfrac{(y-k)^2}{b^2} = 1$.

The equation of the hyperbola is $\dfrac{(x-3)^2}{9} - \dfrac{(y-1)^2}{7} = 1$.

2 Write an equation of a hyperbola with vertices $(2, -1)$ and $(2, 7)$, and foci $(2, 10)$ and $(2, -4)$.

3 EXAMPLE Real-World Connection

Navigation Some ships navigate using LORAN. The ship's equipment calculates the difference between the arrival times of simultaneously broadcast radio signals. The difference in arrival times indicates how much closer the ship is to one transmitter than to the other. The navigator then locates the ship on a hyperbola shown in red. The process is repeated using a second pair of transmitters to locate the ship on a hyperbola shown in blue.

All points on hyperbola #25800 as shown in the diagram are 48 mi closer to one transmitter than the other. The transmitters, at the foci, are 200 mi apart and are located at $(0, 0)$ and $(200, 0)$. Find the equation of hyperbola #25800.

Step 1 Find c. Since the foci are 200 mi apart, $2c = 200$, $c = 100$, and the center of the hyperbola is at $(100, 0)$.

Step 2 Find a by calculating the difference in the distances from the vertex at $(a + 100, 0)$ to the two foci.
$$48 = (a + 100) - [200 - (a + 100)]$$
$$= 2a$$
$$24 = a$$

Step 3 Find b^2.
$$c^2 = a^2 + b^2$$
$$(100)^2 = (24)^2 + b^2$$
$$10{,}000 = 576 + b^2$$
$$b^2 = 9424$$

The equation of the hyperbola is $\dfrac{(x-100)^2}{24^2} - \dfrac{y^2}{9424} = 1$ or $\dfrac{(x-100)^2}{576} - \dfrac{y^2}{9424} = 1$.

✓ **Check Understanding** **3** Use the information from Example 3. Find the equation of the hyperbola with all points 56 mi closer to one transmitter than the other. $\dfrac{(x-100)^2}{784} - \dfrac{y^2}{9216} = 1$

The equation $Ax^2 + Bxy + Cy^2 + Dx + Ey + F = 0$ is the general equation for all conic sections, where A and C are not both equal to zero. To determine which conic section the equation represents, write the equation in standard form by completing the square for the x- and y-terms.

4 **EXAMPLE** **Identifying a Translated Conic Section**

Identify the conic section with equation $4x^2 + y^2 - 24x + 6y + 9 = 0$. If it is a parabola, give the vertex. If it is a circle, give the center and radius. If it is an ellipse or a hyperbola, give the center and foci. Sketch the graph.

Complete the square for the x- and y-terms to write the equation in standard form.

$$4x^2 + y^2 - 24x + 6y + 9 = 0$$

$$4x^2 - 24x + y^2 + 6y = -9 \qquad \text{Group the } x\text{- and } y\text{-terms.}$$

$$4(x^2 - 6x + \blacksquare) + (y^2 + 6y + \blacksquare) = -9 \qquad \text{Complete the square.}$$

$$4(x^2 - 6x + (-3)^2) + (y^2 + 6y + 3^2) = -9 + 4(-3)^2 + 3^2 \qquad \begin{array}{l}\text{Add } 4(-3)^2 \text{ and } 3^2 \\ \text{to each side.}\end{array}$$

$$4(x^2 - 6x + 9) + (y^2 + 6y + 9) = -9 + 36 + 9 \qquad \text{Simplify.}$$

$$4(x - 3)^2 + (y + 3)^2 = 36 \qquad \begin{array}{l}\text{Write the trinomials} \\ \text{as binomials squared.}\end{array}$$

$$\frac{4(x-3)^2}{36} + \frac{(y+3)^2}{36} = 1 \qquad \text{Divide each side by 36.}$$

$$\frac{(x-3)^2}{9} + \frac{(y+3)^2}{36} = 1 \qquad \text{Simplify.}$$

The equation represents an ellipse. The center is $(3, -3)$. The major axis is vertical. Since $b^2 = 9, b = 3$. Since $a^2 = 36, a = 6$.

$$c^2 = a^2 - b^2 = 36 - 9$$
$$= 27$$
$$c = 3\sqrt{3}$$

The distance from the center of the ellipse to the foci is $3\sqrt{3}$. Since the ellipse is centered at $(3, -3)$ and the major axis is vertical, the foci are located $3\sqrt{3}$ above and below this center. The foci are at $(3, -3 + 3\sqrt{3})$ and $(3, -3 - 3\sqrt{3})$.

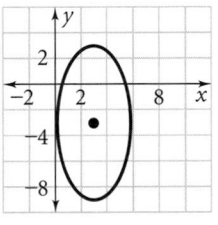

4. circle with center $(6, -2)$ and radius $4\sqrt{3}$;

✓ **Check Understanding** **4** Identify the conic section represented by $x^2 + y^2 - 12x + 4y = 8$. Sketch the graph. **See left.**

EXERCISES

For more practice, see *Extra Practice*.

Practice and Problem Solving

A **Practice by Example**

Example 1
(page 571)

1–4. See margin.

Write an equation of an ellipse with the given characteristics. Check your answers.

1. center $(-2, 1)$, horizontal major axis of length 6, minor axis of length 4

2. center $(5, 3)$, vertical major axis of length 12, minor axis of length 8

3. center $(0, -4)$, horizontal major axis of length 12, minor axis of length 10

4. center $(3, -6)$, vertical major axis of length 14, minor axis of length 6

Lesson 10-6 Translating Conic Sections **573**

Assignment Guide

1 **Objective**
Ⓐ Ⓑ **Core** 1–11, 28–35, 37–40, 49–54
Ⓒ **Extension** 56, 57

2 **Objective**
Ⓐ Ⓑ **Core** 12–27, 36, 41–48, 55
Ⓒ **Extension** 58

Standardized Test Prep 59–63

Mixed Review 64–73

pages 573–576 **Exercises**

1. $\dfrac{(x+2)^2}{9} + \dfrac{(y-1)^2}{4} = 1$

2. $\dfrac{(x-5)^2}{16} + \dfrac{(y-3)^2}{36} = 1$

3. $\dfrac{x^2}{36} + \dfrac{(y+4)^2}{25} = 1$

4. $\dfrac{(x-3)^2}{9} + \dfrac{(y+6)^2}{49} = 1$

Error Prevention

Exercises 37–48 Clarify that the equations given may represent conic sections that have already been translated from the origin. However, students are to translate these graphs 3 units right and 5 units up.

Careers

Exercise 56 Anthropologists study the beliefs, customs, and origins of people. Analyzing patterns often plays an important role in their work.

pages 573–576   Exercises

24. Translate the equation $\frac{x^2}{16} - \frac{y^2}{8} = 1$, a hyperbola centered at (0, 0), 3 units left.

26a. h is added to each x-coordinate, and k is added to each y-coordinate.

b. The lengths of the major and minor axes are unchanged; the x-coordinates of the vertices are increased (or decreased) by the same amount, and the same is true for the y-coordinates. A similar remark holds for the co-vertices.

27. The hyperbola originally had center (0, 0) and a horizontal or vertical transverse axis. If the new center is (h, k), then the equations of the new asymptotes are obtained by replacing x with $x - h$ and y with $y - k$ in the equations of the original asymptotes.

28. Multiplying both sides of the equation by 16 gives $x^2 + y^2 = 16$. This is an equation of the circle with center (0, 0) and radius 4.

574

Example 2
(page 572)

Write an equation of a hyperbola with the given characteristics.

5. vertices $(1, -3)$ and $(-7, -3)$, foci $(2, -3)$ and $(-8, -3)$ $\frac{(x + 3)^2}{16} - \frac{(y + 3)^2}{9} = 1$

6. vertices $(4, -1)$ and $(4, -5)$, foci $(4, 3)$ and $(4, -9)$ $\frac{(y + 3)^2}{4} - \frac{(x - 4)^2}{32} = 1$

7. vertices $(2, 2)$ and $(-4, 2)$, foci $(6, 2)$ and $(-8, 2)$ $\frac{(x + 1)^2}{9} - \frac{(y - 2)^2}{40} = 1$

8. vertices $(-1, 4)$ and $(-1, -6)$, foci $(-1, 8)$ and $(-1, -10)$

8. $\frac{(y + 1)^2}{25} - \frac{(x + 1)^2}{56} = 1$

9. vertices $(0, -2)$ and $(0, 4)$, foci $(0, 6)$ and $(0, -4)$ $\frac{(y - 1)^2}{9} - \frac{x^2}{16} = 1$

Example 3
(page 572)

For Exercises 10–11, find the equation of each hyperbola described.

10. All points on the hyperbola are 72 units closer to one focus than the other. The foci are located at $(0, 0)$ and $(300, 0)$. $\frac{(x - 150)^2}{1296} - \frac{y^2}{21,204} = 1$

11. All points on the hyperbola are 88 units closer to one focus than the other. The foci are located at $(0, 0)$ and $(350, 0)$. $\frac{(x - 175)^2}{1936} - \frac{y^2}{28,689} = 1$

Example 4
(page 573)

Identify the conic section represented by each equation by writing the equation in standard form. For a parabola, give the vertex. For a circle, give the center and the radius. For an ellipse or a hyperbola, give the center and the foci. Sketch the graph.

12–23. See back of book.

12. $x^2 - 8x - y + 19 = 0$ **13.** $x^2 + y^2 + 12x = 45$

14. $3x^2 + 6x + y^2 - 6y = -3$ **15.** $x^2 + y^2 - 2x + 6y = 3$

16. $y^2 - x^2 + 6x - 4y = 6$ **17.** $x^2 - 4y^2 - 2x - 8y = 7$

18. $x^2 + y^2 + 14y = -13$ **19.** $y^2 - 2x - 4y = -10$

20. $4x^2 + 9y^2 + 16x - 54y = -61$ **21.** $x^2 - y^2 + 6x + 10y = 17$

22. $x^2 + 4y^2 - 2x - 15 = 0$ **23.** $9x^2 - 4y^2 - 24y = 72$

 **Apply Your Skills**

24. A conic section centered at the origin is translated. Describe the translation that would produce the equation $x^2 - 2y^2 + 6x - 7 = 0$.   **See margin.**

25. Critical Thinking Use the equation $Ax^2 + Bxy + Cy^2 + Dx + Ey + F = 0$ to identify the shape of the graph that results in each case.
a. $A = C = D = E = 0, B \neq 0, F \neq 0$ **hyperbola**
b. $A = B = C = 0, D \neq 0, E \neq 0, F \neq 0$ **line**

26. a. How does the translation of an ellipse or hyperbola from center $(0, 0)$ to center (h, k) affect the coordinates of the vertices and foci?
b. How does the translation of an ellipse affect the length of its major and minor axes? Justify your answer.   **a–b. See margin.**

 27. Writing Describe how the translation of a hyperbola affects the equations of its asymptotes.   **See margin.**

28. Error Analysis Your friend claims that the equation $\frac{x^2}{16} + \frac{y^2}{16} = 1$ represents an ellipse. Explain why your friend is wrong.   **See margin.**

Write an equation for each conic section. Then sketch the graph.

29. circle with center $(-6, 9)$ and radius 9   **29–32. See back of book.**

30. ellipse with center $(3, 2)$, vertices $(9, 2)$ and $(-3, 2)$, and co-vertices $(3, 5)$ and $(3, -1)$

31. parabola with vertex $(2, -3)$ and focus $(2, 5)$

32. hyperbola with center $(6, -3)$, one focus $(6, 0)$, and one vertex $(6, -1)$

33. $\frac{(x-1)^2}{9} + \frac{(y+1)^2}{16} = 1$

34. $\frac{(x-3)^2}{36} - \frac{(y+2)^2}{15.84} = 1$

37. $(x-8)^2 + (y-2)^2 = 4$

38. $\frac{(x-6)^2}{64} + \frac{(y-2)^2}{36} = 1$

39. $y - 5 = 4(x-3)^2$

40. $\frac{(x-3)^2}{16} - \frac{(y-5)^2}{9} = 1$

41. $\frac{(x-5)^2}{36} - \frac{(y-8)^2}{25} = 1$

42. $\frac{(x-6)^2}{4} + \frac{(y-9)^2}{9} = 1$

43. $\frac{(x-2)^2}{16} + \frac{(y-7)^2}{9} = 1$

44. $\frac{x^2}{16} + \frac{(y-5)^2}{4} = 1$

45. $\frac{(x-4)^2}{16} - (y-9)^2 = 1$

46. $(x-8)^2 = 12(y-11)$

47. $\frac{x^2}{16} + \frac{(y-10)^2}{25} = 1$

48. $x^2 - (y-10)^2 = 1$

Write the equation of each graph. In Exercise 35, each interval represents one unit.

33.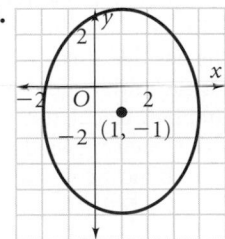

34.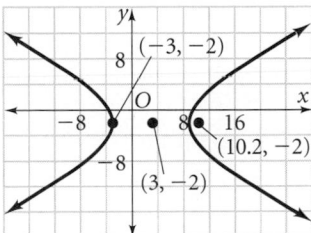

35.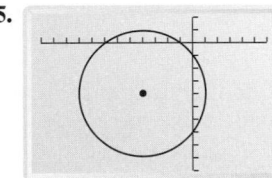

$(x+4)^2 + (y+4)^2 = 25$

36.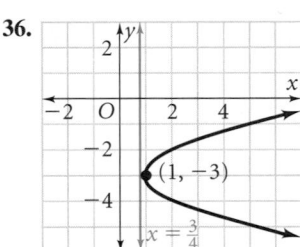

$x - 1 = (y+3)^2$

The graph of each equation is to be translated 3 units right and 5 units up. Write each new equation.   37–48. See left.

37. $(x-5)^2 + (y+3)^2 = 4$

38. $\frac{(x-3)^2}{64} + \frac{(y+3)^2}{36} = 1$

39. $y = 4x^2$

40. $9x^2 + 3x + 10 = 16y^2 + 154 + 3x$

41. $\frac{(x-2)^2}{36} - \frac{(y-3)^2}{25} = 1$

42. $\frac{(x-3)^2}{4} + \frac{(y-4)^2}{9} = 1$

43. $9x^2 + 16y^2 + 18x = 64y + 71$

44. $x^2 + 4y^2 + 6x - 7 = 0$

45. $x^2 - 16y^2 - 2x + 128y = 271$

46. $(x-5)^2 = 12(y-6)$

47. $25x^2 + 16y^2 + 150x = 160y - 225$

48. $x^2 - y^2 + 6x + 10y = 17$

Graph each pair of functions. Identify the conic section represented by the graph and write each equation in standard form.   49–54. See back of book.

49. $y = \sqrt{36 - 4x^2}$
    $y = -\sqrt{36 - 4x^2}$

50. $y = \sqrt{4x^2 - 36}$
    $y = -\sqrt{4x^2 - 36}$

51. $y = \sqrt{4x^2 + 36}$
    $y = -\sqrt{4x^2 + 36}$

52. $y = \sqrt{36 - x^2}$
    $y = -\sqrt{36 - x^2}$

53. $y = 0.5\sqrt{36 - x^2}$
    $y = -0.5\sqrt{36 - x^2}$

54. $y = \sqrt{x - 4}$
    $y = -\sqrt{x - 4}$

Ⓒ Challenge

55. **Open-Ended** On a graphing calculator, create a design using three translated quadratic relations.   **Check students' work.**

56. **History** Some symbols of the writing system of the Ejagham, people who lived in Nigeria and Cameroon, are shown. The symbol for marriage consists of two parabolic shapes. Reproduce this symbol on a graphing calculator. What equations did you use?
    Check students' work.

speech   divorce

discussion   marriage

a–b.

57. Consider equations of the form $Ax^2 + By^2 + Cx + Dy + E = 0$. **See margin.**
    a. What must be true about A and B for the graph of the equation to be a circle? To be an ellipse? To be a hyperbola? To be a parabola?
    b. Suppose $A = 1$ and $B = 1$. Must the graph be a circle? Explain.
    c. Suppose $A = 1, B = -1$, and $C = D = E = 0$. Describe the graph.
    two intersecting lines ($y = x$ and $y = -x$).

Lesson 10-6   Translating Conic Sections   **575**

57a. $A = B$; $A \neq B$ and A and B have the same sign; A and B have opposite signs; $A = 0$ or $B = 0$, but not both A and B are zero.

b. No; answers may vary. Sample: If $C = D = E = 0$, then the graph will be the single point (0, 0).

c. two intersecting lines ($y = x$ and $y = -x$)

Real-World 🌐 Connection

This Nigerian cloth combines writing symbols and patterns.

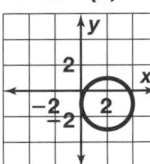
575

Standardized Test Prep

Resources

For additional practice with a variety of test item formats:
- Standardized Test Prep, p. 583
- Test-Taking Strategies, p. 578
- Test-Taking Strategies with Transparencies

pages 573–576   Exercises

58a. Earth:

$$\frac{x^2}{(149.60)^2} + \frac{y^2}{(149.58)^2} = 1$$

Mars:

$$\frac{x^2}{(227.9)^2} + \frac{y^2}{(226.9)^2} = 1$$

Mercury:

$$\frac{x^2}{(57.9)^2} + \frac{y^2}{(56.6)^2} = 1$$

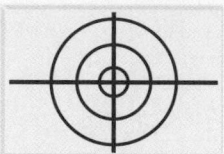

WINDOW FORMAT
Xmin=−379.0322...
Xmax=379.03225...
Xscl=1
Ymin=−250
Ymax=250
Yscl=1

63. **[4]** First group the x- and y-terms so the equation is $x^2 - 14x + y^2 + 10y = 26$. Complete the square for both the x and y groups of terms and factor; $(x - 7)^2 + (y + 5)^2 = 100$ is the equation of a circle with center $(7, -5)$ and radius 10.

[3] does not add 49 and 25 to 26 when completing the square

[2] errors in completing the square and factoring leading to wrong equation

[1] answer only, without explanation

576

---

 58. Astronomy The dimensions of the elliptical orbits of three planets are given in millions of kilometers in the table. The sun is at one focus. The other focus is on the positive x-axis.
a. Write an equation for each orbit and draw the curves on your graphing calculator. (Remember to adjust the viewing window.) **See margin.**
b. Reasoning Which orbit is most circular? Justify your reasoning. **Earth: $\frac{a}{b}$ is closest to 1 for Earth.**

Planet	a	b
Earth	149.60	149.58
Mars	227.9	226.9
Mercury	57.9	56.6

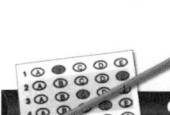

Standardized Test Prep

Quantitative Comparison Compare the boxed quantity in Column A with the boxed quantity in Column B. Choose the best answer.
- **A.** The quantity in Column A is greater.
- **B.** The quantity in Column B is greater.
- **C.** The two quantities are equal.
- **D.** The relationship cannot be determined from the information given.

	Column A	**Column B**
59. C	distance from a focus to the center on the graph of $3x^2 + 4y^2 - 12x + 8y = 32$	distance from a focus to the nearest vertex on the graph of $3x^2 + 4y^2 - 12x + 8y = 32$
60. A	length of the major axis on the graph of $4x^2 - 24x = 64 - 25y^2$	length of the minor axis on the graph of $4x^2 - 24x = 64 - 25y^2$
61. A	number of horizontal units shifted in translating from $x^2 - 4y^2 = 16$ to $x^2 - 2x - 4y^2 = 15$	number of vertical units shifted in translating from $x^2 - 4y^2 = 16$ to $x^2 - 2x - 4y^2 = 15$

Take It to the NET
Online lesson quiz at **www.PHSchool.com**
Web Code: aga-1006

Multiple Choice

62. Which conic section is represented by the equation $x^2 + y^2 = 6x - 14y - 9$? **F**
F. circle **G.** ellipse **H.** parabola **I.** hyperbola

Extended Response

63. Explain how you can tell which conic section is represented by the equation $x^2 + y^2 - 26 = 14x - 10y$. Describe the conic section. **See margin.**

Mixed Review

Lesson 10-5 Find the foci of each hyperbola. Draw the graph. **64–66. See margin.**

64. $\frac{x^2}{49} - \frac{y^2}{36} = 1$ **65.** $8y^2 - 6x^2 = 72$ **66.** $4y^2 - 100x^2 = 400$

Lesson 9-6 Solve each equation. Check your answers.

67. $\frac{1}{3x + 1} = \frac{1}{x^2 - 3}$ **−1, 4**   **68.** $\frac{2}{x + 2} = \frac{6}{x^2 - 4}$ **5**   **69.** $\frac{5}{x^2 - x} + \frac{3}{x - 1} = 6$
about −0.4315, 1.9315

Lesson 8-6 Simplify each expression.

70. $\ln e$ **1**   **71.** $2 \ln e$ **2**   **72.** $\ln e^3$ **3**   **73.** $4 \ln e^2$ **8**

64. $(\sqrt{85}, 0), (-\sqrt{85}, 0)$ **65.** $(0, \sqrt{21}), (0, -\sqrt{21})$ **66.** $(0, 2\sqrt{26}), (0, -2\sqrt{26})$

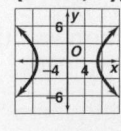   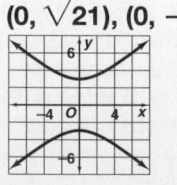   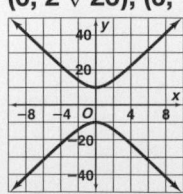

Solving Quadratic Systems

FOR USE WITH LESSON 10-6

In Chapter 3 you solved systems of linear equations algebraically and graphically. You can use the same methods to solve systems that include quadratic equations.

1 EXAMPLE Solving Algebraically

Solve the system algebraically. $\begin{cases} x^2 - y^2 = 9 \\ x^2 + 9y^2 = 169 \end{cases}$

$x^2 - y^2 = 9$
$\underline{x^2 + 9y^2 = 169}$
$-10y^2 = -160$ **Subtract like terms to eliminate the x^2 terms.**
$y = 4 \text{ or } y = -4$ **Solve for y.**

$x^2 - (4)^2 = 9$ **Substitute the values of y into** $x^2 - (-4)^2 = 9$
$x^2 = 25$ **one of the original equations.** $x^2 = 25$

$x = 5 \text{ or } x = -5$ **Solve for x.** $x = 5 \text{ or } x = -5$

● The ordered pairs $(5, 4), (-5, 4), (5, -4),$ and $(-5, -4)$ are solutions to the system.

2 EXAMPLE Solving Graphically

Solve the system by graphing. $\begin{cases} x^2 + y^2 = 36 \\ y = (x - 2)^2 - 3 \end{cases}$

$x^2 + y^2 = 36$
$y = \pm\sqrt{36 - x^2}$ **Solve the first equation for y.**

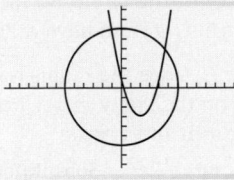

Graph the equations and find the point(s) of intersection.
● The solutions are approximately $(-1, 6)$ and $(4.6, 3.8)$.

EXERCISES

3. $\left(\pm\dfrac{21 + \sqrt{41}}{10}, \dfrac{9 - 21\sqrt{41}}{50}\right), \left(\pm\dfrac{21 - \sqrt{41}}{10}, \dfrac{9 + 21\sqrt{41}}{50}\right)$
or about $(\pm 2.74, -2.51), (\pm 1.46, 2.87)$

Solve each quadratic system.

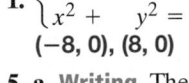

1. $\begin{cases} x^2 + 64y^2 = 64 \\ x^2 + y^2 = 64 \end{cases}$
$(-8, 0), (8, 0)$

2. $\begin{cases} 2x^2 - y^2 = 2 \\ x^2 + y^2 = 25 \end{cases}$
$(3, 4), (-3, 4), (3, -4), (-3, -4)$

3. $\begin{cases} 9x^2 + 25y^2 = 225 \\ y = -x^2 + 5 \end{cases}$

4. $\begin{cases} 4x^2 + 4y^2 = 100 \\ 3x^2 + 3y^2 = 27 \end{cases}$
no solutions

5. a. Writing The system that consists of $y = -3x + 6$ and $y = x^2 - 4x$ is a linear-quadratic system. How would you solve the system algebraically? Graphically? **See margin.**
b. Solve the system in part (a). $(-2, 12), (3, -3)$

Identify each system as linear-quadratic or quadratic-quadratic. Then solve. **6–9. See margin.**

6. $\begin{cases} y = x - 1 \\ x^2 + y^2 = 25 \end{cases}$

7. $\begin{cases} 9x^2 + 4y^2 = 36 \\ x^2 - y^2 = 4 \end{cases}$

8. $\begin{cases} -x + y = 4 \\ y = x^2 - 4x + 2 \end{cases}$

9. $\begin{cases} 4x^2 + 25y^2 = 100 \\ y = x + 2 \end{cases}$

Solving Quadratic Systems

Students solve systems that include quadratic equations both algebraically and graphically.

Resources

 Technology
Computer Test Generator CD-ROM, Chapter 10, Extension Topics

Teaching Notes

Error Prevention
Some students may initially think that all quadratic systems involve two equations of the form $y = ax^2 + bx + c$, where $a \neq 0$. Point out that quadratic systems can also involve quadratic equations in two variables such as circles, ellipses, and hyperbolas.

Math Tip
Quadratic systems can have from 0 to 4 solutions. Encourage students to sketch graphs to represent each of these situations.

---

page 577 Extension

5a. Algebraically: substitute $-3x + 6$ for y in $y = x^2 - 4x$, solve for x, and then substitute each of the solutions in $y = -3x + 6$ to find corresponding values for y. Graphically: Graph both relations. Then use the Intersect feature on the CALC menu to find the coordinates of all points where the graphs intersect.

6. linear-quadratic; $(-3, -4), (4, 3)$

7. quadratic-quadratic; $(\pm 2, 0)$

8. linear-quadratic; $\left(\dfrac{5 + \sqrt{33}}{2}, \dfrac{13 + \sqrt{33}}{2}\right),$ $\left(\dfrac{5 - \sqrt{33}}{2}, \dfrac{13 - \sqrt{33}}{2}\right)$

9. linear-quadratic; $(0, 2),$ $\left(-\dfrac{100}{29}, -\dfrac{42}{29}\right)$

Choosing *Cannot Be Determined*

This feature helps students understand the importance of carefully examining all of the information given and all answer choices for multiple choice questions, before choosing the answer choice "cannot be determined."

Resources

PRENTICE HALL
ASSESSMENT SYSTEM

Test-Taking Strategies with Transparencies
• Transparency 10
• Practice Sheet p. 34

Teaching Notes

Error Prevention

Exercise 4 Students may initially think that the center of the parabola must be at the origin and that the parabola opens upward. Show students how sketching a picture can help them determine that they can find more than one parabola whose focus is at (0, 3). Hence, the equation of the directrix cannot be determined.

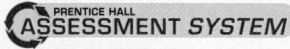

Test-Taking Strategies with Transparencies

Test-Taking Strategy: Choosing "Cannot Be Determined"

When you are not given enough information, you may not be able to determine the answer.

Example The area of a rectangle is 12. What is its perimeter?
A. 14   B. 16   C. 26   D. cannot be determined

12 factors into 3×4, 2×6, and 1×12.
The rectangle could have perimeter
$3 + 4 + 3 + 4 = 14$,
$2 + 6 + 2 + 6 = 16$, or
$1 + 12 + 1 + 12 = 26$.
There is not enough information to decide the correct answer. The answer choice must be **D**, cannot be determined.

Choose the correct answer. If your choice is "cannot be determined," explain.

1. In isosceles $\triangle ABC$, $AB = 5$. How does BC compare to 5?
   A. $BC > 5$ B. $BC = 5$
   C. $BC < 5$ D. cannot be determined
2. In right $\triangle DEF$, $DE = 3$ and $EF = 4$. What is DF?
   F. $\sqrt{7}$ G. 5   H. 7   I. cannot be determined
3. What is the solution of the inequality $ay + 3 > x$?
   A. $y > \frac{x-3}{a}$ B. $y > \frac{x}{a} - 3$
   C. $y < \frac{x-3}{a}$ D. cannot be determined

Solutions
1. D; the congruent sides are not known.
2. D; the sides that are the legs are not known.
3. D; it is not known whether a is positive or negative.

Transparency 10

Some multiple-choice questions cannot be answered. If so, then one of the answer choices will be *cannot be determined*. Be careful, however. Sometimes the answer choice *cannot be determined* is included as a distractor.

1 EXAMPLE

Find an equation of a circle that passes through the points $(0, 0), (1, 0)$ and $(2, 0)$.

   A. $(x - 1)^2 + y^2 = 1$
   B. $\left(x - \frac{1}{2}\right)^2 + y^2 = \frac{1}{4}$
   C. $\left(x - \frac{3}{2}\right)^2 + y^2 = \frac{1}{4}$
   D. cannot be determined

Since the y-coordinates of all three points are zero, the points are collinear. A circle cannot pass through three collinear points. The correct answer is D.

2 EXAMPLE

Which of the following completely describes the graphs of $(x - r)^2 + (y - r)^2 = 2r^2$?

   A. circles of radius r with centers on the line $y = x$
   B. circles with centers (r, r)
   C. circles with centers on the line $y = x$ and passing through $(0, 0)$
   D. cannot be determined

The standard form of an equation of a circle is $(x - h)^2 + (y - k)^2 = r^2$, where (h, k) is the center of the circle. So the equation in Example 2 describes circles that have centers at (r, r) and have radius $\sqrt{2r^2}$, or $r\sqrt{2}$.

Eliminate choice A, since the radius is incorrect. Since the centers of the circles are (r, r), they all lie on the line $y = x$. Choices B and C could be correct. Test choice C by substituting $x = 0$ and $y = 0$.
$$(0 - r)^2 + (0 - r)^2 \stackrel{?}{=} 2r^2 \quad \textbf{Substitute (0, 0) for } x \textbf{ and } y.$$
$$(r)^2 + (r)^2 \stackrel{?}{=} 2r^2 \quad \textbf{Simplify.}$$
$$2r^2 = 2r^2$$

The circles pass through the point $(0, 0)$. The correct answer is C. Choice D is a distractor.

EXERCISES

If the answer to an exercise can be determined, write the answer. If not, write *cannot be determined* and explain your reasoning.

1. Find the radius of the circle defined by $x^2 + y^2 - 4x - 2y + 14 = 0$. **See above.**

> 1. Cannot be determined because the radius would be the square root of a negative number.

2. Find the number of points of intersection of the graphs of $y = x^2$ and $y = 2ax - a^2$. **1**

3. Given that $x^2 - y^2 = 12$, find y when $x = 3$. **Cannot be determined because if $x = 3$, y^2 is a negative number.**

4. The focus of a parabola is $(0, 3)$. Find the equation of the directrix.
Cannot be determined because many parabolas have (0, 3) as their focus.

Chapter Review

Vocabulary

center (p. 549)
circle (p. 549)
conic section (p. 535)
co-vertices (p. 556)
directrix (p. 543)
ellipse (p. 556)

focus of a parabola (p. 543)
focus of an ellipse (p. 556)
focus of a hyperbola (p. 563)
hyperbola (p. 563)
major axis (p. 556)
minor axis (p. 556)

radius (p. 549)
standard form of an equation of a
   circle (p. 549)
transverse axis (p. 563)
vertices of an ellipse (p. 556)
vertices of a hyperbola (p. 563)

 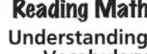 **Reading Math**
Understanding
Vocabulary

 **Take It to the NET**
Online vocabulary quiz
at www.PHSchool.com
Web Code: agj-1051

Choose the correct vocabulary term to complete each sentence.

1. In the definition of a parabola, the fixed line is the ? . **directrix**

2. The vertices of an ellipse are on its ? . **major axis**

3. $(x - h)^2 + (y - k)^2 = r^2$ is the ? . **standard form of an equation of a circle**

4. The distance from a point on a circle to its center is the ? of the circle. **radius**

5. The vertices of a hyperbola are on its ? . **transverse axis**

Skills and Concepts

10-1 Objectives

▼ To graph conic sections (p. 535)

▼ To identify conic sections (p. 537)

A **conic section** is a curve formed by the intersection of a plane and a double cone. Circles, ellipses, parabolas, and hyperbolas are all conic sections.

Graph each equation. Identify the conic section and describe the graph and its lines of symmetry. Then find the domain and range.   6–9. See back of book.

6. $\frac{x^2}{49} + \frac{y^2}{121} = 1$ **7.** $x^2 + y^2 = 4$ **8.** $\frac{x^2}{25} - \frac{y^2}{4} = 1$ **9.** $x = 2y^2 + 5$

Identify the center, the intercepts, and the domain and range of each graph.

10. center (0, 0); (±4, 0);
   domain: $x \geq 4$ or $x \leq -4$
   range: all real numbers

11. center (0, 0); (0, ±2),
   (±3, 0);
   domain: $-3 \leq x \leq 3$
   range: $-2 \leq y \leq 2$

10.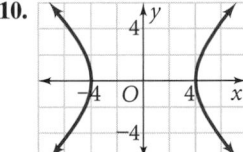

11.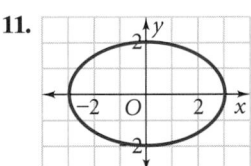

10-2 Objectives

▼ To write the equation of a parabola (p. 543)

▼ To graph parabolas (p. 545)

In a plane, a parabola is the set of all points that are the same distance c from a fixed line, the **directrix**, and a fixed point not on the line, the **focus.**

For $y = ax^2$ when $a > 0$, the parabola opens upward. The focus is $(0, c)$ and the directrix is $y = -c$. When $a < 0$, the parabola opens downward. The focus is $(0, -c)$ and the directrix is $y = c$. For $x = ay^2$, when $a > 0$, the parabola opens to the right. The focus is $(c, 0)$ and directrix is $x = -c$. When $a < 0$, the parabola opens to the left. The focus is $(-c, 0)$ and the directrix is $x = c$. Always, $|a| = \frac{1}{4c}$.

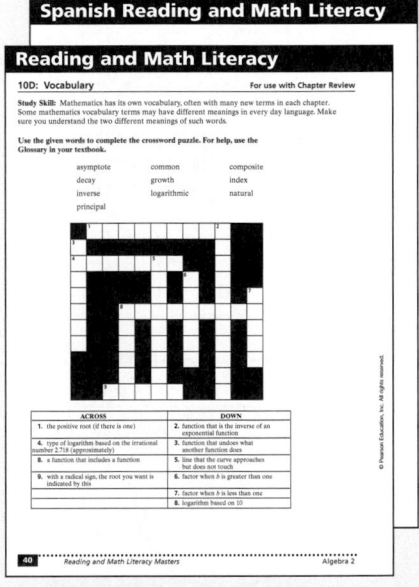

19. $\left(0, \frac{1}{20}\right)$, $y = -\frac{1}{20}$

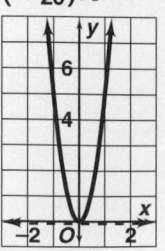

20. $\left(\frac{1}{8}, 0\right)$, $x = -\frac{1}{8}$

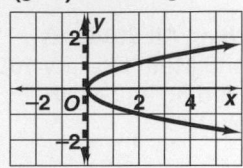

21. $(-2, 0)$, $x = 2$

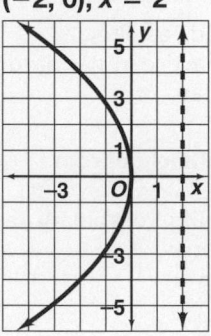

28. center $(1, 0)$, radius 8

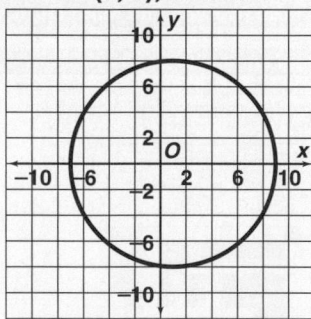

29. center $(-7, -3)$, radius 7

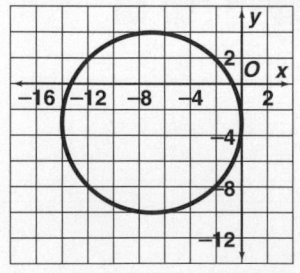

16. $y = \frac{1}{24}x^2$

17. $y = \frac{1}{10}x^2$

18. $y = 3x^2$

Write an equation for a graph that is the set of all points in the plane that are equidistant from the given point and the given line.

12. $F(0, 3)$, $y = -1$ $y = \frac{1}{8}x^2 + 1$

13. $F(-2, 0)$, $x = 4$ $x = -\frac{1}{12}y^2 + 1$

Write an equation of a parabola with a vertex at the origin and the given focus.

14. focus at $(5, 0)$ $x = \frac{1}{20}y^2$ **15.** focus at $(0, -5)$
$y = -\frac{1}{20}x^2$
16. focus at $(0, 6)$

Write an equation of a parabola opening upward with a vertex at the origin.

17. focus is 2.5 units from the vertex   **18.** focus is $\frac{1}{12}$ of a unit from the vertex

Find the focus and the directrix of the graph of each equation. Sketch the graph.

19. $y = 5x^2$ **20.** $x = 2y^2$ **21.** $x = -\frac{1}{8}y^2$

19–21. See margin.

10-3 Objectives

▼ To write and graph the equation of a circle (p. 549)

▼ To find the center and radius of a circle and use it to graph the circle (p. 551)

In a plane, a **circle** is the set of all points at a given distance, the **radius** r, from a given point, the **center** (h, k). The **standard form of an equation of a circle** is $(x - h)^2 + (y - k)^2 = r^2$.

Write an equation in standard form of the circle with the given center and radius.

22. center $(0, 0)$, radius 4 $x^2 + y^2 = 16$ **23.** center $(8, 1)$, radius 5
$(x - 8)^2 + (y - 1)^2 = 25$

Write an equation for each translation of $x^2 + y^2 = r^2$ with the given radius.

24. left 3 units, up 2 units; radius 10   **25.** right 5 units, down 3 units; radius 8
$(x + 3)^2 + (y - 2)^2 = 100$ $(x - 5)^2 + (y + 3)^2 = 64$

Write an equation for each circle. Each interval represents one unit.

26.

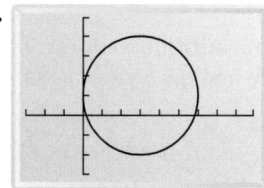

$(x - 3)^2 + (y - 1)^2 = 9$

27.

$(x + 1)^2 + y^2 = 4$

Find the center and the radius of each circle. Sketch the graph.

28. $(x - 1)^2 + y^2 = 64$ **29.** $(x + 7)^2 + (y + 3)^2 = 49$

28–29. See margin.

10-4 Objectives

▼ To write the equation of an ellipse (p. 556)

▼ To find the foci of an ellipse, and to graph an ellipse (p. 558)

In a plane, an **ellipse** is the set of all points P, the sum of whose distances to two fixed points, the **foci,** is constant. The **major axis** is the segment that contains the foci and has endpoints called the **vertices of an ellipse.** The **minor axis** is perpendicular to the major axis and has endpoints called the **co-vertices.**

There are two standard forms of an ellipse centered at the origin. If $\frac{x^2}{a^2} + \frac{y^2}{b^2} = 1$, the major axis is horizontal with vertices $(\pm a, 0)$ and co-vertices $(0, \pm b)$, where $a > b > 0$.

If $\frac{x^2}{b^2} + \frac{y^2}{a^2} = 1$, the major axis is vertical with vertices $(0, \pm a)$ and co-vertices $(\pm b, 0)$. In either case, you can find the foci c using the relationship $c^2 = a^2 - b^2$.

30. $\frac{x^2}{17} + \frac{y^2}{16} = 1$

31. $\frac{x^2}{25} + \frac{y^2}{29} = 1$

32. $\frac{x^2}{9} + \frac{y^2}{10} = 1$

33. $\frac{x^2}{40} + \frac{y^2}{36} = 1$

Write an equation of an ellipse in standard form with a center at the origin and with the given characteristics.

30. foci $(\pm 1, 0)$, co-vertices $(0, \pm 4)$

31. vertex $(0, \sqrt{29})$, co-vertex $(-5, 0)$

32. focus $(0, 1)$, vertex $(0, \sqrt{10})$

33. foci $(\pm 2, 0)$, co-vertices $(0, \pm 6)$

34. Write the equation of an ellipse centered at the origin with height 8 units and width 16 units. $\frac{x^2}{64} + \frac{y^2}{16} = 1$

35. Graph $\frac{x^2}{4} + \frac{y^2}{9} = 1$. Identify the foci. **See margin.**

10-5 Objectives

▼ To graph hyperbolas (p. 562)

▼ To find and use the foci of a hyperbola (p. 564)

In a plane, a **hyperbola** is the set of all points P such that difference between the distances from P to two fixed points, the **foci,** is constant. The foci lie on the line containing the **transverse axis.** Each branch of a hyperbola intersects the transverse axis at a **vertex of the hyperbola.** Each branch approaches the two asymptotes, which contain the diagonals of the central rectangle.

There are two standard forms of hyperbolas centered at the origin. If $\frac{x^2}{a^2} - \frac{y^2}{b^2} = 1$, the asymptotes are $y = \pm \frac{b}{a}x$, the transverse axis is horizontal with vertices $(\pm a, 0)$, and the foci are $(\pm c, 0)$. If $\frac{y^2}{a^2} - \frac{x^2}{b^2} = 1$, the asymptotes are $y = \pm \frac{a}{b}x$, the transverse axis is vertical with vertices $(0, \pm a)$, and the foci are $(0, \pm c)$. In either case, you can find the value of b using the relationship $c^2 = a^2 + b^2$.

Find the foci of each hyperbola. Draw the graph. 36–38. See margin.

36. $\frac{x^2}{36} - \frac{y^2}{225} = 1$

37. $\frac{y^2}{400} - \frac{x^2}{169} = 1$

38. $\frac{x^2}{121} - \frac{y^2}{81} = 1$

39. Find an equation that models the path of a spacecraft around a planet if $a = 107{,}124$ and $c = 213{,}125.9$. $\frac{x^2}{1.148 \times 10^{10}} - \frac{y^2}{3.395 \times 10^{10}} = 1$

10-6 Objectives

▼ To write the equation of a translated conic section (p. 570)

▼ To identify the equation of a translated conic section (p. 573)

41. $\frac{(x-6)^2}{9} - \frac{(y-3)^2}{16} = 1$

You can substitute $(x - h)$ for x and $(y - k)$ for y to translate graphs of an ellipse or a hyperbola. A translated ellipse or hyperbola has center (h, k).

Write an equation of a conic section with the given characteristics.

40. an ellipse with center $(3, -2)$, vertical major axis of length 6; minor axis of length 4 $\frac{(x-3)^2}{4} + \frac{(y+2)^2}{9} = 1$

41. a hyperbola with vertices $(3, 3)$ and $(9, 3)$, foci $(1, 3)$ and $(11, 3)$

42. All points on the hyperbola are 81 units closer to one focus than the other. The foci are at $(0, 0)$ and $(155, 0)$. $\frac{(x - 77.5)^2}{1640.25} - \frac{y^2}{4366} = 1$

Identify the conic section represented by each equation by writing the equation in standard form. For a parabola, give the vertex. For a circle, give the center and the radius. For an ellipse or a hyperbola, give the center and the foci. Sketch the graph. 43–46. See margin.

43. $-x^2 + y^2 + 4y - 16 = 0$

44. $x^2 + y^2 + 3x - 4y - 9 = 0$

45. $x^2 + x - y - 42 = 0$

46. $2x^2 + 3y^2 - 4x + 12y - 20 = 0$

Chapter 10   Chapter Review   **581**

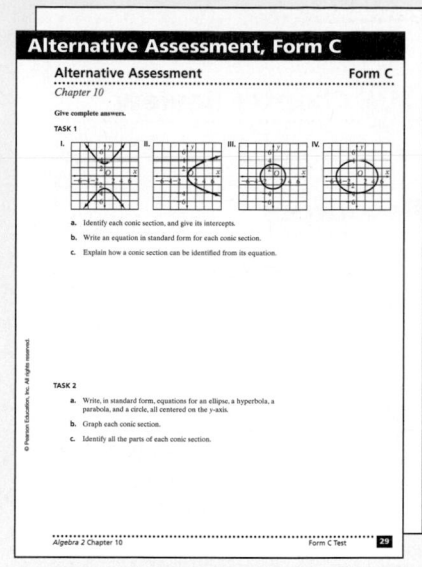
43. hyperbola; center $(0, -2)$, foci $(0, -2 \pm 2\sqrt{10})$

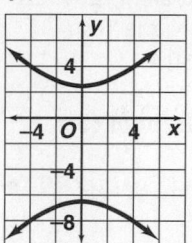

44. circle, center $\left(-\frac{3}{2}, 2\right)$, radius $\frac{\sqrt{61}}{2}$

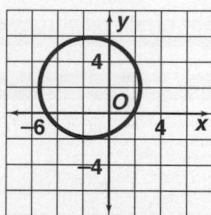

45. parabola; vertex $\left(-\frac{1}{2}, -\frac{169}{4}\right)$

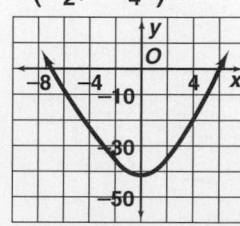

46. ellipse; center $(1, -2)$, foci $\left(\frac{3 \pm \sqrt{51}}{3}, -2\right)$

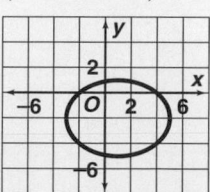

35.

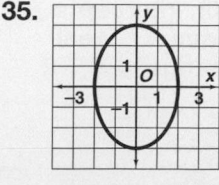

foci $(0, \pm\sqrt{5})$

36.

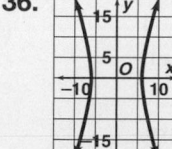

foci $(\pm 3\sqrt{29}, 0)$

37.

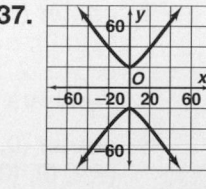

foci $(0, \pm\sqrt{569})$

38.

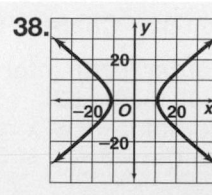

foci $(\pm\sqrt{202}, 0)$

Chapter Test

Take It to the NET
Online chapter test at
www.PHSchool.com
Web Code: aga-1052

Identify the center and intercepts of each conic section. Give the domain and range of each graph. 1–4. See margin.

1.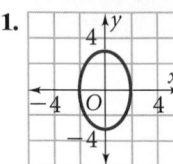

2.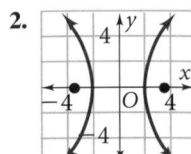

3.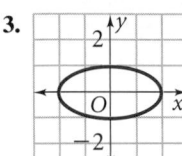

4.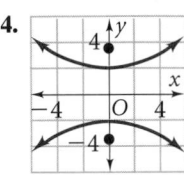

5. Writing Explain how you can tell what kind of conic section a quadratic equation describes without graphing the equation. **Write the equation in standard form.**

Identify the focus and the directrix of the graph of each equation. 6–9. See back of book.

6. $y = 3x^2$

7. $x = -2y^2$

8. $x + 5y^2 = 0$

9. $9x^2 - 2y = 0$

Write an equation of a parabola with a vertex at the origin and the given characteristic.

10. focus at $(0, -2)$ $y = -\frac{1}{8}x^2$

11. focus at $(3, 0)$ $x = \frac{1}{12}y^2$

12. directrix $x = 7$ $x = -\frac{1}{28}y^2$

13. directrix $y = -1$ $y = \frac{1}{4}x^2$

Find the center and radius of the circle. Sketch the circle. 14–17. See back of book.

14. $(x - 2)^2 + (y - 3)^2 = 36$

15. $(x + 5)^2 + (y + 8)^2 = 100$

16. $(x - 1)^2 + (y + 7)^2 = 81$

17. $(x + 4)^2 + (y - 10)^2 = 121$

Find an equation of an ellipse for each given height and width. Assume that the center of the ellipse is $(0, 0)$.

18. height 10 units, width 16 units $\frac{x^2}{64} + \frac{y^2}{25} = 1$

19. height 2 units, width 12 units $\frac{x^2}{36} + y^2 = 1$

20. height 9 units, width 5 units $\frac{x^2}{6.25} + \frac{y^2}{20.25} = 1$

Find the foci for each ellipse. Sketch the ellipse.

21. $\frac{x^2}{81} + \frac{y^2}{36} = 1$

22. $\frac{x^2}{25} + \frac{y^2}{121} = 1$

23. $x^2 + \frac{y^2}{49} = 1$

24. $4x^2 + y^2 = 4$

21–24. See back of book.

25. Critical Thinking What is the shape of an ellipse whose height and width are equal? **circle**

Find the foci for each hyperbola. Sketch the hyperbola. 26–29. See back of book.

26. $\frac{x^2}{144} - \frac{y^2}{100} = 1$

27. $\frac{y^2}{169} - \frac{x^2}{400} = 1$

28. $\frac{x^2}{64} - \frac{y^2}{4} = 1$

29. $y^2 - \frac{x^2}{225} = 1$

30. Open-Ended Write the equation of a hyperbola with a transverse axis on the x-axis. **Check students' work.**

Write an equation of an ellipse with the given characteristics. 31–33. See back of book.

31. center $(0, 0)$, vertex $(4, 0)$, co-vertex $(0, -3)$

32. center $(-2, 7)$, horizontal major axis of length 8, minor axis of length 6

33. center $(3, -2)$, vertical major axis of length 12, minor axis of length 10

Write an equation of a hyperbola with the given characteristics. 34–36. See back of book.

34. vertices $(\pm 3, 7)$, foci $(\pm 5, 7)$

35. vertices $(2, \pm 5)$, foci $(2, -7), (2, 7)$

36. vertices $(-3, -1), (-5, -1)$, foci $(0, -1), (-8, -1)$

Identify the conic section represented by each equation. If it is a parabola, give the vertex. If it is a circle, give the center and radius. If it is an ellipse or a hyperbola, give the center and foci. Sketch the graph. 37–40. See back of book.

37. $3y^2 - x - 6y + 5 = 0$

38. $x^2 + y^2 - 4x - 6y + 4 = 0$

39. $4x^2 + y^2 - 16x - 6y + 9 = 0$

40. $4x^2 - y^2 - 16x + 6y - 9 = 0$

page 582   Chapter Test

1. center $(0, 0)$, intercepts $(\pm 2, 0)$, $(0, \pm 3)$; domain: $-2 \leq x \leq 2$, range: $-3 \leq y \leq 3$

2. center $(0, 0)$, intercepts $(\pm 2, 0)$; domain: $x \leq -2$ or $x \geq 2$, range: all real numbers

3. center $(0, 0)$, intercepts $(\pm 2, 0)$, $(0, \pm 1)$; domain: $-2 \leq x \leq 2$, range: $-1 \leq y \leq 1$

4. center $(0, 0)$, intercepts $(0, \pm 2)$; domain: all real numbers, range: $y \leq -2$ or $y \geq 2$

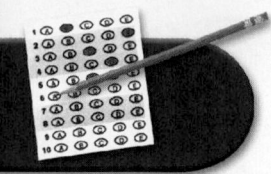

Standardized Test Prep

Standardized Test Prep

Multiple Choice

For Exercises 1–7, choose the correct letter.

1. Which equation represents a circle with center $(-3, 8)$ and radius 12? **C**
   A. $(x - 8)^2 + (y + 3)^2 = 144$
   B. $(x - 8)^2 - (y + 3)^2 = 144$
   C. $(x + 3)^2 + (y - 8)^2 = 144$
   D. $(x - 3)^2 - (y - 8)^2 = 144$

2. Which function has a growth factor of 1.25? **G**
   F. $y = 1.25x$
   G. $y = 4.1(1.25)^x$
   H. $y = 1.25(3.7)^x$
   I. $y = 1.25(0.9)^x$

3. What is the product $\frac{x^2(x - 2)}{x + 4} \cdot \frac{2(2x + 8)}{x^3 - x^2}$? **D**

   A. $\frac{x^4(x - 1)(x - 2) - 4(x + 4)^2}{x^2(x - 1)(x + 4)}$

   B. $\frac{12x^4 + 14x^3 - 32x^2}{x^4 + 2x^3 - 4x^2}$

   C. $\frac{x^4(x - 1)(x - 2)}{4(x + 4)^2}$

   D. $\frac{4(x - 2)}{x - 1}$

4. The equation $y = (x - 4)^2$ represents which conic section? **H**
   F. circle
   G. ellipse
   H. parabola
   I. hyperbola

5. Which events are dependent? **B**
   I. spinning a spinner three times
   II. choosing three students from a class
   III. tossing two coins and a number cube
   A. I only   B. II only   C. III only   D. I and II

6. The graph below represents which function? **G**

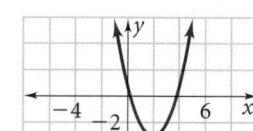

   F. $y = \frac{x^2 - 4}{x + 4}$
   G. $y = x^2 - 4x + 1$
   H. $y = |x + 4|$
   I. $y = x^3 + x^2 - 4$

7. Which equation has roots -3, 0, 1, and 2? **A**
   A. $x^4 - 7x^2 + 6x = 0$
   B. $x^4 - 6x^3 + 11x - 6x = 0$
   C. $x^4 - 4x^3 + x^2 - 6x = 0$
   D. $x^4 - 7x^2 - 6 = 0$

Quantitative Comparison

Compare the boxed quantity in Column A with the boxed quantity in Column B. Choose the best answer.

F. The quantity in Column A is greater.
G. The quantity in Column B is greater.
H. The two quantities are equal.
I. The relationship cannot be determined from the information given.

Column A	Column B
the radius of the circle $x^2 + (y - 1)^2 = 34$	the radius of the circle $(x - 4)^2 + y^2 = 48$

8. **G**

Column A	Column B
$_7C_2$	$_7C_5$

9. **H**

Column A	Column B
$4^{-\frac{2}{3}}$	$4^{-\frac{3}{2}}$

10. **F**

Gridded Response

11. Simplify $\dfrac{1 - \frac{1}{8}}{2 - \frac{3}{4}}$. **0.7**

12. A and B are not mutually exclusive events. $P(A) = \frac{1}{4}$ and $P(B) = \frac{1}{5}$. Find $P(A \text{ or } B)$. **$\frac{2}{5}$**

Short Response

13. $\begin{bmatrix} 1 & 0 \\ 0 & 2 \\ 1 & 3 \end{bmatrix} + \begin{bmatrix} 2 & 1 \\ 1 & 3 \\ 0 & 0 \end{bmatrix}$ **[2]** $\begin{bmatrix} 3 & 1 \\ 1 & 5 \\ 1 & 3 \end{bmatrix}$

   [1] one or 2 errors

14. Find the zeros of the function $y = x^2 - 2x$. Show your work. **See back of book.**

Extended Response

15. a. Write an equation of a line perpendicular to $y = 3x + 2$.
    b. Write an equation of a line parallel to $y = 3x + 2$. **See back of book.**

16. Find $\dfrac{x + 4}{x^2 + 6x + 8} \div \dfrac{x^2 - 16}{x^2 + 8x + 12}$.
    What are the restrictions on the variable? **See margin.**

Resources

Teaching Resources
Cumulative Review

Reaching All Students
Spanish Cumulative Review

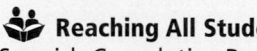
ASSESSMENT SYSTEM

Standardized Test Prep
• Ch. 10 Standardized Test Practice
Assessment Masters
• Cumulative Review
Computer Test Generator CD
• Standarized Test Practice

www.PHSchool.com
• Standarized Test Practice
• Resources

Plus **iTEXT**

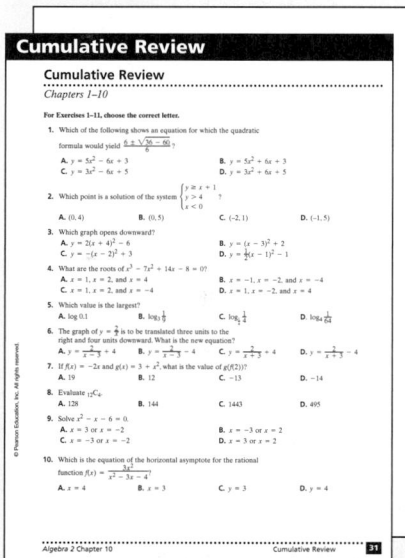

Item	Lesson	Item	Lesson
1	10-3	9	6-7
2	8-1	10	7-4
3	9-4	11	9-4
4	10-1	12	6-7
5	9-7	13	4-2
6	9-3	14	6-2
7	6-5	15	2-2
8	10-3	16	9-4

page 583   Cumulative Review

16. **[4]**

$\dfrac{x + 4}{(x + 4)(x + 2)} \div \dfrac{(x - 4)(x + 4)}{(x + 6)(x + 2)}$

$= \dfrac{x + 4}{(x + 4)(x + 2)} \cdot \dfrac{(x + 6)(x + 2)}{(x - 4)(x + 4)}$

$= \dfrac{(x + 4)(x + 6)(x + 2)}{(x + 4)(x + 2)(x - 4)(x + 4)}$

$= \dfrac{x + 6}{(x - 4)(x + 4)} = \dfrac{x + 6}{x^2 - 16}$;

$x \neq -6, -4, -2, 4$

[3] answer correct, but one restriction missing

[2] answer correct but all restrictions missing OR either numerator or denominator correct, but 1 or 2 restrictions missing.

[1] answer incorrect, restrictions correct

583

Martian Math

In these activities students apply their knowledge of functions, ratios, and conic sections, particularly the ellipse.

Connecting to Prior Knowledge

Have students discuss what they know about planets, and about Mars in particular. Elicit information about the various ways that scientists have gathered information about the Red Planet.

Teaching Notes

Have a volunteer read the introductory paragraph. Ask: *What characteristics of Mars would help to make it a relatively easy place to land a human space expedition? What characteristics would make this difficult?*

Teaching Tip

Ask a volunteer to review the difference between mass (*constant*) and weight (*varies with gravitational attraction*).

Tactile Learners

Have students use a pencil and a string about 10 inches long, fastened at each end by two tacks that are about 4 inches apart, to draw an ellipse. Ask students to identify the foci for this demonstration (*the two tacks*) and the constant sum of the two distances (*the length of the string*).

English Learners

Have a volunteer explain what is meant by the *eccentricity* of a planet's orbit.

Real-World Snapshots

Martian Math

Applying Conic Sections Even though we haven't discovered life on Mars, we know a lot of other things about the planet. Mars has a day about 25 hours long, a pattern of seasons similar to Earth's, and polar icecaps. Mars also has surface temperatures that rarely rise above freezing and almost no oxygen in its atmosphere. Mars is often called the Red Planet because red deserts cover its surface.

Activity 1

a. Mars travels in an elliptical orbit with the sun at one of its foci. Use the data from the diagram to calculate a, b, and c of this elliptical orbit.

b. Point P is the midpoint between Mars' closest and farthest distances to the sun. Use your values of a and b to write an equation of the elliptical orbit of Mars relative to a coordinate system drawn through point P (y-axis in gray). Use distances in millions of kilometers.

c. It is also useful to define Mars' motion relative to the sun. Imagine a new coordinate system (y-axis in black) with its origin at the center of the sun. Rewrite your equation for the ellipse in this new coordinate system.

d. **Critical Thinking** Explain how the eccentricity of a planet's orbit can affect its annual weather cycle.

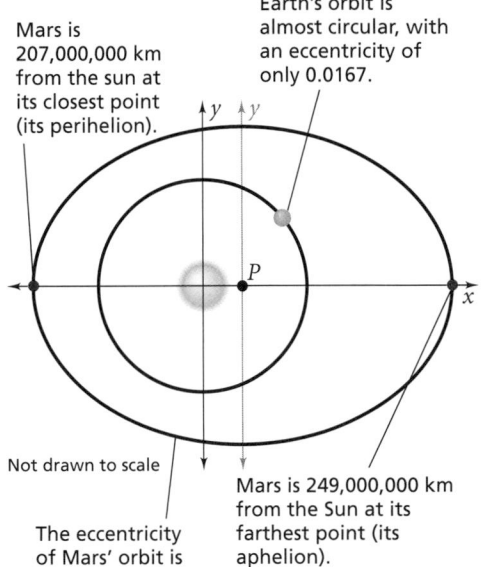

Mars is 207,000,000 km from the sun at its closest point (its perihelion).

Earth's orbit is almost circular, with an eccentricity of only 0.0167.

Not drawn to scale

The eccentricity of Mars' orbit is 0.0934.

Mars is 249,000,000 km from the Sun at its farthest point (its aphelion).

Martian sand dunes

Antenna

Deflated air bag

Solar Panels

Ramp for Sojourner

584 All photographs © Dorling Kindersley Limited unless otherwise credited on acknowledgments page

pages 584–585   Real-World Snapshots

Activity 1

a. $a = 228{,}000{,}000$ km,
$b = 227{,}000{,}000$ km,
$c = 21{,}000{,}000$ km

b. $\dfrac{x^2}{228^2} + \dfrac{y^2}{227^2} = 1$

c. $\dfrac{(x - 21)^2}{228^2} + \dfrac{y^2}{227^2} = 1$

d. Answers may vary. Sample: For an orbit of high eccentricity, the planet's distance from the sun and the amount of the heat that the planet receives will change.

Activity 2

Astronauts who walked on the moon felt as if they weighed about one sixth of their weight on Earth. This is because the weight of an object is determined by the gravitational attraction between the object and the planet (or moon) it's on. You can use the following formula to estimate the weight of an object on the surface of any of the planets: gravitational force $= \frac{GmM}{r^2}$, where $G =$ universal gravitational constant, $m =$ mass of the object, $M =$ mass of the planet, and $r =$ radius of the planet. For a given object, G and m remain constant, so the force of gravity depends only on the variables M and r.

a. Use the data below. Write a ratio to determine the factor by which you would multiply the weight of a 150-lb person on Earth to find his or her weight on Mars.

b. Find the person's weight on Mars.

c. Repeat parts (a) and (b) for two other planets.

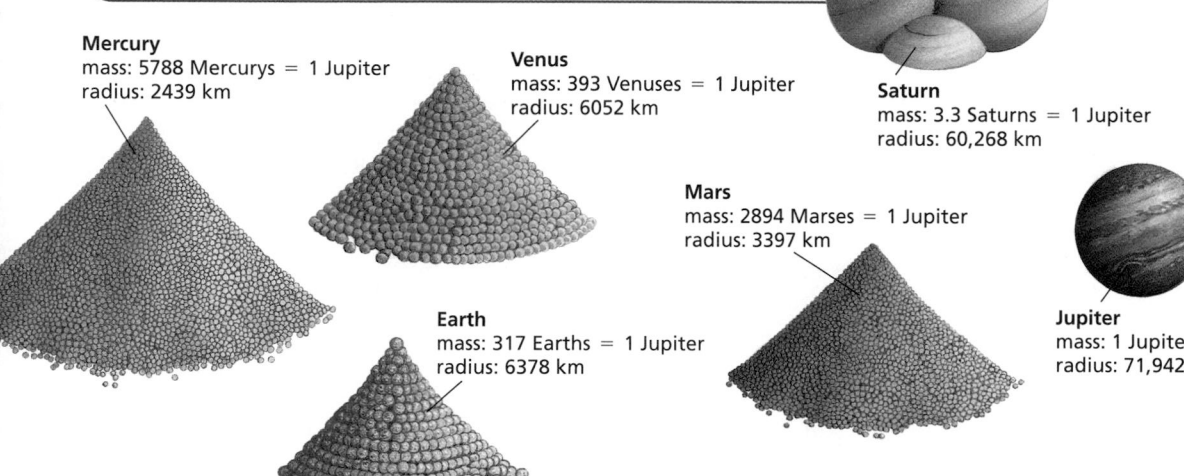

Mercury
mass: 5788 Mercurys = 1 Jupiter
radius: 2439 km

Venus
mass: 393 Venuses = 1 Jupiter
radius: 6052 km

Saturn
mass: 3.3 Saturns = 1 Jupiter
radius: 60,268 km

Mars
mass: 2894 Marses = 1 Jupiter
radius: 3397 km

Earth
mass: 317 Earths = 1 Jupiter
radius: 6378 km

Jupiter
mass: 1 Jupiter
radius: 71,942 km

 Take It to the NET For more information about Mars, go to www.PHSchool.com.
Web Code: age-1053

Man on the Moon
On July 20, 1969, U.S. astronauts first set foot on the moon.

Sojourner rover

Bouncing to a Stop
The Pathfinder Probe parachuted onto Mars inside a giant "beach ball"—a set of air bags designed to cushion the probe's landing. The probe bounced 15 times across the rocky ground and rolled to a stop. Its airbags deflated. Three panels then folded out like petals, exposing the probe's instruments and the Sojourner rover to the Martian landscape.

585

Activity 2

a. 0.386

b. 57.9 lb

c. **Answers may vary.**
Sample: Mercury: 0.3745, 56.2 lb; Jupiter: 2.49, 373.5 lb

Sequences and Series

Chapter at a Glance

11-1	**Mathematical Patterns**
NCTM 1, 2, 3, 8	▼ Identifying Mathematical Patterns
	▼ Using Formulas to Generate Mathematical Patterns

11-2	**Arithmetic Sequences**
NCTM 2, 8, 9, 10	▼ Identifying and Generating Arithmetic Sequences

11-3	**Geometric Sequences**
NCTM 2, 3, 8, 10	▼ Identifying and Generating Geometric Sequences

11-4	**Arithmetic Series**
NCTM 2, 6, 10	▼ Writing and Evaluating Arithmetic Series
	▼ Using Summation Notation

11-5	**Geometric Series**
NCTM 2, 6, 10	▼ Evaluating a Finite Geometric Series
	▼ Evaluating an Infinite Geometric Series

11-6	**Area Under a Curve**
NCTM 2, 3, 4, 7	▼ Finding Area Under a Curve

NCTM STANDARDS 2000

1	Number and Operations	6	Problem Solving
2	Algebra	7	Reasoning and Proof
3	Geometry	8	Communication
4	Measurement	9	Connections
5	Data Analysis and Probability	10	Representation

Pacing Options

This chart suggests pacing only for the lessons and their parts. It is provided as a possible guide. It will help you determine how much time you have in your schedule to cover other components, such as the features, Chapter Review, and Chapter Test.

Day	Traditional (45 min.)	Block (90 min.)
1	11-1 ▼	11-1 ▼ ▼
2	11-1 ▼	11-2 ▼
3	11-2 ▼	11-3 ▼
4	11-3 ▼	11-4 ▼ ▼
5	11-3 ▼	11-5 ▼ ▼
6	11-4 ▼	11-6 ▼
7	11-4 ▼	
8	11-5 ▼ ▼	
9	11-6 ▼	
10	11-6 ▼	

NAEP Correlation (National Assessment of Educational Progress 2000 Mathematics Objectives)

11-1	11-2	11-3	11-4	11-5	11-6
N6b, A1a, A1b	A1c, A1e, A8b	A1e, A8b, A8c	A1e, A8b, A8c	A8b, A8c	G8, A8b, A10

N = Number Sense, Properties, and Operations; **M** = Measurement; **G** = Geometry and Spatial Sense; **D** = Data Analysis, Statistics, and Probability; **A** = Algebra and Functions

Math Background

Chapter Overview

This chapter introduces sequences as lists of numbers that are generated according to a pattern. Sequences can be defined recursively by telling how the sequence starts and then giving instructions for using known terms as "stepping stones" to get to the next terms. Sequences can also be defined by an explicit formula that gives the value of a term as a function of its position in the sequence. Using either an explicit or a recursive formula to describe a sequence depends on the nature of the problem at hand. Recursive formulas are often useful in programming computers to solve problems, since recursive definitions usually make it easy to create program loops.

Series are defined as expressions for the sum of the terms of a sequence. Students investigate arithmetic and geometric series. They see that under certain conditions an infinite geometric series converges to a finite sum.

The final lesson shows how inscribed rectangles and circumscribed rectangles can be used to approximate the area under a curve. In addition to this brief glimpse at a problem that is treated later in calculus, the chapter has feature pages that discuss the Fibonacci sequence and mathematical induction.

Mathematical Patterns   11-1

Patterns often exist in the natural world. Examples may be the shape of a leaf, or the anatomy of the shell of the chambered nautilus. Students may not realize that in indicating a pattern of a sequence of numbers the ellipsis follows three repetitions of the pattern. This is a generally accepted convention, but it is always possible to find a sequence for which a triple repetition does not determine the pattern—more explicit means must be used to convey the content of such a sequence. For example, for the sequence 2, 4, 8, . . . it is impossible to tell whether 16 (the next power of 2) or 14 (add 2, add 4, add 6, . . .) is the next term.

Arithmetic Sequences   11-2

A sequence can be thought of as a function whose domain is a subset of the integers. For example, consider the sequence of positive even numbers (2, 4, 6, 8, . . .). Let the x-coordinate be the number of the term and the y-coordinate be the term itself. Then we can write the function $f = \{(x, y): (1, 2), (2, 4), (3, 6), (4, 8), \ldots\}$. When we graph these points, they all fall on the line that has equation $y = 2x$. This is no surprise since the explicit definition of the arithmetic sequence is $a_n = 2n$. Notice that the slope of the

line equals the common difference of the sequence. An important distinction to make between the equation and the sequence is that the equation is a *continuous* function while the sequence is a *discrete* function. The graph of the sequence consists of a set of discrete points, while the graph of the equation consists of every point on the line.

Geometric Sequences   11-3

Just as an arithmetic sequence is related to a linear function, a geometric sequence is related to an exponential function. For example, consider the sequence of powers of 2: 2, 4, 8, 16, ... Again, consider the sequence as a function. Then we can write the ordered pairs $\{(x, y): (1, 2), (2, 4), (3, 8), (4, 16), \ldots\}$. When we graph these points, they all fall on the exponential curve that has equation $y = 2^x$. This is no surprise since the explicit definition of the geometric sequence is $a_n = 2 \cdot 2^{n-1}$, or $a_n = 2^n$. Notice that the base of the exponential equation equals the common ratio r of the sequence. Have students graph equations such as $y = 3^n$ and $y = \left(\frac{1}{3}\right)^n$ to establish that, when $|r| > 1$, exponential growth is modeled, and that, when $|r| < 1$, exponential decay is modeled. (Refer back to exponential functions in Chapter 8 as needed.)

Arithmetic Series   11-4

You may wish to challenge interested students to prove the formula for the sum S_n of an arithmetic series. Students will need summation notation in future math courses.

Geometric Series   11-5

When you discuss convergent and divergent geometric series, ask students whether an infinite arithmetic sequence converges or diverges. Examples and reasoning can be used to convince them that it is impossible for an infinite arithmetic series to converge. Students usually have little difficulty understanding the difference between a *finite* series and an *infinite series*.

Area Under a Curve   11-6

You may want to point out that we are only using portions of curves that touch or lie above the x-axis. Some students may observe that they can improve on the area approximations in this lesson by first using inscribed rectangles, then circumscribed rectangles, and finally the average of the two approximations.

 # Ongoing Assessment and Intervention

Tools for Monitoring Student Progress

The Prentice Hall *Algebra 2* program provides you with many options for assessment in the Student Edition, the Teacher's Edition and the teaching resources. From these options you may choose instructional materials and techniques that are appropriate for your students and support your district's curriculum requirements.

Instant Check System™ in Chapter 11

Allows students to check their own learning before, during, and after each lesson.

Diagnosing Readiness before the chapter (p. 586)

Check Skills You'll Need exercises in each lesson (pp. 588, 594, 600, 607, 614, 623)

Check Understanding questions with each Example (pp. 589, 590, 594, 595, 601, 602, 608, 609, 615, 616, 624, 625)

Checkpoint Quiz (pp. 605, 619)

Test Prep in Chapter 11

Teaches students strategies and gives them practice with all the test item formats they will encounter on state tests and standardized national exams.

Standardized Test Prep exercises in each lesson (pp. 593, 598, 604, 605, 612, 618, 627)

Test-Taking Strategies (p. 628)

Standardized Test Prep (p. 633)

 PRENTICE HALL ASSESSMENT SYSTEM

All your assessment needs in one place!

Program Assessment

Assess student progress throughout the *Algebra 2* text with blackline masters and CD-ROM.

Assessment Resources

- Checkpoint Quizzes 1 & 2
- Chapter Test, Forms A & B
- Chapter Alternative Assessment

Spanish versions available.

Computer Test Generator

- Unlimited questions of varying difficulty for every lesson objective.
- Create your own practice sheets, quizzes, and tests, or use the pre-made Chapter Tests.
- Diagnose readiness with questions on prerequisite skills.
- Prepare students by making tests based on standardized test objectives.
- Access Algebra 1, Geometry, and Algebra 2 content—all on one CD-ROM.

Test Preparation

A three-step approach to preparing students for high stakes, national, and state exams.

❶ **Diagnose & Prescribe**

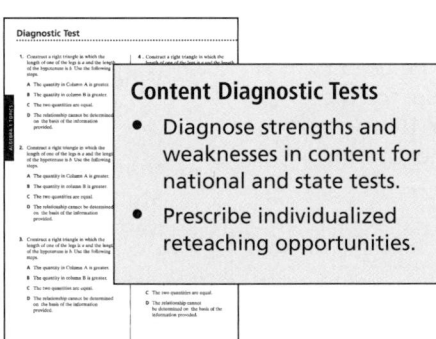

Content Diagnostic Tests

- Diagnose strengths and weaknesses in content for national and state tests.
- Prescribe individualized reteaching opportunities.

❷ **Review & Reteach**

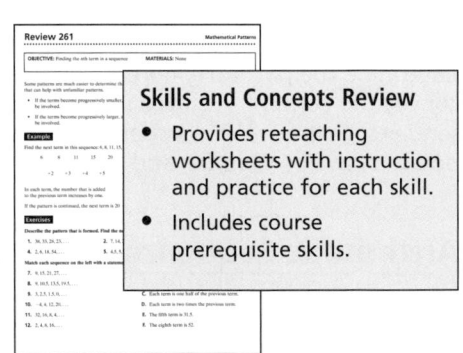

Skills and Concepts Review

- Provides reteaching worksheets with instruction and practice for each skill.
- Includes course prerequisite skills.

❸ **Practice & Assess**

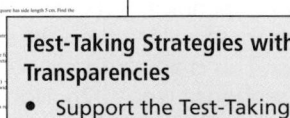

Test Preparation

- Features practice tests for End-of-Course and SAT/ACT exams.
- Includes standardized test practice by chapter for ongoing review.

Teacher's Guide with answers and correlations.

Test-Taking Strategies with Transparencies

- Support the Test-Taking Strategies pages in the Student Edition.
- Provide a teaching transparency and a practice worksheet for each strategy.

 # Reaching All Students

Support in the Student Text and Additional Resources

The textbook, the iText, and other technology components provide numerous opportunities to reach students of various ability levels and learning styles. Each Teacher's Edition lesson suggests how you can help *all* your students be successful and understand the mathematics in Chapter 11.

Below Level

Student Edition
- Diagnosing Readiness*: p. 586
- Check Skills You'll Need*: pp. 588, 594, 600, 607, 614, 623

Reteaching
Chapter 11 Support File: pp. 8–13

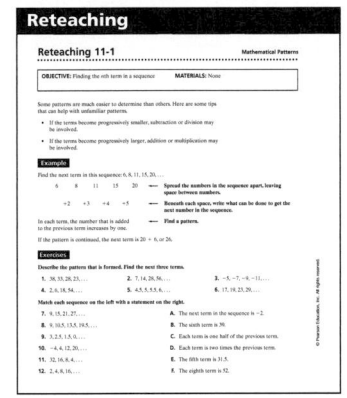

Advanced Learners

Student Edition
- Challenge exercises: pp. 592, 597, 603, 611, 618, 626
- Extension, pp. 599, 620, 621

Enrichment
Chapter 11 Support File: pp. 14–19

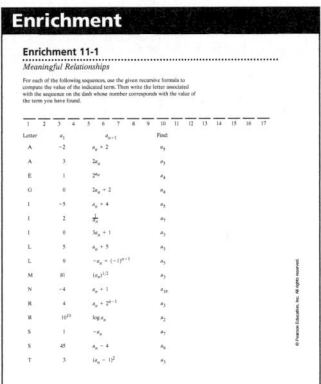

Connections to Precalculus Masters
Chapter 11 Enrichment Topic:
   Area Under a Curve

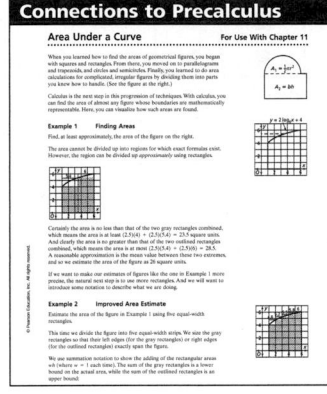

Reading and Math Literacy

Student Edition
- Vocabulary: pp. 587, 629, *plus* in every Lesson Preview
- Reading Math: pp. 594, 603, 606, 607, 609, 617
- Illustrated Glossary: pp. 871–913

Reading and Math Literacy Masters
Chapter 11: pp. 41–44

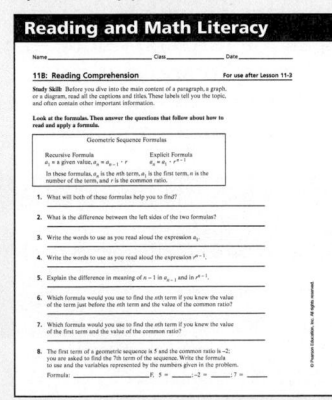

English Learners

Student Edition
- English/Spanish Illustrated Glossary: pp. 871–913

Workbook and Masters
Spanish Practice Workbook: pp. 2–7
Spanish Reading and Math Literacy
   Masters: pp. 41–44

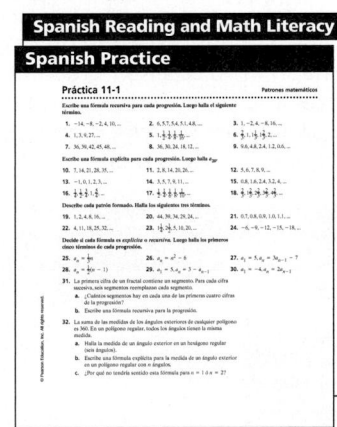

Learning Styles

Student Edition
- Investigation: pp. 588, 600, 607, 613
- Technology: pp. 600, 617, 622, 625
- Writing: pp. 592, 596, 603, 605, 611, 618, 626, 629, 630, 632

Activity Masters
Hands-On Activities: 53, 54
Technology Activities: 35

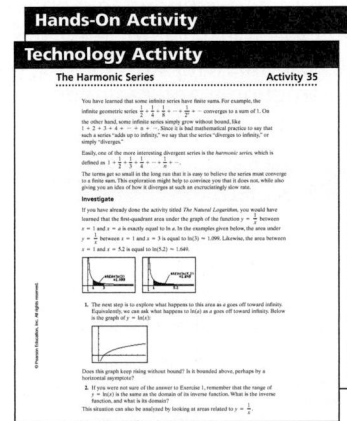

Program Resources

	Teaching Resources in Grab & Go™ Files				Resources for Reaching All Students			Spanish Resources			Transparencies				Presentation Assistant Plus!
	Practice	Reteach	Enrich	Checkpoint Quiz	Reading & Math Literacy	Technology Activities	Hands-On Activities	Practice	Reading & Math Literacy	Checkpoint Quiz	Skills Check	Additional Examples	Answers to Exercises	Lesson Quiz	Prentice Hall Presentation Pro CD-ROM
11-1	■	■	■		■		■	■	■		■	■	■	■	■
11-2	■	■	■		■			■	■		■	■	■	■	■
11-3	■	■	■	■	■			■	■	■	■	■	■	■	■
11-4	■	■	■				■	■	■		■	■	■	■	■
11-5	■	■	■	■	■	■		■	■	■	■	■	■	■	■
11-6	■	■	■					■			■	■	■	■	■
For the chapter	Chapter Tests, Alternative Assessment, Cumulative Review, Cumulative Assessment				Connections to Precalculus Masters			Spanish Chapter Tests, Alternative Assessment, Cumulative Review, Cumulative Assessment			Classroom Aid Transparencies				

Also available for use with the chapter:

 *See page 586C.*

- Practice Workbook
- Solution Key

- For teacher support and access to student Web site materials, use Web Code agk-5500.
- For additional online and technology resources, see below.

Technology

iTEXT Online and on CD-ROM

Complete Interactive Student Text online and on CD-ROM—with instant feedback assessment, tutorial help, dynamic activities, instructional and real-world videos, audio, and additional practice.

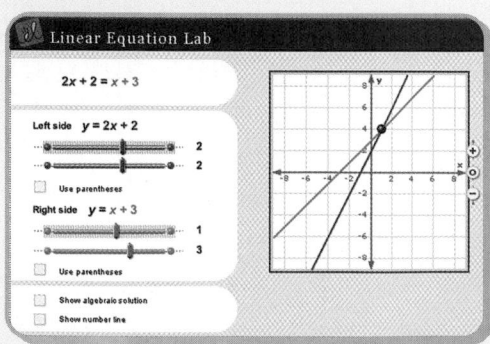

www.PHSchool.com For Students

Use **Web Codes** for easy access to online activities, chapter projects, self-grading lesson quizzes and chapter tests, vocabulary quizzes, updated data sources, graphing calculator procedures, and more.

PH SuccessNet For Teachers

Online lesson planning with built-in state correlations, all the teaching resources, complete reference library, your own calendar and Teacher Web page, professional development, and more.

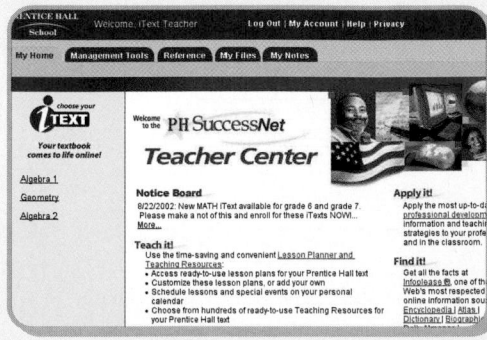

Presentation Assistant Plus!

The Prentice Hall *Presentation Assistant Plus!* provides you with the material you need to teach a lesson from beginning to end. Two easy-to-use formats—Transparencies and CD-ROM—allow you to present a lesson the way you are most comfortable.

 ## Transparencies

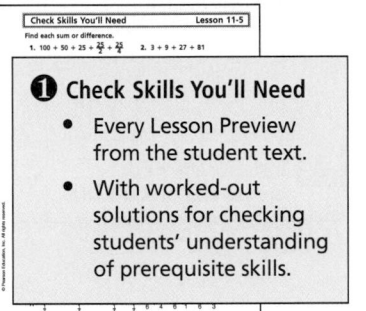

❶ Check Skills You'll Need
- Every Lesson Preview from the student text.
- With worked-out solutions for checking students' understanding of prerequisite skills.

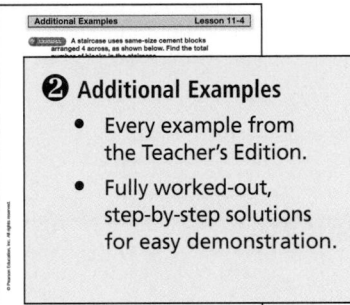

❷ Additional Examples
- Every example from the Teacher's Edition.
- Fully worked-out, step-by-step solutions for easy demonstration.

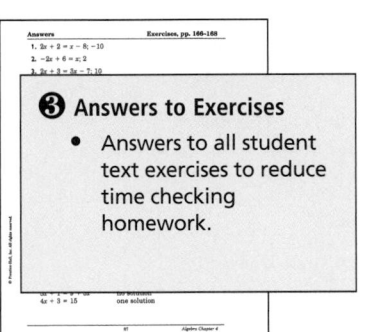

❸ Answers to Exercises
- Answers to all student text exercises to reduce time checking homework.

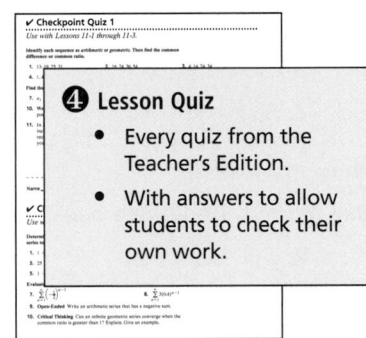

❹ Lesson Quiz
- Every quiz from the Teacher's Edition.
- With answers to allow students to check their own work.

 Throughout the Teacher's Edition, this symbol indicates material that is available on transparency in the Presentation Assistant Plus!

 ## Prentice Hall Presentation Pro CD-ROM

- Includes all Transparencies.
- Conveniently organized by lesson so you can easily ❶ Introduce, ❷ Teach, ❸ Check Homework, and ❹ Assess each lesson.
- Animated examples allow step-by-step instruction at your own pace.
- Easy to edit so you can create custom presentations.

Teaching Chapter 11 Using Presentation Assistant Plus!

	❶ Introduce	❷ Teach	❸ Check Homework	❹ Assess
	Check Skills You'll Need	Additional Examples	Student Edition Answers	Lesson Quiz
11-1	p. 71	pp. 211–212	✔	p. 154
11-2	p. 72	pp. 213–214	✔	p. 155
11-3	p. 73	pp. 215–216	✔	p. 155
11-4	p. 74	pp. 216–218	✔	p. 156
11-5	p. 75	pp. 219–220	✔	p. 157
11-6	p. 76	pp. 221–222	✔	p. 158

 ## Prentice Hall Presentation Pro

CD-ROM with dynamic PowerPoint® presentations for every lesson. Helps you introduce and develop concepts, check homework, and assess progress. Part of Presentation Assistant Plus! *(See above.)*

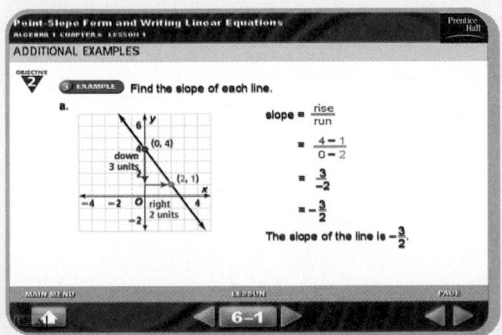

 ## Computer Test Generator

CD-ROM to create practice sheets and tests for course objectives and standardized tests. Includes Instant Chapter Tests™, online testing, and student reports. Part of the PH Assessment System. *(See page 586C.)*

 ## Resource Pro® with Planning Express®

CD-ROM with a lesson planning tool that allows you to import state and local objectives. Includes electronic versions of all the teaching resources.

Sequences and Series

 Diagnosing Readiness

Students will find answers to these exercises in the back of their textbooks.

For intervention, direct students to:

Evaluating Functions
Lesson 2-1: Example 6
Exercises 22–30
Extra Practice, p. 823

Graphing Quadratic Functions
Lesson 5-2: Example 1
Exercises 1–9
Extra Practice, p. 826

Evaluating Radical Expressions
Lesson 7-1: Example 2
Exercises 13–20
Extra Practice, p. 828.

Simplifying Complex Fractions
Lesson 9-5: Example 5
Exercises 22–30
Extra Practice, p. 830

---

page 586 Diagnosing Readiness

7.
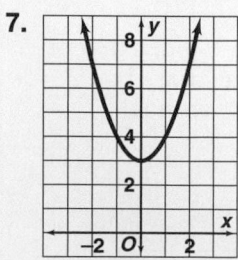

8.
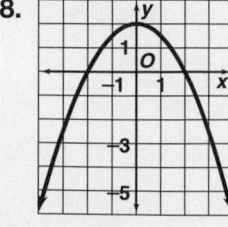

586

Where You've Been

- In Chapter 2, you learned to evaluate functions in function notation.
- In Chapter 5, you learned to use parabolas for graphing quadratic functions.
- In Chapter 7, you learned to evaluate radical expressions.
- In Chapter 9, you learned to simplify complex fractions, which are fractions that have fractions in the numerator or denominator or in both the numerator and denominator.

Diagnosing Readiness   (For help, go to the Lesson in green.)

Instant self-check online and on CD-ROM

Evaluating Functions (Lesson 2-1)

For each function, find $f(1), f(2), f(3)$, and $f(4)$.

1, 6, 11, 16   0.9, 1.1, 1.3, 1.5
1. $f(x) = 2x + 7$ **2.** $f(x) = 5x - 4$ **3.** $f(x) = 0.2x + 0.7$
9, 11, 13, 15
4. $f(x) = -5x + 3$ **5.** $f(x) = 4x - \frac{2}{3}$ **6.** $f(x) = -3x - 9$
$-2, -7, -12, -17$ $3\frac{1}{3}, 7\frac{1}{3}, 11\frac{1}{3}, 15\frac{1}{3}$ $-12, -15, -18, -21$

Graphing Quadratic Functions (Lesson 5-2)

Graph each function.   **7–9. See margin. 10–12. See back of book.**

7. $y = x^2 + 3$ **8.** $y = -\frac{1}{2}x^2 + 2$ **9.** $y = 4x^2 - 1$

10. $y = 2x^2 - 7x + 3$ **11.** $y = -4x^2 + 8x + 5$ **12.** $y = x^2 + 3x + 4$

Evaluating Radical Expressions (Lesson 7-1)

Find each real-number root.

13. $\sqrt{16}$ **4**   **14.** $-\sqrt{16}$ **−4**   **15.** $\sqrt{0.16}$ **0.4**   **16.** $\sqrt{2500}$ **50**

Simplify each radical expression. Use absolute value symbols as needed.

17. $\sqrt{25x^4}$ **$5x^2$**   **18.** $-\sqrt{0.09y^8}$ **$-0.3y^4$**   **19.** $\sqrt{x^6 y^{10}}$ **$x^3 y^5$**   **20.** $\sqrt{121y^{24}}$ **$11y^{12}$**

Simplifying Complex Fractions (Lesson 9-5)

Simplify each complex fraction.

21. $\dfrac{1 - \frac{1}{3}}{\frac{1}{2}}$ **$\frac{4}{3}$**   **22.** $\dfrac{\frac{1}{3} + \frac{1}{6}}{\frac{2}{3}}$ **$\frac{3}{4}$**   **23.** $\dfrac{1}{1 - \frac{2}{5}}$ **$\frac{5}{3}$**   **24.** $\dfrac{1 - \frac{3}{8}}{2 + \frac{1}{4}}$ **$\frac{5}{18}$**

9.
(graph in margin)

Sequences and Series

Chapter 11

Key Vocabulary

- arithmetic mean (p. 595)
- arithmetic sequence (p. 594)
- arithmetic series (p. 608)
- circumscribed rectangles (p. 623)
- common difference (p. 594)
- common ratio (p. 600)
- converge (p. 615)
- diverge (p. 615)
- explicit formula (p. 590)
- geometric mean (p. 602)
- geometric sequence (p. 600)
- geometric series (p. 614)
- inscribed rectangles (p. 623)
- limit (p. 609)
- recursive formula (p. 590)
- sequence (p. 588)
- series (p. 607)
- term (p. 588)

Chapter 11 Overview

This chapter begins to introduce students to sequences and series with a lesson on mathematical patterns. Students are then introduced to arithmetic and geometric series. Finally, students conclude the chapter with a lesson on the area under a curve.

📖 Reading Math
Reading For Problem Solving, p. 606

📖 Vocabulary
A complete list of terms, plus vocabulary exercises, appears in the Chapter Review, p. 629.

📖 Illustrated Glossary
Examples for each vocabulary term, plus definitions in both English and Spanish, appear starting on p. 871.

Test-Taking Strategies
Using Estimation, p. 628

🌐 Real-World Connections
Some of the applications you will find in this chapter are physics (11-1), fund raising (11-2), design (11-3), crafts (11-4), financial planning (11-5), and data analysis (11-6).

💻 www.PHSchool.com
Internet support for this chapter includes:
- Self-grading Vocabulary and Chapter 11 Tests
- Chapter Project
- Chapter Planner
- Chapter 11 Resources

Plus **📱TEXT**

Where You're Going

- In Chapter 11, you will learn to identify and generate arithmetic sequences and geometric sequences.

- You will learn to evaluate arithmetic series and geometric series.

- You will use rectangles to approximate the area under a curve.

 Real-World Connection Applying what you learn, on page 623 you will solve a problem involving the speed of a falcon.

587

Lesson Preview

✓ **Check Skills You'll Need** 📖

Skills Handbook: p. 838

Lesson Resources

📁 **Teaching Resources**
Practice, Reteaching, Enrichment

👥 **Reaching All Students**
Practice Workbook 11-1
Spanish Practice Workbook 11-1
Reading and Math Literacy 11A
Spanish Reading & Literacy 11A
Hands-On Activities 53

⏰ **Presentation Assistant Plus!**
Transparencies
• Check Skills You'll Need 11-1
• Additional Examples 11-1
• Student Edition Answers 11-1
• Lesson Quiz 11-1
PH Presentation Pro CD 11-1

🔷 **ASSESSMENT SYSTEM**

Computer Test Generator CD

💿 **Technology**
Resource Pro® CD-ROM
Computer Test Generator CD
Prentice Hall Presentation Pro CD

💻 **www.PHSchool.com**
Student Site
• Teacher Web Code: agk-5500
• Graphing Calculator,
  Procedure 3
• Self-grading Lesson Quiz
Teacher Center
• Lesson Planner
• Resources

Plus 🔲**TEXT**

11-1

Mathematical Patterns

Lesson Preview

What You'll Learn

OBJECTIVE 1 To identify mathematical patterns

OBJECTIVE 2 To use a formula for finding the *n*th term of a sequence

. . . And Why

To predict the height of a bouncing ball, as in Example 2

✓ **Check Skills You'll Need**   (For help, see Skills Handbook p. 838.)

Find the next two numbers of each pattern. Then write a rule to describe the pattern.   2–6. See back of book.

1. $1, 3, 5, 7, 9, 11, \ldots$ **13, 15; add 2.**

2. $-2, -4, -6, -8, -10, -12, \ldots$

3. $0.2, 1, 5, 25, 125, 625, \ldots$

4. $50, 45, 40, 35, 30, 25, \ldots$

5. $512, 256, 128, 64, 32, 16, \ldots$

6. $2, 5, 8, 11, 14, 17, \ldots$

7. $16, 32, 64, \ldots$ **128, 256; multiply by 2.**

8. $-3, -7, -11, -15, \ldots$
−19, −23; subtract 4.

New Vocabulary   • sequence   • term   • recursive formula   • explicit formula

---

OBJECTIVE 1 **Identifying Mathematical Patterns**

🔲**TEXT** Interactive lesson includes instant self-check, tutorials, and activities.

Investigation: Generating a Pattern

Suppose each student in your math class has a phone conversation with every other member of the class. What is the minimum number of calls required?

Instead of actually making the calls, you can represent telephone conversations by drawing diagrams like the ones below.

1. How many calls are necessary for two people to have a conversation?
1 call

2. How many calls are necessary for everyone to talk to everyone else in a group of three people? In a group of four people?   **3 calls; 6 calls**

3. Use a diagram to find the number of calls needed for five people.
See back of book.

4. **Reasoning** Which of the following formulas can you use to find the pattern for the telephone calls?   **C**

   A. $2n - 3$ **B.** $n(n - 1) - 5$ **C.** $\dfrac{n(n - 1)}{2}$

5. Use the formula from Question 4 to find the number of calls needed for a group of seven students.   **21**

6. How many calls would be needed for your class?   **Check students' work.**

Sometimes steps in a process form a pattern. You can describe some patterns with a **sequence,** or ordered list of numbers. Each number in a sequence is a **term.**

⚡ **Ongoing Assessment and Intervention**

Before the Lesson	**During the Lesson**	**After the Lesson**
Diagnose prerequisite skills using:	**Monitor progress using:**	**Assess knowledge using:**
• Check Skills You'll Need	• Check Understanding	• Lesson Quiz
	• Additional Examples	• Computer Test Generator CD
	• Standardized Test Prep	

When you apply the construction from Example 1 to an equilateral triangle, you form the Koch snowflake.

1 EXAMPLE Generating a Sequence

a. To create one side of the Koch snowflake, replace each ——— with ⌃. Draw the first four figures of the pattern.

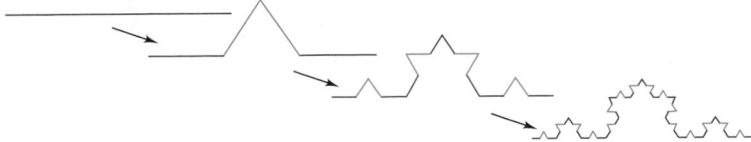

b. Write the number of segments in each figure above as a sequence.

$1, 4, 16, 64, \ldots$

c. Predict the next term of the sequence. Explain your choice.

Each term is 4 times the preceding term. The next term is $64 \cdot 4$, or 256. There will be 256 segments in the next figure in the pattern.

✓ **Check Understanding** ❶ Describe the pattern formed. Find the next three terms.

a. $27, 34, 41, 48, \ldots$
   Add 7; 55, 62, 69.

b. $243, 81, 27, 9, \ldots$
   Divide by 3; 3, 1, $\frac{1}{3}$.

Sometimes you can find the next term in a sequence by using a pattern from the terms that come before it.

2 EXAMPLE Real-World Connection

Physics Suppose you drop a handball from a height of 10 ft. After the ball hits the floor, it rebounds to 85% of its previous height. How high will the ball rebound after its fourth bounce?

Original height of ball: 10 ft →

After 1st bounce: 85% of $10 = 0.85(10) = 8.5$ →

After 2nd bounce: $0.85(8.5) = 7.225$ →

After 3rd bounce: $0.85(7.225) \approx 6.141$ →

After 4th bounce: $0.85(6.141) \approx 5.220$ →

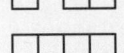

The ball will rebound about 5.2 ft after the fourth bounce.

✓ **Check Understanding** ❷ a. About how high will the ball rebound after the seventh bounce?
   b. After what bounce will the rebound height be less than 2 ft?
   a. 3.2 ft   **b. 10th bounce**

You can use a variable, such as a, with positive integer subscripts to represent the terms in a sequence.

1st term	2nd term	3rd term	...	$n-1$ term	nth term	$n+1$ term	...
↓	↓	↓		↓	↓	↓	
a_1	a_2	a_3	...	a_{n-1}	a_n	a_{n+1}	...

2. Teach

Professional Development

Math Background

Sequences are functions whose domain is usually the set of natural or the set of whole numbers. Sometimes a_n is written $a(n)$.

OBJECTIVE
❶ Teaching Notes

Investigation (Optional)
Teaching Tip

Help students understand that each time a new person is added to the group, the number of new calls will equal the number of people who were already in the group.

1 EXAMPLE Connection to Topology

You may wish to tell students that the Koch snowflake is an example of a *fractal*. Fractals have been the subject of much mathematical research since the mid-twentieth century.

Additional Examples

❶ a. Start with a square with sides 1 unit long. On the right side, add on a square of the same size. Continue adding one square at a time in this way. Draw the first four figures of the pattern.

▭ ▭▭ ▭▭▭

▭▭▭▭

b. Write the number of 1-unit segments in each figure above as a sequence. **4, 7, 10, 13, . . .**
c. Predict the next term of the sequence. Explain your choice. **16; Each term is 3 more than the preceding term.**

❷ Suppose you drop a ball from a height of 100 cm. It bounces back to 80% of its previous height. How high will it go after its fifth bounce? **about 32.8 cm**

👥 Reaching All Students

Below Level Have students working in pairs each create a sequence. Then have students exchange sequences and find the next terms in each other's sequences.	**Advanced Learners** Have students compare the recursive formula (p. 590) with the composition of a function with itself (Chapter 7, p. 393).	**Auditory Learners** See note on page 590. **Tactile Learners** See note on page 591.

3 EXAMPLE Auditory Learners

Ask a volunteer to look up the word *recur* in a dictionary and to read the definition aloud to the class. Have a class discussion about how the definition is related to the adjective recursive.

A **recursive formula** defines the terms in a sequence by relating each term to the ones before it. The pattern in Example 2 was recursive because the height of the ball after each bounce was 85% of its previous height. The recursive formula that describes the ball's height is $a_n = 0.85a_{n-1}$, where $a_1 = 10$.

4 EXAMPLE Alternative Method

To help students visually identify the pattern, have them graph each pair (Length of Side, Perimeter). Ask: *What type of pattern is formed?* **linear** Then, have students find an equation to represent the pattern. $p = 4n$, **where p represents the perimeter of a square whose sides measure n units.** Finally, have students connect this alternative method with the method presented in Example 4.

3 EXAMPLE Using a Recursive Formula

a. Describe the pattern that allows you to find the next term in the sequence $2, 4, 6, 8, 10, \ldots$. Write a recursive formula for the sequence.

The terms of the sequence are the even numbers. Add 2 to a term to find the next term. A recursive formula is $a_n = a_{n-1} + 2$, where $a_1 = 2$.

b. Find the sixth and seventh terms in the sequence.

Since $a_5 = 10$, $a_6 = 10 + 2 = 12$, and $a_7 = 12 + 2 = 14$.

c. Find the value of term a_9 in the sequence.

Term a_9 is the ninth term. $a_9 = a_8 + 2 = (a_7 + 2) + 2 = (14 + 2) + 2 = 18$

✓ **Check Understanding** **3** Find terms a_{11} and a_{15} in the sequence.   **22, 30**

Additional Examples

3 **a.** Describe the pattern that allows you to find the next term in the sequence 2, 6, 18, 54, 162, ... Write a recursive formula for the sequence. **Multiply a term by 3 to get the next term;**
$a_n = 3a_{n-1}$, where $a_1 = 2$
b. Find the sixth and seventh terms in the sequence.   **486, 1458**
c. Find the value of a_{10} in the sequence.   **39,366**

4 The spreadsheet shows the perimeters of regular pentagons with sides from 1 to 4 units long. The numbers in each row form a sequence.

	a1	a2	a3	a4
Length of a Side	1	2	3	4
Perimeter	5	10	15	20

a. For each sequence, find the next term (a_5) and the twentieth term (a_{20}).   **row 2: 5, 20; row 3: 25, 100**
b. Write an explicit formula for each sequence.   **row 2: $a_n = n$; row 3: $a_n = 5n$**

Need Help?

Many explicit formulas are proved by mathematical induction (p. 620).

Sometimes you can find the value of a term of a sequence without knowing the preceding term. Instead, you can use the number of the term to calculate its value. A formula that expresses the *n*th term in terms of *n* is an **explicit formula**.

4 EXAMPLE Real-World Connection

Geometry The spreadsheet below shows the perimeters of squares with sides from 1 to 6 units long. The numbers in each row form a sequence.

	A	B	C	D	E	F	G	H
1		a1	a2	a3	a4	a5	a6	. . .
2	Length of a Side	1	2	3	4	5	6	. . .
3	Perimeter	4	8	12	16	20	24	. . .

a. For each sequence, find the next term (a_7) and the twenty-fifth term (a_{25}).

In the sequence in row 2, each term is the same as its subscript. Therefore, $a_7 = 7$ and $a_{25} = 25$.
In the sequence in row 3, each term is 4 times its subscript. Therefore, $a_7 = 4(7) = 28$ and $a_{25} = 4(25) = 100$.

b. Write an explicit formula for each sequence.

The explicit formula for the sequence in row 2 is $a_n = n$. The explicit formula for the sequence in row 3 is $a_n = 4n$.

✓ **Check Understanding** **4** **a.** Write the first six terms in the sequence showing the areas of the squares in Example 4. Then find a_{20}.   **1, 4, 9, 16, 25, 36; 400**
b. Write an explicit formula for the sequence from part (a). $a_n = n^2$
c. **Critical Thinking** Given the recursive formula $a_n = a_{n-1} + 3$, can you find the fourth term in the sequence? Explain.   **No; a_1 is not given.**

Closure

Ask students to describe two ways that they might use to completely describe the pattern in a sequence of numbers. **Answers may vary. Sample: Study the** pattern and, if possible, write an explicit formula involving an expression in the variable *n* that can be evaluated to find the value of any term a_n. If you cannot do that, describe how the pattern can be used to get from a previous term to the next term.

Practice and Problem Solving

For more practice, see *Extra Practice.*

Ⓐ **Practice by Example**

Examples 1 and 2
(page 589)

1. Subtract 3; 65, 62, 59.

2. Multiply by 2; 128, 256, 512.

Describe each pattern formed. Find the next three terms. 3–9. See back of book.

1. 80, 77, 74, 71, 68, . . .

2. 4, 8, 16, 32, 64, . . .

3. 0, 3, 7, 12, 18, . . .

4. 1, 4, 7, 10, 13, . . .

5. 100, 10, 1, 0.1, 0.01, . . .

6. $\frac{1}{2}, \frac{1}{4}, \frac{1}{8}, \frac{1}{16}, \frac{1}{32}, \ldots$

7. 4, −8, 16, −32, 64, . . .

8. 1, 2, 6, 24, 120, . . .

9. 0, 1, 0, $\frac{1}{3}$, 0, $\frac{1}{5}$, . . .

Fractal Geometry Draw the first four figures of the sequence described.

10.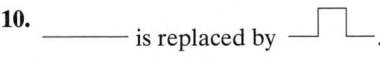

11.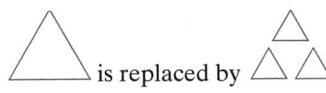

10–11. See back of book.

Example 3
(page 590)

Write a recursive formula for each sequence. Then find the next term.

12. −2, −1, 0, 1, 2, . . .

13. 43, 41, 39, 37, 35, . . .

14. 40, 20, 10, 5, $\frac{5}{2}$, . . .

15. 6, 1, −4, −9, . . .

16. 144, 36, 9, $\frac{9}{4}$, . . .

17. $\frac{1}{2}, \frac{1}{4}, \frac{1}{8}, \frac{1}{16}, \frac{1}{32}, \ldots$

12–20. See margin.

Example 4
(page 590)

Write an explicit formula for each sequence. Then find a_{12}.

18. 4, 5, 6, 7, 8, . . .

19. $\frac{1}{2}, \frac{1}{3}, \frac{1}{4}, \frac{1}{5}, \frac{1}{6}, \ldots$

20. 4, 7, 10, 13, 16, . . .

21. 3, 7, 11, 15, 19, . . .
$a_n = 4n - 1$; 47

22. $-2\frac{1}{2}, -2, -1\frac{1}{2}, -1, \ldots$
$a_n = \frac{n - 6}{2}$; 3

23. 2, 5, 10, 17, 26, . . .
$a_n = n^2 + 1$; 145

Ⓑ **Apply Your Skills**

31. recursive; 340, 323, 306, 289, 272

Decide whether each formula is *explicit* or *recursive*. Then find the first five terms of each sequence. 24–29. See back of book.

24. $a_n = 2a_{n-1} + 3$, where $a_1 = 3$

25. $a_n = \frac{1}{2}(n)(n - 1)$

26. $(n - 5)(n + 5) = a_n$

27. $a_n = -3a_{n-1}$, where $a_1 = -2$

28. $a_n = -4n^2 - 2$

29. $a_n = 2n^2 + 1$

30. $a_n = 5n$ explicit; 5, 10, 15, 20, 25

31. $a_n = a_{n-1} - 17$, where $a_1 = 340$

Real-World 🌐 Connection

Bryan Berg built a 24-ft 4-in. 127-story freestanding house of cards.

🌐 **32. Entertainment** Suppose you are building a tower of cards with levels as displayed below. Complete the table, assuming the pattern continues.

Levels	1	2	3	4	5
Cards Needed	2	7	■	■	■

15 26 40

Find the next two terms in each sequence. Write a formula for the *n*th term. Identify each formula as *explicit* or *recursive*. 33–41. See back of book.

33. 5, 8, 11, 14, 17, . . .

34. 3, 6, 12, 24, 48, . . .

35. 1, 8, 27, 64, 125, . . .

36. 4, 16, 64, 256, 1024, . . .

37. 49, 64, 81, 100, 121, . . .

38. −1, 1, −1, 1, −1, 1, . . .

39. −16, −8, −4, −2, . . .

40. −75, −68, −61, −54, . . .

41. 21, 13, 5, −3, . . .

Lesson 11-1 Mathematical Patterns **591**

Assignment Guide

1 **Objective**
Ⓐ Ⓑ **Core** 1–11, 32, 45–51

2 **Objective**
Ⓐ Ⓑ **Core** 12–31, 33–44
Ⓒ **Extension** 52–57

Standardized Test Prep 58–62

Mixed Review 63–71

Error Prevention

Exercises 12–17 Students may forget to specify the value of a_1. Remind them that a recursive formula always has two parts.

Diversity

Exercise 42 Some students may not be familiar with the idea of counting sheep as a way to induce sleep. Invite a student to explain to the class what it means to count sheep. Ask students to describe techniques they use to help them fall asleep.

Tactile Learners

Exercise 51 Students might use plastic or wooden cubes to model the stacks of boxes.

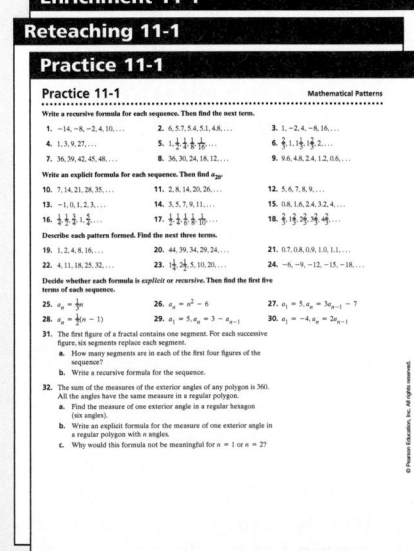

pages 591–593 Exercises

12. $a_n = a_{n-1} + 1, a_1 = -2$; 3

13. $a_n = a_{n-1} - 2, a_1 = 43$; 33

14. $a_n = \frac{a_{n-1}}{2}, a_1 = 40$; $\frac{5}{4}$

15. $a_n = a_{n-1} - 5, a_1 = 6$; −14

16. $a_n = \frac{a_{n-1}}{4}, a_1 = 144$; $\frac{9}{16}$

17. $a_n = a_{n-1} \cdot \frac{1}{2}, a_1 = \frac{1}{2}$; $\frac{1}{64}$

18. $a_n = n + 3$; 15

19. $a_n = \frac{1}{n+1}$; $\frac{1}{13}$

20. $a_n = 3n + 1$; 37

Lesson Quiz 11-1

For Exercises 1 and 2, describe each pattern. Find the next three terms.

1. 5, 15, 25, 35, . . . **Each new term is 10 more than the preceding term; 45, 55, 65**

2. $1, \frac{2}{3}, \frac{4}{9}, \frac{8}{27}, \ldots$ **Each new term is $\frac{2}{3}$ of the preceding term; $\frac{16}{81}, \frac{32}{243}, \frac{64}{729}$**

3. Write a recursive formula for the sequence 7, −1, −9, −17, ... Then find the next term. $a_n = a_{n-1} - 8$, where $a_1 = 7$; −25

4. Write an explicit formula for the sequence $1, \frac{1}{4}, \frac{1}{9}, \frac{1}{16}, \ldots$. Then find a_{15}. $a_n = \frac{1}{n^2}$; $\frac{1}{225}$

5. A recursive formula for a sequence is $a_n = a_{n-1} + 2n$, where $a_1 = 1$. Write the first five terms of the sequence. **1, 5, 11, 19, 29**

Alternative Assessment

Have students work individually. Ask students to select two of the sequences from Exercises 12–17. Then, ask students to write an explicit formula for each sequence they picked. Ask them to show work verifying that the explicit formulas generate the same sequences as those given in the exercises. Then ask students to select two sequences from Exercises 18–23 and write a recursive formula for each sequence. Ask them to show work verifying that the recursive formulas generate the same sequences as those given in the exercises.

pages 591–593 Exercises

43. **Answers may vary. Sample: A recursive formula requires that the previous term be known to find a given term. An explicit formula only requires the number of the term.**

44a–c. Answers may vary. Sample:

a. 1, −2, 4, −8...

b. $a_n = -2(a_{n-1})$; $a_n = (-2)^{n-1}$

45. 26, 677; 458, 330; 2.1×10^{11}

46. 24, 78, 240, 726

56a. $a_n = a_{n-1} + 5$, $a_1 = 25$; $a_n = 20 + 5n$

---

42. Suppose the cartoon at the right included one sheep to the left and another sheep to the right of the three shown. What "names" would you give these sheep? a_{n-2}, a_{n+2}

43. **Writing** Explain the difference between a recursive formula and an explicit formula. **See margin.**

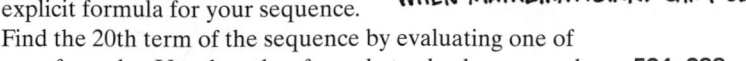

WHEN MATHEMATICIANS CAN'T SLEEP

44. a. **Open-Ended** Write four terms of a sequence of numbers that you can describe both recursively and explicitly.

b. Write a recursive formula and an explicit formula for your sequence.

c. Find the 20th term of the sequence by evaluating one of your formulas. Use the other formula to check your work. **−524, 288**

Use the given rule to write the 4th, 5th, 6th, and 7th terms of each sequence.

45. $a_1 = -1, a_n = (a_{n-1})^2 + 1$

46. $a_1 = -2, a_n = 3(a_{n-1} + 2)$

47. $a_n = (n + 1)^2$ **25, 36, 49, 64**

48. $a_n = 2(n - 1)^3$ **54, 128, 250, 432**

49. $a_n = \frac{n^2}{n + 1}$ **$\frac{16}{5}, \frac{25}{6}, \frac{36}{7}, \frac{49}{8}$**

50. $a_n = \frac{n + 1}{n + 2}$ **$\frac{5}{6}, \frac{6}{7}, \frac{7}{8}, \frac{8}{9}$**

51. **Geometry** Suppose you are stacking boxes in levels that form squares. The numbers of boxes in successive levels form a sequence. The figure at the left shows the top four levels as viewed from above. **25 boxes**

a. How many boxes of equal size would you need for the next lower level?

b. How many boxes of equal size would you need to add three levels? **110 boxes**

c. Suppose you are stacking a total of 285 boxes. How many levels will you have? **9 levels**

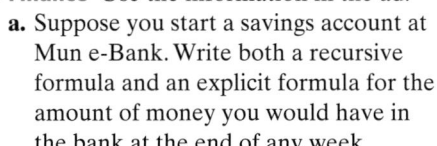 **Challenge**

Use each recursive formula to write an explicit formula for the sequence.

52. $a_1 = 10, a_n = 2a_{n-1}$ $a_n = 10 \cdot 2^n$

53. $a_1 = -5, a_n = a_{n-1} - 1$ $a_n = -n - 4$

54. $a_1 = -2, a_n = \frac{1}{2}a_{n-1}$ $a_n = -2 \cdot \left(\frac{1}{2}\right)^{n-1}$

55. $a_1 = 1, a_n = a_{n-1} + 4$ $a_n = 1 + 4(n - 1)$

56. **Finance** Use the information in the ad.

a. Suppose you start a savings account at Mun e-Bank. Write both a recursive formula and an explicit formula for the amount of money you would have in the bank at the end of any week.

b. How much money would you have in the bank after four weeks? **$40**

c. Assume the bank pays interest every four weeks. To calculate your interest, multiply the balance at the end of the four weeks by 0.005. Then add that much to your account on the last day of the four-week period. Write a recursive formula for the amount of money you have after each interest payment. $a_n = (a_{n-1} + \$20) \cdot 1.005, a_1 = \$40.20$

d. **Critical Thinking** What is the bank's annual interest rate? **6.5%**

Mun e-Bank

is offering a **GREAT** deal right now!

Start a savings club account by depositing only $25 today and $5 a week starting next week.

See how easy it is to save!

57a. 15, 21

b. $a_n = a_{n-1} + n$, $a_1 = 1$

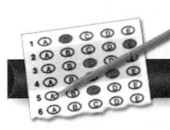

57. **Geometry** The triangular numbers form a sequence. The diagram represents the first three triangular numbers: 1, 3, and 6.

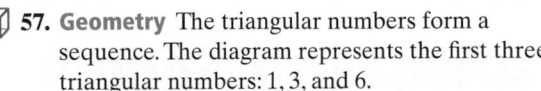

   a. Find the fifth and sixth triangular numbers. $n = 1$ $n = 2$ $n = 3$
   b. Write a recursive formula for the nth triangular number.
   c. Is the explicit formula $a_n = \frac{1}{2}(n^2 + n)$ the correct formula for this sequence? How do you know?   **Yes; the formula yields the same value as the recursive formula.**

Standardized Test Prep

Multiple Choice

58. What is the difference between the third term in the sequence whose recursive formula is $a_1 = -5$, $a_n = 2a_{n-1} + 1$ and the third term in the sequence whose recursive formula is $a_1 = -3$, $a_n = -a_{n-1} + 3$?   **B**
   A. 2   **B.** 14   **C.** 20   **D.** 32

59. What is a recursive formula for the sequence whose explicit formula is $a_n = (n + 1)^2$?   **G**

   F. $a_1 = 1$, $a_n = (a_{n-1} + 1)^2$ **G.** $a_1 = 4$, $a_n = \left(\sqrt{a_{n-1}} + 1\right)^2$

   H. $a_1 = n$, $a_n = a_{n-1} + n$ **I.** $a_1 = n^2$, $a_n = (a_{n-1})^2 + 1$

Use the figure below for Exercises 60–62.

62. [2] $a_n = a_{n-1} + n^2$, $a_1 = 1$; **Each term consists of the previous term added to the square of the number of the term.**

[1] **incorrect formula OR no explanation OR incorrect explanation**

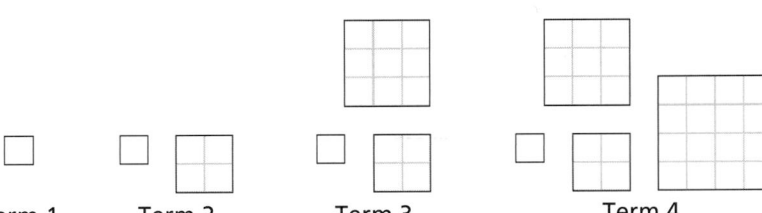

Term 1   Term 2   Term 3   Term 4

60. How many 1×1 squares are in the sixth term of the sequence?   **C**
   A. 21   **B.** 36   **C.** 91   **D.** 441

61. Which expressions represent the first three terms of the sequence?   **I**
   F. $1^2, 2^2, 3^2, \ldots$ **G.** $1, 1 + 2, 1 + 2 + 3, \ldots$
   H. $1^2, (1 + 2)^2, (1 + 2 + 3)^2, \ldots$ **I.** $1^2, 1^2 + 2^2, 1^2 + 2^2 + 3^2, \ldots$

Short Response

62. Write a recursive formula for the sequence in the figure above. Explain your reasoning.   **See left.**

Mixed Review

64. $\frac{(x + 1)^2}{36} + \frac{(y + 2)^2}{36} = 1$

Lesson 10-6

The graph of each equation is translated 2 units left and 3 units down. Write each new equation.

63. $(x + 2)^2 + (y - 1)^2 = 5$ 64. $\frac{(x - 1)^2}{36} + \frac{(y - 1)^2}{36} = 1$
   $(x + 4)^2 + (y + 2)^2 = 5$

Lesson 9-1

Each point is from an inverse variation. Write an equation to model the data.

68. $xy = 27$

72. $xy = 100$

65. $(1, 20)$ $xy = 20$ 66. $(5, 2)$ $xy = 10$ 67. $(9, 13)$ $xy = 117$ 68. $(-3, -9)$

69. $(2, 5)$ $xy = 10$ 70. $(-6, -12)$ $xy = 72$ 71. $\left(\frac{1}{2}, -\frac{1}{2}\right)$ $xy = -\frac{1}{4}$ 72. $(-10, -10)$

Standardized Test Prep

☐ **Resources**
For additional practice with a variety of test item formats:
• Standardized Test Prep, p. 633
• Test-Taking Strategies, p. 628
• Test-Taking Strategies with Transparencies

Exercise 59 Two of the answer choices (H and I) can be eliminated immediately because a_1 is not a specific number. To select the correct choice from the two that remain, use the explicit formula to find the value of a_1.

✓ **Check Skills You'll Need**

Look for a Pattern
Skills Handbook: p. 838,
Exercises 1–8

Lesson Resources

📁 **Teaching Resources**
Practice, Reteaching, Enrichment

👥 **Reaching All Students**
Practice Workbook 11-2
Spanish Practice Workbook 11-2

⏱ **Presentation Assistant Plus!**
Transparencies
• Check Skills You'll Need 11-2
• Additional Examples 11-2
• Student Edition Answers 11-2
• Lesson Quiz 11-2
PH Presentation Pro CD 11-2

 **ASSESSMENT** *SYSTEM*

Computer Test Generator CD

💿 **Technology**
Resource Pro® CD-ROM
Computer Test Generator CD
Prentice Hall Presentation Pro CD

💻 **www.PHSchool.com**
Student Site
• Teacher Web Code: agk-5500
• Self-grading Lesson Quiz
Teacher Center
• Lesson Planner
• Resources

Plus

11-2 Arithmetic Sequences

Lesson Preview

What You'll Learn

OBJECTIVE 1 To identify and generate arithmetic sequences

. . . And Why

To determine the amount of money raised during a fundraiser, as in Example 2

✓ **Check Skills You'll Need** (For help, see Skills Handbook p. 838)

Describe the pattern in each sequence. Use at least one of the words *add*, *subtract*, or *difference*.

1. $10, 8, 6, 4, 2, 0, \ldots$ **Subtract 2.**

2. $100, 117, 134, 151, 168, \ldots$ **Add 17.**

3. $\frac{5}{7}, \frac{8}{7}, \frac{11}{7}, 2, \ldots$ **Add $\frac{3}{7}$.**

4. $-\frac{1}{4}, -\frac{1}{2}, -\frac{3}{4}, -1, -\frac{5}{4}, -\frac{3}{2}, \ldots$ **Subtract $\frac{1}{4}$.**

New Vocabulary • arithmetic sequence • common difference • arithmetic mean

---

OBJECTIVE 1

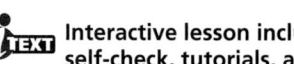 Interactive lesson includes instant self-check, tutorials, and activities.

Identifying and Generating Arithmetic Sequences

📖 **Reading Math**

The stress in the noun *arithmetic* is on the second syllable (uh RITH muh tik). The stress in the adjective *arithmetic* is on the third syllable (ar ith MET ik).

In an **arithmetic sequence,** the difference between consecutive terms is constant. This difference is called the **common difference.** The common difference can be positive (the terms of the sequence are increasing in value) or negative (the terms of the sequence are decreasing in value).

1 EXAMPLE **Identifying an Arithmetic Sequence**

Is the given sequence arithmetic?

a. $2, 4, 8, 16, \ldots$

$$2, \quad 4, \quad 8, \quad 16, \ldots$$
$$+2 \quad\quad +4 \quad\quad +8$$
$$4 - 2 = 2 \quad 8 - 4 = 4 \quad 16 - 8 = 8$$

There is no common difference. This is *not* an arithmetic sequence.

b. the golf ball pattern at the right

$$6, \quad 12, \quad 18, \ldots$$
$$+6 \quad\quad +6$$
$$12 - 6 = 6 \quad 18 - 12 = 6$$

The common difference is 6. The dots on the golf ball form an arithmetic sequence.

✓ **Check Understanding** **1** Is the given sequence arithmetic? If so, identify the common difference.
a. $2, 5, 7, 12, \ldots$ **b.** $48, 45, 42, 39, \ldots$
no **yes; −3**

You can use an explicit formula to find the value of the *n*th term of an arithmetic sequence when the previous term is unknown.

---

594 Chapter 11 Sequences and Series

 Ongoing Assessment and Intervention

Before the Lesson	During the Lesson	After the Lesson
Diagnose prerequisite skills using:	**Monitor progress using:**	**Assess knowledge using:**
• Check Skills You'll Need	• Check Understanding	• Lesson Quiz
	• Additional Examples	• Computer Test Generator CD
	• Standardized Test Prep	

Property	Arithmetic Sequence Formulas
Recursive Formula	**Explicit Formula**

$a_1 = $ a given value, $a_n = a_{n-1} + d$ $a_n = a_1 + (n-1)d$

In these formulas, a_n is the nth term, a_1 is the first term, n is the number of the term, and d is the common difference.

Real-World Connection

The AIDSRide raises money for AIDS services in locations across the United States.

2 EXAMPLE Real-World Connection

Fund-Raising Suppose you participate in a bike-a-thon for charity. The charity starts with $1100 in donations. Each participant must raise at least $35 in pledges. What is the minimum amount of money raised if there are 75 participants?

Find the 76th term of the sequence 1100, 1135, 1170, . . .

$a_n = a_1 + (n-1)d$	**Use the explicit formula.**
$a_{76} = 1100 + (76-1)(35)$	**Substitute $a_1 = 1100$, $n = 76$, and $d = 35$.**
$= 1100 + (75)(35)$	**Subtract within parentheses.**
$= 3725$	**Simplify.**

● With 75 participants, the bike-a-thon will raise a minimum of $3725.

 **Check Understanding**

2a. The first term in the sequence, 1100, was the amount of money with *no* participants, so there is one more term than the number of participants.

2 a. **Critical Thinking** In Example 2, why find the value of the 76th term, not the 75th term?
   b. Use the explicit formula to find the 25th term in the sequence 5, 11, 17, 23, 29, . . .
   149

The **arithmetic mean** of any two numbers is the average of the two numbers.

$$\text{arithmetic mean} = \frac{\text{sum of two numbers}}{2}$$

For any three sequential terms in an arithmetic sequence, the middle term is the arithmetic mean of the first and third terms.

Graphs of arithmetic sequences are linear. Two terms of an arithmetic sequence and their arithmetic mean lie on the same line.

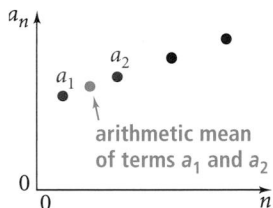
arithmetic mean of terms a_1 and a_2

You can use the arithmetic mean to find a missing term of an arithmetic sequence.

3 EXAMPLE Using the Arithmetic Mean

Find the missing term of the arithmetic sequence 84, ■, 110.

$\text{arithmetic mean} = \frac{84 + 110}{2}$	**Write the average.**
$= 97$	**Simplify.**

3b. $\frac{a_6 + a_7}{2}$

● The missing term is 97.

Check Understanding

3 a. Find the missing term of the arithmetic sequence 24, ■, 57. **40.5**
   b. Write an expression for the arithmetic mean of a_6 and a_7.

Reaching All Students

Below Level Have students list sequences that they already know, and identify the common differences.	**Advanced Learners** Have students find examples of sequences that are neither arithmetic nor geometric. One example is the Fibonacci sequence.	**Inclusion** See note on page 595. **Error Prevention** See note on page 596.

2. Teach

Professional Development

Math Background

An arithmetic sequence is a special case of a linear function. The domain is the set of natural numbers.

OBJECTIVE
1 Teaching Notes

1 EXAMPLE Inclusion

Students with vision problems may have difficulty counting the "dimples" on the golf ball. Draw the pattern for them using dots on a large sheet of paper.

Additional Examples

1 Is the given sequence arithmetic?
a. 7, 10, 13, 16, . . . **yes**
b. the sequence of dots in the "triangles" shown below **no**

2 Suppose you have already saved $75 toward the purchase of a new CD player and speakers. You plan to save at least $12 a week from money you earn at a part-time job. In all, what is the minimum amount you will have after 26 weeks? **$387**

3 Find the missing term of the arithmetic sequence 50, ■, 92. **71**

Closure

Ask students how they can write an explicit formula and a recursive formula for an arithmetic sequence with first term a_1 and common difference d. **Answers may vary. Sample: In an arithmetic sequence, you can add the common difference to a term to get to the next term. To get to the nth term, you can start with a_1 and add d a total of $n - 1$ times. So $a_n = a_1 + (n-1)d$. This is an explicit formula. Using $a_n = a_{n-1} + d$ and $a_1 = $ (given number), you have a recursive formula.**

Assignment Guide

1 Objective
Ⓐ Ⓑ Core 1–74
Ⓒ Extension 75–86

Standardized Test Prep 87–92

Mixed Review 93–101

Error Prevention

Exercises 1–10 When students are deciding whether a sequence is an arithmetic sequence, they should be careful to subtract each term from the term that immediately succeeds it. Subtracting terms from the terms that preceed them will give the wrong common difference for any sequence that is arithmetic.

Technology Tip

Exercise 44 There are several ways to generate arithmetic sequences with a graphing calculator. You may want to suggest that students explore generating sequences with the Table feature, sequence mode, and the seq(feature on the LIST OPS menu.

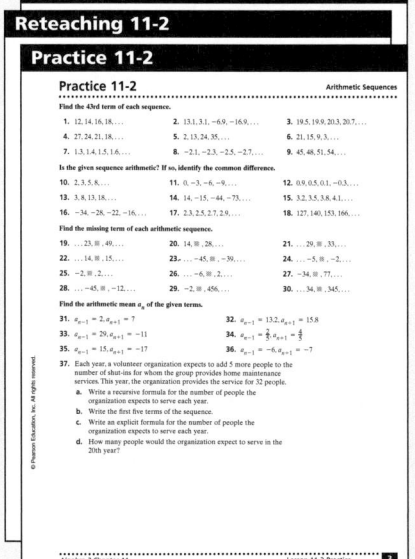

EXERCISES

For more practice, see *Extra Practice*.

Practice and Problem Solving

Ⓐ **Practice by Example**

Example 1
(page 594)

Is the given sequence arithmetic? If so, identify the common difference.

1. $1, 4, 9, 16, \ldots$ **no**   **2.** $10, 20, 30, 40, \ldots$ **yes; 10**

3. $1, 1, 2, 3, 5, 8, \ldots$ **no**   **4.** $0, 1, 3, 6, 10, \ldots$ **no**

5. $-21, -18, -15, -12, \ldots$ **yes; 3**   **6.** $97, 86, 75, 64, \ldots$ **yes; −11**

7. $3, 7, 11, 15, \ldots$ **yes; 4**   **8.** $100, 10, 1, 0.1, \ldots$ **no**

9. $\frac{1}{2}, \frac{1}{4}, \frac{1}{8}, \frac{1}{16}, \ldots$ **no**   **10.** $-5, 5, -5, 5, -5, \ldots$ **no**

Example 2
(page 595)

Find the 32nd term of each sequence.

11. $34, 37, 40, 43, \ldots$ **127**   **12.** $-9, -8.7, -8.4, \ldots$ **0.3**

13. $0.1, 0.5, 0.9, 1.3, \ldots$ **12.5**   **14.** $0.0023, 0.0025, 0.0027, \ldots$ **0.0085**

15. $101, 105, 109, 113, \ldots$ **225**   **16.** $213, 201, 189, 177, \ldots$ **−159**

17. $3, 1, -1, -3, \ldots$ **−59**   **18.** $23, 30, 37, 44, \ldots$ **240**

19. $9, 4, -1, -6, -11, \ldots$ **−146**   **20.** $13, 17, 21, 25, \ldots$ **137**

Example 3
(page 595)

Find the missing term of each arithmetic sequence.

21. $-16, \blacksquare, 1, \ldots$ **−7.5**   **22.** $14, \blacksquare, 28, \ldots$ **21**

23. $\ldots 5, \blacksquare, 21, \ldots$ **13**   **24.** $\frac{13}{2}, \blacksquare, \frac{51}{2}, \ldots$ **16**

25. $101, \blacksquare, -115, \ldots$ **−7**   **26.** $203, \blacksquare, 1117, \ldots$ **660**

27. $25, \blacksquare, -10, \ldots$ **7.5**   **28.** $\ldots 65, \blacksquare, -60, \ldots$ **2.5**

29. $\ldots a_{10}, \blacksquare, a_{12}, \ldots$ **a_{11}**   **30.** $\ldots 99, \blacksquare, 66, \ldots$ **82.5**

Ⓑ **Apply Your Skills**

Find the arithmetic mean a_n of the given terms.

31. $a_{n-1} = 7, a_{n+1} = 1$ **4**   **32.** $a_{n-1} = 4, a_{n+1} = -3$ **$\frac{1}{2}$**

33. $a_{n-1} = 21, a_{n+1} = 5$ **13**   **34.** $a_{n-1} = 100, a_{n+1} = 140$ **120**

35. $a_{n-1} = -18, a_{n+1} = -21$ **−19.5**   **36.** $a_{n-1} = 0.3, a_{n+1} = 1.9$ **1.1**

37. $a_{n-1} = 9, a_{n+1} = -11$ **−1**   **38.** $a_{n-1} = \frac{3}{5}, a_{n+1} = 1$ **$\frac{4}{5}$**

39. $a_{n-1} = r, a_{n+1} = s$ **$\frac{r+s}{2}$**   **40.** $a_{n-1} = r, a_{n+1} = r + s$ **$\frac{2r+s}{2}$**

41. $a_{n-1} = -2x, a_{n+1} = 2x$ **0**   **42.** $a_{n-1} = x + 3, a_{n+1} = 3x - 1$ **$2x + 1$**

43. The student assumed that the sequence was $a_n = 2^{n-1}$. However, $a_1 = 2^0 = 1$, not 0 as given in the problem.

43. Error Analysis A student claims that the next term of the arithmetic sequence $0, 2, 4, \ldots$ is 8. What error did the student make? **See left.**

 44. a. Open-Ended Use your calculator to generate an arithmetic sequence with a common difference of -7. How could you use a calculator to find the 6th term? The 8th term? The 20th term? **a–b. See margin.**

    b. Critical Thinking Explain how your answer to part (a) relates to the explicit formula $a_n = a_1 + (n-1)d$.

45. Writing Describe some advantages and some disadvantages of a recursive formula and an explicit formula. **See margin pp. 596–597.**

pages 596–598 **Exercises**

44a. Answers may vary. Sample: 25, 18, 11, 4, −3, −10…; to find the *n*th term, multiply $n - 1$ times (-7) and add to a_1.

b. Answers may vary. Sample: Start with the first term and continue to subtract 7 for each term. For each term, you subtract 7*x* (term number −1) from the first term.

45. Answers may vary. Sample: An advantage of a recursive formula is that only the preceding term must be known to find the next term; a disadvantage is that many calculations

Find the 17th term of each sequence.

46. $a_{16} = 18, d = 5$ **23**

47. $a_{16} = 18, d = -3$ **15**

48. $a_{16} = 18, d = \frac{1}{2}$ **18.5**

49. $a_{18} = 18, d = -4$ **22**

50. $a_{18} = 18, d = 12$ **6**

51. $a_{18} = 18, d = -11$ **29**

Write an explicit and a recursive formula for each sequence. **52–61. See margin.**

52. $2, 4, 6, 8, 10, \ldots$

53. $0, 6, 12, 18, 24, \ldots$

54. $-5, -4, -3, -2, -1, \ldots$

55. $-4, -8, -12, -16, -20, \ldots$

56. $-2, 5, 12, 19, 26, 33, \ldots$

57. $27, 15, 3, -9, -21, \ldots$

58. $-5, -3.5, -2, -0.5, 1, \ldots$

59. $-32, -20, -8, 4, 16, \ldots$

60. $1, 1\frac{1}{3}, 1\frac{2}{3}, 2, \ldots$

61. $0, \frac{1}{8}, \frac{1}{4}, \frac{3}{8}, \ldots$

 **62. Transportation** Suppose a trolley stops at a certain intersection every 14 min. The first trolley of the day gets to the stop at 6:43 A.M. How long do you have to wait for a trolley if you get to the stop at 8:15 A.M.? At 3:20 P.M.?   **6 min; 1 min**

Find the missing terms of each arithmetic sequence. (*Hint:* The arithmetic mean of the first and fifth terms is the third term.)

63. $2, \blacksquare, \blacksquare, \blacksquare, -22, \ldots$ **−4, −10, −16**

64. $10, \blacksquare, \blacksquare, \blacksquare, -11.6, \ldots$ **4.6, −0.8, −6.2**

65. $1, \blacksquare, \blacksquare, \blacksquare, -35, \ldots$ **−8, −17, −26**

66. $\ldots \frac{13}{5}, \blacksquare, \blacksquare, \blacksquare, \frac{37}{5}, \ldots$ $\frac{19}{5}, 5, \frac{31}{5}$

67. $17, \blacksquare, \blacksquare, \blacksquare, 17, \ldots$ **17, 17, 17**

68. $660, \blacksquare, \blacksquare, \blacksquare, 744, \ldots$ **681, 702, 723**

69. $\ldots -17, \blacksquare, \blacksquare, \blacksquare, 1, \ldots$ **−12.5, −8, −3.5**

70. $\ldots a + 1, \blacksquare, \blacksquare, \blacksquare, a + 17, \ldots$ **a + 5, a + 9, a + 13**

 **71. Savings** In February you start a holiday savings account with a deposit of $20. You increase each monthly deposit by five dollars until the end of the year.   **a–b. See margin.**
   a. Write the amount in the account after each deposit.
   b. Write a recursive formula for the sequence of balances.
   c. How much money will you have saved by the end of the year?   **$495**

Graph the arithmetic sequence generated by each formula over the domain $1 \le n \le 10$.   **72–73. See back of book.**

72. $a_1 = -60, a_n = a_{n-1} + 9$

73. $a_n = 50 - 7n$

74. Critical Thinking Suppose you turn the water on in an empty bathtub with vertical sides. After 20 s, the water has reached a level of 1.15 in. You then leave the room. You want to turn the water off when the level in the bathtub is 8.5 in. How many minutes later should you return? (*Hint:* Begin by identifying two terms of an arithmetic sequence.)   **2.46 min or 2 min 28 s**

C Challenge

75. The arithmetic mean of two terms in an arithmetic sequence is 42. One term is 30. Find the other term.   **54**

76. The arithmetic mean of two terms in an arithmetic sequence is −6. One term is −20. Find the other term.   **8**

77. In an arithmetic sequence with $a_1 = 4$ and $d = 9$, which term is 184?   **21st term**

78. In an arithmetic sequence with $a_1 = 2$ and $d = -2$, which term is −82?   **43rd term**

Real-World Connection

San Francisco's historic cable cars move by gripping and releasing a moving steel cable under the street.

may be required to find a term. An advantage of an explicit formula is that it is easy to find any term.

52. $a_n = 2 + 2(n - 1)$, $a_n = a_{n-1} + 2, a_1 = 2$

53. $a_n = 0 + 6(n - 1)$, $a_n = a_{n-1} + 6, a_1 = 0$

54. $a_n = -5 + 1(n - 1)$, $a_n = a_{n-1} + 1, a_1 = -5$

55. $a_n = -4 - 4(n - 1)$, $a_n = a_{n-1} - 4, a_1 = -4$

56. $a_n = -2 + (n - 1)7$; $a_n = a_{n-1} + 7, a_1 = -2$

57. $a_n = 27 - (n - 1)12$; $a_n = a_{n-1} - 12, a_1 = 27$

58. $a_n = -5 + (n - 1)1.5$; $a_n = a_{n-1} + 1.5, a_1 = -5$

59. $a_n = -32 + (n - 1)12$; $a_n = a_{n-1} + 12$, $a_1 = -32$

60. $a_n = 1 + (n - 1)\frac{1}{3}$; $a_n = a_{n-1} + \frac{1}{3}, a_1 = 1$

61. $a_n = \frac{1}{8}(n - 1)$; $a_n = a_{n-1} + \frac{1}{8}, a_1 = 0$

71a. $20, $45, $75, $110, $150, $195, $245, $300, $360, $425, $495

b. $a_n = a_{n-1} + \$20 + \$5(n - 1), a_1 = \$20$

597

 **Resources**

For additional practice with a variety of test item formats:
- Standardized Test Prep, p. 633
- Test-Taking Strategies, p. 628
- Test-Taking Strategies with Transparencies

Exercise 87 One way to see that B is the correct answer choice is to note that the common difference is 10. Every term of the sequence will therefore have 1 as its final digit. But 33 ends with the digit 3.

pages 596–598 Exercises

91. [2] The third term, 31, is the mean of the first and fifth terms. The second term, 23, is the mean of the first and third terms. The fourth term, 39, is the mean of the third and fifth terms.

[1] incomplete explanation OR incorrect term values

92. [4] 696; $a_2 - a_1 = 10 - 3 = 7$, so the common difference is 7. Use $a_1 = 3$, $d = 7$, and $n = 100$ in the formula $a_n = a_1 + (n - 1)d$ to find a_{100}.

[3] explanation correct, but computational error

[2] incomplete explanation

[1] correct number, but no explanation

---

79. $a_1 = -1$, $d = 3$

80. $a_1 = -4$, $d = 4$

81. $a_1 = 52$, $d = -10$

82. $a_1 = -21\frac{1}{4}$, $d = 4\frac{1}{4}$

83. $a_1 = -100.5$, $d = 22$

84. $a_1 = -9$, $d = 2.2$

Given two terms of each arithmetic sequence, find a_1 and d. See left.

79. $a_3 = 5$ and $a_5 = 11$

80. $a_4 = 8$ and $a_7 = 20$

81. $a_3 = 32$ and $a_7 = -8$

82. $a_{10} = 17$ and $a_{14} = 34$

83. $a_4 = -34.5$ and $a_5 = -12.5$

84. $a_4 = -2.4$ and $a_6 = 2$

Find the indicated term of each arithmetic series.

85. $a_1 = k$, $d = k + 4$; a_9 **9k + 32**

86. $a_1 = k + 7$, $d = 2k - 5$; a_{11} **21k − 43**

Standardized Test Prep

Multiple Choice

87. Which arithmetic sequence DOES NOT include the term 33? **B**
A. 1, 5, 9, 13, . . .   B. 1, 11, 21, . . .
C. 3, 9, 15, . . .   D. 85, 72, 59, . . .

88. Which arithmetic sequence includes the term 27? **I**
I. $a_1 = 7$, $a_n = a_{n-1} + 5$ II. $a_n = 3 + (n - 1)4$ III. $a_n = 57 - 6n$
F. I only   G. I and II only   H. II and III only   I. I, II, and III

Take It to the NET
Online lesson quiz at
www.PHSchool.com
Web Code: aga-1102

89. The arithmetic mean of the monthly salaries of two people is $2955. One person earns $2760 per month. What is the monthly salary of the other person? **B**
A. $2857.50   B. $3150   C. $5520   D. $5715

90. What is the 30th term of the sequence 7, 16, 25, 34, . . . ? **H**
F. 277   G. 270   H. 268   I. 261

Short Response

91. Explain how to use the arithmetic mean to find the missing terms in the arithmetic sequence 15, ■, ■, ■, 47, . . . **See margin.**

Extended Response

92. Find the 100th term of the arithmetic sequence 3, 10, 17, 24, 31, . . . Explain your steps. **See margin.**

Mixed Review

Lesson 11-1

Decide whether each formula is *explicit* or *recursive*. Then find the first five terms of each sequence.

93. recursive;
−2, −7, −12, −17, −22

93. $a_1 = -2$, $a_n = a_{n-1} - 5$

94. $a_n = 3n(n + 1)$ explicit; 6, 18, 36, 60, 90

95. $a_n = n^2 - 1$ explicit; 0, 3, 8, 15, 24

96. $a_1 = -121$, $a_n = a_{n-1} + 13$
recursive;
−121, −108, −95, −82, −69

Lesson 10-6

Find the foci of each ellipse.

98. $(-4\sqrt{2}, 0)$ and $(4\sqrt{2}, 0)$

97. $\frac{x^2}{4} + \frac{y^2}{9} = 1$ $(0, -\sqrt{5})$ and $(0, \sqrt{5})$

98. $\frac{x^2}{36} + \frac{y^2}{4} = 1$ **See left.**

99. $\frac{(x - 1)^2}{121} + \frac{y^2}{100} = 1$
$(1 - \sqrt{21}, 0)$ and $(1 + \sqrt{21}, 0)$

100. $\frac{(x - 1)^2}{64} + \frac{(y - 3)^2}{25} = 1$
$(1 + \sqrt{39}, 3)$ and $(1 - \sqrt{39}, 3)$

Lesson 7-2 **101. Geometry** The formula for volume V of a sphere with radius r is $V = \frac{4}{3}\pi r^3$. Find the radius of a sphere as a function of its volume. Rationalize the denominator. $r = \frac{\sqrt[3]{6\pi^2 V}}{2\pi}$

The Fibonacci Sequence

FOR USE WITH LESSON 11-2

One famous mathematical sequence is the Fibonacci sequence. You can find each term of the sequence using addition, but the sequence is not arithmetic.

EXAMPLE **Generating the Fibonacci Sequence**

The recursive formula for the Fibonacci sequence is $F_n = F_{n-2} + F_{n-1}$, with $F_1 = 1$ and $F_2 = 1$. Use the formula to generate the first five terms of the sequence.

$F_1 = 1$

$F_2 = 1$

$F_3 = F_1 + F_2 = 1 + 1 = 2$

$F_4 = F_2 + F_3 = 1 + 2 = 3$

$F_5 = F_3 + F_4 = 2 + 3 = 5$

2. Answers may vary. Sample: Each entry is the sum of the two entries above it.

The first five terms of the Fibonacci sequence are $1, 1, 2, 3, 5$.

EXERCISES

1. Nature The numbers of the Fibonacci sequence are often found in other areas, especially in nature. Which term of the Fibonacci sequence does each picture represent?

a. **b.** **c.** **d.**

  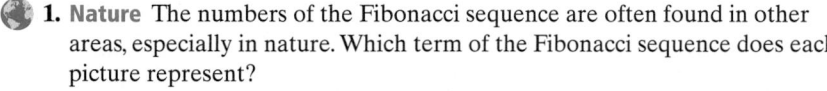 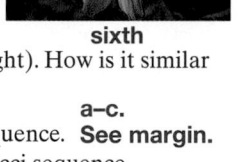

| fifth | seventh | sixth | fourth |

2. Critical Thinking Study Pascal's Triangle (at the right). How is it similar to the Fibonacci sequence? **See above.**

3. a. Generate the first ten terms of the Fibonacci sequence. **See margin.**
b. Find the sum of the first ten terms of the Fibonacci sequence. Divide the sum by 11. What do you notice?
c. **Open-Ended** Choose two numbers other than 1 and 1. Generate a Fibonacci-like sequence from them. Write the first ten terms of your sequence, find the sum, and divide the sum by 11. What do you notice?
d. **Make a Conjecture** What is the sum of the first ten terms of any Fibonacci-like sequence? **It will be 11 times the seventh term.**

a–c.
```
         1
        1 1
       1 2 1
      1 3 3 1
     1 4 6 4 1
   1 5 10 10 5 1
1 ■ ■ ■ ■ ■ ■ ■
```

4. a. Study the pattern at the right. Write the next line.
b. Without calculating, use the pattern to predict the sum of squares of the first ten terms of the Fibonacci sequence.
c. Verify the prediction you made in part (b).

$1^2 + 1^2 = 2 = 1 \cdot 2$

$1^2 + 1^2 + 2^2 = 6 = 2 \cdot 3$

$1^2 + 1^2 + 2^2 + 3^2 = 15 = 3 \cdot 5$

$1^2 + 1^2 + 2^2 + 3^2 + 5^2 = 40 = 5 \cdot 8$

a. $1^2 + 1^2 + 2^2 + 3^2 + 5^2 + 8^2 = 104 = 8 \cdot 13$

b. 4895

c. Check students' work.

 Extension

The Fibonacci Sequence

Students explore a famous sequence that arises in a variety of situations in mathematics, nature, and the sciences.

Resources

 Technology
Computer Test Generator CD-ROM, Chapter 0, Extension Topics

Teaching Notes

Teaching Tip
For Exercise 2, it may help students to show Pascal's Triangle in the form shown below. Have students calculate the sum of the numbers on each diagonal, from the top downward.

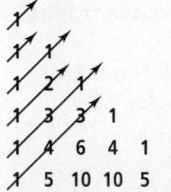

Error Prevention

Exercise 3 For part (c), you may need to explain that the term *Fibonacci-like sequence* means a sequence for which the first two terms are numbers other than 1 and 1 but for which the equation $F_n = F_{n-2} + F_{n-1}$ still holds.

page 599   Extension

3a. 1, 1, 2, 3, 5, 8, 13, 21, 34, 55

b. 143; 13; the answer is the seventh term.

c. Check students' work; the answer is the seventh term.

Lesson Preview

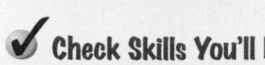 **Check Skills You'll Need**

Mathematical Patterns
Lesson 11-1: Examples 3, 4
Exercises 12–23
Extra Practice, p. 832

Lesson Resources

📁 **Teaching Resources**
Practice, Reteaching, Enrichment
Checkpoint Quiz 1

👥 **Reaching All Students**
Practice Workbook 11-3
Spanish Practice Workbook 11-3
Reading and Math Literacy 11B
Spanish Reading & Literacy 11B
Spanish Checkpoint Quiz 1
Hands-On Activities 57

⏱ **Presentation Assistant Plus!**
Transparencies
• Check Skills You'll Need 11-3
• Additional Examples 11-3
• Student Edition Answers 11-3
• Lesson Quiz 11-3
PH Presentation Pro CD 11-3

(**ASSESSMENT** *SYSTEM*)

Checkpoint Quiz 1
Computer Test Generator CD

💿 **Technology**
Resource Pro® CD-ROM
Computer Test Generator CD
Prentice Hall Presentation Pro CD

💻 **www.PHSchool.com**
Student Site
• Teacher Web Code: agk-5500
• Self-grading Lesson Quiz
Teacher Center
• Lesson Planner
• Resources

Plus

11-3

Geometric Sequences

Lesson Preview

What You'll Learn

OBJECTIVE 1
To identify and generate geometric sequences

... And Why

To find the size of a reduced logo, as in Example 2

✓ Check Skills You'll Need

(For help, go to Lesson 11-1.)

Find the next term in each sequence.

1. $1, 2, 4, 8, \ldots$ **16**

2. $336, 168, 84, 42, \ldots$ **21**

3. $0.1, 1, 10, 100, \ldots$ **1000**

4. $900, 300, 100, \ldots$ $\frac{100}{3}$

New Vocabulary • geometric sequence • common ratio • geometric mean

---

🔳 Interactive lesson includes instant self-check, tutorials, and activities.

OBJECTIVE

1 **Identifying and Generating Geometric Sequences**

4a. Check students' work.

b. Check students' work; they multiply the previous term by a constant.

c. Check students' work.

d. Check students' work.

Graphing Calculator Hint

Enter the values of n and a_n into lists. Then use the STAT and 2nd STAT PLOT features to graph the sequences.

Investigation: Geometric Sequences

• Make a large right isosceles triangle out of colored paper.

• Cut the triangle into two congruent isosceles triangles.

• Place one triangle on top of the other and repeat the previous step.

1. Copy and complete the sequence below. **1, 2, 4, 8**

 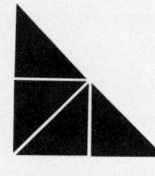 

$a_1 = \blacksquare$ $a_2 = \blacksquare$ $a_3 = \blacksquare$ $a_4 = \blacksquare$

2. Is the sequence in Question 1 arithmetic? Explain why or why not. **No; there is no common difference.**

3. a. Find the sixth term, a_6, of the sequence. **32**

  b. Write a formula for a_6 in terms of a_5. $a_6 = a_5 \cdot 2$

  c. Write a general formula for a_n in terms of a_{n-1}. $a_n = a_{n-1} \cdot 2, a_1 = 1$

4. a. Open-Ended Generate two sequences by multiplying by a constant factor. Write each sequence.

  b. Write a recursive formula for each sequence. What do these formulas and the formula for a_n from Question 3 have in common?

  c. Graph all three sequences. Then sketch each graph.

  d. Compare all three graphs. Write a description of the pattern.

In a **geometric sequence,** the ratio between consecutive terms is constant. This ratio is called the **common ratio.** Unlike in an arithmetic sequence, the difference between consecutive terms varies.

600 Chapter 11 Sequences and Series

🔳 **Ongoing Assessment and Intervention**

Before the Lesson	**During the Lesson**	**After the Lesson**
Diagnose prerequisite skills using:	**Monitor progress using:**	**Assess knowledge using:**
• Check Skills You'll Need	• Check Understanding	• Lesson Quiz
	• Additional Examples	• Computer Test Generator CD
	• Standardized Test Prep	• Checkpoint Quiz 1 (p. 605)

1 EXAMPLE — Identifying a Geometric Sequence

Is the given sequence geometric? If so, identify the common ratio.

a. $5, 15, 45, 135, \ldots$

$$5, \longrightarrow 15, \longrightarrow 45, \longrightarrow 135, \ldots$$

$$\times 3 \qquad \times 3 \qquad \times 3$$

$$15 \div 5 = 3 \qquad 45 \div 15 = 3 \qquad 135 \div 45 = 3$$

There is a common ratio of 3. This is a geometric sequence.

b. $15, 30, 45, 60, \ldots$

$$15, \longrightarrow 30, \longrightarrow 45, \longrightarrow 60, \ldots$$

$$\times 2 \qquad \times 1\tfrac{1}{2} \qquad \times 1\tfrac{1}{3}$$

$$30 \div 15 = 2 \qquad 45 \div 30 = 1\tfrac{1}{2} \qquad 60 \div 45 = 1\tfrac{1}{3}$$

There is no common ratio. This is *not* a geometric sequence.

1a. 5, 15, 45, 135, 405, 1215, 3645, 10,935, 32,805, 98,415; the tenth term is the ninth term times 3.

b. Geometric; the common ratio is -4.

c. Arithmetic; the common difference is $+12$.

✓ Check Understanding

1 a. Write the first ten terms of the geometric sequence from Example 1. Explain how you found the tenth term in the sequence, a_{10}.

b. Is the sequence $6, -24, 96, -384, \ldots$ *arithmetic, geometric,* or *neither?* Explain.

c. Is the sequence $8, 20, 32, 44, \ldots$ *arithmetic, geometric,* or *neither?* Explain.

🔑 Key Concepts

Property	Geometric Sequence Formulas
Recursive Formula	**Explicit Formula**
$a_1 = $ a given value, $a_n = a_{n-1} \cdot r$	$a_n = a_1 \cdot r^{n-1}$

In these formulas, a_n is the nth term, a_1 is the first term, n is the number of the term, and r is the common ratio.

As with an arithmetic sequence, you can use an explicit formula to find the value of the nth term when the previous term is unknown.

2 EXAMPLE — Real-World 🌐 Connection

Real-World 🌐 Connection

Careers Graphic designers use math to lay out pages of books and magazines.

Design Suppose you want a reduced copy of a photograph. The actual length of the photograph is 10 in. The smallest size the copier can make is 64% of the original. Find the length of the photograph after five reductions at 64%.

For five reductions, you need to find the 6th term of the geometric sequence $10, 6.4, \ldots$

$a_n = a_1 \cdot r^{n-1}$	Use the explicit formula.
$a_6 = 10 \cdot 0.64^{6-1}$	Substitute $a_1 = 10$, $n = 6$, and $r = 0.64$.
$= 10 \cdot 0.64^5$	Simplify the exponent.
≈ 1.07	Use a calculator.

After five reductions of 64%, the photograph is about 1 in. long.

✓ Check Understanding

2 Find the 19th term in each sequence.

a. $11, 33, 99, 297, \ldots$ **4,261,625,379**

b. $20, 17, 14, 11, 8, \ldots$ **−34**

Lesson 11-3 Geometric Sequences **601**

Math Background

Arithmetic sequences are based on addition, and geometric sequences are based on multiplication. A geometric sequence is a special case of an exponential function. The domain is the set of natural numbers.

OBJECTIVE 1 Teaching Notes

Investigation (Optional)
Visual Learners

When students copy the sequence in Part 1, encourage them to number each individual triangle within a figure so they can better see the number of triangles in each.

1 EXAMPLE — Teaching Tip

Make it clear that the common ratio for a geometric sequence cannot be 0. Also, the first term of a geometric sequence cannot be 0.

2 EXAMPLE — Careers

Show students how graphic designers reduce the pages of the student book and place them in the Teachers' Edition.

3 EXAMPLE — Connection to Physics

Friction between the swing and child with the air molecules causes the wind resistance. Some students may not realize that the child on the swing is slowing down to a stop. The arc decreases as the swing comes to a stop.

📋 Additional Examples

1 Is the given sequence geometric? If so, identify the common ratio.
a. $1, -6, 36, -216, \ldots$ **yes; −6**
b. $2, 4, 6, 8, \ldots$ **no**

2 Suppose you want to enlarge a photo to 120% of its original size. A photo has a length of 10 cm. Find the length of the photo after five enlargements at 120%? **about 25 cm**

601

👥 Reaching All Students

Below Level Have students generate a list of practical applications of geometric sequences, such as depreciation, compound interest, and amortization tables.	**Advanced Learners** Have students use the definition of a geometric sequence to show that $a_{k+1} = \sqrt{a_k \cdot a_{k+2}}$.	**Error Prevention** See note on page 603. **Error Prevention** See note on page 606.

③ A family purchased a home for $150,000. Two years later the home was valued at $188,160. If the value of the home is increasing geometrically, how much was the home worth after one year? $168,000

Closure

Ask students to explain what a geometric sequence is. Then ask them to explain how they can generate a geometric sequence whose first term is 5. **A geometric sequence is a sequence in which the ratio between consecutive terms is always the same number. To generate a geometric sequence whose first term is 5, you can pick a nonzero number r and multiply 5 by r repeatedly.**

pages 603–605   Exercises

13. $a_n = 5 \cdot (-3)^{n-1}$; 5, −15, 45, −135, 405

14. $a_n = 0.0237 \cdot 10^{n-1}$; 0.0237, 0.237, 2.37, 23.7, 237

15. $a_n = \frac{1}{2}\left(\frac{2}{3}\right)^{n-1}$; $\frac{1}{2}, \frac{1}{3}, \frac{2}{9}, \frac{4}{27}, \frac{8}{81}$

16. $a_n = 0.5^{n-1}$; 1, 0.5, 0.25, 0.125, 0.0625

17. $a_n = 100(-20)^{n-1}$; 100, −2000, 40,000, −800,000, 16,000,000

18. $a_n = 7 \cdot 1^{n-1}$; 7, 7, 7, 7, 7

19. $a_n = 1024(0.5)^{n-1}$; 1024, 512, 256, 128, 64

20. $a_n = 4(0.1)^{n-1}$; 4, 0.4, 0.04, 0.004, 0.0004

21. $a_n = 10(-1)^{n-1}$; 10, −10, 10, −10, 10

The graphs of arithmetic and geometric sequences have different shapes.

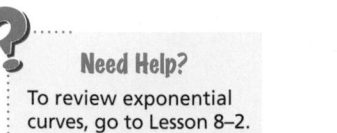

Arithmetic graphs are linear.   Geometric graphs are exponential.

Need Help?
To review exponential curves, go to Lesson 8–2.

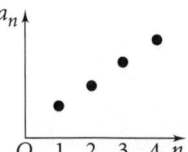

You can find the **geometric mean** of any two positive numbers by taking the positive square root of the product of the two numbers.

$$\text{geometric mean} = \sqrt{\text{product of the two numbers}}$$

You can use the geometric mean to find a missing term of a geometric sequence.

③ EXAMPLE   **Real-World** 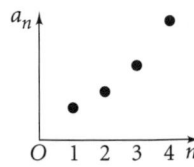 **Connection**

Physics When a child swings without being pushed, air resistance causes the length of the arc of the swing to decrease geometrically. Find the missing arc length.

Find the geometric mean of the two arc lengths.

$$\begin{aligned}\text{geometric mean} &= \sqrt{8 \cdot 6\tfrac{1}{8}} \\ &= \sqrt{49} \\ &= 7\end{aligned}$$

8 ft
■ ft
$6\frac{1}{8}$ ft

● On the second swing, the length of the arc is 7 ft.

 **Check Understanding** **③** Find the missing term of each geometric sequence.
  a. 20, ■, 80, . . . **40**   **b.** 3, ■, 18.75, . . . **7.5**   **c.** 28, ■, 5103, . . . **378**

EXERCISES

For more practice, see *Extra Practice*.

Practice and Problem Solving

Ⓐ **Practice by Example**

Example 1
(page 601)

4–9. See margin p. 603.

Is the given sequence geometric? If so, identify the common ratio and find the next two terms.

1. $1, 2, 4, 8, . . .$ **yes; 2; 16, 32**

2. $1, 2, 3, 4, . . .$ **no**

3. $1, -2, 4, -8, . . .$ **yes; −2; 16, −32**

4. $-1, 1, -1, 1, . . .$

5. $10, 4, 1.6, 0.64, . . .$

6. $7, 0.7, 0.07, 0.007, . . .$

7. $18, -6, 2, -\frac{2}{3}, . . .$

8. $1, \frac{1}{2}, \frac{1}{3}, \frac{1}{4}, . . .$

9. $10, 15, 22.5, 33.75, . . .$

10. $2, -10, 50, -250, . . .$
    yes; −5; 1250, −6250

11. $-1, -6, -36, -216, . . .$
    yes; 6; −1296, −7776

12. $\frac{1}{2}, \frac{1}{4}, \frac{1}{6}, \frac{1}{8}, . . .$
    no

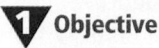
Example 2
(page 601)

Write the explicit formula for each sequence. Then generate the first five terms.

13. $a_1 = 5, r = -3$ **14.** $a_1 = 0.0237, r = 10$ **15.** $a_1 = \frac{1}{2}, r = \frac{2}{3}$

16. $a_1 = 1, r = 0.5$ **17.** $a_1 = 100, r = -20$ **18.** $a_1 = 7, r = 1$

19. $a_1 = 1024, r = 0.5$ **20.** $a_1 = 4, r = 0.1$ **21.** $a_1 = 10, r = -1$

13–21. See margin.

Example 3
(page 602)

Find the missing term of each geometric sequence.

22. $5, \blacksquare, 911.25, \ldots$ **67.5**   **23.** $9180, \blacksquare, 255, \ldots$ **1530**   **24.** $\frac{2}{5}, \blacksquare, \frac{8}{45}, \ldots$ $\frac{4}{15}$

25. $3, \blacksquare, 0.75, \ldots$ **1.5**   **26.** $5, \blacksquare, 2.8125, \ldots$ **3.75**   **27.** $12, \blacksquare, 3, \ldots$ **6**

B   **Apply Your Skills**

28. geometric; 720, 1440

29. arithmetic; 125, 150

30. geometric; 3, −3

31. arithmetic; 50, 55

32. geometric; −80, 160

33. geometric; 0.125, 0.0625

Identify each sequence as *arithmetic, geometric,* or *neither.* Then find the next two terms.

28. $45, 90, 180, 360, \ldots$ **29.** $25, 50, 75, 100, \ldots$ **30.** $3, -3, 3, -3, \ldots$

31. $30, 35, 40, 45, \ldots$ **32.** $-5, 10, -20, 40, \ldots$ **33.** $2, 1, 0.5, 0.25, \ldots$

34. $5, 6, 8, 11, 15, \ldots$
neither; 20, 26
    35. $2, 2, 2, 2, \ldots$
geometric; 2, 2
    36. $1, 4, 9, 16, \ldots$
neither; 25, 36

Find the missing terms of each geometric sequence. (*Hint:* The geometric mean of the first and fifth terms is the third term.)   37–40. See margin.

37. $19{,}683; \blacksquare; \blacksquare; \blacksquare; 243; \ldots$ **38.** $2.5, \blacksquare, \blacksquare, \blacksquare, 202.5, \ldots$

39. $12.5, \blacksquare, \blacksquare, \blacksquare, 5.12, \ldots$ **40.** $-4, \blacksquare, \blacksquare, \blacksquare, -30\frac{3}{8}, \ldots$

Reading Math

For help with reading and solving Exercise 37, see p. 606.

41a–d. Answers may vary. Sample:

a. 3 and 12; 6

b. 3, 6, 12; 2

41. a. Open-Ended Choose two positive numbers. Find their geometric mean.
    b. Find the common ratio for a geometric sequence that includes the terms from part (a) in order from least to greatest or from greatest to least.
    c. Find the 9th term of the geometric sequence from part (b).   **768**
    d. Find the geometric mean of the term from part (c) and the first term of your sequence. What term of the sequence have you just found?   **48; 5th term**

For the geometric sequence $3, 12, 48, 192, \ldots$, find the indicated term.

42. 5th term   **768**   **43.** 7th term   **12,288**   **44.** 10th term   **786,432**

45. 14th term   **201,326,592**   **46.** 17th term   **1.3 × 10¹⁰**   **47.** nth term   **$3(4^{n-1})$**

Find the 10th term of each sequence.

48. $a_9 = 8, r = \frac{1}{2}$ **4**   **49.** $a_{11} = 8, r = \frac{1}{2}$ **16**

50. $a_9 = -5, r = -\frac{1}{2}$ **2.5**   **51.** $a_{11} = -5, r = -\frac{1}{2}$ **10**

52. $a_9 = -\frac{1}{3}, r = \frac{1}{2}$ $-\frac{1}{6}$ **53.** $a_{11} = -\frac{1}{3}, r = \frac{1}{2}$ $-\frac{2}{3}$

 54. Writing Describe the similarities and differences between a common difference and a common ratio.   **See margin.**

C   **Challenge**

55. $142.79, $613.59, $28.62, $58.92, $105.82, $262.94

 **55. Banking** Copy and complete the table below. Use the geometric mean. Assume compound interest is earned and no withdrawals are made.

Period 1	$140.00	$600.00	$25.00	$57.50	$100.00	$250.00
Period 2	■	■	■	■	■	■
Period 3	$145.64	$627.49	$32.76	$60.37	$111.98	$276.55

Assignment Guide

1 **Objective**
   A B Core 1–54
   C Extension 55–60

Standardized Test Prep 61–67

Mixed Review 68–76

Diversity

Exercise 56 You may want to ask a volunteer to explain the basics of golf to students who are not familiar with the game.

Error Prevention

Exercise 58 Some students may choose 0.25 as r. Help students see that r is the same as the decay factor in an exponential function. Therefore, you must subtract 0.25 from 1 to find r.

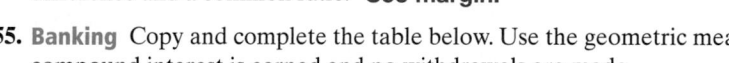

Enrichment 11-3

Reteaching 11-3

Practice 11-3

---

pages 603–605   Exercises

4. yes; −1; −1, 1

5. yes; 0.4; 0.256, 0.1024

6. yes; 0.1; 0.0007, 0.00007

7. yes; $-\frac{1}{3}; \frac{2}{9}, -\frac{2}{27}$

8. no

9. yes; 1.5; 50.625, 75.9375

37. 6561, 2187, 729

38. 7.5, 22.5, 67.5

39. 10, 8, 6.4

40. −6.64, −11.02, −18.30

54. Both the common difference and the common ratio are used to find the next term in a sequence, but a common difference is added and a common ratio is multiplied.

Lesson Quiz 11-3

Is the given sequence geometric? If so, identify the common ratio and find the next two terms.

1. 1, 2, 6, 12, . . . **no**

2. 2, 1, 0.5, 0.25, . . . **yes; 0.5; 0.125, 0.0625**

3. −9, 81, −729, 6561, . . .
   yes; −9; −59,049, 531,441

4. Write the explicit formula for the geometric sequence for which $a_1 = 7$ and $r = \frac{1}{3}$. Then generate the first five terms. $a_n = 7 \cdot \left(\frac{1}{3}\right)^{n-1}$; $7, \frac{7}{3}, \frac{7}{9}, \frac{7}{27}, \frac{7}{81}$

5. Find the missing term for the geometric sequence
   3, ■, 48, . . . **12**

Alternative Assessment

Have students work individually. Ask students to write six different geometric sequence formulas. Three of the sequences should be recursive and three should be explicit. Instruct them to find the first four terms of each sequence, and then to find a_6. Finally, ask students to pick two nonzero numbers p and q. Ask them to write an explicit formula for a sequence for which $a_1 = p$ and $a_3 = q$.

Standardized Test Prep

Resources

For additional practice with a variety of test item formats:
- Standardized Test Prep, p. 633
- Test-Taking Strategies, p. 628
- Test-Taking Strategies with Transparencies

Math Tip

Exercises 63–65 For any geometric sequence, if two of three consecutive terms are known, it is possible to find the value of the remaining term. This tells you that choice D cannot be the correct answer for any of these three exercises.

604

56a. $d, \frac{1}{2}d, \frac{1}{4}d, \frac{1}{8}d, \frac{1}{16}d,$ $\frac{1}{32}d$

  b. Yes; the common ratio is $\frac{1}{2}$.

  c. $a_n = a_{n-1} \cdot \frac{1}{2}$

57. Both arithmetic and geometric sequence explicit formulas use the first term a_1, $n - 1$, and a common term. The recursive formulas both use a_{n-1} and a common term.

58c. **375.42 cm³**

56. **Golf** Each of the putts misses the hole and continues past it for half the distance.
   a. Write a sequence to represent the ball's distance from the hole before each of his first six putts.
   b. Is this sequence geometric? Explain your reasoning.
   c. Write a recursive formula for the sequence.

57. **Critical Thinking** How are the formulas for a geometric sequence similar to the formulas for an arithmetic sequence?

58. Suppose a balloon loses one fourth of its helium each day. The balloon starts with a volume of 5000 cm³.
   a. Write the geometric sequence that shows the amount of helium in the balloon at the start of each day for five days. **5000, 3750, 2812.5, 2109.38, 1582.03**
   b. What is the common ratio of the sequence? $\frac{3}{4}$ **375.42 cm³**
   c. How much helium will be left in the balloon at the start of the tenth day?
   d. Graph the sequence. Then sketch the graph. **See back of book.**
   e. **Critical Thinking** How does the common ratio affect the shape of the graph? **See margin.**

Find a_1 for a geometric sequence with the given terms.

59. $a_5 = 112$ and $a_7 = 448$ **7**

60. $a_9 = \frac{1}{2}$ and $a_{12} = \frac{1}{16}$ **128**

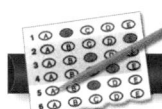

Standardized Test Prep

Multiple Choice

Take It to the NET
Online lesson quiz at
www.PHSchool.com
Web Code: aga-1103

Quantitative Comparison

61. Which geometric sequence DOES NOT include the term 100? **A**
   A. 5, 10, 20, . . .   B. 337.5, 225, 150, . . .
   C. $a_1 = 25$, $a_n = 2a_{n-1}$ D. $a_n = 4 \cdot 5^n$

62. What is the product of the geometric mean of 2 and 32 and the geometric mean of 1 and 4? **F**
   F. 16   G. 19   H. 32   I. 256

Compare the boxed quantity in Column A with the boxed quantity in Column B. Choose the best answer.
   A. The quantity in Column A is greater.
   B. The quantity in Column B is greater.
   C. The two quantities are equal.
   D. The relationship cannot be determined from the information given.

Each group of three terms represents a geometric sequence.

	Column A	Column B
63. A	the missing term in 5, ■, 125	the missing term in 5, 10, ■
64. C	the missing term in 10, 100, ■	the missing term in ■, 200, 40
65. B	the missing term in 15, 45, ■	the missing term in ■, 280, 560

pages 603–605   Exercises

58e. **The common ratio $\frac{3}{4}$ is less than one, so the graph is decreasing.**

66. **[2] geometric mean =** $\sqrt{4 \cdot 16} = \sqrt{64} = 8$ **arithmetic mean =** $\frac{4 + 16}{2} = \frac{20}{2} = 10$ **The arithmetic mean is greater.**

[1] correct answer with no work shown

Short Response

66. Which is greater, the geometric mean of 4 and 16 or the arithmetic mean of 4 and 16? Show your work.   **See margin p. 604.**

Extended Response

67. In a geometric sequence, $a_1 = 3$ and $a_4 = 192$. Explain how to find a_2 and a_3.   **See margin.**

Mixed Review

Lesson 11-2   **Write an explicit and a recursive formula for each arithmetic sequence.**

68. $-3, 0, 3, 6, \ldots$ **69.** $17, 8, -1, \ldots$ **70.** $-2, -13, -24, \ldots$
68–73. See margin.

Lesson 10-3   **Write an equation of the circle with the given center and radius. Graph the circle.**

71. center $(0, 0)$, radius 3   **72.** center $(-3, 1)$, radius 5   **73.** center $(1, 1)$, radius 2

Lesson 9-3   **Find the vertical asymptotes of each function.**

74. $y = \dfrac{x - 3}{x + 3}$ $x = -3$ **75.** $y = \dfrac{x - 3}{x + 1}$ $x = -1$ **76.** $y = \dfrac{x - 3}{x(x - 1)}$ $x = 0, 1$

✓ Checkpoint Quiz 1   Lessons 11-1 through 11-3

 **Instant self-check quiz online and on CD-ROM**

Identify each sequence as *arithmetic* or *geometric*. Then find the common difference or common ratio.   **1–3. See margin.**

1. $15, 30, 45, 60, \ldots$ **2.** $2, 6, 18, 54, \ldots$ **3.** $37, 34, 31, 28, 25, \ldots$

4. $700, 350, 175, 87.5, \ldots$ **5.** $8, -4, 2, -1, 0.5, \ldots$ **6.** $4, 2, 0, -2, -4, \ldots$
    geometric; 0.5   **geometric; −0.5**   **arithmetic; −2**

Find the fifth term of each sequence.

7. $a_1 = 100, a_n = \frac{1}{2}a_{n-1}$ **8.** $a_1 = 2, a_n = 3a_{n-1} - 2$ **9.** $a_n = -n + 6$
   6.25   **82**   **1**

10. Writing Explain how to compute the arithmetic mean and the geometric mean of two terms of a sequence.   **See margin.**

A P●int in Time

In 1276, the Chinese astronomer Guo Shoujing built a device to study the sun. A hole in the tower of his observatory faced due south. At noon, a horizontal pole in the tower cast a shadow on a low wall that extended north from the building. Guo Shou jing learned about the sun's movements by studying the geometric pattern of the shadows on the wall.

Take It to the NET For more information about techniques for measuring the sun's position, go to **www.PHSchool.com**.
Web Code: age-2032

Lesson 11-3   Geometric Sequences   **605**

67. [4] Since $a_4 = a_3 \cdot r = a_2 \cdot r^2 = a_1 \cdot r^3$, $192 = 3 \cdot r^3$. So $r^3 = 64$, and $r = \sqrt[3]{64} = 4$. Then $a_2 = a_1 \cdot r = 3 \cdot 4 = 12$ and $a_3 = a_2 \cdot r = 12 \cdot 4 = 48$.

[3] appropriate methods, but with one computational error

[2] correct answer, but with minimal explanation

[1] correct answer, but with no explanation

68. $a_n = -6 + 3n$; $a_n = a_{n-1} + 3, a_1 = -3$

69. $a_n = 26 - 9n$; $a_n = a_{n-1} - 9, a_1 = 17$

Teaching Resources
Checkpoint Quiz 1 (also in Prentice Hall Assessment System)

Reaching All Students
Reading and Math Literacy 11B

Spanish versions available

70. $a_n = 9 - 11n$; $a_n = a_{n-1} - 11, a_1 = -2$

71. $x^2 + y^2 = 9$

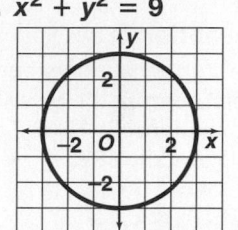

72. $(x + 3)^2 + (y - 1)^2 = 25$

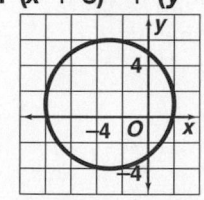

73. $(x - 1)^2 + (y - 1)^2 = 4$

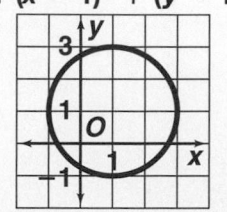

page 605   Checkpoint Quiz 1

1. arithmetic; 15

2. geometric; 3

3. arithmetic; −3

10. To find the arithmetic mean, add the terms and divide by 2. To find the geometric mean, multiply the terms and find the square root of the product.

605

Reading For Problem Solving

Students read an example problem in which they are asked to find the missing terms in a geometric sequence. In addition to being worked out, the problem includes notes that explain each step of the work.

Teaching Notes

Suggest that students review the definition of a geometric mean if they have trouble following the sequence of steps taken to solve this problem.

Error Prevention

Make sure students understand that the first term in the given geometric sequence is 19,683, and not 19, followed by 683.

Exercises

Make sure students label the terms so they can keep track of each term as they find it.

Read the problem below. Then follow along with Wanda as she solves the problem. Check your understanding with the exercise at the bottom of the page.

Find the missing terms of the geometric sequence. (*Hint:* The geometric mean of the first and fifth terms is the third term.

19,683; ■; ■; ■; 243; …

What Wanda Thinks

In this geometric sequence, the numbers decrease.

The hint tells me information about terms in the sequence. I'll label the terms.

The hint says that the geometric mean of the first and fifth terms is the third term. That makes sense, because the third term is the middle term. I'll write that relationship and substitute.

Perfect. I have the third term in the sequence.

I can rewrite the sequence to include the third term.

Now I can find the 2nd and 4th terms in the same way, because they are between terms I know.

I'll rewrite the sequence with the missing terms filled in.

What Wanda Writes

19,683; ■; ■; ■; 243; …

1st term = 19,683
2nd term = ■
3rd term = ■
4th term = ■
5th term = 243

Geometric mean of 1st and 5th terms is 3rd term

3rd term = $\sqrt{19,683 \cdot 243}$
3rd term = $\sqrt{4,782,969}$
3rd term = 2187

19,683; ■; 2187; ■; 243; …

2nd term = $\sqrt{19,683 \cdot 2187}$ = 6561

4th term = $\sqrt{2187 \cdot 243}$ = 729

The sequence is
19,683; 6561; 2187; 729; 243; …

EXERCISES

Find the missing terms of each geometric sequence.

1. 12,312; ■; ■; ■; 152; …
 4104, 1368, 456

2. 1.7; ■; ■; ■; 1239.3; …
 8.8, 45.9, 238.5

Arithmetic Series

Lesson Preview

What You'll Learn

 OBJECTIVE 1 To write and evaluate arithmetic series

 OBJECTIVE 2 To use summation notation

. . . And Why

To find the number of stitches in a cross-stitch pattern, as in Example 2

✓ Check Skills You'll Need

(For help, go to Lesson 11-1.)

Find each sum.

1. $2 + 3.5 + 5 + 6.5 + 8$ **25**

2. $-17 + (-13) + (-9) + (-5) + (-1) + 3$ **−42**

Write an explicit formula for each sequence.

3. $4, 6, 8, 10, 12, \ldots$ $a_n = 2 + 2n$

4. $1, 4, 7, 10, 13, 16, \ldots$ $a_n = -2 + 3n$

5. $-17, -23, -29, -35, \ldots$ $a_n = -11 - 6n$

6. $10, 1, -8, -17, \ldots$ $a_n = 19 - 9n$

New Vocabulary • series • arithmetic series • limit

 iTEXT Interactive lesson includes instant self-check, tutorials, and activities.

OBJECTIVE 1 Writing and Evaluating Arithmetic Series

Investigation: Arithmetic Series

Use the sequence 1, 2, 3, 4, . . . 97, 98, 99, 100 to answer each question.

1. Is it *arithmetic, geometric,* or *neither?* Justify your reasoning.

2. a. Add the first and last terms of the sequence and write down the answer. Then add the second and next-to-last terms. Continue adding terms until you get to the middle of the sequence.

   b. **Reasoning** What patterns do you notice in your answers to part (a)?
   All of the sums are 101.

3. Use your answer to Question 2 to find the sum of the terms of the sequence. **5050**

4. a. Describe a short method for finding the following sum.
   $5 + 10 + 15 + 20 + 25 + 30 + 35 + 40 + 45 + 50$

   b. Find the sum. **275**

1. The sequence is arithmetic because it has a common difference of 1.

2a. $1 + 100 = 101$
$2 + 99 = 101$
$\vdots \qquad \vdots \qquad \vdots$
$50 + 51 = 101$

4a. Add the first and last terms. Multiply this sum by the number of terms divided by 2.

Reading Math

Ellipsis points are three dots indicating a missing part of a statement.

A **series** is the expression for the sum of the terms of a sequence. Finite sequences and series have terms that you can count individually from 1 to a final whole number n. Infinite sequences and series continue without end. You indicate an infinite sequence or series with ellipsis points.

Finite sequence	Finite series
$6, 9, 12, 15, 18$	$6 + 9 + 12 + 15 + 18$
Infinite sequence	**Infinite series**
$3, 7, 11, 15, \ldots$	$3 + 7 + 11 + 15 + \ldots$

1. Plan

Lesson Preview

✓ **Check Skills You'll Need**

Mathematical Patterns
Lesson 11-1: Example 4
Exercises 18–23
Extra Practice, p. 822

Lesson Resources

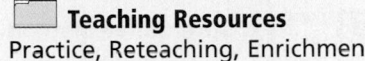 **Teaching Resources**
Practice, Reteaching, Enrichment

 **Reaching All Students**
Practice Workbook 11-4
Spanish Practice Workbook 11-4
Hands-On Activities 54

 **Presentation Assistant Plus!**
Transparencies
• Check Skills You'll Need 11-4
• Additional Examples 11-4
• Student Edition Answers 11-4
• Lesson Quiz 11-4
PH Presentation Pro CD 11-4

 **ASSESSMENT SYSTEM**

Computer Test Generator CD

 Technology
Resource Pro® CD-ROM
Computer Test Generator CD
Prentice Hall Presentation Pro CD

 www.PHSchool.com
Student Site
• Teacher Web Code: agk-5500
• Self-grading Lesson Quiz
Teacher Center
• Lesson Planner
• Resources

Plus  **iTEXT**

Ongoing Assessment and Intervention

Before the Lesson	**During the Lesson**	**After the Lesson**
Diagnose prerequisite skills using:	Monitor progress using:	Assess knowledge using:
• Check Skills You'll Need	• Check Understanding • Additional Examples • Standardized Test Prep	• Lesson Quiz • Computer Test Generator CD

Math Background

Convergence (the existence of a finite sum) of a series is a classical concern of calculus and analysis, but also has importance in chaos theory.

OBJECTIVE

1 **Teaching Notes**

Investigation (Optional)
Teaching Tip
You may wish to review the definitions of *finite* and *infinite*.

1 **EXAMPLE** **Alternative Method**

You may wish to show how to use addition of equations to find the value of the series. Let *S* be the value of the series. You can write the series with the terms arranged in the given order or in reverse order. Write two equations, add, and solve the resulting equation.

$$S = 2 + 11 + 20 + 29 + 38 + 47$$
$$\underline{S = 47 + 38 + 29 + 20 + 11 + 2}$$
$$2S = 49 + 49 + 49 + 49 + 49 + 49$$
$$2S = 294$$
$$S = 147$$

2 **EXAMPLE** **English Learners**

You may need to explain the terms *embroidery, cross-stitch, table linens,* and *woven fabric.* Bring in samples, or ask a student to do so.

Additional Examples

1 Use the sequence 5, 9, 13, 17, 21, 25, 29. Write the related series. Evaluate the series.
5 + 9 + 13 + 17 + 21 + 25 + 29; 119

2 A staircase uses same-size cement blocks arranged 4 across, as shown below. Find the total number of blocks in the staircase.
60 blocks

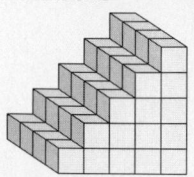

608

1a. $0.3 + 0.6 + 0.9 + 1.2 + 1.5 + 1.8 + 2.1 + 2.4 + 2.7 + 3.0$; **16.5**

b. $100 + 125 + 150 + 175 + 200 + 225$; **975**

✔ **Check Understanding**

Key Concepts

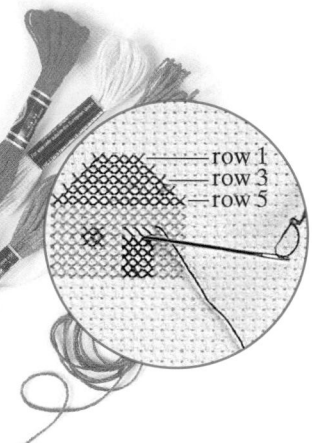

— row 1
— row 3
— row 5

---

1 **EXAMPLE** **Writing and Evaluating a Series**

Use the finite sequence 2, 11, 20, 29, 38, 47. Write the related series. Then evaluate the series.

 Related series → $2 + 11 + 20 + 29 + 38 + 47 = 147$ ← **Add to evaluate.**

The sum of the terms of the sequence is 147.

1 Write the related series for each finite sequence. Then evaluate the series.
 a. 0.3, 0.6, 0.9, 1.2, 1.5, 1.8, 2.1, 2.4, 2.7, 3.0   **b.** 100, 125, 150, 175, 200, 225

An **arithmetic series** is a series whose terms form an arithmetic sequence. When a sequence has many terms, or when you know only the first and last terms of the sequence, you can use a formula to evaluate the related series quickly.

Property	**Sum of a Finite Arithmetic Series**

The sum S_n of a finite arithmetic series $a_1 + a_2 + a_3 + \ldots + a_n$ is

$$S_n = \frac{n}{2}(a_1 + a_n)$$

where a_1 is the first term, a_n is the nth term, and n is the number of terms.

2 **EXAMPLE** **Real-World** 🌐 **Connection**

Crafts Embroidery such as cross-stitch frequently decorates table linens and clothing, although it was originally used to strengthen and repair woven fabric.

Several rows of cross-stitches make up the green roof. Find the total number of green cross-stitches in the roof.

Relate $\boxed{\text{sum of the series}}$ is $\boxed{\dfrac{\text{number of terms}}{2}}$ times   ($\boxed{\text{the first term}}$ plus $\boxed{\text{the last term}}$)

Define   Let S_n = total number of cross-stitches,

    and let n = the number of rows.

    Then a_1 = the number of cross-stitches in the first row,

    and a_n = the number of cross-stitches in the last row.

Write $S_n = \frac{n}{2}(a_1 + a_n)$ **Use the formula.**

    $= \frac{5}{2}(5 + 13)$ **Substitute n = 5, a_1 = 5, and a_n = 13.**

    $= 2.5(18)$ **Simplify.**

    $= 45$ **Multiply.**

There are 45 cross-stitches in the green roof.

✔ **Check Understanding** **2** Suppose the pattern from Example 2 extends to 14 rows of cross-stitches.
 a. Find the 14th term of the sequence. **31**
 b. Use the formula to find the value of the series to the 14th term. **252**

👥 Reaching All Students

Below Level Have students work in pairs to make up arithmetic series for each other to sum. Then have them write the series using summation notation.	**Advanced Learners** Have students explain why the sum of an infinite arithmetic series is always infinite.	**English Learners** See note on page 608. **English Learners** See note on page 610.

Reading Math

Σ is the Greek letter sigma, the equivalent of the English letter S (for summation).

You can use the summation symbol Σ to write a series. Then you can use limits to indicate how many terms you are adding. **Limits** are the least and greatest integral values of n.

upper limit, greatest value of n — explicit formula for the sequence

$$\sum_{n=1}^{3} (5n + 1)$$

lower limit, least value of n

3 **EXAMPLE** **Writing a Series in Summation Notation**

Use summation notation to write the series $3 + 6 + 9 + \ldots$ for 33 terms.

$3 \cdot 1 = 3, 3 \cdot 2 = 6, 3 \cdot 3 = 9, \ldots$ **The explicit formula for the sequence is 3n.**

$3 + 6 + 9 + \ldots + 99 = \sum\limits_{n=1}^{33} 3n$ **The lower limit is 1 and the upper limit is 33.**

✓ **Check Understanding** **3** Use summation notation to write each series for the specified number of terms.
a. $1 + 2 + 3 + \ldots; n = 6$ **a–b. See left.**
b. $3 + 8 + 13 + 18 + \ldots; n = 9$

3a. $\sum\limits_{n=1}^{6} n$

b. $\sum\limits_{n=1}^{9} (5n - 2)$

To expand a series from summation notation, you can substitute each value of n into the explicit formula and add the results.

4 **EXAMPLE** **Finding the Sum of a Series**

Use the series $\sum\limits_{n=1}^{3} (5n + 1)$.

a. Find the number of terms in the series.
Since the values of n are 1, 2, and 3, there are three terms in the series.

b. Find the first and last terms of the series.
The first term of the series is $5n + 1 = 5(1) + 1 = 6$.
The last term of the series is $5n + 1 = 5(3) + 1 = 16$.

c. Evaluate the series.

$\sum\limits_{n=1}^{3} (5n + 1) = (5(1) + 1) + (5(2) + 1) + (5(3) + 1)$ **Substitute.**

$= 6 + 11 + 16$ **Simplify within parentheses.**

$= 33$ **Add.**

The sum of the series is 33.

✓ **Check Understanding** **4** For each sum, find the number of terms, the first term, and the last term. Then evaluate the series.
a. $\sum\limits_{n=1}^{10} (n - 3)$ **b.** $\sum\limits_{n=1}^{4} \left(\frac{1}{2}n + 1\right)$ **c.** $\sum\limits_{n=2}^{5} n^2$
10, −2, 7; 25 **4, $\frac{3}{2}$, 3; 9** **4, 4, 25; 58**

Lesson 11-4 Arithmetic Series **609**

OBJECTIVE
2 **Teaching Notes**

3 **EXAMPLE** **Math Tip**

Tell students that they can read $\sum\limits_{n=1}^{33} 3n$ as "the sum of the values of $3n$ from n equals 1 to n equals 33."

4 **EXAMPLE** **Teaching Tip**

Ask students how they know that this series is arithmetic. **The value of 5n + 1 increases by 5 if n increases by 1.** You may want to point out that summation notation can be used with any type of series, arithmetic or non-arithmetic. Also, stress that the parentheses around $5n + 1$ are essential.

Additional Examples

3 Use summation notation to write the series $8 + 16 + 24 + \ldots$ for 50 terms. $\sum\limits_{n=1}^{50} 8n$

4 Use the series $\sum\limits_{n=1}^{4} (-2n + 3)$.
a. Find the number of terms in the series. **4 terms**
b. Find the first and last terms of the series. **1, −5**
c. Evaluate the series. **−8**

Closure

Ask students what formula they can use to find the sum of the first n terms of an arithmetic sequence with first term a_1 and nth term a_n. Then ask them how they would use the formula to find the value of $\sum\limits_{n=1}^{10} 7n$.
$S_n = \frac{n}{2}(a_1 + a_n)$; The series $\sum\limits_{n=1}^{10} 7n$ is an arithmetic series with $a_1 = 7$ and $a_{10} = 70$. The series has 10 terms. So $\sum\limits_{n=1}^{10} 7n = \frac{10}{2}(7 + 70) = 5(77) = 385$.

For more practice, see *Extra Practice*.

EXERCISES

Practice and Problem Solving

Assignment Guide

1 Objective
Ⓐ Ⓑ **Core** 1–12, 25–33, 35–41
Ⓒ **Extension** 43–46

2 Objective
Ⓐ Ⓑ **Core** 13–24, 34, 42
Ⓒ **Extension** 47–48

Standardized Test Prep 49–54

Mixed Review 55–66

Error Prevention

Exercises 13–18 Remind students to use parentheses around the expression following the summation symbol where necessary. For example, the value of $\sum_{n=1}^{8} (n + 7)$ is 92, but the value of $\sum_{n=1}^{8} n + 7$ is 43.

English Learners

Exercise 41 For part b, explain that *pros and cons* is a phrase meaning "arguments for and against."

Ⓐ **Practice by Example**

Example 1
(page 608)

Write the related series for each finite sequence. Then evaluate each series.

1. 21, 18, 15, 12, 9, 6, 3

2. −5, −15, −25, −35, −45

3. 100, 99, 98, . . . , 95

4. 0.5, 0.25, 0, . . . , −0.75

5. 17.3, 19.6, 21.9, 24.2, 26.5

6. 4.5, 5.6, 6.7, . . . , 11.1

1–6. See margin.

Example 2
(page 608)

Each sequence has eight terms. Evaluate each related series.

7. $\frac{1}{2}, \frac{3}{2}, \frac{5}{2}, \ldots, \frac{15}{2}$ **32**

8. 1, −1, −3, . . . , −13 **−48**

9. 5, 13, 21, . . . , 61 **264**

10. −3.5, −1.25, 1, . . . , 12.25 **35**

11. 1765, 1414, 1063, . . . , −692 **4292**

12. −13, −14.5, −16, . . . , −23.5 **−146**

Example 3
(page 609)

Use summation notation to write each arithmetic series for the specified number of terms. **13–18. See margin pp. 610–611.**

13. 2 + 4 + 6 + . . . ; n = 4

14. 8 + 9 + 10 + . . . ; n = 8

15. 5 + 6 + 7 + . . . ; n = 7

16. 1 + 4 + 7 + 10 + . . . ; n = 11

17. 7 + 14 + 21 + . . . ; n = 15

18. (−3) + (−6) + (−9) + . . . ; n = 5

Example 4
(page 609)

For each sum, find the number of terms, the first term, and the last term. Then evaluate the series.

5, 1, 9; 25   **5, −3, −11; −35**   **6, 4, −1; 9**

19. $\sum_{n=1}^{5} (2n - 1)$

20. $\sum_{n=1}^{5} (-2n - 1)$

21. $\sum_{n=3}^{8} (7 - n)$

22. $\sum_{n=1}^{5} (0.2n - 0.2)$

23. $\sum_{n=2}^{10} \frac{4n}{3}$ **9, $\frac{8}{3}$, $\frac{40}{3}$; 72**

24. $\sum_{n=5}^{10} (20 - n)$

5, 0, 0.8; 2   **6, 15, 10; 75**

Ⓑ **Apply Your Skills**

Tell whether each list is a *sequence* or a *series*. Then tell whether it is *finite* or *infinite*.

sequence; finite

25. 1, 2, 4, 8, 16, 32, . . . **sequence; infinite** **26.** 1, 0.5, 0.25, 0.125, 0.0625

27. 5 + 10 + . . . + 25 **series; finite**

28. −0.5 − 0.25 − 0.125 − . . . **series; infinite**

29. $\frac{4}{3}, \frac{7}{3}, \frac{10}{3}, \frac{13}{3}, \frac{16}{3}, \ldots$ **sequence; infinite** **30.** 2.3 + 4.6 + 9.2 + 18.4 **series; finite**

Real-World 🌐 **Connection**

The seats in a theater are staggered so people don't block the view of those in the row behind them.

31. Architecture A 20-row theater has two aisles. The two side sections have four chairs in the first row and one more chair in each succeeding row. The middle section has 10 chairs in the first row and one more chair in each succeeding row. **a–c. See margin p. 611.**

a. Find the total number of chairs in each section. Then find the total seating capacity of the theater.

b. Write an arithmetic series to represent each section.

c. After every five rows, the ticket price goes down by $5. Front-row tickets cost $60. What is the total amount of money generated by a full house?

32. a. Consider the finite arithmetic series 10 + 13 + 16 + . . . + 31. How many terms are in it? Explain. **8; the formula for the corresponding sequence is 3n + 7. Solving 3n + 7 = 31 for n shows that n = 8.**

b. Evaluate the series. **164**

---

2. (−5) + (−15) + (−25) + (−35) + (−45); −125

3. 100 + 99 + 98 + 97 + 96 + 95; 585

4. 0.5 + 0.25 + 0 + (−0.25) + (−0.5) + (−0.75); −0.75

5. 17.3 + 19.6 + 21.9 + 24.2 + 26.5; 109.5

6. 4.5 + 5.6 + 6.7 + 7.8 + 8.9 + 10 + 11.1; 54.6

13. $\sum_{n=1}^{4} 2n$

14. $\sum_{n=1}^{8} (n + 7)$

15. $\sum_{n=1}^{7} (n + 4)$

pages 610–612 Exercises

1. 21 + 18 + 15 + 12 + 9 + 6 + 3; 84

33. Education Luis has taken three math tests so far this semester. The spreadsheet shows his grades.

	A	B	C	D
1	Student Name	Test 1	Test 2	Test 3
2	Luis Ortez	75	79	83
3	Marie Bova	78	85	84
4	Lasheha Brown	87	82	91

  a. Suppose his test grades continue to improve at the same rate. What will be his grade on the fifth (and final) test? **91**

  b. What will his test average be for this grading period? (Assume each test is worth 100 points.) **83**

 **34. a.** A supermarket displays cans in a triangle. Write an explicit formula for the sequence of the number of cans. $a_n = n + 1$

  b. Use summation notation to write the related series for a triangle with 10 cans in the bottom row. **b–d. See margin.**

  c. Suppose the triangle had 17 rows. How many cans would be in the 17th row?

  d. Critical Thinking Could the triangle have 110 cans? 140 cans? Justify your reasoning.

Evaluate each series to the given term.

35. $2 + 4 + 6 + 8 + \ldots$; 10th term **110**   **36.** $-5 - 25 - 45 - \ldots$; 9th term **−765**

37. $2 + 3 + 4 + 5 + \ldots$; 100th term **5150**   **38.** $\frac{5}{2} + 1 - \frac{1}{2} - 2 - \ldots$; 8th term **−22**

39. $0.17 + 0.13 + 0.09 + 0.05 + \ldots$; 12th term **−0.6**

40. $1500 + 1499 + 1498 + 1497 + \ldots$; 1000th term **1,000,500**

 41. Technology A school committee has decided to spend a large portion of its annual technology budget on graphing calculators. This year, the technology coordinator bought 75 calculators, and plans to buy 25 new calculators each year from now on.

  a. Suppose the school committee has decided that each student in the school should have access to a graphing calculator within seven years. The school population is 500. Will the technology coordinator meet this goal? Explain your reasoning. **No; 75 + 25(6) = 225, which is less than 500.**

 b. Writing What are some pros and cons of buying calculators in this manner? If you could change the plan, would you? If so, how would you change it?

42. a. Open-Ended Write two explicit formulas for arithmetic sequences.

  b. Write the first five terms of each related series.   **a–d. Check**

  c. Use summation notation to rewrite each series.   **students' work.**

  d. Evaluate each series.

41b. Answers may vary. Sample: Pro: spreading the cost over several years, con: calculators purchased first may be outdated by the time 500 calculators have been purchased; check student's work.

 Challenge

Use the values of a_1 and S_n to find the value of a_n.

43. $a_1 = 4$ and $S_{40} = 6080$; a_{40} **300**   **44.** $a_1 = -6$ and $S_{50} = -5150$; a_{50} **−200**

Find a_1 for each arithmetic series.

45. $S_8 = 440$ and $d = 6$ **34**   **46.** $S_{30} = 240$ and $d = -2$ **37**

47. Evaluate S_{10} for the series $x + (x + y) + (x + 2y) + \ldots$ **10x + 45y**

48. Evaluate S_{15} for the series $3x + (3x - 2y) + (3x - 4y) + \ldots$ **45x − 210y**

Lesson 11-4 Arithmetic Series   **611**

16. $\displaystyle\sum_{n=1}^{11} (3n - 2)$

17. $\displaystyle\sum_{n=1}^{15} 7n$

18. $\displaystyle\sum_{n=1}^{5} -3n$

31a. **270 chairs on each side, 390 chairs middle, 930 chairs total**

b. each side: $\displaystyle\sum_{n=1}^{20} (n + 3)$;

middle: $\displaystyle\sum_{n=1}^{20} (n + 9)$

c. **$46,950**

Lesson Quiz 11-4

1. Write an addition expression for the finite series represented by $\displaystyle\sum_{n=1}^{8} 10n$. **10 + 20 + 30 + 40 + 50 + 60 + 70 + 80**

Write each finite arithmetic series using summation notation. Then find the sum of each series.

2. $102 + 104 + 106 + 108 + 110 + 112$
$\displaystyle\sum_{n=1}^{6} (100 + 2n)$; **642**

3. $10 + 5 + 0 + (-5) + (-10) + (-15)$ $\displaystyle\sum_{n=1}^{6} (15 - 5n)$; **−15**

4. Write the arithmetic series to the given term using summation notation. Then find the sum of the series.
$3 + 6 + 9 + 12 + \ldots$; 100th
$\displaystyle\sum_{n=1}^{100} 3n$; **15,150**

Alternative Assessment

Have students work in pairs. Ask each student to write three finite arithmetic series, each with at least six terms. Students trade series. Each student should use summation notation to represent the series he or she received. The student should then evaluate the series. Ask students to check one another's work.

34b. $\displaystyle\sum_{n=1}^{9} (n + 1)$

c. **18 cans**

d. **No; no; 13 rows have 104 cans, 14 rows have 119 cans, 15 rows have 135 cans, and 16 rows have 152 cans. The number of rows would not be an integer for 110 cans or 140 cans.**

Exercise 50 If the expression in parentheses after the summation sign is linear in the variable n, then the series is an arithmetic series, and the common difference for the related sequence is equal to the coefficient of n.

pages 610–612 Exercises

55. $a_n = 2^{n-1}$; 1, 2, 4

56. $a_n = 5^{n-1}$; 1, 5, 25

57. $a_n = -1\,(-1)^{n-1}$; −1, 1, −1

58. $a_n = 3\left(\frac{3}{2}\right)^{n-1}$; $3, \frac{9}{2}, \frac{27}{4}$

59. $a_n = -7(0.1)^{n-1}$; −7, −0.7, −0.07

60. $a_n = 20(-0.5)^{n-1}$; 20, −10, 5

61.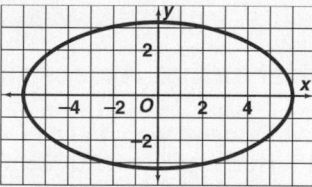

ellipse: x- and y-axes; domain: $-6 \le x \le 6$; range: $-2\sqrt{3} \le y \le 2\sqrt{3}$

62.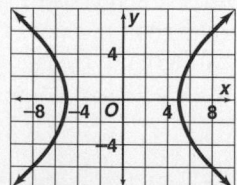

hyperbola: x- and y-axes; domain: $x \le -5$ or $x \ge 5$; range: $-\infty \le y \le \infty$

63.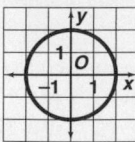

circle: all lines through the origin; domain: $-2 \le x \le 2$; range: $-2 \le y \le 2$

612

Standardized Test Prep

Multiple Choice

49. Which expression represents the sum of the finite series $10 + 20 + 30 + 40$? **B**

   I. $\displaystyle\sum_{n=1}^{4} 10n$ II. $\displaystyle\sum_{n=10}^{40} 10n$ III. $10\left(\displaystyle\sum_{n=1}^{4} n\right)$

   A. I and II only **B.** I and III only **C.** II and III only **D.** I, II, and III

50. What is the value of $\displaystyle\sum_{n=1}^{5} (2n - 3)$? **G**

   F. 6 **G.** 15 **H.** 17 **I.** $10n - 15$

51. Which expression defines the series $14 + 20 + 26 + 32 + 38 + 44 + 50$? **C**

   A. $\displaystyle\sum_{n=2}^{8} (7n - 1)$ **B.** $\displaystyle\sum_{n=3}^{8} (6n - 4)$ **C.** $\displaystyle\sum_{n=3}^{9} (6n - 4)$ **D.** $\displaystyle\sum_{n=8}^{14} (n + 6)$

Quantitative Comparison

Compare the boxed quantity in Column A with the boxed quantity in Column B. Choose the best answer.
- **A.** The quantity in Column A is greater.
- **B.** The quantity in Column B is greater.
- **C.** The two quantities are equal.
- **D.** The relationship cannot be determined from the information given.

Column A	Column B
52. **A** $\displaystyle\sum_{n=1}^{10} n$	$\displaystyle\sum_{n=1}^{10} (n - 1)$
53. **C** $\displaystyle\sum_{n=1}^{5} (2n + 12)$	$\displaystyle\sum_{n=2}^{4} 10n$
54. **B** $\displaystyle\sum_{n=1}^{4} n^2$	$\displaystyle\sum_{n=5}^{8} 2n$

Take It to the NET
Online lesson quiz at
www.PHSchool.com
Web Code: aga-1104

Mixed Review

Lesson 11-3

Write the explicit formula for each geometric sequence. Then generate the first three terms. 55–60. See margin.

55. $a_1 = 1, r = 2$ 56. $a_1 = 1, r = 5$ 57. $a_1 = -1, r = -1$

58. $a_1 = 3, r = \frac{3}{2}$ 59. $a_1 = -7, r = 0.1$ 60. $a_1 = 20, r = -0.5$

Lesson 10-1

Graph each equation. Describe each graph and its lines of symmetry. Give the domain and range for each graph. 61–63. See margin.

61. $x^2 + 3y^2 = 36$ 62. $x^2 - y^2 = 25$ 63. $x^2 + y^2 = 4$

Lesson 9-4

Simplify each rational expression. 64–66. See margin.

64. $\dfrac{x^2 + 4x + 3}{x^2 - 3x - 4}$ 65. $\dfrac{c^2 - 8c + 12}{c^2 - 11c + 30}$ 66. $\dfrac{3z^4 + 36z^3 + 60z^2}{3z^3 - 3z^2}$

64. $\dfrac{x + 3}{x - 4}$

65. $\dfrac{c - 2}{c - 5}$

66. $\dfrac{z^2 + 12z + 20}{z - 1}$

Geometry and Infinite Series

You can use geometric figures to model some infinite series.

1 EXAMPLE Modeling an Infinite Series

Geometry Draw a geometric figure to model the series.
$$\frac{1}{2} + \left(\frac{1}{2}\right)^2 + \left(\frac{1}{2}\right)^3 + \ldots + \left(\frac{1}{2}\right)^n + \ldots$$

Use a square grid. Shade one half of the grid. Then shade one half of the remaining area. Continue until the grid is full.

So the series

$$\frac{1}{2} + \left(\frac{1}{2}\right)^2 + \left(\frac{1}{2}\right)^3 + \ldots + \left(\frac{1}{2}\right)^n + \ldots$$

appears to have a sum of 1.

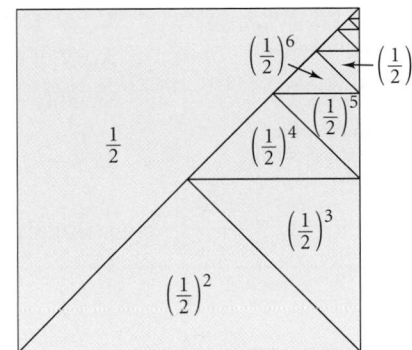

You can write an infinite series from a geometric model.

2 EXAMPLE Writing an Infinite Series

Geometry Write the series modeled by the trapezoids. Estimate the sum of the series. Explain your reasoning.

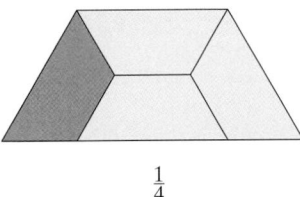   +   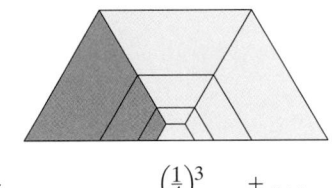   + $\left(\frac{1}{4}\right)^3$ + ...

$\frac{1}{4}$ $\left(\frac{1}{4}\right)^2$

The red area approaches one third of the figure.
So the series $\frac{1}{4} + \left(\frac{1}{4}\right)^2 + \left(\frac{1}{4}\right)^3 + \ldots + \left(\frac{1}{4}\right)^n + \ldots$ appears to have a sum of $\frac{1}{3}$.

EXERCISES   1–3. See margin.

1. a. Write the series modeled by the figure at the right.
b. Evaluate the series. Explain your reasoning.

2. Draw a figure to model the series. Begin with a 10×10 square.
$$\frac{1}{5} + \left(\frac{1}{5}\right)^2 + \left(\frac{1}{5}\right)^3 + \ldots + \left(\frac{1}{5}\right)^n + \ldots$$

3. Make a Conjecture Consider the series
$$\frac{1}{c} + \left(\frac{1}{c}\right)^2 + \left(\frac{1}{c}\right)^3 + \ldots + \left(\frac{1}{c}\right)^n + \ldots$$
What is the sum of the series? Explain your reasoning.

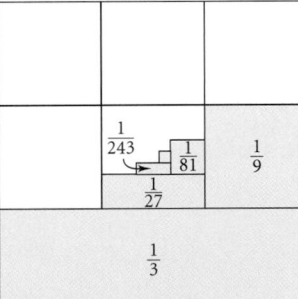

Geometry and Infinite Series

In this investigation, students use geometric figures to develop an intuitive feel for geometric series that converge to a limit. The ideas explored will be helpful in Lesson 11-5.

Teaching Notes

1 EXAMPLE Math Tip

Be sure students understand that it is not literally possible to shade an infinite number of triangles. So, in a theoretical sense, the grid does not get completely shaded.

Error Prevention

Exercise 3 Students may not consider all of the possible values of c. Be sure they consider values for which $c \le 1$.

page 613   Investigation

1a. $\frac{1}{3} + \left(\frac{1}{3}\right)^2 + \left(\frac{1}{3}\right)^3 +$ $\ldots + \left(\frac{1}{3}\right)^n + \ldots$

b. $\frac{1}{2}$; the shaded area approximates one half of the figure.

2. Answers may vary. Sample:

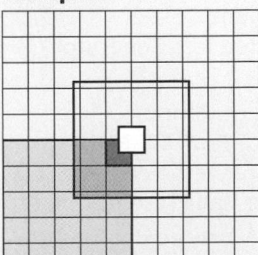

3. Answers may vary. Sample: The sum of the series is $\frac{1}{c-1}$; the examples and the other exercises seem to suggest that pattern.

Lesson Preview

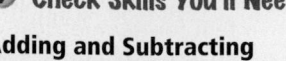 **Check Skills You'll Need**

**Adding and Subtracting
Rational Expressions**
Lesson 9-5: Example 5
Exercises 22–30
Extra Practice p. 830

Lesson Resources

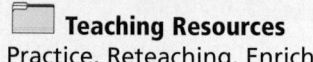 **Teaching Resources**
Practice, Reteaching, Enrichment
Checkpoint Quiz 2

Reaching All Students
Practice Workbook 11-5
Spanish Practice Workbook 11-5
Reading and Math Literacy 11C
Spanish Reading & Literacy 11C
Spanish Checkpoint Quiz 2
Technology Activities 35
Hands-On Activities 58

Presentation Assistant Plus!
Transparencies
• Check Skills You'll Need 11-5
• Additional Examples 11-5
• Student Edition Answers 11-5
• Lesson Quiz 11-5
PH Presentation Pro CD 11-5

 **ASSESSMENT SYSTEM**

Checkpoint Quiz 2
Computer Test Generator CD

 **Technology**
Resource Pro® CD-ROM
Computer Test Generator CD
Prentice Hall Presentation Pro CD

www.PHSchool.com
Student Site
• Teacher Web Code: agk-5500
• Self-grading Lesson Quiz
Teacher Center
• Lesson Planner
• Resources

Plus

 **11-5**

Geometric Series

Lesson Preview

What You'll Learn

OBJECTIVE **1** To evaluate a finite geometric series

OBJECTIVE **2** To evaluate an infinite geometric series

. . . And Why

To find the length of a chambered nautilus shell, as in Example 4

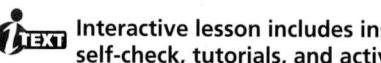 **Check Skills You'll Need** (For help, go to Lesson 9-5.)

Find each sum or difference.

1. $100 + 50 + 25 + \frac{25}{2} + \frac{25}{4}$ **$193\frac{3}{4}$** **2.** $3 + 9 + 27 + 81$ **120**

3. $-2 + 4 - 8 + 16 - 32$ **-22** **4.** $-5 - 10 - 20 - 40$ **-75**

Simplify each fraction.

5. $\dfrac{1 - \frac{1}{5}}{\frac{1}{3}}$ **$\frac{12}{5}$** **6.** $\dfrac{1}{1 - \frac{1}{4}}$ **$\frac{4}{3}$** **7.** $\dfrac{\frac{1}{2} - \frac{1}{3}}{\frac{1}{4}}$ **$\frac{2}{3}$** **8.** $\dfrac{2 + \frac{1}{16}}{\frac{1}{3}}$ **$\frac{99}{16}$**

New Vocabulary • geometric series • converges • diverges

OBJECTIVE **1**

Evaluating a Finite Geometric Series

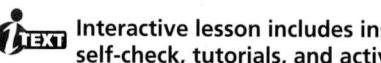 Interactive lesson includes instant self-check, tutorials, and activities.

A **geometric series** is the expression for the sum of the terms of a geometric sequence. As with arithmetic series, you can use a formula to evaluate a finite geometric series.

Key Concepts

Property	**Sum of a Finite Geometric Series**

The sum S_n of a finite geometric series $a_1 + a_2 + a_3 + \ldots + a_n, r \neq 1$, is

$$S_n = \frac{a_1(1 - r^n)}{1 - r}$$

where a_1 is the first term, r is the common ratio, and n is the number of terms.

1 EXAMPLE **Using the Geometric Series Formula**

Use the formula to evaluate the series $3 + 6 + 12 + 24 + 48 + 96$.

The first term is 3, and there are six terms in the series.

The common ratio is $\frac{6}{3} = \frac{12}{6} = \frac{24}{12} = \frac{48}{24} = \frac{96}{48} = 2$.

So $a_1 = 3, r = 2$, and $n = 6$.

$S_n = \dfrac{a_1(1 - r^n)}{1 - r}$ Write the formula.

$S_6 = \dfrac{3(1 - 2^6)}{1 - 2}$ Substitute $a_1 = 3$, $r = 2$, and $n = 6$.

$= \dfrac{-189}{-1} = 189$ Simplify.

The sum of the series is 189.

Need Help?
For more practice with ratios, see Skills Handbook p. 844.

Ongoing Assessment and Intervention

Before the Lesson
Diagnose prerequisite skills using:
• Check Skills You'll Need

During the Lesson
Monitor progress using:
• Check Understanding
• Additional Examples
• Standardized Test Prep

After the Lesson
Assess knowledge using:
• Lesson Quiz
• Computer Test Generator CD
• Checkpoint Quiz 2 (p. 619)

✓ **Check Understanding**

1a. $a_1 = -45, r = -3,$
$n = 5; -2745$

b. $a_1 = \frac{1}{3}, r = \frac{1}{3}, n = 4;$
$\frac{40}{81}$

1 Identify a_1, r, and n for each series. Then evaluate each series.

a. $-45 + 135 - 405 + 1215 - 3645$ **b.** $\frac{1}{3} + \frac{1}{9} + \frac{1}{27} + \frac{1}{81}$

You can use the formula to solve problems involving geometric series.

2 EXAMPLE Real-World 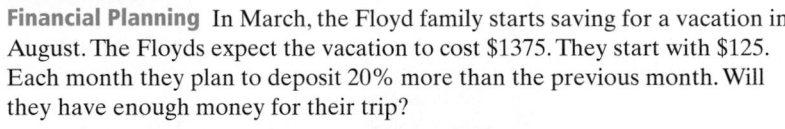 Connection

Financial Planning In March, the Floyd family starts saving for a vacation in August. The Floyds expect the vacation to cost $1375. They start with $125. Each month they plan to deposit 20% more than the previous month. Will they have enough money for their trip?

Relate $S_n = \dfrac{a_1(1 - r^n)}{1 - r}$ **Write the formula for the sum of a geometric series.**

Define S_n = total amount saved

$a_1 = 125$ initial amount

$r = 1.2$ common ratio

$n = 6$ number of months (March through August)

Write $S_6 = \dfrac{125(1 - 1.2^6)}{1 - 1.2}$ **Substitute.**

   $= 1241.24$ **Simplify.**

The final balance will be $1241.24. The Floyds will *not* have enough money for their trip in August.

Real-World 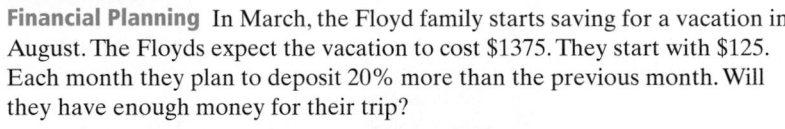 **Connection**

Careers Financial planners use math to help families plan savings for college, retirement, and vacations.

✓ **Check Understanding**

2 a. Reasoning Explain how the common ratio 1.2 was found.
   b. Suppose each month the Floyds deposit 25% more than the previous month. Describe how this changes the problem. **a–b. See below left.**
   c. At this rate of saving, will they have enough money for their trip? Explain. **Yes; they will have $1407.35.**

OBJECTIVE

2 **Evaluating an Infinite Geometric Series**

2a. To find the amount 20% larger than a given amount, multiply by 1.2, which is equivalent to 120%.

b. The common ratio becomes 1.25.

In some cases you can evaluate an infinite geometric series. When $|r| < 1$, the series **converges**, or gets closer and closer, to the sum S. When $|r| \geq 1$, the series **diverges**, or approaches no limit.

3 EXAMPLE Determining Divergence and Convergence

Decide whether each infinite geometric series *diverges* or *converges*. State whether the series has a sum.

a. $1 - \frac{1}{3} + \frac{1}{9} - \ldots$

$a_1 = 1, a_2 = -\frac{1}{3}$

$r = -\frac{1}{3} \div 1 = -\frac{1}{3}$

Since $|r| < 1$, the series converges, and the series has a sum.

b. $\displaystyle\sum_{n=1}^{\infty} 5(2)^{n-1}$

$a_1 = 5(2^0) = 5, a_2 = 5(2^1) = 10$

$r = 10 \div 5 = 2$

Since $|r| \geq 1$, the series diverges, and the series does not have a sum.

✓ **Check Understanding**

3 Determine whether each series has a sum.
   a. $1 + \frac{1}{5} + \frac{1}{25} + \ldots$ **yes**   **b.** $4 + 8 + 16 + \ldots$ **no**

Math Background

The sum $S_n = a_1 + a_2 + a_3 + \ldots + a_n$ of a finite geometric series can be written as $S_n = a_1 + a_1 r + a_1 r^2 + \ldots + a_1 r^{n-1}$. If you multiply both sides by r, you get $r S_n = a_1 r + a_1 r^2 + a_1 r^3 + \ldots + a_1 r^n$. When you subtract this equation from the preceding equation, most of the terms on the right side cancel out, and you get $S_n - r S_n = a_1 - a_1 r^n$. Factor on both sides to get the equation $S_n(1 - r) = a_1(1 - r^n)$. When you divide both sides by $1 - r$ (assuming $r \neq 1$), you obtain $S_n = \dfrac{a_1(1 - r^n)}{1 - r}$, which is the formula for the sum of the geometric series.

OBJECTIVE

1 Teaching Notes

Additional Examples

1 Use the formula to evaluate the series
$5 + 15 + 45 + 135 + 405 + 1215$.
1820

2 The Floyd family starts saving for a vacation that is one year away. They start with $125. Each month they save 8% more than the previous month. How much money will they have saved 12 months later? **$2372.14**

OBJECTIVE

2 Teaching Notes

3 EXAMPLE Math Tip

In part b, call attention to the symbol ∞ above the sigma symbol. Explain that the infinity symbol is used to indicate that there is no upper limit for the number of terms for the summation.

👫 **Reaching All Students**

| **Below Level** Have students graph arithmetic and geometric sequences. Explain why arithmetic sequences are called linear and geometric sequences are called exponential. | **Advanced Learners** Have students look up Zeno's paradox and discuss with the class why Zeno's logic was faulty. | **English Learners** See note on page 617. **Visual Learners** See note on page 620. |

Connection to Biology

A classic work on the relation between mathematics and biology is *On Growth and Form* by D'Arcy Wentworth Thompson. This famous book is still in print and is also available in libraries.

Additional Examples

3 Decide whether each infinite geometric series *diverges* or *converges*. State whether the series has a sum.

a. $\displaystyle\sum_{n=1}^{\infty}\left(\frac{2}{3}\right)^{n}$ converges; has a sum

b. $2 + 6 + 18 + \ldots$ diverges; does not have a sum

4 The weight at the end of a pendulum swings through an arc of 30 inches on its first swing. After that, each successive swing is 85% of the length of the previous swing. What is the total distance the weight will swing by the time it comes to rest? **200 in.**

Closure

Ask students what formula they can use to evaluate the sum of the first n terms of a geometric series with first term a_1 and common ratio r ($r \neq 1$). Then ask them how they can tell whether an infinite geometric series converges or diverges. Finally, ask how one can find the sum if the series converges. $S_n = \dfrac{a_1(1 - r^n)}{1 - r}$; converges if and only if $|r| < 1$; Use $S = \dfrac{a_1}{1 - r}$.

pages 616–619   Exercises

 9. converges; has a sum

10. converges; has a sum

11. converges; has a sum

12. diverges; no sum

13. diverges; no sum

14. converges; has a sum

Key Concepts

Definition	Sum of an Infinite Geometric Series

An infinite geometric series with $|r| < 1$ converges to the sum

$$S = \frac{a_1}{1 - r}$$

where a_1 is the first term and r is the common ratio.

You can use the sum formula to evaluate some infinite geometric series.

4 EXAMPLE   Real-World 🌐 Connection

Biology The length of the outside shell of each closed chamber of a chambered nautilus is 0.9 times the length of the larger chamber next to it. Estimate the total length of the outside shell for the enclosed chambers.

The outside edge of the largest enclosed chamber is 27 mm long, so $a_1 = 27$.

27 mm

$S = \dfrac{a_1}{1 - r}$ Use the formula.

$= \dfrac{27}{1 - 0.9}$ Substitute.

$= 270$ Simplify.

● The total length of the outside shell for the enclosed chambers is about 270 mm.

✔ **Check Understanding** 4 Evaluate each infinite geometric series.

a. $1 + \frac{1}{2} + \frac{1}{4} + \frac{1}{8} + \ldots$ **2**

b. $3 - \frac{3}{2} + \frac{3}{4} - \frac{3}{8} + \ldots$ **2**

EXERCISES

For more practice, see *Extra Practice*.

Practice and Problem Solving

A Practice by Example

Examples 1 and 2
(pages 614 and 615)

Evaluate the series to the given term.

1. $1 + 2 + 4 + \ldots; S_8$ **255**

2. $4 + 12 + 36 + \ldots; S_6$ **1456**

3. $3 + 6 + 12 + \ldots; S_7$ **381**

4. $7 - 35 + 175 - \ldots; S_5$ **3647**

5. $-5 - 10 - 20 - \ldots; S_{11}$ **−10,235**

6. $-\frac{1}{6} + 1 - 6 + 36 - \ldots; S_5$ **$-\frac{1111}{6}$**

7. $\frac{1}{2} + \frac{1}{4} + \frac{1}{8} + \ldots; S_8$ **$\frac{255}{256}$**

8. $1 - 3 + 9 - 27 + \ldots; S_8$ **−1640**

Example 3
(page 615)

Decide whether each infinite geometric series *diverges* or *converges*. State whether each series has a sum. 9–14. See margin.

9. $1 + \frac{1}{4} + \frac{1}{16} + \ldots$

10. $1 - \frac{1}{2} + \frac{1}{4} - \ldots$

11. $4 + 2 + 1 + \ldots$

12. $1 + 2 + 4 + \ldots$

13. $6 + 18 + 54 + \ldots$

14. $-54 - 18 - 6 - \ldots$

15. $1 - 1 + 1 - \ldots$
 diverges; no sum

16. $1 + \frac{1}{5} + \frac{1}{25} + \ldots$
 converges; has a sum

17. $\frac{1}{4} + \frac{1}{2} + 1 + 2 + \ldots$
 diverges; no sum

Example 4
(page 616)

Evaluate each infinite geometric series.

18. $1.1 + 0.11 + 0.011 + \ldots$ **$1.\overline{2}$** **19.** $1.1 - 0.11 + 0.011 - \ldots$ **1**

20. $1 - \frac{1}{5} + \frac{1}{25} - \frac{1}{125} + \ldots$ **$\frac{5}{6}$** **21.** $3 + 1 + \frac{1}{3} + \frac{1}{9} + \ldots$ **$\frac{9}{2}$**

22. $3 + 2 + \frac{4}{3} + \frac{8}{9} + \ldots$ **9** **23.** $3 - 2 + \frac{4}{3} - \frac{8}{9} + \ldots$ **$\frac{9}{5}$**

B **Apply Your Skills**

Determine whether each series is *arithmetic* or *geometric*. Then evaluate the series to the given term.

arithmetic; 420

24. geometric; 2046

24. $2 + 4 + 8 + 16 + \ldots ; S_{10}$ **25.** $2 + 4 + 6 + 8 + \ldots ; S_{20}$

26. geometric; $-1,627,605$

26. $-5 + 25 - 125 + 625 - \ldots ; S_9$ **27.** $6.4 + 8 + 10 + 12.5 + \ldots ; S_7$

27. geometric; 96.47

28. $1 + 2 + 3 + 4 + \ldots ; S_{1000}$ **29.** $81 + 27 + 9 + 3 + \ldots ; S_{200}$
arithmetic; 500,500 **geometric; $\approx$121.5**

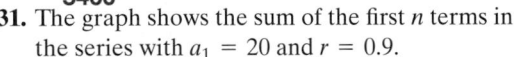 **30. Communications** Many companies use a telephone chain to notify employees of a closing due to bad weather. Suppose the first person in the chain calls four people. Then each of these people calls four others, and so on.
  a. Make a tree diagram to show the first three stages in the telephone chain. How many calls are made at each stage? **See back of book.**
  b. Write the series that represents the total number of calls made through the first six stages. **4 + 16 + 64 + 256 + 1024 + 4096**
  c. How many employees have been notified after stage six?
  5460

31a. 20, 18, 16.2, 14.58

c. $S = \frac{20}{1 - 0.9} = 200$

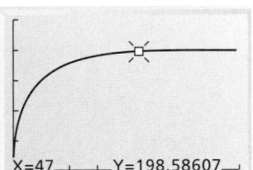 **31.** The graph shows the sum of the first n terms in the series with $a_1 = 20$ and $r = 0.9$.
  a. Write the first four terms of the series.
  b. Use the graph to evaluate the series to the 47th term. **198.59**
  c. Write and evaluate the formula for the sum of the series.
  d. Graph the sum using the window values shown. Use the graph to verify your answer to part (c). **Check students' work.**

X=47   Y=198.58607

Xmin=0   Ymin=0
Xmax=94   Ymax=250
Xscl=10   Yscl=50

Evaluate each infinite series that has a sum.

Reading Math

In $\sum\limits_{n=1}^{\infty}$, the symbol for infinity ∞ indicates that the series continues without end.

32. $\sum\limits_{n=1}^{\infty} \left(\frac{1}{5}\right)^{n-1}$ **$\frac{5}{4}$** **33.** $\sum\limits_{n=1}^{\infty} 3\left(\frac{1}{4}\right)^{n-1}$ **4** **34.** $\sum\limits_{n=1}^{\infty} \left(-\frac{1}{3}\right)^{n-1}$ **$\frac{3}{4}$**

35. $\sum\limits_{n=1}^{\infty} 7(2)^{n-1}$ **no sum** **36.** $\sum\limits_{n=1}^{\infty} (-0.2)^{n-1}$ **$0.8\overline{3}$** **37.** $\sum\limits_{n=1}^{\infty} 2(1.2)^{n-1}$
  no sum

38. A bouncing ball reaches heights of 16 cm, 12.8 cm, and 10.24 cm on three consecutive bounces.
  a. If the ball started at a height of 25 cm, how many times has it bounced when it reaches a height of 16 cm? **2**
  b. Write a geometric series for the downward distances the ball travels from its release at 25 cm. **25 + 20 + 16 + 12.8 + 10.24 + . . .**
  c. Write a geometric series for the upward distances the ball travels from its first bounce. **20 + 16 + 12.8 + 10.24 + . . .**
  d. Find the total vertical distance the ball travels before it comes to rest.
  225 cm

39. Open-Ended Write an infinite geometric series that converges to 3. Use the formula to evaluate the series. **Check students' work.**

Lesson 11-5 Geometric Series **617**

Error Prevention

Exercises 11–13, 17 Students sometimes want to say that a series for which $a_n > 0$ and $r > 1$ converges to ∞. Be sure to point out that we say a series converges *only* if it converges to a real number. The symbol ∞ does not represent a real number.

English Learners

Exercise 48 You may need to explain the terms *friction* and *pendulum*. Let students tie a small object onto the end of a piece of string to simulate the movement of a pendulum.

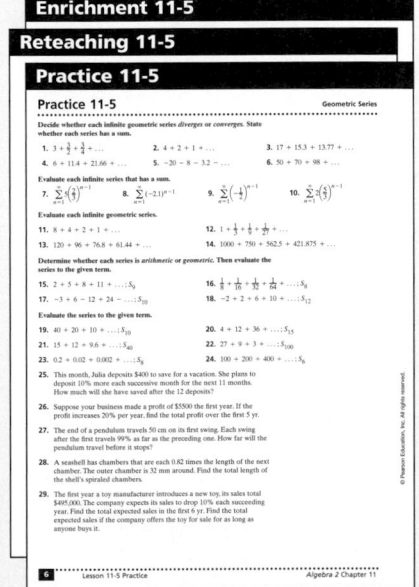

1. Find the sum of the geometric series. $3 - 30 + 300 - 3000 + 30,000$ **27,273**

2. Find the sum of the first twelve terms of the geometric series. Round your answer to the nearest thousandth. $16 + 8 + 4 + \ldots$ **31.992**

3. How can you tell whether an infinite geometric series converges or diverges? **Check the common ratio r. If $|r| < 1$, the series converges. Otherwise, it diverges.**

4. Find the sum of the infinite geometric series. $16 + 8 + 4 + \ldots$ **32**

5. Find the sum of the infinite geometric series. $15 + 5 + \frac{5}{3} + \frac{5}{9} + \ldots$ **22.5**

Alternative Assessment

Have students work individually. Ask students to write two finite geometric series with at least five terms. Ask them to find the sum of each series. Then ask them to write two infinite geometric series, one that diverges and one that converges. Ask them to find the sum of the series that converges.

Standardized Test Prep

A sheet of blank grids is available in the Test-Taking Strategies with Transparencies booklet. Give this sheet to students for practice with filling in the grids.

Resources
For additional practice with a variety of test item formats:
• Standardized Test Prep, p. 633
• Test-Taking Strategies, p. 628
• Test-Taking Strategies with Transparencies

Exercise 52 Students should note that the given terms have not one but *two* terms between them.

40a. No; the sum of a series of positive numbers will be positive.

   b. He did not check to see if $|r|$ was less than 1.

43. (b); (a) yields $26,000; using the formula for finding the sum of a finite geometric series, (b) yields $1,342,177.26.

 **Challenge**

49a. $S = \dfrac{0.142857}{1 - 0.000001} = \dfrac{0.142857}{0.999999} = \dfrac{1}{7}$

---

40. **a.** A classmate uses the formula for the sum of an infinite geometric series to evaluate $1 + 1.1 + 1.21 + 1.331 + \ldots$ and gets -10. Is your classmate's answer reasonable? Explain.
   b. Error Analysis What did your classmate fail to check before using the formula?

Critical Thinking Find the specified value for each infinite geometric series.

41. $a_1 = 12, S = 96$; find r. **$\frac{7}{8}$**   42. $S = 12, r = \frac{1}{6}$; find a_1. **10**

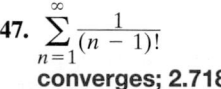 43. **Writing** Suppose you are to receive an allowance each week for the next 26 weeks. Would you rather receive (a) $1000 per week or (b) 2¢ the first week, 4¢ the second week, 8¢ the third week, and so on for the 26 weeks? Justify your answer.

44. The sum of an infinite geometric series is twice its first term.
   a. Error Analysis A student says the common ratio of the series is $\frac{3}{2}$. What is the student's error? **See margin.**
   b. Find the common ratio of the series. **$\frac{1}{2}$**

Technology Create a spreadsheet to evaluate the first n terms of each series. Determine whether each infinite series converges to a sum. If so, estimate the sum.

45. $\sum_{n=1}^{\infty} \frac{1}{2^n}$ **converges; 1**

46. $\sum_{n=1}^{\infty} \frac{100}{n}$ **diverges**

47. $\sum_{n=1}^{\infty} \frac{1}{(n-1)!}$ **converges; 2.718**

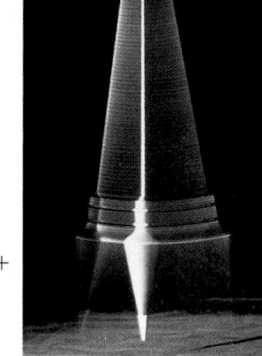

48. **Physics** Because of friction and air resistance, each swing of a pendulum is a little shorter than the previous one. The lengths of the swings form a geometric sequence. Suppose the first swing of a pendulum has a length of 100 cm and the return swing is 99 cm.
   a. On which swing will the arc first have a length less than 50 cm? **69th swing**
   b. Find the total distance traveled by the pendulum until it comes to rest. **10,000 cm**

49. **a.** Show that the infinite geometric series $0.142857 + 0.000000142857 + \ldots$ has a sum of $\frac{1}{7}$.
   b. Find the fraction form of the repeating decimal $0.428571428571\ldots$ **$\frac{3}{7}$**

50. The function $S(n) = \dfrac{10(1 - 0.8^n)}{0.2}$ represents the sum of the first n terms of an infinite geometric series.
   a. What is the domain of the function? **a–b. See margin.**
   b. Find $S(n)$ for $n = 1, 2, 3, \ldots, 10$. Sketch the graph of the function.
   c. Find the sum S of the infinite geometric series. **50**

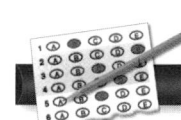

Standardized Test Prep

Gridded Response

51. What is the common ratio for the geometric series $\sum_{n=1}^{10} 7\left(\frac{4}{7}\right)^{n-1}$? Enter your answer as a fraction. **$\frac{4}{7}$**

52. What is the common ratio in a geometric series if $a_2 = \frac{2}{5}$ and $a_5 = \frac{16}{135}$? Enter your answer as a fraction. **$\frac{2}{3}$**

---

pages 616–619 Exercises

44a. Answers may vary. Sample: The student used $r - 1$ instead of $1 - r$ in the formula for the sum of an infinite geometric series.

50a. all integers greater than or equal to 1

   b. 10; 18; 24.4; 29.52; 33.62; 36.89; 39.51; 41.61; 43.29; 44.63;

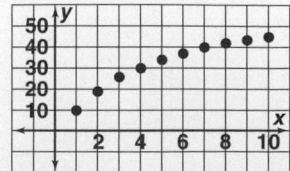

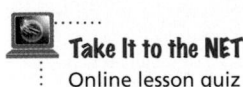
Take It to the NET
Online lesson quiz at
www.PHSchool.com
Web Code: aga-1105

53. Evaluate the infinite geometric series $\frac{2}{5} + \frac{4}{25} + \frac{8}{125} + \dots$ Enter your answer as a fraction. **$\frac{2}{3}$**

54. Find the sum of the two infinite series $\sum\limits_{n=1}^{\infty} \left(\frac{2}{3}\right)^{n-1}$ and $\sum\limits_{n=1}^{\infty} \left(\frac{2}{3}\right)^{n}$. **5**

55. Evaluate the sum $\sum\limits_{n=1}^{3} \left(\frac{1}{n+1}\right)^{2}$. Enter your answer as a decimal to the nearest thousandth. **0.424**

56. Car 1 cost $22,600 when new and depreciated 14% each year for 5 years. The same year, Car 2 cost $17,500 when new and depreciated 7% each year for 5 years. To the nearest dollar, what was the difference in the values of the two cars after 5 years? **1543**

Mixed Review

Lesson 11-4   **Evaluate each series to the given term.**

57. $12.5 + 15 + 17.5 + 20 + 22.5 + \dots$; 7th term   **140**

58. $-100 - 95 - 90 - 85 - \dots$; 11th term   **−825**

59. $-17 - 11 - 5 + 1 + 7 + 13 + \dots$; 25th term   **1375**

Lesson 10-2   **Identify the focus and directrix of each parabola. Then graph the parabola.**

60. $y = \frac{1}{16}x^2$ **61.** $x = -\frac{1}{4}y^2$ **62.** $x^2 = -9y$
60–62. See margin.

Lesson 9-5   **Add or subtract. Simplify where possible.**

64. $\dfrac{10(2y + 3)}{(y + 3)(y - 3)}$

63. $\dfrac{7}{2c} - \dfrac{2}{c^2}$ $\dfrac{7c - 4}{2c^2}$

64. $\dfrac{5}{y + 3} + \dfrac{15}{y - 3}$

65. $\dfrac{4}{x^2 - 36} + \dfrac{x}{x - 6}$ $\dfrac{x^2 + 6x + 4}{(x + 6)(x - 6)}$

66. $\dfrac{15}{3 - d} - \dfrac{-3}{9 - d^2}$ $\dfrac{-3(5d + 16)}{(d + 3)(d - 3)}$

 **Checkpoint Quiz 2**   **Lessons 11-4 through 11-5**

i TEXT Instant self-check
quiz online and
on CD-ROM

1. **arithmetic; 900**

2. **geometric; 29,524**

3. **geometric; −7.9375**

4. **arithmetic; 1200**

Determine whether each series is *arithmetic* or *geometric*. Then evaluate the series to the given term.

1. $1 + 3 + 5 + 7 + \dots$; S_{30} **2.** $1 + 3 + 9 + 27 + \dots$; S_{10}

3. $-4 - 2 - 1 - 0.5 - \dots$; S_7 **4.** $500 + 380 + 260 + 140 + \dots$; S_6

5. $120 + 60 + 30 + 15 + \dots$; S_8 **6.** $-175 - 50 + 75 + 200 + \dots$; S_{12}
   geometric; 239.0625   **arithmetic; 6150**

Evaluate each infinite geometric series.

7. $\sum\limits_{n=1}^{\infty} \left(\frac{1}{15}\right)^{n-1}$ $\frac{15}{14}$ **8.** $\sum\limits_{n=1}^{\infty} 2(0.5)^{n-1}$ **4**

9–10. See margin.

9. Open-Ended Write a finite geometric series with a sum less than 1.

10. Critical Thinking Can an infinite arithmetic series converge? Explain.

✓ **Chapter Checkpoint 2**

**To check understanding of
Lessons 11-4 to 11-5:**

Checkpoint Quiz 2 (p. 619)

📁 **Teaching Resources**
Checkpoint Quiz 2 (also in
   Prentice Hall Assessment
   System)

👥 **Reaching All Students**
Reading and Math Literacy 11C

Spanish versions available

---

page 619   Checkpoint Quiz 2

**9. Answers may vary.
   Sample:**

$$\frac{1}{2} + \frac{1}{4} + \frac{1}{8}$$

**10. No; the common
    difference causes
    arithmetic series to
    diverge.**

---

60. (0, 4), $y = -4$;

61. (−1, 0), $x = 1$;

62. $\left(0, -\frac{9}{4}\right)$, $y = \frac{9}{4}$;

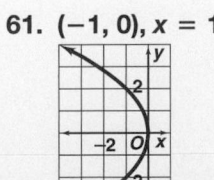

 Extension

Mathematical Induction

Students use the Principle of Mathematical Induction to prove statements are true for all positive integers *n*.

Resources

Technology

Computer Test Generator CD-ROM, Chapter 0, Extension Topics

Teaching Notes

Visual Learners

Set up a domino "chain" and show students how knocking over the first domino results in knocking over all of the dominoes.

Consider the pattern in the following statements.

$$1 = 1$$
$$1 + 3 = 4$$
$$1 + 3 + 5 = 9$$
$$1 + 3 + 5 + 7 = 16$$
$$1 + 3 + 5 + 7 + 9 = 25$$

If this pattern continues without end, then the statement

$$1 + 3 + 5 + 7 + \ldots + (2n - 1) = n^2$$

is true for all positive integers *n*.

The general statement above is true for the first several values of *n*. There is, however, no number of examples that would prove it true for all positive integers. To prove such a statement true for all positive integers, you can use a method called mathematical induction.

Theorem	Principle of Mathematical Induction

Let *S* be a statement involving a positive integer *n*.

Then *S* is true for all positive integers if the following two conditions hold.

1. *S* is true for $n = 1$.

2. For any positive integer *k*, if *S* is true for *k*, then *S* is true for $k + 1$.

The principle of mathematical induction is like a chain reaction in an infinite line of dominoes. Proving that a statement is true for $n = 1$ is like knocking over the first domino. Knowing that if the statement is true for any value of *k* then it will be true for $k + 1$ is like knowing that if any domino is knocked over the one after it will be knocked over also.

EXAMPLE Using Mathematical Induction

Prove that the following statement is true for all positive integers *n*.

$$1 + 3 + 5 + \ldots + (2n - 1) = n^2$$

Proof First show that the statement is true for $n = 1$.

$2n - 1 = n^2$	**Use the statement.**
$2(1) - 1 \stackrel{?}{=} 1^2$	**Substitute 1 for *n*.**
$2 - 1 \stackrel{?}{=} 1^2$	**Multiply.**
$1 = 1 ✓$	**Simplify.**

The statement is true for $n = 1$.

Next, assume that the statement is true for k.

$$1 + 3 + 5 + \ldots + (2k - 1) = k^2$$

From this assumption, prove that the statement is true for $k + 1$.

$$1 + 3 + 5 + \ldots + [2(k + 1) - 1] \overset{?}{=} (k + 1)^2 \qquad \textbf{Write the statement for } k + 1.$$

$$1 + 3 + 5 + \ldots + (2k + 1) \overset{?}{=} (k + 1)^2 \qquad \textbf{Simplify the left side.}$$

$$1 + 3 + 5 + \ldots + (2k - 1) + (2k + 1) \overset{?}{=} (k + 1)^2 \qquad \textbf{Rewrite to show the odd number preceding } (2k + 1).$$

$$k^2 + (2k + 1) \overset{?}{=} (k + 1)^2 \qquad \textbf{Substitute from the assumption.}$$

$$(k + 1)^2 = (k + 1)^2 \checkmark \qquad \textbf{Factor the left side.}$$

The proof shows that conditions 1 and 2 of the principle of mathematical induction are true. By the principle, then, $1 + 3 + 5 + \ldots + (2n - 1) = n^2$ is true for all positive integers, which is what we wanted to prove.

EXERCISES   1–10. See back of book.

1. Test the statement from the example to verify that it is true for $n = 6, 7$, and 8.

2. Complete the mathematical induction steps below to prove that
$$2 + 4 + 6 + \ldots + 2n = n(n + 1)$$
is true for all positive integers n.
  a. Show that the statement is true for $n = 1$.
  b. What statement will you assume to be true?
  c. What statement will you prove true using the assumption from part (b)?
  d. Express the sum in your statement from part (c) in terms of what you assumed. Then substitute and simplify to complete the proof.

Use mathematical induction to prove that each statement is true for all positive integers n.

3. $\dfrac{1}{1 \cdot 2} + \dfrac{1}{2 \cdot 3} + \dfrac{1}{3 \cdot 4} + \ldots + \dfrac{1}{n(n + 1)} = \dfrac{n}{n + 1}$

4. $1 + 2 + 3 + \ldots + n = \dfrac{n(n + 1)}{2}$

5. $1 + 4 + 7 + \ldots + (3n - 2) = \dfrac{n(3n - 1)}{2}$

6. $\dfrac{1}{2} + \left(\dfrac{1}{2}\right)^2 + \left(\dfrac{1}{2}\right)^3 + \left(\dfrac{1}{2}\right)^4 + \ldots + \left(\dfrac{1}{2}\right)^n = 1 - \left(\dfrac{1}{2}\right)^n$

7. $n^2 + n$ is divisible by 2.

8. $1 \cdot 2 + 2 \cdot 3 + 3 \cdot 4 + \ldots + n(n + 1) = \dfrac{n(n + 1)(n + 2)}{3}$

9. $1^2 + 2^2 + 3^2 + \ldots + n^2 = \dfrac{n(n + 1)(2n + 1)}{6}$

10. $a_1 + a_1 r + a_1 r^2 + a_1 r^3 + \ldots + a_1 r^{n - 1} = \dfrac{a_1(1 - r^n)}{1 - r}, r \neq 1$

(This is the formula for the sum of a finite geometric series, page 614.)

Evaluating Series

Students use features on the LIST OPS and LIST MATH menus of a graphing calculator to explore two ways of calculating the sum of a series. These ideas can be applied to earlier work on series as well as in Lesson 11-6.

Resources

Students may use any graphing calculator that has features for automatically generating a sequence and evaluating the corresponding series.

Teaching Notes

Students may want to use the techniques explained here to take another look at sums of arithmetic and geometric series.

Error Prevention

When students use the procedure from Example 2, they may forget to identify the variable used in the explicit formula after they enter the formula itself. The calculator will announce a syntax error. Remind students that it is essential to identify the variable.

page 622 Technology

7. Answers may vary.
   Sample: The method from Example 1 is best to use with a short series of numbers; if given a series in summation notation use the method from Example 2, a long series may be converted to summation notation to take advantage of the Example 2 method as well.

Technology

Evaluating Series

You can use a graphing calculator to evaluate series with limits.

1 EXAMPLE Using the Sum Feature

Find the sum of the terms of the sequence: 15, 30, 45, 60, 75, 90, 105.

Step 1 Enter the sequence in a list. Exit using **QUIT**.

Step 2 Select 5 from the **MATH** menu of the **LIST** feature.

Step 3 Enter the list number. Press **ENTER**.

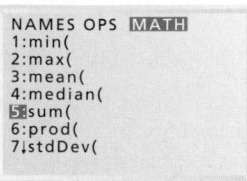

● The sum of the series $15 + 30 + 45 + \ldots + 105$ is 420.

2 EXAMPLE Evaluating a Sum

Use your graphing calculator to evaluate $\sum_{n=1}^{5} \frac{n^2}{2}$.

Step 1 Access the **SUM** feature (Step 2 above).

Step 2 Select 5 from the **OPS** menu of the **LIST** feature.

Step 3 Enter the explicit formula, N, the lower limit, the upper limit, and 1 (because n increases by 1 each time). Press **ENTER**.

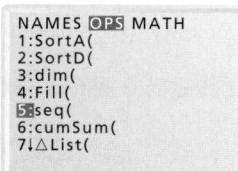

The value of $\sum_{n=1}^{5} \frac{n^2}{2}$ is 27.5.

EXERCISES

Evaluate each series.

1. $595 + 495 + 395 + 295$ **1780**

2. $3 + 9 + 27 + 81$ **120**

3. $4 + 2 + 1 + \ldots + \frac{1}{8}$ **$7\frac{7}{8}$**

4. $\sum_{n=1}^{5} (2n^2 - 5)$ **85**

5. $\sum_{x=1}^{5} 2^x$ **62**

6. $\sum_{n=1}^{5} -\sqrt{n^2}$ **−15**

7. **Writing** Compare the examples. When would you use the method from Example 1? When would you use the method from Example 2? Explain. **See margin.**

Area Under a Curve

Lesson Preview

What You'll Learn

OBJECTIVE
1 To find area under a curve

...And Why

To estimate the distance traveled by a peregrine falcon, as in Example 1

✔ **Check Skills You'll Need** (For help, go to Skills Handbook page 847.)

Find the area of a rectangle with the given length and width.

1. $\ell = 4$ ft, $w = 1$ ft **4 ft²**

2. $\ell = 5.5$ m, $w = 0.5$ m **2.75 m²**

3. $\ell = 6.2$ cm, $w = 0.1$ cm **0.62 cm²**

4. $\ell = 9\frac{1}{2}$ in., $w = 3\frac{5}{8}$ in. **See below.**

New Vocabulary • inscribed rectangles • circumscribed rectangles

4. $34\frac{7}{16}$ in.²

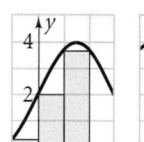 **Interactive lesson includes instant self-check, tutorials, and activities.**

OBJECTIVE

1 **Finding Area Under a Curve**

You can easily calculate the exact area under part of a line parallel to the x-axis, but it is not so easy to calculate the exact area under part of a curve. You can use rectangles to estimate the area under a curve and analyze data.

Inscribed rectangles are completely under the curve. The approximation is less than the area.

Circumscribed rectangles are partially above the curve. The approximation is greater than the area.

Real-World Connection

Adult peregrine falcons can reach speeds of 200 mi/h in a dive.

1 EXAMPLE **Real-World Connection**

Data Analysis The curve at the right approximates the speed of a peregrine falcon during the first 20 s of a high-speed dive.

a. What does the area under the curve represent?

$$\text{area} = \frac{\text{meters}}{\text{second}} \cdot \text{seconds}$$ **Use dimensional analysis.**

$$= \text{meters}$$ **Simplify.**

The area under the curve approximates the total distance traveled by the peregrine falcon.

b. Use inscribed rectangles 5 units wide to estimate the area under the curve.

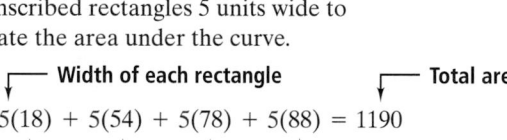

        ┌─ **Width of each rectangle**   ┌─ **Total area**

$$5(18) + 5(54) + 5(78) + 5(88) = 1190$$

Value of curve at upper edge of each rectangle

The area under the curve is about 1190 units². The peregrine falcon traveled about 1190 m during the first 20 s of its dive. The estimate is low because inscribed rectangles were used.

Time (s) — *Meters per second*

Lesson Preview

✔ **Check Skills You'll Need**

Area and Volume
Skills Handbook: p. 847,
Example 1, Exercises 1–4

Lesson Resources

📁 **Teaching Resources**
Practice, Reteaching, Enrichment

👥 **Reaching All Students**
Practice Workbook 11-6
Spanish Practice Workbook 11-6
Hands-On Activities 59

⏱ **Presentation Assistant Plus!**
Transparencies
• Check Skills You'll Need 11-6
• Additional Examples 11-6
• Student Edition Answers 11-6
• Lesson Quiz 11-6
PH Presentation Pro CD 11-6

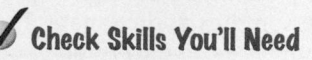 **ASSESSMENT SYSTEM**

Computer Test Generator CD

🌀 **Technology**
Resource Pro® CD-ROM
Computer Test Generator CD
Prentice Hall Presentation Pro CD

💻 **www.PHSchool.com**
Student Site
• Teacher Web Code: agk-5500
• Self-grading Lesson Quiz
Teacher Center
• Lesson Planner
• Resources

Plus

✔ Ongoing Assessment and Intervention

Before the Lesson	**During the Lesson**	**After the Lesson**
Diagnose prerequisite skills using:	**Monitor progress using:**	**Assess knowledge using:**
• Check Skills You'll Need	• Check Understanding	• Lesson Quiz
	• Additional Examples	• Computer Test Generator CD
	• Standardized Test Prep	

Math Background

In earlier work, students have found the approximate area of an irregularly shaped figure by placing the figure on a grid. In this lesson they approximate the area under a curve by using rectangles.

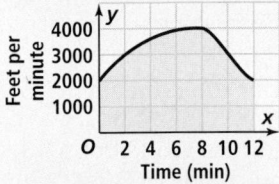

Additional Examples

1 The curve shown below approximates the speed of a car during a 12-minute drive.

a. What does the area under the curve represent? **total feet traveled in 12 min**

b. Use inscribed rectangles 2 units wide to estimate the area under the curve. **about 35,000 ft**

2 Estimate the area under the curve $f(x) = -0.5x^2 + 6$ for the domain $0 \le x \le 2$ by evaluating $A = \sum_{n=1}^{4} (0.5)f(a_n)$, where $a_1 = 0.5, a_2 = 1, a_3 = 1.5$, and $a_4 = 2$. **10.125 units²**

3 Use a graphing calculator to graph $f(x) = -x^2 + 4x + 5$. Find the area under the curve for the domain $1 \le x \le 4$. **24 units²**

Closure

Ask how the size of the rectangle will affect the approximation of the area under a curve. **Smaller rectangles yield a better approximation.**

✓ **Check Understanding**

1a. Answers may vary. Sample: 1545; it is much larger.

b. 1367.5; the mean is most accurate; it is between the other measures known to be smaller and larger than the actual value.

2a.

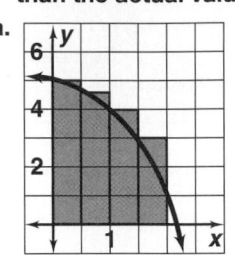

b. The left side values give the height of the circumscribed rectangles.

c. $0.5(5) + 0.5(4.75) + 0.5(4) + 0.5(2.75) = 8.25$ units²; it is greater than Example 2.

Need Help?

The area could also be estimated by evaluating $\sum_{n=1}^{8} (0.25)f(a_n)$ because there are 8 rectangles of width 0.25 between 0 and 2.

---

1 The graph at the right shows the curve from Example 1, but it shows circumscribed rectangles.

a. Estimate the area under the curve using circumscribed rectangles. How does your answer differ from the answer to Example 1?

b. Critical Thinking Find the mean of the answer using inscribed rectangles and the answer using circumscribed rectangles. Of the three answers, which is the most accurate? Explain. **a–b. See left.**

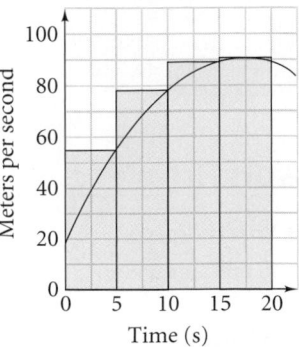

You can use summation notation to represent the area of a series of rectangles and to approximate the area under the curve $f(x)$. Let a_n represent a point on the base of the nth rectangle.

$$A = \sum_{n=1}^{b} (w)f(a_n)$$

b ← number of rectangles
width of each rectangle — function value at a_n

The expression $f(a_n)$ gives the height of the nth rectangle.

2 EXAMPLE Using a Sum to Estimate Area Under a Curve

Estimate the area under the curve $f(x) = -x^2 + 5$ for the domain $0 \le x \le 2$ by evaluating the sum A.

$$A = \sum_{n=1}^{4} (0.5)f(a_n)$$

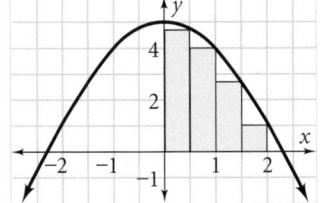

Evaluate the function at the right side of each rectangle.

$a_1 = 0.5, a_2 = 1, a_3 = 1.5, a_4 = 2$ Use an endpoint on the x-axis and on the right side of each rectangle.

$A = 0.5f(0.5) + 0.5f(1) + 0.5f(1.5) + 0.5f(2)$ Add the areas of the rectangles.

$= 0.5(4.75 + 4 + 2.75 + 1)$ total area = width of each rectangle · sum of the heights

$= 0.5(12.5)$ Add within parentheses.

$= 6.25$ Simplify.

● The indicated area is about 6.25 units².

✓ **Check Understanding**

2 a. Sketch the graph from Example 2 and draw circumscribed rectangles for the domain $0 \le x \le 2$. **a–c. See above left.**

b. Critical Thinking To find the area using these rectangles, you should evaluate the function at the left side of each rectangle. Explain why.

c. Use the circumscribed rectangles to write and evaluate a sum that approximates the area under the curve for the domain $0 \le x \le 2$. Compare your answer to the answer in Example 2.

---

624   Chapter 11   Sequences and Series

👥 Reaching All Students

| **Below Level** Show that the height of the right-most circumscribed rectangle in Exercise 1a does not occur at the right or left of the interval. | **Advanced Learners** Print curve and carefully cut out the area. Weigh the piece on a balance. Cut out and weigh a piece of paper one unit on each side. Then divide to get the area. | **Error Prevention** See note on page 625. **Alternative Method** See note on page 624. |

You can use a graphing calculator to find the exact area under a curve.

3 EXAMPLE Using a Graphing Calculator

Graph the function $f(x) = -2x^2 + 5$. Find the area under the curve for the domain $-1 \le x \le 1.5$.

Step 1 Input the equation. Adjust the window values.

Step 2 Access the $\int f(x)dx$ feature from the CALC menu.

Step 3 Use the lower limit of $x = -1$.

Step 4 Use the upper limit of $x = 1.5$.

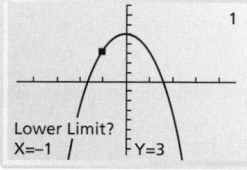

Lower Limit?
X=−1   Y=3

Xmin=−4.7   Ymin=−7
Xmax=4.7   Ymax=8
Xscl=1   Yscl=1

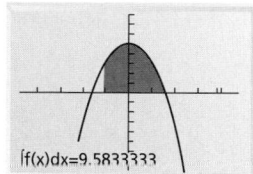

∫f(x)dx=9.5833333

Graphing Calculator Hint

To move the cursor by tenths along the x-axis, set your x window values to multiples of 4.7 or press **ZOOM** 4.

● The area under the curve between $x = -1$ and $x = 1.5$ is $9.58\overline{3}$ units^2.

✓ **Check Understanding** ❸ Use the equation from Example 3 and a graphing calculator. Find the area under the curve for each domain.

a. $0 \le x \le 1$ **4.3̄**   b. $-1 \le x \le 1$ **8.6̄**   c. $-1.5 \le x \le 0$ **5.25**

EXERCISES

For more practice, see *Extra Practice*.

Practice and Problem Solving

A Practice by Example

Example 1
(page 623)

Given each set of axes, what does the area under the curve represent?

1. y-axis: production rate, x-axis: time **total produced**

2. y-axis: rate of growth, x-axis: time **amount of growth**

3. y-axis: miles per gallon, x-axis: gallons **miles**

4. y-axis: distance traveled per year, x-axis: years **distance traveled**

5. y-axis: price per pound of gold, x-axis: pounds of gold **total price**

Use the given rectangles to estimate each area.

6.
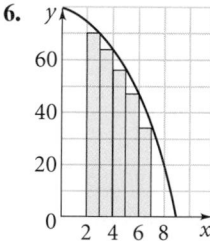
270 units^2

7.
110 units^2

8.
480 units^2

Lesson 11-6 Area Under a Curve **625**

3. Practice

Assignment Guide

▼ **Objective**
  Ⓐ Ⓑ Core 1–41
  Ⓒ Extension 42–45

Standardized Test Prep 46–50

Mixed Review 51–58

Teaching Tip

Exercises 1–5 You may need to give a hint if students have trouble knowing what units to use in the answers. Use ideas from dimensional analysis. For instance, in Exercise 1, time $\times \frac{\text{units produced}}{\text{time}} = $ units produced.

Error Prevention

Exercises 24–29 Watch for students who use circumscribed rather than inscribed rectangles. You may need to help them understand the difference.

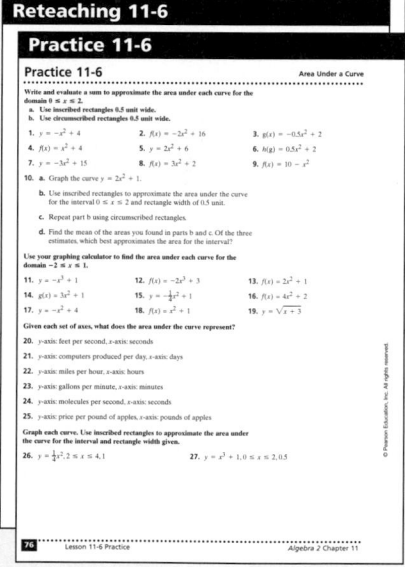

Alternative Assessment

Have students work individually. They will need a graphing calculator. Ask them to construct three functions whose graphs are above the x-axis for $2 \le x \le 5$. Ask them to approximate the area under the graph of each function for this domain by using rectangles of width 0.5. Then have them use the calculator to find each area by using the $\int f(x)dx$ feature on the CALC menu.

pages 625–627   Exercises

32. 9 units²

33. 7.5 units²

34. 15 units²

35. 3.46 units²

36. 8.05 units²

37. 9.75 units²

626

Example 2
(page 624)

Write and evaluate a sum to approximate the area under each curve for the domain $0 \le x \le 2$.   9–17. See back of book.
a. Use inscribed rectangles 1 unit wide.
b. Use circumscribed rectangles 1 unit wide.

9. $f(x) = \frac{1}{2}x^2$ 10. $y = -x^2 + 5$ 11. $g(x) = x^2 + 1$

12. $y = -x^2 + 4$ 13. $y = \frac{2}{3}x^2 + 5$ 14. $h(x) = 5x^2$

15. $y = 4 - \frac{1}{4}x^2$ 16. $h(x) = -(x - 2)^2 + 5$ 17. $y = (x - 2)^2 + 2$

Example 3
(page 625)

Find the area under each curve for the domain $0 \le x \le 1$.

18. 1.6 units²

18. $y = -x^2 + 2$ 19. $f(x) = x + 2$ **2.5 units²** 20. $y = x^3$ **0.25 units²**

21. $y = -x^4 + 2x^3 + 3$ 22. $y = x^5 - x^2 + 2.5$ 23. $y = -(x - 1)^3 + 3$
    3.3 units²   **2.3 units²**   **3.25 units²**

B **Apply Your Skills**

Graph each curve. Use inscribed rectangles to approximate the area under the curve for the interval and rectangle width given.   24–29. See back of book.

24. $y = x^2 + 1, 1 \le x \le 3, 0.5$ 25. $y = 3x^2 + 2, 2 \le x \le 4, 1$

26. $y = x^2, 3 \le x \le 5, 0.5$ 27. $y = 2x^2, 3 \le x \le 5, 1$

28. $y = x^3, 1 \le x \le 3, 0.25$ 29. $y = x^2 + 4, -2 \le x \le 2, 0.5$

30. **a.** Graph the curve $y = \frac{1}{3}x^3$. **a, c–d. See back of book.**
    b. Use inscribed rectangles to approximate the area under the curve for the interval $0 \le x \le 3$ and rectangle width of 1 unit. **3 units²**
    c. Repeat part (b) using circumscribed rectangles.
    d. Find the mean of the areas you found in parts (b) and (c). Of the three estimates, which best approximates the area for the interval? Explain.

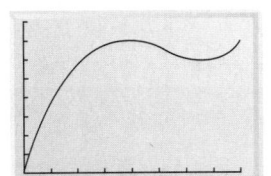

Xmin: 0   Ymin: 0
Xmax: 200   Ymax: 70
Xscl: 25   Yscl: 10

31. The graph at the left approximates the speed of a car as it enters a highway from a stopped position and merges with traffic. The x-axis represents time in seconds, and the y-axis represents miles per hour.
    a. Copy the graph. Use inscribed rectangles half the width of a grid square to estimate the total distance the car traveled in 50 s. **a–b. See back of book.**
    b. **Writing** How does your choice of inscribed or circumscribed rectangles in part (a) affect your area estimate?

Evaluate the area under each curve for $-1 \le x \le 2$. 32–37. See margin.

32. $f(x) = -x^2 + 4$ 33. $y = (x - 0.5)^2 + 1.75$ 34. $g(x) = 2 + 3x^2$

35. $y = \sqrt{1 + x}$ 36. $g(x) = 2^x + 1$ 37. $y = x^3 + 2$

38. $y = -(x - 1)^2 + 4\frac{1}{3}$ 39. $h(x) = \sqrt{x^2}$ 40. $f(x) = -x^4 + 2x^3 + 3$
    10 units²   **2.5 units²**   **9.9 units²**

41. **Open-Ended** Write equations for three curves that are positive for $1 \le x \le 3$. Use your graphing calculator to find the area under each curve for this domain. **Check students' work.**

C **Challenge**

42c. The estimate in (a) is closer to the actual area because there is less area between the curve and the rectangles when more rectangles are used.

42. Approximate the area under the curve $f(x) = x^2$ for the interval $0 \le x \le 4$ by evaluating each sum. Use inscribed rectangles.
    a. $\sum_{n=1}^{8} (0.5)f(a_n)$ **17.5 units²**   **b.** $\sum_{n=1}^{4} (1)f(a_n)$ **14 units²**
    c. Which estimate is closer to the actual area under the curve? Explain.

43. **a.** Graph $y = \frac{1}{4}x^3 + 1$ and $y = 1$ over the domain $-4.7 \le x \le 4.7$.
    b. **Critical Thinking** Evaluate the area under each curve for the interval $-1.5 \le x \le 1.5$. What do you notice? Explain. **a–b. See margin.**

43a.

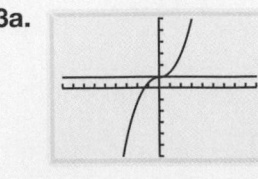

b. The area under both curves is the same, 3 units², over the interval $-1.5 \le x \le 1.5$; this is true because the amount of area *above* $y = \frac{1}{4}x^3 + 1$ and *below* $y = 1$ on the left side of the y-axis is equal to the area *below* $y = \frac{1}{4}x^3 + 1$ and *above* $y = 1$ on the right side of the y-axis.

45b.

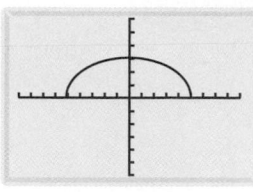

23.56 units²

44. Critical Thinking Use your graphing calculator to find the area of the triangle with vertices $(-3, 0), (-1, 3)$, and $(1, 0)$. (*Hint:* First find the function whose graph makes a peak at $(-1, 3)$.) **6 units²**

45. a. Write the equation $\frac{x^2}{25} + \frac{y^2}{9} = 1$ in calculator-ready form. $y = \sqrt{9 - \frac{9x^2}{25}}$

b. Graph the top half of the ellipse. Calculate the area under the curve for the interval $-5 \le x \le 5$.

c. Use symmetry to find the area of the entire ellipse. **47.12 units²**

d. Open-Ended Find the area of another symmetric shape by graphing part of it. Sketch your graph and show your calculations. **Check students' work.**

Standardized Test Prep

Multiple Choice

Use the graph of $f(x) = \sqrt{x} + 2$ for Exercises 46–49.

46. Which series represents the area of four inscribed rectangles? **A**
A. $(1)(2) + (1)(3) + (1)(3.4) + (1)(3.7)$
B. $(1)(3) + (1)(3.4) + (1)(3.7) + (1)(4)$
C. $(1 + 2 + 3 + 4)(0 + 1 + 2 + 3)$
D. $(1 + 2 + 3 + 4)(3 + 3.4 + 3.7 + 4)$

47. Which series represents the area of four circumscribed rectangles? **G**
F. $(1)(2) + (1)(3) + (1)(3.4) + (1)(3.7)$
G. $(1)(3) + (1)(3.4) + (1)(3.7) + (1)(4)$
H. $(1 + 2 + 3 + 4)(0 + 1 + 2 + 3)$
I. $(1 + 2 + 3 + 4)(3 + 3.4 + 3.7 + 4)$

48. Which of the following is the most accurate value of the area under $f(x) = \sqrt{x} + 2$ for $0 \le x \le 4$? **B**
A. 12.1   B. 14.1   C. 16.1   D. 24.0

49. Which expression does NOT represent a reasonable estimate of the area under $f(x) = \sqrt{x} + 2$ for $0 \le x \le 4$? **G**
F. $\sum_{n=1}^{4} f(a_n)$ G. $\sum_{n=1}^{5} (0.2) f(a_n)$ H. $\sum_{n=1}^{8} (0.5) f(a_n)$ I. $\sum_{n=1}^{10} (0.4) f(a_n)$

Short Response

50. The area under a curve is estimated using inscribed rectangles and circumscribed rectangles. Explain why the mean of these two values might be a more accurate estimate than either one. **See margin.**

Take It to the NET
Online lesson quiz at
www.PHSchool.com
Web Code: aga-1106

Mixed Review

Lesson 11-5

Determine whether the sum of each infinite geometric series exists.

51. $4 + 2 + 1 + \frac{1}{2} + \frac{1}{4} + \dots$ **has a sum**

52. $-972 - 324 - 108 - \dots$ **has a sum**

Lesson 10-5

Write the equation of each hyperbola in standard form. Sketch the graph.

53. $9x^2 - 16y^2 = 144$ **54.** $x^2 - 25y^2 = 25$ **55.** $16x^2 - 10y^2 = 160$
53–55. See margin.

Lesson 9-6

Solve each equation. Check your solution.

56. $\frac{x}{4} = \frac{x-3}{8} - 3$ **57.** $\frac{5}{2-x} = \frac{4}{2x+1}$ $\frac{3}{14}$ **58.** $\frac{x}{x+1} - \frac{x}{x-3} = 9$ $\frac{7 \pm 2\sqrt{73}}{9}$

Lesson 11-6 Area Under a Curve   **627**

Standardized Test Prep

Resources
For additional practice with a variety of test item formats:
- Standardized Test Prep, p. 633
- Test-Taking Strategies, p. 628
- Test-Taking Strategies with Transparencies

Technology Tip
Exercise 48 If graphing calculators are allowed for the test, the fastest way to answer this kind of question is probably to use the $\int f(x)dx$ feature on the CALC menu. (Read the integral of f of x d x; this function from Calculus gives the limiting value of approximations to the desired area.)

50. [2] The mean might be a better estimate since it is between the estimate using inscribed rectangles, which is too low, and the estimate using circumscribed rectangles, which is too high.

[1] incomplete explanation

53. $\frac{x^2}{16} - \frac{y^2}{9} = 1;$
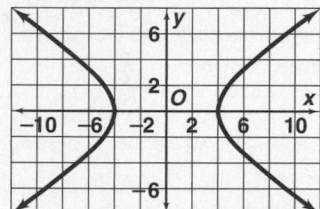

54. $\frac{x^2}{25} - \frac{y^2}{1} = 1;$
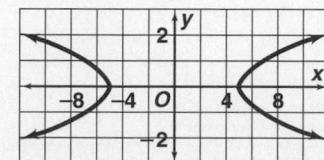

55. $\frac{x^2}{10} - \frac{y^2}{16} = 1;$
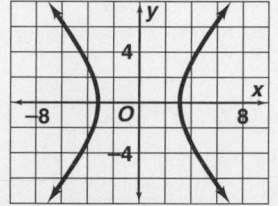

Using Estimation

Estimation is a useful skill in eliminating choices and in checking the reasonableness of answers obtained by using pencil and paper calculations or a calculator.

Resources

Test-Taking Strategies with Transparencies
• Transparency 11
• Practice sheet p. 35

Teaching Notes

1 EXAMPLE **Teaching Tip**

A diagram can be very helpful in making sure you have taken all aspects of this situation into consideration. Estimation is helpful in eliminating answer choices A and B. You must be careful when you decide between C and D. Remember that when the ball bounces, it travels up a certain distance and then down that same distance before it bounces again.

Test-Taking Strategies with Transparencies

Test-Taking Strategy: Using Estimation

Sometimes you can estimate to find the answer.

Example Shannon used a calculator to find 7.95 × 13. Which is a reasonable number to see in the calculator display?

A. 1.0335   B. 10.335   C. 103.35   D. 1033.5

Estimate: Round to the nearest whole number.

7.95 × 13

8 × 13 = 104

Only C is near 104.

The answer is 103.35, or choice C.

Estimate to find the answer.

1. A pair of shoes is on sale for 33% off the original price of $47.99. About how much will the shoes cost on sale?

A. $64   B. $48   C. $32   D. $16

2. The circumference of a circle with radius 5 in. is about

F. 29 in.   G. 31 in.   H. 33 in.   I. 35 in.

3. Estimate the value of $2x^2 + 5$ when $x = 4.1$.

A. 69   B. 37   C. 23   D. 21

Solutions

1. C
2. G
3. B

Transparency 11

Estimating the answer to a test question may help you eliminate one or more answers, find the answer, or check your answer.

1 EXAMPLE

A ball drops from a height of 2 m. After it hits the floor, it rebounds to 60% of its previous height. Find the total distance the ball travels before it comes to rest.

    A. 3 m   **B.** 3.5 m   **C.** 5 m   **D.** 10 m

Estimate the distance the ball travels before the second bounce. The ball rebounds about one-half its previous height, so it travels down 2 m, then up about 1 m, and then down about 1 m. Since $2 + 1 + 1 = 4$, the ball travels about 4 m before the second bounce. You can eliminate answer choices A and B.

Since the distance the ball travels on each bounce models a geometric sequence with $r < 1$, the final answer will be closer to 4 than to 10. The answer is C.

2 EXAMPLE

A student jogs 3.8 mi around a local reservoir five afternoons a week. The student claims to have run about 990 mi around the reservoir last year. Is the student correct? Explain.

$3.8 \cdot 5 \cdot 52 \approx 4 \cdot 5 \cdot 50$ **distance · days per week · weeks per year**

         $= 20 \cdot 50 = 1000$ **Simplify and multiply.**

The student ran about 1000 mi around the reservoir last year. The student is correct.

EXERCISES

Choose the best estimate.

1. A square is inscribed in a circle. The square has side length 4 cm. Find the approximate area of the circle. **A**
    A. 25 cm^2 **B.** 16 cm^2 **C.** 15 cm^2 **D.** 12 cm^2

2. Find the approximate area of the region between the function $y = (x - 1)^2$, the x-axis, and the y-axis. **D**
    A. 2 units^2 **B.** 1.5 units^2 **C.** 1 units^2 **D.** 0.5 units^2

Estimate the answer to each problem.

3. Suppose your aunt gives you $100 on your birthday, along with a promise to give you one half the previous year's amount each year until the amount reaches 1¢. What is the total amount of money that your aunt will give you? **$200**

4. If two numbers a and b are approximately equal, their arithmetic mean and their geometric mean are approximately equal. Use this fact to estimate the value of $\sqrt{56}$. **7.5**

Chapter Review

Vocabulary

arithmetic mean (p. 595)
arithmetic sequence (p. 594)
arithmetic series (p. 608)
circumscribed rectangles (p. 623)
common difference (p. 594)
common ratio (p. 600)

converge (p. 615)
diverge (p. 615)
explicit formula (p. 590)
geometric mean (p. 602)
geometric sequence (p. 600)
geometric series (p. 614)

inscribed rectangles (p. 623)
limit (p. 609)
recursive formula (p. 590)
sequence (p. 588)
series (p. 607)
term (p. 588)

 Reading Math
Understanding Vocabulary

Take It to the NET
Online vocabulary quiz at www.PHSchool.com
Web Code: agj-1151

Choose the correct vocabulary term to complete each sentence.

1. When using Σ to write a series, you can use __?__ to indicate how many terms you are adding. **limits**

2. Using __?__ to approximate the area under a curve will result in an approximation that is greater than the area. **circumscribed rectangles**

3. An ordered list of terms is a __?__. **sequence**

4. If an infinite geometric series __?__, then it must have a sum. **converges**

5. There is a __?__ between consecutive terms in a geometric sequence. **common ratio**

Skills and Concepts

11-1 Objectives

▼ To identify mathematical patterns (p. 588)

▼ To use a formula for finding the nth term of a sequence (p. 590)

6. $a_n = a_{n-1} + 17, a_1 = 5$; 73, 90, 107

7. $a_n = -7 \cdot a_{n-1}, a_1 = 1$; 2401, −16,807, 117,649

8. $a_n = a_{n-1} + 9, a_1 = -2$; 34, 43, 52

A **sequence** is an ordered list of numbers called **terms**. A **recursive formula** gives the first term and defines the other terms in a sequence by relating each term to the one before it. An **explicit formula** expresses the nth term in a sequence in terms of n, where n is a positive integer.

Write a recursive formula for each sequence. Then find the next three terms.

6. 5, 22, 39, 56, . . .   7. 1, −7, 49, −343, . . .   8. −2, 7, 16, 25, . . .

Write an explicit formula for each sequence. Then find a_{12}.

9. 1, 4, 7, 10, . . .
$a_n = 3n - 2$; 34

10. 2, 4, 8, 16, . . .
$a_n = 2^n$; 4096

11. −24, −6, 24, 66, . . .
$a_n = 6n^2 - 30$; 834

12. **Writing** Explain how you decide whether a formula is explicit or recursive.
See margin.

11-2 Objectives

▼ To identify and generate arithmetic sequences (p. 594)

In an **arithmetic sequence,** the difference between consecutive terms is constant. The difference is the **common difference.** A recursive formula for an arithmetic sequence is $a_n = a_{n-1} + d$, given a_1. An explicit formula for an arithmetic sequence is $a_n = a_1 + (n - 1)d$. In each case, a_n is the nth term, a_1 is the first term, n is the number of the term, and d is the common difference. The **arithmetic mean** of any two numbers (or terms in a sequence) is the average of the two numbers.

$$\text{arithmetic mean} = \frac{\text{sum of two numbers}}{2}$$

- Self-grading Vocabulary Test

Chapter 11   Chapter Review   **629**

The sidebar (Resources):

11 Chapter Review

Resources

Student Edition
Extra Practice, Ch. 11, p. 832
English/Spanish Glossary, p. 871
Properties and Formulas, p. 865
Table of Symbols, p. 861

Reaching All Students
Reading and Math Literacy 11D
Spanish Reading and Math Literacy 11D

ASSESSMENT SYSTEM

Standardized Test Prep
- Ch. 11 practice in standardized test formats

www.PHSchool.com
Student Site
- Self-grading Vocabulary Test
Teacher Center
- Resources

Plus **iTEXT**

pages 629–631   Chapter Review

12. Answers may vary. Sample: If the formula uses the previous term, then it is recursive; otherwise it is explicit.

629

34. $\displaystyle\sum_{n=1}^{5} 13 - 3n;\ 20$

35. $\displaystyle\sum_{n=1}^{7} 45 + 5n;\ 455$

36. $\displaystyle\sum_{n=1}^{11} 4.6 + 1.4n;\ 143$

37. $\displaystyle\sum_{n=1}^{8} 23 - 2n;\ 112$

Is each given sequence arithmetic? If so, identify the common difference and find the 32nd term of the sequence.

13. $2, 4, 7, 10, 13, \ldots$ **no**   **14.** $3, 18, 33, 48, \ldots$ **15.** $7, 10, 13, 16, \ldots$
                                 yes; $d = 15; a_{32} = 468$ **yes;** $d = 3; a_{32} = 100$

Find the missing term(s) of each arithmetic sequence.

16. $1, \blacksquare, 9, \ldots$ **5**   **17.** $104, \blacksquare, 99, \ldots$ **101.5**   **18.** $-4.6, \blacksquare, -5.2, \ldots$ $\overset{-4.9}{}$

19. $-1, \blacksquare, 11, \ldots$ **5**   **20.** $-13, \blacksquare, \blacksquare, \blacksquare, -3, \ldots$ **21.** $2, \blacksquare, \blacksquare, \blacksquare, -0.4, \ldots$
                                 −10.5, −8, −5.5   **1.4, 0.8, 0.2**

Find a_n, the arithmetic mean of the given terms.

22. $a_{n-1} = 7, a_{n+1} = 15$ **11**   **23.** $a_{n-1} = -2, a_{n+1} = 3$ **0.5**

 24. Writing Explain how you can determine if a sequence is arithmetic.
If the terms of the sequence have a common difference, then the sequence is arithmetic.

11-3 Objectives

▼ To identify and generate geometric sequences (p. 600)

In a **geometric sequence,** the ratio of consecutive terms is constant. The ratio is the **common ratio.** You can use recursive or explicit formulas to express a geometric sequence.

A recursive formula for a geometric sequence is $a_n = a_{n-1} \cdot r$, given a_1. An explicit formula for a geometric sequence is $a_n = a_1 \cdot r^{n-1}$. In each case, a_n is the nth term, a_1 is the first term, n is the number of the term, and r is the common ratio.

You can find the geometric mean of two positive numbers by taking the positive square root of the product of the two numbers.

$$\text{geometric mean} = \sqrt{\text{product of two numbers}}$$

25. yes; $r = \frac{1}{2}, a_n = 1\left(\frac{1}{2}\right)^{n-1}$, $\frac{1}{16}, \frac{1}{32}$

26. no

27. yes; $r = 1.2, a_n = 3(1.2)^{n-1}$, 6.2208, 7.46496

31. $-10, -5, -2.5$

32. $-\frac{1}{3}, -\frac{2}{3}, -\frac{4}{3}$

33. $3\frac{1}{2}, 12\frac{1}{4}, 42\frac{7}{8}$

The middle term of any three consecutive terms in a geometric sequence is the geometric mean of the first and third terms.

Is the given sequence geometric? If so, identify the common ratio, write the explicit formula for the sequence, and find the next two terms.

25. $1, \frac{1}{2}, \frac{1}{4}, \frac{1}{8}, \ldots$ **26.** $1, 3, 5, 7, \ldots$ **27.** $3, 3.6, 4.32, 5.184, \ldots$

Find the missing term(s) of each geometric sequence.

28. $3, \blacksquare, 12, \ldots$ **6**   **29.** $60, \blacksquare, \frac{20}{3}, \ldots$ **20**   **30.** $0.004, \blacksquare, 0.4, \ldots$ $\overset{0.04}{}$

31. $-20, \blacksquare, \blacksquare, \blacksquare, -1.25, \ldots$ **32.** $-\frac{1}{6}, \blacksquare, \blacksquare, \blacksquare, -2\frac{2}{3}, \ldots$ **33.** $1, \blacksquare, \blacksquare, \blacksquare, 150\frac{1}{16}, \ldots$

11-4 Objectives

▼ To write and evaluate arithmetic series (p. 607)

▼ To evaluate a given number of terms of a series (p. 609)

A **series** is the expression for the sum of the terms of a sequence. Whether the sequence is finite or infinite determines whether the series is finite or infinite.

An **arithmetic series** is the expression for the sum of the terms of an arithmetic sequence. The sum S_n of the first n terms of an arithmetic series is $S_n = \frac{n}{2}(a_1 + a_n)$.

You can use a summation symbol, Σ, and **limits** to write a series. Limits are the least and greatest integral values of n.

Use summation notation to write each arithmetic series for the specified number of terms. Then evaluate the sum.   34–37. See margin.

34. $10 + 7 + 4 + \ldots; n = 5$ **35.** $50 + 55 + 60 + \ldots; n = 7$

36. $6 + 7.4 + 8.8 + \ldots; n = 11$ **37.** $21 + 19 + 17 + \ldots; n = 8$

Find the number of terms in each series, the first term, and the last term. Then evaluate the sum.

11, $-\frac{10}{3}$, -10; $-\frac{220}{3}$

38. $\sum\limits_{n=1}^{3} (17n - 25)$ **3, −8, 26; 27**

39. $\sum\limits_{n=2}^{10} \left(\frac{1}{2}n + 3\right)$ **9, 4, 8; 54**

40. $\sum\limits_{n=5}^{15} \left(-\frac{2}{3}n\right)$

 41. Business Deanna Jones opened a video rental store this year with 400 tapes. She plans to buy 150 new tapes each year from now on. Deanna expects to have 1300 tapes available during her fifth year in business. At her current purchasing rate, will she reach her goal? Explain. **No; she will have only 1150 available by the end of the fifth year.**

11-5 Objectives

▼ To evaluate a finite geometric series (p. 614)

▼ To evaluate an infinite geometric series (p. 615)

A **geometric series** is the sum of the terms of a geometric sequence. The sum S_n of the first n terms of a geometric series is $S_n = \frac{a_1(1 - r^n)}{1 - r}$.

You can find the sum of some infinite geometric series. When $|r| < 1$, the series gets closer and closer, or **converges**, to $S = \frac{a_1}{1 - r}$. When $|r| \geq 1$, the series **diverges**, or approaches no limit.

Find the sum of the series to the given term.

42. $3 + 1 + \frac{1}{3} + \ldots ; S_7$ $4\frac{121}{243}$

43. $1 + 2 + 4 + \ldots ; S_5$ **31**

44. $80 - 40 + 20 - \ldots ; S_8$ **53.125**

45. $12 + 2 + \frac{1}{3} + \ldots ; S_4$ $14\frac{7}{18}$

Decide whether each infinite geometric series *converges* or *diverges*. Then state whether each series has a sum, and if it does, find the sum.

46. converges; S = 187.5

47. diverges; no sum

46. $150 + 30 + 6 + \ldots$

47. $2.2 + 2.42 + 2.662 + \ldots$

48. $-10 - 20 - 40 - \ldots$
   diverges; no sum

49. $\frac{2}{3} + \frac{4}{9} + \frac{8}{27} + \ldots$
   converges; S = 2

11-6 Objective

▼ To find the area under a curve (p. 623)

You can approximate the area under a curve by using **inscribed rectangles** or **circumscribed rectangles.** If you use inscribed rectangles, the approximation is less than the area under the curve. If you use circumscribed rectangles, the approximation is greater than the area under the curve. You can use summation notation to represent the area of a series of rectangles and the approximate area under a curve $f(x)$:

$$A = \sum_{n=1}^{b} (w)f(a_n),$$

where b is the number of rectangles, w is the width of each rectangle, a_n is a point on the base of the nth rectangle, and $f(a_n)$ is the function value at a_n.

Write and evaluate a sum to approximate the area under each curve for the domain $0 \leq x \leq 2$. 50–55. See margin.

a. Use inscribed rectangles 1 unit wide.
b. Use circumscribed rectangles 1 unit wide.
c. Use a graphing calculator to find the exact area under the curve.

50. $y = x^2$ **51.** $y = x^3 + 1$ **52.** $y = -2x^2 + 8$

53. $y = -x + 5$ **54.** $y = x^3 + 4$ **55.** $y = x^2 + 3$

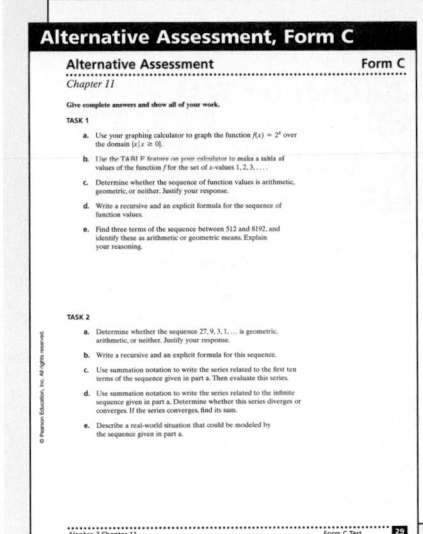

50. $A = \sum\limits_{n-1}^{2} 1 \cdot f(a_n)$

a. **1 unit²**
b. **5 units²**
c. $\frac{8}{3}$ **units²**

51. $A = \sum\limits_{n=1}^{2} 1 \cdot f(a_n)$

a. **3 units²**
b. **11 units²**
c. **6 units²**

52. $A = \sum\limits_{n=1}^{2} 1 \cdot f(a_n)$

a. **6 units²**
b. **14 units²**
c. **10.$\overline{6}$ units²**

53. $A = \sum\limits_{n=1}^{2} 1 \cdot f(a_n)$

a. **7 units²**
b. **9 units²**
c. **8 units²**

54. $A = \sum\limits_{n=1}^{2} 1 \cdot f(a_n)$

a. **9 units²**
b. **17 units²**
c. **12 units²**

55. $A = \sum\limits_{n=1}^{2} 1 \cdot f(a_n)$

a. **7 units²**
b. **11 units²**
c. $8\frac{2}{3}$ **units²**

Resources

Chapter Test — Form B

Chapter Test — Form A

 **Chapter 11**
Chapter Test

💻 ······· **Take It to the NET**
Online chapter test at
www.PHSchool.com
Web Code: aga-1152

Write a recursive and an explicit formula for each sequence. Then find a_{12}. 1–3. See margin.

1. $7, 13, 19, 25, 31, \ldots$ **2.** $10, 20, 40, 80, 160, \ldots$

3. After one month at a new job, you have saved $50. You decide to save $5 more each month.
   a. Write an explicit formula to model the amounts you save each month.
   b. How much will you save in the sixth month?

Determine whether each sequence is *arithmetic*, *geometric*, or *neither*. Then find the tenth term.

4. $23, 27, 31, 35, 39, \ldots$ **arithmetic; 59**   **5.** $-12, -5, 2, 9, 16, \ldots$ **arithmetic; 51**

6. $-5, 15, -45, 135, -405, \ldots$ **geometric; 98,415**

Find the arithmetic mean a_n of the given terms.

7. $a_{n-1} = 4, a_{n+1} = 12$ **8**

8. $a_{n-1} = -11, a_{n+1} = 23$ **6**

9. Open-Ended Write an arithmetic sequence. Then write an explicit formula for it.
   Check students' work.

Determine whether each sequence is *arithmetic* or *geometric*. Then identify the common difference or the common ratio.

10. $1620, 540, 180, 60, 20, \ldots$ **geometric; $r = \frac{1}{3}$**

11. $78, 75, 72, 69, 66, 63, 60, \ldots$ **arithmetic; $d = -3$**

12. $\frac{3}{32}, \frac{3}{16}, \frac{3}{8}, \frac{3}{4}, \frac{3}{2}, 3, 6, \ldots$ **geometric; $r = 2$**

In Exercises 13–16, a_1 is the first term of a sequence, r is a common ratio, and d is a common difference. Write the first five terms. 13–15. See margin.

13. $a_1 = 2, r = -2$ **14.** $a_1 = 3, d = 7$

15. $a_1 = -100, r = \frac{1}{5}$ **16.** $a_1 = 19, d = -4$
                                              19, 15, 11, 7, 3

Find the missing term of each geometric sequence.

17. $2, \blacksquare, 0.5, \ldots$ **1**   **18.** $2, \blacksquare, 8, \ldots$ **4**

Find the sum of each infinite geometric series.

19. $0.5 + 0.05 + 0.005 + \ldots$ $\frac{5}{9}$

20. $1 - \frac{1}{2} + \frac{1}{4} - \ldots$ $\frac{2}{3}$ **21.** $6 + 5 + \frac{25}{6} + \ldots$ **36**

Determine whether each series is *arithmetic* or *geometric*. Then find the sum to the given term.

22. $2 + 7 + 12 + \ldots; S_8$ **arithmetic; 156**

23. $5000 + 1000 + 200 + \ldots; S_{15}$ **geometric; 6250**

24. $1 + 0.01 - 0.98 - \ldots; S_5$ **arithmetic; −4.9**

For each sum, find the number of terms, the first term, and the last term. Then evaluate the sum.

25. $\sum_{n=1}^{5} (3n + 1)$ **5, 4, 16; 50** **26.** $\sum_{n=1}^{8} \frac{2n}{3}$ **8, $\frac{2}{3}$, $\frac{16}{3}$; 24**

27. $\sum_{n=4}^{10} (0.8n - 0.4)$ **7, 2.8, 7.6; 36.4** **28.** $\sum_{n=2}^{6} (-2)^{n-1}$ **5, −2, −32; −22**

29. Critical Thinking How can you tell whether or not a geometric series converges? Include examples of both types of series. Evaluate the series that converges. **See margin.**

🌐 **30. Investments** A diamond is purchased for $2500. Suppose its value increases 5% each year. Find the value of the diamond after 8 years. **$3693.64**

🌐 **31. Physics** A ball on a pendulum moves 40 cm on its first swing. On each succeeding swing back or forth it moves 90% of the distance of the previous swing. Write the first four terms of the sequence of swing lengths. **40, 36, 32.4, 29.16**

Given each set of axes, what does the area under the curve represent?

32. y-axis: miles per hour, x-axis: hours **miles**

33. y-axis: pounds per in.^{2}, x-axis: in.^{2} **pounds**

34. y-axis: dollars per gallon, x-axis: gallons **dollars**

Use left endpoints in the given interval and inscribed rectangles 1 unit wide to approximate the area under the curve $y = f(x)$. 35–38. See back of book.

35. $y = 2x^2; 0 \le x \le 2$

36. $y = x^2 + 1; -1 \le x \le 2$

37. $y = x^3; 1 \le x \le 3$

✏️ **38. Writing** Explain how you could use circumscribed and inscribed rectangles to estimate the area under a curve.

page 632   Chapter Test

1. $a_n = a_{n-1} + 6, a_1 = 7,$
   $a_n = 1 + 6n$; **73**

2. $a_n = a_{n-1} \cdot 2, a_1 = 10,$
   $a_n = 10 \cdot 2^{n-1}$; **20,480**

3a. savings = 50
   + 5(months − 1)

b. $75

13. 2, −4, 8, −16, 32

14. 3, 10, 17, 24, 31

15. $-100, -20, -4, -\frac{4}{5}, -\frac{4}{25}$

29. If the absolute value of the common ratio is less than 1, then it will converge; check students' work.

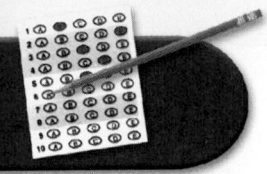
Standardized Test Prep

Reading Comprehension Read the passage below. Then answer the questions on the basis of what is *stated* or *implied* in the passage.

Arcs To cut an arc-topped shape from a rectangular board, carpenters may choose a circular arc or an elliptical arc.

Suppose the length of the board is $2m$ and the height is n.

For a circular arc, the carpenter can find the radius of the circle by using the formula $r = \frac{m^2 + n^2}{2n}$. Using a tack at the center C, and a piece of string of length r, the carpenter can draw a circular arc through points P, T, and Q.

For an elliptical arc, the carpenter can find points A and B on $\overline{PQ}$ that are $\sqrt{m^2 - n^2}$ units from point Z. Using tacks at A and B and a piece of string of length $2m$, the carpenter can draw an elliptical arc through points P, T, and Q.

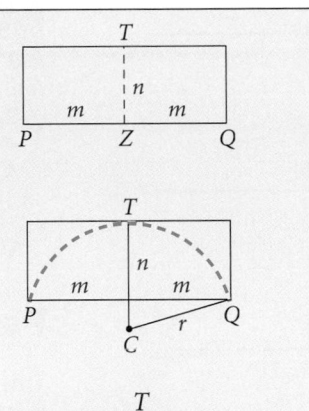

Students must be able to extract information from reading passages, answer multiple choice questions, and construct responses in order to be successful on current state and national assessments.

To answer the questions, students apply skills and concepts from this chapter and previous chapters.
Multiple Choice: Items 1–5
Extended Response: Items 6–9

Resources

Teaching Resources
Cumulative Review

Reaching All Students
Spanish Cumulative Review

ASSESSMENT SYSTEM

Standardized Test Prep
• Ch. 11 Standardized Test Practice
Assessment Masters
• Cumulative Review
Computer Test Generator CD
• Standardized Test Practice

www.PHSchool.com
• Standardized Test Practice
• Resources

Plus

1. What is the value of PQ? **C**
   A. $m + n$
   B. $2n$
   C. $2m$
   D. $\sqrt{m^2 + n^2}$

2. For a circular arc, what is the distance from point C to point Z? **G**
   F. r
   G. $r - n$
   H. $r - m$
   I. $\frac{m^2 + n^2}{2n}$

3. Suppose $m = 21$ in. and $n = 7$ in. For a circular arc, what length of string should the carpenter use? **D**
   A. 19.8 in.
   B. 22.1 in.
   C. 28 in.
   D. 35 in.

4. Suppose $\overline{PQ}$ is on the x-axis of a coordinate system and $\overline{TZ}$ is on the y-axis. What are the coordinates of the foci of the ellipse needed to draw an elliptical arc? **I**
   F. $(m, 0)$ and $(-m, 0)$
   G. $(0, n)$ and $(0, -n)$
   H. $(\sqrt{m^2 + n^2}, 0)$ and $(-\sqrt{m^2 + n^2}, 0)$
   I. $(\sqrt{m^2 - n^2}, 0)$ and $(-\sqrt{m^2 - n^2}, 0)$

5. Suppose $m = 70$ cm and $n = 9$ cm. For an elliptical arc, what length of string should the carpenter use? **C**
   A. 18 cm
   B. 70.58 cm
   C. 140 cm
   D. 276.72 cm

6. Use the Pythagorean Theorem and a diagram of a circular arc to derive the formula $r = \frac{m^2 + n^2}{2n}$. **See margin.**

7. A carpenter wants to cut the largest possible circular arc-topped shape from a board that is 40 in. by 12 in. Find the length of string the carpenter should use. $72\frac{2}{3}$ **in.**

8. Using a board the same size as the one in Question 7, a carpenter wants to cut the largest possible elliptical arc-topped shape. What length of string should the carpenter use? Where should the carpenter attach the string? **See margin.**

9. A board is 30 in. by 15 in. Compare the largest circular and elliptical arc-topped shapes that can be cut from the board. **They are the same.**

page 633   Standardized Test Prep

6.

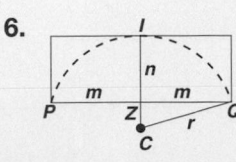

Consider $\triangle ZQC$.
$$r^2 = m^2 + (r - n)^2$$
$$r^2 = m^2 + r^2 - 2nr + n^2$$
$$r^2 - r^2 + 2nr = m^2 + r^2 - 2nr + n^2 - r^2 + 2nr$$
$$2nr = m^2 + n^2$$
$$r = \frac{m^2 + n^2}{2n}$$

8. 40 in.; one end should be attached 16 in. from point Z along $\overline{PZ}$, and the other end should be attached 16 in. from point Z along $\overline{QZ}$.

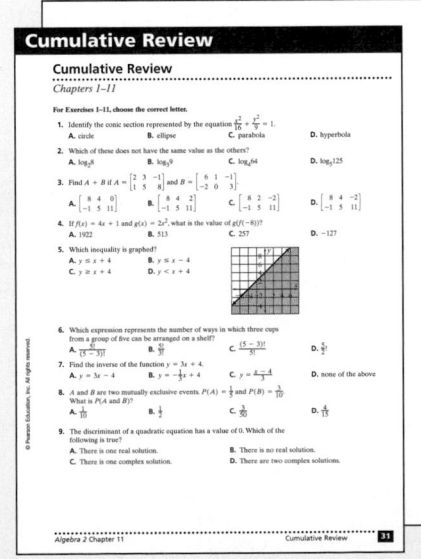

Probability and Statistics

Chapter at a Glance

12-1 Probability Distributions

NCTM 5, 10
- ▼ Making a Probability Distribution
- ▽ Using a Probability Distribution

12-2 Conditional Probability

NCTM 5, 10
- ▼ Finding Conditional Probabilities
- ▽ Using Formulas and Tree Diagrams

12-3 Analyzing Data

NCTM 4, 5
- ▼ Measures of Central Tendency
- ▽ Box-and-Whisker Plots

12-4 Standard Deviation

NCTM 4, 5, 10
- ▼ Finding Standard Deviation
- ▽ Using Standard Deviation

12-5 Working With Samples

NCTM 4, 5, 6
- ▼ Sampling Without Bias
- ▽ Sample Size

12-6 Binomial Distributions

NCTM 5, 6, 8, 9
- ▼ Finding Binomial Probabilities
- ▽ Using a Binomial Distribution

12-7 Normal Distributions

NCTM 5, 6, 8, 9
- ▼ Using a Normal Distribution
- ▽ Using the Standard Normal Curve

NCTM STANDARDS 2000

1 Number and Operations
2 Algebra
3 Geometry
4 Measurement
5 Data Analysis and Probability
6 Problem Solving
7 Reasoning and Proof
8 Communication
9 Connections
10 Representation

Pacing Options

This chart suggests pacing only for the lessons and their parts. It is provided as a possible guide. It will help you determine how much time you have in your schedule to cover other components, such as the features, Chapter Review, and Chapter Test.

Day	Traditional (45 min.)	Block (90 min.)
1	12-1 ▼	12-1 ▼ ▽
2	12-1 ▽	12-2 ▼ ▽
3	12-2 ▼	12-3 ▼ ▽
4	12-2 ▼ ▽	12-4 ▼ ▽
5	12-3 ▼	12-5 ▼ ▽
6	12-3 ▽	12-6 ▼ ▽
7	12-4 ▼	12-7 ▼ ▽
8	12-4 ▽	
9	12-5 ▼ ▽	
10	12-6 ▼	
11	12-6 ▽	
12	12-7 ▼	
13	12-7 ▽	

NAEP Correlation (National Assessment of Educational Progress 2000 Mathematics Objectives)

12-1	12-2	12-3	12-4	12-5	12-6	12-7
D2a, D8, D3c	D11d, D9	D1a, D2c, D2d	D4, D5a	D3a, D3b	D9	D5b, D10c

N = Number Sense, Properties, and Operations; **M** = Measurement; **G** = Geometry and Spatial Sense; **D** = Data Analysis, Statistics, and Probability; **A** = Algebra and Functions

Math Background

Chapter Overview

The study of probability and statistics emerged in the seventeenth and eighteenth centuries. Their development was motivated by studies of games of chance, errors in measurements, and numerical data about political units such as cities and counties. Formal development has continued since then and both have found numerous applications in many fields of human endeavor. This chapter introduces students to probability distributions, ways of organizing and displaying data, and measures of central tendency. Students study measures of variation to describe how data in a data set are spread out. They consider samples and the relationship between sample size and margin of error. Finally, they learn about binomial experiments, binomial distributions, and normal distributions.

Probability Distributions 12-1

Everyone knows that when rolling two number cubes, a sum of 7 is the most likely outcome, but why? A frequency table showing a probability distribution will easily answer this question. Probability distributions are needed for the rest of this chapter.

Conditional Probability 12-2

Deciding the likelihood of an event can be influenced by knowing that some other event has taken place. The *conditional probability* of *B*, given that event *A* has taken place, is the fraction of those times when *A* happens that event *B* also happens. The definition is an extension of the original definition of a probability as the ratio of favorable outcomes to total possible outcomes. Here, 'total possible outcomes' is the restricted sample space where *B* occurs.

Analyzing Data 12-3

As a society, we are somewhat obsessed with data. Newspaper articles, television news reports, and advertisements are common places to find data and statistics presented as factual support for certain conclusions. Because we are bombarded with so much data, it is important to be able to analyze data, in order to make our own conclusions about the data. The measures of central tendency that are presented in this lesson provide several such ways to analyze data.

Note that the mean is affected by an outlier, the median may or may not be, and the mode is not. Note also that a mode may not be near the center of the data set at all; many statisticians do not include it as a measure of *central* tendency.

Standard Deviation 12-4

When we say that the standard deviation for a set of data is large or small, it is important to interpret "large" and "small" in relation to the size of the data values.

The *range* of a data set is not to be confused with the *range* of a relation. Some calculators provide a list of one-variable statistics when a set of data is entered. The statistics may include mean, sum of data values, sum of squared data values, sample standard deviation, population standard deviation, number of data points, minimum value, maximum value, median, first quartile (lower hinge), and third quartile (upper hinge).

Working with Samples 12-5

The term *population* is used in statistics as a carryover from the time when statistics was used mainly to study sociological and economical phenomena. Today, the term is applied to sets or collections of objects, actual or conceptual, and mainly to sets of numbers, measurements, or observations—in any case, the data to be studied. A *sample* is simply part of the population—a subset of the possible data.

Sampling procedures that are based on random processes provide every element of the population with an equal and independent chance of being chosen. Such procedures aim to provide information about the sample that can be generalized to the population. Random sampling procedures can be contrasted with sampling that is not based on random processes—for example, questionnaires, which are more susceptible to *bias*. To illustrate, a person who responds to a questionnaire *voluntarily* provides information and may be more likely to have a strong opinion than a person who chooses not to respond to the questionnaire. In this situation the sample and the total population may differ significantly.

Understanding samples is crucial to interpreting data. In today's world, surveys are commonly used to sway public opinion. The validity of a survey, however, depends on the sample. Being able to understand samples will help students interpret the surveys they hear about on the news or read about in the newspaper.

Binomial and Normal Distributions 12-6, 12-7

Note that the binomial distribution is not identical to the normal distribution but can only be approximated by it under certain conditions. The *standard* normal distribution is the normal distribution with mean 0 and standard deviation 1. You may wish to tell students that the equation for the standard normal distribution is $y = \frac{\sqrt{2}}{2} e^{-\frac{x^2}{2}}$. As is necessary for a probability distribution, the total area between the *x*-axis and the curve is one—another example of a limiting value, since the curve does not touch the *x*-axis.

Students can easily compute the exact percentages for the various regions under the normal curve.

Some students may observe that $P(z < a) = P(z \le a)$. In terms of area, the inclusion of $z = a$ makes no difference—a line has no width. Various practical problems may or may not include an endpoint of the interval.

Ongoing Assessment and Intervention

Tools for Monitoring Student Progress

The Prentice Hall *Algebra 2* program provides you with many options for assessment in the Student Edition, the Teacher's Edition and the teaching resources. From these options you may choose instructional materials and techniques that are appropriate for your students and support your district's curriculum requirements.

Instant Check System™ in Chapter 12

Allows students to check their own learning before, during, and after each lesson.

Diagnosing Readiness before the chapter (p. 634)

Check Skills You'll Need exercises in each lesson (pp. 636, 642, 648, 656, 663, 671, 678)

Check Understanding questions with each Example (pp. 636, 637, 638, 639, 642, 643, 644, 648, 649, 650, 651, 652, 657, 658, 659, 660, 663, 664, 665, 666, 672, 673, 674, 678, 679, 680)

Checkpoint Quiz (pp. 655, 677)

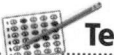 Test Prep in Chapter 12

Teaches students strategies and gives them practice with all the test item formats they will encounter on state tests and standardized national exams.

Standardized Test Prep exercises in each lesson (pp. 641, 646, 654, 655, 662, 668, 669, 676, 683, 684)

Test-Taking Strategies (p. 686)

Standardized Test Prep (p. 691)

All your assessment needs in one place!

Program Assessment

Assess student progress throughout the *Algebra 2* text with blackline masters and CD-ROM.

Assessment Resources

- Checkpoint Quizzes 1 & 2
- Chapter Test, Forms A & B
- Chapter Alternative Assessment

Spanish versions available.

Computer Test Generator

- Unlimited questions of varying difficulty for every lesson objective.
- Create your own practice sheets, quizzes, and tests, or use the pre-made Chapter Tests.
- Diagnose readiness with questions on prerequisite skills.
- Prepare students by making tests based on standardized test objectives.
- Access Algebra 1, Geometry, and Algebra 2 content—all on one CD-ROM.

Test Preparation

A three-step approach to preparing students for high stakes, national, and state exams.

❶ **Diagnose & Prescribe**

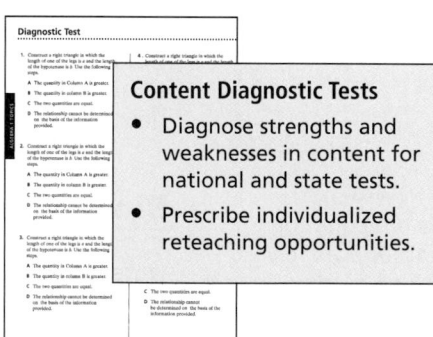

Content Diagnostic Tests
- Diagnose strengths and weaknesses in content for national and state tests.
- Prescribe individualized reteaching opportunities.

❷ **Review & Reteach**

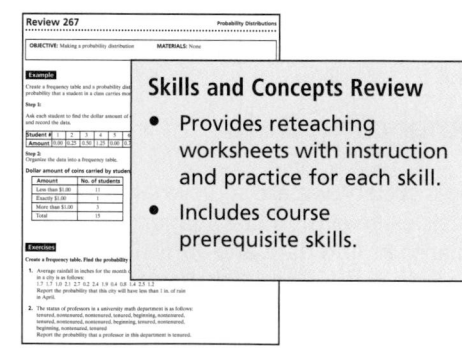

Skills and Concepts Review
- Provides reteaching worksheets with instruction and practice for each skill.
- Includes course prerequisite skills.

❸ **Practice & Assess**

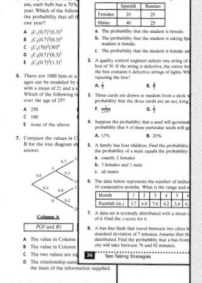

Test Preparation
- Features practice tests for End-of-Course and SAT/ACT exams.
- Includes standardized test practice by chapter for ongoing review.

Teacher's Guide with answers and correlations.

Test-Taking Strategies with Transparencies
- Support the Test-Taking Strategies pages in the Student Edition.
- Provide a teaching transparency and a practice worksheet for each strategy.

# Reaching All Students

Support in the Student Text and Additional Resources

The textbook, the iText, and other technology components provide numerous opportunities to reach students of various ability levels and learning styles. Each Teacher's Edition lesson suggests how you can help *all* your students be successful and understand the mathematics in Chapter 12.

Below Level

Student Edition
- Diagnosing Readiness*: p. 634
- Check Skills You'll Need*: pp. 636, 642, 648, 656, 663, 671, 678

Reteaching
Chapter 12 Support File: pp. 8–14

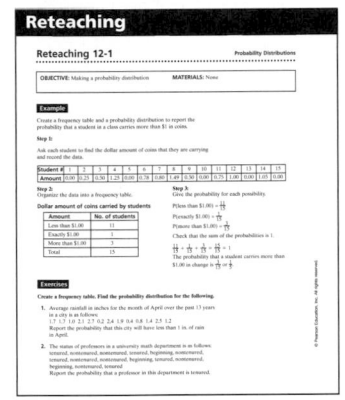

Advanced Learners

Student Edition
- Challenge exercises: pp. 641, 645, 646, 654, 662, 668, 676, 683
- Extension, p. 647

Enrichment
Chapter 12 Support File: pp. 15–21

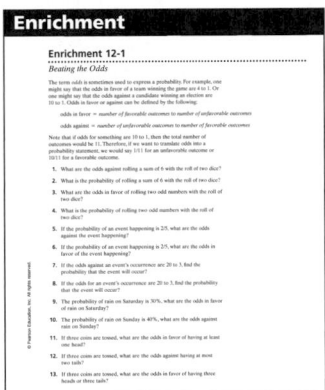

Connections to Precalculus Masters
Chapter 12 Enrichment Topic: Combinatorics

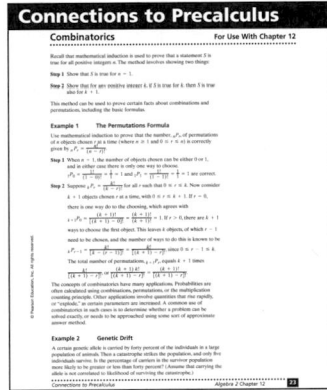

* Can be used with all ability levels to ensure mastery of prerequisite skills.

Reading and Math Literacy

Student Edition
- Vocabulary: pp. 635, 687, *plus* in every Lesson Preview
- Reading Math: pp. 636, 648, 650, 657, 658, 664, 668, 670
- Illustrated Glossary: pp. 871–913

Reading and Math Literacy Masters
Chapter 12: pp. 45–48

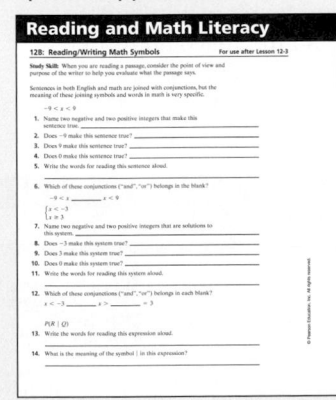

English Learners

Student Edition
- English/Spanish Illustrated Glossary: pp. 871–913

Workbook and Masters
Spanish Practice Workbook: pp. 1–7
Spanish Reading and Math Literacy Masters: pp. 45–48

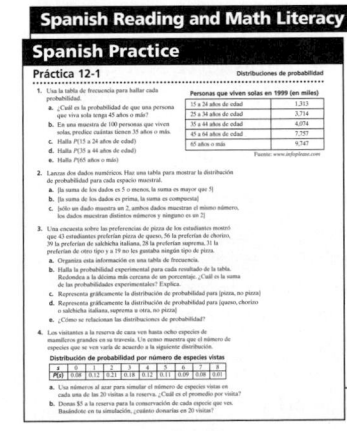

Learning Styles

Student Edition
- Investigation: pp. 656, 671
- Technology: pp. 649, 651, 676, 685
- Writing: pp. 640, 645, 647, 653, 654, 655, 661, 662, 667, 675, 680, 681, 690
- DK Activities: pp. 692–693

Activity Masters
Hands-On Activities: 55, 56

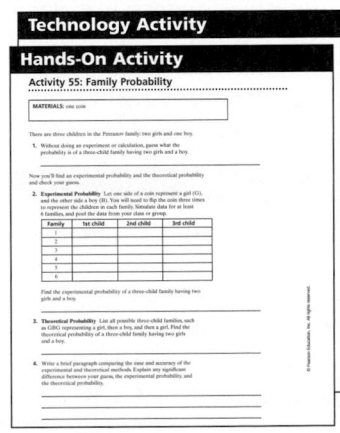

Program Resources

	Teaching Resources in Grab & Go™ Files				Resources for Reaching All Students			Spanish Resources			Presentation Assistant Plus! — Transparencies				Prentice Hall Presentation Pro CD-ROM
	Practice	Reteach	Enrich	Checkpoint Quiz	Reading & Math Literacy	Technology Activities	Hands-On Activities	Practice	Reading & Math Literacy	Checkpoint Quiz	Skills Check	Additional Examples	Answers to Exercises	Lesson Quiz	
12-1	■	■	■		■		■	■			■	■	■	■	■
12-2	■	■	■					■			■	■	■	■	■
12-3	■	■	■	■	■			■	■	■	■	■	■	■	■
12-4	■	■	■					■			■	■	■	■	■
12-5	■	■	■					■				■	■	■	■
12-6	■	■	■	■	■			■	■	■		■	■	■	■
12-7	■	■	■				■	■			■	■	■	■	■
For the chapter	Chapter Tests, Alternative Assessment, Cumulative Review, Cumulative Assessment				Connections to Precalculus Masters			Spanish Chapter Tests, Alternative Assessment, Cumulative Review, Cumulative Assessment			Classroom Aid Transparencies				

Also available for use with the chapter:

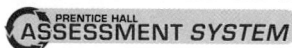 PRENTICE HALL **ASSESSMENT *SYSTEM***   *See page 634C.*

- Practice Workbook
- Solution Key

- For teacher support and access to student Web site materials, use Web Code agk-5500.
- For additional online and technology resources, see below.

Technology

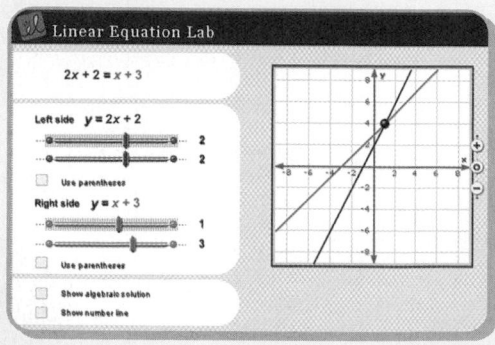 Online and on CD-ROM

Complete Interactive Student Text online and on CD-ROM—with instant feedback assessment, tutorial help, dynamic activities, instructional and real-world videos, audio, and additional practice.

www.PHSchool.com For Students

Use **Web Codes** for easy access to online activities, chapter projects, self-grading lesson quizzes and chapter tests, vocabulary quizzes, updated data sources, graphing calculator procedures, and more.

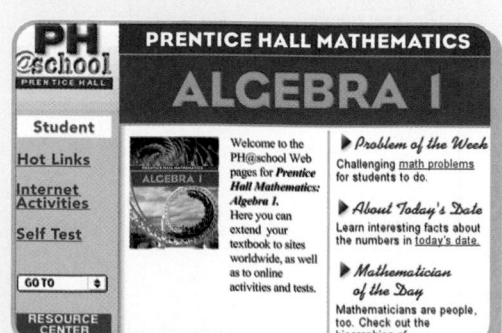

PH Success*Net* For Teachers

Online lesson planning with built-in state correlations, all the teaching resources, complete reference library, your own calendar and Teacher Web page, professional development, and more.

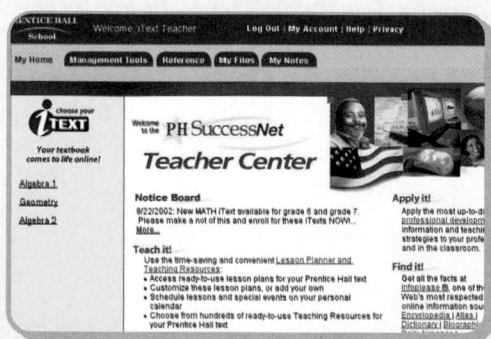

Presentation Assistant Plus!

The Prentice Hall *Presentation Assistant Plus!* provides you with the material you need to teach a lesson from beginning to end. Two easy-to-use formats—Transparencies and CD-ROM—allow you to present a lesson the way you are most comfortable.

Transparencies

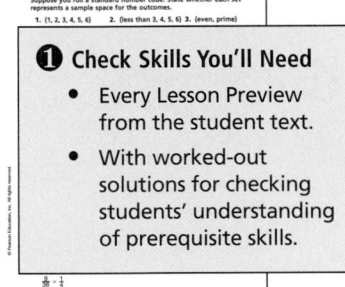

❶ Check Skills You'll Need
- Every Lesson Preview from the student text.
- With worked-out solutions for checking students' understanding of prerequisite skills.

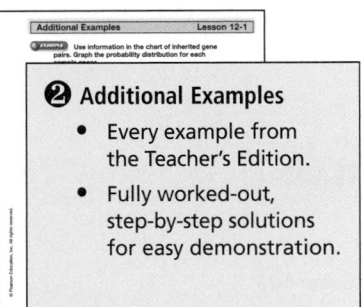

❷ Additional Examples
- Every example from the Teacher's Edition.
- Fully worked-out, step-by-step solutions for easy demonstration.

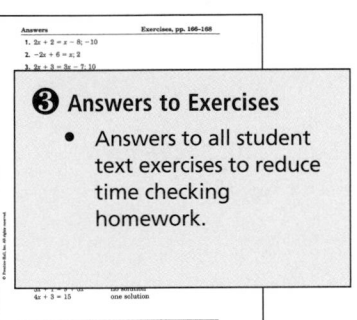

❸ Answers to Exercises
- Answers to all student text exercises to reduce time checking homework.

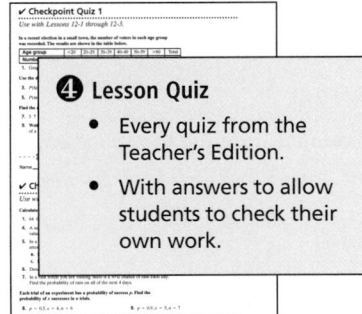

❹ Lesson Quiz
- Every quiz from the Teacher's Edition.
- With answers to allow students to check their own work.

Prentice Hall Presentation Pro CD-ROM

- Includes all Transparencies.
- Conveniently organized by lesson so you can easily ❶ Introduce, ❷ Teach, ❸ Check Homework, and ❹ Assess each lesson.
- Animated examples allow step-by-step instruction at your own pace.
- Easy to edit so you can create custom presentations.

Teaching Chapter 12 Using Presentation Assistant Plus!

	❶ Introduce	❷ Teach	❸ Check Homework	❹ Assess
	Check Skills You'll Need	Additional Examples	Student Edition Answers	Lesson Quiz
12-1	p. 77	pp. 223–227	✔	p. 159
12-2	p. 78	pp. 228–230	✔	p. 160
12-3	p. 79	pp. 231–235	✔	p. 161
12-4	p. 80	pp. 235–237	✔	p. 161
12-5	p. 81	pp. 238–240	✔	p. 162
12-6	p. 82	pp. 241–244	✔	p. 163
12-7	p. 83	pp. 244–246	✔	p. 164

 Throughout the Teacher's Edition, this symbol indicates material that is available on transparency in the Presentation Assistant Plus!

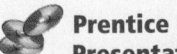 **Prentice Hall Presentation Pro**

CD-ROM with dynamic PowerPoint® presentations for every lesson. Helps you introduce and develop concepts, check homework, and assess progress. Part of Presentation Assistant Plus! *(See above.)*

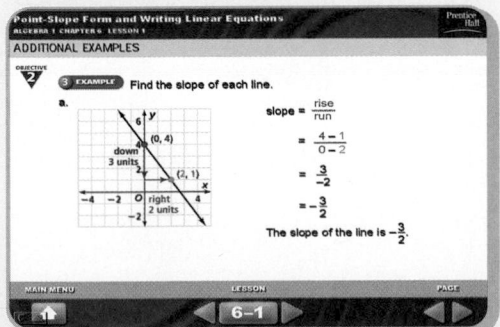

 Computer Test Generator

CD-ROM to create practice sheets and tests for course objectives and standardized tests. Includes Instant Chapter Tests™, online testing, and student reports. Part of the PH Assessment System. *(See page 634C.)*

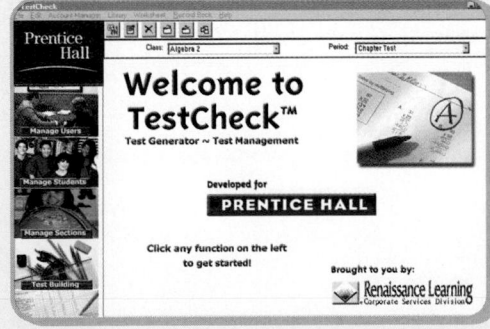

 Resource Pro® with Planning Express®

CD-ROM with a lesson planning tool that allows you to import state and local objectives. Includes electronic versions of all the teaching resources.

Chapter 12

Probability and Statistics

 Diagnosing Readiness

Students will find answers to these exercises in the back of their textbooks.

For intervention, direct students to:

Evaluating Expressions
Lesson 6-7: Example 3
Exercises 22–31
Extra Practice, p. 827

Expanding Binomials
Lesson 6-8: Example 2
Exercises 1–12
Extra Practice, p. 827

Finding Real Roots
Lesson 7-1: Example 1
Exercises 1–12
Extra Practice, p. 828

Finding Probability
Lesson 9-7: Example 2
Exercises 5–9
Extra Practice, p. 830

page 634   Diagnosing Readiness

7. $a^5 + 5a^4b + 10a^3b^2 + 10a^2b^3 + 5ab^4 + b^5$

8. $j^3 + 9j^2k + 27jk^2 + 27k^3$

9. $m^2 + 1.4m + 0.49$

10. $0.000064 + 0.00192t + 0.024t^2 + 0.16t^3 + 0.6t^4 + 1.2t^5 + t^6$

Where You've Been

- In Chapter 1, you learned to find theoretical and experimental probabilities.
- In Chapter 6, you learned to use the Binomial Theorem.
- In Chapter 9, you learned to find the probability of multiple events.

 **Diagnosing Readiness**

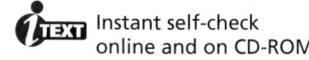 Instant self-check online and on CD-ROM

(For help, go to the Lesson in green.)

Evaluating Expressions (Lesson 6-7)

Evaluate each expression.

1. $5!$ **120**
2. $6!$ **720**
3. $4! \cdot 3!$ **144**
4. $_5C_5$ **1**
5. $_6C_1$ **6**
6. $_7C_4$ **35**

Expanding Binomials (Lesson 6-8)

Use Pascal's Triangle or the Binomial Theorem to expand each binomial. **7–10. See margin.**

7. $(a + b)^5$
8. $(j + 3k)^3$
9. $(m + 0.7)^2$
10. $(0.2 + t)^6$

Finding Real Roots (Lesson 7-1)

Find the real square roots of each number. Round to the nearest thousandth.

11. $\frac{1}{100}$ **±0.1**
12. $\frac{1}{200}$ **±0.071**
13. $\frac{1}{250}$ **±0.063**
14. $\frac{1}{391}$ **±0.051**
15. $\frac{1}{435}$ **±0.048**
16. $\frac{1}{757}$ **±0.036**

Finding Probability (Lesson 9-7)

A and *B* are independent events. Find *P*(*A* and *B*).

17. $P(A) = 0.4, P(B) = 0.2$ **0.08**
18. $P(A) = 0.25, P(B) = 0.5$ **0.125**
19. $P(A) = 0.85, P(B) = 0.10$ **0.085**

20. Find *P*(*A* or *B*) for the events in Exercise 19. **0.865**

 21. **Data Analysis** While processing a day's worth of new checkbook orders, a data entry operator notices that thirty percent of customers prefer the leather checkbook cover to the vinyl checkbook cover. Twenty percent prefer script lettering on their checks to any other kind of lettering. Find the probability that an order selected at random is for a leather checkbook cover with script lettering on the checks. **0.06**

Probability and Statistics

LESSONS

12-1 Probability Distributions

12-2 Conditional Probability

12-3 Analyzing Data

12-4 Standard Deviation

12-5 Working With Samples

12-6 Binomial Distributions

12-7 Normal Distributions

Key Vocabulary

- binomial probability (p. 673)
- box-and-whisker plot (p. 650)
- conditional probability (p. 642)
- cumulative probability (p. 636)
- interquartile range (p. 657)
- margin of error (p. 665)
- measures of central tendency (p. 648)
- measures of variation (p. 657)
- normal distribution (p. 678)
- outlier (p. 652)
- percentile (p. 651)
- probability distribution (p. 637)
- quartiles (p. 650)
- sample (p. 663)
- sample proportion (p. 663)
- standard deviation (p. 657)
- standard normal curve (p. 679)
- z-score (p. 659)

635

Chapter 12 Overview

Students begin their investigation into probability and statistics by learning about probability distributions and conditional probability. Next, students delve into statistics with lessons on analyzing data, standard deviation, and working with samples. The chapter is rounded out with lessons on binomial distributions and normal distributions.

Reading Math
Reading for Math Vocabulary, p. 670

Vocabulary
A complete list of terms, plus vocabulary exercises, appears in the Chapter Review, p. 687.

Illustrated Glossary
Examples for each vocabulary term, plus definitions in both English and Spanish, appear starting on p. 871.

Real-World Snapshots
See pages 692–693 for a real-world application of functions that utilizes Dorling Kindersley's (DK) unique graphic presentation.

Test-Taking Strategies
Answering the Question Asked, p. 686

Real-World Connections
Some of the applications you will find in this chapter are social science (12-1), oceanography (12-3), energy (12-4), quality control (12-6), and medicine (12-7).

www.PHSchool.com
Internet support for this chapter includes:
- Self-grading Vocabulary and Chapter 12 Tests
- Chapter Project
- Chapter Planner
- Chapter 12 Resources

Plus

Where You're Going

- In Chapter 12, you will learn to make and use a probability distribution to conduct a simulation.

- You will learn to use formulas, tree diagrams, and normal distributions to find the probability of an event.

- You will learn to use measures of central tendency and measures of variation to compare data in real-world problems.

Applying what you learn, on pages 692–693 you will do activities involving trains.

Probability Distributions

Lesson Preview

Lesson Resources

📁 Teaching Resources
Practice, Reteaching, Enrichment

👥 Reaching All Students
Practice Workbook 12-1
Spanish Practice Workbook 12-1
Reading and Math Literacy 12A
Spanish Reading & Literacy 12A
Hands-On Activities 55

⏱ Presentation Assistant Plus!
Transparencies
• Check Skills You'll Need 12-1
• Additional Examples 12-1
• Student Edition Answers 12-1
• Lesson Quiz 12-1
PH Presentation Pro CD 12-1

🖥 PRENTICE HALL ASSESSMENT SYSTEM
Computer Test Generator CD

💿 Technology
Resource Pro® CD-ROM
Computer Test Generator CD
Prentice Hall Presentation Pro CD

💻 www.PHSchool.com
Student Site
• Teacher Web Code: agk-5500
• Updated data
• Self-grading Lesson Quiz
Teacher Center
• Lesson Planner
• Resources

Plus 📘TEXT

What You'll Learn

OBJECTIVE 1 To make a probability distribution

OBJECTIVE 2 To use a probability distribution in conducting a simulation

... And Why

To conduct market research, as in Example 5

✓ Check Skills You'll Need (For help, go to Lesson 1-6.)

Suppose you roll a standard number cube. State whether each set represents a sample space for the outcomes.

1. {1, 2, 3, 4, 5, 6} **yes**   **2.** {less than 3, 4, 5, 6} **no**   **3.** {even, prime} **no**

Find each probability for two tosses of a number cube.

4. P(4 and 3) $\frac{1}{18}$ **5.** P(two odd numbers) $\frac{1}{4}$ **6.** P(two integers) **1**

New Vocabulary
• frequency table • cumulative probability
• probability distribution

OBJECTIVE 1 📘TEXT Interactive lesson includes instant self-check, tutorials, and activities.

Making a Probability Distribution

A **frequency table** is a list of the outcomes in a sample space and the number of times each outcome occurs.

1 EXAMPLE Making a Frequency Table

Below are three types of triangles: equilateral, isosceles, and scalene. Make a frequency table. For isosceles, use triangles with exactly two congruent sides.

Reading Math
Scalene comes from the Latin word for uneven.

Step 1 Count the number of each type.

Equilateral	⁄⁄⁄⁄ ⁄	
Isosceles	⁄⁄⁄⁄ ⁄⁄⁄⁄ ⁄	
Scalene	⁄⁄⁄⁄ ⁄⁄⁄	

Total number of triangles: 25

Step 2 Make a table.

Type	Number
Equilateral	6
Isosceles	11
Scalene	8
Total	25

1.

Type	Number
Acute	13
Right	7
Obtuse	5
Total	25

✓ Check Understanding

1 The triangles in Example 1 can also be described as acute, right, and obtuse. Make a frequency table using those categories. **See left.**

Probability over a continuous range of events is **cumulative probability**. You can use a frequency table to find cumulative probability.

636 Chapter 12 Probability and Statistics

✓ Ongoing Assessment and Intervention

Before the Lesson
Diagnose prerequisite skills using:
• Check Skills You'll Need

During the Lesson
Monitor progress using:
• Check Understanding
• Additional Examples
• Standardized Test Prep

After the Lesson
Assess knowledge using:
• Lesson Quiz
• Computer Test Generator CD

636

Need Help?

The experimental probability of an event is the ratio of the number of times the event occurs to the number of trials.

2 EXAMPLE Real-World  Connection

Social Science Use the frequency table. Find the probability that an elderly person living alone will have contact with his or her children more than once a week.

Contact Between Children and Elderly Who Live Alone

How Often Contact Is Made	Number of Elderly
7 times per week	680
2–6 times per week	276
1 time per week	236
Less than 1 time per week	199
Total	1391

Source: *Statistical Handbook on the American Family*

$P(\text{7 times per week}) = \frac{680}{1391}$ Find the experimental probability for each event in the table that represents contact more than once a week.

$P(\text{2–6 times per week}) = \frac{276}{1391}$

$\frac{680}{1391} + \frac{276}{1391} = \frac{956}{1391} \approx 0.687$ Add to find cumulative probability.

● The probability of contact more than once a week is about 0.687, or 68.7%.

✓ **Check Understanding** ❷ Find $P(\text{once a week or more})$.   **≈0.857, or 85.7%**

A **probability distribution** is a function that gives the probability of each event in a sample space. You can use a table or a graph to show a probability distribution.

3 EXAMPLE Probability Distributions

Suppose you roll two number cubes. Show the probability distribution for the sum of the numbers.

Method 1   Make a frequency table. Then extend the table to include probabilities.

Rolling Two Number Cubes

Sum	2	3	4	5	6	7	8	9	10	11	12
Frequency	1	2	3	4	5	6	5	4	3	2	1
Probability	$\frac{1}{36}$	$\frac{2}{36}$	$\frac{3}{36}$	$\frac{4}{36}$	$\frac{5}{36}$	$\frac{6}{36}$	$\frac{5}{36}$	$\frac{4}{36}$	$\frac{3}{36}$	$\frac{2}{36}$	$\frac{1}{36}$

← There are 36 possible outcomes.

← Divide to find the probability.

Method 2   Draw a graph.

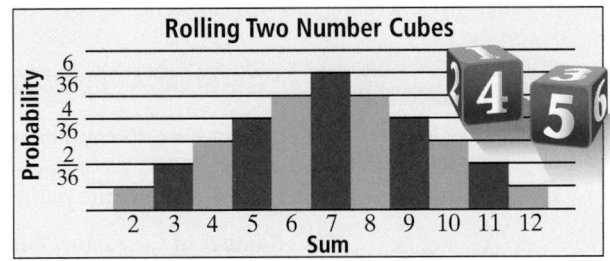

✓ **Check Understanding** ❸ Use a table or a graph to show the probability distribution for the roll of one number cube. **See back of book.**

 Reaching All Students

Below Level Graphs can help students understand frequency distributions. Have students create graphs for frequency tables to help them interpret the data.	**Advanced Learners** Have students discuss the frequency distribution of the heights of all high school seniors, and how the graph might change if only males were included.	**Tactile Learners** See note on page 637. **Error Prevention** See note on page 639.

2. Teach

Math Background

Recalling that the sum of the probabilities for a sample space must total 1 may help students compute cumulative probabilities correctly.

OBJECTIVE

1 **Teaching Notes**

1 EXAMPLE Tactile Learners

Suggest that students trace the triangles onto paper. Then they can cut out the triangles and sort them into categories in order to complete a frequency table.

Additional Examples

❶ Take a survey of your classmates' eye colors and make a frequency table with the data.
Answers may vary. Sample:

Eye Color	Number
Brown	15
Green	6
Blue	4
Total	25

❷ Use the frequency table. Find the probability that a student is involved in at least one extra-curricular activity.

Number of Activities	Number of Students
More than one activity	144
One activity	360
No activities	216
Total Students	720

0.7, or 70%

❸ Suppose you spin two spinners. Each spinner has 4 possible outcomes: 1, 2, 3, or 4. Show the probability distribution for the sum of the numbers.

Spinning Two Spinners

Sum	2	3	4	5	6	7	8
Frequency	1	2	3	4	3	2	1
Probability	$\frac{1}{16}$	$\frac{2}{16}$	$\frac{3}{16}$	$\frac{4}{16}$	$\frac{3}{16}$	$\frac{2}{16}$	$\frac{1}{16}$

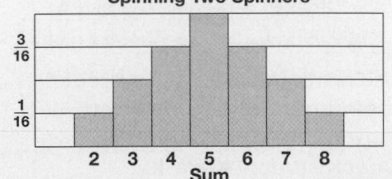

4️⃣ Use information in the chart of inherited gene pairs. Graph the probability distribution for each sample space.

Inherited Gene Pairs from One Recessive and One Hybrid Pea Plant

		Parent Plant	
		r	r
Parent	R	Rr	Rr
Plant	r	rr	rr

RR = dominant gene pair (red flower)
Rr = hybrid gene pair (pink flower)
rr = recessive gene pair (white flower)

a. Genotype Distribution

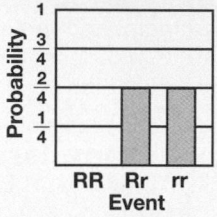

RR Rr rr
Event

b. Plant Color Distribution

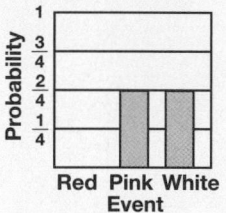

Red Pink White
Event

5️⃣ EXAMPLE **Technology Tip**

Students can type the command =INT(RAND()*100+1) into a spreadsheet cell to generate random numbers. Then they press *enter* to get a random number and copy and paste the cell to generate additional random numbers. Other commands allow students to test the random numbers and answer questions about a distribution.

🔖 **Additional Example**

5️⃣ The probability of an information desk at a community library receiving calls each hour varies according to the following distribution.

Number of Calls Each Hour

c	0	1	2	3	4	5
P(c)	0.05	0.15	0.25	0.3	0.2	0.05

Use random numbers to predict the number of calls received during an eight-hour shift.
Check students' work.

638

A situation may be described by more than one sample space. In that case, each sample space has its own probability distribution.

4️⃣ **EXAMPLE** **Real-World 🌐 Connection**

Genetics Use the information in the chart of inherited gene pairs. Graph the probability distribution for each sample space.

Inherited Gene Pairs From Two Hybrid Corn Plants

		Parent Plant	
		G	w
Parent	G	GG	Gw
Plant	w	Gw	ww

GG = dominant gene pair (green plant)
Gw = hybrid gene pair (green plant)
ww = recessive gene pair (white plant)

a. Genotype Distribution
{GG, Gw, ww}

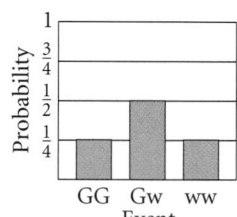

GG Gw ww
Event

b. Plant Color Distribution
{green, white}

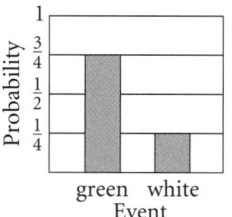

green white
Event

✔ **Check Understanding** 4️⃣ a. **Critical Thinking** Which probability distribution would be more useful to a farmer who wants to avoid raising white corn plants? Explain.
b. Make a probability distribution table for each sample space in Example 4.
a–b. See back of book.

You can design a simulation based on a probability distribution. First, use the probabilities to assign numbers to each event in the sample space. For example, if P(event) = 0.15, assign 15 out of 100 numbers to that event. Then you can conduct trials by generating random numbers.

5️⃣ **EXAMPLE** **Real-World 🌐 Connection**

Market Research At a certain store, the number of customers c who arrive at the checkout counters each minute varies according to the distribution below. Simulate the number of customers over a ten-minute period.

Number of Customers Each Minute

c	0	1	2	3	4	5	6
P(c)	0.15	0.24	0.28	0.17	0.09	0.05	0.02

Closure

Ask students to explain what a probability distribution is and how to use random numbers with the probability distribution to conduct a simulation.
A probability distribution is a function that gives the probability of each event in the sample space. Assign numbers to each outcome based on its probability.
Conduct the simulation and interpret.

Step 1 Define how the simulation will be done. Use random numbers. Assign numbers from 1 to 100 to the events, based on the probability of each event. Use cumulative probabilities to help you assign the numbers.

Graphing Calculator Hint

Use the command int(100*rand) + 1 to generate random numbers from 1 to 100. Press MATH and use the int option under the NUM menu and the rand option under the PRB menu.

Event	Probability	Cumulative Probability	Assigned Numbers
0	0.15	0.15	01–15
1	0.24	0.39	16–39
2	0.28	0.67	40–67
3	0.17	0.84	68–84
4	0.09	0.93	85–93
5	0.05	0.98	94–98
6	0.02	1.00	99–100

Since $P(0) = 0.15$, assign 15 numbers to this outcome.

There are 17 numbers from 68 to 84.

Step 2 Conduct the simulation. Model a ten-minute period by generating ten random numbers from 1 to 100.

Minute →	1st	2nd	3rd	4th	5th	6th	7th	8th	9th	10th
Random numbers →	81	29	83	93	18	9	40	97	47	16
Number of customers →	3	1	3	4	1	0	2	5	2	1

The random number 9 is assigned to the outcome 0 customers.

Step 3 Interpret the simulation. Based on this simulation, a total of 22 customers would arrive at checkout counters over a ten-minute period.

✔ **Check Understanding** **5** Conduct a simulation for Example 5 over a 20-minute period.
Check students' work.

EXERCISES

For more practice, see *Extra Practice*.

Practice and Problem Solving

A **Practice by Example**

Example 1
(page 636)

In the game Rock-Paper-Scissors, the scissors cut the paper, the rock dulls the scissors, and the paper covers the rock. Use the results below for Exercises 1 and 2.

Rock-Paper-Scissors

Player 1	R	S	P	P	S	R	S	S	R	P	S	S	R	S	P	P	R	S
Player 2	S	P	R	S	P	P	R	S	R	S	R	R	P	P	R	S	S	S

R = Rock   P = Paper   S = Scissors   **Bold** = Winner

1. Make a frequency table for the objects played: rock, paper, or scissors.

2. Make a frequency table for the winning players: Player 1, Player 2, or tie.
1–2. See margin.

Example 2
(page 637)

The table shows the frequency of responses to editorials. Find each probability.

Number of Responses	0	1	2	3	4	5	6 or more	Total
Number of Editorials	20	30	56	38	34	16	6	200

3. $P(5$ or more responses$)$
0.11

4. $P($at most 4 responses$)$
0.89

5. $P(0-2$ responses$)$
0.53

Lesson 12-1 Probability Distributions **639**

Assignment Guide

▼1 Objective
A B Core 1–9, 12–16, 18
C Extension 19

▼2 Objective
A B Core 10, 11, 17
C Extension 20

Standardized Test Prep 21–23

Mixed Review 24–30

Error Prevention

Exercises 10, 11 Caution students that rounding may introduce a slight error.

Enrichment 12-1

Reteaching 12-1

Practice 12-1

pages 639–641 Exercises

1.

Object	Frequency
Rock	11
Paper	10
Scissors	15
Total	36

2.

Player	Wins
1	7
2	8
Tie	3
Total	18

Lesson Quiz 12-1

1. During lunch on Monday, the cafeteria deli sold soft drinks to 32 customers, bottled waters to 12 customers, sandwiches to 16 customers, tacos to 12 customers, salads to 13 customers, and baked potatoes to 9 customers. There were a total of 50 customers during lunch on Monday.

a. Make a frequency table for the data. Extend the table to include probability distribution.

Item	Freq.	Prob.
Soft drinks	32	$\frac{32}{50}$
Bottled Water	12	$\frac{12}{50}$
Sandwiches	16	$\frac{16}{50}$
Tacos	12	$\frac{12}{50}$
Salads	13	$\frac{13}{50}$
Baked potatoes	9	$\frac{9}{50}$
Total customers	50	

b. What is the probability that the next customer will order a drink? **0.88**

2. Given the data on the number of bus rides per week for 100 people surveyed, conduct a simulation for the number of bus rides per week for the next ten people surveyed.

Rides per Week	P(Rides per Week)
0	0.52
1	0.25
2	0.13
3	0.08
4 or more	0.02

See answer below.

Alternative Assessment

Have students make a spinner and conduct 100 spins to create a frequency table for the outcomes. Then, based on the frequency table, have students run a simulation for the outcomes of 10 more spins.

Example 3
(page 637)

6. Use a table and a graph to show the probability distribution for the spinner {red, green, blue, yellow}. **See back of book.**

7. Use a table and a graph to show the probability distribution for the number of days {28, 29, 30, 31} in each of 48 consecutive months. **See margin p. 641.**

Example 4
(page 638)

Suppose you roll two number cubes. Graph the probability distribution for each sample space. 8–9. See back of book.

8. {sum of numbers even, sum of numbers odd}

9. {both numbers even, both numbers odd, one number even and the other odd}

Example 5
(pages 638–639)

10. Design and conduct a simulation to determine the ages of 20 licensed drivers chosen at random in the United States. **See back of book.**

Licensed Drivers in the United States, by Age

a	< 20	20–29	30–39	40–49	50–59	60–69	70–79	≥ 80
$P(a)$	0.051	0.176	0.211	0.211	0.156	0.096	0.070	0.029

SOURCE: U.S. Department of Transportation. Go to www.PHSchool.com for a data update. Web Code: agg-2041

11. Design and conduct a simulation to determine the size and type of 30 cars purchased from U.S. car dealerships. **See back of book.**

U.S. Car Sales by Vehicle Size and Type

t	Luxury	Large	Midsize	Small
$P(t)$	0.165	0.076	0.527	0.232

SOURCE: Ward's Communications

 Apply Your Skills

Weather Conditions in Dayton, Ohio

Type of Weather	Days Per Year
Clear	82
Partly Cloudy	118
Mostly Cloudy	34
Rain	75
Light Snow (< 1.5 in.)	45
Snow (≥ 1.5 in.)	11
Total	365

SOURCE: *The USA Today Weather Almanac*

Graph the probability distribution described by each function. 12–13. See margin p. 641.

12. $P(x) = \frac{x}{10}$ for $x = 1, 2, 3,$ and 4

13. $P(x) = \frac{2x + 1}{15}$ for $x = 1, 2,$ and 3

14. **Weather** Refer to the table at the left. **a–b. See back of book.**

a. Make a table showing the probability distribution for weather in Dayton.

b. Define the independent and dependent variables.

c. Find the probability that a day in Dayton will include rain or snow.

15. **Data Collection** Find weather data for a city near you. Draw a graph to show the probability distribution of weather conditions. **Check students' work.**

16. a. **Transportation** Sometimes a probability distribution is shown as a circle graph. Define the independent and dependent variables in the distribution at the right.

b. Draw the distribution as a bar graph.

c. Find P(the tank is at least half full when a driver buys gas).
a–c. See back of book.

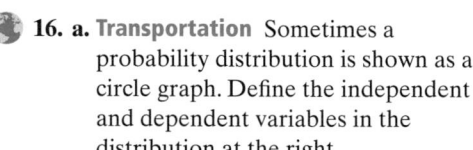

17. **Writing** In a simulation, how do equally likely outcomes help you represent the probability distribution? **See margin p. 641.**

18. **Odds** The odds in favor of an event equal the ratio of the number of times the event occurs to the number of times the event does not occur. The odds in favor of event A are 1 : 4. The odds in favor of event B are 2 : 3. The odds in favor of event C are 1 : 3. The odds in favor of event D are 3 : 17. Graph the probability distribution of events A, B, C, and D. **See margin p. 641.**

Lesson Quiz 12-1

2. Answers will vary. Sample: Use random numbers. Assign numbers from 1 to 100 to events based on the probability of each event.

Person Surveyed	1	2	3	4	5	6	7	8	9	10
Random Numbers	40	19	91	92	92	33	38	52	74	4
Rides per week	0	0	3	3	3	0	0	0	1	0

C Challenge **19. Safety** The table shows data for 911 calls in a town.

a. Conduct a simulation for the number of 911 calls over a 24-hour period.

b. If there are two response teams available, and each response takes about an hour, how many callers in your simulation have to wait?

c. Find P(caller will have to wait). $\frac{10}{47}$

d. Critical Thinking Use your simulation to determine whether additional response teams are needed for this town. Explain your reasoning. **a–b, d. See back of book.**

20. Marketing A company includes instant-win tickets with 10,000,000 of its products. Of the prizes offered, one is a large cash prize, 1,600,000 are small cash prizes, and the other prizes are free samples of the company's products.

a. Find the theoretical probability of winning each type of prize.

b. Design and conduct a simulation to determine the prizes for 100 products.

c. Find the experimental probability for winning each type of prize.

a. 0.0000001, 0.16, ≈0.84

b–c. Check students' work.

Probability Distribution for Number of 911 Calls Each Hour

c	P(c)
0	0.21
1	0.30
2	0.18
3	0.13
4	0.09
5	0.05
6	0.03
7	0.01

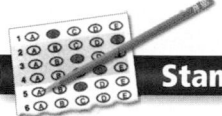

Real-World Connection

More than 93% of the U.S. population is covered by 911 service.

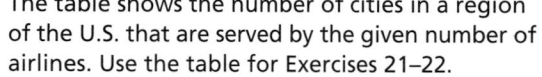

Standardized Test Prep

Multiple Choice

Take It to the NET
Online lesson quiz at
www.PHSchool.com
Web Code: aga-1201

The table shows the number of cities in a region of the U.S. that are served by the given number of airlines. Use the table for Exercises 21–22.

Number of Airlines	Number of Cities
1	27
2	14
3	15
4	18
5	14
6	11

21. What is the probability that a city chosen at random is served by exactly 4 airlines? **C**

A. $\frac{1}{18}$ **B.** $\frac{4}{21}$ **C.** $\frac{2}{11}$ **D.** $\frac{2}{9}$

22. What is the probability that a city chosen at random is served by at least 1 airline? **I**

F. 0 **G.** $\frac{1}{99}$ **H.** $\frac{3}{11}$ **I.** 1

Extended Response

23. A spinner has 4 sections labeled A, B, C, and D. Can the spinner be designed so $P(A) = \frac{1}{12}$, $P(B) = \frac{1}{6}$, $P(C) = \frac{1}{3}$, and $P(D) = \frac{5}{12}$? If so, explain how. **See margin.**

Mixed Review

Lesson 11-6 Find the area under each curve for the domain $0 \le x \le 1$.

24. $y = 3$ **3 units²** **25.** $y = 4x + 2$ **4 units²** **26.** $y = 4x^3 + 1$ **2 units²**

Lesson 10-6 Sketch the graph of each equation. **27–28. See margin.**

27. $x^2 - 4y^2 + 2x + 24y = 51$ **28.** $20y^2 - 40y - x = -25$

Lesson 9-7 Classify each pair of events as *dependent* or *independent*.

29. Choose one item from a buffet. Then choose a different item from the buffet. **dependent**

30. Choose a size for your drink. Then select a flavor. **independent**

Lesson 12-1 Probability Distributions **641**

Standardized Test Prep

Resources

For additional practice with a variety of test item formats:
• Standardized Test Prep, p. 691
• Test-Taking Strategies, p. 686
• Test-Taking Strategies with Transparencies

17. Answers may vary. Sample: Suppose the events in a probability distribution are *not* equally likely. By assigning the appropriate number of *equally likely* outcomes to each event, you can design a simulation that reflects the actual probabilities expected.

18.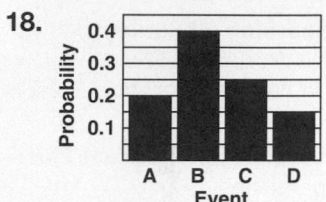

23. [4] Since $\frac{1}{12} + \frac{1}{6} + \frac{1}{3} + \frac{5}{12} = 1$, such a spinner is possible. Divide the spinner into 12 equal parts. Label 1 part A, 2 parts B, 4 parts C, and 5 parts D.

[3] incorrectly divides the 12 parts

[2] does not explain answer

[1] incorrectly adds probabilities

27.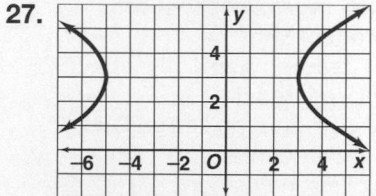

28.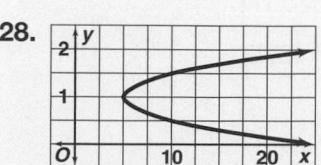

pages 639–641 Exercises

7. Number of Days Per Month

Days	28	29	30	31
Frequency	3	1	16	28
Probability	$\frac{3}{48}$	$\frac{1}{48}$	$\frac{16}{48}$	$\frac{28}{48}$

11. 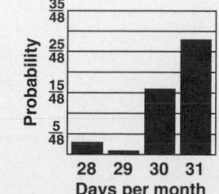 **12.** 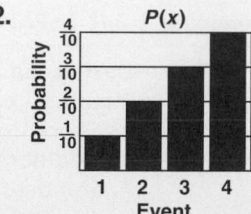 **13.**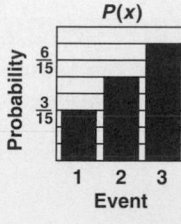

641

Lesson Preview

 **Check Skills You'll Need**

Finding Theoretical Probability
Lesson 9-7: Example 2
Exercises 5–9
Extra Practice, p. 830

Lesson Resources

 **Teaching Resources**
Practice, Reteaching, Enrichment

Reaching All Students
Practice Workbook 12-2
Spanish Practice Workbook 12-2

Presentation Assistant Plus!
Transparencies
• Check Skills You'll Need 12-2
• Additional Examples 12-2
• Student Edition Answers 12-2
• Lesson Quiz 12-2
PH Presentation Pro CD 12-2

ASSESSMENT SYSTEM

Computer Test Generator CD

Technology
Resource Pro® CD-ROM
Computer Test Generator CD
Prentice Hall Presentation Pro CD

 **www.PHSchool.com**
Student Site
• Teacher Web Code: agk-5500
• Updated data
• Self-grading Lesson Quiz
Teacher Center
• Lesson Planner
• Resources

Plus **iTEXT**

12-2
Conditional Probability

Lesson Preview

 What You'll Learn

OBJECTIVE 1 To find conditional probabilities

OBJECTIVE 2 To use formulas and tree diagrams

... And Why

To find the probability of school closings after snowfall, as in Example 4

New Vocabulary • conditional probability

 Check Skills You'll Need   (For help, go to Lesson 9-7.)

A spinner has four equal sections that are red, blue, green, and yellow. Find each probability for two spins.

1. P(blue, then blue) $\frac{1}{16}$
2. P(red, then yellow) $\frac{1}{16}$
3. P(not yellow, then green) $\frac{3}{16}$
4. P(not blue, then not red) $\frac{9}{16}$
5. P(at least one green) $\frac{7}{16}$
6. P(neither spin red) $\frac{9}{16}$

---

iTEXT Interactive lesson includes instant self-check, tutorials, and activities.

OBJECTIVE 1 Finding Conditional Probabilities

A **conditional probability** contains a condition that may limit the sample space for an event. You can write a conditional probability using the notation $P(B \mid A)$, read "the probability of event B, given event A."

1 EXAMPLE Finding Conditional Probability

The table shows the results of a class survey. Find P(did a chore | male).

The condition *male* limits the sample space to 15 possible outcomes. Of the 15 males, 7 did a chore. Therefore, P(did a chore | male) equals $\frac{7}{15}$.

Did you do a household chore last night?

	Yes	No
Male	7	8	← 15 males
Female	7	6	← 13 females

✓ **Check Understanding** ① Use the data in Example 1 to find P(female | did a chore). $\frac{7}{14}$, or $\frac{1}{2}$

2 EXAMPLE Real-World Connection

Recycling Americans recycle more and more material through municipal waste collection each year. Use the information in the table, based on a recent year, to find the probability that a sample of recycled waste was paper.

Municipal Waste Collected in the U.S. (millions of tons)

Material	Recycled	Not Recycled
Paper	34.9	48.9
Metal	6.5	10.1
Glass	2.9	9.1
Plastic	1.1	20.4
Other	15.3	67.8

SOURCE: U.S. Environmental Protection Agency.
Go to **www.PHSchool.com** for a data update.
Web Code: agg-2041

642 Chapter 12 Probability and Statistics

Ongoing Assessment and Intervention

Before the Lesson
Diagnose prerequisite skills using:
• Check Skills You'll Need

During the Lesson
Monitor progress using:
• Check Understanding
• Additional Examples
• Standardized Test Prep

After the Lesson
Assess knowledge using:
• Lesson Quiz
• Computer Test Generator CD

The given condition limits the sample space to *recycled* waste. A favorable outcome is recycled paper.

$$P(\text{paper} \mid \text{recycled}) = \frac{34.9}{34.9 + 6.5 + 2.9 + 1.1 + 15.3}$$

$$\approx 0.57$$

The probability that the recycled waste was paper is about 57%.

 Check Understanding ❷ Find the probability that a sample of recycled waste was plastic.
≈0.018

OBJECTIVE

2 **Using Formulas and Tree Diagrams**

You can use a formula to find conditional probability.

 Key Concepts

Property	Conditional Probability Formula

For any two events *A* and *B* from a sample space with $P(A) \neq 0$,

$$P(B \mid A) = \frac{P(A \text{ and } B)}{P(A)}$$

Using the formula, you can calculate a conditional probability from other probabilities.

3 EXAMPLE **Real-World** 🌐 **Connection**

Market Research Researchers asked shampoo users whether they apply shampoo directly to the head, or indirectly using a hand. Find the probability that a respondent applies shampoo directly to the head, given that the respondent is female.

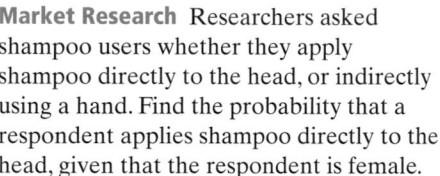

Applying Shampoo

	Directly Onto Head	Into Hand First
Male	2	18
Female	6	24

Relate $P(\text{female}) = \frac{30}{50}$

$P(\text{female } and \text{ applies directly to head}) = \frac{6}{50}$

Define Let A = female.

Let B = applies directly to head.

Write $P(B \mid A) = \dfrac{P(A \text{ and } B)}{P(A)}$

$= \dfrac{\frac{6}{50}}{\frac{30}{50}}$ **Substitute.**

$= \frac{6}{30} = \frac{1}{5}$ **Simplify.**

The probability that a respondent applies shampoo directly to the head, given that the respondent is female, is $\frac{1}{5}$, or 20%.

 Check Understanding ❸ Eighty percent of an airline's flights depart on schedule. Seventy-two percent of its flights depart and arrive on schedule. Find the probability that a flight that departs on time also arrives on time. **0.9**

Lesson 12-2   Conditional Probability   **643**

👥 **Reaching All Students**

Below Level Suggest that students think of conditional probability in terms of deciding what to order at a restaurant. The food you order is going to depend on the type of restaurant.	**Advanced Learners** Make sure students understand under what conditions $P(A\mid B)$ and $P(B\mid A)$ are the same. Have them give an example illustrating their answer.	**English Learners** See note on page 643. **Error Prevention** See note on page 645.

Additional Example

4 A student made the following observations of the weather in his hometown.

- On 28% of the days, the sky is mostly clear.
- During the mostly clear days, it rained 4% of the time.
- During the cloudy days, it rained 31% of the time.

Use a tree diagram to find the probability that a day will start out clear, and then it will rain.

about 1%

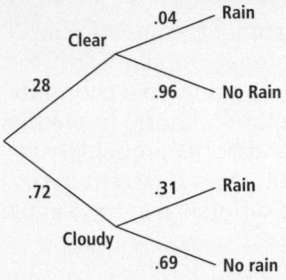

Closure

Ask students to give an example of a sample space and create a conditional probability problem using a subset of the sample space.
Check students' work.

pages 644–646   Exercises

11.

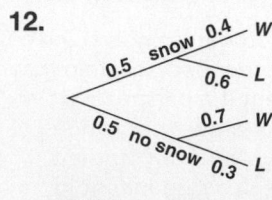

M = male
F = female
R = right
L = left

0.1, 0.114

12.

```
        0.4 W
  snow
0.5    0.6 L
        0.7 W
  no snow
0.5      0.3 L
```

P(W) = 0.55

You can use tree diagrams to solve problems involving conditional probabilities.

4 EXAMPLE   Making a Tree Diagram

A student in Buffalo, New York, made the observations below.

- Of all snowfalls, 5% are heavy (at least 6 in.).
- After a heavy snowfall, schools are closed 67% of the time.
- After a light (less than 6 in.) snowfall, schools are closed 3% of the time.

Find the probability that the snowfall is light and the schools are open.

Make a tree diagram. Use *H* for heavy snowfall, *L* for light snowfall, *C* for schools closed, and *O* for schools open. Find *P*(*L* and *O*).

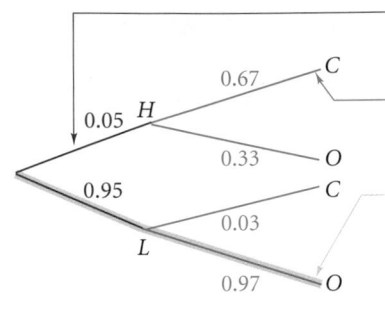

Each first branch represents a simple probability. $P(H) = 0.05$

Each second branch represents a conditional probability. $P(C|H) = 0.67$

The highlighted path represents $P(L \text{ and } O)$.
$P(L \text{ and } O) = P(L) \cdot P(O|L)$
$= 0.95 \cdot 0.97$
$= 0.92$

● The probability that the snowfall is light and the schools are open is about 92%.

Real-World ⊕ Connection

During some winters, Buffalo gets more than 100 inches of snow.

✔ **Check Understanding**   **4** Find *P*(schools open, given heavy snow). **0.33**

EXERCISES

For more practice, see *Extra Practice*.

Practice and Problem Solving

A   Practice by Example

Example 1
(page 642)

Use the table to find each probability.

1. *P*(has diploma)   **0.9**

2. *P*(has diploma and experience)   **0.6**

3. *P*(has experience | has diploma)   **0.6̄**

4. *P*(has no diploma | has experience)   **≈0.085**

Characteristics of Job Applicants

		Has Experience	
		Yes	No
Has High School Diploma	Yes	54	27
	No	5	4

Example 2
(pages 642–643)

Use the table below to find each probability.

5. *P*(The recipient is male.)   **≈0.406**

6. *P*(The degree is a bachelor's.)   **≈0.529**

7. *P*(The recipient is female, given that the degree is advanced.)   **≈0.568**

8. *P*(The degree is *not* an associate's, given that the recipient is male.)   **≈0.780**

Projected Number of Degree Recipients in 2010 (thousands)

Degree	Male	Female
Associate's	224	387
Bachelor's	547	776
Advanced	245	322

SOURCE: U.S. National Center for Education Statistics

Example 3
(page 643)

Use the survey results below for Exercises 9 and 10.

9. Find the probability that a respondent has a pet, given that the respondent has had a pet. **≈45%**

10. Find the probability that a respondent has never had a pet, given that the respondent does not have a pet now. **≈23%**

> 39% have a pet now and have had a pet.
> 61% do not have a pet now.
> 86% have had a pet.
> 14% do not have a pet now and have never had a pet.

Example 4
(page 644)

11. Make a tree diagram based on the survey results below . Then find P(a female respondent is left-handed) and P(a respondent is both male and right-handed). **11–12. See margin p. 644.**
- Of all the respondents, 17% are male.
- Of the male respondents, 33% are left-handed.
- Of female respondents, 90% are right-handed.

12. A football team has a 70% chance of winning when it doesn't snow, but only a 40% chance of winning when it snows. Suppose there is a 50% chance of snow. Make a tree diagram to find the probability that the team will win.

B **Apply Your Skills**

13d. The fact that $P(A) = P(A|B)$ illustrates that the probability of A is the same, regardless of the occurrence of B.

13. Suppose A and B are independent events, with $P(A) = 0.60$ and $P(B) = 0.25$. Find each probability.
  a. $P(A$ and $B)$ **0.15**
  b. $P(A \mid B)$ **0.60**
  c. What do you notice about $P(A)$ and $P(A \mid B)$? **$P(A)$ is equal to $P(A \mid B)$**
  d. **Critical Thinking** One way to describe A and B as independent events is *The occurrence of B has no effect on the probability of A*. Explain how the answer to part (c) illustrates this relationship.

🌐 Surveys Conduct a survey in your class. Then find each probability. **14–18. Check students' work.**

14. P(left-handed | left shoe)

15. P(left-handed | not the right shoe)

16. P(left shoe | right-handed)

17. P(first shoe picked up | right-handed)

18. P(don't know)

Which Shoe Do You Put on First?		Dominant Hand	
		Right	Left
First Shoe Put On	Right	▪	▪
	Left	▪	▪
	First One Grabbed	▪	▪
	Don't Know	▪	▪

🌐 Weather Use probability notation to describe the chance of each event. Let S, C, W, and R represent sunny, cloudy, windy, and rainy weather, respectively.

19. cloudy weather **$P(C)$**

20. sunny and windy weather **$P(S$ and $W)$**

21. rainy weather if it is windy **$P(R \mid W)$**

22. windy weather if it is sunny **$P(W \mid S)$**

C **Challenge** ✏️

23. a. **Writing** Explain which branches of the tree diagram at the right represent conditional probabilities. Give a specific example.
  b. Are the event of having a license and the event of being an adult independent events? Justify your answer.
  c. **Open-Ended** Estimate probabilities for each branch of the tree diagram for your city or town. Then find $P(L)$. **a–c. See margin.**

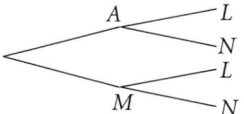

A = adult (21 or older)
M = minor (under 21)
L = licensed driver
N = not licensed to drive

Lesson 12-2 Conditional Probability **645**

Assignment Guide

1 Objective
  Ⓐ Ⓑ **Core** 1–8, 13–22

2 Objective
  Ⓐ Ⓑ **Core** 9–12
  Ⓒ **Extension** 23, 24

Standardized Test Prep 25–28

Mixed Review 29–38

Error Prevention

Exercises 1–13 Urge students to be careful when substituting values into the conditional probability formula. It is important to correctly identify the limited sample space.

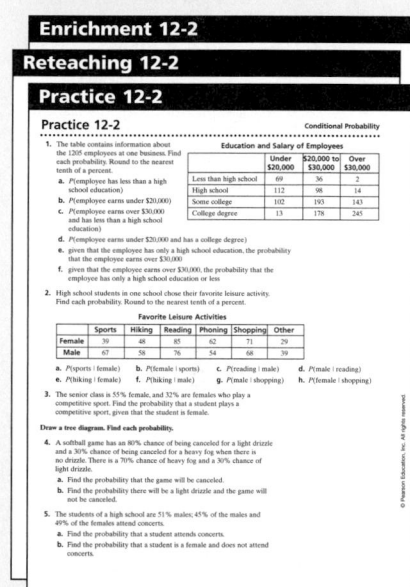

23a. The four right branches represent probabilities conditional upon the person being an adult or a minor. For example, the top branch

represents the probability that a person is licensed given that he or she is an adult.

b. No; the probability of a minor being licensed is

not the same as the probability of an adult being licensed.

c. Check students' work.

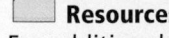

Lesson Quiz 12-2

1. A study was conducted at Central High School to find out how much television students watch per night. Thirty eight percent of the respondents were freshmen. Twenty-two percent of all respondents were freshman who said that they watch at least one hour of television per night. Find the probability that a freshman respondent watches at least one hour of television per night. **about 58%**

2. The tree diagram below shows the probabilities that Jose will or will not cook breakfast on weekends or weekdays. Find the probability that Jose will cook breakfast on any given day. **about 38%**

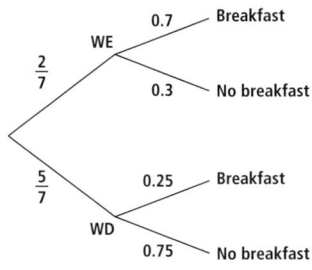

Alternative Assessment

Group students in pairs. Have each student create a tree diagram of a conditional probability problem in Exercises 1–10 or 18–22. Then ask students to share their diagrams with each other. The students should try to interpret each other's diagram, and find one of the conditional probabilities.

Standardized Test Prep

📁 **Resources**

For additional practice with a variety of test item formats:
- Standardized Test Prep, p. 691
- Test-Taking Strategies, p. 686
- Test-Taking Strategies with Transparencies

646

---

24. Critical Thinking Sixty percent of a company's sales representatives have completed training seminars. Of these, 80% have had increased sales. Overall, 56% of the representatives (whether trained or not) have had increased sales. Use a tree diagram to find the probability of increased sales, given that a representative has not been trained. $P(I|N) = 0.2$

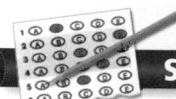

Standardized Test Prep

Multiple Choice

A school library classifies its books as hardback or paperback, fiction or nonfiction, and illustrated or nonillustrated. Use the table at the right for Exercises 25–27.

		Illustrated	Non-illustrated
Hardback	Fiction	420	780
	Nonfiction	590	250
Paperback	Fiction	150	430
	Nonfiction	110	880

Take It to the NET
Online lesson quiz at
www.PHSchool.com
Web Code: aga-1202

25. What is the probability that a book selected at random is a paperback, given that it is illustrated? **C**

A. $\frac{260}{3610}$ B. $\frac{150}{1270}$ C. $\frac{260}{1270}$ D. $\frac{110}{150}$

26. What is the probability that a book selected at random is nonfiction, given that it is a nonillustrated hardback? **H**

F. $\frac{250}{2040}$ G. $\frac{780}{1030}$ H. $\frac{250}{1030}$ I. $\frac{250}{780}$

27. What is the probability that a book selected at random is a paperback? **D**

A. $\frac{1}{1570}$ B. $\frac{260}{1310}$ C. $\frac{1570}{2040}$ D. $\frac{1570}{3610}$

Short Response

28. In another library, the probability that a book is a hardback, given that it is illustrated, is 0.40. The probability that the book is hardback *and* illustrated is 0.20. Find the probability that a book is illustrated. **See margin.**

Mixed Review

Lesson 12-1

29. Consider a February that is not in a leap year. Graph the probability distribution for the sample space {weekdays, weekend days}. **See back of book.**

Lesson 11-1 🌐 **30. Construction** An earthmover purchased for $600,000 loses 18% of its value each year. What is the value of the earthmover after one year? After three years? **$492,000; $330,821**

Lesson 10-1

31. Identify the center and intercepts of the conic section at the right. Then find the domain and range. **See margin.**

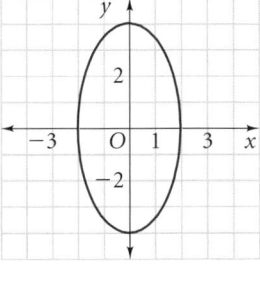

Lesson 8-5 **Solve each equation. If necessary, round to the nearest thousandth.**

32. $2^x = 4$ **2** **33.** $4^{2x} = 10$ **0.830** **34.** $4^{x+1} = 28$ **1.404**

35. $7 - 3^x = -38$ **3.465** **36.** $\log x = -1$ **0.1**

37. $2 \log x = 1$ **3.162** **38.** $\log (2x + 2) = 2$ **49**

---

pages 644–646 Exercises

28. [2] $P(B \mid A) = \frac{P(A \text{ and } B)}{P(A)}$,

where *A* is "the book is illustrated" and *B* is "the book is hardback".

$0.40 = \frac{0.20}{P(A)}$

$0.40 \cdot P(A) = 0.20$

$P(A) = 0.5$

[1] answer only OR minor error

31. center (0, 0)
x-intercepts (2, 0), (−2, 0)
y-intercepts (0, 4), (0, −4);
domain: {x | −2 ≤ x ≤ 2};
range: {y | −4 ≤ y ≤ 4}

You can use a tree diagram like the one at the right to find the conditional probability $P(P \mid D)$, which is the probability that a person with a disease will test positive for it. In this case, $P(P \mid D) = 0.99$.

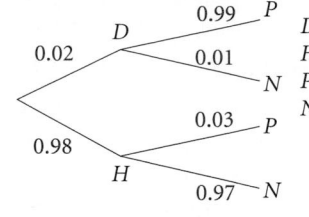

D = person has the disease
H = person is healthy
P = person tests positive
N = person tests negative

Scientists also look at $P(H \mid P)$, the probability of a "false positive," which is the probability that a person who tests positive is actually healthy. Since this probability is not found on a branch in the diagram, you must use the formula for conditional probability.

EXAMPLE

Use the tree diagram above to find $P(H \mid P)$.

Since $P(H \mid P) = \dfrac{P(H \text{ and } P)}{P(P)}$, find $P(H \text{ and } P)$ and $P(P)$.

$$\begin{aligned} P(H \text{ and } P) &= 0.98 \cdot 0.03 & P(P) &= P(D \text{ and } P) \text{ or } P(H \text{ and } P) \\ &= 0.0294 & &= 0.02 \cdot 0.99 + 0.98 \cdot 0.03 \\ & & &= 0.0492 \end{aligned}$$

So $P(H \mid P) = \dfrac{P(H \text{ and } P)}{P(P)}$

$\qquad = \dfrac{0.0294}{0.0492}$ **Substitute.**

$\qquad \approx 0.598$ **Simplify.**

About 60% of the people who test positive do not actually have the disease.

EXERCISES

Use the tree diagram in the Example to find each probability.

1. $P(N)$ **0.9508**　　　**2.** $P(H \text{ and } N)$ **0.9506**　　**3.** $P(H \mid N)$ **0.9998**　　**4.** $P(D \mid N)$ **0.0002**

5. Writing Explain the difference in meaning between $P(P \mid D)$ and $P(D \mid P)$ for the test in the Example. Compare the values of $P(P \mid D)$ and $P(D \mid P)$. What is the best use for this test? Explain.　**See margin.**

The tree diagram relates snowfall and school closings. Find each probability.

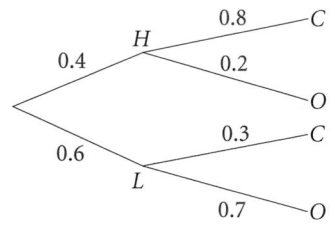

H = heavy snowfall
L = light snowfall
C = schools closed
O = schools open

6. $P(C)$　**0.5**　　　**7.** $P(H \text{ and } O)$

8. $P(H \mid C)$　**0.64**　　**9.** $P(L \mid O)$

10. $P(L \mid C)$　**0.36**　**11.** $P(H \mid O)$
　　　　　　　　　　　0.16

7. **0.08**　　　　　**9.** **0.84**

Extension

Comparing Conditional Probabilities

Students learn to compare conditional probabilities using a tree diagram.

Resources

Computer Test item Generator CD-ROM, Chapter 0, Extension Topics

Teaching Notes

Students may expect that the probability of a false positive is 0.01 since the given probability of testing positive and having the disease is 0.99. Explain that the "false positive" probability speaks to the reliability of the test. Ask students to comment on the reliability of the test if the person is actually healthy.

Visual Learners

Make sure students write the formula for each probability statement in the exercises before they consult the tree diagram for the probabilities to substitute into the formulas.

647

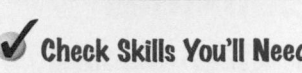

Finding Theoretical Probability
Lesson 1-1: Example 3
Exercises 17–28
Extra Practice, p. 822

Lesson Resources

 **Teaching Resources**
Practice, Reteaching, Enrichment
Checkpoint Quiz 1

Reaching All Students
Practice Workbook 12-3
Spanish Practice Workbook 12-3
Reading and Math Literacy 12B
Spanish Reading & Literacy 12B
Spanish Checkpoint Quiz 1

Presentation Assistant Plus!
Transparencies
• Check Skills You'll Need 12-3
• Additional Examples 12-3
• Student Edition Answers 12-3
• Lesson Quiz 12-3
PH Presentation Pro CD 12-3

ASSESSMENT SYSTEM

Checkpoint Quiz 1
Computer Test Generator CD

Technology
Resource Pro® CD-ROM
Computer Test Generator CD
Prentice Hall Presentation Pro CD

 **www.PHSchool.com**
Student Site
• Teacher Web Code: agk-5500
• Graphing Calculator,
  Procedure 21
• Self-grading Lesson Quiz
Teacher Center
• Lesson Planner
• Resources

Plus iTEXT

 **12-3**

Analyzing Data

Lesson Preview

What You'll Learn

OBJECTIVE 1 To calculate measures of central tendency

OBJECTIVE 2 To draw and interpret box-and-whisker plots

. . . And Why

To analyze a set of water temperatures, as in Example 2

✓ Check Skills You'll Need (For help, go to Lesson 1-1.)

Order each set of values from least to greatest. Then find the middle value.

1. 0.2 0.3 0.6 1.2 0.7 0.9 0.8   **2.** 11 23 15 17 21 18 21

3. 7.8 2.6 3.9 15.6 9.1 11.7 10.4   **4.** 76 89 80 82 86 84 86

1–4. See margin p. 649.

New Vocabulary • measures of central tendency • mean • median • mode
• bimodal • quartiles • box-and-whisker plot • percentiles
• outlier

 Interactive lesson includes instant self-check, tutorials, and activities.

OBJECTIVE 1
Measures of Central Tendency

Statistics is the study of data analysis and interpretation. The mean, the median, and the mode are single, central values that help describe a set of data. They are called **measures of central tendency.**

 Key Concepts

Definition	Measures of Central Tendency	
Measure	**Definition**	**Example, using {1, 2, 2, 3, 5, 5}**
Mean	$\frac{\text{sum of the data values}}{\text{number of data values}}$	$\frac{1 + 2 + 2 + 3 + 5 + 5}{6} = \frac{18}{6} = 3$
Median	middle value *or* mean of the two middle values	$\frac{2 + 3}{2} = 2.5$
Mode	most frequently occurring value	2 and 5

A **bimodal** data set has two modes. If a data set has more than two modes, then the modes are probably not statistically useful. If no value occurs more frequently than any other, then there is no mode.

1 EXAMPLE Finding Measures of Central Tendency

Find the mean, median, and mode for these values: 98, 95, 99, 97, 89, 92, 97, 62, 90.

$$\bar{x} = \frac{98 + 95 + 99 + 97 + 89 + 92 + 97 + 62 + 90}{9} = \frac{819}{9} = 91$$ Use the symbol $\bar{x}$ to designate the mean.

Reading Math
Read $\bar{x}$ as "the mean of x" or "x bar."

62 89 90 92 95 97 97 98 99   Find the median and the mode by ordering the values numerically.
             ↑ ↑ ↑
          Median Mode

● The mean is 91, the median is 95, and the mode is 97.

✓ Check Understanding 1 Find the mean, median, and mode for these values: 2.4, 4.3, 3.7, 3.9, 2.8, 5.4, 2.8.
≈3.6, 3.7, 2.8

648 Chapter 12 Probability and Statistics

Ongoing Assessment and Intervention

Before the Lesson	**During the Lesson**	**After the Lesson**
Diagnose prerequisite skills using:	**Monitor progress using:**	**Assess knowledge using:**
• Check Skills You'll Need	• Check Understanding	• Lesson Quiz
	• Additional Examples	• Computer Test Generator CD
	• Standardized Test Prep	• Chapter Checkpoint 1 (p. 655)

You can use a graphing calculator to find the measures of central tendency.

2 EXAMPLE Real-World Connection

Oceanography Find the mean, the median, and the mode of all the water temperatures listed for the eastern coast of the Gulf of Mexico.

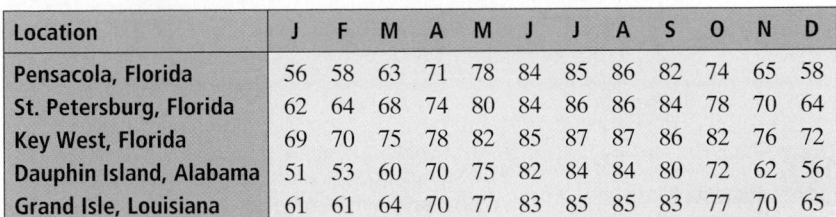

Gulf of Mexico Eastern Coast Water Temperatures (°F)

Location	J	F	M	A	M	J	J	A	S	O	N	D
Pensacola, Florida	56	58	63	71	78	84	85	86	82	74	65	58
St. Petersburg, Florida	62	64	68	74	80	84	86	86	84	78	70	64
Key West, Florida	69	70	75	78	82	85	87	87	86	82	76	72
Dauphin Island, Alabama	51	53	60	70	75	82	84	84	80	72	62	56
Grand Isle, Louisiana	61	61	64	70	77	83	85	85	83	77	70	65

Step 1 Use the STAT feature to enter the data as L1 in your graphing calculator.

Step 2 Use the LIST feature to access the MATH menu. Find the mean.

```
NAMES OPS MATH
1:min(
2:max(
3:mean(
4:median(
5:sum(
6:prod(
7↓stdDev(
```

```
mean (L1)
              73.65
```

Step 3 Return to the same menu to find the median.

```
NAMES OPS MATH
1:min(
2:max(
3:mean(
4:median(
5:sum(
6:prod(
7↓stdDev(
```

```
mean (L1)
              73.65
median (L1)
              75
```

Step 4 Use the STAT PLOT feature to access Plot 1. Choose the histogram, L1, and

```
Plot1 Plot2  Plot3
On  Off
Type: ⊔ ⩘ ⊞
      ⊡ ⊡ ⊿
Xlist: L1
Freq: 1
```

```
WINDOW
Xmin = 50
Xmax = 90
Xscl = 1
Ymin = −2
Ymax = 8
Yscl = 1
Xres = 1
```

Frequency 1 options. Then enter an appropriate viewing window.

Step 5 Graph the data. Use the TRACE feature to move the cursor to the highest points of the graph.

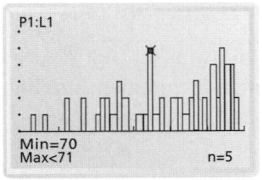

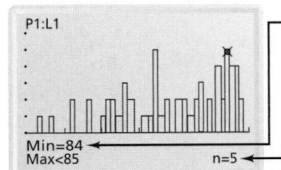

On the screen, the mode appears as the minimum value for the cursor. The modes are 70 and 84.

The modes both occur five times in the data.

The mean is 73.65°F, the median is 75°F, and the modes are 70°F and 84°F.

✓ **Check Understanding** ② Find the mean, median, and mode for the water temperatures in Grand Isle, Louisiana. ≈73.42°F; 73.5°F; 61°F, 70°F, 77°F, 83°F, 85°F

👥 Reaching All Students

Below Level Suggest that students think of the box portion of a box-and-whisker plot as a fence that surrounds the majority of the data and tells how close together data values fall.	**Advanced Learners** Around 80% of adult drivers consider themselves above average. Have students discuss whether 80% of drivers can be above the mean, median, or mode.	**English Learners** See note on page 649. **Error Prevention** See note on page 652.

Math Background

The mean and the median are the most useful classical measures of central tendency. Box-and-whisker plots were invented by John Tukey in the 1970s.

OBJECTIVE 1 Teaching Notes

1 EXAMPLE English Learners

To help students understand the meaning of *bimodal*, have them list words beginning with the prefix bi-, such as bicycle, biplane, bifocal, and bicultural and discuss their meanings.

2 EXAMPLE Technology Tip

When finding the mean and the median, press 2nd 1 to enter L1. When students use the TRACE feature, *min* represents the temperature and *n* represents the number of times that temperature is listed in the table.

✎ Additional Examples

① Find the mean, median, and mode for these values: 78, 87, 84, 75, 80, 98, 78, 95, 72. **83; 80; 78**

② Using the data in the table in Example 2, find the mean, the median, and the mode for the water temperatures in Dauphin Island, AL. **69.1; 71; 84**

page 648 Check Skills You'll Need

1. 0.2 0.3 0.6 0.7 0.8 0.9 1.2; 0.7

2. 11 15 17 18 21 21 23; 18

3. 2.6 3.9 7.8 9.1 10.4 11.7 15.6; 9.1

4. 76 80 82 84 86 86 89; 84

649

3 EXAMPLE **Teaching Tip**

Point out to students that not only are the minimum, maximum, median, and quartiles easily visible but also the range of the data.

4 EXAMPLE **Technology Tip**

Students may enter the data for this example in any list; they must then make certain that they select the appropriate list after selecting the type of plot using the STAT PLOT feature.

5 EXAMPLE **Teaching Tip**

Point out to students that scores for the SAT and ACT are often reported using percentiles. Ask students why knowing the percentile of their score might be beneficial? **The percentile will show how they scored compared to others who took the tests.**

6 EXAMPLE **Math Tip**

Often, when making a box-and-whisker plot, the "whiskers" of the plot are not extended to any outliers. In such cases, the "whiskers" would be extended only to the least or greatest values that are not outliers.

OBJECTIVE
2 Box-and-Whisker Plots

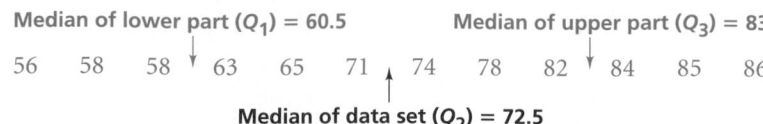

If you arrange data in increasing order, then the median divides the data set into two equal parts. You can use the median of each of the parts to divide the set further, into four equal parts. The values separating the four parts are called **quartiles.** Quartiles are shown below for the 12 water temperatures from Pensacola in Example 2.

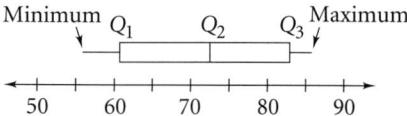

Median of lower part (Q_1) = 60.5   Median of upper part (Q_3) = 83

56   58   58   63   65   71   74   78   82   84   85   86

Median of data set (Q_2) = 72.5

📖 **Reading Math**

Quartiles are sometimes called "hinges."

The values Q_1, Q_2, and Q_3 are the first, second, and third quartiles. A **box-and-whisker plot** is a method of displaying data that uses quartiles to form the center box and the minimum and maximum values to form the whiskers.

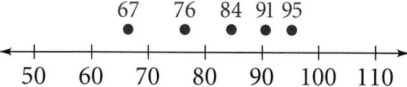

3 EXAMPLE **Making a Box-and-Whisker Plot**

Make a box-and-whisker plot for these values: 84, 79, 90, 73, 95, 88, 92, 81, 67.

Step 1 Find the quartile values, the minimum value, and the maximum value.

67 73 79 81 84 88 90 92 95

$$Q_2 = \text{median} = 84$$

When the median is a value of the data set, it is removed for the calculation of Q_1 and Q_3.

67 73 79 81   88 90 92 95

$$Q_1 = \frac{73 + 79}{2} = 76 \qquad\qquad Q_3 = \frac{90 + 92}{2} = 91$$

The minimum value is 67, and the maximum value is 95.

Step 2 Draw a number line for the base of your box-and-whisker plot. Above the number line, plot the three quartiles, the minimum value, and the maximum value.

67   76   84 91 95

50   60   70   80   90   100   110

Step 3 Finish your box-and-whisker plot by drawing a box through Q_1 and Q_3, a vertical line through the median, and line segments from the box outward to the minimum and maximum values.

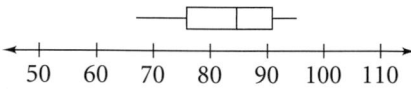

50   60   70   80   90   100   110

3.

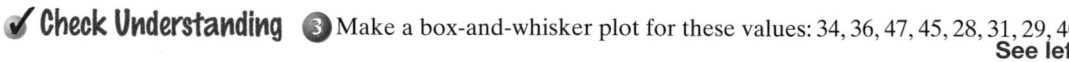

25 30 35 40 45 50

✓ **Check Understanding** **3** Make a box-and-whisker plot for these values: 34, 36, 47, 45, 28, 31, 29, 40.
See left.

4 EXAMPLE Real-World  Connection

Oceanography Use a graphing calculator to find the quartiles of the water temperature data in Example 2.

Use the STAT PLOT feature to select a box-and-whisker plot. Enter the window values. Graph the box-and-whisker plot.

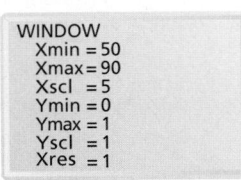
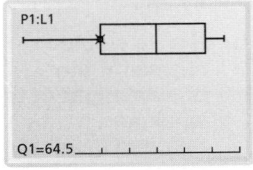

• Use the TRACE feature to find the quartiles: $Q_1 = 64.5$, $Q_2 = 75$, and $Q_3 = 83.5$.

4.

$Q_1 = 84$, $Q_2 = 85$,
$Q_3 = 86$

✓ **Check Understanding** **4** Use the data for just the summer months, as shown in the graph below. Find the quartiles by graphing the box-and-whisker plot. **See left.**

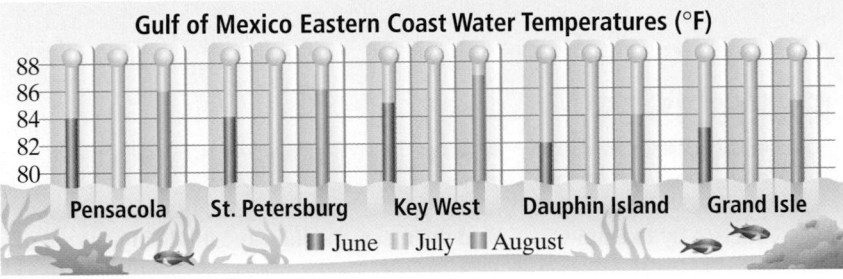

Gulf of Mexico Eastern Coast Water Temperatures (°F)

Pensacola   St. Petersburg   Key West   Dauphin Island   Grand Isle

■ June ■ July ■ August

A **percentile** is a value that divides the range of a data set into two parts such that the part below the percentile contains a given percent of the data. If a number x is at the 63rd percentile in a data set, then about 63% of the data are less than x.

5 EXAMPLE Using Percentiles

Find the values at the 20th and 65th percentiles for the values below.
  54 98 45 87 98 64 21 61 71 82 93 65 62 98 87 24 65 97 31 47

Step 1 Order the values.
  21 24 31 45 47 54 61 62 64 65 65 71 82 87 87 93 97 98 98 98

Step 2 Find the number of values that fall below the 20th percentile and the number that fall below the 65th percentile.

Of the 20 values, 20% should fall below the 20th percentile and 65% should fall below the 65th percentile.

$20 \cdot 20\% = 20 \cdot 0.20 = 4$ $20 \cdot 65\% = 20 \cdot 0.65 = 13$

Since 47 is greater than 4 values, 47 is at the 20th percentile.   Since 87 is greater than 13 values, 87 is at the 65th percentile.

• The value at the 20th percentile is 47 and the value at the 65th percentile is 87.

✓ **Check Understanding** **5** Find the value at each percentile for the data in Example 5.
  a. 0th percentile **21**   **b.** 45th percentile **65**   **c.** 55th percentile **71**

Lesson 12-3 Analyzing Data **651**

Additional Examples

3 Make a box-and-whisker plot for these values: 91, 95, 88, 85, 90, 97, 94, 100, 81. **See answer below.**

4 Use a graphing calculator to find the quartiles of the water temperature data for Dauphin Island, AL in Example 2. $Q_1 = 58$, $Q_2 = 71$, $Q_3 = 81$

5 Find the values of the 30th and 60th percentiles for the values given in Example 5. **61; 82**

6 Identify an outlier for this set of values: 15 34 28 32 30 26 34. **15**

Closure

Ask students to explain what the measures of central tendency are. The mean is the average of a set of data. The median is the middle value or mean of the two middle values. The mode is the data value that occurs the most. Ask students what must be done to a set of data before finding measures of central tendency or making box-and-whisker plots. **Data sets must be placed in order before finding medians or making box-and-whisker plots.**

page 651 Additional Examples

3.

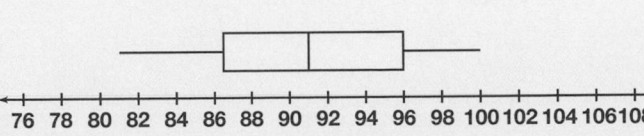

76 78 80 82 84 86 88 90 92 94 96 98 100 102 104 106 108

Assignment Guide

1 Objective
Ⓐ Ⓑ Core 1–3, 12, 20

2 Objective
Ⓐ Ⓑ Core 4–11, 13–19
Ⓒ Extension 21, 22

Standardized Test Prep 23–26

Mixed Review 27–34

Error Prevention

Exercises 1–11 Remind students that data sets must be placed in increasing or decreasing order before finding medians.

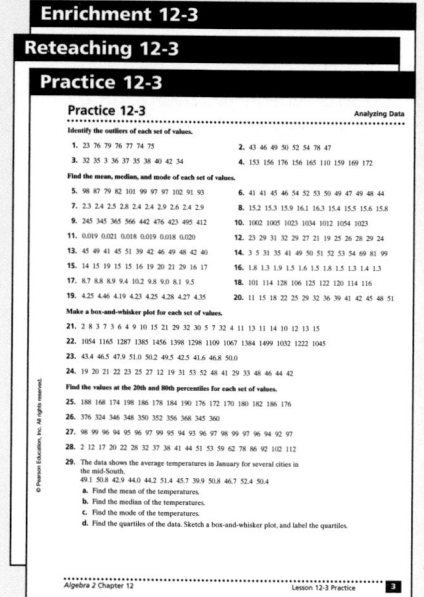

pages 652–655 Exercises

4.
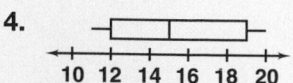
10 12 14 16 18 20

5.
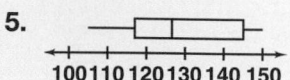
100 110 120 130 140 150

6.
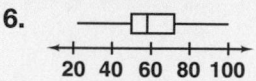
20 40 60 80 100

7.
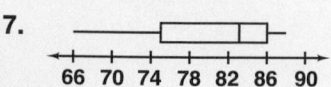
66 70 74 78 82 86 90

652

6a. Yes; it is unlikely that the water temperature of a lake would change by 25°.

b. No; 98 would represent the busiest night of the week and it may relate to a weekly event.

✔ **Check Understanding**

An **outlier** is an item of data with a value substantially different from the rest of the items in the data set. Sometimes an outlier is an important part of the data. At other times it can represent a false reading. When you think an outlier has resulted from an error, you may remove it from the data set.

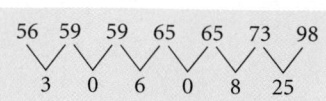 **6 EXAMPLE** Identifying an Outlier

Identify an outlier for this set of values: 56 65 73 59 98 65 59.

| 56 | 59 | 59 | 65 | 65 | 73 | 98 | Order the data.

    3   0   6   0   8   25   Find the differences between adjacent values.

● 98 is substantially different, so 98 is an outlier.

6 a. Suppose the values in Example 6 are measurements of the water temperature of a lake. Would you discard the outlier? Explain. **a–b. See left.**
    b. Suppose the data represent the number of customers in a small restaurant each night during one week. Would you discard the outlier? Explain.

EXERCISES

For more practice, see *Extra Practice*.

Practice and Problem Solving

Ⓐ **Practice by Example**

Find the mean, median, and mode of each set of values. **1–2. See below left.**

Examples 1 and 2
(pages 648 and 649)

1. 5 9 1 2 7 3 1 8 8 1 3   **2.** 307 309 323 304 390 398

3. 475 722 499 572 402 809 499 828 405 499 800 422 672 800
                                               600.3, 535.5, 499

Examples 3 and 4
(pages 650 and 651)

1. 4.36, 3, 1

2. 338.5, 316, no mode

Make a box-and-whisker plot for each set of values. **4–7. See margin.**

4. 12 11 15 12 19 20 19

5. 120 145 133 105 117 150

6. 49 57.5 58 49.2 62 22.2 67 52.1 77 99.9 80 51.7 64

7. Weather The table shows the high temperatures for one day at different locations on the island of Maui, Hawaii. Make a box-and whisker plot of the data.

High Temperatures on Maui

Location	Temperature
Kahului	88°F
Kihei	85°F
Lahaina	86°F
Hana	82°F
Haleakala	66°F
Kula	75°F

Example 5
(page 651)

Find the values at the 30th and 90th percentiles for each set of values.

8. 6283 5700 6381 6274 5700 5896 5972 6075 5993 5581 **5896, 6381**

9. 7 12 3 14 17 20 5 3 17 4 13 2 15 9 15 18 16 9 1 6 **6, 18**

Example 6
(page 652)

Identify the outlier of each set of values.

10. 3.4 4.5 2.3 5.9 9.8 3.3 2.1 3.0 2.9 **9.8**

11. 17 21 19 10 15 19 14 0 11 16 **0**

652 Chapter 12 Probability and Statistics

Dilbert

MY MARKET RESEARCH INDICATES THAT 50% OF YOUR CUSTOMERS ARE ABOVE THE MEDIAN AGE.

BUT THE SHOCKING DISCOVERY WAS THAT 50% WERE BELOW THE MEDIAN AGE.

WHAT PERCENT ARE EXACTLY THE MEDIAN AGE?

I'M PROPOSING TO STUDY THAT IN PHASE TWO.

B **Apply Your Skills**

Major Tornadoes in Oklahoma, May 3, 1999

Length of Path (miles)	Intensity
6	F3
9	F3
4	F2
38	F5
7	F2
12	F3
8	F2
7	F2
15	F4
20	F4
1	F5
22	F3
16	F3
8	F2
13	F3
2	F2

SOURCE: National Oceanic & Atmospheric Administration

13b. 38

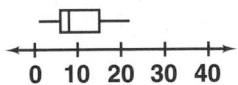

0 10 20 30 40

12. a. What percent of the customers in the cartoon are exactly the median age? **0%**
 b. Must one item from a data set fall exactly at the median? Explain.
 c. Can the company do anything about the shocking discovery? Explain.
 b–c. See margin.

13. Meteorology On May 3, 1999, 59 tornadoes hit Oklahoma in the largest tornado outbreak ever recorded in the state. Sixteen of these were classified as strong (F2 or F3) or violent (F4 or F5).
 a. Make a box-and-whisker plot of the data. **a, c. See margin.**
 b. Identify the outlier. Remove it from the data set and make a revised box-and-whisker plot. **b. See below left.**
 c. Writing How does the removal of the outlier affect the box-and-whisker plot? How does it affect the median of the data set?

Identify the outlier of each set of values. Then describe how its value affects the mean of the data.

103; this value lowers the mean.

14. 947 757 103 619 661 582 626 900 869 728 1001 596 515

15. 87 104 381 215 174 199 233 186 142 228 9 53 117 129

381; this value raises the mean.

For Exercises 16–18, use the set of values below.
1 1 1 1 1 1 2 3 5 8 13 21 34 55 89 89 89 89 89 89

16. At what percentile is 1? **0th**   **17.** At what percentile is 34? **60th**

18. Error Analysis A student claims that 89 is at the 100th percentile. Explain the student's error. **See margin.**

19. Geology The table below shows the number of major earthquakes (magnitude 7.0 or greater) worldwide in the ten-year period from 1991 through 2000.

Major Earthquakes Worldwide (Magnitude 7.0 and Greater)

Year	1991	1992	1993	1994	1995	1996	1997	1998	1999	2000
Earthquakes	11	23	16	15	25	22	20	16	23	18

SOURCE: U.S. Geological Survey National Earthquake Information Center

 a. Find the mean and the median of the numbers of annual earthquakes. **18.9, 19**
 b. Do the data include an outlier that you should discard? Explain. **b–c. See margin.**
 c. Compare the box-and-whisker plots at the right. One shows the data above. The other shows worldwide earthquake data from 1900 through 2000. What conclusions can you draw about recent earthquakes? Justify your reasoning.

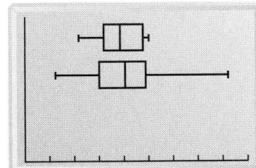

Xmin = 0   Ymin = 0
Xmax = 45 Ymax = 1
Xscl = 5   Yscl = 1

Connection to Geology

Exercise 19 The magnitudes of earthquakes are measured on the Richter scale. It is a scale from 0 to 9 used to measure the severity of earthquakes according to the amount of energy released, with a higher number indicating stronger tremors. Each increase of magnitude of 1 on the scale represents a release of about 30 times as much energy.

12b. No; if there are an even number of items in a data set, the median may lie between data values.

 c. No; 50% of a data set will always lie at or below the median.

13a.

0 10 20 30 40

 c. The main effect of removing the outlier is a shortening of the long whisker. The median decreases from 8.5 to 8.

18. Only 14 out of 20 values are below 89, so 89 is at the 70th percentile. For a number to be at the 100th percentile, 100% of the values must be below that number. That is impossible since a number cannot be less than itself.

19b. No; none of the values is significantly less or greater than the others.

 c. Recent earthquakes have been more consistent in their numbers, with fewer light years as well as fewer extremely heavy years; this is indicated by the shorter whiskers on the box-and-whisker plot for 1991 through 2000.

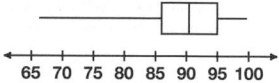
Alternative Assessment

Write several sets of data on the chalkboard or overhead projector. Then give students one box and whisker plot that matches one of the sets of data. Ask students to identify the set of data that the plot represents. Then ask students to describe the median, quartiles, minimum, maximum, and any outliers.

Standardized Test Prep

📁 **Resources**

For additional practice with a variety of test item formats:
- Standardized Test Prep, p. 691
- Test-Taking Strategies, p. 686
- Test-Taking Strategies with Transparencies

20. The median is a better representation for the data; a few outliers can heavily influence the mean without drastically affecting the median.

---

20. Critical Thinking Which measure better represents a data set with several outliers—the mean or the median? Justify your answer. **See margin.**

C Challenge 🌎 **21. Track and Field** The table shows the qualifying distances for the shot put events for both men and women during the 1996 Olympics in Atlanta, Georgia.

1996 Olympic Qualifying Distances for Shot Put (meters)

Men									
	20.43	20.42	19.81	19.61	19.57	19.40	19.12	19.07	19.05
	19.01	18.98	18.48	18.39	18.37	18.21	13.02	NM	NM
	20.58	20.54	20.23	19.95	19.45	19.39	19.39	19.37	18.96
	18.69	18.67	18.53	18.29	18.23	18.22	17.98	17.29	16.51
Women	19.93	19.08	19.04	18.92	18.55	18.39	18.23	18.16	17.69
	17.14	16.40	15.91	DNS	19.36	19.29	19.22	19.03	19.02
	18.61	18.56	18.55	17.48	16.92	16.49	15.28	13.74	DNS

NM = No Measure   DNS = Did Not Show

a. Identify and remove any outliers from the men's results and from the women's results. **men's: 13.02, women's: 13.74**
b. Using the same number line base for both plots, make a box-and-whisker plot for the men's results and another for the women's results.
✏️ **c. Writing** Compare your box-and-whisker plots. Describe any conclusions you can draw about Olympic-level male and female shot-putters. **b–c. See margin.**

🌎 **22. a. Government** Make a box-and-whisker plot for the data from each of the three types of elections shown in the table below. **a–b. See margin p. 655.**

Voter Turnout (percent of voting-age population)

Presidential Year	1972	1976	1980	1984	1988	1992	1996
Voting for President	55.2	53.5	52.8	53.3	50.3	55.1	49.0
Voting for Representatives	50.7	48.9	47.6	47.8	44.9	50.8	45.8
Non-Presidential Year	1974	1978	1982	1986	1990	1994	1998
Voting for Representatives	35.9	34.9	38.0	33.5	33.1	36.6	32.9

SOURCE: U.S. Census Bureau. Go to **www.PHSchool.com** for a data update.
Web Code: agg-2041

✏️ **b. Writing** How does a Presidential election in the United States affect the voter turnout rate in elections for the House of Representatives? Use your box-and-whisker plots to describe any effect that you see.

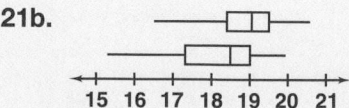

Standardized Test Prep

Multiple Choice

A person checked for e-mail four times each day. The table shows the number of new e-mails she received each time she checked during 5 days.

Day 1	Day 2	Day 3	Day 4	Day 5
6, 3, 1, 5	5, 3, 7, 2	6, 7, 3, 2	8, 2, 6, 9	7, 7, 6, 11

23. Which value is the greatest? **D**
  A. the mean number of e-mails for checks made on days 1–3
  B. the mean number of e-mails for checks made on days 2–4
  C. the mean number of e-mails for checks made on days 2–3
  D. the median number of e-mails for checks made on days 3–4

21b.
```
├──┼──┼──┼──┼──┼──┼──┤
 15 16 17 18 19 20 21
```

c. Answers may vary. Sample: The range for women's shot put is greater than men's. The men are more consistent, as indicated by the shorter box and whiskers. Overall the men tend to throw farther, with the men's median equal to the women's third quartile.

Short Response

Extended Response

24. Which statement(s) is (are) true? **G**

I. The mean number of e-mails for checks made over the 5 days was 5.3.
II. The mean number of e-mails for checks made on day 5 was 7.75.
III. The median number of e-mails for checks made over the 5 days was 6.5.

    F. I only   **G.** I and II only   **H.** II and III only   **I.** I, II, and III

25. Describe how you could find the scores at the 20th and 60th percentiles in a set of 80 scores. **See margin.**

26. Draw a box-and-whisker plot for this set of values: 123, 127, 127, 142, 118, 131, 137, 125, 131.   **See margin.**

Mixed Review

Lesson 12-2

Of all the respondents to a survey, 59% are girls. Of the girls, 61% read horror stories. Of the boys, 49% read horror stories.

27. Find P(boy and reads horror stories).   28. Find P(reads horror stories).
                                          ≈0.20   **≈0.56**

Lesson 11-2

Is the sequence arithmetic? If so, identify the common difference.

29. $16, 7, -2, \ldots$ 30. $34, 51, 68, \ldots$ 31. $2, 2.2, 2.22, \ldots$ 32. $1, 1, 1, \ldots$
    yes; −9   **yes; 17**   **no**   **yes; 0**

Lesson 10-2

Graph each equation. **33–34. See margin.**

33. $y^2 - x - 2y + 1 = 0$ 34. $x^2 + 4x + 144y + 4 = 0$

Checkpoint Quiz 1   Lessons 12-1 through 12-3

 Instant self-check quiz online and on CD-ROM

In a poll, gymnasts were asked, "How many seconds long was your longest handstand on the balance beam?" Use the results below for Exercises 1 and 2.

Longest Handstand

Duration (seconds)	0–2	3–5	6–10	11–20	21–30	31–60	>60	Total
Number of Respondents	14	27	19	18	13	15	24	130

1. Graph the probability distribution.   2. Find $P(6-30 \text{ seconds})$.
      See margin.   **0.385**

3. Writing Could the function $P(x) = \frac{x-2}{2}$ for $x = 1, 2, 3,$ or 4, represent a probability distribution? Explain. **See left.**

3. No; when $x = 1$, $P(x) = -\frac{1}{2}$, and probability is never negative.

Use the table at the right to find each probability.

4. $P(\text{teacher} \mid \text{yes})$ 5. $P(\text{no} \mid \text{teacher})$ $\frac{5}{8}$

6. $P(\text{student} \mid \text{no})$ 7. $P(\text{yes} \mid \text{student})$ $\frac{45}{68}$

4. $\frac{12}{57}$

6. $\frac{23}{43}$

Did You Eat Breakfast Today?

	Yes	No
Teachers	12	20
Students	45	23

Find the mean, median, and mode of each data set.

8. 7 4 9 3 5 4 4 7 9 10 3 1 8 **5.69, 5, 4**

9. 1.2 2.1 4.6 2.5 9.7 6.2 2.6 2.4 3.1 3.8 **3.82, 2.85, no mode**

10. **Open-Ended** Write a data set that includes an outlier. Make a box-and-whisker plot of your data set with and without the outlier. **Check students' work.**

Lesson 12-3   Analyzing Data   **655**

22a.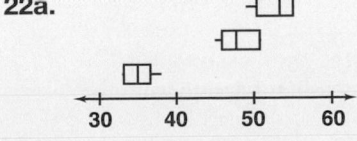

b. A Presidential election greatly increases voter turnout rate for the House of Representatives. The median turnout increases by 12.9%. The minimum turnout in a Presidential election year is 6.9% greater than the maximum turnout for a non-Presidential election year.

To check understanding of Lessons 12-1 to 12-3:

Checkpoint Quiz 1 (p. 655)

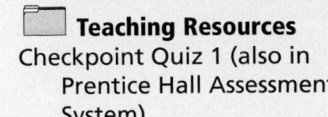 **Teaching Resources**
Checkpoint Quiz 1 (also in Prentice Hall Assessment System)

Reaching All Students
Reading and Math Literacy 12B

Spanish versions available

25. **[2]** Order the 80 scores from lowest to highest. The 20th percentile is the score that is greater than 20%, or 16, of the values; the 60th percentile is the score that is greater than 60% or 48, of the values.

[1] minor error

26. **[4]**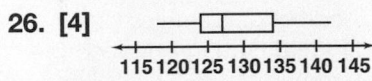
    115 120 125 130 135 140 145

[3] 4 correct values out of 5

[2] 3 correct values

[1] 1 correct value

33.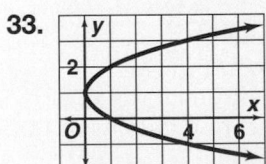

34.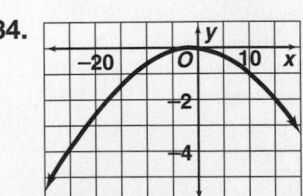

page 655   **Checkpoint Quiz 1**

1.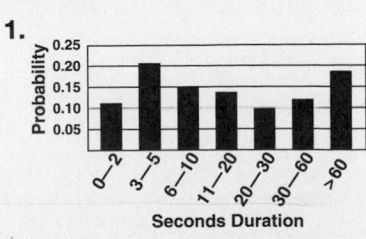

Lesson Preview

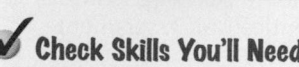 **Check Skills You'll Need**

**Simplifying Expressions
with Integers**
Skills Handbook: p. 845
Examples 3, 4
Exercises 11–32

Lesson Resources

📁 **Teaching Resources**
Practice, Reteaching, Enrichment

👥 **Reaching All Students**
Practice Workbook 12-4
Spanish Practice Workbook 12-4

⏰ **Presentation Assistant Plus!**
Transparencies
• Check Skills You'll Need 12-4
• Additional Examples 12-4
• Student Edition Answers 12-4
• Lesson Quiz 12-4
PH Presentation Pro CD 12-4

PRENTICE HALL ASSESSMENT SYSTEM

Computer Test Generator CD

💿 **Technology**
Resource Pro® CD-ROM
Computer Test Generator CD
Prentice Hall Presentation Pro CD

💻 **www.PHSchool.com**
Student Site
• Teacher Web Code: agk-5500
• Updated data
• Self-grading Lesson Quiz
Teacher Center
• Lesson Planner
• Resources

 Plus 🄸TEXT

 **12-4**

Standard Deviation

Lesson Preview

 What You'll Learn

OBJECTIVE 1
To find the standard deviation of a set of values

OBJECTIVE 2
To use standard deviation in real-world situations

 . . . And Why

To analyze energy demand, as in Example 3

✔ **Check Skills You'll Need**   (For help, go to Skills Handbook page 845.)

Simplify each expression. If necessary, round to the nearest hundredth.

1. $\frac{34.3}{7}$ **4.9**

2. $\frac{6}{2.4}$ **2.5**

3. $8.4 \cdot 1.25$ **10.5**

4. $12 - 6 \cdot 0.5$ **9**

5. $\frac{1}{3}[(2-6)^2 + (7-6)^2 + (8-6)^2]$ **7**

6. $\sqrt{\frac{1}{2}(4-3)^2 + (5+3)^2}$ **8.03**

New Vocabulary   • measures of variation   • range of a set of data
• interquartile range   • standard deviation   • z-score

OBJECTIVE 1   **Finding Standard Deviation**

🄸TEXT **Interactive lesson includes instant self-check, tutorials, and activities.**

1a. Set 1: 80, 80, 80
Set 2: 80, 80, 80
Set 3: 80, 80, 80
Set 4: 80, 80, 80

b. No; although the measures of central tendency are the same, the data in each set are different.

2. Set 1: 6
Set 2: 120
Set 3: 60
Set 4: 120
These differences tell you only how far apart the min. and max. values are.

3. Set 1: 78.5, 80, 81.5
Set 2: 65, 80, 95
Set 3: 65, 80, 95
Set 4: 35, 80, 125

4. Set 1: 3
Set 2: 30
Set 3: 30
Set 4: 90

Investigation: Analyzing Data Spread

1. a. Find the mean, the median, and the mode of each set of data.

Set 1	77	78	79	80	80	81	82	83
Set 2	20	60	70	80	80	90	100	140
Set 3	50	60	70	80	80	90	100	110
Set 4	20	30	40	80	80	120	130	140

b. Are the sets the same? Explain.

2. Find the difference between the greatest and least values in each set of data. What do these differences tell you about each set of data?

3. Find the quartiles of each set of data.

4. For each set, half of the data lie between Q_1 and Q_3. The value $Q_3 - Q_1$ gives you an idea of how the data are spread out. Find $Q_3 - Q_1$ for each set of data.

5. a. Give an example of two sets of data that are spread out differently, though the differences between their extreme values are the same.

b. Give an example of two sets of data that are spread out differently, though their values of $Q_3 - Q_1$ are the same.

5–6. See back of book.

6. a. Summarize the similarities and differences among the four sets in terms of central tendency and spread. Which is the most spread-out set? Which is the least? Explain.

b. Make box-and-whisker plots of the four sets of data. Do the plots support your conclusions from part (a)?

656   Chapter 12   Probability and Statistics

 Ongoing Assessment and Intervention

Before the Lesson
Diagnose prerequisite skills using:
• Check Skills You'll Need

During the Lesson
Monitor progress using:
• Check Understanding
• Additional Examples
• Standardized Test Prep

After the Lesson
Assess knowledge using:
• Lesson Quiz
• Computer Test Generator CD

Statisticians use several **measures of variation** to describe how the data in a data set are spread out.

The **range of a set of data** is the difference between the greatest and least values. The **interquartile range** is the difference between the third and first quartiles.

1 EXAMPLE Real-World Connection

Thirteen men qualified for the 2002 U.S. Men's Alpine Ski Team. Find the range and the interquartile range of their ages at the time of qualification: 27, 28, 29, 23, 25, 26, 26, 28, 22, 23, 23, 21, 25.

$$\text{greatest value} - \text{least value} = 29 - 21 \qquad \textbf{Find the range.}$$
$$= 8$$

Median $\qquad$ **Find the median.**
$\downarrow$

21 22 23 23 23 25 **25** 26 26 27 28 28 29

$\uparrow \qquad\qquad\qquad\qquad\qquad \uparrow$

$Q_1 = 23 \qquad\qquad Q_3 = \dfrac{27 + 28}{2} = 27.5 \quad$ **Find Q_1 and Q_3.**

$Q_3 - Q_1 = 27.5 - 23 \qquad\qquad\qquad$ **Find the interquartile range.**
$= 4.5$

- The range is 8 years. The interquartile range is 4.5 years.

✓ **Check Understanding** **1 a.** Seventeen women qualified for the 2002 U.S. Women's Alpine Ski Team. Find the range and the interquartile range of their ages: 24, 30, 29, 21, 22, 22, 28, 21, 16, 17, 25, 22, 21, 18, 19, 18, 19. **range: 14, interquartile range: 6**
 b. Critical Thinking Can the variation, or spread, in two sets of data be different, even though they have the same range? Give an example.
 c. Can the variation in two sets of data be different, even though they have the same interquartile range? Give an example. **b–c. See back of book.**

Reading Math

The lower case Greek letter σ corresponds to the English letter s.

Another measure of variation is the **standard deviation,** a measure of how each value in a data set varies, or deviates, from the mean. The Greek letter σ (sigma) represents standard deviation.

You can use the following procedure to calculate standard deviation.

Key Concepts

Summary	Finding Standard Deviation

- Find the mean of the data set: $\overline{x}$.

- Find the difference between each value and the mean: $x - \overline{x}$.

- Square each difference: $(x - \overline{x})^2$.

- Find the average (mean) of these squares: $\dfrac{\sum (x - \overline{x})^2}{n}$.

- Take the square root to find the standard deviation:

$$\sigma = \sqrt{\dfrac{\sum (x - \overline{x})^2}{n}}.$$

Need Help?

Σ means summation.

❷ Find the mean and standard deviation for the values 78.2, 90.5, 98.1, 93.7, 94.5 **91; about 6.8**

❸ Use the information from Example 3 to find the mean and standard deviation for daily energy demand on the *weekends* only. **about 36.1; about 3.6**

2 EXAMPLE Math Tip

Greek letters are often used in mathematics as variables or to represent special numbers. Some examples are σ, and π. Explain that the Greek letters have upper- and lower-case forms like the Latin letters we use in English. In the case of sigma, the upper- and lower-case forms have very different meaning in mathematics. The upper-case form, Σ, means summation. The lower-case form, σ, represents standard deviation. Suggest that students record the meanings of Σ, and σ in their notebooks.

3 EXAMPLE Alternative Method

The square of the standard deviation, also known as the variance, can be calculated by subtracting the square of the mean from the mean of the squares of the data values. The square root of this value is the standard deviation. Have students use the information displayed in the first three lines by the 1-Var Stats function to calculate the standard deviation for the data given in Example 3 using this alternative method. This value should agree with the value displayed as σx.

---

2 EXAMPLE Finding the Standard Deviation

Find the mean and the standard deviation for the values: 48.0, 53.2, 52.3, 46.6, 49.9.

$$\bar{x} = \frac{48.0 + 53.2 + 52.3 + 46.6 + 49.9}{5} = 50.0$$ **Find the mean.**

Organize the next steps in a table.

x	$\bar{x}$	$x - \bar{x}$	$(x - \bar{x})^2$
48.0	50.0	−2.0	4.00
53.2	50.0	3.2	10.24
52.3	50.0	2.3	5.29
46.6	50.0	−3.4	11.56
49.9	50.0	−0.1	0.01

Sum: 31.1

$$\sigma = \sqrt{\frac{\sum (x - \bar{x})^2}{n}}$$ **Find the standard deviation.**

$$= \sqrt{\frac{31.1}{5}} \approx 2.5$$

● The mean is 50.0, and the standard deviation is about 2.5.

✓ **Check Understanding** ❷ Find the mean and the standard deviation for these values: 50, 60, 70, 80, 80, 90, 100, 110. **80, ≈18.7**

Standard deviation is like a custom-made measuring stick for the variation in a set of data. A small standard deviation (compared to actual data values) indicates that the data are clustered tightly around the mean. As the data become more spread out, the standard deviation increases.

3 EXAMPLE Real-World 🌐 Connection

Energy Find the mean and the standard deviation of the data for daily energy demand in a small town during August.

... Reading Math

The watt is the metric unit of measurement for power. One million watts of power delivered for one hour results in one megawatt-hour (MWh).

Daily Energy Demand During August (MWh)

Sun.	Mon.	Tues.	Wed.	Thurs.	Fri.	Sat.
		53	52	47	50	39
33	40	41	44	47	49	43
39	47	49	54	53	46	36
33	45	45	42	43	39	33
33	40	40	41	42		

Step 1 Use the STAT feature to enter the data as L1.

Step 2 Use the CALC menu of STAT to access the 1-Var Stats option.

The mean is about 43.2 MWh; the standard deviation is about 6.0 MWh.

```
1-Var Stats
x̄=43.16129032      ← mean
Σx=1338
Σx²=58872
Sx=6.116081394
σx=6.016626288     ← standard deviation
↓n=31
```

✓ Check Understanding ③ Find the mean and standard deviation for this data set: 2 mm, 3 mm, 4 mm, 6 mm, 7 mm, 9 mm, 10 mm, 12 mm, 13 mm, 14 mm.   **8, 4.0**

In a data list, every value falls within some number of standard deviations of the mean. When a value falls within one standard deviation of the mean, it is in the range of values from one standard deviation below the mean to one standard deviation above. For example, if the mean is 50 and the standard deviation is 10, then a value x within one standard deviation of the mean must be in the range $40 \leq x \leq 60$.

4 EXAMPLE   **Real-World**  **Connection**

Energy Use the energy demand data from Example 3. Within how many standard deviations of the mean do all of the values fall? How might the company supplying power to the town use this information?

Real-World  **Connection**

Careers Dispatchers coordinate a utility's power supply and demand.

Step 1 Draw a number line. Plot the data values and the mean.

Step 2 Mark off intervals of 6.0 on either side of the mean.

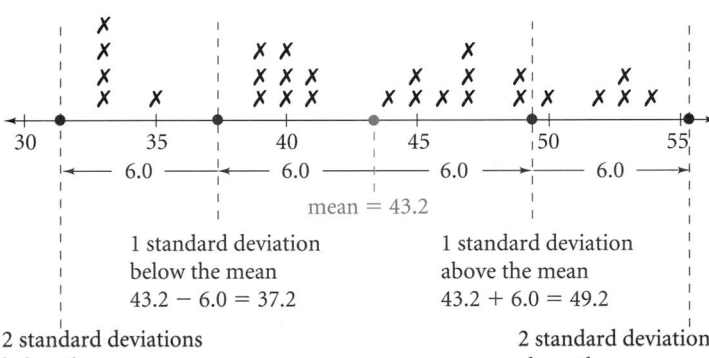

mean = 43.2

1 standard deviation below the mean
43.2 − 6.0 = 37.2

1 standard deviation above the mean
43.2 + 6.0 = 49.2

2 standard deviations below the mean
43.2 − 2(6.0) = 31.2

2 standard deviations above the mean
43.2 + 2(6.0) = 55.2

All of the values fall within two standard deviations of the mean. Therefore, the power company can expect that the daily demand on most days in August will fall within two standard deviations of the mean.

✓ Check Understanding ④ **a.** Within how many standard deviations of the mean for August is a demand of 38.5 MWh? **1**

4b. No; three standard deviations from the mean is 46.3, which is less than 48.

b. In May, the mean daily energy demand is 35.8 MWh, with a standard deviation of 3.5 MWh. The power company prepares for any demand within three standard deviations of the mean. Are they prepared for a demand of 48 MWh? Explain.

The **z-score** is the number of standard deviations that a value is from the mean. In Example 4, the value 49.2 is one standard deviation above the mean, so it has a z-score of 1. The value 37.2, which is one standard deviation below the mean, has a z-score of -1.

OBJECTIVE
2 Teaching Notes

4 EXAMPLE   Math Tip

Make sure students understand that two standard deviations on the number line is 12 units. So all of the values are less than 12 units from the mean.

Additional Examples

④ The number of points that Darden scored in each of 11 basketball games is listed below. Within how many standard deviations of the mean do all of the values fall? What can Darden's coach do with this information? 8, 12, 13, 10, 7, 5, 10, 9, 13, 11, 8
2; The coach can predict that his score in the next game will fall within two standard deviations of the mean.

⑤ A set of values has a mean of 22 and a standard deviation of 5. Find the z-score for a value of 30.
1.6

Closure

Give students the following situation: *Suppose two baseball players have the same mean number of hits per game. However, player A's data has a standard deviation of 0.5 and player B's data has a standard deviation of 2. Which one is most likely to get a hit at his next at-bat? Explain.* **Player A. His lower standard deviation means that he is more consistent.**

3. Practice

Assignment Guide

1 Objective
  Ⓐ Ⓑ **Core** 1–7, 15–19,
    22–26, 28
  Ⓒ **Extension** 29

2 Objective
  Ⓐ Ⓑ **Core** 8–14, 20,
    21, 27
  Ⓒ **Extension** 30

Standardized Test Prep 31–34

Mixed Review 35–41

Error Prevention

Exercises 8, 9 Caution students that they must use the number of standard deviations that includes *all* data values, both above and below the mean.

Enrichment 12-4
Reteaching 12-4
Practice 12-4

pages 660–662 Exercises

15. 14.6, 52.3; the bird speeds are more spread out than the cat speeds.

16. 4.1, 2.0; the number of buttons is more spread out than the number of pockets.

660

---

5 EXAMPLE Finding the *z*-score

A set of values has a mean of 85 and a standard deviation of 6. Find the *z*-score of the value 76.

$$z\text{-score} = \frac{\text{value} - \text{mean}}{\text{standard deviation}}$$

$$= \frac{76 - 85}{6} \quad \text{Substitute.}$$

$$= \frac{-9}{6} \quad \text{Simplify.}$$

$$= -1.5$$

✔ **Check Understanding** ⑤ Use the mean and standard deviation from Example 5. Find the value that has a *z*-score of 2.5. **100**

EXERCISES

For more practice, see *Extra Practice*.

Practice and Problem Solving

Ⓐ **Practice by Example**

Example 1 (page 657)

Find the range and the interquartile range of each set of values.

1. 5 6 7 3 4 5 6 7 8 **5, 2.5**
2. 56 78 125 34 67 91 20 **105, 57**

3. 724 786 670 760 300 187 190 345 456 732 891 879 324
    704, 461

Examples 2 and 3 (page 658)

Find the mean and the standard deviation for each set of values.

4. 78 90 456 673 111 381 21
5. 13 15 17 18 12 21 10

4. 258.6, 228.3
5. 15.1, 3.5
6. 2866.87, 137.69
7. 10,567.45, 435.16

6. The Dow Jones Industrial average for the first 24 weeks of 1991:

2501.50	2646.80	2659.40	2730.70	2830.70	2934.70
2889.40	2909.90	2955.20	2948.30	2558.90	2913.90
2896.80	2920.80	2965.60	2912.40	2938.90	2920.20
2886.60	2913.90	3027.50	2976.70	3000.50	2965.60

7. The Dow Jones Industrial average for the first 24 weeks of 2001:

10662.01	10525.38	10587.59	10659.98	10864.10	10781.45
10799.82	10441.90	10466.31	10644.62	9823.41	9504.78
9878.78	9791.09	10126.94	10579.85	10810.05	10951.24
10821.31	11301.74	11005.37	10990.41	10977.00	10623.64

Example 4 (page 659)

Determine the whole number of standard deviations that includes all data values.

8. The mean price of the nonfiction books on a best-sellers list is $25.07; the standard deviation is $2.62. **2 standard deviations**
$26.95, $22.95, $24.00, $24.95, $29.95, $19.95, $24.95, $24.00, $27.95, $25.00

9. The mean length of Beethoven's nine symphonies is 37 minutes; the standard deviation is 12 minutes. **3 standard deviations**
27 min, 30 min, 47 min, 35 min, 30 min, 40 min, 35 min, 22 min, 65 min

Example 5 (page 660)

A data set has mean 25 and standard deviation 5. Find the *z*-score of each value.

10. 39 **2.8**
11. 18 **−1.4**
12. 125 **20**
13. 25 **0**
14. 11 **−2.8**

18. The range in 1998 was 8489, while in 1999 it dropped to 7891. While overall farm income dropped, there was less variability in 1999.

19. σ for 1998 was ≈2926, while in 1999 it was ≈2779. In 1999 incomes were more tightly clustered about the mean.

22. ≈10.9; ≈3.3
23. ≈75.8; ≈8.7
24. ≈1.9; ≈1.4
25. ≈0.007; ≈0.08

Apply Your Skills **Find the standard deviation for each data set. Use the standard deviations to compare each pair of data sets. 15–16. See margin p. 660.**

15. fastest recorded speeds of various large wild cats (miles per hour):
70 50 30 40 35 30 30 40 15
fastest recorded speeds of various birds in flight (miles per hour):
217 106 95 56 65 37 50 31 53 25 25 25

16. the number of buttons on selected outfits:
11 5 12 8 3 12 10 10 0 5 0 2 7 10
the number of pockets in the same outfits:
5 5 5 2 2 5 3 2 0 2 0 0 5 5

Income   Use the chart at the right for Exercises 17–20.

17. Find the mean income for each year. **1998: ≈7576; 1999: ≈6945**

18. **Writing** Use the range of the data for each year to describe how farm income varied from 1998 to 1999. **See margin p. 660.**

19. Find the standard deviation for each year. In which year did farm income cluster more tightly around the mean? **See margin p. 660.**

20. Which state's 1998 income has a z-score of about 1.6? **Iowa**

Farm Income in Midwestern States (millions of dollars)

State	1998	1999
Iowa	12,153	10,812
Kansas	8688	8565
Minnesota	8971	8010
Missouri	5464	4902
Nebraska	9827	9429
North Dakota	3664	2921
South Dakota	4264	3974

Real-World Connection

The fastest wild cat is the cheetah, which can run as fast as 70 mi/h.

21a. 53.8, ≈3.4
  b. 7; 9; 10

21. **a. Energy** Find the mean and the standard deviation for daily energy usage during ten days in June: 51.8 MWh, 53.6 MWh, 54.7 MWh, 51.9 MWh, 49.3 MWh, 52.0 MWh, 53.5 MWh, 51.2 MWh, 60.7 MWh, 59.3 MWh.
   b. How many items in the data set fall within one standard deviation of the mean? Within two standard deviations? Within three standard deviations?

 Another measure of variation is *variance*, which equals σ^2. Find the variance and the standard deviation of each data set.   22–27. See margin.

22. 12 h   3 h   2 h   4 h   5 h   7 h

23. 60 m   40 m   35 m   45 m   39 m

24. $6.99 $5.50 $7.10 $9.22 $8.99

25. 0.7 g   0.84 g   0.9 g   0.8 g   0.69 g

26. **Critical Thinking** From your results in Exercises 22–25, which do you think is a better measure of variation—variance or standard deviation? Explain.

27. **Error Analysis** Minh says that the data below fall within three standard deviations of the mean. Marsha disagrees, saying that the data fall within six standard deviations of the mean. With whom do you agree? Explain.

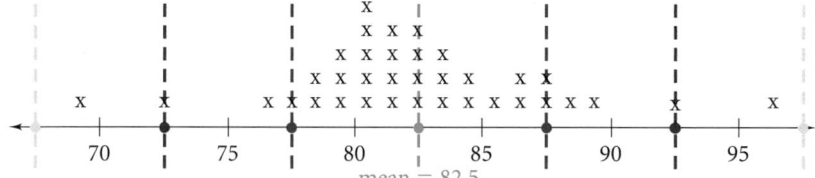

mean = 82.5

Lesson 12-4   Standard Deviation   **661**

26. **Answers may vary. Sample: standard deviation, because it has the same units of measure as the data, and it doesn't magnify the** variation as much as the variance does.

27. **Minh; one standard deviation encompasses all values within one** standard deviation above and below the mean. The graph actually shows that all values are within 3 standard deviations of the mean.

Lesson Quiz 12-4

Use the following set of data for items 1 through 3 below.

13, 10, 11, 8, 14, 13, 13, 14, 30

1. Find the range and interquartile range for the above set of data. **22; 3.5**

2. Find the mean and standard deviation for the above set of data. **14; about 6.0**

3. Within how many standard deviations of the mean do all of the above data values fall? **3**

4. A set of values has a mean of 34 and a standard deviation of 4. Find the z-score of the value 26. **−2**

Careers

Exercises 17–20 Ask students why they think farm income has decreased. Some reasons may be: droughts, floods, or other natural phenomenon. Tell students that the number of farms is decreasing. Some farmers are finding it more profitable to sell their land to community developers or to large farming companies, rather than keep their land as a personal or family farm.

Diversity

Exercise 30 Be sensitive to the disparity between earnings since some students in your class may have family members that work in the listed occupations.

Alternative Assessment

Organize students in pairs or small groups. Have each group toss two number cubes 50 times, recording the results for each trial. Then ask students to find the mean and standard deviation for the data, and compare these results with those of other groups. Based on their comparisons, have students draw conclusions about which numbers are more likely than others to come up on a random toss of the number cubes.

661

Resources

For additional practice with a variety of test item formats:
- Standardized Test Prep, p. 691
- Test-Taking Strategies, p. 686
- Test-Taking Strategies with Transparencies

pages 660–662   Exercises

29a. men: 14; 22.9; 3.2
women: 12; 25.9; 3.8

b. No; the men's team has a broader range of ages, but a smaller standard deviation than the women's team.

30a. union: $641; $279
nonunion: $564; $317

b. union: $98
nonunion: $92

c. union: 3;
nonunion: 2

d. On average, union workers are paid more than nonunion workers. The pay range is broader for nonunion workers. Union workers' pay is more broadly distributed than nonunion workers'.

35.

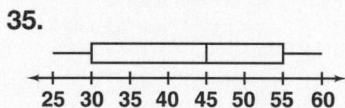

36.

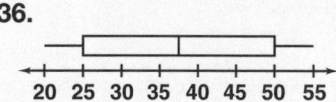

40.

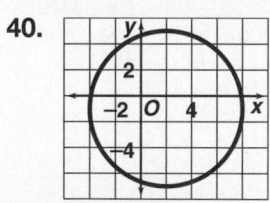

41.

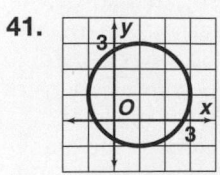

28. **a. Data Collection** Make a table showing the number of siblings of each student in the class.
   b. Find the mean and standard deviation of the data.   **Check students' work.**

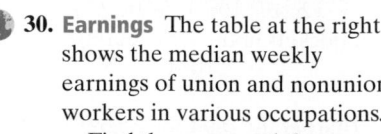

C Challenge

Ages of the Members of the 2000 U.S. Olympic Soccer Teams

Men		Women	
23	32	32	29
29	23	29	22
23	23	32	28
22	23	25	23
21	18	22	22
19	22	20	24
20	23	32	25
23	21	29	27
26	22	24	22

29. **a.** Use the table at the left to find the range, the mean, and the standard deviation of the ages for each team.   **a–b. See margin.**
   b. Critical Thinking For two data sets, does the set with the larger range necessarily have the larger standard deviation? Support your answer with your results from part (a).

30. **Earnings** The table at the right shows the median weekly earnings of union and nonunion workers in various occupations.
   a. Find the mean and the range of the data for union workers and for nonunion workers.
   b. Find the standard deviation for each set of data.
   c. Within how many standard deviations of the mean are earnings of $395 for union workers? For nonunion workers?

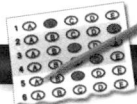

   d. Writing Compare the wages of union and nonunion workers. Use your results from parts (a) through (c).
   a–d. See margin.

Worker's Median Weekly Earnings, 1999

Occupation	Union	Nonunion
Construction	$778	$509
Transportation and public utilities	$748	$613
Trade	$499	$418
Manufacturing	$614	$561
Services	$554	$515
Finance, insurance, and real estate	$582	$599
Mining	$710	$735

SOURCE: U.S. Bureau of Labor Statistics.
Go to **www.PHSchool.com** for a data update.
Web Code: agg-2041

Gridded Response

Take It to the NET
Online lesson quiz at
www.PHSchool.com
Web Code: aga-1204

For Exercises 31–32, use the following bowling scores for six members of a bowling team: 175, 210, 180, 195, 208, 196.

31. What is the mean of the scores?   **194**

32. What is the standard deviation of the scores?   **13.0**

33. At a second bowling tournament, the mean of all the scores was 205, with a standard deviation of 14. What was the *z*-score for a score of 282?   **5.5**

34. At the second tournament, a participant had a *z*-score of −2.5. What was the participant's bowling score?   **170**

Mixed Review

Lesson 12-3   Make a box-and-whisker plot for each set of values.   **35–36. See margin.**

35. 25, 25, 30, 35, 45, 45, 50, 55, 60, 60   36. 20, 23, 25, 36, 37, 38, 39, 50, 52, 55

Lesson 11-3   Find the missing positive term in each geometric sequence.

37. 64, ■, 4, . . . **16**   38. 20, ■, 0.05, . . . **1**   39. 29, ■, 65.25, . . . **43.5**

Lesson 10-3   Graph each circle.   **40–41. See margin.**

40. $(x - 2)^2 + (y + 1)^2 = 36$ 41. $(x - 1)^2 + (y - 1)^2 = 4$

12-5

Working With Samples

Lesson Preview

What You'll Learn

 OBJECTIVE 1 To find sample proportions

 OBJECTIVE 2 To find the margin of error

. . . And Why

To analyze data from a poll, as in Example 5

 Check Skills You'll Need   (For help, go to Lesson 7-1.)

Simplify each expression.

1. $\frac{1}{\sqrt{4}}$ $\frac{1}{2}$

2. $-\frac{1}{\sqrt{9}}$ $-\frac{1}{3}$

3. $\frac{1}{\sqrt{36}}$ $\frac{1}{6}$

4. $-\frac{1}{\sqrt{121}}$ $-\frac{1}{11}$

5. $\frac{1}{\sqrt{50}}$ $\frac{\sqrt{2}}{10}$

6. $-\frac{1}{\sqrt{81}}$ $-\frac{1}{9}$

New Vocabulary • **sample** • **sample proportion** • **random sample**
• **margin of error**

 OBJECTIVE 1 Sampling Without Bias

 Interactive lesson includes instant self-check, tutorials, and activities.

Suppose you want to know what percent of all teenagers recognize the word that means "to pass the summer in a state of slumber." Since it is too costly and time consuming to ask every teenager, use a sample. A **sample** gathers information from only part of a population.

Using any sample, you can find a sample proportion. The **sample proportion** is the ratio $\frac{x}{n}$, where x is the number of times an event occurs in a sample of size n.

> **Word Wise**
>
> Which word means "to pass the summer in a state of slumber"?
>
> A. stridulate
> B. ruminate
> C. estivate
> D. somnambulate

1 EXAMPLE   Finding the Sample Proportion

In a sample of 350 teenagers, 294 have never made a snow sculpture. Find the sample proportion for those who have never made a snow sculpture. Write the answer as a percent.

sample proportion $= \frac{x}{n}$ **Write the formula.**

$= \frac{294}{350}$ **Substitute 294 for *x* and 350 for *n*.**

$= 0.84$ **Simplify.**

The sample proportion is 84%.

 Check Understanding **1** In a poll of 1085 voters, 564 favor Candidate A. Find the sample proportion for those who favor Candidate A.   **52%**

> **Reading Math**
> Bias means "slant."

Samples vary in how well they reflect the entire population. In a **random sample**, all members of the population are equally likely to be chosen.

When a part of a population is overrepresented or underrepresented in a sample, the sample is biased. A random sample can help avoid bias in gathering data.

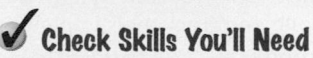 **12-5**

1. Plan

Lesson Preview

 Check Skills You'll Need

Finding Roots
Lesson 7-1: Example 2
Exercises 13–20
Extra Practice, p. 828

Lesson Resources

 Teaching Resources
Practice, Reteaching, Enrichment

Reaching All Students
Practice Workbook 12-5
Spanish Practice Workbook 12-5

Presentation Assistant Plus!
Transparencies
• Check Skills You'll Need 12-5
• Additional Examples 12-5
• Student Edition Answers 12-5
• Lesson Quiz 12-5
PH Presentation Pro CD 12-5

PRENTICE HALL ASSESSMENT SYSTEM

Computer Test Generator CD

Technology
Resource Pro® CD-ROM
Computer Test Generator CD
Prentice Hall Presentation Pro CD

 **www.PHSchool.com**
Student Site
• Teacher Web Code: agk-5500
• Self-grading Lesson Quiz
Teacher Center
• Lesson Planner
• Resources

Plus **iTEXT**

Ongoing Assessment and Intervention

Before the Lesson
Diagnose prerequisite skills using:
• Check Skills You'll Need

During the Lesson
Monitor progress using:
• Check Understanding
• Additional Examples
• Standardized Test Prep

After the Lesson
Assess knowledge using:
• Lesson Quiz
• Computer Test Generator CD

Math Background

When it is not practical to collect data on an entire population, a sample, or smaller portion of the population is often surveyed. The data collected from the sample is then assumed to reflect data of the entire population. When using samples, care must be taken to assure that the members of a sample are selected randomly from the members of a population. Also, the size of a sample reflects the reliability of its data. Larger samples tend to more accurately reflect the entire population.

OBJECTIVE

▼1 Teaching Notes

2 EXAMPLE Teaching Tip

Ask students to conjecture why random sampling techniques might be especially important to minority groups within a community.

Additional Examples

1 In a sample of 500 teenagers, 328 had never attended a popular music concert. Find the sample proportion for those who have never attended a popular music concert. Write the answer as a percent. **about 66%**

2 The Sunnyvale High School student council dance committee is trying to decide whether to have a band or a DJ for the fall dance. They decided that each of the four committee members should survey the students in their homeroom classes. Identify any bias in this sampling method. **This is a convenience sample that is convenient for the committee members. Four homerooms may not accurately reflect the opinions of the entire school. The opinions of the committee members may influence the opinions of their homeroom students.**

664

---

2 EXAMPLE Real-World 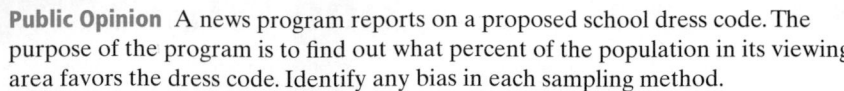 Connection

Public Opinion A news program reports on a proposed school dress code. The purpose of the program is to find out what percent of the population in its viewing area favors the dress code. Identify any bias in each sampling method.

a. Viewers are invited to call the program and express their preferences.

The people who decide to call in may over- or underrepresent some views. For example, members of a group favoring the new dress code might encourage its members to call in. This type of sample is called a "self-selected" sample.

b. A reporter interviews people on the street near the local high school.

This is a "convenience" sample, since it is convenient for the reporter to stay in one place. Because the location is near the school, students may be overrepresented in the sample and the results will be biased.

c. During the program, 300 people are selected at random from the viewing area. Then each person is contacted.

This sampling method contains the least bias. It is a random sample.

✓ **Check Understanding** **2 a.** Suppose the 350 teenagers in Example 1 all live in Florida. Is there bias in this sample? Explain. **a–b. See margin p. 665.**

b. **Critical Thinking** The only way to know a true population proportion is to poll every person in the population. Such a poll is no longer a sample, but a census. Describe a situation in which a sample is unsatisfactory and a census is required.

OBJECTIVE

▼2 Sample Size

The size of a sample affects its reliability. With a small sample size, you are likely to get a wide range of sample proportions. For example, in some samples, no one will recognize the word that means "to pass the summer in a state of slumber." In other samples, everyone will recognize *estivate*. With larger sample sizes, you are less likely to have a sample containing an "all or nothing" result.

The Law of Large Numbers states that the variation in a data set decreases as the sample size increases. By comparing the variation in samples, you can get an idea of their relative sizes.

3 EXAMPLE Comparing Sample Sizes

Each graph below shows the sample proportions for 20 samples. Match each graph to the most likely sample size.

a. 20 people per sample   **b.** 5 people per sample

Distributions of Sample Proportions

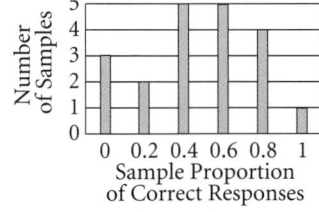

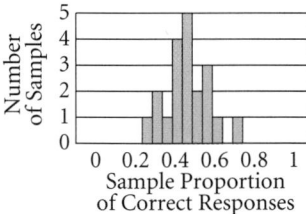

664 Chapter 12 Probability and Statistics

🧑‍🤝‍🧑 Reaching All Students

| **Below Level** Have students discuss what sample of the population it might be useful to choose when trying to predict the outcome of an election. **likely voters** | **Advanced Learners** Have students research the difference between population standard deviation and sample standard deviation. | **Error Prevention** See note on page 667. |

a. The graph on the right shows less variation, so it is more likely to be based on samples of a larger size, 20 people per sample.

b. The graph on the left shows more variation, so it is more likely be based on 5 people per sample.

✓ Check Understanding

3. B; a larger sample has less variation, which corresponds to a smaller standard deviation.

3 A science class measured the heights of blades of grass behind the school. The class took three samples. Use the information in the table below to decide which sample most likely was the greatest in size. Explain your reasoning.

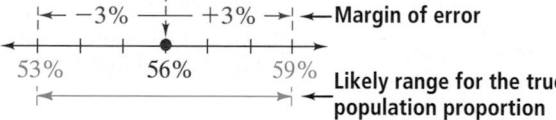

Sample	Standard Deviation (in.)
A	1.45
B	1.09
C	1.26

A sample proportion should be reported with an estimate of error, called the **margin of error.** The margin of error is based on the standard deviation in graphs like those in Example 3. The larger the sample size, the smaller the margin of error.

Key Concepts

Property	Margin of Error Formula

When a random sample of size n is taken from a large population, the sample proportion has a margin of error of approximately $\pm\frac{1}{\sqrt{n}}$.

4 EXAMPLE Using the Margin of Error

A poll reports that 56% of voters favor Candidate B, with a margin of error of $\pm 3\%$. Estimate the number of voters in the poll.

$$\text{margin of error} = \pm\frac{1}{\sqrt{n}} \qquad \text{Write the formula.}$$

$$\pm\sqrt{n} = \frac{1}{\text{margin of error}} \qquad \text{Rewrite the equation.}$$

$$= \frac{1}{0.03} \qquad \text{Substitute 0.03 for margin of error.}$$

$$\approx 33.33 \qquad \text{Simplify.}$$

$$n \approx 1111 \qquad \text{Square each side.}$$

The poll included about 1100 voters.

✓ Check Understanding

4 Estimate the sample size for each margin of error.
   a. $\pm 10\%$ **100**   **b.** $\pm 4\%$ **625**   **c.** $\pm 2\%$ **2500**

You can use the margin of error to determine the likely range for the true population proportion. The graph below shows the range for the population in Example 4.

Sample Proportion

$\leftarrow -3\% \quad\mid\quad +3\% \rightarrow\mid\leftarrow$ **Margin of error**

53%   56%   59% **Likely range for the true population proportion**

4 EXAMPLE Math Tip

Explain to students that when solving for n, both sides of the equation are squared, which eliminates the $\pm$ sign. Additionally, a negative number of voters would not make sense.

5 EXAMPLE Teaching Tip

Challenge students to use their knowledge of reciprocals to explain what happens to the margin of error as n increases and decreases. **As n increases, the margin of error decreases, and as n decreases, the margin of error increases.**

Additional Examples

3 In a survey, teenagers were asked to rank the importance of their relationships with their parents. The response scale ranged from 1 to 5, with 5 being extremely important. Use the information in the table to decide which sample was most likely the greatest in size.

Sample	Score	Standard Deviation
A	4.4	1.4
B	4.6	0.6
C	4.6	1.2

Sample B was most likely the greatest in size since it has the smallest standard deviation.

4 An opinion poll about the popularity of the mayor has a margin of error of $\pm 5\%$. Estimate the number of people who were surveyed. **about 400 people**

page 664 Check Understanding

2a. Yes; the sample is biased because it overrepresents students who live in a warm climate.

b. Answers may vary. Sample: Every 10 years, the United States conducts a census of the population to find exactly how many people live in the country.

665

5 A survey of 528 high school seniors found that 65% already had career plans after high school.
a. Find the margin of error for the sample. **about ±4%**
b. Use the margin of error to find an interval that is likely to contain the true population proportion. **61–69%**

Closure

Ask volunteers to compare and contrast the importance of sampling without bias and sample size. Ask: *Is one aspect more important than the other when working with samples?* **Answers may vary. Sample: Sampling without bias is important to get a sample that is representative of the entire population. Size of the sample is important to the reliability of the sample. Both are equally important when working with samples.**

pages 666–669   Exercises

6. **If students walk or drive to school, or are involved in other after-school activities, they are underrepresented by this sample method.**

Real-World Connection

Some retail businesses cater to left-handers.

5 EXAMPLE   Real-World Connection

Genetics A survey of 2580 students found that 9% are left-handed.

a. Find the margin of error for the sample.

$$\text{margin of error} = \pm\frac{1}{\sqrt{n}} \qquad \text{Use the formula.}$$
$$= \pm\frac{1}{\sqrt{2580}} \qquad \text{Substitute.}$$
$$\approx \pm 0.0197 \qquad \text{Use a calculator.}$$

The margin of error is about ±2%.

b. Use the margin of error to find an interval that is likely to contain the true population proportion.

The margin of error forms an interval with the sample proportion at its midpoint.

Sample Proportion

$\leftarrow -2\% \xrightarrow{\ \ } +2\% \rightarrow$

7%   9%   11%

The proportion of students who are left-handed is likely to be from 7% to 11%.

 Check Understanding

5 In a poll of 123 students, 87 have never ridden a ferry. Find the sample proportion, the margin of error, and the interval likely to contain the true population proportion. **71%, ±9%, 62% to 80%**

EXERCISES

For more practice, see *Extra Practice.*

Practice and Problem Solving

A Practice by Example

Example 1
(page 663)

For each sample, find the sample proportion. Write it as a percent.

1. 837 out of 1150 insurance applicants have no citations on their driving record. **73%**

2. 27 out of 60 shoppers prefer generic brands when available. **45%**

3. 532 out of 580 households own a color television set. **92%**

Example 2
(page 664)

4. This sampling method overrepresents shoppers buying greeting cards.

Identify any bias in each sampling method.

4. A supermarket wants to find the proportion of shoppers who use reduced-price coupons. A manager interviews every shopper entering the greeting card aisle.

5. A maintenance crew wants to estimate how many of 3000 air filters in an office building need replacing. The crew examines five filters chosen at random on each floor of the building. **very little bias**

6. The student government wants to find out how many students have after-school jobs. A pollster interviews students selected at random as they board buses at the end of the school day. **See margin.**

Example 3
(pages 664–665)

7. C; this sample has the smallest standard deviation, which most likely indicates a larger sample.

7. In a survey, teenagers were asked the importance of "making your own things." The response scale ranged from 1 to 5, with 5 being extremely important. Which sample most likely was largest? Explain.

Sample	Score	Standard Deviation
A	3.6	1.2
B	3.8	1.0
C	3.8	0.5

8. Group B probably was the smaller sample; it has the greater variation in the percentages represented in the graph.

8. The table below shows the results of a poll asking students, "How many hours a week would you say you spend doing academic homework?" Which sample most likely was smaller? Explain.

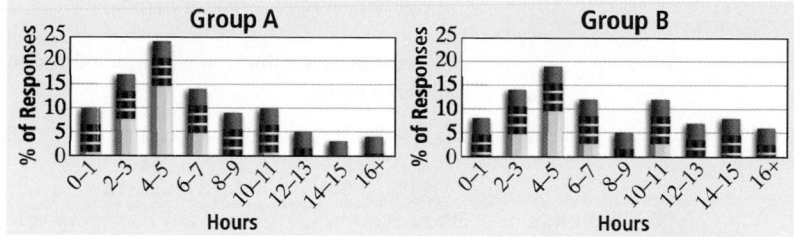

Example 4
(page 665)

Find the margin of error for the sample proportion, given each sample of size n.

9. $n = 200$ ±7%   **10.** $n = 800$ ±4%   **11.** $n = 1200$ ±3%

Find the sample size that produces each margin of error.

12. ±8%   **156**   **13.** ±5%   **400**   **14.** ±1%   **10,000**

Example 5
(page 666)

For each situation, find the margin of error for the sample. Then find an interval likely to contain the true population proportion.

15. Of 750 teenagers polled, 59% think boys and girls are portrayed as equals on television.   **±4%; 55% to 63%**

16. Of 400 teenagers surveyed, 62% do not plan to stay in their community after finishing their education.   **±5%; 57% to 67%**

B Apply Your Skills   🌐 **Surveys** For each sample, find (a) the sample proportion, (b) the margin of error, and (c) the interval likely to contain the true population proportion.

17. In a random sample of 408 grocery shoppers, 258 prefer one large trip per week to several smaller ones.   **a. 63% b. ±5% c. 58% to 68%**

18. Of 500 teenagers surveyed, 460 would like to see adults in their community do more to solve drug problems.   **a. 92% b. ±4% c. 88% to 96%**

19. In a survey of 32 people, 30 return a milk carton to the refrigerator immediately after using it.   **a. 94% b. ±18% c. 76% to 100%**

20. In a survey of 16 people, one person never locks his car.
a. 6% b. ±25% c. 0% to 31%

✏️ **21. Writing** Write a news article describing the sample proportion and margin of error for the poll results shown at the right.
Check students' work.

22. Reasoning How is the margin of error affected if you double the sample size? Explain.
See margin.

23. a. Data Collection Write a survey question to find out the number of students at your school who plan to continue their education after high school
b. Describe the sampling method you would use.
c. Conduct your survey.   **a–c. Check students' work.**

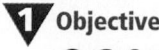

24. A sample proportion is an experimental probability; it is based on actual measurements.

24. Critical Thinking A sample proportion provides an estimate for the percent of an entire population that favors an event. Is a sample proportion an experimental or a theoretical probability? Explain.

3. Practice

Assignment Guide

▼**1** Objective
🅐 🅑 **Core** 1–6, 23–25
🅒 **Extension** 32

▼**2** Objective
🅐 🅑 **Core** 7–22, 26–29
🅒 **Extension** 30, 31

Standardized Test Prep 33–37

Mixed Review 38–46

Error Prevention

Exercises 15, 16 Make sure students select an interval centered on the sample proportion.

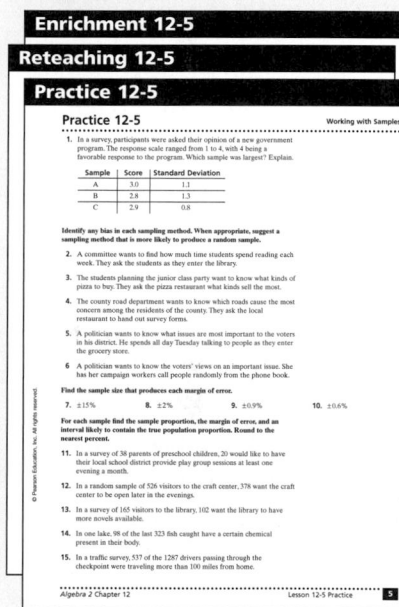

22. Doubling a sample size multiplies the margin of error by $\frac{1}{\sqrt{2}} \approx 0.71$, so the margin is about 71% of its former value.

Lesson Quiz 12-5

1. If 412 of 1720 students at a high school participate in extra-curricular sports activities, what is the proportion of the students who participate in sports? Write the proportion as a percent. **about 24%**

2. A radio talk show found that over 90% of listeners who called in were against building a community recreation center. Identify any bias in this sampling method. **This is a self-selected sample, and the people who call in are likely to over- or under-represent certain viewpoints.**

3. A biology class counted the number of microorganisms in drops of water from a nearby pond. The class took three samples. Use the information in the table to decide which sample was largest. Explain your reasoning.

Sample	Standard Deviation
A	1.2
B	1.7
C	2.1

Sample A; Sample A has the lowest standard deviation suggesting that it was the largest sample.

4. A survey of voters found that 61% of voters supported building a new high school, with a margin of error of 2%. Estimate the number of voters in the poll. **about 2500 voters**

5. Jill conducted a survey of 100 drivers and found that 72% thought that improperly timed traffic lights were the city's worst traffic problem. Find the margin of error and the interval that is likely to contain the true population proportion. **10%; 62–82%**

Reading Math

For help with reading and solving Exercise 25, see p. 670.

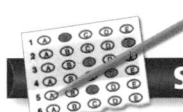

Challenge

30b. $50,000; more than doubling the cost of the survey has made only a small improvement in the margin of error.

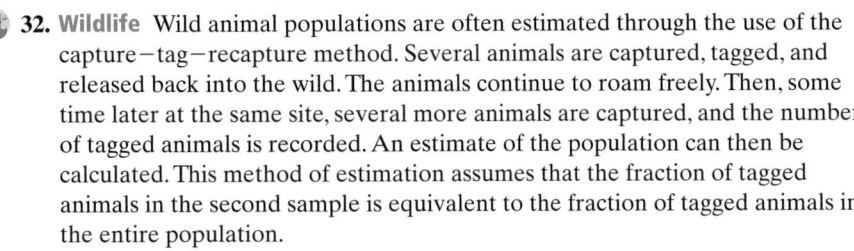

Exercise 32

25. **Computer Use** An online advertisement asks you to participate in a survey. The survey asks how much time you spend online each week. Identify any bias in this method. If appropriate, suggest a method more likely to produce a random sample. **See margin.**

An event occurs x times in a sample of size n. Find its sample proportion and margin of error.

26. $x = 96$
    $n = 900$
    11%, ±3%

27. $x = 20$
    $n = 64$
    31%, ±13%

28. $x = 100$
    $n = 250$
    40%, ±6%

29. $x = 273$
    $n = 435$
    63%, ±5%

30. **a.** It costs $20 to interview each person for a survey. Find the cost to obtain a ±3% margin of error. **$22,220**
    b. Critical Thinking Find the cost to obtain a ±2% margin of error. Why do you think polls with smaller margins of error are rare?

31. **a. Elections** A poll of 150 voters shows that a candidate is preferred by 56% of the voters while 44% prefer the opponent. Should the candidate be concerned? Explain. **a–b. See margin.**
    b. A later poll of 600 voters shows the candidate is preferred by 55% of the voters. Should this candidate feel more or less confident, given the results of the second poll? Explain.

32. **Wildlife** Wild animal populations are often estimated through the use of the capture−tag−recapture method. Several animals are captured, tagged, and released back into the wild. The animals continue to roam freely. Then, some time later at the same site, several more animals are captured, and the number of tagged animals is recorded. An estimate of the population can then be calculated. This method of estimation assumes that the fraction of tagged animals in the second sample is equivalent to the fraction of tagged animals in the entire population.

$$\frac{\text{tagged animals in second sample}}{\text{animals in second sample}} = \frac{\text{tagged animals in population}}{\text{population }(P)}$$

Use the formula above to predict the black bear population of the northern coastal plain of South Carolina. Researchers tagged fourteen black bears in the fall and captured eleven bears the following summer. Of the eleven bears, three were tagged. **51 black bears**

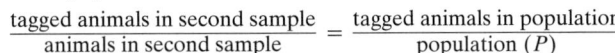

Standardized Test Prep

Multiple Choice

33. In a sample of 625 airline travelers, 485 collected "airline miles" toward free trips. What does the number $\frac{140}{625}$ represent? **B**
    A. the probability that a passenger collects airline miles
    B. the sample proportion of the travelers who do not collect airline miles
    C. the sample proportion of the travelers who collect airline miles
    D. the margin of error for the sample

34. A random sample of people answered the question "Do you collect airline miles?" The margin of error for the sample was ±2%. The sample proportion of people who answered no was $\frac{3}{10}$. How many people in the sample answered no? **H**
    F. 15   G. 225   H. 750   I. 2500

pages 666–669   Exercises

25. **This method is biased because it overrepresents people who respond to the online advertisement.**

A less biased method could involve surveying a group of people selected at random.

31a. There is an 8% margin of error; the candidate should be aware that 52% of the voters could actually prefer the opponent.

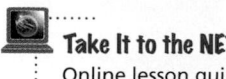
Take It to the NET
Online lesson quiz at
www.PHSchool.com
Web Code: aga-1205

35. A research group had a stack of survey responses. The number of respondents was more than 5000 and fewer than 5500. When the researchers divided the respondents into 13 equal groups, there were no extra respondents. Similarly, there were no extra respondents when they divided the responses into 7 equal groups or 11 equal groups. How many respondents were there? **B**

A. 1001   B. 5005   C. 5031   D. 500,500

Short Response

36. What is the margin of error for a random sample of size 3600? Show your work. **See margin.**

Extended Response

37. In a poll of 2750 airline travelers, 138 said they never check their luggage when they fly. Find the sample proportion, the margin of error, and the interval likely to contain the true population proportion. **See margin.**

Mixed Review

Lesson 12-4   Find the mean and the standard deviation for each data set.

38. 0 km, 1 km, 1 km, 1 km, 2 km, 2 km, 2 km, 3 km, 3 km, 4 km, 5 km, 10 km

$\approx 2.8, \approx 2.5$

39. 1 oz, 1 oz, 2 oz, 2 oz, 3 oz, 4 oz, 5 oz, 6 oz, 8 oz, 9 oz, 10 oz, 10 oz, 12 oz, 20 oz

$\approx 6.6, \approx 5.1$

Lesson 11-4   Use summation notation to write each arithmetic series for the specified number of terms.   40–43. See margin.

40. $3 + 8 + 13 + \ldots; n = 5$ 41. $41 + 33 + 25 + \ldots; n = 8$

42. $-14 + (-8) + (-2) + \ldots; n = 6$ 43. $-27 + (-21) + (-15) + \ldots; n = 10$

Lesson 10-4   Find the equation of each ellipse centered at the origin.

44. height: 20 units
width: 6 units
$\frac{x^2}{9} + \frac{y^2}{100} = 1$

45. height: 12 units
width: 10 units
$\frac{x^2}{25} + \frac{y^2}{36} = 1$

46. height: 24 units
width: 36 units
$\frac{x^2}{324} + \frac{y^2}{144} = 1$

Algebra at Work

·········· Market Researcher

When questions arise about consumer products or services, a market researcher gathers statistical information to help answer the questions. The information a market researcher collects and analyzes helps companies improve their products and make decisions about their customer base. Quantitative research allows a market researcher to analyze data from a large population of potential customers. Market research strategies for gathering information include the following.

- mail surveys
- focus groups
- telephone surveys
- in-person interviews

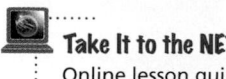
Take It to the NET For more information about market research, go to **www.PHSchool.com**.
Web Code: agb-2031

Lesson 12-5   Working With Samples   **669**

b. The candidate should feel more confident after the second poll; it has a margin of error of only 4%, which means this candidate is preferred by at least 51% of voters.

36. [2] For a random sample of size n, the margin of error is approximately $\pm\frac{1}{\sqrt{n}}$.
For $n = 3600$, the margin of error is approximately $\pm\frac{1}{\sqrt{3600}} = \pm\frac{1}{60} \approx \pm 0.02 \approx \pm 2\%$.

[1] answer only or a calculation error

Alternative Assessment

Have students find poll results in newspapers, magazines, or on the Internet. Direct them to analyze the polls for potential bias, and use the margin of error to estimate the sample size of the polls. Ask volunteers to share their findings with the class.

Standardized Test Prep

📁 **Resources**
For additional practice with a variety of test item formats:
- Standardized Test Prep, p. 691
- Test-Taking Strategies, p. 686
- Test-Taking Strategies with Transparencies

37. [4] The sample proportion is $\frac{138}{2750} \approx$ 5%. The margin of error is $\pm\frac{1}{\sqrt{2750}} \approx \pm\frac{1}{52.44} \approx \pm 0.019 \approx \pm 1.9\%$. The interval is $(5\% - 2\%)$ to $(5\% + 2\%)$, or 3% to 7%.

[3] minor error, but all parts of the question answered

[2] more than one part of the answer is correct

[1] answer only OR only one part of the question answered correctly

40. $\sum\limits_{n=1}^{5} (-2 + 5n)$

41. $\sum\limits_{n=1}^{8} (49 - 8n)$

42. $\sum\limits_{n=1}^{6} (-20 + 6n)$

43. $\sum\limits_{n=1}^{10} (-33 + 6n)$

Reading Math Vocabulary

Students compare the common English meanings of words with their mathematical meanings, and learn that it is important to know the mathematical meanings of words in a problem before solving the problem.

Teaching Notes

Write the words *sample, bias,* and *random* on the chalkboard. Ask students to discuss the meanings of these words, both mathematical and common, before they read the meanings in the table. Record student responses on the chalkboard.

Tactile Learners

Give students note cards with mathematical words on them. Give them separate note cards with the mathematical and common definitions of these words. Have students arrange the cards with the words alongside the cards with their correct definitions.

Exercise

Students may be able to think of more than one other way the sample could be biased. Accept all reasonable responses.

Read the problem below. Notice that the mathematical meaning of a word may differ from the English meaning. Check your understanding with the exercise at the bottom of the page.

Computer Use An online advertisement asks you to participate in a survey. The survey asks how much time you spend online each week. Identify any bias in this method. If appropriate, suggest a method more likely to produce a random sample.

The table below shows both English and mathematical meanings for the words *sample, bias,* and *random.* In mathematics, an English word can be used either

- in a way that makes use of its common English meaning and applies that meaning to mathematical concepts, or
- in a way that differs from its common English meaning.

WORD	ENGLISH MEANING	MATHEMATICAL MEANING
Sample	an example (noun); or to test or try out (verb)	a part of a group or population
Bias	a tendency to prejudge (noun); or to influence in a way that would cause prejudgment (verb)	A sample is *biased* if it does not represent the population.
Random	by chance or without planning (adjective)	A *random sample* is a part of a population chosen in such a way that all members have an equal chance of being chosen.

If you have questions about the meaning of a word, look it up in the dictionary before you begin working. A good dictionary includes mathematical meanings.

Take a look at Exercise 25.

What bias is there in asking you how much time you spend online each week?

The advertisement was posted online, so only people online would be able to see and take the survey. This automatically excludes people who rarely go online, which would bias the sample by overrepresenting people who go online.

If appropriate, suggest a method more likely to produce a random sample.

One way would be to conduct a survey by phone of a specific number of households, chosen at random throughout a given geographical area.

EXERCISE

Think of another way the sample might be biased.
Answers may vary. Sample: The same person might answer the survey more than once.

12-6 Binomial Distributions

Lesson Preview

What You'll Learn

 OBJECTIVE 1 To find binomial probabilities

OBJECTIVE 2 To use binomial distributions

. . . And Why

To find the probability of winning a prize, as in Example 2

 Check Skills You'll Need (For help, go to Lessons 6-7 and 6-8.)

Evaluate each expression.

1. $_4C_2$ **6** 2. $_3C_3$ **1** 3. $_5C_2$ **10**

Use the binomial theorem to expand each binomial. **5–9. See back of book.**

4. $(x + 2)^3$ $x^3 + 6x^2 + 12x + 8$ 5. $(w - y)^4$
6. $(m + n)^3$ 7. $(t + 3s)^4$
8. $(a + 2b)^5$ 9. $(p + q)^6$

New Vocabulary • binomial experiment • binomial probability

 **1. Plan**

OBJECTIVE 1 — Finding Binomial Probabilities

 Interactive lesson includes instant self-check, tutorials, and activities.

> ### Investigation: Binomial Probability
>
> 1. Examine the situations described in the chart below. What do the situations printed in blue have in common?
>
> **1. Each situation has only two possible outcomes.**
>
> | |
> |---|
> | receive a numerical grade |
> | receive a pass/fail grade |
> | wear soccer, running, basketball, or street shoes |
> | wear shoes with cleats or no cleats |
> | guess on a matching test |
> | guess on a true/false test |
>
> 2. Suppose you guess each answer on a ten-question true-or-false test. Are you likely to get 70% or more right?
>   a. Design and conduct a simulation for this situation.
>   b. Run your simulation 10 times. Make a frequency table of the scores. **See back of book.**
>   c. Find P(70% or more right). **20%**

2a. Answers may vary. Sample: Generate random integers from 1 to 100. Odd numbers represent a wrong answer. 10 numbers represent one test.

Need Help?

You can use a coin, a number cube, or random numbers to conduct a simulation.

A **binomial experiment** has three important features:

• The situation involves repeated trials.

• Each trial has two possible outcomes (success or failure).

• The probability of success is constant throughout the trials. (The trials are independent.)

Lesson Preview

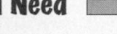 **Check Skills You'll Need**

Permutations and Combinations
Lesson 6-7: Examples 3, 4
Exercises 22–29
Extra Practice, p. 827

The Binomial Theorem
Lesson 6-8: Example 3
Exercises 13–20
Extra Practice, p. 827

Lesson Resources

Teaching Resources
Practice, Reteaching, Enrichment
Checkpoint Quiz 2

Reaching All Students
Practice Workbook 12-6
Spanish Practice Workbook 12-6
Reading and Math Literacy 12C
Spanish Reading & Literacy 12C
Spanish Checkpoint Quiz 2

Presentation Assistant Plus!
Transparencies
• Check Skills You'll Need 12-6
• Additional Examples 12-6
• Student Edition Answers 112-6
• Lesson Quiz 12-6
PH Presentation Pro CD 12-6

PRENTICE HALL ASSESSMENT SYSTEM

Checkpoint Quiz 2
Computer Test Generator CD

Technology
Resource Pro® CD-ROM
Computer Test Generator CD
Prentice Hall Presentation Pro CD

www.PHSchool.com
Student Site
• Teacher Web Code: agk-5500
• Graphing Calculator, Procedure 24
• Self-grading Lesson Quiz
Teacher Center
• Lesson Planner
• Resources

Plus

Ongoing Assessment and Intervention

Before the Lesson
Diagnose prerequisite skills using:
• Check Skills You'll Need

During the Lesson
Monitor progress using:
• Check Understanding
• Additional Examples
• Standardized Test Prep

After the Lesson
Assess knowledge using:
• Lesson Quiz
• Computer Test Generator CD
• Chapter Checkpoint 2 (p. 677)

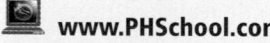

Math Background

In statistics, students will learn conditions under which a normal distribution can be used to approximate a binomial distribution. Computers calculate either easily.

OBJECTIVE

▼ Teaching Notes

Investigation
Teaching Tip

Ask students to list possible outcomes for each situation in order to see that the situations printed in green have only two outcomes.

1 EXAMPLE Tactile Learners

Let students use a spinner with five possible outcomes to help them develop their random number tables.

2 EXAMPLE Teaching Tip

Students have used tree diagrams to represent conditional probabilities in the past. Have students make a table to write similarities and differences between a tree diagram for a conditional probability and a tree diagram for a binomial probability. The table might include the following:

Conditional probability tree diagram: represents the probability that an outcome occurs, given that there is a condition that limits the sample space; it applies to all conditional events, whether they are independent or dependent; the probabilities may vary for each set of branches, as long as they add up to 1; multiplication is used to compute each probability.

Binomial probability tree diagram: represents an experiment that contains the three important features listed on page 671 (encourage students to list them in their own words); multiplication is used to compute each probability.

---

1 EXAMPLE Designing a Binomial Experiment

Suppose that you guess the answers to three questions of a multiple-choice test. Each question has five choices, with one correct choice.

a. Describe a trial for this situation. How many trials are there?

Each guess is a trial. Since you are guessing three times, there are three trials.

b. Describe a success. What is the probability of success on any single trial?

Each correct answer is a success. Since there are five possible answers, all of them equally likely, the probability of success on any single trial is 0.2.

c. Design and conduct a simulation to determine the probability of getting at least two answers correct. Run the simulation 10 times.

Assign each number from 1 to 5 to an outcome, based on each outcome's probability. Let 1 represent a correct response. Let $2-5$ represent incorrect responses. Generate random numbers from 1 to 5.

Simulation	1	2	3	4	5	6	7	8	9	10
Number Generated, Trial 1	2	4	2	5	5	2	1	5	1	2
Number Generated, Trial 2	1	1	5	4	4	5	1	4	5	1
Number Generated, Trial 3	1	3	1	2	2	5	4	2	3	2
Number of Correct Guesses	2	1	1	0	0	0	2	0	1	1

Two of the simulations result in two or more correct guesses. So the experimental probability of getting at least two answers correct is $\frac{2}{10}$, or 20%.

✓ Check Understanding **1** Run the simulation an additional 15 times. Use the results of all 25 simulations to find the experimental probability of getting at least two answers correct.
Check students' work.

You can use a tree diagram to analyze binomial probabilities.

2 EXAMPLE Real-World Connection

Merchandising As part of a promotion, a store is giving away scratch-off cards. Prizes are awarded on 40% of the game cards. Suppose you have three cards. Find the probability that exactly two of the three cards will reveal a prize.

Each card represents a trial with a probability of success of 0.4. The probability of failure is 0.6. The tree diagram below shows the probabilities along each path.

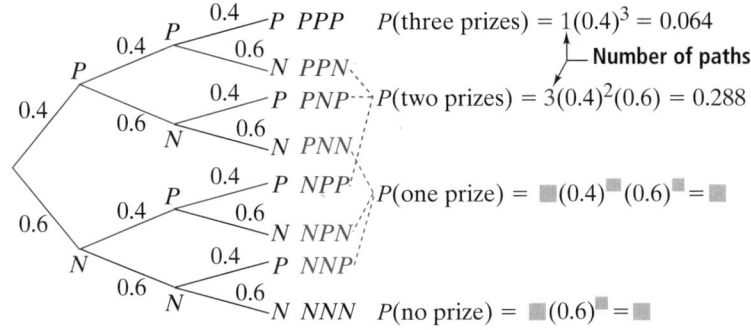

$P(\text{three prizes}) = 1(0.4)^3 = 0.064$
— Number of paths
$P(\text{two prizes}) = 3(0.4)^2(0.6) = 0.288$
$P(\text{one prize}) = \blacksquare(0.4)^\blacksquare(0.6)^\blacksquare = \blacksquare$
$P(\text{no prize}) = \blacksquare(0.6)^\blacksquare = \blacksquare$

The probability that exactly two of three cards will reveal a prize is 0.288.

👥 Reaching All Students

Below Level Use a tree diagram to calculate the probability of flipping two heads in three trials of the binomial experiment *flip-a-coin*.	**Advanced Learners** Have students find out what other probability distribution can be used to calculate the accident rate per mile of highway.	**Inclusion** See note on page 675. **Tactile Learners** See note on page 672.

2 **a.** Complete the tree diagram in Example 2 by finding the probability of receiving one prize and the probability of receiving no prize.

b. Verify your work by adding the probabilities for three, two, one, and no prizes. What answer should you get? **1**

2a. P (one prize) =
$3(0.4)^1(0.6)^2 = 0.432$;
P(no prize) =
$1(0.6)^3 = 0.216$

The relationships you have seen are summarized in the following formula.

🔑 **Key Concepts**

? **Need Help?**
$$_nC_r = \frac{n!}{r!(n-r)!}$$

Definition	Binomial Probability

Suppose you have repeated independent trials, each with a probability of success p and a probability of failure q (with $p + q = 1$). Then the probability of x successes in n trials is the following product.

$$_nC_x p^x q^{n-x}$$

3 **EXAMPLE** Real-World 🌐 Connection

Quality Control A calculator contains four batteries. With normal use, each battery has a 90% chance of lasting for one year. What is the probability that all four batteries will last a year?

Relate This is a binomial experiment.

- There are four batteries.
- Each battery may succeed or fail.
- The probability of success is 0.9 for each battery.

Define Let $n = 4$.   Let $x = 4$.
Let $p = 0.9$.   Let $q = 0.1$.

Write $_nC_x p^x q^{n-x} = {}_4C_4(0.9)^4(0.1)^0$ **Substitute.**
$= (1)(0.9)^4(1)$ **Simplify.**
$= 0.6561$ **Simplify.**

```
(4 nCr 4) *0.9^4*0.1^0
                  .6561
```

The probability that all four batteries will last one year is about 66%.

✓ **Check Understanding** **3** Find the probability of x successes in n trials for the given probability of success p on each trial.

a. $x = 2, n = 5, p = 0.25$
0.2637

b. $x = 8, n = 10, p = 0.7$
0.2335

OBJECTIVE

2 **Using a Binomial Distribution**

To find the full probability distribution for a binomial experiment, expand the binomial $(p + q)^n$. For example, suppose you guess on four questions of a five-choice multiple choice test. For four questions, $n = 4$, $p = 0.2$, and $q = 0.8$.

$$
\begin{array}{cccccccccc}
& & 4\text{ correct} & & 3\text{ correct} & & 2\text{ correct} & & 1\text{ correct} & & 0\text{ correct} \\
(p+q)^4 & = & 1p^4 & + & 4p^3q & + & 6p^2q^2 & + & 4pq^3 & + & 1q^4 \\
& = & (0.2)^4 & + & 4(0.2)^3(0.8) & + & 6(0.2)^2(0.8)^2 & + & 4(0.2)(0.8)^3 & + & (0.8)^4 \\
& = & 0.0016 & + & 0.0256 & + & 0.1536 & + & 0.4096 & + & 0.4096
\end{array}
$$

1 Suppose you and a friend flip a coin three times to find out who gets to play an arcade game first. The person who gets two out of three flips wins. Your winning side is heads.
a. Describe a trial for this situation. How many trials are there? **Each flip is a trial and there are three trials.**
b. Describe a success. What is the probability of a success on each trial? **Heads is a success; 0.5**
c. Conduct a simulation to find the probability of getting heads two out of three times. Run the simulation ten times. **Check students' work.**

2 A fast food restaurant is attaching prize cards to every one of its soft drink cups. The restaurant awards free drinks as prizes on three out of four cards. Suppose you have three cards. Find the probability that exactly one of these cards will reveal a free soft drink as its prize. **about 0.14**

3 Alicia walks to school with her friend Juana. Juana is on time 80% of the time. What is the probability that Juana will be on time five days in a row? **about 33%**

Students may make mistakes when expanding the binomial $(p + q)^n$. Help students see the following:

1) The exponent of p decreases as the exponent of q increases.

2) The sum of the exponents in each term must equal n.

3) There is one more term than the power to which the binomial is being raised.

Additional Example

4 When it rains, there is a 70% chance that Malcolm's soccer practice will be cancelled. If it rains for the next three days, what is the probability that Malcolm's practice will be cancelled on at least one of the days? **about 97%**

Closure

Ask students to explain why, for a binomial probability, $p + q$ must equal 1. **In any probability distribution the sum of the probabilities must be 1. Since there are only two possible outcomes, p and q, $p + q$ must equal 1.**

pages 674–677 Exercises

1. **Each guess is a trial. There are 5 trials. Each correct answer is a success. The probability of a success on a single trial is 0.5. Check students' designs and simulations.**

2. **Each voter selected is a trial. There are 10 trials. A vote in favor of the bond is a success. The probability of a success on a single trial is 0.4. Check students' designs and simulations.**

3. **Each shift is a trial. There are 3 trials. Not experiencing a breakdown is a success. The probability of a success on a single trial is 0.9. Check students' designs and simulations.**

674

Real-World Connection

The air pressure inside a teardrop-shaped weather balloon remains constant as the balloon rises. Lower outside air pressure at higher altitudes causes the balloon to expand.

Of course, you can display a binomial distribution as a graph.

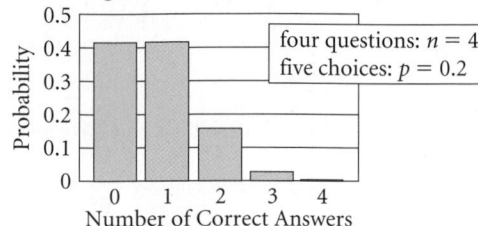

Guessing on a Multiple-Choice Test

four questions: $n = 4$
five choices: $p = 0.2$

Weather A scientist hopes to launch a weather balloon on one of the next three mornings. For each morning, there is a 40% chance of suitable weather. What is the probability that there will be at least one morning with suitable weather?

Use the expansion for $(p + q)^n$, with $n = 3$, $p = 0.4$, and $q = 0.6$.

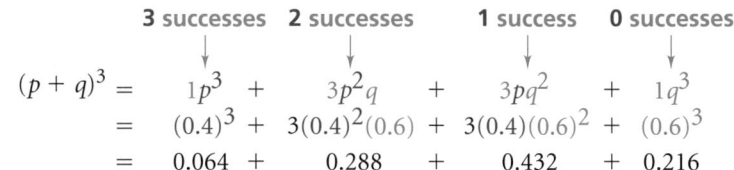

$$3 \text{ successes} \quad 2 \text{ successes} \quad 1 \text{ success} \quad 0 \text{ successes}$$

$$(p + q)^3 = 1p^3 + 3p^2q + 3pq^2 + 1q^3$$
$$= (0.4)^3 + 3(0.4)^2(0.6) + 3(0.4)(0.6)^2 + (0.6)^3$$
$$= 0.064 + 0.288 + 0.432 + 0.216$$

$P(\text{at least 1 success}) = P(1 \text{ success}) + P(2 \text{ successes}) + P(3 \text{ successes})$
$$= 0.432 + 0.288 + 0.064$$
$$= 0.784$$

The probability of at least one morning with suitable weather is about 78%.

✓ Check Understanding **4** One survey found that 80% of respondents eat corn on the cob in circles rather than from side to side. Assume that this sample accurately represents the population. What is the probability that, out of five people you know, at least two of them eat corn on the cob in circles? **0.9933**

EXERCISES

For more practice, see *Extra Practice*.

Practice and Problem Solving

A **Practice by Example**

For each situation, describe a trial and a success. Then design and run a simulation to find the probability. **1–3. See margin.**

Example 1
(page 672)

1. On a true-or-false test, you guess the answers to five questions. Find the probability of guessing the correct answers to exactly three of the five questions.

2. A poll shows that 40% of the voters in a city favor passage of a bond issue to finance park improvements. If ten voters are selected at random, find the probability that exactly four of them will vote in favor of it.

3. A plant production line has a 90% probability of not experiencing a breakdown during an eight-hour shift. Find the probability that three successive shifts will not have a breakdown.

21. Each term of a binomial expansion $(p + q)^n$ contains a power of p times a power of q. The coefficient of each term is the number of times that a combination of powers results when $(p + q)^n$ is expanded. In a binomial experiment of n trials, each trial results in success or failure, with probabilities p and q. The probability of each outcome contains n factors, each of which is either p or q. The coefficient of each term is the number of ways that outcome can be achieved.

Example 2
(page 672)

Suppose you guess on a true-or-false test. Use a tree diagram to find each probability.

4. $P(4$ correct in 4 guesses$)$ **6.25%**   **5.** $P(1$ correct in 4 guesses$)$ **25%**

6. $P(3$ correct in 4 guesses$)$ **25%**   **7.** $P(6$ correct in 4 guesses$)$ **0%**

Example 3
(page 673)

Find the probability of x successes in n trials for the given probability of success p on each trial.

8. $x = 3, n = 8, p = 0.3$ **0.2541**   **9.** $x = 4, n = 8, p = 0.3$ **0.1361**

10. $x = 5, n = 10, p = 0.5$ **0.2461**   **11.** $x = 5, n = 10, p = 0.1$ **0.0015**

Example 4
(page 674)

Use the binomial expansion of $(p + q)^n$ to calculate and graph each binomial distribution.   **12–14. See back of book.**

12. $n = 6, p = 0.3$ **13.** $n = 6, p = 0.5$ **14.** $n = 6, p = 0.9$

 Apply Your Skills **Marketing** A fruit company guarantees that 90% of the pineapples it ships will be ripe within four days. Find each probability for a case containing 12 pineapples.

15. 0.2824

16. 0.8891

15. All 12 are ripe within four days.   **16.** At least 10 are ripe within four days.

17. No more than 9 are ripe within four days. **0.1109**

Sociology A study shows that 50% of the families in a community watch television during dinner. Suppose you select 10 families at random from this population. Find each probability.

18. $P(5$ of the 10 families watch television during dinner$)$ **0.2461**

19. $P(6$ of the 10 families watch television during dinner$)$ **0.2051**

20. $P($at least 5 of the 10 families watch television during dinner$)$ **0.6230**

21. Writing Explain how a binomial experiment is related to a binomial expansion. **See margin p. 674.**

22. Quality Control A company claims that 99% of its cereal boxes have at least as much cereal by weight as the amount stated on the box.
  a. At a quality control checkpoint, one box out of a random sample of ten boxes falls short of its stated weight. What is the probability of this happening due to chance variation in box weights? **0.0914**
  b. Suppose three of ten boxes fail to have the claimed weight. What would you conclude? Explain why. **See margin.**

23. Data Collection Use the current winning percentage of a local sports team as its probability of success. Find the team's probability of winning at least three of any five games. **Check students' work.**

Real-World 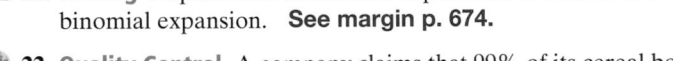 **Connection**

Manufacturers ensure the quality of their products by inspecting raw materials, machinery, and procedures, as well as finished products.

24. Genetics About 11% of the general population is left-handed. At a school with an average class size of 30, each classroom contains four left-handed desks. Does this seem adequate? Justify your answer. **See margin.**

25. For a group of 40 people, what is the probability that exactly three people in the group will celebrate their birthdays on a Wednesday this year?
  a. Find the probability by using the binomial probability formula.
  b. Find the probability by designing and running a simulation.
  c. Compare your results for parts (a) and (b). Explain any discrepancy.
      a–c. See back of book.

26. Open-Ended Describe a binomial experiment that can be solved using the expression $_7C_2(0.6)^2(0.4)^5$. **See back of book.**

Lesson 12-6 Binomial Distributions   **675**

Assignment Guide

1 **Objective**
  Ⓐ Ⓑ **Core** 1–11, 18–21, 24, 26
  Ⓒ **Extension** 27

2 **Objective**
  Ⓐ Ⓑ **Core** 12–17, 22, 23, 25
  Ⓒ **Extension** 28

Standardized Test Prep 29–32

Mixed Review 33–45

Inclusion

Exercise 24 Invite left-handed students to describe to the class what difficulties they have getting along in a world dominated by right-handed people. Ask them to describe specific tools and devices they have difficulty using because the tools are designed for right-handed people.

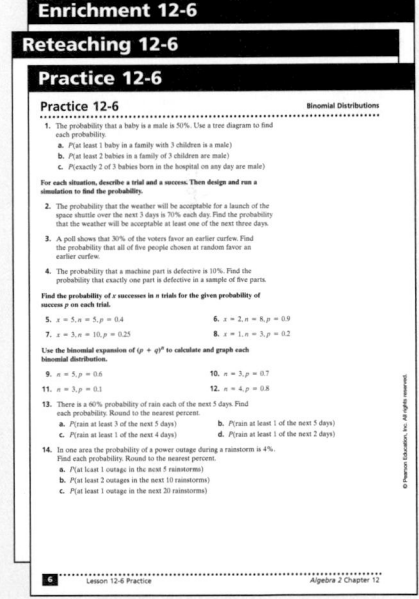

22b. The probability that 3 boxes would be underweight is 0.0001. Thus I would conclude that there is a malfunction in the machinery that must be corrected.

24. The probability of a group of 30 students having 4 or fewer left-handed students is 77.05%. This percentage means that more than three quarters of the classes will have enough left-handed desks; 4 is an adequate number.

Alternative Assessment

Instruct each student to write a problem similar to Example 3. Direct students to exchange problems. Have each student describe a trial and success, use a tree diagram to find the probability, then use the binomial expansion of $(p + q)^n$ to check that their tree diagram is correct. Have students graph the binomial distribution.

Standardized Test Prep

Resources

For additional practice with a variety of test item formats:
- Standardized Test Prep, p. 691
- Test-Taking Strategies, p. 686
- Test-Taking Strategies with Transparencies

 **Challenge**

28a. The graph is symmetrical about the line $x = 3.5$.

b.

x	y
0	0.0078
1	0.0547
2	0.1641
3	0.2734
4	0.2734
5	0.1641
6	0.0547
7	0.0078

27. Statistics A multiple-choice test has ten questions. Each question has five choices, with only one correct.
   a. Statisticians consider a "rare" event to have less than a 5% chance of occurring. According to this standard, what grades would be rare on this test if you guess? Justify your answer. **See margin.**
   b. Design and conduct a simulation to model this situation. Gather results of simulations from your classmates. Do these results confirm the grades you identified as rare in part (a)? Explain. **Check students' work.**

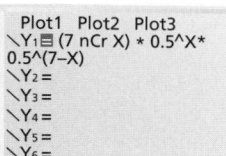 **28.** Enter the binomial probability formula as shown. Set the window and table shown. (To get integer values of x, you may need to adjust your window.)

Plot1 Plot2 Plot3	WINDOW	TABLE SETUP
\Y₁☰ (7 nCr X) * 0.5^X* 0.5^(7−X)	Xmin = −1.7	TblStart = 0
\Y₂=	Xmax = 7.7	ΔTbl = 1
\Y₃=	Xscl = 1	Indpnt: Auto Ask
\Y₄=	Ymin = −.2	Depend: Auto Ask
\Y₅=	Ymax = .5	
\Y₆=	Yscl = .1	
	Xres = 1	

   a. Examine the graph of $y = {}_7C_x(0.5)^x(0.5)^{7-x}$. Describe any symmetry you see in the graph. **a–b. See left.**
   b. Verify the symmetry by displaying values of the function in table form.
   c. Change the graph to $y = {}_7C_x(0.6)^x(0.4)^{7-x}$. Does this graph have any symmetry? Explain. **No; the bulge in the graph has shifted right.**

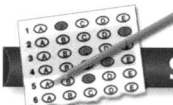

Standardized Test Prep

Quantitative Comparison

 Take It to the NET
Online lesson quiz at
www.PHSchool.com
Web Code: aga-1206

Compare the boxed quantity in Column A with the boxed quantity in Column B. Choose the best answer.
   A. The quantity in Column A is greater.
   B. The quantity in Column B is greater.
   C. The two quantities are equal.
   D. The relationship cannot be determined from the information given.

Column A	Column B
29. $_3C_2(0.6)^2(0.4)^1$	$_6C_4(0.6)^4(0.4)^2$
A	

A survey shows that 60% of the adults in a community floss their teeth every day. Consider a sample of 10 adults.

Column A	Column B
30. P(at least 4 of the 10 adults floss every day)	P(at most 7 of the 10 adults floss every day)
A	

Short Response

31. Evaluate $_nC_x p^x q^{n-x}$ for $n = 7$, $x = 4$, $p = 0.2$, and $q = 0.8$. Round your answer to the nearest thousandth. **See margin p. 677.**

Extended Response

32. A bank of track lights contains several bulbs. The chance that some number of the bulbs will last for at least 2 years is given by the expression $_5C_2(0.15)^2 (0.85)^3$. **a–c. See margin p. 677.**
   a. What is the number of bulbs in the track?
   b. How many bulbs should last at least 2 years?
   c. What is the probability that all the bulbs will last at least 2 years?

pages 674–677 Exercises

27a. Getting 5 or more items right by guessing would be statistically rare. The probability of getting 10, 9, 8, 7, or 6 correct is each less than 1%. The probability of getting 5 right is 2.6%. The probability of getting 4 right is 8.8%.

Lesson 12-5

33. The table contains information from a study of the prices of comparable airline tickets. Which sample most likely was greater in size, A or B? Explain.

33. Sample B was larger because it had a smaller standard deviation.

Sample	Standard Deviation
A	$10.81
B	$3.97

Lesson 11-5

Find the sum of each geometric series to the given term.

34. 394.0625

35. ≈18.18

34. $8 + 12 + 18 + \ldots; n = 8$

35. $20 + (-2) + 0.2 + \ldots; n = 12$

36. $729 + 243 + 81 + \ldots; n = 9$
    1093.$\overline{4}$

37. $\frac{1}{16} + \frac{1}{4} + 1 + \ldots; n = 6$
    85.3125

Lesson 10-5

Find the equation of a hyperbola with horizontal transverse axis, centered at the origin, for the given a and c values.   38–39. See margin.

38. $a = 897$ units, $c = 1024$ units

39. $a = 20$ units, $c = 29$ units

Lesson 5-4

Factor each expression.   40–43. See margin.

40. $x^2 + 6x + 9$

41. $x^2 + x - 6$

42. $x^2 - 7x + 10$

43. $3x^2 + 12x + 9$

44. $2x^2 - x - 6$
    $(2x + 3)(x - 2)$

45. $5x^2 + 5x - 10$
    $5(x - 1)(x + 2)$

 Checkpoint Quiz 2   **Lessons 12-4 through 12-6**

 Instant self-check quiz online and on CD-ROM

Calculate the mean, range, and standard deviation for each set of data.

1. 34 36 29 45 34 25
   33.8$\overline{3}$, 20, 6.20

2. 12 9 10 11 14 10
   11, 5, 1.63

3. 1 5 2 1 4 1 3 2
   2.375, 4, 1.41

4. A set of values has a mean of 300 and a standard deviation of 60. What value has a z-score of -1.2?   **228**

5a. This survey may be biased because it overrepresents people who shop for CDs online and entirely misses those who do not have internet access.

b. Answers may vary. Sample: Survey a random selection of students in homerooms for each grade level.

5. A survey on the Web site of an online CD store includes the question, "Who is your favorite singer?"   **a–b. See left.**
   a. Explain why the results of the survey may be biased.
   b. **Open-Ended** Suggest a way to make the survey an unbiased representation of the population of your high school.

6. **Consumer Spending** In a survey of 683 car owners selected at random, 235 reported paying cash for their first car.
   a. Find the sample proportion.   **0.3441 ≈ 34.4%**
   b. Find the margin of error.   **±3.8%**
   c. Find an interval likely to contain the true population proportion.
      30.6% to 38.2%

7. Determine the sample size that produces a margin of error of ±20%.   **25**

8. Seventy percent of the time, a friend of yours is more than 10 minutes late to meet you for a movie. What is the probability that your friend will be more than 10 minutes late to meet you for all of the next three movies you see?   **0.343**

Each trial of an experiment has a probability of success p. Find the probability of x successes in n trials.

9. $p = 0.8, x = 4, n = 5$ **0.4096**

10. $p = 0.4, x = 4, n = 5$ **0.0768**

✓ **Chapter Checkpoint 2**

To check understanding of Lessons 12-4 to 12-6:

Checkpoint Quiz 2 (p. 677)

📁 **Teaching Resources**
Checkpoint Quiz 2 (also in Prentice Hall Assessment System)

👥 **Reaching All Students**
Reading and Math Literacy 12C

Spanish versions available

---

31. [2] $_nC_x p^x q^{n-x} =$
    $_7C_4(0.2)^4(0.8)^{7-4} =$
    $\frac{7!}{4!3!} \cdot (0.2)^4(0.8)^3 =$
    $35(0.0016)(0.512) \approx$
    0.029

    [1] answer only OR incomplete solution

32. [4] If $_nC_x p^x q^{n-x} =$
    $_5C_2(0.15)^2(0.85)^3$, then
    $n = 5, x = 2, p = 0.15$,
    and $q = 0.85$.

    a. The number of bulbs in the track is n, or 5, bulbs.

    b. The number that are supposed to last at least 2 years is x, or 2, bulbs.

    c. The probability that all the bulbs will last at least 2 years is $_5C_5(0.15)^5(0.85)^0$ ≈ 0.000076.

    [3] a minor error

    [2] at least 1 part correct

    [1] answers only OR at least some correct information

38. $\frac{x^2}{804{,}609} - \frac{y^2}{243{,}967} = 1$

39. $\frac{x^2}{400} - \frac{y^2}{441} = 1$

40. $(x + 3)(x + 3)$

41. $(x + 3)(x - 2)$

42. $(x - 5)(x - 2)$

43. $3(x + 1)(x + 3)$

 **Check Skills You'll Need**

Standard Deviation
Lesson 12-4: Example 4
Exercises 8, 9
Extra Practice, p. 833

Lesson Resources

📁 **Teaching Resources**
Practice, Reteaching, Enrichment

 **Reaching All Students**
Practice Workbook 12-7
Spanish Practice Workbook 12-7
Hands-On Activities 56

⏰ **Presentation Assistant Plus!**
Transparencies
• Check Skills You'll Need 12-7
• Additional Examples 12-7
• Student Edition Answers 12-7
• Lesson Quiz 12-7
PH Presentation Pro CD 12-7

ASSESSMENT SYSTEM

Computer Test Generator CD

💊 **Technology**
Resource Pro® CD-ROM
Computer Test Generator CD
Prentice Hall Presentation Pro CD

 **www.PHSchool.com**
Student Site
• Teacher Web Code: agk-5500
• Self-grading Lesson Quiz
Teacher Center
• Lesson Planner
• Resources

Plus 🅘TEXT

 **12-7**

Normal Distributions

Lesson Preview

What You'll Learn

 OBJECTIVE 1 To use a normal distribution

 OBJECTIVE 2 To use the standard normal curve

... And Why

To describe the jaws of great white sharks, as in Example 2

✓ **Check Skills You'll Need**   (For help, go to Lesson 12-4.)

Find the numbers that are one and two standard deviations above and below each given mean. Write these numbers from least to greatest. 1–6. See below left.

1. $\bar{x} = 12, \sigma = 2$ **2.** $\bar{x} = 16.7, \sigma = 1$ **3.** $\bar{x} = 7, \sigma = 1.5$

4. $\bar{x} = 22, \sigma = 1.7$ **5.** $\bar{x} = 17.5, \sigma = 0.9$ **6.** $\bar{x} = 33.1, \sigma = 1.2$

New Vocabulary • normal distribution • standard normal curve

🅘TEXT **Interactive lesson includes instant self-check, tutorials, and activities.**

 OBJECTIVE 1

Using a Normal Distribution

1. 8, 10, 14, 16

2. 14.7, 15.7, 17.7, 18.7

3. 4, 5.5, 8.5, 10

A **normal distribution** shows data that vary randomly from the mean. The pattern the data form is a bell-shaped curve called a normal curve.

1 EXAMPLE  **Real-World Connection**

Medicine The bar graph below gives the birth weights of a population of 100 babies. The red curve shows how the weights are normally distributed about the mean, 3250 g. Estimate the percent of babies weighing 2500–3999 g.

Real-World Connection

Careers Neonatal nurses specialize in the nursing care of newborns and babies up to 30 days old.

4. 18.6, 20.3, 23.7, 25.4

5. 15.7, 16.6, 18.4, 19.3

6. 30.7, 31.9, 34.3, 35.5

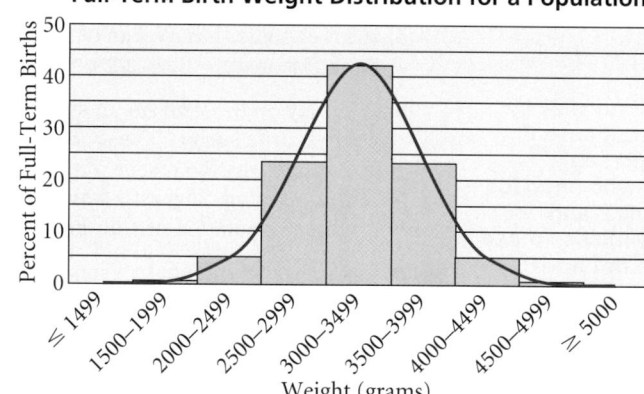

Full-Term Birth Weight Distribution for a Population

Estimate and add the percents for 2500–2999, 3000–3499, and 3500–3999.

$23\% + 42\% + 23\% = 88\%$

About 88% of the babies weigh 2500–3999 g.

✓ **Check Understanding** ❶ **a.** Estimate the percent of babies weighing less than 3500 g.   **71%**
b. The standard deviation in birth weights is about 500 g. Estimate the percent of babies whose birth weights are within 1.5 standard deviations of the mean.   **88%**

678   Chapter 12   Probability and Statistics

Ongoing Assessment and Intervention

Before the Lesson
Diagnose prerequisite skills using:
• Check Skills You'll Need

During the Lesson
Monitor progress using:
• Check Understanding
• Additional Examples
• Standardized Test Prep

After the Lesson
Assess knowledge using:
• Lesson Quiz
• Computer Test Generator CD

Every normal curve has a symmetric bell shape. When outcomes are normally distributed, you can sketch the graph of the distribution.

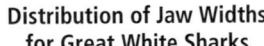 **2 EXAMPLE** Real-World Connection

Biology Refer to the photo. For the given population of sharks, the standard deviation of the jaw widths is 2.8 inches. Sketch a normal curve showing the jaw widths at one, two, and three standard deviations from the mean.

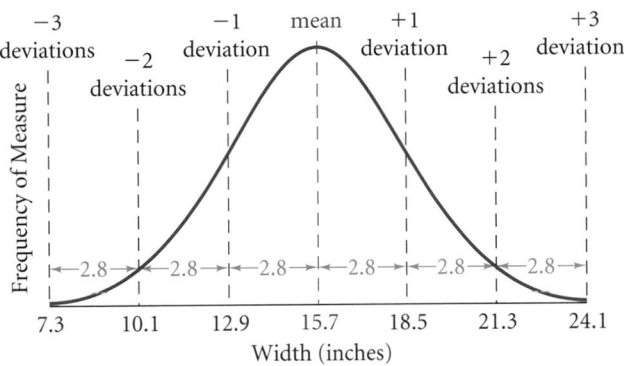

Distribution of Jaw Widths for Great White Sharks

Real-World Connection

The jaw widths of a population of great white sharks are normally distributed about a mean of 15.7 inches.

✓ **Check Understanding** **2** Suppose the mean in Example 2 is 15.4 inches and the standard deviation is 3.1 inches. Sketch a normal curve showing the jaw widths at one, two, and three standard deviations from the mean. **See back of book.**

OBJECTIVE

2 **Using the Standard Normal Curve**

When you show a probability distribution as a bar graph, the height of the bar for each outcome indicates the probability. For a normal curve, however, the area between the curve and the *x*-axis represents the probability.

The **standard normal curve** is a normal distribution centered on the *y*-axis. The mean of the standard normal curve is 0. The standard deviation is 1.

The Standard Normal Curve

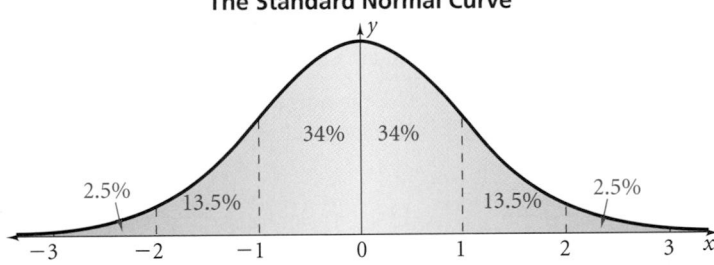

Need Help?

The *z*-score of a value is the number of standard deviations that the value is from the mean.

Every normal curve contains the same probability distribution. When a data set is normally distributed, about 68% of the data fall within one standard deviation of the mean. About 95% of the data fall within two standard deviations of the mean. To find the values that are two standard deviations away from the mean, find the values that have *z*-scores of −2 and 2.

Lesson 12-7 Normal Distributions **679**

👥 **Reaching All Students**

Below Level Have students discuss the advantages of converting data to *z*-scores. Make sure they understand that not all data will match the standard normal curve.	**Advanced Learners** Teachers sometimes "curve" grades. Discuss what conditions would be needed for grades to match a normal distribution.	**Visual Learners** See note on page 679. **Tactile Learners** See note on page 679.

2. Teach

Professional Development

Math Background

Much of mathematical statistics is directed at relating data sets to a normal distribution. This is because the normal distribution supports hypothesis testing, which depends on the distribution of data within 1, 2, and 3 standard deviations of the mean of a normal distribution.

OBJECTIVE

1 **Teaching Notes**

1 EXAMPLE **Visual Learners**

Ask students to bring a bell from home. Encourage all shapes and sizes. Tape a sheet of butcher paper on the board. Have students trace the vertical outline of their bell on the paper.

2 EXAMPLE **Tactile Learners**

Suggest students fold a piece of paper in half lengthwise. Then fold it into thirds lengthwise. They can use the fold lines to mark the standard deviations.

Additional Examples

1 Use the data from Example 1 to estimate the number of babies whose birth weights are between one and two standard deviations from the mean. The standard deviation in birth weights is about 500g. **about 10%**

2 A survey of the employees of the XYZ Corporation found that the mean morning commute time to work was 18 minutes. The standard deviation was 4 minutes. Sketch a normal curve showing the commute times at one, two, and three standard deviations from the mean.

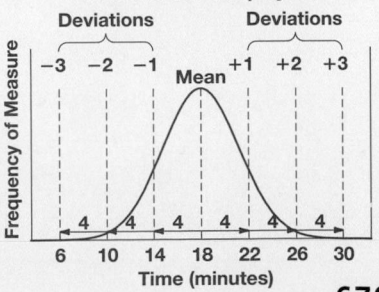

Distribution for Commute Times for XYZ Employees

679

Instruct students to draw an *x*-axis and a *y*-axis on their paper. They can use string to estimate the shape of the bell curve on the paper. Encourage students to use this paper and string when working the Exercises.

Additional Examples

3 In a survey, the responses to the question, "How much time do you spend in the shower every day?" were normally distributed. The mean was 15 minutes; the standard deviation was 2 minutes.
a. What values are one standard deviation from the mean?
13 minutes and 17 minutes
b. What percent of the responses would you expect to find that are less than 13 and greater than 17?
32%

4 Use the distribution from Example 4 to answer the following question. Assume there are 92 students in the lecture class. The professor has found that students who score between one and two standard deviations below the mean need to attend study sessions in order to pass the class. How many students need to attend study sessions? **about 12 students**

Closure

Ask students to list some data that is likely to be normally distributed. Some possibilities are shoe size, test scores, and birth weight. Ask students to explain the definition of the mean and standard deviation as it relates to their data.

---

3 EXAMPLE **Using the Standard Normal Curve**

In a survey, the responses to the question "How much time do you spend at meals in one week?" were normally distributed. The mean was 13 h; the standard deviation was 3 h.

a. What values are one standard deviation from the mean?

Values that are one standard deviation from the mean have *z*-scores of -1 and 1.

$$z\text{-score} = \frac{\text{value } - \text{ mean}}{\text{standard deviation}}$$

$$-1 = \frac{v - 13}{3} \qquad 1 = \frac{u - 13}{3}$$

$$v = 10 \qquad\qquad u = 16$$

The values 10 h and 16 h are one standard deviation away from the mean.

b. What percent of the responses would you expect to find from 10 h to 16 h?

The responses are normally distributed, and 10 h and 16 h are the values that are one standard deviation from the mean. Since 68% of the data are within one standard deviation of the mean, 68% should be values from 10 h to 16 h.

✔ **Check Understanding** **3** **a.** Suppose there were 100 responses to the survey question. How many responses would you expect to be values from 10 h to 16 h? **68 responses**
b. Of 100 responses, how many would you expect to be values from 16 h to 19 h?
13 or 14 responses

4 EXAMPLE **Real-World** **Connection**

Education In a university lecture class with 174 students, the final exam scores have a mean of 68.5 and a standard deviation of 7.3. The grades on the exams are all whole numbers, and the grade pattern follows a normal curve.

a. Find the number of students who receive grades from one to two standard deviations above the mean.

Use the normal curve. About 13.5% of the students receive grades from one to two standard deviations above the mean.

Distribution of Final Exam Scores

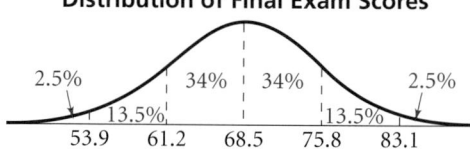

$0.135(174) = 23.49$ **Find the number of students that corresponds to 13.5%.**

About 23 or 24 students receive grades from one to two standard deviations above the mean.

b. Find the number of students who receive grades of 61 or below.

Use the normal curve from part (a). A grade of 61 is about one standard deviation below the mean.

4b. 76 is about 1 SD above the mean. About 13.5% + 2.5% should receive grades above 76. 16% of 140 is about 22.

$13.5\% + 2.5\% = 16\%$ **Find the % at least 1 standard deviation below the mean.**

$0.16(174) = 27.84$ **Find the number of students.**

About 28 students receive grades of 61 or below.

✔ **Check Understanding** **4** **a.** Suppose there are 140 students in the class in Example 4. About how many would receive grades from 69 to 75? **47 or 48 students**
b. Writing How do you know that in a class of 140 students, about 22 students receive grades of 76 or higher? **See left.**

EXERCISES

Practice and Problem Solving

For more practice, see *Extra Practice*.

3. Practice

A Practice by Example

Example 1
(page 678)

Biology The heights of men in a survey are distributed normally about the mean. Use the graph for Exercises 1–4.

Heights of Men Ages 25–34

1. About what percent of men aged 25 to 34 are 69–71 inches tall? **43%**

2. About what percent of men aged 25 to 34 are less than 70 inches tall? **39%**

3. Suppose the survey included data on 100 men. About how many would you expect to be 69–71 inches tall? **43 men**

4. The mean of the data is 70, and the standard deviation is 2.5. About what percent of men are within one standard deviation of the mean in height? **66%**

Example 2
(page 679)

Sketch a normal curve for each distribution. Label the x-axis values at one, two, and three standard deviations from the mean. **5–8. See margin.**

5. mean = 45, standard deviation = 5

6. mean = 45, standard deviation = 10

7. mean = 45, standard deviation = 2

8. mean = 45, standard deviation = 3.5

Examples 3 and 4
(page 680)

A set of data with a mean of 62 and a standard deviation of 5.7 is normally distributed. Find each value, given its distance from the mean.

9. +3 standard deviations **79.1**

10. −1 standard deviation **56.3**

A set of data has a normal distribution with a mean of 50 and a standard deviation of 8. Find the percent of data within each interval.

11. from 42 to 58 **68%**

12. greater than 34 **97.5%**

13. less than 50 **50%**

14. **Test Scores** The scores on an exam are normally distributed, with a mean of 85 and a standard deviation of 5. What percent of the scores are from 85 to 95? **47.5%**

B Apply Your Skills

15. The numbers of paper clips in a truckload of boxes are normally distributed, with a mean of 100 and a standard deviation of 5. Find the probability that a box will *not* contain from 95 to 105 clips. **32%**

16. The student's grade is an outlier; 99% of all grades are expected to be within 3 standard deviations of the mean; and this score is 4.4 standard deviations above the mean.

16. **Writing** In a class of 25, one student receives a grade of 100 on a test. The grades are distributed approximately normally, with a mean of 78 and a standard deviation of 5. Do you think the student's grade is an outlier? Explain. **See left.**

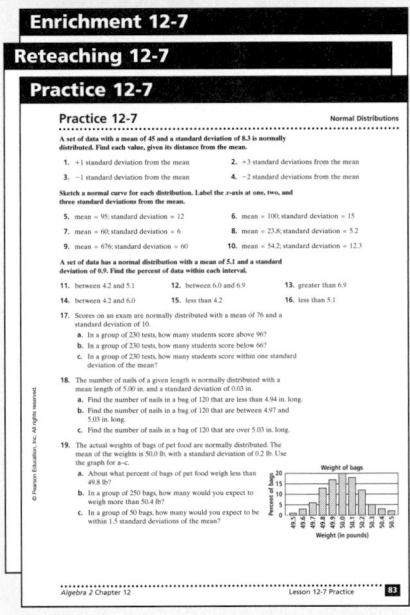
pages 681–684 Exercises

5.
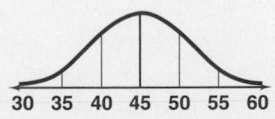

6.
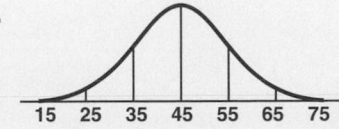

7.
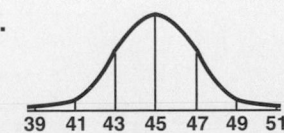

8.
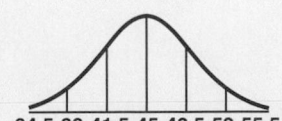

17a. set 2

b–c.

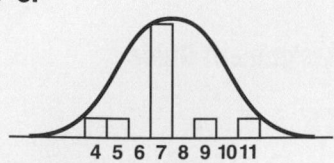

4 5 6 7 8 9 10 11

28a.

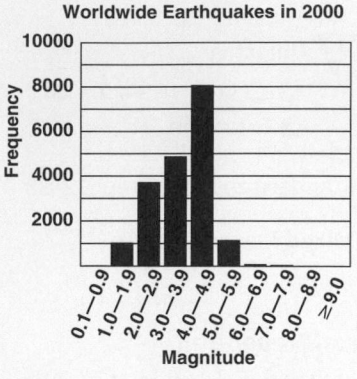

Worldwide Earthquakes in 2000

(Frequency vs. Magnitude histogram with intervals 0.1–0.9, 1.0–1.9, 2.0–2.9, 3.0–3.9, 4.0–4.9, 5.0–5.9, 6.0–6.9, 7.0–7.9, 8.0–8.9, ≥9.0)

b. The data do not fit a normal curve; the data are too skewed to the left.

26. The first plant was in the top 16% of its group.

17. a. From the table at the right, select the set of values that appears to be distributed normally.
   b. Using the set you chose in part (a), make a histogram of the values.   **a–c. See margin.**
   c. Sketch a normal curve over your graph.

18. Track To qualify as a contestant in a race, a runner has to be in the fastest 16% of all applicants. The running times are normally distributed, with a mean of 63 min and a standard deviation of 4 min. To the nearest minute, what is the qualifying time for the race?
   59 minutes

19. Agriculture To win a prize, a tomato must be greater than 4 in. in diameter. The diameters of a crop of tomatoes grown in a special soil are normally distributed, with a mean of 3.2 in. and a standard deviation of 0.4 in. Find the probability that the crop will contain a winning tomato.   **2.5%**

Set 1	Set 2	Set 3
1	5	5
10	7	6
5	7	9
19	7	1
2	4	1
7	11	5
1	7	11
7	7	1
2	7	10
10	9	4
6	7	2
9	7	8

A normal distribution has a mean of 100 and a standard deviation of 10. Find the probability that a value selected at random is in the given interval.

20. from 80 to 100   **47.5%**   **21.** from 70 to 130   **100%**   **22.** from 90 to 120   **81.5%**

23. at least 100   **50%**   **24.** at most 110   **84%**   **25.** at least 80   **97.5%**

26. Two tomato plants were chosen from two groups of plants grown in different soils. Each sample plant produced 23 tomatoes. The mean number of tomatoes for plants in the first soil was 17, with a standard deviation of 5. The mean number of tomatoes for plants in the second soil was 18, with a standard deviation of 6. Determine which plant, if either, is in the top 16% of its group.

27. In a set of data, the value that is −3 standard deviations from the mean is 86. The value that is +1 standard deviation from the mean is 250.
   a. Find the mean.   **209**
   b. Find the standard deviation.   **41**
   c. Find an interval with an end value of 250 that contains about 81.5% of the data.   **127–250**

28. Seismology The table below shows the number of earthquakes worldwide in 2000.
   a. Draw a histogram to represent the data.   **a–b. See margin.**
   b. Does the histogram approximate a normal curve? Explain.

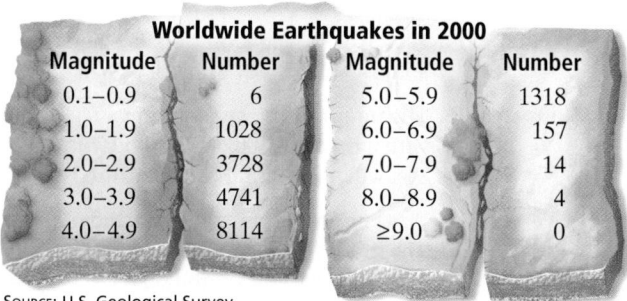

Worldwide Earthquakes in 2000

Magnitude	Number	Magnitude	Number
0.1–0.9	6	5.0–5.9	1318
1.0–1.9	1028	6.0–6.9	157
2.0–2.9	3728	7.0–7.9	14
3.0–3.9	4741	8.0–8.9	4
4.0–4.9	8114	≥9.0	0

Source: U.S. Geological Survey

29. Critical Thinking Jake and Elena took the same standardized test, but with different groups of students. They both received a score of 87. In Jake's group, the mean was 80 and the standard deviation was 6. In Elena's group, the mean was 76 and the standard deviation was 4. Did either student score in the top 10% of his or her group? Explain. **See margin.**

C Challenge **30. Quality Control** Tubs of Better Butter weigh 1.0 lb each, with a standard deviation of 0.06 lb. At a quality control checkpoint, 12 of the tubs taken as samples weighed less than 0.88 lb. Assume that the weights of the samples were normally distributed. How many tubs of butter were taken as samples?

30. 480 tubs

31. Games In the Japanese game pachinko, a player launches small steel balls from the bottom of a playing frame to the top. The balls then fall through pins and bounce around haphazardly. They land in slots at the bottom of the game and form a normal distribution. If a ball falls into a specially marked slot, the player wins additional balls with which to play again in the next round. If a ball does not fall into a marked slot, the player loses that ball.

a. Suppose that all slots between one and two standard deviations from the center are marked. When a ball lands in one of the marked slots, you win the ball back along with two others. If you begin with 200 balls, how many balls should you have after one round? **162 balls**

b. Suppose that there are two sets of marked slots. One set is within one standard deviation of the center and the other set is more than two standard deviations from the center. When a ball lands in one of the slots in the first set, you win the ball back. When a ball lands in one of the slots in the second set, you win the ball back, along with four others. If you begin with 1000 balls, how many balls should you have after one round? **930 balls**

c. Open-Ended Using your knowledge of normal distributions, design a pachinko game with both winning and losing slots in which you would theoretically have the same number of balls after each round as when you started. You can adjust the number of balls at the beginning of the game, the placement of the winning slots, and the number balls won per slot. **Check students' work.**

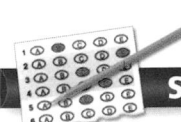

Standardized Test Prep

Multiple Choice

For a daily airline flight between two cities, the number of pieces of checked luggage has a mean of 380 and a standard deviation of 20. Use this information for Exercises 32–33.

32. On what percent of the flights would you expect from 340 to 420 pieces of checked luggage? **D**
A. 34% B. 47.5% C. 68% D. 95%

33. What number of pieces of checked luggage is 3 standard deviations above the mean? **H**
F. 60 G. 97.5 H. 440 I. 1140

34. A set of data is normally distributed with a mean of 44 and a standard deviation of 3.2. Which statements are NOT true? **A**
I. 68% of the values are between 37.6 and 50.4
II. 13.5% of the values are less than 40.8
III. 5% of the values are lower than 37.6 or higher than 50.4.
A. I and II only B. I and III only C. II and III only D. I, II, and III

Lesson 12-7 Normal Distributions **683**

29. Elena scored within the top 10% of her group. Her score is 2.75 std. dev. above the mean, which places her in the top 1%.

Jake did not score in the top 10%. His score is 1.16 std. dev. above the mean, or at the 88th percentile.

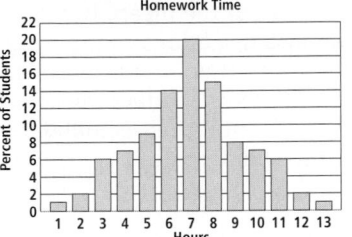

Lesson Quiz 12-7

1. The bar graph below gives the hours of homework per week of surveyed students.

Homework Time

(bar graph: Percent of Students vs. Hours, 1–13)

a. About what percent of students have between 5 and 9 hours of homework per week? **about 66%**

b. Suppose the survey included 500 students. About how many have between 5 and 9 hours of homework per week? **about 330 students**

c. The mean of the data is seven hours and the standard deviation is two. About what percentage of students have an amount of homework within 2 standard deviations of the mean? **about 92%**

2. A biology class did a survey of an open field for the number of visible insects per square foot of ground. The results were normally distributed. The mean was 28 insects and the standard deviation was 5.

a. What values are 1 standard deviation from the mean? **23 and 33 insects**

b. Suppose the class surveyed 50 one-foot square plots. Find the number of plots that contained a number of insects within one standard deviation of the mean. **34 plots**

683

Alternative Assessment

Have students come up with an idea for a survey of students in the school that would collect data that should be normally distributed. Ask them to use the standard normal curve to predict the number of students who should fall within one standard deviation of the mean, two standard deviations of the mean, and so on. Then, if it is feasible, have students conduct the survey and find out if their actual data is normally distributed.

Standardized Test Prep

 **Resources**

For additional practice with a variety of test item formats:
- Standardized Test Prep, p. 691
- Test-Taking Strategies, p. 686
- Test-Taking Strategies with Transparencies

pages 681–684   Exercises

35. **[2] For Distribution A, with 50 data values, 25 values are at or below 40, which is the mean. For Distribution B, with 30 data values, 15 values are at or below the mean 40. So Distribution A has more values at or below 40.**

    [1] answer only OR error

39. **Answers may vary. Sample: For each trial generate 4 random numbers 1–100. If all 4 numbers are less than or equal to 95, the trial is a success. Repeat for 10 trials.**

40. **total garbage generated over *x* years**

41. **total number of bus passengers over *x* hours**

43. **Answers may vary. Sample: $\frac{x^2}{16} + \frac{y^2}{9} = 1$**

44. **Answers may vary. Sample: $\frac{x^2}{4} - \frac{y^2}{4} = 1$**

Short Response

35. Distribution A has 50 data values with mean 40 and standard deviation 2.4. Distribution B has 30 data values with mean 40 and standard deviation 2.8. Which distribution has more data values at or below 40? Show your work.   **See margin.**

Reading Comprehension

Read the article below. Then answer Exercises 36–38.

College Entrance Exam Results for 2000

In 2000, over 1.2 million students across the country took college entrance exams. The average score on the verbal section showed no improvement over the average scores of the previous four years. The average score on the mathematics section was three points higher than the previous year's average.

Section	Mean	Standard Deviation
Math	505	111
Verbal	514	113

 Take It to the NET
Online lesson quiz at
www.PHSchool.com
Web Code: aga-1207

36. What is the probability that a student's score on the verbal section is from 401 to 514?   **0.34**

37. What is the probability that a student's score on the math section is greater than 727?   **0.025**

38. Both Susanna's math score and her verbal score were more than one standard deviation above the mean, but less than two standard deviations above the mean. What are the lower and upper limits of Susanna's combined score?   **1243 and 1467 points**

Mixed Review

Lesson 12-6   39. **Production** A plant production line has a 95% probability of not experiencing a breakdown during a six-hour shift. The plant managers want to know the probability that four successive shifts will not have a breakdown. Design and run a simulation to find the probability. Include an explanation of what constitutes a trial and a success.   **See margin.**

Lesson 11-6   **For each set of axes, what does the area under the curve represent?**   40–41. See margin.

40. *y*-axis: tons of garbage generated per year, *x*-axis: years

41. *y*-axis: bus passengers per hour, *x*-axis: hours

Lesson 10-6   42. **Coordinate Geometry** Write the equation of a circle centered at $(4, -5)$ with radius 7. $(x - 4)^2 + (y + 5)^2 = 49$

Open-Ended Write the equation of a conic section with the given characteristics.   43–44. See margin.

43. an ellipse with a major axis 8 units long

44. a hyperbola with an asymptote at $y = -x$

Lesson 9-1   **Suppose that *x* and *y* vary inversely. Write a function to model inverse variation.**

45. $x = 1$ when $y = 5$ 46. $x = -1$ when $y = 10$ 47. $x = -3$ when $y = 3$

48. $x = 25$ when $y = -5$ 49. $x = 1.8$ when $y = -6$ 50. $x = 7.5$ when $y = 50$

45–50. See margin.

684   Chapter 12   Probability and Statistics

45. $y = \frac{5}{x}$ 48. $y = -\frac{125}{x}$

46. $y = -\frac{10}{x}$ 49. $y = -\frac{10.8}{x}$

47. $y = -\frac{9}{x}$ 50. $y = \frac{375}{x}$

Area Under a Curve

FOR USE WITH LESSON 12-7

Statisticians use the function $f(x) = \frac{1}{\sqrt{2\pi}} e^{-\frac{x^2}{2}}$ to model data such as height or birth weight. You can use the area under the graph of the function to find probabilities.

EXAMPLE

In a population of 100 babies, the weights are normally distributed about the mean, 3250 g. The standard deviation is 500 g. Find the probability that a baby chosen at random weighs from 2250 g to 4250 g.

Step 1 Find the z-scores of the lower and upper limits.

$$z\text{-score} = \frac{\text{value} - \text{mean}}{\text{standard deviation}}$$

$$z_1 = \frac{2250 - 3250}{500} = \frac{-1000}{500} = -2$$

$$z_2 = \frac{4250 - 3250}{500} = \frac{1000}{500} = 2$$

Step 2 Enter $f(x) = \frac{1}{\sqrt{2\pi}} e^{-\frac{x^2}{2}}$ as Y_1. Adjust the window values.

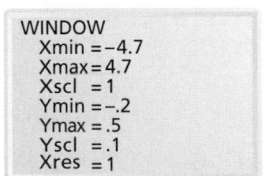

```
WINDOW
 Xmin =-4.7
 Xmax=4.7
 Xscl =1
 Ymin =-.2
 Ymax =.5
 Yscl =.1
 Xres =1
```

Step 3 Use the CALC feature and press 7 to access the $\int f(x)dx$ feature. Move the cursor until the lower limit is $x = -2$. Press ENTER. Move the cursor until the upper limit is $x = 2$. Press ENTER.

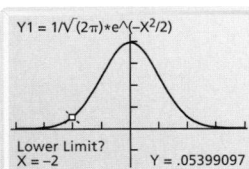
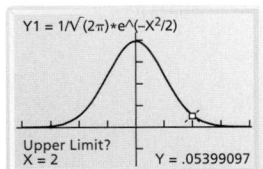
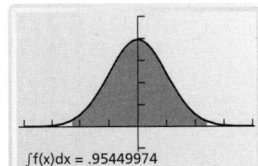

The area under the curve from $x = -2$ to $x = 2$ is about 0.95. So the probability that a baby weighs from 2250 g to 4250 g is about 95%.

EXERCISES

Use the data and the function in the example. Find the probability that the weight of a baby chosen at random falls within each interval.

1. 3150–4150 g   **0.543**   **2.** 4300–4500 g   **0.012**   **3.** less than 1800 g   **0.002** **4.** more than 4550 g   **0.005**

 5. Manufacturing A battery company manufactures batteries having life spans that are normally distributed, with a mean of 45 months and a standard deviation of 5 months. Find the probability that a battery chosen at random will have each life span.
a. 45–52 months   **0.419**   **b.** 48–50 months   **0.116**

Probability and the Area Under a Curve

Students use the graphing calculator to graph a normal distribution curve and then use the numerical integral function $\int f(x)dx$ to find an area under the curve. This area represents the probability that a baby weighs within two standard deviations of the given mean birth weight.

Resources

Students may use any graphing calculator.

Teaching Notes

Students already know that every standard normal curve contains the same probability distribution. So they should expect that 95% of the data should fall within two standard deviations of the mean. When the standard normal curve is centered on the y-axis, the mean of the curve is 0, and the standard deviation is 1. For two standard deviations, the data would fall between x-values of -2 and 2 on the curve.

Connection to Calculus

In this exercise, the students learn that the area under the standard normal curve between -2 and 2 on the x-axis is equal to about 0.95, which is also the probability that data will fall within two standard deviations of the mean. Explain that finding the area under a curve involves integrating between two points on the curve. This is a calculus operation represented by the expression $\int f(x)dx$.

Answering the Question Asked

This feature helps students devise strategies for carefully identifying the specific question being asked. This is an important strategy because answer choices are often correct for questions that are closely related to the question being asked.

Resources

Test-Taking Strategies with Transparencies
- Transparency 12
- Practice sheet p. 36

Teaching Notes

Ask students if they have ever seen questions on standardized tests where more than one answer seemed correct. Explain that good test questions often include incorrect choices (distracters) that seem to be correct if the student does not read the question carefully. Therefore it is critical that students identify the question being asked.

Test-Taking Strategies with Transparencies

> *Test-Taking Strategy: Answering the Question Asked*
> ....
> Incorrect choices may answer related questions.
>
> | *Example* A savings account earns interest compounded annually at a rate of 7%. If $1000 is deposited, what is the account balance after 1 year? |
> | --- |
> | A. $1000   B. $70   C. $1070   D. $7000 |
>
> Calculate the interest earned: $0.07 \times 1000 = \$70$
>
> Choice B is $70, but this is the interest earned, not the account balance.
>
> Calculate the account balance: $1000 + 70 = \$1070$
>
> The answer is $1070, or choice C.
>
> Answer the question asked. Explain your reasoning.
> 1. Seven friends went bowling. Here are their scores.
>   78 110 99 81 104 84 81
>   Find the mean of the scores.
>   A. 81   B. 84   C. 78   D. 91
> 2. If $3x - 7 = 8$, what is the value of $4x$? Write in your response on the grid.
> 3. Write in standard form the equation of the line perpendicular to $y = x - 6$ through $(-2, 3)$.
>   A. $x - y = -5$ B. $x + y = 1$
>   C. $-x + y = -6$ D. $x + y = -1$
>
> Solutions
> 1. D
> 2. 20
> 3. B
>
> Transparency 12

When answering a question, be sure to answer the question that is asked. Read the question carefully and identify the quantity that you are asked to find. Some answer choices are answers to related questions, so you have to be careful that you are answering the right question.

EXAMPLE

There are five puppies in a litter. If the probability that a puppy is male is 0.5, what is the probability that at most one puppy in the litter is male?

A. 0.15625   **B.** 0.1875   **C.** 0.5   **D.** 0.96875

The problem is asking for the probability of "at most" one male puppy. Do not confuse this with "exactly" or "at least" one male puppy.

$$P(\text{at most one male puppy}) = P(\text{no male puppies}) + P(\text{exactly 1 male puppy})$$
$$= {}_5C_0(0.5)^0(0.5)^5 + {}_5C_1(0.5)^1(0.5)^4$$
$$= 0.03125 + 0.15625 = 0.1875$$

The correct answer is B.

Choices A and D are answers to related, but different, questions.

$$P(\text{exactly one male puppy}) = {}_5C_1(0.5)^1(0.5)^4 = 0.15625$$
$$P(\text{at least one male puppy}) = P(\text{exactly 1 male}) + \ldots + P(\text{exactly 5 males})$$
$$= {}_5C_1(0.5)^1(0.5)^4 + \ldots + {}_5C_5(0.5)^5(0.5)^0$$
$$= 0.15625 + \ldots + 0.03125$$
$$= 0.96875$$

EXERCISES

Identify the quantity that is being asked for. Then answer the question.

1. A box contains four quarters. Exactly two of the quarters have the American eagle on the back. Suppose you draw two quarters with replacement at random from the box.
   a. What is the probability that both have the American eagle on the back?
   b. What is the probability that neither has the American eagle on the back?
   c. What is the probability that at least one has the American eagle on the back? **a–c. See margin.**

2. In a survey, 28% of respondents say they are left-handed, 64% say they are right-handed, and 8% say they are ambidextrous. If the ambidextrous people are omitted, about what percent of those remaining are left-handed? **See margin p. 687.**
   A. 28%   **B.** 30%   **C.** 32%   **D.** 34%

3. A student conducted a survey at school and found that 75% of the boys and 65% of the girls like to watch hockey games. There are an equal number of boys and girls in the school. If someone does not like to watch hockey games, what is the approximate probability that the person is a boy? **See margin p. 688.**
   A. 25%   **B.** 42%   **C.** 55%   **D.** 75%

---

page 686   Test-Taking Strategies

1a. Out of the possible pairs of quarters, the pair drawn have the American eagle on the back.
$\frac{1}{4}$ or 0.25

b. Out of the possible pairs of quarters, the pair drawn do not have the American eagle on the back.
$\frac{1}{4}$ or 0.25

c. Out of the possible pairs of quarters, the pair drawn have at least one quarter with the American eagle on the back. $\frac{3}{4}$ or 0.75

Chapter Review

Vocabulary

bimodal (p. 648)
binomial experiment (p. 671)
binomial probability (p. 673)
box-and-whisker plot (p. 650)
conditional probability (p. 642)
cumulative probability (p. 636)
frequency table (p. 636)
interquartile range (p. 657)
margin of error (p. 665)

mean (p. 648)
measures of central tendency (p. 648)
measures of variation (p. 657)
median (p. 648)
mode (p. 648)
normal distribution (p. 678)
outlier (p. 652)
percentile (p. 651)
probability distribution (p. 637)

quartiles (p. 650)
random sample (p. 663)
range of a set of data (p. 657)
sample (p. 663)
sample proportion (p. 663)
standard deviation (p. 657)
standard normal curve (p. 679)
z-score (p. 659)

 **Reading Math**
Understanding
Vocabulary

Take It to the NET
Online vocabulary quiz
at www.PHSchool.com
Web Code: agj-1251

Choose the correct term to complete each sentence.

1. A(n) __?__ is part of a population. **sample**

2. A(n) __?__ has a value substantially different from other data in a set. **outlier**

3. A function that gives the probability of each event in a sample space is a(n) __?__. **probability distribution**

4. A(n) __?__ involves repeated trials, each of which has two possible outcomes whose probabilities are constant throughout the trials. **binomial experiment**

5. Dispersion of data in a data set can be measured by __?__. **measures of variation**

Skills and Concepts

12-1 and 12-2 Objectives

▼ To make a probability distribution (p. 636)

▼ To use a probability distribution in conducting a simulation (p. 638)

▼ To find conditional probabilities (p. 642)

▼ To use formulas and tree diagrams (p. 643)

A **probability distribution** is a function that gives the probability of each event in a sample space. A **frequency table** lists outcomes and the number of times each occurs. A frequency table can be used to find **cumulative probability**, which is the probability of a range of events.

A **conditional probability** limits the sample space to a given event. The probability of event A, given event B, is written $P(A \mid B)$. You can find a conditional probability from a table, a tree diagram, or by the conditional probability formula.

$$P(A \mid B) = \frac{P(A \text{ and } B)}{P(B)}$$

6. Use the results in the table below for the Rock-Paper-Scissors game.
   a. Make a frequency table for the winner: Player 1, Player 2, or tie.
   b. Find $P(\text{Player 2 wins})$. $P(\text{Player 2 wins}) = \frac{4}{15}$

6a.

Winner	Freq.
Player 1	8
Player 2	4
Ties	3
Total	15

Rock-Paper-Scissors

Player 1	S	P	P	R	R	P	**P**	**P**	P	**S**	R	S	**P**	**S**	R
Player 2	P	R	**S**	S	**P**	S	R	R	P	P	R	S	R	P	**P**

R = Rock   P = Paper   S = Scissors   **Bold** = Winner

7. Two number cubes are rolled. Use a table to show the probability distribution for the product of the two numbers. **See back of book.**

Resources

Student Edition
Extra Practice, Ch. 12, p. 833
English/Spanish Glossary, p. 871
Properties and Formulas, p. 865
Table of Symbols, p. 861

 **Reaching All Students**
Reading and Math Literacy 12D
Spanish Reading and Math
Literacy 12D

 PRENTICE HALL
ASSESSMENT *SYSTEM*

Standardized Test Prep Workbook
• Ch. 12 practice in standardized test formats

 www.PHSchool.com
Student Site
• Self-grading Vocabulary Test
Teacher Center
• Resources

Plus **TEXT**

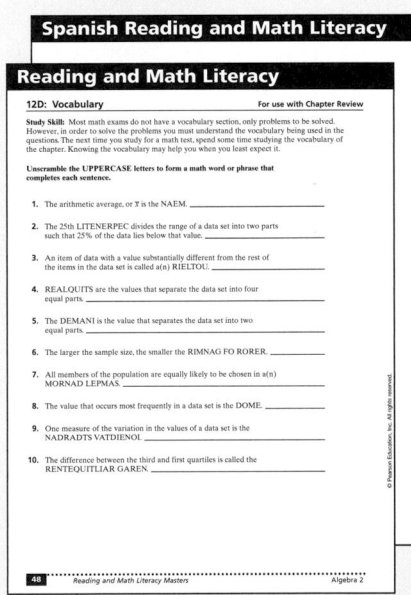

2. of the respondents who are not ambidextrous, the percentage who are left-handed, B

3. of the percentage of students who do not like to watch hockey, the probability that the student will be male, B

11.

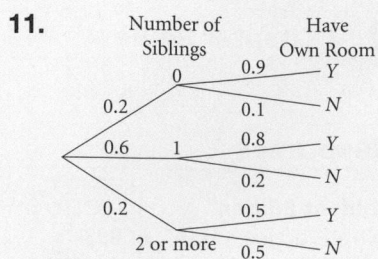

Number of Siblings — Have Own Room

- 0: 0.2, then 0.9 Y, 0.1 N
- 1: 0.6, then 0.8 Y, 0.2 N
- 2 or more: 0.2, then 0.5 Y, 0.5 N

14. 14.4; 14; 12, 13, 14

15.

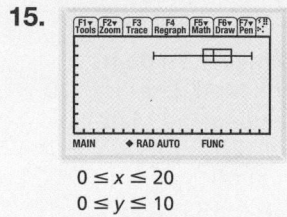

$0 \le x \le 20$
$0 \le y \le 10$

16. 20th percentile = 13,
90th percentile = 18

17. 53rd percentile

---

8. At a bank, the number of customers c who arrive at the teller counters each minute varies according to the distribution below. Simulate the number of customers over a ten-minute period. **Check students' work.**

Number of Customers Each Minute

c	0	1	2	3	4	5	6	7
$P(c)$	0.16	0.28	0.25	0.18	0.09	0.02	0.01	0.01

Use the frequency table below for Exercises 9 and 10.

Birthday Months of Respondents to a Survey

Month	J	F	M	A	M	J	J	A	S	O	N	D
Male	0	1	2	1	1	3	2	0	1	1	0	2
Female	0	1	0	1	0	2	1	3	1	0	4	1

9. Find P(birthday in August | female respondent). $\frac{3}{14}$

10. Find P(male respondent | birthday in June). $\frac{3}{5}$

Use these survey results for Exercises 11–13.

- Of all respondents, 60% have 1 sibling and 20% have 2 or more siblings.
- Of the respondents with 0 siblings, 90% have their own room.
- Of the respondents with 1 sibling, 20% do not have their own room.
- Of the respondents with 2 or more siblings, 50% have their own room.

11. Make a tree diagram that reflects the results of the survey. **See margin.**

12. Find P(own room | 0 siblings). **0.9**   **13.** Find P(share room | 1 sibling). **0.2**

12-3 Objectives

▼ To calculate measures of central tendency (p. 648)

▼ To draw and interpret box-and-whisker plots (p. 650)

You can use **measures of central tendency** to analyze data. The **mean** $\bar{x}$ equals the sum of the values divided by the number of values. The **median** is the middle value of a data set in numerical order. If the set has an even number of values, then the median is the mean of the middle two values. The **mode** is the most frequently occurring value. There can be more than one mode or no mode. A **bimodal** distribution has 2 modes. The second quartile is the median of the whole set. The first and third **quartiles** are, respectively, the medians of the values less than and greater than the median. A **box-and-whisker plot** displays data by using the quartiles to form a box and the minimum and maximum values to form whiskers. A **percentile** divides the range of a data set into two parts such that the part lying below the value contains a given percentage of the data. An **outlier** is a data value substantially different from the rest of the data.

Use the following set of values for Exercises 14–19.   **14–17. See margin.**

13 12 15 18 14 16 18 12 13 14 14 17 15 8 17
16 12 16 14 15 13 13 17 15 14 18 16 12 12 13

14. Find the mean, median, and mode.   **15.** Make a box-and-whisker plot.

16. Find the 20th and 90th percentiles.   **17.** At what percentile is 15?

18. Identify the outlier. **8**   **19.** Find the range without the outlier.

6

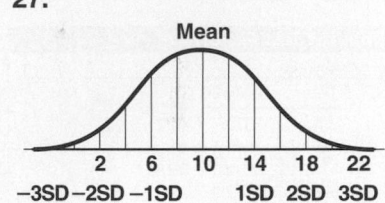
12-4 Objectives

▼ To find the standard deviation of a set of values (p. 656)

▼ To use standard deviation in real-world situations (p. 659)

You can use **measures of variation** to describe the spread of data. The **range of a set of data** is the difference between the maximum and minimum values. The **interquartile range** is the difference between the third and first quartiles. The **standard deviation** is a measure of how the data values vary from the mean. To find the standard deviation, (1) find the mean, (2) find the difference between each data value and the mean, (3) square each difference, (4) find the mean of the squares, and (5) take the square root of this mean. The **z-score** of a value is the number of standard deviations that value is from the mean.

Use the following set of values for Exercises 20–22.

$1.95 $1.27 $1.81 $1.33 $1.30 $.99 $1.63 $1.49 $1.39 $1.25 $1.50

20. Find the standard deviation. **≈0.26**

21. Within how many standard deviations of the mean do all of the values fall? **2**

22. Find the z-score of the value $1.85, to the nearest hundredth. **≈1.56**

12-5 Objectives

▼ To find sample proportions (p. 663)

▼ To find the margin of error (p. 664)

A **sample** is part of a population. For a **random sample**, all members of the population are equally likely to be chosen for the sample. When an event occurs x times in a sample of size n, the **sample proportion** is the ratio $\frac{x}{n}$. When a random sample of size n is taken from a large population, the sample proportion has a **margin of error** of approximately $\pm \frac{1}{\sqrt{n}}$.

23. Of 50 people who rented clubs at a golf course, 38 were right-handed.
  a. Find the sample proportion as a percent. **76%**
  b. Find the margin of error. **±14%**
  c. Find an interval likely to contain the true population proportion. **from 62% to 90%**

12-6 and 12-7 Objectives

▼ To find binomial probabilities (p. 671)

▼ To use binomial distributions (p. 673)

▼ To use a normal distribution (p. 678)

▼ To use the standard normal curve (p. 679)

A **binomial experiment** has repeated independent trials, each trial having two possible outcomes. In a binomial experiment with probability of success p and of failure $q (p + q = 1)$, the probability of x successes in n trials is $_nC_x p^x q^{n-x}$. This value is the **binomial probability**.

A **normal distribution** shows data that vary from the mean in a random manner. The pattern they form is a bell-shaped curve called a normal curve. The **standard normal curve** is a normal distribution centered on the y-axis. The mean is 0 and the standard deviation is 1. When a data set follows the normal curve, about 68% of the data fall within one standard deviation of the mean. About 95% of the data fall within two standard deviations of the mean.

24. A true-or-false quiz contains four questions. Design and describe a simulation you could use to find the probability of guessing three questions correctly. **See margin.**

25. Find the probability of 13 successes in 24 trials, given that the probability of success is 0.6 for each trial. **0.137**

26. Use the binomial expansion of $(p + q)^n$ to write the binomial distribution for $n = 5$ and $p = 0.7$. **See back of book.**

27. Sketch a curve for a normal distribution with mean 10 and standard deviation 4. Label the x-axis at one, two, and three standard deviations from the mean. **See margin.**

24. Answers may vary. Sample: Each guess is a trial. There are 4 trials. Since there are 2 equally likely answers, the probability of success is 0.5. Let 1 represent a correct response and 2 an incorrect response. Generate 4 random numbers, either 1 or 2, 10 times. The probability is one tenth the number of times there are exactly three 1's.

27.

Mean

2   6   10   14   18   22
−3SD −2SD −1SD   1SD 2SD 3SD

Resources

📁 **Teaching Resources**
Ch. 12 Test, Forms A & B
Ch. 12 Alternative Assessment,
Form C

👥 **Reaching All Students**
Spanish Ch. 12 Test, Forms A & B
Spanish Ch. 12 Alternative
Assessment, Form C

PRENTICE HALL
ASSESSMENT SYSTEM

Assessment Masters
• Ch. 12 Test, Forms A & B
• Ch. 12 Alternative Assessment,
  Form C
Computer Test Generator CD
• Ch. 12 pre-made Test
• Make your own Ch. 12 test

💻 **www.PHSchool.com**
Student Site
• Self-grading Chapter 12 Test
Teacher Center
• Resources

 Plus  **TEXT**

Chapter Test — Form B

Chapter Test — Form A

Chapter Test	Form A
Chapter 12	

1. At a store, you buy 8 plums, 4 bananas, 6 apples, and 12 carrots.
   a. Graph the probability distribution for the items purchased.
   b. Find the probability that one food item chosen at random is a piece of fruit.

Use the results of the survey below to find each conditional probability.

How many pets do you have in your home?

	0 Pets	1 Pet	2 Pets	3+ Pets
Male respondents	5	10	5	2
Female respondents	4	13	6	2

2. P(male | 2 pets)
3. P(2 pets | male)
4. P(0 pets | female)
5. P(0 pet | male)
6. Which of these is equal to 0.18, according to the tree diagram?
   A. P(: A)
   B. P(C and B)
   C. P(D : C)
   D. P(A and D)

7. **Writing** Explain how to find the median of a set of data.

Use the following set of values for Exercises 8–13.
8.3 9.6 8.9 1.3 9.4 8.6 1.2 1.4 1.1 6.2 6.2

8. Find the mean, median, and mode(s) of the data set. Round answers to the nearest hundredth, if necessary.
9. Draw a box-and-whisker plot.
10. Find the range.
11. Find the interquartile range.
12. Find the standard deviation. Round to the nearest hundredth.
13. Find the 25th and 75th percentiles.
14. **Open-Ended** Write two data sets with a range equal to 35 but with different standard deviations. You do not need to calculate the standard deviations.

| Algebra 2 Chapter 12 | Form A Test | 27 |

4.

	Number of
AGE	**Respondents**
< 30	25
≥ 30	25

Chapter 12

Chapter Test

 **Take It to the NET**
Online chapter test at
www.PHSchool.com
······· Web Code: aga-1252

Graph the probability distribution for each sample space when two number cubes are rolled.

1. {both cubes the same number, each cube a different number} **1–3. See back of book.**

2. {prime sum, composite sum}

3. ✏️ **Writing** Describe how a situation can have more than one sample space. Include an example.

Use the table below for Exercises 4–8.

How Many Current Music Groups Can You Name?

Age of Respondent	Number of Groups	
	0 – 4	**5 or more**
< 30	7	18
≥ 30	13	12

4. Make a frequency table for the ages of the respondents. **4–5. See margin.**

5. Make a frequency table for the number of groups named.

6. Find $P(5 \text{ or more})$. $\frac{3}{5}$

7. Find $P(5 \text{ or more} \mid \text{age} < 30)$. $\frac{18}{25}$

8. Find $P(\text{age} \geq 30 \mid 0\text{–}4)$. $\frac{13}{20}$

9. Find the mean, median, and mode for this set of values: 8, 9, 11, 12, 13, 15, 16, 18, 20. **See margin.**

10. Make a box-and-whisker plot for this set of values: 36, 36, 48, 65, 75, 82, 92, 101. **See margin.**

11. Find the 20th and 60th percentiles for this set of values: 36, 38, 42, 47, 51, 56, 62, 69, 70, 74. **42, 62**

12. Given the set of values below, at what percentiles are 78 and 81?
    43 58 64 78 78 81 89 89 91 93
    78 at 30th percentile, 81 at 50th percentile

13. Identify the outlier of this set of values: 17, 15, 16, 15, 9, 18, 16. **9**

14. **Open-Ended** Write a set of values that has a range of 10, a mean of 86, and a mode of 85. **See margin.**

15. Find the mean and the standard deviation for this set of values: 15, 17, 19, 20, 14, 23, 12. **See margin.**

16. A data set has a mean 30 and a standard deviation of 3. Find the z-score of the value 38.
    z-score ≈ 2.67

Find the margin of error for each sample. Then find an interval likely to contain the true population proportion. 17–18. See margin.

17. 15% of 457 teachers

18. 47% of 296 teens

19. 56% of 87 musicians **±10.7%; 45.3%–66.7%**

20. 23% of 100 bakers **±10%; 13%–33%**

A newspaper wants to take a poll about which candidate voters prefer for President. Identify any bias in each sampling method.

21. The newspaper interviews people at a political debate. **bias toward active voters**

22. The newspaper publishes a number for people to call and express their opinion. **See margin.**

23. The newspaper calls people selected at random from the local telephone book.
    bias toward voters with listed numbers

Find the probability of x successes in n trials for the given probability of success p on each trial.

24. $x = 4, n = 10, p = 0.2$ **0.088**

25. $x = 3, n = 8, p = 0.6$ **0.124**

26. At a high school, 30% of the students buy class rings. You select five students at random. Find $P(\text{exactly two buy rings})$ and $P(\text{at least two buy rings})$. **0.309, 0.472**

27. A student guesses the answers to three questions on a true-or-false test. Design and describe a simulation to find the probability that the student guesses at least one of the questions correctly.
    See margin p. 691.

A set of data has a normal distribution with a mean of 29 and a standard deviation of 4. Find the percent of data within each interval.

28. from 25 to 33 **68%**   29. from 21 to 25 **13.5%**

30. greater than 29 **50%**   31. less than 21 **2.5%**

32. A data set is normally distributed with a mean of 37 and a standard deviation of 8.1. Sketch a normal curve for the distribution. Label the x-axis values at one, two, and three standard deviations from the mean. **See margin p. 691.**

5.

Number of Groups	Number of Respondents
0–4	20
5 or more	30

9. mean ≈ 13.56, median = 13, no mode

10.

30 40 50 60 70 80 90 100

14. Answers may vary. Sample: 82, 85, 85, 92

15. mean ≈ 17.14, standard deviation ≈ 3.523

17. ±4.7%; 10.3%–19.7%

18. ±5.8%; 41.2%–52.8%

22. bias toward newspaper subscribers and people motivated to call

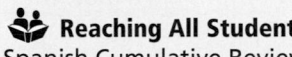
Multiple Choice

For Exercises 1–8, choose the correct letter.

1. Which polynomial has $(x - 1)$ as a factor?   **C**
  A. $x^2 + 3x + 2$
  B. $x^2 + 2x + 1$
  C. $x^3 - x^2 - x + 1$
  D. $x^3 - 3x - 2$

2. Which is the equation of an inverse variation for which $x = 5$ when $y = -28$?   **I**
  F. $y = \frac{-x}{140}$ G. $y = \frac{-130}{x}$
  H. $y = \frac{-x}{130}$ I. $y = \frac{-140}{x}$

3. Which parabola has focus $(3, 0)$ and directrix $x = -3$?   **C**
  A. $y = \frac{1}{12}x^2$ B. $y = -\frac{1}{3}x^2$
  C. $x = \frac{1}{12}y^2$ D. $x = \frac{1}{3}y^2$

4. Which is greatest for these data?   **F**
  9 10 10 10 11 12 12 13 15
  F. mean   G. median
  H. range   I. mode

5. What are the quartiles of these data?   **A**
  18 19 20 20 22 23 25 28 32
  A. $Q_1 = 19.5, Q_2 = 22, Q_3 = 26.5$
  B. $Q_1 = 20, Q_2 = 21, Q_3 = 26.5$
  C. $Q_1 = 20, Q_2 = 22, Q_3 = 25$
  D. $Q_1 = 19, Q_2 = 22.5, Q_3 = 28$

6. In which interval is the area above the x-axis and under the curve $y = 4x^2 + 1$ greatest?   **F**
  F. $-5 \leq x \leq 1$ G. $1 \leq x \leq 3$
  H. $1 \leq x \leq 4$ I. $2 \leq x \leq 5$

7. What are the foci of $\frac{x^2}{64} + \frac{y^2}{36} = 1$?   **B**

  A. $(0, \pm10)$ B. $(\pm2\sqrt{7}, 0)$
  C. $(\pm10, 0)$ D. $(0, \pm2\sqrt{7})$

8. Which graph has an asymptote at $x = 3$?   **I**
  F. $y = \frac{1}{x + 3}$
  G. $y = \frac{3}{x - 1}$
  H. $y = \frac{x - 3}{x + 3}$
  I. $y = \frac{3}{x - 3}$

Quantitative Comparison

Compare the boxed quantity in Column A with the boxed quantity in Column B. Choose the best answer.

  A. The quantity in Column A is greater.
  B. The quantity in Column B is greater.
  C. The two quantities are equal.
  D. The relationship cannot be determined from the information given.

Column A	Column B
$P(A) = \frac{1}{2}$, $P(A \text{ and } B) = \frac{1}{3}$	

9.
B

$P(A)$	$P(B \mid A)$

10.
A

the value that is three standard deviations above the mean, for mean 18 and standard deviation 2.8	the value that is two standard deviations below the mean, for mean 27 and standard deviation 1.5

Gridded Response

11. Evaluate $\sum\limits_{n=1}^{8} \frac{3n}{2}$.   **54**

12. Write the sum of the infinite geometric series as a fraction. $1 - 0.2 + 0.04 - \ldots$ $\frac{5}{6}$

Short Response

13. Solve the equation $\frac{x}{6} = \frac{x + 4}{9}$. Check your solution. Show your work.   **13–14. See back of book.**

14. State the property or properties used to justify the identity $9 \log 3 - 3 \log 9 = \log 27$.

Extended Response

15. Find the vertices, intercepts, asymptotes, and foci of the hyperbola $\frac{x^2}{16} - \frac{y^2}{9} = 1$.   **15–16. See back of book.**

16. Determine whether the series below is *arithmetic* or *geometric*. Then find the sum of the first eight terms.
  $10,000 + 1000 + 100 + 10 + \ldots$

Resources

Cumulative Review

Cumulative Review
Chapters 1–12

Item	Lesson	Item	Lesson
1	6-2	9	9-7
2	9-1	10	12-4
3	10-2	11	11-4
4	12-3	12	11-5
5	12-3	13	9-6
6	11-6	14	8-4
7	10-4	15	10-5
8	9-3	16	11-4/5

27. Answers may vary.
Sample: Flip a coin. Let heads represent a correct guess, and let tails represent an incorrect guess. A trial is 3 tosses.

Run the simulation 10 times and count the number of trials with at least 1 H. Divide the result by 10.

32.
12.7 20.8 28.9 37 45.1 53.2 61.3

691

Training Day

In these activities students apply their knowledge of geometric and arithmetic sequences and explore transforming a drawing by dilation.

Connecting to Prior Knowledge

Have students discuss various two-dimensional representations they have seen of three-dimensional objects. Examples could include plans for building model planes, ships, or houses, maps, and pictures of geometric shapes such as cubes and pyramids. Ask students to point out various ways that three dimensions are reduced to two.

Teaching Notes

Have a volunteer read the introductory paragraph. Discuss optical illusions in general. Point out the contrast between what is known (the parallel train tracks do not meet) and the illusion (to create a sense of distance, they do meet in the drawing).

Teaching Tip

Ask students to review the meaning and definition of a geometric sequence, as applied in this activity.

Tactile Learners

Have students use integer lengths for their railroad ties, and have them create a collage picture using spaghetti or thin wood sticks for the ties, glued to a piece of cardboard.

Connection to Art History

Have students research when perspective drawing, with parallel lines meeting in a vanishing point, was first studied and used by famous artists.

English Learners

Ask students to point to the *ties* and the *tracks* in the figure, to make sure that everyone understands the difference between these terms.

692

Training Day

Applying Sequences The world is three-dimensional, but drawings are done on a two-dimensional surface. We know that railroad tracks are parallel, but to create a feeling of depth in a drawing, tracks are often drawn as though they meet. The point where they seem to meet is called a vanishing point. This technique is called perspective drawing.

Strong-Armed Laborer
To build the track of the Canadian Pacific railroad, a freight car loaded with crossties was hauled to the end of the trails. Workers carried the crossties farther down the roadbed to extend the rails.

Legendary Locomotive
During the Civil War, this engine was hijacked by Union soldiers who planned to blow up a bridge. Confederate troops pursued them, and after an 18-hour, 139-km (87-mile) chase, caught up with the engine and recaptured it.

Activity 1

Materials: paper and pencil, ruler

a. Draw a set of railroad tracks such that the lengths of the horizontal ties form a geometric sequence.

b. Write the first four terms of the sequence.

c. Write a recursive formula for the sequence.

d. Write an explicit formula for the sequence.

Spanning Three Generations
These three trains represent more than 25 years of development. The original "Bullet Train" (on the right) was built in 1964. Series 300 (on the left) was built in 1992. It has a top speed of 168 mi/h.

All photographs © Dorling Kindersley Limited unless otherwise credited on acknowledgments page

pages 692–693 **Real-World Snapshots**

Activity 1

a–d. Check students' work.

Activity 2

Find a small picture or drawing you want to enlarge. Follow the steps below to enlarge the drawing. Use the diagram below as a guide.

Step 1 Choose a point O to the right of the drawing.

Step 2 Choose and label some key points on the drawing as A, B, C, etc.

Step 3 Lightly draw $\overrightarrow{OA}$.

Step 4 To make a drawing with dimensions that are *three times* the size of the original picture, locate point A' on $\overrightarrow{OA}$ so that $OA' = 3 \cdot OA$.

Step 5 Repeat Steps 3 and 4 for the remaining points on the picture (each ray begins at point O). Use the new points to help you draw the figure with new dimensions. (In this example, the new drawing will have a scale factor of 3.)

Energy for Trains

Before the invention of the steam engine, heavy loads were transported along railroads using human or animal power. Steam locomotives have nearly disappeared in America. Locomotives are now diesel or electric.

Activity 3

a. Begin with a small, simple drawing (perhaps one of your own or a cartoon). Use the method from Activity 2 to create at least two size changes of the original drawing so that the scale factors form an arithmetic sequence. (The original drawing has a scale factor of 1.)

b. Write the first four terms of the arithmetic sequence of scale factors.

c. Write a recursive formula for the sequence.

d. Write an explicit formula for the sequence.

Take It to the NET For more information about trains, go to **www.PHSchool.com**. Web Code: age-1253

693

Teaching Tip

Before students begin the activities, discuss the illustrations and their captions. Have students work in pairs or in small groups to complete the activities. Have each team read through all the activities before beginning to work.

Activity 1

Materials: paper and pencil, ruler, small picture or drawing to enlarge

Teaching Tip

Have a student explain the difference between a recursive and an explicit formula for a sequence.

Activity 2

Materials: paper and pencil, ruler, small picture or drawing to enlarge

Teaching Tip

Encourage students to choose a fairly simple line drawing to enlarge.

Activity 3

Materials: large piece of paper, pencil, ruler

Scoring Rubric

This scoring rubric can be used for evaluating student work on each of the activities. Share this scoring rubric with students before they begin work.

4 Drawings, formulas, and calculations are correct. Steps are neat, accurate, and clearly show the mathematics.

3 Drawings, formulas, and calculations are mostly correct, with some minor errors. Steps are neat and mostly accurate.

2 Drawings, formulas, and calculations contain both major and minor errors.

1 Correct answer, but no work is shown.

Activity 2

Check students' work.

Activity 3

Check students' work.

Periodic Functions and Trigonometry

Chapter at a Glance

13-1 Exploring Periodic Data

NCTM
1, 2, 3, 4, 5
- ▼ Identifying Periodic Functions
- ▼ Finding the Amplitude of a Periodic Function

13-2 Angles and the Unit Circle

NCTM
2, 3, 4, 8
- ▼ Working with Angles in Standard Position
- ▼ Using the Unit Circle

13-3 Radian Measure

NCTM
2, 3, 4, 9
- ▼ Using Radian Measure
- ▼ Finding the Length of an Arc

13-4 The Sine Function

NCTM
2, 3, 9, 10
- ▼ Interpreting Sine Functions
- ▼ Graphing Sine Functions

13-5 The Cosine Function

NCTM
2, 3, 7, 10
- ▼ Graphing and Writing Cosine Functions
- ▼ Solving Trigonometric Equations

13-6 The Tangent Function

NCTM
2, 3, 7, 8
- ▼ Graphing the Tangent Function

13-7 Translating Sine and Cosine Functions

NCTM
2, 3, 7, 8
- ▼ Graphing Translations of Trigonometric Functions
- ▼ Writing Equations of Translations

13-8 Reciprocal Trigonometric Functions

NCTM
2, 3, 7, 8
- ▼ Evaluating Reciprocal Trigonometric Functions
- ▼ Graphing Reciprocal Trigonometric Functions

NCTM STANDARDS 2000

1 Number and Operations	6 Problem Solving
2 Algebra	7 Reasoning and Proof
3 Geometry	8 Communication
4 Measurement	9 Connections
5 Data Analysis and Probability	10 Representation

Pacing Options

This chart suggests pacing only for the lessons and their parts. It is provided as a possible guide. It will help you determine how much time you have in your schedule to cover other components, such as the features, Chapter Review, and Chapter Test.

Day	Traditional (45 min.)	Block (90 min.)
1	13-1 ▼ ▼	13-1 ▼ ▼
2	13-2 ▼	13-2 ▼ ▼
3	13-2 ▼	13-3 ▼ ▼
4	13-3 ▼ ▼	13-4 ▼ ▼
5	13-4 ▼	13-5 ▼ ▼
6	13-4 ▼	13-6 ▼
7	13-5 ▼	13-7 ▼ ▼
8	13-5 ▼	13-8 ▼ ▼
9	13-6 ▼	
10	13-7 ▼	
11	13-7 ▼	
12	13-8 ▼ ▼	

NAEP Correlation (National Assessment of Educational Progress 2000 Mathematics Objectives)

13-1	13-2	13-3	13-4	13-5	13-6	13-7	13-8
A14c	A14b, A14c	A14b, A14c	A14c	A14c	A14c	N4d, A3d, A14c	A14c

N = Number Sense, Properties, and Operations; **M** = Measurement; **G** = Geometry and Spatial Sense; **D** = Data Analysis, Statistics, and Probability; **A** = Algebra and Functions

Math Background

Chapter Overview

Chapter 13 introduces the concept of a periodic function. After a discussion of measures of angles in standard position in the coordinate plane, the sine and cosine functions are defined in terms of the *x*- and *y*-coordinates of points on the unit circle. Students learn about radian measure, examine the graphs of sine and cosine functions, and learn how to find the amplitude and period of such functions.

The tangent function is defined in relation to the unit circle. Students learn about phase shifts and translations of graphs of sine and cosine functions. Finally, they consider the cosecant, secant, and cotangent functions, which are defined as the reciprocals of the sine, cosine, and tangent functions.

Exploring Periodic Data   13-1

The term *periodic* means repetitive or cyclic. Therefore, periodic functions must be somehow cyclic or repetitive. As students explore the graphs of periodic functions, make sure they understand how each is repetitive. The relation to a circle will follow in the next lesson.

Angles and the Unit Circle   13-2

Many geometry courses treat angle measure in such a way that no angle can have a measure greater than 180°. There are many sound reasons for doing so. In trigonometry, it is more helpful to relate angle measure to the concept of rotations, and permit angle measures of *any* size, positive or negative. The unit circle definitions of the sine and cosine functions make it easy to see why these are periodic functions.

Radian Measure   13-3

Some students are so accustomed to degree measure and unfamiliar with radian measure that it may take a little time for them to appreciate the many advantages of radian measure. Defining the sine and cosine functions as functions of real numbers with no explicit unit of angle measure attached is analogous to specifying coordinates of points in the coordinate plane, where we use "pure" numbers that have no specific units of length attached. There is also a very convenient relationship between angle measures in radians and arc lengths determined by a central angle in a circle.

The Sine and Cosine Functions   13-4, 13-5

When students have completed these lessons, they should be able to inspect an equation of the form $y = a \sin b\theta$ or $y = a \cos b\theta$ ($a \neq 0$, $b > 0$, θ in radians), specify its amplitude and period, and sketch a rough graph. The exercises in these lessons will help students appreciate how versatile the sine and cosine functions are in modeling situations involving periodic data.

The Tangent Function   13-6

The tangent function can be defined as the quotient of the sine and cosine functions or as the *y*-coordinate of the point where the terminal side of an angle in standard position intersects the line $x = 1$ (the line tangent to the unit circle at (1, 0)). This lesson uses the second approach since it gives an immediate geometric interpretation and makes it easy to determine the period of the tangent function.

Translating Sine and Cosine Functions   13-7

By now, many students can probably anticipate what equations for translations of the graphs of $y = a \sin bx$ or $y = a \cos bx$ will look like. The concepts of phase shifts and vertical shifts fit naturally with what students know about translations.

Use of a graphing calculator is effective in showing how trigonometric graphs are stretched or shrunk. Make sure students understand that if a graph is changed vertically, then the amplitude changes, and if a graph is changed horizontally, the period may change.

Reciprocal Trigonometric Functions   13-8

The cosecant, secant, and cotangent functions are defined as the respective reciprocals of the sine, cosine, and tangent functions. Some students need to be reminded that the $\sin^{-1}$, $\cos^{-1}$, and $\tan^{-1}$ functions on the calculator are not reciprocals, but rather inverse functions, which they will learn about in Chapter 14. Vertical asymptotes are necessary for the graphs of the tangent, secant, cosecant, and cotangent functions. Students should be encouraged to review the occurrence of vertical asymptotes in the graphs of rational functions. (See Chapter 9.)

Ongoing Assessment and Intervention

Tools for Monitoring Student Progress

The Prentice Hall *Algebra 2* program provides you with many options for assessment in the Student Edition, the Teacher's Edition and the teaching resources. From these options you may choose instructional materials and techniques that are appropriate for your students and support your district's curriculum requirements.

Instant Check System™ in Chapter 13

Allows students to check their own learning before, during, and after each lesson.

Diagnosing Readiness before the chapter (p. 694)

Check Skills You'll Need exercises in each lesson (pp. 696, 704, 712, 720, 729, 735, 742, 749)

Check Understanding questions with each Example (pp. 697, 698, 699, 704, 705, 707, 708, 713, 714, 715, 720, 721, 722, 723, 724, 730, 731, 736, 737, 742, 743, 744, 745, 746, 749, 750, 751, 752)

Checkpoint Quiz (pp. 719, 748)

 Test Prep in Chapter 13

Teaches students strategies and gives them practice with all the test item formats they will encounter on state tests and standardized national exams.

Standardized Test Prep exercises in each lesson (pp. 701, 710, 718, 727, 734, 740, 748, 755)

Test-Taking Strategies (p. 756)

Standardized Test Prep (p. 761)

All your assessment needs in one place!

Program Assessment

Assess student progress throughout the *Algebra 2* text with blackline masters and CD-ROM.

Assessment Resources

- Checkpoint Quizzes 1 & 2
- Chapter Test, Forms A & B
- Chapter Alternative Assessment

Spanish versions available.

Computer Test Generator

- Unlimited questions of varying difficulty for every lesson objective.
- Create your own practice sheets, quizzes, and tests, or use the pre-made Chapter Tests.
- Diagnose readiness with questions on prerequisite skills.
- Prepare students by making tests based on standardized test objectives.
- Access Algebra 1, Geometry, and Algebra 2 content—all on one CD-ROM.

Test Preparation

A three-step approach to preparing students for high stakes, national, and state exams.

❶ Diagnose & Prescribe

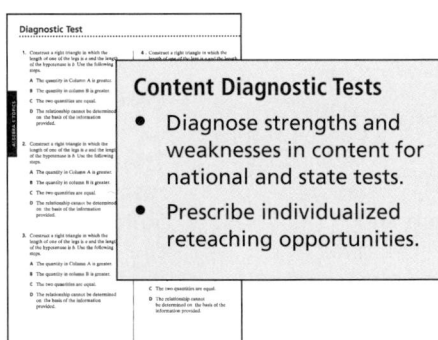

Content Diagnostic Tests
- Diagnose strengths and weaknesses in content for national and state tests.
- Prescribe individualized reteaching opportunities.

❷ Review & Reteach

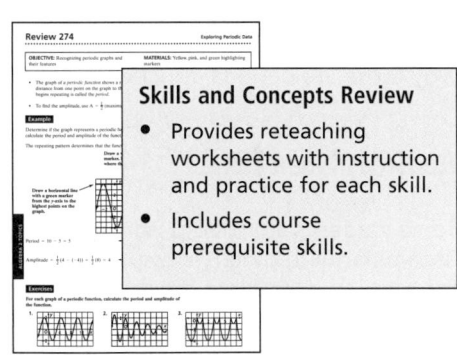

Skills and Concepts Review
- Provides reteaching worksheets with instruction and practice for each skill.
- Includes course prerequisite skills.

❸ Practice & Assess

Test Preparation
- Features practice tests for End-of-Course and SAT/ACT exams.
- Includes standardized test practice by chapter for ongoing review.

Teacher's Guide with answers and correlations.

Test-Taking Strategies with Transparencies
- Support the Test-Taking Strategies pages in the Student Edition.
- Provide a teaching transparency and a practice worksheet for each strategy.

Reaching All Students

Support in the Student Text and Additional Resources

The textbook, the iText, and other technology components provide numerous opportunities to reach students of various ability levels and learning styles. Each Teacher's Edition lesson suggests how you can help *all* your students be successful and understand the mathematics in Chapter 13.

Below Level

Student Edition
- Diagnosing Readiness*: p. 694
- Check Skills You'll Need*: pp. 696, 704, 712, 720, 729, 735, 742, 749

Reteaching
Chapter 13 Support File: pp. 8–14

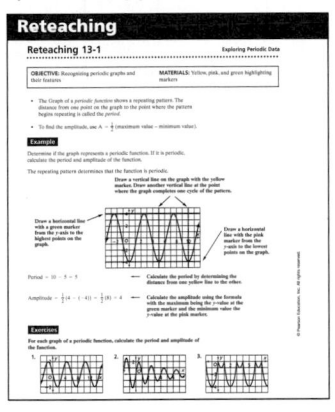

Advanced Learners

Student Edition
- Challenge exercises: pp. 701, 702, 709, 710, 718, 719, 726, 727, 733, 734, 739, 740, 747, 754, 755

Enrichment
Chapter 13 Support File: pp. 15–21

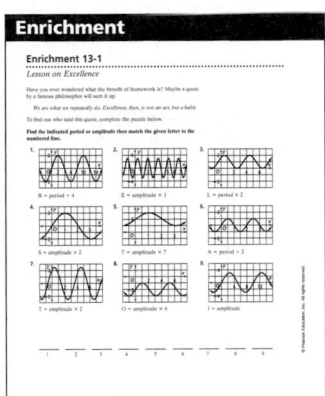

Connections to Precalculus Masters
Chapter 13 Enrichment Topic:
The "Standard Form"

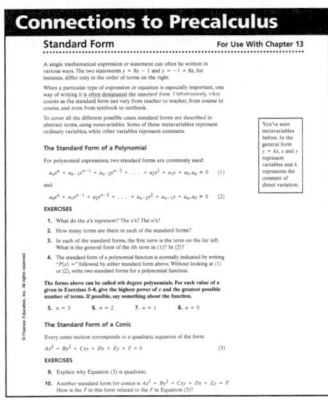

* Can be used with all ability levels to ensure mastery of prerequisite skills.

Reading and Math Literacy

Student Edition
- Vocabulary: pp. 695, 757, *plus* in every Lesson Preview
- Reading Math: pp. 698, 706, 712, 720, 739, 741
- Illustrated Glossary: pp. 871–913

Reading and Math Literacy Masters
Chapter 13: pp. 49–52

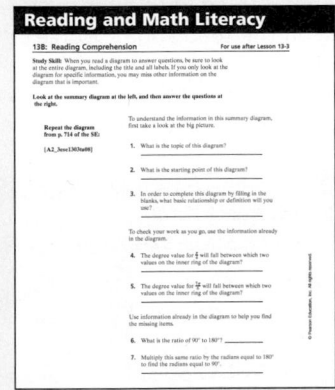

English Learners

Student Edition
- English/Spanish Illustrated Glossary: pp. 871–913

Workbook and Masters
Spanish Practice Workbook: pp. 2–7
Spanish Reading and Math Literacy Masters: pp. 49–52

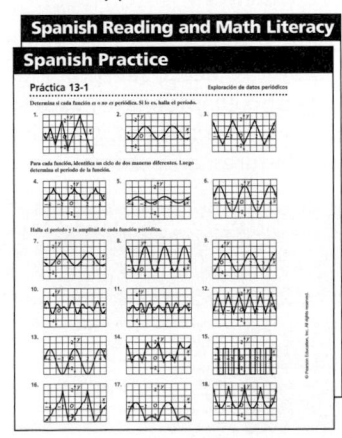

Learning Styles

Student Edition
- Investigation: pp. 696, 706, 711
- Technology: pp. 714, 718, 721, 722, 728, 731, 747, 749, 751
- Writing: pp. 700, 709, 718, 726, 733, 739, 747, 753, 754, 760

Activity Masters
Hands-On Activities: 57
Technology Activities: 14, 37

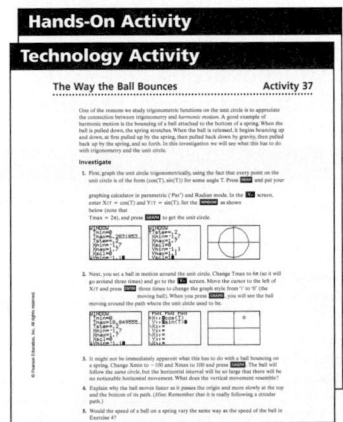

Program Resources

	Teaching Resources in Grab & Go™ Files				Resources for Reaching All Students			Spanish Resources			Transparencies				Presentation Assistant Plus!
	Practice	Reteach	Enrich	Checkpoint Quiz	Reading & Math Literacy	Technology Activities	Hands-On Activities	Practice	Reading & Math Literacy	Checkpoint Quiz	Skills Check	Additional Examples	Answers to Exercises	Lesson Quiz	Prentice Hall Presentation Pro CD-ROM
13-1	■	■	■		■			■	■		■	■	■	■	■
13-2	■	■	■					■			■	■	■	■	■
13-3	■	■	■	■	■			■	■	■	■	■	■	■	■
13-4	■	■	■					■			■	■	■	■	■
13-5	■	■	■			■		■			■	■	■	■	■
13-6	■	■	■					■			■	■	■	■	■
13-7	■	■	■		■		■	■	■		■	■	■	■	■
13-8		■						■			■	■	■	■	■
For the chapter	Chapter Tests, Alternative Assessment, Cumulative Review, Cumulative Assessment				Connections to Precalculus Masters			Spanish Chapter Tests, Alternative Assessment, Cumulative Review, Cumulative Assessment			Classroom Aid Transparencies				

Also available for use with the chapter:

 *See page 694C.*

- Practice Workbook
- Solution Key

- For teacher support and access to student Web site materials, use Web Code agk-5500.
- For additional online and technology resources, see below.

Technology

iTEXT Online and on CD-ROM

Complete Interactive Student Text online and on CD-ROM—with instant feedback assessment, tutorial help, dynamic activities, instructional and real-world videos, audio, and additional practice.

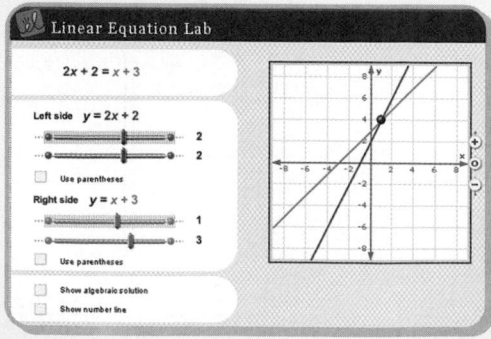

www.PHSchool.com For Students

Use **Web Codes** for easy access to online activities, chapter projects, self-grading lesson quizzes and chapter tests, vocabulary quizzes, updated data sources, graphing calculator procedures, and more.

PH SuccessNet For Teachers

Online lesson planning with built-in state correlations, all the teaching resources, complete reference library, your own calendar and Teacher Web page, professional development, and more.

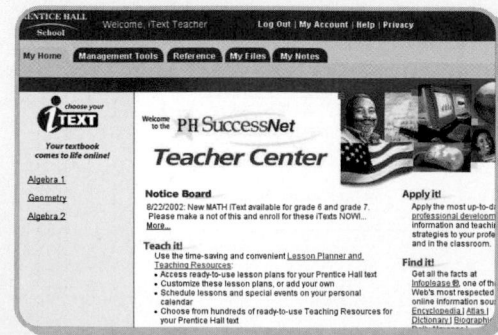

Presentation Assistant Plus!

The Prentice Hall *Presentation Assistant Plus!* provides you with the material you need to teach a lesson from beginning to end. Two easy-to-use formats—Transparencies and CD-ROM—allow you to present a lesson the way you are most comfortable.

Transparencies

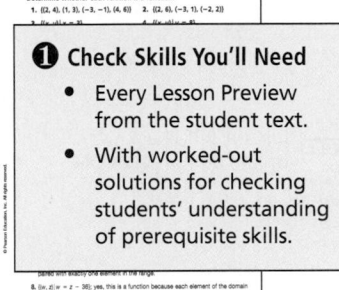

❶ **Check Skills You'll Need**
- Every Lesson Preview from the student text.
- With worked-out solutions for checking students' understanding of prerequisite skills.

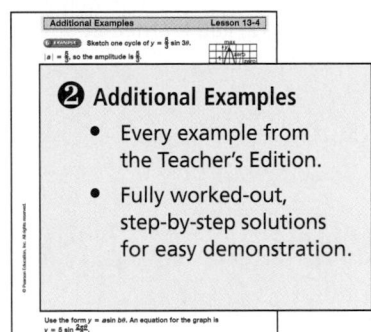

❷ **Additional Examples**
- Every example from the Teacher's Edition.
- Fully worked-out, step-by-step solutions for easy demonstration.

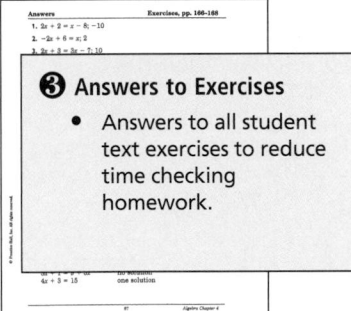

❸ **Answers to Exercises**
- Answers to all student text exercises to reduce time checking homework.

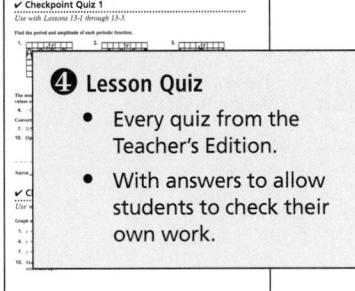

❹ **Lesson Quiz**
- Every quiz from the Teacher's Edition.
- With answers to allow students to check their own work.

 Throughout the Teacher's Edition, this symbol indicates material that is available on transparency in the Presentation Assistant Plus!

Prentice Hall Presentation Pro CD-ROM

- Includes all Transparencies.
- Conveniently organized by lesson so you can easily ❶ Introduce, ❷ Teach, ❸ Check Homework, and ❹ Assess each lesson.
- Animated examples allow step-by-step instruction at your own pace.
- Easy to edit so you can create custom presentations.

Teaching Chapter 13 Using Presentation Assistant Plus!

	❶ Introduce Check Skills You'll Need	❷ Teach Additional Examples	❸ Check Homework Student Edition Answers	❹ Assess Lesson Quiz
13-1	p. 84	pp. 247–250	✔	p. 165
13-2	p. 85	pp. 251–253	✔	p. 166
13-3	p. 86	pp. 254–257	✔	p. 166
13-4	p. 87	pp. 258–262	✔	p. 167
13-5	p. 88	pp. 263–265	✔	p. 168
13-6	p. 89	pp. 265–266	✔	p. 169
13-7	p. 90	pp. 267–269	✔	p. 169
13-8	p. 91	pp. 270–273	✔	p. 170

Prentice Hall Presentation Pro

CD-ROM with dynamic PowerPoint® presentations for every lesson. Helps you introduce and develop concepts, check homework, and assess progress. Part of Presentation Assistant Plus! *(See above.)*

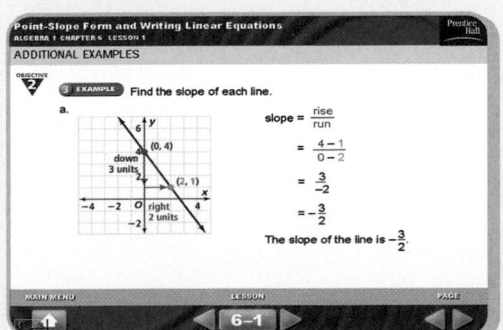

Computer Test Generator

CD-ROM to create practice sheets and tests for course objectives and standardized tests. Includes Instant Chapter Tests™, online testing, and student reports. Part of the PH Assessment System. *(See page 694C.)*

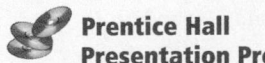

Resource Pro® with Planning Express®

CD-ROM with a lesson planning tool that allows you to import state and local objectives. Includes electronic versions of all the teaching resources.

Chapter 13

Periodic Functions and Trigonometry

 Diagnosing Readiness

Students will find answers to these exercises in the back of their textbooks.

For intervention, direct students to:

Analyzing graphs of rational functions
Lesson 9-3; Example 2
Exercises 7–12
Extra Practice, p. 830

Simplifying complex fractions
Lesson 9-5; Example 5
Exercises 22–30
Extra Practice, p. 830

Translating conic sections
Lesson 10-6; Example 4
Exercises 12–21
Extra Practice, p. 831

Writing formulas for sequences
Lesson 11-1; Example 3
Exercises 12–17
Extra Practice, p. 832

page 694 Diagnosing Readiness

12. $(x - 1)^2 + (y + 4)^2 = 16;$

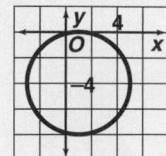

13. $\dfrac{(x - 2)^2}{9} + \dfrac{(y - 5)^2}{4} = 1;$

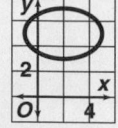

694

Where You've Been

- In Chapter 9, you learned to graph rational functions, some of which have graphs that are discontinuous in the coordinate plane.

- In Chapter 10, you learned to write and graph equations representing circles, ellipses, hyperbolas, and parabolas.

- In Chapters 11 and 12, you learned about patterns and probability.

 **iTEXT** Instant self-check online and on CD-ROM

Diagnosing Readiness (For help, go to the Lesson in green.)

Analyzing Graphs of Rational Functions (Lesson 9-3)

Describe the vertical asymptotes and holes for each rational function.

1. $y = \dfrac{2}{x - 3}$
vertical asymptote $x = 3$

2. $y = \dfrac{(x - 5)(x - 1)}{x - 1}$
hole at $x = 1$

3. $y = \dfrac{x + 2}{(2x + 1)(x - 4)}$
vertical asymptotes $x = -\frac{1}{2}$ and $x = 4$

Simplifying Complex Fractions (Lesson 9-5)

Simplify each complex fraction.

4. $\dfrac{\frac{2}{a}}{\frac{1}{b}}$ $\dfrac{2b}{a}$

5. $\dfrac{5 + \frac{1}{2}}{2 - \frac{1}{5}}$ $\dfrac{55}{18}$

6. $\dfrac{\frac{3}{c + d}}{2}$ $\dfrac{3}{2(c + d)}$

7. $\dfrac{\frac{1}{4}}{\frac{4}{c}}$ $\dfrac{c}{16}$

8. $\dfrac{\frac{2}{3}}{\frac{6}{c + 4}}$ $\dfrac{c + 4}{9}$

9. $\dfrac{\frac{4}{x}}{\frac{2}{8}}$ $\dfrac{16}{x}$

10. $\dfrac{3 - \frac{1}{2}}{\frac{7}{6}}$ $\dfrac{15}{7}$

11. $\dfrac{\frac{9}{m - n}}{\frac{3}{2m - 2n}}$ 6

Translating Conic Sections (Lesson 10-6)

Write an equation for each conic section. Then sketch the graph. **12–15. See margin.**

12. circle with center at $(1, -4)$ and radius 4

13. ellipse with center at $(2, 5)$, vertices at $(5, 5)$ and $(-1, 5)$, and co-vertices at $(2, 3)$ and $(2, 7)$

14. parabola with vertex at $(0, -3)$ and focus at $(0, 5)$

15. hyperbola with center at $(6, 1)$, one focus at $(6, 6)$, and one vertex at $(6, -2)$

Writing Formulas for Sequences (Lesson 11-1)

Find the next two terms in each sequence. Write a formula for the nth term. Identify each formula as *explicit* or *recursive*. **16–18. See margin p. 695.**

16. $16, 13, 10, 7, \ldots$

17. $-1, -8, -27, -64, -125, \ldots$

18. $9, 3, 1, \frac{1}{3}, \ldots$

---

14. $y = \frac{1}{32}x^2 - 3;$

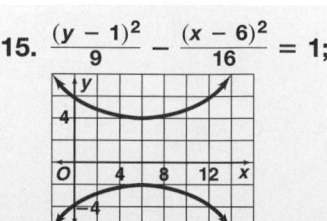

15. $\dfrac{(y - 1)^2}{9} - \dfrac{(x - 6)^2}{16} = 1;$

Periodic Functions and Trigonometry

Where You're Going

- In Chapter 13, you will learn how geometric measurement relates to trigonometry.

- You will learn to use radian measure.

- You will learn how to write and graph functions that describe periodic data.

Real-World Connection Applying what you learn, on page 715 you will solve a problem involving a satellite's orbit.

Key Vocabulary

- amplitude (p. 698)
- central angle (p. 712)
- cosecant (p. 749)
- cosine function (p. 729)
- cosine of θ (p. 706)
- cotangent (p. 749)
- coterminal angles (p. 705)
- cycle (p. 697)
- initial side (p. 704)
- intercepted arc (p. 712)
- period (p. 697)
- periodic function (p. 697)
- phase shift (p. 742)
- radian (p. 712)
- secant (p. 749)
- sine curve (p. 721)
- sine function (p. 720)
- sine of θ (p. 706)
- standard position (p. 704)
- tangent function (p. 735)
- tangent of θ (p. 735)
- terminal side (p. 704)
- unit circle (p. 706)

Chapter 13 Overview

This chapter begins with an exploration of periodic data in which students are introduced to cycles, periods, and amplitudes. The chapter continues with lessons that introduce the unit circle and radian measure. Students then complete lessons on the sine, cosine, and tangent functions. The chapter concludes with lessons on translating trigonometric functions and reciprocal trigonometric functions.

📖 **Reading Math**
Reading a Graph, p. 741

📖 **Vocabulary**
A complete list of terms, plus vocabulary exercises, appears in the Chapter Review, p. 757.

📖 **Illustrated Glossary**
Examples for each vocabulary term, plus definitions in both English and Spanish, appear starting on p. 871.

📶 **Test-Taking Strategies**
Using Mental Math, p. 756

🌐 **Real-World Connections**
Some of the applications you will find in this chapter are physics (13-1), space (13-3), wave motion (13-5), and indirect measurement (13-8).

💻 **www.PHSchool.com**
Internet support for this chapter includes:
- Self-grading Vocabulary and Chapter 13 Tests
- Chapter Project
- Chapter Planner
- Chapter 13 Resources

Plus 🖳**TEXT**

695

---

16. **4, 1;** $a_n = 19 - 3n$;
    explicit or $a_1 = 16$,
    $a_n = a_{n-1} - 3$; recursive

17. **−216, −343;** $a_n = -n^3$;
    explicit

18. $\frac{1}{9}, \frac{1}{27}$; $a_n = 9\left(\frac{1}{3}\right)^{n-1}$;
    explicit or $a_1 = 9$,
    $a_n = \frac{1}{3} \cdot a_{n-1}$; recursive

Lesson Preview

✓ **Check Skills You'll Need**

Determining Whether Relations are Functions
Lesson 2-1: Example 4
Exercises 10–13
Extra Practice, p. 824

Lesson Resources

📁 **Teaching Resources**
Practice, Reteaching, Enrichment

👥 **Reaching All Students**
Practice Workbook 13-1
Spanish Practice Workbook 13-1
Reading and Math Literacy 13A
Spanish Reading & Literacy 13A
Hands-On Activities 63

⏰ **Presentation Assistant Plus!**
Transparencies
• Check Skills You'll Need 13-1
• Additional Examples 13-1
• Student Edition Answers 13-1
• Lesson Quiz 13-1
PH Presentation Pro CD 13-1

 **ASSESSMENT** *SYSTEM*

Computer Test Generator CD

💿 **Technology**
Resource Pro® CD-ROM
Computer Test Generator CD
Prentice Hall Presentation Pro CD

🖥️ **www.PHSchool.com**
Student Site
• Teacher Web Code: agk-5500
• Self-grading Lesson Quiz
Teacher Center
• Lesson Planner
• Resources

Plus 🄸TEXT

13-1

Exploring Periodic Data

Lesson Preview

What You'll Learn

OBJECTIVE 1 To identify cycles and periods of periodic functions

OBJECTIVE 2 To find the amplitude of periodic functions

. . . And Why

To make predictions about sound waves, as in Example 4

✓ **Check Skills You'll Need**   (For help, go to Lesson 2-1.)

Determine whether each relation is a function.

1. $\{(2,4),(1,3),(-3,-1),(4,6)\}$ **yes**

2. $\{(2,6),(-3,1),(-2,2)\}$ **yes**

3. $\{(x,y)\mid x=3\}$ **no**

4. $\{(x,y)\mid y=8\}$ **yes**

5. $\{(x,y)\mid x=y^2\}$ **no**

6. $\{(x,y)\mid x^2+y^2=36\}$ **no**

7. $\{(a,b)\mid a=b^3\}$ **yes**

8. $\{(w,z)\mid w=z-36\}$ **yes**

New Vocabulary • periodic function • cycle • period • amplitude

---

OBJECTIVE 1   **Identifying Periodic Functions**

🄸TEXT Interactive lesson includes instant self-check, tutorials, and activities.

Investigation: Periodic Cycles

Use the diagram below. Suppose you and a friend are the last two people seated on a Ferris wheel. Once the ride begins, the wheel moves at a constant speed. It takes 36 seconds to complete one revolution.

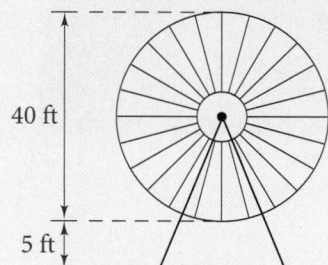 

40 ft

5 ft

1. a. At 0 seconds, when the ride starts, how high above the ground are you? **5 ft**
   b. At what height are you at 9 seconds? At 18 seconds? At 27 seconds? **25 ft; 45 ft; 25 ft**
   c. At what height are you at 126 seconds? How many revolutions have you made? **45 ft; 3.5 revolutions**
   d. Predict where you will be at 3 minutes. **5 ft**

2. Sketch a graph showing the relationship between your height above the ground and the time since the ride began. Use $0 \le t \le 144$ for the domain, where $t = 0$ is the time at which the ride starts. **See back of book.**

3. Critical Thinking How far (in feet) have you traveled after one revolution of the wheel? How far have you traveled at 144 seconds? **about 125.66 ft; about 502.65 ft**

Ongoing Assessment and Intervention

Before the Lesson	**During the Lesson**	**After the Lesson**
Diagnose prerequisite skills using:	**Monitor progress using:**	**Assess knowledge using:**
• Check Skills You'll Need	• Check Understanding	• Lesson Quiz
	• Additional Examples	• Computer Test Generator CD
	• Standardized Test Prep	

A **periodic function** repeats a pattern of *y*-values (outputs) at regular intervals. One complete pattern is a **cycle.** A cycle may begin at any point on the graph of the function. The **period** of a function is the horizontal length of one cycle.

1 EXAMPLE Identifying Cycles and Periods

Analyze the periodic function below. Identify one cycle in two different ways. Then determine the period of the function.

Begin at any point on the graph. Trace one complete pattern.

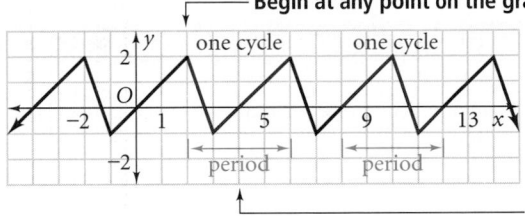

The beginning and ending *x*-values of each cycle determine the period of the function.

● Each cycle is 4 units long. The period of the function is 4.

✓ **Check Understanding** ❶ For each function, identify one cycle in two different ways. Then determine the period of the function.

a.
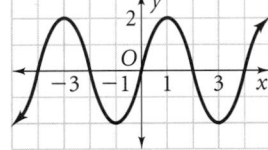

b.
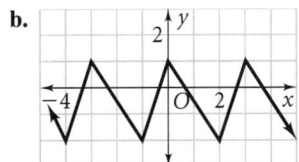

from −3 to 1 or 0 to 4; 4   from −4 to −1 or 0 to 3; 3

You can determine whether a function is periodic by analyzing its graph.

2 EXAMPLE Identifying Periodic Functions

Determine whether each function *is* or *is not* periodic. If it is, find the period.

a.
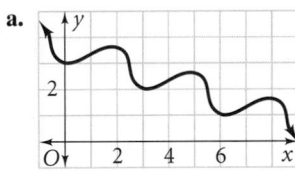

Although the graph shows similar curves, the *y*-values from one section do not repeat in other sections. The function *is not* periodic.

b.
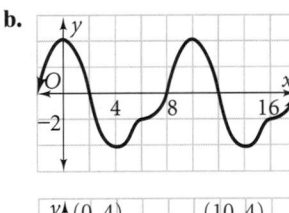

The pattern of *y*-values in one section repeats exactly in other sections. The function *is* periodic.

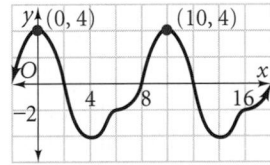

Find points at the beginning and end of one cycle. Subtract the *x* values of the points: 10 − 0 = 10. The pattern in the graph repeats every 10 units, so the period is 10.

Math Background

Trigonometric functions are probably the periodic functions most accessible to students, but there are many others. There are machines that display periodic graphs, for example heart monitors and oscilloscopes.

OBJECTIVE
1 Teaching Notes

Investigation (Optional)
Direct students' attention to the diagram of the Ferris wheel. Ask how many revolutions were made after 9 s, 18 s and 27 s. $\frac{1}{4}$, $\frac{1}{2}$, and $\frac{3}{4}$ **of a revolution**

Suggest that students connect the points with smooth curves rather than straight lines. They may need to plot more points to draw the curves accurately.

Additional Examples

❶ Analyze this periodic function. Identify one cycle in two different ways. Then determine the period of the function. **A cycle could begin, for example, at (−5, 0) or at (−3, 2). Each cycle is 7 units long; the period is 7.**

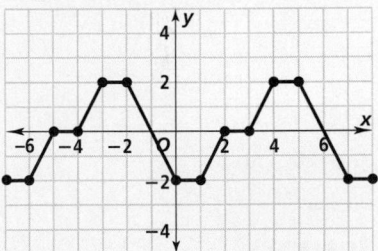

❷ Determine whether each function *is* or *is not* periodic. If it is, find the period.
a.
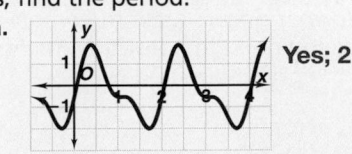
Yes; 2

b.
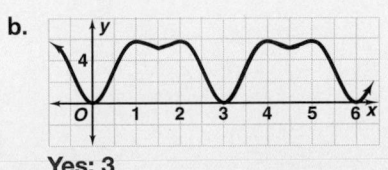

Yes; 3

697

👥 Reaching All Students

| **Below Level** Ask students to explain why the motion of a piston in a cylinder, tides in the oceans, the motion of a pendulum, etc. are periodic. | **Advanced Learners** A function is periodic if, for some non-zero real number α, $f(x + \alpha) = f(x)$ for every x in the domain. Discuss the meaning of the smallest possible value of α. | **Inclusion** See note on page 699. **Error Prevention** See note on page 698. |

698

OBJECTIVE 2 Teaching Notes

3 EXAMPLE **Error Prevention**

Students may incorrectly assume that all periodic functions are symmetric about the *x*-axis. Point out that the line of symmetry for this function is $x = 5$ or any multiple of 5.

4 EXAMPLE **Teaching Tip**

For simplicity, units of measure are given only for the values of time *t*. The amplitude of sound waves is generally measured in units of pressure, such as *pascals*.

⬛ Additional Examples

3 Find the amplitudes of the two functions in Additional Example 2.
a) 2   b) 3

4 The oscilloscope screen below shows the graph of the alternating current electricity *s*, in volts, supplied to homes in the United States. Find the period and amplitude.

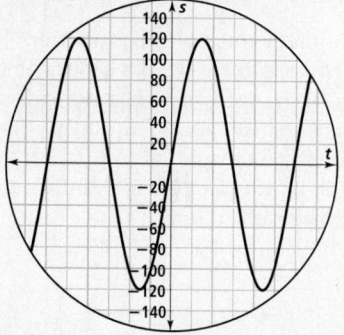

1 unit on the *t*-axis $= \frac{1}{360}$ s
$\frac{1}{60}$ s; 120 volts

Closure

Ask students: *If you know the period and the amplitude of a graph, do you have enough information to sketch the graph?* **No, you need to know the shape of the graph during a cycle.**

✔ **Check Understanding** **2** Determine whether each function *is* or *is not* periodic. If it is, find the period.

a.
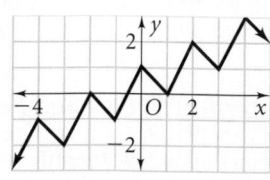
not periodic

b.
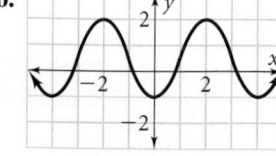
periodic; 4

Finding the Amplitude of a Periodic Function

Reading Math

Amplitude modulation (AM) radio works by varying the amplitude of radio waves.

The amplitude of a periodic function measures the amount of variation in the function values.

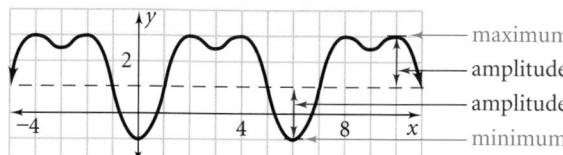

 Key Concepts

Definition	**Amplitude of a Periodic Function**

The **amplitude** of a periodic function is half the difference between the maximum and minimum values of the function.

3 EXAMPLE **Finding Amplitude of a Periodic Function**

Find the amplitude of the periodic function at the right.

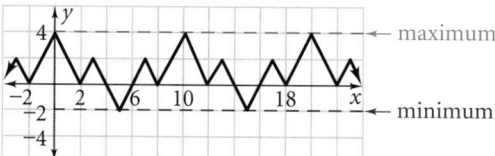

amplitude $= \frac{1}{2}$(maximum value − minimum value)   **Use the definition of amplitude.**

$= \frac{1}{2}[4 - (-2)]$ **Substitute.**

$= \frac{1}{2}(6) = 3$ **Subtract within parentheses and simplify.**

● The amplitude of the function is 3.

✔ **Check Understanding** **3** Find the amplitude of each function.

a.
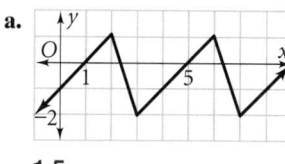
1.5

b.
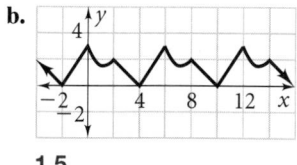
1.5

You can model some data with periodic functions. The rotation of a Ferris wheel, the beating of a heart, and the movement of sound waves are all examples of real-world events that generate periodic data.

 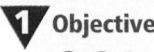
4 EXAMPLE Real-World Connection

Sound Waves Sound is produced by periodic changes in air pressure called sound waves. The oscilloscope at the right shows the graph of a pure tone from a tuning fork. Find the period and the amplitude of the sound wave.

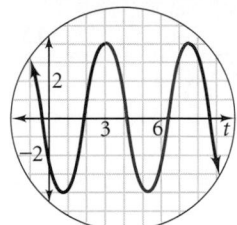

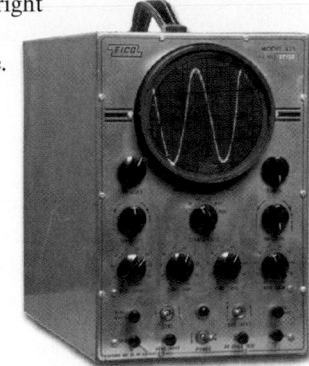

1 unit on the *t*-axis = 0.001 s

One cycle of the sound wave occurs from 0.003 s to 0.0075 s. The maximum value of the function is 4, and the minimum value is −4.

period $= 0.0075 - 0.003$ **Use the definitions.** amplitude $= \frac{1}{2}[4 - (-4)]$

$= 0.0045$ **Simplify.** $= \frac{1}{2}(8) = 4$

● The period of the sound wave is 0.0045 s. The amplitude is 4.

✓ **Check Understanding** 4 Sketch the graph of a sound wave with a period of 0.004 s and an amplitude of 2. **See margin.**

EXERCISES

For more practice, see *Extra Practice*.

Practice and Problem Solving

A Practice by Example

Example 1 (page 697)

Identify one cycle in two different ways. Then determine the period of the function.

1. 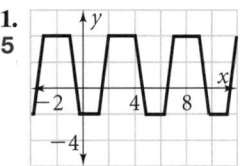 **2.** 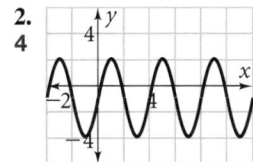 **3.**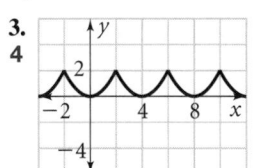

Example 2 (page 697)

Determine whether each function *is* or *is not* periodic. If it is, find the period.

4. not periodic

5. periodic; 12

6. not periodic

7. not periodic

8. periodic; 8

9. periodic; 7

4. 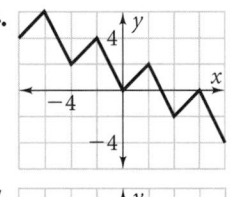 **5.** 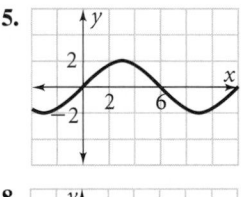 **6.**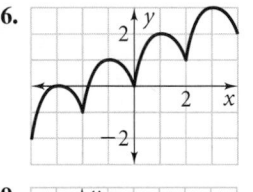

7. 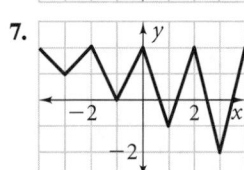 **8.** 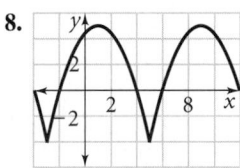 **9.**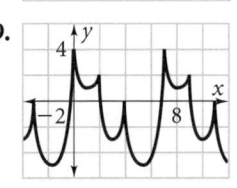

pages 697–699 Check Understanding

4.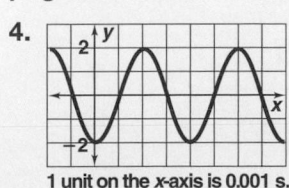

1 unit on the *x*-axis is 0.001 s.

3. Practice

Find the amplitude of each periodic function.

10. **4**

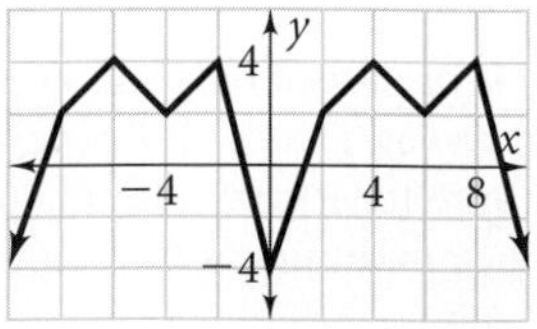

11. **3**

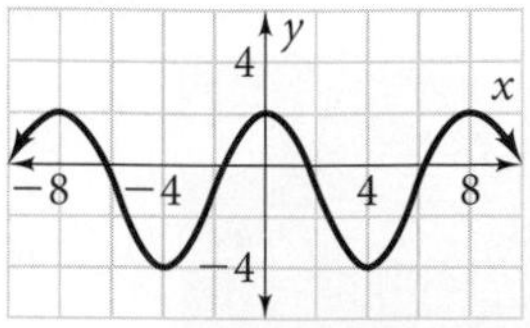

12. **1**

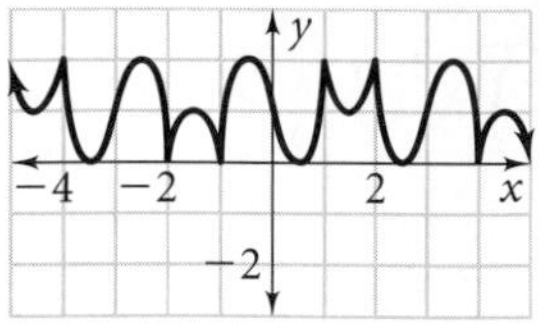

13. **2**

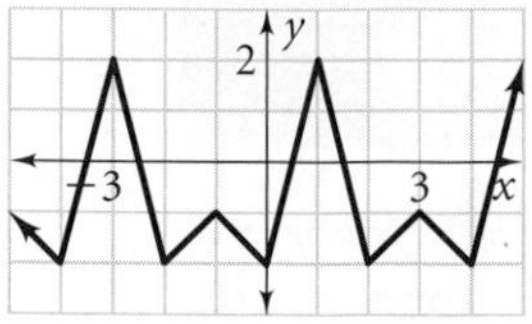

B Apply Your Skills

Sketch the graph of a sound wave with the given period and amplitude.

14. period 0.02, amplitude 4 **15.** period 0.005, amplitude 9

14–15. See margin.

16. Complete each statement with *x* or *y*.

a. You use ■-values to compute the amplitude of a function. ***y***

b. You use ■-values to compute the period of a function. ***x***

Writing **Could you use a periodic function to represent each situation described below? Explain. 18–19. See margin.**

17. the average monthly temperature in your community, recorded every month for three years

18. the population in your community, recorded every year for the last 50 years

19. the number of cars per hour that pass through an intersection near where you live, recorded for two consecutive work days

17. Answers may vary. Sample: Yes; average monthly temperatures for three years should be cyclical due to the variation of the seasons.

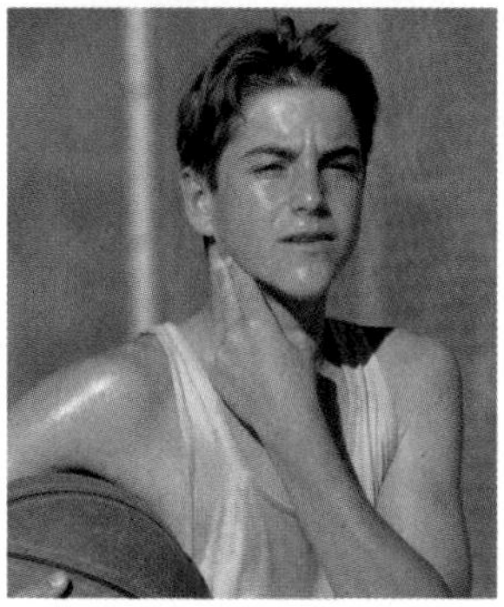

Real-World Connection

The carotid artery of the neck is a commonly used pulse point.

Health **Use the graph below for Exercises 20 and 21.**

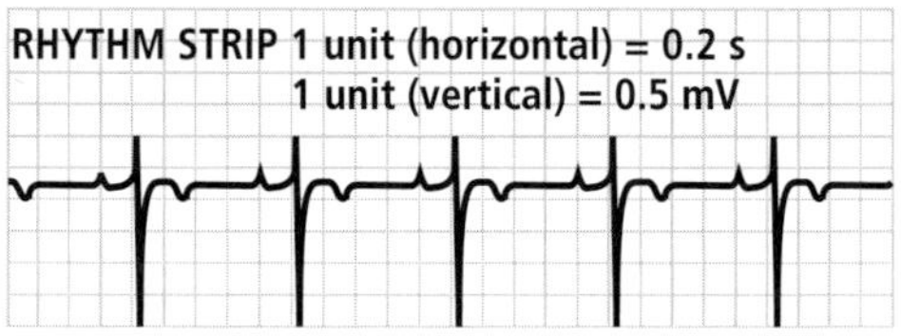
RHYTHM STRIP 1 unit (horizontal) = 0.2 s
1 unit (vertical) = 0.5 mV

20. A person's pulse rate is the number of times his or her heart beats in one minute. Each cycle in the graph represents one heartbeat. Find the pulse rate. **60 beats per min**

21. An electrocardiogram (EKG or ECG) measures the electrical activity of a person's heart in millivolts over time.

a. What is the period of the EKG shown above? **1 s**

b. What is the amplitude of the EKG? **1.5 mV**

22. **Open-Ended** Sketch a graph of a periodic function that has a period of 3 and an amplitude of 2. **Check students' work.**

Find the maximum, minimum, and period of each periodic function. Then copy the graph and sketch two more cycles. 23–25. See margin.

23.

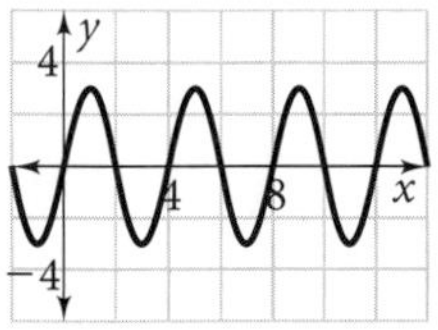

24.

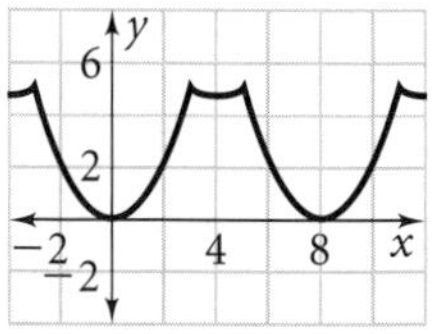

25.

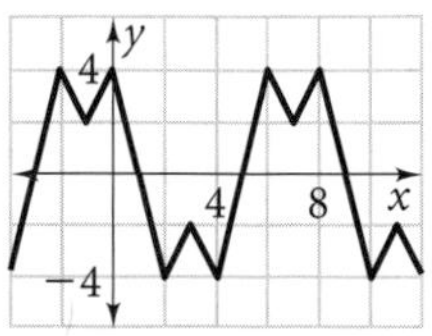

pages 699–702 Exercises

14.

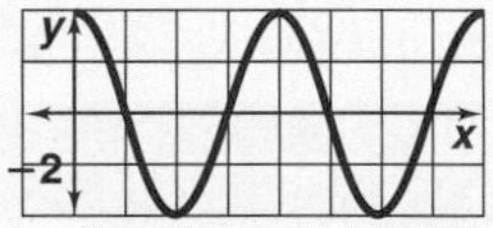

1 unit on the *x*-axis is 0.005 s.

15.

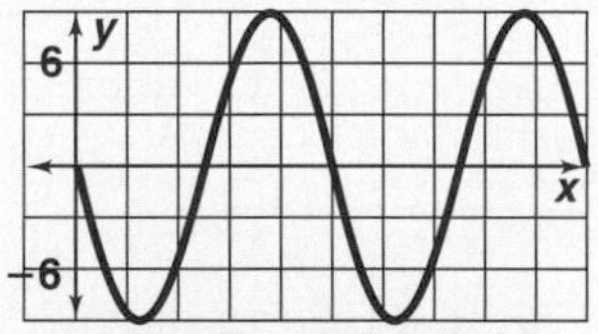

1 unit on the *x*-axis is 0.001 s.

18. Answers may vary. Sample: No; population usually increases or decreases but is not cyclical.

19. Answers may vary. Sample: Yes; traffic that passes through an intersection should be at the same levels for the same times of day for two consecutive work days.

23. 3, −3, 4;

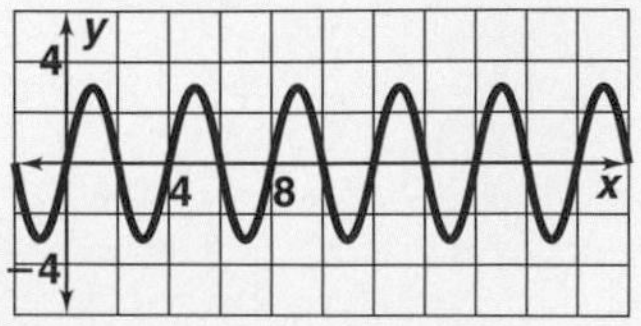

24. 5, 0, 8;

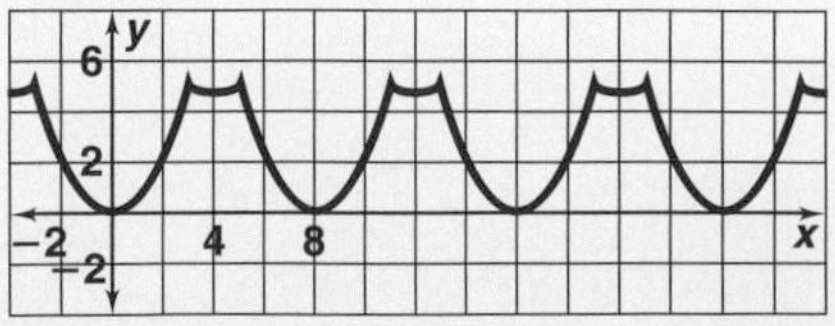

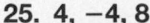

25. 4, −4, 8;

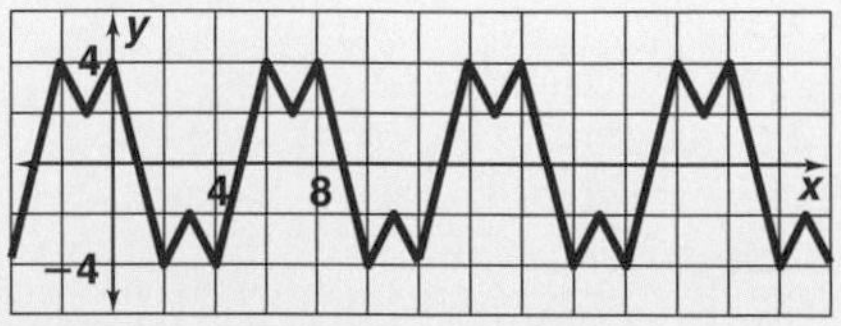

Language Arts Functions that repeat over time are common in everyday life. The English language has many words that stand for common periods of time. State the period of time from which each term derives.

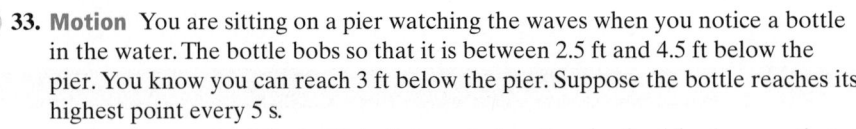
26. annual	27. biweekly	28. quarterly	29. hourly	30. circadian
1 yr	**2 weeks**	**3 months**	**1 hour**	**1 day**

C **Challenge**

31. Suppose f is a periodic function. The period of f is 5 and $f(1) = 2$. Find $f(6)$, $f(11)$, and $f(-4)$. **2, 2, 2**

32. Suppose g is a periodic function. The period of g is 24, $g(3) = 67$, and $g(8) = 70$. Find each function value.
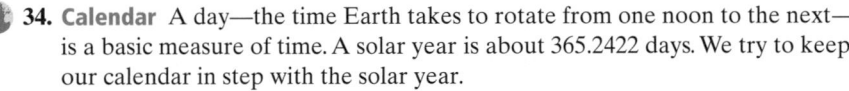
   a. $g(27)$ **67**   b. $g(80)$ **70**   c. $g(-16)$ **70**   d. $g(51)$ **67**

33. **Motion** You are sitting on a pier watching the waves when you notice a bottle in the water. The bottle bobs so that it is between 2.5 ft and 4.5 ft below the pier. You know you can reach 3 ft below the pier. Suppose the bottle reaches its highest point every 5 s.
   a. Sketch a graph of the bottle's distance below the pier for 15 s. Assume that at $t = 0$, the bottle is closest to the pier. **See back of book.**
   b. Find the period and the amplitude of the function. **5 s, 1 ft**
   c. **Estimation** Use your graph to estimate the length of time the bottle is within reach during each cycle. **Answers may vary. Sample: about $1\frac{1}{3}$ s**

34. **Calendar** A day—the time Earth takes to rotate from one noon to the next—is a basic measure of time. A solar year is about 365.2422 days. We try to keep our calendar in step with the solar year.
   a. If every calendar year has 365 days, by how many days would the calendar year and the solar year differ after 100 years? **24.22 days**
   b. If every fourth year has an extra "leap" day added, by how many days would the two systems differ after 100 years? **0.78 day**
   c. If every hundred years the "leap" day is omitted, by how many days would the two systems differ after 100 years? **0.22 day**
   d. **Critical Thinking** Why is it important for the difference between the calendar year and the solar year to be zero? **See margin.**

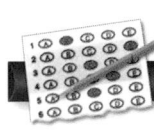

Real-World **Connection**

Coast Guard rescue jumpers time their pickups for the crests of the waves.

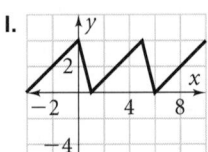 **Standardized Test Prep**

Multiple Choice

35. A periodic function goes through 5 complete cycles in 4 min. What is the period of the function? **C**
   A. $\frac{1}{5}$ min   B. $\frac{1}{4}$ min   C. 48 s   D. 75 s

36. The period of a periodic function is 8 s. How many cycles does it go through in 30 s? **G**
   F. $\frac{4}{15}$ cycle   G. 3.75 cycles   H. 22 cycles   I. 240 cycles

37. Which graph is NOT the graph of a periodic function? **B**

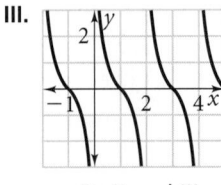

   I.   II.   III.

   A. I only   B. II only   C. III only   D. II and III

Lesson 13-1 Exploring Periodic Data   **701**

34d. **Answers may vary. Sample: The calendar year is meant to predict events in the solar year. Keeping the difference between the two minimal is necessary for the calendar year to be useful.**

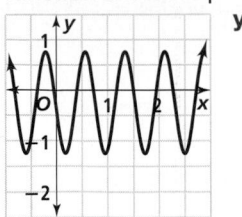
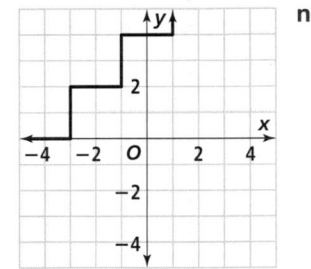
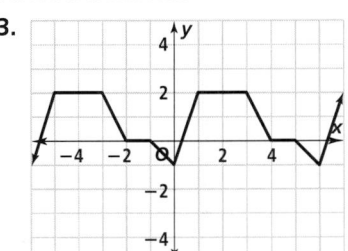
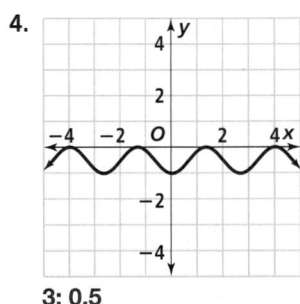
701

Standardized Test Prep

Resources

For additional practice with a variety of test item formats:
- Standardized Test Prep, p. 761
- Test-Taking Strategies, p. 756
- Test-Taking Strategies with Transparencies

38. The amplitude of a periodic function is 2.5 and its minimum value is 0. What is the function's maximum value? **D**

   A. −2.5   **B.** 0   **C.** 2.5   **D.** 5.0

Short Response

39. A periodic function completes *m* cycles in *n* seconds. What is the period of the function? Show your work. **See margin.**

Extended Response

Take It to the NET
Online lesson quiz at **www.PHSchool.com**
Web Code: aga-1301

40. A machine begins recording two periodic functions at the same time. The first has a period of 6 s. The second has a period of 7 s. After 20 s, the machine begins recording a third periodic function, with a period of 8 s. How many seconds after the machine begins recording the third function are all three functions at the beginning of their periods? Explain. **See margin.**

Mixed Review

Lesson 12-7

41. Sketch a normal curve for a distribution that has mean 57 and standard deviation 12. Label the *x*-axis values at one, two, and three standard deviations from the mean. **See back of book.**

Lesson 11-1

Find the next two terms in each sequence. Write a formula for the *n*th term. Identify each formula as *explicit* or *recursive*. 42–44. See margin.

42. $1, 3, 5, 7, 9, \ldots$ **43.** $4, 6, 8, 10, 12, \ldots$ **44.** $3, 6, 11, 18, 27, \ldots$

Lesson 10-6

Write an equation for each conic section. Then sketch the graph.

45. parabola with vertex $(-3, 2)$ and focus $(-3, 7)$ **45–47. See margin.**

46. hyperbola with center $(5, -3)$, one focus at $(5, 0)$, and one vertex at $(5, -1)$

47. ellipse with center $(-2, 1)$, vertices at $(-6, 1)$ and $(2, 1)$, and co-vertices at $(-2, 3)$ and $(-2, -1)$

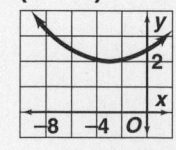

A Point in Time

1500   1600   1700   1800   1900   2000

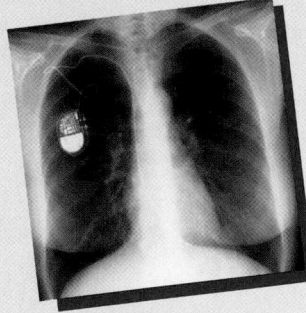

To human beings, the most important periodic function is the rhythm of the heart. About once per second, a nerve in the heart generates an electrical signal. This causes the heart to contract and force blood through the body.

In 1958, doctors placed the first pacemaker in a patient with a malfunctioning nerve. The creator of the device's control unit was Otis Boykin, an inventor from Dallas, Texas. He began his career testing automatic airplane controls. Today, more than a million pacemakers are helping people worldwide enjoy the normal rhythms of the human heart.

Take It to the NET For more information about pacemakers, go to **www.PHSchool.com**.
Web Code: age-2032

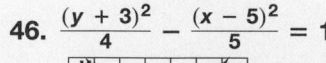
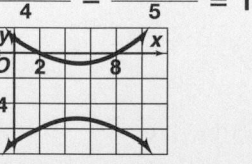
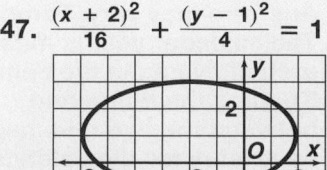

Special Right Triangles

FOR USE WITH LESSON 13-2

In Geometry you learned about two special right triangles, the 45°-45°-90° triangle and the 30°-60°-90° triangle. The figures at the right summarize the relationships among the lengths of the sides of each triangle.

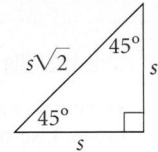
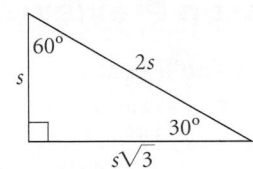

1 EXAMPLE Finding Side Lengths in a 45°-45°-90° Triangle

Find the missing side lengths in each figure.

a.

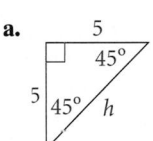

$h = \sqrt{2} \cdot 5$ hypotenuse $= \sqrt{2} \cdot$ leg

$h = 5\sqrt{2}$ **Simplify.**

b.

$5 = \sqrt{2} \cdot s$

$s = \dfrac{5}{\sqrt{2}}$

$s = \dfrac{5\sqrt{2}}{2}$

2 EXAMPLE Finding Side Lengths in a 30°-60°-90° Triangle

Find the missing side lengths in the triangle at the right.

$4 = \sqrt{3} \cdot s$ longer leg $= \sqrt{3} \cdot$ shorter leg

$s = \dfrac{4}{\sqrt{3}} = \dfrac{4\sqrt{3}}{3}$ **Divide and simplify.**

$h = 2s$ hypotenuse $= 2 \cdot$ shorter leg

$= 2 \cdot \dfrac{4\sqrt{3}}{3} = \dfrac{8\sqrt{3}}{3}$ **Substitute $\dfrac{4\sqrt{3}}{3}$ for s and simplify.**

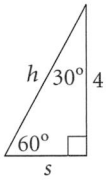

EXERCISES

Use the given information to find the missing side length(s) in each 45°-45°-90° triangle. Rationalize any denominators. 1–4. See right.

1. hypotenuse 1 in.   **2.** leg 2 cm   **3.** hypotenuse $\sqrt{3}$ ft   **4.** leg $2\sqrt{5}$ m

Use the given information to find the missing side lengths in each 30°-60°-90° triangle. Rationalize any denominators. 5–13. See margin.

5. shorter leg 3 in.   **6.** longer leg 1 cm   **7.** hypotenuse 1 ft

8. shorter leg $\sqrt{3}$ cm   **9.** hypotenuse $2\sqrt{2}$ ft   **10.** longer leg $2\sqrt{3}$ in.

11. hypotenuse $3\sqrt{2}$ m   **12.** longer leg $\sqrt{5}$ cm   **13.** shorter leg $\sqrt{13}$ mm

1. $\dfrac{\sqrt{2}}{2}$ in.

2. $2\sqrt{2}$ cm

3. $\dfrac{\sqrt{6}}{2}$ ft

4. $2\sqrt{10}$ m

---

page 703 Geometry Review

5. hypotenuse: 6 in., longer leg: $3\sqrt{3}$ in.

6. shorter leg: $\dfrac{\sqrt{3}}{3}$ cm, hypotenuse: $\dfrac{2\sqrt{3}}{3}$ cm

7. shorter leg: $\dfrac{1}{2}$ ft, longer leg: $\dfrac{\sqrt{3}}{2}$ ft

8. hypotenuse: $2\sqrt{3}$ cm, longer leg: 3 cm

9. shorter leg: $\sqrt{2}$ ft, longer leg: $\sqrt{6}$ ft

Special Right Triangles

Students review the special right triangles from geometry in preparation for learning about the unit circle and the definitions of trigonometric functions.

Resources

Technology
Computer Test Item Generator CD-ROM, Chapter 0, Geometry and Measurement

Teaching Notes

1 EXAMPLE **Teaching Tip**

Remind students that the hypotenuse is always the longest side of a right triangle.

2 EXAMPLE **Error Prevention**

Suggest to students that, as a memory aid and in order to prevent confusing these two special triangles, they record the two special right triangles in their notebooks. Then they can refer to them in the future for problems involving special triangles.

Connection to Algebra

Remind students that they are rationalizing the denominator in the second step in Example 1b. Rationalizing the denominator means multiplying by 1, here $\dfrac{\sqrt{2}}{\sqrt{2}}$, in order that roots appear only in the numerator.

10. shorter leg: 2 in., hypotenuse: 4 in.

11. shorter leg: $\dfrac{3\sqrt{2}}{2}$ m, longer leg: $\dfrac{3\sqrt{6}}{2}$ m

12. shorter leg: $\dfrac{\sqrt{15}}{3}$ cm, hypotenuse: $\dfrac{2\sqrt{15}}{3}$ cm

13. hypotenuse: $2\sqrt{13}$, longer leg: $\sqrt{39}$

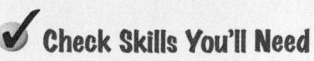 **Check Skills You'll Need**

Skills Handbook p. 848
Exercises 1–12
Extra Practice, p. 834

Lesson Resources

📁 **Teaching Resources**
Practice, Reteaching, Enrichment

👥 **Reaching All Students**
Practice Workbook 13-2
Spanish Practice Workbook 13-2
Technology Activities 37

⏱ **Presentation Assistant Plus!**
Transparencies
• Check Skills You'll Need 13-2
• Additional Examples 13-2
• Student Edition Answers 13-2
• Lesson Quiz 13-2
PH Presentation Pro CD 13-2

ASSESSMENT SYSTEM

Computer Test Generator CD

💿 **Technology**
Resource Pro® CD-ROM
Computer Test Generator CD
Prentice Hall Presentation Pro CD

💻 **www.PHSchool.com**
Student Site
• Teacher Web Code: agk-5500
• Self-grading Lesson Quiz
Teacher Center
• Lesson Planner
• Resources

Plus 📘**TEXT**

13-2

Angles and the Unit Circle

Lesson Preview

What You'll Learn

OBJECTIVE 1 To work with angles in standard position

OBJECTIVE 2 To find coordinates of points on the unit circle

. . . And Why

To use an ancient calendar, as in Example 3

✓ **Check Skills You'll Need** (For help, go to page 54.)

For each measure, draw an angle with its vertex at the origin of the coordinate plane. Use the positive *x*-axis as one ray of the angle. **1–6. See margin p. 706.**

1. 90°   **2.** 45°   **3.** 30°
4. 150°   **5.** 135°   **6.** 120°

New Vocabulary • standard position • initial side • terminal side • coterminal angles • unit circle • cosine of θ • sine of θ

OBJECTIVE

1 **Working With Angles in Standard Position**

📘**TEXT** Interactive lesson includes instant self-check, tutorials, and activities.

An angle is in **standard position** when the vertex is at the origin and one ray is on the positive *x*-axis. The ray on the *x*-axis is the **initial side** of the angle; the other ray is the **terminal side** of the angle.

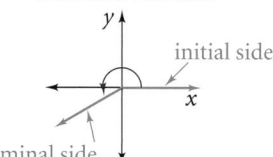

Standard Position

To measure an angle in standard position, find the amount of rotation from the initial side to the terminal side.

1 EXAMPLE **Measuring an Angle in Standard Position**

Find the measure of the angle at the right.

The angle measures 20° more than a straight angle of 180°.

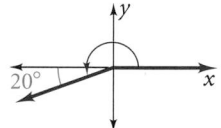

Since 180 + 20 = 200, the measure of the angle is 200°.

✓ **Check Understanding** **1** One full rotation contains 360 degrees. How many degrees are in one quarter of a rotation? In one half of a rotation? In three quarters of a rotation? **90°; 180°; 270°**

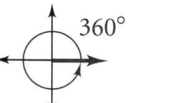 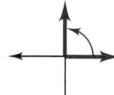 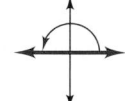 

---

704 Chapter 13 Periodic Functions and Trigonometry

Ongoing Assessment and Intervention

Before the Lesson Diagnose prerequisite skills using:	**During the Lesson** Monitor progress using:	**After the Lesson** Assess knowledge using:
• Check Skills You'll Need	• Check Understanding • Additional Examples • Standardized Test Prep	• Lesson Quiz • Computer Test Generator CD

2a.

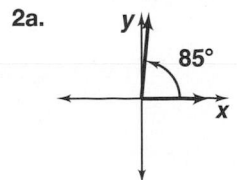

The measure of an angle is positive when the rotation from the initial side to the terminal side is in the counterclockwise direction. The measure is negative when the rotation is clockwise.

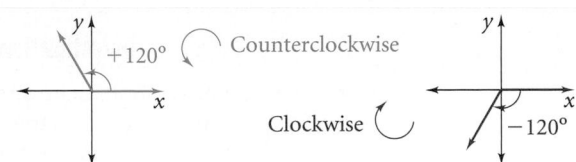

b.

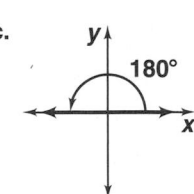

2 EXAMPLE **Sketching an Angle in Standard Position**

Sketch each angle in standard position.

a. 36° **b.** 315° **c.** −150°

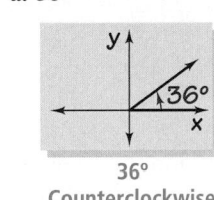 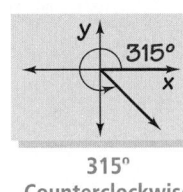 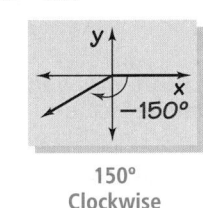

36° 315° 150°
Counterclockwise Counterclockwise Clockwise

c.

✓ **Check Understanding** **2** Sketch each angle in standard position. **a–c. See left.**
  a. 85° **b.** −320° **c.** 180°

Two angles in standard position are **coterminal angles** if they have the same terminal side.

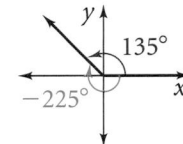

Angles that have measures 135° and −225° are coterminal.

3 EXAMPLE **Real-World** **Connection**

Real-World **Connection**

Archaeologists assembling a sample of Mesoamerican hieroglyphic text

History The Aztec calendar stone has 20 divisions for the 20 days in each month of the Aztec year. The yellow angle marks the passage of 11 days. Find the measures of two coterminal angles that coincide with the angle. The terminal side of the angle is $\frac{11}{20}$ of a full rotation from the initial side.

$$\frac{11}{20} \cdot 360° = 198°$$

To find a coterminal angle, subtract one full rotation.

$$198° − 360° = −162°$$

Two coterminal angle measures for the angle in the photograph are 198° and −162°.

✓ **Check Understanding** **3 a.** Find another angle coterminal with 198° by adding one full rotation. **558°**
  b. Reasoning Are angles with measures of 40° and 680° coterminal? Explain.
  c. Make a Conjecture Generalize how the measures of two coterminal angles are related. **b–c. See margin p. 706.**

Lesson 13-2 Angles and the Unit Circle **705**

---

2. Teach

Professional Development

Math Background

The arrow arc drawn to show the rotation to the terminal side of an angle in standard position is important. It distinguishes between positive and negative coterminal angles, such as an angle of −30° and one of 330°. The arrow can also be used to show an angle that has a measure greater than 360°. For example, the angle formed by one-and-a-half complete rotations, 540°. This angle is coterminal with an angle whose measure is 180°.

OBJECTIVE
1 Teaching Notes

3 EXAMPLE **Diversity**

If any students are of Mexican ancestry, they may share what they know of Aztec history. Explain that the Aztec civilization migrated into central Mexico from the north, and then moved by way of Chapultepec to settle in the area that is now Mexico City, around 1325 AD. The Aztecs were in control of most of central Mexico when the Spaniards arrived in 1519.

Additional Examples

1 Find the measure of the angle. **150°**

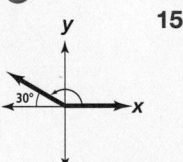

2 Sketch each angle in standard position.
a. 48° **b.** 310°

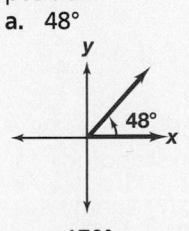 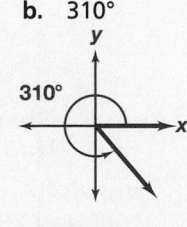

c. −170°

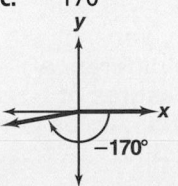

705

Investigation

Some students may need help with using the compass and protractor. Ask a student who is familiar with these to act as a coach. As the students are making their conjectures, point out again that the radius of the circle that they drew is 1 unit.

Additional Examples

3 An angle on the Aztec calendar shows the passage of 16 days. Find the measures of the two coterminal angles that coincide with the angle. **288° and −72°**

page 704 Check Skills You'll Need

1.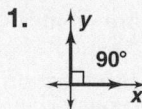
90°

2.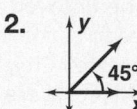
45°

3.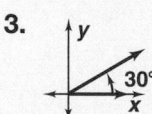
30°

4.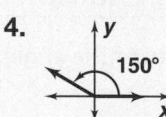
150°

5.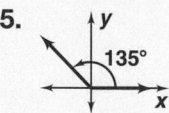
135°

6.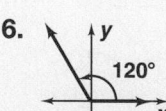
120°

page 705 Check Understanding

3b. No; 40° is coterminal with 400° and 760°.

c. Answers may vary. Sample: The difference between measures of two coterminal angles is a multiple of 360°.

706

Investigation: Angles in a Circle

- Use a compass. Construct a circle with a radius of 1 unit on the coordinate plane. Place the center of the circle at the origin.

- Use a protractor. Draw an angle of 30°. Place one ray along the positive *x*-axis. Place the other ray in Quadrant I. Label the point where the second ray intersects the circle *P(x, y)*.

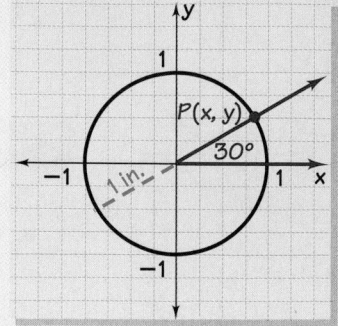

1. Identify the methods you could use to find the coordinates of *P*.

2. Choose one method and find the values of *x* and *y*. Express the coordinates in decimal form. **(0.87, 0.5)**

3. Use a calculator to find the values of cos 30° (read "cosine of 30 degrees") and sin 30° (read "sine of 30 degrees"). Compare these values to the values you found in Question 2.

4. a. Repeat the steps above using an angle of 45°. What are the coordinates of the new point *P*? **(0.707, 0.707)**
   b. Find cos 45° and sin 45° using your calculator. How do these values compare to those you found in part (a)?
   c. **Make a Conjecture** What is the relationship between the coordinates of a point *P* on the circle and the values of the sine and cosine of the angle containing *P*?

1. Answers may vary. Sample: Use a 30°-60°-90° triangle.

3. 0.87, 0.5; these values are the same as those in Question 2.

4b. 0.707, 0.707; these values are the same as those in part (a).

c. The *x*-coordinate of *P* equals the cosine of the angle containing *P*, and the *y*-coordinate equals the sine of the angle.

Reading Math

The Greek letter *θ* (pronounced THAY-tuh) is a variable frequently used to symbolize an angle.

The **unit circle** has a radius of 1 unit and its center at the origin of the coordinate plane. Points on the unit circle are related to periodic functions.

You can use the symbol *θ* for the measure of an angle in standard position.

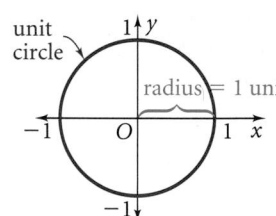

Key Concepts

Definition	**Cosine and Sine of an Angle**

Suppose an angle in standard position has measure *θ*. The **cosine of θ** (cos *θ*) is the *x*-coordinate of the point at which the terminal side of the angle intersects the unit circle. The **sine of θ** (sin *θ*) is the *y*-coordinate.

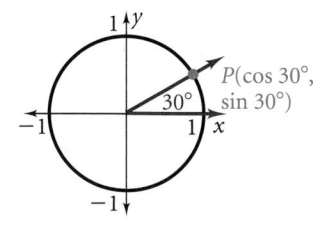

4 **EXAMPLE** Finding the Cosine and Sine of an Angle

Find the cosine and sine of 60°.

From the figure, the x-coordinate of point A is $\frac{1}{2}$, so $\cos 60° = \frac{1}{2}$, or 0.5.

Use a 30°-60°-90° right triangle to find sin 60°.

$$\text{longer leg} = \sqrt{3} \cdot \text{shorter leg}$$
$$= \sqrt{3} \cdot \frac{1}{2} \quad \text{Substitute.}$$
$$= \frac{\sqrt{3}}{2} \quad \text{Multiply.}$$
$$\approx 0.87 \quad \text{Simplify.}$$

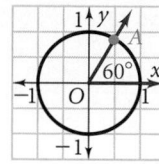

The coordinates of the point at which the terminal side of a 60° angle intersects the unit circle are about $(0.5, 0.87)$, so $\cos 60° = 0.5$ and $\sin 60° = \frac{\sqrt{3}}{2} \approx 0.87$.

? Need Help?

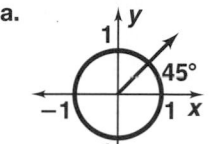

✓ **Check Understanding**

4 Draw each angle in a unit circle. Then find the cosine and sine of each angle.

a. 45°   **b.** 30°   **c.** 120°

4a.

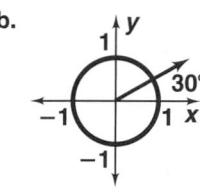

$\frac{\sqrt{2}}{2} \approx 0.707,\ \frac{\sqrt{2}}{2} \approx 0.707$

b.

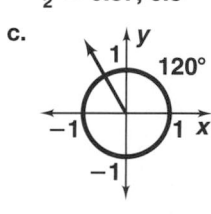

$\frac{\sqrt{3}}{2} \approx 0.87,\ 0.5$

c.

$-0.5,\ \frac{\sqrt{3}}{2} \approx 0.87$

Notice that the y-value 0.87 from Example 4 is an *approximate* value of sin 60°. For some angles, you can use right triangles to find the *exact* cosine and sine.

5 **EXAMPLE** Finding Exact Values of Cosine and Sine

Find the exact values of $\cos(-120°)$ and $\sin(-120°)$.

Step 1 Sketch an angle of $-120°$ in standard position. Sketch a unit circle.

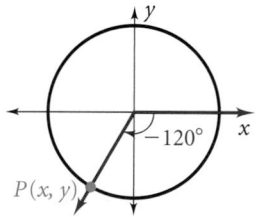

$x\text{-coordinate} = \cos(-120°)$
$y\text{-coordinate} = \sin(-120°)$

Step 2 Sketch a right triangle. Place the hypotenuse on the terminal side of the angle. Place one leg on the x-axis. (The other leg will be parallel to the y-axis.)

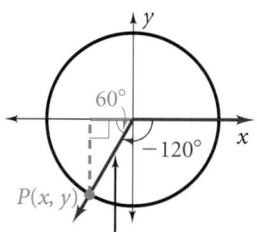

The triangle contains angles of 30°, 60°, and 90°.

Step 3 Find the length of each side of the triangle.

$$\text{hypotenuse} = 1 \quad \text{The hypotenuse is a radius of the unit circle.}$$
$$\text{shorter leg} = \frac{1}{2} \quad \text{The shorter leg is half the hypotenuse.}$$
$$\text{longer leg} = \frac{1}{2}\sqrt{3} \quad \text{The longer leg is } \sqrt{3} \text{ times the short leg.}$$
$$= \frac{\sqrt{3}}{2}$$

Since the point lies in Quadrant III, both coordinates are negative. The shorter leg lies along the x-axis, so $\cos(-120°) = -\frac{1}{2}$, and $\sin(-120°) = -\frac{\sqrt{3}}{2}$.

Lesson 13-2 Angles and the Unit Circle   **707**

Additional Examples

4 Find the cosine and sine of 135°. about −0.71; about 0.71

5 Find the exact values of $\cos(-150°)$ and $\sin(-150°)$. $-\frac{\sqrt{3}}{2}$; $-\frac{1}{2}$

Closure

Ask students: *What do the sine and cosine of an angle represent on the unit circle?* **The sine is the y-coordinate of the point where the terminal side of the angle intersects the unit circle; the cosine is the x-coordinate of the point where the terminal side of the angle intersects the unit circle.**

Since perpendicular lines form right angles, point out that the right triangle is always formed by drawing a line perpendicular to the x-axis from the point where the terminal side intersects the unit circle.

Assignment Guide

▼ **1 Objective**
  Ⓐ Ⓑ **Core** 1–20, 37–49
  Ⓒ **Extension** 62

▼ **2 Objective**
  Ⓐ Ⓑ **Core** 21–36, 50–52
  Ⓒ **Extension** 53–61

Standardized Test Prep 63–68

Mixed Review 69–77

Error Prevention

Exercises 21–28 Tell students to pay close attention to the quadrant in which the terminal side of the angle lies. The quadrant determines whether or not the *x*- and *y*-coordinates are negative, and therefore affects whether the sine and cosine of the angle are negative.

Teaching Tip

Exercises 29–36 The Greek letter θ is read as "theta."

✓ **Check Understanding**

5a. −0.5, −0.87; −0.5, −0.87; the values are equal and are the rounded decimal values of $-\frac{1}{2}$ and $-\frac{\sqrt{3}}{2}$.

5 **a.** Find the decimal values of $-\frac{1}{2}$ and $-\frac{\sqrt{3}}{2}$. Then use a calculator to find cos (−120°) and sin (−120°). How do these values compare to each other? How do they compare to the exact values found in Example 5?
b. Find the exact values of cos 135° and sin 135°. Use properties of a 45°-45°-90° triangle. Use a calculator to find the decimal equivalents. $-\frac{\sqrt{2}}{2}, \frac{\sqrt{2}}{2}$; ≈ −0.707, ≈ 0.707
c. Find the exact values of cos 150° and sin 150°.
c. $-\frac{\sqrt{3}}{2}, \frac{1}{2}$

EXERCISES

For more practice, see *Extra Practice*.

Practice and Problem Solving

Ⓐ **Practice by Example**

Find the measure of each angle in standard position.

Example 1
(page 704)

1. 45° 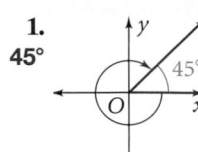   **2.** −135° 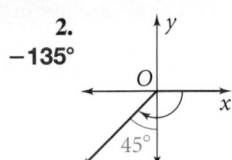   **3.** 240°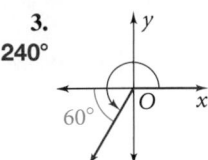

4. 115° 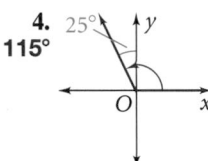   **5.** −120° 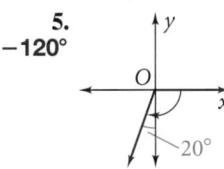   **6.** −340°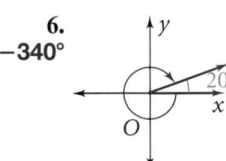

Example 2
(page 705)

Sketch each angle in standard position. 7–11. See back of book.

7. 40°   **8.** −130°   **9.** −270°   **10.** 120°   **11.** 95°

Example 3
(page 705)

Find the measure of an angle between 0° and 360° coterminal with each given angle.

12. 385° **25°**   **13.** 575° **215°**   **14.** −405° **315°**   **15.** −356° **4°**

16. 500° **140°**   **17.** −210° **150°**   **18.** 415° **55°**   **19.** −180° **180°**

20. Telephones Rotary telephones were widely used until the 1980s. Dialing a higher number (or 0) took longer because the dial moved through a larger central angle. Estimate the measures of two coterminal angles that coincide with the angle at the right. **−135°, 585°**

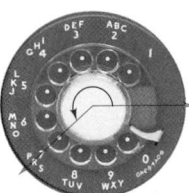

Examples 4 and 5
(page 707)

Find the exact values of the cosine and sine of each angle. Then find the decimal values. Round your answers to the nearest hundredth. 23–28. See margin.

21. 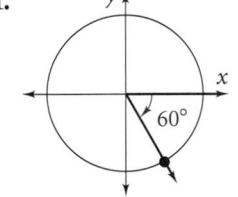   **22.** 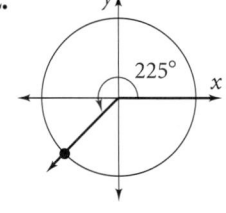   **23.**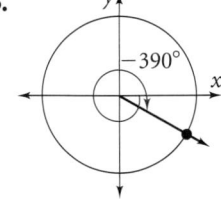

21. $\frac{1}{2}, \frac{\sqrt{3}}{2}$; 0.50, 0.87

22. $-\frac{\sqrt{2}}{2}, -\frac{\sqrt{2}}{2}$; −0.71, −0.71

24. −240°   **25.** 390°   **26.** 315°   **27.** −30°   **28.** 135°

pages 708–710 **Exercises**

23. $\frac{\sqrt{3}}{2}, -\frac{1}{2}$; 0.87, −0.50

24. $-\frac{1}{2}, \frac{\sqrt{3}}{2}$; −0.50, 0.87

25. $\frac{\sqrt{3}}{2}, \frac{1}{2}$; 0.87, 0.50

26. $\frac{\sqrt{2}}{2}, -\frac{\sqrt{2}}{2}$; 0.71, −0.71

27. $\frac{\sqrt{3}}{2}, -\frac{1}{2}$; 0.87, −0.50

28. $-\frac{\sqrt{2}}{2}, \frac{\sqrt{2}}{2}$; −0.71, 0.71

50a.

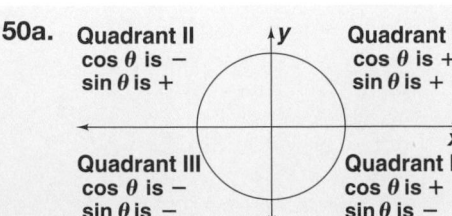

Quadrant II	Quadrant I
cos θ is −	cos θ is +
sin θ is +	sin θ is +
Quadrant III	**Quadrant IV**
cos θ is −	cos θ is +
sin θ is −	sin θ is −

B **Apply Your Skills**

For each angle θ, find the values of $\cos \theta$ and $\sin \theta$. Round your answers to the nearest hundredth.

29. 0° **1.00, 0.00**
30. 32° **0.85, 0.53**
31. −45° **0.71, −0.71**
32. −210° **−0.87, 0.50**

33. −95° **−0.09, −1.00**
34. −10° **0.98, −0.17**
35. 154° **−0.90, 0.44**
36. 90° **0.00, 1.00**

Open-Ended Find a positive and a negative coterminal angle for the given angle.

37–44. Answers may vary. Samples:

37. **405°, −315°**
38. **235°, −485°**
39. **45°, −315°**
40. **40°, −320°**

37. 45°
38. −125°
39. −675°
40. 400°

41. −85° **275°, −445°**
42. −425° **295°, −65°**
43. 213° **573°, −147°**
44. −57° **303°, −417°**

In which quadrant, or on which axis, does the terminal side of each angle lie?

45. 150° **II**
46. 210° **III**
47. 540° **negative x-axis**
48. −60° **IV**
49. 0° **positive x-axis**

50. **a.** Copy and complete the chart at the right. **See margin p. 708.**
   b. Suppose you know that $\cos \theta$ is negative and $\sin \theta$ is positive. In which quadrant does the terminal side of the angle lie? **II**
   c. **Writing** Summarize how the quadrant in which the terminal side of an angle lies affects the sign of the sine and cosine of that angle. **See margin.**

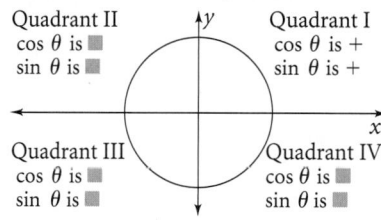

Quadrant II
$\cos \theta$ is ■
$\sin \theta$ is ■

Quadrant I
$\cos \theta$ is +
$\sin \theta$ is +

Quadrant III
$\cos \theta$ is ■
$\sin \theta$ is ■

Quadrant IV
$\cos \theta$ is ■
$\sin \theta$ is ■

51. **a.** Use a calculator to find the value of each expression: $\cos 40°$, $\cos 400°$, and $\cos (−320°)$. **0.77, 0.77, 0.77**
   b. **Critical Thinking** What do you notice about the values you found in part (a)? Explain. **See margin.**

52. **Writing** Explain how to find the sine and cosine of angles with measures of 0°, 90°, 180°, 270°, and 360° without using a calculator. **See margin.**

C **Challenge**

Sketch each angle in standard position. Use the unit circle and a right triangle to find exact values of the cosine and the sine of the angle. **53–58. See back of book.**

53. −300°
54. 120°
55. 225°

56. −780°
57. −405°
58. 1020°

59. **Design** Navaho sand paintings like the one at the right have many lines of symmetry. Suppose point A is on a unit circle. Find the coordinates of A. $\left(-\dfrac{\sqrt{2}}{2}, \dfrac{\sqrt{2}}{2}\right)$

60. **Open-Ended** Find the measures of four angles in standard position that have a sine of 0.5. (*Hint:* Use the unit circle and right triangles.)

60. Answers may vary. Sample: 30°, 150°, −210°, 390°

61. **Critical Thinking** Suppose θ is an angle in standard position and $\cos \theta = -\dfrac{1}{2}$ and $\sin \theta = -\dfrac{\sqrt{3}}{2}$. Can the value of θ be 60°? Can it be −120°? Draw a diagram and justify your reasoning. **See margin.**

Lesson 13-2 Angles and the Unit Circle **709**

50c. If the terminal side of an angle is in Quadrants I or II, then the sine of the angle is positive; otherwise it is not. If the terminal side of an angle is in Quadrants I or IV, then the cosine of the angle is positive; otherwise it is not.

51b. The cosines of the three angles are equal because the angles are coterminal.

52. The x-coordinate of a point on the ray defined by angle θ is equal to cos θ; similarly for the y-coordinate and sin θ. The angles 0°, 180°, and 360° lie on the x-axis, and

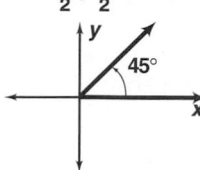
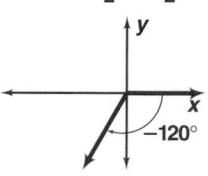
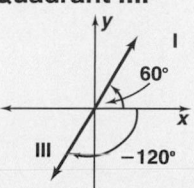
709

 **Resources**

For additional practice with a variety of test item formats:
• Standardized Test Prep, p. 761
• Test-Taking Strategies, p. 756
• Test-Taking Strategies with Transparencies

Exercise 65 Place the angle in the correct quadrant, and then use the signs of the coordinates for a point in that quadrant to eliminate some answer choices.

pages 708–710   Exercises

72.

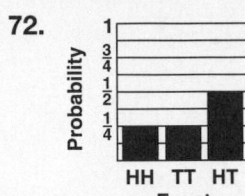

73.

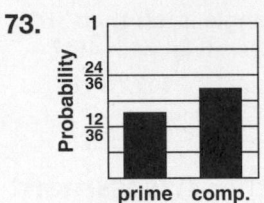

74. $(0, 2\sqrt{5})$, $(0, -2\sqrt{5})$

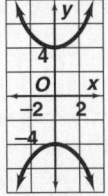

75. $(0, 5\sqrt{5})$, $(0, -5\sqrt{5})$

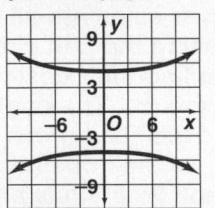

 62. Navigation When navigators locate an object, they measure in a clockwise direction from due north. The measure of the angle is called the bearing. Suppose a lighthouse's bearing is 110° from a ship.
  a. Sketch the diagram at the right on a coordinate plane. Place north along the positive *y*-axis.
  b. Express the location of the lighthouse in terms of an angle in standard position.   **a. Check students' work.**
    b. −20°

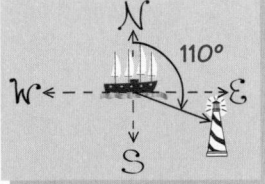

Standardized Test Prep

Multiple Choice

63. Which angle, in standard position, is NOT coterminal with the others?   **A**
  A. −190°   **B.** −170°   **C.** 190°   **D.** 550°

64. An angle drawn in standard position has a terminal side that passes through the point $(\sqrt{2}, -\sqrt{2})$. What is one possible measure of the angle?
  F. 45°   **G.** 225°   **H.** 315°   **I.** 330°   **H**

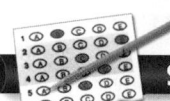
Take It to the NET
Online lesson quiz at
www.PHSchool.com
········· Web Code: aga-1302

65. An angle of 120° is in standard position. What are the coordinates of the point at which the terminal side intersects the unit circle?   **D**
  A. $\left(\frac{1}{2}, \frac{\sqrt{3}}{2}\right)$ **B.** $\left(-\frac{1}{2}, -\frac{\sqrt{3}}{2}\right)$ **C.** $\left(-\frac{\sqrt{3}}{2}, \frac{1}{2}\right)$ **D.** $\left(-\frac{1}{2}, \frac{\sqrt{3}}{2}\right)$

66. An angle of −225° is in standard position. Which points can lie on the terminal side of the angle?   **F**
  I. $\left(\frac{\sqrt{2}}{2}, -\frac{\sqrt{2}}{2}\right)$ **II.** $\left(-\frac{\sqrt{2}}{2}, \frac{\sqrt{2}}{2}\right)$ **III.** $\left(-\frac{\sqrt{2}}{2}, -\frac{\sqrt{2}}{2}\right)$ **IV.** $(-1, 1)$
  F. I and II   **G.** II and III   **H.** II and IV   **I.** I and III

Short Response   **67.** What is the exact value of cos (−210)°? Show your work. **See back of book.**

Extended Response   **68.** Use an angle in standard position to find the exact value of $[\sin (-135°)]^2 + [\cos (-135°)]^2$. Show your work.   **See back of book.**

Mixed Review

Lesson 13-1   Determine whether each function *is* or *is not* periodic. If it is, find the period.

69.

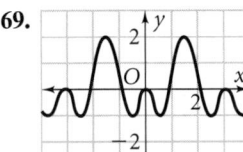

periodic; 3

70.

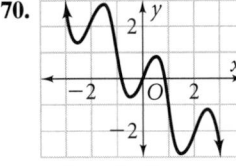

not periodic

71.

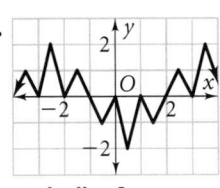

periodic; 6

Lesson 12-1   Graph the probability distribution for each sample space.

72. {two coins heads, two coins tails, one coin heads and the other tails}

73. {the sum of two number cubes a prime number, the sum a composite number}
72–77. See margin.

Lesson 10-5   Find the foci of each hyperbola. Draw the graph.

74. $\frac{y^2}{16} - \frac{x^2}{4} = 1$ **75.** $\frac{y^2}{25} - \frac{x^2}{100} = 1$ **76.** $\frac{x^2}{36} - \frac{y^2}{49} = 1$ **77.** $\frac{x^2}{81} - \frac{y^2}{64} = 1$

76. $(\sqrt{85}, 0)$, $(-\sqrt{85}, 0)$

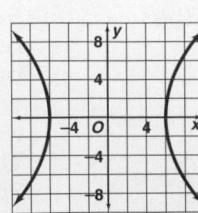

77. $(\sqrt{145}, 0)$, $(-\sqrt{145}, 0)$

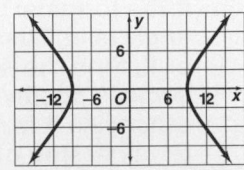

Measuring Radians

FOR USE WITH LESSON 13-3

In the past, you have used degrees to measure angles. When angles are used in periodic functions, they are often measured in larger units called radians.

1. Measure the diameter of a cylinder and calculate its radius. On a piece of string, mark off a "number line" with each unit equal to the radius. Mark at least seven units. **1–5. Check students' work.**

2. Wrap the string around the cylinder. How many radius units are needed to go around the cylinder one time?

3. Use the end of the cylinder to draw a circle on a sheet of paper. Keep the cylinder in place and wrap the string around it on the paper. Mark an arc of the circle equal to one radius unit of length.

4. Remove the cylinder and string. Use paper folding to locate the center of the circle. (Fold the circle onto itself and crease the paper along a diameter. Repeat to get a second diameter.) Draw a central angle that intercepts one radius unit of arc.

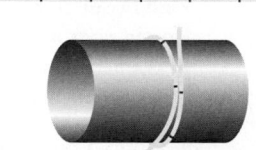
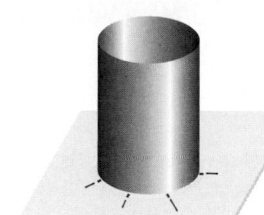
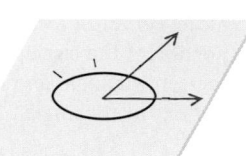

The measure of the angle you drew in Question 4 is 1 radian.

5. Use a protractor to measure the angle from Question 4 in degrees.

6. **Critical Thinking** The formula $C = 2\pi r$ relates the circumference of a circle C to its radius r. *Exactly* how many radians are in a 360° angle? Explain.

6. **2π; a circle has an angle measure of 360°. Dividing the circumference, $2\pi r$, by the length of a radius, r, we find there are 2π radians in 360°.**

The diagram at the right shows that a rotation of 180° is equivalent to π radians.

7. Find the number of degrees in one radian by dividing 180 by π. How does your answer compare to the measurement you made in Question 5?   **57.30°; the numbers are very close.**

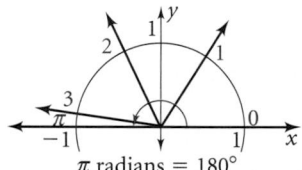

π radians = 180°

EXERCISES

Use the proportion $\frac{d°}{180°} = \frac{r \text{ radians}}{\pi \text{ radians}}$ to find the number of radians in each given degree measure.

1. 10° $\frac{\pi}{18}$ **radians**   2. 45° $\frac{\pi}{4}$ **radians**   3. 90° $\frac{\pi}{2}$ **radians**   4. 120° $\frac{2\pi}{3}$ **radians**   5. 270° $\frac{3\pi}{2}$ **radians**

6. 310° $\frac{31\pi}{18}$ **radians** 7. 50° $\frac{5\pi}{18}$ **radians**   8. 415° $\frac{83\pi}{36}$ **radians** 9. 170° $\frac{17\pi}{18}$ **radians** 10. 380° $\frac{19\pi}{9}$ **radians**

Measuring Radians

Students investigate how many times a length of string equal to the radius of a circle will wrap around the circumference of that same circle. This experiential learning leads to a better understanding of the definition of a radian.

Resources

Cylinder, ruler, string, protractor

Teaching Notes

Math Tip
The number of radians in a central angle of a circle is the measure of the intercepted arc in radian units.

Teaching Tip
Emphasize to students that a radian is a unit used to measure an angle. They may want to think of a degree as measuring an angle by comparing it to the whole *inside* of a circle, while a radian measures an angle by comparing it to the whole *outside* of a circle.

Lesson Preview

 Check Skills You'll Need

Finding the Circumference of a Circle
Formulas: p. 870

Lesson Resources

 Teaching Resources
Practice, Reteaching, Enrichment
Checkpoint Quiz 1

 Reaching All Students
Practice Workbook 13-3
Spanish Practice Workbook 13-3
Reading and Math Literacy 13B
Spanish Reading & Literacy 13B
Spanish Checkpoint Quiz 1

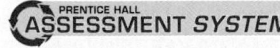 **Presentation Assistant Plus!**
Transparencies
• Check Skills You'll Need 13-3
• Additional Examples 13-3
• Student Edition Answers 13-3
• Lesson Quiz 13-3
PH Presentation Pro CD 13-3

PRENTICE HALL
ASSESSMENT SYSTEM

Checkpoint Quiz 1
Computer Test Generator CD

 Technology
Resource Pro® CD-ROM
Computer Test Generator CD
Prentice Hall Presentation Pro CD

 www.PHSchool.com
Student Site
• Teacher Web Code: agk-5500
• Graphing Calculator,
  Procedure 19
• Self-grading Lesson Quiz
Teacher Center
• Lesson Planner
• Resources

Plus

 **13-3**

Radian Measure

Lesson Preview

What You'll Learn

OBJECTIVE 1 To use radian measure for angles

OBJECTIVE 2 To find the length of an arc of a circle

. . . And Why

To solve problems involving the orbits of satellites, as in Example 5

 Check Skills You'll Need (For help, go to page 870.)

Find the circumference of a circle with the given radius or diameter. Round your answer to the nearest tenth.

1. radius 4 in. **25.1 in.**
2. diameter 70 m **219.9 m**
3. radius 8 mi **50.3 mi**
4. diameter 3.4 ft **10.7 ft**
5. radius 5 mm **31.4 mm**
6. diameter 6.3 cm **19.8 cm**

New Vocabulary • central angle • intercepted arc • radian

OBJECTIVE

1 **Using Radian Measure**

 Interactive lesson includes instant self-check, tutorials, and activities.

A **central angle** of a circle is an angle with a vertex at the center of a circle. An **intercepted arc** is the portion of the circle with endpoints on the sides of the central angle and remaining points within the interior of the angle.

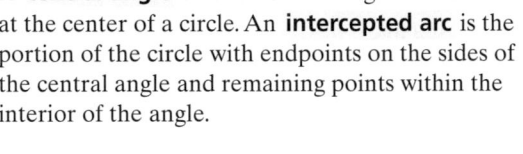

 Reading Math
Radian is a shortened form of the phrase *radial angle*.

When a central angle intercepts an arc that has the same length as a radius of the circle, the measure of the angle is defined to be one **radian.** Like degrees, radians measure the amount of rotation from the initial side to the terminal side of an angle.

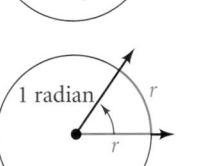

Real-World **Connection**

Some pendulum rides travel through a complete revolution of 2π radians.

Because the circumference of a circle is $2\pi r$, there are 2π radians in any circle. Since 2π radians $= 360°$, and therefore π radians $= 180°$, you can use a proportion such as $\frac{d°}{180°} = \frac{r \text{ radians}}{\pi \text{ radians}}$ to convert between degrees and radians.

1 **EXAMPLE** **Using a Proportion**

a. Find the radian measure of an angle of 60°.

$$\frac{60°}{180°} = \frac{r \text{ radians}}{\pi \text{ radians}}$$ Write a proportion.

$$60 \cdot \pi = 180 \cdot r$$ Write the cross-products.

$$r = \frac{60 \cdot \pi}{180}$$ Divide each side by 180.

$$= \frac{\pi}{3} \approx 1.05$$ Simplify.

An angle of 60° measures about $\frac{5\pi}{2}$... 1.05 radians.

b. Find the degree measure of $\frac{5\pi}{2}$ radians.

712   Chapter 13   Periodic Functions and Trigonometry

 Ongoing Assessment and Intervention

Before the Lesson
Diagnose prerequisite skills using:
• Check Skills You'll Need

During the Lesson
Monitor progress using:
• Check Understanding
• Additional Examples
• Standardized Test Prep

After the Lesson
Assess knowledge using:
• Lesson Quiz
• Computer Test Generator CD
• Chapter Checkpoint 1 (p. 719)

$$\frac{\frac{5\pi}{2}\text{ radians}}{\pi\text{ radians}} = \frac{d^\circ}{180^\circ} \qquad \textbf{Write a proportion.}$$

$$\frac{\frac{5\pi}{2}}{\pi} = \frac{d}{180}$$

$$\frac{5\pi}{2} \cdot 180 = \pi \cdot d \qquad \textbf{Write the cross-products.}$$

$$\frac{5\pi \cdot 180}{2 \cdot \pi} = d \qquad \textbf{Divide each side by } \pi.$$

$$d = \frac{5\pi \cdot 180^{90}}{{}_{1}2 \cdot \pi} \qquad \textbf{Simplify.}$$

$$= 450$$

● An angle of $\frac{5\pi}{2}$ radians measures 450°.

✓ **Check Understanding** ➊ Use a proportion for each conversion.
   a. 85° to radians **≈1.48 radians**   **b.** 2.5 radians to degrees **≈143.24°**

The proportion $\frac{d^\circ}{180^\circ} = \frac{r\text{ radians}}{\pi\text{ radians}}$ leads to the following two convenient conversion factors.

🔑 **Key Concepts**

Summary	Converting Between Radians and Degrees

To convert degrees to radians, multiply by $\frac{\pi\text{ radians}}{180^\circ}$.

To convert radians to degrees, multiply by $\frac{180^\circ}{\pi\text{ radians}}$.

You can use the conversion factors and dimensional analysis to convert between angle measurement systems.

➋ **EXAMPLE** **Using Dimensional Analysis**

a. Find the degree measure of an angle of $-\frac{3\pi}{4}$ radians.

$$-\frac{3\pi}{4}\text{ radians} = -\frac{3\pi}{4}\text{ radians} \cdot \frac{180^\circ}{\pi\text{ radians}} \qquad \textbf{Multiply by } \frac{180^\circ}{\pi\text{ radians}}.$$

$$= -\frac{3\pi}{{}_14}\text{radians} \cdot \frac{{}^{45}180^\circ}{\pi\text{ radians}} \qquad \textbf{Simplify.}$$

$$= -135^\circ$$

An angle of $-\frac{3\pi}{4}$ radians measures -135°.

b. Find the radian measure of an angle of 27°.

$$27^\circ = 27^\circ \cdot \frac{\pi}{180^\circ}\text{ radians} \qquad \textbf{Multiply by } \frac{\pi\text{ radians}}{180^\circ}.$$

$$= {}^327^\circ \cdot \frac{\pi}{{}_{20}180^\circ}\text{ radians} \qquad \textbf{Simplify.}$$

$$= \frac{3\pi}{20}\text{ radians}$$

● An angle of 27° measures $\frac{3\pi}{20}$ radians.

✓ **Check Understanding** ➋ Use dimensional analysis to convert each degree measure from degrees to radians or from radians to degrees. (Express radian measures in terms of π.)
   a. $\frac{\pi}{2}$ radians **90°**   **b.** 225° $\frac{5\pi}{4}$ **radians**   **c.** 2 radians **≈114.59°**   **d.** 150° $\frac{5\pi}{6}$ **radians**

👐 **Reaching All Students**

Below Level Remind students that when an angle measure is reported in radians the unit is normally not written. Since the radian angle measure is a ratio between two lengths, it has no units.	**Advanced Learners** You may wish to require students to memorize the radian measures for 30°, 45°, 60°, 90°, and the related angles in other quadrants.	**English Learners** See note on page 714. **Visual Learners** See note on page 716.

2. Teach

Math Background

The radian measure of an angle can also be expressed as a ratio: radian measure of an angle = $\frac{\text{arc length}}{\text{radius}}$. When the arc length is the radius, the value of this ratio is one. When the arc length is the whole circle, or $2\pi r$, then the value of this ratio is 2π.

OBJECTIVE
➊ **Teaching Notes**

➊ **EXAMPLE** **Error Prevention**

Suggest that students can find their own errors if they use the basic relationship 360° = 2π radians, or about 6.28 radians, to help them form a rough estimate of the size of the answer before they calculate.

➋ **EXAMPLE** **Auditory Learners**

Ask student volunteers to explain how they decide which form of the unit fraction to use, $\frac{180^\circ}{\pi\text{ radians}}$ or $\frac{\pi\text{ radians}}{180^\circ}$.

➌ **EXAMPLE** **Teaching Tip**

Emphasize that radian measures are often written with fractions. This notation has the advantage of giving exact values instead of decimal approximations. However, when measuring lengths or distances in an actual situation, the decimal value may be required.

Additional Examples

➊ **a.** Find the radian measure of an angle of 45°.
about 0.79 radians
b. Find the degree measure of $\frac{13\pi}{6}$ radians. **390°**

➋ **a.** Find the degree measure of an angle of $-\frac{3\pi}{2}$ radians. **−270°**
b. Find the radian measure of an angle of 54°. $\frac{3\pi}{10}$ **radians**

713

3 Find the exact values of
cos ($\frac{\pi}{3}$ radians) and sin ($\frac{\pi}{3}$ radians).
$\frac{1}{2}$; $\frac{\sqrt{3}}{2}$

OBJECTIVE
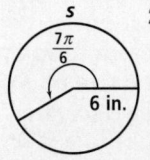 **Teaching Notes**

4 **EXAMPLE** **English Learners**

Verify that students understand
the meaning of *intercepted arc* by
asking them to use a colored
pencil to mark this arc on a sketch
of the circle.

Additional Examples

4 Use this circle to find length *s*
to the nearest tenth.

22.0 in.

5 A satellite completes one
orbit around Earth every 4 h. The
satellite orbits 6400 km above
Earth's surface. How far does the
satellite travel in 1 h?
about 20,100 km

Closure

Ask students: *What is a radian
and how is it used?* **A radian is
the measure of a central angle
that intercepts an arc equal in
length to the radius of a circle.
Radians are used to measure
angles.**

You can find the sine and cosine of angles in radian measure by first converting the radian measure to degrees and then using the unit circle.

3 **EXAMPLE** **Finding Cosine and Sine of Radian Measures**

Find the exact values of cos ($\frac{\pi}{4}$ radians) and sin ($\frac{\pi}{4}$ radians).

$\frac{\pi}{4}$ radians · $\frac{180°}{\pi \text{ radians}}$ = 45°   **Convert radians to degrees.**

Draw the angle. Complete a
45°-45°-90° triangle. Since the
hypotenuse has length 1, both
legs have length $\frac{\sqrt{2}}{2}$.

Thus, cos ($\frac{\pi}{4}$ radians) = $\frac{\sqrt{2}}{2}$

and sin ($\frac{\pi}{4}$ radians) = $\frac{\sqrt{2}}{2}$.

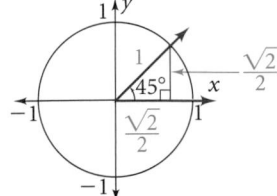

3a. 0.71, 0.71; these
values are the
rounded decimal
equivalent of $\frac{\sqrt{2}}{2}$.

b. π radians = 180°, so $\frac{\pi}{4}$
radians becomes $\frac{180°}{4}$,
which is 45°.

 Check Understanding **3** **a.** Use a calculator to find cos ($\frac{\pi}{4}$ radians) and sin ($\frac{\pi}{4}$ radians). How do these values compare to the coordinates found in Example 3?   **a–b. See left.**
 b. Explain how to use mental math to convert $\frac{\pi}{4}$ radians to degrees. (*Hint:* Begin with the relationship π radians = 180°.)

OBJECTIVE
2 **Finding the Length of an Arc**

You can find the length of an intercepted arc by using the proportion

$$\frac{\text{arc length } s}{\text{circumference } 2\pi r} = \frac{\text{central angle measure } \theta \text{ radians}}{2\pi \text{ radians}}.$$

Simplifying this proportion results in the formula below.

Key Concepts

Property	**Length of an Intercepted Arc**
For a circle of radius *r* and a central angle of measure θ (in radians), the length *s* of the intercepted arc is $s = r\theta$.	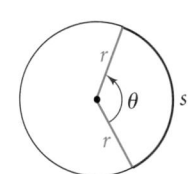

4 **EXAMPLE** **Finding the Length of an Arc**

Use the circle at the right. Find length *s* to the nearest tenth.

$s = r\theta$ **Use the formula.**

$= 3 \cdot \frac{5\pi}{6}$ **Substitute 3 for *r* and $\frac{5\pi}{6}$ for θ.**

$= \frac{5\pi}{2}$ **Simplify.**

≈ 7.9 **Use a calculator.**

The arc has length 7.9 in.

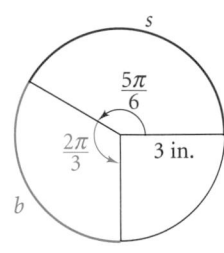

 Check Understanding **4** Find length *b* in Example 4. Round your answer to the nearest tenth. **6.3 in.**

Real-World **Connection**

The National Air and Space Museum in Washington, D.C., holds over 8500 artifacts from the history of space exploration.

Weather Satellite A weather satellite in a circular orbit around Earth completes one orbit every 2 h. The radius of Earth is about 6400 km, and the satellite orbits 2600 km above Earth's surface. How far does the satellite travel in 1 h?

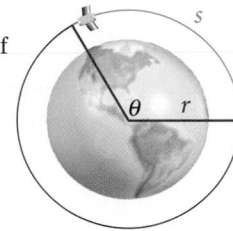

Since one complete rotation (orbit) takes 2 h, the satellite completes $\frac{1}{2}$ of a rotation in 1 h.

Step 1 Find the radius of the satellite's orbit.

$$r = 6400 + 2600$$ Add the radius of Earth and the distance from Earth's surface to the satellite.

$$= 9000$$ Simplify.

Step 2 Find the measure of the central angle the satellite travels through in 1 h.

$$\theta = \frac{1}{2} \cdot 2\pi$$ Multiply the fraction of the rotation by the number of radians in one complete rotation.

$$= \pi$$ Simplify.

Step 3 Find s for $\theta = \frac{2\pi}{3}$.

$$s = r\theta$$ Use the formula.

$$= 9000\pi$$ Substitute 9000 for r and π for θ.

$$\approx 28,274$$ Simplify.

The satellite travels about 28,000 km in 1 h.

✓**Check Understanding** 5 Find the length of the arc intercepted by each angle.
a. $\angle AOB$
b. $\angle COD$
c. $\angle AOC$
d. $\angle AOD$

5a. ≈3.14 units
b. ≈4.19 units
c. ≈6.28 units
d. ≈10.47 units

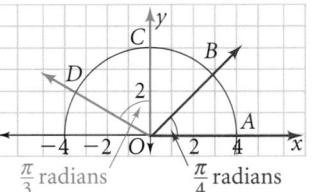

$\frac{\pi}{3}$ radians $\frac{\pi}{4}$ radians

EXERCISES

For more practice, see *Extra Practice*.

Practice and Problem Solving

A **Practice by Example**

Examples 1 and 2
(pages 712 and 713)

Write each measure in radians. Express the answer in terms of π and as a decimal rounded to the nearest hundredth.

1. $-300°$ $-\frac{5\pi}{3}$, **−5.24**
2. $150°$ $\frac{5\pi}{6}$, **2.62**
3. $-90°$ $-\frac{\pi}{2}$, **−1.57**
4. $-60°$ $-\frac{\pi}{3}$, **−1.05**
5. $160°$ $\frac{8\pi}{9}$, **2.79**
6. $20°$ $\frac{\pi}{9}$, **0.35**

Write each measure in degrees. Round your answer to the nearest degree, if necessary.

7. 3π radians **540°**
8. $\frac{11\pi}{10}$ radians **198°**
9. $-\frac{2\pi}{3}$ radians **−120°**
10. -3 radians **−172°**
11. 1.57 radians **90°**
12. 4.71 radians **270°**

3. Practice

Assignment Guide

▼**1** **Objective**
Ⓐ Ⓑ **Core** 1–19, 31–44, 46, 49
Ⓒ **Extension** 52–55, 57

▼**2** **Objective**
Ⓐ Ⓑ **Core** 20–30, 45, 47, 48, 50, 51
Ⓒ **Extension** 56

Standardized Test Prep 58–62

Mixed Review 63–74

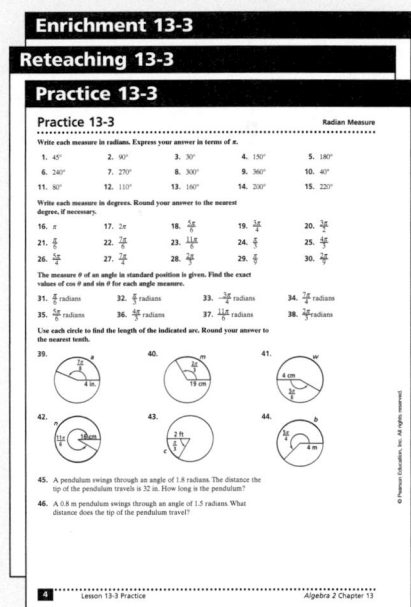

Enrichment 13-3
Reteaching 13-3
Practice 13-3

Visual Learners

Exercise 13 Encourage students to make posters of the diagram to display in the classroom.

pages 715–719 Exercises

37.

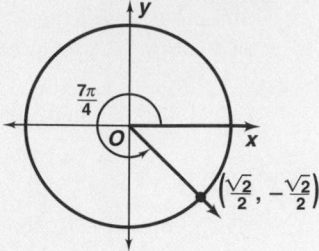

$\frac{7\pi}{4}$

$\left(\frac{\sqrt{2}}{2}, -\frac{\sqrt{2}}{2}\right)$

0.71, −0.71

38.

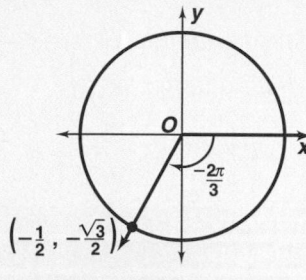

$-\frac{2\pi}{3}$

$\left(-\frac{1}{2}, -\frac{\sqrt{3}}{2}\right)$

−0.50, −0.87

39.

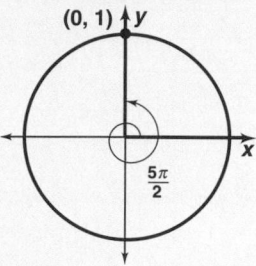

(0, 1)

$\frac{5\pi}{2}$

0.00, 1.00

---

13. Copy and complete the diagram at the right. Fill in the missing measures in radians or degrees. **See back of book.**

Example 3 (page 714)

The measure θ of an angle in standard position is given. Find the exact values of $\cos \theta$ and $\sin \theta$ for each angle measure.

14. $\frac{\sqrt{3}}{2}, \frac{1}{2}$

15. $\frac{1}{2}, \frac{\sqrt{3}}{2}$

17. $-\frac{1}{2}, \frac{\sqrt{3}}{2}$

18. $-\frac{\sqrt{3}}{2}, \frac{1}{2}$

14. $\frac{\pi}{6}$ radians

15. $\frac{\pi}{3}$ radians

16. $\frac{\pi}{2}$ radians **0, 1**

17. $\frac{2\pi}{3}$ radians

18. $\frac{5\pi}{6}$ radians

19. $-\frac{\pi}{2}$ radians **0, −1**

Example 4 (page 714)

Use each circle to find the length of the indicated arc. Round your answer to the nearest tenth.

20. 3.1 cm
$\frac{\pi}{3}$ t 3 cm

21. c 10.5 m
$\frac{2\pi}{3}$ 5 m

22. 51.8 ft m
$\frac{11\pi}{6}$ 9 ft

23. a
$\frac{4\pi}{3}$ 6 in.
25.1 in.

24. 2 m
$\frac{3\pi}{4}$ w
4.7 m

25. $\frac{5\pi}{4}$ 11 cm z
43.2 cm

Example 5 (page 715)

Find the length of each arc.

26.

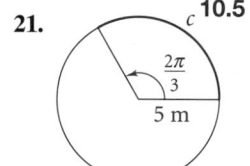

255° 24 in.

≈107 in.

27.

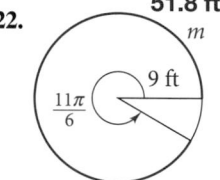

1.45 radians 22 ft

≈32 ft

28. **Space** A geostationary satellite is positioned 35,800 km above Earth's surface. It takes 24 h to complete one orbit. The radius of Earth is about 6400 km.
   a. What distance does the satellite travel in 1 h? **≈11,048 km**
   b. What distance does the satellite travel in 3 h? **≈33,144 km**
   c. What distance does the satellite travel in 2.5 h? **≈27,620 km**
   d. What distance does the satellite travel in 25 h? **≈276,198 km**
   e. **Critical Thinking** After how many hours has the satellite traveled 200,000 km?
   18.1 h

29. Automobile Design Suppose a windshield wiper arm has a length of 22 in. and rotates through an angle of 110°. What distance does the tip of the wiper travel as it moves once across the windshield? ≈**42.2 in.**

 30. Geography The 24 lines of longitude that approximate the 24 standard time zones are equally spaced around the equator.

30a. 15°, $\frac{\pi}{12}$ radians

    a. Suppose you use 24 central angles to divide a circle into 24 equal arcs. Express the measure of each angle in degrees and in radians.

    b. The radius of the equator is about 3960 mi. About how wide is each time zone at the equator? ≈**1036.7 mi**

    c. The radius of the Arctic Circle is about 1580 mi. About how wide is each time zone at the Arctic Circle? ≈**413.6 mi**

In which quadrant, or on which axis, does the terminal side of each angle lie?

31. $\frac{4\pi}{3}$ radians **III**
   32. $-\frac{5\pi}{4}$ radians **II**
   33. $\frac{9\pi}{2}$ radians **positive y-axis**

34. $\frac{5\pi}{6}$ radians **II**
   35. $-\pi$ radians **negative x-axis**
   36. $\frac{6\pi}{5}$ radians **III**

Draw an angle in standard position with each given measure. Then find the values of the cosine and sine of the angle to the nearest hundredth. **37–42. See margin pp. 716–717.**

37. $\frac{7\pi}{4}$ radians
   38. $-\frac{2\pi}{3}$ radians
   39. $\frac{5\pi}{2}$ radians

40. -2π radians
   41. $\frac{7\pi}{6}$ radians
   42. $-\frac{\pi}{5}$ radians

 43. a. Geometry Draw a unit circle on the coordinate plane. Then draw five angles in standard position measuring $\frac{\pi}{5}$, $\frac{4\pi}{5}$, $\frac{6\pi}{5}$, $\frac{9\pi}{5}$, and $\frac{3\pi}{10}$ radians.

    b. For each angle, complete a right triangle. Place the hypotenuse along the terminal side (from the origin to the unit circle). Place one leg along the x-axis. The other leg will be parallel to the y-axis.

    c. Critical Thinking Are the five triangles congruent? Justify your answer by using the values of sin θ and cos θ for each angle. **a–c. See margin.**

Need Help?
Two triangles are congruent if their corresponding sides are congruent and their corresponding angles are congruent.

44. Open-Ended Draw an angle in standard position. Draw a circle with its center at the vertex of the angle. Find the measure of the angle in radians and degrees. **Check students' work.**

 45. Transportation Suppose the radius of a bicycle wheel is 13 in. (measured to the outside of the tire). Find the number of radians through which a point on the tire turns when the bicycle has moved forward a distance of 12 ft. ≈**11 radians**

46. Error Analysis A student wanted to rewrite $\frac{9\pi}{4}$ radians in degrees. The screen shows her calculation. What error did the student make? **The student forgot to include parentheses.**

```
9*π/4*360/2*π
          3997.189782
```

Find the length of each arc. Then find the measures of two angles coterminal with the given angle.

47. ≈**798 ft; −55°, 665°**

48. ≈**23.6 in.;** $-\frac{7\pi}{6}$, $\frac{17\pi}{6}$

47.

150 ft
−305°

48.
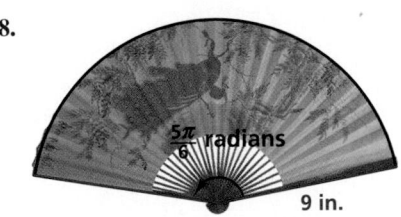
$\frac{5\pi}{6}$ radians
9 in.

Connection to Geography
Exercise 30 Remind students that lines of longitude are perpendicular to the equator and lines of latitude are parallel to the equator.

40.
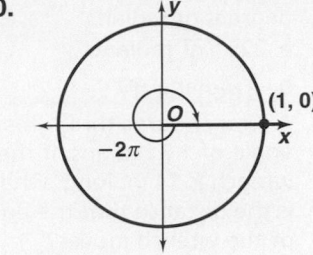
-2π
(1, 0)
1.00, 0.00

41.
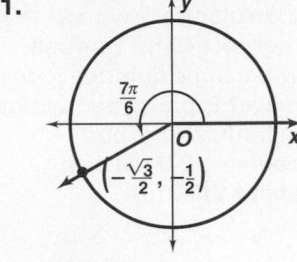
$\frac{7\pi}{6}$
$\left(-\frac{\sqrt{3}}{2}, -\frac{1}{2}\right)$
−0.87, −0.50

42.
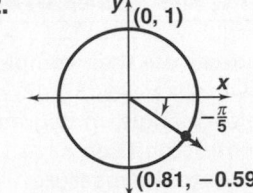
(0, 1)
$-\frac{\pi}{5}$
(0.81, −0.59)
0.81, −0.59

43a-b.
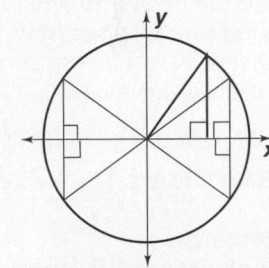

c. All five triangles are congruent by SSS. All have a hypotenuse of 1 unit, a long leg of 0.81 unit, and a short leg of 0.59 unit.

$\cos\frac{\pi}{5} = 0.81$, $\sin\frac{\pi}{5} = 0.59$;
$\sin\frac{3\pi}{10} = 0.81$, $\cos\frac{3\pi}{10} = 0.59$;
$\cos\frac{4\pi}{5} = -0.81$, $\sin\frac{4\pi}{5} = 0.59$;
$\cos\frac{6\pi}{5} = -0.81$, $\sin\frac{6\pi}{5} = -0.59$;
$\cos\frac{9\pi}{5} = 0.81$, $\sin\frac{9\pi}{5} = -0.59$

717

Lesson Quiz 13-3

1. Rewrite each angle measure using the other unit, either degrees or radians.
   a. 225° $\frac{5\pi}{4}$ **radians**
   b. $\frac{\pi}{2}$ **radians 90°**

2. A wrench turns through an angle of 1.5 radians. If the wrench is 14 in. long, what is the distance that the end of the wrench moves?
   21 in.

3. A jogger runs 100 m around a circular track with a radius of 40 m. Through what angle does the jogger move? Express your answer in both radians and degrees. **2.5 radians; about 143.2°**

Alternative Assessment

Have students use their completed drawings for Exercises 37–42, and measure each angle, in degrees, with a protractor. Then have them calculate the measure of each angle in degrees by multiplying the radian measure by $\frac{180}{\pi}$. Finally ask them to compare the measured and calculated results to see how close their measurements came to the calculated values.

Standardized Test Prep

📁 **Resources**
For additional practice with a variety of test item formats:
• Standardized Test Prep, p. 761
• Test-Taking Strategies, p. 756
• Test-Taking Strategies with Transparencies

Exercise 59 Suggest that students first draw a quick sketch to place the angle in the correct quadrant. This will help to eliminate any response with the incorrect sign.

---

49. **If two angles measured in radians are coterminal, the difference of their measures will be evenly divisible by 2π.**

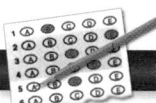

C Challenge

56.
$$\frac{\theta}{2\pi} = \frac{s}{2\pi r}$$
$$\frac{\theta}{2\pi} \cdot 2\pi r = \frac{s}{2\pi r} \cdot 2\pi r$$
$$\theta r = s$$
$$s = r\theta$$

57a. 0.5017962; 0.4999646; the first four terms

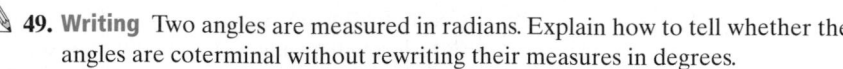

49. **Writing** Two angles are measured in radians. Explain how to tell whether the angles are coterminal without rewriting their measures in degrees.

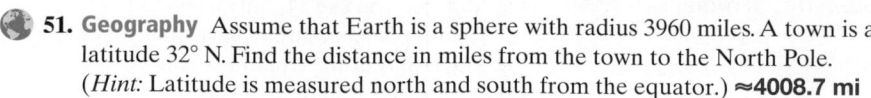

50. **Music** A CD with diameter 12 cm spins in a CD player. Calculate how much farther a point on the outside edge of the CD travels in one revolution than a point 1 cm closer to the center of the CD. **≈6.3 cm**

51. **Geography** Assume that Earth is a sphere with radius 3960 miles. A town is at latitude 32° N. Find the distance in miles from the town to the North Pole. (*Hint:* Latitude is measured north and south from the equator.) **≈4008.7 mi**

The given angle θ is in standard position. Find the radian measure of the angle that results after the given number of revolutions from the terminal side of θ.

52. $\theta = \frac{\pi}{2}$; 1 clockwise revolution $-\frac{3\pi}{2}$ **radians**

53. $\theta = \frac{\pi}{3}$; 2 clockwise revolutions $-\frac{11\pi}{3}$ **radians**

54. $\theta = -\frac{2\pi}{3}$; 1 counterclockwise revolution $\frac{4\pi}{3}$ **radians**

55. $\theta = \frac{5\pi}{6}$; $2\frac{1}{2}$ counterclockwise revolutions $\frac{35\pi}{6}$ **radians**

56. **Reasoning** Use the proportion $\frac{\text{measure of central angle}}{\text{measure of one complete rotation}} = \frac{\text{length of arc}}{\text{circumference}}$ to derive the formula $s = r\theta$. Use θ for the central angle measure and s for the arc length. Measure the rotation in radians.

57. **a.** Use the cartoon below. Use a calculator to evaluate the first three terms of Jason's expression to seven decimal places. Then evaluate the first four terms. Which is a better estimate of cos 60°?

FOX TROT by Bill Amend

b. Jason's expression will approximate the cosine of any angle if you know its radian measure. Write a general form of his expression by substituting x for $\frac{\pi}{3}$. **57b.** $1 - \frac{x^2}{2!} + \frac{x^4}{4!} - \frac{x^6}{6!} + \frac{x^8}{8!} - \ldots$
c. Use the general formula you wrote in part (b) to estimate $\cos\left(\frac{\pi}{10}\text{ radians}\right)$ to the nearest thousandth. What is the angle measure, in degrees? **≈0.951; 18°**

Standardized Test Prep

Multiple Choice

58. Which pairs of measurements represent the same angle measures? **C**

   I. 240°, $\frac{7\pi}{6}$ radians **II.** 135°, $\frac{3\pi}{4}$ radians **III.** 150°, $\frac{5\pi}{6}$ radians

   A. I and II only **B.** I and III only **C.** II and III only **D.** I, II, and III

59. What is the exact value of cos $\left(\frac{5\pi}{4}\text{ radians}\right)$? **G**

F. $-\frac{\sqrt{3}}{2}$ G. $-\frac{\sqrt{2}}{2}$ H. $-\frac{1}{2}$ I. $\frac{\sqrt{2}}{2}$

60. In a circle, an arc of length 8π cm is intercepted by a central angle of $\frac{2\pi}{3}$ radians. What is the radius of the circle? **D**

A. $\frac{3\pi}{16}$ cm   B. $\frac{16\pi}{3}$ cm   C. $\frac{16\pi^2}{3}$ cm   D. 12 cm

61. Two arcs have the same length. One arc is intercepted by an angle of $\frac{3\pi}{2}$ radians in a circle of radius 15 cm. If the radius of the other circle is 25 cm, what central angle intercepts the arc? **G**

F. $\frac{3\pi}{2}$ radians   G. $\frac{9\pi}{10}$ radians   H. $\frac{3\pi}{2}$ radians   I. $\frac{5\pi}{3}$ radians

Short Response   **62.** Describe the relationship between a central angle of one radian and the radius of the circle. **See margin.**

Mixed Review

Lesson 13-2   **Sketch each angle in standard position. 63–67. See margin.**

63. 15°   **64.** −75°   **65.** 150°   **66.** −270°   **67.** −85°

Lesson 12-4   **Find the mean and the standard deviation for each set of values.**

68. 6 1 9 12 4 15 21 7 8 8 **9.1, 5.41**

69. 12 13 15 9 16 5 18 16 12 11 15 **12.9, 3.53**

70. 21 29 35 26 25 28 27 51 24 34 **30, 8.09**

Lesson 10-3   **Write an equation of a circle with the given center and radius.**

71. $x^2 + y^2 = 64$

72. $x^2 + (y + 5)^2 = 16$

71. center $(0, 0)$, radius 8   **72.** center $(0, -5)$, radius 4

73. center $(3, 7)$, radius 6.5   **74.** center $(-8, 4)$, radius 3
$(x - 3)^2 + (y - 7)^2 = 42.25$ $(x + 8)^2 + (y - 4)^2 = 9$

✓ Checkpoint Quiz 1   Lessons 13-1 through 13-3

Instant self-check quiz online and on CD-ROM

Find the period and the amplitude of each periodic function.

1.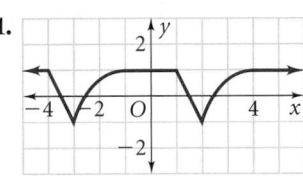

2.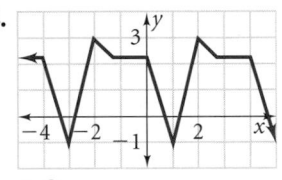

5, 1   **4, 2**

Find the exact values of sin θ and cos θ for an angle in standard position with each measure θ.

3. −45° $-\frac{\sqrt{2}}{2}, \frac{\sqrt{2}}{2}$ **4.** 210° $-\frac{1}{2}, -\frac{\sqrt{3}}{2}$ **5.** π radians **0, −1**   **6.** $\frac{\pi}{6}$ radians $\frac{1}{2}, \frac{\sqrt{3}}{2}$

Convert each angle measure into its equivalent in radians or degrees.

7. −180° $-\pi$ **radians**   **8.** 36° $\frac{\pi}{5}$ **radians**   **9.** π radians **180°**   **10.** $\frac{4\pi}{3}$ radians **240°**

Lesson 13-3   Radian Measure   **719**

Take It to the NET
Online lesson quiz at
www.PHSchool.com
Web Code: aga-1303

✓ Chapter Checkpoint 1

To check understanding of Lessons 13-1 to 13-3:

Checkpoint Quiz 1 (p. 719)

📁 **Teaching Resources**
Checkpoint Quiz 1 (also in Prentice Hall Assessment System)

👥 **Reaching All Students**
Reading and Math Literacy 13B

Spanish versions available

---

pages 716–719 Exercises

62. **[2] For a central angle of 1 radian, the length of the intercepted arc is the length of the radius.**

[1] incomplete explanation

63.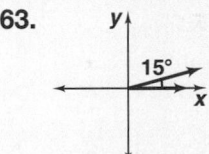

64.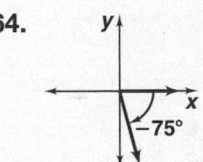

65.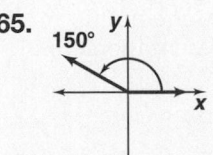

66.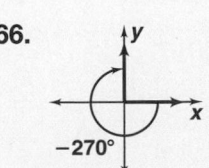

67.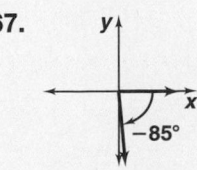

719

13-4

The Sine Function

Lesson Preview

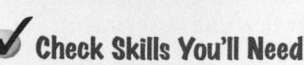

Check Skills You'll Need

Exploring Periodic Data
Lesson 13-1: Example 3
Exercises 10–13
Extra Practice, p. 834

Lesson Resources

📁 **Teaching Resources**
Practice, Reteaching, Enrichment

👥 **Reaching All Students**
Practice Workbook 13-4
Spanish Practice Workbook 13-4

⏱ **Presentation Assistant Plus!**
Transparencies
• Check Skills You'll Need 13-4
• Additional Examples 13-4
• Student Edition Answers 13-4
• Lesson Quiz 13-4
PH Presentation Pro CD 13-4

ASSESSMENT SYSTEM
Computer Test Generator CD

💿 **Technology**
Resource Pro® CD-ROM
Computer Test Generator CD
Prentice Hall Presentation Pro CD

🖥 **www.PHSchool.com**
Student Site
• Teacher Web Code: agk-5500
• Graphing Calculator,
  Procedure 11
• Self-grading Lesson Quiz
Teacher Center
• Lesson Planner
• Resources

Plus **iTEXT**

Lesson Preview

What You'll Learn

 OBJECTIVE 1 To identify properties of the sine function

OBJECTIVE 2 To graph sine curves

. . . And Why

To model light waves, as in Example 7

✔ **Check Skills You'll Need**   (For help, go to Lesson 13-1.)

Use the graph. Find the value(s) of each of the following.

1. the period   **2**
2. the domain   **all real numbers**
3. the amplitude   **1**
4. the range   **all real numbers between −1 and 1, inclusive**

New Vocabulary   • sine function   • sine curve

OBJECTIVE
1 **Interpreting Sine Functions**

📖 **Reading Math**

Sine comes from the Latin word *sinus*, meaning "bay," a reference to the shape of the sine curve.

iTEXT Interactive lesson includes instant self-check, tutorials, and activities.

The **sine function,** $y = \sin \theta$, matches the measure θ of an angle in standard position with the y-coordinate of a point on the unit circle. This point is where the terminal side of the angle intersects the unit circle.

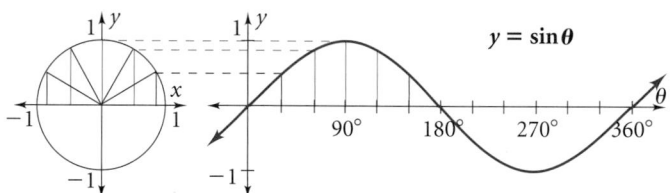

1 EXAMPLE **Interpreting the Sine Function in Degrees**

Use the graph of the sine function.

a. What is the value of $y = \sin \theta$ for $\theta = 270°$?

The value of the function at $\theta = 270°$ is −1.

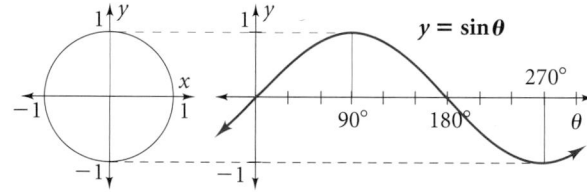

b. For what value of θ between 0° and 360° does the graph of $y = \sin \theta$ reach the maximum value of 1?

When $y = 1, \theta = 90°$.

1a. yes; at 450°

 b. Yes; the y-values repeat at regular intervals.

✔ **Check Understanding** **1 a.** Extend the graph from Example 1 to include angle measures from 270° to 720°. Will the graph reach the maximum value of 1 again, and if so, where?
b. Reasoning Is the sine function a periodic function? Explain.

720   Chapter 13   Periodic Functions and Trigonometry

 **Ongoing Assessment and Intervention**

Before the Lesson
Diagnose prerequisite skills using:
• Check Skills You'll Need

During the Lesson
Monitor progress using:
• Check Understanding
• Additional Examples
• Standardized Test Prep

After the Lesson
Assess knowledge using:
• Lesson Quiz
• Computer Test Generator CD

As you have seen, an angle measure θ can be expressed in degrees or in radians. In this book, when no unit is mentioned you should use radians.

You can graph the sine function in radians. In the unit circle, you can show radian measures along the circle as lengths of arcs. In the graphs below, the points for 1, 2, and 3 radians are marked on the unit circle and on the θ-axis.

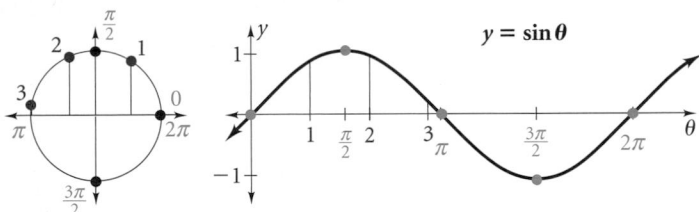

Real-World **Connection**

If you mark a point on one of the blades of an eggbeater and plot the point's horizontal distance over time from the center of the eggbeater, the graph is a sine curve.

2 EXAMPLE Estimating Sine Values in Radians

Estimate each value from the graph. Check your estimate with a calculator.

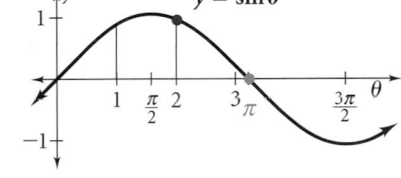

a. sin 2

The sine function reaches its maximum value of 1 at $\frac{\pi}{2} \approx 1.57$. The value of the function at 2 is slightly less than 1, or about 0.9.

sin 2 ≈ 0.9092974268   **Use a calculator in radian mode.**

b. sin π

The sine function crosses the x-axis at π, so sin π = 0.

sin π = 0   **Use a calculator in radian mode.**

✓ Check Understanding **2** Use the graphs of sin θ from Examples 1 and 2.
a. Find the amplitude of the sine function. **1**   **b. 360°, 2π radians**
b. Express the period of the sine function in degrees and in radians.
c. What are the domain and range of the sine function?
   domain: all real numbers, range: all real numbers between −1 and 1, inclusive

The graph of a sine function is called a **sine curve.** By varying the period, you get different sine curves.

3 EXAMPLE Finding the Period of a Sine Curve

Use the graph of $y = \sin 4\theta$ at the right.

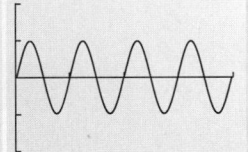

Xmin=0
Xmax=2π
Xscl=π/2
Ymin=−2
Ymax=2
Yscl=1

a. How many cycles occur in the graph at the right? How is the number of cycles related to the coefficient of θ in the equation?

The graph shows 4 cycles. The number of cycles is equal to the coefficient of θ.

? Need Help?

The period of a function is the horizontal length of one cycle.

b. Find the period of $y = \sin 4\theta$.

$2\pi \div 4 = \frac{\pi}{2}$ **Divide the interval of the graph by the number of cycles.**

The period of $y = \sin 4\theta$ is $\frac{\pi}{2}$.

Lesson 13-4 The Sine Function   **721**

👥 Reaching All Students

Below Level Review the meanings of *period* and *amplitude*.	**Advanced Learners** Have students research alternating current electricity, and explain how it can be represented by a sine curve.	**Tactile Learners** See note on page 721. **Error Prevention** See note on page 722.

2. Teach

Math Background

The sine function and sine curves have many applications. Mathematical analysis of sound waves yields a sine function in which the loudness of the sound depends upon the amplitude, and the pitch depends upon the number of cycles per second.

OBJECTIVE
1 Teaching Notes

1 EXAMPLE Tactile Learners

To help students see how the points on the sine function represent an unrolling of the circle, have them place one finger on the circle and another on the graph. Then move their fingers simultaneously to see how the points on the circle and graph correspond.

Additional Examples

1 Use the graph of the sine function shown in Example 1.
a. What is the value of $y = \sin \theta$ for $\theta = 180°$? **0**
b. For what other values of θ, on the interval shown, does the graph of sin θ have the same value as for $\theta = 180°$? **0°, 360°**

2 Estimate each value from the graph shown in Example 2. Check your estimate with a calculator.
a. sin 3 **about 0.1**
b. sin $\frac{\pi}{2}$ **1**

3 Use this graph of $y = \sin 6\theta$, for $0 \le \theta \le 2\pi$.

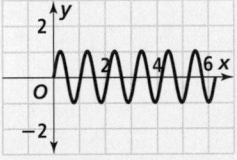

a. How many cycles occur in this graph? How is the number of cycles related to the coefficient of θ in the equation? **6; They are equal.**
b. Find the period of $y = \sin 6\theta$.
$\frac{\pi}{3}$

721

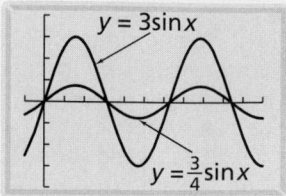

4 Here is the graph of
$y = a \sin \theta$ for values of $a = \frac{3}{4}$
and $a = 3$.

a. Find the amplitude of each
sine curve. How does the value of
a affect the amplitude? $\frac{3}{4}$, 3; The
amplitude is $|a|$.
b. How would a negative value of
a affect each graph? **A negative
value of a reflects the graph in
the x-axis.**

OBJECTIVE
2 **Teaching Notes**

5 **EXAMPLE** **Teaching Tip**

Remind students to connect the
five points in the pattern with
curves rather than straight lines.

6 **EXAMPLE** **Error Prevention**

Students may think that a cycle is
just the part of the curve between
two zero y-values. In this case, the
part of the curve between two
zeros is only half of the cycle.

✓ **Check Understanding** **3** Find the period of each sine curve below. For each graph, the θ-axis shows values from 0 to 2π.

a.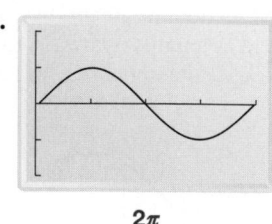

b.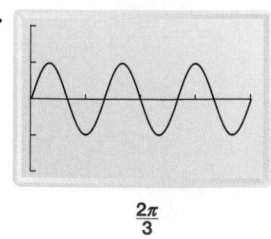

2π $\frac{2\pi}{3}$

You can also vary the amplitude of a sine curve.

4 **EXAMPLE** **Finding the Amplitude of a Sine Curve**

The graphing calculator
screens at the right show
several graphs of
$y = a \sin \theta$. Each θ-axis
shows values from 0 to 2π.

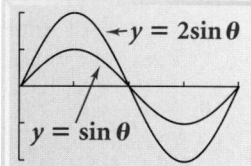 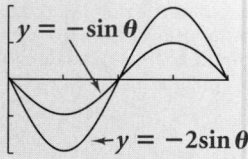

a. Find the amplitude of
each sine curve. How
does the value of a affect the amplitude?

The amplitude of $y = \sin \theta$ is 1, and the amplitude of $y = 2 \sin \theta$ is 2.
The amplitude of $y = -\sin \theta$ is 1, and the amplitude of $y = -2 \sin \theta$ is 2.
In each case, the amplitude of the curve is $|a|$.

b. How does a negative value of a affect the position of the curve?
When a is negative, the graph is a reflection in the x-axis.

Need Help?
The amplitude of a
function is half the
difference between
its maximum and
minimum values.

✓ **Check Understanding** **4** Find the amplitude of each sine curve. Each interval on the y-axis represents one unit.

a. 4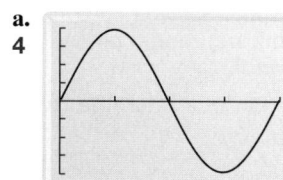

b. 3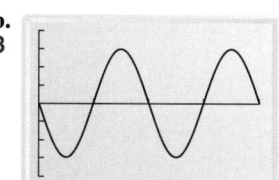

The summary box below lists the properties of sine functions.

Key Concepts

Summary	**Properties of Sine Functions**

Suppose $y = a \sin b\theta$, with $a \neq 0, b > 0$, and θ in radians.

- $|a|$ is the amplitude of the function.
- b is the number of cycles in the interval from 0 to 2π.
- $\frac{2\pi}{b}$ is the period of the function.

OBJECTIVE 2 — Graphing Sine Functions

You can use five points equally spaced through one cycle to sketch a sine curve. For $a > 0$, this five-point pattern is *zero–max–zero–min–zero*.

5 EXAMPLE — Sketching a Graph

a. Sketch one cycle of a sine curve with amplitude 2 and period 4π.

5a.
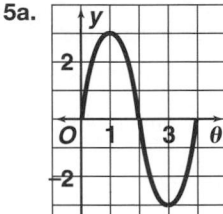

Step 1 Choose scales for the y-axis and the θ-axis that are about equal ($\pi \approx 3$ units). On the θ-axis, mark one period (4π).

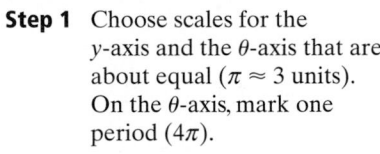

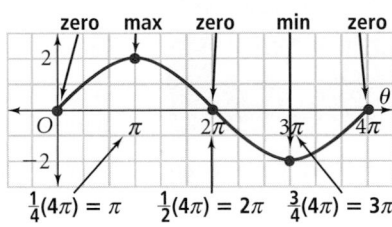

Step 2 Mark equal spaces through one cycle by dividing the period into fourths.

$\frac{1}{4}(4\pi) = \pi \qquad \frac{1}{2}(4\pi) = 2\pi \qquad \frac{3}{4}(4\pi) = 3\pi$

Step 3 Since the amplitude is 2, the maximum is 2 and the minimum is -2. Plot the five points and sketch the curve.

c.

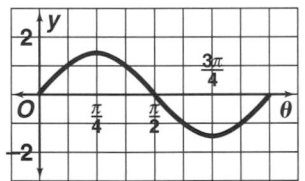

b. Use the form $y = a \sin b\theta$. Write an equation with $a > 0$ for the sine curve in part (a).

The amplitude is 2, and $a > 0$, so $a = 2$.
The period is 4π, and $4\pi = \frac{2\pi}{b}$, so $b = \frac{1}{2}$.
An equation for the function is $y = 2 \sin \frac{1}{2}\theta$.

✔ **Check Understanding** **5 a.** Sketch one cycle of a sine curve with amplitude 3, period 4, and $a > 0$.
b. **Critical Thinking** Predict the five-point pattern for graphing a sine curve when $a < 0$. **zero-min-zero-max-zero**
c. Sketch one cycle of a sine curve with amplitude 2, period $\frac{2\pi}{3}$, and $a < 0$.
a, c. See left.

You can also graph sine functions from a given function rule.

6a.
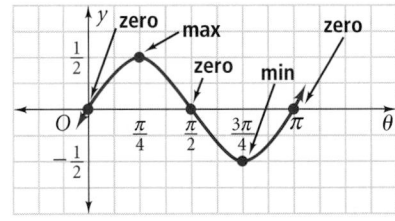

6 EXAMPLE — Graphing From a Function Rule

Sketch one cycle of $y = \frac{1}{2} \sin 2\theta$.

$|a| = \frac{1}{2}$, so the amplitude is $\frac{1}{2}$.

$b = 2$, so there are 2 cycles from 0 to 2π.

$\frac{2\pi}{b} = \frac{2\pi}{2} = \pi$, so the period is π.

b.

Divide the period into fourths.

Using the values of the amplitude and period, plot the *zero–max–zero–min–zero* pattern.

Sketch the curve.

✔ **Check Understanding** **6** Sketch one cycle of the graph of each sine function. **a–b. See left.**
a. $y = 1.5 \sin 2\theta$ **b.** $y = 3 \sin \frac{\pi}{2}\theta$

Lesson 13-4 The Sine Function 723

Additional Examples

5 a. Sketch one cycle of a sine curve with amplitude 3 and period 4.
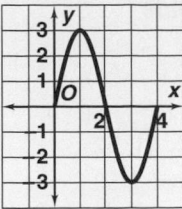

b. Use the form $y = a \sin b\theta$. Write an equation with $a > 0$ for the sine curve in part a.
$y = 3 \sin \frac{\pi}{2} x$

6 Sketch one cycle of $y = \frac{5}{3} \sin 3\theta$.
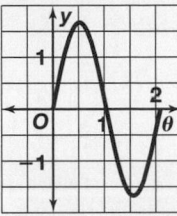

7 Find the period of the following sine curve. Then write an equation for the curve.
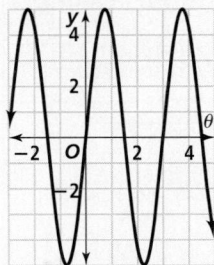

$3; \ y = 5 \sin \left(\frac{2\pi\theta}{3}\right)$

Closure

Ask students: *What have you learned about the graph of the sine function? What does the shape of the sine graph depend on?* **The graph of a sine function is a periodic curve. For the function $y = a \sin b\theta$, the amplitude of the graph is $|a|$, and the number of cycles between 0 and 2π is b. The period of the function is $\frac{2\pi}{b}$, $b > 0$.**

723

Assignment Guide

▼**1 Objective**
- Ⓐ Ⓑ **Core** 1–15, 34–39, 42–44, 51, 52
- Ⓒ **Extension** 53–58

▼**2 Objective**
- Ⓐ Ⓑ **Core** 16–33, 40, 41, 45–50
- Ⓒ **Extension** 59

Standardized Test Prep 60–65

Mixed Review 66–74

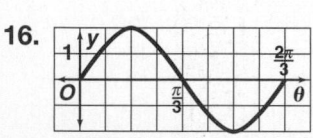
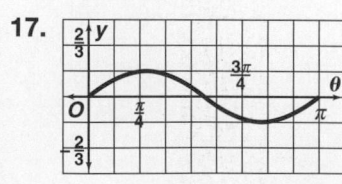
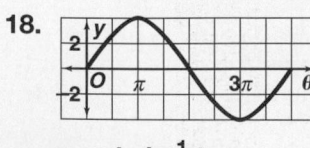

You can use sine functions to model real-world situations.

Real-World 🌎 Connection

Light can be modeled as waves. Changes in wavelength (period) change the color that the eye perceives. Changes in amplitude affect the intensity of the color.

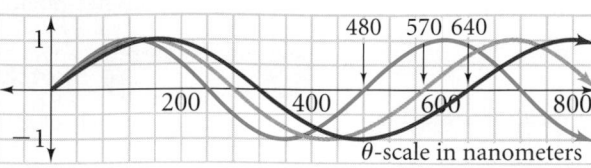

7 EXAMPLE **Real-World 🌎 Connection**

Optics The graph at the right models waves of red, blue, and yellow light. Find the period of the sine curve representing blue. Then write the equation.

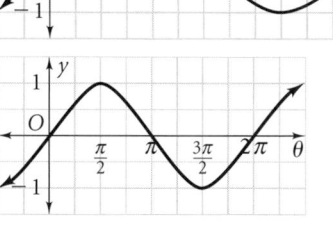

According to the graph, one blue cycle takes 480 nanometers to complete, so the period is 480.

To write the equation, first find b.

$$period = \frac{2\pi}{b}$$ Use the relationship between the period and b.

$$480 = \frac{2\pi}{b}$$ Substitute.

$$b = \frac{2\pi}{480}$$ Multiply each side by $\frac{b}{480}$.

$$\approx 0.013$$ Simplify.

● Use the form $y = \sin b\theta$. An equation for blue light is $y = \sin 0.013\theta$.

✔ **Check Understanding** **7** Write equations for the sine curves that model the red and yellow light waves in Example 7. $y = \sin 0.010\theta, y = \sin 0.011\theta$

EXERCISES

For more practice, see *Extra Practice*.

Practice and Problem Solving

Ⓐ **Practice by Example**

Example 1 (page 720)

Use the graph at the right to find the value of $y = \sin \theta$ for each value of θ.

1. 30° $\frac{1}{2}$ 2. 45° ≈**0.7**   3. 120° ≈**0.9**

4. 180° **0**   5. 240° ≈**−0.9**   6. 300° ≈**−0.9**

Example 2 (page 721)

Use the graph at the right to find the value of $y = \sin \theta$ for each value of θ.

7. $\frac{\pi}{2}$ radians **1**   8. 3 radians ≈**0.1**

9. ≈**−0.8**

9. 4 radians   10. 5 radians ≈**−1**

11. $\frac{3\pi}{2}$ radians**−1**12. $\frac{7\pi}{4}$ radians ≈**−0.7**

Examples 3 and 4 (pages 721 and 722)

How many cycles does each sine function have in the interval from 0 to 2π? Find the amplitude and period of each function.

13. **3; 2, $\frac{2\pi}{3}$**

14. **$\frac{1}{2}$; 1, 4π**

15. **2; 3, π**

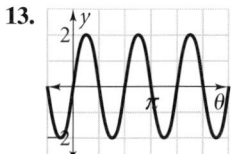

13.

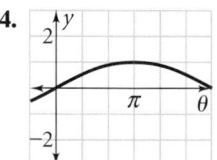

14.

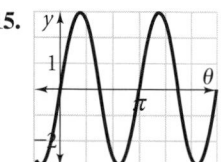

15.

724   Chapter 13   Periodic Functions and Trigonometry

16.

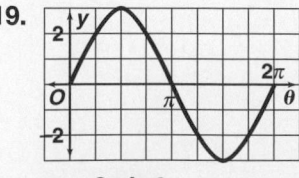

$y = 2 \sin 3\theta$

17.

$y = \frac{1}{3} \sin 2\theta$

18.

$y = 4 \sin \frac{1}{2}\theta$

19.

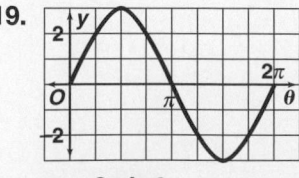

$y = 3 \sin\theta$

20.

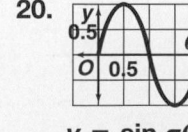

$y = \sin \pi\theta$

21.

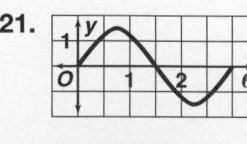

$y = \frac{3}{2} \sin \frac{2\pi}{3}\theta$

22.

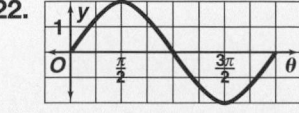

724

Example 5
(page 723)

Sketch one cycle of each sine curve. Assume $a > 0$. Write an equation for
each graph.   16–21. See margin p. 724.

16. amplitude 2, period $\frac{2\pi}{3}$

17. amplitude $\frac{1}{3}$, period π

18. amplitude 4, period 4π

19. amplitude 3, period 2π

20. amplitude 1, period 2

21. amplitude 1.5, period 3

Example 6
(page 723)

Sketch one cycle of the graph of each sine function.   22–27. See margin.

22. $y = 2 \sin \theta$ **23.** $y = \sin 3\theta$ **24.** $y = -\sin \frac{\pi}{2}\theta$

25. $y = 2 \sin \pi\theta$ **26.** $y = 4 \sin \frac{1}{2}\theta$ **27.** $y = -4 \sin \frac{1}{2}\theta$

Example 7
(page 724)

Find the period of each sine curve. Then write an equation for each
sine function.

28. 2π; $y = 2 \sin \theta$

29. 2π; $y = -3 \sin \theta$

30. π; $y = \frac{5}{2} \sin 2\theta$

31. $\frac{\pi}{3}$; $y = \frac{1}{2} \sin 6\theta$

28.
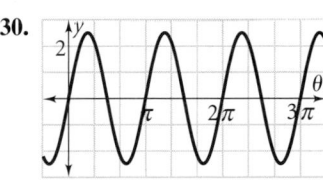

29.
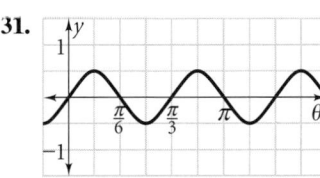

30.
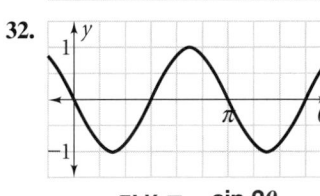

31.
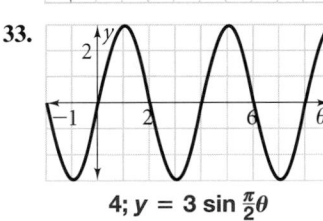

32.
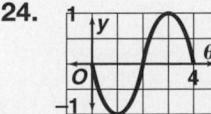

π; $y = -\sin 2\theta$

33.
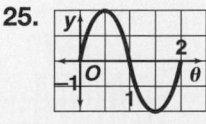

4; $y = 3 \sin \frac{\pi}{2}\theta$

B **Apply Your Skills**

How many cycles does each sine function have in the interval from 0 to 2π?
Find the amplitude and period of each function.

34. $y = \sin \theta$ **1; 1, 2π**   **35.** $y = \sin 5\theta$ **5; 1, $\frac{2\pi}{5}$**   **36.** $y = \sin \pi\theta$ **π; 1, 2**

37. $y = 3 \sin \theta$ **1; 3, 2π**   **38.** $y = -5 \sin \theta$ **1; 5, 2π**   **39.** $y = -5 \sin 2\pi\theta$
2π; 5, 1

40. a. Graph the functions $y = \sin \theta$, $y = 2 \sin \theta$, and $y = 3 \sin \theta$ on the
same screen. **a–b. See margin.**
   b. Critical Thinking If a is positive, how does the graph of $y = a \sin \theta$
   change as the value of a changes?

41. a. Graph the functions $y = 3 \sin \theta$ and $y = -3 \sin \theta$ on the same screen. How
are the two graphs related? **a–c. See margin.**
   b. Graph the functions $y = \sin 3\theta$ and $y = \sin (-3\theta)$ on the same screen. How
   are the two graphs related?
   c. Critical Thinking How does the graph of $y = a \sin b\theta$ change when a is
   replaced with its opposite? How does the graph change when b is replaced
   with its opposite?

42. Use the formula period $= \frac{2\pi}{b}$ to find the period of each sine function.
   a. $y = 1.5 \sin 2\theta$ **π**   **b.** $y = 3 \sin \frac{\pi}{2}\theta$ **4**

Connection to Algebra
Exercise 52c To help students
recall the basics of translations,
ask: *What equation would you
write to translate $y = x^2$ to the
right 3 units?* $y = (x - 3)^2$

27.
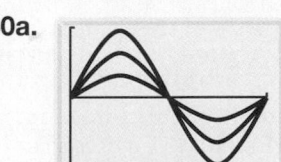

40a.
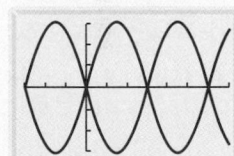

**b. As a increases, the
amplitude of the
graph increases.**

41a.
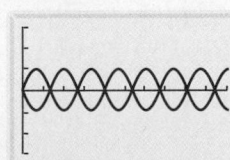

**They are reflections
of each other in the
x-axis.**

b.

**They are reflections
of each other in the
x-axis.**

**c. When either a or b is
replaced by its opposite,
the graph is a reflection
of the original graph in
the x-axis.**

23.
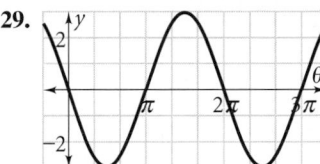

24.

25.

26.
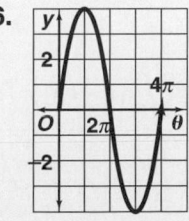

725

1. Sketch the graph of $y = 3 \sin 2\theta$ in the interval from 0 to 2π.

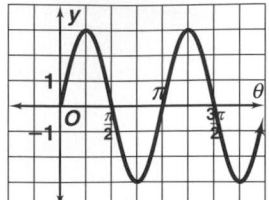

2. Write an equation of the sine function for this graph.

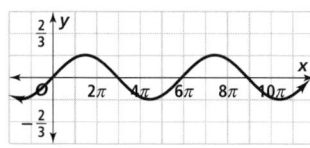

$y = \frac{1}{3} \sin \frac{x}{3}$

3. What is the amplitude of the graph in Question 2? $\frac{1}{3}$

Alternative Assessment

Have students use the drawings for Exercises 13–15 and write an equation of the sine function for each graph.
$y = 2 \sin 3\theta$; $y = \sin \frac{1}{2}\theta$,
$y = 3 \sin 2\theta$

---

pages 724–727 Exercises

44. • $|a|$ is the amplitude of the function.

• b is the number of cycles in the interval 0° to 360°.

• $\frac{360}{b}$ is the period of the function. The properties relating to number of cycles and period are affected.

45. $\frac{2\pi}{5}$, 3.5

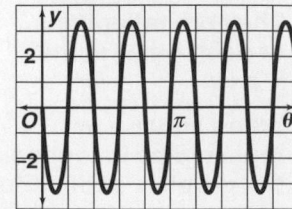

Real-World **Connection**

Careers Sound engineers working on music videos use sound boards to control hundreds of sound waves.

---

 43. **Music** The sound wave for the note A above middle C can be modeled by the function $y = 0.001 \sin 880\pi\theta$.
   a. What is the period of the function? $\frac{1}{440}$
   b. What is the amplitude of the function? **0.001**
   c. How many cycles of the graph are between 0 and 2π? **880π**

 44. **Writing** Suppose the independent variable θ is measured in degrees. Restate the properties of the sine function $y = a \sin b\theta$ on page 722 in terms of degrees. Which properties are affected by the conversion to degrees? **See margin.**

Find the period and amplitude of each sine function. Then sketch each function from 0 to 2π. 45–50. See margin pp. 726–727.

45. $y = -3.5 \sin 5\theta$ 46. $y = \frac{5}{2} \sin 2\theta$ 47. $y = -2 \sin 2\pi\theta$

48. $y = 0.4 \sin 3\theta$ 49. $y = 0.5 \sin \frac{\pi}{3}\theta$ 50. $y = -1.2 \sin \frac{5\pi}{6}\theta$

51. **Open-Ended** Write the equations of three sine functions with the same amplitude that have periods of 2, 3, and 4. Then sketch all three graphs on the same coordinate axes. **Check students' work.**

52. **Electricity** One type of electric generator consists of a rotating magnetic field surrounded by stationary coils. The voltages produced by the generator can be modeled by sine curves. Suppose three coils are placed symmetrically around a magnetic field. The graph below shows the voltages produced in each coil.

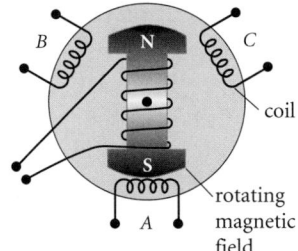

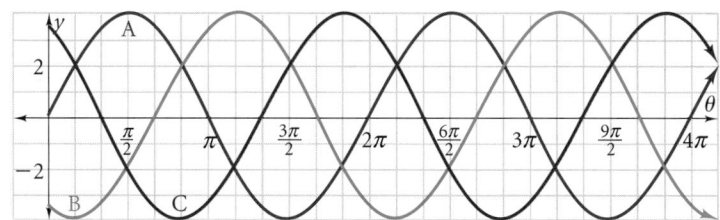

a. Find the amplitude and period of each sine curve. **4, 2π**

52b. $y = 4 \sin \theta$

b. Write an equation for the graph that models the voltage produced by coil A.

c. **Critical Thinking** One of the graphs has the equation $y = 4 \sin\left(\theta - \frac{2\pi}{3}\right)$. Use your knowledge of translations in the coordinate plane to predict whether this is the equation for coil B or coil C. Check your prediction using a graphing calculator. **coil B**

 **Challenge** **Sound** For sound waves, the period and the frequency of a pitch are reciprocals of each other: period = $\frac{\text{seconds}}{\text{cycle}}$ and frequency = $\frac{\text{cycles}}{\text{second}}$. Write an equation for each pitch. Let θ = time in seconds. Use $a = 1$.

53. the lowest pitch easily heard by humans: 30 cycles per second $y = \sin 60\pi\theta$

54. the lowest pitch heard by elephants: 15 cycles per second $y = \sin 30\pi\theta$

55. the highest pitch heard by bats: 120,000 cycles per second $y = \sin 240{,}000\pi\theta$

56–58. See margin p. 727.
Find the period and amplitude of each function. Sketch each function from 0 to 2π.

56. $y = \sin(\theta + 2)$ 57. $y = \sin(\theta - 3)$ 58. $y = \sin(2\theta + 4)$

726   Chapter 13 Periodic Functions and Trigonometry

---

46. $\pi, \frac{5}{2}$

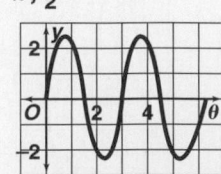

47. 1, 2

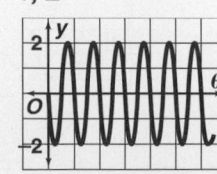

48. $\frac{2\pi}{3}$, 0.4

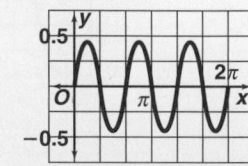

49. 6, 0.5

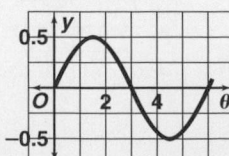

Solar Year

March 21st
equal day and night

June 21st
longest day

Dec. 21st
shortest day

Sept. 22nd
equal day and night

Not drawn to scale

🌐 59. **Astronomy** Sunrise and sunset are defined as the times when someone at sea level sees the uppermost edge of the sun on the horizon. In Houston, Texas, at the spring equinox (March 21), there are 12 hours and 9 minutes of sunlight. Throughout the year, the variation from 12 hours 9 minutes of sunlight can be modeled by a sine function. The longest day (June 21) has 1 hour 55 minutes more sunlight than at the equinox. The shortest day (December 21) has 1 hour 55 minutes less sunlight.
   a. Define the independent and dependent variables for a function that models the variation in hours of sunlight in Houston. **a–b. See margin.**
   b. What are the amplitude and period of the function measured in days?
   c. Write a function that relates the number of days away from the spring equinox to the variation in hours of sunlight in Houston. $y = \frac{23}{12} \sin \frac{2\pi x}{365}$
   d. **Estimation** Use your function from part (c). In Houston, about how much less sunlight does February 14 have than March 21? **1.1 h**
   e. **Research** Find the number of hours of sunlight in your area on June 21 and on December 21. Develop a sunlight model from your data. Use your model to predict the number of hours of sunlight you will have one week from now.
   Check students' work.

Resources

For additional practice with a variety of test item formats:
● Standardized Test Prep, p. 761
● Test-Taking Strategies, p. 756
● Test-Taking Strategies with Transparencies

Exercise 63 Point out that, since the period $= \frac{2\pi}{b}$, the value of b in $y = a \sin b\theta$ is $\frac{1}{2}$. This eliminates all but one of the responses.

Standardized Test Prep

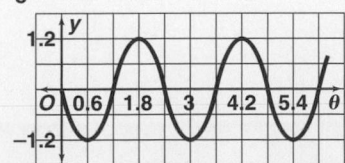

Multiple Choice

60. Which value is NOT the same as the other three values? **C**
   A. sin 100°　　　**B.** sin 80°　　　**C.** sin −80°　　　**D.** sin −260°

61. What is the amplitude of $y = 3 \sin 4\theta$? **G**
   F. $\frac{4}{3}$　　　**G.** 3　　　**H.** 4　　　**I.** 2π

62. Which answer choice describes $y = -\sin 2\theta$? **B**
   A. amplitude −1, period 4π　　**B.** amplitude 1, period π
   C. amplitude 2, period $-\pi$　　**D.** amplitude 2π, period 1

63. Which function has a period of 4π and an amplitude of 8?　**G**
   F. $y = -8 \sin 8\theta$　**G.** $y = -8 \sin \frac{1}{2}\theta$　**H.** $y = 8 \sin 2\theta$　**I.** $y = 4 \sin 8\theta$

Short Response

64. Find the value of θ that is between 90° and 180° such that $\sin \theta = \sin 60°$. Show your work. **See margin.**

Extended Response

65. The period of a sine function is 30° and its amplitude is 1. Write the function in the form $y = a \sin b\theta$, where θ is in radians. Show your work.
   See margin.

Take It to the NET
Online lesson quiz at
www.PHSchool.com
Web Code: aga-1304

Mixed Review

Lesson 13-3　Write each measure in radians. Express the answer in terms of π and as a decimal rounded to the nearest hundredth. **66–70. See margin.**
   66. −80°　　　**67.** 150°　　　**68.** −240°　　　**69.** 320°　　　**70.** −450°

Lesson 12-2　71. A poll of teenagers in one town showed that 43% play a team sport. It also showed that 21% play varsity team sports. Find the probability that a teenager plays varsity sports, given that the teenager plays a team sport. **≈49%**

Lesson 11-1　Write an explicit formula for each sequence. Then find a_{15}.
   72. 6, 5, 4, 3, . . .　　**73.** 15, 18, 21, 24, . . .　　**74.** 0.6, 1.4, 2.2, 3, . . .
   $a_n = 7 - n$; −8　　　$a_n = 12 + 3n$; 57　　　$a_n = 0.8n - 0.2$; 11.8

Lesson 13-4　The Sine Function　**727**

59a. days from spring equinox, hours of sunlight

b. $\frac{23}{12}$ h, about 365 days

c. $y = \frac{23}{12} \sin \frac{2\pi x}{365}$

64. **[2]** Since sine is always positive in the first and second quadrants, a value of θ where its sine is equal to the sin 60° would have a reference angle of 60°. 180° − 60° is equal to 120°.
   [1] answer only, with no work shown

65. **[4]** The amplitude is 1, so $a = 1$.
   $30° \cdot \frac{\pi \text{ radians}}{180°} = \frac{\pi}{6}$ radians, so $b = 2\pi \div \frac{\pi}{6} = 2\pi \cdot \frac{6}{\pi} = 12$.
   The function is $y = \sin 12\theta$.
   [3] one calculation error
   [2] incomplete explanation
   [1] answer only, with no work shown

66. $-\frac{4\pi}{9}$ radians, −1.40 radians

67. $\frac{5\pi}{6}$ radians, 2.62 radians

68. $-\frac{4\pi}{3}$ radians, −4.19 radians

69. $\frac{16\pi}{9}$ radians, 5.59 radians

70. $-\frac{5\pi}{2}$ radians, −7.85 radians

50. $\frac{12}{5}$, 1.2

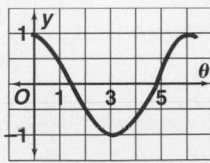

56. 2π, 1

57. 2π, 1

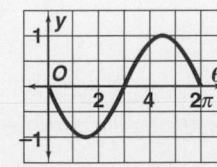

58. π, 1

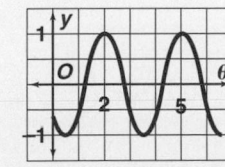

Graphing Trigonometric Functions

Students use a graphing calculator to graph both $y = \sin x$ and $y = \cos x$, for x in radians or degrees.

Resources

Any graphing calculator

Teaching Notes

1 EXAMPLE

Ask students: *Compare the window setting for Xmin for the two graphs.* **They are the same; one is in radians and the other is in degrees.**

Error Prevention

2 EXAMPLE

If students are having difficulty with graphing correctly, or using the TRACE function, have them work with a partner. Suggest that partners compare screens at each step to find errors.

Connection to History

In the early nineteenth century, French mathematical physicist Joseph Fourier, during his studies of heat flow, showed that many mathematical curves can be considered as the sum of simple sine and cosine functions. This is the basis of the oscilloscope.

page 728 Technology

2. 2π radians, 360°; 1

3. $\frac{2\pi}{3}$ radians, 120°; −1

4. 2π radians, 360°; −3

5. 2π radians, 360°; −0.5

You can use a graphing calculator to graph trigonometric functions in radians or degrees.

Take It to the NET
Graphing Calculator procedures online at
www.PHSchool.com
Web Code: age-2111

1 EXAMPLE **Comparing Graphs in Radians and Degrees**

Compare the graphs of $y = \cos x$ from −360° to 360° and from −2π to 2π radians.

Step 1 Press **MODE** to change the mode to degrees. Adjust the window values. Graph the function.

Step 2 Change the mode to radians. Graph the function.

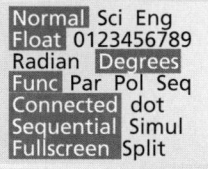

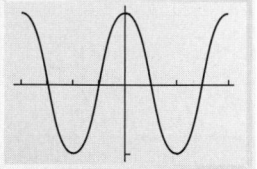

Xmin = −360   Ymin = −1.2
Xmax = 360   Ymax = 1.2
Xscl = 90   Yscl = 1

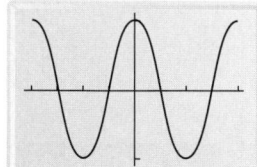
Xmin = −2π Ymin = −1.2
Xmax = 2π Ymax = 1.2
Xscl = π/2   Yscl = 1

The graphs appear to be identical, although in different windows. The function has a period of 360° or 2π radians.

You can use the **TRACE** feature to evaluate trigonometric functions.

2 EXAMPLE **Using the Trace Function**

Graph the function $y = \sin x$. Find sin 30° and sin 150°.

Step 1 Change the mode to degrees. Adjust the window values.

Step 2 Graph the function. Use the **TRACE** key to find the y-values when $x = 30$ and $x = 150$.

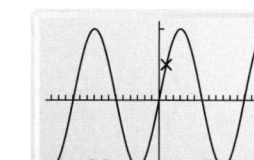
WINDOW FORMAT
Xmin=−470
Xmax=470
Xscl=30
Ymin=−1.2
Ymax=1.2
Yscl=1

Use these values to trace easily.

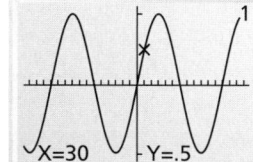
X=30   Y=.5

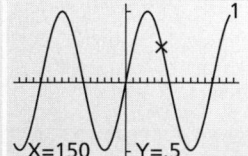
X=150   Y=.5

EXERCISES

Use appropriate window values to identify the period of each function in radians and in degrees. Then evaluate each function at 90°. 2–5. See margin.

1. $y = \cos x$ 2. $y = \sin x$ 3. $y = \sin 3x$ 4. $y = -3\sin x$ 5. $y = \cos(x + 30°)$

2π radians, 360°; 0

6. **Writing** Graph $y = \sin x$ and $y = \cos x$ in the same window. Compare the graphs. How are they similar? How are they different? **The graphs of $y = \sin x$ and $y = \cos x$ have the same period and amplitude. However, the graph of $y = \cos x$ is the graph of $y = \sin x$ translated horizontally $-\frac{\pi}{2}$ units.**

The Cosine Function

Lesson Preview

What You'll Learn

OBJECTIVE 1 To graph and write cosine functions

OBJECTIVE 2 To solve trigonometric equations

. . . And Why

To model wave motion, as in Example 3

✓ **Check Skills You'll Need**   (For help, go to Lesson 13-2.)

Find the x-coordinate of each point on the unit circle at the right.

1. A **1**   2. B **0**
3. C **−1**   4. D **0**

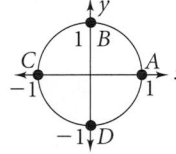

New Vocabulary • cosine function

Lesson Preview

✓ **Check Skills You'll Need**

Angles and the Unit Circle
Lesson 13-2: Example 4
Exercises 21–28
Extra Practice, p. 834

Lesson Resources

📁 **Teaching Resources**
Practice, Reteaching, Enrichment

👥 **Reaching All Students**
Practice Workbook 13-5
Spanish Practice Workbook 13-5
Technology Activities 14
Hands-On Activities 64

⏱ **Presentation Assistant Plus!**
Transparencies
• Check Skills You'll Need 13-5
• Additional Examples 13-5
• Student Edition Answers 13-5
• Lesson Quiz 13-5
PH Presentation Pro CD 13-5

ASSESSMENT SYSTEM

Computer Test Generator CD

💿 **Technology**
Resource Pro® CD-ROM
Computer Test Generator CD
Prentice Hall Presentation Pro CD

🖥 **www.PHSchool.com**
Student Site
• Teacher Web Code: agk-5500
• Self-grading Lesson Quiz
Teacher Center
• Lesson Planner
• Resources

Plus **iTEXT**

OBJECTIVE 1

Graphing and Writing Cosine Functions

iTEXT Interactive lesson includes instant self-check, tutorials, and activities.

The **cosine function,** $y = \cos \theta$, matches the measure θ of an angle in standard position with the x-coordinate of a point on the unit circle. This point is where the terminal side of the angle intersects the unit circle.

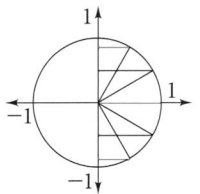 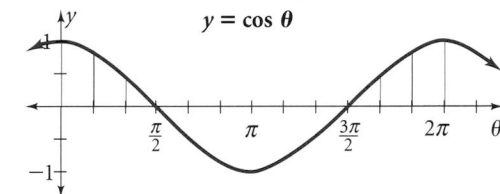

1 EXAMPLE **Interpreting the Graph of Cos θ**

Use the graph shown above.

a. Find the domain, period, range, and amplitude of the cosine function.

The domain of the function is all real numbers.

The function goes from its maximum value of 1 and back again in an interval from 0 to 2π. The period is 2π.

The function has a maximum value of 1 and a minimum value of -1. The range is $-1 \le y \le 1$.

$$\text{amplitude} = \tfrac{1}{2}(\text{maximum} - \text{minimum})$$
$$= \tfrac{1}{2}[1 - (-1)]$$
$$= 1$$

b. Examine the cycle of the cosine function in the interval from 0 to 2π. Where in the cycle does the maximum value occur? Where does the minimum occur? Where do the zeros occur?

The maximum value occurs at 0 and 2π. The minimum value occurs at π. The zeros occur at $\frac{\pi}{2}$ and $\frac{3\pi}{2}$.

Real-World 🌐 **Connection**

The distance over time between the center line of a metronome and a point on the metronome's swinging arm can be modeled with a cosine function.

✓ **Ongoing Assessment and Intervention**

Before the Lesson
Diagnose prerequisite skills using:
• Check Skills You'll Need

During the Lesson
Monitor progress using:
• Check Understanding
• Additional Examples
• Standardized Test Prep

After the Lesson
Assess knowledge using:
• Lesson Quiz
• Computer Test Generator CD

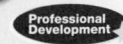

2. Teach

Professional Development

Math Background

The term "cosine" was first used by Edmund Gunter in 1620, who suggested combining the terms "complement" and "sine" into *cosinus* which was anglicized to "cosine." The sine was originally called *jya*, a Hindu word that means half-chord. This word was incorrectly translated (around 1150) into the Latin word *sinus* which is the term we now use in the form sine.

OBJECTIVE 1

Teaching Notes

1 EXAMPLE Visual Learners

Draw a sine curve on a transparency. Place it on the overhead projector over a transparency with a coordinate system. Ask a student to shift (or translate) the sine curve so that it shows the cosine curve.

Additional Examples

1 Use the graph shown below.

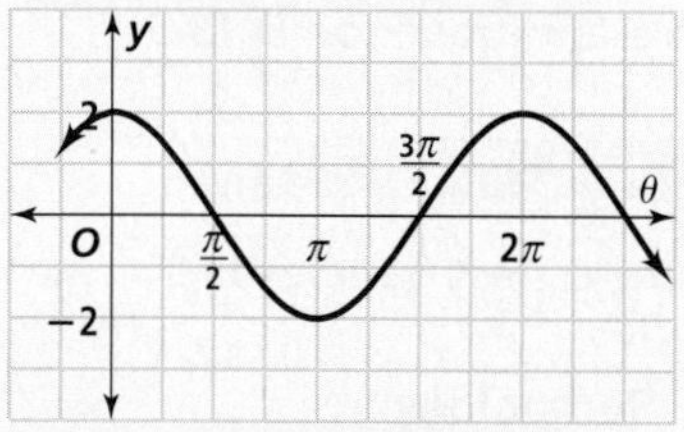

a. Find the domain, period, range, and amplitude of the cosine function. **all real numbers; 2π; $-2 \le y \le 2$; 2**

b. Examine the cycle of the cosine function in the interval from 0 to 2π. Where in the cycle does the maximum value occur? Where does the minimum occur? Where do the zeros occur? **0, 2π; π; $\frac{\pi}{2}$, $\frac{3\pi}{2}$**

2 Sketch the graph of $y = -2 \cos \pi\theta$ in the interval from 0 to 4.

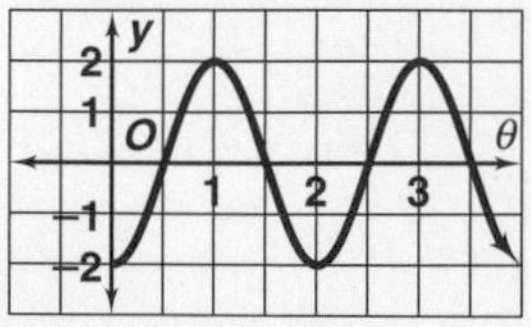

Check Understanding 1 Use the graphs below. How are the graphs of the sine and cosine functions alike? How are they different?

1. They are the same curve translated $\frac{\pi}{2}$ units horizontally.

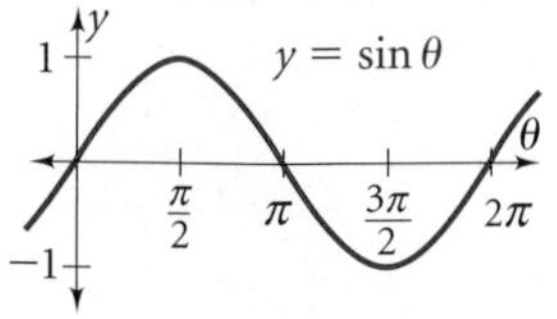

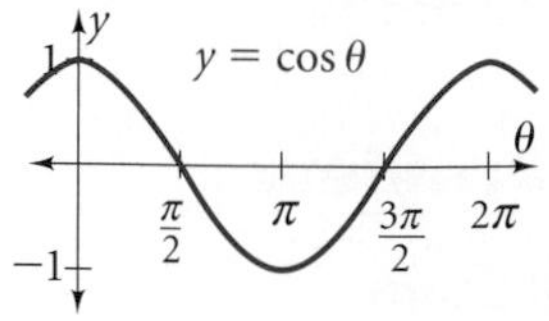

The cosine function has some of the same properties as the sine function.

Key Concepts

Summary **Properties of Cosine Functions**

Suppose $y = a \cos b\theta$, with $a \neq 0$, $b > 0$, and θ in radians.

- $|a|$ is the amplitude of the function.
- b is the number of cycles in the interval from 0 to 2π.
- $\frac{2\pi}{b}$ is the period of the function.

To graph a cosine function, locate five points equally spaced through one cycle. For $a > 0$, this five-point pattern is *max–zero–min–zero–max.*

2 EXAMPLE Sketching the Graph of a Cosine Function

Sketch the graph of $y = 1.5 \cos 2\theta$ in the interval from 0 to 2π.

$|a| = 1.5$, so the amplitude is 1.5.

$b = 2$, so the graph has two full cycles from 0 to 2π.

$\frac{2\pi}{b} = \pi$, so the period is π.

Divide the period into fourths. Plot five points for the first cycle. Use 1.5 for the maximum and −1.5 for the minimum. Repeat the pattern for the second cycle.

Sketch the curve.

Choose scales for axes that are about equal ($\frac{\pi}{3} \approx 1$).

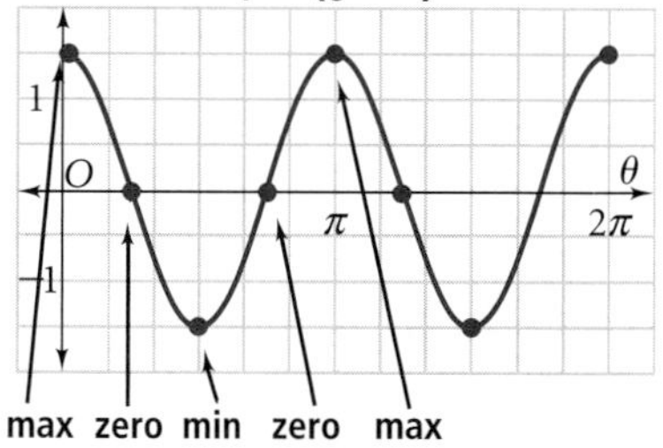

2a.

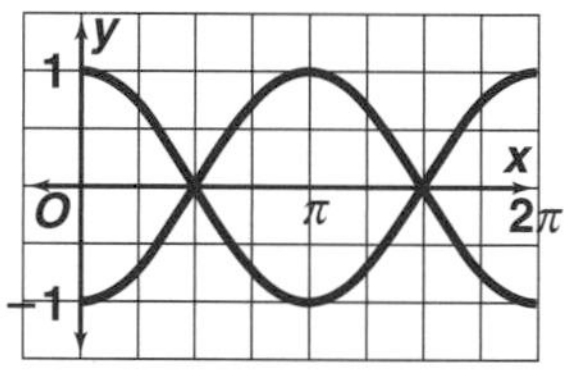

They are reflections of each other over the *x*-axis.

b. min-zero-max-zero-min

Check Understanding 2 a. Graph the equations $y = \cos x$ and $y = -\cos x$ on the same coordinate plane. Compare the graphs. **a–b. See left.**

b. **Critical Thinking** Write the five-point pattern to graph $y = a \cos b\theta$ when $a < 0$.

c. Sketch the cosine curve $y = -\frac{1}{2} \cos \pi\theta$ in the interval from 0 to 2π.

See margin p. 731.

OBJECTIVE 2

Solving Trigonometric Equations

Waves of water show periodic motion. Away from the shore, individual water molecules move up and down, returning to their initial position after a wave passes. Their height can be modeled with a cosine function.

Reaching All Students

Below Level Make sure students understand that because the sine and cosine function are the same curve, shifted $\frac{\pi}{2}$ radians, the functions have the same maximum and minimum values.	**Advanced Learners** Ask students to use the unit circle and the Pythagorean theorem to justify the equation $(\sin \theta)^2 + (\cos \theta)^2 = 1$, and share their justifications.	**Visual Learners** See note on page 730. **Tactile Learners** See note on page 731.

Real-World  **Connection**

The regular waves in a wave pool can be modeled with a cosine function.

---

3 EXAMPLE Real-World 🌐 Connection

Wave Motion The figures at the right show the vertical motion of a water molecule as a wave moves by. Suppose 10-in. waves occur every 4 s. Write an equation that models the height of the water molecule as it moves from crest to crest.

wave direction ──▶

10 in.

Particle is at the crest of the wave.

The equation will have the form $y = a \cos b\theta$. Find values for a and b.

$a = \frac{10}{2}$ **amplitude** $= \frac{\text{maximum} - \text{minimum}}{2}$

$= 5$ **Simplify.**

period $= \frac{2\pi}{b}$ **Use the formula for the period.**

$4 = \frac{2\pi}{b}$ **The period is 4. Substitute.**

$b = \frac{2\pi}{4}$ **Multiply each side by $\frac{b}{4}$.**

$= \frac{\pi}{2}$ **Simplify.**

Particle is in the trough of the wave.

An equation that models the height of the water molecule is $y = 5 \cos \frac{\pi}{2}\theta$.

✓ **Check Understanding** ③ Write a cosine function for each description. Choose $a > 0$.
 a. amplitude 4, period 6π **a.** $y = 4 \cos \frac{1}{3}\theta$
 b. amplitude 2.5, period 8   **b.** $y = 2.5 \cos \frac{\pi}{4}\theta$

You can solve an equation by graphing to find an exact location along a sine or cosine curve.

4 EXAMPLE Solving a Cosine Equation

Suppose you want to find the time t in seconds when the water particle from Example 3 is exactly 3 in. above the average height represented by $y = 0$. Solve $5 \cos \frac{\pi}{2}t = 3$ in the interval from 0 to 8.

Graphing Calculator Hint

When you use the Intersect feature, move the cursor close to the desired point after the Guess? prompt appears.

Step 1 Use two equations. Graph the equations $y = 3$ and $y = 5 \cos \frac{\pi}{2}t$ on the same screen.

Step 2 Use the Intersect feature to find the points at which the two graphs intersect.

The graph shows four solutions in the interval. They are $t \approx 0.6$, 3.4, 4.6, and 7.4.

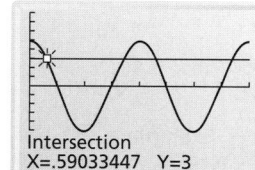

Xmin=0
Xmax=8
Xscl=1
Ymin=−8
Ymax=8
Yscl=1

Intersection
X=.59033447 Y=3

The water particle is 3 in. above the average height at about 0.6, 3.4, 4.6, and 7.4 s.

✓ **Check Understanding** ④ Find all solutions in the interval from 0 to 2π.
 a. $3 \cos 2t = -2$ **a.** 1.2, 2.0, 4.3, 5.1
 b. $-2 \cos \theta = 1.2$ **b.** 2.2, 4.1
 c. Critical Thinking In the interval from 0 to 2π, when is $-2 \cos \theta$ less than 1.2? Greater than 1.2? **$0 \le \theta < 2.2$ and $4.1 < \theta \le 2\pi$; $2.2 < \theta < 4.1$**

---

3 EXAMPLE Connection to Oceanography

Tsunami is a Japanese word derived from the characters "harbor" and "wave.". Tsunamis are giant waves, usually caused by earthquakes under the ocean. A tsunami with waves as high as 15 meters occurred in 1998 in Papua, New Guinea.

4 EXAMPLE Tactile Learners

To model the nature of a wave, bring a few yards of cloth to class. You hold one end of the cloth still while a volunteer generates waves by moving the other end up and down. Have a second volunteer hold a yardstick horizontally to show the average height.

4 EXAMPLE Technology Tip

The graphing calculator must be set to radians to use the given window settings.

Additional Examples

③ Suppose 8-in. waves occur every 6 s. Write an equation that models the height of a water molecule as it moves from crest to crest. $y = 4 \cos \frac{\pi}{3}\theta$.

④ Solve the equation $1 = -2 \cos \left(\frac{2x}{3}\right)$ in the interval from 0 to 10. **about 3.14 and 6.28, or π and 2π.**

Closure

Ask students: *How is the graph of the cosine function different from the graph of the sine function? How is it the same?* **The graphs are both the same periodic curve, except the graph of the cosine function is translated 90°, or $\frac{\pi}{2}$ radians to the left of the graph of the sine function.**

---

page 730 Check Understanding

2c.

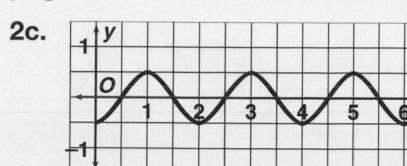

731

Error Prevention

Exercises 5–9 Remind students that these are cosine functions, so the *y*-value at zero radians is the maximum or minimum value for the function, not zero as it is for a sine function.

Careers

Exercise 35 Oceanographers collect many kinds of data every day, such as making measurements of wave heights, tides, and the width of the beach in order to measure erosion over a period of time.

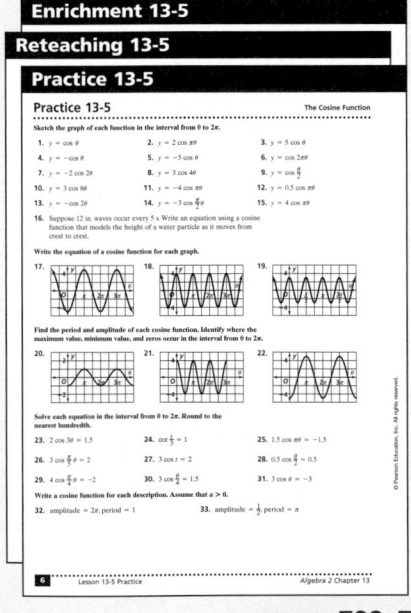

EXERCISES

For more practice, see *Extra Practice*.

Practice and Problem Solving

Ⓐ **Practice by Example**

Example 1
(page 729)

1. 2π, 3; max: 3, min: -3, zeros: $\frac{\pi}{2}$, $\frac{3\pi}{2}$

2. $\frac{2\pi}{3}$, 1; max: 1, min: -1, zeros: $\frac{\pi}{6}$, $\frac{\pi}{2}$, $\frac{5\pi}{6}$, $\frac{7\pi}{6}$, $\frac{3\pi}{2}$, $\frac{11\pi}{6}$

3. π, 1; max: 1, min: -1, zeros: $\frac{\pi}{4}$, $\frac{3\pi}{4}$, $\frac{5\pi}{4}$, $\frac{7\pi}{4}$

4. 2π, 2; max: 2, min: -2, zeros: $\frac{\pi}{2}$, $\frac{3\pi}{2}$

Find the period and amplitude of each cosine function. At what values of *x* for $0 \le x \le 2\pi$ do the maximum value(s), minimum value(s), and zeros occur?

1.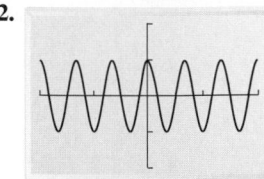
Xmin=-2π
Xmax=2π
Xscl=π
Ymin=-4
Ymax=4
Yscl=1

2.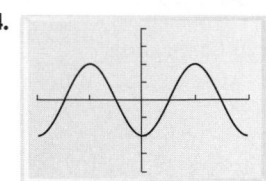
Xmin=-2π
Xmax=2π
Xscl=π
Ymin=-2
Ymax=2
Yscl=1

3.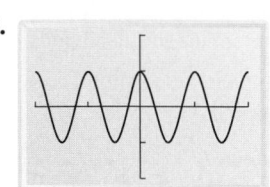
Xmin=-2π
Xmax=2π
Xscl=π
Ymin=-2
Ymax=2
Yscl=1

4.
Xmin=-2π
Xmax=2π
Xscl=π
Ymin=-4
Ymax=4
Yscl=1

Example 2
(page 730)

Sketch the graph of each function in the interval from 0 to 2π.

5. $y = \cos 2\theta$ 6. $y = -3 \cos \theta$ 7. $y = -\cos 3t$ 8. $y = \cos \frac{\pi}{2}\theta$ 9. $y = -\cos \pi\theta$
5–9. See margin pp. 732–733.

Example 3
(page 731)

Write a cosine function for each description. Assume that $a > 0$.

10. amplitude 2, period π 11. amplitude $\frac{\pi}{2}$, period 3   12. amplitude π, period 2
   $y = 2 \cos 2\theta$ $y = \frac{\pi}{2} \cos \frac{2\pi}{3}\theta$ $y = \pi \cos \pi\theta$

Write an equation of a cosine function for each graph.

13.

14.

$y = -3 \cos 2\theta$ $y = 2 \cos \frac{\pi}{4}\theta$

15. **Wave Motion** Suppose 8-in. waves pass every 3 s. Write an equation that models the height of a water molecule as it moves from crest to crest.
  $y = 4 \cos \frac{2\pi}{3}\theta$

16. 0.52, 2.62, 3.67, 5.76

17. 1.98, 4.30

18. 0.55, 1.45, 2.55, 3.45, 4.55, 5.45

Example 4
(page 731)

Solve each equation in the interval from 0 to 2π. Round to the nearest hundredth.

16. $\cos 2t = \frac{1}{2}$ 17. $20 \cos t = -8$ 18. $-2 \cos \pi\theta = 0.3$

19. $3 \cos \frac{t}{3} = 2$ **2.52**   20. $\cos \frac{1}{4}\theta = 1$ **0.00**   21. $8 \cos \frac{\pi}{3}t = 5$
                                                    0.86, 5.14

Ⓑ **Apply Your Skills**

Identify the period, range, and amplitude of each function.

22. $y = 3 \cos \theta$ 23. $y = -\cos 2t$ 24. $y = 2 \cos \frac{1}{2}t$ 25. $y = \frac{1}{3} \cos \frac{\theta}{2}$

26. $y = 3 \cos \left(-\frac{\theta}{3}\right)$ 27. $y = -\frac{1}{2} \cos 3\theta$ 28. $y = 16 \cos \frac{3\pi}{2}t$ 29. $y = 0.7 \cos \pi t$
22–29. See margin p. 733.

Solve each equation in the interval from 0 to 2π. Round your answers to the nearest hundredth.

30. $\sin \theta = 0.6$ 31. $-3 \sin 2\theta = 1.5$ 32. $\sin \pi\theta = 1$
   0.64, 2.50   **1.83, 2.88, 4.97, 6.02**   **0.50, 2.50, 4.50**

732   **Chapter 13** Periodic Functions and Trigonometry

pages 732–734 **Exercises**

5.

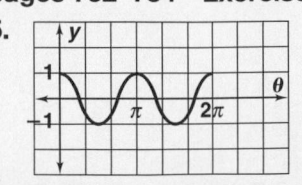

6.

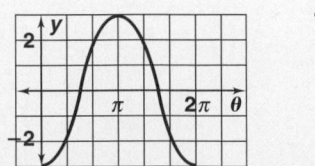

7.

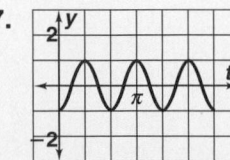

8.

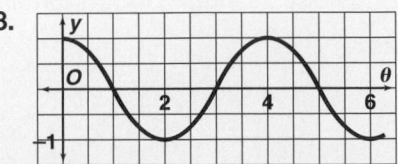

33. a. Solve $-2 \sin \theta = 1.2$ in the interval from 0 to 2π. **3.79, 5.64**
  b. Solve $-2 \sin \theta = 1.2$ in the interval $2\pi \leq \theta \leq 4\pi$. How are these solutions related to the solutions in part (a)?

34. a. Graph the equation $y = 5 \cos \frac{\pi}{2}\theta$ from Example 3. **a–b. See back of book.**
  b. The independent variable θ represents time (in seconds). Find four times at which the particle is at the crest of a wave.
  c. For how many seconds during each cycle is the particle above the line $y = 0$? Below $y = 0$? **2 s; 2 s**

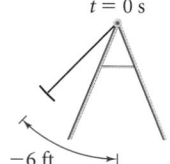 **35. Tides** The table at the right shows the times for high tide and low tide. The markings on the side of a local pier showed a high tide of 7 ft and a low tide of 4 ft on the previous day.

Tide Table	
High tide	4:03 A.M.
Low tide	10:14 A.M.
High tide	4:25 P.M.
Low tide	10:36 P.M.

  a. What is the average depth of water at the pier? What is the amplitude of the variation from the average depth? **a–b. See left.**
  b. How long is one cycle of the tide?
  c. Write a cosine function that models the relationship between the depth of water and the time of day. Use $y = 0$ to represent the average depth of water. Use $t = 0$ to represent the time 4:03 A.M. $y = 1.5 \cos \frac{2\pi t}{742}$
  d. Critical Thinking Suppose your boat needs at least 5 ft of water to approach or leave the pier. Between what times could you come and go?
    12:17 A.M.–7:49 A.M., 12:39 P.M.–8:11 P.M.

Real-World  **Connection**

Commercial fishermen, including clam diggers, work in relation to the tides.

35a. 5.5 ft; 1.5 ft

  b. about 12 h 22 min

36c.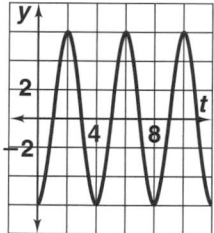

5

e. Yes; at 13.5 s you are 4.24 ft and the puddle is from 4 to 6 ft.

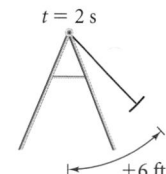 **36. Recreation** Suppose a friend gives you a push on a swing. Your friend starts by pulling you backward six feet and letting go.

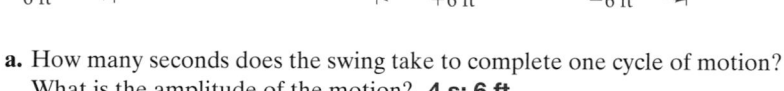

  a. How many seconds does the swing take to complete one cycle of motion? What is the amplitude of the motion? **4 s; 6 ft**
  b. Modeling Suppose you maintain the rate and amplitude of your swinging. Express your arc distance from the resting point of the swing as a function of time. Use a cosine function. $y = -6 \cos \frac{\pi}{2}t$
  c. Graph the function you wrote in part (b). In the interval from 0 s to 10 s, how many times do you pass the resting point of the swing? **See left.**
  d. Write an equation to find the times in the first 10 s that you are exactly 3 ft forward (of the resting point) in your swing. $-6 \cos \frac{\pi}{2}t = 3$
  e. Writing Refer to the diagram at the right. Suppose you jump from the swing 13.5 s after you start. Will you land in the puddle? Justify your answer. **See left.**

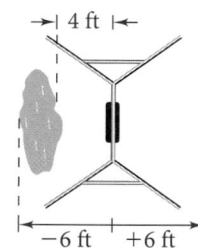

C Challenge 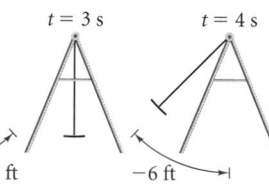 **37. a.** Graph $y = \cos \theta$ and $y = \cos\left(\theta - \frac{\pi}{2}\right)$ in the interval from 0 to 2π. What translation of the graph of $y = \cos \theta$ produces the graph of $y = \cos\left(\theta - \frac{\pi}{2}\right)$?
  b. Graph $y = \cos\left(\theta - \frac{\pi}{2}\right)$ and $y = \sin \theta$ in the interval from 0 to 2π. What do you notice? **a–c. See margin.**
  c. Critical Thinking Explain how you could rewrite a sine function as a cosine function.

9.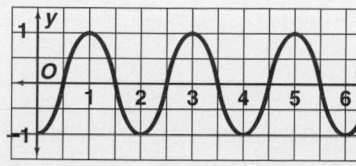

22. 2π, $-3 \leq y \leq 3$, 3
23. π, $-1 \leq y \leq 1$, 1
24. 4π, $-2 \leq y \leq 2$, 2
25. 4π, $-\frac{1}{3} \leq y \leq \frac{1}{3}$, $\frac{1}{3}$
26. 6π, $-3 \leq y \leq 3$, 3
27. $\frac{2\pi}{3}$, $-\frac{1}{2} \leq y \leq \frac{1}{2}$, $\frac{1}{2}$
28. $\frac{4}{3}$, $-16 \leq y \leq 16$, 16
29. 2, $-0.7 \leq y \leq 0.7$, 0.7

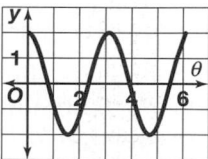
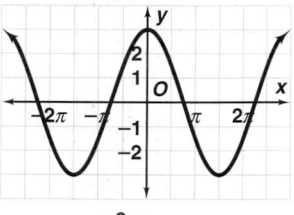 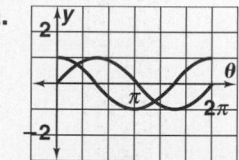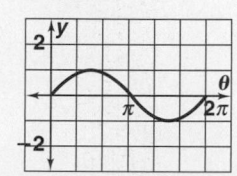

Standardized Test Prep

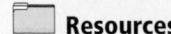

Resources

For additional practice with a variety of test item formats:
- Standardized Test Prep, p. 761
- Test-Taking Strategies, p. 756
- Test-Taking Strategies with Transparencies

pages 732–734   Exercises

39. On the unit circle, the x-values of $-\theta$ are equal to the x-values of θ, 10 $\cos(-\theta) = \cos \theta$. $-\cos \theta$ is the opposite of $\cos \theta$, so these graphs are reflections of each other over the x-axis.

46.

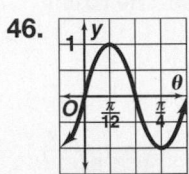

$y = \sin 6\theta$

47.

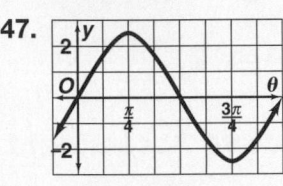

$y = \frac{5}{2} \sin 2\theta$

48.

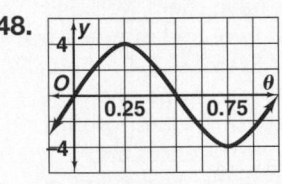

$y = 4 \sin 2\pi\theta$

52. $a_n = 10 \cdot 3^{n-1}$; 10, 30, 90, 270, 810

53. $a_n = 12(-0.3)^{n-1}$; 12, −3.6, 1.08, −0.324, 0.0972

54. $a_n = 900\left(-\frac{1}{3}\right)^{n-1}$; 900, −300, 100, $-\frac{100}{3}$, $\frac{100}{9}$

38. Biology A helix is a three-dimensional spiral. The coiled strands of DNA and the edges of twisted crepe paper are examples of helixes. In the diagram, the y-coordinate of each edge illustrates a cosine function. Write an equation for the y-coordinate of one edge. $y = \cos \frac{\pi}{12}x$ or $y = -\cos \frac{\pi}{12}x$

39. Graph one cycle of $y = \cos \theta$, one cycle of $y = -\cos \theta$, and one cycle of $y = \cos(-\theta)$ on the same set of axes. Use the unit circle to explain any relationships you see among these graphs. **See margin.**

Standardized Test Prep

Multiple Choice

40. Which statement(s) is (are) true? **A**

I. $\cos \theta = \cos(-\theta)$ II. $\cos(\theta + 2\pi) = \cos \theta$ III. $\cos \pi = -\cos \pi$

A. I and II only   B. II only   C. I and III only   D. I, II, and III

Quantitative Comparison

Compare the boxed quantity in Column A with the boxed quantity in Column B. Choose the best answer.

A. The quantity in Column A is greater.
B. The quantity in Column B is greater.
C. The two quantities are equal.
D. The relationship cannot be determined from the information given.

Take It to the NET
Online lesson quiz at
www.PHSchool.com
Web Code: aga-1305

	Column A	Column B
41. A	$\sin \frac{\pi}{2}$	$\cos(-\pi)$
42. C	$\sin \frac{\pi}{2}$	$\cos 0$
43. D	$\cos \theta$	$\sin 2\theta$
44. C	$\cos(\theta + 2\pi)$	$\cos(-\theta)$
45. C	$\cos \pi$	$\sin \frac{3\pi}{2}$

Mixed Review

Lesson 13-4

Sketch one cycle of each sine curve. Assume that $a > 0$. Then write an equation for each graph. **46–48. See margin.**

46. amplitude 1, period $\frac{\pi}{3}$ **47.** amplitude 2.5, period π **48.** amplitude 4, period 1

Lesson 12-5

Find the sample size that produces each margin of error.

49. ±3% **about 1111**   **50.** ±7% **about 204**   **51.** ±11% **about 83**

Lesson 11-3

Write the explicit formula for each sequence. Then generate the first five terms.

52. $a_1 = 10, r = 3$ **53.** $a_1 = 12, r = -0.3$ **54.** $a_1 = 900, r = -\frac{1}{3}$
52–54. See margin.

The Tangent Function

Lesson Preview

What You'll Learn

 OBJECTIVE To graph the tangent function

...And Why

To model the facade of a building, as in Example 3

✔ **Check Skills You'll Need** (For help, go to Lesson 13-3.)

Use a calculator to find the sine and cosine of each value of θ. Then calculate the ratio $\frac{\sin \theta}{\cos \theta}$.

1. $\frac{\pi}{3}$ radians ≈0.87, 0.5; 1.73
2. 30 degrees 0.5, ≈0.87; ≈0.58
3. 90 degrees 1, 0; undefined
4. $\frac{5\pi}{6}$ radians 0.5, ≈−0.87; ≈−0.58
5. $\frac{5\pi}{2}$ radians 1, 0; undefined
6. 0 degrees 0, 1; 0

New Vocabulary • tangent of θ • tangent function

OBJECTIVE

1 Graphing the Tangent Function

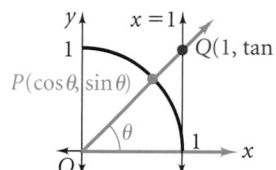 **Interactive lesson includes instant self-check, tutorials, and activities.**

? **Need Help?**

A line tangent to a circle intersects the circle at exactly one point.

The sine and cosine of an angle derive from the coordinates of a point on the unit circle. The tangent of an angle derives from the coordinates of a point on a line *tangent* to the unit circle.

For an angle θ in standard position, the **tangent of θ** is the y-coordinate of the point where the line containing the terminal side of the angle intersects the tangent line $x = 1$.

The line containing the terminal side of θ intersects the line $x = 1$ at Q.

The graph below shows one cycle of the **tangent function,** $y = \tan \theta$. Since the period is π, the asymptote that occurs at $\theta = \frac{\pi}{2}$ repeats every π units.

$y = \tan \theta$

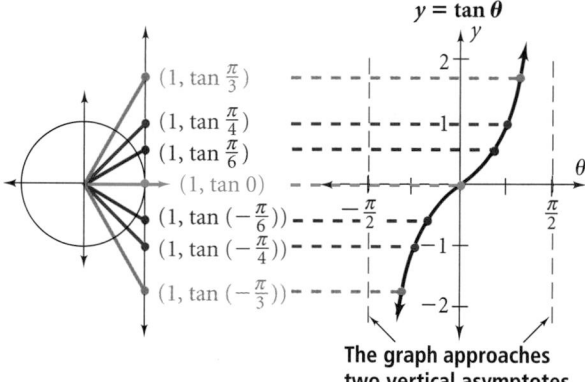

The graph approaches two vertical asymptotes.

You can estimate function values from the graph of the tangent function.

 Ongoing Assessment and Intervention

Before the Lesson	During the Lesson	After the Lesson
Diagnose prerequisite skills using:	**Monitor progress using:**	**Assess knowledge using:**
• Check Skills You'll Need	• Check Understanding	• Lesson Quiz
	• Additional Examples	• Computer Test Generator CD
	• Standardized Test Prep	

Lesson Preview

✔ **Check Skills You'll Need**

Angles and the Unit Circle
Lesson 13-4: Example 4
Exercises 24–28
Extra Practice, p. 834

Lesson Resources

📁 **Teaching Resources**
Practice, Reteaching, Enrichment

👥 **Reaching All Students**
Practice Workbook 13-6
Spanish Practice Workbook 13-6
Hands-On Activities 65

⏱ **Presentation Assistant Plus!**
Transparencies
• Check Skills You'll Need 13-6
• Additional Examples 13-6
• Student Edition Answers 13-6
• Lesson Quiz 13-6
PH Presentation Pro CD 13-6

PRENTICE HALL ASSESSMENT SYSTEM

Computer Test Generator CD

🖥 **Technology**
Resource Pro® CD-ROM
Computer Test Generator CD
Prentice Hall Presentation Pro CD

💻 **www.PHSchool.com**
Student Site
• Teacher Web Code: agk-5500
• Self-grading Lesson Quiz
Teacher Center
• Lesson Planner
• Resources

Plus

Math Background

The sine and cosine functions were first used in the context of astronomy, but the tangent function was developed in response to requirements for practical measurements of heights and distances.

OBJECTIVE

Teaching Notes

1 **EXAMPLE** English Learners

Review the meaning and pronunciation of asymptote (AS-im-tote).

Additional Examples

1 Use the graph of the tangent function shown in Example 1 to find each value.
a. $\tan -45°$ **−1**
b. $\tan 0°$ **0**
c. $\tan 45°$ **1**

2 Sketch two cycles of the graph of $y = \tan \frac{\theta}{2}$

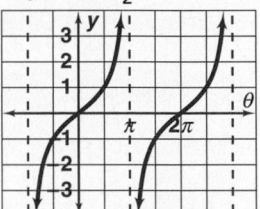

3 What is the height of the triangle in the design from Example 3 when $\theta = 18°$? What is the height when $\theta = 20°$? **about 32.5 ft; about 36.4 ft**

Closure

Ask students: *How is the graph of the tangent function the same as the graphs of the cosine and sine functions? How is it different?*
The graph of the tangent function is periodic like the sine and cosine functions, but unlike those functions, the graph has vertical asymptotes at $x = \pm\frac{\pi}{2}$ and every odd multiple of $\pm\frac{\pi}{2}$.

736

---

1 **EXAMPLE** **Finding Tangent Values From a Graph**

Use the graph of $y = \tan \theta$ at the right to find each value.

a. $\tan\left(-\frac{\pi}{4}\right)$ $\quad \tan\left(-\frac{\pi}{4}\right) = -1$
b. $\tan 0$ $\quad \tan 0 = 0$
c. $\tan \frac{\pi}{4}$ $\quad \tan \frac{\pi}{4} = 1$

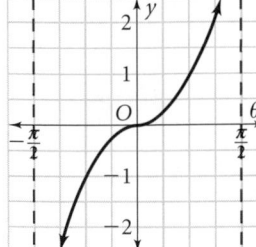

✓ **Check Understanding** **1** a. Use the graph in Example 1 to find $\tan \frac{\pi}{8}$ and $\tan\left(-\frac{\pi}{8}\right)$. **0.4, −0.4**
b. **Critical Thinking** Explain why the terminal side of an angle with measure $\frac{\pi}{2}$ *does not intersect* the tangent line. **The terminal side of $\frac{\pi}{2}$ lies on the line $x = 0$, which cannot intersect $x = 1$.**

The graph in Example 1 shows one cycle of the tangent function, $y = \tan \theta$. Since the period is π, the asymptote that occurs at $\theta = \frac{\pi}{2}$ is repeated every π units.

🔧 **Key Concepts**

Summary	**Properties of Tangent Functions**

Suppose $y = a \tan b\theta$, with $b > 0$ and θ in radians.
- $\frac{\pi}{b}$ is the period of the function.
- One cycle occurs in the interval from $-\frac{\pi}{2b}$ to $\frac{\pi}{2b}$.
- There are vertical asymptotes at each end of the cycle.

You can use asymptotes and three points to sketch one cycle of a tangent curve. As with sine and cosine, the five elements are equally spaced through one cycle. Use the pattern *asymptote–(−a)–zero–(a)–asymptote*. In the graph at the right, $a = b = 1$.

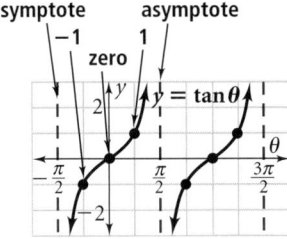

The next example shows how to use the period, asymptotes, and points to graph a tangent function.

2 **EXAMPLE** **Graphing a Tangent Function**

Sketch two cycles of the graph of $y = \tan \pi\theta$.

$period = \frac{\pi}{b}$ **Use the formula for the period.**

$\quad\quad\quad = \frac{\pi}{\pi} = 1$ **Substitute π for b and simplify.**

One cycle occurs in the interval from $-\frac{1}{2}$ to $\frac{1}{2}$.
Asymptotes occur every 1 unit, at $\theta = -\frac{1}{2}, \frac{1}{2},$ and $\frac{3}{2}$.
Since $a = 1$, $\left(-\frac{1}{4}, -1\right)$ and $\left(\frac{1}{4}, 1\right)$ are on the graph.
Plot three points in each cycle. Sketch the curve.

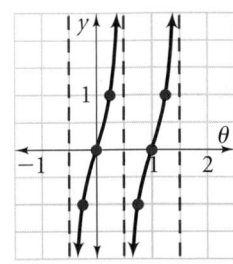

736 Chapter 13 Periodic Functions and Trigonometry

👥 **Reaching All Students**

Below Level Defining the tangent function as $\tan \theta = \frac{y}{x} = \frac{\sin \theta}{\cos \theta}$ may help some students see why some values of θ must be excluded from the domain.	**Advanced Learners** Have students research and report on how the trigonometric functions are defined in terms of a right triangle.	**English Learners** See note on page 736. **Error Prevention** See note on page 738.

✓ **Check Understanding** ② Sketch the graph of each tangent curve from 0 to π. **See below left.**
   a. $y = \tan 3\theta$ **b.** $y = \tan \frac{\pi}{2}\theta$

You can use the tangent function and a graphing calculator to solve problems involving angles.

2a.
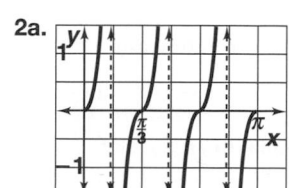

b.
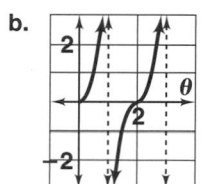

③ **EXAMPLE**   **Real-World** 🌐 **Connection**

Design An architect is designing the front facade of a building to include a triangle, as shown in the figure. The base of the triangle is 200 ft wide. The function $y = 100 \tan \theta$ models the height of the triangle, where θ is the angle indicated. Graph the function in degree mode. What is the height of the triangle when $\theta = 16°$? What is the height when $\theta = 22°$?

Not drawn to scale

Step 1 Graph the function.

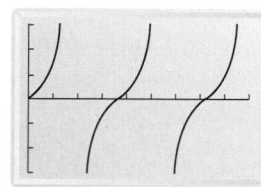

Xmin=0
Xmax=470
Xscl=50
Ymin=−300
Ymax=300
Yscl=90

Step 2 Use the TABLE feature.

X	Y₁
16	28.675
17	30.573
18	32.492
19	34.433
20	36.397
21	38.386
22	40.403
X=16	

When $\theta = 16°$, the height of the triangle is about 28.7 ft. When $\theta = 22°$, the height of the triangle is about 40.4 ft.

✓ **Check Understanding** ③ **a.** What is the height of the triangle when $\theta = 25°$? ≈**46.6 ft**
   b. Reasoning The architect wants the triangle to be at least one story tall. The average height of a story is 14 ft. What must the measure of θ be for the height of the triangle to be at least 14 ft? ≈**8°**

Assignment Guide

▼ **Objective**
   Ⓐ Ⓑ Core 1–42
   Ⓒ Extension 43–45

Standardized Test Prep 46–52

Mixed Review 53–67

Enrichment 13-6
Reteaching 13-6
Practice 13-6

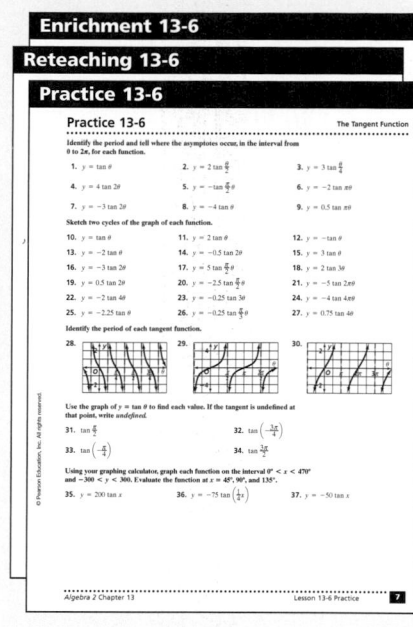

EXERCISES

For more practice, see *Extra Practice*.

Practice and Problem Solving

Ⓐ **Practice by Example**

Example 1
(page 736)

Use the graph of $y = \tan \theta$ to find each value. If the tangent is undefined at that point, write *undefined*.

1. $\tan(-\pi)$ **0**   **2.** $\tan \pi$ **0**

3. $\tan \frac{3\pi}{4}$ **−1**   **4.** $\tan \frac{\pi}{2}$ **undefined**

5. $\tan\left(-\frac{7\pi}{4}\right)$ **1**   **6.** $\tan 2\pi$ **0**

7. $\tan\left(-\frac{3\pi}{4}\right)$ **1**   **8.** $\tan \frac{3\pi}{2}$
                                                 undefined

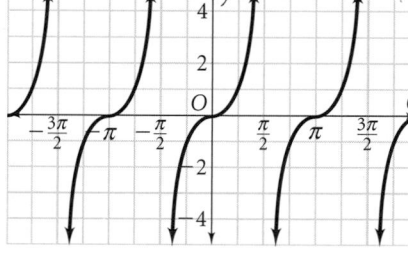

pages 737–740 Exercises

15.

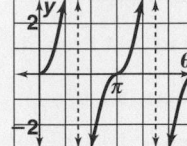

16.

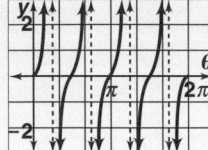

17.

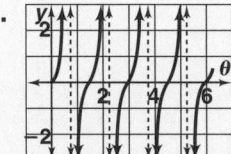

18.

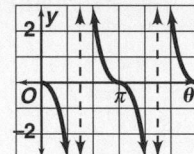

19.

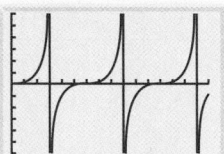

50, undefined, −50

20.

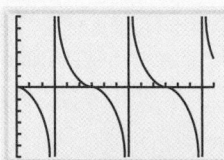

−100, undefined, 100

21.

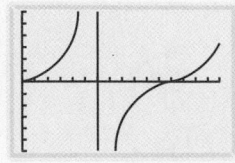

51.8, 125, 301.8

22a.

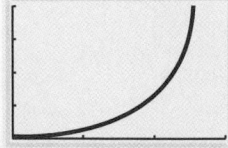

738

Example 2
(page 736)

Each graphing calculator screen shows the interval 0 to 2π. What is the period of each graph?

9.
π

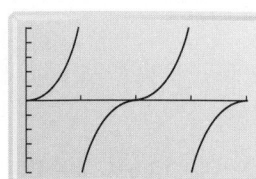

10.
$\frac{\pi}{2}$

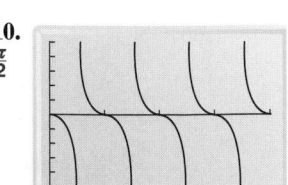

11. $\frac{\pi}{5}$, $\theta = -\frac{\pi}{10}, \frac{\pi}{10}$

12. $\frac{2\pi}{3}$, $\theta = -\frac{\pi}{3}, \frac{\pi}{3}$

13. $\frac{\pi}{4}$, $\theta = -\frac{\pi}{8}, \frac{\pi}{8}$

14. $\frac{3\pi^2}{2}$, $\theta = -\frac{3\pi^2}{4}, \frac{3\pi^2}{4}$

Identify the period and tell where two asymptotes occur for each function.

11. $y = \tan 5\theta$ **12.** $y = \tan \frac{3\theta}{2}$ **13.** $y = \tan 4\theta$ **14.** $y = \tan \frac{2}{3\pi}\theta$

Sketch the graph of each tangent curve in the interval from 0 to 2π.

15. $y = \tan \theta$ **16.** $y = \tan 2\theta$ **17.** $y = \tan \frac{2\pi}{3}\theta$ **18.** $y = \tan(-\theta)$
15–18. See margin.

Example 3
(page 737)

Graph each function on the interval $0° < x < 470°$ and $-300 < y < 300$. Evaluate the function at $x = 45°, 90°,$ and $135°$.   **19–21. See margin.**

19. $y = 50 \tan x$ **20.** $y = -100 \tan x$ **21.** $y = 125 \tan\left(\frac{1}{2}x\right)$

22. Suppose the architect in Example 3 reduces the length of the base of the triangle to 100 ft. The function that models the height of the triangle becomes $y = 50 \tan \theta$.
 a. Graph the function on a graphing calculator. **See margin.**
 b. What is the height of the triangle when $\theta = 16°$? ≈14.3 ft
 c. What is the height of the triangle when $\theta = 22°$? ≈20.2 ft

B **Apply Your Skills**

Identify the period for each tangent function. Then graph each function in the interval from -2π to 2π.   **23–25. See margin.**

23. $y = \tan \frac{\pi}{6}\theta$ **24.** $y = \tan 2.5\theta$ **25.** $y = \tan\left(-\frac{3}{2\pi}\theta\right)$

Solve each equation in the interval from 0 to 2π. Round your answers to the nearest hundredth.

26. $\tan \theta = 2$ **27.** $\tan \theta = -2$ **28.** $6 \tan 2\theta = 1$
 1.11, 4.25   **2.03, 5.18**   **0.08, 1.65, 3.22, 4.79**

29. a. Set your graphing calculator to Degree mode. Use window values $0 \le x \le 141$ and $-500 \le y \le 500$. Graph the functions $y = 100 \tan 2x$, $y = 200 \tan 2x$, and $y = 400 \tan 2x$ on the same set of axes. Sketch the graphs.
 b. Choose five values for x. Compare the y values. Explain how doubling the coefficient of the tangent function affects the output.
 c. Without graphing, make a prediction about the difference between the y-values of $y = 200 \tan x$ and $y = 600 \tan x$. Check your prediction on your graphing calculator.   **a–c. See margin p. 739.**

30. Ceramics An artist is creating triangular ceramic tiles for a triangular patio. The patio will be an equilateral triangle with base 18 ft and height 15.6 ft.
 a. Find the area of the patio in square feet.   **140.4 ft²**
 b. The artist uses tiles that are isosceles triangles with base 6 in. The function $y = 3 \tan \theta$ models the height of the tiles, where θ is the measure of one of the base angles. Graph the function. Find the height of the tile when $\theta = 30°$ and when $\theta = 60°$.   **b–d. See margin p. 739.**
 c. Find the area of one tile in square inches when $\theta = 30°$ and when $\theta = 60°$.
 d. Find the number of tiles the patio will require if $\theta = 30°$ and if $\theta = 60°$.

738 Chapter 13 Periodic Functions and Trigonometry

Real-World Connection

Careers Ceramic artists work with a variety of geometric shapes.

---

23. 6

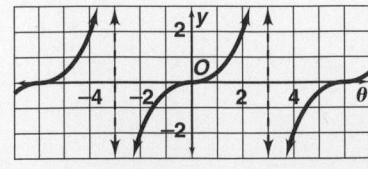

24. $\frac{2\pi}{5}$

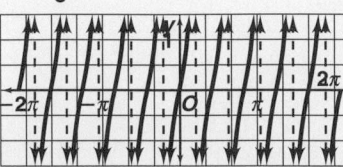

25. $\frac{2\pi^2}{3}$

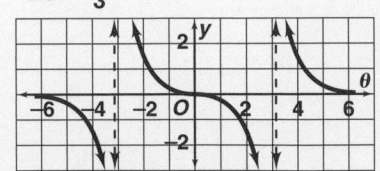

31. a. Open-Ended Write a tangent function. **Check students' work.**
  b. Graph the function on the interval -2π to 2π.
  c. Identify the period and the asymptotes of the function.

 32. Writing Explain how you can find the equations of the asymptotes of $y = \tan b\theta$.

32. The asymptotes occur at $-\frac{\pi}{2b}$ and $\frac{\pi}{2b}$; adding or subtracting multiples of their difference will give other asymptote values.

Use the function $y = 200 \tan x$ on the interval $0° \le x \le 141°$. Complete each ordered pair. Round your answers to the nearest whole number.

33. $(45°, \blacksquare)$ **34.** $(\blacksquare°, 0)$ **35.** $(\blacksquare°, -200)$ **36.** $(141°, \blacksquare)$ **37.** $(\blacksquare°, 550)$
   200   **0**   **135**   **−162**   **70**

Write an equation of a tangent function for each graph.

Reading Math
For help with reading and solving Exercise 38, see p. 741.

38. $y = \tan\left(\frac{1}{2}x\right)$

39. $y = -\tan\left(\frac{1}{2}x\right)$

40. $y = -\tan x$ or $y = \tan(-x)$

41. $y = \tan(2x)$

38.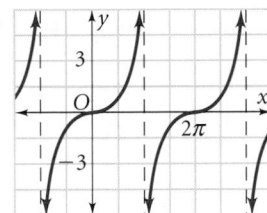

39.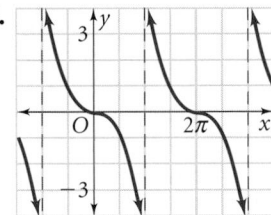

40.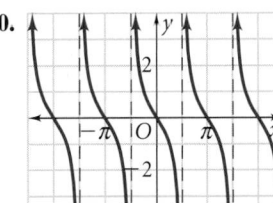

41.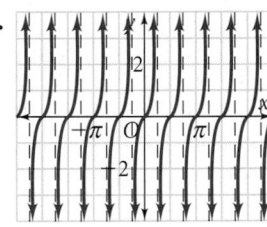

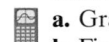 **42. Construction** An architect is designing a hexagonal gazebo. The floor is a hexagon made up of six isosceles triangles. The function $y = 4 \tan \theta$ models the height of one triangle, where θ is the measure of one of the base angles and the base of the triangle is 8 ft long. **a. See margin.**
  a. Graph the function. Find the height of one triangle when $\theta = 60°$.
  b. Find the area of one triangle in square feet when $\theta = 60°$. **27.7 ft²**
  c. Find the area in square feet covered by the gazebo when the triangles forming the hexagon are equilateral. **166.3 ft²**

C Challenge

43a.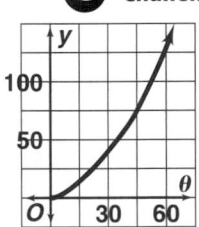

43. Geometry The base of a square pyramid has side length 150 ft. The function $y = 75 \tan \theta$ models the slant height ℓ of the pyramid, where θ is the angle indicated in the figure.
  a. Graph the function on a graphing calculator. Sketch the graph.
  b. Find the slant height of the pyramid when $\theta = 60°$. **130 ft**
  c. Find the surface area of the pyramid. (*Hint:* Don't forget to include the base of the pyramid.) **61,500 ft²**

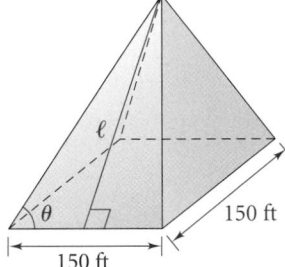

44. a. Graph $y = \tan x$, $y = a \tan x$ (with $a > 0$), and $y = a \tan x$ (with $a < 0$) on the same coordinate plane. **Check students' work.**
  b. Critical Thinking Recall the pattern of five elements for graphing a tangent function: *asymptote−(−1)−zero−(1)−asymptote*. How does the value of a affect this pattern?
  The new pattern is asymptote–(−a)–zero–(a)–asymptote.

Lesson 13-6   The Tangent Function   **739**

29a.

b. Check students' work; doubling the coefficient of the tangent function also doubles the output.

c. Answers may vary. Sample: the values of $y = 600 \tan x$ will be three times greater than the values of $y = 200 \tan x$.

Lesson Quiz 13-6

1. Sketch the graph of $y = \frac{1}{2} \tan 2\theta$ in the interval from 0 to 2π.

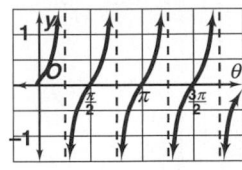

2. What is the period of the graph in Question 1? $\frac{\pi}{2}$

3. Write an equation of a tangent function that has an asymptote at $x = 2$. **Answers may vary. Sample:** $y = \tan \frac{\pi}{4}x$.

Alternative Assessment

Have students in small groups prepare a presentation, illustrated by a poster, of the unit circle and the graph of one of the three functions: sine, cosine, or tangent. Then let the groups present their posters and explanations to the class.

Standardized Test Prep

Resources
For additional practice with a variety of test item formats:
• Standardized Test Prep, p. 759
• Test-Taking Strategies, p. 754
• Test-Taking Strategies with Transparencies

30b.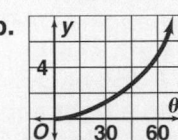

1.7 in., 5.2 in.

c. 5.2 in.², 15.6 in.²

d. 3888 tiles, 1297 tiles

42a.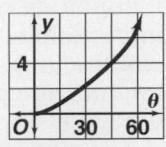

6.9 ft

739

45. Geometry Use the drawing at the right and similar triangles. Justify the statement that $\tan \theta = \frac{\sin \theta}{\cos \theta}$. **See margin.**

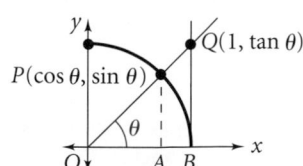

Multiple Choice

46. Which value is NOT defined? **C**

A. $\tan 0$ **B.** $\tan \pi$ **C.** $\tan \frac{3\pi}{2}$ **D.** $\frac{1}{\tan \frac{\pi}{4}}$

47. What is the exact value of $\tan \frac{7\pi}{6}$? **H**

F. $-\sqrt{3}$ **G.** $-\frac{\sqrt{3}}{3}$ **H.** $\frac{\sqrt{3}}{3}$ **I.** $\sqrt{3}$

Take It to the NET
Online lesson quiz at
www.PHSchool.com
Web Code: aga-1306

48. Which pair of values are NOT equal? **D**

A. $\tan \frac{\pi}{4}$, $-\tan \frac{3\pi}{4}$ **B.** $\tan \frac{\pi}{4}$, $\tan \frac{5\pi}{4}$

C. $\tan \theta$, $-\tan (-\theta)$ **D.** $\tan \theta$, $\tan (\pi - \theta)$

49. Which equation does NOT represent a vertical asymptote of the graph of $y = \tan \theta$? **G**

F. $\theta = -\frac{\pi}{2}$ **G.** $\theta = 0$ **H.** $\theta = \frac{\pi}{2}$ **I.** $\theta = \frac{3\pi}{2}$

50. Which function has a period of 4π? **D**

A. $y = \tan 4\theta$ **B.** $y = \tan 2\theta$ **C.** $y = \tan \frac{1}{2}\theta$ **D.** $y = \tan \frac{1}{4}\theta$

Short Response

51. Explain why there is no discussion of the amplitude of the tangent function in the lesson. **See margin.**

Extended Response

52. Compare the period of $y = \tan \theta$ with the period of $y = \sin \theta$. Use a graph of the two functions to support your statements. **See margin.**

Mixed Review

Lesson 13-5

Solve each equation in the interval from 0 to 2π. Round your answer to the nearest hundredth.

1.93, 4.35

53. $\cos t = \frac{1}{4}$ **1.32, 4.97**   **54.** $10 \cos t = -2$ **1.77, 4.51**   **55.** $-2 \cos \theta = 0.7$

56. $3 \cos \frac{t}{5} = 1$ **6.15**   **57.** $\cos \frac{3}{4}\theta = -0.6$ **58.** $5 \cos \pi t = 0.9$

2.95, 5.43   **0.44, 1.56, 2.44,**

Lesson 12-3   Find the mean, median, and mode for each set of values.   **3.56, 4.44, 5.56**

59. 9   6   8   1   3   4   5   2   6   8   4   9   12   3   4   10   7   6 $\approx$**5.9, 6, 4 and 6**

60. 45   42   39   35   41   45   49   42   43   48   32   51   42   **42.6, 42, 42**

61. 7.1   8.5   7.0   7.6   8.5   8.1   7.9   8.2   7.3   9.1   8.7   7.9 $\approx$**8, 8, 7.9 and 8.5**

Lesson 11-2   Find the 27th term of each sequence.

62. $5, 8, 11, \ldots$ **83**   **63.** $59, 48, 37, \ldots$ **−227**   **64.** $1, 3.5, 6, 8.5, \ldots$ **66**

65. $2.1, 1.7, 1.3, \ldots$ **−8.3**   **66.** $-11, -5, 1, \ldots$ **145**   **67.** $6, -7, -20, \ldots$ **−332**

---

pages 737–740 Exercises

45. Answers may vary. Sample: Triangles *OAP* and *OBQ* both share the angle θ and each triangle has a right angle, so they are similar by AA.
$\frac{\sin \theta}{\cos \theta} = \frac{AP}{OA} = \frac{BQ}{OB} = \frac{\tan \theta}{1}$.
Thus $\frac{\sin \theta}{\cos \theta} = \tan \theta$.

51. **[2]** There is no discussion of the amplitude of the tangent function because the tangent function has no upper or lower limit.

[1] incomplete explanation

740

52. **[4]** (Student graphs $y = \tan \theta$ and $y = \sin \theta$ correctly, showing 2 periods of $y = \tan \theta$ and 1 period of $y = \sin \theta$.) The period of $y = \tan \theta$ is half of the period of $y = \sin \theta$.

[3] statement correct and graph accurate, but doesn't illustrate 2 periods of $y = \tan \theta$

[2] accurate graph with incorrect answer OR inaccurate graph with correct answer

[1] answer only, with no graph

Reading a Graph

Read the problem below to understand how to read a graph. Check your understanding with the exercise at the bottom of the page.

Write an equation of a tangent function for the graph.

A graph shows data points of a function on a coordinate grid. When you read a graph, you identify information from the graph to help you solve the problem. As you look at a graph, ask yourself the following questions.

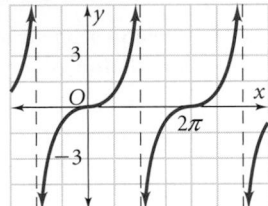

What relationship is shown in the graph?

The problem states that the graph shows a tangent function.

What information can I obtain from the graph?

Scale The scale on the y-axis shows that two grid lines represent 3 units. The scale on the x-axis shows that four grid lines represent 2π units, which means two grid lines represent π units. Redraw the graph and add labels to the x-axis.

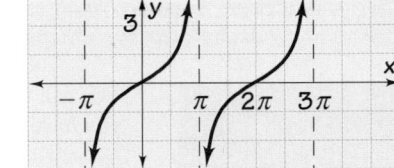

Asymptotes A tangent function has vertical asymptotes. Now that you've added labels, you can see that asymptotes occur at x-values of $-\pi, \pi,$ and 3π.

Period The period is the horizontal distance between asymptotes.

$$\text{period} = \text{distance between asymptotes} = \pi - (-\pi) = 2\pi$$

Now you can use the information you've obtained from the graph to write an equation for the tangent function shown. The standard form for the equation of a tangent function is $y = \tan bx$. Since you know the period, you can find b.

$\text{period} = \frac{\pi}{b}$, so $b = \frac{\pi}{\text{period}} = \frac{\pi}{2\pi} = \frac{1}{2}$

Since $\left(-\frac{\pi}{2}, -1\right)$ is on the graph, $a = 1$.

An equation for the tangent function is $y = \tan \frac{1}{2}x$.

EXERCISE

Use the graph of a tangent function at the right.
a. Identify the asymptotes of the function. $-\frac{\pi}{2}, \frac{\pi}{2}$
b. Identify the period of the function. π
c. Write an equation for the function. $y = \tan x$

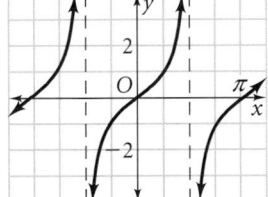

Reading a Graph

Students learn to read and interpret information from problems involving graphs.

Teaching Notes

Using the graph, show students how to determine the scale on the x- and y-axes. Explain that not all graphs have each tick mark on the axes labeled, so care must be taken to determine the value represented by each mark. Also tell students to be mindful that the x- and y-axes may not have the same scale.

Visual Learners

Have students copy the graph and annotate their copy noting the scale, asymptotes, and period. Students may use this annotated copy for future reference.

Exercise

Have students first note the differences in scale, asymptotes, and period between this graph, and the graph in the Example.

Translating Sine and Cosine Functions

Lesson Preview

Lesson Preview

What You'll Learn

OBJECTIVE 1 To graph translations of trigonometric functions

OBJECTIVE 2 To write equations of translations

...And Why

To analyze temperature data, as in Example 6

✓ Check Skills You'll Need

(For help, go to Lesson 2-6.)

Graph each pair of equations on the same coordinate plane. Identify each translation as *horizontal*, *vertical*, or *diagonal*.   **1–6. See back of book.**

1. $y = 2x, y = 2x + 5$

2. $g(x) = |x|, f(x) = |x + 3|$

3. $y = -x, y = -x - 1$

4. $g(x) = |x|, h(x) = |x| - 4$

5. $y = -|x|, y = -|x - 2| + 1$

6. $y = x^2, y = (x + 3)^2 - 2$

New Vocabulary   • phase shift

Lesson Resources

📁 Teaching Resources
Practice, Reteaching, Enrichment
Checkpoint Quiz 2

👥 Reaching All Students
Practice Workbook 13-7
Spanish Practice Workbook 13-7
Reading and Math Literacy 13C
Spanish Reading & Literacy 13C
Spanish Checkpoint Quiz 2
Hands-On Activities 57

⏱ Presentation Assistant Plus!
Transparencies
• Check Skills You'll Need 13-7
• Additional Examples 13-7
• Student Edition Answers 13-7
• Lesson Quiz 13-7
PH Presentation Pro CD 13-7

ASSESSMENT SYSTEM
Checkpoint Quiz 2
Computer Test Generator CD

💿 Technology
Resource Pro® CD-ROM
Computer Test Generator CD
Prentice Hall Presentation Pro CD

🖥 www.PHSchool.com
Student Site
• Teacher Web Code: agk-5500
• Self-grading Lesson Quiz
Teacher Center
• Lesson Planner
• Resources

Plus 📱**iTEXT**

OBJECTIVE 1

Graphing Translations of Trigonometric Functions

Real-World 🌐 Connection

A modem (modulator-demodulator) uses phase shifts to convert data between digital signals, which use binary digits, and analog signals, which use waves.

> 📱**iTEXT** Interactive lesson includes instant self-check, tutorials, and activities.

You can translate periodic functions horizontally and vertically using the methods you have used for other functions.

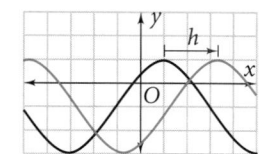

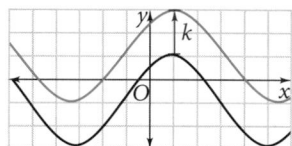

$g(x)$: horizontal translation of $f(x)$
$$g(x) = f(x - h)$$

$h(x)$: vertical translation of $f(x)$
$$h(x) = f(x) + k$$

A horizontal translation of a periodic function is a **phase shift**.

When $g(x) = f(x - h)$, the value of h is the amount of the shift left or right. If $h > 0$, the shift is to the right. If $h < 0$, the shift is to the left.

1 EXAMPLE   Identifying Phase Shifts

What is the value of h in each translation? Describe each phase shift (use a phrase such as *3 units to the left*).

a. $g(x) = f(x - 2)$

   $h = 2$; the phase shift is 2 units to the right.

b. $y = |x + 4|$
   $= |x - (-4)|$
   $h = -4$; the phase shift is 4 units to the left.

✓ Check Understanding 1

What is the value of h in each translation? Describe each phase shift (use a phrase such as *3 units to the left*).

a. $g(t) = f(t - 5)$ **5; 5 units to the right**

b. $y = \sin(x + 3)$ **−3; 3 units to the left**

🔄 Ongoing Assessment and Intervention

Before the Lesson	**During the Lesson**	**After the Lesson**
Diagnose prerequisite skills using:	Monitor progress using:	Assess knowledge using:
• Check Skills You'll Need	• Check Understanding	• Lesson Quiz
	• Additional Examples	• Computer Test Generator CD
	• Standardized Test Prep	• Chapter Checkpoint 2 (p. 748)

You can analyze a translation to determine how it relates to the parent function.

2 EXAMPLE Graphing Translations

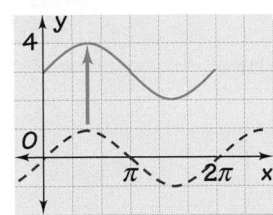

Use the graph of the parent function $y = \sin x$ at the left. Sketch each translation of the graph in the interval $0 \le x \le 2\pi$.

a. $y = \sin x + 3$

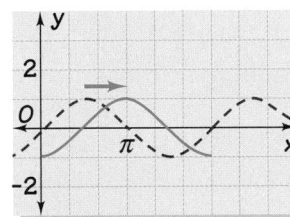

Translate the graph of $y = \sin x$ 3 units up.

b. $y = \sin\left(x - \frac{\pi}{2}\right)$

Translate the graph of $y = \sin x$ $\frac{\pi}{2}$ units to the right.

✔ Check Understanding

2 Use the graph of $y = \sin x$ from Example 2. Sketch each translation of the graph in the interval $0 \le x \le 2\pi$. Which translation is a phase shift? **a–b. See left.**
a. $y = \sin x - 2$ **b.** $y = \sin (x - 2)$

2a.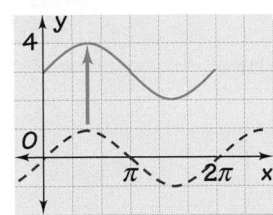

b.

(b) is a phase shift.

You can combine vertical and horizontal translations to produce diagonal translations.

3 EXAMPLE Graphing a Diagonal Translation

Use the graph of the parent function $y = \sin x$ in Example 2. Sketch the translation $y = \sin (x + \pi) - 2$ in the interval $0 \le x \le 2\pi$.

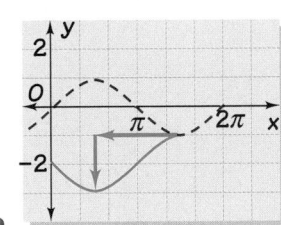

Translate the parent function π units to the left and 2 units down.

3a.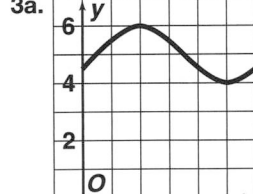

b.

✔ Check Understanding

3 The graph at the right shows $y = \cos x$. Use it to graph each diagonal translation.
a. $y = \cos (x - 2) + 5$ **a–b. See left.**
b. $y = \cos (x + 1) + 3$

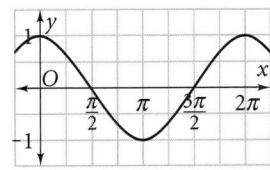

Lesson 13-7 Translating Sine and Cosine Functions **743**

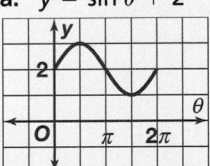
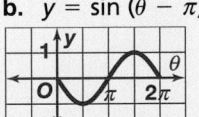
743

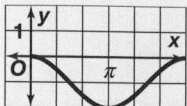
3 Use the graph of $y = \sin x$ in Example 2. Sketch the translation $y = \sin\left(x + \frac{\pi}{2}\right) - 1$ in the interval $0 \le x \le 2\pi$.

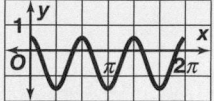

4 Sketch the graph of $y = \sin 3\left(x - \frac{\pi}{2}\right) - \frac{1}{2}$ in the interval from 0 to 2π.

OBJECTIVE

2 **Teaching Notes**

5 **EXAMPLE** Inclusion

For students who may have trouble organizing a problem requiring several steps, help them make their own list of procedures. Begin with the basic equation and then list each variable with what it means in terms of a translation. Color-code the letter in the basic equation and in the list of descriptions.

6 **EXAMPLE** Connection to Meteorology

Tell the students that data about weather is a particularly rich resource for scientists and mathematicians of all kinds. This is because records have been kept all over the world for a great many years, so there is an enormous database in which to look for patterns.

4a.

b.

Key Concepts

The translations graphed in Examples 2 and 3 show the following properties of translations of sine and cosine functions.

Summary	Translations of Sine and Cosine Functions

Parent Function
$y = a \sin bx$
$y = a \cos bx$

Translated Function
$y = a \sin b(x - h) + k$
$y = a \cos b(x - h) + k$

- $|a|$ = amplitude
- $\frac{2\pi}{b}$ = period (when x is in radians and $b > 0$)
- h = phase shift, or horizontal shift
- k = vertical shift

You can analyze an equation before graphing it to determine the parent function of the graph.

4 **EXAMPLE** Graphing a Translation of $y = \sin 2x$

Sketch the graph of $y = \sin 2\left(x - \frac{\pi}{3}\right) - \frac{3}{2}$ in the interval from 0 to 2π.

Since $a = 1$ and $b = 2$, the graph is a translation of $y = \sin 2x$.

Step 1 Sketch one cycle of $y = \sin 2x$. Use five points in the pattern $zero-max-zero-min-zero$.

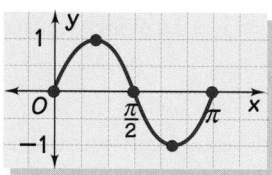

Step 2 Since $h = \frac{\pi}{3}$ and $k = -\frac{3}{2}$, translate the graph $\frac{\pi}{3}$ units to the right and $\frac{3}{2}$ units down. Extend the periodic pattern from 0 to 2π. Sketch the graph.

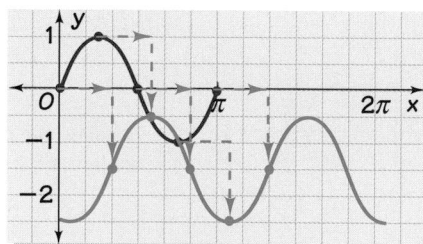

The blue curve above is the graph of $y = \sin 2\left(x - \frac{\pi}{3}\right) - \frac{3}{2}$.

✓ Check Understanding **4** Sketch each graph in the interval from 0 to 2π. **a–b. See left.**
   a. $y = -3 \sin 2\left(x - \frac{\pi}{3}\right) - \frac{3}{2}$
   b. $y = 2 \cos \frac{\pi}{2}(x + 1) - 3$

2 Writing Equations of Translations

You can write an equation to describe a translation.

5 EXAMPLE Writing a Translation

Write an equation for each translation.

a. $y = \sin x$, π units down

π units down means $k = \pi$.

An equation is $y = \sin x - \pi$.

b. $y = -\cos x$, 2 units to the left

2 units to the left means $h = 2$.

An equation is $y = -\cos(x - (-2))$.

✓ **Check Understanding** ⑤ Write an equation for each translation.
a. $y = \cos x$, $\frac{\pi}{2}$ units up $y = \cos x + \frac{\pi}{2}$ **b.** $y = 2\sin x$, $\frac{\pi}{4}$ units to the right

$$y = 2\sin\left(x - \frac{\pi}{4}\right)$$

6 EXAMPLE Real-World Connection

Temperature Cycles The table at the left gives the typical high temperature in New Orleans, Louisiana, on several days of the year (January 1 = 1, February 1 = 32, and so on). Plot the data in the table. Write a cosine model for the data.

Day of Year	Temperature (°F)
16	62
47	65
75	71
106	79
136	85
167	90
197	91
228	90
259	87
289	79
320	70
350	64

Plot the data.

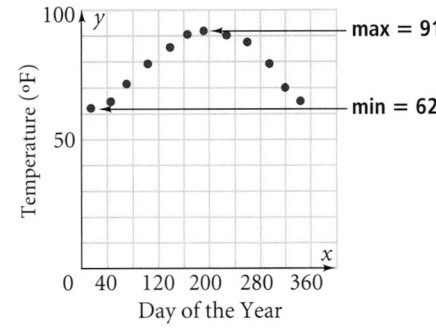

Use the form $y = a\cos b(x - h) + k$. Find values a, b, h, and k.

amplitude $= \frac{1}{2}(\text{max} - \text{min})$

$= \frac{1}{2}(91 - 62)$

$= 14.5$

period $= \frac{2\pi}{b}$

$365 = \frac{2\pi}{b}$ **One complete cycle takes 365 days.**

$b = \frac{2\pi}{365}$

So (choosing $a > 0$), $a = 14.5$.

To find the values h and k,

compare $y = 14.5\cos\frac{2\pi}{365}x$

with the plot of the data.

phase shift: $h = 197 - 0$

$= 197$

vertical shift: $k = 91 - 14.5$

$= 76.5$

A model for the data is

$y = 14.5\cos\frac{2\pi}{365}(x - 197) + 76.5$.

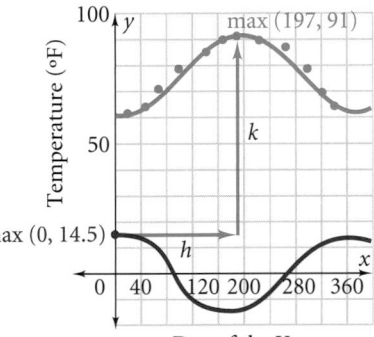

Day of the Year

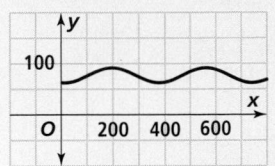
⑤ Write an equation for each translation.
a. $y = \cos x$, π units up
$y = \cos x + \pi$
b. $y = -\sin x$, 3 units to the right
$y = -\sin(x - 3)$

⑥ Use the following graph, which shows the model for the data given in Example 6, to draw some conclusions about the weather in New Orleans.

Answers may vary. Be sure students mention the highs and lows as well as the fact that the graph shows that fluctuations are moderate and do not go below 50°F nor above 100 degrees.

Closure

Ask students: *How do you translate a sine or cosine curve in the coordinate plane? What are the effects of the various parts of the equation $y = a\cos b(x - h) + k$?* The basic shape of a curve remains the same when translated. In the equation above, $|a|$ is the amplitude, $\frac{2\pi}{b}$ is the period, when $b > 0$. The phase shift, or horizontal shift is represented by h and k is the vertical shift.

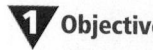

3. Practice

Assignment Guide

1 Objective

Ⓐ Ⓑ Core 1–30, 43, 45, 46

Ⓒ Extension 47–50

2 Objective

Ⓐ Ⓑ Core 31–42, 44

Ⓒ Extension 51–54

Standardized Test Prep 55–60

Mixed Review 61–72

Exercise 37 Ask students: *Do you think a cosine model will always fit a table of temperatures at one place on earth? What constraints might there be for this model to fit?* **No, this model only fits where the fluctuations recur in a certain pattern that does not show either extreme variation or no variation at all.**

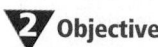

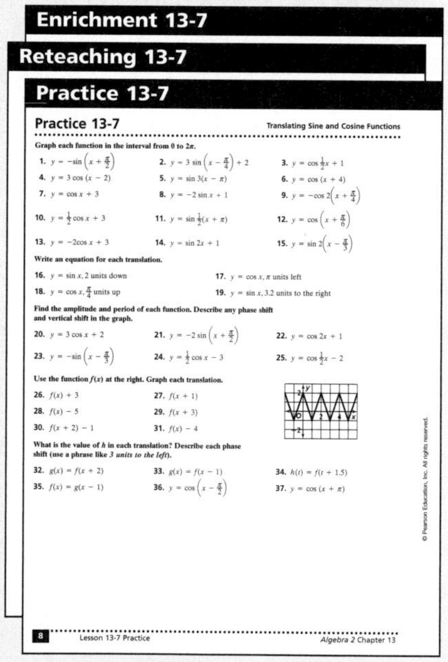

Enrichment 13-7

Reteaching 13-7

Practice 13-7

Practice 13-7 — Translating Sine and Cosine Functions

Graph each function in the interval from 0 to 2π.

1. $y = -\sin\left(x + \frac{\pi}{2}\right)$ 2. $y = 3\sin\left(x - \frac{\pi}{4}\right) + 2$ 3. $y = \cos\frac{1}{2}x + 1$
4. $y = 3\cos(x - 2)$ 5. $y = \sin 3(x - \pi)$ 6. $y = \cos(x + 4)$
7. $y = \cos x + 3$ 8. $y = -2\sin x + 1$ 9. $y = -\cos 2\left(x + \frac{\pi}{4}\right)$
10. $y = \frac{1}{2}\cos x + 3$ 11. $y = \sin\frac{1}{2}(x + \pi)$ 12. $y = \cos\left(x + \frac{\pi}{6}\right)$
13. $y = -2\cos x + 3$ 14. $y = \sin 2x + 1$ 15. $y = \sin 2\left(x - \frac{\pi}{3}\right)$

Write an equation for each translation.

16. $y = \sin x$, 2 units down 17. $y = \cos x$, π units left
18. $y = \cos x$, $\frac{\pi}{4}$ units up 19. $y = \sin x$, 3.2 units to the right

Find the amplitude and period of each function. Describe any phase shift and vertical shift in the graph.

20. $y = 3\cos x + 2$ 21. $y = -2\sin\left(x + \frac{\pi}{2}\right)$ 22. $y = \cos 2x + 1$
23. $y = -\sin\left(x - \frac{\pi}{3}\right)$ 24. $y = \frac{1}{2}\cos x - 3$ 25. $y = \cos\frac{1}{2}x - 2$

Use the function $f(x)$ at the right. Graph each translation.

26. $f(x) + 3$ 27. $f(x + 1)$
28. $f(x) - 5$ 29. $f(x + 3)$
30. $f(x + 2) - 1$ 31. $f(x) - 4$

What is the value of h in each translation? Describe each phase shift (use a phrase like *3 units to the left*).

32. $g(x) = f(x + 2)$ 33. $g(x) = f(x - 1)$ 34. $h(t) = f(t + 1.5)$
35. $f(x) = g(x - 1)$ 36. $y = \cos\left(x - \frac{\pi}{2}\right)$ 37. $y = \cos(x + \pi)$

8 Lesson 13-7 Practice Algebra 2 Chapter 13

pages 746–748 Exercises

1. **−1; 1 unit to the left**
2. **−2; 2 units to the left**
3. **1.6; 1.6 units to the right**
4. **3; 3 units to the right**
5. **$-\pi$; π units to the left**
6. **$\frac{5\pi}{7}$; $\frac{5\pi}{7}$ units to the right**

Check Understanding 6 **a.** **Estimation** Use the model from Example 6. Estimate the high temperature in New Orleans on September 1 (day 244). **86.5°**

b. **Graphing Calculator** Graph the model on your calculator. Use it to estimate the first day of the year that the high temperature is likely to reach 75°F. **day 100**

EXERCISES

For more practice, see *Extra Practice*.

Practice and Problem Solving

Ⓐ Practice by Example

Example 1 (page 742)

What is the value of h in each translation? Describe each phase shift (use a phrase like *3 units to the left*). **1–6. See margin.**

1. $g(x) = f(x + 1)$
2. $g(t) = f(t + 2)$
3. $h(z) = g(z - 1.6)$
4. $h(x) = f(x - 3)$
5. $y = \sin(x + \pi)$
6. $y = \cos\left(x - \frac{5\pi}{7}\right)$

Example 2 (page 743)

Use the function $f(x)$ at the right. Graph each translation.

7. $f(x) + 1$
8. $f(x) - 3$
9. $f(x + 2)$
10. $f(x - 1)$

7–10. See margin pp. 746–747.

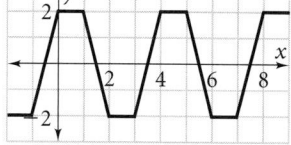

Graph each translation of $y = \cos x$ in the interval from 0 to 2π.

11. $y = \cos(x + 3)$
12. $y = \cos x + 3$
13. $y = \cos x - 4$
14. $y = \cos(x - 4)$
15. $y = \cos x + \pi$
16. $y = \cos(x - \pi)$

11–16. See back of book.

Example 3 (page 743)

Find the amplitude and period of each function. Describe any phase shift and vertical shift in the graph. **17–20. See left.**

17. $y = 3\sin x + 1$
18. $y = -4\cos 2(x + 1) - 2$
19. $y = -\sin\left(x + \frac{\pi}{2}\right) + 2$
20. $y = -\cos\pi(x - 3) + 2$

17. **3, 2π; 1 unit up**
18. **4, π; 1 unit left and 2 units down**
19. **1, 2π; $\frac{\pi}{2}$ units left and 2 units up**
20. **1, 2; 3 units right and 2 units up**

Graph each function in the interval from 0 to 2π.

21. $y = -2\sin\left(x + \frac{\pi}{4}\right) - 1$
22. $y = \sin 3\left(x + \frac{\pi}{3}\right) + 1$
23. $y = -\cos(x - \pi) - 3$
24. $y = 2\sin\left(x - \frac{\pi}{6}\right) + 2$

21–24. See back of book.

Example 4 (page 744)

Graph each function in the interval from 0 to 2π.

25. $y = 3\sin\frac{1}{2}x$
26. $y = \cos 2\left(x + \frac{\pi}{2}\right) - 2$
27. $y = \frac{1}{2}\sin 2x - 1$
28. $y = \sin 3\left(x + \frac{\pi}{3}\right)$
29. $y = \sin 2(x + 3) - 2$
30. $y = 3\sin\left(\frac{\pi}{2}x - \pi\right)$

25–30. See back of book.

Example 5 (page 745)

Write an equation for each translation. **31–36. See margin p. 747.**

31. $y = \sin x$, π units to the left
32. $y = \cos x$, $\frac{\pi}{2}$ units down
33. $y = \sin x$, 3 units up
34. $y = \cos x$, 1.5 units to the right
35. $y = \cos x$, $\frac{3}{2\pi}$ units to the left
36. $y = \sin x$, 3π units down

7.

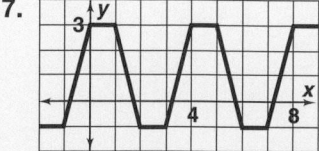

8.

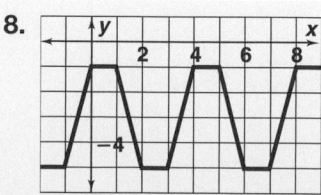

9.

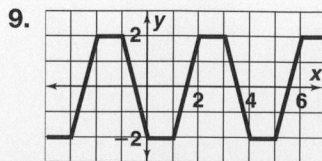

Example 6
(page 745)

37. Temperature The table below shows water temperatures at a buoy in the Gulf of Mexico on several days of the year.

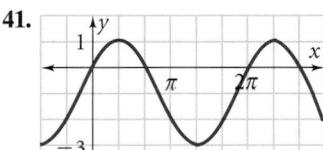

Water Temperatures in the Gulf of Mexico

Day of the Year	16	47	75	106	136	167	197	228	259	289	320	350
Temperature (°F)	71	69	70	73	77	82	85	86	84	82	78	74

SOURCE: *The USA Today Weather Almanac*

a. Plot the data.   **See back of book.**   **b.** Write a cosine model for the data.
$y = 8.5 \cos \frac{2\pi}{365}(x - 228) + 77.5$

B Apply Your Skills

Write an equation for each translation.

38. $y = \sin x$, 2 units to the right and 4 units down $y = \sin(x - 2) - 4$

39. $y = \cos x$, 3 units to the left and π units up $y = \cos(x + 3) + \pi$

41. $y = 2\cos\left(x - \frac{\pi}{3}\right) - 1$;
$y = 2\sin\left(x + \frac{\pi}{6}\right) - 1$

40. $y = \sin x$, $\frac{\pi}{2}$ units to the right and 3.5 units up $y = \sin\left(x - \frac{\pi}{2}\right) + 3.5$

42. $y = -10\cos 18x$;
$y = 10\sin 18(x - 5)$

Write a cosine function for each graph. Then write a sine function for each graph.

41.

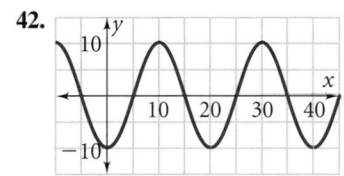

42.

43. The graphs of $y = \sin x$ and $y = \cos x$ are shown at the left.   **a–b. See left.**
   a. What phase shift will translate the cosine graph onto the sine graph? Write your answer as an equation in the form $\sin x = \cos(x - h)$.
   b. What phase shift will translate the sine graph onto the cosine graph? Write your answer as an equation in the form $\cos x = \sin(x - h)$.

43a. $\frac{\pi}{2}$; $\sin x = \cos\left(x - \frac{\pi}{2}\right)$
b. $-\frac{\pi}{2}$; $\cos x = \sin\left(x + \frac{\pi}{2}\right)$

44. a. Critical Thinking Use a sine function to model the normal daily high temperature in New Orleans. Use the data given in Example 6 on page 745.
   b. Writing How do the sine and cosine models differ?   **a–b. See margin.**
   c. Estimation Use your sine model to estimate the high temperature in New Orleans on December 1 (day 334).   **about 66°**
   d. Graph your model. Use it to estimate the first day of the year that the high temperature is likely to reach 70°F.   **March 20 (day 79)**

45a. Check students' work.

45. a. Open-Ended Draw a periodic function. Find its amplitude and period. Then sketch a translation of your function 3 units down and 4 units to the left.
   b. Critical Thinking Suppose your original function is $f(x)$. Describe your translation using the form $g(x) = f(x - h) + k$. $g(x) = f(x + 4) - 3$

46. a. Write $y = 3\sin(2x - 4) + 1$ in the form $y = a\sin b(x - h) + k$. (*Hint:* Factor where possible.) $y = 3\sin 2(x - 2) + 1$
   b. Find the amplitude and period. Describe any translations.
   3, π; 2 units right and 1 unit up

C Challenge   Use a graphing calculator to graph each function in the interval from 0 to 2π. Then sketch each graph.   **47–54. See back of book.**

47. $y = \sin x + x$ **48.** $y = \sin x + 2x$

49. $y = \sin x - 0.5x$ **50.** $y = \cos x - x$

51. $y = \cos x - 2x$ **52.** $y = \cos x + x$

53. $y = \sin(x + \cos x)$ **54.** $y = \sin(x + 2\cos x)$

Graphing Calculator Hint
You may need to change your window values between exercises to see each function clearly.

10.
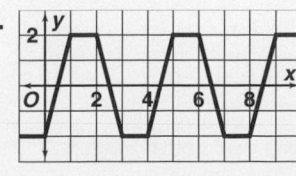

31. $y = \sin(x + \pi)$

32. $y = \cos x - \frac{\pi}{2}$

33. $y = \sin x + 3$

34. $y = \cos(x - 1.5)$

35. $y = \cos\left(x + \frac{3}{2\pi}\right)$

36. $y = \sin x - 3\pi$

4. Assess

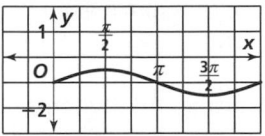

Lesson Quiz 13-7

1. Sketch the graph of $y = \frac{1}{2}\sin x - 1$ in the interval from 0 to 2π.

2. What is the value of h in the translation $g(x) = f(x + 4)$? $h = -4$

3. Describe the phase shift in the translation $g(x) = f(x + 4)$.
four units to the left

4. Write an equation for the translation of $y = \sin x$, $\frac{\pi}{2}$ units down. $y = \sin x - \frac{\pi}{2}$

Alternative Assessment

Ask students to write a journal page or two about what they have learned in this lesson, including examples and sketches of graphs. Ask them to describe any points about which they are still confused.

Standardized Test Prep

Resources
For additional practice with a variety of test item formats:
• Standardized Test Prep, p. 761
• Test-Taking Strategies, p. 756
• Test-Taking Strategies with Transparencies

Teaching Tip

Exercises 55–57, 59 Ask students to share memory aids they have developed to help them remember the various translations of the graphs that result from changes to the function.

44a. $14.5\sin\frac{2\pi}{365}(x - 105.75) + 76.5$

b. The difference between the two models is the horizontal shift factor.

747

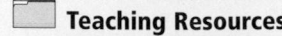
To check understanding of
Lessons 13-4 to 13-7:

Checkpoint Quiz 2 (p. 748)

Teaching Resources
Checkpoint Quiz 2 (also in
Prentice Hall Assessment
System)

Reaching All Students
Reading and Math Literacy 13C

Spanish versions available

---

pages 746–748   Exercises

58. **[2]** If the function $y = \cos \theta$ is shifted to the right by $\frac{\pi}{2}$ radians, the result is $y = \cos \left(\theta - \frac{\pi}{2} \right)$, which is the same as $y = \sin \theta$. So $a = 1$, and $b = -\frac{\pi}{2}$.

   [1] answer only, with no work shown

59. **[2]** If the minimum value is 1 and the amplitude is 4, the graph is $1 + 4 = 5$ units above the *x*-axis. The graph is translated 5 units up. The amplitude is 4, so the function is $y = 4 \sin \theta + 5$.

   [1] answer only, with no work shown

60. **[4]** $\sin \theta = 3 \sin \theta$
   $\sin \theta - \sin \theta$
   $\quad = 3 \sin \theta - \sin \theta$
   $0 = 2 \sin \theta$
   $\frac{0}{2} = \frac{2 \sin \theta}{2}$
   $0 = \sin \theta$
   $\sin \theta = 0$ at $-\pi, 0, \pi,$ and 2π

   [3] one calculation error

   [2] incomplete answer

   [1] answer only, with no work shown

61. $\frac{\pi}{6}$; $\theta = -\frac{\pi}{12}, \frac{\pi}{12}$

62. 4π; $\theta = -2\pi, 2\pi$

63. $\frac{2\pi}{3}$; $\theta = -\frac{\pi}{3}, -\frac{\pi}{3}$

64. 6π; $\theta = -3\pi, 3\pi$

Standardized Test Prep

Multiple Choice

55. Which function is a phase shift of $y = \sin \theta$ by 5 units to the left?   **C**
   A. $y = 5 \sin \theta$ **B.** $y = \sin \theta + 5$ **C.** $y = \sin (\theta + 5)$ **D.** $y = \sin 5\theta$

56. Which function is a translation of $y = \cos \theta$ by 5 units down?   **I**
   F. $y = -5 \cos \theta$ **G.** $y = \cos \theta - 5$
   H. $y = \cos (\theta - 5)$ **I.** $y = \cos (-5\theta)$

Take It to the NET
Online lesson quiz at
www.PHSchool.com
Web Code: aga-1307

57. Which function is a translation of $y = \sin \theta$ that is $\frac{\pi}{3}$ units up and $\frac{\pi}{2}$ units to the left?   **B**
   A. $y = \sin \left(\theta + \frac{\pi}{3} \right) + \frac{\pi}{2}$ **B.** $y = \sin \left(\theta + \frac{\pi}{2} \right) + \frac{\pi}{3}$
   C. $y = \sin \left(\theta - \frac{\pi}{2} \right) + \frac{\pi}{3}$ **D.** $y = \sin \left(\theta - \frac{\pi}{3} \right) - \frac{\pi}{2}$

Short Response

58. Find values of *a* and *b* such that the function $y = \sin \theta$ can be expressed as $y = a \cos (\theta + b)$.   **See margin.**

59. Write a function that is a transformation of $y = \sin \theta$ so that its amplitude is 4 and its minimum value is 1. Show your work.   **See margin.**

Extended Response

60. Find all the values of θ between $-\pi$ and 2π for which $\sin \theta = 3 \sin \theta$. Show your work.   **See margin.**

Mixed Review

Lesson 13-6

Identify the period of each function. Then tell where two asymptotes occur for each function.   **61–64. See margin.**

61. $y = \tan 6\theta$ 62. $y = \tan \frac{\theta}{4}$ 63. $y = \tan 1.5\theta$ 64. $y = \tan \frac{\theta}{6}$

Lesson 12-6

For the given probability of success *p* on each trial, find the probability of *x* successes in *n* trials.

65. $x = 4, n = 5, p = 0.2$ **0.0064**   66. $x = 3, n = 5, p = 0.6$ **0.3456**
67. $x = 4, n = 8, p = 0.7$ **≈0.136**   68. $x = 7, n = 8, p = 0.7$ **≈0.198**

Lesson 11-5

Find the sum of the series to the given term.

69. $2 + 4 + 8 + \ldots ; S_5$ **62**   70. $3 + 12 + 48 + \ldots ; S_7$ **16,383**
71. $-1 - 6 - 36 + \ldots ; S_8$ **−335,923**   72. $120 - 30 + 7.5 - \ldots ; S_5$ **96.09375**

 Checkpoint Quiz 2   **Lessons 13-4 through 13-7**

TEXT Instant self-check
quiz online and
on CD-ROM

Graph each function in the interval from -2π to 2π.   **1–10. See back of book.**

1. $y = \sin 4x$ 2. $y = 3 \cos x$ 3. $y = -2 \sin \pi x$
4. $y = 2 \cos \frac{\pi}{2} x$ 5. $y = \tan 2x$ 6. $y = -\tan x$
7. $y = \cos (x - 2)$ 8. $y = \sin x + 4$ 9. $y = 3 \tan \frac{\pi}{4} x$

10. Sketch the graph of $y = \sin 3x$ after a translation of 2 units to the right and π units down.

13-8 · Reciprocal Trigonometric Functions

Lesson Preview

What You'll Learn

 OBJECTIVE 1
To evaluate reciprocal trigonometric functions

 OBJECTIVE 2
To graph reciprocal trigonometric functions

. . . And Why

To find indirect measurements, as in Example 6

 Check Skills You'll Need (For help, go to Lesson 7-8.)

Find the reciprocal of each fraction.

1. $\frac{9}{13}$ $\frac{13}{9}$ 2. $\frac{-5}{8}$ $-\frac{8}{5}$ 3. $\frac{1}{2\pi}$ 2π 4. $\frac{4m}{15}$ $\frac{15}{4m}$ 5. $\frac{14}{-t}$ $-\frac{t}{14}$

Graph each pair of relations on the same coordinate plane. 6–9. See back

6. $y = x, y = -x$

7. $y = x^2, y = \pm\sqrt{x}$ of book.

8. $y = |2x|, y = -|2x|$

9. $y = -6x^2, y = \pm\sqrt{6x}$

New Vocabulary • cosecant • secant • cotangent

Lesson Preview

 Check Skills You'll Need

Graphing Two-Variable Equations
Skills Handbook: p. 851
Example 1, Exercises 1–12

Lesson Resources

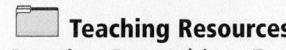 **Teaching Resources**
Practice, Reteaching, Enrichment

Reaching All Students
Practice Workbook 13-8
Spanish Practice Workbook 13-8

Presentation Assistant Plus!
Transparencies
• Check Skills You'll Need 13-8
• Additional Examples 13-8
• Student Edition Answers 13-8
• Lesson Quiz 13-8
PH Presentation Pro CD 13-8

 **PRENTICE HALL**
ASSESSMENT SYSTEM

Computer Test Generator CD

Technology
Resource Pro® CD-ROM
Computer Test Generator CD
Prentice Hall Presentation Pro CD

 **www.PHSchool.com**
Student Site
• Teacher Web Code: agk-5500
• Self-grading Lesson Quiz
Teacher Center
• Lesson Planner
• Resources

Plus **iTEXT**

OBJECTIVE

1 Evaluating Reciprocal Trigonometric Functions

iTEXT Interactive lesson includes instant self-check, tutorials, and activities.

In earlier lessons in this chapter, you studied three trigonometric functions—sine, cosine, and tangent. Three other functions—cosecant, secant, and cotangent—are reciprocals of the three you have used.

 Key Concepts

Definition	**Cosecant, Secant, and Cotangent Functions**

The cosecant (csc), secant (sec), and cotangent (cot) functions are defined as reciprocals. Their domains include all real numbers θ except those that make a denominator zero.

$$\csc \theta = \frac{1}{\sin \theta} \qquad \sec \theta = \frac{1}{\cos \theta} \qquad \cot \theta = \frac{1}{\tan \theta}$$

You can evaluate reciprocal trigonometric functions by using the definitions.

 Graphing Calculator Hint

Caution! The keys for $\sin^{-1}$, $\cos^{-1}$, and $\tan^{-1}$ do not give reciprocals. They represent inverse trigonometric functions, which you will study in Chapter 14.

1 **EXAMPLE** **Using Reciprocals**

a. Find csc 60°.

Use a calculator in degree mode.

1/sin (60)	
	1.154700538

Use the definition.
$\csc 60° = \frac{1}{\sin 60°}$

b. Suppose $\cos \theta = \frac{5}{13}$. Find $\sec \theta$.

$\sec \theta = \frac{1}{\cos \theta}$ **Use the definition.**

$= \frac{1}{\frac{5}{13}}$ **Substitute.**

$= \frac{13}{5}$ **Simplify.**

 Check Understanding **1 a.** Suppose $\sin \theta = \frac{15}{8}$. Find $\csc \theta$. $\frac{8}{15}$

b. Find cot 55° to the nearest hundredth. ≈0.70

Ongoing Assessment and Intervention

Before the Lesson
Diagnose prerequisite skills using:
• Check Skills You'll Need

During the Lesson
Monitor progress using:
• Check Understanding
• Additional Examples
• Standardized Test Prep

After the Lesson
Assess knowledge using:
• Lesson Quiz
• Computer Test Generator CD

2. Teach

Professional Development

Math Background

Students may have used trigonometric functions previously in problems involving indirect measurement. If so, they know that these functions can also be defined as the ratio of sides in a right triangle. Defining sine as the ratio of the lengths of the leg opposite the acute angle and the hypotenuse makes clear the reciprocal relationship with cosecant.

OBJECTIVE

▼ Teaching Notes

1 EXAMPLE Visual Learners

Draw the following chart on the board as a memory aid for the reciprocal relationships.

sin x ←┐
cos x ←┐
tan x ←┐
cot x ←┘
sec x ←┘
csc x ←┘

2 EXAMPLE Alternative Method

Since the reciprocal of $\frac{a}{b}$ is always $\frac{b}{a}$ (a and $b \neq 0$), the reciprocal of $\frac{\sqrt{3}}{2}$ can be written directly as $\frac{2}{\sqrt{3}}$. Rationalizing the denominator produces the result csc 60° = $\frac{2\sqrt{3}}{3}$.

3 EXAMPLE Technology Tip

Ask students what would happen if you left the calculator in degree mode to do these calculations. The angle $\frac{\pi}{3}$ is interpreted as an angle of a little more than one degree rather than 60 degrees.

📖 Additional Examples

1 a. Find csc 45°. **about 1.41**
   b. Suppose $\cos \theta = \frac{4}{5}$. Find sec θ. **$\frac{5}{4}$**

2 Find the exact value of csc 45°.

$\sqrt{2}$

3 Use a calculator to evaluate each expression. Round to the nearest thousandth.
   a. cot $\frac{\pi}{5}$ **1.376**
   b. sec (−2) **−2.403**

750

You can use what you know about the unit circle to find exact values for reciprocal trigonometric functions.

2 EXAMPLE Finding Exact Values

Find the exact value of csc 60°.

Use the unit circle to find the exact value of sin 60°. Then write the reciprocal.

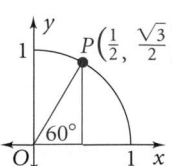

The *y*-coordinate of point *P* is $\frac{\sqrt{3}}{2}$.

$\csc 60° = \dfrac{1}{\sin 60°}$ **Use the definition.**

$= \dfrac{1}{\frac{\sqrt{3}}{2}}$ **Substitute.**

$= \dfrac{2}{\sqrt{3}}$ **Simplify.**

$= \dfrac{2\sqrt{3}}{3}$ **Rationalize the denominator.**

✓ **Check Understanding** **2** Find each exact value.
   a. sec 60° **2**
   b. cot 45° **1**
   c. csc 30° **2**

You can also evaluate the reciprocal functions in radians.

3 EXAMPLE Using Radians

Evaluate each expression. Use your calculator's radian mode. Round to the nearest thousandth.

a. cot $\frac{\pi}{3}$

$\cot \frac{\pi}{3} = \dfrac{1}{\tan \frac{\pi}{3}}$

1/tan (π/3)
.5773502692

cot $\frac{\pi}{3} \approx 0.577$

b. sec (−1)

$\sec (-1) = \dfrac{1}{\cos (-1)}$

1/cos (−1)
1.850815718

sec (−1) ≈ 1.851

✓ **Check Understanding** **3** Use a calculator to evaluate each expression. Each angle is given in radians. Round to the nearest thousandth.
   a. csc (−1.5) **−1.003**
   b. sec 2 **−2.403**
   c. cot π **undefined**

750 Chapter 13 Periodic Functions and Trigonometry

👥 Reaching All Students

Below Level Point out to students that the definitions of the reciprocal trig functions are true for all values of A for which both functions are defined. So they are identities.	**Advanced Learners** Students who created a table for the trigonometric functions in terms of a right triangle can now expand that table to the reciprocal functions.	**Visual Learners** See note on page 750. **Error Prevention** See note on page 752.

Graphing Reciprocal Trigonometric Functions

The graphs of reciprocal trigonometric functions have asymptotes where their denominators are zero.

4 EXAMPLE Sketching a Graph

Sketch the graphs of $y = \sin x$ and $y = \csc x$ in the interval from 0 to 2π.

Step 1 Make a table of values.

x	0	$\frac{\pi}{6}$	$\frac{\pi}{3}$	$\frac{\pi}{2}$	$\frac{2\pi}{3}$	$\frac{5\pi}{6}$	π	$\frac{7\pi}{6}$	$\frac{4\pi}{3}$	$\frac{3\pi}{2}$	$\frac{5\pi}{3}$	$\frac{11\pi}{6}$	2π
$\sin x$	0	0.5	0.9	1	0.9	0.5	0	−0.5	−0.9	−1	−0.9	−0.5	0
$\csc x$	■	2	1.2	1	1.2	2	■	−2	−1.2	−1	−1.2	−2	■

Step 2 Plot the points and sketch the graphs.

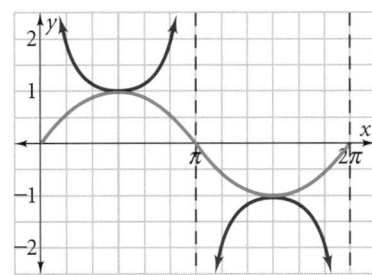

$y = \csc x$ will have a vertical asymptote wherever its denominator ($\sin x$) is 0.

✓**Check Understanding** ④ Graph $y = \tan x$ and $y = \cot x$ in the interval from 0 to 2π. **See left.**

4.
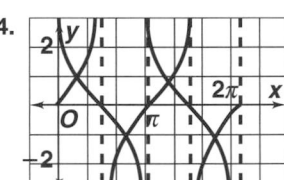

You can use a graphing calculator to graph trigonometric functions quickly.

5 EXAMPLE Using Technology to Graph Reciprocals

Graph $y = \sec x$. Find the value of sec 20°.

Step 1 Use degree mode.
Graph $y = \frac{1}{\cos x}$.

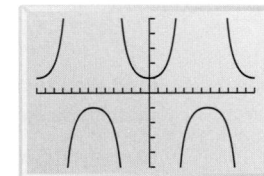

Xmin=−360
Xmax=360
Xscl=30
Ymin=−5
Ymax=5
Yscl=1

Step 2 Use the TABLE feature.

X	Y1
20	1.0642
21	1.0711
22	1.0785
23	1.0864
24	1.0946
25	1.0089
26	1.5458

X=20

sec 20° ≈ 1.0642

✓**Check Understanding** ⑤ Use the graph of the reciprocal trigonometric function to find csc 45°. **≈1.4142**

④ EXAMPLE **Connection to Algebra**

Ask where the graph of $y = \sec x$ will have a vertical asymptote in the interval from 0 to 2π. $\frac{\pi}{2}, \frac{3\pi}{2}$

⑥ EXAMPLE **Teaching Tip**

Point out that the units in which the string is measured must be feet because the height of the person is given in feet.

Additional Examples

④ Graph $y = \cos x$ and $y = \sec x$ in the interval from 0 to 2π.

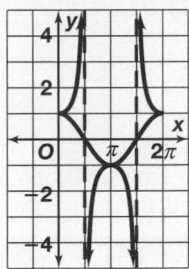

⑤ Use the graph of $y = \sec x$ in Example 5 to find the value of sec 13°. **about 1.0263**

⑥ Use the function in Example 6 to find the length of string needed to form an angle of 55°. **about 10.5 ft**

Closure

Ask: *How can you graph the cotangent, secant, and cosecant functions on the calculator? Where are the asymptotes for these functions?* **You can graph these functions by graphing the reciprocals of the tangent, cosine, and sine functions. For example, enter 1/tan(x) to graph cot(x). The asymptotes will be located wherever tan(x) = 0, cos(x) = 0 or sin(x) = 0.**

Assignment Guide

1 Objective
- **A B Core** 1–28, 42–49, 54–58, 70
- **C Extension** 71, 72

2 Objective
- **A B Core** 29–41, 50–53, 59–69
- **C Extension** 73, 74

Standardized Test Prep 75–82

Mixed Review 83–92

Error Prevention

Exercises 56–58 Make sure students remember that division by zero is undefined.

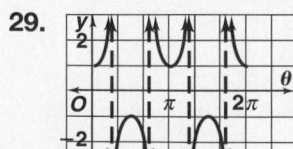

Enrichment 13-8
Reteaching 13-8
Practice 13-8

You can use a reciprocal trigonometric function to solve a real-world problem.

6 EXAMPLE Real-World Connection

Indirect Measurement A handler of a parade balloon holds a line of length y. The length is modeled by the function $y = d \sec \theta$, where d is the distance from the handler of the balloon to the point on the ground just below the balloon, and θ is the angle formed by the line and the ground. Graph the function for $h = 6$. Find the length of line needed to form an angle of 60°.

$$y = 6 \sec \theta = 6\left(\frac{1}{\cos \theta}\right) = \frac{6}{\cos \theta}$$ **Use the definition of secant. Simplify.**

Graph the function. Use the **value** feature.

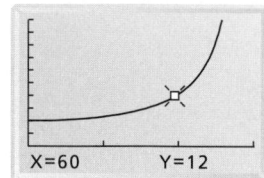

Xmin=0
Xmax=90
Xscl=30
Ymin=0
Ymax=30
Yscl=3

X=60   Y=12

● To form an angle of 60°, the line must be 12 ft long.

✓ **Check Understanding** **6** How long must the line be to form an angle of 60°? Of 45°? Of 5°?
6.9 ft; 8.5 ft; 68.8 ft

Real-World Connection

Some large parade balloons need more than 50 physically fit, trained handlers.

EXERCISES

For more practice, see *Extra Practice*.

Practice and Problem Solving

A Practice by Example

Example 1
(page 749)

Evaluate each expression. Give your answer as a decimal rounded to the nearest hundredth.

1. csc 100° **1.02**
2. csc 80° **1.02**
3. cot $(-55°)$ **−0.70**
4. sec 200° **−1.06**

Evaluate each expression. Write your answer in exact form.

5. Suppose $\tan \theta = \frac{20}{15}$. Find $\cot \theta$. **$\frac{3}{4}$**
6. Suppose $\sin \theta = \frac{13}{18}$. Find $\csc \theta$. **$\frac{18}{13}$**

7. Suppose $\cos \theta = -\frac{21}{35}$. Find $\sec \theta$. **$-\frac{5}{3}$**
8. Suppose $\tan \theta = -\frac{4}{3}$. Find $\cot \theta$. **$-\frac{3}{4}$**

Example 2
(page 750)

Find the exact value of each expression. If the expression is undefined, write *undefined*.

9. sec 45° **$\sqrt{2}$**
10. cot 60° **$\frac{\sqrt{3}}{3}$**
11. cot 90° **0**
12. sec 180° **−1**

13. csc 0° **undefined**
14. csc 60° **$\frac{2\sqrt{3}}{3}$**
15. cot 0° **undefined**
16. cot 30° **$\sqrt{3}$**

17. sec 90° **undefined**
18. csc 30° **2**
19. sec 60° **2**
20. csc 45° **$\sqrt{2}$**

Example 3
(page 750)

Evaluate each expression to the nearest hundredth. Each angle is given in radians.

21. cot 3 **−7.02**
22. sec π **−1**
23. csc $\frac{\pi}{2}$ **1**
24. sec $(-\pi)$ **−1**

25. sec 2.5 **−1.25**
26. csc (-3.2) **17.13**
27. cot $\frac{\pi}{6}$ **1.73**
28. csc (-4.5) **1.02**

Example 4
(page 751)

Graph each function in the interval from 0 to 2π. **29–32. See margin.**

29. $y = \sec 2\theta$
30. $y = \cot \theta$
31. $y = \csc 2\theta - 1$
32. $y = \csc 2\theta$

pages 752–755 Exercises

29.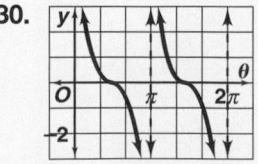

30.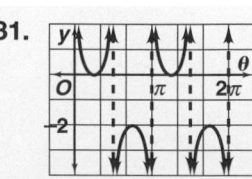

31.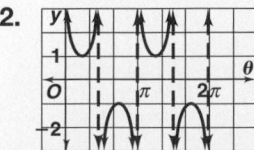

32.

Example 5
(page 751)

Use the graph of the appropriate reciprocal trigonometric function to find each value. Round to four decimal places.

33. sec 30° **1.1547** **34.** sec 80° **5.7588** **35.** sec 110° **−2.9238** **36.** csc 30° **2**

37. csc 70° **1.0642** **38.** csc 130° **1.3054** **39.** cot 30° **1.7321** **40.** cot 60° **0.5774**

Example 6
(page 752)

 **41. Indirect Measurement** A communications tower has wires anchoring it to the ground. Each wire is attached to the tower at a height 20 ft above the ground. The length y of the wire is modeled with the function $y = 20 \csc \theta$, where θ is the measure of the angle formed by the wire and the ground.
a. Graph the function. **See back of book.**
b. Find the length of wire needed to form an angle of 45°. **≈28.3 ft**
c. Find the length of wire needed to form an angle of 60°. **≈23.1 ft**
d. Find the length of wire needed to form an angle of 75°. **≈20.7 ft**

B **Apply Your Skills**

Evaluate each expression. Write your answer in exact form. If appropriate, also state it as a decimal rounded to the nearest hundredth. If the expression is undefined, write *undefined*.

42. cot (−45°) **−1**

43. sec (−30°) $\frac{2\sqrt{3}}{3}$; **1.15**

44. csc (−90°) **−1**

45. sec (−180°) **−1**

Graph each function in the interval from 0 to 2π. **46–49. See margin.**

46. $y = \csc \theta - \frac{\pi}{2}$

47. $y = \sec \frac{1}{4}\theta$

48. $y = -\sec \pi\theta$

49. $y = \cot \frac{\theta}{3}$

Match each function with its graph.

50. $y = \frac{1}{\sin x}$ **B**

51. $y = \frac{1}{\cos x}$ **C**

52. $y = -\frac{1}{\sin x}$ **A**

53. $y = \frac{1}{\tan x}$ **D**

A.
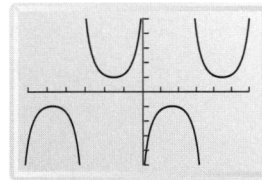

B.
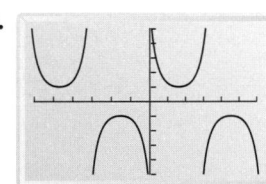

C.
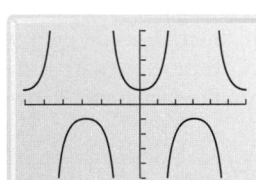

D.
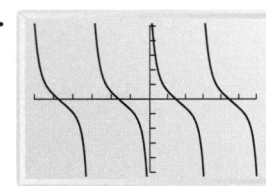

54a. domain: all real numbers except multiples of π; range: all real numbers ≥1 or ≤−1; period 2π

54. a. What are the domain, range, and period of $y = \csc x$? **See left.**
b. What is the relative minimum in the interval $0 \le x \le \pi$? **1**
c. What is the relative maximum in the interval $\pi \le x \le 2\pi$? **−1**

55. Reasoning Use the relationship $\csc x = \frac{1}{\sin x}$ to explain why each statement is true. **Reciprocals have the same sign.**
a. When the graph of $y = \sin x$ is positive, so is the graph of $y = \csc x$.
b. When the graph of $y = \sin x$ is near a y-value of −1, so is the graph of $y = \csc x$. **The reciprocal of −1 is −1.**

46.
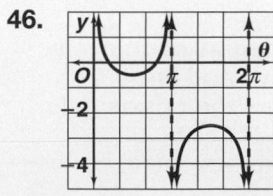

47.
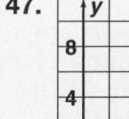

48.
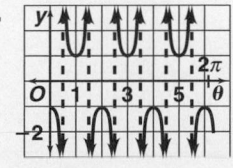

49.
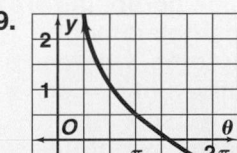

Lesson Quiz 13-8

1. What are the equations of the two lines that define the maximum and minimum values for the graphs of $y = \sin x$ and $y = \cos x$?
$y = 1$ and $y = -1$

2. Which basic trigonometric functions have vertical asymptotes?
$y = \tan x$, $y = \cot x$, $y = \sec x$, $y = \csc x$

3. What are not in the ranges of $y = \sec x$ and $y = \csc x$?
$-1 < y < 1$

Alternative Assessment

Have students work in small groups to make a poster that includes the graphs of all six of the trigonometric functions. Have groups exchange and check and correct the work before displaying the posters in the classroom.

Exercises 75–82 Suggest that students begin by drawing a right triangle that has sides in the correct proportions such that the angle θ has the function value that is given.

pages 752–755 Exercises

56. csc 180° is undefined because sin 180° is 0 and csc 180° is $\frac{1}{\sin 180°}$.

57. sec 90° is undefined because cos 90° is 0 and sec 90° is $\frac{1}{\cos 90°}$.

58. cot 0° is undefined because tan 0° is 0 and cot 0° is $\frac{1}{\tan 0°}$.

60a.

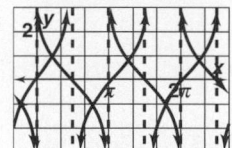

b. The domain of $y = \tan x$ is all real numbers except odd multiples of $\frac{\pi}{2}$, which are its asymptotes. The domain of $y = \cot x$ is all real numbers except multiples of π, which are its asymptotes. The range of both functions is all real numbers.

c. The graphs have the same period and range. Their asymptotes are shifted by $\frac{\pi}{2}$.

d. Answers may vary. Sample: $x = \frac{\pi}{4}, x = \frac{3\pi}{4}$

71. $y = \sec x$ and $y = \csc x$ are not parabolas because parabolas are not restricted by asymptotes, whereas the curves of $y = \sec x$ and $y = \csc x$ are between asymptotes.

✏️ **Writing** Explain why each expression is undefined. **56–58. See margin.**

56. csc 180°   57. sec 90°   58. cot 0°

59a–b. See left.

🌐 59. **Indirect Measurement** The function $y = 60 \sec \theta$ models the length y of a fire ladder as a function of the measure of the angle θ formed by the ladder and the horizontal when the hinge of the ladder is 60 ft from the building.

59a.

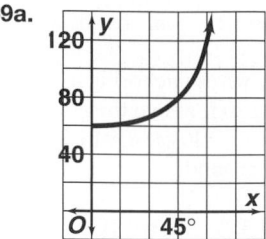

b. **63.9 ft**

a. Graph the function.
b. In the photo, $\theta = 20°$. How far is the ladder extended?
c. How far is the ladder extended when it forms an angle of 30°? **69.3 ft**
d. Suppose the ladder is extended to its full length of 80 ft. What angle does it form with the horizontal? How far up a building can the ladder reach when fully extended? (*Hint:* Use the information in the photo.) **52.9 ft**

60. a. Graph $y = \tan x$ and $y = \cot x$ on the same axes. **a–d. See margin.**
✏️ b. State the domain, the range, and the asymptotes of each function.
✏️ c. **Writing** Compare the two graphs. How are they alike? How are they different?
⬛ d. **Geometry** The graph of the cotangent function can be reflected about a line to graph the tangent function. Name at least two lines that have this property.

🖩 Graph each function in the interval from 0 to 2π. Describe any phase shift and vertical shift in the graph. **61–68. See back of book.**

61. $y = \sec 2\theta + 3$
62. $y = \sec 2\left(\theta + \frac{\pi}{2}\right)$
63. $y = \csc 2\theta - 1$
64. $y = \csc 2\left(\theta - \frac{\pi}{2}\right)$
65. $y = -2 \sec (x - 4)$
66. $f(x) = 3 \csc (x + 2) - 1$
67. $y = \cot 2(x + \pi) + 3$
68. $g(x) = 2 \sec \left(3\left(x - \frac{\pi}{6}\right)\right) - 2$

69. a. Graph $y = -\cos x$ and $y = -\sec x$ on the same axes. **a–e. See back of book.**
b. State the domain, the range, and the period of each function.
✏️ c. For which values of x does $-\cos x = -\sec x$? Justify your answer.
✏️ d. **Writing** Compare the two graphs. How are they alike? How are they different?
e. **Reasoning** Is the value of $-\sec x$ positive when $-\cos x$ is positive and negative when $-\cos x$ is negative? Justify your answer.

🖩 70. a. **Critical Thinking** Evaluate each expression below. Tell which one gives the correct value of csc 60°. **II**
   I. $\sin ((60^{-1})°)$ **II.** $(\sin 60°)^{-1}$ **III.** $\sin^{-1} 60°$
b. Which expression in part (a) represents $\sin \left(\frac{1}{60}\right)°$? **I**

ⓒ **Challenge**

71. **Reasoning** Each branch of $y = \sec x$ and $y = \csc x$ is a curve. Explain why these curves cannot be parabolas. (*Hint:* Do parabolas have asymptotes?) **See margin.**

754   Chapter 13 Periodic Functions and Trigonometry

73a.

b. **Answers may vary. Sample:** Given $y = b \cot x$, as $|b|$ decreases, the period increases; as $|b|$ increases, the period decreases. If $b < 0$, cot x begins each cycle negative and ends positive; the opposite is true for $b > 0$.

72. $y = \cos 3x$ cycles 3 times for each cycle of $y = \cos x$. Thus, for each cycle of $y = \sec x$, $y = \sec 3x$ cycles 3 times, and each cycle of $y = \sec 3x$ is $\frac{1}{3}$ as wide as one cycle of $y = \sec x$.

72. Reasoning Consider the relationship between the graphs of $y = \cos x$ and $y = \cos 3x$. Use the relationship to explain the distance between successive branches of the graphs of $y = \sec x$ and $y = \sec 3x$.

73. a. Graph $y = \cot x, y = \cot 2x, y = \cot(-2x)$, and $y = \cot \frac{1}{2}x$ on the same axes.   **a–b. See margin p. 754.**

b. Make a Conjecture Describe how the graph of $y = \cot bx$ changes as the value of b changes.

74. a. Graph $y = \sec x, y = 2 \sec x, y = -3 \sec x$, and $y = \frac{1}{2} \sec x$ on the same axes.   **a–b. See margin.**

b. Make a Conjecture Describe how the graph of $y = b \sec x$ changes as the value of b changes.

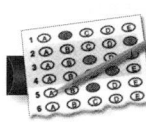

Gridded Response

For Exercises 75–78, suppose $\cos \theta = \frac{9}{41}$ and $\sin \theta > 0$. Enter each answer as a fraction.

75. What is $\tan \theta$? $\frac{40}{9}$

76. What is $\sec \theta$? $\frac{41}{9}$

77. What is $\cot \theta$? $\frac{9}{40}$

78. What is $\csc \theta$? $\frac{41}{40}$

Take It to the NET
Online lesson quiz at
www.PHSchool.com
Web Code: aga-1308

For Exercises 79–82, suppose $\tan \theta = \frac{4}{3}$, $\sin \theta > 0$, and $-\frac{\pi}{2} \le \theta < \frac{\pi}{2}$. Enter each answer as a decimal.

79. What is $\cot \theta + \cos \theta$? **1.35**

80. What is $(\sin \theta)(\cot \theta)$? **0.6**

81. What is $\sec \theta \div \tan \theta$? **1.25**

82. What is $\sin \theta + \cos \theta + \cot \theta + \csc \theta$? **3.4**

Mixed Review

Lesson 13-7

Find the amplitude and period of each function. Describe any phase shift and vertical shift in the graph.   **83–86. See margin.**

83. $y = 2 \sin x - 5$

84. $y = -\cos(x + 4) - 7$

85. $y = -3 \sin\left(x + \frac{\pi}{6}\right) + 4$

86. $y = 5 \cos \pi(x - 1.5) - 8$

Lesson 12-7

Sketch a normal curve for each distribution. Label the x-axis values at one, two, and three standard deviations from the mean.   **87–88. See margin.**

87. mean = 25, standard deviation = 5

88. mean = 25, standard deviation = 10

Lesson 11-6

Write and evaluate a sum to approximate the area under each curve for the domain $-1 \le x \le 2$.   **89–92. See margin.**
a. Use inscribed rectangles 1 unit wide.
b. Use circumscribed rectangles 1 unit wide.

89. $f(x) = 3x^2$

90. $y = x^2 + 4$

91. $g(x) = -x^2 + 4$

92. $g(x) = -x^2 + 8$

Lesson 13-8   Reciprocal Trigonometric Functions   **755**

86. 5, 2; 1.5 units right, 8 units down

87.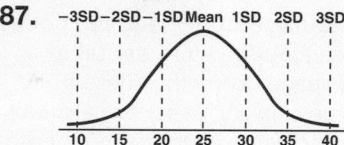

88.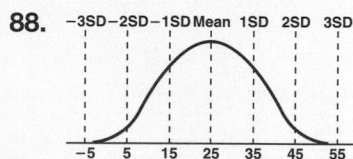

89a. $\displaystyle\sum_{n=-1}^{2} (1) f(a_n)$, 3 units^2

b. $\displaystyle\sum_{n=-1}^{2} (1) f(a_n)$, 18 units^2

90a. $\displaystyle\sum_{n=-1}^{2} (1) f(a_n)$, 13 units^2

b. $\displaystyle\sum_{n=-1}^{2} (1) f(a_n)$, 18 units^2

91a. $\displaystyle\sum_{n=-1}^{2} (1) f(a_n)$, 6 units^2

b. $\displaystyle\sum_{n=-1}^{2} (1) f(a_n)$, 11 units^2

92a. $\displaystyle\sum_{n=-1}^{2} (1) f(a_n)$, 18 units^2

b. $\displaystyle\sum_{n=-1}^{2} (1) f(a_n)$, 23 units^2

74a.

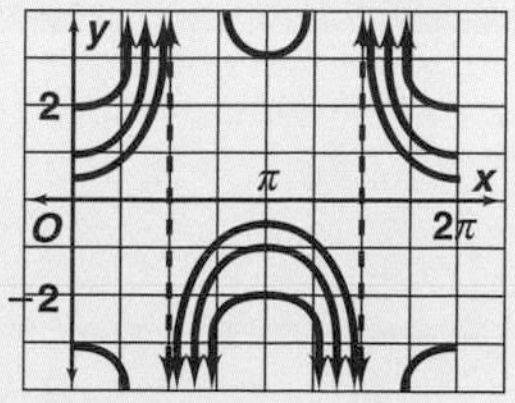

b. Answers may vary. Sample:
Given $y = b \sec x$, as $|b|$ increases, the curve is narrower; as $|b|$ decreases, the curve is wider. If $b < 0$, it is a reflection in the x-axis of $y = |b| \sec x$.

83. 2, 2π; 5 units down

84. 1, 2π; 4 units left, 7 units down

85. 3, 2π; $\frac{\pi}{6}$ units left, 4 units up

Using Mental Math

This feature explains how to use the memorization of the sine and cosine of special angles and the pattern of y-values of periodic functions to answer test items using mental math.

Resources

Test-Taking Strategies with Transparencies
- Transparency 13
- Practice sheet p. 37

Teaching Notes

Encourage students to memorize the values given in the table on this page. Knowing these basic values makes it easy to calculate and solve problems using mental math.

Test-Taking Strategies with Transparencies

Test-Taking Strategy: Using Mental Math

Sometimes, it is easiest to compute mentally.

Example Find the 7th term in the pattern.

1, 2, 4, 8, . . .

A. 16   B. 32   C. 64   D. 128

To find the pattern, mentally compute how the terms relate to their position in the list.

1   2   4   8
×2 ×2 ×2

The terms can be rewritten as $2^0, 2^1, 2^2, 2^3, ...$
So the 7th term must be 2^6.

The answer is 64, or choice C.

Use mental math to find the answer. Explain your reasoning.

1. Complete the table below, using the rule $y = 2x - 1$.

x	−1	0	1	2	3
y	−3	−1	1		

A. 4, 6   B. 2, 4   C. 3, 5   D. 3, 7

2. Which pattern has the rule that the nth term is 3 − 2n?
F. 1, −1, −3, −5, . . .   G. −1, 1, 3, 5, . . .
H. −2, −4, −6, −8, . . .   I. 1, −1, −3, −15, . . .

Solutions
1. C
2.

Transparency 13

You can solve many problems quickly when you know the sine and cosine of special angles and the pattern of the y-values of the periodic function.

θ	0° or 0 radians	30° or $\frac{\pi}{6}$ radians	45° or $\frac{\pi}{4}$ radians	60° or $\frac{\pi}{3}$ radians	90° or $\frac{\pi}{2}$ radians
$\sin \theta$	0	$\frac{1}{2}$	$\frac{\sqrt{2}}{2}$	$\frac{\sqrt{3}}{2}$	1
$\cos \theta$	1	$\frac{\sqrt{3}}{2}$	$\frac{\sqrt{2}}{2}$	$\frac{1}{2}$	0

1 EXAMPLE

Find each exact value.

a. sin 150°

The terminal side of the angle lies in Quadrant II and forms an angle of 30° with the x-axis.

$\sin 150° = \sin 30° = \frac{1}{2}$

b. $\cos\left(-\frac{\pi}{4}\right)$

The terminal side of the angle lies in Quadrant IV and forms an angle of $\frac{\pi}{4}$ radians with the x-axis.

$\cos\left(-\frac{\pi}{4}\right) = \cos\frac{\pi}{4} = \frac{\sqrt{2}}{2}$

2 EXAMPLE

Solve each equation in the interval from 0° to 360°. Give exact answers.

a. $\sin \theta = -\frac{\sqrt{2}}{2}$

The sine is negative, so the terminal side of the angle must lie in Quadrant III or IV. It forms an angle of 45° with the x-axis.

$\theta = 180° + 45° = 225°$

$\theta = 360° - 45° = 315°$

The solutions are 225° and 315°.

b. $\cos\left(\frac{\theta}{2}\right) = 0$

The cosine is 0, so the terminal side of the angle must lie on the y-axis. The angle must be 90° or 270°.

If $\frac{\theta}{2} = 90°$, then $\theta = 180°$.

If $\frac{\theta}{2} = 270°$, then $\theta = 540°$.

Since 540° > 360°, the only solution is 180°.

EXERCISES

Find each exact value.

1. cos 150° $-\frac{\sqrt{3}}{2}$

2. sin −120° $-\frac{\sqrt{3}}{2}$

3. $\sin\left(\frac{5\pi}{6}\right)$ $\frac{1}{2}$

4. $\cos\left(\frac{\pi}{3}\right)$ $\frac{1}{2}$

Solve each equation in the interval from 0° to 360°. Give exact answers.

5. $\cos \theta = \frac{1}{2}$ **60°, 300°**

6. $\sin \theta = \frac{\sqrt{2}}{2}$ **45°, 135°**

7. $\sin \theta = 1$ **90°**

8. $\cos\left(\frac{\theta}{4}\right) = \frac{1}{2}$ **240°**

Chapter Review

Vocabulary

amplitude (p. 698)
central angle (p. 712)
cosecant (p. 749)
cosine function (p. 729)
cosine of θ (p. 706)
cotangent (p. 749)
coterminal angles (p. 705)
cycle (p. 697)

initial side (p. 704)
intercepted arc (p. 712)
period (p. 697)
periodic function (p. 697)
phase shift (p. 742)
radian (p. 712)
secant (p. 749)
sine curve (p. 721)

sine function (p. 720)
sine of θ (p. 706)
standard position (p. 704)
tangent function (p. 735)
tangent of θ (p. 735)
terminal side (p. 704)
unit circle (p. 706)

 Reading Math
Understanding Vocabulary

 Take It to the NET
Online vocabulary quiz
at www.PHSchool.com
Web Code: agj-1351

Choose the correct term to complete each sentence.

1. The __?__ of a function is the length of one cycle. **period**

2. Centered at the origin of the coordinate plane, the __?__ has a radius of 1 unit.
   unit circle

3. The asymptote of the __?__ occurs at $\theta = \frac{\pi}{2}$ and repeats every π units.
   tangent function

4. A horizontal translation of a periodic function is a(n) __?__. **phase shift**

5. The __?__ is the reciprocal of the cosine function. **secant function**

Skills and Concepts

13-1 Objectives

▼ To identify cycles and periods of periodic functions (p. 696)

▼ To find the amplitude of periodic functions (p. 698)

A **periodic function** repeats a pattern of *y*-values at regular intervals. One complete pattern is called a **cycle.** A cycle may begin at any point on the graph. The **period** of a function is the length of one cycle. The **amplitude** of a periodic function is half the difference between its maximum and minimum values.

6. Determine whether the function at the right *is* or *is not* periodic. If it is, identify one cycle in two different ways. Then determine the period and amplitude. **periodic; 4, 2**

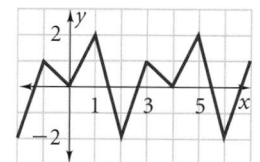

7. Sketch the graph of a wave with a period of 0.5 and an amplitude of 3.
   See margin.

13-2 Objectives

▼ To work with angles in standard position (p. 704)

▼ To find coordinates of points on the unit circle (p. 706)

An angle is in **standard position** if the vertex is at the origin and one ray, the **initial side**, is on the positive *x*-axis. The other ray is the **terminal side** of the angle. Two angles in standard position are **coterminal** if they have the same terminal side.

The **unit circle** has a radius of 1 unit and its center at the origin. The **cosine of θ** (cos θ) is the *x*-coordinate of the point where the terminal side of the angle intersects the unit circle. The **sine of θ** (sin θ) is the *y*-coordinate.

8. Find the measure of the angle in standard position at the right. **−225°**

9. Sketch a −30° angle in standard position.
   See margin.

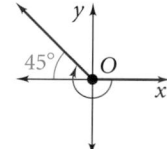

pages 757–759 **Chapter Review**

7. **Answers may vary. Sample:**

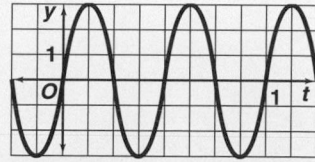

9.

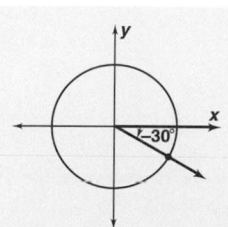

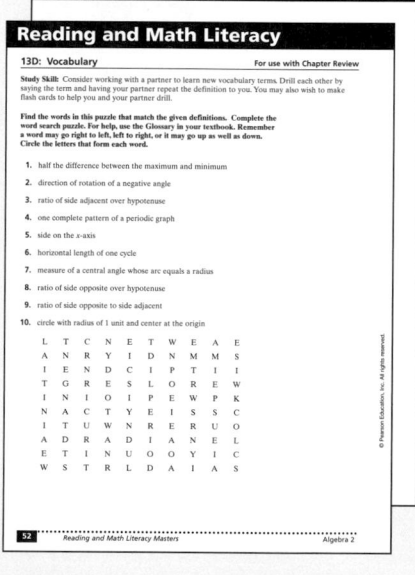

19.

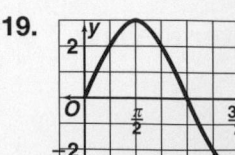

20.

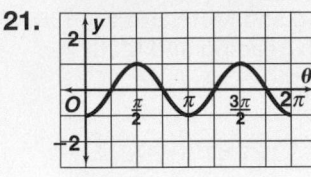

21.

10. 240°

10. Find the measure of an angle between 0° and 360° coterminal with a −120° angle.

11. Find the exact coordinates of the point at which the terminal side of a 315° angle intersects the unit circle. Then find the decimal equivalents. Round your answers to the nearest hundredth. $\left(\frac{\sqrt{2}}{2}, -\frac{\sqrt{2}}{2}\right)$; **(0.71, −0.71)**

13-3 Objectives

▼ To use radian measure for angles (p. 712)

▼ To find the length of an arc of a circle (p. 714)

12a. $\frac{\pi}{3}$

  b. $\frac{1}{2}, \frac{\sqrt{3}}{2}$

13a. $-\frac{\pi}{4}$

  b. $\frac{\sqrt{2}}{2}, -\frac{\sqrt{2}}{2}$

14a. π

  b. **−1, 0**

15a. 360°

  b. 1, 0

16a. 150°

  b. $-\frac{\sqrt{3}}{2}, \frac{1}{2}$

A **central angle** of a circle is an angle whose vertex is at the center of a circle and whose sides are radii of the circle. An **intercepted arc** is the portion of the circle whose endpoints are on the sides of the angle and whose remaining points lie in the interior of the angle. A **radian** is the measure of a central angle that intercepts an arc equal in length to a radius of the circle.

To convert degrees to radians, multiply by $\frac{\pi \text{ radians}}{180°}$. To convert radians to degrees, multiply by $\frac{180°}{\pi \text{ radians}}$. When the measure of an angle θ is in radians and r is the radius, the length s of the intercepted arc is $s = r\theta$.

The measure θ of an angle in standard position is given.
a. Write each degree measure in radians and each radian measure in degrees rounded to the nearest degree.
b. Find the exact values of cos θ and sin θ for each angle measure.

12. 60°   **13.** −45°   **14.** 180°

15. 2π radians   **16.** $\frac{5\pi}{6}$ radians   **17.** $-\frac{3\pi}{4}$ radians

                                                       17a. −135°

18. Use the circle to find the length of the indicated arc. Round your answer to the nearest tenth. **26.2 ft**

                                                    b. $-\frac{\sqrt{2}}{2}, -\frac{\sqrt{2}}{2}$

m $\frac{5\pi}{3}$ 5 ft

13-4 and 13-5 Objectives

▼ To identify properties of the sine function (p. 720)

▼ To graph sine curves (p. 723)

▼ To graph and write cosine functions (p. 729)

▼ To solve trigonometric equations (p. 730)

The **sine function** $y = \sin \theta$ matches the measure θ of an angle in standard position with the y-coordinate of a point on the unit circle. This point is where the terminal side of the angle intersects the unit circle. The graph of a sine function is called a **sine curve**.

The **cosine function** $y = \cos \theta$ matches the measure θ of an angle in standard position with the x-coordinate of a point on the unit circle. This point is where the terminal side of the angle intersects the unit circle.

For the sine function $y = a \sin b\theta$ and the cosine function $y = a \cos b\theta$, the amplitude equals $|a|$, there are b cycles from 0 to 2π, and the period is $\frac{2\pi}{b}$.

Sketch the graph of each function in the interval from 0 to 2π.

19. $y = 3 \sin \theta$ **20.** $y = 2 \cos\left(\frac{\pi}{2}\right)t$ **21.** $y = -\cos 2\theta$
19–21. See margin.

22. How many cycles does the sine function have in the interval from 0 to 2π? Find the amplitude and period of the function. Then write an equation for the sine function.

     3 cycles; 1, $\frac{2\pi}{3}$; $y = -\sin 3\theta$

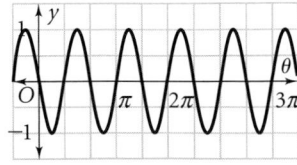

Write an equation of the function for each description or graph.

23. sine function, $a > 0$, amplitude 4, period 0.5π $y = 4 \sin 4\theta$

24. cosine function, $a > 0$, amplitude 3, period π $y = 3 \cos 2\theta$

25.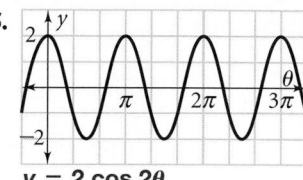

$y = 2 \cos 2\theta$

Solve each equation in the interval from 0 to 2π. Round to the nearest hundredth.

26. $\sin \theta = -0.7$
3.92, 5.51

27. $\sin \left(\frac{\pi}{2}\right) \theta = 0.25$
0.16, 1.84, 4.16, 5.84

28. $3 \cos 4\theta = -2$
0.58, 1.00, 2.15, 2.57, 3.72, 4.14, 5.29, 5.71

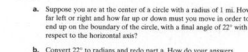
13-6 Objectives

▼ To graph the tangent function (p. 735)

The **tangent** of an angle θ in standard position is the y-coordinate of the point where the terminal side of the angle intersects the tangent line $x = 1$. A **tangent function** in the form $y = a \tan b\theta$ has a period of $\frac{\pi}{b}$.

Graph each function in the interval from 0 to 2π. Then evaluate the function at $t = \frac{\pi}{4}$ and $t = \frac{\pi}{2}$. If the tangent is undefined at that point, write *undefined*.

29. $y = \tan \left(\frac{1}{2}\right) t$
30. $y = \tan 3t$
31. $y = 2 \tan t$
29–31. See margin.

13-7 Objectives

▼ To graph translations of trigonometric functions (p. 742)

▼ To write equations of translations (p. 745)

A horizontal translation of a periodic function is a **phase shift.** When $g(x) = f(x - h) + k$, the value of h is the amount of the horizontal shift and the value of k is the amount of the vertical shift.

Graph each function in the interval from 0 to 2π. **32–34. See margin.**

32. $y = \cos \left(x + \frac{\pi}{2}\right)$
33. $y = 2 \sin x - 4$
34. $y = \sin (x - \pi) + 3$

Write an equation for each translation.

35. $y = \sin x, \frac{\pi}{4}$ units to the right
$y = \sin \left(x - \frac{\pi}{4}\right)$

36. $y = \cos x, 2$ units down
$y = \cos x - 2$

13-8 Objectives

▼ To evaluate reciprocal trigonometric functions (p. 749)

▼ To graph reciprocal trigonometric functions (p. 751)

The **cosecant** (csc), **secant** (sec), and **cotangent** (cot) functions are defined as reciprocals for all real numbers θ (except those that make a denominator zero).

$$\csc \theta = \frac{1}{\sin \theta} \qquad \sec \theta = \frac{1}{\cos \theta} \qquad \cot \theta = \frac{1}{\tan \theta}$$

Evaluate each expression. Write your answer in exact form.

37. $\sec (-45°)$ $\sqrt{2}$
38. $\cot 120°$ $-\frac{\sqrt{3}}{3}$
39. $\csc 150°$ **2**

Graph each function in the interval from 0 to 2π. **40–42. See margin.**

40. $y = 2 \csc \theta$
41. $y = \sec \theta - 1$
42. $y = \cot \left(\frac{1}{4}\right) \theta$

32.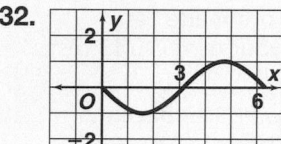

33.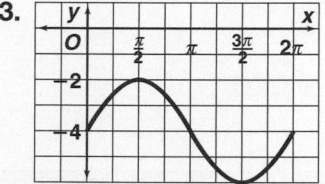

34.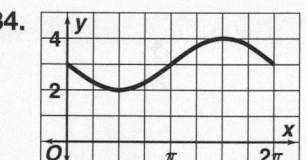

40.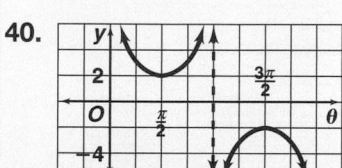

41.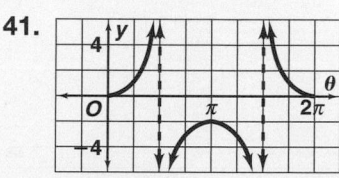

29.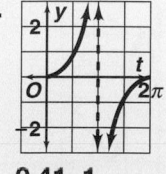
0.41, 1

30.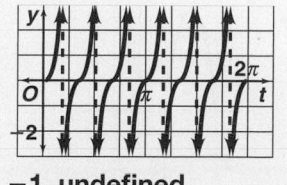
−1, undefined

31.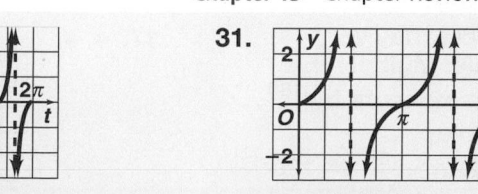
2, undefined

42.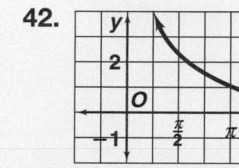

Chapter 13 Chapter Test

Take It to the NET
Online chapter test at
www.PHSchool.com
Web Code: aga-1352

Determine whether each function *is* or *is not* periodic. If it is periodic, find the period and amplitude.

1.

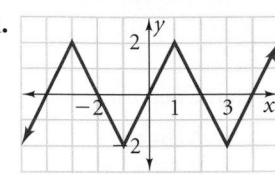

periodic; 4, 2

2.

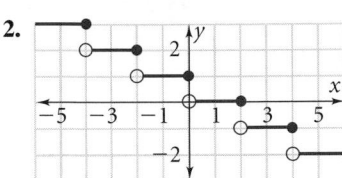

not periodic

Find the measure of an angle between 0° and 360° coterminal with the given angle.

3. $-32°$ **328°**   **4.** $-229°$ **131°**   **5.** $375°$ **15°**

Write each measure in radians. Express the answer in terms of π and also as a decimal rounded to the nearest hundredth. **6–8. See margin.**

6. $-225°$ **7.** $120°$ **8.** $600°$

Write each measure in degrees. If necessary, round your answer to the nearest degree.

9. $\frac{5\pi}{6}$ **150°**   **10.** -2.5π **−450°**   **11.** 0.8 **46°**

How many cycles does each sine function have in the interval from 0 to 2π? Find the amplitude and period of each function.

12.

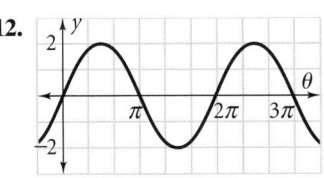

1 cycle; 2, 2π

13.

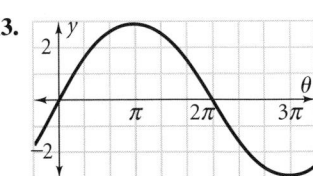

$\frac{1}{2}$ cycle; 3, 4π

14. Open-Ended Sketch a function with period 7.
Check students' work.

15. Writing Explain how to convert an angle measure in radians to an angle measure in degrees. Include an example. **See margin.**

16. Physics A pendulum 18 inches long swings through an angle of $\frac{3\pi}{4}$ radians. How far does the tip of the pendulum travel in one swing? Round your answer to the nearest inch. **42 in.**

17–18. See margin.
Find the amplitude and period of each function. Then sketch one cycle of the graph of each function.

17. $y = 4 \sin (2x)$ **18.** $y = 2 \sin (4x)$

Solve each equation in the interval from 0 to 2π. Give an exact answer and an answer rounded to the nearest hundredth. **19–21. See margin p. 761.**

19. $\cos t = \frac{1}{2}$ **20.** $2 \sin t = \sqrt{3}$

21. $3 \tan 2t = \sqrt{3}$ **22.** $\cos \frac{t\pi}{4} = 1$ **0**

Graph each function in the interval from 0 to 2π.

23. $y = 2 \cos x$ **24.** $y = -\cos \frac{\theta}{\pi}$

25. $y = 4 \sin x - 2$ **26.** $y = \cos (x + \pi)$

27. $y = \tan \frac{\theta}{3}$ **28.** $y = \tan \frac{\pi}{3}\theta$

23–28. See back of book.
Write an equation for each translation.

29. $y = \sin x$, 1 unit down $y = \sin x - 1$

30. $y = \cos x$, 7.5 units to the right

31. $y = \sin x$, 3 units to the left, 1.5 units down

32. $y = \cos x$, $\frac{\pi}{2}$ units to the right, 8 units up

30–32. See margin p. 761.
Evaluate each expression. Write your answer in exact form. If the expression is undefined, write *undefined*.

33. $\sin 30°$ $\frac{1}{2}$ **34.** $\cos 60°$ $\frac{1}{2}$

35. $\sin (-330°)$ $\frac{1}{2}$ **36.** $\csc (-330°)$ **2**

37. $\sec 270°$ **undefined**   **38.** $\tan 60°$ $\sqrt{3}$

39. $\cos 45°$ $\frac{\sqrt{2}}{2}$ **40.** $\cot (-60°)$ $-\frac{\sqrt{3}}{3}$

Graph each function in the interval from 0 to 2π.
41–44. See back of book.

41. $y = \cot \theta$ **42.** $y = \sec \theta + 1$

43. $y = \csc \frac{\theta}{2}$ **44.** $y = \csc (\theta + 1)$

15. Answers may vary.
Sample: Multiply the
radian measure by $\frac{180}{\pi}$.
Example:
$\frac{2\pi}{3}$ radians $\cdot \frac{180°}{\pi} = 120°$

17. 4, π

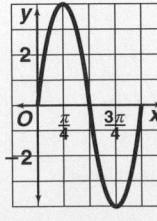

18. 2, $\frac{\pi}{2}$

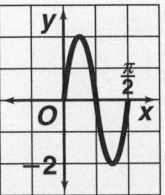

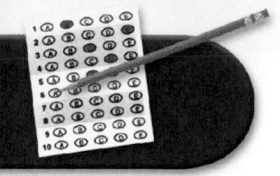
Standardized Test Prep

Reading Comprehension Read the passage below. Then answer the questions on the basis of what is *stated* or *implied* in the passage.

The Birthday Problem Suppose you are in a room of 25 people. How likely is it that at least two of the people celebrate their birthdays on the same day of the year? What about in a room of 100 people? Assume that no birthday occurs on February 29.

To answer such questions, first ask a related question: For any group of people, what is the probability that *no two* in the group have the same birthday? For a group of four people, using 365 as the number of days in a year, the probability is $\frac{365}{365} \cdot \frac{364}{365} \cdot \frac{363}{365} \cdot \frac{362}{365}$, or about 0.984. (For each person after the first, the number of days available for a "different birthday" decreases by 1.) Then it is easy to calculate the probability that at least two of the four have the same birthday: about $1 - 0.984$, or 0.016.

So you can calculate the probability that at least two of 25 people share a birthday by using the following expression.

$$1 - \frac{365}{365} \cdot \frac{364}{365} \cdot \frac{363}{365} \cdot \frac{362}{365} \cdot \ldots \cdot \frac{343}{365} \cdot \frac{342}{365} \cdot \frac{341}{365}$$

---

1. Which expression gives the probability that no two of three people have the same birthday? **B**
   - A. $\frac{364}{365} \cdot \frac{363}{365} \cdot \frac{362}{365}$
   - B. $\frac{365}{365} \cdot \frac{364}{365} \cdot \frac{363}{365}$
   - C. $1 - \frac{364}{365} \cdot \frac{363}{365} \cdot \frac{362}{365}$
   - D. $1 - \frac{365}{365} \cdot \frac{364}{365} \cdot \frac{363}{365}$

2. Which expression gives the probability that at least two of three people have the same birthday? **I**
   - F. $\frac{364}{365} \cdot \frac{363}{365} \cdot \frac{362}{365}$
   - G. $\frac{365}{365} \cdot \frac{364}{365} \cdot \frac{363}{365}$
   - H. $1 - \frac{364}{365} \cdot \frac{363}{365} \cdot \frac{362}{365}$
   - I. $1 - \frac{365}{365} \cdot \frac{364}{365} \cdot \frac{363}{365}$

3. Here is a different question: You meet 25 strangers, one at a time. With each meeting, what is the probability that a person has the same birthday as you? **D**
   - A. $\frac{340}{365}$
   - B. $\frac{25}{365}$
   - C. $\frac{1}{25}$
   - D. $\frac{1}{365}$

4. In a group of 366, what is the probability that at least two people have the same birthday? **H**
   - F. $\frac{1}{366}$
   - G. $1 - \frac{365}{366}$
   - H. 1
   - I. $\frac{366}{365}$

5. The reading passage contains the expression
   $$1 - \frac{365}{365} \cdot \frac{364}{365} \cdot \frac{363}{365} \cdot \frac{362}{365} \cdot \ldots \cdot \frac{343}{365} \cdot \frac{342}{365} \cdot \frac{341}{365}.$$
   What is another way to write that expression? **C**
   - A. $1 - \frac{365 \cdot 364 \cdot 363 \ldots \cdot 341}{365!}$
   - B. $1 - \frac{365!}{341! \cdot 365^{25}}$
   - C. $1 - \frac{365!}{340! \cdot 365^{25}}$
   - D. $\frac{1 - 365!}{340! \cdot 365^{25}}$

6. In a group of five people, what is the probability that no two have the same birthday? What is the probability that at least two people in the group have the same birthday? **about 0.973; about 0.027**

7. In a group of 15 people, what is the probability that no two have the same birthday? What is the probability that at least two people in the group have the same birthday? **about 0.747; about 0.253**

8. Suppose you want a group for which the probability that at least two people have the same birthday is at least 50%. How many people do you need? **23 people**

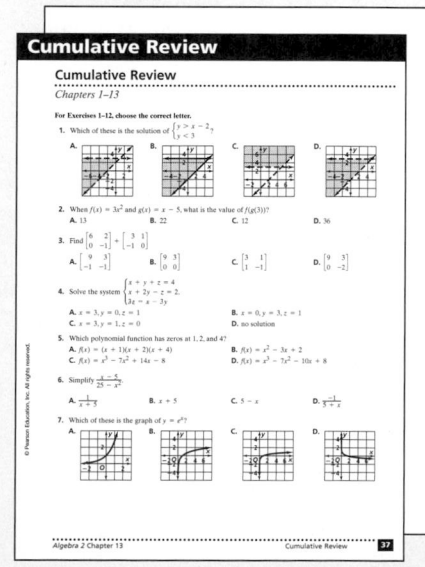
19. $\frac{\pi}{3}, \frac{5\pi}{3}$; 1.05, 5.26

20. $\frac{\pi}{3}, \frac{2\pi}{3}$; 1.05, 2.09

21. $\frac{\pi}{12}, \frac{7\pi}{12}, \frac{13\pi}{12}, \frac{19\pi}{12}$; 0.26, 1.83, 3.40, 4.97

30. $y = \cos(x - 7.5)$

31. $y = \sin(x + 3) - 1.5$

32. $y = \cos\left(x - \frac{\pi}{2}\right) + 8$

Chapter 14

Trigonometric Identities and Equations

Chapter at a Glance

14-1 Trigonometric Identities

NCTM 2, 9, 10
- ▼ Verifying Trigonometric Identities

14-2 Solving Trigonometric Equations Using Inverses

NCTM 2, 7
- ▼ Inverses of Trigonometric Functions
- ▼ Solving Trigonometric Equations

14-3 Right Triangles and Trigonometric Ratios

NCTM 2, 3, 8, 10
- ▼ Finding the Lengths of Sides in a Right Triangle
- ▼ Finding the Measures of Angles in a Right Triangle

14-4 Area and the Law of Sines

NCTM 2, 3, 4, 7
- ▼ Area and the Law of Sines

14-5 The Law of Cosines

NCTM 2, 7
- ▼ The Law of Cosines

14-6 Angle Identities

NCTM 2, 7, 8
- ▼ Angle Identities
- ▼ Sum and Difference Identities

14-7 Double-Angle and Half-Angle Identities

NCTM 2, 7, 8
- ▼ Double-Angle Identities
- ▼ Half-Angle Identities

NCTM STANDARDS 2000

1	Number and Operations	6	Problem Solving
2	Algebra	7	Reasoning and Proof
3	Geometry	8	Communication
4	Measurement	9	Connections
5	Data Analysis and Probability	10	Representation

Pacing Options

This chart suggests pacing only for the lessons and their parts. It is provided as a possible guide. It will help you determine how much time you have in your schedule to cover other components, such as the features, Chapter Review, and Chapter Test.

Day	Traditional (45 min.)	Block (90 min.)
1	14-1 ▼	14-1 ▼
2	14-2 ▼	14-2 ▼ ▼
3	14-2 ▼	14-3 ▼ ▼
4	14-3 ▼	14-4 ▼
5	14-3 ▼	14-5 ▼
6	14-4 ▼	14-6 ▼ ▼
7	14-5 ▼	14-7 ▼ ▼
8	14-6 ▼	
9	14-6 ▼	
10	14-7 ▼	
11	14-7 ▼	

NAEP Correlation (National Assessment of Educational Progress 2000 Mathematics Objectives)

14-1	14-2	14-3	14-4	14-5	14-6	14-7
A14b	A14b, A14c	A14a, A14c, G6e	A14a, A14c	A14a, A14c	A14a, A14b, A14c	A5b

N = Number Sense, Properties, and Operations; **M** = Measurement; **G** = Geometry and Spatial Sense;
D = Data Analysis, Statistics, and Probability; **A** = Algebra and Functions

Math Background

Chapter Overview

Chapter 14 begins by examining the concept of a trigonometric identity. Students see that many identities can be verified by using the unit circle definitions of the sine and cosine functions or definitions of the cofunctions. Students then see how to solve trigonometric equations by using graphs and the unit circle definitions of trigonometric functions. Inverse trigonometric functions are considered next, and students see how to use them in solving equations.

Trigonometry originated with the study of triangles, most especially right triangles. Lessons 9-3, 9-4, and 9-5 address right-triangle trigonometry and the use of trigonometry to study triangles in general. The chapter concludes with a study of the formulas for sums and differences of angles, double angles, and half angles.

Trigonometric Identities   14-1

Students have seen many examples of algebraic equations that are true for all values of their variables. Trigonometric identities are true for all values for which the functions exist. Emphasize to students that there are probably multiple ways to establish an identity. They may also need to recognize that establishing the truth of any trigonometric equation is essentially discovering an identity.

Solving Trigonometric Equations Using Inverses   14-2

The trigonometric functions are not one-to-one functions, so one must pay careful attention to domains and ranges to arrive at useful definitions of inverse trigonometric functions. Some students may be interested in researching the several ways the inverse trigonometric functions can be defined.

Right Triangles and Trigonometric Ratios   14-3

In Geometry, students learned the relationships between the side lengths for right triangles such as 45°-45°-90° and 30°-60°-90° triangles. Students who confuse similarity (same shape) with congruence (same size and shape) may need to review both concepts, and some of the theorems about similarity. They should recall the theorem usually called Angle-Angle: two triangles are similar if two angles of one have the same measure as two angles of the other. This is, of course, based on the theorem stating that the sum of the measures of the angles in a triangle is 180°. Students for whom this fact seems a dim memory may benefit

from tearing a paper triangle and assembling the corners to show the 3 angles form a line.

It may also help students to review the relationship between angle measure and side length in a triangle. This will help emphasize that the longest side of a right triangle is always the hypotenuse because it is opposite the angle with the greatest measure (the right angle).

Area and the Law of Sines   14-4

Prior to this lesson, students have found angle measures and side lengths of *right* triangles. It is important for students to realize that the Law of Sines allows them to find missing measures in *any* triangle. In the derivation of the Law of Sines, the altitude h is drawn. Recall that an *altitude* of a triangle is the perpendicular segment from a vertex to the line containing the opposite side. Since perpendicular lines form right angles, a right triangle is formed.

Note that the Law of Sines is applicable in two situations: (1) the measures of two angles and any side are known, and (2) the measures of two sides and the angle opposite one side are known (the ambiguous case). The Law of Sines cannot be used without a known angle measure. (The Law of Cosines, treated in the next lesson, deals with this case.)

The Law of Cosines   14-5

Students may find it helpful to observe that the Law of Cosines can be thought of as an "adjusted" version of the Pythagorean Theorem. The final term is the 'correction term.' There is no ambiguous case related to the Law of Cosines.

Angle Identities   14-6

Discuss how the negative angle identities and cofunction identities are related to the unit-circle and right-triangle definitions of the trigonometric functions. Students can benefit from seeing how the angle difference identities for $\sin (A - B)$ and $\tan (A - B)$ can be derived by using the identity for $\cos (A - B)$.

Double-Angle and Half-Angle Identities   14-7

The identities in this lesson grow out of those in Lesson 9-6. You may wish to challenge students to describe the angles θ for which they can compute exact values for a function such as the sine function. Students may also enjoy trying to show two or three different ways to establish these identities.

Ongoing Assessment and Intervention

Tools for Monitoring Student Progress

The Prentice Hall *Algebra 2* program provides you with many options for assessment in the Student Edition, the Teacher's Edition and the teaching resources. From these options you may choose instructional materials and techniques that are appropriate for your students and support your district's curriculum requirements.

Instant Check System™ in Chapter 14

Allows students to check their own learning before, during, and after each lesson.

Diagnosing Readiness before the chapter (p. 762)

Check Skills You'll Need exercises in each lesson (pp. 764, 769, 778, 787, 794, 800, 807)

Check Understanding questions with each Example (pp. 765, 766, 769, 770, 771, 772, 779, 780, 781, 787, 788, 789, 795, 796, 801, 802, 803, 808, 809)

Checkpoint Quiz (pp. 785, 806)

Test Prep in Chapter 14

Teaches students strategies and gives them practice with all the test item formats they will encounter on state tests and standardized national exams.

Standardized Test Prep exercises in each lesson (pp. 768, 776, 784, 785, 792, 799, 805, 806, 811)

Test-Taking Strategies (p. 812)

Standardized Test Prep (pp. 817–819)

All your assessment needs in one place!

Program Assessment

Assess student progress throughout the *Algebra 2* text with blackline masters and CD-ROM.

Assessment Resources

- Checkpoint Quizzes 1 & 2
- Chapter Test, Forms A & B
- Chapter Alternative Assessment

Spanish versions available.

 Computer Test Generator

- Unlimited questions of varying difficulty for every lesson objective.
- Create your own practice sheets, quizzes, and tests, or use the pre-made Chapter Tests.
- Diagnose readiness with questions on prerequisite skills.
- Prepare students by making tests based on standardized test objectives.
- Access Algebra 1, Geometry, and Algebra 2 content—all on one CD-ROM.

Test Preparation

A three-step approach to preparing students for high stakes, national, and state exams.

❶ **Diagnose & Prescribe**

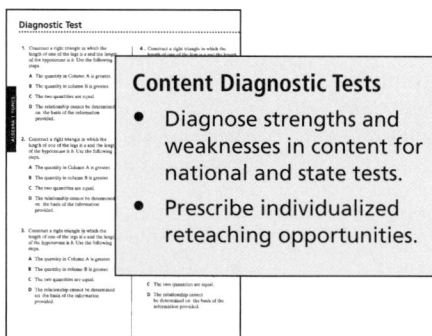

Content Diagnostic Tests
- Diagnose strengths and weaknesses in content for national and state tests.
- Prescribe individualized reteaching opportunities.

❷ **Review & Reteach**

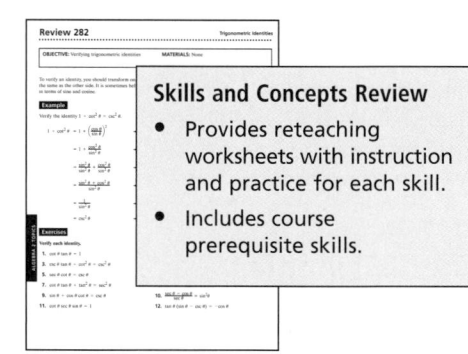

Skills and Concepts Review
- Provides reteaching worksheets with instruction and practice for each skill.
- Includes course prerequisite skills.

❸ **Practice & Assess**

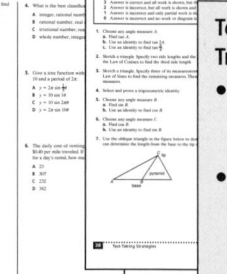

Test Preparation
- Features practice tests for End-of-Course and SAT/ACT exams.
- Includes standardized test practice by chapter for ongoing review.

Teacher's Guide with answers and correlations.

Test-Taking Strategies with Transparencies
- Support the Test-Taking Strategies pages in the Student Edition.
- Provide a teaching transparency and a practice worksheet for each strategy.

 # Reaching All Students

Support in the Student Text and Additional Resources

The textbook, the iText, and other technology components provide numerous opportunities to reach students of various ability levels and learning styles. Each Teacher's Edition lesson suggests how you can help *all* your students be successful and understand the mathematics in Chapter 14.

Below Level

Student Edition
- Diagnosing Readiness*: p. 762
- Check Skills You'll Need*: pp. 764, 769, 778, 787, 794, 800, 807

Reteaching
Chapter 14 Support File: pp. 8–14

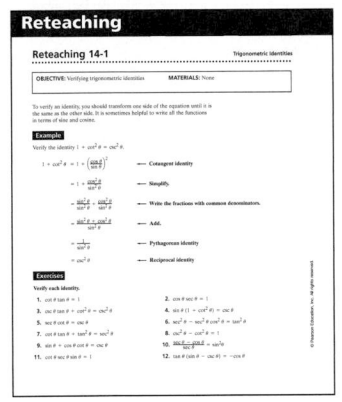

Advanced Learners

Student Edition
- Challenge exercises: pp. 767, 775, 784, 791, 798, 805, 811
- Extension, pp. 777, 793

Enrichment
Chapter 14 Support File: pp. 15–21

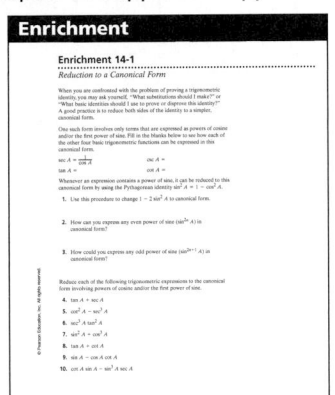

Connections to Precalculus Masters
Chapter 14 Enrichment Topic: Function "Behavior"

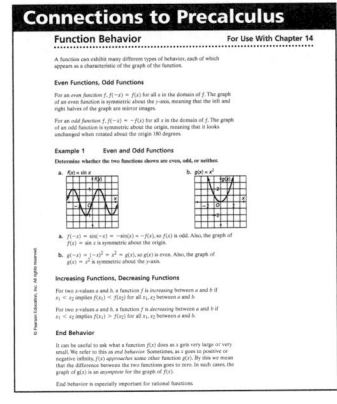

* Can be used with all ability levels to ensure mastery of prerequisite skills.

Reading and Math Literacy

Student Edition
- Vocabulary: pp. 763, 813, *plus* in every Lesson Preview
- Reading Math: pp. 765, 770, 779, 783, 786, 788, 801
- Illustrated Glossary: pp. 871–913

Reading and Math Literacy Masters
Chapter 14: pp. 53–56

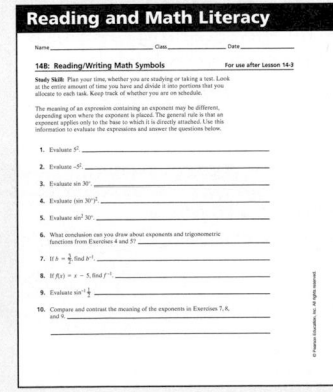

English Learners

Student Edition
- English/Spanish Illustrated Glossary: pp. 871–913

Workbook and Masters
Spanish Practice Workbook: pp. 1–7
Spanish Reading and Math Literacy Masters: pp. 53–56

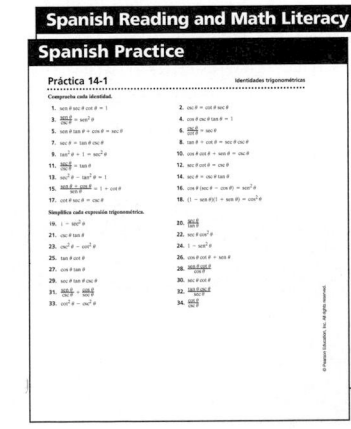

Learning Styles

Student Edition
- Investigation: pp. 764, 778
- Technology: pp. 764, 771, 780, 814
- Writing: pp. 767, 774, 775, 791, 793, 798, 805, 810, 816
- DK Activities: pp. 820–821

Activity Masters
Hands-On Activities: 58, 59

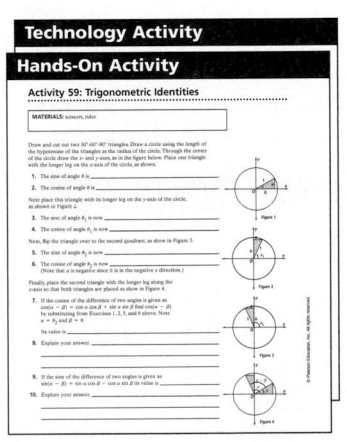

Program Resources

	Teaching Resources in Grab & Go™ Files				Resources for Reaching All Students			Spanish Resources			Presentation Assistant Plus! Transparencies				Prentice Hall Presentation Pro CD-ROM
	Practice	Reteach	Enrich	Checkpoint Quiz	Reading & Math Literacy	Technology Activities	Hands-On Activities	Practice	Reading & Math Literacy	Checkpoint Quiz	Skills Check	Additional Examples	Answers to Exercises	Lesson Quiz	
14-1	■	■	■		■			■			■	■	■	■	■
14-2	■	■	■				■	■			■	■	■	■	■
14-3	■	■	■	■	■			■	■	■	■	■	■	■	■
14-4	■	■	■					■			■	■	■	■	■
14-5	■	■	■					■			■	■	■	■	■
14-6	■	■	■	■	■		■	■	■	■	■	■	■	■	■
14-7	■	■	■					■			■	■	■	■	■
For the chapter	Chapter Tests, Alternative Assessment, Cumulative Review, Cumulative Assessment				Connections to Precalculus Masters			Spanish Chapter Tests, Alternative Assessment, Cumulative Review, Cumulative Assessment			Classroom Aid Transparencies				

Also available for use with the chapter:

 PRENTICE HALL ASSESSMENT *SYSTEM*   *See page 762C.*

- Practice Workbook
- Solution Key

- For teacher support and access to student Web site materials, use Web Code agk-5500.
- For additional online and technology resources, see below.

Technology

 iTEXT Online and on CD-ROM

Complete Interactive Student Text online and on CD-ROM—with instant feedback assessment, tutorial help, dynamic activities, instructional and real-world videos, audio, and additional practice.

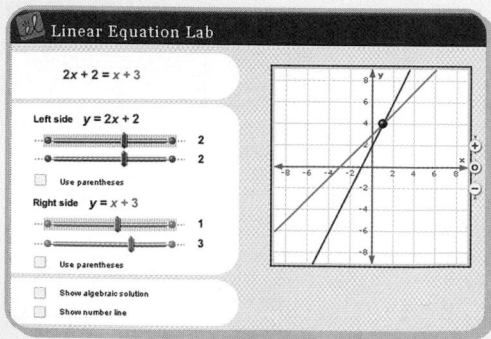

www.PHSchool.com For Students

Use **Web Codes** for easy access to online activities, chapter projects, self-grading lesson quizzes and chapter tests, vocabulary quizzes, updated data sources, graphing calculator procedures, and more.

PH SuccessNet For Teachers

Online lesson planning with built-in state correlations, all the teaching resources, complete reference library, your own calendar and Teacher Web page, professional development, and more.

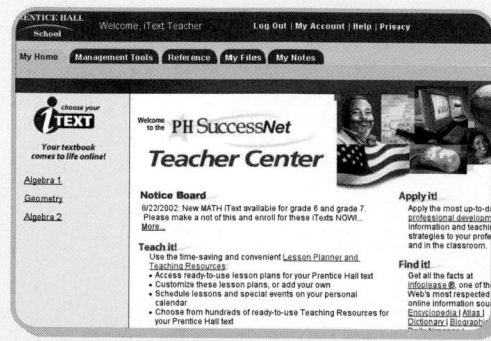

Presentation Assistant Plus!

The Prentice Hall *Presentation Assistant Plus!* provides you with the material you need to teach a lesson from beginning to end. Two easy-to-use formats—Transparencies and CD-ROM—allow you to present a lesson the way you are most comfortable.

Transparencies

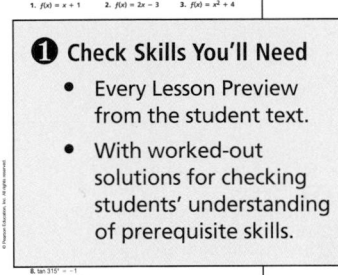

❶ Check Skills You'll Need
- Every Lesson Preview from the student text.
- With worked-out solutions for checking students' understanding of prerequisite skills.

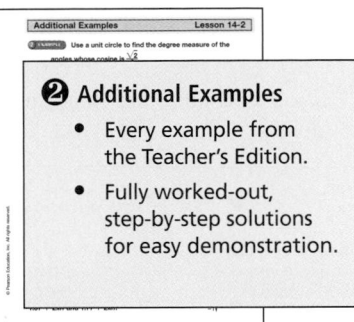

❷ Additional Examples
- Every example from the Teacher's Edition.
- Fully worked-out, step-by-step solutions for easy demonstration.

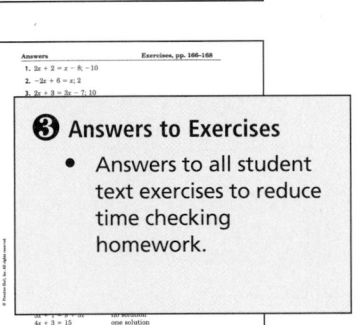

❸ Answers to Exercises
- Answers to all student text exercises to reduce time checking homework.

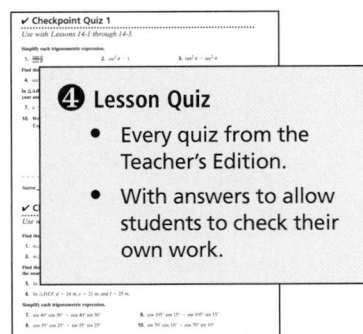

❹ Lesson Quiz
- Every quiz from the Teacher's Edition.
- With answers to allow students to check their own work.

Prentice Hall Presentation Pro CD-ROM

- Includes all Transparencies.
- Conveniently organized by lesson so you can easily ❶ Introduce, ❷ Teach, ❸ Check Homework, and ❹ Assess each lesson.
- Animated examples allow step-by-step instruction at your own pace.
- Easy to edit so you can create custom presentations.

Teaching Chapter 14 Using Presentation Assistant Plus!

	❶ **Introduce**	❷ **Teach**	❸ **Check Homework**	❹ **Assess**
	Check Skills You'll Need	Additional Examples	Student Edition Answers	Lesson Quiz
14-1	p. 92	p. 274	✔	p. 171
14-2	p. 93	pp. 275–279	✔	p. 172
14-3	p. 94	pp. 280–283	✔	p. 173
14-4	p. 95	pp. 283–285	✔	p. 174
14-5	p. 96	pp. 285–287	✔	p. 175
14-6	p. 97	pp. 288–290	✔	p. 175
14-7	p. 98	pp. 290–294	✔	p. 176

Throughout the Teacher's Edition, this symbol indicates material that is available on transparency in the Presentation Assistant Plus!

Prentice Hall Presentation Pro

CD-ROM with dynamic PowerPoint® presentations for every lesson. Helps you introduce and develop concepts, check homework, and assess progress. Part of Presentation Assistant Plus! *(See above.)*

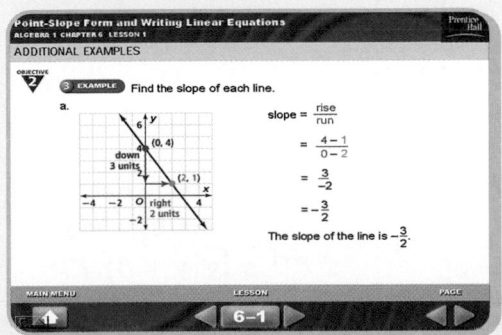

Computer Test Generator

CD-ROM to create practice sheets and tests for course objectives and standardized tests. Includes Instant Chapter Tests™, online testing, and student reports. Part of the PH Assessment System. *(See page 762C.)*

Resource Pro® with Planning Express®

CD-ROM with a lesson planning tool that allows you to import state and local objectives. Includes electronic versions of all the teaching resources.

Trigonometric Identities and Equations

  Diagnosing Readiness

Students will find answers to these exercises in the back of their textbooks.

For intervention, direct students to:

Solving Quadratic Equations
Lesson 5-5: Example 3
Exercises 7–12
Extra Practice, p. 826

Finding the Inverse of a Function
Lesson 7-7: Examples 4, 5
Exercises 17–22
Extra Practice, p. 828

Solving Exponential and Logarithmic Equations
Lesson 8-5: Example 5
Exercises 11–18
Extra Practice, p. 829

Evaluating Trigonometric Functions
Lesson 13-2: Example 4
Exercises 21–28
Lesson 13-6: Example 1
Exercises 1–8
Extra Practice, p. 832

page 762 Diagnosing Readiness

7. Domain of f is all real numbers, range of f is all real numbers; $f^{-1}(x) = \frac{x-2}{5}$, domain of f^{-1} is all real numbers, range of f^{-1} is all real numbers. f^{-1} is a function.

8. Domain of f is $\{x \mid x \geq -3\}$, the range of f is $\{y \mid y \geq 0\}$; $f^{-1}(x) = x^2 - 3$, the domain of f^{-1} is all real numbers, the range of f^{-1} is $\{y \mid y \geq -3\}$. f^{-1} is a function.

762

Where You've Been

● In Chapter 5, you learned to solve quadratic equations by finding square roots.

● In Chapter 7, you learned to find the inverse of a function.

● In Chapter 8, you learned about exponential and logarithmic functions, which are inverse functions. You learned to solve exponential and logarithmic equations by using inverse functions.

● In Chapter 13, you learned to use the sine, cosine, and tangent functions.

 **Diagnosing Readiness**

TEXT Instant self-check online and on CD-ROM

(For help, go to the Lesson in green.)

Solving Quadratic Equations (Lesson 5-5)

Solve each equation.

1. $4x^2 = 25$ $\pm\frac{5}{2}$
2. $x^2 - 23 = 0$ $\pm\sqrt{23}$
3. $3x^2 = 80$ $\pm\frac{4\sqrt{15}}{3}$
4. $8x^2 - 44 = 0$ $\pm\frac{\sqrt{22}}{2}$
5. $0.5x^2 = 15$ $\pm\sqrt{30}$
6. $6x^2 - 13 = 11$ ± 2

Finding the Inverse of a Function (Lesson 7-7)

For each function f, find f^{-1} and the domain and range of f and f^{-1}. Determine whether f^{-1} is a function. **7–12. See margin.**

7. $f(x) = 5x + 2$
8. $f(x) = \sqrt{x+3}$
9. $f(x) = \sqrt{3x-4}$
10. $f(x) = \frac{5}{x}$
11. $f(x) = \frac{10}{x-1}$
12. $f(x) = \frac{10}{x} - 1$

Solving Exponential and Logarithmic Equations (Lesson 8-5)

Solve each equation.

13. $4^x = \frac{1}{8}$ -1.5
14. $\log 5x + 1 = -1$ 0.002
15. $7^{3x} = 500$ ≈ 1.065
16. $\log 3x + \log x = 9$ $\approx 18{,}257$
17. $\log(4x+3) - \log x = 5$ $\approx 3 \times 10^{-5}$
18. $3^x = 243$ 5

Evaluating Trigonometric Functions (Lessons 13-2 and 13-6)

For each value of θ, find the values of $\cos\theta$, $\sin\theta$, and $\tan\theta$. Round your answers to the nearest hundredth.

19. $48°$
   0.67, 0.74, 1.11
20. $-105°$
   $-0.26, -0.97, 3.73$
21. $16°$
   0.96, 0.28, 0.29
22. $\frac{5\pi}{6}$
   $-0.87, 0.5, -0.58$

9. Domain of f is $\{x \mid x \geq \frac{4}{3}\}$, the range of f is $\{y \mid y \geq 0\}$; $f^{-1}(x) = \frac{x^2+4}{3}$, the domain of f^{-1} is $\{x \mid x \geq 0\}$, the range of f^{-1} is $\{y \mid y \geq \frac{4}{3}\}$. f^{-1} is a function.

10. Domain of f is $\{x \mid x \neq 0\}$, range of f is $\{y \mid y \neq 0\}$; $f^{-1}(x) = \frac{5}{x}$, domain of f^{-1} is $\{x \mid x \neq 0\}$, range of f^{-1} is $\{y \mid y \neq 0\}$. f^{-1} is a function.

Trigonometric Identities and Equations

LESSONS

14-1 Trigonometric Identities

14-2 Solving Trigonometric Equations Using Inverses

14-3 Right Triangles and Trigonometric Ratios

14-4 Area and the Law of Sines

14-5 The Law of Cosines

14-6 Angle Identities

14-7 Double-Angle and Half-Angle Identities

Key Vocabulary

- Law of Cosines (p. 794)
- Law of Sines (p. 787)
- trigonometric identity (p. 764)
- trigonometric ratios for a right triangle (p. 778)

763

Chapter 14 Overview

This chapter begins with an introduction to trigonometric identities. Students then learn how to solve trigonometric equations using inverses. Then students are introduced to the trigonometric ratios of right triangles. In subsequent lessons, students learn about area and the Law of Sines, the Law of Cosines, and angle identities. The chapter concludes with a lesson on double-angle and half-angle identities.

📖 **Reading Math**
Reading a Diagram, p. 786

📖 **Vocabulary**
A complete list of terms, plus vocabulary exercises, appears in the Chapter Review, p. 813.

📖 **Illustrated Glossary**
Examples for each vocabulary term, plus definitions in both English and Spanish, appear starting on p. 871.

🧮 **Test-Taking Strategies**
Answering Open Ended Questions, p. 812

DK **Real-World Snapshots**
See pages 820–821 for a real-world application of trigonometry that utilizes Dorling Kindersley's (DK) unique graphic presentation.

🌐 **Real-World Connections**
Some of the applications you will find in this chapter are physics (14-2), construction (14-3), surveying (14-4), and sailing (14-5).

💻 **www.PHSchool.com**
Internet support for this chapter includes:
- Self-grading Vocabulary and Chapter 14 Tests
- Chapter Project
- Chapter Planner
- Chapter 14 Resources

Plus

Where You're Going

- In Chapter 14, you will learn to verify trigonometric identities.

- You will learn to solve trigonometric equations.

- By using trigonometric ratios, you will solve real-wold problems involving right triangles.

 Applying what you learn, on pages 820–821 you will do activities involving angles and balance .

---

11. Domain of f is $\{x \mid x \neq 1\}$, range of f is $\{y \mid y \neq 0\}$; $f^{-1}(x) = \frac{10}{x} + 1$, domain of f^{-1} is $\{x \mid x \neq 0\}$, range of f^{-1} is $\{y \mid y \neq 1\}$. f^{-1} is a function.

12. Domain of f is $\{x \mid x \neq 0\}$, range of f is $\{y \mid y \neq -1\}$; $f^{-1}(x) = \frac{10}{x + 1}$, domain of f^{-1} is $\{x \mid x \neq -1\}$, range of f^{-1} is $\{y \mid y \neq 0\}$. f^{-1} is a function.

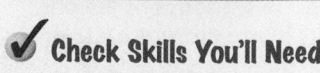

Trigonometric Identities

Lesson Preview

Lesson Preview

 Check Skills You'll Need

Properties of Real Numbers
Lesson 1-1: Example 1
Exercises 1–8
Extra Practice, p. 822

Algebraic Expressions
Lesson 1-2: Example 4
Exercises 21–35
Extra Practice, p. 822

Rational Expressions
Lesson 9-4: Example 1
Exercises 1–6
Extra Practice, p. 830

Lesson Resources

 **Teaching Resources**
Practice, Reteaching, Enrichment

Reaching All Students
Practice Workbook 14-1
Spanish Practice Workbook 14-1
Reading and Math Literacy 14A
Spanish Reading & Literacy 14A

Presentation Assistant Plus!
Transparencies
• Check Skills You'll Need 14-1
• Additional Examples 14-1
• Student Edition Answers 14-1
• Lesson Quiz 14-1
PH Presentation Pro CD 14-1

ASSESSMENT SYSTEM
PRENTICE HALL

Computer Test Generator CD

Technology
Resource Pro® CD-ROM
Computer Test Generator CD
Prentice Hall Presentation Pro CD

 **www.PHSchool.com**
Student Site
• Teacher Web Code: agk-5500
• Self-grading Lesson Quiz
Teacher Center
• Lesson Planner
• Resources

Plus **iTEXT**

764

What You'll Learn

OBJECTIVE 1
To verify trigonometric identities

... And Why

To use trigonometric identities in simplifying expressions

New Vocabulary
• trigonometric identity

✓ **Check Skills You'll Need** (For help, go to Lessons 1-1, 1-2, and 9-4.)

Determine whether each equation is true for all real numbers x. Explain your reasoning. 1–4. See back of book.

1. $2x + 3x = 5x$

2. $-(4x - 10) = 10 - 4x$

3. $\frac{4x^2}{x} = 4x$

4. $\frac{x^2 + 1}{x - 1} = x + 1$

 Interactive lesson includes instant self-check, tutorials, and activities.

OBJECTIVE 1 **Verifying Trigonometric Identities**

> ## Investigation: Trigonometric Identities
>
> **1.** Use a graphing calculator to graph $y_1 = \tan x$ and $y_2 = \frac{\sin x}{\cos x}$. If your calculator has the "animate" graph style, use it for y_2.
>
> **2.** Graph $y_1 = (\cos x)^2 + (\sin x)^2$ and $y_2 = 1$. **1–2. See back of book.**
>
> **3.** **Make a Conjecture** In Questions 1 and 2, are there any values of x for which $y_1 \neq y_2$? **no**

Real-World Connection

Astronomers use trigonometry to determine the angles that locate an object in the celestial coordinate system. This system is similar to the system of latitude and longitude used on Earth.

A trigonometric equation such as $\csc \theta = \frac{1}{\sin \theta}$ is true for all values of θ except those for which $\sin \theta = 0$. A **trigonometric identity** is a trigonometric equation that is true for all values except those for which the expressions on either side of the equal sign are undefined. The three equations $\csc \theta = \frac{1}{\sin \theta}$, $\sec \theta = \frac{1}{\cos \theta}$, and $\tan \theta = \frac{1}{\cot \theta}$ are known as the reciprocal identities.

You can derive some other identities from the unit circle definitions of sine, cosine, and tangent. In the diagram below, $\cos \theta$, $\sin \theta$, and $\tan \theta$ are the coordinates of points P and Q. You can use the slope of $\overleftrightarrow{PQ}$ to show that $\tan \theta = \frac{\sin \theta}{\cos \theta}$.

slope $\overleftrightarrow{PQ} = \frac{\sin \theta - 0}{\cos \theta - 0}$ slope $= \frac{y_2 - y_1}{x_2 - x_1}$

$\quad = \frac{\sin \theta}{\cos \theta}$

slope $\overleftrightarrow{PQ} = \frac{\tan \theta - 0}{1 - 0}$ slope $= \frac{y_2 - y_1}{x_2 - x_1}$

$\quad = \tan \theta$

So, $\tan \theta = \frac{\sin \theta}{\cos \theta}$.   **Transitive Property of Equality**

[Diagram: unit circle with $P(\cos \theta, \sin \theta)$, line $x = 1$, angle θ, and $Q(1, \tan \theta)$]

Ongoing Assessment and Intervention

Before the Lesson
Diagnose prerequisite skills using:
• Check Skills You'll Need

During the Lesson
Monitor progress using:
• Check Understanding
• Additional Examples
• Standardized Test Prep

After the Lesson
Assess knowledge using:
• Lesson Quiz
• Computer Test Generator CD

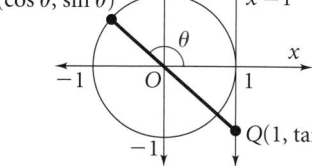

Using the reciprocal identity $\cot\theta = \frac{1}{\tan\theta}$ and the Tangent Identity $\tan\theta = \frac{\sin\theta}{\cos\theta}$, you can derive the Cotangent Identity $\cot\theta = \frac{\cos\theta}{\sin\theta}$.

$$\cot\theta = \frac{1}{\tan\theta} \quad \textbf{Reciprocal identity}$$

$$= \frac{1}{\frac{\sin\theta}{\cos\theta}} \quad \textbf{Substitute using the Tangent Identity.}$$

$$= \frac{\cos\theta}{\sin\theta} \quad \textbf{Divide.}$$

You can derive another identity from the definitions of $\cos\theta$ and $\sin\theta$. The ordered pair $(\cos\theta, \sin\theta)$ is a point on the unit circle, and for any point (x, y) on the unit circle, $x^2 + y^2 = 1$. So $\cos^2\theta + \sin^2\theta = 1$. This is one of the three Pythagorean identities.

To verify an identity, you should transform one side of the equation until it is the same as the other side. This eliminates the possibility of introducing errors that can be caused by squaring both sides of an equation or multiplying both sides of an equation by an expression that equals 0. These are the errors that can introduce extraneous roots when solving equations.

It is sometimes helpful to write all the functions in terms of sine and cosine.

1 **EXAMPLE** **Verifying Identities**

Verify the Pythagorean identity $1 + \tan^2\theta = \sec^2\theta$.

$$1 + \tan^2\theta = 1 + \left(\frac{\sin\theta}{\cos\theta}\right)^2 \quad \textbf{Tangent Identity}$$

$$= 1 + \frac{\sin^2\theta}{\cos^2\theta} \quad \textbf{Simplify.}$$

$$= \frac{\cos^2\theta}{\cos^2\theta} + \frac{\sin^2\theta}{\cos^2\theta} \quad \textbf{Write the fractions with common denominators.}$$

$$= \frac{\cos^2\theta + \sin^2\theta}{\cos^2\theta} \quad \textbf{Add.}$$

$$= \frac{1}{\cos^2\theta} \quad \textbf{Pythagorean identity}$$

$$= \sec^2\theta \quad \textbf{Reciprocal identity}$$

The left side of the equation has been transformed into the right side. Therefore the equation is an identity.

1.
$$1 + \cot^2\theta = 1 + \left(\frac{\cos\theta}{\sin\theta}\right)^2$$
$$= 1 + \frac{\cos^2\theta}{\sin^2\theta} = 1 + \frac{1 - \sin^2\theta}{\sin^2\theta}$$
$$= 1 + \frac{1}{\sin^2\theta} - \frac{\sin^2\theta}{\sin^2\theta}$$
$$= 1 + \csc^2\theta - 1$$
$$= \csc^2\theta$$

✔ **Check Understanding** **1** Verify the third Pythagorean identity, $1 + \cot^2\theta = \csc^2\theta$. **See left.**

 Key Concepts

Properties	Trigonometric Identities

Reciprocal identities

$$\csc\theta = \frac{1}{\sin\theta} \qquad \sec\theta = \frac{1}{\cos\theta} \qquad \cot\theta = \frac{1}{\tan\theta}$$

Tangent and cotangent identities

$$\tan\theta = \frac{\sin\theta}{\cos\theta} \qquad \cot\theta = \frac{\cos\theta}{\sin\theta}$$

Pythagorean identities

$$\cos^2\theta + \sin^2\theta = 1 \qquad 1 + \tan^2\theta = \sec^2\theta \qquad 1 + \cot^2\theta = \csc^2\theta$$

There are many trigonometric identities in addition to the identities named in the summary above.

Additional Examples

1 Verify the identity
$(\sin x + \cos x)^2 = 1 + 2\sin x \cos x$.
Answers may vary. Sample:
$(\sin x + \cos x)^2$
$= \sin^2 x + 2 \sin x \cos x + \cos^2 x$
$= (\sin^2 x + \cos^2 x) + 2 \sin x \cos x$
$= 1 + 2 \sin x \cos x$

2 Verify the identity
$\frac{\sin \theta}{\tan \theta} + \frac{\cos \theta}{\cot \theta} = \sin \theta + \cos \theta$.
Answers may vary. Sample:
$\frac{\sin \theta}{\tan \theta} + \frac{\cos \theta}{\cot \theta}$
$= \frac{\sin \theta}{\left(\frac{\sin \theta}{\cos \theta}\right)} + \frac{\cos \theta}{\left(\frac{\cos \theta}{\sin \theta}\right)}$
$= \sin \theta \cdot \frac{\cos \theta}{\sin \theta} + \cos \theta \cdot \frac{\sin \theta}{\cos \theta}$
$= \cos \theta + \sin \theta$
$= \sin \theta + \cos \theta$

3 Simplify the trigonometric
expression $(1 + \cot^2 \theta)(\sec^2 \theta - 1)$.
$\sec^2 \theta$

Closure

Ask students to explain what a
trigonometric identity is. Then ask
them to explain the procedure
they would use to verify that a
trigonometric equation is an
identity. **Answers may vary.**
Sample: A trigonometric identity
is an equation which involves
trigonometric functions and
which is true for all values of
the variable for which the
expressions in the equation
are defined. To verify that an
equation is an identity, select
one side of the equation, and
transform it until it is the other
side of the equation.

pages 766–768   Exercises

1. $\cos \theta \cot \theta =$
$\cos \theta \left(\frac{\cos \theta}{\sin \theta}\right) =$
$\frac{1 - \sin^2 \theta}{\sin \theta} = \frac{1}{\sin \theta} - \sin \theta$

2. $\sin \theta \cot \theta =$
$\sin \theta \left(\frac{\cos \theta}{\sin \theta}\right) = \cos \theta$

3. $\cos \theta \tan \theta =$
$\cos \theta \left(\frac{\sin \theta}{\cos \theta}\right) = \sin \theta$

4. $\sin \theta \sec \theta =$
$\sin \theta \left(\frac{1}{\cos \theta}\right) = \frac{\sin \theta}{\cos \theta} =$
$\tan \theta$

5. $\cos \theta \sec \theta =$
$\cos \theta \left(\frac{1}{\cos \theta}\right) = 1$

766

---

2 **EXAMPLE**   Verifying Identities

Verify the identity $\tan^2 \theta - \sin^2 \theta = \tan^2 \theta \sin^2 \theta$.

$\tan^2 \theta - \sin^2 \theta = \left(\frac{\sin \theta}{\cos \theta}\right)^2 - \sin^2 \theta$ **Tangent Identity**

$= \frac{\sin^2 \theta}{\cos^2 \theta} - \sin^2 \theta$ **Simplify.**

$= \frac{\sin^2 \theta}{\cos^2 \theta} - \frac{\sin^2 \theta \cos^2 \theta}{\cos^2 \theta}$ **Write fractions with common denominators.**

$= \frac{\sin^2 \theta - \sin^2 \theta \cos^2 \theta}{\cos^2 \theta}$ **Subtract.**

$= \frac{\sin^2 \theta (1 - \cos^2 \theta)}{\cos^2 \theta}$ **Factor.**

$= \frac{\sin^2 \theta (\sin^2 \theta)}{\cos^2 \theta}$ **Pythagorean identity**

$= \frac{\sin^2 \theta}{\cos^2 \theta} \sin^2 \theta$ **Rewrite the fraction.**

$= \tan^2 \theta \sin^2 \theta$ **Tangent Identity**

✓ **Check Understanding** **2** Verify the identity $\sec^2 \theta - \sec^2 \theta \cos^2 \theta = \tan^2 \theta$. **See left.**

2. $\sec^2 \theta - \sec^2 \theta \cos^2 \theta$
$= \left(\frac{1}{\cos \theta}\right)^2 - \left(\frac{1}{\cos \theta}\right)^2 \cos^2 \theta$
$= \frac{1}{\cos^2 \theta} - \frac{1}{\cos^2 \theta} \cdot \cos^2 \theta$
$= \frac{1}{\cos^2 \theta} - \frac{\cos^2 \theta}{\cos^2 \theta} = \frac{1 - \cos^2 \theta}{\cos^2 \theta}$
$= \frac{\sin^2 \theta}{\cos^2 \theta} = \tan^2 \theta$

You can use the trigonometric identities to simplify trigonometric expressions.
Again, it is often helpful to write all the functions in terms of sines and cosines.

3 **EXAMPLE**   Simplifying Expressions

Simplify the trigonometric expression $\csc \theta \tan \theta$.

$\csc \theta \tan \theta = \frac{1}{\sin \theta} \cdot \tan \theta$ **Reciprocal Identity**

$= \frac{1}{\sin \theta} \cdot \frac{\sin \theta}{\cos \theta}$ **Tangent Identity**

$= \frac{\sin \theta}{\sin \theta \cos \theta}$ **Multiply.**

$= \frac{1}{\cos \theta}$ **Simplify.**

$= \sec \theta$ **Reciprocal identity**

So $\csc \theta \tan \theta = \sec \theta$.

Need Help?

To help remember the
sec and csc reciprocal
identities, notice that
the initial letters of
the functions in each
identity are different.

✓ **Check Understanding** **3** Simplify the trigonometric expression $\sec \theta \cot \theta$. **csc θ**

EXERCISES

For more practice, see *Extra Practice*.

Practice and Problem Solving

A   Practice by Example

Examples 1 and 2
(pages 765 and 766)

Verify each identity.   **1–8. See margin.**

1. $\cos \theta \cot \theta = \frac{1}{\sin \theta} - \sin \theta$

2. $\sin \theta \cot \theta = \cos \theta$

3. $\cos \theta \tan \theta = \sin \theta$

4. $\sin \theta \sec \theta = \tan \theta$

5. $\cos \theta \sec \theta = 1$

6. $\tan \theta \cot \theta = 1$

7. $\sin \theta \csc \theta = 1$

8. $\cot \theta = \frac{\csc \theta}{\sec \theta}$

---

6. $\tan \theta \cot \theta =$
$\left(\frac{\sin \theta}{\cos \theta}\right)\left(\frac{\cos \theta}{\sin \theta}\right) = 1$

7. $\sin \theta \csc \theta =$
$\sin \theta \left(\frac{1}{\sin \theta}\right) = \frac{\sin \theta}{\sin \theta} = 1$

8. $\cot \theta = \frac{\cos \theta}{\sin \theta} =$
$\frac{1}{\sin \theta} \cdot \frac{\cos \theta}{1} = \frac{1}{\sin \theta} \div$
$\frac{1}{\cos \theta} = \frac{\csc \theta}{\sec \theta}$

39. $\pm\sqrt{1 - \cos^2 \theta}$

40. $\frac{\pm\sqrt{1 - \cos^2 \theta}}{\cos \theta}$

41. $\frac{\pm\sqrt{1 - \sin^2 \theta}}{\sin \theta}$

42. $\pm\sqrt{1 + \cot^2 \theta}$

43. $\pm\sqrt{\csc^2 \theta - 1}$

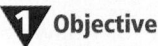
Example 3
(page 766)

Simplify each trigonometric expression.

9. $\tan \theta \cot \theta$ **1**

10. $1 - \cos^2 \theta$ **$\sin^2 \theta$**

11. $\sec^2 \theta - 1$ **$\tan^2 \theta$**

12. $1 - \csc^2 \theta$ **$-\cot^2 \theta$**

13. $\sec \theta \cot \theta$ **$\csc \theta$**

14. $\cos \theta \tan \theta$ **$\sin \theta$**

15. $\sin \theta \cot \theta$ **$\cos \theta$**

16. $\sin \theta \csc \theta$ **1**

17. $\sec \theta \cos \theta \sin \theta$ **$\sin \theta$**

18. $\sin \theta \sec \theta \cot \theta$ **1**

19. $\sec^2 \theta - \tan^2 \theta$ **1**

20. $\dfrac{\sin \theta}{\cos \theta \tan \theta}$ **1**

B **Apply Your Skills**

Simplify each trigonometric expression.

21. $\cos \theta + \sin \theta \tan \theta$ **$\sec \theta$**

22. $\csc \theta \cos \theta \tan \theta$ **1**

23. $\tan \theta (\cot \theta + \tan \theta)$ **$\sec^2 \theta$**

24. $\sin^2 \theta + \cos^2 \theta + \tan^2 \theta$ **$\sec^2 \theta$**

25. $\cos^2 \theta \sec \theta \csc \theta$ **$\cot \theta$**

26. $\sin \theta (1 + \cot^2 \theta)$ **$\csc \theta$**

27. $\cot \theta \tan \theta - \sec^2 \theta$ **$-\tan^2 \theta$**

28. $\sin^2 \theta \csc \theta \sec \theta$ **$\tan \theta$**

29. $\cos \theta (1 + \tan^2 \theta)$ **$\sec \theta$**

30. $\sin \theta (1 + \cot^2 \theta)$ **$\csc \theta$**

31. $\sec \theta \cos \theta - \cos^2 \theta$ **$\sin^2 \theta$**

32. $\sin \theta \csc \theta - \cos^2 \theta$ **$\sin^2 \theta$**

33. $\csc \theta - \cos \theta \cot \theta$ **$\sin \theta$**

34. $\cos \theta + \sin \theta \tan \theta$ **$\sec \theta$**

35. $\sec \theta (1 + \cot^2 \theta)$ **$\sec \theta \csc^2 \theta$**

36. $\csc^2 \theta (1 - \cos^2 \theta)$ **1**

37. $\dfrac{\cos \theta \csc \theta}{\cot \theta}$ **1**

38. $\dfrac{\sin^2 \theta \csc \theta \sec \theta}{\tan \theta}$ **1**

Express the first trigonometric function in terms of the second.

39. $\sin \theta, \cos \theta$

40. $\tan \theta, \cos \theta$

41. $\cot \theta, \sin \theta$

42. $\csc \theta, \cot \theta$

43. $\cot \theta, \csc \theta$

44. $\sec \theta, \tan \theta$

39–44. See margin pp. 766–767.

Verify each identity. **45–50. See back of book.**

45. $\sin^2 \theta \tan^2 \theta = \tan^2 \theta - \sin^2 \theta$

46. $\sec \theta - \sin \theta \tan \theta = \cos \theta$

47. $\sin \theta \cos \theta (\tan \theta + \cot \theta) = 1$

48. $\dfrac{1 - \sin \theta}{\cos \theta} = \dfrac{\cos \theta}{1 + \sin \theta}$

49. $\dfrac{\sec \theta}{\cot \theta + \tan \theta} = \sin \theta$

50. $(\cot \theta + 1)^2 = \csc^2 \theta + 2 \cot \theta$

51. Express $\cos \theta \csc \theta \cot \theta$ in terms of $\sin \theta$. $\dfrac{1 - \sin^2 \theta}{\sin^2 \theta}$

52. Express $\dfrac{\cos \theta}{\sec \theta + \tan \theta}$ in terms of $\sin \theta$. **$1 - \sin \theta$**

53. **Open-Ended** Create a trigonometric identity. (*Hint:* Start with a simple trigonometric expression and work backward.) **Check students' work.**

54. **Writing** Describe the similarities and differences in solving an equation and in verifying an identity. **See margin.**

C **Challenge**

Verify each identity. **55–56. See margin.**

55. $1 + \sec \theta = \dfrac{1 + \cos \theta}{\cos \theta}$

56. $\dfrac{1 + \tan \theta}{\tan \theta} = \cot \theta + 1$

57. $\dfrac{\cot \theta \sin \theta}{\sec \theta} + \dfrac{\tan \theta \cos \theta}{\csc \theta} = 1$

58. $\sin^2 \theta \tan^2 \theta + \cos^2 \theta \tan^2 \theta = \sec^2 \theta - 1$

57–58. See back of book.

Simplify each trigonometric expression.

59. $\dfrac{\cot^2 \theta - \csc^2 \theta}{\tan^2 \theta - \sec^2 \theta}$ **1**

60. $(1 - \sin \theta)(1 + \sin \theta) \csc^2 \theta + 1$ **$\csc^2 \theta$**

---

44. $\pm\sqrt{1 + \tan^2 \theta}$

54. When checking a root of an equation, you substitute the solution into the equation to see if it is true. When verifying an identity, you substitute equivalent expressions until both sides are the same.

55. $1 + \sec \theta = 1 + \dfrac{1}{\cos \theta} = \dfrac{1}{\cos \theta} + 1 = \dfrac{1 + \cos \theta}{\cos \theta}$

56. $\dfrac{1 + \tan \theta}{\tan \theta} = \dfrac{1}{\tan \theta} + \dfrac{\tan \theta}{\tan \theta} = \cot \theta + 1$

767

Error Prevention

Exercises 9–38 A common mistake when applying Reciprocal Identities is to use $\csc \theta = \dfrac{1}{\cos \theta}$ rather than $\csc \theta = \dfrac{1}{\sin \theta}$ or to use $\sec \theta = \dfrac{1}{\sin \theta}$ rather than $\sec \theta = \dfrac{1}{\cos \theta}$. Urge students to commit the Reciprocal Identities to memory and to refer to the Key Concepts box on page 765 frequently to double check that they recall all of these identities correctly.

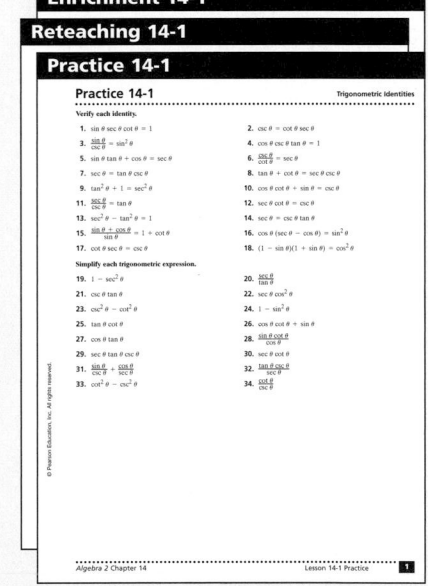

Lesson Quiz 14-1

1. Verify the identity
$\frac{1 + \cot^2 \theta}{\cot^2 \theta} = \sec^2 \theta$. **Answers may vary. Sample:**
$$\frac{1 + \cot^2 \theta}{\cot^2 \theta} = \frac{1}{\cot^2 \theta} + \frac{\cot^2 \theta}{\cot^2 \theta}$$
$$= \tan^2 \theta + 1$$
$$= 1 + \tan^2 \theta$$
$$= \sec^2 \theta$$

2. Simplify $(1 - \sec \theta)(1 + \sec \theta)$.
$-\tan^2 \theta$

3. Express $\frac{1 + \tan^2 \theta}{1 - \tan^2 \theta}$ in terms of $\cos \theta$. $\frac{1}{2 \cos^2 \theta - 1}$

Alternative Assessment

Have students work in groups of three. Ask each student to create a trigonometric identity. Each student in the group should then verify the identities created by the other two students. Have students check one another's work.

Standardized Test Prep

Resources

For additional practice with a variety of test item formats:
- Standardized Test Prep, p. 817
- Test-Taking Strategies, p. 812
- Test-Taking Strategies with Transparencies

Exercise 62 One way to arrive at the answer quickly is to note that one of the expressions is defined for $\theta = 0$, while the other three are not.

pages 766–768 Exercises

66. [2] $(\sec \theta + 1)(\sec \theta - 1)$
$= \sec^2 \theta + \sec \theta -$
$\sec \theta - 1$
$= \sec^2 \theta - 1 = \tan^2 \theta$

[1] does not show work

69.
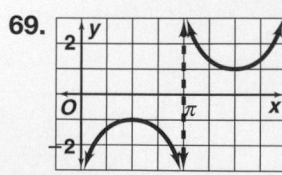

---

61. If $n_2 > n_1$, then
$\theta_1 > \theta_2$; if $n_2 < n_1$,
then $\theta_1 < \theta_2$; if
$n_2 = n_1$, then $\theta_1 = \theta_2$.

 61. Physics When a ray of light passes from one medium into a second, the angle of incidence θ_1 and the angle of refraction θ_2 are related by Snell's law: $n_1 \sin \theta_1 = n_2 \sin \theta_2$, where n_1 is the index of refraction of the first medium and n_2 is the index of refraction of the second medium. How are θ_1 and θ_2 related if $n_2 > n_1$? If $n_2 < n_1$? If $n_2 = n_1$?

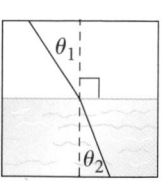

Standardized Test Prep

Multiple Choice

62. Which expression is NOT equal to the other three expressions? **C**

 A. $\frac{2}{\tan \theta}$ 　　 B. $\frac{\cot \theta}{\frac{1}{2}}$ 　　 C. $\frac{\sin \theta}{\frac{1}{2} \cos \theta}$ 　　 D. $\frac{2 \cos \theta}{\sin \theta}$

63. Which equation is NOT true? **H**

 F. $\cos^2 \theta = 1 - \sin^2 \theta$ 　　 G. $\cot^2 \theta = \csc^2 \theta - 1$
 H. $\sin^2 \theta = \cos^2 \theta - 1$ 　　 I. $\tan^2 \theta = \sec^2 \theta - 1$

Take It to the NET
Online lesson quiz at
www.PHSchool.com
.... Web Code: aga-1401

64. Which expressions are equivalent? **C**

 I. $(\sin \theta)(\csc \theta - \sin \theta)$ 　 II. $\sin^2 \theta - 1$ 　　 III. $\cos^2 \theta$
 A. I and II only 　　　　　　　 B. II and III only
 C. I and III only 　　　　　　　 D. I, II, and III

65. How can you express $\csc^2 \theta - 2 \cot^2 \theta$ in terms of $\sin \theta$ and $\cos \theta$? **F**

 F. $\frac{1 - 2 \cos^2 \theta}{\sin^2 \theta}$ 　　　　　 G. $\frac{1 - 2 \sin^2 \theta}{\sin^2 \theta}$

 H. $\sin^2 \theta - 2 \cos^2 \theta$ 　　　　 I. $\frac{1}{\sin^2 \theta} - \frac{2}{\tan^2 \theta}$

Short Response

66. Show that $(\sec \theta + 1)(\sec \theta - 1) = \tan^2 \theta$ is an identity. **See margin.**

Extended Response

67. Explain how to simplify the expression $\frac{\tan \theta}{\cos \theta - \sec \theta}$. **67–68. See back of book.**

68. Explain how to verify the identity $\frac{\cos x}{1 - \sin^2 x} = \sec x$.

Mixed Review

Lesson 13-8

Graph each function in the interval from 0 to 2π. **69–72. See margin.**

69. $y = \csc (-\theta)$ 　　　 70. $y = -\cot \theta$ 　　　 71. $y = -\sec 0.5\theta$

72. $y = -\sec (0.5\theta + 2)$ 　 73. $y = \cot \frac{\theta}{5}$ 　　　 74. $y = \pi \sec \theta$
　　　　　　　　　　　　 73–74. See back of book.

Lesson 13-2

Find the measure of an angle between 0° and 360° that is coterminal with the given angle.

75. 395° **35°** 　 76. 405° **45°** 　 77. −225° **135°** 　 78. −149° **211°**

79. 627° **267°** 　 80. −281° **79°** 　 81. 493° **133°** 　 82. −609° **111°**

Lesson 12-3

Make a box-and-whisker plot for each set of values. **83–84. See back of book.**

83. 300 345 333 295 302 321

84. 32 48 87 43 62 15 49 51 47 36 50 109 64

70.
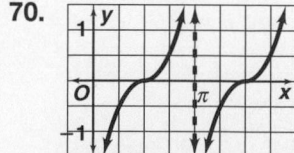

71.
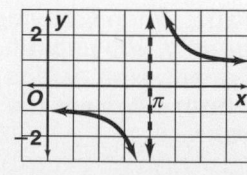

72.
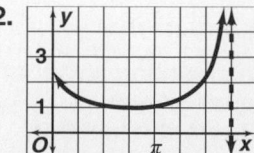

14-2 Solving Trigonometric Equations Using Inverses

Lesson Preview

What You'll Learn

OBJECTIVE 1
To evaluate inverses of trigonometric functions

OBJECTIVE 2
To solve trigonometric equations

... And Why

To solve problems involving springs, as in Example 7

✓ **Check Skills You'll Need**   (For help, go to Lessons 7-7, 13-2, and 13-6.)

For each function f, find f^{-1}. **1–2. See below.**

1. $f(x) = x + 1$
2. $f(x) = 2x - 3$
3. $f(x) = x^2 + 4$ $f^{-1}(x) = \pm\sqrt{x - 4}$

Find each value.

4. $\sin 30°$ **0.5**
5. $\cos \frac{\pi}{4}$ $\frac{\sqrt{2}}{2}$
6. $\cos 135°$ $-\frac{\sqrt{2}}{2}$

7. $\tan(-\pi)$ **0**
8. $\tan 315°$ **−1**
9. $\sin\left(-\frac{7\pi}{3}\right)$ $-\frac{\sqrt{3}}{2}$

1. $f^{-1}(x) = x - 1$
2. $f^{-1}(x) = \frac{x + 3}{2}$

Lesson Preview

✓ **Check Skills You'll Need**

Inverse Relations and Functions
Lesson 7-7: Examples 4, 5
Exercises 17–22
Extra Practice, p. 828

Angles and the Unit Circle
Lesson 13-2: Example 4
Exercises 29–36
Extra Practice, p. 834

The Tangent Function
Lesson 13-6: Example 1
Exercises 1–8
Extra Practice, p. 834

Lesson Resources

Teaching Resources
Practice, Reteaching, Enrichment

Reaching All Students
Practice Workbook 14-2
Spanish Practice Workbook 14-2
Hands-On Activities 58

Presentation Assistant Plus!
Transparencies
• Check Skills You'll Need 14-2
• Additional Examples 14-2
• Student Edition Answers 14-2
• Lesson Quiz 14-2
PH Presentation Pro CD 14-2

PRENTICE HALL ASSESSMENT SYSTEM

Computer Test Generator CD

Technology
Resource Pro® CD-ROM
Computer Test Generator CD
Prentice Hall Presentation Pro CD

www.PHSchool.com
Student Site
• Teacher Web Code: agk-5500
• Self-grading Lesson Quiz
Teacher Center
• Lesson Planner
• Resources

Plus

OBJECTIVE 1

Inverses of Trigonometric Functions

iTEXT Interactive lesson includes instant self-check, tutorials, and activities.

The cosine function $y = \cos\theta$ is periodic, so a horizontal line, such as the x-axis, can intersect the graph of $y = \cos\theta$ in infinitely many points. Therefore a vertical line can intersect the graph of the inverse of $y = \cos\theta$ in infinitely many points. The inverse of $y = \cos\theta$ is a relation that is not a function.

You can use a graph of an inverse function to find the measures of angles that have a given value of the function.

1 EXAMPLE   Using a Graph to Find Angles With a Given Cosine

Use the graph of the inverse of $y = \cos\theta$ at the right.

a. Find the radian measures of the angles whose cosine is −1.

The line $x = -1$ intersects the graph at $(-1, \pi)$ and $(-1, -\pi)$. So the measures of two angles whose cosine is −1 are π and $-\pi$.

Other points of intersection are $(-1, \pm 3\pi)$, $(-1, \pm 5\pi)$, and so on. The measures of all the angles whose cosine is −1 can be written as $\pi + 2\pi n$, where n is any integer.

b. Find the radian measures of the angles θ whose cosine is 2.

The line $x = 2$ does not intersect the graph. 2 is not in the domain of the inverse of $y = \cos\theta$. There is no angle whose cosine is 2.

Inverse of $y = \cos\theta$

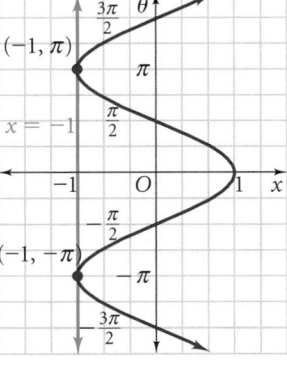

✓ **Check Understanding** **①** What are the radian measures of the angles whose cosine is 1.1? Whose cosine is 0? Whose cosine is −1.1?   **none, $\frac{\pi}{2} + \pi n$, none**

Ongoing Assessment and Intervention

Before the Lesson
Diagnose prerequisite skills using:
• Check Skills You'll Need

During the Lesson
Monitor progress using:
• Check Understanding
• Additional Examples
• Standardized Test Prep

After the Lesson
Assess knowledge using:
• Lesson Quiz
• Computer Test Generator CD

2. Teach

Math Background

You can restrict the domains of the secant, cosecant, and cotangent trigonometric functions in such a way that the inverses are functions, but there is no universal agreement as to the most useful choice of domain.

OBJECTIVE

1 Teaching Notes

1 EXAMPLE Alternative Method

Students can use a graphing calculator to display the graph of the inverse relation for $y = \cos x$. One approach is to graph $y = \cos x$ and then use the DrawInv feature on the DRAW menu. Another approach is to use a parametric graph. Set the calculator to parametric mode. Use the equations $X_{1T} = T$ and $Y_{1T} = \cos(T)$ to display the graph of the cosine function. For the inverse relation, use $X_{2T} = \cos(T)$ and $Y_{2T} = T$.

3 EXAMPLE Technology Tip

Have students use their graphing calculators to check that $\sin^{-1}(-0.9) \approx -1.12$. Before they do this, they should check that the calculator is set to Radian mode.

4 EXAMPLE Teaching Tip

You may want to point out that the Quadrant II angle is obtained by adding the negative angle in Quadrant IV to π. As a result, you can specify all the angles whose tangent is -0.84 with the single expression $-0.70 + \pi n$.

2a. $120° + n \cdot 360°$ and $240° + n \cdot 360°$

b. $150° + n \cdot 360°$ and $210° + n \cdot 360°$

c. $45° + n \cdot 360°$ and $315° + n \cdot 360°$

✓ Check Understanding

Reading Math

For a number x, x^{-1} is the multiplicative inverse of x, or $\frac{1}{x}$.

For the cos function, $\cos^{-1}$ is the relation that is the inverse of cos.

$\cos^{-1} x \neq \frac{1}{\cos x}$

$(\cos x)^{-1} = \frac{1}{\cos x}$

You can also use a unit circle to find the measures of angles that have a given value for sine or cosine.

2 EXAMPLE Using a Unit Circle

Use a unit circle to find the degree measures of the angles whose cosine is $\frac{1}{2}$.

Draw a unit circle and mark the points on the circle that have x-coordinates of $\frac{1}{2}$. These points and the origin form 30°-60°-90° triangles. 60° and 300° are the measures of two angles whose cosine is $\frac{1}{2}$. All their coterminal angles also have a cosine of $\frac{1}{2}$. The measures of all the angles whose cosine is $\frac{1}{2}$ can be written as $60° + n \cdot 360°$ and $300° + n \cdot 360°$.

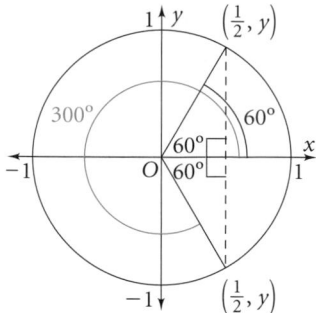

② Check Understanding Use a unit circle to find the measure in degrees of all the angles with the given cosine. **a–c. See left.**

a. $-\frac{1}{2}$ **b.** $-\frac{\sqrt{3}}{2}$ **c.** $\frac{\sqrt{2}}{2}$

The domain of the cosine function can be restricted to $0 \leq \theta \leq \pi$ so that its inverse is a function. The inverse function is written $\theta = \cos^{-1} x$ and is read as "θ is the angle whose cosine is x."

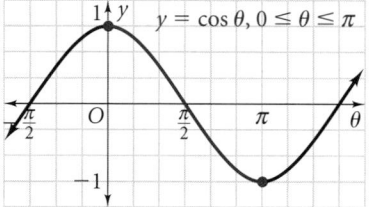 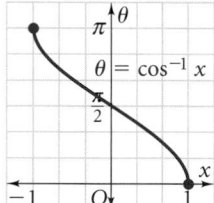

Similarly, the ranges of $y = \sin \theta$ and $y = \tan \theta$ are restricted to $-\frac{\pi}{2} \leq \theta \leq \frac{\pi}{2}$ to obtain the inverse functions $\theta = \sin^{-1} x$ and $\theta = \tan^{-1} x$.

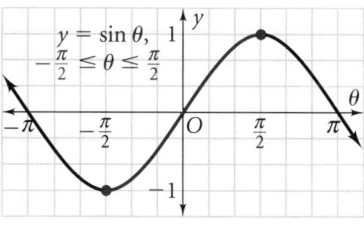 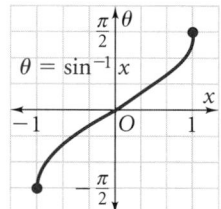

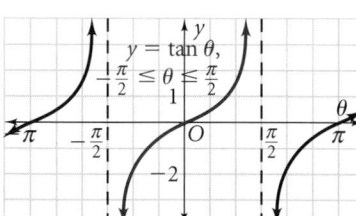 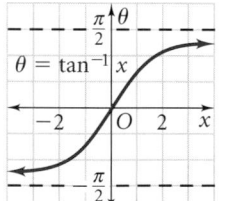

770   Chapter 14   Trigonometric Identities and Equations

👥 Reaching All Students

Below Level Remind students that if a vertical line intersects a graph at more than one point, the graph is not a function. That is why the inverse of $y = \cos \theta$ is not a function.	**Advanced Learners** Have students research the restricted domains of functions such as Sine θ (with an upper case "S") that have inverses that are functions.	**Visual Learners** See note on page 771. **Error Prevention** See note on page 773.

3 EXAMPLE Using a Calculator to Find the Inverse of Sine

Use a calculator and an inverse function to find the radian measures of all the angles whose sine is −0.9.

$\sin^{-1}(-0.9) \approx -1.12$ **Use a calculator.**

This angle is in Quadrant IV. The sine function is also negative in Quadrant III, as shown in the figure at the right. So $\pi + 1.12 \approx 4.26$ is another solution.

The radian measures of all the angles whose sine is −0.9 can be written as

$-1.12 + 2\pi n$ and $4.26 + 2\pi n$.

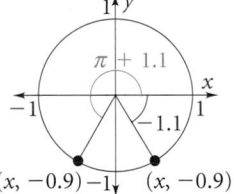

3a. 0.46 + 2πn and
2.69 + 2πn

b. −0.82 + 2πn and
3.96 + 2πn

✓ **Check Understanding** ③ Find the radian measures of the angles. **a–b. See left.**

a. angles whose sine is 0.44   **b.** angles whose sine is −0.73

4 EXAMPLE Using a Calculator to Find the Inverse of Tangent

Use a calculator and an inverse function to find the measure in radians of all the angles whose tangent is −0.84.

$\tan^{-1}(-0.84) \approx -0.70$ **Use a calculator.**

The tangent function is also negative in Quadrant II, as shown in the figure at the right. So $\pi - 0.70 \approx 2.44$ is another solution.

The radian measures of all the angles whose tangent is −0.84 can be written as

$-0.70 + 2\pi n$ and $2.44 + 2\pi n$.

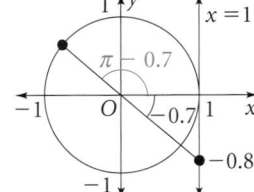

✓ **Check Understanding** ④ Find the radian measures of the angles.

a. angles whose tangent is 0.44   **b.** angles whose tangent is −0.73
   0.41 + 2πn and 3.56 + 2πn   **−0.63 + 2πn and 2.51 + 2πn**

OBJECTIVE

2 Solving Trigonometric Equations

In contrast to trigonometric identities, most trigonometric equations are true for only certain values of the variable.

5 EXAMPLE Solving Trigonometric Equations

Solve $4\cos\theta - 1 = \cos\theta$ for $0 \le \theta < 2\pi$.

$4\cos\theta - 1 = \cos\theta$

$3\cos\theta = 1$ **Add 1 − cos θ to each side.**

$\cos\theta = \frac{1}{3}$ **Divide each side by 3.**

$\cos^{-1}\frac{1}{3} \approx 1.23$ **Use the inverse function to find one value of θ.**

The cosine function is also positive in Quadrant IV. So another value of θ is $2\pi - 1.23 \approx 5.05$. The two solutions between 0 and 2π are approximately 1.23 and 5.05.

❶ Refer to the graph of the inverse of $y = \cos\theta$ in Example 1.
a. Find the radian measures of the angles whose cosine is 0.
$\frac{\pi}{2} + \pi n$, **where n is any integer**
b. Find the radian measures of the angles θ whose cosine is −1.5.
There are no such angles.

❷ Use a unit circle to find the degree measure of the angles whose cosine is $\frac{\sqrt{2}}{2}$. **45° + n · 360°, 315° + n · 360°**

❸ Use a calculator and an inverse function to find the radian measures of all the angles whose sine is 0.98.
≈ 1.37 + 2πn, ≈ 1.77 + 2πn

❹ Use a calculator and an inverse function to find the measures in radians of all the angles whose tangent is 1.34. **≈ 0.93 + 2πn, ≈ 4.07 + 2πn**

OBJECTIVE
2 Teaching Notes

5 EXAMPLE Visual Learners

Students can get visual reinforcement of the results by using a graphing calculator to graph $Y_1 = 4\cos x - 1$ and $Y_2 = \cos x$. Have them use a window with Xmin = 0, Xmax = 2π, Ymin = −5, Ymax = 5. The solutions are the x-coordinates of the points where the graphs intersect.

5 Solve $7 \cos \theta - 3 = 2 \cos \theta$ for $0 \le \theta < 2\pi$. $\approx 0.93, \approx 5.36$

6 Solve $2 \sin \theta \cos \theta - \cos \theta = 0$ for $0 \le \theta < 2\pi$. $\frac{\pi}{6}, \frac{\pi}{2}, \frac{5\pi}{6}, \frac{3\pi}{2}$

7 In decibels, the noise level d close to an electronic alarm device is modeled by $d = 40 \sin \frac{\pi(t-6)}{12} + 40$, where t is the number of seconds after the device is activated. How many seconds after the device is activated does it take for the sound to reach a noise level of 60 decibels? **8 s**

Closure

Ask students to describe two methods they might use to find the value of an angle measure θ if they know the value of a trigonometric function of θ. **Answers may vary. Sample: If the value is one associated with a 30°-60°-90° or a 45°-45°-90°, triangle, you may use the triangle to determine the angle measure. Otherwise, use the inverse trigonometric functions on a graphing calculator.**

✓ **Check Understanding** **5** Solve $3 \sin \theta + 1 = \sin \theta$ for $0 \le \theta < 2\pi$. $\frac{11\pi}{6}$ and $\frac{7\pi}{6}$

Sometimes you can solve trigonometric equations by factoring.

6 **EXAMPLE** **Solving by Factoring**

Solve $2 \cos \theta \sin \theta + \sin \theta = 0$ for $0 \le \theta < 2\pi$.

$$2 \cos \theta \sin \theta + \sin \theta = 0$$
$$\sin \theta \,(2 \cos \theta + 1) = 0 \qquad \text{Factor.}$$
$$\sin \theta = 0 \quad \text{or} \quad 2 \cos \theta + 1 = 0 \qquad \text{Zero-Product Property}$$
$$\sin \theta = 0 \qquad\qquad \cos \theta = -\frac{1}{2} \qquad \text{Solve for } \cos \theta.$$
$$\theta = 0 \text{ and } \pi \qquad\qquad \theta = \frac{2\pi}{3} \text{ and } \frac{4\pi}{3} \qquad \text{Use the unit circle.}$$

The four values of θ are $0, \pi, \frac{2\pi}{3}$, and $\frac{4\pi}{3}$.

✓ **Check Understanding** **6** Solve $\sin \theta \cos \theta - \cos \theta = 0$ for $0 \le \theta < 2\pi$. $\frac{\pi}{2}$ and $\frac{3\pi}{2}$

You can use trigonometric equations to solve problems involving repetitive events.

7 **EXAMPLE** **Real-World** **Connection**

Real-World **Connection**

The motion of an oscillating spring is called simple harmonic motion.

7b. **Yes; at 2 s, the toy will reach a maximum at 4 in. and then come back down, again hitting 2 in. at 2 s.**

c. **Let $y_1 = -4 \cos \frac{2\pi}{3} t$ and let $y_2 = 2$. Graph. Trace and calculate the intersection.**

Physics The spring at the left is stretched and released. The equation $h = -4 \cos \frac{2\pi}{3} t$ models the toy's height h in inches above or below the rest position as a function of time t in seconds. When will the toy first be 2 in. above the rest position?

$$h = -4 \cos \frac{2\pi}{3} t$$
$$2 = -4 \cos \frac{2\pi}{3} t \qquad \text{Substitute 2 for } h.$$
$$-\frac{2}{4} = \cos \frac{2\pi}{3} t \qquad \text{Divide each side by } -4.$$
$$-\frac{1}{2} = \cos \frac{2\pi}{3} t \qquad \text{Simplify.}$$
$$\cos^{-1}\left(-\frac{1}{2}\right) = \frac{2\pi}{3} t \qquad \text{Use the inverse of the cosine to solve for } t.$$
$$2.0944 \approx \frac{2\pi}{3} t \qquad \text{Evaluate the inverse.}$$
$$\frac{3}{2\pi}(2.0944) \approx t \qquad \text{Multiply each side by } \frac{3}{2\pi}.$$
$$1 \approx t \qquad \text{Simplify.}$$

The toy is 2 in. above the rest position at 1 s.

✓ **Check Understanding** **7** **a.** When will the toy in Example 7 first be 2 in. below the rest position? When will the toy next be 4 in. below the rest position? $\frac{1}{2}$ s; 3 s

b. You found that the toy in Example 7 is 2 in. above the rest position after 1 s. Will it ever be at that same position again? Explain. **b–c. See left.**

c. How could you use a graphing calculator to solve Example 7?

EXERCISES

Practice and Problem Solving

A **Practice by Example**

Example 1
(page 769)

1. $-\frac{\pi}{2} + 2\pi n$

Use the graph of the inverse of $y = \sin \theta$ at the right.

1. Find the measures of the angles whose sine is -1.

2. Find the measures of the angles whose sine is 0.
   $0 + \pi n$

3. Find the measures of the angles whose sine is 1.
   $\frac{\pi}{2} + 2\pi n$

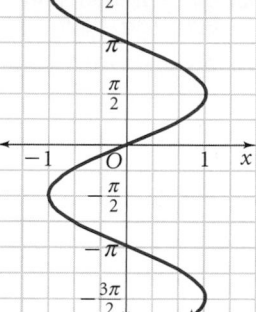

Example 2
(page 770)

5. $30° + n \cdot 360°$ and $210° + n \cdot 360°$ or $30° + n \cdot 180°$

Use a unit circle and 30°-60°-90° triangles to find the degree measures of the angles.

4. angles whose sine is $\frac{1}{2}$ $30° + n \cdot 360°$ and $150° + n \cdot 360°$

5. angles whose tangent is $\frac{\sqrt{3}}{3}$

6. angles whose sine is $-\frac{1}{2}$ $210° + n \cdot 360°$ and $330° + n \cdot 360°$

7. angles whose tangent is $-\sqrt{3}$
   $120° + n \cdot 360°$ and $300° + n \cdot 360°$ or $120° + n \cdot 180°$

Examples 3 and 4
(page 771)

Use a calculator and inverse functions to find the radian measures of the angles.

8. angles whose tangent is 1

9. angles whose sine is 0.37

10. angles whose sine is (-0.78)

11. angles whose tangent is (-3)

12. angles whose cosine is (-0.89)

13. angles whose sine is (-1.1)

14. angles whose tangent is 5
15. angles whose cosine is 0.58

8–15. See margin.

Example 5
(page 771)

Solve each equation for $0 \le \theta < 2\pi$.

16. $2 \sin \theta = 1$ $\frac{\pi}{6}, \frac{5\pi}{6}$

17. $2 \cos \theta - \sqrt{3} = 0$ $\frac{\pi}{6}, \frac{11\pi}{6}$

18. $4 \tan \theta = 3 + \tan \theta$ $\frac{\pi}{4}, \frac{5\pi}{4}$

19. $2 \sin \theta - \sqrt{2} = 0$ $\frac{\pi}{4}, \frac{3\pi}{4}$

20. $3 \cos \theta = 2$ **0.84, 5.44**

21. $3 \tan \theta - 1 = \tan \theta$ **0.46, 3.61**

22. $\sqrt{2} \cos \theta - \sqrt{2} = 0$ **0**

23. $3 \tan \theta + 5 = 0$ **2.11, 5.25**

24. $2 \sin \theta = 3$ **no solution**

25. $2 \sin \theta = -\sqrt{3}$ $\frac{4\pi}{3}, \frac{5\pi}{3}$

Example 6
(page 772)

26. $(\cos \theta)(\cos \theta + 1) = 0$ $\frac{\pi}{2}, \pi, \frac{3\pi}{2}$

27. $(\sin \theta - 1)(\sin \theta + 1) = 0$ $\frac{\pi}{2}, \frac{3\pi}{2}$

28. $\tan^2 \theta + \tan \theta = 0$ $0, \pi, \frac{3\pi}{4}, \frac{7\pi}{4}$

29. $2 \sin^2 \theta - 1 = 0$ $\frac{\pi}{4}, \frac{3\pi}{4}, \frac{5\pi}{4}, \frac{7\pi}{4}$

30. $\tan \theta = \tan^2 \theta$ $0, \frac{\pi}{4}, \pi, \frac{5\pi}{4}$

31. $\sin^2 \theta + 3 \sin \theta = 0$ **0, π**

32. $\sin \theta = -\sin \theta \cos \theta$ **0, π**

33. $2 \sin^2 \theta - 3 \sin \theta = 2$ $\frac{7\pi}{6}, \frac{11\pi}{6}$

Example 7
(page 772)

34. **Physics** Two students set up a spring experiment similar to the one in Example 7. In their experiment, a weight was released 4 cm below the rest position. It rose to 4 cm above the rest position and returned to 4 cm below the rest position once every 4 seconds. The equation $h = -4 \cos\left(\frac{\pi}{2}t\right)$ models the height above and below the rest position at t seconds.
    a. Solve the equation for t. $t = \frac{2}{\pi} \cdot \cos^{-1}\left(\frac{h}{-4}\right)$
    b. Find the times at which the weight is first at a height of 1 cm, 2 cm, and 3 cm above the rest position. **1.16 s, 1.33 s, 1.54 s**
    c. Find the times at which the weight is at a height of 1 cm, 2 cm, and 3 cm below the rest position for the second time. **3.16 s, 3.33 s, 3.54 s**

Assignment Guide

▼1 Objective
   Ⓐ Ⓑ Core 1–15, 35–37

▼2 Objective
   Ⓐ Ⓑ Core 16–34, 38–66
   Ⓒ Extension 67–74

Standardized Test Prep 75–81

Mixed Review 82–92

Error Prevention

Exercises 4–12, 14, 15 Students may not name all the angles for which the given functions have the given value. Remind them that they must use what they know about the period of each function to specify all the values.

Enrichment 14-2

Reteaching 14-2

Practice 14-2

---

pages 773–776 **Exercises**

8. **0.79 + $2\pi n$ and 3.93 + $2\pi n$**

9. **0.46 + $2\pi n$ and 2.69 + $2\pi n$**

10. **−0.89 + $2\pi n$ and 4.04 + $2\pi n$**

11. **1.89 + $2\pi n$ and 5.03 + $2\pi n$ or 189 + πn**

12. **2.67 + $2\pi n$ and 3.61 + $2\pi n$**

13. **no solution**

14. **1.37 + $2\pi n$ and 4.51 + $2\pi n$**

15. **0.95 + $2\pi n$ and 5.33 + $2\pi n$**

Exercises 46–51 Students may find the "basic" solutions graphically. They must then use periodicity to describe all the solutions.

Exercises 67–72 You may wish to ask students to describe values of *y* for which each equation has no solutions.

Connection to Astronomy

Exercise 74 Suggest that students research what affects ocean tides.

pages 773–776   Exercises

46. $0 + 2\pi n, \frac{2}{3}\pi + 2\pi n,$
    $\frac{4}{3}\pi + 2\pi n$

47. $\frac{\pi}{2} + 2\pi n, \frac{3\pi}{2} + 2\pi n$

48. $\frac{\pi}{6} + 2\pi n, \frac{5\pi}{6} + 2\pi n,$
    $\frac{3\pi}{2} + 2\pi n$

49. $\frac{\pi}{4} + \frac{\pi}{2}n$

50. $\frac{\pi}{6} + 2\pi n, \frac{5\pi}{6} + 2\pi n,$
    $\frac{\pi}{2} + \pi n$

51. $0 + 2\pi n, \pi + 2\pi n,$
    $1.25 + 2\pi n, 4.39 + 2\pi n$

52. $\frac{\pi}{2} + 2\pi n, \frac{7\pi}{6} + 2\pi n,$
    $\frac{11\pi}{6} + 2\pi n$

53. $0.524 + \pi n, 2.62 + \pi n$

54. $\frac{\pi}{6} + 2\pi n, \frac{5\pi}{6} + 2\pi n$

55. $\frac{7\pi}{20} + \pi n, \frac{3\pi}{4} + \pi n$

B **Apply Your Skills**

35. $30° + n \cdot 360°$ and
    $150° + n \cdot 360°$

36. $60° + n \cdot 360°$ and
    $300° + n \cdot 360°$

37. $210° + n \cdot 360°$ and
    $330° + n \cdot 360°$

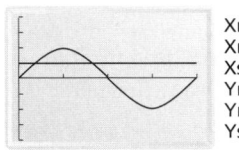

Real-World **Connection**

Electric generators convert mechanical energy into electricity. A generator may be larger than a house and generate enough electricity for a million homes.

Each diagram shows one solution to the equation below it. Find the complete solution of each equation.

35. 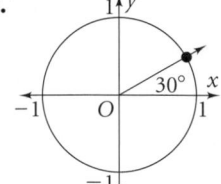   36. 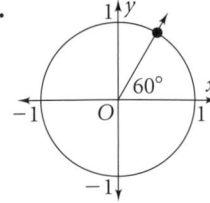   37.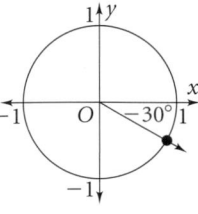

$5 \sin \theta = 1 + 3 \sin \theta$ $6 \cos \theta - 5 = -2$ $4 \sin \theta + 3 = 1$

Solve each equation for $0 \le \theta < 2\pi$.

38. $\sec \theta = 2$ $\frac{\pi}{3}, \frac{5\pi}{3}$ 39. $\csc \theta = -1$ $\frac{3\pi}{2}$

40. $\cot \theta = 10$ **0.10, 3.24**   41. $\csc \theta = 3$ **0.34, 2.80**

42. $\cot \theta = -10$ **3.04, 6.18**   43. $\sec \theta = 1$ **0**

 44. **Electricity** The function $I = 40 \sin 60\pi t$ models the current I in amps that the electric generator shown at the left is producing after t seconds. When is the first time that the current will reach 20 amps? -20 amps?   **0.0028 s; 0.019 s**

45. **Critical Thinking** The graphing calculator screen below shows a portion of the graphs of $y = \sin \theta$ and $y = 0.5$.

Xmin=0
Xmax=360
Xscl=90
Ymin=−2
Ymax=2
Yscl=0.5

   a. $30° + n \cdot 360°$
     $\le x \le 150° +$
     $n \cdot 360°$

   b. $150° + n \cdot 360°$
     $\le x \le 390° +$
     $n \cdot 360°$

a. Write the complete solution of $\sin \theta \ge 0.5$.
b. Write the complete solution of $\sin \theta \le 0.5$.
c. Writing Explain how you can solve inequalities involving trigonometric functions. **Find the values of x where the graphs intersect, and then choose the appropriate interval.**

Find the complete solution in radians of each equation.   **46–55. See margin.**

46. $2 \sin^2 \theta + \cos \theta - 1 = 0$ 47. $\sin^2 \theta - 1 = \cos^2 \theta$

48. $2 \sin \theta + 1 = \csc \theta$ 49. $3 \tan^2 \theta - 1 = \sec^2 \theta$

50. $\sin \theta \cos \theta = \frac{1}{2} \cos \theta$ 51. $\tan \theta \sin \theta = 3 \sin \theta$

52. $2 \cos^2 \theta + \sin \theta = 1$ 53. $\sin \theta \cot^2 \theta - 3 \sin \theta = 0$

54. $4 \sin^2 \theta + 1 = 4 \sin \theta$ 55. $\tan \theta \cot \theta - \tan \theta + 2 \cot \theta = 0$

56. **Error Analysis** A student solved an equation as shown below. What error did the student make?

$$\theta = \cos^{-1} 0.5$$
$$= \frac{1}{\cos 0.5}$$
$$\approx \frac{1}{0.88}$$
$$\approx 1.14$$

The student misinterpreted the meaning of $\cos^{-1} 0.5$ as being equal to $\frac{1}{\cos 0.5}$.

57. Error Analysis A student solved the equation $\sin^2 \theta = \frac{1}{2}\sin\theta$, $0 \le \theta < 2\pi$, as shown below. What error did the student make?

$$\sin^2 \theta = \tfrac{1}{2}\sin\theta$$
$$\sin\theta = \tfrac{1}{2}$$
$$\theta = \tfrac{\pi}{6} \text{ and } \tfrac{5\pi}{6}$$

The student divided both sides of the equation by sin θ, which in the given interval can be equal to zero. Since division by zero is not possible, this is where the error was.

Find the x-intercepts of the graph of each function.

58. $2.09 + 2\pi n$, $4.19 + 2\pi n$

59. $0.79 + \pi n$, $2.36 + \pi n$

58. $y = 2\cos\theta + 1$

59. $y = 2\sin^2\theta - 1$

60. $y = \cos^2\theta - 1$ **$0 + \pi n$**

61. $y = \tan^2\theta - 1$ **$0.79 + \pi n$, $2.36 + \pi n$**

62. $y = 2\sin^4\theta - \sin^2\theta$ **$0 + \pi n$, $0.79 + \pi n$, $2.36 + \pi n$**

63. $y = 2\cos^2\theta - 3\cos\theta - 2$ **$2.09 + 2\pi n$, $4.19 + 2\pi n$**

 **64. Writing** Describe the similarities and differences in solving the equations $4x + 1 = 3$ and $4\sin\theta + 1 = 3$. **See margin.**

65. Find the complete solution of $\sin^2\theta + 2\sin\theta + 1 = 0$. (*Hint:* How would you solve $x^2 + 2x + 1 = 0$?) **$\frac{3\pi}{2} + 2\pi n$**

66. a. Open-Ended Write three trigonometric equations whose complete solution is $\pi + 2\pi n$. **a–b. See margin.**
   b. Describe how you found the equations in part (a).

 Challenge

Solve each trigonometric equation for θ in terms of y.

Sample $y = 2\sin 3\theta + 4$

$$\sin 3\theta = \frac{y - 4}{2}$$
$$3\theta = \sin^{-1}\left(\frac{y - 4}{2}\right)$$
$$\theta = \frac{1}{3}\sin^{-1}\left(\frac{y - 4}{2}\right)$$

67. $y = 2\sin\theta$ **$\sin^{-1}\left(\frac{y}{2}\right)$**

68. $y = \cos 2\theta$ **$\frac{1}{2}\cos^{-1}(y)$**

69. $y = 3\sin(\theta + 2)$ **$\sin^{-1}\left(\frac{y}{3}\right) - 2$**

70. $y = -4\cos 2\pi\theta$ **$\frac{1}{2\pi}\cos^{-1}\left(-\frac{y}{4}\right)$**

71. $y = \cos\theta + 1$ **$\cos^{-1}(y - 1)$**

72. $y = 2\cos\pi\theta + 1$ **$\frac{1}{\pi}\cos^{-1}\left(\frac{y - 1}{2}\right)$**

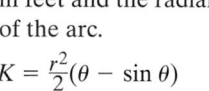 **73. Parks** A segment of a circle is the region formed by an arc of a circle and the line segment joining the endpoints of the arc. (The measure of the arc must be between 0 and 2π.) The expression below gives the area K in square feet of a segment in terms of the radius of the circle r in feet and the radian measure θ of the arc.

50 ft

$$K = \frac{r^2}{2}(\theta - \sin\theta)$$

   a. Suppose a circular park has a radius of 50 ft. Write an equation for the area of any segment of the park using $r = 50$. **$k = 1250(\theta - \sin\theta)$ ft^2**
   b. Use trial and error to approximate the measure of θ that makes the area of the segment 1500 ft^2. **≈ 2.08**

Lesson Quiz 14-2

1. Use a unit circle and 30°-60°-90° triangles to find the degree measures of the angles that have a sine of $-\frac{\sqrt{3}}{2}$. **240° + $n \cdot$ 360°, 300° + $n \cdot$ 360°**

2. Use a calculator and inverse functions to find the radian measures of the angles whose cosine is 0.75. **$\approx 0.72 + 2\pi n$, $\approx 5.56 + 2\pi n$**

Solve each equation for $0 \le \theta < 2\pi$.

3. $2\cos^2\theta - 1 = 0$ **$\frac{\pi}{4}, \frac{3\pi}{4}, \frac{5\pi}{4}, \frac{7\pi}{4}$**

4. $\sqrt{2}\sin\theta\cos\theta + \cos\theta = 0$ **$\frac{\pi}{2}, \frac{5\pi}{4}, \frac{3\pi}{2}, \frac{7\pi}{4}$**

Alternative Assessment

Have students work individually. Ask them to select a real number between −1 and 1. Ask them to find all angles that have their sine equal to that number, and then find all the angles that have their tangent equal to that number. Next ask students to create and solve two equations that involve trigonometric functions of an angle θ. Ask the students to find all solutions θ for $0 \le \theta < 2\pi$.

64. Answers may vary. Sample: In the first equation, you isolate the variable x to get the solution. In the trigonometric equation, you first isolate the trig. part, $\sin\theta$, but then you must continue to solve for θ.

66a. Answers may vary. Sample: $\cos\theta = -1$, $2\cos\theta = -2$, $3\cos\theta = -3$

b. Start with $\cos\theta = -1$, and then multiply both sides of equation by any nonzero number.

775

Standardized Test Prep

Resources

For additional practice with a variety of test item formats:

- Standardized Test Prep, p. 817
- Test-Taking Strategies, p. 812
- Test-Taking Strategies with Transparencies

pages 773–776   Exercises

81. [4] $2 \sin^2 \theta = -\sin \theta$
$2 \sin^2 \theta + \sin \theta = 0$
$\sin \theta (2 \sin \theta + 1) = 0$
So $\sin \theta = 0$
$\sin^{-1} 0 = 0, \pi$
or $2 \sin \theta + 1 = 0$
$\sin \theta = -\frac{1}{2}$
$\sin^{-1}\left(-\frac{1}{2}\right) =$
$\frac{11\pi}{6}, \frac{7\pi}{6}$

[3] appropriate methods, with minor error

[2] answer only, without work shown

[1] finds only one solution for each instance where it might equal 0

74a. 1:55 A.M., 11:05 A.M., and 2:55 P.M.

b. 12:00 midnight to 1:55 A.M., 11:05 A.M. to 2:55 P.M.

 74. Tides One day the tides at a point in Maine could be modeled by $h = 5 \cos \frac{2\pi}{13}t$, where h is the height of the tide in feet above the mean water level and t is the number of hours past midnight.
  a. At what times that day will the tide be 3 ft above the mean water level?
  b. At what times that day will the tide be *at least* 3 ft above the mean water level?

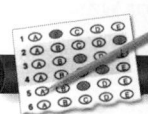
Standardized Test Prep

Multiple Choice

80. [2] $2 \cos \theta = \sqrt{2}$
$\cos \theta = \frac{\sqrt{2}}{2}$
$\cos^{-1} \frac{\sqrt{2}}{2} = \theta$
$\theta = \frac{\pi}{4}$ and $\frac{7\pi}{4}$

[1] finds solution in Quadrant I only

 Take It to the NET
Online lesson quiz at **www.PHSchool.com**
········ Web Code: aga-1402

75. Which of the following is NOT equal to 60°? **D**
A. $\sin^{-1} \frac{\sqrt{3}}{2}$ B. $\cos^{-1} \frac{1}{2}$ C. $\tan^{-1} \sqrt{3}$ D. $\tan^{-1} \frac{\sqrt{3}}{3}$

76. In which quadrants are the solutions to $\tan \theta + 1 = 0$? **H**
  F. Quadrants I and II   G. Quadrants II and III
  H. Quadrants II and IV   I. Quadrants III and IV

77. Which of these angles have a sine of about -0.6? **C**
  I. 143.1°   II. 216.9°   III. 323.1°
  A. I and II only   B. I and III only
  C. II and III only   D. I, II, and III

78. What is the solution of $2 \sin \theta - \sqrt{3} = 0$ for $0 \le \theta < 2\pi$? **G**
  F. $\frac{\pi}{6}$ and $\frac{5\pi}{6}$ G. $\frac{\pi}{3}$ and $\frac{2\pi}{3}$
  H. $\frac{2\pi}{3}$ and $\frac{4\pi}{3}$ I. $\frac{4\pi}{3}$ and $\frac{5\pi}{3}$

79. Suppose $a > 0$. Under what conditions for a and b will $a \sin \theta = b$ have exactly two solutions in the interval $0 \le \theta < 2\pi$? **D**
  A. $a = b$ B. $b > a$
  C. $a = -b$ D. $a > b > -a$

Short Response

80. Solve $2 \cos \theta = \sqrt{2}$ for $0 \le \theta < 2\pi$. **See left.**

Extended Response

81. Solve $2 \sin^2 \theta = -\sin \theta$ for $0 \le \theta < 2\pi$. Show your work. **See margin.**

Mixed Review

Lesson 14-1   **Simplify each expression.**

82. $\cos^2 \theta \sec \theta \csc \theta$ **$\cot \theta$**   **83.** $\sin \theta \sec \theta \tan \theta$ **$\tan^2 \theta$**

84. $\csc^2 \theta (1 - \cos^2 \theta)$ **1**   **85.** $\frac{\cos \theta \csc \theta}{\cot \theta}$ **1**

86. $\frac{\sec \theta}{\cot \theta + \tan \theta}$ **$\sin \theta$**   **87.** $\frac{\sin \theta + \tan \theta}{1 + \cos \theta}$ **$\tan \theta$**

Lesson 13-5   **Write a cosine function for each description.**

88. amplitude 4, period 8 **$y = 4 \cos \frac{\pi}{4}\theta$**   **89.** amplitude 3, period 2π **$y = 3 \cos \theta$**

90. amplitude 3π, period 1   **91.** amplitude $\frac{\pi}{4}$, period 3π
 $y = 3\pi \cos 2\pi\theta$ **$y = \frac{\pi}{4} \cos \frac{2}{3}\theta$**

Lesson 12-2 **92. Transportation** Ninety-eight percent of a railroad's trains depart on schedule. Eighty-nine percent of its trains depart and arrive on schedule. Find the probability that a train that departs on time also arrives on time. $\frac{91}{100}$

Lissajous Figures

A clock pendulum swings in only one plane. Its oscillating path projected on a sheet of paper below it would be a segment. A pendulum supported by a string can move so that its path is a circle, ellipse, or other complicated curve. These curves are called Lissajous figures.

Lissajous figures can be described by parametric equations of this form.

$$x = a_1 \sin b_1(t - h_1)$$
$$y = a_2 \sin b_2(t - h_2)$$

x represents the oscillating motion in one direction and y represents the oscillating motion in the perpendicular direction. t is time, $|a_1|$ and $|a_2|$ are amplitudes of the oscillations, $\frac{b_1}{2\pi}$ and $\frac{b_2}{2\pi}$ are cycles per second, and h_1 and h_2 are phase shifts.

The parametric equations can be graphed with a graphing calculator. See page 126.

EXAMPLE

Set the calculator to radian and parametric mode. Set the window values as shown.

```
WINDOW
 Tmin=0
 Tmax=7
 Tstep=.05
 Xmin=-3
 Xmax=3
 Xscl=1
↓Ymin=-2
```

```
WINDOW
↑Tstep=.05
 Xmin=-3
 Xmax=3
 Xscl=1
 Ymin=-2
 Ymax=2
 Yscl=1
```

Graph each pair of parametric equations.

a. $x = 3 \sin 2(t - \pi)$
$y = 2 \sin 4(t - \pi)$

b. $x = 3 \sin 2\left(t - \frac{\pi}{3}\right)$
$y = 2 \sin 4(t - \pi)$

c. $x = 3 \sin 2(t - 1)$
$y = 2 \sin 3(t - 1)$

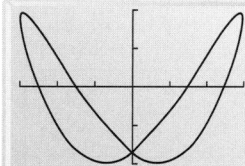

EXERCISES

Use your calculator to graph each pair of parametric equations. Sketch each graph.   1–3. See margin.

1. $x = 2.1 \sin (t - 1)$
$y = 1.8 \sin (t - 2)$

2. $x = 3 \sin 2\left(t - \frac{3}{2}\right)$
$y = 2 \sin 3\left(t - \frac{2}{3}\right)$

3. $x = 3 \sin 3(t - 1)$
$y = 2 \sin 2(t - 1)$

4. Open-Ended Graph other Lissajous figures by changing the numbers in the equations. Sketch the interesting graphs and record their equations.
Check students' work.

Extension   Lissajous Figures   **777**

Extension

Lissajous Figures

Students use a graphing calculator to graph parametric equations for Lissajous figures. This feature shows students the variety of complicated curves that parametric equations can describe.

Resources

Any graphing calculator that has parametric graphing capabilities

Teaching Notes

Teaching Tip

Suggest that students also try non-integer rational values for b_1 and b_2. The curves for rational values of b_1 and b_2 are *unicursal*, meaning that they are closed curves that can be traced entirely and without retracing by moving a pencil point over the curve one time.

Technology Tip

In Exercise 4, if students change the values of a_1 and a_2, they may need to change the window settings for the axes. Changes in b_1 and b_2 may require a change in the value of Tmax.

page 777   Extension

1.
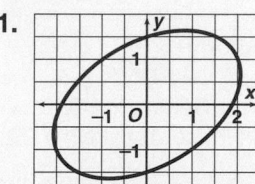

2.
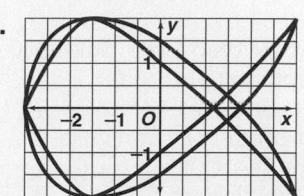

3.
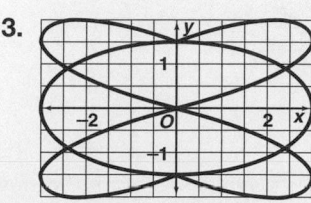

Right Triangles and Trigonometric Ratios

Lesson Preview

✓ **Check Skills You'll Need**

Ratios and Proportions
Skills Handbook: p. 844,
Example 3
Exercises 16, 17

Lesson Resources

📁 **Teaching Resources**
Practice, Reteaching, Enrichment
Checkpoint Quiz 1

👥 **Reaching All Students**
Practice Workbook 14-3
Spanish Practice Workbook 14-3
Reading and Math Literacy 14B
Spanish Reading & Literacy 14B
Spanish Checkpoint Quiz 1

⏱ **Presentation Assistant Plus!**
Transparencies
• Check Skills You'll Need 14-3
• Additional Examples 14-3
• Student Edition Answers 14-3
• Lesson Quiz 14-3
PH Presentation Pro CD 14-3

PRENTICE HALL ASSESSMENT SYSTEM

Checkpoint Quiz 1
Computer Test Generator CD

💿 **Technology**
Resource Pro® CD-ROM
Computer Test Generator CD
Prentice Hall Presentation Pro CD

🖥 **www.PHSchool.com**
Student Site
• Teacher Web Code: agk-5500
• Graphing Calculator,
  Procedure 12
• Self-grading Lesson Quiz
Teacher Center
• Lesson Planner
• Resources

Plus

Lesson Preview

What You'll Learn

OBJECTIVE 1
To find lengths of sides in a right triangle

OBJECTIVE 2
To find measures of angles in a right triangle

. . . And Why

To design bridges, as in Example 3

✓ **Check Skills You'll Need** (For help, go to Skills Handbook page 844.)

$\triangle ABC$ is similar to $\triangle RST$. Complete the following proportions.

1. $\dfrac{a}{b} = \dfrac{r}{\blacksquare}$ **s**   **2.** $\dfrac{a}{c} = \dfrac{\blacksquare}{t}$ **r**

3. $\dfrac{t}{r} = \dfrac{c}{\blacksquare}$ **a**   **4.** $\dfrac{c}{b} = \dfrac{\blacksquare}{s}$ **t**

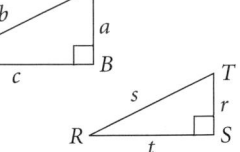

New Vocabulary • trigonometric ratios for a right triangle

OBJECTIVE 1

Finding the Lengths of Sides in a Right Triangle

🖥 **i TEXT** Interactive lesson includes instant self-check, tutorials, and activities.

Investigation: Right Triangle Ratios

Draw three right triangles, each one having an acute angle of 53°. Make the hypotenuse of the first triangle 10 cm long, and make the other two hypotenuses differ by at least 5 cm. Label the triangles 1, 2, and 3.

1. In each triangle, measure the lengths of the hypotenuse, the leg opposite the 53° angle, and the leg adjacent to the 53° angle. Copy the table below and record your measurements. Then calculate the three ratios for each triangle.

Triangle	Hyp. (cm)	Leg opp. ∠A (cm)	Leg adj. to ∠A (cm)	opp. hyp.	adj. hyp.	opp. adj.
1	10	8.0	6.0	0.80	0.60	1.33
2	■20	■16	■12	■0.8	■0.6	■1.33
3	■30	■24	■18	■0.8	■0.6	■1.33

2. Reasoning What patterns do you see in the last three columns of the table? Check your results with others. **Ratios are the same within each column.**

3. Make a Conjecture What is true about these ratios for all right triangles that have an acute angle of 53°? **The ratios are a constant for all right triangles that have an acute angle of 53°.**

The **trigonometric ratios for a right triangle** are the six different ratios of the sides of a right triangle. These ratios do not depend on the size of the right triangle. They depend only on the measures of the acute angles in the triangle.

✓ **Ongoing Assessment and Intervention**

Before the Lesson
Diagnose prerequisite skills using:
• Check Skills You'll Need

During the Lesson
Monitor progress using:
• Check Understanding
• Additional Examples
• Standardized Test Prep

After the Lesson
Assess knowledge using:
• Lesson Quiz
• Computer Test Generator CD
• Chapter Checkpoint 1 (p. 785)

Reading Math

Some students use the fictitious name "SOHCAHTOA" to remember definitions.

Sine:
Opposite over
Hypotenuse

Cosine:
Adjacent over
Hypotenuse

Tangent:
Opposite over
Adjacent

In a right triangle that has an acute $\angle A$, the ratios are defined as follows.

$$\sin A = \frac{\text{length of leg opposite } \angle A}{\text{length of hypotenuse}} = \frac{a}{c}$$

$$\cos A = \frac{\text{length of leg adjacent to } \angle A}{\text{length of hypotenuse}} = \frac{b}{c}$$

$$\tan A = \frac{\text{length of leg opposite } \angle A}{\text{length of leg adjacent to } \angle A} = \frac{a}{b}$$

$$\csc A = \frac{1}{\sin A} = \frac{\text{length of hypotenuse}}{\text{length of leg opposite } \angle A} = \frac{c}{a}$$

$$\sec A = \frac{1}{\cos A} = \frac{\text{length of hypotenuse}}{\text{length of leg adjacent to } \angle A} = \frac{c}{b}$$

$$\cot A = \frac{1}{\tan A} = \frac{\text{length of leg adjacent to } \angle A}{\text{length of leg opposite } \angle A} = \frac{b}{a}$$

1 EXAMPLE **Real-World** **Connection**

In the pyramid of Khafre, $AC \approx 108$ m and $m\angle A \approx 53°$.

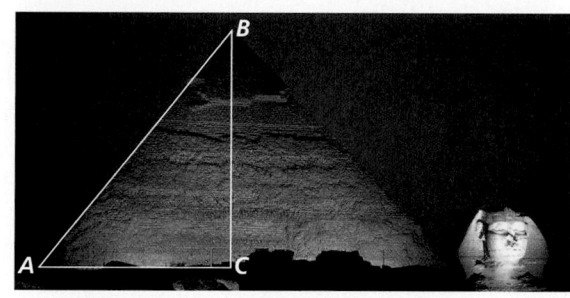

Egyptology Given that $\sin 53° \approx 0.80$, $\cos 53° \approx 0.60$, and $\tan 53° \approx 1.33$, find the height BC of the pyramid.

$$\tan A = \frac{BC}{AC} \quad \text{definition of tan}$$

$$1.33 = \frac{BC}{108} \quad \text{Substitute.}$$

$$BC = 108\,(1.33) \approx 144$$

The height of the pyramid of Khafre is about 144 m.

✓ **Check Understanding** **1** Find the length of a lateral edge of the pyramid. **180 m**

For acute angles, the unit circle definition of sine is equivalent to the definition of sine for right triangles.

sin θ using the unit circle

$\sin \theta = y$-coordinate of P

$\quad = PQ$

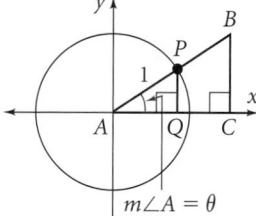

sin A using a right triangle

$$\sin A = \frac{\text{length of leg opposite } \angle A}{\text{length of hypotenuse}}$$

$$= \frac{BC}{AB}$$

Since $\triangle APQ$ and $\triangle ABC$ are similar triangles, $\frac{PQ}{PA} = \frac{BC}{AB}$.

So $\sin \theta = PQ = \frac{PQ}{1} = \frac{PQ}{PA} = \frac{BC}{AB} = \sin A$.

Lesson 14-3 Right Triangles and Trigonometric Ratios **779**

---

2. Teach

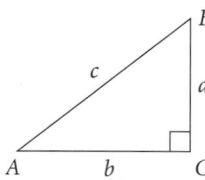

Math Background

Every right triangle that has an acute angle of measure $A°$ is similar to every other right triangle that has an acute angle of measure $A°$. As a result, all ratios of corresponding sides of a right triangle are completely determined by the measures of its acute angles. This makes it possible to define the trigonometric functions of angles with measures between 0° and 90° in terms of ratios of the side lengths of a right triangle. These definitions are consistent with the unit circle definitions of the functions of such angles.

OBJECTIVE

▼ 1 Teaching Notes

Investigation (Optional)
This investigation will help students see that once you have specified the measure of an acute angle and the length of the hypotenuse of a right triangle, the lengths of the legs and the ratios of the sides are determined. Encourage students to draw their triangles carefully and accurately. Stress the importance of accurate measurements. Suggest that all lengths be measured to the nearest tenth of a centimeter.

1 EXAMPLE **Connection to History**

You may want to mention that the oldest pyramid in Egypt dates back to about 2700 B.C. Other ancient civilizations had pyramids. Especially notable are the pyramids of Mexico and Central America. The largest pyramid ever constructed is in Mexico at Cholula de Rivadabia. This pyramid has a base area of nearly 45 acres.

👥 Reaching All Students

Below Level Have students determine the height of the school building, flagpole, or tall tree using a protractor and measuring tape.	**Advanced Learners** Have students calculate the angles of a triangle with sides in the ratio of $3:4:5$.	**Inclusion** See note on page 781. **English Learners** See note on page 783.

EXAMPLE 2 — Math Tip

Point out that the units used in the diagram are not crucial. A rough sketch is all that is needed. The diagram is used merely as an aid to see how to use the Pythagorean Theorem and to see which legs are opposite from and adjacent to the acute angle A.

EXAMPLE 3 — Careers

Many large cities in the U.S. have extensive park systems. These systems provide job opportunities in park planning, landscaping, sports and recreation activities, and park maintenance.

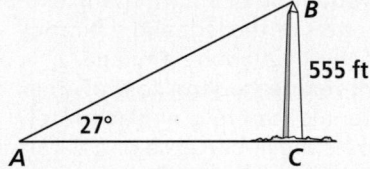

Additional Examples

1 A tourist visiting Washington D.C. is seated on the grass at point A and is looking up at the top of the Washington Monument. The angle of her line of sight with the ground is 27°. Given that sin 27° ≈ 0.45, cos 27° ≈ 0.89, and tan 27° ≈ 0.51, find her approximate distance AC from the base of the monument.

≈ 1088 ft

2 In △PQR, ∠R is a right angle and cos $P = \frac{7}{25}$. Find sin P, tan P, and cos Q in fraction and in decimal form. **sin $P = \frac{24}{25} = 0.96$, tan $P = \frac{24}{7} ≈ 3.4286$, cos $Q = \frac{24}{25} = 0.96$**

3 A man 6 feet tall is standing 50 feet from a tree. When he looks at the top of the tree, the angle of elevation is 42°. Find the height of the tree to the nearest foot. **51 ft**

You can use the same figure to show that the definitions of the other five ratios are equivalent for acute angles.

EXAMPLE 2

In △ABC, ∠C is a right angle and sin $A = \frac{5}{13}$. Find cos A, cot A, and sin B in fraction and in decimal form.

Step 1 Draw a diagram.

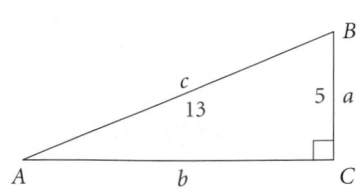

Step 2 Use the Pythagorean Theorem to find b.

$$c^2 = a^2 + b^2$$
$$13^2 = 5^2 + b^2$$
$$169 = 25 + b^2$$
$$144 = b^2$$
$$12 = b$$

Step 3 Calculate the ratios.

$$\cos A = \frac{\text{length of leg adjacent to } \angle A}{\text{length of hypotenuse}} = \frac{b}{c} = \frac{12}{13} ≈ 0.9231$$

$$\cot A = \frac{\text{length of leg adjacent to } \angle A}{\text{length of leg opposite } \angle A} = \frac{b}{a} = \frac{12}{5} = 2.4$$

$$\sin B = \frac{\text{length of leg opposite } \angle B}{\text{length of hypotenuse}} = \frac{b}{c} = \frac{12}{13} ≈ 0.9231$$

✔ Check Understanding **2** In △DEF, ∠D is a right angle and tan $E = \frac{3}{4}$. Draw a diagram and find sin E and sec F in fraction and in decimal form. **See left.**

2.

$\frac{3}{5} = 0.6, \frac{5}{3} ≈ 1.67$

If you are given the measures of an acute angle and a side of a right triangle, you can find the length of another side of the triangle.

EXAMPLE 3 — Real-World Connection

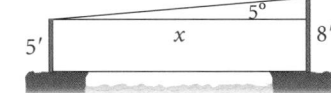

Planning Park planners would like to build a bridge across a creek. Surveyors have determined that from 5 ft above the ground the angle of elevation to the top of an 8-ft pole on the opposite side of the creek is 5°. Find the length of the bridge to the nearest foot.

In the right triangle, the length of the leg opposite the 5° angle is 8 − 5, or 3 ft. You need to find the length of the leg adjacent to the 5° angle. Use the tangent ratio.

$\tan 5° = \frac{3}{x}$

$x = \frac{3}{\tan 5°}$ **Solve for x.**

$≈ 34.29$ **Use a calculator in degree mode.**

The bridge will be about 34 ft long.

Real-World Connection

Careers Park planners are often licensed in landscape architecture. They are usually employed by government agencies.

✔ Check Understanding **3 a. Critical Thinking** What are the advantages and disadvantages of using cot 5° instead of tan 5° in solving Example 3? **See margin.**

b. Find the length of the bridge in Example 3 by using the 85° angle in the right triangle instead of the 5° angle. **≈34.29 ft**

page 780 Check Understanding

3a. Answers may vary. Sample: An advantage is that simplification of the equation is easier. A

disadvantage is that you have to press an extra button on the calculator to get the cotangent function.

Finding the Measures of Angles in a Right Triangle

To find the measure of an acute angle in a right triangle, you can use the inverses of the trigonometric functions.

4 EXAMPLE Finding Angle Measures

In $\triangle DEF$, $\angle F$ is a right angle, $f = 13$, and $e = 5$. Find $m\angle D$ to the nearest tenth of a degree.

Step 1 Draw a diagram.

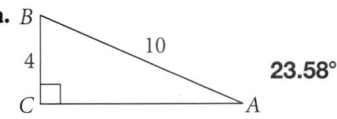

13 ← Side f is opposite $\angle F$.

5 ← Side e is opposite $\angle E$.

Step 2 Use a cosine ratio.

$$\cos D = \frac{5}{13}$$

$$m\angle D = \cos^{-1}\frac{5}{13}$$

$$\approx 67.38° \quad \textbf{Use a calculator.}$$

To the nearest tenth of a degree, $m\angle D$ is 67.4°.

5. D

e 10

F 7 E

$e \approx 7.14$; $m\angle E \approx$
$45.6°$, $m\angle D \approx 44.4°$

✓ **Check Understanding** **4** Use a trigonometric ratio to find $m\angle A$ in each triangle.

a. B

4 10

C A **23.58°**

b. C **56.25°**

5

A 9 B

5 EXAMPLE Real-World 🌐 Connection

Construction A wheelchair ramp must be constructed so the slope is not more than 1 in. of rise for every 1 ft of run. What is the maximum angle that the ramp can make with the ground, to the nearest tenth of a degree?

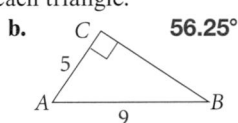

Surface of ramp

θ 1 in. Rise

1 ft

Horizontal projection or run

Not drawn to scale

Let $\theta =$ the measure of the angle the ramp makes with the ground.

You know the length of the leg opposite the angle you need to find. You know the length of the leg adjacent to the angle you need to find. So, use the tangent ratio.

$$\tan \theta = \frac{1}{12} \quad \textbf{Rewrite 1 ft as 12 in.}$$

$$\theta = \tan^{-1}\frac{1}{12} \quad \textbf{Use the inverse of the tangent function.}$$

$$\theta \approx 4.8 \quad \textbf{Use a calculator.}$$

The angle between the ramp and the ground will be about 4.8°.

Real-World 🌐 Connection

Federal regulations define allowable slopes for handicap-accessible facilities.

✓ **Check Understanding** **5** In $\triangle DEF$, $\angle F$ is a right angle, $d = 7$, and $f = 10$. Draw a diagram and find the remaining side length and angle degree measures. Round to the nearest tenth.

See above left.

OBJECTIVE
2 **Teaching Notes**

5 EXAMPLE Inclusion

Inform students that many cities have guidelines that specify acceptable slopes for ramps used as building access for people using wheelchairs and walkers.

Additional Examples

4 In $\triangle KMN$, $\angle N$ is a right angle, $m = 7$, and $n = 25$. Find $m\angle K$ to the nearest tenth of a degree. **73.7°**

5 A straight road that goes up a hill is 800 feet higher at the top than at the bottom. The horizontal distance covered is 6515 feet. To the nearest degree, what angle does the road make with level ground? **7°**

Closure

Ask students to name one piece of additional information that would allow them to find all the other side lengths and angle measures of a right triangle if they are given the measure of one of the acute angles. Then tell them to suppose that they know the lengths of two sides of a right triangle. Ask what other information they would need about the sides to find the length of the third side and the measures of the angles. **length of opposite leg, length of adjacent leg, or length of hypotenuse; You would need to know whether both are legs or whether one is a leg and the other is the hypotenuse.**

3. Practice

Assignment Guide

1 Objective
A B Core 1–8, 25–34, 42–48
C Extension 49–51

2 Objective
A B Core 9–24, 35–41
C Extension 52, 53

Standardized Test Prep 54–59

Mixed Review 60–70

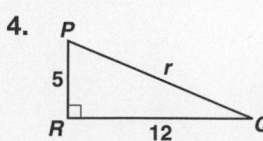

Enrichment 14-3
Reteaching 14-3
Practice 14-3

pages 782–785 Exercises

4.

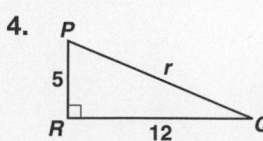

P, R, Q triangle with 5, r, 12

$\sin P = \frac{12}{13} \approx 0.92,$

$\cos P = \frac{5}{13} \approx 0.38,$

$\tan P = \frac{12}{5} \approx 2.40,$

$\csc P = \frac{13}{12} \approx 1.08,$

$\sec P = \frac{13}{5} \approx 2.60$

782

EXERCISES

For more practice, see *Extra Practice*.

Practice and Problem Solving

A Practice by Example

Example 1 (page 779)

1. Ballooning From a hot-air balloon 3000 ft above the ground, you see a clearing whose angle of depression is 20°. Given that sin 20° ≈ 0.34, cos 20° ≈ 0.94, and tan 20° ≈ 0.36, find each distance to the nearest foot.

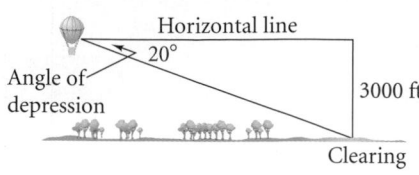

a. your horizontal distance from the clearing ≈ **8333 ft**
b. your direct distance from the clearing ≈ **8824 ft**

Example 2 (page 780)

2a. $\frac{15}{17} \approx 0.88$

b. $\frac{17}{8} \approx 2.13$

c. $\frac{8}{15} \approx 0.53$

d. $\frac{17}{8} \approx 2.13$

e. $\frac{17}{15} \approx 1.13$

f. $\frac{8}{15} \approx 0.53$

2. In △*ABC*, find each value as a fraction and as a decimal. Round to the nearest hundredth.

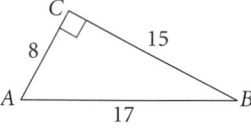

a. sin *A*   **b.** sec *A*
c. cot *A*   **d.** csc *B*
e. sec *B*   **f.** tan *B*

3. In △*GHI*, ∠*H* is a right angle, *GH* = 40, and cos *G* = $\frac{40}{41}$. Draw a diagram and find each value in fraction and in decimal form. **a–f. See below left.**
a. sin *G*   **b.** sin *I*   **c.** cot *G*
d. csc *G*   **e.** cos *I*   **f.** sec *H*

4. In △*PQR*, ∠*R* is a right angle and cot *P* = $\frac{5}{12}$. Draw a diagram. Find the values of the other five trigonometric functions of ∠*P* in fraction and in decimal form. **See margin.**

Example 3 (page 780)

3.

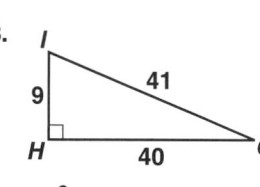

9, 41, 40, H, G, I

a. $\frac{9}{41} \approx 0.22$

b. $\frac{40}{41} \approx 0.98$

c. $\frac{40}{9} \approx 4.44$

d. $\frac{41}{9} \approx 4.56$

e. $\frac{9}{41} \approx 0.22$

f. not defined

Find each length *x*. Round to the nearest tenth.

5.

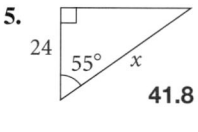

24, 55°, x, **41.8**

6.

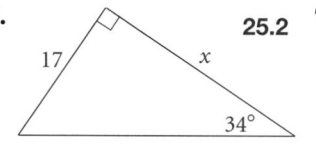

17, x, 34°, **25.2**

7.

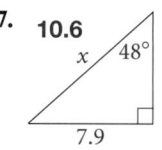

10.6, x, 48°, 7.9

8. Indirect Measurement The tallest flagpole in the world was built in San Francisco in 1915.

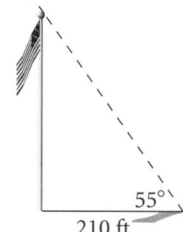

a. When the angle of elevation of the sun was 55°, the length of the shadow cast by this flagpole was 210 ft. Find the height of the flagpole to the nearest foot. **300 ft**
b. What was the length of the shadow when the angle of elevation of the sun was 34°? **445 ft**
c. What do you need to assume about the flagpole and the shadow to solve these problems? Explain why. **See margin.**

Examples 4 and 5 (page 781)

Find each angle measure to the nearest tenth of a degree.

9. $\cos^{-1}\frac{\sqrt{2}}{2}$ **45.0°**   10. $\tan^{-1} 0.3333$ **18.4°**   11. $\sin^{-1}\frac{3}{4}$ **48.6°**

12. $\tan^{-1}\sqrt{3}$ **60.0°**   13. $\sin^{-1} 0.335$ **19.6°**   14. $\cos^{-1} 0.992$ **7.3°**

15. $\tan^{-1} 3.552$ **74.3°**   16. $\sin^{-1} 0.052$ **3.0°**   17. $\cos^{-1}\frac{3}{8}$ **68.0°**

8c. **Answers may vary. Sample: The flagpole must be straight, the ground must be flat, and the flagpole and the ground must be perpendicular. You assume these things so that the flagpole and the ground form a right angle. By having a right triangle you can use its properties to find the missing parts.**

18. $a \approx 8.7$, $\angle A = 60.0°$, $\angle B = 30.0°$

19. $c \approx 7.8$, $\angle A = 39.8°$, $\angle B = 50.2°$

20. $a \approx 9.0$, $\angle A = 36.9°$, $\angle B = 53.1°$

In $\triangle ABC$, $\angle C$ is a right angle. Find the remaining sides and angles. Round your answers to the nearest tenth. **21–23. See margin.**

18. $b = 5, c = 10$ **19.** $a = 5, b = 6$ **20.** $b = 12, c = 15$

21. $a = 8.1, b = 6.2$ **22.** $b = 4.3, c = 9.1$ **23.** $a = 17, c = 22$

24. Rocketry An observer on the ground at point A watches a rocket ascend. The observer is 1200 ft from the launch point B. As the rocket rises, the distance d from the observer to the rocket increases.
    a. Write a model for $m\angle A$. $m\angle A = \cos^{-1}\left(\frac{1200}{d}\right)$
    b. Find $m\angle A$ if $d = 1500$ ft. Round your answer to the nearest degree.   **37°**
    c. Find $m\angle A$ if $d = 2000$ ft. Round your answer to the nearest degree.   **53°**

 B **Apply Your Skills**

Sketch a right triangle with θ as the measure of one acute angle. Find the other five trigonometric ratios of θ.   **25–33. See margin.**

Reading Math
For help with reading and solving Exercise 25, see p. 786.

25. $\sin \theta = \frac{3}{8}$ **26.** $\cos \theta = \frac{7}{20}$ **27.** $\cos \theta = \frac{1}{5}$

28. $\tan \theta = \frac{24}{7}$ **29.** $\csc \theta = \frac{21}{12}$ **30.** $\sec \theta = \frac{16}{9}$

31. $\cot \theta = \frac{5}{4}$ **32.** $\sin \theta = 0.35$ **33.** $\csc \theta = 5.2$

34. a. Engineering A radio tower has supporting cables attached to it at points 100 ft above the ground. Write a model for the length d of each supporting cable as a function of the angle θ that it makes with the ground. $d = \frac{100}{\sin \theta}$
    b. Find d when $\theta = 60°$ and when $\theta = 50°$.   **115.5 ft, 130.5 ft**

In $\triangle ABC$, $\angle C$ is a right angle. Two measures are given. Find the remaining sides and angles. Round your answers to the nearest tenth.

35–40. See back of book.

35. $b = 8, c = 17$ **36.** $a = 7, b = 10$

37. $m\angle A = 52°, c = 10$ **38.** $m\angle A = 34.2°, b = 5.7$

39. $m\angle B = 17.2°, b = 8.3$ **40.** $m\angle B = 8.3°, c = 20$

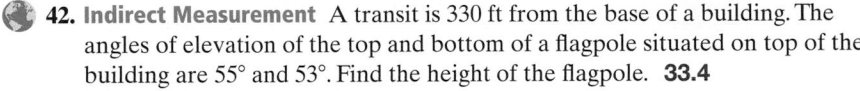

100 ft d θ

41. A 150-ft pole casts a shadow 210 ft long. Find the measure of the angle of elevation of the sun.   **35.5°**

42. Indirect Measurement A transit is 330 ft from the base of a building. The angles of elevation of the top and bottom of a flagpole situated on top of the building are 55° and 53°. Find the height of the flagpole.   **33.4**

45b.
Answers may vary.
Sample:
$\cos E = \frac{EF}{13}$
$\sin E = \frac{5}{13} \approx 0.385$
$m\angle E = \sin^{-1} 0.385 \approx 22.6°$
$EF = 13 \cos 22.6° \approx 12$

46–47. See back of book.

43. Geometry An altitude inside a triangle forms angles of 36° and 42° with two of the sides. The altitude is 5 m long. Find the area of the triangle.   **20.3 m²**

44. a. Construction When a crane's boom is elevated to an angle of 70°, it extends to a height of 128 ft. How far is the crane's cab from the point where materials will be dropped?   **46.6 ft**
    b. Find the length of the boom.   **136.2 ft**

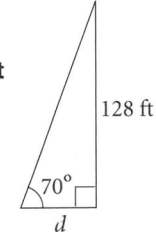

128 ft
70°
d

45. a. In Example 4, use the Pythagorean Theorem to find EF.   **13**
    b. Use a trigonometric ratio to find EF.   **See left.**

46. Open-Ended If $\sin \theta = \frac{1}{2}$, describe a method you could use to find all the angles between 0° and 360° that satisfy this equation.

47. Reasoning Show that $\cos A$ defined as a ratio equals $\cos \theta$ using the unit circle.

21. $c \approx 10.2$, $\angle A = 52.6°$, $\angle B = 37.4°$

22. $a \approx 8.0$, $\angle A = 61.8°$, $\angle B = 28.2°$

23. $b \approx 14.0$, $\angle A = 50.6°$, $\angle B = 39.4°$

25. $\cos \theta = \frac{\sqrt{55}}{8}$, $\tan \theta = \frac{3\sqrt{55}}{55}$, $\csc \theta = \frac{8}{3}$, $\sec \theta = \frac{8\sqrt{55}}{55}$, $\cot \theta = \frac{\sqrt{55}}{3}$

26. $\sin \theta = \frac{3\sqrt{39}}{20}$, $\tan \theta = \frac{3\sqrt{39}}{7}$, $\csc \theta = \frac{20\sqrt{39}}{117}$, $\sec \theta = \frac{20}{7}$, $\cot \theta = \frac{7\sqrt{39}}{117}$

Error Prevention

Exercises 18–23 Students who draw diagrams for these exercises may not label the sides with the appropriate lengths. Remind them that for a triangle whose vertices are labeled with capital letters, it is customary to use the corresponding small letters for the lengths of the opposite sides.

English Learners

Exercise 44 You may need to explain what is meant by a *crane*, the *boom* of a crane, and the *cab* of a crane. Point to each in the photo as they are explained.

27. $\sin \theta = \frac{2\sqrt{6}}{5}$, $\tan \theta = 2\sqrt{6}$, $\csc \theta = \frac{5\sqrt{6}}{12}$, $\sec \theta = 5$, $\cot \theta = \frac{\sqrt{6}}{12}$

28. $\sin \theta = \frac{24}{25}$, $\cos \theta = \frac{7}{25}$, $\csc \theta = \frac{25}{24}$, $\sec \theta = \frac{25}{7}$, $\cot \theta = \frac{7}{24}$

29. $\sin \theta = \frac{4}{7}$, $\cos \theta = \frac{\sqrt{33}}{7}$, $\tan \theta = \frac{4\sqrt{33}}{33}$, $\sec \theta = \frac{7\sqrt{33}}{33}$, $\cot \theta = \frac{\sqrt{33}}{4}$

30. $\sin \theta = \frac{5\sqrt{7}}{16}$, $\cos \theta = \frac{9}{16}$, $\tan \theta = \frac{5\sqrt{7}}{9}$, $\csc \theta = \frac{16\sqrt{7}}{35}$, $\cot \theta = \frac{9\sqrt{7}}{35}$

31. $\sin \theta = \frac{4\sqrt{41}}{41}$, $\cos \theta = \frac{5\sqrt{41}}{41}$, $\tan \theta = \frac{4}{5}$, $\csc \theta = \frac{\sqrt{41}}{4}$, $\sec \theta = \frac{\sqrt{41}}{5}$

32. $\cos \theta = 0.937$, $\tan \theta = 0.374$, $\csc \theta = 2.857$, $\sec \theta = 1.068$, $\cot \theta = 2.676$

33. $\sin \theta = 0.192$, $\cos \theta = 0.981$, $\tan \theta = 0.196$, $\sec \theta = 1.019$, $\cot \theta = 5.103$

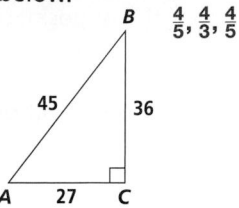

Lesson Quiz 14-3

1. Find sin A, tan A, and cos B for the triangle shown below. $\frac{4}{5}, \frac{4}{3}, \frac{4}{5}$

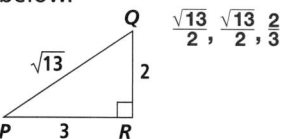

2. Find csc P, sec Q, and cot Q for the triangle shown below. $\frac{\sqrt{13}}{2}, \frac{\sqrt{13}}{2}, \frac{2}{3}$

3. In $\triangle KST$, $\angle S$ is a right angle, $s = 17$, and $t = 15$. Find $m\angle T$ and $m\angle K$ to the nearest tenth of a degree. **61.9°, 28.1°**

4. A flagpole that is 35 feet tall casts a shadow 22 feet long at a certain time of the morning. What is the angle of elevation of the sun to the nearest degree? **58°**

Alternative Assessment

Have students work in pairs. Ask each one to sketch a right triangle and indicate the right angle. Tell one student to label two sides with their lengths. Tell the other student to label one acute angle and the hypotenuse with their measures. Instruct the pairs to exchange triangles and find all the missing measures of sides and angles in each triangle. Finally, ask students to select one acute angle of their triangle and to give the values of all six trigonometric functions for those angles. Students exchange triangles again and check each other's work.

---

 48. Baseball The bases on a baseball diamond form a square 90 ft on a side. The pitcher's plate is 60 ft 6 in. from the back corner of home plate.

a. About how far is the pitcher's plate from second base? ≈**67 ft**

b. A line drive is 10 ft high when it passes over the third baseman, who is 100 ft from home plate. At what angle did the ball leave the bat? (Assume the ball is 4 ft above the ground when it is hit.) ≈**3.4°**

49. $\sec A \stackrel{?}{=} \frac{1}{\cos A}$

$\frac{c}{b} \stackrel{?}{=} \frac{1}{\frac{b}{c}}$

$\frac{c}{b} = \frac{c}{b}$

C **Challenge**

50. $\tan A \stackrel{?}{=} \frac{\sin A}{\cos A}$

$\frac{a}{b} \stackrel{?}{=} \frac{\frac{a}{c}}{\frac{b}{c}}$

$\frac{a}{b} = \frac{a}{b}$

51. $\cos^2 A + \sin^2 A \stackrel{?}{=} 1$

$\left(\frac{b}{c}\right)^2 + \left(\frac{a}{c}\right)^2 \stackrel{?}{=} 1$

$b^2 + a^2 \stackrel{?}{=} c^2$

$c^2 = c^2$

Need Help?

A regular polygon has congruent sides and congruent angles.

Use the definitions of trigonometric ratios in right $\triangle ABC$ to verify each identity.

49. $\sec A = \frac{1}{\cos A}$ **50.** $\tan A = \frac{\sin A}{\cos A}$ **51.** $\cos^2 A + \sin^2 A = 1$

52. a. In $\triangle DEF$ below, h is the length of an altitude. Find h to the nearest tenth.
b. For $DF = 10.8$, find the area of $\triangle DEF$ to the nearest tenth.
c. Find the area of $\triangle RST$ to the nearest tenth.

a. 5.9 units
b. 31.9 units²
c. 6.2 units²

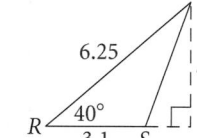

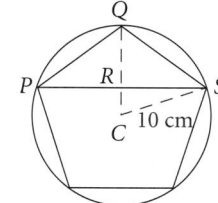

53. Geometry A regular pentagon is inscribed in a circle of radius 10 cm.
a. Find the measure of $\angle C$. **72°**
b. Find the length of the diagonal PS. (*Hint*: First find RS.) **19.0 cm**

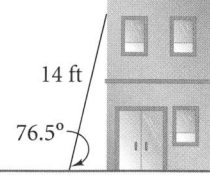

Standardized Test Prep

Multiple Choice

54. A ladder rests against a vertical building, as shown at the right. The ladder is 14 ft long and forms an angle of 76.5° with the ground. Which statement is NOT true? **A**

A. The bottom of the ladder is 13.6 ft from the base of the building.
B. The bottom of the ladder is 3.3 ft from the base of the building.
C. The top of the ladder is 13.6 ft from the ground.
D. The ladder forms an angle of 13.5° with the building.

55. The sides of a rectangle are 25 cm and 8 cm. What is the measure of the angle formed by the short side and the diagonal of the rectangle? **I**
F. 17.7°   **G.** 18.7°   **H.** 71.3°   **I.** 72.3°

784 Chapter 14 Trigonometric Identities and Equations

---

pages 782–785 Exercises

64.

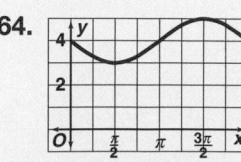

65.

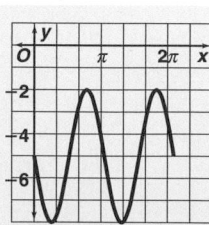

66.

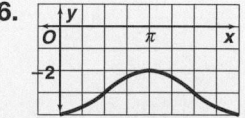

56. The figure at the right is a rectangle. What is the value of x? **A**

A. 31.0 B. 36.9
C. 53.1 D. 59.0

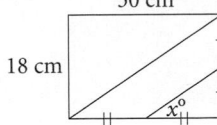
30 cm / 18 cm / $x°$

Take It to the NET
Online lesson quiz at
www.PHSchool.com
Web Code: aga-1403

57. In $\triangle XYZ$, $\angle Z$ is a right angle and $\tan X = \frac{8}{15}$.
What is $\sin Y$? **G**

F. $\frac{8}{17}$ G. $\frac{15}{17}$ H. $\frac{17}{15}$ I. $\frac{15}{8}$

58. In the right triangle at the right, $\cos y° = \frac{5}{13}$.
If $x + 2z = 7.1$, what is the value of z? **C**

A. 67.3 B. 22.6
C. −7.76 D. −30.1

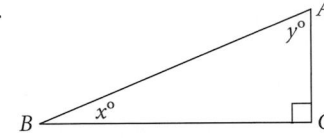
A / $y°$ / B / $x°$ / C

Short Response

59. Find the measures of the acute angles of a right triangle, to the nearest tenth, if the legs are 135 cm and 95 cm.
See back of book.

Mixed Review

Lesson 14-2

Find the complete solution of each equation. Express your answer in degrees.

60. $\sec^2 \theta + \sec \theta = 0$ **$180° + n \cdot 360°$**

61. $2 \cos^2 \theta + 1 = 0$ **no solution**

62. $\cot \theta = \cot^2 \theta$ **$45° + n \cdot 180°$**

63. $\sin^2 \theta + 5 \sin \theta = 0$
$0 + n \cdot 360°$ and $180° + n \cdot 360°$

Lesson 13-7

Graph each function in the interval from 0 to 2π.

64. $y = \sin (x - \pi) + 4$

65. $y = 3 \sin 2\left(x + \frac{\pi}{2}\right) - 5$

66. $y = \cos (x + \pi) - 3$

67. $y = -2 \cos \left(x - \frac{\pi}{3}\right) - 4$
64–67. See margin pp. 784–785.

Lesson 12-6

Use the binomial expansion of $(p + q)^n$ to calculate and graph each binomial distribution. 68–70. See margin.

68. $n = 8, p = 0.2$ **69.** $n = 8, p = 0.4$ **70.** $n = 8, p = 0.8$

Checkpoint Quiz 1 · Lessons 14-1 through 14-3

TEXT Instant self-check quiz online and on CD-ROM

Simplify each trigonometric expression.

1. $\sec \theta \cot \theta$ **$\csc \theta$**

2. $\sec^2 \theta - 1$ **$\tan^2 \theta$**

3. $-1 - \cot^2 \theta$ **$-\csc^2 \theta$**

Find the value of each expression to the nearest thousandth.

4. $\cos^{-1}\left(-\frac{\pi}{5}\right)$ **2.250**

5. $\sin^{-1} \frac{\pi}{10}$ **0.320**

6. $\tan^{-1} 4.35$ **1.345**

7. $a \approx 7.7, m\angle A \approx 29.0°,$ $m\angle B \approx 61.0°$

8. $c \approx 10.0, m\angle A \approx 51.9°,$ $m\angle B \approx 38.1°$

9. $a \approx 19.6, m\angle A \approx 34.0°,$ $m\angle B \approx 56.0°$

In $\triangle ABC$, $\angle C$ is a right angle. Find the remaining sides and angles. Round your answers to the nearest tenth.

7. $b = 14, c = 16$ **8.** $a = 7.9, b = 6.2$ **9.** $b = 29, c = 35$

10. Open-Ended Draw a right triangle. Measure the lengths of two sides, and then find the remaining sides and angles without measuring. **Check students' work.**

67.

68. $P(0) \approx 0.167772$
$P(1) \approx 0.335544$
$P(2) \approx 0.293601$
$P(3) \approx 0.146801$
$P(4) \approx 0.045875$
$P(5) \approx 0.009175$
$P(6) \approx 0.001147$
$P(7) \approx 0.000082$
$P(8) \approx 0.000003$

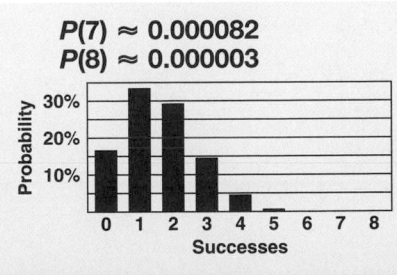

Standardized Test Prep

Resources
For additional practice with a variety of test item formats:
• Standardized Test Prep, p. 817
• Test-Taking Strategies, p. 812
• Test-Taking Strategies with Transparencies

Chapter Checkpoint 1

To check understanding of Lessons 14-1 to 14-3:

Checkpoint Quiz 1 (p. 785)

Teaching Resources
Checkpoint Quiz 1 (also in Prentice Hall Assessment System)

Reaching All Students
Reading and Math Literacy 14B

Spanish versions available

69. $P(0) \approx 0.016796$
$P(1) \approx 0.089580$
$P(2) \approx 0.209019$
$P(3) \approx 0.278692$
$P(4) \approx 0.232243$
$P(5) \approx 0.123863$
$P(6) \approx 0.041288$
$P(7) \approx 0.007864$
$P(8) \approx 0.000655$

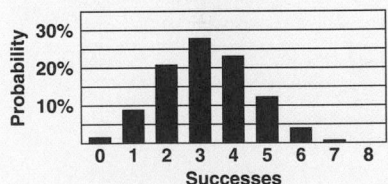

70. $P(0) \approx 0.000003$
$P(1) \approx 0.000082$
$P(2) \approx 0.001147$
$P(3) \approx 0.009175$
$P(4) \approx 0.045875$
$P(5) \approx 0.146801$
$P(6) \approx 0.293601$
$P(7) \approx 0.335544$
$P(8) \approx 0.167772$

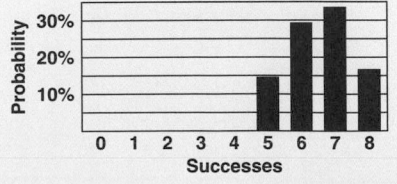

Reading a Diagram

Students learn to use information in a trigonometric ratio problem to create a diagram of a triangle, then use the diagram to find other trigonometric ratios.

Teaching Notes

For the sake of drawing a diagram to find trigonometric ratios, it does not matter which acute angle is labeled theta, nor which leg has length 3 or length $\sqrt{55}$. However, 3 is less than $\sqrt{55}$, so the angle theta should actually be the angle opposite the shorter leg.

Auditory Learners

Place students in pairs. Have one student read aloud the given information while the other student labels the diagram.

Exercise

Some students may mistakenly assume that the legs of this triangle have lengths of 3 and 4, with a hypotenuse length of 5. Caution students to draw the diagram after carefully analyzing the given ratio.

 **Reading Math**

Reading a Diagram

FOR USE WITH PAGE 783, EXERCISE 25

Read the solution of the problem below to understand how to use and read a diagram. Check your understanding with the exercise at the bottom of the page.

Sketch a right triangle with θ as the measure of an acute angle. Find the other five trigonometric ratios of θ.

$$\sin \theta = \frac{3}{8}$$

A diagram provides information in the form of a picture. Diagrams are often given, but this problem asks you to create a diagram based on certain information, and then use that diagram to find additional information.

What information am I given?

To create the diagram, you'll need to understand the given information. Begin with the definition of $\sin \theta$.

$$\sin \theta = \frac{\text{length of leg opposite } \theta}{\text{length of hypotenuse}} = \frac{3}{8}$$

This means that I should . . .

- draw a right triangle
- label one of its acute angles θ
- label the side opposite θ 3, and label the hypotenuse 8

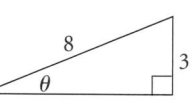

Using your diagram

The problem now asks you to find the other five trigonometric ratios of θ. To do this, you'll need to know the lengths of all three sides of the triangle, but if you look at your diagram, you'll notice that the length of one side is missing.

$$a^2 + b^2 = c^2 \qquad \textbf{Use the Pythagorean Theorem.}$$
$$a^2 + 3^2 = 8^2 \qquad \textbf{Substitute 3 for } b \textbf{ and 8 for } c.$$
$$a^2 + 9 = 64 \qquad \textbf{Simplify.}$$
$$a^2 = 55 \qquad \textbf{Subtract 9 from each side.}$$
$$a = \sqrt{55} \qquad \textbf{Take the square root of each side.}$$

Add this new piece of information to your diagram. Now you can find the other trigonometric ratios. Refer to page 779 for definitions, and refer to your diagram to substitute the corresponding information. Here's one.

$$\cos \theta = \frac{\text{length of leg adjacent to } \theta}{\text{length of hypotenuse}} = \frac{\sqrt{55}}{8}$$

EXERCISE

Suppose $\cos \theta = \frac{3}{4}$. Sketch a right triangle with θ as one of the acute angles. Find the five other trigonometric ratios of θ.

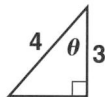

$\sin \theta = \frac{\sqrt{7}}{4}$, $\tan \theta = \frac{\sqrt{7}}{3}$,
$\cot \theta = \frac{3\sqrt{7}}{7}$, $\sec \theta = \frac{4}{3}$,
$\csc \theta = \frac{4\sqrt{7}}{7}$

786   **Reading Math**   Reading a Diagram

Area and the Law of Sines

Lesson Preview

What You'll Learn

OBJECTIVE
1 To find the area of any triangle and to use the Law of Sines

. . . And Why

To measure heights, as in Example 4

✓ Check Skills You'll Need

(For help, go to Lesson 13-4.)

Simplify each expression.

1. $\dfrac{\sin 30°}{6}$ **$\dfrac{1}{12}$**

2. $\dfrac{\sin 45°}{4}$ **$\dfrac{\sqrt{2}}{8}$**

3. $\dfrac{\sin 60°}{10}$ **$\dfrac{\sqrt{3}}{20}$**

4. $\dfrac{\sin 30°}{12}$ **$\dfrac{1}{24}$**

5. $\dfrac{\sin 45°}{8}$ **$\dfrac{\sqrt{2}}{16}$**

6. $\dfrac{\sin 60°}{9}$ **$\dfrac{\sqrt{3}}{18}$**

Find the area of a triangle with the given base b and height h.

7. $b = 3$ cm, $h = 4$ cm **6 cm^2**

8. $b = 6$ in., $h = 15$ in. **45 in.^{2}**

9. $b = 5.2$ mm, $h = 12.6$ mm **32.8 mm^2**

10. $b = 6.17$ ft, $h = 3.25$ ft **10.03 ft^2**

New Vocabulary • Law of Sines

Lesson Preview

✓ **Check Skills You'll Need**

The Sine Function
Lesson 13-4: Example 1
Exercises 1–6
Extra Practice, p. 834

Lesson Resources

 Teaching Resources
Practice, Reteaching, Enrichment

 Reaching All Students
Practice Workbook 14-4
Spanish Practice Workbook 14-4

 Presentation Assistant Plus!
Transparencies
• Check Skills You'll Need 14-4
• Additional Examples 14-4
• Student Edition Answers 14-4
• Lesson Quiz 14-4
PH Presentation Pro CD 14-4

 **ASSESSMENT SYSTEM**

Computer Test Generator CD

 Technology
Resource Pro® CD-ROM
Computer Test Generator CD
Prentice Hall Presentation Pro CD

 www.PHSchool.com
Student Site
• Teacher Web Code: agk-5500
• Self-grading Lesson Quiz
Teacher Center
• Lesson Planner
• Resources

Plus **iTEXT**

OBJECTIVE
1 Area and the Law of Sines

 Interactive lesson includes instant self-check, tutorials, and activities.

Need Help?

An oblique triangle is a triangle that does not contain a right angle.

The formula for the area K of a triangle is $K = \frac{1}{2}bh$.

In any oblique $\triangle ABC$ with side lengths $a, b,$ and $c, h = c \sin A$. Therefore $K = \frac{1}{2}bh = \frac{1}{2}bc \sin A$. Similarly, $K = \frac{1}{2}ac \sin B$ and $K = \frac{1}{2}ab \sin C$.

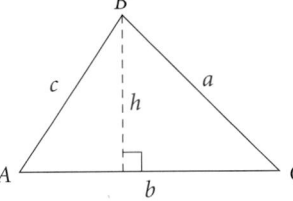

1 EXAMPLE Finding the Area of a Triangle

Find the area of the triangle at the right.

In the triangle, $b = 5, c = 10,$ and $m\angle A = 31°$.

$K = \frac{1}{2}bc \sin A = \frac{1}{2}(5)(10) \sin 31°$

≈ 12.9

● The area is about 12.9 mi^2.

✓ **Check Understanding** **1** A triangle has sides of lengths 12 in. and 15 in., and the measure of the angle between them is 24°. Find the area of the triangle. **36.6 in.^{2}**

Combining the three equations for the area of $\triangle ABC$ yields a useful formula.

$\frac{1}{2}bc \sin A = \frac{1}{2}ac \sin B = \frac{1}{2}ab \sin C$ **Transitive Property of Equality**

$\dfrac{\sin A}{a} = \dfrac{\sin B}{b} = \dfrac{\sin C}{c}$ **Divide by $\frac{1}{2}abc$.**

This relationship of the lengths of the sides of any triangle to the sines of the angles opposite them is known as the **Law of Sines.**

Ongoing Assessment and Intervention

Before the Lesson	During the Lesson	After the Lesson
Diagnose prerequisite skills using:	**Monitor progress using:**	**Assess knowledge using:**
• Check Skills You'll Need	• Check Understanding • Additional Examples • Standardized Test Prep	• Lesson Quiz • Computer Test Generator CD

Math Background

You can prove that, for any triangle, the area of the triangle is equal to one-half the product of the lengths of two sides and the sine of their included angle. From this it follows that the ratio of the sine of an angle to the length of the side opposite the angle is the same for all the angles of the triangle. This result is known as the Law of Sines.

OBJECTIVE

▼ 1 Teaching Notes

1 EXAMPLE Alternative Method

Show how to calculate the area of the triangle by using the altitude from the vertex of the obtuse angle to the longest side of the triangle. The altitude will have a length of $5 \sin 31°$. So the area will be $\frac{1}{2} \cdot 10 \cdot 5 \sin 31°$.

2 EXAMPLE Math Tip

Ask students why knowing two angle measures and one side length is always enough to permit them to find the remaining angle measure and side lengths. **You can subtract the sum of the given angle measures from 180° to find the measure of the third angle. You then have enough information to use the Law of Sines to find the remaining side lengths.**

4 EXAMPLE English Learners

You may need to explain that the *summit* of a mountain is the highest point on the mountain.

Additional Example

1 Find the area of the triangle shown below. $\approx 194.4\ cm^2$

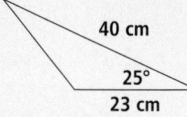

40 cm

25°

23 cm

788

🔑 Key Concepts

Theorem	Law of Sines

In $\triangle ABC$, let a, b, and c represent the lengths of the sides opposite $\angle A$, $\angle B$, and $\angle C$, respectively. Then $\frac{\sin A}{a} = \frac{\sin B}{b} = \frac{\sin C}{c}$.

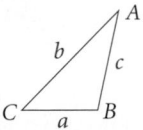

📖 Reading Math

In math, law refers to a general property. The Law of Sines could have been named the Property of Sines.

You can use the Law of Sines to find missing measures of any triangle when you know the measures of

- two angles and any side, or
- two sides and the angle opposite one of them.

In Example 2, you are given the measures of two angles and a side.

2 EXAMPLE Finding a Side of a Triangle

In $\triangle PQR$, $m\angle R = 39°$, $m\angle Q = 32°$, and $PQ = 40$ cm. Find RQ.

Step 1 Draw and label a diagram.

Step 2 Find the measure of the angle opposite $\overline{RQ}$.

$$m\angle P = 180° - 39° - 32° = 109°$$

Step 3 Find RQ.

$\dfrac{\sin 109°}{RQ} = \dfrac{\sin 39°}{40}$ **Law of Sines**

$RQ = \dfrac{40 \sin 109°}{\sin 39°}$ **Solve for RQ.**

$RQ \approx 60.1$ cm   **Use a calculator.**

✓ **Check Understanding** **2** In $\triangle KLM$, $m\angle K = 120°$, $m\angle M = 50°$, and $ML = 35$ yd. Find KL. **31.0 yd**

In Example 3, you are given the measures of two sides and an angle opposite one of the sides.

3 EXAMPLE Finding an Angle of a Triangle

In $\triangle RST$, $t = 7$, $r = 9$, and $m\angle R = 110°$. Find $m\angle S$.

Step 1 Draw and label a diagram.

Step 2 Find the measure of the angle opposite t.

$\dfrac{\sin T}{7} = \dfrac{\sin 110°}{9}$ **Law of Sines.**

$\sin T = \dfrac{7 \sin 110°}{9}$ **Solve for sin T.**

$m\angle T = \sin^{-1}\left(\dfrac{7 \sin 110°}{9}\right)$ **Solve for $m\angle T$.**

$m\angle T \approx 47°$ **Use a calculator.**

Step 3 Find the measure of $\angle S$.

$$m\angle S \approx 180° - 110° - 47° = 23°$$

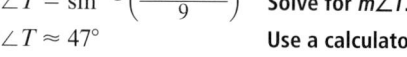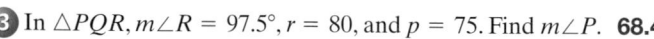

✓ **Check Understanding** **3** In $\triangle PQR$, $m\angle R = 97.5°$, $r = 80$, and $p = 75$. Find $m\angle P$. **68.4°**

👥 Reaching All Students

Below Level Make sure students understand that they only need to form a proportion with two of the ratios in the Law of Sines to solve for a missing angle or side length.	**Advanced Learners** Have students investigate what happens to the Law of Sines if angle C is a right angle. Ask students to share their results with the class.	**English Learners** See note on page 788. **Error Prevention** See note on page 790.

Surveyors can use the Law of Sines to indirectly measure the height of a mountain.

4 EXAMPLE **Real-World Connection**

Real-World Connection

The modern transit measures distances with a laser beam and stores data electronically.

Surveying A surveyor locates points A and B at the same elevation and 3950 ft apart. At A, the angle of elevation to the summit of the mountain is 18°. At B, the angle of elevation is 31°.

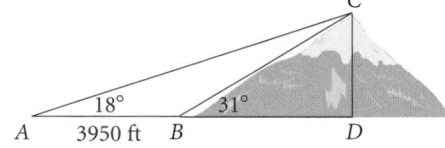

a. Find BC, the distance from B to the summit.

First find $m\angle ABC$ and $m\angle ACB$.

$m\angle ABC = 180° - 31° = 149°$
$m\angle ACB = 180° - 18° - 149° = 13°$

Now use the Law of Sines in $\triangle ABC$. Write a proportion that includes the side you know, AB, and the side you want, BC.

$\dfrac{\sin A}{BC} = \dfrac{\sin C}{AB}$ **Law of Sines**

$\dfrac{\sin 18°}{BC} = \dfrac{\sin 13°}{3950}$ **Substitute.**

$BC = \dfrac{3950 \sin 18°}{\sin 13°}$ **Solve for BC.**

$BC \approx 5426$ **Simplify.**

The distance from B to the summit is about 5426 ft.

b. Find CD, the height of the mountain.

In right $\triangle BCD$, you know BC and $m\angle B$. Use the sine ratio.

$\sin 31° \approx \dfrac{CD}{5426}$ **Definition of Sine**

$CD \approx 5426 \sin 31°$ **Solve for CD.**

$CD \approx 2795$ **Use a calculator.**

The summit is about 2795 ft higher than points A and B.

✔ Check Understanding **4** In $\triangle MNP$, $m\angle M = 35°$, $m\angle N = 120°$, and $MN = 48$. Find the length of the altitude of $\triangle MNP$ from vertex P.   **56.4**

EXERCISES

For more practice, see *Extra Practice*.

Practice and Problem Solving

 Practice by Example

Example 1
(page 787)

Find the area of each triangle. Round your answer to the nearest tenth.

1. **18.7 cm²**
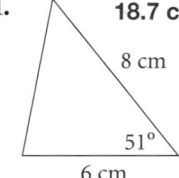
8 cm
51°
6 cm

2. **9.1 in.²**
10 in.
15°
7 in.

3. **81.9 m²**
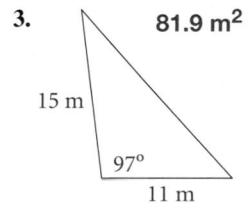
15 m
97°
11 m

4. A triangle has sides of lengths 10 cm and 16 cm, and the measure of the angle between them is 130°. Find the area of the triangle. **61.3 cm²**

Lesson 14-4 Area and the Law of Sines   **789**

Additional Examples

2 In $\triangle ABC$, $m\angle A = 33°$, $m\angle C = 64°$, and $BC = 8$ cm. Find AC. ≈ **14.6 cm**

3 In $\triangle PQR$, $p = 7$ in., $q = 10$ in., and $m\angle Q = 98°$. Find $m\angle R$. ≈ **38°**

4 Two observers view the same mountain peak from two points on level ground and 2 miles apart, as shown in the diagram. The angle of elevation at T to the peak for the observer most distant from the mountain is 31°. For the other observer, the angle of elevation at S to the peak is 58°.
a. Find TK, the distance from T to the summit. ≈ **3.74 mi**
b. Find RK, the height of the mountain. ≈ **1.93 mi**

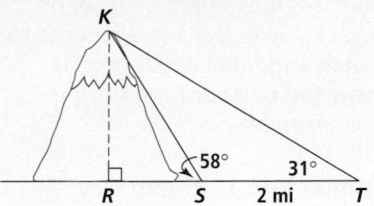

Closure

Have students write a paragraph explaining how they can find the area of a triangle if they know the measures of its sides and angles. **Find half the product of the measures of two sides and the sine of their included angle.** Ask: *What information must be given to use the Law of Sines to find missing measures of any triangle?* **Answers may vary: Sample: two angles and any side, or, two sides and the angle opposite one of them**

789

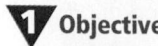

Assignment Guide

1 Objective

Ⓐ Ⓑ Core 1–42

Ⓒ Extension 43–45

Standardized Test Prep 46–49

Mixed Review 50–63

Error Prevention

Exercises 8–10 Students who do not sketch diagrams for these exercises may apply the Law of Sines incorrectly. Urge students to sketch and label a diagram to show the given information for each exercise.

Connection to Geometry

Exercise 29 Be sure students recall the relevant inequality theorem from geometry. An angle of greater measure is always opposite a side of greater length.

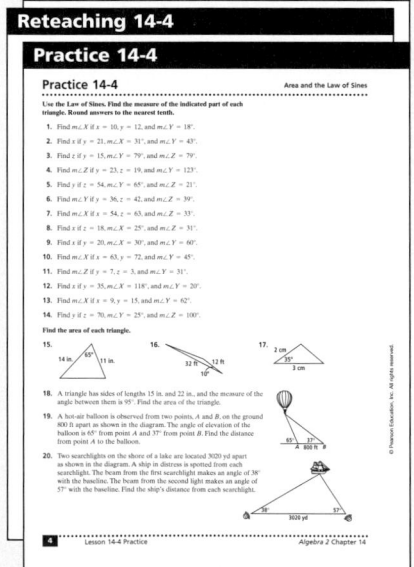

Enrichment 14-4

Reteaching 14-4

Practice 14-4

Example 2
(page 788)

Use the Law of Sines. Find the measure x to the nearest tenth.

5.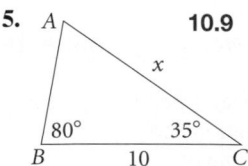

6.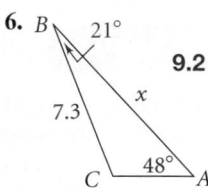

7.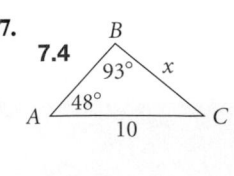

8. In $\triangle RST$, $m\angle R = 78°$, $m\angle T = 39°$, and $TS = 19$ in. Find RS. **12.2 in.**

9. In $\triangle JKL$, $m\angle L = 64°$, $j = 18$ m, and $m\angle K = 36°$. Find k. **10.7 m**

10. In $\triangle RNP$, $m\angle N = 58°$, $n = 20$ in., and $m\angle R = 42°$. Find r. **15.8 in.**

Example 3
(page 788)

Use the Law of Sines. Find the measure x to the nearest tenth.

11.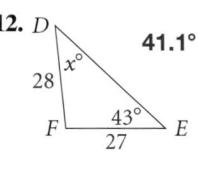

12.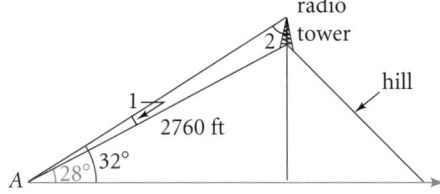

13. In $\triangle DEF$, $m\angle F = 43°$, $d = 16$ mm, and $f = 24$ mm. Find $m\angle D$. **27.0°**

14. In $\triangle ABC$, $m\angle A = 52°$, $c = 10$ ft, and $a = 15$ ft. Find $m\angle C$. **31.7°**

15. In $\triangle XYZ$, $m\angle Z = 33°$, $z = 35$ cm, and $x = 31$ cm. Find $m\angle X$. **28.8°**

Example 4
(page 789)

16. **Surveying** The distance from point A to the top of the hill is 2760 ft. The angle of elevation from A to the base of the tower is 28° and the angle of elevation from A to the top of the tower is 32°.

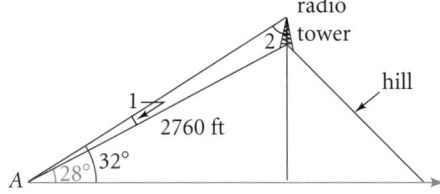

a. Find the measures of $\angle 1$ and $\angle 2$. **$m\angle 1 = 4°$, $m\angle 2 = 58°$**

b. Find to the nearest foot the height of the tower above the top of the hill. **227 ft**

Ⓑ **Apply Your Skills**

Find the remaining sides and angles in each triangle. Round your answers to the nearest tenth.   20–24. See margin.

17. $m\angle D = 100°$,
$e = 22.3°$,
$f = 34.2$

17.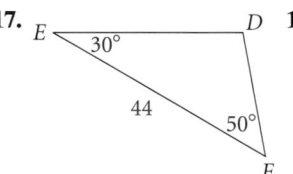

18.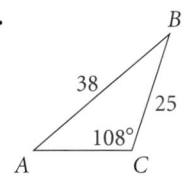

19.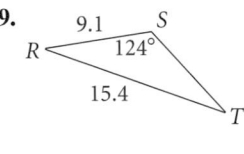

18. $m\angle A = 38.70$,
$m\angle B = 33.3°$,
$b = 21.9$

19. $m\angle T = 29.3°$,
$m\angle R = 26.7°$,
$r = 8.3$

20.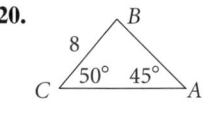

21.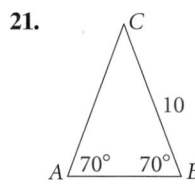

22.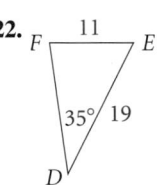

23. In $\triangle DEF$, $m\angle D = 54°$, $m\angle E = 54°$, and $d = 20$ in.

24. In $\triangle DEF$, $m\angle D = 54°$, $e = 8$ m, and $d = 10$ m.

pages 789–792   Exercises

20. $m\angle B = 85°$, $b = 11.3$,
$c = 8.7$

21. $m\angle C = 40°$, $b = 10$,
$c = 6.8$

22. $m\angle E = 62.8°$,
$m\angle F = 82.2°$, $e = 17.1$

23. $m\angle F = 72°$, $e = 20$ in.,
$f = 23.5$

24. $m\angle E = 40.3°$,
$m\angle F = 85.7°$, $f = 12.3$ m

25. Critical Thinking In $\triangle ABC$, $a = 10$ and $b = 15$. **a–c. See margin.**
   a. Does the triangle have a greater area when $m\angle C = 1°$ or when $m\angle C = 50°$?
   b. Does the triangle have a greater area when $m\angle C = 50°$ or when $m\angle C = 179°$?
   c. For what measure of $\angle C$ does $\triangle ABC$ have the greatest area? Explain.

26. a. Open-Ended Sketch a triangle. Specify three of its measures so that you can use the Law of Sines to find the remaining measures.
   b. Solve for the remaining measures of the triangle. **Check students' work.**

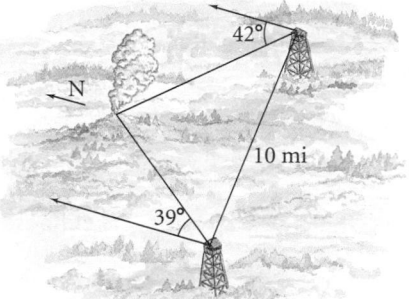

27. Forestry A forest ranger in an observation tower sights a fire 39° east of north. A ranger in a tower 10 miles due east of the first tower sights the fire at 42° west of north. How far is the fire from each tower? **7.5 mi, 7.9 mi**

28. Geometry One of the congruent sides of an isosceles triangle is 10 cm long. One of the congruent angles has a measure of 54°. Find the perimeter of the triangle. Round your answer to the nearest centimeter. **32 cm**

29. Geometry The sides of a triangle are 15 in., 17 in., and 16 in. long. The smallest angle has a measure of 53°. Find the measure of the largest angle. Round your answer to the nearest degree. **65°**

Find the area of $\triangle ABC$. Round your answer to the nearest tenth.

30. $m\angle C = 68°$, $b = 12.9$, $c = 15.2$ **77.1**   **31.** $m\angle A = 52°$, $a = 9.71$, $c = 9.33$ **44.5**

32. $m\angle A = 23°$, $m\angle C = 39°$, $b = 14.6$ **33.** $m\angle B = 87°$, $a = 10.1$, $c = 9.8$ **49.4**

34. $m\angle A = 96°$, $m\angle C = 18°$, $a = 43.4$ **35.** $m\angle C = 33°$, $a = 1.2$, $b = 0.9$ **0.5**

36. $m\angle B = 40°$, $m\angle C = 80°$, $c = 5.5$ **6.3**   **37.** $m\angle A = 20°$, $b = 1$, $c = 5$ **0.9**

32. 33.6
34. 267.6

In $\triangle ABC$, $m\angle A = 40°$ and $m\angle B = 30°$. Find each value to the nearest tenth.

38. Find AC for $BC = 10.5$ m. **8.2 m**   **39.** Find BC for $AC = 21.8$ ft. **28.0 ft**

40. Find AC for $AB = 81.2$ yd. **43.2 yd**   **41.** Find BC for $AB = 5.9$ cm. **4.0 cm**

42. Measurement A vacant lot is in the shape of an isosceles triangle. It is between two streets that intersect at an 85.9° angle. Each of the sides of the lot that face these streets is 150 ft long. Find the length of the third side, to the nearest foot. **204.4 ft**

C Challenge **43. Sailing** Buoys are located in the sea at points A, B, and C. $\angle ACB$ is a right angle. $AC = 3.0$ mi, $BC = 4.0$ mi, and $AB = 5.0$ mi. A ship is located at point D on $\overline{AB}$ so that $m\angle ACD = 30°$. How far is the ship from the buoy at point C? Round your answer to the nearest tenth of a mile. **2.4 miles**

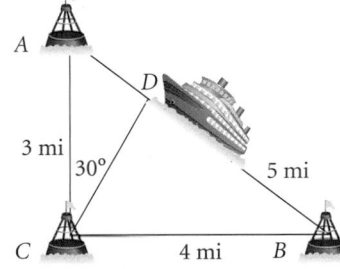

44. Writing Suppose you know the measures of all three angles of a triangle. Can you use the Law of Sines to find the lengths of the sides? Explain. **No; you need at least one side in order to set up a proportion you can solve.**

Lesson 14-4 Area and the Law of Sines **791**

25a. **when $m\angle C = 50$**

  b. **when $m\angle C = 50$**

  c. **90°; a right triangle has the greatest height.**

---

4. Assess

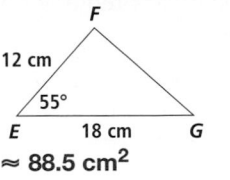

Lesson Quiz 14-4

1. Find the area of $\triangle EFG$.

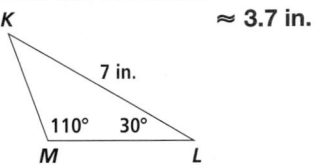

  ≈ 88.5 cm²

2. Find KM in $\triangle KLM$. **≈ 3.7 in.**

3. In $\triangle ABC$, $m\angle A = 56°$, $AB = 11$ ft, and $BC = 13$ ft. Find $m\angle C$. **≈ 44.5°**

4. In $\triangle PQR$, $m\angle P = 49°$, $m\angle R = 37°$, and $PR = 26$ cm. Find QR and the area of $\triangle PQR$. **≈ 19.7 cm; ≈ 154 cm²**

Alternative Assessment

Have students work in groups of three. Ask each student to create two problems about triangles. One problem should involve finding the area of a triangle, given the lengths of two sides and the measure of the included angle. The other problem should involve using the Law of Sines to find a missing side length or angle measure. Each student should solve the problems created by the other two students. Ask students to check one another's work. If students create problems that are examples of the ambiguous case, point out that they will learn how to solve these triangles in the Extension for use with Lesson 14-4.

Resources

For additional practice with a variety of test item formats:
- Standardized Test Prep, p. 817
- Test-Taking Strategies, p. 812
- Test-Taking Strategies with Transparencies

Exercise 49 This exercise does not require trigonometry. Plane geometry is sufficient.

pages 789–792   Exercises

54. $a = 3, m\angle A = 36.9°,$ $m\angle C = 53.1°$

55. $b = 3\sqrt{2}, m\angle A = 45°,$ $m\angle C = 45°$

56. $c = 11.2, m\angle A = 41.8°,$ $m\angle C = 48.2°$

57. $b = 8.3, m\angle A = 11.1°,$ $m\angle C = 78.9°$

58. $c = 8.5, m\angle A = 25.9°,$ $m\angle C = 64.1°$

59. $c = 89.3, m\angle A = 63.3°,$ $m\angle C = 26.7°$

60.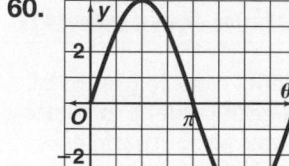

61.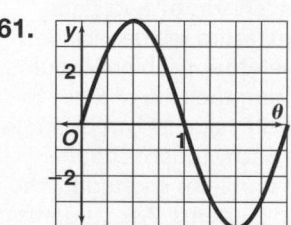

62.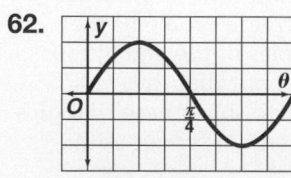

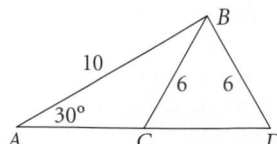

45. a. In the diagram at the left, $m\angle A = 30°$, $AB = 10$, and $BC = BD = 6$. Use the Law of Sines to find $m\angle D$. **56.4°**
b. Find $m\angle ABD$ and $m\angle ABC$. **93.6°, 26.4°**
c. Reasoning Notice that two sides and a nonincluded angle of $\triangle ABC$ are congruent to the corresponding parts of $\triangle ABD$, but the triangles are not congruent. Must $\triangle EFG$ be congruent to $\triangle ABD$ if $EF = 10$, $FG = 6$, and $\angle E \cong \angle A$? Explain. **No; $\triangle EFG$ could be congruent to $\triangle ABC$ instead of $\triangle ABD$.**

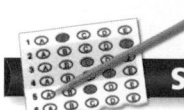

Quantitative Comparison

Use the triangle at the right for Questions 46–49. Compare the boxed quantity in Column A with the boxed quantity in Column B. Choose the best answer.
A. The quantity in Column A is greater.
B. The quantity in Column B is greater.
C. The two quantities are equal.
D. The relationship cannot be determined from the information given.

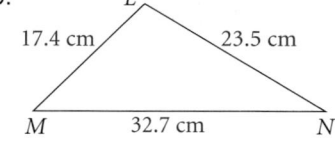

Take It to the NET
Online lesson quiz at
www.PHSchool.com
Web Code: aga-1404

	Column A	Column B
46. A	$\dfrac{\sin M}{\sin N}$	$\dfrac{\sin N}{\sin M}$
47. B	$\dfrac{\sin N}{\sin L}$	$\dfrac{\sin L}{\sin N}$
48. B	$\dfrac{\sin M}{\sin L}$	$\dfrac{\sin L}{\sin M}$
49. C	the product of MN and the length of the altitude from L	the product of ML and the length of the altitude from N

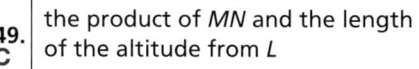
Mixed Review

Lesson 14-3   Find each angle measure to the nearest tenth of a degree.

50. 53.1°
51. 24.6°
52. 38.7°
53. 54.7°

50. $\cos^{-1}\dfrac{3}{5}$ **51.** $\tan^{-1} 0.4569$ **52.** $\sin^{-1}\dfrac{5}{8}$ **53.** $\tan^{-1}\sqrt{2}$

In $\triangle ABC$, $\angle B$ is a right angle. Find the remaining sides and angles. Round your answers to the nearest tenth. **54–59. See margin.**

54. $b = 5, c = 4$ **55.** $a = 3, c = 3$ **56.** $a = 10, b = 15$
57. $a = 1.6, c = 8.1$ **58.** $a = 4.1, b = 9.4$ **59.** $b = 100, c = 45$

Lesson 13-4   Sketch one cycle of the graph of each sine function. **60–62. See margin.**

60. $y = 4 \sin \theta$ **61.** $y = 4 \sin \pi\theta$ **62.** $y = \sin 4\theta$

Lesson 12-4   **63.** A set of values has a mean of 36 and a standard deviation of 5. Find the z-score of the value 43. $\dfrac{7}{5}$

The Ambiguous Case

The triangles at the right have one pair of congruent angles and two pairs of congruent sides. But the triangles are not congruent. Notice that each of the congruent angles is opposite one of the congruent sides.

When you know the measures of two sides of a triangle and one of the opposite angles, there may be two triangles with those measurements. You can use the Law of Sines to find the other measures for both triangles.

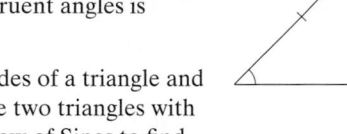

EXAMPLE

In each $\triangle ABC$ at the right, $m\angle A = 35°$, $a = 11$, and $b = 15$. Find $m\angle B$.

$\dfrac{\sin A}{a} = \dfrac{\sin B}{b}$ **Law of Sines**

$\dfrac{\sin 35°}{11} = \dfrac{\sin B}{15}$ **Substitute.**

$\sin B = \dfrac{15 \sin 35°}{11}$ **Solve for sin B.**

$m\angle B \approx \sin^{-1}\left(\dfrac{15 \sin 35°}{11}\right)$ **Find one value of m∠B.**

$m\angle B \approx 51°$ **Use a calculator.**

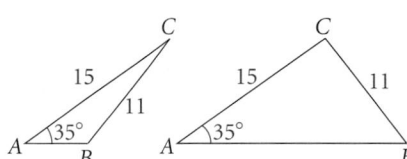

The sine function is also positive in Quadrant II. So another value of $m\angle B$ is about $180° - 51° = 129°$.

Because there are two possible angle measures for $\angle B$, there are two triangles that satisfy the given conditions. In one triangle the angle measures are about 35°, 51°, and 94°. In the other, the angle measures are about 35°, 129°, and 16°.

EXERCISES

In each $\triangle ABC$, find the measures for $\angle B$ and $\angle C$ that satisfy the given conditions. Draw diagrams to help you decide whether two triangles are possible. Remember that a triangle can have only one obtuse angle. **1–4. See margin.**

1. $m\angle A = 62°$, $a = 30$, and $b = 32$

2. $m\angle A = 16°$, $a = 12$, and $b = 37.5$

3. $m\angle A = 48°$, $a = 93$, and $b = 125$

4. $m\angle A = 112°$, $a = 16.5$, and $b = 5.4$

5. $m\angle A = 23.6°$, $a = 9.8$, and $b = 17$
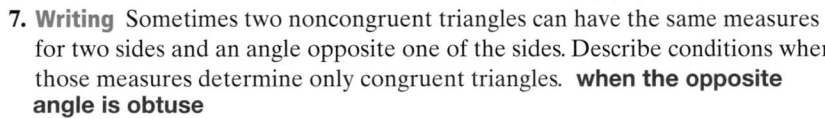
44.0° and 112.4°, or 136.0° and 20.4°

6. $m\angle A = 155°$, $a = 12.5$, and $b = 8.4$
16.5° and 8.5°

7. Writing Sometimes two noncongruent triangles can have the same measures for two sides and an angle opposite one of the sides. Describe conditions when those measures determine only congruent triangles. **when the opposite angle is obtuse**

Extension

The Ambiguous Case

This extension will demonstrate the need for caution when using the Law of Sines to find missing side lengths and angle measures in a triangle.

Resources

protractor, compass, centimeter ruler, graphing calculator

Teaching Notes

Teaching Tip
You may need to provide some guidance if students have trouble drawing the diagrams for Exercises 1–6. Suggest that they use millimeters for side lengths.

Error Prevention
Students may fail to see that two sets of angle measures are possible for Exercises 1–3 and 5. Urge them to draw diagrams for the exercises *before* they undertake the calculations.

page 793   Extension

1. **70.4 and 47.6°, or 109.6° and 8.4°**

2. **59.5° and 104.5°, or 120.5° and 43.5°**

3. **87.3° and 44.7°, or 92.7° and 39.3°**

4. **17.7° and 50.3°**

Lesson Preview

 Check Skills You'll Need

Area and the Law of Sines
Lesson 14-4: Example 3
Exercises 10–14
Extra Practice, p. 835

Lesson Preview

What You'll Learn

 OBJECTIVE 1
To use the Law of Cosines in finding the measures of sides and angles of a triangle

... And Why

To find the length of a sailing course, as in Example 1

 Check Skills You'll Need   (For help, go to Lesson 14-4.)

Use the Law of Sines.

1. In $\triangle ABC$, $m\angle C = 33°$, $a = 17$, and $c = 21$. Find $m\angle A$. **26.2°**

2. In $\triangle RST$, $m\angle R = 59°$, $m\angle S = 45°$, and $r = 16$. Find t. **18.1**

3. In $\triangle DEF$, $m\angle D = 55°$, $d = 18$, and $e = 21$. Find $m\angle F$. **52.1°**

New Vocabulary • Law of Cosines

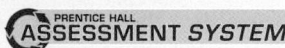

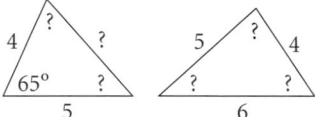 Interactive lesson includes instant self-check, tutorials, and activities.

OBJECTIVE 1 The Law of Cosines

Since you can't use the Law of Sines to find the missing measures in the triangles at the right, another formula is needed.

In this oblique $\triangle ABC$ with altitude h, let $AD = x$.

Then $DB = c - x$.

In $\triangle ADC$,
$b^2 = x^2 + h^2$ and
$\cos A = \frac{x}{b}$ or $x = b \cos A$.

In $\triangle CBD$,

$$a^2 = (c - x)^2 + h^2$$ **Pythagorean Theorem**
$$= c^2 - 2cx + x^2 + h^2$$ **Square the binomial.**
$$= c^2 - 2cx + b^2$$ **Substitute b^2 for $x^2 + h^2$.**
$$= c^2 - 2cb \cos A + b^2$$ **Substitute $b \cos A$ for x.**
$$= b^2 + c^2 - 2bc \cos A$$ **Commutative Property of Addition**

The last equation relates the length of a side of any triangle to the measure of the opposite angle. It applies to any of the three sides and is called the **Law of Cosines.**

 Key Concepts

Theorem	**Law of Cosines**

In $\triangle ABC$, let a, b, and c represent the lengths of the sides opposite $\angle A$, $\angle B$, and $\angle C$, respectively.

$$a^2 = b^2 + c^2 - 2bc \cos A$$

$$b^2 = a^2 + c^2 - 2ac \cos B$$

$$c^2 = a^2 + b^2 - 2ab \cos C$$

 Ongoing Assessment and Intervention

Before the Lesson
Diagnose prerequisite skills using:
• Check Skills You'll Need

During the Lesson
Monitor progress using:
• Check Understanding
• Additional Examples
• Standardized Test Prep

After the Lesson
Assess knowledge using:
• Lesson Quiz
• Computer Test Generator CD

You can use the Law of Cosines to find missing measures in any triangle when you know the measures of

- two sides and the angle between them, or
- all three sides.

Real-World Connection

One leg of a race course is laid out close to the wind to test the capability of the boats and the skill of the crews.

In this example, you are given the measures of two sides and the included angle.

1 EXAMPLE Real-World Connection

Sailing A racing committee wants to lay out a triangular course with a 40° angle between two sides of 3.5 mi and 2.5 mi. What will be the length of the third side?

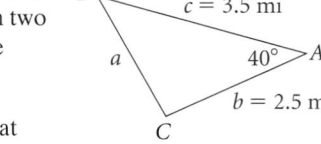

Choose the form of the Law of Cosines that has a^2 on one side.

$a^2 = b^2 + c^2 - 2bc \cos A$

$a^2 = 2.5^2 + 3.5^2 - 2(2.5)(3.5) \cos 40°$ **Substitute.**

≈ 5.094 **Use a calculator.**

$a \approx 2.3$ **Use a calculator.**

The third side of the triangular course will be about 2.3 mi long.

✓ **Check Understanding** ❶ The lengths of two sides of a triangle are 8 and 10, and the measure of the angle between them is 40°. Find the length of the third side. **6.4**

In this example, you are given the measures of three sides.

2 EXAMPLE Finding an Angle Measure

Find the measure of $\angle C$ in the triangle below. Round your answer to the nearest tenth of a degree.

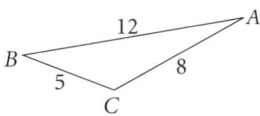

Choose the form of the Law of Cosines that contains $\angle C$.

$c^2 = a^2 + b^2 - 2ab \cos C$

$12^2 = 5^2 + 8^2 - 2(5)(8) \cos C$ **Substitute.**

$144 = 25 + 64 - 80 \cos C$ **Simplify.**

$55 = -80 \cos C$ **Combine like terms.**

$-\frac{55}{80} = \cos C$ **Solve for cos C.**

$\cos^{-1}\left(-\frac{55}{80}\right) = m\angle C$ **Solve for $m\angle C$.**

$m\angle C \approx 133.4°$ **Use a calculator.**

✓ **Check Understanding** ❷ The lengths of the sides of a triangle are 10, 14, and 15. Find the measure of the angle opposite the longest side. **75.3°**

Lesson 14-5   The Law of Cosines   **795**

---

2. Teach

Professional Development ★

Math Background

The Law of Cosines is, in a sense, an extension of the Pythagorean Theorem. But while the Pythagorean Theorem applies only to right triangles, the Law of Cosines applies to all triangles.

OBJECTIVE
1 Teaching Notes

2 EXAMPLE Tactile Learners

Students can cut narrow strips of paper to the lengths given and fit them together to form a triangle to convince themselves that all triangles with these side lengths are congruent.

Additional Examples

❶ Suppose two stars are 9.5 and 4.6 light years from Earth. When an astronomer observes the stars with the Earth as vertex, the angle between the stars is about 43°. What is the approximate distance between the stars? **≈ 6.9 light years**

❷ A triangle has sides of lengths 9 cm, 11 cm, and 14 cm. Find the measure of the angle opposite the longest side. Round your answer to the nearest tenth of a degree. **≈ 88.3°**

❸ In $\triangle PQR$, $r = 10$, $q = 12$, and $m\angle P = 32°$. Find $m\angle Q$. **≈ 91.6°**

Closure

Ask students to state the Law of Cosines in words. **The square of the length of any side of a triangle is equal to the sum of the squares of the lengths of the other two sides minus twice the product of the cosine of their included angle and the lengths of these two sides.**

795

Assignment Guide

▼ Objective

Ⓐ Ⓑ **Core** 1–49

Ⓒ **Extension** 50–52

Standardized Test Prep 53–58

Mixed Review 59–67

Error Prevention

Exercises 15–17 Students may have errors that result from rounding to too few decimals places at intermediate stages of the solution process. Since students will be using calculators for these exercises, encourage them to use several decimal places, if they use intermediate rounding, to ensure that the final answer will have the desired accuracy.

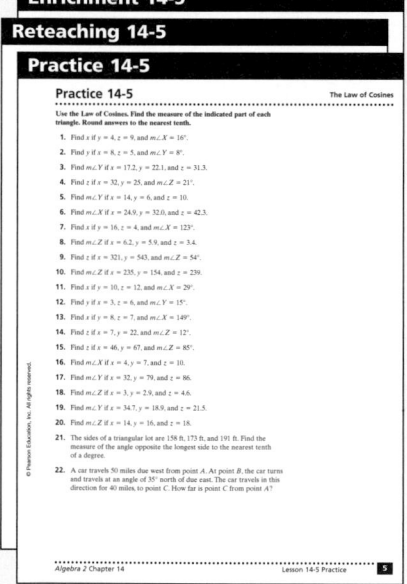

Sometimes you need to use the Law of Cosines followed by the Law of Cosines again or by the Law of Sines.

3 EXAMPLE Finding an Angle Measure

In $\triangle ABC$, $b = 6.2$, $c = 7.8$, and $m\angle A = 45°$. Find $m\angle B$.

Step 1 Draw a diagram.

Step 2 Find a. Since you cannot find $m\angle B$ directly, use the Law of Cosines to find a.

$a^2 = b^2 + c^2 - 2bc \cos A$

$a^2 = 6.2^2 + 7.8^2 - 2(6.2)(7.8) \cos 45°$ **Substitute.**

≈ 30.89 **Simplify.**

$a \approx \sqrt{30.89}$ **Solve for a.**

$a \approx 5.56$ **Find the principal square root.**

Step 3 Now you can use the Law of Sines or the Law of Cosines to find $m\angle B$.

$\dfrac{\sin B}{6.2} \approx \dfrac{\sin 45°}{5.56}$ **Law of Sines**

$\sin B \approx \dfrac{6.2 \sin 45°}{5.56}$ **Solve for sin B.**

$m\angle B \approx \sin^{-1}\left(\dfrac{6.2 \sin 45°}{5.56}\right)$ **Solve for m∠B. (∠B is not obtuse because b < c.)**

$\approx 52°$ **Use a calculator.**

? Need Help?

To help remember the formulas for the Law of Cosines, notice that the first and last letters are the same and the last one is capitalized.

✓ **Check Understanding** ❸ In $\triangle RST$, $s = 41$, $t = 53$, and $m\angle R = 126°$. Find $m\angle T$. **30.7°**

EXERCISES

For more practice, see *Extra Practice*.

Practice and Problem Solving

Ⓐ **Practice by Example**

Example 1
(page 795)

Use the Law of Cosines. Find the length of x to the nearest tenth.

1.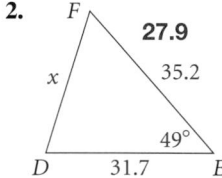

2.

3.

4. In $\triangle DEF$, $m\angle E = 54°$, $d = 14$ ft, and $f = 20$ ft. Find e. **16.3 ft**

5. In $\triangle RST$, $m\angle T = 32°$, $r = 10$ cm, and $s = 17$ cm. Find t. **10.0 cm**

6. In $\triangle ABC$, $m\angle B = 52°$, $a = 15$ in., and $c = 10$ in. Find b. **11.8 in.**

Example 2
(page 795)

Use the Law of Cosines. Find the measure of x to the nearest tenth of a degree.

7. **47.3°**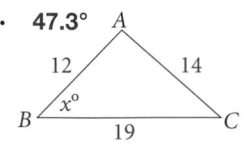

8. **27.0°**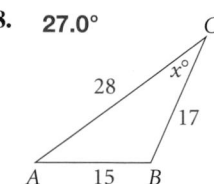

9. **125.1°**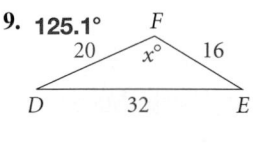

796 Chapter 14 Trigonometric Identities and Equations

10. In $\triangle DEF$, $d = 15$ in., $e = 18$ in., and $f = 10$ in. Find $m\angle F$. **33.7°**

11. In $\triangle ABC$, $a = 20$ m, $b = 14$ m, and $c = 16$ m. Find $m\angle A$. **83.3°**

12. In $\triangle DEF$, $d = 12$ ft, $e = 10$ ft, and $f = 9$ ft. Find $m\angle F$. **47.2°**

Example 3
(page 796)

Use the Law of Cosines and the Law of Sines. Find x to the nearest tenth.

13.

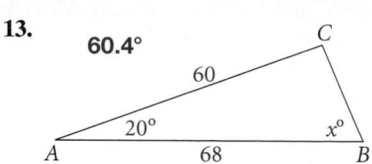

14. 50.9°

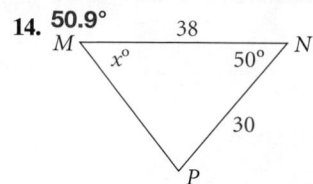

15. In $\triangle ABC$, $b = 4$ in., $c = 6$ in., and $m\angle A = 69°$. Find $m\angle C$. **71.7°**

16. In $\triangle RST$, $r = 17$ cm, $s = 12$ cm, and $m\angle T = 13°$. Find $m\angle S$. **26.7°**

17. In $\triangle DEF$, $d = 20$ ft, $e = 25$ ft, and $m\angle F = 98°$. Find $m\angle D$. **35.5°**

B **Apply Your Skills**

For each triangle, write the correct form of the Law of Cosines or the Law of Sines to solve for the measure in red. Use only the information given in blue.

18. $b^2 = a^2 + c^2 - 2ab \cos B$

19. $c^2 = a^2 + b^2 - 2ab \cos C$

20. $\dfrac{\sin B}{b} = \dfrac{\sin C}{c}$

21. $\dfrac{\sin A}{a} = \dfrac{\sin B}{b}$

18.

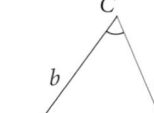

19.

20.

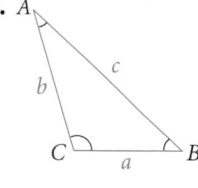

21.

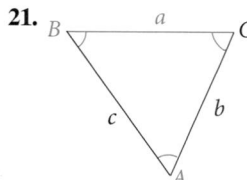

22.

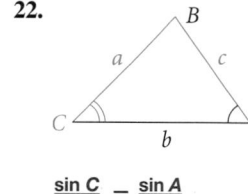

$\dfrac{\sin C}{c} = \dfrac{\sin A}{a}$

23.

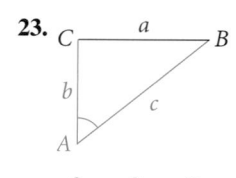

$a^2 = b^2 + c^2 - 2bc \cos A$

Find the remaining sides and angles in each triangle. Round your answers to the nearest tenth. 24–29. See margin.

24.

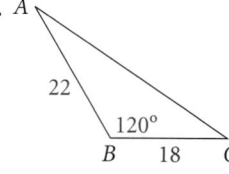

25.

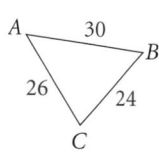

26.

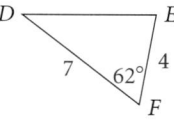

27.

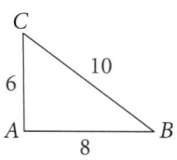

28.

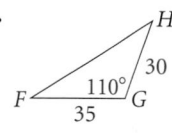

29.

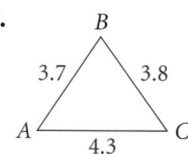

30. a. Open-Ended Sketch a triangle. Specify three of its measures so that you can use the Law of Cosines to find the remaining measures.
   b. Solve for the remaining measures of the triangle.
   a–b. Check students' work.

31. Sports A softball diamond is a square that is 65 ft on a side. The pitcher's mound is 46 ft from home plate. How far is the pitcher from third base? **38.9 ft**

Exercise 31 Some students may not be familiar with softball. You may want to call on a volunteer to explain how it differs from baseball.

pages 796–799 Exercises

24. $b = 34.7$, $m\angle A = 26.7°$, $m\angle B = 33.3°$

25. $m\angle A = 50.1°$, $m\angle B = 56.3°$, $m\angle C = 73.6°$

26. $f = 5.5$, $m\angle D = 42.5°$, $m\angle E = 75.5°$

27. $m\angle A = 90°$, $m\angle B = 36.9°$, $m\angle C = 53.1°$

28. $g = 53.3$, $m\angle F = 31.9°$, $m\angle H = 38.1°$

29. $m\angle A = 56.1°$, $m\angle B = 70°$, $m\angle C = 53.9°$

Alternative Assessment

Ask students to create three problems that involve finding missing measures of sides or angles of triangles. Each problem should be solvable by making use of the Law of Cosines. Ask students to draw diagrams to show the given information. Then ask them to solve each problem. Have them discuss their problems with a neighbor to verify their results.

English Learners

Exercise 34 Use a map or compass to help explain what is meant by *due north, change course,* and *east of north.*

pages 796–799   Exercises

32. Assume one side is 1. Then use that side and its corresponding angle to find the ratio of the lengths of the other two sides.

Real-World 🌐 Connection

Careers Pilots need navigation skills that include plotting a course on an aeronautical chart and computing flight time, headings, and fuel requirements.

49. Yes; since cos 90° = 0, $c^2 = a^2 + b^2 - 2ab \cos C$ reduces to $c^2 = a^2 + b^2$.

C Challenge

✏️ 32. **Writing** Given the measures of three angles of a triangle, explain how to find the ratio of the lengths of two sides of the triangle. **See margin.**

📦 33. **Geometry** The lengths of the sides of a triangle are 7.6 cm, 8.2 cm, and 5.2 cm. Find the measure of the largest angle. **77.2°**

🌐 34. **Navigation** A pilot is flying from city A to city B, which is 85 mi due north. After flying 20 mi, the pilot must change course and fly 10° east of north to avoid a cloudbank.
   a. If the pilot remains on this course for 20 mi, how far will the plane be from city B? **45.4 mi**
   b. How many degrees will the pilot have to turn to the left to fly directly to city B? How many degrees from due north is this course?
   14.4° left; 4.4° west of north

In △*ABC*, *m*∠*A* = 53° and *c* = 7 cm. Find each value to the nearest tenth.

35. Find *m*∠*B* for *b* = 6.2 cm. **57.1°**   36. Find *a* for *b* = 13.7 cm. **11.0 cm**

37. Find *a* for *b* = 11 cm. **8.8 cm**   38. Find *m*∠*C* for *b* = 15.2 cm. **27.0°**

39. Find *m*∠*B* for *b* = 37 cm. **62.5°**   40. Find *a* for *b* = 16 cm. **13.0 cm**

In △*RST*, *t* = 7 ft and *s* = 13 ft. Find each value to the nearest tenth.

41. Find *m*∠*T* for *r* = 11 ft. **32.6°**   42. Find *m*∠*T* for *r* = 6.97 ft. **21.5°**

43. Find *m*∠*S* for *r* = 14 ft. **67.2°**   44. Find *r* for *m*∠*R* = 35°. **8.3 ft**

45. Find *m*∠*S* for *m*∠*R* = 87°. **64.4°**   46. Find *m*∠*R* for *m*∠*S* = 70°. **80.0°**

📦 47. **Geometry** The lengths of the adjacent sides of a parallelogram are 54 cm and 78 cm. The larger angle measures 110°. What is the length of the longer diagonal? Round your answer to the nearest centimeter. **109 cm**

📦 48. **Geometry** The lengths of the adjacent sides of a parallelogram are 21 cm and 14 cm. The smaller angle measures 58°. What is the length of the shorter diagonal? Round your answer to the nearest centimeter. **18 cm**

49. **Critical Thinking** Does the Law of Cosines apply to a right triangle? That is, does $c^2 = a^2 + b^2 - 2ab \cos C$ remain true when ∠*C* is a right angle? Justify your answer.

🌐 50. **Physics** A pendulum 36 in. long swings 30° from the vertical. How high above the horizontal is the pendulum at the end of its swing? Round your answer to the nearest tenth of an inch. **4.8 in.**

51. **a.** Find the length of the altitude to $\overline{PQ}$ in the triangle below. **2.1 m**
    b. Find the area of △*PQR*. **9.975 m²**

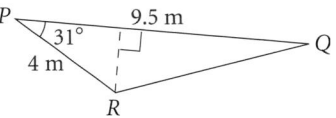

52. Find *x* in △*ABC*. **3.0**

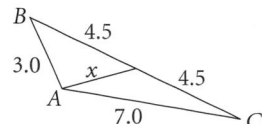

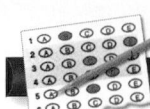
Gridded Response

Use the diagram below for Questions 53–58.

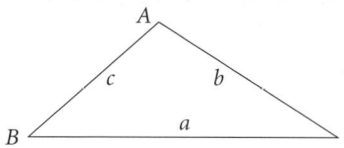

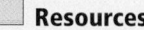
53. Let $a = 23.2$, $b = 18.5$, and $m\angle C = 42°$. Find c to the nearest tenth. **15.6**

54. Use the information in Question 53 to find $m\angle A$ to the nearest tenth. **85.4°**

55. Suppose $a = 45.25$, $b = 39.75$, and $c = 20.65$. Find $m\angle B$ to the nearest tenth. **61.4**

56. Use the information in Question 55 to find $m\angle C$ to the nearest tenth. **27.1**

57. Suppose $b = 11.0$, $c = 11.7$, and $m\angle A = 22$. Find the length of the altitude from A to the nearest hundredth. **10.99**

58. Use the information in Question 57 to find the area of $\triangle ABC$ to the nearest tenth. **24.1**

Mixed Review

Lesson 14-4

59. In $\triangle RST$, $m\angle R = 37°$, $m\angle T = 59°$, and $TS = 12$ in. Find RS. **17.1 in.**

60. In $\triangle JKL$, $m\angle L = 71°$, $j = 11$ m, and $m\angle K = 46°$. Find k. **8.9 m**

61. In $\triangle MNP$, $m\angle N = 42°$, $n = 21$ in., and $m\angle M = 57°$. Find m. **26.3 in.**

62. In $\triangle DEF$, $m\angle F = 91°$, $d = 17$ mm, and $f = 21$ mm. Find $m\angle D$. **54.0°**

Lesson 13-6

Identify the period and tell where two asymptotes occur for each function.

63–67. See margin.

63. $y = \tan 0.5\theta$ **64.** $y = \tan \frac{3\pi\theta}{2}$ **65.** $y = \tan(-3\theta)$ **66.** $y = \tan \frac{2\pi}{5}\theta$

Lesson 12-1

67. Use a table and a graph to show the probability distribution for the sum of two octahedral number cubes. $\{2, 3, 4, 5, 6, 7, 8, 9, 10, 11, 12, 13, 14, 15, 16\}$

Algebra at Work

·····Acoustical Physicist

Acoustical physicists study sound to design concert halls, theaters, and auditoriums. They consider building materials, the shape of the hall, and the placement of people and equipment. Acoustical physicists ensure that sound is distributed evenly so that all of the people in the theater or auditorium hear equally well.

A blank sheet of grids is available in the Test-Taking Strategies with Transparencies booklet. Give this sheet to students for practice with filling in grids.

Resources

For additional practice with a variety of test item formats:
- Standardized Test Prep, p. 817
- Test-Taking Strategies, p. 812
- Test-Taking Strategies with Transparencies

63. 2π, $x = \pm\pi$

64. $\frac{2}{3}$, $x = \pm\frac{1}{3}$

65. $\frac{\pi}{3}$, $x = \pm\frac{\pi}{6}$

66. $\frac{5}{2}$, $x = \pm\frac{5}{4}$

67.

x	$P(x)$
2	0.016
3	0.031
4	0.047
5	0.063
6	0.078
7	0.094
8	0.109
9	0.125
10	0.109
11	0.094
12	0.078
13	0.063
14	0.047
15	0.031
16	0.016

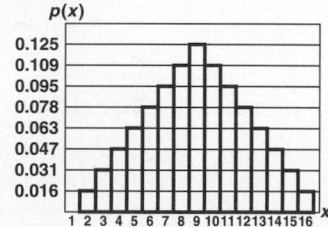

Lesson Preview

✓ **Check Skills You'll Need**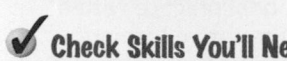

Trigonometric Identities
Lesson 14-1: Example 3
Exercises 11–19
Extra Practice, p. 835

Lesson Resources

📁 **Teaching Resources**
Practice, Reteaching, Enrichment
Checkpoint Quiz 2

👥 **Reaching All Students**
Practice Workbook 14-6
Spanish Practice Workbook 14-6
Reading and Math Literacy 14C
Spanish Reading & Literacy 14C
Spanish Checkpoint Quiz 2
Hands-On Activities 59

⏱ **Presentation Assistant Plus!**
Transparencies
• Check Skills You'll Need 14-6
• Additional Examples 14-6
• Student Edition Answers 14-6
• Lesson Quiz 14-6
PH Presentation Pro CD 14-6

PRENTICE HALL
ASSESSMENT SYSTEM

Checkpoint Quiz 2
Computer Test Generator CD

💿 **Technology**
Resource Pro® CD-ROM
Computer Test Generator CD
Prentice Hall Presentation Pro CD

💻 **www.PHSchool.com**
Student Site
• Teacher Web Code: agk-5500
• Self-grading Lesson Quiz
Teacher Center
• Lesson Planner
• Resources

Plus

Lesson Preview

What You'll Learn

OBJECTIVE 1 To verify and use angle identities

OBJECTIVE 2 To verify and use sum and difference identities

... And Why

To simplify trigonometric expressions and find values of trigonometric functions

✓ **Check Skills You'll Need** (For help, go to Lesson 14-1.)

Complete the three reciprocal identities.

1. $\csc \theta = \frac{1}{\blacksquare}$ $\sin \theta$ **2.** $\sec \theta = \frac{1}{\blacksquare}$ $\cos \theta$ **3.** $\cot \theta = \frac{1}{\blacksquare}$ $\tan \theta$

Complete the three Pythagorean identities.

4. $\cos^2 \theta + \sin^2 \theta = \blacksquare$ **1**   **5.** $1 + \tan^2 \theta = \blacksquare$ $\sec^2 \theta$ **6.** $1 + \cot^2 \theta = \blacksquare$
$\csc^2 \theta$

 Interactive lesson includes instant self-check, tutorials, and activities.

OBJECTIVE 1 — **Angle Identities**

Real-World 🌐 Connection

Over 2000 years ago, the Greek astronomer Hipparchus needed a table of trigonometric ratios to calculate the positions of the stars. He had to compute the table himself and he used angle identities to make the computations easier.

In the figure at the right, angles θ and $-\theta$ have the same amount of rotation, but the rotations are in opposite directions.

Point Q is a reflection of P in the x-axis. The x-coordinates of P and Q are the same and their y-coordinates are opposites. So $\cos(-\theta) = \cos\theta$ and $\sin(-\theta) = -\sin\theta$.

Similarly, R is the reflection of S in the x-axis. So $\tan(-\theta) = -\tan\theta$.

In the figure at the right, θ is a counterclockwise rotation from the positive x-axis and $\frac{\pi}{2} - \theta$ is the same amount of rotation clockwise from the positive y-axis.

Point Q is a reflection of P in the line $y = x$. If (x, y) are the coordinates of P, then (y, x) are the coordinates of Q. So $\cos\left(\frac{\pi}{2} - \theta\right) = \sin\theta$ and $\sin\left(\frac{\pi}{2} - \theta\right) = \cos\theta$.

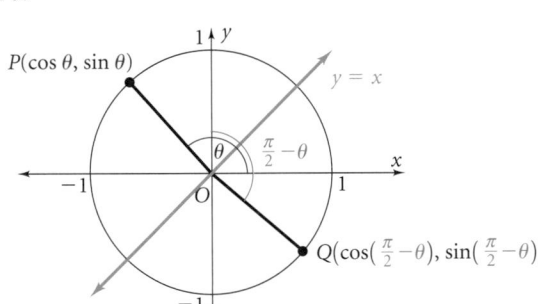

Then, by the Tangent Identity, $\tan\left(\frac{\pi}{2} - \theta\right) = \dfrac{\sin\left(\frac{\pi}{2} - \theta\right)}{\cos\left(\frac{\pi}{2} - \theta\right)} = \dfrac{\cos\theta}{\sin\theta} = \cot\theta$.

INSTANT CHECK SYSTEM 🔄 **Ongoing Assessment and Intervention**

Before the Lesson
Diagnose prerequisite skills using:
• Check Skills You'll Need

During the Lesson
Monitor progress using:
• Check Understanding
• Additional Examples
• Standardized Test Prep

After the Lesson
Assess knowledge using:
• Lesson Quiz
• Computer Test Generator CD
• Chapter Checkpoint 2 (p. 806)

Key Concepts

Properties	Angle Identities

Negative angle identities

$$\sin(-\theta) = -\sin\theta \qquad \cos(-\theta) = \cos\theta \qquad \tan(-\theta) = -\tan\theta$$

Cofunction identities

$$\sin\left(\frac{\pi}{2} - \theta\right) = \cos\theta \qquad \cos\left(\frac{\pi}{2} - \theta\right) = \sin\theta \qquad \tan\left(\frac{\pi}{2} - \theta\right) = \cot\theta$$

Reading Math

The word cofunction is derived from complementary angle *function*.

1 EXAMPLE **Verifying Angle Identities**

Verify the identity $\sin\left(\theta - \frac{\pi}{2}\right) = -\cos\theta$.

$$\sin\left(\theta - \frac{\pi}{2}\right) = \sin\left(-\left(\frac{\pi}{2} - \theta\right)\right) \qquad -(a - b) = b - a$$
$$= -\sin\left(\left(\frac{\pi}{2} - \theta\right)\right) \qquad \sin(-\theta) = -\sin\theta$$
$$= -\cos\theta \qquad \sin\left(\frac{\pi}{2} - \theta\right) = \cos\theta$$

✓ **Check Understanding** **1** Verify the identity $\cos\left(\theta - \frac{\pi}{2}\right) = \sin\theta$.

$$\cos\left(\theta - \frac{\pi}{2}\right) = \cos\left(-\left(\frac{\pi}{2} - \theta\right)\right)$$
$$= \cos\left(\frac{\pi}{2} - \theta\right)$$
$$= \sin\theta$$

You can use angle identities to solve trigonometric equations.

2 EXAMPLE **Solving Trigonometric Equations**

Solve $\sin\theta = \sin\left(\frac{\pi}{2} - \theta\right)$ for $0 \le \theta < 2\pi$.

$$\sin\theta = \sin\left(\frac{\pi}{2} - \theta\right)$$
$$\sin\theta = \cos\theta \qquad \textbf{cofunction identity}$$
$$\frac{\sin\theta}{\cos\theta} = 1 \qquad \textbf{Divide by } \cos\theta.$$
$$\tan\theta = 1 \qquad \textbf{Tangent Identity}$$
$$\theta = \tan^{-1} 1 \qquad \textbf{Solve for one value of } \theta.$$
$$\theta = \frac{\pi}{4}$$

Another solution is $\frac{\pi}{4} + \pi + \frac{5\pi}{4}$.

✓ **Check Understanding** **2** Solve $\sin\left(\frac{\pi}{2} - \theta\right) = \sec\theta$ for $0 \le \theta < 2\pi$. **0 + 2πn, π + 2πn**

3 EXAMPLE **Cofunction Identities in a Right Triangle**

The cofunction identities were derived using the unit circle. So they apply to an angle θ of any size. Use the definitions of the trigonometric ratios for a right triangle to derive a cofunction identity for $\sin(90° - A)$.

In a right triangle, the acute angles are complementary. So $A + B = 90°$ and $B = 90° - A$, where A and B are the measures of the acute angles.

$$\sin(90° - A) = \sin B \qquad \textbf{A and B are complementary angles.}$$
$$= \frac{b}{a} \qquad \textbf{definition of sine in a right triangle}$$
$$= \cos A \qquad \textbf{definition of cosine in a right triangle}$$

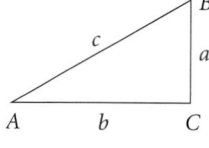

Math Background

The negative angle, cofunction, angle difference, and angle sum identities play an important role in simplifying and manipulating calculations. For instance, in calculus, the angle sum identities for sine and cosine are used in computing the slopes of the tangent lines to the graphs of $y = \sin x$ and $y = \cos x$, respectively.

OBJECTIVE

▼ 1 Teaching Notes

3 EXAMPLE **Auditory Learners**

Students may find it helpful to use oral repetition to memorize a statement that summarizes the cofunction identities. Suggest the following statement: *A trigonometric function of an acute angle is equal to the cofunction of the complement of the angle.*

Additional Examples

1 Use the fact that $\pi - \theta = \frac{\pi}{2} - \left(\theta - \frac{\pi}{2}\right)$ to verify the identity $\sin(\pi - \theta) = \sin\theta$.
$$\sin(\pi - \theta) = \sin\left[\frac{\pi}{2} - \left(\theta - \frac{\pi}{2}\right)\right]$$
$$= \cos\left(\theta - \frac{\pi}{2}\right)$$
$$= \cos\left(\frac{\pi}{2} - \theta\right)$$
$$= \sin\theta$$

2 Solve $\cos\left(\frac{\pi}{2} - \theta\right) = \sin\left(\frac{\pi}{2} - \theta\right)$ for $0 \le \theta < 2\pi$. $\frac{\pi}{4}, \frac{5\pi}{4}$

3 Find a cofunction identity for $\tan(90° - A)$, where A is an acute angle of a right triangle. **tan (90° − A) = cot A**

👥 Reaching All Students

Below Level Show students how the angle identities on p. 801 come from the definitions of trigonometric functions and the unit circle.	**Advanced Learners** Students may like to show that the cofunction identities on p. 801 can also be verified using the translation relations $g(x) = f(x - h)$.	**Auditory Learners** See note on page 801. **Error Prevention** See note on page 804.

Teaching Tip
You may want to show students that the identities for cos (A − B) and sin (A − B) can be used to verify simpler identities. For example to recall that cos (−θ) = cos θ, note that −θ = 0 − θ and use the identity for the difference of two angle measures.

$$\cos (-\theta) = \cos (0 - \theta)$$
$$= \cos 0 \cos \theta + \sin 0 \sin \theta$$
$$= 1 \cdot \cos \theta + 0 \cdot \sin \theta$$
$$= \cos \theta$$

✓ **Check Understanding** ③ Derive a cofunction identity for sec (90° − A). **sec (90° − A) = csc A**

OBJECTIVE

2

Sum and Difference Identities

In the cofunction identities, any angle θ is subtracted from $\frac{\pi}{2}$. There are also identities for subtracting any two angles.

It is convenient to start with an identity for finding the cosine of the difference of two angles.

In the figure below, angles A, B, and $A - B$ are shown. Use the distance formula to find the square of the distance between P and Q.

$$(PQ)^2 = (x_1 - x_2)^2 + (y_1 - y_2)^2$$
$$= (\cos A - \cos B)^2 + (\sin A - \sin B)^2$$
$$= \cos^2 A - 2 \cos A \cos B + \cos^2 B + \sin^2 A - 2 \sin A \sin B + \sin^2 B$$
$$= 2 - 2 \cos A \cos B - 2 \sin A \sin B \quad \text{Use the Pythagorean identity } \sin^2 \theta + \cos^2 \theta = 1.$$

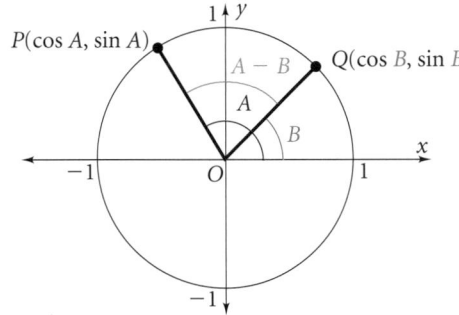

Now use the Law of Cosines to find $(PQ)^2$ in $\triangle POQ$.
$$(PQ)^2 = (PO)^2 + (QO)^2 - 2(PO)(QO) \cos (A - B)$$
$$= 1^2 + 1^2 - 2(1)(1) \cos (A - B)$$
$$= 2 - 2 \cos (A - B)$$

The Transitive Property for Equality tells you that the two expressions for $(PQ)^2$ are equal.

$$2 - 2 \cos (A - B) = 2 - 2 \cos A \cos B - 2 \sin A \sin B$$
$$-2 \cos (A - B) = -2 \cos A \cos B - 2 \sin A \sin B \quad \text{Subtract 2 from each side.}$$
$$\cos (A - B) = \cos A \cos B + \sin A \sin B \quad \text{Divide each side by } -2.$$

You can also derive an identity for sin (A − B). Then you can use the Tangent Identity to derive an identity for tan (A − B).

 Key Concepts

Properties	**Angle Difference Identities**
$\sin (A - B) = \sin A \cos B - \cos A \sin B$	
$\cos (A - B) = \cos A \cos B + \sin A \sin B$	
$\tan (A - B) = \frac{\tan A - \tan B}{1 + \tan A \tan B}$	

4 EXAMPLE Using Angle Difference Identities

Find the exact value of cos 15°.

You know exact values for 30°, 60°, and 45°. Use the fact that 15° = 60° − 45°.

$$\cos (A - B) = \cos A \cos B + \sin A \sin B$$ **Cosine Angle Difference Identity**

$$\cos (60° - 45°) = \cos 60° \cos 45° + \sin 60° \sin 45°$$ **Substitute 60° for A and 45° for B.**

$$= \frac{1}{2}\left(\frac{\sqrt{2}}{2}\right) + \frac{\sqrt{3}}{2}\left(\frac{\sqrt{2}}{2}\right)$$ **Replace with exact values.**

$$= \frac{\sqrt{2}}{4} + \frac{\sqrt{6}}{4}$$ **Simplify.**

$$= \frac{\sqrt{2} + \sqrt{6}}{4}$$

So cos 15° = $\frac{\sqrt{2} + \sqrt{6}}{4}$.

✓ **Check Understanding**   **4** Find the exact value of sin 15°. $\frac{\sqrt{6} - \sqrt{2}}{4}$

You can use the Negative Angle Identities and the Sine Angle Difference Identity to derive an identity for sin (A + B).

$$\sin (A + B) = \sin (A - (-B))$$ **Rewrite as subtraction.**

$$= \sin A \cos (-B) - \cos A \sin (-B)$$ **Sine Angle Difference Identity**

$$= \sin A \cos B - \cos A (-\sin B)$$ **negative angle identities**

$$= \sin A \cos B + \cos A \sin B$$ **Simplify.**

You can similarly derive an identity for cos (A + B). You can use the Tangent Identity to derive tan (A + B).

🔑 **Key Concepts**

Properties	**Angle Sum Identities**

$$\sin (A + B) = \sin A \cos B + \cos A \sin B$$

$$\cos (A + B) = \cos A \cos B - \sin A \sin B$$

$$\tan (A + B) = \frac{\tan A + \tan B}{1 - \tan A \tan B}$$

5 EXAMPLE Using Angle Sum Identities

Find the exact value of sin 105°.

Use the fact that 105° = 60° + 45°.

$$\sin (A + B) = \sin A \cos B + \cos A \sin B$$ **Sine Angle Sum Identity**

$$\sin (60° + 45°) = \sin 60° \cos 45° + \cos 60° \sin 45°$$ **Substitute 60° for A and 45° for B.**

$$= \frac{\sqrt{3}}{2}\left(\frac{\sqrt{2}}{2}\right) + \frac{1}{2}\left(\frac{\sqrt{2}}{2}\right)$$ **Replace with exact values.**

$$= \frac{\sqrt{6}}{4} + \frac{\sqrt{2}}{4}$$ **Simplify.**

$$= \frac{\sqrt{6} + \sqrt{2}}{4}$$

So, sin 105° = $\frac{\sqrt{6} + \sqrt{2}}{4}$.

✓ **Check Understanding**   **5** Find the exact value of tan 105°.   **−2 − $\sqrt{3}$**

4 Find the exact value of cos 165°. $-\frac{\sqrt{2} + \sqrt{6}}{4}$

5 Find the exact value of sin 195°. $\frac{\sqrt{2} - \sqrt{6}}{4}$

Closure

Ask students to state the negative angle identities in words. Then ask them to summarize the cofunction identities in words. Finally, ask them to state the identity for cos (A − B) in words. **The sine of the opposite of θ is equal to the opposite of the sine of θ, the cosine of the opposite of θ is equal to the cosine of θ, and the tangent of the opposite of θ is equal to the opposite of the tangent of θ; A trigonometric function of an angle measure that is in radians is equal to the cofunction of π over 2 minus the angle measure; The cosine of the difference of two angle measures is the product of their cosines plus the product of their sines.**

3. Practice

Assignment Guide

1 Objective
A B Core 1–16, 50, 52

2 Objective
A B Core 17–51
C Extension 53–57

Standardized Test Prep 58–64

Mixed Review 65–78

Error Prevention

Exercise 15 Students sometimes think that the cofunction for the cosecant function is the sine function. They are confusing cofunctions with reciprocal functions. Point out that all they need to do is drop the letters "co-" from cosecant to see that the cofunction for the cosecant function is the secant function.

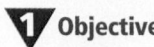

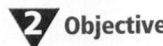

EXERCISES

For more practice, see *Extra Practice*.

Practice and Problem Solving

A Practice by Example

Example 1 (page 801)

Verify each identity. 1–6. See back of book.

1. $\csc\left(\theta - \frac{\pi}{2}\right) = -\sec\theta$

2. $\sec\left(\theta - \frac{\pi}{2}\right) = \csc\theta$

3. $\cot\left(\frac{\pi}{2} - \theta\right) = \tan\theta$

4. $\csc\left(\frac{\pi}{2} - \theta\right) = \sec\theta$

5. $\tan\left(\theta - \frac{\pi}{2}\right) = -\cot\theta$

6. $\sec\left(\frac{\pi}{2} - \theta\right) = \csc\theta$

Example 2 (page 801)

Solve each trigonometric equation for $0 \le \theta < 2\pi$.

7. $\cos\left(\frac{\pi}{2} - \theta\right) = \csc\theta$ $\frac{\pi}{2}, \frac{3\pi}{2}$

8. $\sin\left(\frac{\pi}{2} - \theta\right) = -\cos(-\theta)$ $\frac{\pi}{2}, \frac{3\pi}{2}$

9. $\frac{\pi}{4}, \frac{3\pi}{4}, \frac{5\pi}{4}, \frac{7\pi}{4}$

9. $\tan\left(\frac{\pi}{2} - \theta\right) + \tan(-\theta) = 0$

10. $\sin^2\theta + \cos^2\theta = \sin\theta$ $\frac{\pi}{2}$

11. $\tan^2\theta - \sec^2\theta = \cos(-\theta)$ π

12. $2\sin\left(\frac{\pi}{2} - \theta\right) = \sin(-\theta)$ 2.034, 5.176

13. $\tan\left(\frac{\pi}{2} - \theta\right) = \cos(-\theta)$ $\frac{\pi}{2}, \frac{3\pi}{2}$

14. $1 + \cot^2\theta = \csc\theta$ $\frac{\pi}{2}$

Example 3 (page 801)

Use the definitions of the trigonometric ratios for a right triangle to derive each cofunction identity.

15. a cofunction identity for $\csc(90° - A)$ **sec A**

16. a cofunction identity for $\cot(90° - A)$ **tan A**

Examples 4 and 5 (page 803)

Mental Math Find the value of each trigonometric expression.

17. $\cos 50° \cos 40° - \sin 50° \sin 40°$ **0**

18. $\sin 80° \cos 35° - \cos 80° \sin 35°$ $\frac{\sqrt{2}}{2}$

19. $\sin 100° \cos 170° + \cos 100° \sin 170°$ **−1**

20. $\cos 183° \cos 93° + \sin 183° \sin 93°$ **0**

Find each exact value. Use a sum or difference identity. 21–31. See margin.

21. $\cos 105°$ 22. $\tan 105°$ 23. $\tan 15°$ 24. $\sin 75°$

25. $\cos 75°$ 26. $\tan 75°$ 27. $\cos 135°$ 28. $\tan 135°$

29. $\sin(-15°)$ 30. $\cos(-15°)$ 31. $\tan(-15°)$ 32. $\sin 225°$ $-\frac{\sqrt{2}}{2}$

33. $\cos 240°$ $-\frac{1}{2}$ 34. $\sin 390°$ $\frac{1}{2}$ 35. $\cos(-300°)$ $\frac{1}{2}$ 36. $\tan 390°$ $\frac{\sqrt{3}}{3}$

B Apply Your Skills

Verify each identity. 37–43. See back of book.

37. $\sin(A - B) = \sin A \cos B - \cos A \sin B$

38. $\tan(A - B) = \dfrac{\tan A - \tan B}{1 + \tan A \tan B}$

39. $\cos(A + B) = \cos A \cos B - \sin A \sin B$

40. $\tan(A + B) = \dfrac{\tan A + \tan B}{1 - \tan A \tan B}$

41. $\sin\left(x + \frac{\pi}{3}\right) + \sin\left(x - \frac{\pi}{3}\right) = \sin x$

42. $\sin\left(\frac{3\pi}{2} - x\right) = -\cos x$

43. **Reasoning** Show that the equation $\sin(A + B) = \sin A + \sin B$ is *not* an identity by finding a counterexample, values for A and B for which the equation is false.

pages 804–806 Exercises

21. $\dfrac{\sqrt{2} - \sqrt{6}}{4}$

22. $-\sqrt{3} - 2$

23. $2 - \sqrt{3}$

24. $\dfrac{\sqrt{2} + \sqrt{6}}{4}$

25. $\dfrac{\sqrt{6} - \sqrt{2}}{4}$

26. $2 + \sqrt{3}$

27. $-\dfrac{\sqrt{2}}{2}$

28. -1

29. $\dfrac{\sqrt{2} - \sqrt{6}}{4}$

30. $\dfrac{\sqrt{6} + \sqrt{2}}{4}$

31. $-2 + \sqrt{3}$

Rewrite each expression as a trigonometric function of a single angle measure.

44. $\sin 3\theta$

45. $\sin 5\theta$

46. $\cos 7\theta$

47. $\cos 5\theta$

44. $\sin 2\theta \cos \theta + \cos 2\theta \sin \theta$

45. $\sin 3\theta \cos 2\theta + \cos 3\theta \sin 2\theta$

46. $\cos 3\theta \cos 4\theta - \sin 3\theta \sin 4\theta$

47. $\cos 2\theta \cos 3\theta - \sin 2\theta \sin 3\theta$

48. $\dfrac{\tan 5\theta + \tan 6\theta}{1 - \tan 5\theta \tan 6\theta}$ $\tan 11\theta$

49. $\dfrac{\tan 3\theta - \tan \theta}{1 + \tan 3\theta \tan \theta}$ $\tan 2\theta$

50. **a.** Graph $y = \sin 2x$ and $y = 2 \sin x$ on the same axes.
   b. Does $\sin 2x = 2 \sin x$ for all values of x? Is $\sin 2x = 2 \sin x$ an identity? Explain.   **a–d. See margin.**
   c. Does $\sin 2x = 2 \sin x$ for any values of x? If so, what are they?
   d. Open-Ended Find an equation of the form $a \sin b = c \sin d$ whose solutions are $2\pi n$.

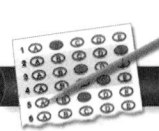
51. **Gears** The diagram at the right shows a gear whose radius is 10 cm. Point A represents a $60°$ counterclockwise rotation of point $P(10, 0)$. Point B represents a θ-degree rotation of point A. The coordinates of B are $(10 \cos (\theta + 60°), 10 \sin (\theta + 60°))$. Write these coordinates in terms of $\cos \theta$ and $\sin \theta$.   **See margin.**

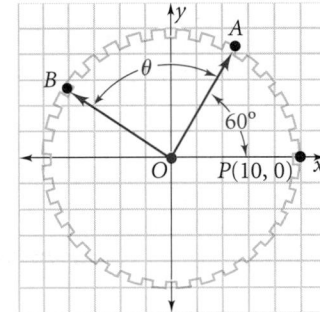

52. **a. Critical Thinking** A function is even if $f(-x) = f(x)$. A function is odd if $f(-x) = -f(x)$. Which trigonometric functions are even? Which are odd?   **a–b. See margin.**
   b. Writing Are all functions either even or odd? Explain your answer. Give a counterexample if possible.

C Challenge

Use the sum and difference formulas to verify each identity. 53–56. See back of book.

53. $\cos (\pi - \theta) = -\cos \theta$

54. $\sin (\pi - \theta) = \sin \theta$

55. $\sin (\pi + \theta) = -\sin \theta$

56. $\cos (\pi + \theta) = -\cos \theta$

57. **Reasoning** For any parallelogram, prove that the sum of the squares of the lengths of the diagonals equals twice the sum of the squares of the lengths of two adjacent sides.   **See back of book.**

Standardized Test Prep

Multiple Choice

58. Which expressions are equivalent?   **D**
   I. $\cos \theta$ II. $\cos (-\theta)$ III. $\dfrac{\sin (-\theta)}{\tan (-\theta)}$
   A. I and II only   **B.** II and III only   **C.** I and III only   **D.** I, II, and III

59. Which expressions are equivalent?   **I**
   I. $-\tan \left(\dfrac{\pi}{2} - \theta\right)$ II. $\tan \left(\theta - \dfrac{\pi}{2}\right)$ III. $\tan \left(-\left(\dfrac{\pi}{2} - \theta\right)\right)$
   F. I and II only   **G.** II and III only   **H.** I and III only   **I.** I, II, and III

60. Which expression is equal to $\cos 50°$?   **D**
   A. $\sin 20° \cos 30° + \cos 20° \sin 30°$ **B.** $\sin 20° \cos 30° - \cos 20° \sin 30°$
   C. $\cos 20° \cos 30° + \sin 20° \sin 30°$ **D.** $\cos 20° \cos 30° - \sin 20° \sin 30°$

61. Which expression is NOT equivalent to $\cos \theta$?   **G**
   F. $-\sin (\theta - 90°)$ **G.** $-\cos (-\theta)$ **H.** $\sin (\theta + 90°)$ **I.** $-\cos (\theta + 180°)$

Lesson 14-6 Angle Identities   **805**

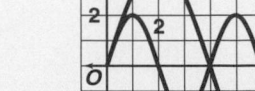
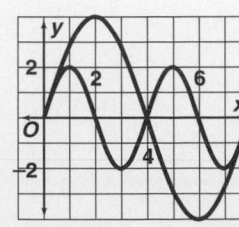
50a.
[graph]

b. No; it is not an identity since it only corresponds for a few specific x-values.

c. yes; $0 + 2\pi n$, $\pi + 2\pi n$

d. Answers may vary. Sample: $\sin x = 2 \sin (0.5x)$

51. $(5 \cos \theta - 5\sqrt{3} \sin \theta,$ $5 \sin \theta + 5\sqrt{3} \cos \theta)$

4. Assess

Lesson Quiz 14-6

1. Show that $\sin \left(\dfrac{\pi}{2} - \theta\right) - \cos \theta = 0$.
   $\sin \left(\dfrac{\pi}{2} - \theta\right) = \cos \theta$, so
   $\sin \left(\dfrac{\pi}{2} - \theta\right) - \cos \theta$
   $= \cos \theta - \cos \theta = 0$

2. Solve the equation $\sec \theta - \tan \theta = 0$ for $0 \le \theta < 2\pi$. $\dfrac{\pi}{2}$

3. Find the value of $\cos 85° \cos 55° + \sin 85° \sin 55°$. $\dfrac{\sqrt{3}}{2}$

4. Write an expression for $\sin 17°$ in terms of sines or cosines of $50°$ and $33°$.
   $\sin 50° \cos 33° - \cos 50° \sin 33°$

Alternative Assessment

Have students work in pairs. Each student should create two trigonometric identities that can be verified by using identities that were developed in this lesson. Each student should verify the identities that the other student wrote. Have students check each other's work.

Standardized Test Prep

Resources
For additional practice with a variety of test item formats:
- Standardized Test Prep, p. 817
- Test-Taking Strategies, p. 812
- Test-Taking Strategies with Transparencies

Exercise 61 It may be easier to use diagrams than identities to answer this exercise.

52a. cosine, secant; sine, cosecant, tangent, and cotangent

   b. No; answers may vary. Sample: $y = \sin (x + 0.5)$ is not odd because $y = \sin (-x + 0.5) = \sin (-(x - 0.5)) = -\sin (x - 0.5) \ne -\sin (x + 0.5)$.

805

To check understanding of Lessons 14-4 to 14-6:

Checkpoint Quiz 2 (p. 806)

Teaching Resources
Checkpoint Quiz 2 (also in Prentice Hall Assessment System)

Reaching All Students
Reading and Math Literacy 14C

Spanish versions available

Take It to the NET
Online lesson quiz at
www.PHSchool.com
Web Code: aga-1406

Short Response

62. Which expression is an exact value for sin 15° ? **B**

A. $\frac{\sqrt{2}}{2} \cdot \frac{\sqrt{3}}{2} + \frac{\sqrt{2}}{2} \cdot \frac{1}{2}$ 　　　　　 B. $\frac{\sqrt{2}}{2} \cdot \frac{\sqrt{3}}{2} - \frac{\sqrt{2}}{2} \cdot \frac{1}{2}$

C. $\frac{\sqrt{2}}{2} \cdot \frac{1}{2} + \frac{\sqrt{2}}{2} \cdot \frac{\sqrt{3}}{2}$ 　　　　　 D. $\frac{\sqrt{2}}{2} \cdot \frac{1}{2} - \frac{\sqrt{2}}{2} \cdot \frac{\sqrt{3}}{2}$

63. Find an exact value for sin 165°. Show your work. **See back of book.**

64. Use the fact that $\frac{\pi}{6} = \frac{\pi}{2} - \frac{\pi}{3}$ to find an exact value for cos $\frac{\pi}{6}$. Show your work. **See back of book.**

Mixed Review

Lesson 14-5

65. In $\triangle RST$, $m\angle S = 24°$, $r = 10$ ft, and $t = 18$ ft. Find s. **9.8 ft**

66. In $\triangle XYZ$, $m\angle Z = 51°$, $x = 13$ cm, and $y = 17$ cm. Find z. **13.4 cm**

67. In $\triangle DEF$, $m\angle F = 68°$, $d = 16$ mm, and $e = 21$ mm. Find f. **21.1 mm**

68. In $\triangle ABC$, $m\angle A = 87°$, $b = 22$ m, and $c = 19$ m. Find a. **28.3 m**

Lesson 13-3

Write each measure in radians. Express the answer in terms of π and as a decimal rounded to the nearest hundredth.

69. 80° 　$\frac{4\pi}{9}$ and 1.40 　　 **70.** −50° 　$-\frac{5\pi}{18}$ and −0.87 　 **71.** −15° 　$-\frac{\pi}{12}$ and −0.26

72. 70° 　$\frac{7\pi}{18}$ and 1.22 　　 **73.** 190° 　$\frac{19\pi}{18}$ and 3.32 　 **74.** 200° 　$\frac{10\pi}{9}$ and 3.49

Lesson 12-7

A set of data with a mean of 39 and a standard deviation of 6.2 is normally distributed. Find each value, given its distance from the mean.

75. +1 standard deviation **45.2** 　　　 **76.** −2 standard deviations **26.6**

77. +3 standard deviations **57.6** 　　　 **78.** −1 standard deviation **32.8**

Checkpoint Quiz 2

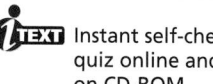

Lessons 14-4 through 14-6

Instant self-check quiz online and on CD-ROM

Find the area of $\triangle ABC$.

1. $m\angle A = 37°$, $b = 10$ cm, and $c = 12$ cm. **36.1 cm²**

2. $m\angle B = 18°$, $a = 20$ ft, and $c = 25$ ft. **77.3 ft²**

3. $m\angle B = 104°$, $a = 8$ m, and $c = 9$ m. **34.9 m²**

4. $m\angle C = 96°$, $a = 26$ in., and $b = 31$ in. **400.8 in.²**

Find the remaining sides and angles in each triangle. Round your answers to the nearest tenth.
$a = 8.2$ ft, $m\angle B = 69.7°$, $m\angle C = 83.3°$
5. In $\triangle ABC$, $m\angle A = 27°$, $b = 17$ ft, and $c = 18$ ft.

6. In $\triangle DEF$, $d = 32$ mm, $e = 30$ mm, and $f = 35$ mm.
$m\angle D = 58.4°$, $m\angle E = 53.0°$, $m\angle F = 68.7°$

Simplify each trigonometric expression.

7. cos 80°

8. sin 63°

7. cos 60° cos 20° − sin 60° sin 20° 　　　 **8.** sin 90° cos 27° − cos 90° sin 27°

9. sin 150° cos 290° + cos 150° sin 290° **sin 80°** 　　 **10.** cos 233° cos 154° + sin 233° sin 154° **cos 79°**

14-7 Double-Angle and Half-Angle Identities

Lesson Preview

 What You'll Learn

OBJECTIVE 1 To verify and use double-angle identities

OBJECTIVE 2 To verify and use half-angle identities

. . . And Why

To find exact values of trigonometric functions

 Check Skills You'll Need (For help, go to Lesson 14-6.)

Complete the following angle identities. 1–4. See margin p. 808.

1. $\cos(A - B) = \blacksquare$

2. $\cos(A + B) = \blacksquare$

3. $\tan(A - B) = \blacksquare$

4. $\sin(A - B) = \blacksquare$

5. $\sin(A + B) = \blacksquare$
 $\sin A \cos B + \cos A \sin B$

6. $\tan(A + B) = \blacksquare$
 $\dfrac{\tan A + \tan B}{1 - \tan A \tan B}$

Lesson Preview

 Check Skills You'll Need

Angle Identities
Lessons 14-6: Examples 4 and 5
Exercises 21–36
Extra Practice, p. 835

Lesson Resources

Teaching Resources
Practice, Reteaching, Enrichment

Reaching All Students
Practice Workbook 14-7
Spanish Practice Workbook 14-7

Presentation Assistant Plus!
Transparencies
• Check Skills You'll Need 14-7
• Additional Examples 14-7
• Student Edition Answers 14-7
• Lesson Quiz 14-7
PH Presentation Pro CD 14-7

ASSESSMENT SYSTEM

Computer Test Generator CD

Technology
Resource Pro® CD-ROM
Computer Test Generator CD
Prentice Hall Presentation Pro CD

 www.PHSchool.com
Student Site
• Teacher Web Code: agk-5500
• Self-grading Lesson Quiz
Teacher Center
• Lesson Planner
• Resources

Plus

OBJECTIVE 1  Interactive lesson includes instant self-check, tutorials, and activities.

1 Double-Angle Identities

You can use the angle sum identities to derive the double-angle identities.

Let $\theta = A = B$.

$\cos(A + B) = \cos A \cos B - \sin A \sin B$ **Cosine Angle Sum Identity**

$\cos(\theta + \theta) = \cos\theta \cos\theta - \sin\theta \sin\theta$ **Substitute θ for A and B.**

$\cos 2\theta = \cos^2\theta - \sin^2\theta$ **Simplify.**

You can use the Pythagorean identity $\sin^2\theta + \cos^2\theta = 1$ in the form $\sin^2\theta = 1 - \cos^2\theta$ to derive another identity for $\cos 2\theta$.

$\cos 2\theta = \cos^2\theta - \sin^2\theta$

$= \cos^2\theta - (1 - \cos^2\theta)$ **Substitute $1 - \cos^2\theta$ for $\sin^2\theta$.**

$= \cos^2\theta - 1 + \cos^2\theta$ **Remove parentheses.**

$= 2\cos^2\theta - 1$ **Simplify.**

You can use the Pythagorean theorem in the form $\cos^2\theta = 1 - \sin^2\theta$ to derive a third identity for $\cos 2\theta$.

$\cos 2\theta = \cos^2\theta - \sin^2\theta$

$= (1 - \sin^2\theta) - \sin^2\theta$ **Substitute $1 - \sin^2\theta$ for $\cos^2\theta$.**

$= 1 - 2\sin^2\theta$ **Simplify.**

You can use the other angle sum identities to derive double-angle identities for the sine and tangent.

 Key Concepts

Properties	**Double-Angle Identities**
$\cos 2\theta = \cos^2\theta - \sin^2\theta$	$\sin 2\theta = 2\sin\theta \cos\theta$
$\cos 2\theta = 2\cos^2\theta - 1$	$\tan 2\theta = \dfrac{2\tan\theta}{1 - \tan^2\theta}$
$\cos 2\theta = 1 - 2\sin^2\theta$	

 ## Ongoing Assessment and Intervention

Before the Lesson
Diagnose prerequisite skills using:
• Check Skills You'll Need

During the Lesson
Monitor progress using:
• Check Understanding
• Additional Examples
• Standardized Test Prep

After the Lesson
Assess knowledge using:
• Lesson Quiz
• Computer Test Generator CD

2. Teach

Math Background

With the double and half-angle identities, students now have the ability to connect the most common trigonometric identities.

OBJECTIVE

1 **Teaching Notes**

2 EXAMPLE **Math Tip**

Point out to students the difficulty of verifying the identity by transforming the left-hand side of the identity to obtain the right-hand side.

Additional Examples

1 Use a double-angle identity to find the exact value of sin 600°.
$-\frac{\sqrt{3}}{2}$

2 Verify the identity
$\frac{\sin 2\theta}{1 - \sin^2 \theta} = 2 \tan \theta$. Transform the left side to obtain the right side.

$\frac{\sin 2\theta}{1 - \sin^2 \theta} = \frac{2 \sin \theta \cos \theta}{\cos^2 \theta}$

$= \frac{2 \sin \theta}{\cos \theta}$

$= 2 \left(\frac{\sin \theta}{\cos \theta}\right)$

$= 2 \tan \theta$

page 807 **Check Skills You'll Need**

1. $\cos A \cos B + \sin A \sin B$

2. $\cos A \cos B - \sin A \sin B$

3. $\frac{\tan A - \tan B}{1 + \tan A \tan B}$

4. $\sin A \cos B - \cos A \sin B$

---

1 EXAMPLE **Using a Double-Angle Identity**

Use a double-angle identity to find the exact value of cos 120°.

$\cos 120° = \cos 2(60°)$ **Rewrite 120 as 2(60).**

$= \cos^2 60° - \sin^2 60°$ **Use a cosine double-angle identity.**

$= \left(\frac{1}{2}\right)^2 - \left(\frac{\sqrt{3}}{2}\right)^2$ **Replace with exact values.**

$= -\frac{1}{2}$ **Simplify.**

✔ **Check Understanding** **1** Use a double-angle identity to find the exact value of sin 120°. $\frac{\sqrt{3}}{2}$

You can use the double-angle identities to verify other identities.

2 EXAMPLE **Verifying an Identity**

Verify the identity $\cos 2\theta = \frac{1 - \tan^2 \theta}{1 + \tan^2 \theta}$.

$\frac{1 - \tan^2 \theta}{1 + \tan^2 \theta} = \frac{1 - \tan^2 \theta}{\sec^2 \theta}$ **Pythagorean identity**

$= \frac{1}{\sec^2 \theta} - \frac{\tan^2 \theta}{\sec^2 \theta}$ **Write as two fractions.**

$= \frac{1}{\frac{1}{\cos^2 \theta}} - \frac{\frac{\sin^2 \theta}{\cos^2 \theta}}{\frac{1}{\cos^2 \theta}}$ **Express in terms of sin θ and cos θ.**

$= \cos^2 \theta - \sin^2 \theta$ **Simplify.**

$= \cos 2\theta$ **double-angle identity**

✔ **Check Understanding** **2** Verify the identity $2 \cos 2\theta = 4 \cos^2 \theta - 2$.
$2 \cos 2\theta = 2(2 \cos^2 \theta - 1) = 4 \cos^2 \theta - 2$

OBJECTIVE

2 **Half-Angle Identities**

You can use double-angle identities to derive half-angle identities.
Let $\theta = \frac{A}{2}$.

$\cos 2\theta = 2 \cos^2 \theta - 1$ **cosine double-angle identity**

$\cos 2\left(\frac{A}{2}\right) = 2 \cos^2 \frac{A}{2} - 1$ **Substitute $\frac{A}{2}$ for θ.**

$\frac{\cos A + 1}{2} = \cos^2 \frac{A}{2}$ **Solve for $\cos^2 \frac{A}{2}$.**

$\pm\sqrt{\frac{\cos A + 1}{2}} = \cos \frac{A}{2}$ **Take the square root of each side.**

Similarly, $\sin \frac{A}{2} = \pm\sqrt{\frac{1 - \cos A}{2}}$ and $\tan \frac{A}{2} = \pm\sqrt{\frac{1 - \cos A}{1 + \cos A}}$.

 Key Concepts

Properties	**Half-Angle Identities**	
$\sin \frac{A}{2} = \pm\sqrt{\frac{1 - \cos A}{2}}$	$\cos \frac{A}{2} = \pm\sqrt{\frac{1 + \cos A}{2}}$	$\tan \frac{A}{2} = \pm\sqrt{\frac{1 - \cos A}{1 + \cos A}}$

Choose the positive or negative sign for each function depending on the quadrant in which $\frac{A}{2}$ lies.

Reaching All Students

Below Level Show students how the double angle identities are derived from the sum identities by adding an angle to itself.	**Advanced Learners** Have students derive double angle and half angle identities for cosecant, secant, and cotangent functions.	**Error Prevention** See note on page 810.

3 EXAMPLE Using Half-Angle Identities

Use the half-angle identities to find each exact value.

a. sin 15°

$$\sin 15° = \sin\left(\frac{30}{2}\right)° \qquad \text{Rewrite 15° as } \frac{30°}{2}.$$

$$= \sqrt{\frac{1 - \cos 30°}{2}} \qquad \text{Use the principal square root, since sin 15° is positive.}$$

$$= \sqrt{\frac{1 - \frac{\sqrt{3}}{2}}{2}} \qquad \text{Substitute the exact value for cos 30°.}$$

$$= \sqrt{\frac{2 - \sqrt{3}}{4}} \qquad \text{Simplify.}$$

$$= \frac{\sqrt{2 - \sqrt{3}}}{2} \qquad \text{Simplify.}$$

b. cos 150°

$$\cos 150° = \cos\left(\frac{300}{2}\right)° \qquad \text{Rewrite 150 as } \frac{300}{2}.$$

$$= -\sqrt{\frac{1 + \cos 300°}{2}} \qquad \text{Use the negative square root, since cos 150° is negative.}$$

$$= -\sqrt{\frac{1 + \left(\frac{1}{2}\right)}{2}} \qquad \text{Replace with an exact value.}$$

$$= -\sqrt{\frac{3}{4}} \qquad \text{Simplify.}$$

$$= -\frac{\sqrt{3}}{2} \qquad \text{Simplify.}$$

✓ **Check Understanding** 3 Use the half-angle identities to find the exact value of each expression.
a. sin 150° $\frac{1}{2}$ **b.** tan 150° $-\frac{\sqrt{3}}{3}$

4 EXAMPLE Using Half-Angle Identities

Given $\sin \theta = -\frac{24}{25}$ and $180° < \theta < 270°$, find $\sin \frac{\theta}{2}$.

First find cos θ.

$$\cos^2 \theta + \sin^2 \theta = 1 \qquad \text{Pythagorean identity}$$

$$\cos^2 \theta + \left(-\frac{24}{25}\right)^2 = 1 \qquad \text{Substitute.}$$

$$\cos^2 \theta = \frac{49}{25^2} \qquad \text{Solve for } \cos^2 \theta.$$

$$\cos \theta = -\frac{7}{25} \qquad \text{Choose the negative square root since } \theta \text{ is in Quadrant III.}$$

Now find $\sin \frac{\theta}{2}$.

Since $180° < \theta < 270°$, $90° < \frac{\theta}{2} < 135°$ and $\frac{\theta}{2}$ is in Quadrant II.

$$\sin \frac{\theta}{2} = \pm\sqrt{\frac{1 - \cos \theta}{2}} \qquad \text{half-angle identity}$$

$$= \sqrt{\frac{1 - \left(-\frac{7}{25}\right)}{2}} \qquad \text{Substitute. Choose the positive square root since } \frac{\theta}{2} \text{ is in Quadrant II.}$$

$$= \frac{4}{5} \qquad \text{Simplify.}$$

4. $-\frac{3}{5}, -\frac{4}{3}$

✓ **Check Understanding** 4 Use the information in Example 4 to find the exact values of $\cos \frac{\theta}{2}$ and $\tan \frac{\theta}{2}$.

3 EXAMPLE Teaching Tip

You may want to challenge students to show that sin 15° can also be expressed as $\frac{\sqrt{6} - \sqrt{2}}{4}$.

Additional Examples

3 Use the half-angle identities to find each exact value.

a. sin 75° $\frac{\sqrt{2 + \sqrt{3}}}{2}$

b. cos 67.5° $\frac{\sqrt{2 - \sqrt{2}}}{2}$

4 Given $\cos \theta = -\frac{12}{13}$ and $90° < \theta < 180°$, find $\sin \frac{\theta}{2}$. $\frac{5\sqrt{26}}{26}$

Closure

Ask students to suppose that they are given the values of sin θ, cos θ, and tan θ for a certain angle θ. Ask them whether it is easier to apply the double-angle formulas or half-angle formulas if they want to find a trigonometric function's value for 2θ and $\frac{\theta}{2}$.
Answers may vary. Sample: Using the half-angle formulas is more difficult, because you must determine in which quadrant $\frac{\theta}{2}$ will be before you can decide whether to use a positive square root or a negative square root.

Need Help?
The quadrant of the terminal side of an angle determines the sign of the function.

Function	Positive in Quadrants
sin	I, II
cos	I, IV
tan	I, III

For more practice, see *Extra Practice*.

EXERCISES

Practice and Problem Solving

Assignment Guide

 **Objective**

Ⓐ Ⓑ **Core** 1–10, 27–29, 33–37, 42–46, 48

Ⓒ **Extension** 51–53

 **Objective**

Ⓐ Ⓑ **Core** 11–26, 30–32, 38–41, 47, 49, 50

Ⓒ **Extension** 54–57

Standardized Test Prep 58–61

Mixed Review 62–66

Error Prevention

Exercises 23–26 Students may have errors if they do not carefully consider the quadrant in which $\frac{\theta}{2}$ will lie.

Enrichment 14-7

Reteaching 14-7

Practice 14-7

Practice 14-7 Double-Angle and Half-Angle Identities

Ⓐ **Practice by Example**

Example 1
(page 808)

Use a double-angle identity to find the exact value of each expression.

1. $\sin 240°$ $-\frac{\sqrt{3}}{2}$
2. $\cos 120°$ $-\frac{1}{2}$
3. $\tan 120°$ $-\sqrt{3}$
4. $\sin 90°$ **1**

5. $\cos 240°$ $-\frac{1}{2}$
6. $\tan 240°$ $\sqrt{3}$
7. $\cos 600°$ $-\frac{1}{2}$
8. $\sin 600°$ $-\frac{\sqrt{3}}{2}$

Example 2
(page 808)

Use an angle sum identity to verify each identity.

9. $\sin 2\theta = 2 \sin \theta \cos \theta$
10. $\tan 2\theta = \frac{2 \tan \theta}{1 - \tan^2 \theta}$

9–18. See margin.

Example 3
(page 809)

Use a half-angle identity to find the exact value of each expression.

11. $\cos 15°$
12. $\tan 15°$
13. $\sin 15°$
14. $\sin 22.5°$

15. $\cos 22.5°$
16. $\tan 22.5°$
17. $\cos 90°$
18. $\sin 7.5°$

Example 4
(page 809)

Given $\cos \theta = -\frac{4}{5}$ and $90° < \theta < 180°$, find the exact value of each expression.

19. $\sin \frac{\theta}{2}$ $\frac{3\sqrt{10}}{10}$
20. $\cos \frac{\theta}{2}$ $\frac{\sqrt{10}}{10}$
21. $\tan \frac{\theta}{2}$ **3**
22. $\cot \frac{\theta}{2}$ $\frac{1}{3}$

Given $\cos \theta = -\frac{15}{17}$ and $180° < \theta < 270°$, find the exact value of each expression.

23. $\sin \frac{\theta}{2}$ $\frac{4\sqrt{17}}{17}$
24. $\cos \frac{\theta}{2}$ $-\frac{\sqrt{17}}{17}$
25. $\tan \frac{\theta}{2}$ -4
26. $\sec \frac{\theta}{2}$ $-\sqrt{17}$

Ⓑ **Apply Your Skills**

27–30. See margin pp. 810–811.

$\triangle RST$ has a right angle at $\angle T$. Use identities to show that each equation is true.

27. $\sin 2R = \frac{2rs}{t^2}$
28. $\cos 2R = \frac{s^2 - r^2}{t^2}$

29. $\sin 2S = \sin 2R$
30. $\sin^2 \frac{S}{2} = \frac{t - r}{2t}$

31. $\tan \frac{R}{2} = \frac{r}{t + s}$
32. $\tan^2 \frac{S}{2} = \frac{t - r}{t + r}$

33. Critical Thinking If $\sin 2A = \sin 2B$, must $A = B$? Explain.

31–33. See back of book.

Given $\cos \theta = \frac{3}{5}$ and $270° < \theta < 360°$, find the exact value of each expression.

34. $\sin 2\theta$ $-\frac{24}{25}$
35. $\cos 2\theta$ $-\frac{7}{25}$
36. $\tan 2\theta$ $-\frac{24}{7}$
37. $\csc 2\theta$ $-\frac{25}{24}$

38. $\sin \frac{\theta}{2}$ $\frac{\sqrt{5}}{5}$
39. $\cos \frac{\theta}{2}$ $-\frac{2\sqrt{5}}{5}$
40. $\tan \frac{\theta}{2}$ $-\frac{1}{2}$
41. $\cot \frac{\theta}{2}$ -2

Use identities to write each equation in terms of the single angle θ. Then solve the equation for $0 \le \theta < 2\pi$. **42–45. See margin p. 811.**

42. $4 \sin 2\theta - 3 \cos \theta = 0$
43. $2 \sin 2\theta - 3 \sin \theta = 0$

44. $\sin 2\theta \sin \theta = \cos \theta$
45. $\cos 2\theta = -2 \cos^2 \theta$

Simplify each expression.

46. $2 \cos^2 \theta - \cos 2\theta$ **1**
47. $\sin^2 \frac{\theta}{2} - \cos^2 \frac{\theta}{2}$ $-\cos \theta$
48. $\frac{\cos 2\theta}{\sin \theta + \cos \theta}$ $\cos \theta - \sin \theta$

49. Open-Ended Choose an angle measure A.
a. Find $\sin A$ and $\cos A$. **a–c. See margin p. 811.**
b. Use an identity to find $\sin 2A$.
c. Use an identity to find $\cos \frac{A}{2}$.

50. Writing Is $\frac{\tan \theta}{4} = \tan \frac{\theta}{4}$ an identity? Explain. **See margin p. 811.**

pages 810–811 Exercises

9. $\sin 2\theta = \sin (\theta + \theta) = \sin \theta \cos \theta + \cos \theta \sin \theta = 2 \sin \theta \cos \theta$

10. $\tan 2\theta = \tan (\theta + \theta) = \frac{\tan \theta + \tan \theta}{1 - \tan \theta \tan \theta} = \frac{2 \tan \theta}{1 - \tan^2 \theta}$

11. $\frac{\sqrt{2 + \sqrt{3}}}{2}$

12. $\sqrt{7 - 4\sqrt{3}}$

13. $\frac{\sqrt{2 - \sqrt{3}}}{2}$

14. $\frac{\sqrt{2 - \sqrt{2}}}{2}$

15. $\frac{\sqrt{2 + \sqrt{2}}}{2}$

16. $\sqrt{3 - 2\sqrt{2}}$

17. 0

18. $\frac{\sqrt{2 - \sqrt{2 + \sqrt{3}}}}{2}$

27. $\sin 2R$
$= 2 \sin R \cos R$
$= 2\frac{r}{t} \cdot \frac{s}{t}$
$= \frac{2rs}{t^2}$

28. $\cos 2R$
$= \cos^2 R - \sin^2 R$
$= \left(\frac{s}{t}\right)^2 - \left(\frac{r}{t}\right)^2$
$= \frac{s^2}{t^2} - \frac{r^2}{t^2}$
$= \frac{s^2 - r^2}{t^2}$

810

 **Challenge**

Use double-angle identities to write each expression, using trigonometric functions of θ instead of 4θ. **51–56. See back of book.**

51. $\sin 4\theta$ **52.** $\cos 4\theta$ **53.** $\tan 4\theta$

Use half-angle identities to write each expression, using trigonometric functions of θ instead of $\frac{\theta}{4}$.

54. $\sin \frac{\theta}{4}$ **55.** $\cos \frac{\theta}{4}$ **56.** $\tan \frac{\theta}{4}$

57. Use the Tangent Half-Angle Identity and a Pythagorean identity to prove each identity. **a–b. See back of book.**

a. $\tan \frac{A}{2} = \frac{\sin A}{1 + \cos A}$ **b.** $\tan \frac{A}{2} = \frac{1 - \cos A}{\sin A}$

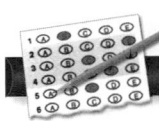

Standardized Test Prep

Multiple Choice

58. If θ is in Quadrant I and $\tan \theta = \frac{5}{12}$, what is the value of $\frac{\tan 4\theta}{5}$ to the nearest hundredth? **D**

A. 18.10 B. 0.33 C. 0.32 D. -23.90

59. If θ is in Quadrant I and $\sin \theta = \frac{3}{5}$, what is an exact value of $\sin 2\theta$? **G**

F. $\frac{9}{25}$ G. $\frac{24}{25}$ H. $\frac{6}{5}$ I. 73.7

Short Response

60. Use a half-angle identity to find an exact value of $\sin 67.5°$. **See back of book.**

Extended Response

61. In the diagram at the right, line ℓ_1 forms an angle of θ with the positive x-axis and crosses the line $x = 1$ at (1, 0.5). Line ℓ_2 forms an angle of 2θ with the positive x-axis. Find the coordinates of the point where ℓ_2 intersects $x = 1$. Show your work. **See back of book.**

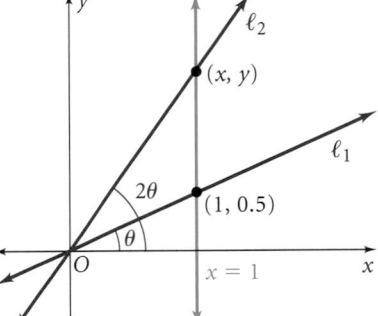

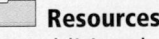 **Take It to the NET**
Online lesson quiz at
www.PHSchool.com
Web Code: aga-1407

Mixed Review

Lesson 14-6

Find each exact value. Use a sum or difference identity.

62. $\cos 405°$ $\frac{\sqrt{2}}{2}$ **63.** $\sin (-300°)$ $\frac{\sqrt{3}}{2}$ **64.** $\tan (-300°)$ $\sqrt{3}$

Lesson 13-1

Find the period and amplitude of each periodic function.

65. 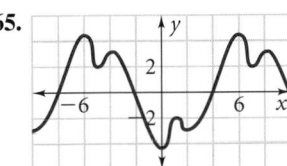 12, about 4.1

66. 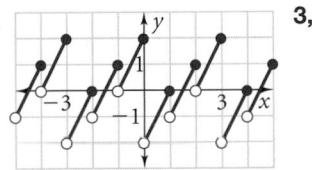 3, 2

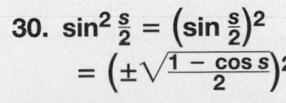

Lesson 14-7 Double-Angle and Half-Angle Identities **811**

---

29. $\sin 2S = 2 \sin S \cos S$
$= 2 \cdot \frac{s}{t} \cdot \frac{r}{t} = \frac{2sr}{t^2}$
$= 2 \sin R \cos R = \sin 2R$

30. $\sin^2 \frac{s}{2} = \left(\sin \frac{s}{2}\right)^2$
$= \left(\pm\sqrt{\frac{1 - \cos s}{2}}\right)^2$

$= \frac{1 - \cos s}{2} = \frac{1 - \frac{r}{t}}{2}$
$= \frac{1}{2} - \frac{r}{2t} = \frac{t - r}{2t}$

42. $\cos \theta (8 \sin \theta - 3) = 0$
$\frac{\pi}{2}, \frac{3\pi}{2}, 0.384, 2.757$

43. $\sin \theta (4 \cos \theta - 3) = 0$
$0, \pi, 0.723, 5.560$

44. $\cos \theta (2 \sin^2 \theta - 1) = 0$
$\frac{\pi}{2}, \frac{3\pi}{2}, \frac{\pi}{4}, \frac{3\pi}{4}, \frac{5\pi}{4}, \frac{7\pi}{4}$

45. $4 \cos^2 \theta - 1 = 0$
$\frac{\pi}{3}, \frac{2\pi}{3}, \frac{4\pi}{3}, \frac{5\pi}{3}$

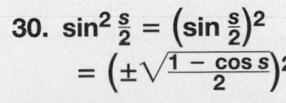

 **4. Assess**

Lesson Quiz 14-7

1. Use a double-angle identity to find the exact value of $\sin 660°$. $-\frac{\sqrt{3}}{2}$

2. Use an angle sum identity and a double-angle identity to verify the identity $\sin 3\theta = 3 \sin \theta - 4 \sin^3\theta$.
$\sin 3\theta = \sin (2\theta + \theta)$
$= \sin 2\theta \cos \theta + \cos 2\theta \sin \theta$
$= (2 \sin \theta \cos \theta)\cos \theta + (\cos^2 \theta - \sin^2 \theta)\sin \theta$
$= 3 \sin \theta \cos^2 \theta - \sin^3 \theta$
$= 3 \sin \theta (1 - \sin^2 \theta) - \sin^3 \theta$
$= 3 \sin \theta - 4 \sin^3 \theta$

3. Use a half-angle identity to find the exact value of $\sin 67.5°$. $\frac{\sqrt{2 + \sqrt{2}}}{2}$

4. Given $\cos \theta = -\frac{20}{29}$ and $180° < \theta < 270°$, find the exact value of $\cos \frac{\theta}{2}$.
$-\frac{3\sqrt{58}}{58}$

Alternative Assessment

Have students work individually to create a problem similar to those in Exercises 1–8 and a problem similar to those in Exercises 19–26. Ask students to solve each of the problems that they create. Suggest they check their results with a calculator.

Standardized Test Prep

Resources
For additional practice with a variety of test item formats:
• Standardized Test Prep, p. 817
• Test-Taking Strategies, p. 812
• Test-Taking Strategies with Transparencies

49. Answers may vary.
Sample:

a. $\sin 60 = \frac{\sqrt{3}}{2}$, $\cos 60 = \frac{1}{2}$

b. $\sin 120 = \frac{\sqrt{3}}{2}$

c. $\cos 30 = \frac{\sqrt{3}}{2}$

Answering Open-Ended Questions

Many assessment tests now require students to answer open-ended questions that are scored according to rubrics. This feature helps students understand the kinds of criteria used in constructing the rubrics. Understanding these criteria will help students think about how to maximize their scores on such test items.

Resources

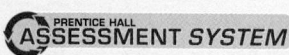

Test-Taking Strategies with Transparencies
• Transparency 14
• Practice sheet p. 38

Teaching Notes

Suggest students use unit circle diagrams to get a clearer under-standing of the conditions for the problems posed in each exercise.

English Learners

Explain that *rubrics* are rules that help both students and teachers classify and evaluate answers to questions.

Test-Taking Strategies with Transparencies

Test-Taking Strategy: Answering Open-Ended Questions

1. Create two different number patterns, so that the first number is the same in both patterns and the second number is the same in both patterns. Write the first 5 numbers in each pattern and describe the pattern.

Scoring Rubric

4 Meets all conditions and follows directions.
3 Meets all conditions, but does not write 5 numbers in each pattern OR does not describe patterns.
2 Meets one or two conditions, OR descriptions do not match patterns.
0 Meets no conditions, OR only one pattern is produced.

2. A clothing store discounts a shirt 30% for a sale. After the sale, a clerk was told to raise the price by 30% of its sale price. The clerk marked the original price on the shirt. Was the clerk right or wrong? Explain.

Scoring Rubric

4 Correctly expresses the current price in terms of the original price, AND concludes the clerk was wrong.
3 Argues convincingly why clerk was wrong, but makes computational errors.
2 Decides clerk was wrong, but presents weak or incomplete argument.
0 Answers inappropriately or not at all.

Transparency 14

812

Open-ended questions ask you to create an example that satisfies certain given conditions. You may need to use your example to answer follow-up questions. As with extended-response questions, you should show all your work since you can receive partial credit.

EXAMPLE

For angles A and B, $A \neq B$ and $\sin A = \sin B$.
a. Find three pairs of values for A and B.
b. Write and prove a relation for A and B.

Here is a scoring rubric for a 4-point response.

[4] **a.** three pairs that satisfy the conditions
b. $A + B = n\pi$, where n is an odd integer, or $A - B = 2n\pi$, or any correct relation with a specific value of n; proves the relation.

[3] **a.** three pairs that satisfy the conditions
b. $A + B = n\pi$, where n is an odd integer, or $A - B = 2n\pi$, or any correct relation with a specific value of n; does not prove the relation.

[2] **a.** three pairs that satisfy the conditions
b. no answer or incorrect answer

[1] **a.** one or two pairs that satisfy the conditions
b. no answer or incorrect answer

The following response is worth 2 points.

a. $A = 0, B = \pi$
$A = 0, B = 2\pi$
$A = \frac{\pi}{6}, B = \frac{5\pi}{6}$

b. $A + B = 2\pi$. Let $A = 2\pi - B$.
$\sin(2\pi - B) = \sin(2\pi)\cos(B) - \cos(2\pi)\sin(B)$
$= 0 - (-1)\sin(B)$
$= \sin(B)$

2a. $A = 0, B = \pi$
$A = 0, B = 2\pi$
$A = \frac{\pi}{6}, B = \frac{5\pi}{6}$

b. $A + B = \pi$
$\sin A = \sin(\pi - B) =$
$\sin \pi \cos B - \cos \pi \cdot$
$\sin B = 0 \cos B -$
$(-1)\sin B = \sin B$

EXERCISES

1. Explain why the response above received only 2 points. **Part (a) is correct but part (b) is incorrect.**

2. Write a 4-point response for the Example. **See right.**

Find three sets of values for A and B, where $A \neq B$, that make each equation true. Write and prove a relation for A and B. 3–4. See margin.

3. $\cos A = \cos B$

4. $\tan A = \tan B$

5. Find three sets of values for A and B such that $\sin(A + B) = \sin A + \sin B$. Write and prove a relation for A and B. **See back of book.**

page 812 Test-Taking Strategies

3. $A = 0, B = 2\pi$
$A = \frac{\pi}{2}, B = \frac{3\pi}{2}$
$A = 2\pi, B = 0;$

$A + B = 2\pi$
$\cos A = \cos(2\pi - B) =$
$\cos 2\pi \cos B +$
$\sin 2\pi \sin B =$
$(1) \cos B + (0) \sin B =$
$\cos B$

4. $A = 0, B = \pi$
$A = \frac{\pi}{4}, B = \frac{5\pi}{4}$
$A = \frac{3\pi}{4}, B = \frac{7\pi}{4};$
$A = B + \pi$

$\tan A = \tan(B + \pi)$
$\frac{\tan B + \tan \pi}{1 - \tan B \tan \pi} =$
$\frac{\tan B + 0}{1 - \tan B \cdot 0} = \frac{\tan B}{1} =$
$\tan B$

Chapter Review

Vocabulary

Law of Cosines (p. 794)
Law of Sines (p. 787)

trigonometric identity (p. 764)

trigonometric ratios for a right
triangle (p. 778)

Reading Math
Understanding
Vocabulary

2. **trigonometric ratios
for a right triangle**

Take It to the NET
Online vocabulary quiz
at www.PHSchool.com
Web Code: agj-1451

4. **trigonometric identity**

Choose the correct vocabulary term to complete each sentence.

1. You can find missing measures of any triangle by using the _?_ if you know the measures of two angles and a side. **Law of Sines**

2. The six ratios of the lengths of the sides of a right triangle are known as the _?_.

3. If you know the measures of two sides and the angle between them, you can use the _?_ to find missing parts of any triangle. **Law of Cosines**

4. A trigonometric equation that is true for all values except those for which the expressions on either side of the equal sign are undefined is a _?_.

5. The _?_ can be used to find missing measures of any triangle when you know two sides and the angle opposite one of them. **Law of Sines**

Skills and Concepts

14-1 Objectives

▼ To verify trigonometric identities (p. 764)

A **trigonometric identity** is a trigonometric equation that is true for all values except those for which the expressions on either side of the equal sign are undefined.

Reciprocal Identities

$$\csc \theta = \frac{1}{\sin \theta}$$

$$\sec \theta = \frac{1}{\cos \theta}$$

$$\cot \theta = \frac{1}{\tan \theta}$$

Tangent and Cotangent Identities

$$\tan \theta = \frac{\sin \theta}{\cos \theta}$$

$$\cot \theta = \frac{\cos \theta}{\sin \theta}$$

Pythagorean Identities

$$\cos^2 \theta + \sin^2 \theta = 1$$

$$1 + \tan^2 \theta = \sec^2 \theta$$

$$1 + \cot^2 \theta = \csc^2 \theta$$

Verify each identity. **6–7. See margin.**

6. $\sin \theta \tan \theta = \frac{1}{\cos \theta} - \cos \theta$

7. $\cos^2 \theta \cot^2 \theta = \cot^2 \theta - \cos^2 \theta$

Simplify each trigonometric expression.

8. $1 - \sin^2 \theta$ **$\cos^2 \theta$**

9. $\frac{\cos \theta}{\sin \theta \cot \theta}$ **1**

10. $\csc^2 \theta - \cot^2 \theta$ **1**

14-2 Objectives

▼ To evaluate inverses of trigonometric functions (p. 769)

▼ To solve trigonometric equations (p. 771)

The function $\cos^{-1} x$ is the inverse of $\cos \theta$ with the restricted domain $0 \le \theta \le \pi$. The functions $\sin^{-1} x$ and $\tan^{-1} x$ are the inverses of $\sin \theta$ and $\cos \theta$, $-\frac{\pi}{2} \le \theta \le \frac{\pi}{2}$.

Use a unit circle and 30°-60°-90° triangles to find the value in degrees of each expression.

11. $\sin^{-1}\left(-\frac{\sqrt{3}}{2}\right)$ **−60°**

12. $\tan^{-1} \sqrt{3}$ **60°**

13. $\tan^{-1}\left(-\frac{\sqrt{3}}{3}\right)$ **−30°**

14. $\cos^{-1} \frac{\sqrt{3}}{2}$ **30°**

pages 813–815   Chapter Review

6. $\sin \theta \tan \theta = \frac{\sin^2 \theta}{\cos \theta}$

$$= \frac{1 - \cos^2 \theta}{\cos \theta} = \frac{1}{\cos \theta} - \frac{\cos^2 \theta}{\cos \theta}$$

$$= \frac{1}{\cos \theta} - \cos \theta$$

7. $\cos^2 \theta \cot^2 \theta = (1 - \sin^2 \theta) \cot^2 \theta$

$$= \cot^2 \theta - \sin^2 \theta \cot^2 \theta$$

$$= \cot^2 \theta - \sin^2 \theta \cdot \frac{\cos^2 \theta}{\sin^2 \theta}$$

$$= \cot^2 \theta - \cos^2 \theta$$

Resources

Student Edition
Extra Practice, Ch. 14, p. 835
English/Spanish Glossary, p. 871
Properties and Formulas, p. 865
Table of Symbols, p. 861

Reaching All Students
Reading and Math Literacy 14D
Spanish Reading and Math
Literacy 14D

ASSESSMENT SYSTEM

Standardized Test Prep
● Ch. 14 practice in standardized test formats

www.PHSchool.com
Student Site
● Self-grading Vocabulary Test
Teacher Center
● Resources

Plus

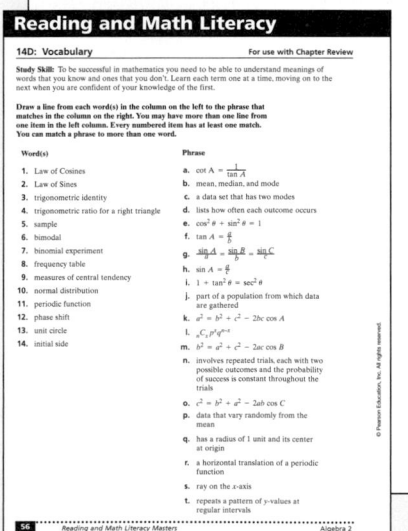

15. $0.34 + 2\pi n$, $2.80 + 2\pi n$

16. $-1.11 + 2\pi n$, $2.03 + 2\pi n$

17. $2.27 + 2\pi n$, $4.02 + 2\pi n$

18. $0.20 + 2\pi n$, $6.08 + 2\pi n$

Use a calculator to find the value in radians of each expression.

15. $\sin^{-1} 0.33$ **16.** $\tan^{-1}(-2)$ **17.** $\cos^{-1}(-0.64)$ **18.** $\cos^{-1} 0.98$

Solve each equation for $0 \le \theta < 2\pi$.

19. $2\cos\theta = 1$
$\frac{\pi}{3}, \frac{5\pi}{3}$

20. $\sqrt{3}\tan\theta = 1$
$\frac{\pi}{6}, \frac{7\pi}{6}$

21. $\sin\theta = \sin^2\theta$
$0, \frac{\pi}{2}, \pi$

14-3 Objectives

▼ To find lengths of sides in a right triangle (p. 778)

▼ To find measures of angles in a right triangle (p. 781)

The six different ratios of the sides of a right triangle are known as the **trigonometric ratios for a right triangle**. These ratios depend on the size of the acute angles in the right triangle.

In a right triangle ABC that has an acute $\angle A$ and right $\angle C$, the ratios are defined as follows.

$$\sin A = \frac{\text{length of leg opposite } \angle A}{\text{length of hypotenuse}} = \frac{a}{c} \qquad \csc A = \frac{\text{length of hypotenuse}}{\text{length of leg opposite } \angle A} = \frac{c}{a}$$

$$\cos A = \frac{\text{length of leg adjacent to } \angle A}{\text{length of hypotenuse}} = \frac{b}{c} \qquad \sec A = \frac{\text{length of hypotenuse}}{\text{length of leg adjacent to } \angle A} = \frac{c}{b}$$

$$\tan A = \frac{\text{length of leg opposite } \angle A}{\text{length of leg adjacent to } \angle A} = \frac{a}{b} \qquad \cot A = \frac{\text{length of leg adjacent to } \angle A}{\text{length of leg opposite } \angle A} = \frac{b}{a}$$

In $\triangle ABC$, $\angle B$ is a right angle, $AB = 30$, and $\sec A = \frac{5}{3}$. Find each value in fraction and in decimal form.

22. $\cos A$ $\frac{3}{5}$, 0.6   **23.** $\sin A$ $\frac{4}{5}$, 0.8   **24.** $\tan C$ $\frac{3}{4}$, 0.75

In $\triangle GHI$, $\angle H$ is a right angle. Find the remaining sides and angles. Round your answers to the nearest tenth.

25. $g = 3$, $i = 9$
$3\sqrt{10}$, 18.4°, 71.6°

26. $g = 12$, $h = 20$
16, 36.9°, 53.1°

27. $h = 55$, $i = 40$
37.7, 43.3°, 46.7°

14-4 Objectives

▼ To find the area of any triangle and to use the Law of Sines (p. 787)

You can find missing measures of any triangle if you know the measures of two angles and any side or if you know the measures of two sides and the angle opposite one of them by using the **Law of Sines.**

The Law of Sines states that for $\triangle ABC$, if a, b, and c represent the lengths of the sides opposite $\angle A$, $\angle B$, and $\angle C$, respectively, then $\frac{\sin A}{a} = \frac{\sin B}{b} = \frac{\sin C}{c}$.

Find the area of each triangle. Round your answers to the nearest hundredth.

28.
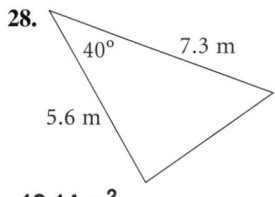
40°, 7.3 m, 5.6 m
13.14 m²

29.
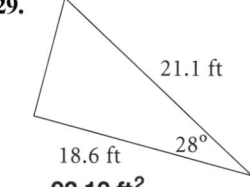
21.1 ft, 28°, 18.6 ft
92.12 ft²

30. **57.81 m²**
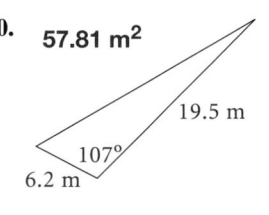
19.5 m, 107°, 6.2 m

31. In $\triangle LMN$, $m\angle L = 67°$, $m\angle N = 24°$, and $MN = 16$ in. Find LM to the nearest tenth. **7.1 in.**

32. In $\triangle XYZ$, $m\angle Z = 34°$, $x = 61$ cm, and $z = 42$ cm. Find $m\angle X$ to the nearest tenth. **54.3° or 125.7°**

14-5 Objectives

▼ To use the Law of Cosines to find the area of any triangle (p. 794)

You can find missing parts of any triangle when you know the measures of two sides and the angle between them, or all three sides, by using the **Law of Cosines.** For $\triangle ABC$, the following are true.

$$a^2 = b^2 + c^2 - 2bc \cos A \quad b^2 = a^2 + c^2 - 2ac \cos B \quad c^2 = a^2 + b^2 - 2ab \cos C$$

33. In $\triangle ABC$, $m\angle B = 45°$, $a = 24$ ft, and $c = 30$ ft. Find b to the nearest tenth.

33. 21.4 ft

34. 43.9°

34. In $\triangle DEF$, $d = 25$ in., $e = 28$ in., and $f = 20$ in. Find $m\angle F$ to the nearest tenth.

35. In $\triangle GHI$, $h = 8$, $i = 12$, and $m\angle G = 96°$. Find $m\angle I$ to the nearest tenth. **52.2°**

14-6 Objectives

▼ To verify angle identities (p. 800)

▼ To verify sum and difference identities (p. 802)

Angle identities are used to solve trigonometric equations.

Negative angle identities

$$\sin(-\theta) = -\sin\theta \qquad \cos(-\theta) = \cos\theta \qquad \tan(-\theta) = -\tan\theta$$

Cofunction identities

$$\sin\left(\frac{\pi}{2} - \theta\right) = \cos\theta \qquad \cos\left(\frac{\pi}{2} - \theta\right) = \sin\theta \qquad \tan\left(\frac{\pi}{2} - \theta\right) = \cot\theta$$

Angle difference identities

$$\sin(A - B) = \sin A \cos B - \cos A \sin B \qquad \tan(A - B) = \frac{\tan A - \tan B}{1 + \tan A \tan B}$$
$$\cos(A - B) = \cos A \cos B + \sin A \sin B$$

Angle sum identities

$$\sin(A + B) = \sin A \cos B + \cos A \sin B \qquad \tan(A + B) = \frac{\tan A + \tan B}{1 - \tan A \tan B}$$
$$\cos(A + B) = \cos A \cos B - \sin A \sin B$$

Verify each identity.   **36–37. See margin.**

36. $\cos\left(\theta + \frac{\pi}{2}\right) = -\sin\theta$ **37.** $\sin^2\left(\theta - \frac{\pi}{2}\right) = \cos^2\theta$

Solve each trigonometric equation for $0 \le \theta < 2\pi$.

38. $\tan\left(\frac{\pi}{2} - \theta\right) = \cos\theta$ $\frac{\pi}{2}$ **and** $\frac{3\pi}{2}$ **39.** $1 + \tan^2\theta = \cos\theta$ **0**

14-7 Objectives

▼ To verify double-angle identities (p. 807)

▼ To verify half-angle identities (p. 808)

You can use double-angle and half-angle identities to find exact values of trigonometric expressions. In the half-angle identities, choose the positive or negative sign for each function depending on the quadrant in which $\frac{A}{2}$ lies.

Double-angle identities

$$\cos 2\theta = \cos^2\theta - \sin^2\theta \qquad \sin 2\theta = 2\sin\theta\cos\theta \qquad \tan 2\theta = \frac{2\tan\theta}{1 - \tan^2\theta}$$
$$\cos 2\theta = 2\cos^2\theta - 1 \qquad \cos 2\theta = 1 - 2\sin^2\theta$$

Half-angle identities

$$\sin\frac{A}{2} = \pm\sqrt{\frac{1 - \cos A}{2}} \qquad \cos\frac{A}{2} = \pm\sqrt{\frac{1 + \cos A}{2}} \qquad \tan\frac{A}{2} = \pm\sqrt{\frac{1 - \cos A}{1 + \cos A}}$$

Use a double-angle identity to find the exact value of each expression.

40. $\sin 120°$ $\frac{\sqrt{3}}{2}$ **41.** $\cos 90°$ **0**   **42.** $\tan 300°$ $-\sqrt{3}$

Use a half-angle identity to find the exact value of each expression.

43. $\cos 180°$ **−1**   **44.** $\tan 60°$ $\sqrt{3}$ **45.** $\sin 120°$ $\frac{\sqrt{3}}{2}$

Chapter 14   Chapter Review   **815**

pages 813–815   **Chapter Review**

36. $\cos\left(\theta + \frac{\pi}{2}\right) = \cos\theta\cos\left(\frac{\pi}{2}\right) - \sin\theta\sin\left(\frac{\pi}{2}\right)$

           $= \cos\theta \cdot 0 - \sin\theta \cdot 1$

           $= -\sin\theta$

37. $\sin^2\left(\theta - \frac{\pi}{2}\right) = \sin^2\left(-\left(\frac{\pi}{2} - \theta\right)\right)$

           $= \left(-\sin\left(\frac{\pi}{2} - \theta\right)\right) \cdot \left(-\sin\left(\frac{\pi}{2} - \theta\right)\right)$

           $= (-\cos\theta)(-\cos\theta)$

           $= \cos^2\theta$

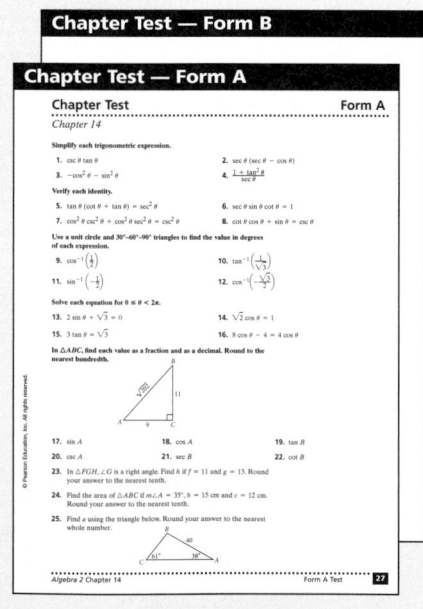
Chapter 14 Chapter Test

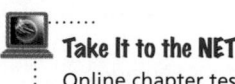 **Take It to the NET**
Online chapter test at
www.PHSchool.com
Web Code: aga-1452

Simplify each trigonometric expression.

1. $\sin\theta + \cos\theta\cot\theta$ **csc θ**

2. $\sec\theta\sin\theta\cot\theta$ **1**

3. $\cot\theta(\tan\theta + \cot\theta)$ **csc² θ**

Verify each identity.   4–7. See margin.

4. $\csc\theta\cos\theta\tan\theta = 1$ 5. $\csc^2\theta - \cot^2\theta = 1$

6. $\sec\theta\cot\theta = \csc\theta$ 7. $\sec^2\theta - 1 = \tan^2\theta$

Use a unit circle and 30°-60°-90° triangles to find the value in degrees of each expression.

8. $\sin^{-1}\left(\frac{\sqrt{3}}{2}\right)$ 9. $\cos^{-1}\left(\frac{\sqrt{3}}{2}\right)$

10. $\cos^{-1}(-1)$ 11. $\tan^{-1}(\sqrt{3})$
   8–12. See margin.

Solve each equation for $0 \le \theta < 2\pi$.

12. $4\sin\theta + 2\sqrt{3} = 0$ 13. $2\cos\theta = 1$ $\frac{\pi}{3}, \frac{5\pi}{3}$

14. $\sqrt{2}\sin\theta - 1 = 0$ $\frac{\pi}{4}, \frac{3\pi}{4}$

In $\triangle ABC$, find each value as a fraction and as a decimal. Round to the nearest hundredth.

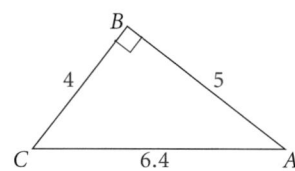

15–20. See
back of book.

15. $\sin A$ 16. $\sec A$ 17. $\cot A$

18. $\csc C$ 19. $\sec C$ 20. $\tan C$

In $\triangle DEF$, $\angle F$ is a right angle. Find the remaining sides and angles. Round your answers to the nearest tenth.

21. $e = 6, f = 10$ 22. $d = 10, e = 12$

23. $e = 21, f = 51$ 24. $d = 5.5, e = 2.6$
21–24. See back of book.

25. Find the area of the triangle.

91.8 m²

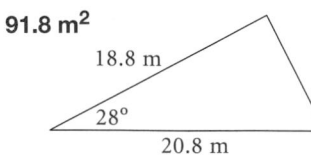

26. In $\triangle ABC, m\angle A = 45°, m\angle C = 23°$, and $BC = 25$ in. Find AB to the nearest tenth. **13.8 in.**

27. In $\triangle DEF, m\angle F = 56°, m\angle E = 34°$, and $DF = 10$ ft. Find EF to the nearest tenth. **17.9 ft**

28. In $\triangle GHI, m\angle I = 45°, g = 32$ cm, and $i = 52$ cm. Find $m\angle G$ to the nearest tenth. **25.8°**

29. In $\triangle JKL, m\angle J = 29°, l = 35$ m, and $j = 56$ m. Find $m\angle L$ to the nearest tenth. **17.6°**

30. **Writing** Suppose you know the lengths of all three sides of a triangle. Can you use the Law of Sines to find the measures of the angles? Explain.
   See margin.

31. In $\triangle MNO, m\angle N = 45°, m = 20$ cm, and $o = 41$ cm. Find n to the nearest tenth. **30.4 cm**

32. In $\triangle PQR, p = 51$ ft, $q = 81$ ft, and $r = 61$ ft. Find $m\angle R$ to the nearest tenth. **48.8°**

33. In $\triangle STU, m\angle S = 96°, t = 8$ in., and $u = 10$ in. Find $m\angle U$ to the nearest tenth. **47.9°**

Verify each identity.   34–37. See back of book.

34. $-\sin\left(\theta - \frac{\pi}{2}\right) = \cos\theta$

35. $\csc\left(\theta + \frac{\pi}{2}\right) = \sec\theta$

36. $\csc\left(\theta - \frac{\pi}{2}\right) = -\sec\theta$

37. $\cos\left(-\theta - \frac{\pi}{2}\right) = \sin(-\theta)$

Solve each trigonometric equation for $0 \le \theta < 2\pi$.
   0, π

38. $\sin\left(\frac{\pi}{2} - \theta\right) = \sec\theta$ 39. $\cos\left(\frac{\pi}{2} - \theta\right) = \csc\theta$
   $\frac{\pi}{2}, \frac{3\pi}{2}$

40. $\cot\left(\frac{\pi}{2} - \theta\right) = \sin\theta$ **0**

Use a double-angle identity to find the exact value of each expression.

41. $\sin 60°$ $\frac{\sqrt{3}}{2}$ 42. $\cos 60°$ $\frac{1}{2}$ 43. $\tan 60°$ $\sqrt{3}$

Use a half-angle identity to find the exact value of each expression.

44. $\tan 30°$ $\frac{\sqrt{3}}{3}$ 45. $\sin 90°$ **1**   46. $\cos 180°$ **−1**

47. **Open-Ended** Choose an angle measure A. Find $\sin A$ and $\cos A$. Then use the identities to find $\cos 2A$ and $\sin\frac{A}{2}$. **Check students' work.**

---

page 816 Chapter Test

4. $\csc\theta\cos\theta\tan\theta =$

$\frac{1}{\sin\theta} \cdot \frac{\cos\theta}{1} \cdot \frac{\sin\theta}{\cos\theta} =$

$\frac{\cos\theta\sin\theta}{\sin\theta\cos\theta} = 1$

5. $\csc^2\theta - \cot^2\theta =$
   $1 + \cot^2\theta - \cot^2\theta = 1$

6. $\sec\theta\cot\theta = \frac{1}{\cos\theta} \cdot \frac{\cos\theta}{\sin\theta}$
   $= \frac{1}{\sin\theta} = \csc\theta$

7. $\sec^2\theta - 1 = 1 + \tan^2\theta - 1$
   $= \tan^2\theta$

8. $60° + 360° \cdot n, 120° + 360° \cdot n$

9. $30° + 360° \cdot n, 330° + 360° \cdot n$

10. $180° + 360° \cdot n$

11. $60° + 360° \cdot n, 240° + 360° \cdot n$

12. $\frac{4\pi}{3}, \frac{5\pi}{3}$

30. No; the Law of Sines requires at least one angle in order to set up a ratio of side-to-angle, which can then be compared to the other sides.

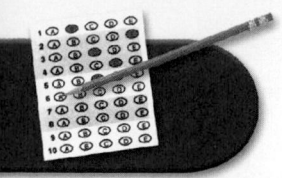

Standardized Test Prep

 CUMULATIVE REVIEW
CHAPTERS 1–14

Take It to the NET
Online end-of-course test
at www.PHSchool.com
Web Code: aga-1454

 **Standardized Test Prep**

Multiple Choice

For Exercises 1–23, choose the correct letter.

1. Which conic section is an ellipse? **C**
   A. $(x - 1)^2 + (y - 2)^2 = 4$
   B. $(x + 4)^2 - (y - 3)^2 = 25$
   C. $\frac{x^2}{36} + \frac{y^2}{81} = 100$
   D. $\frac{x^2}{9} - \frac{y^2}{49} = 121$

2. How many solutions does the system
$\begin{cases} y = \frac{1}{2}x^3 - 1 \\ y = -x^2 + 4 \end{cases}$ have? **G**
   F. 0   G. 1   H. 2   I. 3

3. In which sequence is a_{25} the greatest? **A**
   A. $a_n = 2a_{n-1} + 7, a_1 = 5$
   B. $a_n = 3n - 10$
   C. $a_n = a_{n-1} + 18, a_1 = -7$
   D. $a_n = n^2 - 200$

4. What is the inverse of the function $f(x) = x^3 + 4$? **H**
   F. $f^{-1}(x) = \frac{1}{3}x - 4$
   G. $f^{-1}(x) = \sqrt[3]{x} - 4$
   H. $f^{-1}(x) = \sqrt[3]{x - 4}$
   I. $f^{-1}(x) = \sqrt[4]{x - 3}$

5. Which function shifts $y = |x + 1| - 3$ right 4 units and down 7 units? **D**
   A. $y = |x - 6| + 1$
   B. $y = |x - 3| + 4$
   C. $y = |x + 5| - 10$
   D. $y = |x - 3| - 10$

6. Which is a direct variation that includes the point (10, 1)? **F**
   I. $y = 10x$ II. $y = 0.1x$
   III. $xy = 10$ IV. $y = 0.5x - 4$

   F. II only   G. I and III only
   H. II, III, and IV   I. I only

7. Which of the following expressions is equivalent to $3 \log x + 2 \log y - \log x$? **D**
   I. $2 \log xy$ II. $\log x^2 + \log y^2$
   III. $2 \log x + 2 \log y$ IV. $4 \log x - y$

   A. I and II only   B. II and III only
   C. III and IV only   D. I, II, and III only

8. Which periodic function is a tangent function? **I**
   F. 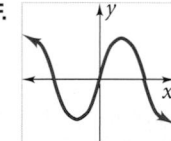   G.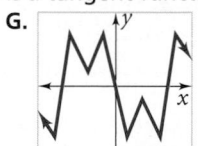
   H. 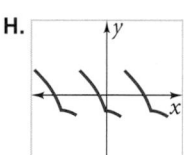   I.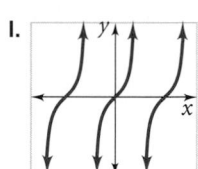

9. What is the solution of the matrix equation
$\begin{bmatrix} 10 & 9 & -5 \\ 3 & 12 & 7 \end{bmatrix} - X = \begin{bmatrix} 4 & -8 & 5 \\ 15 & -3 & 0 \end{bmatrix}$? **A**
   A. $\begin{bmatrix} 6 & 17 & -10 \\ -12 & 15 & 7 \end{bmatrix}$
   B. $\begin{bmatrix} 14 & 1 & 0 \\ 18 & 9 & 7 \end{bmatrix}$
   C. $\begin{bmatrix} 15 & 1 & -1 \\ 3 & 9 & 22 \end{bmatrix}$
   D. $\begin{bmatrix} -6 & -17 & 10 \\ 12 & -15 & -7 \end{bmatrix}$

10. What is the distance of $4 - 5i$ from the origin? **G**
   F. 9 units
   G. $\sqrt{41}$ units
   H. 3 units
   I. 1 unit

11. Which of the following is a simplification of $\frac{x^2 y^3 z}{4x} \div \frac{3xy^4 z^2}{2z}$? **D**
   A. $\frac{3x^3 y^7 z^3}{8xz}$
   B. $\frac{3x^2 y^7 z^2}{8}$
   C. $\frac{2x^2 y^3 z^2}{12x^2 y^4 z^2}$
   D. $\frac{1}{6y}$

Resources

📁 **Teaching Resources**
Cumulative Review
Quarter 4 Test, Forms A & B
End-of-Course Test, Forms A & B

👥 **Reaching All Students**
Spanish Cumulative Review
Spanish Quarter 4 Test,
   Forms A & B
Spanish End-of-Course Test,
   Forms A & B

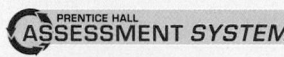 **PRENTICE HALL ASSESSMENT SYSTEM**

Standardized Test Prep
● Ch. 14 Standardized Test Practice
Assessment Masters
● Cumulative Review
● Quarter 4 Test, Forms A & B
● End-of-Course Test, Forms A & B
Computer Test Generator CD
● Standarized Test Practice

 www.PHSchool.com
● Standarized Test Practice
● Resources

Plus

Item	1	2	3	4	5	6	7	8	9	10	11
Lesson	10-4	3-1/2	11-2/3	7-7	2-6	2-3	8-4	13-6	4-2	5-6	7-2

Item	Lesson
12	3-4
13	14-4
14	13-4
15	13-3
16	6-1
17	8-2
18	8-4
19	13-5
20	11-2
21	12-3

12. Which point is a solution of the following system? **H**

$$\begin{cases} y \le 3x - 2 \\ y < 2x \\ x \ge -1 \\ y \ge -4 \end{cases}$$

F. $(0, 7)$
G. $(-4, 1)$
H. $(3, 1)$
I. $(-1, -5)$

13. The Law of Sines cannot be used as the first step in solving which of these triangles? **C**

A.
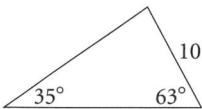

B.
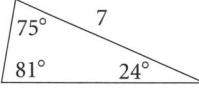

C.
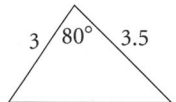

D.
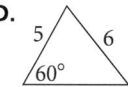

14. What is the amplitude of $y = -4 \sin \frac{1}{2}x$? **G**
F. 4π
G. 4
H. $\frac{1}{2}$
I. -4

15. What is $\frac{5\pi}{6}$ radians in degrees? **B**
A. 300°
B. 150°
C. 170°
D. 80°

16. For $f(x) = x^2 - 1$ and $g(x) = |2x + 3|$, which has the greatest value? **I**
F. $f(g(3))$
G. $g(f(2))$
H. $g(f(-1))$
I. $f(g(10))$

17. Which is the graph of an exponential function? **C**

A.
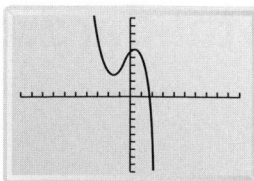

B.
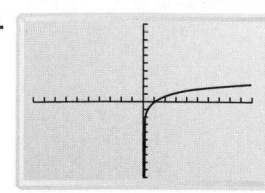

C.
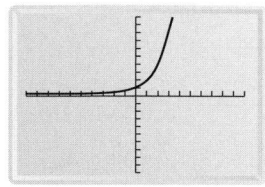

D.
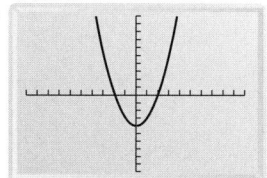

18. Which of the following expressions is equivalent to $3 \log x - 2 \log 2x$? **I**
F. $-\log x$ 　　　 **G.** $\log (-x)$
H. $\log \frac{x}{2}$ 　　　 **I.** $\log \frac{x}{4}$

19. In $\triangle ABC$, $m\angle A = 36°$, $b = 12$, and $c = 25$. What is the length of a rounded to the nearest hundredth? **D**
A. 15.94 　　　 **B.** 253.95
C. 283.59 　　　 **D.** 16.84

20. Which sequence has a common difference of 3? **G**
I. $a_n = a_{n-1} - 3$, $a_1 = 2$
II. $a_n = 3$
III. $a_n = a_{n-1} + 3$, $a_1 = -7$
IV. $a_n = n^2 + 3$

F. I only 　　　 **G.** III only
H. I and III 　　　 **I.** II and IV

21. Which is greatest for the following data? **D**

3, 4, 5, 5, 5, 5, 6, 7, 8, 9

A. mean 　　　 **B.** mode
C. median 　　　 **D.** range

22. Which of the following equations represents an ellipse? **H**
   F. $3y^2 - x - 6y + 5 = 0$
   G. $x^2 + y^2 - 4x - 6y + 4 = 0$
   H. $4x^2 + y^2 - 16x - 6y + 9 = 0$
   I. $4x^2 - y^2 - 16x + 6y - 9 = 0$

23. Which curve has a period of 3? **C**
   A. $y = 3 \sin 3\theta$ B. $y = \cos \frac{\pi}{3} \theta$
   C. $y = \tan \frac{\pi}{3} \theta$ D. $y = \frac{1}{3} \cos \theta$

Quantitative Comparison

Compare the boxed quantity in Column A with the boxed quantity in Column B. Choose the best answer.

   A. The quantity in Column A is greater.
   B. The quantity in Column B is greater.
   C. The two quantities are equal.
   D. The relationship cannot be determined from the information given.

	Column A	Column B
24. A	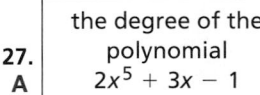 $\sin\frac{\pi}{2}$	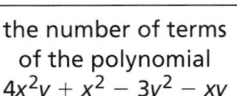 $\cos\frac{\pi}{2}$
25. D	$\sin\theta$	$\cos\theta$
26. B	a_5 when $a_n = 4n - 1$	a_5 when $a_n = 2n^2 - 30$
27. A	the degree of the polynomial $2x^5 + 3x - 1$	the number of terms of the polynomial $4x^2y + x^2 - 3y^2 - xy$
28. D	the third quartile of a given data set	the median of the same data set
29. C	the sum of the solutions of $x^2 + 5x + 6 = 0$	the sum of the solutions of $x^2 + 5x + 4 = 0$

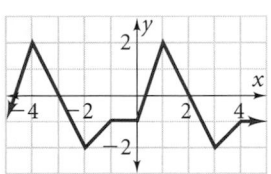

30. A	the period	the amplitude

Gridded Response

31. Express $\frac{5\pi}{9}$ radians in degrees. **100**

32. A pendulum is 18 in. long. It swings through an angle of $\frac{3\pi}{4}$ radians. How far does the tip of the pendulum travel in one swing? Round your answer to the nearest inch. **42**

33. Find a_{33} in the product $\begin{bmatrix} 2 & 1 \\ -6 & 5 \\ -1 & 3 \end{bmatrix} \cdot \begin{bmatrix} 8 & -2 & 0.5 \\ 4 & -7 & 10 \end{bmatrix}$.
   29.5

Short Response   34–42. See back of book.

34. In $\triangle ABC$, $m\angle A = 56°$, $a = 8$, and $c = 6$. Show how to find $m\angle C$. Round to the nearest tenth.

35. Graph the function $y = \sin\left(x + \frac{\pi}{2}\right)$.

36. Divide $2x^4 + 4x^3 + 5x^2 + 9x - 2$ by $x + 2$. Show your work.

37. Write the equation of a rational function with asymptotes $y = 4$ and $x = -2$. Explain your work.

38. Simplify $(5 + 2i)(-3 + i)$. Show your work.

39. You put $600 into an account earning 5% annual interest, compounded continuously. How much will you have after 18 months? Show your work.

40. You roll three number cubes. Can the three events {rolling three of the same number, rolling exactly two of the same number, rolling all different numbers} be used to form a probability distribution? Explain.

41. You roll three number cubes. Find P(all three show the same number).

42. Find the inverse of the matrix $\begin{bmatrix} 6 & -2 \\ 11 & 3 \end{bmatrix}$.

Extended Response   43–44. See back of book.

43. In $\triangle ABC$, $m\angle A = 65°$, $b = 23$, and $c = 19$. Show how to find a. Round to the nearest hundredth.

44. Suppose you receive $350 for your birthday. You can put the money into an account earning 4.5% annual interest compounded continuously, or into an account earning 5% annual interest compounded monthly. Write and solve the equations that show how much you would have in each account after one year and after five years.

Item	Lesson
22	10-4
23	13-4/5/6
24	13-3
25	13-2
26	11-4/5
27	6-1
28	12-4
29	5-8
30	13-4/5/6
31	13-3
32	13-3
33	4-3
34	14-4
35	13-4
36	6-3
37	10-5
38	5-6
39	8-5
40	12-1
41	12-1
42	4-7
43	14-5
44	8-5

A Question of Balance

In these activities students apply their knowledge of formulas and angle measures.

Connecting to Prior Knowledge

Have students share their experiences with balancing a structure—perhaps as they were building a house of cards, or making towers of dominoes or blocks. Or, have students with experience discuss the importance of balance in gymnastics.

Teaching Notes

Have a volunteer read the introductory paragraph. Ask: *What factors make you feel more or less stable when you are on top of a ladder or a fence?*

Teaching Tip

Ask a nearby lumber store or a parent who does construction to give you scraps of two-by-four in lengths of 4, 8, 12, and 16 in. to use for these activities.

Tactile Learners

Have students experiment with plastic bottles of various widths and heights to determine what ratio of height to circumference tends to make such vessels unstable.

Connection to Building Trades

To make clear why wood this size is called "two-by-four," have students research how lumber is sold and measured, and have them find the actual dimensions of a piece of lumber that is labeled two-by-four.

English Learners

Use objects in the classroom to demonstrate the meanings for *unstable, tips over,* and *balance.*

820

DK Real-World Snapshots

A Question of Balance

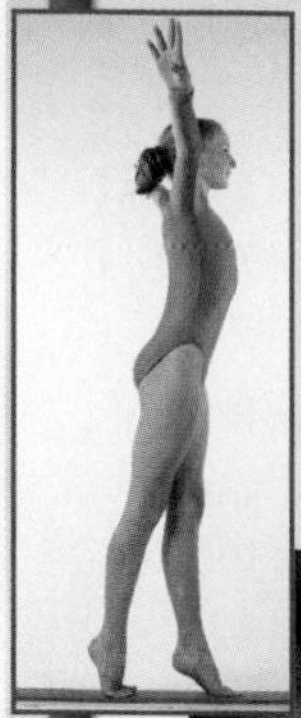

Applying Trigonometry Why is it so difficult to walk on a balance beam? It is difficult because you must keep your body's center of gravity over a narrow base of support to maintain your balance. You can use this idea to calculate the maximum angle any object (or person) can tip without falling over.

The Balance Beam

The balance beam, used only in women's gymnastics, is 5 m long but only 10 cm wide. A beam exercise lasts between 70 and 90 s. Each movement on the balance beam flows freely into the next, with the gymnast pausing only to hold the balance positions.

Activity 1

Materials: four pieces of 2×4 wood (16 in., 12 in., 8 in., 4 in. long), pencil, protractor

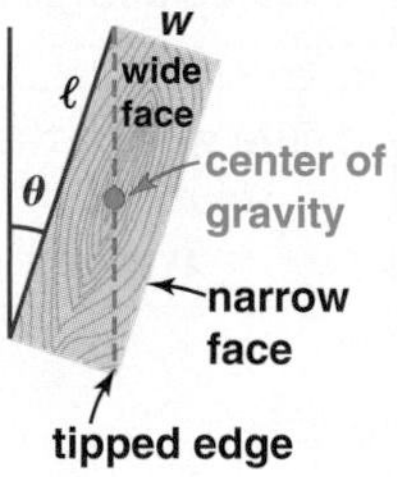

a. Use the diagram to write an equation relating θ to w and the length ℓ of the 2×4.

b. Tip a 16-in.-long piece of 2×4 on the edge of its narrow face. Use a protractor to measure the maximum angle the piece of 2×4 can tip without falling over. Use the equation from part (a) as a check.

c. Repeat part (b) for pieces of 2×4 that measure 4 in., 8 in., and 12 in.

d. Reasoning Suppose you tip the 2×4 on the edge of its wide face instead of its narrow face. Write a new equation relating θ to ℓ and to n, the width of the narrow face. Use your new equation to calculate the value of θ for each of the 2×4 pieces from parts (b) and (c).

Diagram labels: w, wide face, ℓ, center of gravity, θ, narrow face, tipped edge

All photographs © Dorling Kindersley Limited unless otherwise credited on acknowledgments page

---

pages 820–821   **Real-World Snapshots**

Activity 1

a. $\tan \theta = \frac{w}{\ell}$

b. 14°

c. 45°, 26.6°, 18.4°

d. $\tan \theta = \frac{n}{\ell}$; 7.1°, 26.6°, 14.0°, 9.5°

Balancing on a surfboard
To balance on a surfboard requires constant shifting of position due to the motion of the board on the water.

Balance in Ballet
To dance *en pointe* (on the tips of their toes), ballerinas rely on specially reinforced shoes.

Take It to the NET For more information about balance, go to **www.PHSchool.com**.
Web Code: age-1453

Balancing Act
The gymnast on the left below is holding a balance. The gymnast in the middle is in a precarious position, with his center of mass tipping over his foot. The gymnast on the right is tipping over, because his center of mass is no longer over his foot.

Activity 2

a. **Writing** Describe a method to measure the angle at which a piece of wood tips. (*Hints:* The diagram shows only one of the many places where you can measure θ. Also, large protractors are more accurate than small ones.)

b. Measure the angle at which each of the four pieces tips over on the edge of its narrow face.

c. Measure the angle at which each of the four pieces tips over on the edge of its wide face.

d. Compare your results from parts (b) and (c) with the angle measures you obtained in Activity 1.

821

Activity 2
a–d. Check students' work.

Teaching Tip
Before students begin the activity, discuss the illustrations and their captions. Have students work in pairs or in small groups to complete the activities. Have each team read through both activities before beginning to work.

Activity 1

Materials: paper and pencil

Teaching Tip
Help students organize their work by making a table for recording the results with the various lengths. Work with students to identify appropriate labels for the rows and columns.

Activity 2

Materials; paper and pencil, protractor, lengths of 2-by-4 that measure 4, 8, 12, and 16 in.

Teaching Tip
Ask students to read the Hint and then discuss why they can measure more accurately with a large protractor than with a small one. Elicit the fact that a measuring error will be less significant with a large protractor.

Scoring Rubric

This scoring rubric can be used for evaluating student work on both activities. Share this scoring rubric with students before they begin work.

4 Equations and calculations are correct.
   Steps are neat, accurate, and clearly show the mathematics. Responses are clearly indicated and give the appropriate units.
3 Equations and calculations are mostly correct, with some minor errors.
   Steps are neat and mostly accurate. Units are not completely accurate.
2 Equations and calculations contain both major and minor errors.
1 Correct answer, but no work is shown.

Left margin column

9. $-102, \frac{1}{102}$

10. $3.7, -\frac{10}{37}$

11. $-2\frac{3}{4}, \frac{4}{11}$

12. $0.04, -25$

13. $-\sqrt{2}, \frac{\sqrt{2}}{2}$

14. $-\pi + 4, \frac{1}{\pi - 4}$

15. $\frac{8}{5}, -\frac{5}{8}$

16. $-1.5, \frac{2}{3}$

17. $-\frac{6}{7}, \frac{7}{6}$

18. $-\frac{3\pi}{2}, \frac{2}{3\pi}$

19. $-0.0001, 10,000$

20. $-5\sqrt{7}, \frac{\sqrt{7}}{35}$

30. ⟨+++●+++⟩ 0 2 4

31. ⟨+++●+++⟩ −4 −2 0

32. ⟨●++++++++⟩ −10 −8 −6 −4 −2 0

33. ⟨+○++++++⟩ −6 −4 −2 0

34. ⟨++++●++++++⟩ −20 −18 −16 −14 −12 −10

35. ⟨+++⊕+++++⟩ 4 6 8 10 12 14

36. $-3 < r < 5$
⟨+⊕++++⊕+⟩ −4 −2 0 2 4

37. $-2 \le z < 1$
⟨●++⊕+⟩ −2 0 2

38. $3 \le x \le 7$
⟨+●++++●++⟩ 2 4 6 8

39. $x < -2, x > 8$
⟨+++++++⊕++⟩ −2 0 2 4 6 8 10 12

40. $5 < b \le 11$
⟨++⊕++++●+⟩ 0 2 4 6 8 10 12

41. $p > -5$
⟨++⊕+++++⟩ −6 −4 −2 0 2

Right main column

Chapter 1 Extra Practice

Lesson 1-1 Replace each ▦ with the symbol <, >, or = to make the sentence true.

1. $-5 \ \blacksquare \ -8$ **>**
2. $7 \ \blacksquare \ 7$ **=**
3. $0.1 \ \blacksquare \ 0.01$ **>**
4. $12 \ \blacksquare \ \sqrt{12}$ **>**
5. $\frac{3}{8} \ \blacksquare \ 0.375$ **=**
6. $\frac{1}{5} \ \blacksquare \ \frac{1}{4}$ **<**
7. $\frac{1}{3} \ \blacksquare \ 0.333$ **>**
8. $\sqrt{6} \ \blacksquare \ 3$ **<**

Lesson 1-1 Find the opposite and the reciprocal of each number. 9–20. See margin.

9. 102
10. -3.7
11. $2\frac{3}{4}$
12. -0.04
13. $\sqrt{2}$
14. $\pi - 4$
15. $-\frac{8}{5}$
16. 1.5
17. $\frac{6}{7}$
18. $\frac{3\pi}{2}$
19. 0.0001
20. $5\sqrt{7}$

Lesson 1-2 Evaluate each expression for the given values of the variables.

21. $6c + 5d - 4c - 3d + 3c - 6d; c = 4$ and $d = -2$ **28**

22. $10a + 3b - 5a + 4b + 1a + 5b; a = -3$ and $b = 5$ **42**

23. $3m + 9n + 6m - 7n - 4m + 2n; m = 6$ and $n = -4$ **14**

Lesson 1-3 Solve each equation. Check your answers.

24. $5 - w = 2w - 1$ **2**
25. $-2s = 3s - 10$ **2**
26. $2(x + 3) + 2(x + 4) = 24$ $\frac{5}{2}$
27. $8z + 12 = 5z - 21$ **−11**
28. $7b - 6(11 - 2b) = 10$ **4**
29. $10k - 7 = 2(13 - 5k)$ $\frac{33}{20}$

Lesson 1-4 Solve each inequality. Graph the solution. 30–35. See margin for graphs.

30. $3x - 8 \ge 1$ $x \ge 3$
31. $7t + 4 \le 3t$ $t \le -1$
32. $3v \le 5v + 18$ $v \ge -9$
33. $4a < 2a - 7$ $a < -\frac{7}{2}$
34. $7 - x \ge 24$ $x \le -17$
35. $2(y - 3) + 7 < 21$ $y < 10$

Lesson 1-4 Solve each compound inequality. Graph the solution. 36–41. See margin.

36. $4r > -12$ and $2r < 10$
37. $5z \ge -10$ and $3z < 3$
38. $7x \ge 21$ and $8x \le 56$
39. $3x < -6$ or $7x > 56$
40. $9b > 27$ and $4b \le 44$
41. $5p \ge 10$ or $-2p < 10$

Lesson 1-5 Solve each equation. Check your answers.

42. $|4m + 2| = 10$ **2, −3**
43. $|9 - 4z| = 53$ **−11, 15.5**
44. $|5x| = 30$ **−6, 6**
45. $|3x - 6| - 7 = 14$ **−5, 9**
46. $3|2d - 1| = 21$ **−3, 4**
47. $|2v + 3| - 6 = 14$ $-\frac{23}{2}, \frac{17}{2}$

Lesson 1-5 Solve each inequality. Graph the solution. 48–53. See margin for graphs.

48. $|3 - k| < 7$ **−4 < k < 10**
49. $|2t + 7| \ge 4$ $t \le -5.5, t \ge -1.5$
50. $|x - 2| < 6$ **−4 < x < 8**
51. $2|w + 6| \le 10$ **−11 ≤ w ≤ −1**
52. $|3y - 5| + 6 > 15$
   $y < -\frac{4}{3}$ or $y > \frac{14}{3}$
53. $3|2z + 5| + 2 \le 8$
   $-\frac{7}{2} \le z \le -\frac{3}{2}$

Lesson 1-6 Suppose you select a number at random from the sample space {1, 2, 3, 4, 5, 6, 7, 8, 9}. Find each theoretical probability.

54. P(a number that is a multiple of 5) $\frac{1}{9}$
55. P(a number that is an integer) **1**
56. P(a number that is a factor of twelve) $\frac{5}{9}$
57. P(a number that is less than or equal to 4) $\frac{4}{9}$
58. P(a number that is greater than 6) $\frac{1}{3}$
59. P(a number that is a composite number) $\frac{4}{9}$

Bottom graphs

48.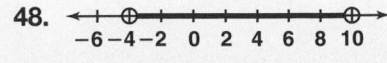
⟨+⊕++++++⊕+⟩ −6 −4 −2 0 2 4 6 8 10

49.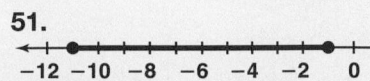
⟨++●+++●++⟩ −8 −6 −4 −2 0

50.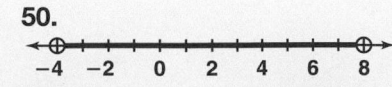
⟨⊕++++++⊕⟩ −4 −2 0 2 4 6 8

51.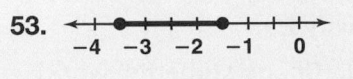
⟨+●+++++●+⟩ −12 −10 −8 −6 −4 −2 0

52.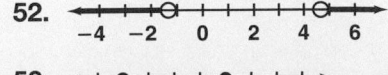
⟨++⊖+++⊖+⟩ −4 −2 0 2 4 6

53. ⟨++●+++●++⟩ −4 −3 −2 −1 0

Extra Practice

● **Lesson 2-1** Determine whether each relation is a function. Justify your answer. 1–6. See margin.

1. $\{(0,1),(1,0),(2,1),(3,1),(4,2)\}$

2. $\{(7,4),(4,9),(-3,1),(1,7),(2,8)\}$

3. $\{(1,4),(3,2),(5,2),(1,-8),(6,7)\}$

4. $\{(-5,1),(0,-3),(-2,1),(10,11),(7,1)\}$

5. $\{(9,3),(6,2),(3,2),(3,1),(6,-2)\}$

6. $\{(4,9),(5,3),(-2,0),(5,4),(8,1)\}$

● **Lesson 2-2** Graph each equation. 7–14. See margin.

7. $y = x - 7$

8. $4x - y = 8$

9. $y = -x + 4$

10. $2x + 5y = 10$

11. $y = -4x + 3$

12. $-6x - 2y = 7$

13. $-2y = x - 2$

14. $3x - 8y = 9$

● **Lesson 2-2** Write in standard form the equation of each line.

15. slope $= 3; (-1,4)$ **$3x - y = -7$**
16. slope $= -1; (0,7)$ **$x + y = 7$**
17. slope $= \frac{3}{4}; (2,8)$ **$3x - 4y = -26$**

18. slope $= -\frac{2}{5}; (3,-9)$
$2x + 5y = -39$
19. slope $= \frac{8}{3}; (-2,0)$ **$8x - 3y = -16$**
20. slope $= -5; (-3,-12)$
$5x + y = -27$

● **Lesson 2-2** Write in point-slope form the equation of the line through each pair of points.

21. $(0,2)$ and $(-1,3)$
$y - 2 = -1(x - 0)$

22. $(1,2)$ and $(-2,-4)$
$y - 2 = 2(x - 1)$

23. $(11,4)$ and $(3,0)$
$y - 0 = \frac{1}{2}(x - 3)$

24. $(-4,-5)$ and $(-1,-8)$
$y + 5 = -1(x + 4)$

25. $(-5,6)$ and $(3,-10)$
$y - 6 = -2(x + 5)$

26. $(12,10)$ and $(0,0)$ **$y = \frac{5}{6}x$**

● **Lesson 2-2** Find the slope, y-intercept, and x-intercept of each line.

27. $y = 2x - 5$ **2, −5, 2.5**
28. $y = -x + 1$ **−1, 1, 1**
29. $y = 4$ **0, 4, none**
30. $y = 5x + 10$ **5, 10, −2**

31. $y = \frac{1}{3}x - 15$ **$\frac{1}{3}$, −15, 45**
32. $x = -7$
undefined, none, −7
33. $y = -6x$ **−6, 0, 0**
34. $y = -\frac{2}{5}x + 20$
−0.4, 20, 50

● **Lesson 2-2** Write each equation in standard form. 35–38. See back of book.

35. $y = 3x + 9$

36. $4x = 6y - 9$

37. $2y = 8x - 7$

38. $y = -x + 1$

39. $0.3x + 1.2y = 2.4$
$3x + 12y = 24$
40. $y = \frac{2}{3}x + 15$
$2x - 3y = -45$
41. $x = 8 - y$
$x + y = 8$
42. $\frac{1}{2}x - \frac{3}{4}y = 1$
$2x - 3y = 4$

● **Lesson 2-3** Write an equation of a direct variation that passes through each point.

43. $(3,7)$ **$y = \frac{7}{3}x$**
44. $(5,-8)$ **$y = -\frac{8}{5}x$**
45. $(-4,-10)$ **$y = 2.5x$**
46. $(-2,9)$ **$y = -4.5x$**

47. $(-6,6)$ **$y = -x$**
48. $(6,-3)$ **$y = -0.5x$**
49. $(12,8)$ **$y = \frac{2}{3}x$**
50. $(-15,-1)$ **$y = \frac{1}{15}x$**

● **Lesson 2-5** Graph each equation by writing two linear equations. 51–58. See back of book.

51. $y = |x - 2|$

52. $y = \left|x + \frac{1}{2}\right|$

53. $y = |4x + 3|$

54. $y = |4x - 3|$

55. $y = -|x + 4|$

56. $y = 2|x - 3|$

57. $y = |x + 4| - 2$

58. $y = \frac{4}{3}|2x - 1|$

● **Lesson 2-7** Graph each inequality. 59–66. See back of book.

59. $y < -x + 5$

60. $0.1x + 0.6y \geq 2$

61. $y \leq 3x - 1$

62. $x + 3y > 12$

63. $y \geq 5x - 3$

64. $6x + 2y \geq 7$

65. $y + 1 > \frac{1}{3}x + 2$

66. $5x - 4y \leq -3$

CHAPTER 2

page 823 Extra Practice

1. Yes; each x-value has exactly one y-value.

2. Yes; each x-value has exactly one y-value.

3. No; the x-value 1 has two y-values.

4. Yes; each x-value has exactly one y-value.

5. No; the x-values 3 and 6 have two y-values.

6. No; the x-value 5 has two y-values.

7.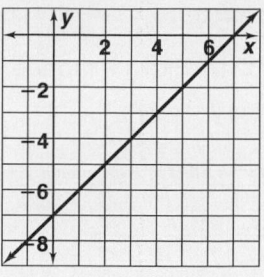

8.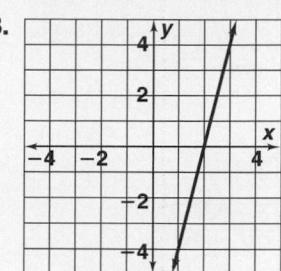

9.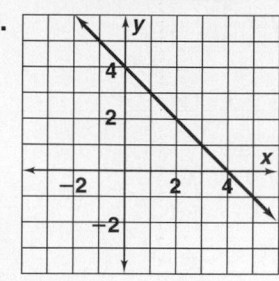

10.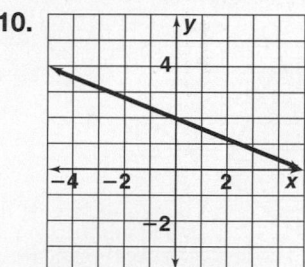

11.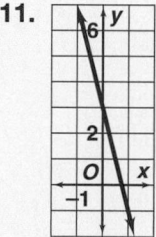

12.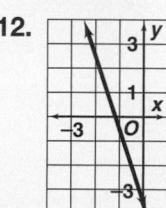

13.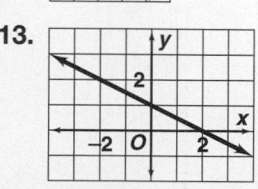

14.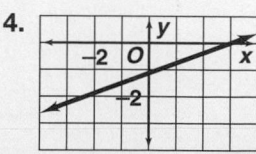

1.
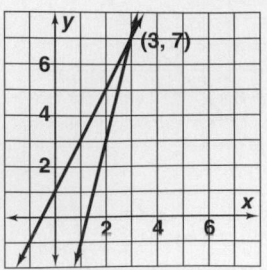

2.
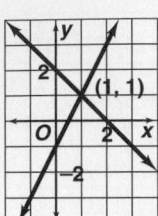

3.
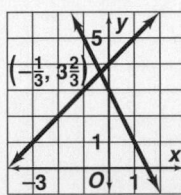

4.
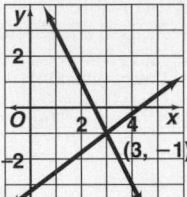

5.
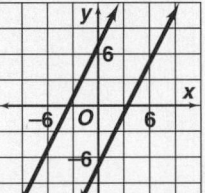

6.
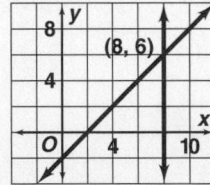

● **Lesson 3-1** Solve each system by graphing.   1–6. See margin.

1. $\begin{cases} y = 2x + 1 \\ y = 4x - 5 \end{cases}$

2. $\begin{cases} x + y = 2 \\ y = 2x - 1 \end{cases}$

3. $\begin{cases} y = x + 4 \\ y = -2x + 3 \end{cases}$

4. $\begin{cases} 3x - 4y = 13 \\ 2x + y = 5 \end{cases}$

5. $\begin{cases} 2x = y - 7 \\ 4x - 2y = 14 \end{cases}$

6. $\begin{cases} x = 8 \\ x - y = 2 \end{cases}$

● **Lesson 3-2** Solve each system of equations.

7. $\begin{cases} x + y = 5 \\ x - y = -3 \end{cases}$ **(1, 4)**

8. $\begin{cases} y = 3x - 1 \\ 2x + y = 14 \end{cases}$ **(3, 8)**

9. $\begin{cases} 3x + 2y = 12 \\ x + y = 3 \end{cases}$ **(6, −3)**

10. $\begin{cases} x - 4y = 16 \\ x + 2y = 4 \end{cases}$ **(8, −2)**

11. $\begin{cases} y = 2x + 5 \\ y = 4 - x \end{cases}$ $\left(-\frac{1}{3}, \frac{13}{3}\right)$

12. $\begin{cases} y = 5x - 1 \\ y = 14 \end{cases}$ **(3, 14)**

● **Lesson 3-3** Solve each system of inequalities by graphing.   13–15. See margin.

13. $\begin{cases} y \geq x - 3 \\ y \leq 3x + 7 \end{cases}$

14. $\begin{cases} 3x + 4y > 8 \\ y < 5x \end{cases}$

15. $\begin{cases} -x - 2y \geq -5 \\ y < 3 \end{cases}$

● **Lesson 3-4** Find the values of x and y that maximize or minimize the objective function.

16. $\begin{cases} x \leq 4 \\ y \leq 3 \\ x \geq 0 \\ y \geq 0 \end{cases}$

17. $\begin{cases} x + y \leq 5 \\ y \geq x \\ x \geq 0 \end{cases}$

18. $\begin{cases} 1 \leq x \leq 6 \\ 2 \leq y \leq 4 \\ x + y \geq 4 \end{cases}$

maximum for
$P = 2x + y$
(4, 3)

minimum for
$C = x + y$
(0, 0)

maximum for
$P = 3x + 2y$
(6, 4)

🌐 **19. Business** A lunch stand makes $.75 in profit on each chef's salad and $1.20 in profit on each Caesar salad. On a typical weekday, it sells between 40 and 60 chef's salads and between 35 and 50 Caesar salads. The total number sold has never exceeded 100 salads. How many of each type of salad should be prepared to maximize profit? **50 chef's salads and 50 Caesar salads**

● **Lesson 3-5** Graph each point in coordinate space.   20–28. See back of book.

20. $(0, 3, 0)$

21. $(4, 0, -2)$

22. $(0, 0, 5)$

23. $(1, 1, 0)$

24. $(0, 4, 2)$

25. $(-1, 2, 2)$

26. $(3, 0, 1)$

27. $(6, 1, 3)$

28. $(3, -1, 4)$

● **Lesson 3-5** Sketch the graph of each equation.   29–34. See back of book.

29. $x - y + z = 4$

30. $2x - y - z = 6$

31. $-x + y + 3z = 9$

32. $x + y + z = 5$

33. $-5x + 2y + 2z = 10$

34. $x - y + 3z = 3$

● **Lesson 3-6** Solve each system of equations.

35. $\begin{cases} x + y + z = 6 \\ x = 2y \\ z = x + 1 \end{cases}$ **(2, 1, 3)**

36. $\begin{cases} x - 2y + z = 8 \\ y - z = 4 \\ z = 3 \end{cases}$ **(19, 7, 3)**

37. $\begin{cases} 3x + y - z = 15 \\ x - y + 3z = -19 \\ 2x + 2y + z = 4 \end{cases}$
(2, 3, −6)

13.
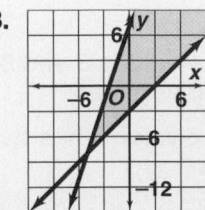

14.
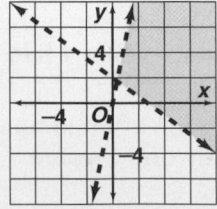

15.
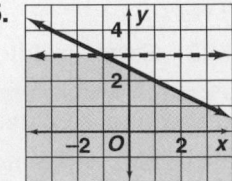

● **Lesson 4-1** State the dimensions of each matrix. Identify the indicated element.

1. $\begin{bmatrix} 3 & 1 & -5 \\ 6 & 9 & 10 \end{bmatrix}; a_{21}$ **2 × 3; 6**

2. $\begin{bmatrix} 0.5 & 6.1 \\ -9.2 & 4.7 \end{bmatrix}; a_{11}$ **2 × 2; 0.5**

3. $\begin{bmatrix} 56 & -83 & 12 \\ 101 & -71 & 49 \end{bmatrix}; a_{12}$ **2 × 3; −83**

4. $\begin{bmatrix} 5 & 8 \\ -2 & 3 \\ 3 & 4 \end{bmatrix}; a_{21}$ **3 × 2; −2**

5. $\begin{bmatrix} \frac{1}{4} & \frac{3}{8} \end{bmatrix}; a_{12}$ **1 × 2; $\frac{3}{8}$**

6. $\begin{bmatrix} 17 & -23 & 79 \\ 47 & 61 & 5 \end{bmatrix}; a_{22}$ **2 × 3; 61**

● **Lesson 4-2** Find each sum or difference.

7. $\begin{bmatrix} -8 & 3 \\ 19 & -45 \end{bmatrix} + \begin{bmatrix} 12 & 64 \\ -7 & 63 \end{bmatrix}$ $\begin{bmatrix} 4 & 67 \\ 12 & 18 \end{bmatrix}$

8. $\begin{bmatrix} 3.6 & -9.8 \\ 4.0 & -1.7 \end{bmatrix} - \begin{bmatrix} 0.8 & 3.4 \\ -6.1 & 7.9 \end{bmatrix}$ $\begin{bmatrix} 2.8 & -13.2 \\ 10.1 & -9.6 \end{bmatrix}$

9. $\begin{bmatrix} 4 & 6 & -3 \\ 8 & -9 & -1 \end{bmatrix} - \begin{bmatrix} 10 & 7 & -3 \\ -9 & 2 & 7 \end{bmatrix}$ $\begin{bmatrix} -6 & -1 & 0 \\ 17 & -11 & -8 \end{bmatrix}$

10. $\begin{bmatrix} -308 & 651 \\ 912 & -347 \end{bmatrix} + \begin{bmatrix} 105 & 318 \\ -762 & -438 \end{bmatrix}$ $\begin{bmatrix} -203 & 969 \\ 150 & -785 \end{bmatrix}$

● **Lesson 4-3** Solve each matrix equation.   **11–14. See margin.**

11. $\begin{bmatrix} 25 & -60 \\ 42 & 91 \end{bmatrix} + X = \begin{bmatrix} -37 & 61 \\ 85 & 37 \end{bmatrix}$

12. $\begin{bmatrix} -8 & 3 & 1 \\ -9 & 6 & 7 \end{bmatrix} - X = \begin{bmatrix} 5 & 8 & 3 \\ 4 & 2 & 6 \end{bmatrix}$

13. $X + \begin{bmatrix} 6 & 2 & 9 \\ 1 & 5 & 10 \end{bmatrix} = \begin{bmatrix} 11 & -5 & 16 \\ 3 & 6 & 8 \end{bmatrix}$

14. $X - \begin{bmatrix} 2.3 & 6.5 \\ 9.4 & -8.2 \end{bmatrix} = \begin{bmatrix} -4.7 & 3.6 \\ 9.4 & -5.8 \end{bmatrix}$

● **Lesson 4-3** For exercises 15–26, use matrices *A*, *B*, *C*, and *D* shown below. Perform the indicated operations if they are defined. If an operation is not defined, label it *undefined*.   **15–26. See margin.**

$$A = \begin{bmatrix} 8 & 1 \\ -2 & 5 \end{bmatrix} \quad B = \begin{bmatrix} -3 & 1 & 0 \\ -2 & -1 & 5 \end{bmatrix} \quad C = \begin{bmatrix} 9 & 4 \\ 5 & 1 \\ 2 & 0 \end{bmatrix} \quad D = \begin{bmatrix} 1 & 7 & 3 \\ 8 & 10 & -2 \end{bmatrix}$$

15. *AB*

16. *BD*

17. 2*A*

18. *CD*

19. *DA*

20. −3*B*

21. 0.2*A*

22. *BA*

23. 5*C*

24. *CB*

25. $\frac{1}{2}D$

26. *BC*

● **Lesson 4-4** Use △*ABC* with coordinates *A*(1, 5), *B*(2, −1), and *C*(4, 3). Write the coordinates of each image in matrix form.   **27–30. See margin.**

27. a dilation 5 times the size

28. a translation 3 units left and 1 unit up

29. a translation 2 units right and 7 units down

30. a dilation one third the size

● **Lesson 4-5** Solve each matrix equation. If an equation cannot be solved, explain why.

31. $\begin{bmatrix} 2 & 1 \\ -1 & 7 \end{bmatrix} X = \begin{bmatrix} 8 & 1 \\ -12 & 41 \end{bmatrix}$

32. $\begin{bmatrix} -1 & 0 \\ 6 & 3 \end{bmatrix} X = \begin{bmatrix} -9 \\ -3 \end{bmatrix} \begin{bmatrix} 9 \\ -19 \end{bmatrix}$

33. $\begin{bmatrix} -3 & 5 \\ 1 & 8 \end{bmatrix} X = \begin{bmatrix} 29 \\ 58 \end{bmatrix} \begin{bmatrix} 2 \\ 7 \end{bmatrix}$

See margin.

● **Lesson 4-7** Solve each system of equations. Check your answers.

34. $\begin{cases} x - y = 3 \\ x + y = 5 \end{cases}$ **(4, 1)**

35. $\begin{cases} x - 2y = 7 \\ x + 3y = 12 \end{cases}$ **(9, 1)**

36. $\begin{cases} 2x + 5y = 10 \\ x + y - 2 \end{cases}$ **(0, 2)**

Extra Practice

19. product undefined

20. $\begin{bmatrix} 9 & -3 & 0 \\ 6 & 3 & -15 \end{bmatrix}$

21. $\begin{bmatrix} 1.6 & 0.2 \\ -0.4 & 1 \end{bmatrix}$

22. product undefined

23. $\begin{bmatrix} 45 & 20 \\ 25 & 5 \\ 10 & 0 \end{bmatrix}$

24. $\begin{bmatrix} -35 & 5 & 20 \\ -17 & 4 & 5 \\ -6 & 2 & 0 \end{bmatrix}$

25. $\begin{bmatrix} 0.5 & 3.5 & 1.5 \\ 4 & 5 & -1 \end{bmatrix}$

26. $\begin{bmatrix} -22 & -11 \\ -13 & -9 \end{bmatrix}$

27. $\begin{bmatrix} 5 & 10 & 20 \\ 25 & -5 & 15 \end{bmatrix}$

28. $\begin{bmatrix} -2 & -1 & 1 \\ 6 & 0 & 4 \end{bmatrix}$

29. $\begin{bmatrix} 3 & 4 & 6 \\ -2 & -8 & -4 \end{bmatrix}$

30. $\begin{bmatrix} \frac{1}{3} & \frac{2}{3} & \frac{4}{3} \\ \frac{5}{3} & -\frac{1}{3} & 1 \end{bmatrix}$

31. $\begin{bmatrix} \frac{68}{15} & -\frac{34}{15} \\ -\frac{16}{15} & \frac{83}{15} \end{bmatrix}$

---

page 825   Extra Practice

11. $\begin{bmatrix} -62 & 121 \\ 43 & -54 \end{bmatrix}$

12. $\begin{bmatrix} -13 & -5 & -2 \\ -13 & 4 & 1 \end{bmatrix}$

13. $\begin{bmatrix} 5 & -7 & 7 \\ 2 & 1 & -2 \end{bmatrix}$

14. $\begin{bmatrix} -2.4 & 10.1 \\ 18.8 & -14 \end{bmatrix}$

15. $\begin{bmatrix} -26 & 7 & 5 \\ -4 & -7 & 25 \end{bmatrix}$

16. product undefined

17. $\begin{bmatrix} 16 & 2 \\ -4 & 10 \end{bmatrix}$

18. $\begin{bmatrix} 41 & 103 & 19 \\ 13 & 45 & 13 \\ 2 & 14 & 6 \end{bmatrix}$

7.

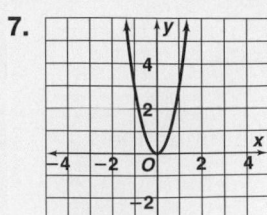

8.

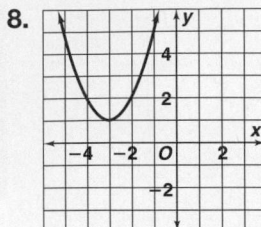

9.

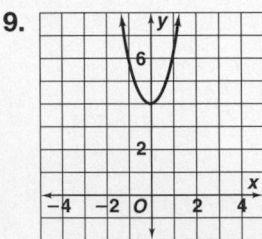

10.

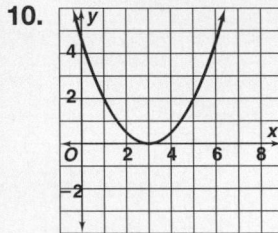

11.

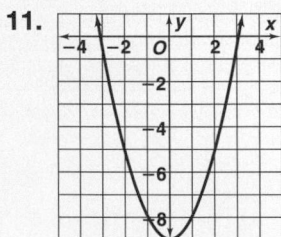

12.

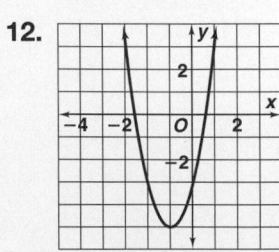

13.

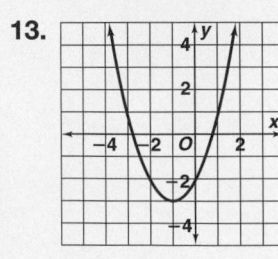

Chapter 5 Extra Practice

● **Lesson 5-1** Determine whether each function is *linear* or *quadratic*. Identify the quadratic, linear, and constant terms.

1. $y = 3x + 4$ **linear; none, 3x, 4** **2.** $y = x^2 + 1$ **quadratic; x^2, none, 1** **3.** $3x + 2y = 1$ **linear; none, $-\frac{3}{2}x, \frac{1}{2}$**

4. $y = (x + 1)(x - 1)$
quadratic; x^2, none, −1

5. $y = 3 - x^2$
quadratic; $-x^2$, none, 3

6. $y = 5x(x + 2)$
quadratic; $5x^2$, 10x, none

● **Lessons 5-2 and 5-3** Graph each function. **7–14. See margin.**

7. $y = 3x^2$

8. $y = (x + 3)^2 + 1$

9. $y = 2x^2 + 4$

10. $y = \frac{1}{2}(x - 3)^2$

11. $y = x^2 - 9$

12. $y = 2(x + 1)^2 - 5$

13. $y = (x + 1)^2 - 3$

14. $y = (x - 2)^2$

● **Lesson 5-4** Factor each expression. **15–22. See margin.**

15. $x^2 + 3x - 54$

16. $x^2 + 10x + 24$

17. $x^2 - 36$

18. $x^2 - 9x - 36$

19. $x^2 - 15x + 56$

20. $25x^2 + 70x + 49$

21. $7x^2 - 20x - 3$

22. $5x^2 + 23x - 10$

23. $\frac{1}{4}x^2 - 4$
$\frac{1}{4}(x - 4)(x + 4)$

24. $x^2 - 6x - 16$
$(x - 8)(x + 2)$

25. $4x^2 + 12x + 40$
$4(x^2 + 3x + 10)$

26. $4x^2 - 6x + 9$
cannot be factored

● **Lesson 5-5** Solve each equation by factoring, by taking square roots, or by graphing. When necessary, round your answer to the nearest hundredth. **27–29. See margin.**

27. $x^2 + 4x - 1 = 0$

28. $4x^2 - 100 = 0$

29. $x^2 = -2x + 1$

30. $x^2 - 9 = 0$ **±3**

31. $2x^2 + 4x = 70$ **−7, 5**

32. $x^2 - 30 = 10$ **±6.32**

33. $x^2 + 4x = 0$ **0, −4**

34. $x^2 + 3x + 2 = 0$
−2, −1

● **Lesson 5-6** Simplify each expression.

35. $(3 - i) + (5 - 2i)$ **8 − 3i**

36. $(4 + 2i)(1 - i)$ **6 − 2i**

37. $(4 + 2i) - (3 + 5i)$ **1 − 3i**

38. $(8 - 3i)(6 + 9i)$ **75 + 54i**

39. $(2 + 5i) - (-6 + i)$ **8 + 4i**

40. $(-2 - 3i)(7 - i)$ **−17 − 19i**

● **Lesson 5-6** Solve each equation. Check your answers.

41. $x^2 + 16 = 0$ **±4i**

42. $4x^2 = -1$ **±$\frac{1}{2}$i**

43. $x^2 = -10$ **±$i\sqrt{10}$**

44. $4x^2 + 48 = 0$ **±$2i\sqrt{3}$**

45. $-2x^2 = 5$ **±$i\frac{\sqrt{10}}{2}$**

46. $x^2 + 3 = 0$ **±$i\sqrt{3}$**

● **Lesson 5-6** Find the first three output values of each fractal-generating function. Use $z = 0$ as the first input value.

47. $f(z) = z^2 - i$ **−i, −1 − i, i**

48. $f(z) = z^2 + 2 + i$ **2 + i, 5 + 5i, 2 + 51i**

● **Lessons 5-7 and 5-8** Solve each equation by completing the square or using the Quadratic Formula.

49. $x^2 + 5x + 8 = 4$ **−1, −4**

50. $8x^2 + 64 = 0$ **±$2i\sqrt{2}$**

51. $2x^2 - 5x + 1 = 0$ **$\frac{5}{4} + \frac{\sqrt{17}}{4}$**

52. $3x^2 = x - 9$ **$\frac{1}{6} \pm \frac{i\sqrt{107}}{6}$**

53. $x^2 + 10 = 4x - 2$ **$2 \pm 2i\sqrt{2}$**

54. $x^2 - 7x = 0$ **0, 7**

55. $x^2 + 4x + 4 = 0$ **−2**

56. $x^2 - 7 = 0$ **±$\sqrt{7}$**

57. $x^2 + 8x - 17 = 0$ **$-4 \pm \sqrt{33}$**

● **Lesson 5-8** Evaluate the discriminant of each equation. Tell how many solutions each equation has and whether the solutions are real or imaginary. **58–61. See margin.**

58. $x^2 + 4x = 17$

59. $2x^2 + x = -1$

60. $x^2 - 4x + 5 = 0$

61. $2x^2 + 5x = 0$

62. $x^2 - 19 = 1$
80; 2, real

63. $3x^2 = 8x - 4$
−16; 2, imaginary

64. $-2x^2 + 1 = 7x$
57; 2, real

65. $4x^2 + 4x = -1$
0; 1, real

14.

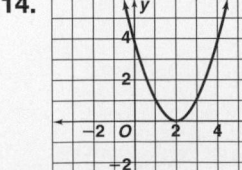

15. $(x + 9)(x - 6)$

16. $(x + 6)(x + 4)$

17. $(x - 6)(x + 6)$

18. $(x - 12)(x + 3)$

19. $(x - 8)(x - 7)$

20. $(5x + 7)^2$

21. $(7x + 1)(x - 3)$

22. $(5x - 2)(x + 5)$

27. 0.41 −2.41

28. ±5

29. 0.41, −2.41

58. 84; 2, real

59. 108; 2, real

60. 24; 2, real

61. 25; 2, real

Extra Practice

● **Lesson 6-1** Write each polynomial in standard form. Then classify it by degree and by number of terms. **1–6. See margin.**

1. $a^2 + 4a - 5a^2 - a$

2. $3x - \frac{1}{3} - 5x$

3. $3n^2 + n^3 - n - 3 - 3n^3$

4. $15 - y^2 - 10y - 8 + 8y$

5. $6c^2 - 4c + 7 - 8c^2$

6. $3x^2 - 5x - x^2 + x + 4x$

● **Lesson 6-2** Write a polynomial function in standard form with the given zeros. **7–14. See margin.**

7. $x = 3, 2, -1$

8. $x = 1, 1, 2$

9. $x = -2, -1, 1$

10. $x = 1, 2, 6$

11. $x = -3, -1, 5$

12. $x = 0, 0, 2, 3$

13. $x = -2, 1, 2, 2$

14. $x = 2, 4, 5, 7$

● **Lesson 6-3** Divide.

15. $(x^3 - 3x^2 + 2) \div (x - 1)$ $x^2 - 2x - 2$

16. $(x^3 - x^2 - 6x) \div (x - 3)$ $x^2 + 2x$

17. $(2x^3 + 10x^2 + 8x) \div (x + 4)$ $2x^2 + 2x$

18. $(x^4 + x^2 - 6) \div (x^2 + 3)$ $x^2 - 2$

19. $(x^2 - 4x + 2) \div (x - 2)$ $x - 2, R -2$

20. $(x^3 + 11x + 12) \div (x + 3)$ $x^2 - 3x + 20, R -48$

● **Lesson 6-4** Solve each equation.

21. $t^3 - 3t^2 - 10t = 0$ $0, -2, 5$

22. $4m^3 + m^2 - m + 5 = 0$ $-1.25, \frac{1}{2} \pm \frac{i\sqrt{3}}{2}$

23. $t^3 - 6t^2 + 12t - 8 = 0$ 2

24. $2c^3 - 7c^2 - 4c = 0$ $0, -\frac{1}{2}, 4$

25. $w^4 - 13w^2 + 36 = 0$ $\pm 3, \pm 2$

26. $x^3 + 2x^2 - 13x + 10 = 0$ $-5, 1, 2$

● **Lesson 6-5** Find the roots of each polynomial equation.

27. $x^3 + 2x^2 + 3x + 6 = 0$ $-2, \pm i\sqrt{3}$

28. $x^3 - 3x^2 + 4x - 12 = 0$ $3, \pm 2i$

29. $3x^4 + 11x^3 + 14x^2 + 7x + 1 = 0$ $-1, \frac{-5 \pm \sqrt{13}}{6}$

30. $3x^4 - x^3 - 22x^2 + 24x = 0$ $-3, 0, \frac{4}{3}, 2$

31. $45x^3 + 93x^2 - 12 = 0$ $-2, -\frac{2}{5}, \frac{1}{3}$

32. $8x^4 - 66x^3 + 175x^2 - 132x - 45 = 0$ $-\frac{1}{4}, \frac{5}{2}, 3$

● **Lesson 6-7** Evaluate each expression.

33. $6!$ 720

34. $3!4!$ 144

35. $\frac{7!}{4!}$ 210

36. $\frac{6!2!}{8!}$ $\frac{1}{28}$

37. $_8P_5$ 6720

38. $_4C_1$ 4

39. $_6C_2$ 15

40. $_6P_2$ 30

41. $_7C_3$ 35

42. $_7P_3$ 210

43. $2(_7C_5)$ 42

44. $\frac{_7C_5}{_5C_2}$ 2.1

● **Lesson 6-7** Indicate whether each situation involves a combination or a permutation. Then answer the question.

45. How many different orders can you choose to read six of the nine books on your summer reading list?   **permutation; 60,480 orders**

46. How many ways are there to choose five shirts out of seven to take to camp?   **combination; 21 ways**

47. How many ways can you choose two out of four kinds of flowers for a bouquet?   **combination; 6 ways**

● **Lesson 6-8** Use the Binomial Theorem to expand each binomial. **48–55. See margin.**

48. $(x - 1)^3$

49. $(3x + 2)^4$

50. $(4x + 10)^3$

51. $(2x + 5y)^4$

52. $(x^2 + 2)^4$

53. $(x + 2y)^7$

54. $(5x - y)^5$

55. $(x - 4y^3)^4$

1. $-4a^2 + 3a$; quadratic binomial

2. $-2x - \frac{1}{3}$; linear binomial

3. $-2n^3 + 3n^2 - n - 3$; cubic polynomial of 4 terms

4. $-y^2 - 2y + 7$; quadratic trinomial

5. $-2c^2 - 4c + 7$; quadratic trinomial

6. $2x^2$; quadratic monomial

7. $y = x^3 - 4x^2 + x + 6$

8. $y = x^3 - 4x^2 + 5x - 2$

9. $y = x^3 + 2x^2 - x - 2$

10. $y = x^3 - 9x^2 + 20x - 12$

11. $y = x^3 - x^2 - 17x - 15$

12. $y = x^4 - 5x^3 + 6x^2$

13. $y = x^4 - 3x^3 - 2x^2 + 12x - 8$

14. $y = x^4 - 18x^3 + 115x^2 - 306x + 280$

48. $x^3 - 3x^2 + 3x - 1$

49. $81x^4 + 216x^3 + 216x^2 + 96x + 16$

50. $64x^3 + 480x^2 + 1200x + 1000$

51. $16x^4 + 160x^3y + 600x^2y^2 + 1000xy^3 + 625y^4$

52. $x^8 + 8x^6 + 24x^4 + 32x^2 + 16$

53. $x^7 + 14x^6y + 84x^5y^2 + 280x^4y^3 + 560x^3y^4 + 672x^2y^5 + 448xy^6 + 128y^7$

54. $3125x^5 - 3125x^4y + 1250x^3y^2 - 250x^2y^3 + 25xy^4 - y^5$

55. $x^4 - 16x^3y^3 + 96x^2y^6 - 256xy^9 + 256y^{12}$

44. $f^{-1}(x) = \frac{x-1}{6}$;
domain of f: all real numbers,
range of f: all real numbers,
domain of f^{-1}: all real numbers,
range of f^{-1}: all reall numbers;
f^{-1} is a function.

45. $f^{-1}(x) = x^2 - 4$, $x \geq 0$;
domain of f: $\{x \geq -4\}$,
range of f: $\{y \geq 0\}$,
domain of f^{-1}: $\{x \geq 0\}$,
range of f^{-1}: $\{y \geq -4\}$;
f^{-1} is a function.

46. $f^{-1}(x) = x^2 + 3$, $x \geq 0$;
domain of f: $\{x \geq 3\}$,
range of f: $\{y \geq 0\}$,
domain of f^{-1}: $\{x \geq 0\}$,
range of $f^{-1}\{y \geq 3\}$;
f^{-1} is a function.

47. $f^{-1}(x) = -\frac{x^2-2}{5}$, $x \geq 0$;
domain of f: $\left\{x \leq \frac{2}{5}\right\}$,
range of f: $\{y \geq 0\}$,
domain of f^{-1}: $\{x \geq 0\}$,
range of f^{-1}: $\left\{y \leq \frac{2}{5}\right\}$;
f^{-1} is a function.

48. $f^{-1}(x) = \pm\sqrt{\frac{x-1}{3}}$;
domain of f: all real numbers,
range of f: $\{y \geq 1\}$,
domain of f^{-1}: $\{x \geq 1\}$,
range of f^{-1}: all real numbers;
f^{-1} is not a function.

49. $f^{-1}(x) = \pm\sqrt{2-x}$;
domain of f: all real numbers,
range of f: $\{y \leq 2\}$,
domain of f^{-1}: $\{x \leq 2\}$,
range of f^{-1}: all real numbers;
f^{-1} is not a function.

Chapter 7 Extra Practice

● **Lesson 7-1** Simplify each radical expression. Use absolute value symbols as needed.

1. $\sqrt{36x^4}$ $6x^2$

2. $\sqrt{c^{80}d^{50}}$ $c^{40}|d^{25}|$

3. $\sqrt[4]{81x^{12}}$ $3|x^3|$

4. $\sqrt[3]{-64}$ -4

5. $\sqrt[5]{-32k^5}$ $-2k$

6. $\sqrt[4]{\frac{1}{16}w^{12}}$ $\frac{1}{2}|w^3|$

7. $\sqrt[4]{m^{18}n^8}$ $m^4n^2\sqrt{m}$

8. $\sqrt[3]{27y^{15}}$ $3y^5$

● **Lesson 7-2** Multiply or divide and simplify. Assume that all variables are positive.

9. $\sqrt{3x^4} \cdot \sqrt{24x^3}$ $6x^3\sqrt{2x}$

10. $\sqrt[3]{4} \cdot \sqrt[3]{18}$ $2\sqrt[3]{9}$

11. $\sqrt{5a^3} \cdot \sqrt{20a}$ $10a^2$

12. $\frac{\sqrt{80}}{\sqrt{5}}$ 4

13. $\frac{\sqrt{18x^5y}}{\sqrt{2x}}$ $3x^2\sqrt{y}$

14. $\frac{\sqrt[3]{640w^3z^8}}{\sqrt[3]{5wz^4}}$ $4z\sqrt[3]{2w^2z}$

● **Lesson 7-3** Simplify.

15. $2\sqrt{7} + 3\sqrt{7}$ $5\sqrt{7}$

16. $\sqrt{32} + \sqrt{8}$ $6\sqrt{2}$

17. $\sqrt{7x} + \sqrt{28x}$ $3\sqrt{7x}$

18. $3\sqrt{18} + 2\sqrt{72}$ $21\sqrt{2}$

19. $\sqrt{27} + \sqrt{48}$ $7\sqrt{3}$

20. $8\sqrt{45} - 3\sqrt{80}$ $12\sqrt{5}$

● **Lesson 7-4** Write each expression in simplest form. Assume that all variables are positive.

21. $\left(x^{-\frac{4}{3}}y^{\frac{3}{5}}\right)^{15}$ $\frac{y^9}{x^{20}}$

22. $\left(x^{\frac{1}{4}}y^{-\frac{3}{8}}\right)^{16}$ $\frac{x^4}{y^6}$

23. $\left(8x^{15}y^{-9}\right)^{-\frac{1}{3}}$ $\frac{y^3}{2x^5}$

24. $\left(-27x^{-9}y^6\right)^{\frac{1}{3}}$ $-\frac{3y^2}{x^3}$

25. $\left(-32x^{-10}y^{15}\right)^{\frac{1}{5}}$ $-\frac{2y^3}{x^2}$

26. $\left(32x^{20}y^{-10}\right)^{-\frac{1}{5}}$ $\frac{y^2}{2x^4}$

27. $\left(\frac{81y^{16}}{16x^{12}}\right)^{\frac{1}{4}}$ $\frac{3y^4}{2x^3}$

28. $\left(\frac{16x^{14}}{81y^{18}}\right)^{\frac{1}{2}}$ $\frac{4x^7}{9y^9}$

● **Lesson 7-5** Solve. Check for extraneous solutions.

29. $\sqrt{13x - 10} = 3x$ no real solution

30. $\sqrt{x + 20} = x$ 5

31. $(4x - 12)^{\frac{1}{2}} + 3 = x$ 3, 7

32. $(7x)^{\frac{1}{3}} = (5x + 2)^{\frac{1}{3}}$ 1

33. $\sqrt{x - 2} - \sqrt{2x + 3} = -2$ 3, 11

34. $\sqrt{10x} - 2\sqrt{5x - 25} = 0$ 10

● **Lesson 7-6** Let $f(x) = x^2$ and $g(x) = 3x + 1$. Evaluate each expression.

35. $(f \circ g)(0)$ 1

36. $(f \circ g)(2)$ 49

37. $(f \circ g)(-3)$ 64

38. $(f \circ g)(5)$ 256

39. $(g \circ f)(0)$ 1

40. $(g \circ f)(1)$ 4

41. $(g \circ f)(-1)$ 4

42. $(f \circ f)(3)$ 81

43. $(g \circ g)(4)$ 40

● **Lesson 7-7** For each function f, find f^{-1} and the domain and range of f and f^{-1}. Determine whether f^{-1} is a function.   44–49. See margin.

44. $f(x) = 6x + 1$

45. $f(x) = \sqrt{x + 4}$

46. $f(x) = \sqrt{x - 3}$

47. $f(x) = \sqrt{-5x + 2}$

48. $f(x) = 3x^2 + 1$

49. $f(x) = 2 - x^2$

● **Lesson 7-8** Graph each function.   50–58. See back of book.

50. $y = \sqrt{x}$

51. $y = \sqrt{x} - 1$

52. $y = \sqrt{x} + 3$

53. $y = \sqrt{x + 3}$

54. $y = 4\sqrt{x}$

55. $y = \frac{3}{4}\sqrt{x}$

56. $y = 2\sqrt{x - 5} + 2$

57. $y = \sqrt[3]{x} + 1$

58. $y = \sqrt[3]{x - 2} - 3$

● **Lesson 8-1** Write an exponential equation $y = ab^x$ whose graph passes through the given points.

1. $(1, 10), (2, 25)$ $y = 4(2.5)^x$

2. $\left(2, 10\frac{2}{3}\right), (-1, 4.5)$ $y = 6\left(\frac{4}{3}\right)^x$

3. $(2, 6), (4, 54)$ $y = \frac{2}{3}(3)^x$

4. $(-2, 0.05), (2, 12.8)$ $y = 0.8(4)^x$

5. $(2, 128), (-1, 16)$ $y = 32(2)^x$

6. $(-1, 12.25), (1, 4)$ $y = 7\left(\frac{4}{7}\right)^x$

● **Lesson 8-1** Without graphing, determine whether each equation represents exponential growth or exponential decay. **7–12. See margin.**

7. $y = 10^x$

8. $y = 327(0.05)^x$

9. $y = 1.023(0.98)^x$

10. $y = 0.5(1.67)^x$

11. $y = 1.14^x$

12. $y = 8(1.3)^x$

13. $y = 2\left(\frac{9}{10}\right)^x$
exponential decay

14. $y = 4.1(0.72)^x$
exponential decay

15. $y = 9.2(2.3)^x$
exponential growth

● **Lessons 8-1 and 8-2** Graph each equation. **16–23. See margin.**

16. $y = 3^x$

17. $y = 2(4)^x$

18. $y = 2^{-x}$

19. $y = \left(\frac{1}{4}\right)^x$

20. $y = 2^{3x}$

21. $y = 9^{-2x}$

22. $y = -0.1^x$

23. $y = -\left(\frac{1}{2}\right)^x$

● **Lesson 8-3** Write each equation in logarithmic form.

24. $100 = 10^2$ **log 100 = 2**

25. $9^3 = 729$ $\log_9 729 = 3$

26. $64 = 4^3$ $\log_4 64 = 3$

27. $\left(\frac{1}{2}\right)^4 = \frac{1}{16}$ $\log_{\frac{1}{2}} \frac{1}{16} = 4$

28. $49^{\frac{1}{2}} = 7$ $\log_{49} 7 = \frac{1}{2}$

29. $\left(\frac{1}{3}\right)^{-3} = 27$ $\log_{\frac{1}{3}} 27 = -3$

30. $625^{\frac{1}{4}} = 5$ $\log_{625} 5 = \frac{1}{4}$

31. $2^{-5} = \frac{1}{32}$ $\log_2 \frac{1}{32} = -5$

32. $6^2 = 36$ $\log_6 36 = 2$

● **Lesson 8-3** Graph each logarithmic function. **33–40. See back of book.**

33. $y = 2 \log x$

34. $y = \log_8 x$

35. $y = \log_4 (x + 1)$

36. $y = 3 + \log x$

37. $y = -1 + \log_2 x$

38. $y = \log (x - 2)$

39. $y = \log (x + 2)$

40. $y = \log (x - 5)$

● **Lesson 8-4** Write each expression as a single logarithm.

41. $\log 8 + \log 3$ **log 24**

42. $4(\log_2 x + \log_2 3)$ $4(\log_2 3x)$

43. $3 \log x + 4 \log x$ $\log x^7$

44. $\log 4 + \log 2 - \log 5$ $\log \left(\frac{8}{5}\right)$

45. $\log r - \log t + 2 \log s$ $\log \left(\frac{rs^2}{t}\right)$

46. $2 \log x - 4 \log y$ $\log \left(\frac{x^2}{y^4}\right)$

● **Lesson 8-4** Expand each logarithm. **47–51. See margin.**

47. $\log_b 2x^2 y^3$

48. $\log_b 3m^3 p^2$

49. $\log_b (4mn)^5$

50. $\log_b \frac{x^2}{2y}$

51. $\log_b \frac{(xy)^4}{2}$

52. $\log_b \sqrt[5]{x^3}$ $\frac{3}{5} \log_b x$

● **Lessons 8-5 and 8-6** Solve each equation.

53. $\sqrt[3]{y^2} = 4$ **±8**

54. $2 - 4^x = -62$ **3**

55. $\log x + \log 2 = 5$ **50,000**

56. $\log_3 (x + 1) = 4$ **80**

57. $e^x = 5$ **1.609**

58. $e^{\frac{x}{4}} = 5$ **6.438**

59. $\ln x - \ln 4 = 7$ **4386.533**

60. $\log 4x = -1$ **0.025**

61. $\log 4 - \log x = -2$ **400**

62. $\ln 2 + \ln x = 4$ **27.299**

63. $4 + 5^x = 29$ **2**

64. $e^{3x} = 20$ **0.99858**

17.
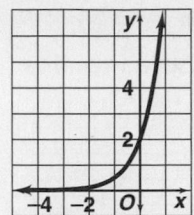

18.
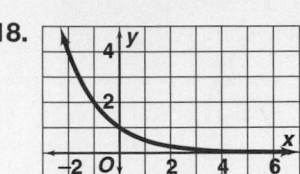

19.
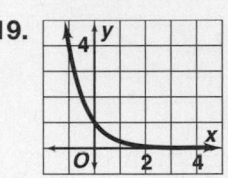

20.
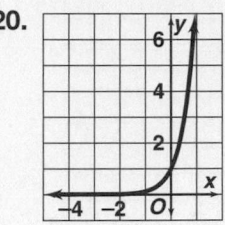

21.
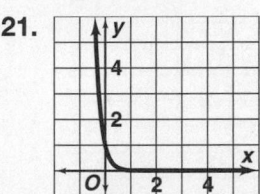

22.
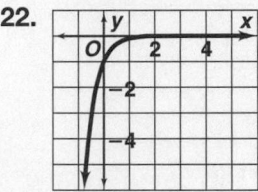

23.
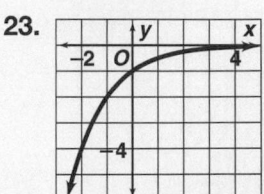

47. $\log_b 2 + 2 \log_b x + 3 \log_b y$

48. $\log_b 3 + 3 \log_b m + 2 \log_b p$

49. $5(\log_b 4 + \log_b m + \log_b n)$

50. $2 \log_b x - (\log_b 2 + \log_b y)$

51. $4(\log_b x + \log_b y) - \log_b 2$

CHAPTER 8

page 829 Extra Practice

7. exponential growth

8. exponential decay

9. exponential decay

10. exponential growth

11. exponential growth

12. exponential growth

16.
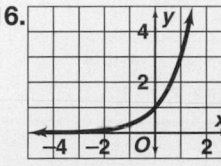

829

7.

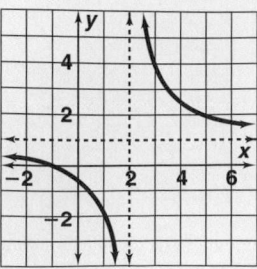

8.

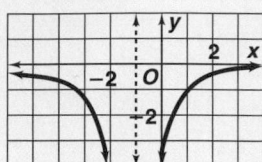

9.

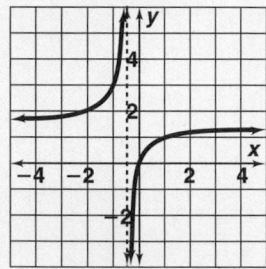

10.

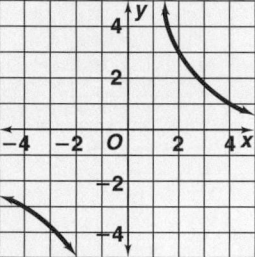

11.

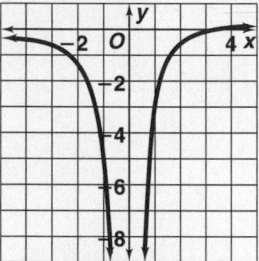

12.

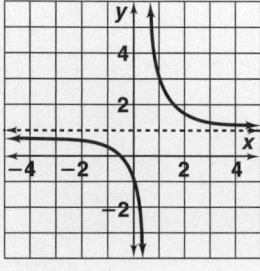

Chapter 9 Extra Practice

● **Lesson 9-1** Suppose that x and y vary inversely. Write a function that models each inverse variation.

1. $x = 3$ when $y = 2$ **$y = \frac{6}{x}$**   **2.** $x = 4$ when $y = -1$ **$y = \frac{-4}{x}$**   **3.** $x = 5$ when $y = 8$ **$y = \frac{40}{x}$**

4. $x = -6$ when $y = -2$ **$y = \frac{12}{x}$**   **5.** $x = -8$ when $y = 3$ **$y = \frac{-24}{x}$**   **6.** $x = 10$ when $y = 15$ **$y = \frac{150}{x}$**

● **Lesson 9-2** Sketch the asymptotes and the graph of each equation.   **7–14. See margin.**

7. $y = \frac{x + 1}{x - 2}$ **8.** $y = \frac{x - 3}{(x + 1)^2}$ **9.** $y = \frac{3x}{2x + 1}$ **10.** $y = \frac{8 - x}{x}$

11. $y = \frac{x - 4}{x^2}$ **12.** $y = \frac{2x + 1}{2x - 1}$ **13.** $y = \frac{x}{x + 3}$ **14.** $y = \frac{x + 2}{x - 4}$

● **Lesson 9-3** Find any points of discontinuity for each rational function.

15. $y = \frac{3x^2 + 2x}{x}$ **0**   **16.** $y = \frac{x^2 - 16}{x^2 + 4}$ **none**   **17.** $y = \frac{(x + 2)(x - 1)}{(x + 2)^2(x - 1)}$ **−2, 1**   **18.** $y = \frac{4}{x - 6}$ **6**

19. $y = \frac{9x}{3x^3 - 6x}$ **0, $\pm\sqrt{2}$**   **20.** $y = \frac{x^2 + 7x + 12}{x + 4}$ **−4**   **21.** $y = \frac{x - 7}{x - 7}$ **7**   **22.** $y = \frac{x^2 - 3x + 2}{x - 1}$ **1**

● **Lesson 9-4** Simplify each rational expression. What are the restrictions on the variables?

23. $\frac{x^2 + 9x + 18}{x + 6}$ **$x + 3$; $x \neq -6$**

24. $\frac{x^2 + 3x + 2}{x - 1} \cdot \frac{1 - x}{x + 2}$ **$-(x + 1)$; $x \neq 1, -2$**

25. $\frac{x^2 - 2x - 8}{x + 3} \div \frac{x - 4}{x + 3}$ **$x + 2$; $x \neq -3, 4$**

26. $\frac{2x^2 + 5x - 3}{x^2 - 4x} \cdot \frac{2x^3 - 8x^2}{x^2 + 6x + 9}$ **$\frac{2x(2x - 1)}{x + 3}$; $x \neq 0, 4, -3$**

27. $\frac{3x + 1}{x^2 - 6x - 6} \div \frac{6x^2 + 11x + 3}{x^2 + 4x + 4}$ **See margin.**

28. $\frac{3x^4 - x^3 - 2x^2}{6x^2 - 2x - 4}$ **$\frac{x^2}{2}$; $x \neq -\frac{2}{3}, 1$**

● **Lesson 9-5** Add or subtract. Simplify where possible.

29. $\frac{6x + 1}{x + 2} + \frac{2x - 5}{2x + 4}$ **$\frac{14x - 3}{2(x + 2)}$**

30. $\frac{8}{x^2 - 25} + \frac{9}{x - 5}$ **$\frac{9x + 53}{(x + 5)(x - 5)}$**

31. $\frac{x - 3}{x^2 + 3x} + \frac{7}{x + 3}$ **$\frac{8x - 3}{x(x + 3)}$**

32. $\frac{3x}{x^2 + 5x + 6} - \frac{2x}{x^2 + 8x + 16}$ **$\frac{x(x^2 + 14x + 36)}{(x + 3)(x + 2)(x + 4)^2}$**

33. $\frac{2}{x^2 - 1} - 3$ **$\frac{-3x^2 + 5}{x^2 - 1}$**

34. $\frac{2x}{x - 5} - \frac{x}{x + 7}$ **$\frac{x(x + 19)}{(x - 5)(x + 7)}$**

● **Lesson 9-6** Solve each equation. Check your answers.

35. $\frac{x}{4} = \frac{x + 1}{3}$ **−4**

36. $\frac{2}{x^2 - 1} = \frac{4}{x + 1}$ **$\frac{3}{2}$**

37. $\frac{3x}{5} + \frac{4}{x} = \frac{4x + 1}{5}$ **−5, 4**

38. $\frac{3x}{x - 2} = 4 + \frac{x}{5}$ **−8, 5**

39. $x + \frac{x}{4} - \frac{x}{5} = 21$ **20**

40. $\frac{3}{x + 4} + \frac{5}{4} = \frac{18}{x + 4}$ **8**

● **Lesson 9-7** Classify each pair of events as dependent or independent.

41. A main dish is selected at random; a type of salad is selected at random.   **independent**

42. A department is selected at random; a class in that department is selected at random.   **dependent**

43. A volleyball team is selected at random from the league; one of the remaining teams is selected at random.   **dependent**

13.

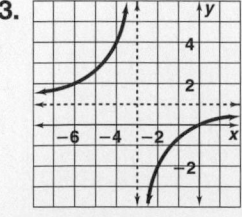

14.

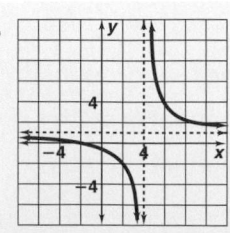

27. $\frac{(x + 2)^2}{(x^2 - 6x - 6)(2x + 3)}$;

$x \neq -\frac{1}{3}, -\frac{3}{2}, 3 \pm \sqrt{15}$

Extra Practice

● **Lesson 10-1** Graph each equation. Identify the conic section and describe the graph and its lines of symmetry. Then find the domain and range.   1–6. See back of book.

1. $x^2 + y^2 = 4$

2. $x^2 - 16y^2 = 64$

3. $4x^2 + 9y^2 = 36$

4. $8x^2 - 16y^2 = 32$

5. $9x^2 + 9y^2 - 36 = 0$

6. $25x^2 + 4y^2 = 100$

● **Lesson 10-2** Write an equation of a parabola with its vertex at the origin.

7. focus at $(0, 3)$ $y = \frac{1}{12}x^2$

8. directrix at $x = 4$ $x = -\frac{1}{16}y^2$

9. focus at $(0, -2)$ $y = -\frac{1}{8}x^2$

10. directrix at $y = \frac{1}{2}$ $y = -\frac{1}{2}x^2$

11. focus at $(0, 1)$ $y = \frac{1}{4}x^2$

12. directrix at $x = 2$ $x = -\frac{1}{8}y^2$

13. directrix at $y = 3$ $y = -\frac{1}{12}x^2$

14. focus at $(0, -5)$ $y = -\frac{1}{20}x^2$

15. focus at $\left(\frac{3}{2}, 0\right)$ $x = \frac{1}{6}y^2$

● **Lesson 10-2** Identify the focus and the directrix of the graph of each equation. Then sketch the graph.   16–23. See back of book.

16. $y = 4x^2$

17. $x = \frac{1}{16}y^2$

18. $-y = 10x^2$

19. $y^2 - 8x = 0$

20. $x^2 = 6y$

21. $y^2 = 20x$

22. $x^2 + 4y = 0$

23. $x^2 = -2y$

● **Lesson 10-3** Write an equation of a circle with the given center and radius.   24–26. See margin.

24. center $(0, 0)$; radius 8

25. center $(-4, -6)$; radius 2

26. center $(-5, 1)$; radius 3

27. center $(1, 4)$; radius 5
$(x - 1)^2 + (y - 4)^2 = 25$

28. center $(3, -2)$; radius 3.5
$(x - 3)^2 + (y + 2)^2 = 12.25$

29. center $(0, -3)$; radius 1
$x^2 + (y + 3)^2 = 1$

● **Lesson 10-3** For each equation, find the center and radius of the circle.

30. $(x + 1)^2 + (y - 3)^2 = 4$ **(−1, 3), 2**

31. $(x + 6)^2 + (y + 9)^2 = 144$ **(−6, −9), 12**

32. $(x - 2)^2 + (y + 4)^2 = 16$ **(2, −4), 4**

33. $(x + 8)^2 + (y - 1)^2 = 100$ **(−8, 1), 10**

34. $(x - 3)^2 + (y + 10)^2 = 25$ **(3, −10), 5**

35. $(x - 7)^2 + (y - 2)^2 = 81$ **(7, 2), 9**

● **Lesson 10-4** Find the foci for each equation of an ellipse. Then graph the ellipse.   36–41. See back of book.

36. $\frac{x^2}{9} + \frac{y^2}{25} = 1$

37. $\frac{x^2}{36} + \frac{y^2}{4} = 1$

38. $\frac{x^2}{100} + \frac{y^2}{121} = 1$

39. $\frac{x^2}{81} + \frac{y^2}{64} = 1$

40. $\frac{x^2}{49} + \frac{y^2}{144} = 1$

41. $\frac{x^2}{4} + y^2 = 1$

● **Lesson 10-5** Graph each equation.   42–47. See back of book.

42. $4x^2 - 25y^2 = 100$

43. $81x^2 - 16y^2 = 1296$

44. $y^2 - 4x^2 = 36$

45. $12x^2 - 3y^2 = 432$

46. $9x^2 - 121y^2 = 1089$

47. $x^2 - 64y^2 = 64$

● **Lesson 10-6** Identify the conic section represented by each equation. If it is a parabola, give the vertex. If it is a circle, give the center and radius. If it is an ellipse or a hyperbola, give the center and foci. Sketch the graph.   48–53. See margin.

48. $(x + 1)^2 + (y - 2)^2 = 7$

49. $\frac{x^2}{89} + \frac{y^2}{62} = 1$

50. $\frac{x^2}{73} - \frac{y^2}{19} = 1$

51. $x + y^2 - 3y + 4 = 0$

52. $x^2 + y^2 + 16x - 6y = 11$

53. $3x^2 - 6x + y - 10 = 0$

24. $x^2 + y^2 = 64$

25. $(x + 4)^2 + (y + 6)^2 = 4$

26. $(x + 5)^2 + (y - 1)^2 = 9$

48. circle; center $(-1, 2)$,
radius $= \sqrt{7}$

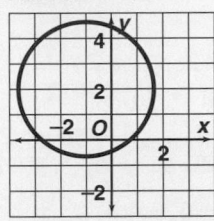

49. ellipse; center $(0, 0)$,
foci $(\pm 3\sqrt{3}, 0)$

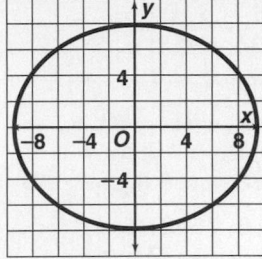

50. hyperbola; center $(0, 0)$,
foci $(\pm\sqrt{92}, 0)$

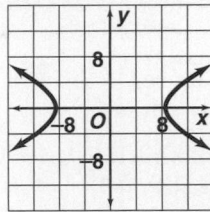

51. parabola; vertex $\left(-\frac{7}{4}, \frac{3}{2}\right)$

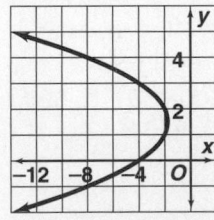

52. circle; center $(-8, 3)$,
radius $= \pm 2\sqrt{21}$

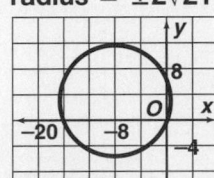

53. parabola; vertex $(1, 13)$

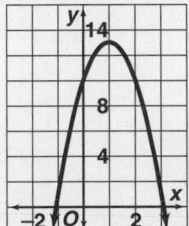

## CHAPTER 11

1. explicit; 5, 8, 11, 14, 17

2. recursive; 4, 11, 18, 25, 32

3. explicit; 15, 40, 75, 120, 175

4. recursive; 2, −1, −4, −7, −10

7. 9, 11, 13; $a_n = 2n + 1$; $a_1 = 3$, $a_n = a_{n-1} + 2$

8. 7, 3, −1; $a_n = -4n + 23$; $a_1 = 19$, $a_n = a_{n-1} - 4$

9. −7.5, −6, −4.5; $a_n = -13.5 + 1.5n$; $a_1 = -12$, $a_n = a_{n-1} + 1.5$

10. 1.1, 1.4, 1.7; $a_n = 0.3n - 0.1$; $a_1 = 0.2$, $a_n = a_{n-1} + 0.3$

11. −62, −75, −88; $a_n = -13n - 10$; $a_1 = -23$, $a_n = a_{n-1} - 13$

12. 62.5, 75, 87.5; $a_n = 12.5n + 12.5$; $a_1 = 25$, $a_n = a_{n-1} + 12.5$

16. $a_n = 6(2)^{n-1}$; 6, 12, 24, 48, 96

17. $a_n = -27\left(\frac{1}{3}\right)^{n-1}$; −27, −9, −3, −1, −$\frac{1}{3}$

18. $a_n = 1900(0.1)^{n-1}$; 1900, 190, 19, 1.9, 0.19

19. $a_n = -5(3)^{n-1}$; −5, −15, −45, −135, −405

20. $a_n = 4^{n-1}$; 1, 4, 16, 64, 256

21. $a_n = 500(0.2)^{n-1}$; 500, 100, 20, 4, 0.8

● **Lesson 11-1** Decide whether each formula is *explicit* or *recursive*. Then find the first five terms of each sequence.   1–4. See margin.

1. $a_n = 3n + 2$

2. $a_1 = 4$; $a_n = a_{n-1} + 7$

3. $a_n = 5n(n + 2)$

4. $a_1 = 2$; $a_n = a_{n-1} - 3$

5. $a_n = 6n^2 - 1$
explicit; 5, 23, 53, 95, 149

6. $a_n = 6 - 2n$
explicit; 4, 2, 0, −2, −4

● **Lesson 11-1** Find the next three terms in each sequence. Write an explicit and a recursive formula for each sequence.   7–12. See margin.

7. $3, 5, 7, \ldots$

8. $19, 15, 11, \ldots$

9. $-12, -10.5, -9, \ldots$

10. $0.2, 0.5, 0.8, \ldots$

11. $-23, -36, -49, \ldots$

12. $25, 37.5, 50, \ldots$

● **Lesson 11-2** Find the arithmetic mean a_n of the given terms.

13. $a_{n-1} = 10$, $a_{n+1} = 20$ **15**

14. $a_{n-1} = 7$, $a_{n+1} = 19$ **13**

15. $a_{n-1} = -2$, $a_{n+1} = -7$ **−4.5**

● **Lesson 11-3** Write the explicit formula for each geometric sequence. Then generate the first five terms.   16–21. See margin.

16. $a_1 = 6$, $r = 2$

17. $a_1 = -27$, $r = \frac{1}{3}$

18. $a_1 = 1900$, $r = 0.1$

19. $a_1 = -5$, $r = 3$

20. $a_1 = 1$, $r = 4$

21. $a_1 = 500$, $r = 0.2$

● **Lesson 11-4** Use summation notation to write each arithmetic series for the specified number of terms. Then evaluate each series.

22. $21, 19, 17, 15, \ldots$; 8 terms $\displaystyle\sum_{n=1}^{8} (-2n + 23)$; **112**

23. $4, 7, 10, 13, 16, 19, \ldots$; 10 terms $\displaystyle\sum_{n=1}^{10} (3n + 1)$; **175**

24. $-35, -28, -21, -14, \ldots$; 7 terms $\displaystyle\sum_{n=1}^{7} (7n - 42)$; **−98**

25. $97, 96, 95, 94, 93, \ldots$; 20 terms $\displaystyle\sum_{n=1}^{20} (-n + 98)$; **1750**

● **Lesson 11-4** For each sum, find the number of terms, the first term, and the last term. Then evaluate the sum.

26. $\displaystyle\sum_{n=1}^{5} (2n + 3)$ **5, 5, 13; 45**

27. $\displaystyle\sum_{n=2}^{7} (4 - n)$ **6, 2, −3; −3**

28. $\displaystyle\sum_{n=1}^{5} (n + 1)$ **5, 2, 6; 20**

29. $\displaystyle\sum_{n=3}^{10} (3n - 5)$ **8, 4, 25; 116**

● **Lesson 11-5** Find the sum of each infinite geometric series.

30. $4 + 2 + 1 + \frac{1}{2} + \ldots$ **8**

31. $3 - 1 + \frac{1}{3} - \frac{1}{9} + \ldots$ **$\frac{9}{4}$**

32. $2.2 - 0.22 + 0.022 - \ldots$ **2**

33. $0.9 + 0.09 + 0.009 + \ldots$ **1**

34. $5 - \frac{5}{2} + \frac{5}{4} - \frac{5}{8} + \ldots$ **$\frac{10}{3}$**

35. $1 + 0.1 + 0.01 + \ldots$ **$\frac{10}{9}$**

● **Lesson 11-5** Determine whether each series is *arithmetic* or *geometric*. Then find the sum to the given term.

arithmetic; 165

36. $3 + 6 + 9 + 12 + 15 + \ldots$; 10th term

geometric; 3069

37. $3 + 6 + 12 + 24 + 48 + \ldots$; 10th term

38. $-1000 + 500 - 250 + 125 - \ldots$; 7th term
geometric; −671.875

39. $87 + 72 + 57 + 42 + \ldots$; 20th term
arithmetic; −1110

● **Lesson 11-6** Write and evaluate sums to approximate the area under each curve for the domain $0 \le x \le 2$. First use inscribed rectangles 1 unit wide. Then use circumscribed rectangles 1 unit wide.

40. $f(x) = 2x^2$
0 + 2 = 2; 2 + 8 = 10

41. $y = x^3$
0 + 1 = 1; 1 + 8 = 9

42. $g(x) = 2x + 3$
3 + 5 = 8; 5 + 7 = 12

43. $h(x) = |x + 3|$
3 + 4 = 7; 4 + 5 = 9

Chapter 12 Extra Practice

Lesson 12-1 Graph the probability distribution for each sample space.

1. {the product of two number cubes an even number, the product an odd number} **See margin.**

2. {the sum of two number cubes a prime number, the sum a composite number} **See margin.**

Lesson 12-2 Use the data in the table to find each probability.

3. P(counselor a junior) $\frac{39}{80}$

4. P(counselor female) $\frac{37}{80}$

5. P(counselor a senior and male) $\frac{25}{80}$

6. P(counselor a junior | counselor female) $\frac{21}{37}$

7. P(counselor male | counselor a senior) $\frac{25}{41}$

Characteristics of Camp Counselors

Grade Level	Male	Female
Junior	18	21
Senior	25	16

Lesson 12-3 Find the mean, median, and mode for each set of values.

8. 3 2 6 4 5 3 4 2 7 5 3 **4, 4, 3**

9. 16 62 24 13 21 35 24 17 20 **25.8, 21, 24**

10. 125 135 126 138 137 135 121 **131, 135, 135**

11. 6.1 9.5 3.8 4.6 6.1 2.3 3.7 2.1 **4.8, 4.2, 6.1**

Lesson 12-4 Find the mean, range, interquartile range, and standard deviation for each set of data.

12. 6 8 5 2 7 3 5 6 7 **5.444, 6, 3, 1.83**

13. 25 29 21 19 30 26 28 **25.429, 11, 8, 3.81**

14. 12 9 10 11 13 9 20 **12, 11, 4, 3.546**

15. 100 98 101 100 102 97 100 **99.71, 5, 3, 1.578**

Lesson 12-5 Find the margin of error for the sample proportion, given each sample size n.

16. $n = 90$ ±11%

17. $n = 300$ ±6%

18. $n = 125$ ±9%

19. $n = 900$ ±3%

20. $n = 1000$ ±3%

21. $n = 5000$ ±1%

Lesson 12-6 Find the probability of x successes in n trials for the given probability of success p on each trial.

22. $x = 2, n = 6, p = 0.7$ 0.0595 ≈ 6%

23. $x = 3, n = 8, p = \frac{2}{5}$ 0.2787 ≈ 28%

24. $x = 9, n = 10, p = 0.3$ 0.0001 ≈ 0.01%

25. $x = 7, n = 9, p = \frac{1}{5}$ 0.0003 ≈ 0.03%

26. $x = 4, n = 12, p = 0.8$ 0.00052 ≈ 0.05%

27. $x = 8, n = 11, p = 0.9$ 0.0710 ≈ 7%

Lesson 12-6 Use the binomial expansion of $(p + q)^n$ to calculate and graph each binomial distribution. **28–33. See back of book.**

28. $n = 5, p = 0.2$

29. $n = 6, p = 0.4$

30. $n = 5, p = 0.7$

31. $n = 4, p = 0.2$

32. $n = 5, p = 0.4$

33. $n = 6, p = 0.8$

Lesson 12-7 Sketch a normal curve for each distribution. Label the x-axis values at one, two, and three standard deviations from the mean. **34–37. See margin.**

34. mean $= 30$, standard deviation $= 4$

35. mean $= 45$, standard deviation $= 11$

36. mean $= 10$, standard deviation $= 2$

37. mean $= 60$, standard deviation $= 12$

1.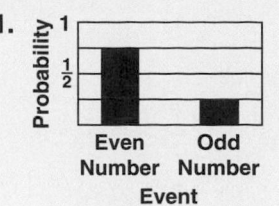

2.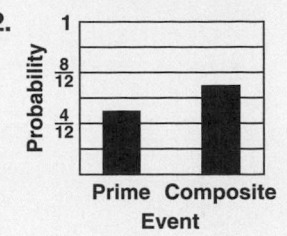

34.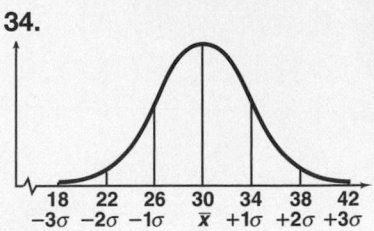

35.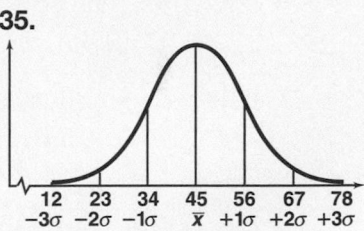

36.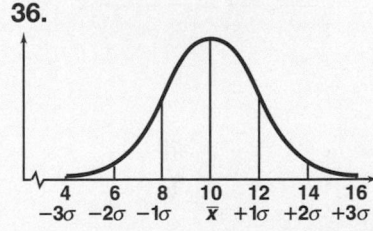

37.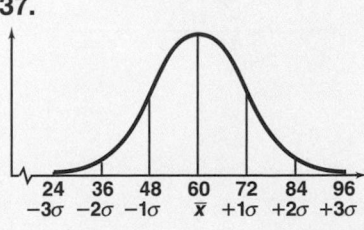

4.

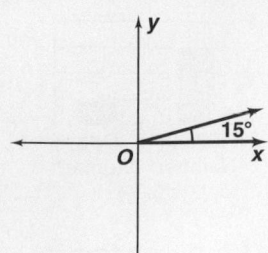

5.

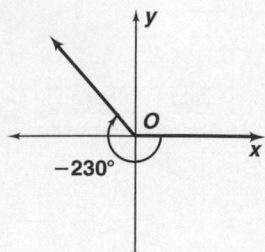

−230°

6.

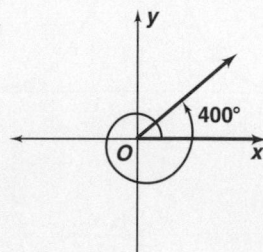

400°

7.

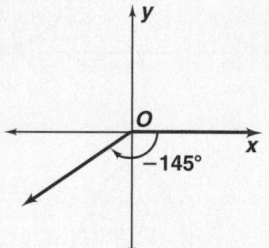

−145°

8.

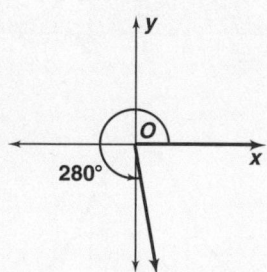

280°

9.

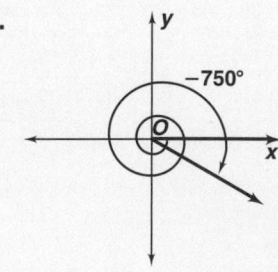

−750°

Chapter **13** **Extra Practice**

● **Lesson 13-1** Find the period and amplitude of each periodic function.

1.

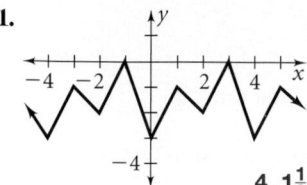

$4, 1\frac{1}{2}$

2.

$1, 2\frac{1}{2}$

3.

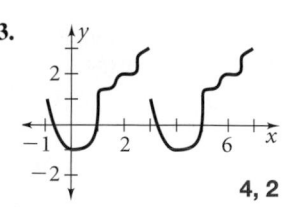

$4, 2$

● **Lesson 13-2** Sketch each angle in standard position.   **4–9. See margin.**

4. $15°$ **5.** $-230°$ **6.** $400°$

7. $-145°$ **8.** $280°$ **9.** $-750°$

● **Lesson 13-3** Write each measure in radians. Express the answer in terms of π and as a decimal rounded to the nearest hundredth.

10. $100°$ $\frac{5\pi}{9}$, **1.75**   **11.** $270°$ $\frac{3\pi}{2}$, **4.71**   **12.** $-45°$ $-\frac{\pi}{4}$, **−0.79**

13. $-550°$ $\frac{-55\pi}{18}$, **−9.60**   **14.** $425°$ $\frac{85\pi}{36}$, **7.42**   **15.** $10°$ $\frac{\pi}{18}$, **0.17**

● **Lesson 13-3** Write each measure in degrees. When necessary, round your answer to the nearest degree.

16. 5π radians **900°**   **17.** -2 radians **−115°**   **18.** $\frac{5\pi}{6}$ radians **150°**

19. -3π radians **−540°**   **20.** $-\frac{13\pi}{10}$ radians **−234°**   **21.** 9 radians **516°**

● **Lessons 13-4, 13-5, and 13-6** Identify the amplitude or asymptotes, and the period for each function.

22. $y = 4 \sin 3x$ $4, \frac{2\pi}{3}$ **23.** $y = \cos 4x$ $1, \frac{\pi}{2}$ **24.** $y = \frac{1}{3} \tan \pi x$ Asymptotes at $x = \frac{1}{2} + n$, n is an integer, 1.

25. $y = 2 \cos \frac{x}{4}$ $2, 8\pi$ **26.** $y = 3 \tan x$ Asymptotes at $x = \frac{\pi}{2} + \pi n$, n is an integer, π.   **27.** $y = \frac{1}{9} \sin 5x$ $\frac{1}{9}, \frac{2\pi}{5}$

● **Lessons 13-4, 13-5, and 13-6** Sketch the graph of each function in the interval from 0 to 2π.   **28–33. See back of book.**

28. $y = 2 \cos x$ **29.** $y = 3 \sin 2x$ **30.** $y = \tan \frac{x}{2}$

31. $y = -\sin 3x$ **32.** $y = -2 \tan \pi x$ **33.** $y = \cos 4x$

● **Lesson 13-7** Graph each function in the interval from 0 to 2π.   **34–37. See margin.**

34. $y = -3 \cos (x + \pi) + 3$ **35.** $y = 2 \sin \left(2x - \frac{\pi}{3}\right) - 2$

36. $y = -\sin \left(x - \frac{\pi}{4}\right) + 1$ **37.** $y = 3 \cos \left(3x + \frac{\pi}{2}\right) - 1$

● **Lesson 13-8** Evaluate each expression in radians.

38. $\cot 1$ **0.6421**   **39.** $\sec 4$ **−1.5299**   **40.** $\csc (-0.8)$ **−1.394**

41. $\sec (-\pi)$ **−1**   **42.** $\cot \frac{3\pi}{2}$ **0**   **43.** $\csc \frac{\pi}{4}$ **1.4142** $\approx \sqrt{2}$

44. $\sec 1.1$ **2.2046**   **45.** $\cot 2$ **−0.4577**   **46.** $\csc 2.5$ **1.6709**

34.

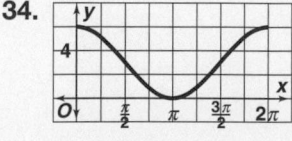

35.

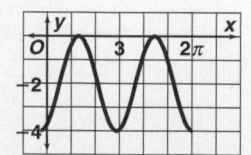

36.

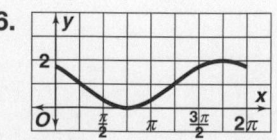

37.

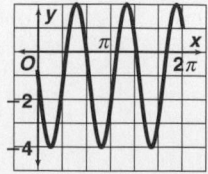

Chapter 14 Extra Practice

● **Lesson 14-2** Use a unit circle and 30°-60°-90° triangles to find the degree measures of the angles.

1. angles whose sine is $\frac{\sqrt{3}}{2}$
$60° + n \cdot 360°$ and $120° + n \cdot 360°$

2. angles whose cosine is $-\frac{1}{2}$
$120° + n \cdot 360°$ and $240° + n \cdot 360°$

3. angles whose tangent is $\sqrt{3}$
$60° + n \cdot 360°$ and $240° + n \cdot 360°$

● **Lesson 14-2** Use a calculator to find the value in radians of each expression.

4. $\tan^{-1}(-1.6)$ **−1.012**   **5.** $\sin^{-1}(-2.8)$ **no solution** **6.** $\sin^{-1}1.2$ **no solution**   **7.** $\tan^{-1}3.8$ **1.313**

8. $\cos^{-1}0.5$ **1.047**   **9.** $\sin^{-1}(-2.1)$ **no solution**   **10.** $\tan^{-1}1.3$ **0.9151**   **11.** $\cos^{-1}(-1)$ **3.14159 ≈ π**

● **Lesson 14-2** Solve each equation for $0 \le \theta \le 2\pi$.

12. $4\cos\theta = 3$ **0.7227, 5.5605**   **13.** $\sqrt{3}\sin\theta + \sqrt{3} = 0$ $\frac{3\pi}{2}$ **14.** $2\tan\theta + 3 = \tan\theta$ **1.8925, 5.034**

15. $(\tan\theta)\left(\tan\theta + \frac{1}{2}\right) = 0$
0, π, 2.6779, 5.8195, 2π

16. $\cos^2\theta - \frac{1}{3}\cos\theta = 0$
$\frac{\pi}{2}, \frac{3\pi}{2}$, **1.2310, 5.0522**

17. $\sin\theta\cos\theta + \sin\theta = 0$ **0, π**

● **Lesson 14-3** In $\triangle ABC$, $\angle C$ is a right angle. Find the remaining sides and angles. Round your answer to the nearest tenth.   **18–23. See margin.**

18. $m\angle A = 29°, b = 8$

19. $a = 7, c = 9$

20. $m\angle B = 52°, b = 10$

21. $a = 2, b = 4$

22. $m\angle A = 37°, c = 12$

23. $b = 5, c = 8$

● **Lesson 14-3** In $\triangle RST$, $\angle S$ is a right angle, $RS = 24$, and $\cos R = \frac{12}{13}$. Draw a diagram and find each value in fraction and decimal form.

24. $\sin R$ $\frac{5}{13}$, **0.385**   **25.** $\sin T$ $\frac{12}{13}$, **0.923**   **26.** $\cos T$ $\frac{5}{13}$, **0.385**   **27.** $\cot R$ $\frac{12}{5}$, **2.4**

● **Lessons 14-4 and 14-5** Use the Law of Sines or the Law of Cosines. Find the measure x to the nearest tenth.

28. 43.0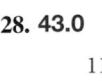

29. 11.3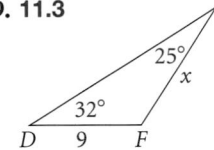

30. **12.6**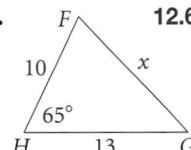

31. **46.3**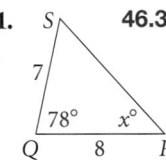

● **Lesson 14-6** Find each exact value. Use a sum or difference identity.

32. $\cos 15°$ $\frac{\sqrt{6} + \sqrt{2}}{4}$

33. $\sin 15°$ $\frac{\sqrt{6} - \sqrt{2}}{4}$

34. $\tan 315°$ **−1**

35. $\cos 390°$ $\frac{\sqrt{3}}{2}$

36. $\sin 105°$ $\frac{\sqrt{6} + \sqrt{2}}{4}$

37. $\tan 225°$ **1**

● **Lesson 14-7** Use a double-angle identity to find the exact value of each expression.

38. $\sin 120°$ $\frac{\sqrt{3}}{2}$

39. $\cos 720°$ **1**

40. $\tan 480°$ $-\sqrt{3}$

41. $\cos 180°$ **−1**

42. $\sin 180°$ **0**

43. $\cos 480°$ $-\frac{1}{2}$

● **Lesson 14-7** Use a half-angle identity to find the exact value of each expression.   **45–49. See margin.**

44. $\sin 90°$ **1**

45. $\cos 75°$

46. $\tan 75°$

47. $\sin 67.5°$

48. $\tan 67.5°$

49. $\cos 7.5°$

CHAPTER 14

page 835 Extra Practice

18. $\angle B = 61°, a = 4.4, c = 9.1$

19. $b = 5.7, \angle A = 51.1°,$
$\angle B = 38.9°$

20. $\angle A = 38°, c = 12.7,$
$a = 7.8$

21. $c = 4.5, \angle A = 26.6°,$
$\angle B = 63.4°$

22. $\angle B = 53°, a = 7.2,$
$b = 9.6$

23. $a = 6.2, \angle B = 38.7°,$
$\angle A = 51.3°$

45. $\sqrt{\dfrac{2 - \sqrt{3}}{2}}$

46. $\sqrt{7 + 4\sqrt{3}}$

47. $\dfrac{\sqrt{2 + \sqrt{2}}}{2}$

48. $\sqrt{3 + 2\sqrt{2}}$

49. $\dfrac{\sqrt{2 + \sqrt{2 + \sqrt{3}}}}{2}$

Skills Handbook

Problem Solving Strategies

You may find these strategies helpful when solving word problems.

STRATEGY	WHEN TO USE IT
Draw a Diagram	The problem describes a picture or diagram.
Try, Check, Revise	Solving the problem directly is too complicated.
Look for a Pattern	The problem describes a relationship.
Make a Table	The problem has data that need to be organized.
Solve a Simpler Problem	The problem is complex or has numbers that are too cumbersome to use at first.
Use Logical Reasoning	You need to reach a conclusion using given information.
Work Backward	You need to find the number that led to the result in the problem.

Problem Solving: Draw a Diagram

2.

> **EXAMPLE**
>
> Two students leave school at the same time and travel in opposite directions along the same road. One walks at a rate of 3 mi/h. The other bikes at a rate of 8.5 mi/h. How far apart are the students after two hours?
>
> Draw a Diagram: walking 3 mi/h • 2h   biking 8.5 mi/h • 2h
>
> 6   3   School   8.5   17

● After two hours, the students will be 6 + 17, or 23 mi apart.

EXERCISES

1. A bug starts at point $P(0, 0)$. Each time it moves, it crawls one half the distance traveled in the previous move. It travels east, north, west, south, east, north, and so on, in order. Its first move is east 16 units. Where is the bug after six moves? $\left(13, 6\frac{1}{2}\right)$

2. Draw a graph to check this statement: The graph of $y = 2(x - 3) + 1$ is the graph of $y = 2x + 1$ shifted to the right 3 units. **See above.**

3. Suppose you have four metal rods with lengths 2 in., 5 in., 7 in., and 9 in. How could you use all four rods to measure a length of 1 in.?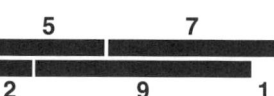

4. Two cars leave Los Angeles at the same time and follow the same route toward the Grand Canyon. The first car averages 55 mi/h. The second car averages 65 mi/h. How far apart are the two cars after five hours? **50 mi**

Problem Solving: Try, Check, Revise

When you are not sure how to start solving a problem, try an answer and then test it. In the process of testing, you may see a way to revise your trial answer to get closer to the actual answer.

● EXAMPLE

The automatic leg-counter at the Brazinski farm counted 114 legs as the pigs and ducks swarmed through the gate at feeding time. A total of 40 animals passed through the gate. How many pigs and how many ducks passed through the gate?

Try	20 pigs	**Test**	$20 \cdot 4 =$	80 legs
	20 ducks		$20 \cdot 2 =$	$\underline{+40 \text{ legs}}$
				120 legs

Revise your guess. You need fewer pigs to bring the total number of legs down.

Try	18 pigs	**Test**	$18 \cdot 4 =$	72 legs
	22 ducks		$22 \cdot 2 =$	$\underline{+44 \text{ legs}}$
				116 legs

The number is still too high.

Try	17 pigs	**Test**	$17 \cdot 4 =$	68 legs
	23 ducks		$23 \cdot 2 =$	$\underline{+46 \text{ legs}}$
				114 legs

● Seventeen pigs and 23 ducks passed through the gate.

EXERCISES

1. Suppose the automatic leg-counter at the Brazinski farm counted 126 legs, but there were still a total of 40 animals. How many pigs and how many ducks passed through the gate? **23 pigs and 17 ducks**

2. Suppose the automatic leg-counter at the Brazinski farm counted 114 legs, but a total of 32 animals passed through the gate. How many pigs and how many ducks passed through the gate? **25 pigs and 7 ducks**

3. Marika biked a total of 110 mi during three days of training for a bicycle race. On the second day of her training session, she biked 15 mi more than on the first day but 5 mi less than on the third day. How many miles did she bike on the third day? **45 mi**

4. Use each of the integers from 1 to 9 once to fill the circles so that the sums along the spokes are equal. (Each spoke contains three numbers.) **See above.**

5. Use each of the integers 2, 4, 6, 8, 12, 14, 16, 18, and 20 to fill the circles so that the sums along the spokes are equal. **See above.**

6. Find a and b such that $x^2 - x - 72 = (x + a)(x + b)$. **$a = 8, b = -9$ or $a = -9, b = 8$**

7. Approximate $\sqrt{385}$ to the nearest tenth. **19.6**

8. Mr. Hoerner spent $45.50 last month to see 11 movies. If video rentals cost $3, movie matinees cost $4.50, and evening movies cost $7, how many of each type of movie did he see? **6, 3, and 2, respectively**

4.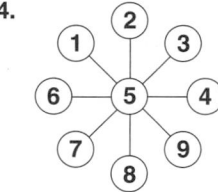

5.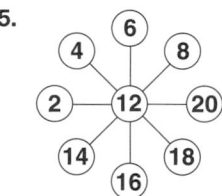

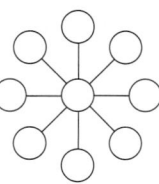

page 838 Problem Solving:
Look for a Pattern
and Make a Table

3a.

Rectangle Perimeter

		length						
		1	**2**	**3**	**4**	**5**	**6**	**7**
width	**1**	4	6	8	10	12	14	16
	2	6	8	10	12	14	16	18
	3	8	10	12	14	16	18	20
	4	10	12	14	16	18	20	22
	5	12	14	16	18	20	22	24
	6	14	16	18	20	22	24	26
	7	16	18	20	22	24	26	28

Rectangle Area

		length						
		1	**2**	**3**	**4**	**5**	**6**	**7**
width	**1**	1	2	3	4	5	6	7
	2	2	4	6	8	10	12	14
	3	3	6	9	12	15	18	21
	4	4	8	12	16	20	24	28
	5	5	10	15	20	25	30	35
	6	6	12	18	24	30	36	42
	7	7	14	21	28	35	42	49

b. yes

Problem Solving: Look for a Pattern and Make a Table

Some problems describe relationships that involve regular sequences of numbers or other things. To solve the problem you need to be able to recognize and describe the *pattern* that shows the relationship among the numbers or things. One way to organize the information is to *make a table*.

EXAMPLE

After scrounging around in the couch cushions, your father tells you he has found $2.40 in equal numbers of quarters, dimes, and nickels. He says you can have the money if you can tell him how many of each coin he has.

Make a table to help find a pattern.

Number of Nickels	1	2	3	4	5	6
Number of Dimes	1	2	3	4	5	6
Number of Quarters	1	2	3	4	5	6
Total Value	$.40	$.80	$1.20	$1.60	$2.00	$2.40

● Your father has six of each type of coin.

EXERCISES

1. Your father tells you that he has found $3.10 in equal numbers of quarters, nickels, and pennies. How many of each coin does he have? **ten of each coin**

2. **a.** A college radio station sponsors a contest once a week. One resident from a dormitory calls in and tries to answer ten questions correctly. Each correct answer earns the dorm $50, but each incorrect answer reduces the winnings by $25. Last week's contestant earned $350. How many answers were correct?
   8 answers
   b. The contest rules were changed so that each incorrect answer reduces the winnings by $50. A contestant earned $100. How many answers were correct?
   6 answers

3. **a.** Make tables to show the perimeters and areas of rectangles whose lengths are 1, 2, 3, 4, 5, 6, and 7 units and whose widths are 1, 2, 3, 4, 5, 6, and 7 units.
   b. Use the tables to find out whether there is a rectangle whose area and perimeter are numerically the same. **a–b. See margin.**

4. Lisa's school uniform is any combination of a white or light blue shirt, a dark blue skirt or a dark blue pair of slacks, and a plaid blazer. How many different outfits can she make? **4 outfits**

5. How many different ways are there to make $.50 in change without using pennies? **11 ways if you include one fifty-cent coin**

6. How many different ways are there to make $.75 in change without using pennies? **22 if you include one fifty-cent coin**

7. How many ways can you roll two standard number cubes and get a sum of 7? **6 ways**

8. Suppose you have five 32¢ stamps and three 20¢ stamps. How many different amounts of postage could you make? **23 amounts**

Problem Solving: Solve a Simpler Problem

By solving one or more simpler problems, you can often find a pattern that will help solve a more complicated problem.

EXAMPLE

One thousand snap-together cubes make up a large cube measuring 10 units along each edge. The large cube is painted red and then taken apart. How many of the snap-together cubes are painted red on two sides?

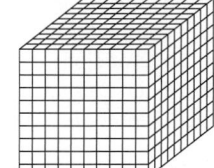

Begin with one snap-together cube, and then add cubes to make a larger cube. Find out whether there is a pattern.

Length of edge	1	2	3	4	5	...
Number of snap-together cubes	1	8	27	64	125	...
Number of cubes with two sides painted	0	0	12	24	36	...
Pattern			12 • 1	12 • 2	12 • 3	...

The pattern is that there are $12 \cdot (n - 2)$ snap-together cubes painted red on two sides.

$12 \cdot (10 - 2) = 12 \cdot 8$ **Substitute 10 for *n*.**

$ = 96$

There are 96 cubes that are painted red on two sides.

EXERCISES

1. Six different cuts are made through the center of a pizza. How many slices are formed? **12 slices**

2. **a.** Find each sum at the right. **4, 9, 16, 25**
   b. Describe a relationship between the number of addends and the sum of each addition in part (a). **(number of addends)² = sum**
   c. Evaluate $1 + 3 + 5 + ... + 997 + 999$. **250,000**

$1 + 3 = \blacksquare$
$1 + 3 + 5 = \blacksquare$
$1 + 3 + 5 + 7 = \blacksquare$
$1 + 3 + 5 + 7 + 9 = \blacksquare$

3. Find the total number of squares of all sizes on a standard checkerboard, a board with eight units on a side. **204 squares**

4. Suppose your heart beats 68 times per minute.
   a. How many times had your heart beaten by your 15th birthday? **536,112,000 times**
   b. If you live to be 87 years old, how many times will your heart have beaten? **3,109,449,600 times**

5. **a.** The Steuben County Regional Soccer League has ten teams. During a season, each team plays every other team twice, once at home and once away. How many games are played in one season? **90 games**
   b. Suppose there are *s* teams in the league. How many games are played in one season? **s(s − 1) games**

6. First, Second, Third, and Fourth Streets run east and west. They intersect A, B, and C Boulevards, which run north and south. How many different one-way paths are there from the intersection of First Street and A Boulevard to the intersection of Fourth Street and C Boulevard? **10 paths**

Problem Solving: Use Logical Reasoning

Some problems can be solved without using numbers. They can be solved by *logical reasoning*, given some information.

> **EXAMPLE**
>
> Four pigs (Julie, Snowball, Ladybug, and Tina) and their owners (Juan, Suzanne, LaShawn, and Trevor) went home happy after winning prizes at the county fair. None of the pigs have the same first initial as their owners. Juan's pig is not Tina. LaShawn's pig got her name because she was born during a blizzard. Match the owners with their pigs.
>
> Make a table to organize what you know.
>
> | | Julie | Snowball | Ladybug | Tina |
> |---|---|---|---|---|
> | Juan | X | X | | X |
> | Suzanne | | X | | |
> | LaShawn | X | ✔ | X | X |
> | Trevor | | X | | X |
>
> Juan's pig is not Tina, so put an X in that box.
>
> **LaShawn's pig must be Snowball.**
>
> Since the pigs and their owners have different first initials, put an X in each box along the main diagonal.
>
> Use *logical reasoning* to complete the table.
>
> | | Julie | Snowball | Ladybug | Tina |
> |---|---|---|---|---|
> | Juan | X | X | ✔ | X |
> | Suzanne | X | X | X | ✔ |
> | LaShawn | X | ✔ | X | X |
> | Trevor | ✔ | X | X | X |
>
> Juan must own Ladybug.
>
> **The only pig left for Suzanne is Tina.**
>
> The only possible pig for Trevor is Julie.
>
> Juan owns Ladybug, Suzanne owns Tina, LaShawn owns Snowball, and Trevor owns Julie.

EXERCISES

1. The junior class is selling mugs with the school logo as part of a school-wide fundraising campaign. The top four salespeople in the class are Pat, Andy, Leon, and Shana. Pat sold more mugs than Andy but fewer than Leon. Shana also sold more than Andy, but she sold fewer than Pat. Andy sold the fewest mugs. Who sold the most mugs in the junior class? **Leon**

2. Gregor has the same number of brothers as sisters. His sister Delores has twice as many brothers as sisters. How many children are in Gregor and Delores' family? **7 children**

3. Ray has the same number of male classmates as female classmates. His classmate Rita has three fourths as many female classmates as male classmates. How many students are in the class? **15 students**

4. Which expression(s) will be positive for all positive integers n? **A, D, and E**
   A. $2^n - n$ **B.** $n - 2^n$ **C.** $(n + 1) - 2^n$ **D.** $2^n - (n - 1)$ **E.** $2^n + n$

5. Four people, Luis, Marisa, Neil, and Ophelia, were on a bus. The florist sat next to Marisa. Luis and the surgeon are married to each other. The caterer, the editor, and Neil don't know each other. The surgeon was sitting behind Ophelia. Luis doesn't make salmon. Which person does which work?
   Luis: editor; Marisa: surgeon; Neil: florist; Ophelia: caterer

3.

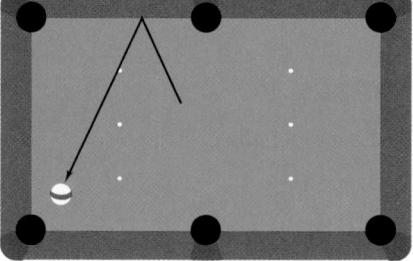

Problem Solving: Work Backward

To solve some problems you need to start with the end result and work backward to the beginning.

 EXAMPLE

A ball bounced four times, reaching one half its previous height with each bounce. After the fourth bounce, the ball reached a height of 2 ft. How high was the ball when it was dropped?

Each bounce reaches one half the previous height. So multiply by two to find the previous height. Work backward.

Bounce	4	3	2	1
Height	2 ft	4 ft	8 ft	16 ft

After the first bounce, the ball reached a height of 16 ft, so it must have been dropped from a height of 2(16) or 32 ft.

EXERCISES

1. A ball bounced four times, reaching three fourths of its previous height with each bounce. After the fourth bounce, the ball reached a height of 27 cm. How high was the ball when it was dropped?   **$85\frac{1}{3}$ cm**

2. On Friday, Kamiko deposited $475 in her account. On Sunday, she withdrew $150. On Tuesday she deposited $25 and withdrew $50. On Wednesday she wrote a check for $127.50. She now has $627.45 in her account. How much was in Kamiko's account before she made Friday's deposit? **$454.95**

3. The diagram at the right shows the final resting place of a ball on a billiard table. Suppose the ball bounced off the cushions of the table four times. Show where the ball was when it was originally set in motion. (*Hint:* The ball makes equal angles with the side when it rebounds.)   **See margin.**

4. Suppose you start with a number. You multiply the number by 3, add 7, divide by $\frac{1}{2}$, subtract 5, and then divide by 12. The result is 5. What number did you start with?   **8.5**

5. Suppose you start with a number. You subtract 10, multiply by 3, add 5, multiply by $\frac{1}{4}$, and divide by $\frac{1}{3}$. The final result is 33. What number did you start with?   **23**

6. Derwood decided to sell a box of pencils. On Monday he sold half the pencils. On Tuesday he sold another 40 pencils. On Wednesday he sold half the pencils that were left. On Thursday he sold the remaining 25 pencils. How many pencils were in the box originally?   **180 pencils**

7. Tian rented a car to drive from his town to Chicago. The rental company charges $53 per day plus $.27 per mile. When Tian dropped the car off in Chicago three days later, his bill from the rental company was $453.57, which included 5% sales tax. How far from Chicago does Tian live? **1011 mi**

Percents and Percent Applications

Percent means "per hundred." Find fraction, decimal, and percent equivalents by replacing one symbol for *hundredths* with another.

1 EXAMPLE Write each number as a percent.

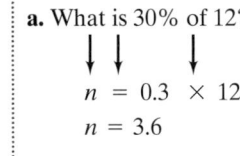   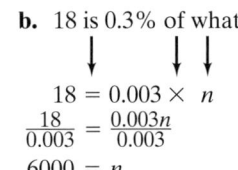   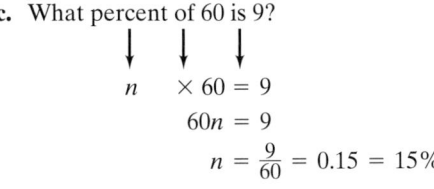

a. $0.082 = 8.2\%$ **b.** $1.20 = 120\%$ **c.** $\frac{3}{5} = \frac{60}{100} = 60\%$ **d.** $1\frac{1}{6} = \frac{7}{6}$
$= 1.166\overline{6}$
$= 116.\overline{6}\%$

Move the decimal point two places to the right and write a percent sign.

Write the fraction as hundredths. Then replace hundredths with a percent sign.

First, use $7 \div 6$ to write $1\frac{1}{6}$ as a decimal.

2 EXAMPLE Write each percent as a decimal.

a. $50\% = 0.50 = 0.5$ **b.** $\frac{1}{2}\% = 0.5\% = 00.5\% = 0.005$

Move the decimal point two places to the left and drop the percent sign.

To model a percent problem with an equation, express each percent as a decimal. There are three basic kinds of percent problems.

3 EXAMPLE Use an equation to solve each percent problem.

a. What is 30% of 12?

$n = 0.3 \times 12$
$n = 3.6$

b. 18 is 0.3% of what?

$18 = 0.003 \times n$
$\frac{18}{0.003} = \frac{0.003n}{0.003}$
$6000 = n$

c. What percent of 60 is 9?

$n \times 60 = 9$
$60n = 9$
$n = \frac{9}{60} = 0.15 = 15\%$

EXERCISES

Write each number as a percent.

1. 0.46 **46%**   **2.** 0.3 **30%**   **3.** 0.294 **29.4%**   **4.** 1.03 **103%**   **5.** 0.007 **0.7%**   **6.** 1.506 **150.6%**

7. $\frac{1}{4}$ **25%**   **8.** $\frac{3}{8}$ **37.5%**   **9.** $\frac{2}{3}$ **66.7%**   **10.** $\frac{4}{9}$ **44.4%**   **11.** $1\frac{3}{20}$ **115%**   **12.** $\frac{1}{200}$ **0.5%**

Write each percent as a decimal.

13. 40% **0.4**   **14.** 8% **0.08**   **15.** 150% **1.5**   **16.** 0.7% **0.007**   **17.** 103.5% **1.035**   **18.** 3.3% **0.033**

Use an equation to solve each percent problem.

19. What is 25% of 50? **12.5**   **20.** What percent of 58 is 37? **63.8%**   **21.** 120% of what is 90? **75**

22. 8 is what percent of 40? **20%**   **23.** 15 is 75% of what? **20**   **24.** 80% of 58 is what? **46.4**

25. In Louisiana the state sales tax is 4%. If you buy a $15,000 car in Louisiana, how much tax will you pay? **$600**

26. The Mississippi River drains about 1,247,300 mi², which is 13.3% of the land area of North America. Estimate the total area of North America. **about 9.4 million mi²**

Operations With Fractions

To add or subtract fractions, use a common denominator. The common denominator is the least common multiple of the denominators.

1 EXAMPLE Simplify $\frac{2}{3} + \frac{3}{5}$.

$\frac{2}{3} + \frac{3}{5} = \frac{10}{15} + \frac{9}{15}$ For 3 and 5, the least common multiple is 15.

                    Write $\frac{2}{3}$ and $\frac{3}{5}$ as equivalent fractions with denominators of 15.

     $= \frac{19}{15}$ or $1\frac{4}{15}$ Add the numerators.

2 EXAMPLE Simplify $5\frac{1}{4} - 3\frac{2}{3}$.

$5\frac{1}{4} - 3\frac{2}{3} = 5\frac{3}{12} - 3\frac{8}{12}$ Write equivalent fractions.

     $= 4\frac{15}{12} - 3\frac{8}{12}$ Write $5\frac{1}{4}$ as $4\frac{15}{12}$ so you can subtract the fractions.

     $= 1\frac{7}{12}$ Subtract the fractions. Then subtract the whole numbers.

To multiply fractions, multiply the numerators and multiply the denominators. You can simplify by using a greatest common factor.

3 EXAMPLE Simplify $\frac{3}{4} \cdot \frac{8}{11}$.

Method 1 $\frac{3}{4} \cdot \frac{8}{11} = \frac{24}{44} = \frac{24 \div 4}{44 \div 4} = \frac{6}{11}$ **Method 2** $\frac{3}{{}_1 4} \cdot \frac{8^2}{11} = \frac{6}{11}$

Divide 24 and 44 by 4, their greatest common factor.   Divide 4 and 8 by 4, their greatest common factor.

To divide fractions, use a reciprocal to change the problem to multiplication.

4 EXAMPLE Simplify $3\frac{1}{5} \div 1\frac{1}{2}$.

$3\frac{1}{5} \div 1\frac{1}{2} = \frac{16}{5} \div \frac{3}{2}$ Write mixed numbers as improper fractions.

     $= \frac{16}{5} \cdot \frac{2}{3}$ Multiply by the reciprocal of the divisor.

     $= \frac{32}{15}$ or $2\frac{2}{15}$ Simplify.

EXERCISES

Perform the indicated operation.

1. $\frac{3}{5} + \frac{4}{5}$ $1\frac{2}{5}$ 2. $\frac{1}{2} + \frac{2}{3}$ $1\frac{1}{6}$ 3. $4\frac{1}{2} + 2\frac{1}{3}$ $6\frac{5}{6}$ 4. $6\frac{4}{5} + 1\frac{1}{9}$ $7\frac{41}{45}$

5. $5\frac{3}{4} + 4\frac{2}{5}$ $10\frac{3}{20}$ 6. $\frac{4}{5} - \frac{1}{5}$ $\frac{3}{5}$ 7. $\frac{2}{3} - \frac{3}{7}$ $\frac{5}{21}$ 8. $5\frac{1}{2} - 3\frac{2}{5}$ $2\frac{1}{10}$

9. $8\frac{2}{5} - 1\frac{1}{10}$ $7\frac{3}{10}$ 10. $7\frac{3}{4} - 4\frac{4}{5}$ $2\frac{19}{20}$ 11. $\frac{3}{4} \cdot \frac{1}{2}$ $\frac{3}{8}$ 12. $\frac{9}{2} \cdot \frac{6}{7}$ $3\frac{6}{7}$

13. $3\frac{4}{5} \cdot 10$ 38 14. $2\frac{1}{2} \cdot 3\frac{1}{5}$ 8 15. $6\frac{3}{4} \cdot 5\frac{2}{3}$ $38\frac{1}{4}$ 16. $\frac{1}{2} \div \frac{1}{3}$ $1\frac{1}{2}$

17. $\frac{6}{5} \div \frac{3}{5}$ 2 18. $8\frac{1}{2} \div 4\frac{1}{4}$ 2 19. $5\frac{5}{6} \div 2\frac{1}{3}$ $2\frac{1}{2}$ 20. $3\frac{1}{6} \div 1\frac{3}{4}$ $1\frac{17}{21}$

21. $7\frac{1}{2} + 3\frac{3}{4}$ $11\frac{1}{4}$ 22. $3\frac{2}{3} \div \frac{1}{2}$ $7\frac{1}{3}$ 23. $\frac{8}{9} - \frac{2}{3}$ $\frac{2}{9}$ 24. $7\frac{2}{7} \div 2\frac{3}{7}$ 3

25. $\frac{7}{8} \cdot 5\frac{1}{2}$ $4\frac{13}{16}$ 26. $2\frac{3}{4} \cdot \frac{5}{8}$ $1\frac{23}{32}$ 27. $8 - 5\frac{5}{6}$ $2\frac{1}{6}$ 28. $14\frac{1}{4} - 5\frac{2}{3}$ $8\frac{7}{12}$

29. $4\frac{2}{3} + 1\frac{6}{11}$ $6\frac{7}{33}$ 30. $5\frac{1}{4} \cdot 8$ 42 31. $3\frac{1}{2} \div 6$ $\frac{7}{12}$ 32. $8 \div 3\frac{5}{6}$ $2\frac{2}{23}$

Ratios and Proportions

A *ratio* is a comparison of two quantities by division. You can write *equal ratios* by multiplying or dividing each quantity by the same nonzero number.

Ways to Write a Ratio
$a : b$ a to b $\frac{a}{b}$ $(b \neq 0)$

1 EXAMPLE Write $3\frac{1}{3} : \frac{1}{2}$ as a ratio in simplest form.

$$3\frac{1}{3} \cdot \frac{1}{2} \longrightarrow \overset{\times 6}{\underset{\times 6}{\frac{3\frac{1}{3}}{\frac{1}{2}}}} = \frac{20}{3} \text{ or } 20 \cdot 3$$

In simplest form, both terms should be integers.
Multiply by the common denominator, 6.

A rate is a ratio that compares different types of quantities. In simplest form for a rate, the second quantity is one unit.

2 EXAMPLE Write 247 mi in 5.2 h as a rate in simplest form.

$$\overset{\div 5.2}{\underset{\div 5.2}{\frac{247 \text{ mi}}{5.2 \text{ h}}}} = \frac{47.5 \text{ mi}}{1 \text{ h}} \text{ or } 47.5 \text{ mi/h}$$ **Divide by 5.2 to make the second quantity one unit.**

A proportion is a statement that two ratios are equal. You can find a missing term in a proportion by using the cross products.

Cross Products of a Proportion
$\frac{a}{b} = \frac{c}{d} \longrightarrow ad = bc$

3 EXAMPLE Write a proportion. Then solve.

The Copy Center charges $2.52 for 63 copies. At that rate, how much will the Copy Center charge for 140 copies?

$$\begin{aligned} \text{cost} \longrightarrow \\ \text{copies} \longrightarrow \end{aligned} \quad \frac{2.52}{63} = \frac{c}{140}$$ **Write each ratio as cost : copies.**

$$2.52 \cdot 140 = 63c$$ **Use cross products.**

$$c = \frac{2.52 \cdot 140}{63}$$ **Solve for c.**

$$= 5.6 \text{ or } \$5.60$$

EXERCISES

Write each ratio or rate in simplest form.

1. 15 to 20 **3 to 4**

2. 85 : 34 **5 : 2**

3. 38 g in 4 oz **9.5 g/oz**

4. 375 mi in 4.3 h **87.21 mi/h**

5. $\frac{84}{30}$ **$\frac{14}{5}$**

Solve each proportion.

6. $\frac{a}{5} = \frac{12}{15}$ **4**

7. $\frac{21}{12} = \frac{14}{x}$ **8**

8. $8 : 15 = n : 25$ **$13\frac{1}{3}$**

9. $2.4 : c = 4 : 3$ **1.8**

10. $\frac{17}{8} = \frac{n}{20}$ **42.5**

11. $\frac{13}{n} = \frac{20}{3}$ **1.95**

12. $5 : 7 = y : 5$ **$3\frac{4}{7}$**

13. $\frac{0.4}{3.5} = \frac{5.2}{x}$ **45.5**

14. $\frac{4}{x} = \frac{7}{6}$ **$3\frac{3}{7}$**

15. $4 : n = n : 9$ **±6**

16. A canary's heart beats 130 times in 12 s. Use a proportion to find how many times its heart beats in 50 s. **about 542 times**

17. According to the label, there are 65 calories in 4 fl oz of pineapple juice. How many calories are in 14 oz of the juice? **227.5 calories**

Simplifying Expressions With Integers

To add two numbers with the same sign, *add* their absolute values. The sum has the same sign as the numbers. To add two numbers with different signs, find the *difference* between their absolute values. The sum has the same sign as the number with the greater absolute value.

1 EXAMPLE Add.

a. $-8 + (-5) = -13$ **b.** $-8 + 5 = -3$ **c.** $8 + (-5) = 3$

To subtract a number, add its opposite.

2 EXAMPLE Subtract.

a. $4 - 7 = 4 + (-7)$ **b.** $-4 - (-7) = -4 + 7$ **c.** $-4 - 7 = -4 + (-7)$
      $= -3$ $= 3$ $= -11$

The product or quotient of two numbers with the same sign is positive. The product or quotient of two numbers with different signs is negative.

3 EXAMPLE Multiply or divide.

a. $(-3)(-5) = 15$ **b.** $-35 \div 7 = -5$ **c.** $24 \div (-6) = -4$

4 EXAMPLE Simplify $2^2 - 3(4 - 6) - 12$.

Use the order of operations shown at the right.

$$2^2 - 3(4 - 6) - 12 = 2^2 - 3(-2) - 12$$
$$= 4 - 3(-2) - 12$$
$$= 4 - (-6) - 12$$
$$= 4 + 6 - 12$$
$$= 10 - 12 = -2$$

Order of Operations

1. Perform any operation(s) inside grouping symbols.
2. Simplify any terms with exponents.
3. Multiply and divide in order from left to right.
4. Add and subtract in order from left to right.

EXERCISES

Simplify each expression.

1. $-4 + 5$ **1**   **2.** $12 - 12$ **0**   **3.** $-15 + (-23)$ **−38**   **4.** $4 - 17$ **−13**   **5.** $-5 - 12$ **−17**

6. $17 + (-18)$ **−1**   **7.** $3 - (-5)$ **8**   **8.** $-8 - (-12)$ **4**   **9.** $-19 + 5$ **−14**   **10.** $-8 + (-8)$ **−16**

11. $(-7)(-4)$ **28**   **12.** $-120 \div 30$ **−4**   **13.** $(-3)(4)$ **−12**   **14.** $75 \div (-3)$ **−25**   **15.** $(-6)(15)$ **−90**

16. $(18)(-4)$ **−72**   **17.** $-84 \div (-7)$ **12**   **18.** $(-13)(-3)$ **39**   **19.** $(-225) \div (-15)$ **15**   **20.** $-16 \div 8$ **−2**

21. $-2(1 + 5) + (-3)(2)$ **−18**   **22.** $-4(-2 - 5) + 3(1 - 4)$ **19**   **23.** $20 - (3)(12) + 4^2$ **0**

24. $\frac{-15}{-5} - \frac{36}{-12} + \frac{-12}{-4}$ **9**   **25.** $5^2 - 6(5 - 9)$ **49**   **26.** $4\left[(12)(3) - \frac{12}{3}\right]$ **128**

27. $(-3 + 2^3)\left(4 + \frac{-42}{7}\right)$ **−10**   **28.** $(3 - 10)^2 + 3(-10)$ **19**   **29.** $(7 + 7)(7 - 7) - \frac{7}{-7}$ **1**

30. $5 - (-4)(-3) + 3^2$ **2**   **31.** $\left(\frac{-15}{5}\right)^2 + (7 - 4)^2$ **18**   **32.** $[4(-3)]^2 + 4(-3)^2$ **180**

13. $\ell = \dfrac{P}{2} - w$

14. $r = \dfrac{d}{t}$

15. $b = c - 2a$

16. $P = \dfrac{I}{rt}$

17. $x = 2y$

18. $a = \dfrac{c}{2} - x$

19. $m = q - (n + p)$

20. $c = 2a - d$

21. $m = \dfrac{q}{np}$

22. $m = \dfrac{y - b}{x}$

23. $r = \dfrac{1 - 3s}{2}$

24. $b = \dfrac{3a}{2}$

25. $b = \dfrac{2A}{h}$

26. $h = \dfrac{V}{\ell w}$

27. $b = \pm\sqrt{c^2 - a^2}$

28. $b = 3m - a - c$

Evaluating Formulas and Solving Literal Equations

To evaluate a formula, first substitute the known values for the variables. Then perform the indicated operations.

1 EXAMPLE   Find the volume of a cone that has a radius of 5 in. and a height of 10 in. Use the formula $V = \frac{1}{3}\pi r^2 h$.

$V = \frac{1}{3}\pi r^2 h$

$\approx \frac{1}{3}(3.14)(5)^2(10)$ **Replace π with 3.14, r with 5, and h with 10.**

≈ 262 in.^{3} **Round your answer.**

Sometimes you do not know values for the variables in a formula, so you cannot substitute. To solve a formula or a literal equation for one of the variables in it, use properties of equality.

2 EXAMPLE   Solve $P = 2(\ell + w)$ for w.

$P = 2(\ell + w)$

$\dfrac{P}{2} = \ell + w$ **Divide each side by 2.**

$\dfrac{P}{2} - \ell = w$ **Subtract ℓ from each side.**

Thus, $w = \dfrac{P}{2} - \ell$.

EXERCISES

Evaluate each formula. Give decimal answers to the nearest tenth.

1. $P = 2(\ell + w); \ell = 3.2, w = 4$ **14.4**

2. $c = 0.5q + 0.5n; q = 3, n = 5$ **4**

3. $d = rt; r = 35, t = 2.4$ **84**

4. $y = 3.5x + 2; x = 1.5$ **7.3**

5. $y = (x + 2)(x - 2); x = 5$ **21**

6. $A = s^2; s = 10.5$ **110.3**

7. $a = \sqrt{c^2 - b^2}; c = 5.5, b = 3$ **4.6**

8. $d = 0.5gt^2; g = -32, t = 4.5$ **−324**

9. $y = 2x^2 - 3x + 1; x = 6$ **55**

10. $A = \frac{1}{2}(b_1 + b_2)h; b_1 = 13, b_2 = 9, h = 8$ **88**

11. $V = \pi r^2 h; r = 4.3, h = 9.1$ **528.6**

12. $A = \frac{1}{2}bh; b = 13.7, h = 8.5$ **58.2**

Solve each equation for the given variable.   **13–28. See margin.**

13. $P = 2(\ell + w); \ell$

14. $d = rt; r$

15. $2a + b = c; b$

16. $I = Prt; P$

17. $\frac{1}{2}x = y; x$

18. $2(x + a) = c; a$

19. $m + n + p = q; m$

20. $\dfrac{c + d}{2} = a; c$

21. $mnp = q; m$

22. $y = mx + b; m$

23. $2r + 3s = 1; r$

24. $3a = 2b; b$

25. $A = \frac{1}{2}bh; b$

26. $V = \ell wh; h$

27. $c^2 = a^2 + b^2; b$

28. $m = \dfrac{a + b + c}{3}; b$

29. The formula $V = \frac{1}{2}\ell(A_1 + A_2)$ relates the volume V of a log to its length ℓ and the areas of the ends A_1 and A_2. Solve the formula for ℓ and find the length of a log that has a volume of 23 ft^3 and end areas of 0.32 ft^2 and 1.58 ft^2. $\ell = \dfrac{2V}{A_1 + A_2}$; **24.2 ft**

30. The formula $A = \frac{1}{2}h(b_1 + b_2)$ relates the area A of a trapezoid to its height h and the lengths of its bases b_1 and b_2. Solve the formula for b_1 and find the length of a base of a trapezoid that has an area of 43 cm^2, a height of 10 cm, and one base of 5.2 cm. $b_1 = \dfrac{2A}{h} - b_2$; **3.4 cm**

Area and Volume

The *area* of a plane figure is the number of square units contained in the figure. The *volume* of a space figure is the number of cubic units contained in the figure. Formulas for area and volume are listed on page 870.

1 EXAMPLE Find the area of each figure.

a.

1.8 cm
3.2 cm

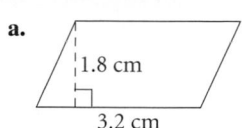

$A = bh$

$= 3.2 \cdot 1.8$

$= 5.76 \approx 5.8 \text{ cm}^2$

b.

$2\frac{1}{10}$ in.

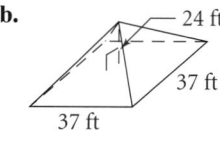

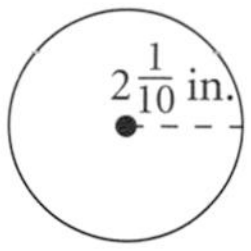

$A = \pi r^2$

$\approx \frac{22}{7} \cdot \left(\frac{21}{10}\right)^2$

$= \frac{693}{50} = 13\frac{43}{50} \text{ in.}^2$

c.

19 mm
8.5 mm
23 mm

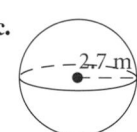

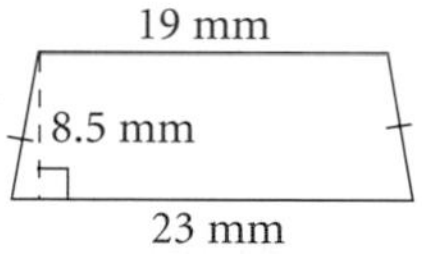

$A = \frac{1}{2}(b_1 + b_2)h$

$= \frac{1}{2}(19 + 23) \cdot 8.5$

$= 178.5 \text{ mm}^2$

2 EXAMPLE Find the volume of each figure.

a.

3.3 cm
5.0 cm
7.5 cm

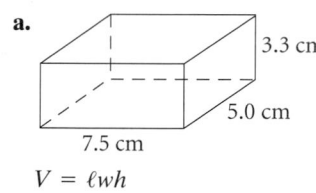

$V = \ell wh$

$= 7.5 \cdot 5.0 \cdot 3.3$

$= 123.75 \approx 124.8 \text{ cm}^3$

b.

24 ft
37 ft
37 ft

$V = \frac{1}{3}Bh$

$= \frac{1}{3}(37^2) \cdot 24$

$= 10{,}952 \text{ ft}^3$

c.

2.7 m

$V = \frac{4}{3}\pi r^3$

$\approx \frac{4}{3} \cdot 3.14 \cdot 2.7^3$

$= 82.40616 \approx 82.4 \text{ m}^3$

EXERCISES

Find the area of each figure.

1.

4 m
7 m

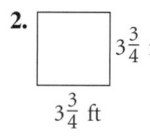

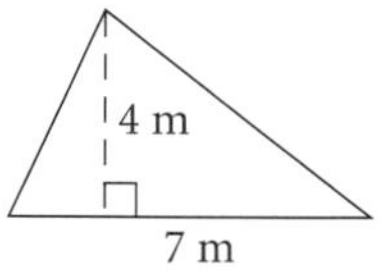

14 m²

2.

$3\frac{3}{4}$ ft
$3\frac{3}{4}$ ft

14.1 ft²

3.

9 cm
5 cm
4 cm
6 cm

30 cm²

4.

10 in.

78.5 in.²

Find the volume of each figure.

5.

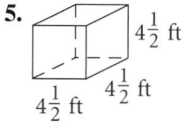

$4\frac{1}{2}$ ft
$4\frac{1}{2}$ ft
$4\frac{1}{2}$ ft

91.1 ft³

6.

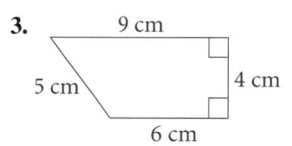

8 m

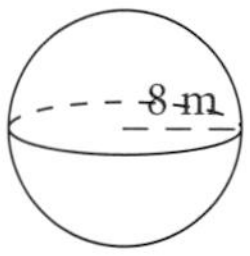

2144.7 m³

7.

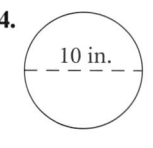

12 in.
5 in.

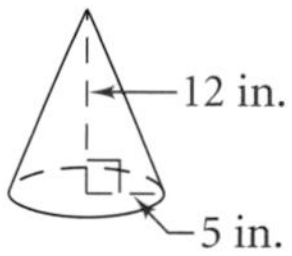

314.2 in.³

8.

50 ft
60 ft
80 ft

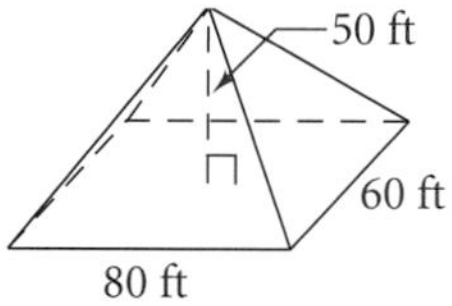

80,000 ft³

9. Find the area of a triangle with a base of 17 in. and a height of 13 in. **110.5 in.²**
10. Find the volume of a box 64 cm long, 48 cm wide, and 58 cm high. **178,176 cm³**
11. Find the surface area of the cube in Exercise 5. **121.5 ft²**
12. Find the surface area of the rectangular solid in Example 2a. **157.5 cm²**

Skills Handbook

847

7–12.

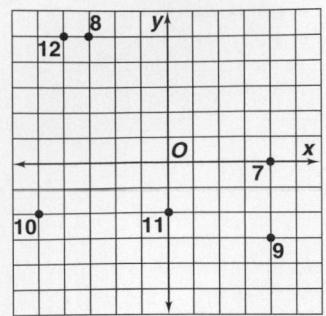

18. $\left(-1, -\frac{1}{2}\right)$

19. $\left(5, -\frac{3}{2}\right)$

20. $\left(-\frac{1}{2}, -\frac{11}{2}\right)$

21. $\left(\frac{5}{2}, -1\right)$

The Coordinate Plane, Slope, and Midpoint

The *coordinate plane* is formed when two number lines intersect at right angles. The ordered pair $(-2, 4)$ identifies the location of a point on the plane. From the origin, move 2 units to the left and 4 units up.

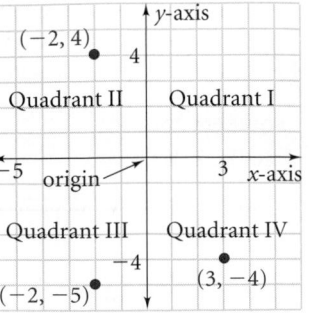

1 EXAMPLE   In which quadrant would you find each point?

   a. $(3, -4)$ Move 3 units right and 4 units down. The point is in Quadrant IV.

   b. $(-2, -5)$ Move 2 units left and 5 units down. The point is in Quadrant III.

To find the slope of a line on the coordinate plane, choose two points on the line and use the slope formula.

2 EXAMPLE   Find the slope of each line.

a.
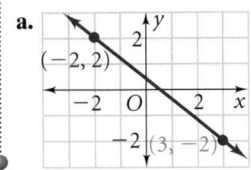

$$m = \frac{y_2 - y_1}{x_2 - x_1}$$
$$= \frac{2 - (-2)}{-2 - 3}$$
$$= \frac{4}{-5} \text{ or } -\frac{4}{5}$$

b.
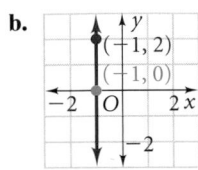

$$m = \frac{y_2 - y_1}{x_2 - x_1}$$
$$= \frac{2 - 0}{-1 - (-1)} = \frac{2}{0}$$

Since you cannot divide by zero, this line has an undefined slope.

Each coordinate of the midpoint of a segment is the mean of the corresponding coordinates of its endpoints. If (x_m, y_m) is the midpoint of the segment joining (x_1, y_1) and (x_2, y_2), then $x_m = \frac{x_1 + x_2}{2}$ and $y_m = \frac{y_1 + y_2}{2}$.

3 EXAMPLE   Find the coordinates of the midpoint of the segment with endpoints $(-2, 5)$ and $(6, -3)$.

$$\frac{-2 + 6}{2} = 2 \text{ and } \frac{5 + (-3)}{2} = 1, \text{ so the midpoint is } (2, 1).$$

EXERCISES

In which quadrant would you find each point?

1. $(3, 2)$ **I**   **2.** $(-4, 3)$ **II**   **3.** $(2, -3)$ **IV**   **4.** $(4, -2)$ **IV**   **5.** $(-4, -5)$ **III**   **6.** $(-1, -3)$ **III**

Graph each point on a coordinate plane.   7–12. See margin.

7. $(4, 0)$ **8.** $(-3, 5)$ **9.** $(4, -3)$ **10.** $(-5, -2)$ **11.** $(0, -2)$ **12.** $(-4, 5)$

Find the slope of each line.

13.
$\frac{3}{4}$
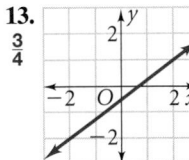

14.
-1
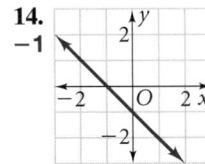

15.
0
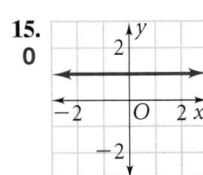

16. the line containing
-2 $(-3, 4)$ and $(2, -6)$

17. the line containing
$\frac{1}{5}$ $(25, 40)$ and $(100, 55)$

Find the midpoint of the segment with the given points.   18–21. See margin.

18. $(-4, 4), (2, -5)$ **19.** $(3, 3), (7, -6)$ **20.** $(-1, -8), (0, -3)$ **21.** $(3, 4), (2, -6)$

Solving Linear Equations and Inequalities

To solve a linear equation having one variable, use inverse operations and properties of equality to get the variable alone on one side of the equal sign.

1 EXAMPLE Solve each equation.

a.
$$3x - 11 = -5$$
$$3x - 11 + 11 = -5 + 11 \quad \textbf{Add 11 to each side.}$$
$$3x = 6$$
$$\frac{3x}{3} = \frac{6}{3} \qquad \textbf{Divide each side by 3.}$$
$$x = 2$$

b.
$$\tfrac{2}{3}x + 1 = -5$$
$$\tfrac{2}{3}x + 1 - 1 = -5 - 1 \quad \textbf{Subtract 1 from each side.}$$
$$\tfrac{2}{3}x = -6$$
$$\tfrac{3}{2} \cdot \tfrac{2}{3}x = \tfrac{3}{2} \cdot (-6) \quad \textbf{Multiply each side by } \tfrac{3}{2}.$$
$$x = -9$$

Sometimes you can use the Distributive Property to simplify an equation.

2 EXAMPLE Solve each equation.

a.
$$2(x + 8) - 5 = 7$$
$$2x + 16 - 5 = 7 \qquad \textbf{Distribute to remove}$$
$$2x = -4 \qquad\qquad \textbf{parentheses.}$$
$$x = -2$$

b.
$$2x + 9 = 6x$$
$$2x - 2x + 9 = 6x - 2x \quad \textbf{Subtract 2x from}$$
$$9 = 4x \qquad\qquad\qquad \textbf{each side.}$$
$$\tfrac{9}{4} = x \text{ (or } x = 2.25)$$

In solving an inequality, you must reverse the order of the inequality when you multiply or divide each side by a negative number.

3 EXAMPLE Solve and graph each inequality.

a.
$$\tfrac{x}{3} - 2 > -4$$
$$\tfrac{x}{3} - 2 + 2 > -4 + 2$$
$$\tfrac{x}{3} > -2$$
$$3 \cdot \tfrac{x}{3} > 3(-2)$$
$$x > -6$$

(number line graph: $-8 \quad -6 \quad -4$, open circle at -6)

b.
$$2x \geq 5x - 9$$
$$2x - 5x \geq 5x - 5x - 9 \quad \textbf{Divide each side}$$
$$-3x \geq -9 \qquad\qquad\quad \textbf{by } -3 \textbf{ and}$$
$$\tfrac{-3x}{-3} \leq \tfrac{-9}{-3} \qquad\qquad \textbf{reverse the order}$$
$$x \leq 3 \qquad\qquad\qquad\quad \textbf{of the inequality.}$$

(number line graph: $0 \ 1 \ 2 \ 3 \ 4 \ 5 \ 6$, closed circle at 3)

EXERCISES

Solve each equation.

1. $x + 4 = 3$ **−1**
2. $3c - 7 = -13$ **−2**
3. $8y - 3 + y = 51$ **6**
4. $6a = -48$ **−8**
5. $\tfrac{1}{2}(s - 6) = 17$ **40**
6. $\tfrac{d}{3} = -8$ **−24**
7. $\tfrac{4}{9}h = \tfrac{2}{3}$ **1.5**
8. $\tfrac{2}{3}r + 9 = 75$ **99**
9. $4(t + 5) = -36$ **−14**
10. $7g - 3g + 2 = 6$ **1**
11. $3(x - 4) = 2x + 1$ **13**
12. $q + 4.5 = 3q - 2.7$ **3.6**

Solve and graph each inequality.   **13–24. See margin.**

13. $9 + x \leq 15$
14. $-g < 5$
15. $7y + 2 \geq -12$
16. $9h > -18$
17. $\tfrac{s}{5} \geq 7$
18. $4 - a \leq 9$
19. $-\tfrac{c}{4} < 7$
20. $-\tfrac{3v}{5} > -\tfrac{9}{10}$
21. $t - 5.3 < -3.3$
22. $4y - 9y > -55$
23. $-5w > 2w - 21$
24. $\tfrac{3c}{7} \leq -\tfrac{2}{3}$

Skills Handbook **849**

---

13. $x \leq 6$

(number line: $0 \ 2 \ 4 \ 6$, closed circle at 6)

14. $g > -5$

(number line: $-5 \ \dots \ 0 \ 1$, open circle at -5)

15. $y \geq -2$

(number line: $-2 \ 0 \ 2 \ 4$, closed circle at -2)

16. $h > -2$

(number line: $-2 \ 0 \ 2 \ 4$, open circle at -2)

17. $s \geq 35$

(number line: $0 \ 20 \ 30 \ 40$, closed circle at 35)

18. $a \geq -5$

(number line: $-5 \ 0 \ 5 \ 10$, closed circle at -5)

19. $c > -28$

(number line: $-30 \ \dots \ -20$, open circle at -28)

20. $v < \tfrac{3}{2}$

(number line: $-1 \ 0 \ 1 \ 2$, open circle at $\tfrac{3}{2}$)

21. $t < 2$

(number line: $-2 \ 0 \ 2 \ 4$, open circle at 2)

22. $y < 11$

(number line: $6 \ 8 \ 10 \ 12$, open circle at 11)

23. $w < 3$

(number line: $-2 \ 0 \ 2 \ 4$, open circle at 3)

24. $c \leq -\tfrac{14}{9}$

(number line: $-2 \ \dots \ -1 \ \dots \ 0$, closed circle at $-\tfrac{14}{9}$)

13. $-3 \le x \le 15$

$$\begin{array}{c} \hline -3\ \ 0\ \ 3\ \ 6\ \ 9\ \ 12\ \ 15\ \ 18 \end{array}$$

14. $a < -10$ or $a > 4$

$$\begin{array}{c} \hline -10\ \ \ \ \ \ \ \ -4\ \ 0\ \ 4 \end{array}$$

15. $r \le -7$ or $r \ge 7$

$$\begin{array}{c} \hline -7\ \ \ \ \ \ \ 0\ \ \ \ \ \ \ 7 \end{array}$$

16. $y < -13$ or $y > 13$

$$\begin{array}{c} \hline -13\ \ -5\ \ 0\ \ 5\ \ \ \ 13 \end{array}$$

17. $-2.4 \le p \le 2.4$

$$\begin{array}{c} \hline -3\ \ \ \ \ \ \ 0\ \ \ \ \ \ \ 3 \end{array}$$

18. $-\frac{1}{2} \le k \le \frac{1}{2}$

$$\begin{array}{c} \hline -1\ \ -\frac{1}{2}\ \ 0\ \ \frac{1}{2}\ \ 1 \end{array}$$

19. $-2 < x < \frac{6}{7}$

$$\begin{array}{c} \hline -2\ \ -1\ \ 0\ \ \frac{6}{7} \end{array}$$

20. $w \le 2$ or $w \ge 8$

$$\begin{array}{c} \hline 0\ \ 2\ \ 4\ \ 6\ \ 8 \end{array}$$

1.

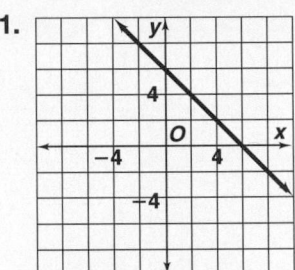

2.

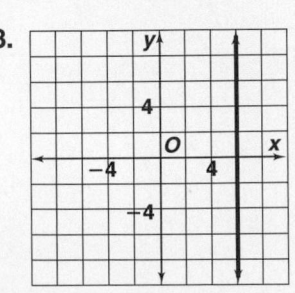

3.

Absolute Value Equations and Inequalities

To solve an absolute value equation, get the absolute value by itself on one side of the equation. Then use the definition of absolute value to write two equations.

1 EXAMPLE Solve $|x| + 3 = 11$.

$|x| + 3 = 11$ **Subtract 3 from each side.**
$\quad |x| = 8$ **The value of x is either 8 or −8.**
$x = 8$ or $x = -8$

2 EXAMPLE Solve $|p - 20| = 4$.

$|p - 20| = 4$ **The value of the expression $p - 20$ is 4 or −4.**
$p - 20 = 4$ or $p - 20 = -4$ **Write two equations.**
$\quad p = 24$ or $\quad\quad p = 16$ **Solve for p.**

To solve an absolute value inequality, write two inequalities. Join the inequalities with *and* when $|x| < c$. Join them with *or* when $|x| > c$.

3 EXAMPLE Solve $|x + 3| < 5$. Graph the solution.

$|x - 3| < 5$
$x - 3 < 5$ and $x - 3 > -5$ **Write two inequalities joined by *and*.**
$\quad x < 8$ and $\quad\quad x > -2$ **The solutions are all numbers less than 8 *and* greater than −2.**

$$\begin{array}{c} \hline -2\ \ 0\ \ 2\ \ 4\ \ 6\ \ 8 \end{array}$$

4 EXAMPLE Solve $|x + 2| \ge 4$. Graph the solution.

$|x + 2| \ge 4$
$x + 2 \ge 4$ or $x + 2 \le -4$ **Write two inequalities joined by *or*.**
$\quad x \ge 2$ or $\quad\quad x \le -6$ **The solutions are all numbers less than or equal to −6 *or* greater than *or* equal to 2.**

$$\begin{array}{c} \hline -6\ \ -4\ \ -2\ \ 0\ \ 2\ \ 4 \end{array}$$

EXERCISES

Solve each equation.

1. $|y| = 8$ **8, −8**
2. $|a| + 4 = 7$ **3, −3**
3. $|c + 4| = 9$ **5, −13**
4. $3|r| = 18$ **6, −6**

5. $|5x| = 35$ **7, −7**
6. $-7|p| + 4 = -17$ **3, −3**
7. $|w - 8| = 7$ **1, 15**
8. $|3t - 2| = 8$ **$-2, \frac{10}{3}$**

9. $\frac{|v|}{4} = 5$ **20, −20**
10. $\left|h + \frac{1}{2}\right| = 5\frac{1}{2}$ **5, −6**
11. $|n - 7| = 0$ **7**
12. $8|z + 3| = 24$ **0, −6**

Solve each inequality. Graph the solution.   **13–20. See margin.**

13. $|x - 6| \le 9$
14. $|a + 3| > 7$
15. $|r| \ge 7$
16. $|3y| > 39$

17. $|5p| \le 12$
18. $4|k| + 3 \le 5$
19. $|7x + 4| < 10$
20. $7|w - 5| \ge 21$

Graphing Two-Variable Equations and Inequalities

An equation in the form $Ax + By = C$ represents a line. To graph the line, first find the x-intercept and the y-intercept.

1 EXAMPLE   Graph $2x - 4y = 16$.

$2x - 4y = 16$
$2x - 4(0) = 16$ **To find the x-intercept, replace y with 0.**
$2x = 16$
$x = 8$ **Solve for x.**

The x-intercept is $(8, 0)$.

$2x - 4y = 16$
$2(0) - 4y = 16$ **To find the y-intercept, replace x with 0.**
$-4y = 16$
$y = -4$ **Solve for y.**

The y-intercept is $(0, -4)$.

Plot the points $(8, 0)$ and $(0, -4)$. Then draw a line through the points.

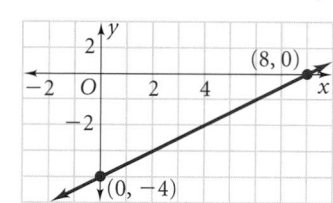

The equation $x = -3$ does not have a y-intercept. In this case, use *any* two points that lie on the line. For example, use $(-3, 1)$ and $(-3, 3)$.

A linear inequality describes a region of the coordinate plane that has a boundary line. Draw a dashed line when the inequality uses $<$ or $>$. Draw a solid line when the inequality uses $\leq$ or $\geq$.

2 EXAMPLE   Graph $2x + y > 5$.

First, graph the boundary line $2x + y = 5$. Use the x-intercept $(2.5, 0)$ and the y-intercept $(0, 5)$. Since the inequality uses $>$, draw a dashed line.

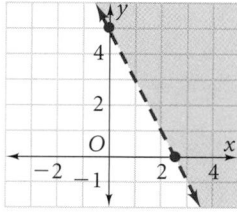

Next, test a point. Use $(0, 0)$. $2x + y > 5$
$2(0) + 0 > 5$
$0 > 5$ **False**

The inequality is *false* for $(0, 0)$.
Shade the region that does *not* contain $(0, 0)$.

EXERCISES

Graph each equation or inequality. 1–9. See margin pp. 850–851. 10–24. See back of book.

1. $x + y = 6$
2. $2x + y = -4$
3. $x = 6$
4. $y = -3$

5. $3x - 2y = 12$
6. $x - 3y = -6$
7. $x - y = -3$
8. $y = x - 4$

9. $3x + 5y = 30$
10. $y = -4x + 5$
11. $2x - 5y = 20$
12. $4x + 7y = -21$

13. $y \geq -2$
14. $x + 2y < 8$
15. $4x - 4y > 8$
16. $x + 3y \leq 12$

17. $x - 5 < 0$
18. $7x - 4y > 12$
19. $y - 3x \leq 6$
20. $5x + 4y \geq 0$

21. $x + 5y \geq -8$
22. $y = \frac{2}{3}x + 2$
23. $\frac{2}{5}x - \frac{1}{2}y > 10$
24. $3y - x \leq 0$

4.
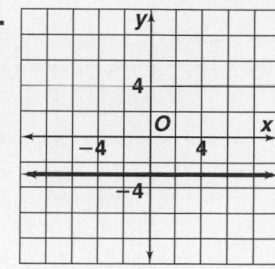

5.
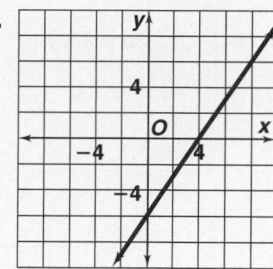

6.
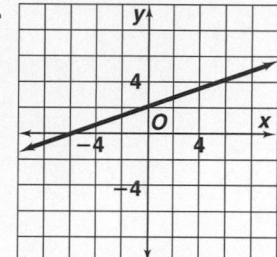

7.
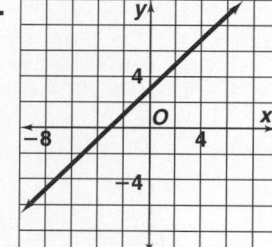

8.
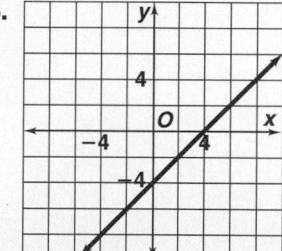

9.
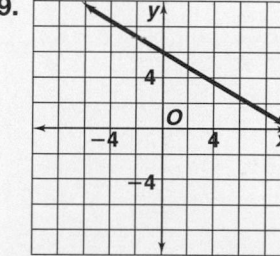

Operations With Exponents

An exponent indicates how many times a number is used as a factor.

1 EXAMPLE Write using exponents.

a. $3 \cdot 3 \cdot 3 \cdot 3 \cdot 3 = 3^5$

　　　　　↑
　　five factors of 3

b. $a \cdot a \cdot b \cdot b \cdot b \cdot b = a^2 b^4$

　　　　↑　　　↑
two factors of a; four factors of b

$2^n = \square$	$10^n = \square$
$2^2 = 4$	$10^2 = 100$
$2^1 = 2$	$10^1 = 10$
$2^0 = 1$	$10^0 = 1$
$2^{-1} = \frac{1}{2}$	$10^{-1} = \frac{1}{10}$
$2^{-2} = \frac{1}{4}$	$10^{-2} = \frac{1}{100}$

The patterns shown at the right indicate that $a^0 = 1$ and that $a^{-n} = \frac{1}{a^n}$.

2 EXAMPLE Write each expression so that all exponents are positive.

a. $a^{-2}b^3 = \frac{1}{a^2} \cdot b^3 = \frac{b^3}{a^2}$

b. $x^3 y^0 z^{-1} = x^3 \cdot 1 \cdot \frac{1}{z} = \frac{x^3}{z}$

You can simplify expressions that contain powers with the same base.

3 EXAMPLE Simplify each expression.

a. $b^5 \cdot b^3 = b^{5+3}$ **Add exponents to multiply powers with the same base.**

$= b^8$

b. $\frac{x^5}{x^7} = x^{5-7}$ **Subtract exponents to divide powers with the same base.**

$= x^{-2} = \frac{1}{x^2}$

You can simplify expressions that contain parentheses and exponents.

4 EXAMPLE Simplify each expression.

a. $\left(\frac{ab}{n}\right)^3 = \frac{a^3 b^3}{n^3}$ **Raise each factor in the parentheses to the third power.**

b. $(c^2)^4 = c^{2 \cdot 4} = c^8$ **Multiply exponents to raise a power to a power.**

EXERCISES

Write each expression using exponents.

1. $x \cdot x \cdot x$　$\mathbf{x^3}$

2. $x \cdot x \cdot x \cdot y \cdot y$　$\mathbf{x^3 y^2}$

3. $a \cdot a \cdot a \cdot b$　$\mathbf{a^4 b}$

4. $\frac{a \cdot a \cdot a \cdot a}{b \cdot b}$　$\mathbf{\frac{a^4}{b^2}}$

Write each expression so that all exponents are positive.

5. c^{-4}　$\mathbf{\frac{1}{c^4}}$

6. $m^{-2} n^0$　$\mathbf{\frac{1}{m^2}}$

7. $x^5 y^{-7} z^{-3}$　$\mathbf{\frac{x^5}{y^7 z^3}}$

8. $ab^{-1} c^2$　$\mathbf{\frac{ac^2}{b}}$

Simplify each expression. Use positive exponents.

9. $d^2 d^6$　$\mathbf{d^8}$

10. $n^4 n$　$\mathbf{n^5}$

11. $r^3 \cdot r^2 \cdot s^7 \cdot s$　$\mathbf{r^5 s^8}$

12. $x^5 y^2 \cdot xy^2 z^6$　$\mathbf{x^6 y^4 z^6}$

13. $\frac{a^5}{a^2}$　$\mathbf{a^3}$

14. $\frac{c^7}{c}$　$\mathbf{c^6}$

15. $\frac{n^3}{n^6}$　$\mathbf{\frac{1}{n^3}}$

16. $\frac{a^5 b^3}{ab^8}$　$\mathbf{\frac{a^4}{b^5}}$

17. $(rt)^3$　$\mathbf{r^3 t^3}$

18. $(3x)^2$　$\mathbf{9x^2}$

19. $\left(\frac{a}{b}\right)^4$　$\mathbf{\frac{a^4}{b^4}}$

20. $\left(\frac{xz}{y}\right)^6$　$\mathbf{\frac{x^6 z^6}{y^6}}$

21. $(c^3)^4$　$\mathbf{c^{12}}$

22. $\left(\frac{x^2}{y^5}\right)^3$　$\mathbf{\frac{x^6}{y^{15}}}$

23. $(u^4 v^2)^3$　$\mathbf{u^{12} v^6}$

24. $(p^5)^{-2}$　$\mathbf{\frac{1}{p^{10}}}$

25. $\frac{(2a^4)(3a^2)}{6a^3}$　$\mathbf{a^3}$

26. $(x^{-2})^3$　$\mathbf{\frac{1}{x^6}}$

27. $(4a^2 b)^3 (ab)^2$　$\mathbf{64a^8 b^5}$

28. $(mg^3)^{-1}$　$\mathbf{\frac{1}{mg^3}}$

29. $g^{-3} g^{-1}$　$\mathbf{\frac{1}{g^4}}$

30. $\frac{x^2 y^3 z^{-1}}{x^5 y z^3}$　$\mathbf{\frac{y^2}{x^3 z^4}}$

31. $\frac{(3a^3)^2}{18a}$　$\mathbf{\frac{a^5}{2}}$

32. $\frac{c^3 d^7}{c^{-3} d^{-1}}$　$\mathbf{c^6 d^8}$

Factoring and Operations With Polynomials

When the terms of a polynomial are in descending order by degree and all like terms have been combined, the polynomial is in standard form.

1 EXAMPLE Perform each operation. Write in standard form.

a. $(3y^2 - 4y + 5) + (y^2 + 9y) = (3y^2 + y^2) + (-4y + 9y) + 5$ **To add, group like terms.**

$= 4y^2 + 5y + 5$ **Write in standard form.**

b. $8a^2(3a^2 - 5a - 2) = 8a^2(3a^2) + 8a^2(-5a) + 8a^2(-2)$ **To multiply, distribute $8a^2$.**

$= 24a^4 - 40a^3 - 16a^2$

c. $(n + 4)(n - 3) = n(n) + n(-3) + 4(n) + 4(-3)$ **Distribute n and 4.**

$= n^2 - 3n + 4n - 12$

$= n^2 + n - 12$

To factor a polynomial, first find the greatest common factor (GCF) of the terms. Then use the distributive property to factor out the GCF.

2 EXAMPLE Factor $6x^3 - 12x^2 + 18x$.

$6x^3 = 6 \cdot x \cdot x \cdot x; -12x^2 = 6 \cdot (-2) \cdot x \cdot x; 18x = 6 \cdot 3 \cdot x$ **List the factors of each term. The GCF is $6x$.**

$6x^3 - 12x^2 + 18x = 6x(x^2) + 6x(-2x) + 6x(3)$ **Use the distributive property to factor out $6x$.**

$= 6x(x^2 - 2x + 3)$

When a polynomial is the product of two binomials, you can work backward to find the factors.

$x^2 + bx + c = (x + \blacksquare)(x + \blacksquare)$ The *sum* of the numbers you use here must equal b.

   The *product* of the numbers you use here must equal c.

3 EXAMPLE Factor $x^2 - 13x + 36$.

Choose numbers that are factors of 36. Look for a pair with the sum -13. The numbers -4 and -9 have a product of 36 and a sum of -13. The factors are $(x - 4)$ and $(x - 9)$. So, $x^2 - 13x + 36 = (x - 4)(x - 9)$.

Factors	Sum
$-6 \cdot (-6)$	-12
$-4 \cdot (-9)$	-13

EXERCISES

Perform the indicated operations. Write each answer in standard form.   1–3. See margin.

1. $(x^2 + 3x - 1) + (7x - 4)$

2. $(5y^2 + 7y) - (3y^2 + 9y - 8)$

3. $4x^2(3x^2 - 5x + 9)$

4. $-5d(13d^2 - 7d + 8)$
$-65d^3 + 35d^2 - 40d$

5. $(x - 5)(x + 3)$
$x^2 - 2x - 15$

6. $(n - 7)(n - 2)$
$n^2 - 9n + 14$

Factor each polynomial.   7–14. See margin.

7. $a^2 - 8a + 12$

8. $b^3 + 6b^2$

9. $n^2 - 2n - 8$

10. $x^2 + 5x + 4$

11. $3m^2 - 9$

12. $y^2 + 5y - 24$

13. $s^3 + 6s^2 + 11s$

14. $2x^3 + 4x^2 - 8x$

15. $y^2 - 10y + 25$
$(y - 5)^2$

16. $3r^2 - 48$
$3(r + 4)(r - 4)$

17. $2x^2 + 5x - 12$
$(2x - 3)(x + 4)$

18. $4w^2 - 9$
$(2w + 3)(2w - 3)$

1. $x^2 + 10x - 5$

2. $2y^2 - 2y + 8$

3. $12x^4 - 20x^3 + 36x^2$

7. $(a - 6)(a - 2)$

8. $b^2(b + 6)$

9. $(n - 4)(n + 2)$

10. $(x + 4)(x + 1)$

11. $3(m^2 - 3)$

12. $(y + 8)(y - 3)$

13. $s(s^2 + 6s + 11)$

14. $2x(x^2 + 2x - 4)$

1. 1.34×10^6

2. 0.0688

3. 7.75×10^{-4}

4. 7.2×10^{-3}

5. 111,300

6. 0.0008

7. 1.895×10^3

8. 2300

9. 1.234×10^5

10. 79,850

11. 6.4×10^5

12. 3.0×10^1

13. $\approx 8.52 \times 10^2$

14. $\approx 2.4 \times 10^2$

15. $\approx 1.8 \times 10^1$

16. $\approx 2.0 \times 10^1$

17. $\approx 8.95 \times 10^{-12}$

18. $\approx 4 \times 10^{18}$

19. $\approx 3.77 \times 10^{10}$

20. $\approx 5.8 \times 10^{-5}$

21. $\approx 1.8 \times 10^{-6}$

22. $\approx 1.9 \times 10^{-8}$

Scientific Notation and Significant Digits

In *scientific notation*, a number has the form $a \times 10^n$, where n is an integer and $1 \le a < 10$.

1 EXAMPLE Write 5.59×10^6 in standard form.

$5.59 \times 10^6 = 5\,590\,000$ **A positive exponent indicates a value greater than 1. Move the decimal point six places to the right.**

$= 5{,}590{,}000$

2 EXAMPLE Write 0.000 031 8 in scientific notation.

$0.0000318 = 3.18 \times 10^{-5}$ **Move the decimal point to create a number between 1 and 10 (five places to the right). Since the original number is less than 1, use a negative exponent.**

When a measurement is in scientific notation, all the digits of the number between 1 and 10 are *significant digits*. When you multiply or divide measurements, your answer should have as many significant digits as the least number of significant digits in any of the numbers involved.

3 EXAMPLE Multiply $(6.71 \times 10^8 \text{ mi/h})$ and $(3.8 \times 10^4 \text{ h})$.

$(6.71 \times 10^8 \text{ mi/h})(3.8 \times 10^4 \text{ h}) = (6.71 \cdot 3.8)(10^8 \cdot 10^4)$ **Rearrange factors.**

$= 25.498 \times 10^{12}$ **Add exponents when multiplying powers of 10.**

$= 2.5498 \times 10^{13}$ **Write in scientific notation.**

$\approx 2.5 \times 10^{13} \text{ mi}$ **Round to two significant digits.**

three significant digits   two significant digits

4 EXAMPLE Simplify $\dfrac{6.332 \times 10^5}{1.6 \times 10^{-2}}$.

$\dfrac{6.332 \times 10^5}{1.6 \times 10^{-2}} = \dfrac{6.332}{1.6} \times 10^{5 - (-2)}$ **Subtract exponents when dividing powers of 10.**

$= 3.9575 \times 10^7$ **Simplify.**

$\approx 4.0 \times 10^7$ **Round to two significant digits.**

EXERCISES

Change each number to scientific notation or to standard form. **1–10. See margin.**

1. 1,340,000   **2.** 6.88×10^{-2} **3.** 0.000775   **4.** 0.0072   **5.** 1.113×10^5

6. 8.0×10^{-4} **7.** 1895   **8.** 2.3×10^3 **9.** 123,400   **10.** 7.985×10^4

Write each product or quotient in scientific notation. Round to the appropriate number of significant digits. **11–22. See margin.**

11. $(1.6 \times 10^2)(4.0 \times 10^3)$ **12.** $(2.5 \times 10^{-3})(1.2 \times 10^4)$ **13.** $(4.237 \times 10^4)(2.01 \times 10^{-2})$

14. $\dfrac{7.0 \times 10^5}{2.89 \times 10^3}$ **15.** $\dfrac{1.4 \times 10^4}{8.0 \times 10^2}$ **16.** $\dfrac{6.48 \times 10^6}{3.2 \times 10^5}$

17. $(1.78 \times 10^{-7})(5.03 \times 10^{-5})$ **18.** $(7.2 \times 10^{11})(5 \times 10^6)$ **19.** $(8.90 \times 10^8) \div (2.36 \times 10^{-2})$

20. $(3.95 \times 10^4) \div (6.8 \times 10^8)$ **21.** $(4.9 \times 10^{-8}) \div (2.7 \times 10^{-2})$ **22.** $(3.972 \times 10^{-5})(4.7 \times 10^{-4})$

Operations With Radicals

To simplify a radical, remove all perfect square factors from the radicand.

1 EXAMPLE Simplify $\sqrt{75}$.

$\sqrt{75} = \sqrt{25 \cdot 3} = \sqrt{25} \cdot \sqrt{3} = 5\sqrt{3}$ Use the property $\sqrt{ab} = \sqrt{a} \cdot \sqrt{b}$.

2 EXAMPLE Simplify $\sqrt{18} - \sqrt{50} + \sqrt{27}$.

$$\sqrt{18} - \sqrt{50} + \sqrt{27} = \sqrt{9 \cdot 2} - \sqrt{25 \cdot 2} + \sqrt{9 \cdot 3} \quad \text{Simplify each radical.}$$
$$= 3\sqrt{2} - 5\sqrt{2} + 3\sqrt{3} \quad \text{Use the distributive property}$$
$$= (3 - 5)\sqrt{2} + 3\sqrt{3} \quad \text{to combine like terms.}$$
$$= -2\sqrt{2} + 3\sqrt{3}$$

To remove a radical from the denominator of a fraction, you *rationalize* the denominator. Make the denominator rational by multiplying by a form of 1.

3 EXAMPLE Simplify each expression.

a. $\dfrac{5}{\sqrt{3}} = \dfrac{5}{\sqrt{3}} \cdot \dfrac{\sqrt{3}}{\sqrt{3}}$ Multiply the fraction by $\dfrac{\sqrt{3}}{\sqrt{3}}$ to make the denominator a rational number.

$= \dfrac{5\sqrt{3}}{\sqrt{9}} = \dfrac{5\sqrt{3}}{3}$

b. $\dfrac{2}{\sqrt{3}} \cdot \sqrt{\dfrac{5}{6}} = \dfrac{2}{\sqrt{3}} \cdot \dfrac{\sqrt{5}}{\sqrt{6}}$ Use the property $\sqrt{\dfrac{a}{b}} = \dfrac{\sqrt{a}}{\sqrt{b}}$.

$= \dfrac{2\sqrt{5}}{\sqrt{18}}$ Multiply radicals.

$= \dfrac{2\sqrt{5}\sqrt{2}}{\sqrt{18}\sqrt{2}}$ Multiply by $\dfrac{\sqrt{2}}{\sqrt{2}}$ to make the denominator a rational number.

$= \dfrac{2\sqrt{10}}{\sqrt{36}}$

$= \dfrac{2\sqrt{10}}{6} = \dfrac{\sqrt{10}}{3}$

EXERCISES

Simplify each radical expression.

1. $\sqrt{36}$ **6**
2. $\sqrt{72}$ **$6\sqrt{2}$**
3. $\sqrt{18}$ **$3\sqrt{2}$**
4. $\sqrt{108}$ **$6\sqrt{3}$**
5. $\sqrt{54}$ **$3\sqrt{6}$**

6. $\sqrt{60}$ **$2\sqrt{15}$**
7. $\sqrt{300}$ **$10\sqrt{3}$**
8. $\sqrt{\dfrac{1}{2}}$ **$\dfrac{\sqrt{2}}{2}$**
9. $\dfrac{2}{\sqrt{3}}$ **$\dfrac{2\sqrt{3}}{3}$**
10. $\dfrac{3}{\sqrt{5}}$ **$\dfrac{3\sqrt{5}}{5}$**

11. $\dfrac{\sqrt{2}}{\sqrt{5}}$ **$\dfrac{\sqrt{10}}{5}$**
12. $\dfrac{\sqrt{3}}{\sqrt{8}}$ **$\dfrac{\sqrt{6}}{4}$**
13. $\dfrac{1}{\sqrt{2}} \cdot \dfrac{\sqrt{3}}{\sqrt{2}}$ **$\dfrac{\sqrt{3}}{2}$**
14. $\sqrt{\dfrac{2}{3}} \cdot \sqrt{\dfrac{5}{6}}$ **$\dfrac{\sqrt{5}}{3}$**
15. $\dfrac{\sqrt{2}}{3} \cdot \sqrt{\dfrac{8}{5}}$ **$\dfrac{4\sqrt{5}}{15}$**

16. $\sqrt{\dfrac{2}{7}} \cdot \sqrt{\dfrac{8}{7}}$ **$\dfrac{4}{7}$**
17. $\dfrac{2}{\sqrt{2}} \cdot \sqrt{\dfrac{5}{3}}$ **$\dfrac{\sqrt{30}}{3}$**
18. $\sqrt{2} + \sqrt{2}$ **$2\sqrt{2}$**

19. $3\sqrt{5} + 2\sqrt{5}$ **$5\sqrt{5}$**
20. $7\sqrt{7} - \sqrt{7}$ **$6\sqrt{7}$**
21. $4\sqrt{3} - 3\sqrt{3}$ **$\sqrt{3}$**

22. $\sqrt{18} + \sqrt{98}$ **$10\sqrt{2}$**
23. $\sqrt{8} - \sqrt{50}$ **$-3\sqrt{2}$**
24. $\sqrt{6} + \sqrt{24}$ **$3\sqrt{6}$**

25. $\sqrt{40} + \sqrt{90}$ **$5\sqrt{10}$**
26. $\sqrt{27} + \sqrt{75} - \sqrt{12}$ **$6\sqrt{3}$**
27. $\sqrt{45} + \sqrt{20} + \sqrt{5}$ **$6\sqrt{5}$**

28. $\sqrt{3} - \sqrt{75} + \sqrt{18}$ **$3\sqrt{2} - 4\sqrt{3}$**
29. $\sqrt{98} + \sqrt{50} - \sqrt{5}$ **$12\sqrt{2} - \sqrt{5}$**
30. $\sqrt{5} + \sqrt{3} - \sqrt{180}$ **$\sqrt{3} - 5\sqrt{5}$**

The Pythagorean Theorem and the Distance Formula

In a right triangle, the sum of the squares of the lengths of the legs is equal to the square of the length of the hypotenuse. Use this relationship, known as the Pythagorean Theorem, to find the length of a side of a right triangle.

The Pythagorean Theorem

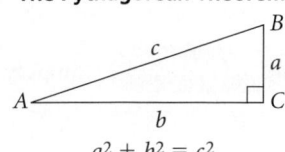

$$a^2 + b^2 = c^2$$

1 EXAMPLE Find m in the triangle below, to the nearest tenth.

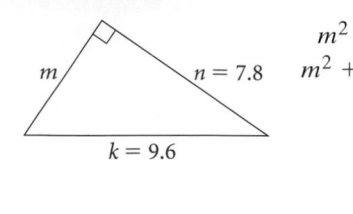

$$m^2 + n^2 = k^2$$
$$m^2 + 7.8^2 = 9.6^2$$
$$m^2 = 9.6^2 - 7.8^2$$
$$m^2 = 31.32$$
$$m = \sqrt{31.32}$$
$$\approx 5.6$$

Thus, m is about 5.6 units.

To find the distance between two points on the coordinate plane, use the distance formula.

The distance d between any two points (x_1, y_1) and (x_2, y_2) is
$$d = \sqrt{(x_2 - x_1)^2 + (y_2 - y_1)^2}.$$

2 EXAMPLE Find the distance between $(-3, 2)$ and $(6, -4)$.

$$d = \sqrt{(6 - (-3))^2 + (-4 - 2)^2}$$
$$= \sqrt{9^2 + (-6)^2}$$
$$= \sqrt{81 + 36}$$
$$= \sqrt{117}$$
$$\approx 10.8$$

Thus, d is about 10.8 units.

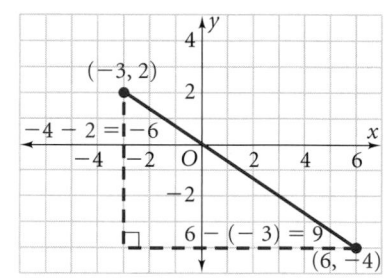

EXERCISES

In each problem, a and b are the lengths of the legs of a right triangle and c is the length of the hypotenuse. Find each missing length.

1. c if $a = 6$ and $b = 8$ **10**
2. a if $b = 12$ and $c = 13$ **5**
3. b if $a = 8$ and $c = 17$ **15**
4. c if $a = 10$ and $b = 3$ **≈10.4**
5. a if $b = 7$ and $c = 25$ **24**
6. b if $a = 24$ and $c = 40$ **32**
7. a if $b = 100$ and $c = 114$ **≈54.7**
8. b if $a = 12.0$ and $c = 30.1$ **≈27.6**
9. c if $a = 8.3$ and $b = 3.3$ **≈8.9**

Find the distance between each pair of points, to the nearest tenth.

10. $(0, 0), (4, -3)$ **5**
11. $(-5, -5), (1, 3)$ **10**
12. $(-1, 0), (4, 12)$ **13**
13. $(0, 15), (17, 0)$ **22.7**
14. $(-4, 2), (4, -2)$ **8.9**
15. $(-8, -8), (8, 8)$ **22.6**
16. $(-1, 1), (1, -1)$ **2.8**
17. $(-2, 9), (0, 0)$ **9.2**
18. $(-5, 3), (4, 3)$ **9**
19. $(-2, 1), (3, 4)$ **5.8**
20. $(3, -2), (3, 5)$ **7**
21. $(5, 4), (-3, 1)$ **8.5**

Bar and Circle Graphs

Sometimes you can draw different graphs to represent the same data, depending on the information you want to share. A *bar graph* is useful for comparing amounts; a *circle graph* is useful for comparing percents.

EXAMPLE Display the 1998 data on immigration to the United States in a bar graph and a circle graph.

Immigration to the United States, 1998

Place of Origin	Immigrants (1000's)
Africa	40.7
Asia	219.7
Europe	90.8
North America	253.0
South America	45.4

SOURCE: U.S. Immigration and Naturalization Service. Go to **www.PHSchool.com** for a data update.

To make a bar graph, place the categories along the bottom axis. Decide on a scale for the side axis. An appropriate scale would be 0–300, marked in intervals of 50. For each data item, draw a bar whose height is equal to the data value.

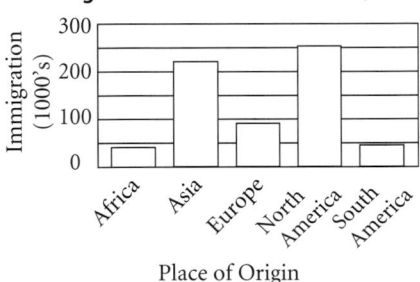

Immigration to the United States, 1998

To make a circle graph, first find the *percent* of the data in each category. Then express each percent as a decimal and multiply by 360° to find the size of each *central angle*.

$$\text{Africa} \rightarrow \frac{40.7}{649.6} \approx 0.06 \text{ or } 6\%$$

$$0.06 \times 360° \approx 22°$$

Draw a circle and use a protractor to draw each central angle.

Immigration to the United States, 1998

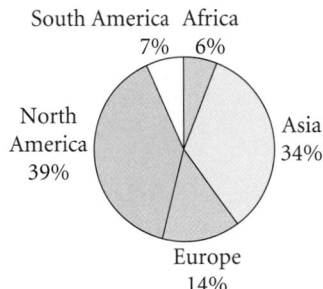

EXERCISES

Display the data from each table in a bar graph and a circle graph. **1–2. See margin.**

1. **NASA Space Shuttle Expenses, 2000**

Operation	Millions of Dollars
Orbiter, integration	698.8
Propulsion	1,053.1
Mission, launch operations	738.8
Flight operations	244.6
Ground operations	510.3

SOURCE: U.S. National Aeronautics and Space Administration. Go to **www.PHSchool.com** for a data update. Web Code: agg-2041

2. **Cable TV Revenue, 1999**

	Millions of Dollars
Advertising, programs	20,068
Basic service	26,890
Pay-per-view, premium services	6,324
Installation	765
Other	5,727

SOURCE: U.S. Census Bureau. Go to **www.PHSchool.com** for a data update. Web Code: agg-2041

1.

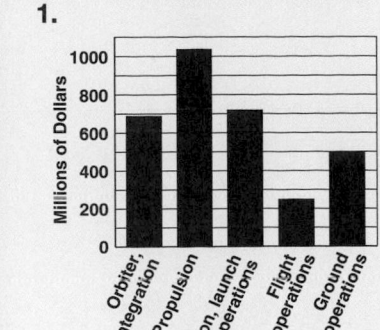

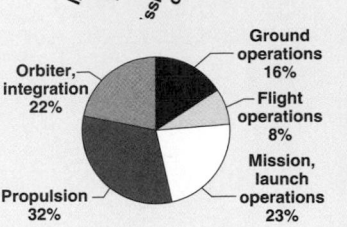

2.

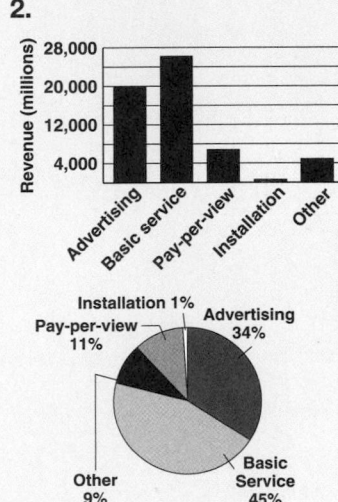

Descriptive Statistics and Histograms

For numerical data, you can find the *mean*, the *median*, and the *mode*.

Mean   The sum of the data values in a data set divided by the number of data values

Median   The middle value of a data set that has been arranged in increasing or decreasing order. If the data set has an even number of values, the median is the mean of the middle two values.

Mode   The most frequently occurring value in a data set

1 EXAMPLE   Find the mean, median, and mode for the following data set.

5 7 6 3 1 7 9 5 10 7

Mean $\dfrac{5 + 7 + 6 + 3 + 1 + 7 + 9 + 5 + 10 + 7}{10} = 6$

Median $5, 7, 6, 3, 1, 7, 9, 5, 10, 7$ **Rearrange the numbers from least to greatest.**

$1, 3, 5, 5, 6, 7, 7, 7, 9, 10$ **The median is the mean of the two middle numbers, 6 and 7.**

The median is $\dfrac{6 + 7}{2} = 6.5$.

Mode   The most frequently occurring data value is 7.

The frequency of a data value is the number of times it occurs in a data set.
A *histogram* is a bar graph that shows the frequency of each data value.

2 EXAMPLE   Use the survey results to make a histogram for the cost of a movie ticket at various theaters.

Survey of Movie Ticket Prices
\$5 \$6 \$5 \$7 \$6 \$7 \$6 \$8 \$6

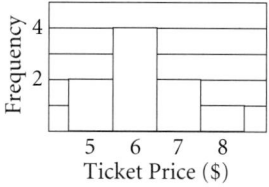

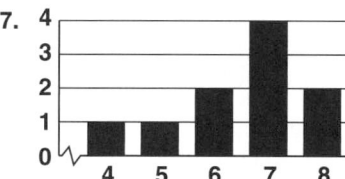

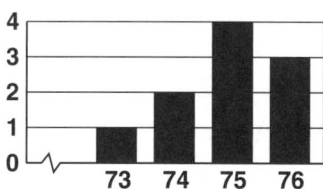

EXERCISES

Find the mean, the median, and the mode of each data set.

1. −3 4 5 5 −2 7 1 8 9   **3.8, 5, 5**

2. 0 0 1 1 2 3 3 5 3 8 7   **3, 3, 3**

3. 2.4 2.4 2.3 2.3 2.4 12.0   **4.0, 2.4, 2.4**

4. 1 1 1 1 2 2 2 3 3 4   **2, 2, 1**

5. 1.2 1.3 1.4 1.5 1.6 1.7 1.8   **1.5, 1.5, no mode**

6. −4 −3 −2 −1 0 1 2 3 4   **0, 0, no mode**

Make a histogram for each data set.   **7–8. See above.**

7. 7 4 8 6 6 8 7 7 5 7

8. 73 75 76 75 74 75 76 74 76 75

Operations With Rational Expressions

A *rational expression* is an expression that can be written in the form $\frac{\text{polynomial}}{\text{polynomial}}$, where a variable is in the denominator. A rational expression is in simplest form if the numerator and denominator have no common factors except 1.

1 EXAMPLE Write the expression $\frac{4x + 8}{x + 2}$ in simplest form.

$\frac{4x + 8}{x + 2} = \frac{4(x + 2)}{x + 2}$ **Factor the numerator.**

$\qquad = 4$ **Divide out the common factor $x + 2$.**

To add or subtract two rational expressions, use a common denominator.

2 EXAMPLE Simplify $\frac{x}{2y} + \frac{x}{3y}$.

$\frac{x}{2y} + \frac{x}{3y} = \frac{x}{2y} \cdot \frac{3}{3} + \frac{x}{3y} \cdot \frac{2}{2}$ **The common denominator of $3y$ and $2y$ is $6y$.**

$\qquad = \frac{3x}{6y} + \frac{2x}{6y}$

$\qquad = \frac{5x}{6y}$ **Add the numerators. Place the sum over the common denominator.**

To multiply rational expressions, first find and divide out any common factors in the numerators and the denominators. Then multiply the remaining numerators and denominators. To divide rational expressions, first use a reciprocal to change the problem to multiplication.

3 EXAMPLE Simplify $\frac{40x^2}{21} \div \frac{5x}{14}$.

$\frac{40x^2}{21} \div \frac{5x}{14} = \frac{40x^2}{21} \cdot \frac{14}{5x}$ **Change dividing by $\frac{5x}{14}$ to multiplying by the reciprocal, $\frac{14}{5x}$.**

$\qquad = \frac{^8 \cancel{40x^2}^{21}}{_3 \cancel{21}} \times \frac{\cancel{14}^2}{_1 \cancel{5x}}$ **Divide out the common factors 5, x, and 7.**

$\qquad = \frac{16x}{3}$ **Multiply the numerators ($8x \cdot 2$). Multiply the denominators ($3 \cdot 1$).**

EXERCISES

Write each expression in simplest form.

1. $\frac{4a^2b}{12ab^3}$ $\frac{a}{3b^2}$

2. $\frac{5n + 15}{n + 3}$ **5**

3. $\frac{x - 7}{2x - 14}$ $\frac{1}{2}$

4. $\frac{28c^2(d - 3)}{35c(d - 3)}$ $\frac{4c}{5}$

Perform the indicated operation.

5. $\frac{3x}{2} + \frac{5x}{2}$ **4x**

6. $\frac{3x}{8} + \frac{5x}{8}$ **x**

7. $\frac{5}{h} - \frac{3}{h}$ $\frac{2}{h}$

8. $\frac{6}{11p} - \frac{9}{11p}$ $\frac{-3}{11p}$

9. $\frac{3x}{5} - \frac{x}{2}$ $\frac{x}{10}$

10. $\frac{13}{2x} - \frac{13}{3x}$ $\frac{13}{6x}$

11. $\frac{7x}{5} + \frac{5x}{7}$ $\frac{74x}{35}$

12. $\frac{5a}{b} + \frac{3a}{5b}$ $\frac{28a}{5b}$

13. $\frac{7x}{8} \cdot \frac{32x}{35}$ $\frac{4x^2}{5}$

14. $\frac{3x^2}{2} \cdot \frac{6}{x}$ **9x**

15. $\frac{8x^2}{5} \cdot \frac{10}{x^3}$ $\frac{16}{x}$

16. $\frac{7x}{8} \cdot \frac{64}{14x}$ **4**

17. $\frac{16}{3x} \div \frac{5}{3x}$ $\frac{16}{5}$

18. $\frac{4x}{5} \div \frac{16}{15x}$ $\frac{3x^2}{4}$

19. $\frac{x^3}{8} \div \frac{x^2}{16}$ **2x**

20. $\frac{3}{n^2} \div 9n^4$ $\frac{1}{3n^6}$

Tables

Table 1 Measures

United States Customary	Metric
Length	
12 inches (in.) = 1 foot (ft)	10 millimeters (mm) = 1 centimeter (cm)
36 in. = 1 yard (yd)	100 cm = 1 meter (m)
3 ft = 1 yd	1000 mm = 1 meter
5280 ft = 1 mile (mi)	1000 m = 1 kilometer (km)
1760 yd = 1 mi	
Area	
144 square inches (in.^2) = 1 square foot (ft^2)	100 square millimeters (mm^2) = 1 square centimeter (cm^2)
9 ft^2 = 1 square yard (yd^2)	10,000 cm^2 = 1 square meter (m^2)
43,560 ft^2 = 1 acre (a)	10,000 m^2 = 1 hectare (ha)
4840 yd^2 = 1 acre	
Volume	
1728 cubic inches (in.^3) = 1 cubic foot (ft^3)	1000 cubic millimeters (mm^3) = 1 cubic centimeter (cm^3)
27 ft^3 = 1 cubic yard (yd^3)	1,000,000 cm^3 = 1 cubic meter (m^3)
Liquid Capacity	
8 fluid ounces (fl oz) = 1 cup (c)	1000 milliliters (mL) = 1 liter (L)
2 c = 1 pint (pt)	1000 L = 1 kiloliter (kL)
2 pt = 1 quart (qt)	
4 qt = 1 gallon (gal)	
Mass	
16 ounces (oz) = 1 pound (lb)	1000 milligrams (mg) = 1 gram (g)
2000 lb = 1 ton (t)	1000 g = 1 kilogram (kg)
	1000 kg = 1 metric ton
Temperature	
32°F = freezing point of water	0°C = freezing point of water
98.6°F = normal body temperature	37°C = normal body temperature
212°F = boiling point of water	100°C = boiling point of water

Time	
60 seconds (s) = 1 minute (min)	365 days = 1 year (yr)
60 minutes = 1 hour (h)	52 weeks (approx.) = 1 year
24 hours = 1 day (d)	12 months = 1 year
7 days = 1 week (wk)	10 years = 1 decade
4 weeks (approx.) = 1 month (mo)	100 years = 1 century

Table 2 Reading Math Symbols

$0.\overline{3}$	0.333 . . .	p. 5
. . .	and so on	p. 5
$\approx$	is approximately equal to	p. 6
$\cdot$	multiplication sign, times (×)	p. 7
( )	parentheses for grouping	p. 7
$\frac{1}{a}$	reciprocal of a, $a \neq 0$	p. 7
$\lvert a \rvert$	absolute value of a	p. 8
π	pi, an irrational number, approximately equal to 3.14	p. 11
$\neq$	is not equal to	p. 12
[ ]	brackets for grouping	p. 14
=	equals	p. 18
$\stackrel{?}{=}$	Is the statement true?	p. 18
°	degree(s)	p. 22
%	percent	p. 22
$a : b$	ratio of a to b	p. 23
$>$	is greater than	p. 26
$\leq$	is less than or equal to	p. 26
$\geq$	is greater than or equal to	p. 26
$<$	is less than	p. 26
$\pm$	plus or minus	p. 29
AB	length of segment AB; distance between points A and B	p. 30
$\triangle ABC$	triangle ABC	p. 30
P(event)	probability of the event	p. 40
(x, y)	ordered pair	p. 54
{ }	set braces	p. 55
$f(x)$	f of x; the function value at x	p. 58
$\{x \mid x > 0\}$	the set of all x, such that x is greater than zero	p. 62
x_1, x_2, etc.	specific values of the variable x	p. 64
y_1, y_2, etc.	specific values of the variable y	p. 64
b	y-intercept of a linear function	p. 65
m	slope of a linear function	p. 65
$[x]$	greatest integer	p. 71
$\begin{bmatrix} 1 & 2 \\ 3 & 4 \end{bmatrix}$	matrix	p. 164
a_{mn}	element in the mth row and nth column of matrix A	p. 165
A'	A prime	p. 188
A^{-1}	inverse of matrix A	p. 195
$\begin{vmatrix} a & b \\ c & d \end{vmatrix}$	determinant of a matrix	p. 196
det A	determinant of matrix A	p. 196
$\sqrt{x}$	nonnegative square root of x	p. 262
i	the imaginary number $\sqrt{-1}$	p. 270
$n!$	n factorial	p. 339
${}_nC_r$	combinations of n things taken r at a time	p. 340
${}_nP_r$	permutations of n things taken r at a time	p. 340
a^n	nth power of a	p. 362
a^{-n}	$\frac{1}{a^n}$, $a \neq 0$	p. 362
$\sqrt[n]{a}$	the principal nth root of a	p. 364
$(g \circ f)(x)$	$g(f(x))$	p. 393
*	multiply (in a spreadsheet formula)	p. 396
$\wedge$	raised to a power (in a spreadsheet formula)	p. 396
$f^{-1}(x)$	the inverse of function f	p. 402
e	the number 2.71828 . . .	p. 433
$\log_b x$	logarithm of x, base b	p. 439
$\ln x$	$\log_e x$	p. 462
$\sum_{n=1}^{5}$	summation	p. 609
∞	infinity	p. 615
$P(A \mid B)$	probability of event A, given event B	p. 642
$\overline{x}$	mean of data values of x	p. 657
σ	sigma	p. 657
θ	theta, measure of an angle	p. 706
$\cos\theta$	cosine of θ	p. 706
$\sin\theta$	sine of θ	p. 706
$\tan\theta$	tangent of θ	p. 735
$\csc\theta$	cosecant of θ	p. 749
$\cot\theta$	cotangent of θ	p. 749
$\sec\theta$	secant of θ	p. 749
$\cos^{-1} x$	the angle whose cosine is x	p. 770
$\sin^{-1} x$	the angle whose sine is x	p. 770
$\tan^{-1} x$	the angle whose tangent is x	p. 770
$\angle A$	angle A	p. 778
$m\angle A$	measure of angle A	p. 781

Table 3 Squares and Square Roots

Number n	Square n^2	Positive Square Root $\sqrt{n}$	Number n	Square n^2	Positive Square Root $\sqrt{n}$	Number n	Square n^2	Positive Square Root $\sqrt{n}$
1	1	1.000	**51**	2601	7.141	**101**	10,201	10.050
2	4	1.414	**52**	2704	7.211	**102**	10,404	10.100
3	9	1.732	**53**	2809	7.280	**103**	10,609	10.149
4	16	2.000	**54**	2916	7.348	**104**	10,816	10.198
5	25	2.236	**55**	3025	7.416	**105**	11,025	10.247
6	36	2.449	**56**	3136	7.483	**106**	11,236	10.296
7	49	2.646	**57**	3249	7.550	**107**	11,449	10.344
8	64	2.828	**58**	3364	7.616	**108**	11,664	10.392
9	81	3.000	**59**	3481	7.681	**109**	11,881	10.440
10	100	3.162	**60**	3600	7.746	**110**	12,100	10.488
11	121	3.317	**61**	3721	7.810	**111**	12,321	10.536
12	144	3.464	**62**	3844	7.874	**112**	12,544	10.583
13	169	3.606	**63**	3969	7.937	**113**	12,769	10.630
14	196	3.742	**64**	4096	8.000	**114**	12,996	10.677
15	225	3.873	**65**	4225	8.062	**115**	13,225	10.724
16	256	4.000	**66**	4356	8.124	**116**	13,456	10.770
17	289	4.123	**67**	4489	8.185	**117**	13,689	10.817
18	324	4.243	**68**	4624	8.246	**118**	13,924	10.863
19	361	4.359	**69**	4761	8.307	**119**	14,161	10.909
20	400	4.472	**70**	4900	8.367	**120**	14,400	10.954
21	441	4.583	**71**	5041	8.426	**121**	14,641	11.000
22	484	4.690	**72**	5184	8.485	**122**	14,884	11.045
23	529	4.796	**73**	5329	8.544	**123**	15,129	11.091
24	576	4.899	**74**	5476	8.602	**124**	15,376	11.136
25	625	5.000	**75**	5625	8.660	**125**	15,625	11.180
26	676	5.099	**76**	5776	8.718	**126**	15,876	11.225
27	729	5.196	**77**	5929	8.775	**127**	16,129	11.269
28	784	5.292	**78**	6084	8.832	**128**	16,384	11.314
29	841	5.385	**79**	6241	8.888	**129**	16,641	11.358
30	900	5.477	**80**	6400	8.944	**130**	16,900	11.402
31	961	5.568	**81**	6561	9.000	**131**	17,161	11.446
32	1024	5.657	**82**	6724	9.055	**132**	17,424	11.489
33	1089	5.745	**83**	6889	9.110	**133**	17,689	11.533
34	1156	5.831	**84**	7056	9.165	**134**	17,956	11.576
35	1225	5.916	**85**	7225	9.220	**135**	18,225	11.619
36	1296	6.000	**86**	7396	9.274	**136**	18,496	11.662
37	1369	6.083	**87**	7569	9.327	**137**	18,769	11.705
38	1444	6.164	**88**	7744	9.381	**138**	19,044	11.747
39	1521	6.245	**89**	7921	9.434	**139**	19,321	11.790
40	1600	6.325	**90**	8100	9.487	**140**	19,600	11.832
41	1681	6.403	**91**	8281	9.539	**141**	19,881	11.874
42	1764	6.481	**92**	8464	9.592	**142**	20,164	11.916
43	1849	6.557	**93**	8649	9.644	**143**	20,449	11.958
44	1936	6.633	**94**	8836	9.695	**144**	20,736	12.000
45	2025	6.708	**95**	9025	9.747	**145**	21,025	12.042
46	2116	6.782	**96**	9216	9.798	**146**	21,316	12.083
47	2209	6.856	**97**	9409	9.849	**147**	21,609	12.124
48	2304	6.928	**98**	9604	9.899	**148**	21,904	12.166
49	2401	7.000	**99**	9801	9.950	**149**	22,201	12.207
50	2500	7.071	**100**	10,000	10.000	**150**	22,500	12.247

Table 4 Trigonometric Ratios

Angle	Sine	Cosine	Tangent	Angle	Sine	Cosine	Tangent
1°	0.0175	0.9998	0.0175	**46°**	0.7193	0.6947	1.0355
2°	0.0349	0.9994	0.0349	**47°**	0.7314	0.6820	1.0724
3°	0.0523	0.9986	0.0524	**48°**	0.7431	0.6691	1.1106
4°	0.0698	0.9976	0.0699	**49°**	0.7547	0.6561	1.1504
5°	0.0872	0.9962	0.0875	**50°**	0.7660	0.6428	1.1918
6°	0.1045	0.9945	0.1051	**51°**	0.7771	0.6293	1.2349
7°	0.1219	0.9925	0.1228	**52°**	0.7880	0.6157	1.2799
8°	0.1392	0.9903	0.1405	**53°**	0.7986	0.6018	1.3270
9°	0.1564	0.9877	0.1584	**54°**	0.8090	0.5878	1.3764
10°	0.1736	0.9848	0.1763	**55°**	0.8192	0.5736	1.4281
11°	0.1908	0.9816	0.1944	**56°**	0.8290	0.5592	1.4826
12°	0.2079	0.9781	0.2126	**57°**	0.8387	0.5446	1.5399
13°	0.2250	0.9744	0.2309	**58°**	0.8480	0.5299	1.6003
14°	0.2419	0.9703	0.2493	**59°**	0.8572	0.5150	1.6643
15°	0.2588	0.9659	0.2679	**60°**	0.8660	0.5000	1.7321
16°	0.2756	0.9613	0.2867	**61°**	0.8746	0.4848	1.8040
17°	0.2924	0.9563	0.3057	**62°**	0.8829	0.4695	1.8807
18°	0.3090	0.9511	0.3249	**63°**	0.8910	0.4540	1.9626
19°	0.3256	0.9455	0.3443	**64°**	0.8988	0.4384	2.0503
20°	0.3420	0.9397	0.3640	**65°**	0.9063	0.4226	2.1445
21°	0.3584	0.9336	0.3839	**66°**	0.9135	0.4067	2.2460
22°	0.3746	0.9272	0.4040	**67°**	0.9205	0.3907	2.3559
23°	0.3907	0.9205	0.4245	**68°**	0.9272	0.3746	2.4751
24°	0.4067	0.9135	0.4452	**69°**	0.9336	0.3584	2.6051
25°	0.4226	0.9063	0.4663	**70°**	0.9397	0.3420	2.7475
26°	0.4384	0.8988	0.4877	**71°**	0.9455	0.3256	2.9042
27°	0.4540	0.8910	0.5095	**72°**	0.9511	0.3090	3.0777
28°	0.4695	0.8829	0.5317	**73°**	0.9563	0.2924	3.2709
29°	0.4848	0.8746	0.5543	**74°**	0.9613	0.2756	3.4874
30°	0.5000	0.8660	0.5774	**75°**	0.9659	0.2588	3.7321
31°	0.5150	0.8572	0.6009	**76°**	0.9703	0.2419	4.0108
32°	0.5299	0.8480	0.6249	**77°**	0.9744	0.2250	4.3315
33°	0.5446	0.8387	0.6494	**78°**	0.9781	0.2079	4.7046
34°	0.5592	0.8290	0.6745	**79°**	0.9816	0.1908	5.1446
35°	0.5736	0.8192	0.7002	**80°**	0.9848	0.1736	5.6713
36°	0.5878	0.8090	0.7265	**81°**	0.9877	0.1564	6.3138
37°	0.6018	0.7986	0.7536	**82°**	0.9903	0.1392	7.1154
38°	0.6157	0.7880	0.7813	**83°**	0.9925	0.1219	8.1443
39°	0.6293	0.7771	0.8098	**84°**	0.9945	0.1045	9.5144
40°	0.6428	0.7660	0.8391	**85°**	0.9962	0.0872	11.4301
41°	0.6561	0.7547	0.8693	**86°**	0.9976	0.0698	14.3007
42°	0.6691	0.7431	0.9004	**87°**	0.9986	0.0523	19.0811
43°	0.6820	0.7314	0.9325	**88°**	0.9994	0.0349	28.6363
44°	0.6947	0.7193	0.9657	**89°**	0.9998	0.0175	57.2900
45°	0.7071	0.7071	1.0000	**90°**	1.0000	0.0000	

Table 5 **Random Numbers**

71133	15379	62220	83119	33872	80881	54263	35427
50631	71600	00133	22447	76212	94621	91026	89499
92641	47157	49324	27674	04501	30142	49180	17909
06747	85629	84240	41917	84067	44264	40953	20516
10967	26366	60323	55523	09686	47962	59778	99479
08945	67385	60015	91676	72694	49757	86540	32359
22437	77933	00815	21862	25049	30840	01760	60655
78658	17681	63881	99741	74067	35810	11989	68048
23006	64650	50777	06226	64703	73487	34815	35296
67218	66215	14219	61908	18165	17261	45017	29303
03020	75784	91506	02237	88056	15027	04040	96770
94965	75820	50994	31050	67304	16730	29373	96700
07845	69584	70548	52973	72302	97594	92241	15204
42665	29990	57260	75846	01152	30141	35982	96088
04003	36893	51639	65625	28426	90634	32979	05449
32959	06776	72420	55622	81422	67587	93193	67479
29041	35939	80920	31801	38638	87905	37617	53135
63364	20495	50868	54130	32625	30799	94255	03514
27838	19139	82031	46143	93922	32001	05378	42457
94248	29387	32682	86235	35805	66529	00886	25875
40156	92636	95648	79767	16307	71133	15714	44142
44293	19195	30569	41277	01417	34656	80207	33362
71878	31767	40056	52582	30766	70264	86253	07179
24757	57502	51033	16551	66731	87844	41420	10084
55529	68560	50069	50652	76104	42086	48720	96632
39724	50318	91370	68016	06222	26806	86726	52832
80950	27135	14110	92292	17049	60257	01638	04460
21694	79570	74409	95087	75424	57042	27349	16229
06930	85441	37191	75134	12845	67868	51500	97761
18740	35448	56096	37910	35485	19640	07689	31027
40657	14875	70695	92569	40703	69318	95070	01541
52249	56515	59058	34509	35791	22150	56558	75286
86570	07303	40560	57856	22009	67712	19435	90250
62962	66253	93288	01838	68388	55481	00336	19271
78066	09117	62350	58972	80778	46458	83677	16125
89106	30219	30068	54030	49295	48985	01624	72881
88310	18172	89450	04987	02781	37935	76222	93595
20942	90911	57643	34009	20728	88785	81212	08214
93926	66687	58252	18674	18501	22362	37319	33201
88294	55814	67443	77285	36229	26886	66782	89931
29751	08485	49910	83844	56013	26596	20875	34568
11169	15529	33241	83594	01727	86595	65723	82322
06062	54400	80649	70749	50395	48993	77447	24862
87445	17139	43278	55031	79971	18515	61850	49101
39283	22821	44330	82225	53534	77235	42973	60190

Properties and Formulas

Order of Operations
1. Perform any operation(s) inside grouping symbols.
2. Simplify any terms with exponents.
3. Multiply and divide in order from left to right.
4. Add and subtract in order from left to right.

Properties of Exponents
For any nonzero number a and any integers m and n:

$a^0 = 1, a \neq 0$ $a^m \cdot a^n = a^{m+n}$

$\dfrac{a^m}{a^n} = a^{m-n}$ $(a^m)^n = a^{mn}$

$a^{-n} = \dfrac{1}{a^n}$ $a^{\frac{1}{n}} = \sqrt[n]{a}$

$(ab)^n = a^n b^n$ $\left(\dfrac{a}{b}\right)^n = \dfrac{a^n}{b^n}$

Properties of Square Roots
For any numbers $a \geq 0$ and $b \geq 0$,
$\sqrt{ab} = \sqrt{a} \cdot \sqrt{b}$.
For any numbers $a \geq 0$ and $b > 0$,
$\sqrt{\dfrac{a}{b}} = \dfrac{\sqrt{a}}{\sqrt{b}}$.

The Pythagorean Theorem
In a right triangle, the sum of the squares of the lengths of the legs is equal to the square of the length of the hypotenuse.
$a^2 + b^2 = c^2$

The Converse of the Pythagorean Theorem
If a triangle has sides of lengths a, b, and c, and $a^2 + b^2 = c^2$, then the triangle is a right triangle with hypotenuse of length c.

The Distance Formula
The distance d between any two points (x_1, y_1) and (x_2, y_2) is $d = \sqrt{(x_2 - x_1)^2 + (y_2 - y_1)^2}$.

The Midpoint Formula
The midpoint M of a line segment with endpoints $A(x_1, y_1)$ and $B(x_2, y_2)$ is $\left(\dfrac{x_1 + x_2}{2}, \dfrac{y_1 + y_2}{2}\right)$.

Summary of Vertical and Horizontal Translations
If k and h are positive numbers and $f(x)$ is a function, then
$f(x) + k$ shifts $f(x)$ up k units;
$f(x) - k$ shifts $f(x)$ down k units;
$f(x + h)$ shifts $f(x)$ left h units;
$f(x - h)$ shifts $f(x)$ right h units.

Multiplication Counting Principle
If there are m ways to make a first selection and n ways to make a second selection, there are $m \times n$ ways to make the two selections.

Number of Permutations
The number of permutations of n items of a set arranged r items at a time is
$_nP_r = \dfrac{n!}{(n-r)!}$ for $1 \leq r \leq n$.

CHAPTER 1

The Identity Properties
For every real number a:
$a + 0 = a$ and $0 + a = a$
$a \cdot 1 = a$ and $1 \cdot a = a$

Closure
For all real numbers a and b, $a + b$ and $a \cdot b$ are real numbers.

The Commutative Properties
For all real numbers a and b:
$a + b = b + a$ and $a \cdot b = b \cdot a$

The Inverse Properties
For every real number a:
$a + (-a) = 0$ and $a \cdot \dfrac{1}{a} = 1$ $(a \neq 0)$

The Associative Properties
For all real numbers a, b, and c:
$(a + b) + c = a + (b + c)$
$(a \cdot b) \cdot c = a \cdot (b \cdot c)$

The Distributive Property
For all real numbers a, b, and c:
$a(b + c) = ab + ac$

Properties of Equality
Let a, b, and c represent real numbers.
Reflexive: $a = a$
Symmetric: If $a = b$, then $b = a$.
Transitive: If $a = b$ and $b = c$, then $a = c$.
Addition: If $a = b$, then $a + c = b + c$.
Subtraction: If $a = b$, then $a - c = b - c$.
Multiplication: If $a = b$, then $ac = bc$.
Division: If $a = b$ and $c \neq 0$, then $\dfrac{a}{c} = \dfrac{b}{c}$.
Substitution: If $a = b$, then b may be substituted for a in any expression to obtain an equivalent expression.

Properties of Inequality
Let a, b, and c represent real numbers.
Transitive: If $a \leq b$ and $b \leq c$, then $a \leq c$.
Addition: If $a \leq b$, then $a + c \leq b + c$.
Subtraction: If $a \leq b$, then $a - c \leq b - c$.
Multiplication:
If $a \leq b$ and $c > 0$, then $ac \leq bc$.
If $a \leq b$ and $c < 0$, then $ac \geq bc$.
Division:
If $a \leq b$ and $c > 0$, then $\dfrac{a}{c} \leq \dfrac{b}{c}$.
If $a \leq b$ and $c < 0$, then $\dfrac{a}{c} \geq \dfrac{b}{c}$.

CHAPTER 2

Slope Formula
$\text{slope} = \dfrac{\text{vertical change (rise)}}{\text{horizontal change (run)}} = \dfrac{y_2 - y_1}{x_2 - x_1}$,
where $x_2 - x_1 \neq 0$.

Point-Slope Equation of a Line
The line through point (x_1, y_1) with slope m has the equation $y - y_1 = m(x - x_1)$.

CHAPTER 3

Vertex Principle of Linear Programming
If there is a maximum or a minimum value of the linear objective function, it occurs at one or more vertices of the feasible region.

CHAPTER 4

Matrix Addition
Let A, B, and C represent $m \times n$ matrices.
Closure: $A + B$ is an $m \times n$ matrix.
Commutative: $A + B = B + A$
Associative: $(A + B) + C = A + (B + C)$
Additive Identity: There exists a unique $m \times n$ matrix O such that $O + A = A + O = A$.
Additive Inverse: For each A, there exists a unique opposite $-A$ such that $A + (-A) = O$.

Matrix Subtraction
If two matrices A and B have the same dimensions, then $A - B = A + (-B)$.

Scalar Multiplication
Let A, B, and O represent $m \times n$ matrices, and let c and d represent scalars.
Closure: cA is an $m \times n$ matrix.
Associative: $(cd)A = c(dA)$
Distributive:
$c(A + B) = cA + cB$
$(c + d)A = cA + dA$
Multiplicative Identity: $1 \cdot A = A$
Zero: $0A = O$ and $cO = O$

Matrix Multiplication
Let A, B, and C represent $n \times n$ matrices.
Closure: AB is an $n \times n$ matrix.
Associative: $(AB)C = A(BC)$
Distributive:
$A(B + C) = AB + AC$
$(B + C)A = BA + CA$
Zero: $OA = AO = O$, where O has the same dimensions as A.

CHAPTER 5

Graph of a Quadratic Function in Standard Form
The graph of $y = ax^2 + bx + c$ is a parabola when $a \neq 0$.
When $a > 0$, the parabola opens up. When $a < 0$, the parabola opens down.
The axis of symmetry is the line $x = -\dfrac{b}{2a}$.
The x-coordinate of the vertex is $-\dfrac{b}{2a}$.
The y-coordinate of the vertex is the value of y when $x = -\dfrac{b}{2a}$, or $y = f\left(-\dfrac{b}{2a}\right)$.
The y-intercept is $(0, c)$.

Graph of a Quadratic Function in Vertex Form
The graph of $y = a(x - h)^2 + k$ is the graph of $y = ax^2$ translated h units horizontally and k units vertically.
When h is positive the graph shifts right; when h is negative the graph shifts left.
When k is positive the graph shifts up; when k is negative the graph shifts down.
The vertex is (h, k), and the axis of symmetry is the line $x = h$.
When $a > 0$, the parabola opens up. When $a < 0$, the parabola opens down.

Factoring Perfect Square Trinomials
$a^2 + 2ab + b^2 = (a + b)^2$
$a^2 - 2ab + b^2 = (a - b)^2$

Factoring a Difference of Two Squares
$a^2 - b^2 = (a + b)(a - b)$

Zero-Product Property
If $ab = 0$, then $a = 0$ or $b = 0$.
Example: If $(x + 3)(x - 7) = 0$, then $(x + 3) = 0$ or $(x - 7) = 0$.

Square Root of a Negative Real Number
For any positive real number a, $\sqrt{-a} = i\sqrt{a}$.
Example: $\sqrt{-4} = i\sqrt{4} = i \cdot 2 = 2i$
Note that $(\sqrt{-4})^2 = (i\sqrt{4})^2 = i^2\sqrt{4}^2 = -1 \cdot 4 = -4$ (not 4).

Quadratic Formula
The roots of $ax^2 + bx + c = 0$ are
$x = \frac{-b \pm \sqrt{b^2 - 4ac}}{2a}$.

The Discriminant
The standard form of a quadratic equation is $ax^2 + bx + c = 0$. The discriminant is the value of the expression $b^2 - 4ac$.
$b^2 - 4ac > 0 \Rightarrow$ two real solutions
$b^2 - 4ac = 0 \Rightarrow$ one real solution
$b^2 - 4ac < 0 \Rightarrow$ two complex solutions

CHAPTER 6

Factor Theorem
The expression $x - a$ is a linear factor of a polynomial if and only if the value a is a zero of the related polynomial function.

Remainder Theorem
If a polynomial $P(x)$ of degree $n \geq 1$ is divided by $(x - a)$, where a is a constant, then the remainder is $P(a)$.

Sum and Difference of Cubes
$a^3 + b^3 = (a + b)(a^2 - ab + b^2)$
$a^3 - b^3 = (a - b)(a^2 + ab + b^2)$

Rational Root Theorem
If $\frac{p}{q}$ is in simplest form and is a rational root of the polynomial equation $a_nx^n + a_{n-1}x^{n-1} + \ldots + a_1x + a_0 = 0$ with integer coefficients, then p must be a factor of a_0 and q must be a factor of a_n.

Irrational Root Theorem
Let a and b be rational numbers and let $\sqrt{b}$ be an irrational number. If $a + \sqrt{b}$ is a root of a polynomial equation with rational coefficients, then the conjugate $a - \sqrt{b}$ also is a root.

Imaginary Root Theorem
If the imaginary number $a + bi$ is a root of a polynomial equation with real coefficients, then the conjugate $a - bi$ also is a root.

Fundamental Theorem of Algebra
If $P(x)$ is a polynomial of degree $n \geq 1$ with complex coefficients, then $P(x) = 0$ has at least one complex root.

Corollary
Including imaginary roots and multiple roots, an nth degree polynomial equation has exactly n roots; the related polynomial function has exactly n zeros.

Binomial Theorem
For every positive integer n,
$(a + b)^n = {}_nC_0a^n + {}_nC_1a^{n-1}b + {}_nC_2a^{n-2}b^2 + \ldots + {}_nC_{n-1}ab^{n-1} + {}_nC_nb^n$.

Chapter 7

nth Root of a^n
For any negative real number a, $\sqrt[n]{a^n} = |a|$ when n is even.

Multiplying Radical Expressions
If $\sqrt[n]{a}$ and $\sqrt[n]{b}$ are real numbers, then $\sqrt[n]{a} \cdot \sqrt[n]{b} = \sqrt[n]{ab}$.

Dividing Radical Expressions
If $\sqrt[n]{a}$ and $\sqrt[n]{b}$ are real numbers and $b \neq 0$, then $\frac{\sqrt[n]{a}}{\sqrt[n]{b}} = \sqrt[n]{\frac{a}{b}}$.

Chapter 8

Properties of Logarithms
For any positive numbers, M, N, and b, $b \neq 1$:
$\log_b MN = \log_b M + \log_b N$
$\log_b \frac{M}{N} = \log_b M - \log_b N$
$\log_b M^x = x \log_b M$

Change of Base Formula
For any positive numbers, M, b, and c, with $b \neq 1$ and $c \neq 1$, $\log_b M = \frac{\log_c M}{\log_c b}$.

Properties and Formulas

Chapter 9

Probability of A and B
If A and B are independent events, then $P(A \text{ and } B) = P(A) \cdot P(B)$.

Probability of A or B
If A and B are mutually exclusive events, then $P(A \text{ or } B) = P(A) + P(B)$.
If A and B are not mutually exclusive events, then $P(A \text{ or } B) = P(A) + P(B) - P(A \text{ and } B)$.

Chapter 10

Conic Section	Form of Equation
Parabola	vertex (h, k) $y = a(x - h)^2 + k$ $x = a(y - k)^2 + h$
Circle	center (h, k) $(x - h)^2 + (y - k)^2 = r^2$
Ellipse	center (h, k) $\frac{(x-h)^2}{a^2} + \frac{(y-k)^2}{b^2} = 1$ $\frac{(x-h)^2}{b^2} + \frac{(y-k)^2}{a^2} = 1$
Hyperbola	center (h, k) $\frac{(x-h)^2}{a^2} - \frac{(y-k)^2}{b^2} = 1$ $\frac{(y-k)^2}{a^2} - \frac{(x-h)^2}{b^2} = 1$

Chapter 11

Arithmetic Sequence Formulas
Recursive: a_1 = a given value; $a_n = a_{n-1} + d$
Explicit: $a_n = a_1 + (n - 1)d$
In these formulas, a_n is the nth term, a_1 is the first term, n is the number of the term, and d is the common difference.

Geometric Sequence Formulas
Recursive: a_1 = a given value; $a_n = a_{n-1} \cdot r$
Explicit: $a_n = a_1 \cdot r^{n-1}$
In these formulas, a_n is the nth term, a_1 is the first term, n is the number of the term, and r is the common ratio.

Sum of a Finite Arithmetic Series
The sum S_n of a finite arithmetic series $a_1 + a_2 + a_3 + \ldots + a_n$ is $S_n = \frac{n}{2}(a_1 + a_n)$, where a_1 is the first term, a_n is the nth term, and n is the number of terms.

Sum of a Finite Geometric Series
The sum S_n of a finite geometric series $a_1 + a_2 + a_3 + \ldots + a_n$ is $S_n = \frac{a_1(1 - r^n)}{1 - r}$, where a_1 is the first term, r is the common ratio, and n is the number of terms.

Sum of an Infinite Geometric Series
An infinite geometric series with $|r| < 1$ converges to the sum S given by the following formula:
$S = \frac{a_1}{1 - r}$

Chapter 12

Conditional Probability Formula
For any two events A and B from a sample space with $P(A) \neq 0$,
$P(B \mid A) = \frac{P(A \text{ and } B)}{P(A)}$

Margin of Error Formula
When a random sample of size n is taken from a large population, the sample proportion has a margin of error of approximately $\pm\frac{1}{\sqrt{n}}$.

Binomial Probability
For repeated independent trials, each with a probability of success p and a probability of failure q (with $p + q = 1$), the probability of x successes in n trials is ${}_nC_xp^xq^{n-x}$.

Chapter 13

Converting Between Radians and Degrees
To convert degrees to radians, multiply by $\frac{\pi \text{ radians}}{180°}$.
To convert radians to degrees, multiply by $\frac{180°}{\pi \text{ radians}}$.

Length of an Intercepted Arc
For a circle of radius r and a central angle of measure θ (in radians), the length s of the intercepted arc is $s = r\theta$.

Properties of Sine Functions
Suppose $y = a \sin b\theta$, with $a \neq 0$, $b > 0$, and θ in radians.
$|a|$ is the amplitude of the function.
b is the number of cycles in the interval from 0 to 2π.
$\frac{2\pi}{b}$ is the period of the function.

Properties & Formulas

Properties of Cosine Functions
Suppose $y = a \cos b\theta$, with $a \neq 0$, $b > 0$, and θ in radians.
$|a|$ is the amplitude of the function.
b is the number of cycles in the interval from 0 to 2π.
$\frac{2\pi}{b}$ is the period of the function.

Properties of Tangent Functions
Suppose $y = a \tan b\theta$, with $b > 0$ and θ in radians.
$\frac{\pi}{b}$ is the period of the function.
One cycle occurs in the interval from $-\frac{\pi}{2b}$ to $\frac{\pi}{2b}$.
There are vertical asymptotes at each end of the cycle.

Translations of Sine and Cosine Functions
$y = a \sin b(x - h) + k$ and $y = a \cos b(x - h) + k$ represent translations of $y = a \sin bx$ and $y = a \cos bx$.
- $|a|$ = amplitude
- $\frac{2\pi}{b}$ = period (when x is in radians and $b > 0$)
- h = phase shift, or horizontal shift
- k = vertical shift

Cosecant, Secant, and Cotangent Functions
The cosecant (csc), secant (sec), and cotangent (cot) functions are defined as reciprocals. Their domains include all real numbers θ except those that make a denominator zero.
$\csc\theta = \frac{1}{\sin\theta}$ $\sec\theta = \frac{1}{\cos\theta}$ $\cot\theta = \frac{1}{\tan\theta}$

Chapter 14

Trigonometric Identities
Reciprocal Identities:
$\csc\theta = \frac{1}{\sin\theta}$ $\sec\theta = \frac{1}{\cos\theta}$ $\cot\theta = \frac{1}{\tan\theta}$
Tangent and Cotangent Identities:
$\tan\theta = \frac{\sin\theta}{\cos\theta}$ $\cot\theta = \frac{\cos\theta}{\sin\theta}$
Pythagorean Identities:
$\cos^2\theta + \sin^2\theta = 1$
$1 + \tan^2\theta = \sec^2\theta$
$1 + \cot^2\theta = \csc^2\theta$

Trigonometric Ratios for a Right Triangle
In $\triangle ABC$ with $\angle C$ a right angle:
$\sin A = \frac{\text{length of leg opposite } \angle A}{\text{length of hypotenuse}} = \frac{a}{c}$
$\cos A = \frac{\text{length of leg adjacent to } \angle A}{\text{length of hypotenuse}} = \frac{b}{c}$
$\tan A = \frac{\text{length of leg opposite } \angle A}{\text{length of leg adjacent to } \angle A} = \frac{a}{b}$
$\csc A = \frac{\text{length of hypotenuse}}{\text{length of leg opposite } \angle A} = \frac{c}{a}$
$\sec A = \frac{\text{length of hypotenuse}}{\text{length of leg adjacent to } \angle A} = \frac{c}{b}$
$\cot A = \frac{\text{length of leg adjacent to } \angle A}{\text{length of leg opposite } \angle A} = \frac{b}{a}$

Law of Sines
In $\triangle ABC$, let a, b, and c represent the lengths of the sides opposite $\angle A$, $\angle B$, and $\angle C$, respectively.
Then $\frac{\sin A}{a} = \frac{\sin B}{b} = \frac{\sin C}{c}$.
You can use the Law of Sines to find missing measures of any triangle when you know the measures of two angles and any side, or two sides and the angle opposite one of them.

Law of Cosines
In $\triangle ABC$, let a, b, and c represent the lengths of the sides opposite $\angle A$, $\angle B$, and $\angle C$, respectively.
$a^2 = b^2 + c^2 - 2bc \cos A$
$b^2 = a^2 + c^2 - 2ac \cos B$
$c^2 = a^2 + b^2 - 2ab \cos C$
You can use the Law of Cosines to find missing parts of any triangle when you know the measures of two sides and the angle between them, or all three sides.

Angle Identities
Negative Angle Identities:
$\sin(-\theta) = -\sin\theta$
$\cos(-\theta) = \cos\theta$
$\tan(-\theta) = -\tan\theta$
Cofunction Identities:
$\sin\left(\frac{\pi}{2} - \theta\right) = \cos\theta$
$\cos\left(\frac{\pi}{2} - \theta\right) = \sin\theta$
$\tan\left(\frac{\pi}{2} - \theta\right) = \cot\theta$

Angle Difference Identities
$\sin(A - B) = \sin A \cos B - \cos A \sin B$
$\cos(A - B) = \cos A \cos B + \sin A \sin B$
$\tan(A - B) = \frac{\tan A - \tan B}{1 + \tan A \tan B}$

Angle Sum Identities
$\sin(A + B) = \sin A \cos B + \cos A \sin B$
$\cos(A + B) = \cos A \cos B - \sin A \sin B$
$\tan(A + B) = \frac{\tan A + \tan B}{1 - \tan A \tan B}$

Double Angle Identities
$\sin 2\theta = 2 \sin\theta \cos\theta$
$\cos 2\theta = \cos^2\theta - \sin^2\theta$
$\cos 2\theta = 2\cos^2\theta - 1$
$\cos 2\theta = 1 - 2\sin^2\theta$
$\tan 2\theta = \frac{2\tan\theta}{1 - \tan^2\theta}$

Properties and Formulas

Formulas from Geometry

You will use a number of geometric formulas as you work through your algebra book. Here are some perimeter, area, and volume formulas.

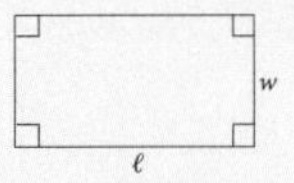

$P = 2\ell + 2w$
$A = \ell w$
Rectangle

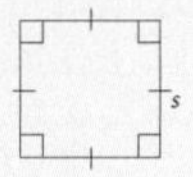

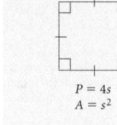

$P = 4s$
$A = s^2$
Square

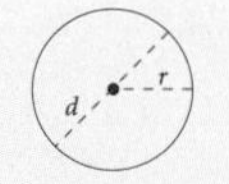

$C = 2\pi r$ or $C = \pi d$
$A = \pi r^2$
Circle

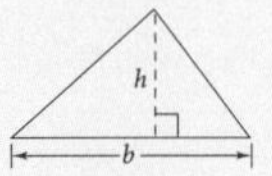

$A = \frac{1}{2}bh$
Triangle

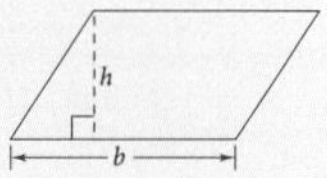

$A = bh$
Parallelogram

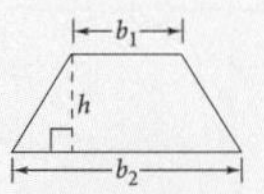

$A = \frac{1}{2}(b_1 + b_2)h$
Trapezoid

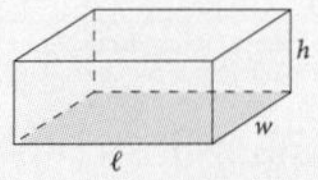

$SA = 2(\ell w + wh + h\ell)$
$V = Bh$
$V = \ell wh$
Rectangular Prism

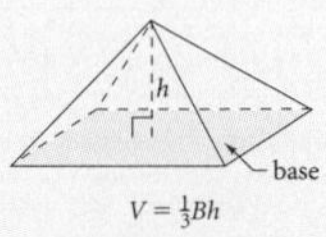

$V = \frac{1}{3}Bh$
Pyramid

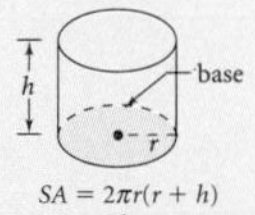

$SA = 2\pi r(r + h)$
$V = Bh$
$V = \pi r^2h$
Cylinder

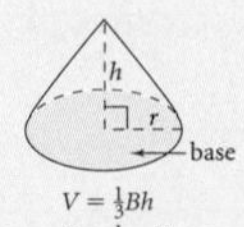

$V = \frac{1}{3}Bh$
$V = \frac{1}{3}\pi r^2h$
Cone

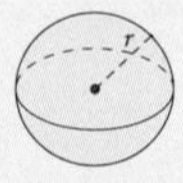

$SA = 4\pi r^2$
$V = \frac{4}{3}\pi r^3$
Sphere

English/Spanish Illustrated Glossary

A

EXAMPLES

Absolute value function (p. 86) A function of the form $f(x) = |mx + b| + c$, where $m \neq 0$, is an absolute value function.

$f(x) = |3x - 2| + 3$
$f(x) = |2x|$

Función de valor absoluto (p. 86) Una función de la forma $f(x) = |mx + b| + c$, donde $m \neq 0$, es una función de valor absoluto.

Absolute value of a complex number (p. 271) The absolute value of a complex number is its distance from the origin on the complex number plane. In general, $|a + bi| = \sqrt{a^2 + b^2}$.

$|3 - 4i| = \sqrt{3^2 + (-4)^2} = 5$

Valor absoluto de un número complejo (p. 271) El valor absoluto de un número complejo es la distancia a la que está del origen en el plano complejo. Generalmente, $|a + bi| = \sqrt{a^2 + b^2}$.

Absolute value of a real number (pp. 8, 33) The absolute value of a real number is its distance from zero on the number line. If $x \geq 0$, then $|x| = x$. If $x < 0$, then $|x| = -x$.

$|3| = 3$
$|-4| = 4$

Valor absoluto de un número real (pp. 8, 33) El valor absoluto de un número real es la distancia a la que se encuentra de cero en la recta numérica. Si $x \geq 0$, entonces $|x| = x$. Si $x < 0$, entonces $|x| = -x$.

Additive inverse (p. 7) The opposite or additive inverse of any number a is $-a$. The sum of opposites is 0.

$3 + (-3) = 0$
$5.2 + (-5.2) = 0$

Inverso aditivo (p. 7) El opuesto o inverso aditivo de cualquier número a es $-a$. La suma de los opuestos es 0.

Algebraic expression (p. 12) An expression that contains one or more variables is called an algebraic expression or a variable expression.

$2x + 3$
$z - y$

Expresión algebraica (p. 12) Una expresión que contiene una o más variables es llamada expresión algebraica o expresión variable.

Amplitude (of a periodic function) (p. 698) The amplitude of a periodic function is half the difference between the maximum and minimum values of the function.

The maximum and minimum values of $y = 4 \sin x$ are 4 and -4, respectively.
amplitude $= \frac{4 - (-4)}{2} = 4$

Amplitud (de una función periódica) (p. 698) La amplitud de una función periódica es la mitad de la diferencia entre los valores máximo y mínimo de la función.

EXAMPLES

Arithmetic mean (p. 595) The arithmetic mean of any two numbers is their sum divided by two.

The arithmetic mean of 12 and 15 is $\frac{12 + 15}{2} = 13.5$.

Media aritmética (p. 595) La media aritmética de dos números cualesquiera es la suma de los números dividida por dos.

Arithmetic sequence (p. 594) In an arithmetic sequence, the difference between consecutive terms is constant. The constant is called the common difference.

The arithmetic sequence $1, 5, 9, 13, \ldots$ has a common difference of 4.

Progresión aritmética (p. 594) En una sucesión numérica la diferencia entre términos consecutivos es un número constante. El número constante se llama la diferencia común.

Arithmetic series (p. 608) An arithmetic series is a series whose terms form an arithmetic sequence.

$1 + 5 + 9 + 13 + 17 + 21$ is an arithmetic series with six terms.

Serie aritmética (p. 608) Una serie aritmética es una serie cuyos términos forman una progresión aritmética.

Asymptote (p. 425) An asymptote is a line that a graph approaches but never reaches.

The function $y = \frac{x + 2}{x - 2}$ has $x = 2$ as a vertical asymptote and $y = 1$ as a horizontal asymptote.

Asíntota (p. 425) Una asíntota es una recta a la que la gráfica se acerca indefinidamente, pero sin encontrarla jamás.

Augmented matrix (p. 218) An augmented matrix contains the coefficients and constants from a system of equations.

linear system   augmented matrix
$\begin{cases} x + 4 = 6 \\ -2x + 5y = 7 \end{cases}$ $\begin{bmatrix} 1 & 4 & 6 \\ -2 & 5 & 7 \end{bmatrix}$

Matriz aumentada (p. 218) Una matriz aumentada contiene los coeficientes y constantes de un sistema de ecuaciones.

Axis of symmetry (p. 235) The axis of symmetry is the line that divides a parabola into two parts that are mirror images.

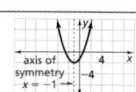

Eje de simetría (p. 235) El eje de simetria es la recta que divide una parábola en dos partes que son imágenes una de la otra.

$y = x^2 + 2x - 1$

B

Bimodal (p. 648) A bimodal data set has two modes.

$\{1, 2, 3, 3, 4, 5, 6, 6\}$
mode $= 3$ and 6

Bimodal (p. 648) Un conjunto bimodal de datos tiene dos modas.

EXAMPLES

Binomial experiment (p. 671) A binomial experiment is one in which the situation involves repeated trials. Each trial has two possible outcomes (success or failure), and the probability of success is constant throughout the trials.

Experimento binomial (p. 671) Un experimento binomial es un experimento que requiere varios ensayos. Cada ensayo tiene dos resultados posibles (éxito o fracaso), y la probabilidad de éxito es constante durante todos los ensayos.

Binomial probability (p. 673) In a binomial experiment with probability of success p and probability of failure q, the probability of x successes in n trials is given by ${}_nC_x \, p^x q^{n-x}$.

Suppose you roll a standard number cube and that you call rolling a 1 a success. Then $p = \frac{1}{6}$ and $q = \frac{5}{6}$. The probability of rolling nine 1's in twenty rolls is ${}_{20}C_9 \left(\frac{1}{6}\right)^9 \left(\frac{5}{6}\right)^{11} \approx 0.0022$.

Probabilidad binomial (p. 673) En un experimento binomial con una probabilidad de éxito p y una probabilidad de fracaso q, la probabilidad de x éxitos en n ensayos se expresa con ${}_nC_x \, p^x q^{n-x}$.

Binomial Theorem (p. 348) For every positive integer n,
$(a + b)^n = {}_nC_0 a^n + {}_nC_1 a^{n-1} b^1 + \ldots + {}_nC_{n-1} a^1 b^{n-1} + {}_nC_n b^n$.

$(x - 3)^3 = {}_3C_0(2x)^3 + {}_3C_1(2x)^2(-3)^1$
$\qquad + {}_3C_2(2x)^1(-3)^2 + {}_3C_3(-3)^3$
$= 8x^3 - 36x^2 + 54x - 27$

Teorema binomial (p. 348) Para todo número entero positivo n,
$(a + b)^n = {}_nC_0 a^n + {}_nC_1 a^{n-1} b^1 + \ldots + {}_nC_{n-1} a^1 b^{n-1} + {}_nC_n b^n$.

Box-and-whisker plot (p. 650) A box-and-whisker plot is a method of displaying data that uses quartiles to form the center box and the maximum and minimum values to form the whiskers.

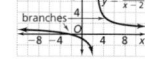

Gráfica de conectores (p. 650) Una gráfica de conectores es un método para mostrar datos que utiliza cuartiles para formar una casilla central y los valores máximos y mínimos para formar los conectores.

Branch (p. 485) Each piece of a discontinuous graph is called a branch.

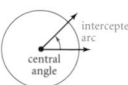

Ramificación (p. 485) Cada segmento de una gráfica discontinua se llama ramificación.

C

Center of a circle (p. 549) The center of a circle is the point that is the same distance from every point on the circle.

intercepted arc
central angle

Centro de un círculo (p. 549) El centro de un círculo es el punto que está situado a la misma distancia de cada punto de la circunferencia.

EXAMPLES

Center of rotation (p. 190) The center of rotation is the fixed point about which a rotation turns.

Center of rotation

Centro de rotación (p. 190) El centro de rotación es el punto fijo alrededor del cual gira un objeto.

Central angle (p. 712) A central angle of a circle is an angle whose vertex is at the center of a circle.

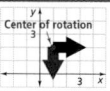

Ángulo central (p. 712) El ángulo central de un círculo es un ángulo cuyo vértice está situado en el centro del círculo.

Change of Base Formula (p. 453) $\log_b M = \frac{\log_c M}{\log_c b}$, where M, b, and c are positive numbers, and $b \neq 1$ and $c \neq 1$.

$\log_3 8 = \frac{\log 8}{\log 3} \approx 1.8928$

Fórmula de cambio de base (p. 453) $\log_b M = \frac{\log_c M}{\log_c b}$, donde M, b y c son números positivos y $b \neq 1$ y $c \neq 1$.

Circle (p. 549) A circle is the set of all points in a plane at a distance r from a given point. The standard form of the equation of a circle with center (h, k) and radius r is $(x - h)^2 + (y - k)^2 = r^2$.

Círculo (p. 549) Un círculo es el conjunto de todos los puntos situados en un plano a una distancia r de un punto dado. La forma normal de la ecuación del círculo cuyo centro es (h, k) y cuyo radio es r es $(x - h)^2 + (y - k)^2 = r^2$.

Circumscribed rectangles (p. 623) When approximating the area under a curve, circumscribed rectangles are partially above the curve. Their area is greater than the area under the curve.

Rectángulos circunscritos (p. 623) Al aproximar el área que queda dentro de una curva, los rectángulos circunscritos quedan parcialmente por fuera de la curva. Su área es mayor que el área dentro de la curva.

Coefficient (p. 13) The numerical factor in a term is the coefficient.

The coefficient of $-3k$ is -3.

Coeficiente (p. 13) El factor numérico de un término es el coeficiente.

Coefficient matrix (p. 210) When representing a system of equations with a matrix equation, the matrix containing the coefficients of the system is the coefficient matrix.

$\begin{cases} x + 2y = 5 \\ 3x + 5y = 14 \end{cases}$

coefficient matrix $\begin{bmatrix} 1 & 2 \\ 3 & 5 \end{bmatrix}$

Matriz de coeficientes (p. 210) Al representar un sistema de ecuaciones con una ecuación de matriz, la matriz que contiene los coeficientes del sistema es la matriz de coeficientes.

Combination (p. 340) Any unordered selection of r objects from a set of n objects is a combination. The number of combinations of n objects taken r at a time is $_nC_r = \frac{n!}{r!(n-r)!}$ for $0 \le r \le n$.

Combinación (p. 340) Cualquier selección no ordenada de r objetos tomados de un conjunto de n objetos es una combinación. El número de combinaciones de n objetos, cuando se toman r objetos cada vez, es $_nC_r = \frac{n!}{r!(n-r)!}$ para $0 \le r \le n$.

The number of combinations of seven items taken four at a time is
$_7C_4 = \frac{7!}{4!(7-4)!} = 5040$.
There are 5040 ways to choose four items from seven items without regard to order.

Combined variation (p. 480) A combined variation combines direct and inverse variations in more complicated relationships.

Variación combinada (p. 480) Una variación combinada combina variaciones directas e inversas en relaciones más complejas.

$y = kx^2$
$z = \frac{kx}{y}$

Common difference (p. 594) A common difference is the difference between consecutive terms of an arithmetic sequence.

Diferencia común (p. 594) La diferencia común es la diferencia entre los términos consecutivos de una progresión aritmética.

The arithmetic sequence $1, 5, 9, 13, \ldots$ has a common difference of 4.

Common logarithm (p. 439) A common logarithm is a logarithm that uses base 10. You can write the common logarithm $\log_{10} y$ as $\log y$.

Logaritmo común (p. 439) El logaritmo común es un logaritmo de base 10. El logaritmo común $\log_{10} y$ se expresa como $\log y$.

$\log 1 = 0$
$\log 10 = 1$
$\log 50 = 1.698970004\ldots$

Common ratio (p. 600) A common ratio is the ratio of consecutive terms of a geometric sequence.

Razón común (p. 600) Una razón común es el número que resulta al dividir términos consecutivos en una progresión geométrica.

The geometric sequence $2.5, 5, 10, 20, \ldots$ has a common ratio of 2.

Completing the square (p. 278) Completing the square is a process for converting a quadratic expression into a perfect square trinomial.

Método de la completación del cuadrado (p. 278) El método de completación del cuadrado es un proceso para convertir una expresión cuadrática en un trinomio cuadrado perfecto.

$x^2 - 12x + \blacksquare$
$x^2 - 12x + \left(\frac{-12}{2}\right)^2$
$x^2 - 12x + 36$

Complex conjugates (p. 332) The complex numbers $a + bi$ and $a - bi$ are complex conjugates.

Conjugados complejos (p. 332) Los números complejos $a + bi$ y $a - bi$ son conjugados complejos.

The complex numbers $2 - 3i$ and $2 + 3i$ are complex conjugates.

Complex fraction (p. 506) A complex fraction is a fraction that has a fraction in its numerator or denominator or in both its numerator and denominator.

Fracción compleja (p. 506) Una fracción compleja es una fracción que contiene otra fracción en el numerador o en el denominador, o en ambos.

$\dfrac{\frac{2}{5}}{3}$

$\dfrac{2}{\frac{9}{2}}$

Complex number plane (p. 271) You can use the complex number plane to represent a complex number geometrically. Locate the real part of the number on the horizontal axis and the imaginary part on the vertical axis.

Plano de números complejos (p. 271) Plano que sirve para representar geométricamente los números complejos. Se localiza la parte real del número en el eje horizontal y la parte imaginaria en el eje vertical.

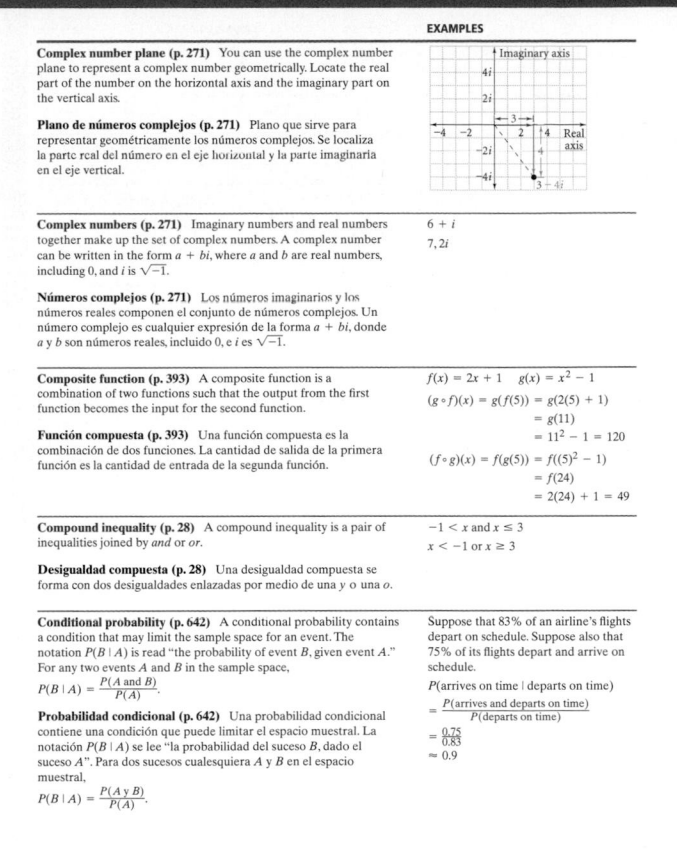

Complex numbers (p. 271) Imaginary numbers and real numbers together make up the set of complex numbers. A complex number can be written in the form $a + bi$, where a and b are real numbers, including 0, and i is $\sqrt{-1}$.

Números complejos (p. 271) Los números imaginarios y los números reales componen el conjunto de números complejos. Un número complejo es cualquier expresión de la forma $a + bi$, donde a y b son números reales, incluido 0, e i es $\sqrt{-1}$.

$6 + i$
$7, 2i$

Composite function (p. 393) A composite function is a combination of two functions such that the output from the first function becomes the input for the second function.

Función compuesta (p. 393) Una función compuesta es la combinación de dos funciones. La cantidad de salida de la primera función es la cantidad de entrada de la segunda función.

$f(x) = 2x + 1 \quad g(x) = x^2 - 1$
$(g \circ f)(x) = g(f(5)) = g(2(5) + 1)$
$= g(11)$
$= 11^2 - 1 = 120$
$(f \circ g)(x) = f(g(5)) = f((5)^2 - 1)$
$= f(24)$
$= 2(24) + 1 = 49$

Compound inequality (p. 28) A compound inequality is a pair of inequalities joined by and or or.

Desigualdad compuesta (p. 28) Una desigualdad compuesta se forma con dos desigualdades enlazadas por medio de una y o una o.

$-1 < x$ and $x \le 3$
$x < -1$ or $x \ge 3$

Conditional probability (p. 642) A conditional probability contains a condition that may limit the sample space for an event. The notation $P(B \mid A)$ is read "the probability of event B, given event A." For any two events A and B in the sample space,
$P(B \mid A) = \frac{P(A \text{ and } B)}{P(A)}$.

Probabilidad condicional (p. 642) Una probabilidad condicional contiene una condición que puede limitar el espacio muestral. La notación $P(B \mid A)$ se lee "la probabilidad del suceso B, dado el suceso A". Para dos sucesos cualesquiera A y B en el espacio muestral,
$P(B \mid A) = \frac{P(A \text{ y } B)}{P(A)}$.

Suppose that 83% of an airline's flights depart on schedule. Suppose also that 75% of its flights depart and arrive on schedule.
$P(\text{arrives on time} \mid \text{departs on time})$
$= \dfrac{P(\text{arrives and departs on time})}{P(\text{departs on time})}$
$= \frac{0.75}{0.83}$
≈ 0.9

Conic section (p. 535) A conic section is a curve formed by the intersection of a plane and a double cone.

Sección cónica (p. 535) Una sección cónica es una curva que se forma por la intersección de un plano con un cono doble.

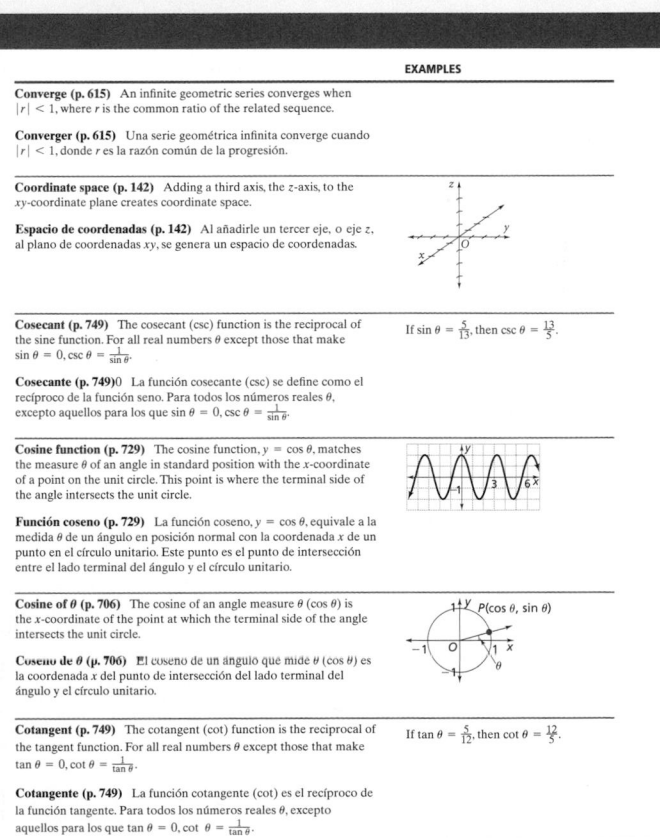

ellipse   hyperbola

Conjugates (p. 331) Number pairs of the form $a + \sqrt{b}$ and $a - \sqrt{b}$ are conjugates.

Conjugados (p. 331) Los pares de números con la forma $a + \sqrt{b}$ y $a - \sqrt{b}$ son conjugados.

$5 + \sqrt{3}$ and $5 - \sqrt{3}$ are conjugates.

Constant matrix (p. 210) When representing a system of equations with a matrix equation, the matrix containing the constants of the system is the constant matrix.

Matriz de constantes (p. 210) Al representar un sistema de ecuaciones con un arreglo matricial, la matriz que contiene las constantes del sistema es la matriz de constantes.

$\begin{cases} x + 2y = 5 \\ 3x + 5y = 14 \end{cases}$

constant matrix $\begin{bmatrix} 5 \\ 14 \end{bmatrix}$

Constant of variation (pp. 72, 478, 480) The constant of variation is the value of k in the direct variation $y = kx$ or the value of k in the indirect variation $xy = k$. A combined variation also has a constant of variation.

Constante de variación (pp. 72, 478, 480) La constante de variación es el valor de k en una variación directa $y = kx$, o el valor de k en la variación indirecta $xy = k$. Una variación combinada también tiene una constante de variación.

In $y = 3.5x$, the constant of variation k is 3.5. In $xy = 5$, the constant of variation k is 5.

Constraints (p. 135) Constraints are limits on the variables in the objective function in a linear programming problem. See **Linear programming**.

Restricciones (p. 135) Las restricciones son los límites a las variables de la función objetiva en un problema de programación lineal. Ver **Linear programming**.

Continuously compounded interest formula (p. 433) The formula for continuously compounded interest is $A = Pe^{rt}$.

Fórmula de interés compuesto continuo (p. 433) La fórmula para el interés compuesto continuo es $A = Pe^{rt}$.

Suppose that $P = \$1200$, $r = 0.05$, and $t = 3$. Then
$A = 1200e^{0.05 \cdot 3}$
$= 1200(2.718\ldots)^{0.15}$
≈ 1394.20

Converge (p. 615) An infinite geometric series converges when $|r| < 1$, where r is the common ratio of the related sequence.

Converger (p. 615) Una serie geométrica infinita converge cuando $|r| < 1$, donde r es la razón común de la progresión.

Coordinate space (p. 142) Adding a third axis, the z-axis, to the xy-coordinate plane creates coordinate space.

Espacio de coordenadas (p. 142) Al añadirle un tercer eje, o eje z, al plano de coordenadas xy, se genera un espacio de coordenadas.

Cosecant (p. 749) The cosecant (csc) function is the reciprocal of the sine function. For all real numbers θ except those that make $\sin \theta = 0$, $\csc \theta = \frac{1}{\sin \theta}$.

Cosecante (p. 749) La función cosecante (csc) se define como el recíproco de la función seno. Para todos los números reales θ, excepto aquellos para los que $\sin \theta = 0$, $\csc \theta = \frac{1}{\sin \theta}$.

If $\sin \theta = \frac{5}{13}$, then $\csc \theta = \frac{13}{5}$.

Cosine function (p. 729) The cosine function, $y = \cos \theta$, matches the measure of an angle θ in standard position with the x-coordinate of a point on the unit circle. This point is where the terminal side of the angle intersects the unit circle.

Función coseno (p. 729) La función coseno, $y = \cos \theta$, equivale a la medida θ de un ángulo en posición normal con la coordenada x de un punto en el círculo unitario. Este punto es el punto de intersección entre el lado terminal del ángulo y el círculo unitario.

Cosine of θ (p. 706) The cosine of an angle measure θ ($\cos \theta$) is the x-coordinate of the point at which the terminal side of the angle intersects the unit circle.

Coseno de θ (p. 706) El coseno de un ángulo que mide θ ($\cos \theta$) es la coordenada x del punto de intersección del lado terminal del ángulo y el círculo unitario.

Cotangent (p. 749) The cotangent (cot) function is the reciprocal of the tangent function. For all real numbers θ except those that make $\tan \theta = 0$, $\cot \theta = \frac{1}{\tan \theta}$.

Cotangente (p. 749) La función cotangente (cot) es el recíproco de la función tangente. Para todos los números reales θ, excepto aquellos para los que $\tan \theta = 0$, $\cot \theta = \frac{1}{\tan \theta}$.

If $\tan \theta = \frac{5}{12}$, then $\cot \theta = \frac{12}{5}$.

Coterminal angles (p. 705) Two angles in standard position are coterminal if they have the same terminal side.

Ángulos coterminales (p. 705) Dos ángulos que están en posición normal son coterminales si tienen el mismo lado terminal.

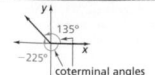

coterminal angles

Angles that have measures 135° and −225° are coterminal.

Co-vertices (of an ellipse) (p. 556) The endpoints of the minor axis of an ellipse are the co-vertices of the ellipse.

Co-vértices (de una elipse) (p. 556) Los puntos de intersección entre una elipse y los ejes menores son los co-vértices de la elipse.

Cramer's Rule (p. 217) Cramer's Rule is a method of solving a system of linear equations using determinants. Form the determinants D_x and D_y by replacing one column of the determinant with the constant terms from the system.

Regla de Cramer (p. 217) La regla de Cramer es un método para resolver por medio de determinantes un sistema de ecuaciones lineales. Se forman los determinantes D_x y D_y al reemplazar una columna del determinante con los términos constantes del sistema.

$$\begin{cases} x + 2y = 6 \\ -x + y = -6 \end{cases}$$

$$D = \begin{vmatrix} 1 & 2 \\ -1 & 1 \end{vmatrix} = -3$$

$$D_x = \begin{vmatrix} 6 & 2 \\ -6 & 1 \end{vmatrix} = -18$$

$$D_y = \begin{vmatrix} 1 & 6 \\ -1 & -6 \end{vmatrix} = 0$$

$$x = \frac{D_x}{D} = 6 \qquad y = \frac{D_y}{D} = 0$$

Cumulative probability (p. 636) Probability over a continuous range of events is cumulative probability.

Probabilidad acumulativa (p. 636) La probabilidad que existe a lo largo de una serie continua de sucesos es la probabilidad acumulativa.

Cycle (p. 697) The cycle of a periodic function is one complete pattern of y-values.

Ciclo (p. 697) El ciclo de una función periódica es un patrón completo de valores y.

D

Decay factor (p. 425) In an exponential decay function of the form $y = ab^x$, with $0 < b < 1$, b is the decay factor.

Factor de decremento (p. 425) En una función exponencial decremental de la forma $y = ab^x$, con $0 < b < 1$, b es el factor de decremento.

In the equation $y = 0.5^x$, 0.5 is the decay factor.

Degree of a polynomial (p. 301) The degree of a polynomial is the largest degree of any term of the polynomial.

Grado de un polinomio (p. 301) El grado de un polinomio es el grado mayor de cualquier término del polinomio.

$P(x) = x^6 + 2x^3 - 3$
degree 6

Degree of a term (p. 301) The exponent in a term determines the degree of the term.

Grado de un término (p. 301) El exponente de un término determina el grado del término.

$x^2 \leftarrow$ degree 2
$3y^3 \leftarrow$ degree 3
$-4a^{12} \leftarrow$ degree 12

Dependent events (p. 519) When the outcome of one event affects the outcome of a second event, the two events are dependent.

Sucesos dependientes (p. 519) Cuando la probabilidad de que ocurra un suceso depende del resultado de otro suceso, los dos sucesos son dependientes.

Suppose two apples and two oranges are in a refrigerator. Two people choose one piece of fruit each, at random. The probability of choosing an apple the first time is $\frac{1}{2}$. The outcome of the second choice depends on the outcome of the first choice. The events are dependent.

Dependent system (p. 118) A system of equations that does not have a unique solution is a dependent system.

Sistema dependiente (p. 118) Un sistema de ecuaciones es dependiente cuando no tiene una solución única.

$\begin{cases} y = 2x + 3 \\ -4x + 2y = 6 \end{cases}$ represents two equations for the same line, so it has many solutions. It is a dependent system.

Dependent variable (p. 62) In a linear equation such as $y = 3x + 2$, y is called the dependent variable because it depends on the value of x.

Variable dependiente (p. 62) En una ecuación lineal tal que $y = 3x + 2$, y es la variable dependiente porque depende del valor de x.

$y = 2x + 1$
y is the dependent variable.

Determinant (p. 196) The determinant of a 2×2 matrix $\begin{bmatrix} a & b \\ c & d \end{bmatrix}$ is the real number $ad - bc$.

Determinante (p. 196) El determinante de una matriz cuadrada $\begin{bmatrix} a & b \\ c & d \end{bmatrix}$ es el número real $ad - bc$.

The determinant of $\begin{bmatrix} 3 & -2 \\ 5 & 6 \end{bmatrix}$ is $3(6) - 5(-2) = 28$.

Difference of cubes (p. 322) A difference of cubes is an expression of the form $a^3 - b^3$. It can be factored as $(a - b)(a^2 + ab + b^2)$.

Diferencia de dos cubos (p. 322) La diferencia de dos cubos es una expresión de la forma $a^3 - b^3$. Se puede factorizar como $(a - b)(a^2 + ab + b^2)$.

$x^3 - 27 = (x - 3)(x^2 + 3x + 9)$

Difference of two squares (p. 259) A difference of two squares is an expression of the form $a^2 - b^2$. It can be factored as $(a + b)(a - b)$.

Diferencia de dos cuadrados (p. 259) La diferencia de dos cuadrados es una expresión de la forma $a^2 - b^2$. Se puede factorizar como $(a + b)(a - b)$.

$25a^2 - 4 = (5a + 2)(5a - 2)$
$m^6 - 1 = (m^3 + 1)(m^3 - 1)$

Dilation (p. 188) A dilation is a transformation that changes the size of a figure. When the center of the dilation is the origin, you can use scalar multiplication to find the coordinates of the vertices of an image.

Dilatación (p. 188) Una dilatación es una transformación que cambia el tamaño de una figura. Cuando el centro de dilatación está en el origen, se hallan las coordenadas de los vértices de la imagen por medio del factor de escala.

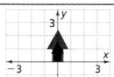

Direct variation (p. 72) A linear function defined by an equation of the form $y = kx$, where $k \neq 0$, represents direct variation.

Variación directa (p. 72) Una función lineal definida por una ecuación de la forma $y = kx$, donde $k \neq 0$, representa una variación directa.

$y = 3.5x, y = 7x, y = -\frac{1}{2}x$

Directrix (p. 543) The directrix of a parabola is the fixed line used to define a parabola. Each point of the parabola is the same distance from the focus and the directrix.

Directriz (p. 543) La directriz de una parábola es la recta fija con que se define una parábola. Cada punto de la parábola está a la misma distancia del foco y de la directriz.

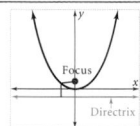

Focus

Directrix

Discriminant (p. 287) The discriminant of a quadratic equation in the form $ax^2 + bx + c = 0$ is $b^2 - 4ac$. The value of the discriminant determines the number of real roots the equation has. If $b^2 - 4ac < 0$, the equation has no roots; if $b^2 - 4ac = 0$, the equation has one root; if $b^2 - 4ac > 0$, the equation has two real roots.

Discriminante (p. 287) El discriminante de una ecuación cuadrática de la forma $ax^2 + bx + c = 0$ es $b^2 - 4ac$. El valor del discriminante determina el número de raíces reales de la ecuación. Si $b^2 - 4ac < 0$, la ecuación no tiene raíces reales; si $b^2 - 4ac = 0$, la ecuación tiene una raíz real; si $b^2 - 4ac > 0$, la ecuación tiene dos raíces reales.

$3x^2 - 6x + 1$
discriminant $= (-6)^2 - 4(3)(1)$
$= 36 - 12 = 24$
The equation has two real roots.

Diverge (p. 615) An infinite geometric series diverges when $|r| \geq 1$, where r is the common ratio of the related sequence.

Divergir (p. 615) Una serie geométrica infinita diverge cuando $|r| \geq 1$, donde r es la razón común de la progresión relacionada.

Domain (p. 56) The domain of a relation is the set of all inputs, or x-coordinates, of the ordered pairs.

Dominio (p. 56) El dominio de una relación es el conjunto de todos los valores de entrada, o coordenadas x, de los pares ordenados.

In the relation $\{(0, 1), (0, 2), (0, 3), (0, 4), (1, 3), (1, 4), (2, 1)\}$, the domain is $[0, 1, 2]$. In the function $f(x) = x^2 - 10$, the domain is all real numbers.

E

Ellipse (p. 556) An ellipse is the set of points P in a plane such that the sum of the distances from P to two fixed points F_1 and F_2 is a given constant k. The standard form of the equation of an ellipse with its center at the origin $\frac{x^2}{a^2} + \frac{y^2}{b^2} = 1$ if the major axis is horizontal and $\frac{x^2}{b^2} + \frac{y^2}{a^2} = 1$ if the major axis is vertical, where $a > b$.

Elipse (p. 556) Una elipse es el conjunto de puntos P situados en un plano tal que la suma de las distancias entre P y dos puntos fijos F_1 y F_2 es una constante dada k. La forma normal de la ecuación de una elipse con su centro en el origen es $\frac{x^2}{a^2} + \frac{y^2}{b^2} = 1$ si el eje mayor es horizontal y $\frac{x^2}{b^2} + \frac{y^2}{a^2} = 1$ si el eje mayor es vertical, donde $a > b$.

$\frac{x^2}{36} + \frac{y^2}{9} = 1$
$F_1 = (-3\sqrt{3}, 0), F_2 = (3\sqrt{3}, 0)$

Equal matrices (p. 173) Equal matrices are matrices with the same dimensions and equal corresponding elements.

Matrices equivalentes (p. 173) Dos matrices son equivalentes si y sólo si tienen las mismas dimensiones y sus elementos correspondientes son iguales.

Matrices A and B are equal.
$A = \begin{bmatrix} 2 & 6 \\ \frac{9}{3} & 1 \end{bmatrix} \quad B = \begin{bmatrix} \frac{6}{3} & 6 \\ 3 & \frac{13}{13} \end{bmatrix}$

Equivalent systems (p. 125) Equivalent systems of equations are systems that have the same solution(s).

Sistemas equivalentes (p. 125) Los sistemas equivalentes de ecuaciones son sistemas que tienen la misma solución o soluciones.

Evaluate (p. 12) Substitute numbers for the variables in an expression and follow the order of operations to evaluate the expression.

Evaluar (p. 12) Al sustituir las variables de una expresión algebraica por números y realizar las operaciones en el orden respectivo, se evalúa la expresión.

When $x = 2$ and $y = -1$,
$2x + 3y$ evaluates to 1.

Expand a binomial (p. 347) You expand a binomial by multiplying and writing the resulting polynomial in standard form.

Desarrollar un binomio (p. 347) Un binomio se desarrolla multiplicándolo y escribiendo el polinomio que resulta en forma normal.

$(x + 4)^3$
$= (x + 4)(x + 4)^2$
$= (x + 4)(x^2 + 8x + 16)$
$= x^3 + 8x^2 + 16x + 4x^2 + 32x + 64$
$= x^3 + 12x^2 + 48x + 64$

EXAMPLES

Experimental probability (p. 40) The experimental probability of an event is the ratio

$$\frac{\text{number of times the event occurs}}{\text{number of trials}}$$

Probabilidad experimental (p. 40) La probabilidad experimental de un suceso es la razón

$$\frac{\text{número de veces que el suceso ocurre}}{\text{número de ensayos}}.$$

Suppose a basketball player has scored 19 times in 28 attempts at a basket. The probability of the player's scoring is $P(\text{score}) = \frac{19}{28} \approx 0.68$, or 68%.

Explicit formula (p. 590) An explicit formula expresses the nth term of a sequence in terms of n.

Fórmula explícita (p. 590) Una fórmula explícita expresa el n-ésimo término de una progresión en función de n.

Let $a_n = 2n + 5$ for positive integers n. If $n = 7$, then $a_7 = 2(7) + 5 = 19$.

Exponential equation (p. 453) An equation of the form $b^{cx} = a$, where the exponent includes a variable, is called an exponential equation. You can solve an exponential equation by taking the logarithm of each side of the equation.

Ecuación exponencial (p. 453) Una ecuación de la forma $b^{cx} = a$, donde el exponente incluye una variable, se llama ecuación exponencial. Dicha ecuación se resuelve hallando el logaritmo de cada lado de la ecuación.

$5^{2x} = 270$
$\log 5^{2x} = \log 270$
$2x \log 5 = \log 270$
$2x = \frac{\log 270}{\log 5}$
$2x \approx 3.4785$
$x \approx 1.7392$

Exponential function (p. 422) The general form of an exponential function is $y = ab^x$, where x is a real number, $a \neq 0$, $b > 0$, and $b \neq 1$. When $b > 1$, the function models exponential growth with growth factor b. When $0 < b < 1$, the function models exponential decay with decay factor b.

Función exponencial (p. 422) La forma general de una función exponencial es $y = ab^x$, donde x es un número real, $a \neq 0$, $b > 0$ y $b \neq 1$. Cuando $b > 1$, la función representa un incremento exponencial con factor incremental b. Cuando $0 < b < 1$, la función representa el decremento exponencial con factor decremental b.

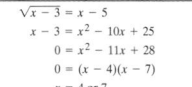

Extraneous solution (p. 34) An extraneous solution is a solution of an equation derived from an original equation that is not a solution of the original equation.

Solución extraña (p. 34) Una solución extraña es una solución de una ecuación derivada de una ecuación dada, pero que no satisface la ecuación dada.

$\sqrt{x - 3} = x - 5$
$x - 3 = x^2 - 10x + 25$
$0 = x^2 - 11x + 28$
$0 = (x - 4)(x - 7)$
$x = 4$ or 7

The number 7 is a solution, but 4 is not, since $\sqrt{4 - 3} \neq 4 - 5$.

F

EXAMPLES

Factor Theorem (p. 309) The expression $x - a$ is a linear factor of a polynomial if and only if the value a is a zero of the related polynomial function.

Teorema de factores (p. 309) La expresión $x - a$ es un factor lineal de un polinomio si y sólo si el valor a es un cero de la función del polinomio.

The value 2 makes the polynomial $x^2 + 2x - 8$ equal to zero. So, $x - 2$ is a factor of $x^2 + 2x - 8$.

Factoring (p. 255) Factoring is rewriting an expression as the product of its factors.

Descomposición factorial (p. 255) Descomponer en factores es convertir una expresión en el producto de sus factores.

expanded form   factored form
$x^2 + x - 56$ $(x + 8)(x - 7)$

Feasible region (p. 136) The feasible region contains all solutions that satisfy the constraints of a system in a linear programming problem. *See* **Linear programming.**

Región factible (p. 136) La región factible contiene todas las soluciones que satisfacen las restricciones de un sistema en un problema de programación lineal. *Ver* **Linear programming.**

Focus (plural: foci) (pp. 543, 556, 563) The focus of a conic section is a point used to define a conic section.

A parabola is the set of all points that are the same distance from the parabola's focus and its directrix. An ellipse is the set of all points P such that the sum of the distances from each point P to the two foci of the ellipse is a constant. A hyperbola is the set of all points P such that the difference of the distances from each point P to the two foci of the hyperbola is a constant.

Foco (pp. 543, 556, 563) El foco de una sección cónica es el punto con el que se define una sección cónica.

Una parábola es el conjunto de todos los puntos que están a la misma distancia del foco y la directriz de la parábola. Una elipse es el conjunto de todos los puntos P tal que la suma de las distancias de cada punto P a los dos focos de la elipse es una constante. Una hipérbola es el conjunto de todos los puntos P tal que la diferencia de las distancias de cada punto P a los dos focos de la hipérbola es una constante.

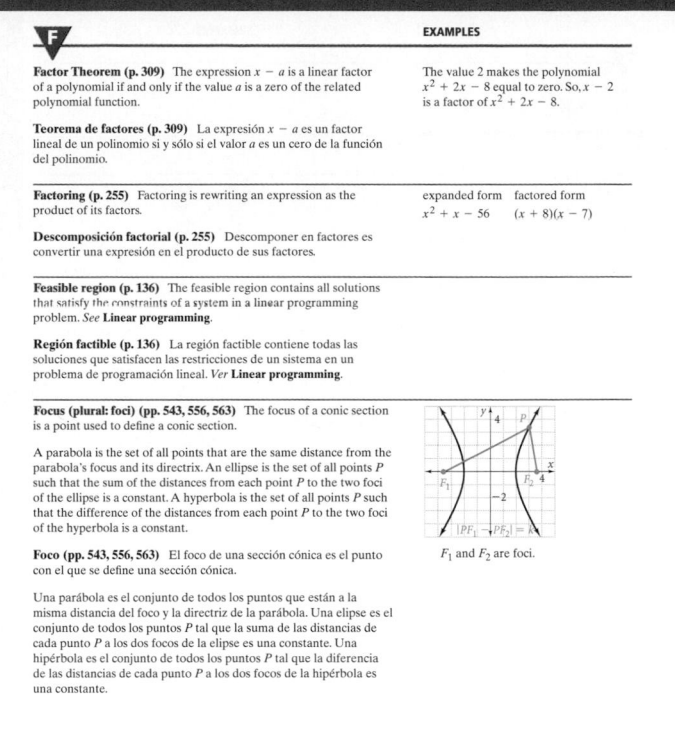

F_1 and F_2 are foci.

EXAMPLES

Frequency table (p. 636) A frequency table is a list of the outcomes in a sample space and the number of times each outcome occurs.

Tabla de frecuencias (p. 636) Una tabla de frecuencias es una lista de los resultados de un espacio muestral y el número de veces que cada resultado ocurre.

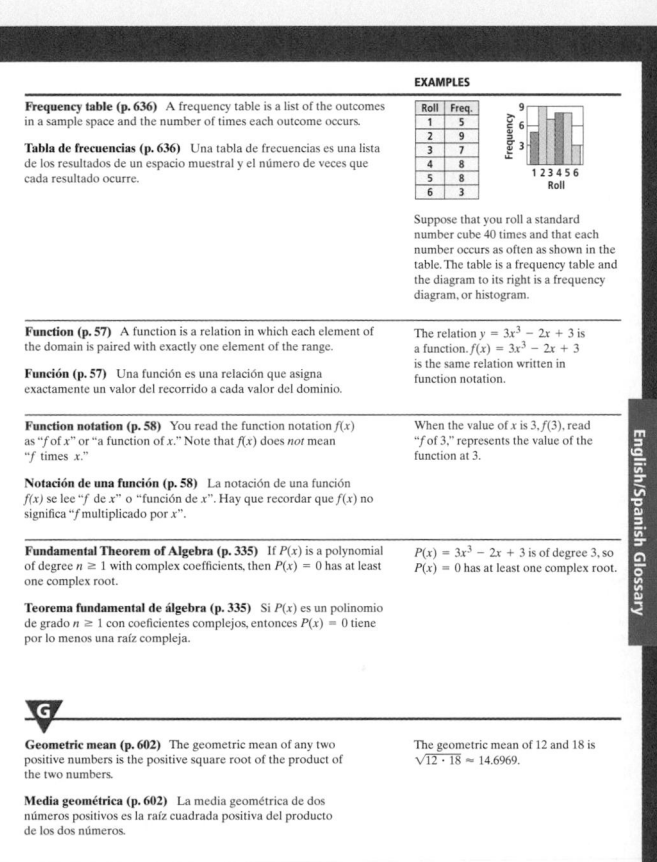

Suppose that you roll a standard number cube 40 times and that each number occurs as often as shown in the table. The table is a frequency table and the diagram to its right is a frequency diagram, or histogram.

Function (p. 57) A function is a relation in which each element of the domain is paired with exactly one element of the range.

Función (p. 57) Una función es una relación que asigna exactamente un valor del recorrido a cada valor del dominio.

The relation $y = 3x^3 - 2x + 3$ is a function. $f(x) = 3x^3 - 2x + 3$ is the same relation written in function notation.

Function notation (p. 58) You read the function notation $f(x)$ as "f of x" or "a function of x." Note that $f(x)$ does *not* mean "f times x."

Notación de una función (p. 58) La notación de una función $f(x)$ se lee "f de x" o "función de x". Hay que recordar que $f(x)$ no significa "f multiplicado por x".

When the value of x is 3, $f(3)$, read "f of 3," represents the value of the function at 3.

Fundamental Theorem of Algebra (p. 335) If $P(x)$ is a polynomial of degree $n \geq 1$ with complex coefficients, then $P(x) = 0$ has at least one complex root.

Teorema fundamental de álgebra (p. 335) Si $P(x)$ es un polinomio de grado $n \geq 1$ con coeficientes complejos, entonces $P(x) = 0$ tiene por lo menos una raíz compleja.

$P(x) = 3x^3 - 2x + 3$ is of degree 3, so $P(x) = 0$ has at least one complex root.

G

Geometric mean (p. 602) The geometric mean of any two positive numbers is the positive square root of the product of the two numbers.

Media geométrica (p. 602) La media geométrica de dos números positivos es la raíz cuadrada positiva del producto de los dos números.

The geometric mean of 12 and 18 is $\sqrt{12 \cdot 18} \approx 14.6969$.

EXAMPLES

Geometric sequence (p. 600) In a geometric sequence, the ratio of consecutive terms is constant. The constant is called the common ratio.

Progresión geométrica (p. 600) En una progresión geométrica, el cociente de términos consecutivos es un valor constante. La constante se llama razón común.

The geometric sequence 2.5, 5, 10, 20, 40, . . . has a common ratio of 2.

Geometric series (p. 614) A geometric series is the sum of the terms in a geometric sequence.

Serie geométrica (p. 614) Una serie geométrica es la suma de términos en una progresión geométrica.

One geometric series with five terms is $2.5 + 5 + 10 + 20 + 40$.

Greatest common factor (GCF) of an expression (p. 255) The greatest common factor (GCF) of an expression is the common factor of each term of the expression that has the greatest coefficient and the greatest exponent.

Máximo factor común de una expresión (p. 255) El máximo común factor de una expresión es el factor común de cada término de la expresión que tiene el mayor coeficiente y el mayor exponente.

The GCF of $4x^2 + 20x - 12$ is 4.

Growth factor (p. 422) In an exponential growth function of the form $y = ab^x$, with $b > 1$, b is the growth factor.

Factor incremental (p. 422) En una función exponencial incremental de la forma $y = ab^x$, con $b > 1$, b es el factor incremental.

In the exponential equation $y = 2^x$, 2 is the growth factor.

H

Hyperbola (p. 563) A hyperbola is a set of points P in a plane such that the difference between the distances from P to the foci F_1 and F_2 is a given constant k. $|PF_1 - PF_2| = k$

The standard form of an equation of a hyperbola centered at $(0, 0)$ is $\frac{x^2}{a^2} - \frac{y^2}{b^2} = 1$ if the transverse axis is horizontal and $\frac{y^2}{a^2} - \frac{x^2}{b^2} = 1$ if the transverse axis is vertical.

Hipérbola (p. 563) Una hipérbola es un conjunto de puntos P en un plano tal que la diferencia entre las distancias de P a los focos F_1 y F_2 es una constante k dada. $|PF_1 - PF_2| = k$

La forma normal de la ecuación de una hipérbola centrada en $(0, 0)$ es $\frac{x^2}{a^2} - \frac{y^2}{b^2} = 1$, si el eje transversal es horizontal, y $\frac{y^2}{a^2} - \frac{x^2}{b^2} = 1$, si el eje transversal es vertical.

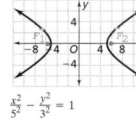

$$\frac{x^2}{5^2} - \frac{y^2}{3^2} = 1$$

T867

I

i **(p. 270)** The imaginary number *i* is defined as the number whose square is -1. So $i^2 = -1$ and $i = \sqrt{-1}$.

i **(p. 270)** El número imaginario *i* se define como el número cuyo cuadrado es -1. Por lo tanto, $i^2 = -1$ e $i = \sqrt{-1}$.

Image (p. 188) An image is a figure obtained by a transformation of a preimage.

Imagen (p. 188) Una imagen es la figura que resulta después de que la pre-imagen sufre una transformación.

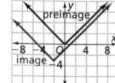

Imaginary number (p. 270) An imaginary number is any number of the form $a + bi$, where $b \neq 0$.

Número imaginario (p. 270) Un número imaginario es todo número de la forma $a + bi$, donde $b \neq 0$.

$2 + 3i$
$7i$
i

Imaginary Root Theorem (p. 332) If the imaginary number $a + bi$ is a root of a polynomial equation with real coefficients, then the conjugate $a - bi$ also is a root.

Teorema de la raíz imaginaria (p. 332) Si el número imaginario $a + bi$ es la raíz de la ecuación de un polinomio con coeficientes reales, entonces el conjugado $a - bi$ también es una raíz.

$2 + 3i$ is a root of $x^2 - 4x + 13 = 0$, so $2 - 3i$ is also a root.

Inconsistent system (p. 118) A system of equations that has no solution is an inconsistent system.

Sistema incompatible (p. 118) Un sistema incompatible es un sistema de ecuaciones para el cual no hay solución.

$\begin{cases} y = 2x + 3 \\ -2x + y = 1 \end{cases}$ is a system of parallel lines, so it has no solution. It is an inconsistent system.

Independent events (p. 519) When the outcome of one event does not affect the outcome of a second event, the two events are independent.

Sucesos independientes (p. 519) Cuando el resultado de un suceso no altera el resultado de otro, los dos sucesos son independientes.

The results of two rolls of a number cube are independent. Getting a 5 on the first roll does not change the probability of getting a 5 on the second roll.

Independent system (p. 118) A system of equations that has a unique solution is an independent system.

Sistema independiente (p. 118) Un sistema de ecuaciones que tenga una sola solución es un sistema independiente.

$\begin{cases} x + 2y = -7 \\ 2x - 3y = 0 \end{cases}$ has the unique solution $(-3, -2)$. It is an independent system.

Independent variable (p. 62) In a linear equation such as $y = 3x + 2$, x is called the independent variable.

Variable independiente (p. 62) En una ecuación lineal de la forma $y = 3x + 2$, x se llama variable independiente.

$y = 2x + 1$
x is the independent variable.

Index (p. 364) With a radical sign, the index indicates the degree of the root.

Índice (p. 364) Con un signo de radical, el índice indica el grado de la raíz.

index 2 index 3 index 4
$\sqrt{16}$ $\sqrt[3]{16}$ $\sqrt[4]{16}$

Inscribed rectangles (p. 623) When approximating the area under a curve, inscribed rectangles are completely under the curve. Their area is less than the area under the curve.

Rectángulos inscritos (p. 623) Cuando se aproxima el área situada dentro de una curva, los rectángulos inscritos quedan completamente contenidos en la curva. Su área es menor que el área dentro de la curva.

Initial side (of an angle) (p. 704) When an angle is in standard position, the side along the x-axis is the initial side of the angle, and the side not along the x-axis is the terminal side of the angle.

Lado inicial (de un ángulo) (p. 704) Cuando un ángulo está en posición normal, el lado que se encuentra sobre el eje x es el lado inicial del ángulo, y el lado terminal del ángulo es el que no está sobre el eje x.

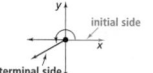

initial side
terminal side

Intercepted arc (p. 712) An intercepted arc is the portion of a circle whose endpoints are on the sides of a central angle of the circle and whose remaining points lie in the interior of the angle.

Arco interceptado (p. 712) Un arco interceptado es la porción de un círculo cuyos extremos quedan sobre los lados de un ángulo central del círculo y cuyos puntos restantes quedan en el interior del ángulo.

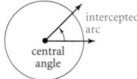

intercepted arc
central angle

Interquartile range (p. 657) The interquartile range of a set of data is the difference between the third and first quartiles.

Intervalo intercuartil (p. 657) El rango intercuartil de un conjunto de datos es la diferencia entre el tercero y el primer cuartiles.

The first and third quartiles of the data set {2, 3, 4, 5, 5, 6, 7, 7} are 3.5 and 6.5. The interquartile range is $6.5 - 3.5 = 3$.

Inverse functions (p. 403) The inverse of function f is denoted by f^{-1}. If f^{-1} is a function then f and f^{-1} are called inverse functions.

Funciones inversas (p. 403) La inversa de la función f se denota con f^{-1}. Si f^{-1} es una función, entonces f y f^{-1} son funciones inversas.

If $f(x) = x + 3$, then $f^{-1}(x) = x - 3$.

Inverse relation (p. 401) If a relation maps element a of its domain to element b of its range, the inverse relation "undoes" the relation and maps b back to a. If (a, b) is an ordered pair of a relation, then (b, a) is an ordered pair of its inverse.

Relación inversa (p. 401) Si una relación muestra el elemento a de su dominio hacia el elemento b de su recorrido, la relación inversa "deshace" la relación y muestra b hacia a. Si (a, b) es un par ordenado de una relación, entonces (b, a) es un par ordenado de su inversa.

Inverse variation (p. 478) An equation of the form $y = \frac{k}{x}$ or $xy = k$, where $k \neq 0$, is an inverse variation with constant of variation k.

Variación inversa (p. 478) Una ecuación de la forma $y = \frac{k}{x}$ ó $xy = k$, donde $k \neq 0$, es una variación inversa con una constante de variación k.

$xy = 5$, or $y = \frac{5}{x}$

Irrational Root Theorem (p. 331) Let a and b be rational numbers and let $\sqrt{b}$ be an irrational number. If $a + \sqrt{b}$ is a root of a polynomial equation with rational coefficients, then the conjugate $a - \sqrt{b}$ also is a root.

Teorema de raíz irracional (p. 331) Sean a y b números racionales y sea $\sqrt{b}$ un número irracional. Si $a + \sqrt{b}$ es una raíz de una ecuación de un polinomio con coeficientes racionales, entonces el conjugado $a - \sqrt{b}$ también es una raíz.

$2 + \sqrt{3}$ is a root of $x^2 - 4x + 1 = 0$, so $2 - \sqrt{3}$ is also a root.

L

Law of Cosines (p. 794) In $\triangle ABC$, let $a, b,$ and c represent the lengths of the sides opposite $\angle A$, $\angle B$, and $\angle C$, respectively. Then
$a^2 = b^2 + c^2 - 2bc \cos A,$
$b^2 = a^2 + c^2 - 2ac \cos B,$ and
$c^2 = a^2 + b^2 - 2ab \cos C$

Ley de cosenos (p. 794) En $\triangle ABC$, sean a, b y c las longitudes de los lados opuestos a $\angle A$, $\angle B$ y $\angle C$, respectivamente. Entonces
$a^2 = b^2 + c^2 - 2bc \cos A,$
$b^2 = a^2 + c^2 - 2ac \cos B$ y
$c^2 = a^2 + b^2 - 2ab \cos C$

$LM^2 = 11.41^2 + 8.72^2 - 2(11.41)(8.72) \cos 18°$
$LM^2 = 16.9754$
$LM \approx 4.12$

Law of Sines (p. 788) In $\triangle ABC$, let $a, b,$ and c represent the lengths of the sides opposite $\angle A$, $\angle B$, and $\angle C$, respectively. Then
$\frac{\sin A}{a} = \frac{\sin B}{b} = \frac{\sin C}{c}$

Ley de senos (p. 788) En $\triangle ABC$, sean a, b y c las longitudes de los lados opuestos a $\angle A$, $\angle B$ y $\angle C$, respectivamente. Entonces
$\frac{\text{sen } A}{a} = \frac{\text{sen } B}{b} = \frac{\text{sen } C}{c}$

$m\angle L = 180 - (120 + 18) = 42°$
$\frac{KL}{\sin 120} = \frac{8.72}{\sin 42°}$
$KL = \frac{8.72 \sin 120}{\sin 42}$
$KL \approx 11.26$

Like radicals (p. 374) Like radicals are radical expressions that have the same index and the same radicand.

Radicales semejantes (p. 374) Los radicales semejantes son expresiones radicales que tienen el mismo índice y el mismo radicando.

$4\sqrt[3]{7}$ and $\sqrt[3]{7}$ are like radicals.

Limits (p. 609) Limits in summation notation are the least and greatest integer values of n.

Límites (p. 580) Los límites en notación de sumatoria son el menor y el mayor valor de n en números enteros.

limits $\sum_{n=1}^{3} 3n + 5$

Linear equation (p. 62) A linear equation is an equation that represents a linear function.

Ecuación lineal (p. 62) Una ecuación lineal es una ecuación que representa una función lineal.

$y = 2x + 1$

Linear function (p. 62) A function whose graph is a line is a linear function. You can represent a linear function with a linear equation.

Función lineal (p. 62) Una función cuya gráfica es una recta es una función lineal. La función lineal se representa con una ecuación lineal.

$y = 2x + 1$

Linear inequality (p. 99) A linear inequality is an inequality in two variables whose graph is a region of the coordinate plane that is bounded by a line. Each point in the region is a solution of the inequality. A sign of $\leq$ or $\geq$ indicates a solid boundary line. A sign of $<$ or $>$ indicates a dashed boundary line.

Desigualdad lineal (p. 99) Una desigualdad lineal es una desigualdad de dos variables cuya gráfica es una región del plano de coordenadas delimitado por una línea. Cada punto de la región es una solución de la desigualdad. El signo $\leq$ o $\geq$ denota que hay una línea de delimitación continua. El signo $<$ o $>$ denota que la línea de delimitación es punteada.

$y > x + 1$

Linear programming (p. 135) Linear programming is a technique that identifies the minimum or maximum value of some quantity. This quantity is modeled with an objective function. Limits on the variables in the objective function are constraints, written as linear inequalities.

Programación lineal (p. 135) La programación lineal es un método que permite identificar las condiciones que elevan al máximo o reducen al mínimo una cantidad. Esta cantidad se modela como una función objetiva. Los límites de las variables en la función objetiva son restricciones, expresadas como desigualdades lineales.

Restrictions: $x \geq 0$, $y \geq 0$, $x + y \leq 7$, and $y \leq -2x + 8$

Objective function: $B = 2x + 4y$

Graph the restrictions to find the coordinates of each vertex.

Evaluate $B = 2x + 4y$ at each vertex. The minimum value of B occurs when $x = 0$ and $y = 0$. The maximum value of B occurs when $x = 0$ and $y = 7$.

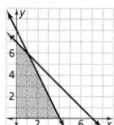

Linear system (p. 116) If the graph of each equation in a system of two variables is a line, then the system is a linear system.

Sistema lineal (p. 116) Si la gráfica de cada ecuación de un sistema de dos variables es una recta, el sistema es un sistema lineal.

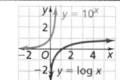

$4x + 5y = 7$ $2x - 3y = -13$

Logarithm (p. 439) A logarithm of a positive number y to the base b is defined as follows:
If $y = b^x$, then $\log_b y = x$.

Logaritmo (p. 439) El logaritmo de un número positivo y de base b se define así:
Si $y = b^x$, entonces $\log_b y = x$.

$\log_2 8 = 3$
$\log_{10} 100 = 2$
$\log_5 5^7 = 7$

Logarithmic equation (p. 455) An equation that includes a logarithmic expression is called a logarithmic equation.

Ecuación logarítmica (p. 455) Una ecuación que incluye una expresión logarítmica se llama ecuación logarítmica.

$\log_3 x = 4$

Logarithmic function (p. 440) A logarithmic function is the inverse of an exponential function.

Función logarítmica (p. 440) Una función logarítmica es la inversa de una función exponencial.

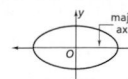

Major axis of an ellipse (p. 556) The major axis of an ellipse is the segment that contains the foci and has its endpoints on the ellipse. These endpoints are vertices of the ellipse.

Eje mayor de una elipse (p. 556) El eje mayor de una elipse es el segmento que contiene los focos y tiene los puntos extremos sobre la elipse. Los extremos son los vértices de la elipse.

Mapping diagram (p. 56) A mapping diagram describes a relation by linking elements of the domain with elements of the range.

Mapa (p. 56) Un mapa describe una relación al unir los elementos del dominio con los elementos del recorrido.

Margin of error (p. 665) A sample proportion should be reported with an estimate of error, called the margin of error. When a random sample of size n is taken from a large population, the sample proportion has a margin of error of about $\pm \frac{1}{\sqrt{n}}$.

Margen de error (p. 665) Una proporción muestral debe incluir una estimación del error, que se llama margen de error. Cuando se hace una muestra aleatoria de tamaño n de una población grande, la proporción muestral tiene un margen de error de aproximadamente $\pm \frac{1}{\sqrt{n}}$.

A set of 500 items is taken from a population for sampling. The margin of error for a sample proportion is about $\pm \frac{1}{\sqrt{500}} = \pm 0.045$.

Matrix (p. 164) A matrix is a rectangular array of numbers written within brackets. A matrix with m horizontal rows and n vertical columns is an $m \times n$ matrix.

Matriz (p. 164) Una matriz es un conjunto de números encerrados en corchetes y dispuestos en forma de rectángulo. Una matriz que contenga m líneas horizontales y n líneas verticales es una matriz $m \times n$.

$A = \begin{bmatrix} 1 & -2 & 0 & 10 \\ 9 & 7 & -3 & 8 \\ 2 & -10 & 1 & -6 \end{bmatrix}$

The number 2 is the element in the third row and first column. A is a 3×4 matrix.

Matrix addition (p. 170) You add two matrices with the same dimensions by adding their corresponding elements.

Suma matricial (p. 170) Para sumar dos matrices que tengan las mismas dimensiones se suman sus elementos correspondientes.

$\begin{bmatrix} 2 & -3 \\ 0 & 4 \end{bmatrix} + \begin{bmatrix} -1 & 0 \\ 5 & -6 \end{bmatrix}$
$= \begin{bmatrix} 2 + (-1) & -3 + 1 \\ 0 + 5 & 4 + (-6) \end{bmatrix}$
$= \begin{bmatrix} 1 & -3 \\ 5 & -2 \end{bmatrix}$

Matrix element (p. 165) Every item listed in a matrix is an element of the matrix. An element is identified by its position in the matrix.

Elemento matricial (p. 165) Cada cifra de una matriz es un elemento de la matriz. El elemento se identifica según la posición que ocupa en la matriz.

$A = \begin{bmatrix} 1 & -2 & 0 & 10 \\ 9 & 7 & -3 & 8 \\ 2 & -10 & 1 & -6 \end{bmatrix}$

Element a_{21} is 9, the element in the second row and first column.

Matrix equation (p. 172) A matrix equation is an equation in which the variable is a matrix.

Ecuación matricial (p. 172) Una ecuación matricial es una ecuación en que la variable es una matriz.

Solve $X + \begin{bmatrix} 3 & -2 \\ 5 & 1 \end{bmatrix} = \begin{bmatrix} 4 & 0 \\ 0 & 3 \end{bmatrix}$.

$X + \begin{bmatrix} 3 & -2 \\ 5 & 1 \end{bmatrix} = \begin{bmatrix} 4 & 0 \\ 0 & 3 \end{bmatrix}$

$X = \begin{bmatrix} 4 & 0 \\ 0 & 3 \end{bmatrix} - \begin{bmatrix} 3 & -2 \\ 5 & 1 \end{bmatrix} = \begin{bmatrix} 1 & 2 \\ -5 & 2 \end{bmatrix}$

Matrix multiplication (p. 180) To find element c_{ij} of the product matrix AB, multiply each element in the ith row of A by the corresponding element in the jth column of B, and then add. If A is an $m \times n$ matrix and B is an $n \times p$ matrix, then the product matrix AB is an $m \times p$ matrix.

Multiplicación matricial (p. 180) Para encontrar el elemento c_{ij} del producto de la matriz AB, se multiplica cada elemento de la línea horizontal i de A por el elemento respectivo de la fila vertical j de B y luego se suma. Si A es una matriz $m \times n$ y B es una matriz $n \times p$, entonces el producto de la matriz AB es una matriz $m \times p$.

$\begin{bmatrix} 1 & 1 \\ 2 & 3 \\ 0 & 2 \end{bmatrix} \begin{bmatrix} 4 & 2 \\ 5 & 6 \end{bmatrix}$
$= \begin{bmatrix} (1)(4) + (1)(5) & (1)(2) + (1)(6) \\ (2)(4) + (3)(5) & (2)(2) + (3)(6) \\ (0)(4) + (2)(5) & (0)(2) + (2)(6) \end{bmatrix}$
$= \begin{bmatrix} 9 & 8 \\ 23 & 22 \\ 10 & 12 \end{bmatrix}$

Mean (p. 648) The sum of the data values divided by the number of data values is the mean.

Media (p. 648) La suma de los valores de datos dividida por el número de valores de datos sumados es la media.

$[1, 2, 3, 3, 6, 6]$
mean $= \frac{1 + 2 + 3 + 3 + 6 + 6}{6}$
$= \frac{21}{6} = 3.5$

Measures of central tendency (p. 648) The mean, the median, and the mode are single, central values that help describe a set of data. They are called measures of central tendency.

Medidas de tendencia central (p. 648) La media, la mediana y la moda son los valores centrales únicos que permiten describir un conjunto de datos. Se llaman medidas de tendencia central.

$[1, 2, 3, 3, 4, 5, 6, 6]$
mean $= 3.75$
median $= 3.5$
mode $= 3$ and 6

Measures of variation (p. 657) Measures of variation, such as the range, the interquartile range, and the standard deviation, describe how the data in a data set are spread out.

Medidas de dispersión (p. 657) Las medidas de dispersión, tal como el rango, el intervalo intercuartil y la desviación normal, describen cómo se dispersan los datos en un conjunto de datos.

Median (p. 648) The median is the middle value in a data set. If the data set contains an even number of values, the median is the mean of the two middle values.

Mediana (p. 648) La mediana es el valor situado en el medio en un conjunto de datos. Si el conjunto de datos contiene un número par de valores, la mediana es la media de los dos valores del medio.

$[1, 2, 3, 3, 4, 5, 6, 6]$
median $= \frac{3 + 4}{2} = \frac{7}{2} = 3.5$

Minor axis of an ellipse (p. 556) The minor axis of an ellipse is the segment perpendicular to the major axis at its midpoint. The endpoints of the minor axis are on the ellipse and are the co-vertices of the ellipse.

Eje menor de una elipse (p. 556) El eje menor de una elipse es el segmento perpendicular al eje mayor en su punto medio. Los extremos del eje menor están sobre la elipse y son los covértices de la elipse.

Mode (p. 648) The mode is the most frequently occurring value (or values) in a set of data.

Moda (p. 648) La moda es el valor o valores que ocurren con mayor frecuencia en un conjunto de datos.

$[1, 2, 3, 3, 4, 5, 6, 6]$
The modes are 3 and 6.

Multiple zero (p. 310) If a linear factor in a polynomial is repeated, the zero related to that factor is a multiple zero.

Ceros múltiples (p. 310) Si un factor lineal se repite en un polinomio, el cero que está relacionado con ese factor es un cero múltiple.

The zeros of the function $P(x) = 2x(x - 3)^2(x + 1)$ are 0, 3, and -1. Since $(x - 3)$ occurs twice as a factor, the zero 3 is a multiple zero.

Multiplicative identity matrix (p. 195) For an $n \times n$ square matrix, the multiplicative identity matrix is an $n \times n$ square matrix I, or $I_{n \times n}$, with 1's along the main diagonal and 0's elsewhere.

Matriz de identidad multiplicativa (p. 195) Para una matriz cuadrada $n \times n$, la matriz de identidad multiplicativa es la matriz cuadrada I de $n \times n$, ó $I_{n \times n}$, con unos por la diagonal principal y ceros en los demás lugares.

$I_{2 \times 2} = \begin{bmatrix} 1 & 0 \\ 0 & 1 \end{bmatrix}$

$I_{3 \times 3} = \begin{bmatrix} 1 & 0 & 0 \\ 0 & 1 & 0 \\ 0 & 0 & 1 \end{bmatrix}$

Multiplicative inverse (p. 7) The multiplicative inverse, or reciprocal, of any nonzero number a is $\frac{1}{a}$. The product of reciprocals is 1.

Inverso multiplicativo (p. 7) El inverso multiplicativo, o recíproco, de todo número racional distinto de cero a es $\frac{1}{a}$. El producto de números recíprocos es 1.

$5 \times \frac{1}{5} = 1$

Multiplicative inverse of a matrix (p. 195) If A and X are $n \times n$ matrices, and $AX = XA = I$, then X is the multiplicative inverse of A, written A^{-1}.

Inverso multiplicativo de una matriz (p. 195) Si A y X son matrices $n \times n$, y $AX = XA = I$, entonces X es el inverso multiplicativo de A, expresado como A^{-1}.

$A = \begin{bmatrix} 2 & 1 \\ 4 & 0 \end{bmatrix}$

$X = \begin{bmatrix} 0 & \frac{1}{4} \\ 1 & -\frac{1}{2} \end{bmatrix}$

$AX = \begin{bmatrix} 1 & 0 \\ 0 & 1 \end{bmatrix} = I$, so $X = A^{-1}$

Multiplicity (p. 310) The multiplicity of a zero of a polynomial function is the number of times the related linear factor is repeated in the factored form of the polynomial.

Multiplicidad (p. 310) La multiplicidad de un cero de una función polinomial es el número de veces que el factor lineal relacionado se repite en la forma factorizada del polinomio.

The zeros of the function
$P(x) = 2x(x-3)^2(x+1)$ are $0, 3$, and -1. Since $(x-3)$ occurs twice as a factor, the zero 3 has multiplicity 2.

Mutually exclusive events (p. 521) When two events cannot happen at the same time, the events are mutually exclusive. If A and B are mutually exclusive events, then $P(A \text{ or } B) = P(A) + P(B)$.

Sucesos mutuamente excluyentes (p. 521) Cuando dos sucesos no pueden ocurrir al mismo tiempo, son mutuamente excluyentes. Si A y B son sucesos mutuamente excluyentes, entonces $P(A \text{ o } B) = P(A) + P(B)$.

Rolling an even number E and rolling a multiple of five M on a standard number cube are mutually exclusive events.
$$P(E \text{ or } M) = P(E) + P(M)$$
$$= \frac{3}{6} + \frac{1}{6}$$
$$= \frac{4}{6}, \text{ or } \frac{2}{3}$$

N

n factorial (p. 339) For any positive integer n, n factorial (or $n!$) is $n(n-1) \times \ldots \times 3 \times 2 \times 1.0! = 1$.

n factorial (p. 339) Para cualquier número entero positivo n, n factorial (o $n!$) es $n(n-1) \times \ldots \times 3 \times 2 \times 1.0! = 1$.

$4! = 4 \times 3 \times 2 \times 1 = 24$

nth root (p. 363) For any real numbers a and b, and any positive integer n, if $a^n = b$, then a is an nth root of b.

raíz n-ésima (p. 363) Para todos los números reales a y b, y todo número entero positivo n, si $a^n = b$, entonces a es la n-ésima raíz de b.

$\sqrt[5]{32} = 2$ because $2^5 = 32$.
$\sqrt[4]{81} = 3$ because $3^4 = 81$.

Natural logarithmic function (p. 462) The function $y = \log_e x$ is the natural logarithmic function. It is the inverse of $y = e^x$. It is commonly written as $y = \ln x$.

Función logarítmica natural (p. 462) La función $y = \log_e x$ es la función logarítmica natural. Es la inversa de $y = e^x$. Generalmente se expresa como $\ln y = x$.

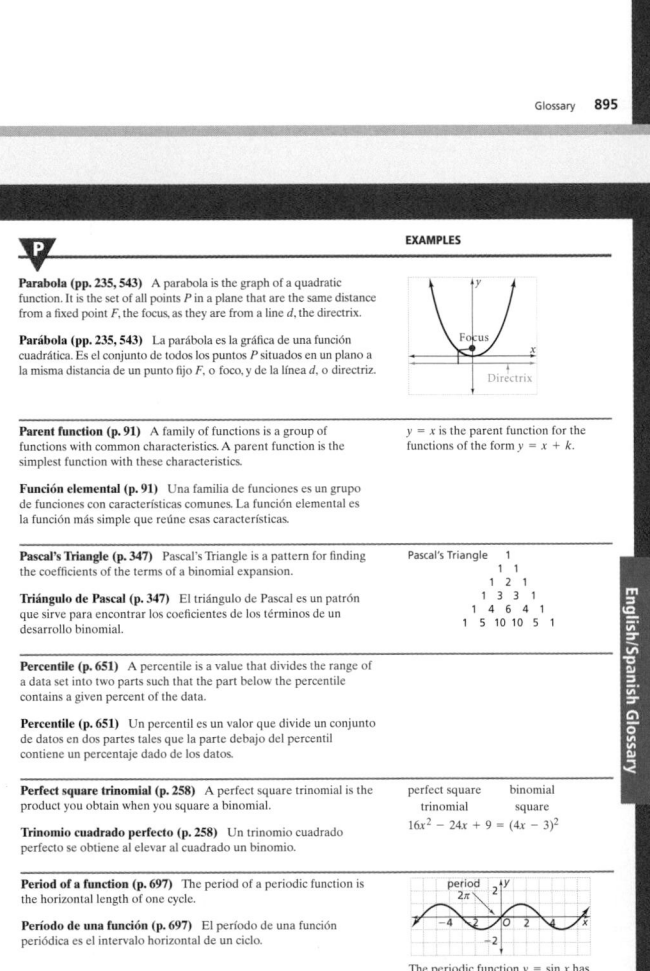

$\ln e^3 = 3$
$\ln 10 \approx 2.3026$
$\ln 36 \approx 3.5835$

Normal distribution (p. 678) A normal distribution shows data that vary randomly from the mean in the pattern of a bell-shaped curve.

Distribución normal (p. 678) En una distribución normal los datos que varían de la media se muestran de manera aproximada en una curva en forma de campana.

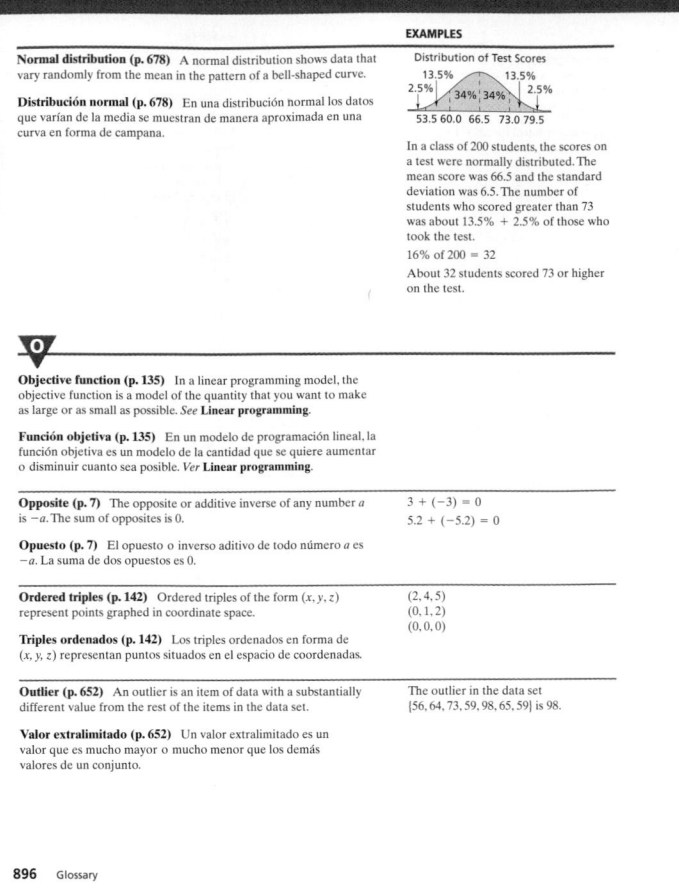

Distribution of Test Scores

In a class of 200 students, the scores on a test were normally distributed. The mean score was 66.5 and the standard deviation was 6.5. The number of students who scored greater than 73 was about $13.5\% + 2.5\%$ of those who took the test.

16% of $200 = 32$

About 32 students scored 73 or higher on the test.

O

Objective function (p. 135) In a linear programming model, the objective function is a model of the quantity that you want to make as large or as small as possible. See **Linear programming**.

Función objetiva (p. 135) En un modelo de programación lineal, la función objetiva es un modelo de la cantidad que se quiere aumentar o disminuir cuanto sea posible. Ver **Linear programming**.

Opposite (p. 7) The opposite or additive inverse of any number a is $-a$. The sum of opposites is 0.

Opuesto (p. 7) El opuesto o inverso aditivo de todo número a es $-a$. La suma de dos opuestos es 0.

$3 + (-3) = 0$
$5.2 + (-5.2) = 0$

Ordered triples (p. 142) Ordered triples of the form (x, y, z) represent points graphed in coordinate space.

Triples ordenados (p. 142) Los triples ordenados en forma de (x, y, z) representan puntos situados en el espacio de coordenadas.

$(2, 4, 5)$
$(0, 1, 2)$
$(0, 0, 0)$

Outlier (p. 652) An outlier is an item of data with a substantially different value from the rest of the items in the data set.

Valor extralimitado (p. 652) Un valor extralimitado es un valor que es mucho mayor o mucho menor que los demás valores de un conjunto.

The outlier in the data set
$\{56, 64, 73, 59, 98, 65, 59\}$ is 98.

P

Parabola (pp. 235, 543) A parabola is the graph of a quadratic function. It is the set of all points P in a plane that are the same distance from a fixed point F, the focus, as they are from a line d, the directrix.

Parábola (pp. 235, 543) La parábola es la gráfica de una función cuadrática. Es el conjunto de todos los puntos P situados en un plano a la misma distancia de un punto fijo F, o foco, y de la línea d, o directriz.

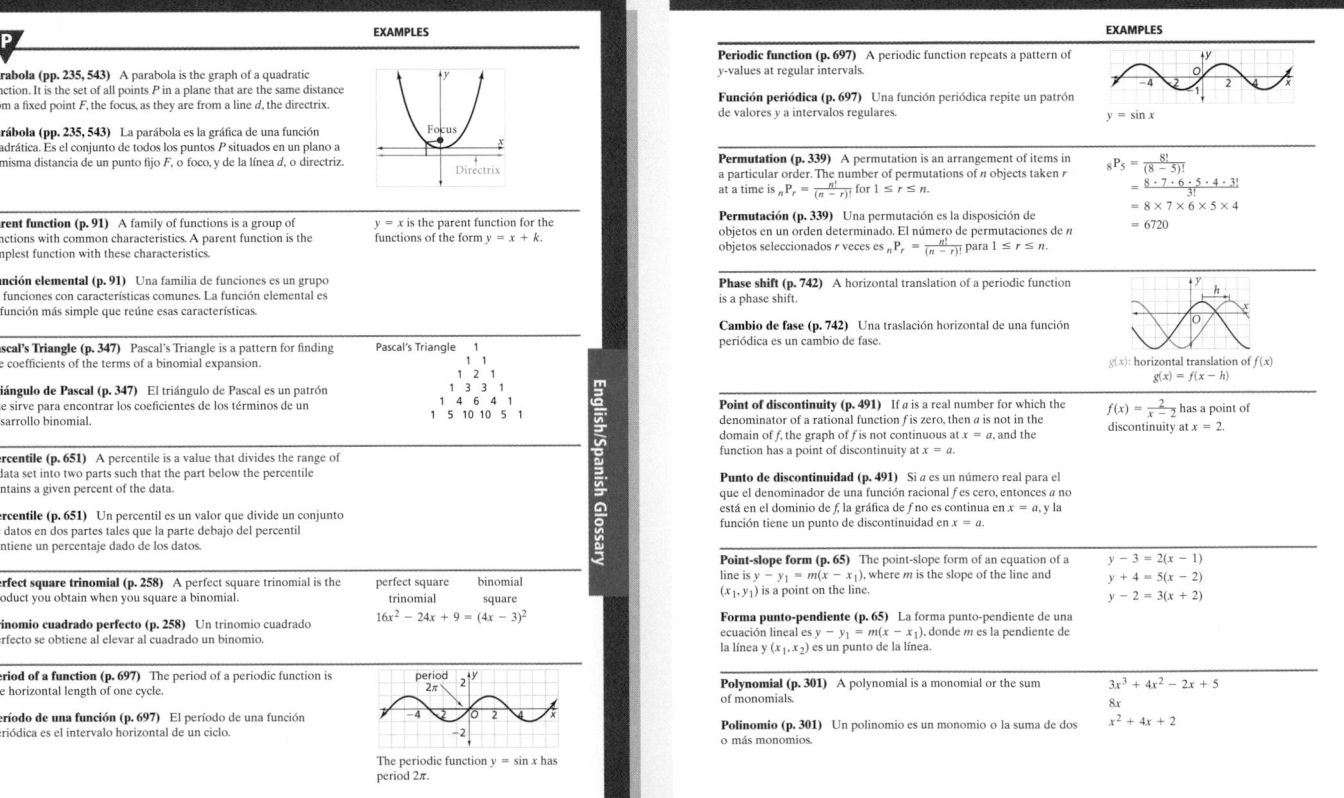

Parent function (p. 91) A family of functions is a group of functions with common characteristics. A parent function is the simplest function with these characteristics.

Función elemental (p. 91) Una familia de funciones es un grupo de funciones con características comunes. La función elemental es la función más simple que reúne esas características.

$y = x$ is the parent function for the functions of the form $y = x + k$.

Pascal's Triangle (p. 347) Pascal's Triangle is a pattern for finding the coefficients of the terms of a binomial expansion.

Triángulo de Pascal (p. 347) El triángulo de Pascal es un patrón que sirve para encontrar los coeficientes de los términos de un desarrollo binomial.

Pascal's Triangle
```
        1
       1 1
      1 2 1
     1 3 3 1
    1 4 6 4 1
   1 5 10 10 5 1
```

Percentile (p. 651) A percentile is a value that divides the range of a data set into two parts such that the part below the percentile contains a given percent of the data.

Percentile (p. 651) Un percentil es un valor que divide un conjunto de datos en dos partes tales que la parte debajo del percentil contiene un percentaje dado de los datos.

Perfect square trinomial (p. 258) A perfect square trinomial is the product you obtain when you square a binomial.

Trinomio cuadrado perfecto (p. 258) Un trinomio cuadrado perfecto se obtiene al elevar al cuadrado un binomio.

perfect square trinomial = binomial square
$16x^2 - 24x + 9 = (4x - 3)^2$

Period of a function (p. 697) The period of a periodic function is the horizontal length of one cycle.

Período de una función (p. 697) El período de una función periódica es el intervalo horizontal de un ciclo.

The periodic function $y = \sin x$ has period 2π.

Periodic function (p. 697) A periodic function repeats a pattern of y-values at regular intervals.

Función periódica (p. 697) Una función periódica repite un patrón de valores y a intervalos regulares.

$y = \sin x$

Permutation (p. 339) A permutation is an arrangement of items in a particular order. The number of permutations of n objects taken r at a time is $_nP_r = \frac{n!}{(n-r)!}$ for $1 \le r \le n$.

Permutación (p. 339) Una permutación es la disposición de objetos en un orden determinado. El número de permutaciones de n objetos seleccionados r veces es $_nP_r = \frac{n!}{(n-r)!}$ para $1 \le r \le n$.

$$_8P_5 = \frac{8!}{(8-5)!}$$
$$= \frac{8 \cdot 7 \cdot 6 \cdot 5 \cdot 4 \cdot 3!}{3!}$$
$$= 8 \times 7 \times 6 \times 5 \times 4$$
$$= 6720$$

Phase shift (p. 742) A horizontal translation of a periodic function is a phase shift.

Cambio de fase (p. 742) Una traslación horizontal de una función periódica es un cambio de fase.

$g(x)$: horizontal translation of $f(x)$
$g(x) = f(x - h)$

Point of discontinuity (p. 491) If a is a real number for which the denominator of a rational function f is zero, then a is not in the domain of f, the graph of f is not continuous at $x = a$, and the function has a point of discontinuity at $x = a$.

Punto de discontinuidad (p. 491) Si a es un número real para el que el denominador de una función racional f es cero, entonces a no está en el dominio de f, la gráfica de f no es continua en $x = a$, y la función tiene un punto de discontinuidad en $x = a$.

$f(x) = \frac{2}{x-2}$ has a point of discontinuity at $x = 2$.

Point-slope form (p. 65) The point-slope form of an equation of a line is $y - y_1 = m(x - x_1)$, where m is the slope of the line and (x_1, y_1) is a point on the line.

Forma punto-pendiente (p. 65) La forma punto-pendiente de una ecuación lineal es $y - y_1 = m(x - x_1)$, donde m es la pendiente de la línea y (x_1, x_2) es un punto de la línea.

$y - 3 = 2(x - 1)$
$y + 4 = 5(x - 2)$
$y - 2 = 3(x + 2)$

Polynomial (p. 301) A polynomial is a monomial or the sum of monomials.

Polinomio (p. 301) Un polinomio es un monomio o la suma de dos o más monomios.

$3x^3 + 4x^2 - 2x + 5$
$8x$
$x^2 + 4x + 2$

English/Spanish Glossary

T870

Polynomial function (p. 301) $P(x) = a_n x^n + a_{n-1} x^{n-1} + \ldots + a_1 x + a_0$ is a polynomial function when n is a nonnegative integer and the coefficients $a_n, \ldots a_0$ are real numbers.

Función polinomial (p. 301) $P(x) = a_n x^n + a_{n-1} x^{n-1} + \ldots + a_1 x + a_0$ es una función polinomial, donde n es un entero cuyo valor no es cero y los coeficientes $a_n, \ldots a_0$ son números reales.

Preimage (p. 188) The preimage is the original figure before a transformation.

Pre-imagen (p. 188) La pre-imagen es la figura original antes de sufrir una transformación.

Principal root (p. 364) When a number has two real roots, the positive root is called the principal root. A radical sign indicates the principal root.

Raíz principal (p. 364) Cuando un número tiene dos raíces reales, la raíz positiva es la raíz principal. El signo del radical indica la raíz principal.

The number 25 has two square roots, 5 and −5. The principal square root, 5, is indicated by the symbols $\sqrt{25}$ or $25^{\frac{1}{2}}$.

Probability distribution (p. 637) A probability distribution is a function that tells the probability of each outcome in a sample space.

Distribución de probabilidades (p. 637) Una distribución de probabilidades es una función que señala la probabilidad de que cada resultado ocurra en un espacio muestral.

Roll	Fr.	Prob.
1	5	0.125
2	9	0.225
3	7	0.175
4	8	0.2
5	8	0.2
6	3	0.075

The table and graph both show the experimental probability distribution for the outcomes of 40 rolls of a standard number cube.

Q

Quadratic Formula (p. 285) A quadratic equation written in standard form $ax^2 + bx + c = 0$, can be solved using the Quadratic Formula.

$x = \frac{-b \pm \sqrt{b^2 - 4ac}}{2a}$

Fórmula cuadrática (p. 285) Toda ecuación cuadrática $ax^2 + bx + c = 0$ escrita en forma normal se puede resolver por medio de la fórmula cuadrática.

$x = \frac{-b \pm \sqrt{b^2 - 4ac}}{2a}$

If $-x^2 + 3x + 2 = 0$, then

$x = \frac{-3 \pm \sqrt{(3)^2 - 4(-1)(2)}}{2(-1)}$

$= \frac{-3 \pm \sqrt{17}}{-2}$

Quadratic function (p. 234) A quadratic function is a function that can be written in the standard form $f(x) = ax^2 + bx + c$, where $a \neq 0$. Its graph is a parabola.

Función cuadrática (p. 234) Una función cuadrática se puede expresar con la forma normal $f(x) = ax^2 + bx + c$, donde $a \neq 0$. Su gráfica es una parábola.

$y = x^2 + 2x - 2$

Quartiles (p. 650) Quartiles are values that separate a finite data set into four equal parts. The second quartile (Q_2) is the median of the data. The first and third quartiles (Q_1 and Q_3) are the medians of the lower half and upper half of the data, respectively.

Cuartiles (p. 650) Los cuartiles son valores que separan un conjunto finito de datos en cuatro partes iguales. El segundo cuartil (Q_2) es la mediana de los datos. Los cuartiles primero y tercero (Q_1 y Q_3) son las medianas de la mitad superior e inferior de los datos, respectivamente.

$\{2, 3, 4, 5, 5, 6, 7, 7\}$
$Q_1 = 3.5$
$Q_2 \text{ (median)} = 5$
$Q_3 = 6.5$

R

Radian (p. 712) One radian is the measure of a central angle of a circle that intercepts an arc equal in length to a radius of the circle. You can use a proportion to convert an angle measure from one unit of measure to the other.

$\frac{\text{degree measure}}{360} = \frac{\text{radian measure}}{2\pi}$

Radián (p. 712) Un radián es la medida del ángulo central de un círculo que corta un arco de la misma longitud que el radio del círculo. Se puede usar una proporción para convertir la medida de un ángulo de una unidad de medida a la otra.

$\frac{\text{medida en grados}}{360} = \frac{\text{medida de radián}}{2\pi}$

$60° \to \frac{60}{360} = \frac{x}{2\pi}$
$x = \frac{60(2\pi)}{360}$
$= \frac{\pi}{3}$
Thus, $60° = \frac{\pi}{3}$ radians.

Radical equation (p. 385) A radical equation is an equation that has a variable in a radicand or has a variable with a rational exponent.

Ecuación radical (p. 385) La ecuación radical es una ecuación que contiene una variable dentro de un radicando o una variable con un exponente racional.

$(\sqrt{x})^3 + 1 = 65$
$x^{\frac{3}{2}} + 1 = 65$

Radical function (p. 409) A radical equation defines a radical function.

Función radical (p. 409) Una ecuación radical define una función radical.

$f(x) = \sqrt{x - 2}$

Radicand (p. 364) The number under a radical sign is the radicand.

Radicando (p. 364) La expresión que aparece debajo del signo radical es el radicando.

The radicand in $3\sqrt[4]{7}$ is 7.

Radius (p. 549) The radius r of a circle is the distance between the center of the circle and any point on the circumference.

Radio (p. 549) El radio r de un círculo es la distancia entre el centro del círculo y cualquier punto de la circunferencia.

Random sample (p. 663) In a random sample, each member of the population is as likely to be chosen for the sample as every other member.

Muestra aleatoria (p. 663) En una muestra aleatoria es igualmente probable que cada miembro de la población sea escogido para la muestra.

Let the set of all females between the ages of 19 and 34 be the population. A random selection of 900 females between those ages would be a sample of the population.

Range (p. 56) The range of a relation is the set of all outputs or y-coordinates of the ordered pairs.

Rango (p. 56) El rango de una relación es el conjunto de todos resultados posibles, o ordenadas y, de los pares ordenados.

In the relation $\{(0, 1), (0, 2), (0, 3), (0, 4), (1, 3), (1, 4), (2, 1)\}$, the range is $\{1, 2, 3, 4\}$. In the function $f(x) = |x - 3|$, the range is the set of real numbers greater than or equal to 0.

Range of a set of data (p. 657) The range of a set of data is the difference between the greatest and least values.

Rango de un conjunto de datos (p. 657) El rango de un conjunto de datos es la diferencia entre el valor máximo y el valor mínimo de los datos.

The range of the set $\{3.2, 4.1, 2.2, 3.4, 3.8, 4.0, 4.2, 2.8\}$ is $4.2 - 2.2 = 2$.

Rational exponent (p. 379) If the nth root of a is a real number and m is an integer, then $a^{\frac{1}{n}} = \sqrt[n]{a}$ and $a^{\frac{m}{n}} = \sqrt[n]{a^m} = (\sqrt[n]{a})^m$. If m is negative, $a \neq 0$.

Exponente racional (p. 379) Si la raíz n-ésima de a es un número real y m es un número entero, entonces $a^{\frac{1}{n}} = \sqrt[n]{a}$ y $a^{\frac{m}{n}} = \sqrt[n]{a^m} = (\sqrt[n]{a})^m$. Si m es negativo, $a \neq 0$.

$4^{\frac{1}{3}} = \sqrt[3]{4}$
$5^{\frac{3}{2}} = \sqrt{5^3} = (\sqrt{5})^3$

Rational function (p. 491) A rational function $f(x)$ can be written as $f(x) = \frac{P(x)}{Q(x)}$, where $P(x)$ and $Q(x)$ are polynomial functions and $Q(x) \neq 0$.

Función racional (p. 491) Una función racional $f(x)$ se puede expresar como $f(x) = \frac{P(x)}{Q(x)}$, donde $P(x)$ y $Q(x)$ son funciones de polinomios y $Q(x) \neq 0$.

The function $y = \frac{x - 2}{x^2 - 9}$ is a rational function with three branches separated by asymptotes $x = -3$ and $x = 3$.

Rational Root Theorem (p. 329) If $\frac{p}{q}$ is in simplest form and is a rational root of the polynomial equation $a_n x^n + a_{n-1} x^{n-1} + \ldots + a_1 x + a_0 = 0$ with integer coefficients, then p must be a factor of a_0 and q must be a factor of a_n.

Teorema de la raíz racional (p. 329) Si $\frac{p}{q}$ está en su forma más simple y es la raíz racional de la ecuación del polinomio $a_n x^n + a_{n-1} x^{n-1} + \ldots + a_1 x + a_0 = 0$ con números enteros como coeficientes, entonces p debe ser factor de a_0 y q debe ser factor de a_n.

The polynomial equation $10x^3 + 6x^2 - 11x - 2 = 0$ has leading coefficient 10 (with factors ± 1, ± 2, ± 5, ± 10) and constant term −2 (with factors ± 1 and ± 2). Its only possible rational roots are ± 1, ± 2, $\pm \frac{1}{2}$, $\pm \frac{1}{5}$, $\pm \frac{2}{5}$, $\pm \frac{1}{10}$.

Rationalize the denominator (p. 370) To rationalize the denominator of an expression, rewrite it so there are no radicals in any denominator and no denominators in any radical.

Racionalizar el denominador (p. 370) Para racionalizar el denominador de una expresión, ésta se escribe de modo que no haya radicales en ningún denominador y no haya denominadores en ningún radical.

$\frac{1}{\sqrt{2}} = \frac{1}{\sqrt{2}} \times \frac{\sqrt{2}}{\sqrt{2}} = \frac{\sqrt{2}}{2}$

Reciprocal (p. 7) The reciprocal or multiplicative inverse of any nonzero number a is $\frac{1}{a}$. The product of reciprocals is 1.

Recíproco (p. 7) El valor recíproco, o inverso multiplicativo, de un número a cuyo valor no es cero es $\frac{1}{a}$. El producto de un número y su valor recíproco es 1.

$5 \times \frac{1}{5} = 1$

Recursive formula (p. 590) A recursive formula defines the terms in a sequence by relating each term to the ones before it.

Fórmula recursiva (p. 590) Una fórmula recursiva define cada término de una progresión en función del término o términos precedentes.

Let $a_n = 2.5a_{n-1} + 3a_{n-2}$. If $a_5 = 3$ and $a_4 = 7.5$, then $a_6 = 2.5(3) + 3(7.5) = 30$.

Reflection (p. 189) A reflection, or flip, is a transformation that maps a point in the plane to its mirror image, using a specific line as the mirror.

Reflexión (p. 189) Una reflexión es una transformación en la que se voltea una figura sobre una línea específica, que actúa de manera espejo.

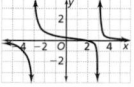

preimage   image

Relation (p. 55) A relation is a set of pairs of input and output values.

Relación (p. 55) Una relación es cualquier conjunto de pares ordenados de valores de entrada y valores de salida.

$\{(0, 1), (0, 2), (0, 3), (0, 4), (1, 3)\}$

T871

Relative maximum (minimum) (p. 309) The *y*-value of a point on the graph of a function that is higher (lower) than the nearby points of the graph is a relative maximum (minimum).

Máximo (mínimo) relativo (p. 309) El valor *y* de un punto en la gráfica de una función que es mayor (menor) que los de los puntos cercanos es un máximo (mínimo) relativo.

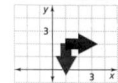

Remainder Theorem (p. 317) If a polynomial $P(x)$ of degree $n \geq 1$ is divided by $(x - a)$, where a is a constant, then the remainder is $P(a)$.

Teorema del residuo (p. 317) Si un polinomio $P(x)$ de grado $n \geq 1$ se divide por $(x - a)$, donde a es una constante, el residuo es $P(a)$.

If $P(x) = x^3 - 4x^2 + x + 6$ is divided by $x - 3$, then the remainder is $P(3) = 3^3 - 4(3)^2 + 3 + 6 = 0$ (which means that $x - 3$ is a factor of $P(x)$).

Rotation (p. 190) A rotation is a transformation that turns a figure about a fixed point called the center of rotation.

Rotación (p. 190) Rotación es una transformación que hace girar una figura alrededor de un punto fijo llamado centro de rotación.

Row operations (p. 219) To solve a system of equations using an augmented matrix, you can use one or more of the following row operations:
• Switch any two rows.
• Multiply a row by a constant.
• Add one row to another.
• Combine one or more of these steps.

Operaciones de líneas horizontales (p. 219) Para resolver un sistema de ecuaciones por medio de una matriz aumentada, se puede usar una o más de las siguientes operaciones de líneas horizontales:
• Intercambiar dos líneas horizontales.
• Multiplicar una línea horizontal por una constante.
• Sumar una línea horizontal a otra.
• Combinar uno o más de estos pasos.

Sample (p. 663) A sample is information gathered from only part of a population.

Muestra (p. 663) Una muestra contiene información reunida solamente de una parte de una población.

Let the set of all males between the ages of 19 and 34 be the population. A random selection of 900 males between those ages would be a sample of the population.

Sample proportion (p. 663) If an event occurs *x* times in a sample of size *n*, the sample proportion is $\frac{x}{n}$.

Proporción muestral (p. 663) Si un suceso ocurre *x* veces en un espacio muestral de tamaño *n*, la proporción de la muestra es $\frac{x}{n}$.

For a random selection of 900 males, 350 preferred red shirts to green shirts. The sample proportion would be $\frac{350}{900} = \frac{7}{18}$.

Sample space (p. 41) The set of all possible outcomes of an experiment is called the sample space.

Espacio muestral (p. 41) El espacio muestral es el conjunto de todos los resultados posibles de un suceso.

When you roll a number cube, the sample space is $\{1, 2, 3, 4, 5, 6\}$.

Scalar (p. 178) A scalar is a number that multiplies a matrix. To find the scalar product, multiply each element in the matrix by the scalar.

Escalar (p. 178) El valor escalar es el número que multiplica una matriz. Para hallar el producto escalar, se multiplica cada elemento de la matriz por el valor escalar.

$$2.5\begin{bmatrix} 1 & 0 \\ -2 & 3 \end{bmatrix} = \begin{bmatrix} 2.5(1) & 2.5(0) \\ 2.5(-2) & 2.5(3) \end{bmatrix}$$
$$= \begin{bmatrix} 2.5 & 0 \\ -5 & 7.5 \end{bmatrix}$$

Scalar product (p. 178) Suppose *c* is a scalar and *A* is a matrix. You find the scalar product *cA* by multiplying each element of *A* by *c*.

Producto escalar (p. 178) Si *c* es un número escalar y *A* es una matriz, el producto escalar *cA* se halla multiplicando cada elemento de *A* por *c*.

$$2.5\begin{bmatrix} 1 & 0 \\ -2 & 3 \end{bmatrix} = \begin{bmatrix} 2.5(1) & 2.5(0) \\ 2.5(-2) & 2.5(3) \end{bmatrix}$$
$$= \begin{bmatrix} 2.5 & 0 \\ -5 & 7.5 \end{bmatrix}$$

Scatter plot (p. 80) A scatter plot is a graph that relates two different sets of data by plotting the data as ordered pairs. You can use a scatter plot to determine a relationship between the data sets.

Diagrama de puntos (p. 80) Un diagrama de puntos es una gráfica que relaciona dos conjuntos de datos presentando los datos como pares ordenados. El diagrama de puntos sirve para definir la relación entre conjuntos de datos.

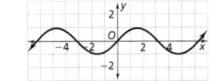

Secant (p. 749) The secant (sec) function is the reciprocal of the cosine function. For all real numbers θ except those that make $\cos \theta = 0$, $\sec \theta = \frac{1}{\cos \theta}$.

Secante (p. 749) La función secante (sec) es el recíproco de la función coseno. Para todos los números reales θ, excepto aquellos para los que $\cos \theta = 0$, $\sec \theta = \frac{1}{\cos \theta}$.

If $\cos \theta = \frac{5}{13}$, then $\sec \theta = \frac{13}{5}$.

Sequence (p. 588) A sequence is an ordered list of numbers.

Progresión (p. 588) Una progresión es una sucesión de números.

$1, 4, 7, 10, \ldots$

Series (p. 607) A series is the sum of the terms of a sequence. The series is finite (infinite) if the corresponding sequence is finite (infinite).

Serie (p. 607) Una serie es la suma de los términos de una progresión. La serie es finita (infinita) si la progresión correspondiente es finita (infinita).

The series $3 + 6 + 9 + 12 + 15$ corresponds to the sequence $3, 6, 9, 12, 15$. The sum of the series is 45.

Simplest form of a rational expression (p. 499) A rational expression is in simplest form when its numerator and denominator are polynomials that have no common divisors.

Forma simplificada de una expresión racional (p. 499) Una expresión racional no se puede simplificar más cuando su numerador y su denominador son polinomios que ya no contienen factores comunes.

$\frac{x^2 - 7x + 12}{x^2 - 9} = \frac{(x - 4)(x - 3)}{(x + 3)(x - 3)}$
$= \frac{x - 4}{x + 3}$, where $x \neq -3$

Simulation (p. 40) When actual trials are difficult to conduct, you can find experimental probability by using a simulation, which is a model of one or more events.

Simulación (p. 40) Cuando es difícil realizar las pruebas de un experimento, se puede determinar la probabilidad experimental por medio de una simulación, o modelo de uno o más sucesos del experimento.

Suppose a weather forecaster predicts a 50% chance of rain for the next three days. You can use three coins landing heads up to simulate three days in a row of rain.

Sine curve (p. 721) A sine curve is the graph of a sine function.

Sinusoide (p. 721) Sinusoide es la gráfica de la función seno.

Sine function (p. 720) The sine function, $y = \sin \theta$, matches the measure θ of an angle in standard position with the *y*-coordinate of a point on the unit circle. This point is where the terminal side of the angle intersects the unit circle.

Función seno (p. 720) La función seno, $y = \text{sen } \theta$, equivale a la medida de θ de un ángulo en posición normal con la coordenada *y* de un punto dado en el círculo unitario. Este punto es la intersección del lado terminal y el círculo unitario.

Sine of θ (p. 706) The sine of an angle measure θ ($\sin \theta$) is the *y*-coordinate of the point at which the terminal side of the angle intersects the unit circle.

Seno de θ (p. 706) El seno de un ángulo que mide θ (sen θ) es la ordenada *y* del punto de intersección entre el lado terminal del ángulo y el círculo unitario.

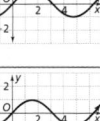

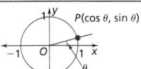

$P(\cos \theta, \sin \theta)$

Slope of a line (p. 64) The slope of a non-vertical line is the ratio of the vertical change to a corresponding horizontal change. The slope of a vertical line is undefined.

slope $= \frac{\text{vertical change}}{\text{horizontal change}} = \frac{y_2 - y_1}{x_2 - x_1}$, where $x_2 - x_1 \neq 0$

Pendiente de una recta (p. 64) La pendiente de una recta no vertical es el cociente del cambio vertical y el cambio horizontal. La pendiente de una recta vertical no está definida.

pendiente $= \frac{\text{cambio vertical}}{\text{cambio horizontal}} = \frac{y_2 - y_1}{x_2 - x_1}$, donde $x_2 - x_1 \neq 0$

The slope of the line through points $(-1, -1)$ and $(1, -2)$ is $\frac{-2 - (-1)}{1 - (-1)} = \frac{-1}{2} = -\frac{1}{2}$.

Slope-intercept form (p. 65) The slope-intercept form of an equation of a line is $y = mx + b$, where *m* is the slope and *b* is the *y*-intercept.

Forma pendiente-ordenada al origen (p. 65) La forma pendiente-ordenada al origen de una ecuación lineal es $y = mx + b$, donde *m* es la pendiente y *b* es el intercepto en *y*.

$y = 8x + 2$

$y = -x + 1$

$y = -\frac{1}{2}x - 14$

Solution of an equation (p. 18) A solution of an equation is a number that makes the equation true.

Solución de una ecuación (p. 18) Una solución de una ecuación es cualquier número que haga verdadera la ecuación.

The solution of $2x - 7 = -12$ is $x = -2.5$.

Square matrix (p. 195) A square matrix is a matrix with equal numbers of columns and rows.

Matriz cuadrada (p. 195) Una matriz cuadrada es la que tiene la misma cantidad de líneas verticales y de líneas horizontales.

Matrix *A* is a square matrix.

$A = \begin{bmatrix} 1 & 2 & 0 \\ -1 & 0 & -2 \\ 1 & 2 & 3 \end{bmatrix}$

Standard deviation (p. 657) Standard deviation is a measure of how much the values in a data set vary, or deviate, from the mean, $\overline{x}$. To find the standard deviation, follow five steps:
• Find the mean of the data set.
• Find the difference between each data value and the mean.
• Square each difference.
• Find the mean of the squares.
• Take the square root of the mean of the squares. This is the standard deviation.

Desviación normal (p. 657) La desviación normal denota cuánto los valores de un conjunto de datos varían, o se desvían, de la media, $\overline{x}$. Para hallar la desviación normal, se siguen cinco pasos:
• Se halla la media del conjunto de datos.
• Se calcula la diferencia entre cada valor de datos y la media.
• Se eleva al cuadrado cada diferencia.
• Se halla la media de los cuadrados.
• Se calcula la raíz cuadrada de la media de los cuadrados. Ésa es la desviación normal.

$\{0, 2, 3, 4, 6, 7, 8, 9, 10, 11\}$
$\overline{x} = 6$
standard deviation $= \sqrt{12} \approx 3.46$

T872

Standard form of a linear equation (p. 63) The standard form of a linear equation is $Ax + By = C$, where A, B, and C are real numbers, and A and B are not both zero.

In standard form, the equation $y = \frac{4}{3}x - 1$ is $4x + -3y = 3$.

Forma normal de una ecuación lineal (p. 63) La forma normal de una ecuación lineal es $Ax + By = C$, donde A, B, y C son números reales, y A y B son valores distintos de cero.

Standard form of an equation of a circle (p. 549) See Circle.

$(x - 3)^2 + (y - 4)^2 = 4$

Forma normal de la ecuación de un círculo (p. 549) Ver Circle.

Standard form of an equation of an ellipse (p. 556) See Ellipse.

$\frac{x^2}{5^2} + \frac{y^2}{3^2} = 1$

Forma normal de la ecuación de una elipse (p. 556) Ver Ellipse.

Standard form of an equation of a hyperbola (p. 563) See Hyperbola.

$\frac{x^2}{5^2} - \frac{y^2}{3^2} = 1$

Forma normal de la ecuación de una hipérbola (p. 563) Ver Hyperbola.

Standard form of a polynomial (p. 301) The standard form of a polynomial has the terms in descending order by degree. A one-variable polynomial in standard form has no two terms with the same degree, since all like terms have been combined.

$2x^3 - 5x^2 - 2x + 5$

Forma normal de un polinomio (p. 301) Un polinomio está en forma normal cuando sus términos están en orden descendente por grados. Un polinomio de una variable en forma normal no tiene dos términos del mismo grado puesto que todos los términos han sido combinados.

Standard form of a quadratic equation (p. 263) The standard form of a quadratic equation is $ax^2 + bx + c = 0$, where $a \neq 0$.

$2x^2 + 5x + 2 = 0$

Forma normal de una ecuación cuadrática (p. 263) La forma normal de una ecuación cuadrática es $ax^2 + bx + c = 0$, donde $a \neq 0$.

Standard form of a quadratic function (p. 234) The standard form of a quadratic function is $f(x) = ax^2 + bx + c$, where $a \neq 0$.

$f(x) = 2x^2 + 5x + 2$

Forma normal de una función cuadrática (p. 234) La forma normal de una función cuadrática es $f(x) = ax^2 + bx + c$, donde $a \neq 0$.

Standard normal curve (p. 679) The standard normal curve is a normal distribution centered on the y-axis. The mean of the standard normal curve is 0. The standard deviation is 1.

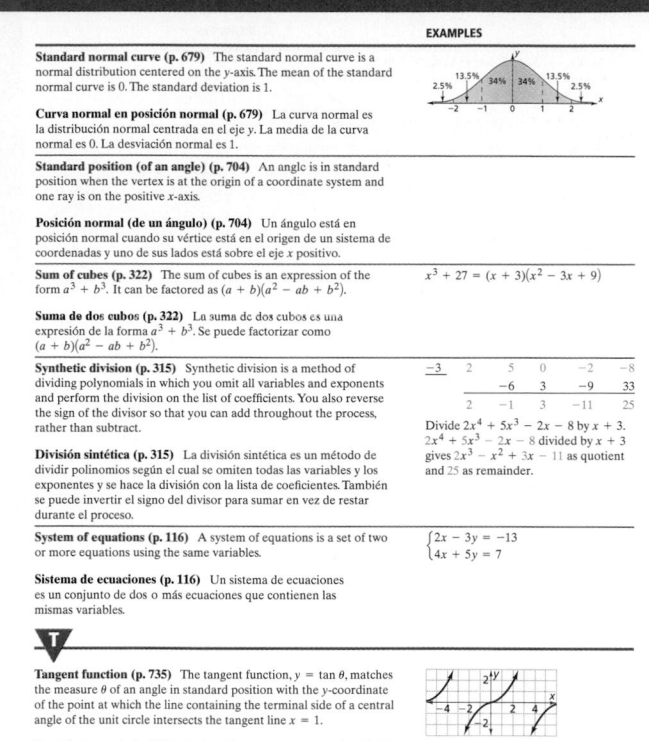

Curva normal en posición normal (p. 679) La curva normal es la distribución normal centrada en el eje y. La media de la curva normal es 0. La desviación normal es 1.

Standard position (of an angle) (p. 704) An angle is in standard position when the vertex is at the origin of a coordinate system and one ray is on the positive x-axis.

Posición normal (de un ángulo) (p. 704) Un ángulo está en posición normal cuando su vértice está en el origen de un sistema de coordenadas y uno de sus lados está sobre el eje x positivo.

Sum of cubes (p. 322) The sum of cubes is an expression of the form $a^3 + b^3$. It can be factored as $(a + b)(a^2 - ab + b^2)$.

$x^3 + 27 = (x + 3)(x^2 - 3x + 9)$

Suma de dos cubos (p. 322) La suma de dos cubos es una expresión de la forma $a^3 + b^3$. Se puede factorizar como $(a + b)(a^2 - ab + b^2)$.

Synthetic division (p. 315) Synthetic division is a method of dividing polynomials in which you omit all variables and exponents and perform the division on the list of coefficients. You also reverse the sign of the divisor so that you can add throughout the process, rather than subtract.

$$\begin{array}{r|rrrr} -3 & 2 & 5 & 0 & -2 & -8 \\ & & -6 & 3 & -9 & 33 \\ \hline & 2 & -1 & 3 & -11 & 25 \end{array}$$

Divide $2x^4 + 5x^3 - 2x - 8$ by $x + 3$.
$2x^4 + 5x^3 - 2x - 8$ divided by $x + 3$ gives $2x^3 - x^2 + 3x - 11$ as quotient and 25 as remainder.

División sintética (p. 315) La división sintética es un método de dividir polinomios según el cual se omiten todas las variables y los exponentes y se hace la división con la lista de coeficientes. También se puede invertir el signo del divisor para sumar en vez de restar durante el proceso.

System of equations (p. 116) A system of equations is a set of two or more equations using the same variables.

$\begin{cases} 2x - 3y = -13 \\ 4x + 5y = 7 \end{cases}$

Sistema de ecuaciones (p. 116) Un sistema de ecuaciones es un conjunto de dos o más ecuaciones que contienen las mismas variables.

T

Tangent function (p. 735) The tangent function, $y = \tan \theta$, matches the measure θ of an angle in standard position with the y-coordinate of the point at which the line containing the terminal side of a central angle of the unit circle intersects the tangent line $x = 1$.

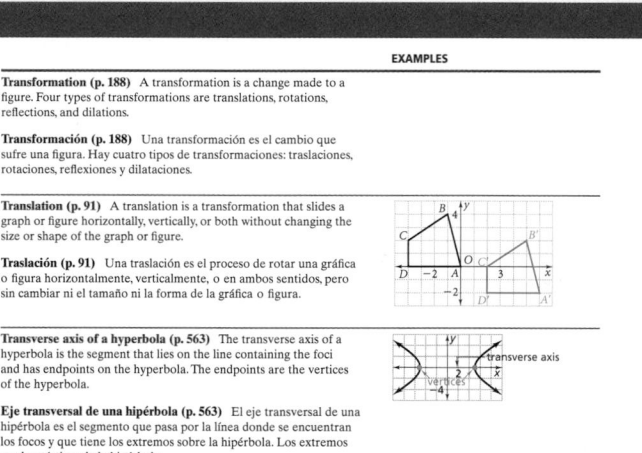

Función tangente (p. 735) La función tangente, $y = \tan \theta$, equivale a la medida θ de un ángulo en posición normal, con la ordenada y del punto donde la línea que contiene el lado terminal de un ángulo central del círculo unitario corta la tangente $x = 1$.

Tangent of θ (p. 735) The tangent of an angle measure θ (tan θ) is the y-coordinate of the point at which the line containing the terminal side of the angle intersects the tangent line $x = 1$.

Tangente de θ (p. 735) La tangente de un ángulo que mide θ (tan θ) es la ordenada y del punto donde la línea que contiene el lado terminal del ángulo corta la tangente $x = 1$.

Term of a sequence (p. 588) Each number in a sequence is a term.

$1, 4, 7, 10, \ldots$
The second term is 4.

Término de una progresión (p. 588) Cada número de una progresión es un término.

Term of an expression (p. 13) A term is a number, a variable, or the product of a number and one or more variables.

The expression $4x^2 - 3y + 7.3$ has 3 terms.

Término de una expresión (p. 13) Un término es un número, una variable, o el producto de un número y una o más variables.

Terminal side (of an angle) (p. 704) See Initial side (of an angle).

Lado terminal (de un ángulo) (p. 704) Ver Lado inicial (de un ángulo).

Theoretical probability (p. 41) If a sample space has n equally likely outcomes, and an event A occurs in m of these outcomes, then the theoretical probability of event A is $P(A) = \frac{m}{n}$.

Use the set $\{1, 4, 9, 16, 25, 36, 49, 64, 81, 100\}$. The probability that a number selected at random is greater than 50 is $P(A) = \frac{3}{10} = 0.3$.

Probabilidad teórica (p. 41) Si un espacio muestral tiene n resultados con la misma probabilidad de ocurrir, y ocurre un suceso A en m de estos resultados, entonces la probabilidad teórica del suceso A es $P(A) = \frac{m}{n}$.

Tolerance (p. 36) The difference between a desired measurement and its maximum and minimum allowable values is the tolerance. The tolerance equals one half of the difference between the maximum and minimum values.

A manufacturing specification calls for a dimension d of 10 cm with a tolerance of 0.1 cm. The allowable difference between d and 10 is less than or equal to 0.1.

Tolerancia (p. 36) La diferencia entre una medida deseada y sus valores máximo y mínimo permitidos es la tolerancia. La tolerancia equivale a la mitad de la diferencia entre los valores máximo y mínimo.

Trace (p. 144) A trace is a set of ordered pairs that result from substituting 0 for one of the variables in the equation of a plane.

Trazo (p. 144) El trazo es un conjunto de pares ordenados que resulta al reemplazar por 0 una de las variables de la ecuación de un plano.

Transformation (p. 188) A transformation is a change made to a figure. Four types of transformations are translations, rotations, reflections, and dilations.

Transformación (p. 188) Una transformación es el cambio que sufre una figura. Hay cuatro tipos de transformaciones: traslaciones, rotaciones, reflexiones y dilataciones.

Translation (p. 91) A translation is a transformation that slides a graph or figure horizontally, vertically, or both without changing the size or shape of the graph or figure.

Traslación (p. 91) Una traslación es el proceso de rotar una gráfica o figura horizontalmente, verticalmente, o en ambos sentidos, pero sin cambiar ni el tamaño ni la forma de la gráfica o figura.

Transverse axis of a hyperbola (p. 563) The transverse axis of a hyperbola is the segment that lies on the line containing the foci and has endpoints on the hyperbola. The endpoints are the vertices of the hyperbola.

Eje transversal de una hipérbola (p. 563) El eje transversal de una hipérbola es el segmento que pasa por la línea donde se encuentran los focos y que tiene los extremos sobre la hipérbola. Los extremos son los vértices de la hipérbola.

Trend line (p. 80) A trend line is a line that approximates the relationship between the data sets of a scatter plot. You can use a trend line to make predictions.

Línea de tendencia (p. 80) La línea de tendencia es una línea que aproxima la relación entre los conjuntos de datos en un diagrama de puntos. La línea de tendencia permite hacer predicciones.

Trigonometric identity (p. 764) A trigonometric identity is a trigonometric equation that is true for all values except those for which an expression on either side of the equal sign is undefined.

$\tan \theta = \frac{\sin \theta}{\cos \theta}$

Identidad trigonométrica (p. 764) Una identidad trigonométrica es una ecuación trigonométrica que satisface todos los valores excepto aquellos para los cuales las expresiones a cada lado del signo igual no están definidas.

Trigonometric ratios for a right triangle (p. 778) The trigonometric ratios for a right triangle are the six different ratios of the sides of a right triangle. These ratios do not depend on the size of the right triangle. They depend only on the size of the acute angles in the triangle. In a right triangle that has an acute $\angle A$, the ratios are defined as follows.

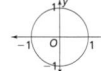

$$\sin A = \frac{a}{c} \qquad \csc A = \frac{1}{\sin A} = \frac{c}{a}$$
$$\cos A = \frac{b}{c} \qquad \sec A = \frac{1}{\cos A} = \frac{c}{b}$$
$$\tan A = \frac{a}{b} \qquad \cot A = \frac{1}{\tan A} = \frac{b}{a}$$

Razones trigonométricas para un triángulo rectángulo (p. 778) Las razones trigonométricas de un triángulo rectángulo son las seis razones de los lados de dicho triángulo. Esas razones no dependen del tamaño del triángulo rectángulo. Dependen sólo de la magnitud de los ángulos agudos del triángulo. En un triángulo rectángulo que tenga un ángulo agudo $\angle A$, las razones se definen así:

$$\operatorname{sen} A = \frac{a}{c} \qquad \csc A = \frac{1}{\operatorname{sen} A} = \frac{c}{a}$$
$$\cos A = \frac{b}{c} \qquad \sec A = \frac{1}{\cos A} = \frac{c}{b}$$
$$\tan A = \frac{a}{b} \qquad \cot A = \frac{1}{\tan A} = \frac{b}{a}$$

 U

Unit circle (p. 706) The unit circle has a radius of 1 unit and its center at the origin of the coordinate plane.

Círculo unitario (p. 706) El círculo unitario tiene un radio de 1 unidad y el centro situado en el origen del plano de coordenadas.

 V

Variable (p. 12) A variable is a symbol, usually a letter, that represents one or more numbers.

x, a, k

Variable (p. 12) Una variable es un símbolo, generalmente una letra, que representa uno o más valores.

Variable expression (p. 12) An expression that contains one or more variables is an algebraic expression, or a variable expression.

$2x + 3, z - y$

Expresión variable (p. 12) Una expresión que contenga uno o más variables es una expresión algebraica o expresión variable.

Variable matrix (p. 210) When representing a system of equations with a matrix equation, the matrix containing the variables of the system is the variable matrix.

$$\begin{cases} x + 2y = 5 \\ 3x + 5y = 14 \end{cases}$$

variable matrix $\begin{bmatrix} x \\ y \end{bmatrix}$

Matriz variable (p. 210) Al representar un sistema de ecuaciones con una ecuación de matrices, la matriz que contenga las variables del sistema es la matriz variable.

Vertex form of a quadratic function (p. 248) The vertex form of a quadratic function is $y = a(x - h)^2 + k$. The coordinates of the vertex of the parabola are (h, k).

$y = x^2 + 2x - 1 = (x + 1)^2 - 2$
The vertex is $(-1, -2)$.

Forma vértice de una función cuadrática (p. 248) La forma vértice de una función cuadrática es $y = a(x - h)^2 + k$. Las coordenadas del vértice de la parábola son (h, k).

Vertex of a parabola (p. 235) The vertex of a parabola is the point at which the parabola intersects the axis of symmetry. The y-value of the vertex is the maximum or minimum value of the function.

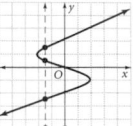

Vértice de una parábola (p. 235) El vértice de una parábola es el punto de intersección entre la parábola y su eje de simetría. El valor y del vértice es el valor máximo o mínimo de la función.

The vertex of the quadratic function $y = x^2 + 2x - 1$ is $(-1, -2)$.

Vertical-line test (p. 57) You can use the vertical-line test to determine whether a relation has at least one element of the domain paired with more than one element of the range. If a vertical line passes through two or more points on the graph, then the relation is *not* a function.

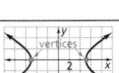

Prueba de la línea vertical (p. 57) La prueba de la línea vertical permite determinar si en una relación hay por lo menos un elemento del dominio al que corresponde más de un elemento del recorrido. Si una recta vertical del sistema de coordenadas pasa por dos o más puntos de la gráfica, quiere decir que la relación *no es* una función.

Vertices of a hyperbola (p. 563) The endpoints of the transverse axis of a hyperbola are the vertices of the hyperbola.

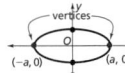

Vértices de una hipérbola (p. 563) Los dos puntos de intersección de la hipérbola y su eje transversal son los vértices de la hipérbola.

Vertices of an ellipse (p. 556) The endpoints of the major axis of an ellipse are the vertices of the ellipse.

Vértices de una elipse (p. 556) Los dos puntos de intersección de la elipse y su eje longitudinal son los vértices de la elipse.

X

x- and y-intercepts (p. 63) The point at which a line crosses the x-axis (or the x-coordinate of that point) is an x-intercept. The point at which a line crosses the y-axis (or the y-coordinate of that point) is a y-intercept.

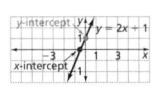

Intercepto en x e intercepto en y (p. 63) El punto donde una recta cruza el eje x (o la coordenada horizontal de ese punto) es el intercepto en x. El punto donde una recta cruza el eje y (o la coordenada vertical de ese punto) es el intercepto en y.

The x-intercept of $y = 2x + 1$ is $\left(-\frac{1}{2}, 0\right)$ or $-\frac{1}{2}$.
The y-intercept of $y = 2x + 1$ is $(0, 1)$ or 1.

Z

Zero matrix (p. 171) The zero matrix O, or $O_{m \times n}$, is the $m \times n$ matrix whose elements are all zeros. It is the additive identity matrix for the set of all $m \times n$ matrices.

$$\begin{bmatrix} 1 & 4 \\ 2 & -3 \end{bmatrix} + O = \begin{bmatrix} 1 & 4 \\ 2 & -3 \end{bmatrix}$$

Matriz cero (p. 171) La matriz cero, O, ó $O_{m \times n}$, es la matriz $m \times n$ cuyos elementos son todos ceros. Es la matriz de identidad aditiva para el conjunto de todas las matrices $m \times n$.

Zero of a function (pp. 264, 309) A zero of a function is any value of the variable for which the function is 0. On the graph of a function, each x-intercept represents a zero.

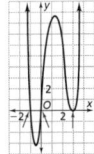

Cero de una función (pp. 264, 309) Un cero de una función es cualquier valor de la variable para el cual la función es 0. En la gráfica de una función, cada intercepto en x representa un cero.

The zeros of the function $P(x) = 2x(x - 3)^2(x + 1)$ are $0, 3$, and -1.

Zero-Product Property (p. 263) If a and b are real numbers and $ab = 0$, then $a = 0$ or $b = 0$, or $a = b = 0$.

$(x - 3)(2x - 5) = 0$
$x - 3 = 0$ or $2x - 5 = 0$

Propiedad del producto cero (p. 263) Si a y b son números reales y $ab = 0$, entonces $a = 0$ ó $b = 0$, ó $a = b = 0$.

z-score (p. 659) The z-score of a value is the number of standard deviations that the value is from the mean.

$\{0, 2, 3, 4, 6, 7, 8, 9, 10, 11\}$
$\bar{x} = 6$
standard deviation $= \sqrt{12} \approx 3.46$
For 8, z-score $= \frac{8 - 6}{\sqrt{12}} \approx 0.58$.

Puntaje z (p. 659) El puntaje z de un valor es el número de desviaciones normales que tiene ese valor de la media.

T874

Answers to Instant Check System™

Chapter 1

Diagnosing Readiness   p. 2

1. 0 **2.** −3 **3.** −2.09 **4.** 8.05 **5.** −$\frac{3}{4}$ **6.** $\frac{11}{12}$ **7.** 10$\frac{7}{10}$
8. 3$\frac{1}{2}$ **9.** −42 **10.** 72 **11.** 9 **12.** −9.8 **13.** −3$\frac{1}{3}$
14. −5$\frac{1}{2}$ **15.** −4$\frac{2}{5}$ **16.** −$\frac{3}{4}$ **17.** −21 **18.** 7.35
19. −$\frac{1}{6}$ **20.** −$\frac{3}{8}$ **21.** −20 **22.** 8 **23.** 0.97 **24.** −5
25. 55 **26.** 3

Lesson 1-1   pp. 4–8

Check Skills You'll Need **1.** 7.2 **2.** 4 **3.** −13.5 **4.** 6.8
5. −5 **6.** −1

Check Understanding **1.** rational numbers; rational numbers
2.

3. −√0.08 > −√0.1, −√0.1 < −√0.08
4a. −400, $\frac{400}{400}$ **b.** −4$\frac{5}{9}$, $\frac{5}{6}$ **c.** 0.002, −500
d. $\frac{4}{9}$, $\frac{4}{9}$ (or −2$\frac{1}{4}$) **5a.** Identity Prop. of Add.
b. Assoc. Prop. of Add. **6a.** 10, 1.5, 3 **b.** for values of x such that $x \le 0$

Lesson 1-2   pp. 12–15

Check Skills You'll Need **1.** 16 **2.** 6 **3.** $\frac{8}{9}$ **4.** 195 **5.** 21
6. −1

Check Understanding **1a.** $\frac{7}{8}$ **b.** 26 **c.** 4 **2a.** −16
b. −3 **c.** −69 **3a.** about 45%; about 43%
b. Answers may vary. Sample: Changing patterns in minority populations might lead to more voter turnout. Less stable international conditions might arouse voter concerns. **4a.** −3x^2 + 6x
b. −4r − 4s **c.** −2y^2 − 1 **5a.** 10x **b.** 10c + 2d
c. 2d

Lesson 1-3   pp. 18–21, 24

Check Skills You'll Need **1.** −4x + 3 **2.** 7x + 3y − 1
3. 8g + 2h **4.** $\frac{4}{5}$ **5.** 2y **6.** −3c + 1

Check Understanding **1a.** −11 **b.** 2 **2a.** 35 **b.** 3
3. b_1 = $\frac{2A}{h}$ − b_2 **4a.** x = $\frac{15}{a+b}$, $a \ne -b$
b. x = $\frac{a(d-b)}{2}$, $a \ne 0$ **5.** 8 cm wide, 16 cm long
6. 36 cm, 39 cm, 45 cm **7.** about 86.4 seconds, or 1 minute 26.4 seconds

Checkpoint Quiz 1 **1.** −1, 0.3, $\frac{2}{3}$, 7 **2.** Comm. Prop. of

Add., Assoc. Prop. of Add., Dist. Prop. **3.** a + 2b
4. a^2 + a − 7 **5.** 5 **6.** $\frac{3}{2}$, or 1$\frac{1}{2}$ **7.** 28 **8.** r = $\frac{A-p}{pt}$,
$p \ne 0, t \ne 0$ **9.** x = $\frac{4b}{7a}$, $a \ne 0$ **10.** width = 76 yd, length = 236 yd

Lesson 1-4   pp. 26–29

Check Skills You'll Need **1.** true **2.** false **3.** false
4. false **5.** true **6.** true **7.** −6 **8.** 15

Check Understanding
1a. x < 11

b. $n \le -2$

2. All real numbers are solutions.

b. no solutions

c. values of a less than or equal to 0; values of a greater than 0 **3.** at least $55,000
4.

5. x < 4 or x > 5

6. by at least 0.03 in., but by no more than 0.43 in.

Lesson 1-5   pp. 33–36, 38

Check Skills You'll Need **1.** 14 **2.** 16 **3.** 2.3 **4.** x > 3
5. $a \ge 4$ **6.** t < 9

Check Understanding **1.** $\frac{5}{2}$, −3 **2.** −$\frac{13}{5}$, 5 **3a.** 1 **b.** no solutions **c.** Answers may vary; any positive real number. **4.** x < −2 or x > 5

5. −8$\frac{2}{5}$ < z < 7$\frac{3}{5}$

6. |C − 28.125| ≤ 0.375

Checkpoint Quiz 1
1. x ≤ 5

2. x < 5$\frac{4}{7}$

3. z > −1

4. w > 1 or w < −3

5. −15 ≤ x ≤ 7

---

6. x < −2 or x > 2

7. −$\frac{5}{2}$, $\frac{11}{2}$ **8.** $\frac{1}{8}$ **9.** 13 < 3n + 3 < 16, n = 4
10. PR − RQ < PQ < PR + RQ; 4 < 26

Lesson 1-6   pp. 39–42

Check Skills You'll Need **1.** 37.5% **2.** 183$\frac{1}{3}$% **3.** 0.43%
4. 0.25% **5.** 104% **6.** 300%

Check Understanding **1.** $\frac{32}{50}$, or 0.64, or 64% **2.** $\frac{3}{50}$, or 6% **3.** $\frac{1}{2}$, or 50% **4.** $\frac{1}{4}$, or 25% **5a.** $\frac{1}{16}$, or 6.25%
b. $\frac{5}{16}$, or 31.25%

Chapter 2

Diagnosing Readiness   p. 52

1.

2.

3.

4. 6s **5.** 4a + b
9. xy − y + x **7.** 1.5g **8.** 0 **9.** 3b − 2c − 2
10. 6f − 5d **11.** 3h + 3g **12.** −2z + 5
13. 2g − 4dg − 12d **14.** 8v − 6 **15.** 7t − 3st − 5s
16. −2 < x < 8

17. $a \le 0$

18. x > −1

19. x < −4 or x > $\frac{10}{3}$

20. −$\frac{1}{2}$ ≤ d ≤ $\frac{25}{4}$

21. −24 ≤ f ≤ 18

22. $\frac{15}{64}$ **23.** $\frac{1}{32}$
24. $\frac{11}{18}$ **25.** $\frac{13}{18}$ **26.** $\frac{61}{72}$ **27.** $\frac{13}{16}$

Lesson 2-1   pp. 55–61

Check Skills You'll Need
1. **2.** **3.**

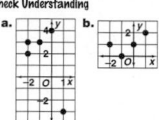

4. 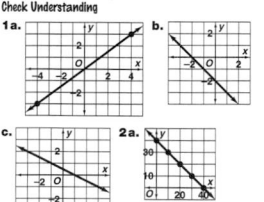 **5.**

6. 1, 2, 4, 7 **7.** 5, 3, −1, −7 **8.** 3, 1, 9, 51
9. 4, 3, 1, 2

Check Understanding
1a. **b.**

2a. domain {−3, 0, 2, 4}, range {2, 1, 4, −3}
b. domain {−3, −1, 1}, range {−4, −2, 1, 3}
3a. domain range **b.** domain range **4a.** function

b. not a function **5a.** not a function **b.** function
c. not a function **6a.** −14, −5, 10 **b.** −$\frac{13}{4}$, −1, $\frac{11}{4}$
c. $\frac{6}{5}$, $\frac{3}{5}$, −$\frac{2}{5}$

Lesson 2-2   pp. 62–70

Check Skills You'll Need **1.** $\frac{17}{7}$, 7, $\frac{23}{7}$, $\frac{29}{7}$ **2.** −$\frac{16}{5}$, −2, −$\frac{7}{5}$, $\frac{6}{5}$
3. −5, 1, 4, 13 **4.** −$\frac{9}{5}$, −8, −$\frac{15}{2}$, −6

Check Understanding
1a. **b.**

c. **2a.**

y = 40 − x, x-intercept (40, 0), y-intercept (0, 40). When there are 0 children, the train holds 40 adults. When there are 0 adults, the train holds 40 children. **b.** Answers may vary. Sample: Each seat holds one person, whether adult or child.

3a. $\frac{2}{3}$ **b.** −$\frac{6}{7}$ **4a.** 2x − y = 10 **b.** $\frac{5}{8}x$ − y = −$\frac{11}{4}$
5a. y − 0 = −$\frac{1}{4}$(x − 5) **b.** y + 1 = −$\frac{5}{3}$(x + 2)
c. y − 1 = $\frac{4}{9}$(x − 5) **6a.** −$\frac{3}{2}$ **b.** −$\frac{4}{3}$ **c.** −$\frac{A}{B}$
7a. y = −$\frac{3}{5}x$ + $\frac{14}{5}$

b. y = $\frac{2}{3}x$ − $\frac{3}{3}$

c. x = 5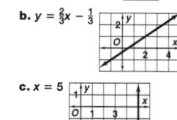

Lesson 2-3   pp. 72–74, 77

Check Skills You'll Need **1.** y = $\frac{x}{4}$ **2.** y = $\frac{5}{12}x$ **3.** y = 20
4. y = 30x **5.** y = 7 **6.** true **7.** true **8.** false
9. true

Check Understanding **1a.** yes; $\frac{1}{3}$, y = $\frac{1}{3}x$ **b.** no
c. no **2a.** yes; k = 0.5 **b.** no **c.** yes; $\frac{5}{9}$ **d.** no
3a. π **b.** 33.4 cm **4a.** 8 **b.** 28 **c.** −0.6 **d.** 0.2

Checkpoint Quiz 1 **1.** (9, 0), (0, −3) **2.** (−$\frac{7}{2}$, 0), (0, 5)
3. (0, 0) **4.** (−$\frac{5}{2}$, 0), (0, 10) **5.** y = 2x − 9
6. y = 4x − 2 **7.** y = −$\frac{2}{3}x$ − 2 **8.** y = −$\frac{2}{3}x$ + 2
9a. y = 27x **b.**

Both intercepts are 0 when no one has bought any tickets. **c.** Answers may vary. Sample: No; the number of people must be a whole number. **10.** A

Lesson 2-4   pp. 78–84

Check Skills You'll Need **1.** 3.6, −1.7 **2.** 1.5, −3.5
3. −1, $\frac{7}{10}$ **4.** −6, −2, −4 **5.** 6, $\frac{11}{3}$, 3

Check Understanding **1a.** d = −20t + 135; the slope is negative. **b.**

The h-intercept (0, 1350) represents the starting height at time 0. **2a.** The candle is burning down at the rate of $\frac{1}{4}$ inch per hour. **b.** the original

height of the candle. **c.** y = −2x + 9 **3a.** 3$\frac{1}{2}$ in.
b. 6$\frac{1}{4}$ in. **c.** after 25 hours
4a.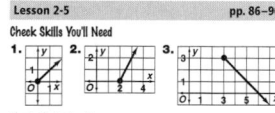

A linear model is reasonable; models may vary. Sample: y = −1.92x + 6
b.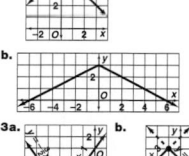

not reasonable

Lesson 2-5   pp. 86–90

Check Skills You'll Need
1. **2.** **3.**

Check Understanding
1a. **b.**

2a.

b.

3a.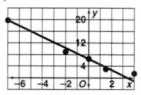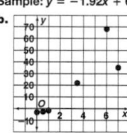

4a. The graph would get narrower.
b.

Lesson 2-6   pp. 91–95, 98

Check Skills You'll Need
1. **2.**

3. **4.**

5. **6.**

Check Understanding **1a.** y = x + 5 is y = x shifted 5 units up. **b.** f(x) = −|x| + 2 is f(x) = −|x| shifted 2 units up. **2a.** y = −|x|, k = −1

b. y = 3x, k = 5

3a. y = |3x| − 2 **b.** y = $\frac{1}{3}x$ + 3 **4a.** y = |x|; h = 1 **b.** y = −|x|; h = $\frac{3}{2}$

5a. y = |x + $\frac{3}{2}$| **b.** y = |x − 4| **6.** Answers may vary. Sample: 4.5 units right and 3 units up
7.

8a. g(x) = |x − 7| − 1 **b.** y = −|x − 3| + 4

Checkpoint Quiz 1
1. **2.** **3.**

4. **5.**

6. **7.** y = x − 4 **8.** y = |x + 5| − 3

9a. 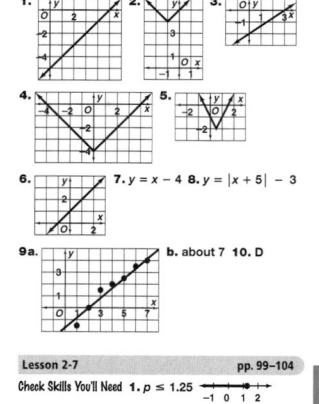 **b.** about 7 **10.** D

Lesson 2-7   pp. 99–104

Check Skills You'll Need **1.** $p \le 1.25$

2. t > 13

3. $t \le -3$

4. c = ±4.5

5. b = 2, 8

6. $h \le -3.5$ or $h \ge 3.5$

Check Understanding
1a. **b.** **c.**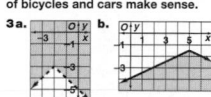

2a. at least 3; (2, 5), (1, 6), (0, 7) **b.** Domain and range are all whole numbers; only whole numbers of bicycles and cars make sense.
3a. **b.**

4a. y ≤ |x + 4| − 3 **b.** y ≥ 2x + 5

Chapter 3

Diagnosing Readiness   p. 114

1. $7x - 1$ 2. $5 - p$ 3. $-6z + 10$ 4. $r - 4$
5. $a \le \frac{3}{2}$
6. $b > 2$
7. $c < -12$
8. $d \le -1$

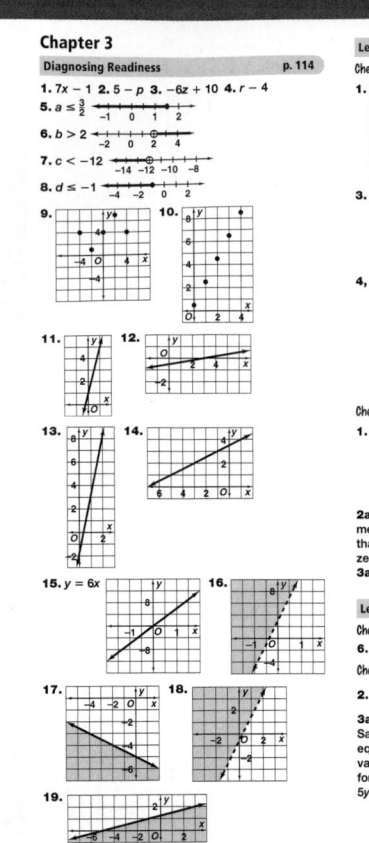

15. $y = 6x$

Lesson 3-1   pp. 116–118
Check Skills You'll Need

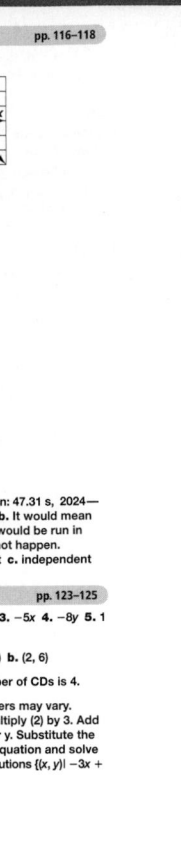

Check Understanding
1. $(1, 3)$
2a. 2008—men: 43.46 s, women: 47.31 s, 2024—men: 43.07 s, women: 45.89 s b. It would mean that eventually the 400-m run would be run in zero seconds, and this could not happen.
3a. inconsistent b. dependent c. independent

Lesson 3-2   pp. 123–125
Check Skills You'll Need 1. -4 2. x 3. $-5x$ 4. $-8y$ 5. 1 6. -2 7. $-\frac{1}{4}$

Check Understanding 1.a. $(-6, -6)$ b. $(2, 6)$
2. $\begin{cases} c = 15.49x \\ c = 6 + 13.99x \end{cases}$ The number of CDs is 4.
3a. $(4, -1)$ b. $(-2, 1)$ 4. Answers may vary. Sample: Multiply (1) by -5. Multiply (2) by 3. Add equations together, solving for y. Substitute the value of y into either original equation and solve for x. 5a. infinite number of solutions $\{(x, y) \mid -3x + 5y = 7\}$ b. no solution

---

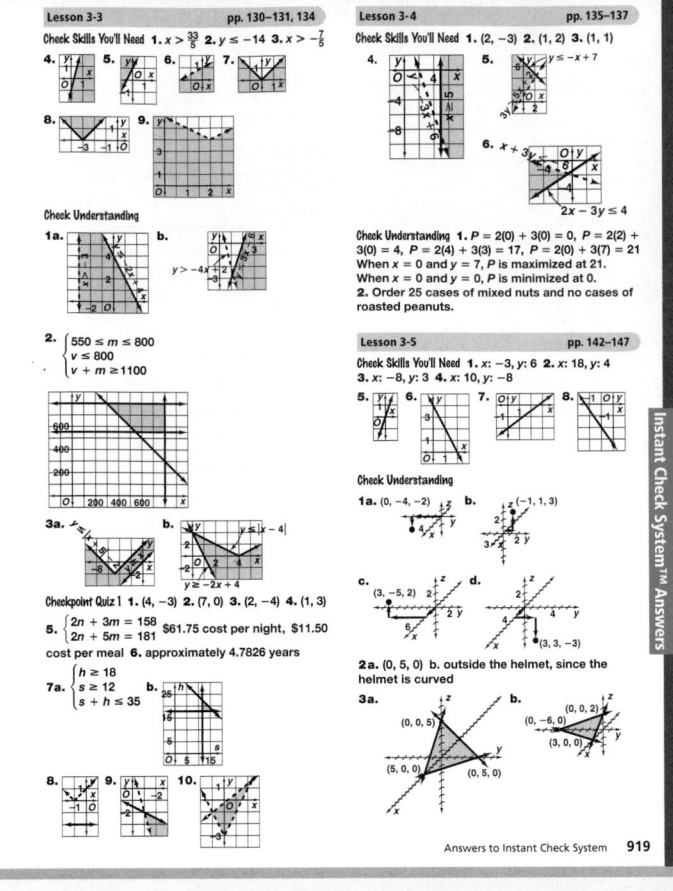

Lesson 3-3   pp. 130–131, 134
Check Skills You'll Need 1. $x > \frac{33}{5}$ 2. $y \le -14$ 3. $x > -\frac{7}{5}$

Check Understanding
1a. ... b. ... $y > -4x$ ...
2. $\begin{cases} 550 \le m \le 800 \\ v \le 800 \\ v + m \ge 1100 \end{cases}$
3a. ... b. ... $y \ge -2x + 4$

Checkpoint Quiz 1 1. $(4, -3)$ 2. $(7, 0)$ 3. $(2, -4)$ 4. $(1, 3)$
5. $\begin{cases} 2n + 3m = 158 \\ 2n + 5m = 181 \end{cases}$ $61.75 cost per night, $11.50 cost per meal 6. approximately 4.7826 years
7a. $\begin{cases} h \ge 18 \\ s \ge 12 \\ s + h \ge 35 \end{cases}$ b. ...

Lesson 3-4   pp. 135–137
Check Skills You'll Need 1. $(2, -3)$ 2. $(1, 2)$ 3. $(1, 1)$
5. $y \le -x + 7$ 6. $x + 3$ ... $2x - 3y \le 4$

Check Understanding 1. $P = 2(0) + 3(0) = 0$, $P = 2(2) + 3(0) = 4$, $P = 2(4) + 3(3) = 17$, $P = 2(0) + 3(7) = 21$. When $x = 0$ and $y = 7$, P is maximized at 21. When $x = 0$ and $y = 0$, P is minimized at 0.
2. Order 25 cases of mixed nuts and no cases of roasted peanuts.

Lesson 3-5   pp. 142–147
Check Skills You'll Need 1. $x: -3, y: 6$ 2. $x: 18, y: 4$ 3. $x: -8, y: 3$ 4. $x: 10, y: -8$

Check Understanding 1a. $(0, -4, -2)$ b. $(-1, 1, 3)$ c. $(3, -5, 2)$ d. $(3, 3, -3)$
2a. $(0, 5, 0)$ b. outside the helmet, since the helmet is curved
3a. $(0, 0, 5)$, $(5, 0, 0)$, $(0, 5, 0)$ b. $(0, -6, 0)$, $(0, 0, 2)$, $(3, 0, 0)$

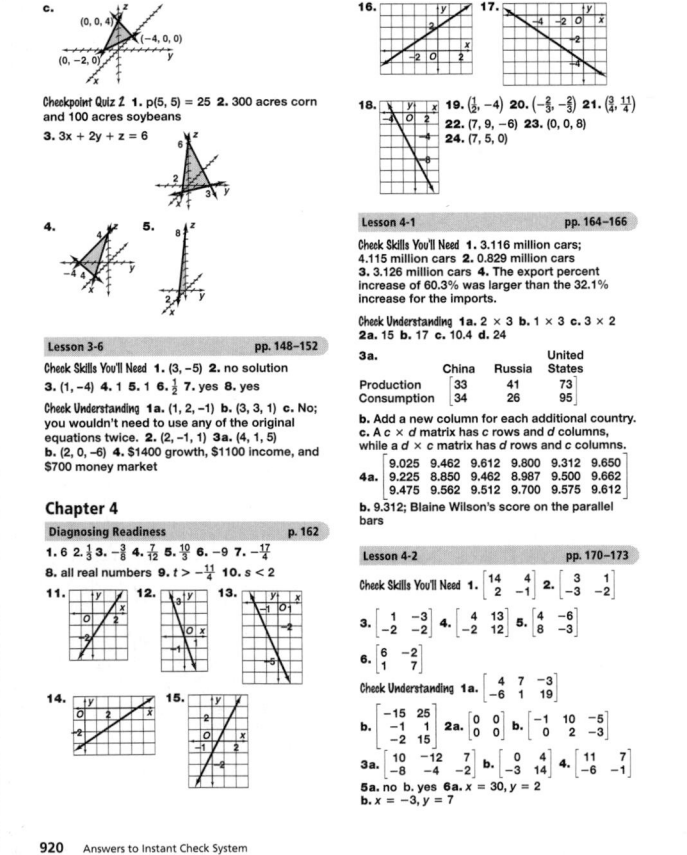

c. $(0, 0, 4)$, $(-4, 0, 0)$, $(0, -2, 0)$

Checkpoint Quiz 2 1. $p(5, 5) = 25$ 2. 300 acres corn and 100 acres soybeans
3. $3x + 2y + z = 6$

Lesson 3-6   pp. 148–152
Check Skills You'll Need 1. $(3, -5)$ 2. no solution
3. $(1, -4)$ 4. 1 5. 1 6. $\frac{1}{2}$ 7. yes 8. yes

Check Understanding 1a. $(1, 2, -1)$ b. $(3, 3, 1)$ c. No; you wouldn't need to use any of the original equations twice. 2. $(2, -1, 1)$ 3a. $(4, 1, 5)$ b. $(2, 0, -6)$ 4. $1400 growth, $1100 income, and $700 money market

Chapter 4
Diagnosing Readiness   p. 162
1. 6 2. $\frac{1}{3}$ 3. $-\frac{3}{8}$ 4. $\frac{10}{3}$ 5. $\frac{10}{3}$ 6. -9 7. $-\frac{17}{4}$
8. all real numbers 9. $t > -\frac{11}{4}$ 10. $s < 2$

Lesson 4-1   pp. 164–166
Check Skills You'll Need 1. 3.116 million cars; 4.115 million cars 2. 0.829 million cars 3. 3.126 million cars 4. The export percent increase of 60.3% was larger than the 32.1% increase for the imports.

Check Understanding 1a. 2×3 b. 1×3 c. 3×2 2a. 15 b. 17 c. 10.4 d. 24
3a.

	China	Russia	United States
Production	33	41	73
Consumption	34	26	95

b. Add a new column for each additional country. c. A $c \times d$ matrix has c rows and d columns, while a $d \times c$ matrix has d rows and c columns.
4a.
$$\begin{bmatrix} 9.025 & 9.462 & 9.612 & 9.800 & 9.312 & 9.650 \\ 9.225 & 8.850 & 9.462 & 8.987 & 9.500 & 9.662 \\ 9.475 & 9.562 & 9.512 & 9.700 & 9.575 & 9.612 \end{bmatrix}$$
b. 9.312; Blaine Wilson's score on the parallel bars

Lesson 4-2   pp. 170–173
Check Skills You'll Need 1. $\begin{bmatrix} 14 & 4 \\ -2 & -1 \end{bmatrix}$ 2. $\begin{bmatrix} 3 & 1 \\ -3 & -2 \end{bmatrix}$
3. $\begin{bmatrix} 1 & -3 \\ -2 & 1 \end{bmatrix}$ 4. $\begin{bmatrix} 4 & 13 \\ -2 & 12 \end{bmatrix}$ 5. $\begin{bmatrix} 4 & -6 \\ 8 & -3 \end{bmatrix}$
6. $\begin{bmatrix} 6 & -2 \\ 1 & 7 \end{bmatrix}$

Check Understanding 1a. $\begin{bmatrix} 4 & 7 & -3 \\ -6 & 1 & 19 \end{bmatrix}$
b. $\begin{bmatrix} -15 & 25 \\ -1 & 1 \\ -2 & 15 \end{bmatrix}$ 2a. $\begin{bmatrix} 0 & 0 \\ 0 & 0 \end{bmatrix}$ b. $\begin{bmatrix} -1 & 10 & -5 \\ 0 & 2 & -3 \end{bmatrix}$
3a. $\begin{bmatrix} 10 & -12 & 7 \\ -8 & -4 & -2 \end{bmatrix}$ b. $\begin{bmatrix} 0 & 4 \\ -3 & 14 \end{bmatrix}$ 4. $\begin{bmatrix} 11 & 7 \\ -6 & -1 \end{bmatrix}$
5a. no b. yes 6a. $x = 30, y = 2$
b. $x = -3, y = 7$

16. 17. 18. 19. $(\frac{1}{2}, -4)$ 20. $(-\frac{2}{3}, -\frac{2}{3})$ 21. $(\frac{3}{4}, \frac{11}{4})$
22. $(7, 9, -6)$ 23. $(0, 0, 8)$
24. $(7, 5, 0)$

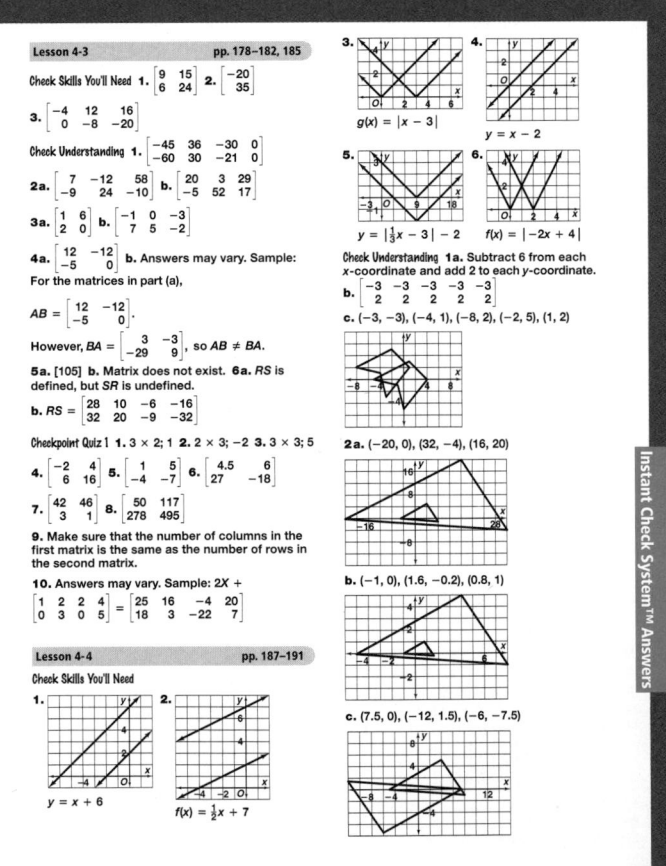

Lesson 4-3   pp. 178–182, 185
Check Skills You'll Need 1. $\begin{bmatrix} 9 & 15 \\ 6 & 24 \end{bmatrix}$ 2. $\begin{bmatrix} -20 \\ 35 \end{bmatrix}$
3. $\begin{bmatrix} -4 & 12 & 16 \\ 0 & -8 & -20 \end{bmatrix}$

Check Understanding 1. $\begin{bmatrix} -45 & 36 & -30 & 0 \\ -60 & 30 & -21 & 0 \end{bmatrix}$
2a. $\begin{bmatrix} 7 & -12 & 58 \\ -9 & 24 & -10 \end{bmatrix}$ b. $\begin{bmatrix} 20 & 3 & 29 \\ -5 & 52 & 17 \end{bmatrix}$
3a. $\begin{bmatrix} 1 & 6 \\ 2 & 0 \end{bmatrix}$ b. $\begin{bmatrix} -1 & 0 & -3 \\ 7 & 5 & -2 \end{bmatrix}$
4a. $\begin{bmatrix} 12 & -12 \\ -5 & 0 \end{bmatrix}$ b. Answers may vary. Sample: For the matrices in part (a),
$AB = \begin{bmatrix} 12 & -12 \\ -5 & 0 \end{bmatrix}$.
However, $BA = \begin{bmatrix} 3 & -3 \\ -29 & 9 \end{bmatrix}$, so $AB \ne BA$.
5a. $[105]$ b. Matrix does not exist. 6a. RS is defined, but SR is undefined.
b. $RS = \begin{bmatrix} 28 & 10 & -6 & -16 \\ 32 & 20 & -9 & -32 \end{bmatrix}$

Checkpoint Quiz 1 1. 3×2; 1 2. 2×3; -2 3. 3×3; 5
4. $\begin{bmatrix} -2 & 4 \\ 6 & 16 \end{bmatrix}$ 5. $\begin{bmatrix} 1 & 5 \\ -4 & -7 \end{bmatrix}$ 6. $\begin{bmatrix} 4.5 & 6 \\ 27 & -18 \end{bmatrix}$
7. $\begin{bmatrix} 42 & 46 \\ 3 & 1 \end{bmatrix}$ 8. $\begin{bmatrix} 50 & 117 \\ 278 & 495 \end{bmatrix}$
9. Make sure that the number of columns in the first matrix is the same as the number of rows in the second matrix.
10. Answers may vary. Sample: $2X + \begin{bmatrix} 1 & 2 & 4 \\ 0 & 3 & 5 \end{bmatrix} = \begin{bmatrix} 25 & 16 & -4 & 20 \\ 18 & 3 & -22 & 7 \end{bmatrix}$

Lesson 4-4   pp. 187–191
Check Skills You'll Need
1. $y = x + 6$ 2. $f(x) = \frac{1}{2}x + 7$

$g(x) = |x - 3|$
$y = x - 2$
$y = \frac{1}{3}x - 3 - 2$
$f(x) = |-2x + 4|$

Check Understanding 1a. Subtract 6 from each x-coordinate and add 2 to each y-coordinate.
b. $\begin{bmatrix} -3 & -4 & -8 & -2 & 1 \\ 2 & 1 & 2 & 5 & 2 \end{bmatrix}$
c. $(-3, -3), (-4, 1), (-8, 2), (-2, 5), (1, 2)$
2a. $(-20, 0), (32, -4), (16, 20)$
b. $(-1, 0), (1.6, -0.2), (0.8, 1)$
c. $(7.5, 0), (-12, 1.5), (-6, -7.5)$

3a. $\begin{bmatrix} 3 & 4 & -1 \\ 0 & 4 & 1 \end{bmatrix}$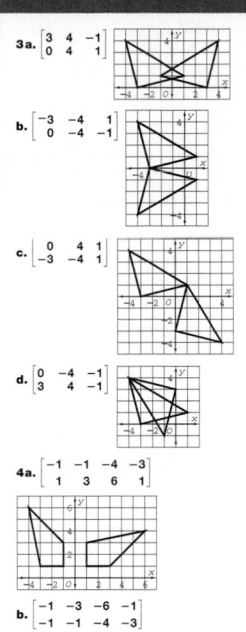

b. $\begin{bmatrix} -3 & -4 & 1 \\ 0 & -4 & -1 \end{bmatrix}$

c. $\begin{bmatrix} 0 & 4 & 1 \\ -3 & -4 & 1 \end{bmatrix}$

d. $\begin{bmatrix} 0 & -4 & -1 \\ 3 & 4 & 1 \end{bmatrix}$

4a. $\begin{bmatrix} -1 & -1 & -4 & -3 \\ 1 & 3 & 6 & 1 \end{bmatrix}$

b. $\begin{bmatrix} -1 & -1 & -3 & -6 & -1 \\ -1 & -1 & -4 & -3 \end{bmatrix}$

c. $\begin{bmatrix} 1 & 1 & 4 & 3 \\ -1 & -3 & -6 & -1 \end{bmatrix}$

d. $\begin{bmatrix} 1 & 3 & 6 & 1 \\ 1 & 1 & 4 & 3 \end{bmatrix}$

Lesson 4-5 pp. 195–199

Check Skills You'll Need 1a. 12 **b.** 12 **c.** 0 **2a.** −12 **b.** −12 **c.** 0 **3a.** 12 **b.** −12 **c.** 24 **4a.** −12 **b.** 12 **c.** −24

Check Understanding 1a. $\begin{bmatrix} 2 & 1 \\ 2.5 & 1 \end{bmatrix} \begin{bmatrix} -2 & 2 \\ 5 & -4 \end{bmatrix} =$

$\begin{bmatrix} 2(-2) + 1(5) & 2(2) + 1(-4) \\ 2.5(-2) + 1(5) & 2(2.5) + 1(-4) \end{bmatrix} = \begin{bmatrix} 1 & 0 \\ 0 & 1 \end{bmatrix}$

b. $\begin{bmatrix} -2 & -5 \\ -3 & -8 \end{bmatrix} \begin{bmatrix} -8 & 5 \\ 3 & -2 \end{bmatrix} =$

$\begin{bmatrix} -2(-8) + (-5)(3) & -2(5) + (-5)(-2) \\ -3(-8) + (-8)(3) & -3(5) + (-8)(-2) \end{bmatrix}$

$= \begin{bmatrix} 1 & 0 \\ 0 & 1 \end{bmatrix}$ **2a.** 0 **b.** 10 **c.** −9

3a. yes; $\begin{bmatrix} 1.5 & -2 \\ -0.5 & 1 \end{bmatrix}$ **b.** yes; $\begin{bmatrix} -\frac{24}{11} & \frac{23}{33} \\ \frac{10}{11} & -\frac{5}{33} \end{bmatrix}$

4a. $\begin{bmatrix} 3 & -4 \\ 4 & -5 \end{bmatrix} \begin{bmatrix} 0 & -2 \\ 0 & 4 \end{bmatrix} = \begin{bmatrix} 0 & -22 \\ 0 & -28 \end{bmatrix}$

b. $\begin{bmatrix} 7 & 5 \\ 3 & 2 \end{bmatrix} \begin{bmatrix} -2 \\ 1 \end{bmatrix} = \begin{bmatrix} -9 \\ 4 \end{bmatrix}$

5a. 43.3%, 62.0%, 70.3%; 73.9% **b.** about 11,830 people **c.** about 102 people

Lesson 4-6 pp. 202–207

Check Skills You'll Need 1. −24 **2.** 0 **3.** −24 **4.** 12 **5.** 12 **6.** 0

Check Understanding 1a. 27 **b.** 22 **c.** 0 **2.** −1087

3a. The matrices $\begin{bmatrix} 0 & 0 & 1 \\ 0.2 & -0.2 & 0 \\ 0 & -1 & 1 \end{bmatrix}$ and

$\begin{bmatrix} 1 & 5 & -1 \\ 1 & 0 & -1 \\ 1 & 0 & 0 \end{bmatrix}$ have a product of $\begin{bmatrix} 1 & 0 & 0 \\ 0 & 1 & 0 \\ 0 & 0 & 1 \end{bmatrix}$, so

they are inverses.

b. The matrices $\begin{bmatrix} 0 & 1 & 0 \\ 1 & 0 & 1 \\ 0 & 1 & 0 \end{bmatrix}$ and $\begin{bmatrix} 3 & 4 & 1 \\ -2 & 0 & 2 \\ 1 & 5 & 3 \end{bmatrix}$ have

a product of $\begin{bmatrix} -2 & 0 & 2 \\ 4 & 9 & 4 \\ -2 & 0 & 2 \end{bmatrix}$, so they are not

inverses.

4a. The matrices $\begin{bmatrix} 0 & 0 & 2 \\ 1 & 3 & -2 \\ 1 & -2 & 1 \end{bmatrix}$ and

$\begin{bmatrix} 0.1 & 0.4 & 0.6 \\ 0.3 & 0.2 & -0.2 \\ 0.5 & 0 & 0 \end{bmatrix}$ have a product of $\begin{bmatrix} 1 & 0 & 0 \\ 0 & 1 & 0 \\ 0 & 0 & 1 \end{bmatrix}$,

so they are inverses.

b. $\begin{bmatrix} 9 \\ -5 \\ 4 \end{bmatrix}$ **5. POETRY**

Checkpoint Quiz 1 1. A'(−2, 8), B'(−8, 0), C'(2, −2) **2.** A'(−4, 7), B'(−7, 3), C'(−2, 2) **3.** A'(4, 1), B'(0, 4), C'(−1, −1) **4.** A'(−4, 1), B'(0, 4), C'(1, −1)

5. $\begin{bmatrix} 2 & 3 \\ -4 & 5 \end{bmatrix}$ **6.** $\begin{bmatrix} 5 \\ 2 \\ 6 \end{bmatrix}$ **7.** $\begin{bmatrix} -2 \\ 8 \end{bmatrix}$ **8.** −10 **9.** 18 **10.** −71

Lesson 4-7 pp. 210–213

Check Skills You'll Need 1. (2, 4) **2.** (0, 6, 3) **3.** (3, −3, 9)

Check Understanding 1a. $\begin{bmatrix} 3 & 2 \\ 1 & 1 \end{bmatrix} \begin{bmatrix} x \\ y \end{bmatrix} = \begin{bmatrix} 16 \\ 5 \end{bmatrix}$;

coefficient matrix is $\begin{bmatrix} 3 & 2 \\ 1 & 1 \end{bmatrix}$, variable matrix is $\begin{bmatrix} x \\ y \end{bmatrix}$,

constant matrix is $\begin{bmatrix} 16 \\ 5 \end{bmatrix}$

b. $\begin{bmatrix} 1 & 1 & -1 \\ 1 & -2 & -1 \\ 2 & -1 & 2 \end{bmatrix} \begin{bmatrix} x \\ y \\ z \end{bmatrix} = \begin{bmatrix} 0 \\ 5 \\ 8 \end{bmatrix}$; coefficient matrix

is $\begin{bmatrix} 1 & 1 & -1 \\ 1 & -2 & -1 \\ 2 & -1 & 2 \end{bmatrix}$, variable matrix is $\begin{bmatrix} x \\ y \\ z \end{bmatrix}$, constant

matrix is $\begin{bmatrix} 0 \\ 5 \\ 8 \end{bmatrix}$ **2a.** (−1, 4) **b.** (−2, 8)

3a. $2(4) + (-10) + 3(1) \overset{?}{=} 1$
$8 - 10 + 3 \overset{?}{=} 1$
$1 = 1$
$5(4) + (-10) - 2(1) \overset{?}{=} 8$
$20 - 10 - 2 \overset{?}{=} 8$
$8 = 8$
$4 - (-10) - 9(1) \overset{?}{=} 5$
$4 + 10 - 9 \overset{?}{=} 5$
$5 = 5$

b. (1.25, 2.5, −1.75)

4. one large bead = $1.95, one small bead = $.55

5a. yes **b.** The graphing calculator indicates that there is a "singular matrix" error.

Lesson 4-8 pp. 217–220

Check Skills You'll Need 1. −3 **2.** 1 **3.** 11 **4.** −18 **5.** 15 **6.** −35

Check Understanding 1. (1, 2) **2a.** In D, replace the coefficients of z with the constants. **b.** y = 1,

z = 1 **3a.** $\begin{vmatrix} 1 & -5 \\ 3 & 3 \end{vmatrix}$ $\begin{vmatrix} 15 \\ 3 \end{vmatrix}$ **b.** $\begin{vmatrix} 1 & 2 & 3 \\ 1 & -2 & -8 \\ 0 & 1 & 1 \end{vmatrix}$ $\begin{vmatrix} 3 \\ 8 \\ 4 \end{vmatrix}$

4a. $\begin{cases} 5x + 7y = -3 \\ -8y = 6 \end{cases}$ $\begin{cases} -x + 3z = -4 \\ 7x + 2y - z = 0 \\ y + 2z = -3 \end{cases}$

5. (−15, 5)

6a. $3(4) - 2(1) + 4(0) \overset{?}{=} 10$
$12 - 2 + 0 \overset{?}{=} 10$
$10 = 10$ ✓
$4 + 4(1) - 2(0) \overset{?}{=} 8$
$4 + 4 - 0 \overset{?}{=} 8$
$8 = 8$ ✓

b. (−1, 2, 3)

Chapter 5

Diagnosing Readiness p.232

1. $4x^2 - 5x$ **2.** $\frac{11x}{30}$ **3.** $-7x^2 - 13x$ **4.** $\frac{2}{3}$ **5.** −1.8 **6.** 1

7. 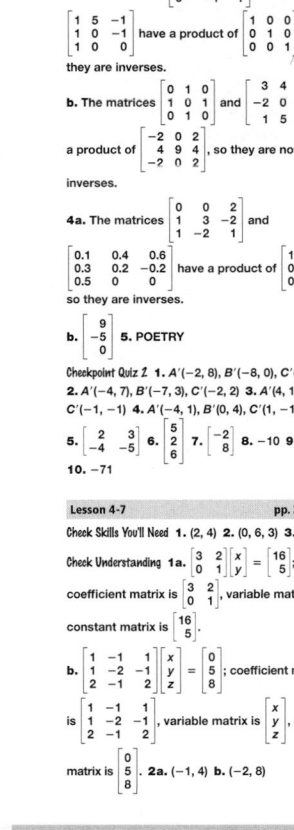 **8.** **9.**

10.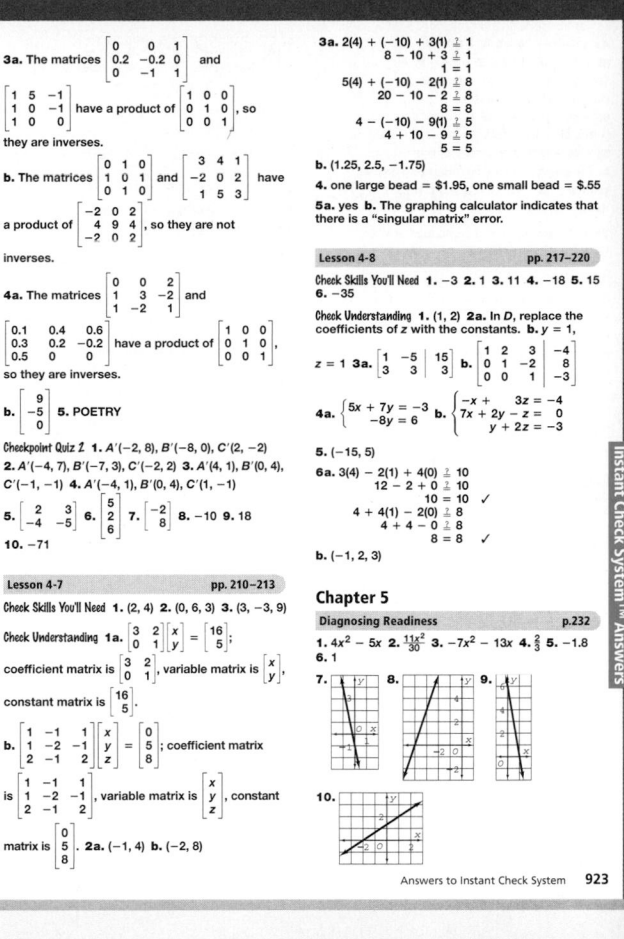

---

11. 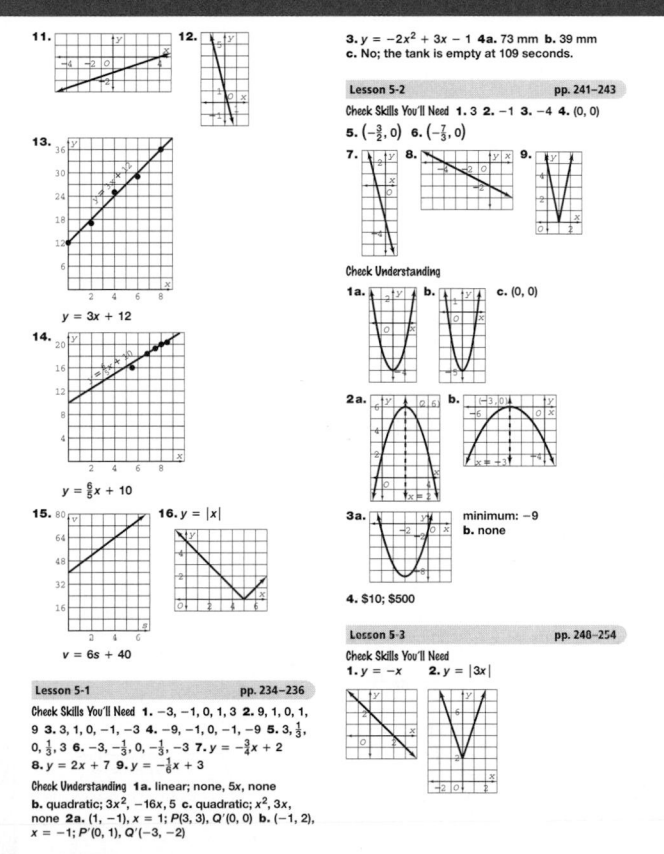 **12.**

13.

$y = 3x + 12$

14.

$y = \frac{6}{5}x + 10$

15. **16.** $y = |x|$

$v = 6s + 40$

Lesson 5-1 pp. 234–236

Check Skills You'll Need 1. −3, −1, 0, 1, 3 **2.** 9, 1, 0, 1, 9 **3.** 3, 1, 0, −1, −3 **4.** −9, −1, 0, −1, −9 **5.** 3, $\frac{1}{3}$, 0, $\frac{1}{3}$, 3 **6.** −3, $-\frac{1}{3}$, 0, $-\frac{1}{3}$, −3 **7.** $y = -\frac{3}{4}x + 2$

8. $y = 2x + 7$ **9.** $y = -\frac{3}{8}x + 3$

Check Understanding 1a. linear; none, 5x, none **b.** quadratic; $3x^2$, −16x, 5 **c.** quadratic; x^2, 3x, none **2a.** (1, −1), x = 1; P(3, 3), Q'(0, 0) **b.** (−1, 2), x = −1; P'(0, 1), Q'(−3, −2)

3. $y = -2x^2 + 3x - 1$ **4a.** 73 mm **b.** 39 mm **c.** No; the tank is empty at 109 seconds.

Lesson 5-2 pp. 241–243

Check Skills You'll Need 1. 3 **2.** −1 **3.** −4 **4.** (0, 0)

5. $\left(-\frac{3}{2}, 0\right)$ **6.** $\left(-\frac{7}{8}, 0\right)$

7. **8.** **9.**

Check Understanding

1a. **b.** **c.** (0, 0)

2. $y = 2(x + 1)^2$ **3.** $y = 0.00015(x - 2000)^2$ **4.** $y = -3(x - 2)^2 + 17$

Checkpoint Quiz 1 1. $y = x^2 + 6x + 3$ **2.** $y = -2x^2 + 4x + 1$ **3.** $y = 5x^2 - 10x$

2a. **b.**

3a. minimum: −9 **b.** none

4. $10; $500

Lesson 5-3 pp. 248–254

Check Skills You'll Need

1. $y = -x$ **2.** $y = |3x|$

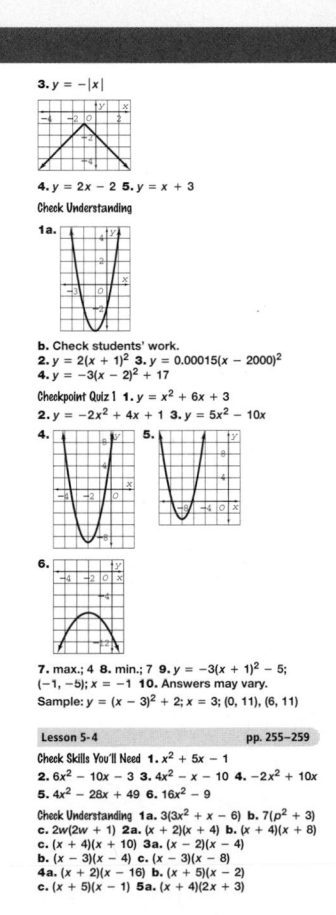

3. $y = -|x|$

4. $y = 2x - 2$ **5.** $y = x + 3$

Check Understanding

1a. **b.** Check students' work.

4. **5.**

6.

7. max.; 4 **8.** min.; 7 **9.** $y = -3(x + 1)^2 - 5$; (−1, −5); x = −1 **10.** Answers may vary.
Sample: $y = (x - 3)^2 + 2$; x = 3; (0, 11), (6, 11)

Lesson 5-4 pp. 255–259

Check Skills You'll Need 1. $x^2 + 5x - 1$
2. $6x^2 - 10x - 3$ **3.** $4x^2 - x - 10$ **4.** $-2x^2 + 10x$ **5.** $4x^2 - 28x + 49$ **6.** $16x^2 - 9$

Check Understanding 1a. $3(3x^2 + x - 6)$ **b.** $7(p^2 + 3)$ **c.** $2w(2w + 1)$ **2a.** $(x + 2)(x + 4)$ **b.** $(x + 4)(x + 8)$ **c.** $(x + 4)(x + 10)$ **3a.** $(x - 2)(x - 4)$ **b.** $(x - 3)(x - 4)$ **c.** $(x - 3)(x - 8)$ **4a.** $(x + 2)(x - 16)$ **b.** $(x + 5)(x - 2)$ **c.** $(x + 5)(x - 1)$ **5a.** $(x + 4)(2x + 3)$

b. $(x + 1)(4x + 3)$ **c.** $(x - 2)(2x - 3)$ **6a.** $(x - 1)(2x + 9)$ **b.** $(x - 6)(3x + 2)$ **c.** $(x + 2)(4x - 4)$ **7a.** $(2x + 3)^2$ **b.** $(8x - 1)^2$ **c.** $(5x + 9)^2$ **8a.** $(x - 8)(x + 8)$ **b.** $(2a + 7)(2a - 7)$

Lesson 5-5 pp. 263–265

Check Skills You'll Need 1. $(x + 7)(x - 2)$ **2.** $4x(x - 3)$ **3.** $(3x - 4)(3x + 4)$

4. 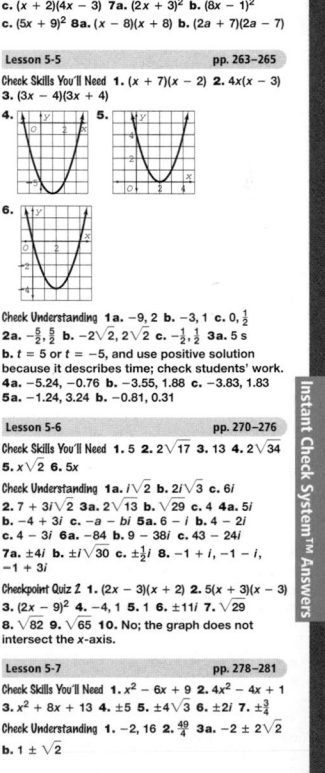 **5.**

6.

Check Understanding 1a. −9, 2 **b.** −3, 1 **c.** 0, $\frac{1}{2}$ **2a.** $-\frac{5}{2}, \frac{5}{2}$ **b.** $-2\sqrt{2}, 2\sqrt{2}$ **c.** $-\frac{1}{2}, \frac{1}{2}$ **3a.** 5 s **b.** t = 5 or t = −5, and use positive solution because it describes time; check students' work. **4a.** −5.24, −0.76 **b.** −3.55, 1.88 **c.** −3.83, 1.83 **5a.** −1.24, 3.24 **b.** −0.81, 0.31

Lesson 5-6 pp. 270–276

Check Skills You'll Need 1. 5 **2.** $2\sqrt{17}$ **3.** 13 **4.** $2\sqrt{34}$ **5.** $x\sqrt{2}$ **6.** 5x

Check Understanding 1a. $i\sqrt{2}$ **b.** $i\sqrt{3}$ **c.** 6i **2.** $7 + 3i\sqrt{2}$ **3a.** $2\sqrt{13}$ **b.** $\sqrt{29}$ **c.** 4 **4a.** 5i **b.** −4 + 3i **c.** −a − bi **5a.** 6 − i **b.** 4 − 2i **c.** 4 − 3i **6a.** −84 **b.** 9 − 38i **c.** 43 − 24i **7a.** ±4i **b.** $\pm i\sqrt{30}$ **c.** $\pm\frac{1}{2}i$ **8.** −1 + i, −1 − i, −1 + 3i

Checkpoint Quiz 1 1. $(2x - 3)(x + 2)$ **2.** $5(x + 3)(x - 3)$ **3.** $(2x - 9)^2$ **4.** −4, 1 **5.** 1 **6.** ±11i **7.** $\sqrt{29}$ **8.** $\sqrt{82}$ **9.** $\sqrt{65}$ **10.** No; the graph does not intersect the x-axis.

Lesson 5-7 pp. 278–281

Check Skills You'll Need 1. $x^2 - 6x + 9$ **2.** $4x^2 - 4x + 1$ **3.** $x^2 + 8x + 13$ **4.** ±5 **5.** $\pm4\sqrt{3}$ **6.** $\pm2i$ **7.** $\pm\frac{3}{4}$

Check Understanding 1. −2, 16 **2.** $\frac{49}{4}$ **3a.** $-2 \pm 2\sqrt{2}$ **b.** $1 \pm \sqrt{2}$

4a. $x^2 - 8x + 36 = 0$; $(4 + 2i\sqrt{5})^2 - 8(4 + 2i\sqrt{5}) + 36 = 16 + 2(8i\sqrt{5}) + (2i\sqrt{5})^2 - 32 - 16i\sqrt{5} + 36 = (16 - 20 - 32 + 36) + (16i\sqrt{5} - 16i\sqrt{5}) = 0$; $(4 - 2i\sqrt{5})^2 - 8(4 - 2i\sqrt{5}) + 36 = 16 + 2(-8i\sqrt{5}) + (-2i\sqrt{5})^2 - 32 + 16i\sqrt{5} + 36 = 16 - 20 - 32 + 36 + (-16i\sqrt{5} + 16i\sqrt{5}) = 0$
b. The graph has no x-intercepts, so no real solutions. **c.** $-3 \pm 5i$ **5a.** $-2, \frac{3}{2}$ **b.** $\frac{3}{4} \pm \frac{i\sqrt{23}}{4}$
6a. $y = (x - 5)^2 - 27$ **b.** $y = \left(x + \frac{5}{2}\right)^2 - \frac{13}{4}$

7a. (280, 38,000) **b.** The coefficient of s^2 is negative, so the parabola opens downward.

Lesson 5-8 pp. 285–289

Check Skills You'll Need **1.** $y = -10x^2 + 8$ **2.** $y = x^2 + 4x + 3$ **3.** $y = -x^2 + 4x + 1$ **4.** $y = 8x^2 - 2x - 1$ **5.** 24 **6.** 84 **7.** −48 **8.** 89

Check Understanding **1.** $-1, \frac{4}{3}$ **2a.** $-1 \pm \frac{i\sqrt{2}}{2}$

b.

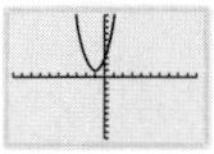

The graph does not intersect the x-axis.
3a. $\frac{1}{2}, \frac{3}{2}$ **b.** $-2 \pm 3\sqrt{5}$; −8.71, 4.71
4a. one real solution **b.** two imaginary solutions
5. yes; the discriminant is positive.

Chapter 6

Diagnosing Readiness p. 298

1. $2x^2 + 1$ **2.** $-\frac{1}{4}x^2 - 1$ **3.** $3x^2 - 6x + 3$

4.

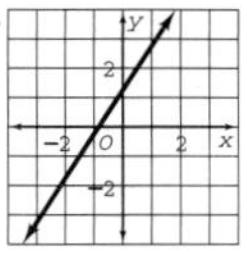

5.

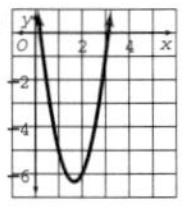

6.

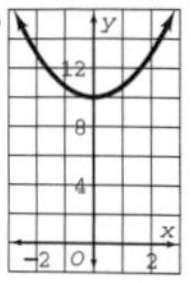

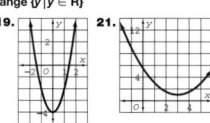

7. $x = -0.25, 1$
8. $x = -6.39, 4.39$
9. $x = -6.38, 0.38$
10. $x = -4, 9$

11. $x = -3, \frac{7}{2}$ **12.** $x = \frac{2 \pm \sqrt{13}}{3}$
13. 24; 2 real solutions **14.** 0; 1 real solution
15. 0; 1 real solution **16.** $\frac{50}{101}$

Lesson 6-1 pp. 300–303

Check Skills You'll Need **1.** x **2.** $3x^2y - 8xy^2$ **3.** $7x^2 - 3x$ **4.** 1 term **5.** 2 terms **6.** 3 terms

Check Understanding **1a.** $-2x + 5$; degree 1, 2 terms **b.** $5x^3 + x^2 - 4x$; degree 3, 3 terms **c.** $-2x^5 + 6$; degree 5, 2 terms **2.** Answers may vary. Sample: No; when $x = 25$ then, based on the cubic model, $y \approx 3.6$, but because of its turning points the cubic model is unreliable. **3.** 78.38 million troy oz

Lesson 6-2 pp. 307–310

Check Skills You'll Need **1.** $(x + 4)(x + 3)$ **2.** $(x + 10)(x - 2)$ **3.** $(x - 12)(x - 2)$ **4.** $x^2 + 4x$
5. $x^2 + 2x + 1$ **6.** $x^3 - 4x^2 - 3x + 18$

Check Understanding **1.** $x^3 + 4x^2 + 5x + 2$
2. $3x(x - 4)(x + 3)$ **3.** $V \approx 3014$ in.^{3}, depth 10.5 in., length 20.5 in., width 13.9 in. **4a.** 7, 5, 3

b.

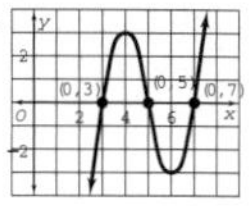

5a. $y = x^3 + 5x^2 + 2x - 8$ **b.** $y = x^3 + 6x^2 + 8x$
c. Answers may vary. Sample: The zero at 0 can be from $x = 0$, $x^2 = 0$, $x^3 = 0$, and so on. Each power will lead to a different answer. **6a.** −1, multiplicity of 3 **b.** 2, multiplicity of 2

Lesson 6-3 pp. 314–317

Check Skills You'll Need **1.** $x^2 - x - 10$ **2.** $2x^2 - 5x - 3$
3. $x^2 + 3x - 9$ **4.** $3x^2 + 9x - 30$ **5.** $4x^3 - 2x^2 + 5x + 9$; 4, −2, 5, 9 **6.** $5x^3 - 9x^2 + 10$; 5, −9, 0, 10
7. $-x^2 + 2x + 7$; −1, 2, 7 **8.** $-3x^4 + x^3 - 7x^2$; −3, 1, −7, 0, 0

Check Understanding **1.** $x + 1$, R 5 **2a.** yes **b.** no
3. $x^2 + 3x - 2$, R −4 **4a.** $x^2 - 4x + 3$
b. $(x + 2)(x - 3)(x - 1)$ **5.** −69

Checkpoint Quiz 1 **1.** Answers may vary. Sample: $y = (x + 1)^2(x + 2)(x + 3)$ **2.** $-3x^3 + 5x + 6$; degree 3, 3 terms **3.** $x^4 - 3x^3 + \frac{3}{2}x$; degree 4, 3 terms **4.** $3x^2 + 9x - 12$; degree 2, 3 terms
5. 1, 2 (mult. 2) **6.** $-\frac{1}{2}$, 4 **7.** 0 (mult. 3), 3, −1 (mult. 2) **8.** $x^2 + 2x + 1$ **9.** $2x^2 - 3x + 1$

Lesson 6-4 pp. 321–324

Check Skills You'll Need

1. (1, 4)

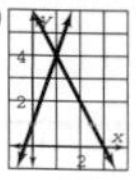

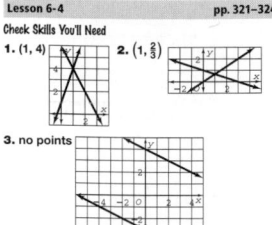

2. $\left(1, \frac{2}{3}\right)$

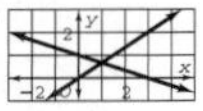

3. no points

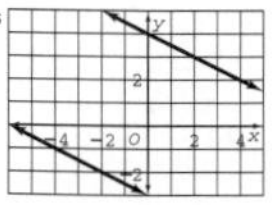

4. $(x - 5)(x + 3)$ **5.** $(x - 7)(x - 2)$ **6.** $(x + 5)(x + 1)$

Check Understanding

1. $x = -1$

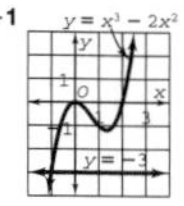

2. 22.7125 in., 25.7125 in., 20.7125 in.
3. $(2x - 1)(4x^2 + 2x + 1)$ **4a.** $-2, 1 \pm i\sqrt{3}$ **b.** $\frac{1}{3}, \frac{-1 \pm i\sqrt{3}}{6}$ **5a.** $(x^2 + 6)(x^2 + 1)$ **b.** $(x^2 - 5)(x^2 + 2)$
6. $3i, -3i, i\sqrt{2}, -i\sqrt{2}$

Lesson 6-5 pp. 329–332

Check Skills You'll Need **1.** ±1, ±2, ±3, ±4, ±6, ±12
2. ±1, ±2, ±3, ±4, ±6, ±8, ±12, ±24 **3.** ±1, ±2, ±3, ±4, ±6, ±9, ±12, ±18, ±36 **4.** ±1, ±2, ±3, ±4, ±6, ±8, ±12, ±16, ±24, ±48
5. $x^3 - 5x^2 + 7x - 35$ **6.** $x^3 + 2x^2 - 3x - 6$

7. A rational number can be written as the quotient of two integers $\frac{a}{b}$, where $b \neq 0$.
8. Irrational numbers cannot be written as quotients of integers. **9.** An imaginary number is a nonreal number of the form $a + bi$, where $b \neq 0$.

Check Understanding **1.** 4 **2a.** $\pm\sqrt{5}$, 2 **b.** $-1, \frac{1 \pm i\sqrt{2}}{3}$
3a. $2 + \sqrt{7}, -\sqrt{5}$ **b.** No; the Irrational Root Theorem does not apply unless you know that all of the coefficients of the polynomial are rational.
4a. $-3i, -2 - i$ **b.** 4 or greater
5a. $x^3 - 3x^2 + x + 5 = 0$ **b.** $x^4 + 5x^2 + 4 = 0$

Lesson 6-6 pp. 335–337

Check Skills You'll Need **1.** degree 2 **3.** degree 5
4. $\pm 4i$ **5.** $1 \pm i\sqrt{2}$ **6.** $\frac{-5 \pm i\sqrt{7}}{4}$

Check Understanding **1.** 4 complex roots, number of real roots: 0, 2, or 4, possible rational roots: ±1, ±3 **2a.** 2, $\pm 2i$ **b.** Graph the equation, and where the graph crosses the x-axis are the real zeros.

Lesson 6-7 pp. 339–341

Check Skills You'll Need **1.** 30, 240 **2.** $\frac{4}{5}$ **3.** 210 **4.** 42
5. 36 **6.** 60 **7.** 192

Check Understanding **1.** 720 **2.** 720 **3a.** 252 **b.** 28
c. 480,700 **4.** 77,520; 125,970 **5.** 638

Checkpoint Quiz 2 **1.** 1, 3, −2 **2.** $\frac{1}{3}, \frac{-1 \pm i\sqrt{3}}{6}$ **3.** $\pm 3, \pm i\sqrt{5}$ **4.** $\frac{1}{2}, \frac{-1 \pm i\sqrt{3}}{2}$ **5.** $-2, 2, -\frac{4}{3}$ **6a.** $3 + 5i, -\sqrt{2}$ **b.** Degree must be ≥ 4. **7.** 5; by the corollary to the Fundamental Theorem of Algebra
8a. 744 **b.** 10 **9a.** 21 **b.** 35 **c.** 35 **d.** 21
10. 5040

Lesson 6-8 pp. 347–349

Check Skills You'll Need **1.** $x^2 + 4x + 4$ **2.** $4x^2 + 12x + 9$ **3.** $x^3 - 9x^2 + 27x - 27$ **4.** $a^4 + 4a^3b + 6a^2b^2 + 4ab^3 + b^4$ **5.** 1 **6.** 5 **7.** 10 **8.** 10 **9.** 5

Check Understanding **1.** $a^8 + 8a^7b + 28a^6b^2 + 56a^5b^3 + 70a^4b^4 + 56a^3b^5 + 28a^2b^6 + 8ab^7 + b^8$
2. $x^4 - 8x^3 + 24x^2 - 32x + 16$ **3a.** $v^9 + 9v^8w + 36v^7w^2 + 84v^6w^3 + 126v^5w^4 + 126v^4w^5 + 84v^3w^6 + 36v^2w^7 + 9vw^8 + w^9$ **b.** $c^5 - 10c^4 + 40c^3 - 80c^2 + 80c - 32$ **4a.** 0.387 **b.** 0.349

Chapter 7

Diagnosing Readiness p. 360

1. $3y^2 - 14y + 8$ **3.** $x^3 + 4x^2 - 15x - 18$ **5.** $8b^3$
7. $6a^6$ **9.** −2, 7 **11.** $-4, \frac{2}{3}$ **15.** domain {1, 2, 3, 4}, range {2, 3, 4, 5} **17.** domain $\{x \mid x \in R\}$, range $\{y \mid y \in R\}$

19.

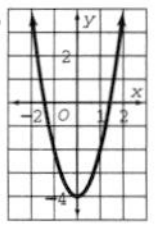

21.

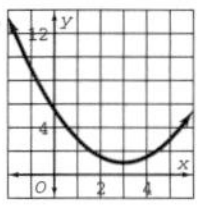

Lesson 7-1 pp. 363–365

Check Skills You'll Need **1.** 5^2 **2.** 0.3^2 **3.** $\left(\frac{2}{7}\right)^2$ **4.** $(x^5)^2$
5. $(x^2y)^2$ **6.** $(13x^3y^6)^2$

Check Understanding **1a.** 0; −1; 2 **b.** 0.01 and −0.01, no real square root, $\frac{6}{11}$ and $-\frac{6}{11}$ **2a.** −3 **b.** 3 **c.** 7
3a. $2|x|y^2$ **b.** $-3c^2$ **c.** $x^2|y^3|$ **4a.** 2.29 in. **b.** 2.8 in.
c. 2.92 in.

Lesson 7-2 pp. 368–371

Check Skills You'll Need **1.** 6 **2.** 3 **3.** 3 **4.** x^2 **5.** ab
6. $5a^3b^4$

Check Understanding **1a.** 6 **b.** −3 **c.** not possible
2. $5x^2\sqrt{2}$; $x\sqrt[3]{18x}$ **3.** $42x^3y\sqrt{3}$ **4a.** 3 **b.** $2x\sqrt{x}$
c. $4x^3\sqrt[4]{x^2}$ **5a.** $\frac{\sqrt{35}}{5}$ b. $\frac{x\sqrt{5y}}{5y}$ **c.** $\frac{\sqrt[3]{18x^2}}{3x}$ **6.** $t = \frac{\sqrt{da}}{a}$

Lesson 7-3 pp. 374–378

Check Skills You'll Need **1.** $15x^2 + 2x - 8$
2. $-24x^2 + 71x - 35$ **3.** $x^2 - 16$ **4.** $16x^2 - 25$
5. $x^2 + 10x + 25$ **6.** $4x^2 - 36x + 81$

Check Understanding **1a.** $5\sqrt{7}$ **b.** cannot combine
c. $9\sqrt{xy}$ **2.** $72\sqrt{2}$ in. or about 101.8 in. **3.** $2\sqrt{2}$
4. $5 - 2\sqrt{6}$ **5.** 3 **6.** $39 + 10\sqrt{15}$

Checkpoint Quiz 1 **1.** $|b|c^2$ **2.** xy^2 **3.** $-a$ **4.** $-y^2$
5. $8\sqrt{3} + 24$ **6.** $12x^3y\sqrt{35}$ **7.** $12\sqrt[3]{3} - 9\sqrt[3]{2}$
8. $\frac{4\sqrt{10x}}{45x}$ **9.** −7 **10.** $\frac{20\sqrt{7} - 25}{87}$

Lesson 7-4 pp. 379–382

Check Skills You'll Need **1.** $\frac{1}{16}$ **2.** $\frac{1}{9x^2}$ **3.** $\frac{1}{125x^6y^3}$ **4.** $\frac{1}{2}$
5. $\frac{16b^{12}}{a^8}$ **6.** $\frac{b^2}{16a^6}$

Check Understanding **1a.** 2 **b.** 2 **c.** 4 **2a.** $\frac{1}{\sqrt[8]{y^3}}, \sqrt[5]{z^2}$
b. $x^{\frac{2}{3}}, y^{\frac{3}{2}}$ **c.** If m is negative, $a^{\frac{m}{n}} = \frac{1}{(\sqrt[n]{a})^m}$, and if $a = 0$, then the denominator of the fraction would be zero. Since this cannot happen, $a \neq 0$.
3. about 0.270 revolutions per second, or about 16 revolutions per minute **4a.** $\frac{1}{125}$ **b.** 8 **c.** 16
5. $\frac{1}{2x^5}$

Lesson 7-5 pp. 385–388

Check Skills You'll Need **1.** −3, 2 **2.** −2, 7 **3.** $1, -\frac{3}{2}$
4. $-\frac{1}{3}, 2$ **5.** $-\frac{5}{2}, \frac{1}{2}$ **6.** $-\frac{2}{3}, \frac{3}{2}$

Check Understanding **1.** 7 **2.** 6 **3.** about 17.84 cm
4. 10 **5.** 5

Lesson 7-6 pp. 392–398

Check Skills You'll Need **1.** D: {0, 2, 4}, R: {−5, −3, −1}
2. D: {−1, 0, 1}, R: 0 **3.** D: all real numbers, R: all real numbers **4.** D: all real numbers, R: all real numbers ≥ 0 **5.** 10 **6.** 28

Check Understanding **1.** $f + g = 5x^2 + x + 1$, domain: all real numbers; $f - g = 5x^2 - 9x - 1$, domain: all real numbers **2.** $f \cdot g = 12x^3 + 8x^2 - 17x + 5$, domain: all real numbers; $\frac{f}{g} = 3x + 5$, domain: all real numbers except $\frac{1}{2}$ **3a.** $(f \circ g)(x) = x^2 - 2$, $(f \circ g)(-5) = 23$ **b.** No; the order in which operations are performed changes between $(f \circ g)$ and $(g \circ f)$, which changes what each composition equals. **4a.** Let $f(x) = 0.9x$ and $g(x) = 0.75x$. Then $(g \circ f)(x) = g(0.9x) = 0.75(0.9x)$.
b. $(f \circ g)(x) = f(0.75x) = 0.9(0.75)x$. **c.** It makes no difference.

Checkpoint Quiz 2 **1.** $81x^4$ **2.** $\frac{1}{4y^2}$ **3.** 5 **4.** $5, -\frac{29}{5}$
5. $-\frac{2}{3}, -1$ **6.** −2 **7.** $\frac{15}{4}$ **8.** 0 **9.** $\frac{7}{2}$ **10.** 43

Lesson 7-7 pp. 400–403

Check Skills You'll Need

1.

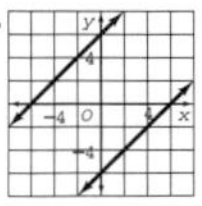

2.

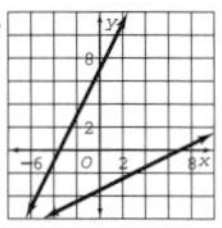

3.

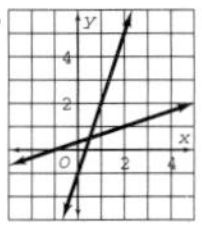

4.

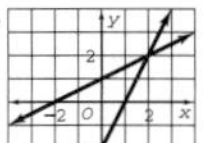

5.

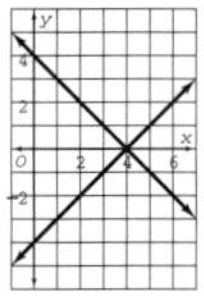

6.

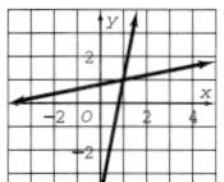

Check Understanding **1a.** The line $y = x$ is the perpendicular bisector of each segment connecting a point in s to the corresponding point in the inverse of s. The graph of the inverse of s is a reflection in the line $y = x$ of the graph of s. **b.** yes; no **2a.** Yes; no; for every x-value except 3 in the domain of the inverse there are two y-values. **b.** $y = \frac{1}{3}x + \frac{10}{3}$; it is a function because for each value of x there is only one y-value.

3.

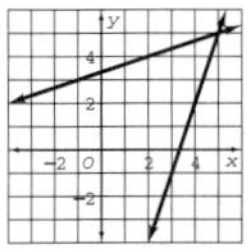

4a. D: all real numbers, R: all real numbers
b. $f^{-1}(x) = \frac{-x + 10}{3}$ **c.** D: all real numbers, R: all real numbers **d.** 3 **e.** 2 **5.** ≈44 ft/s
6. 777, −5802

Lesson 7-8 pp. 408–411

Check Skills You'll Need

1.

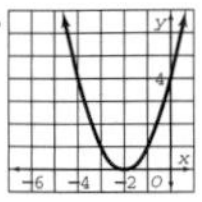

2.

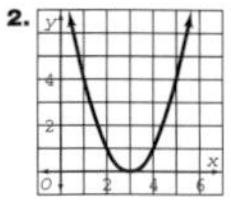

3.

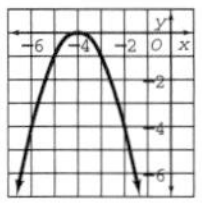

4.

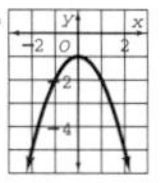

5.

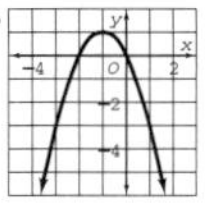

6.

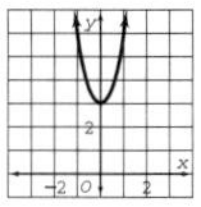

Check Understanding

1.

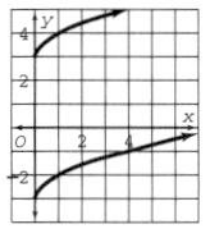

2.

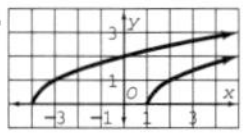

3.

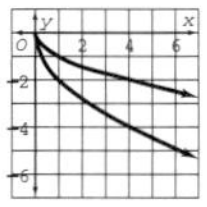

4.

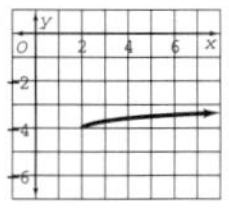

5. 512 kg

6.

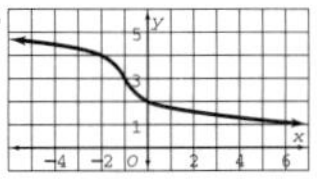

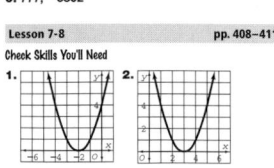

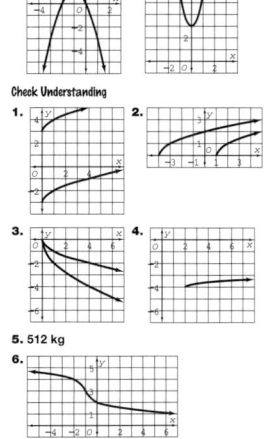

7. $y = 2\sqrt[3]{x - 3} + 3$; the graph is the graph of $y = 2\sqrt[3]{x}$ translated 3 units right and 3 units up.

Chapter 8

Diagnosing Readiness p. 420

1. 0.1, 1, 10, 100, 1000 **2.** $\frac{4}{9}, \frac{2}{3}, 1, \frac{3}{2}, \frac{9}{4}$
3. 12, 0, 0, 0, 12

4a. $n = 3d$

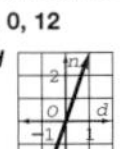

b. 84 acorns **c.** The function would be $n = 9 + 3d$ and the graph would shift 9 units upward.

5. $y = x^2 - 4x$ **6.** $y = 3x^2 - 2x + 7$

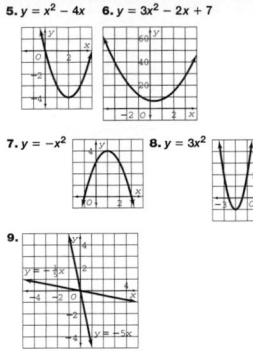

7. $y = -x^2$ **8.** $y = 3x^2$

9.

10. $y = \frac{x^2}{5}$

$y = \pm\sqrt{5x + 12}$

11.

Lesson 8-1   pp. 422–426
Check Skills You'll Need **1.** 8 **2.** 16 **3.** 2 **4.** 9 **5.** 1 **6.** $\frac{1}{4}$

Check Understanding

1a.   **b.**

2a. about 338 million **b.** The growth factor may change. **c.** about 346 million **3.** $y = 0.25(4)^x$

4a. exponential decay **b.** exponential growth **c.** exponential decay

5a. $y = 0$ **b.** $y = 0$

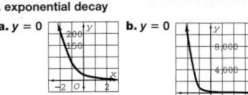

6. about $3900

Lesson 8-2   pp. 431–438
Check Skills You'll Need **1.** $y = |x + 2| + 1$ **2.** $y = -|x| - 2$ **3.** $y = (x - 1)^2 - 2$ **4.** $y = -(x + 1)^2 + 3$ **5.** $y = x^{-5}$ **6.** $y = x$ **7.** $y = x^5$ **8.** $33

Check Understanding

1a.   **b.**

2a.   **b.**

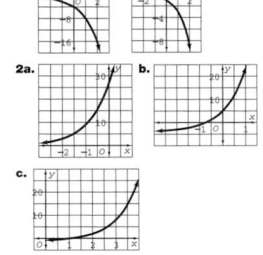

c.

3. $y = 90\left(\frac{1}{2}\right)^{\frac{3}{4}x}$; about 71 mg **4a.** 54.5982 **b.** 0.0498 **c.** 1.6487 **5.** $1479.00

Checkpoint Quiz 1 **1.** exponential growth; 45% increase **2.** exponential decay; 1% decrease **3.** exponential growth; 70% increase **4.** exponential decay; 20% decrease
5.   **6.**

---

7.   **8.**

9. Answers may vary. Sample: The population of Smallville was 1200 in 1990. It was growing at a rate of 1%. **10.** $y = 100\left(\frac{1}{2}\right)^{\frac{1}{50}x}$; 9.9 mg

Lesson 8-3   pp. 438–441
Check Skills You'll Need **1.** 2 **2.** 16 **3.** 4 **2.** 4

5.   **6.**

7.   **8.**

Check Understanding **1.** The earthquake in California released about 1265 times as much energy as the earthquake in Alabama. **2a.** $\log_3 729 = 6$
b. $3 = \log_5\left(\frac{1}{8}\right)$ **c.** $0 = \log_{10} 1$ **3a.** $-\frac{5}{6}$ **b.** $\frac{3}{2}$ **c.** 2
4. 3.2×10^{-9}

5.   **6.**

Lesson 8-4   pp. 446–448
Check Skills You'll Need **1.** 5 **2.** −1 **3.** $\frac{2}{3}$ **4.** 24 **5.** 2187
6. $\frac{1}{27}$ **7.** 36

Check Understanding **1a.** Product Property **b.** Power Property, Quotient Property **2a.** $\log 2$ **b.** No; they do not have the same base. **3a.** $\log_2 7 + \log_2 b$
b. $2 \log y - 2 \log 3$ **c.** $3 \log_7 a + 4 \log_7 b$
4. about 6 decibels

Lesson 8-5   pp. 435–460
Check Skills You'll Need **1.** 1 **2.** 2 **3.** $\frac{4}{3}$ **4.** $\frac{1}{25}$

Check Understanding **1a.** 1.2619 **b.** 0.8496 **c.** 0.2009
2a. 3.7227, $\log_6 2301$ **b.** Answers may vary. Sample: Use a calculator to raise 2 to the 2.465 power. **3.** 0.8229 **4.** 0.4634 **5.** 2068 **6.** 3.45 **7.** 200

Checkpoint Quiz 2

1.   **2.**

3. $5 \log s - 5 \log r$ **4.** $\log_6 3 + 2 \log_6 x + 2 \log_6 y$
5. $\log_6 4 + \frac{1}{2} \log_6 x$ **6.** 3 **7.** 20 **8.** 1000
9. 0.3010, 0.6309, 1.5850, 8, 9 **10.** Rewrite $\log_2 10$ as $\frac{\log 10}{\log 2}$ and evaluate it to get ≈ 3.219. Then set $3.219 = \log_3 x$. Rewrite to get $3.219 = \frac{\log x}{\log 3}$ and solve. Convert $\log x = 1.585$ to $10^{1.585} = x$ or $x \approx 38.45$. So $\log_2 10 = \log_3 38.45$.

Lesson 8-6   pp. 462–464
Check Skills You'll Need **1.** 148.413 **2.** 40.171 **3.** 0.135
4. 0.368 **5.** 11.417 **6.** 81 **7.** $\frac{1}{2}$ **8.** 65,536

Check Understanding **1a.** $\ln 8$ **b.** $\ln x^3 y$ **c.** $\ln \sqrt[4]{3x}$
2a. ≈ 5.4 km/s; no **b.** One could increase its mass ratio or its exhaust velocity. **3a.** 1.105
b. 439,605,248 **c.** 488,262 **4a.** 2.401 **b.** 1.605
5. 6.5%

Chapter 9
Diagnosing Readiness   p. 476
1. $\frac{1}{27}$ **2.** $\frac{1}{3}$ **3.** $\frac{5}{6}$ **4.** $\frac{22}{25}$ **5.** $\frac{22}{25}$ **6.** $\frac{19}{2}$ **7.** $-\frac{3}{4}$ **8.** $-\frac{8}{3}$; 2
9. $-\frac{10}{3}$; 10 **10.** $-\frac{19}{7}$; $\frac{48}{7}$ **11.** $(x + 2)(x - 2)$
12. $(4x + 5)(x + 3)$ **13.** $(3x - 5)(3x + 5)$
14. $(x - 6)^2$ **15.** $(3x + 4)(x + 2)$ **16.** $(x - 3)(x - 2)$
17. 1, −8 **18.** −6, −8 **19.** 4, 2 **20.** 0, $-\frac{5}{3}$ **21.** 8, $\frac{1}{2}$
22. 15, −2

Lesson 9-1   pp. 478–480
Check Skills You'll Need **1.** 10 **2.** 15 **3.** 1.2

Check Understanding **1.** $y = \frac{0.42}{x}$ **2a.** inverse; $y = \frac{0.72}{x}$
b. neither **c.** direct; $y = 15x$

3a. about 5,000,000 min, or about 10 yr **b.** about 27 beats per min
4. A varies jointly with the height and the sum of the bases. **5.** $V = \frac{\sqrt{2}}{6} e^3$

Lesson 9-2   pp. 485–488
Check Skills You'll Need **1.** 2 units up **2.** 2 units left
3. 3 units down **4.** 3 units right **5.** 4 units left and 5 units down **6.** 10 units right and 7 units up

Check Understanding

1.   **2.**

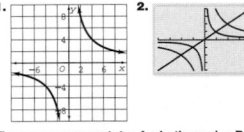

The axes are asymptotes for both graphs. Both graphs are symmetric with respect to $y = x$ and $y = -x$. The branches of $y = \frac{25}{x}$ are closer to the axes than are the branches of $y = \frac{100}{x}$; the intersections of $y = \frac{25}{x}$ and $y = x$ are closer to the origin than those of $y = \frac{100}{x}$. **3.** The axes are asymptotes for both graphs. Both graphs are symmetric with respect to $y = x$ and $y = -x$. Each graph is a 90° rotation about the origin of the other graph. **4a.** 2.28 ft, 1.81 ft, 1.52 ft **b.** As the pipe becomes very short, the pitch becomes very high (great frequency). As the pipe becomes very long, the pitch becomes low (frequency near 0).

5. $x = -7$ and $y = -3$

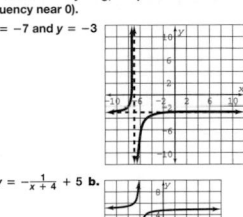

6a. $y = -\frac{1}{x + 4} + 5$ **b.**

Lesson 9-3   pp. 491–498
Check Skills You'll Need **1.** $(x + 3)(x + 2)$
2. $(x - 4)(x - 2)$ **3.** $(x - 3)(x - 9)$
4. $(2x - 7)(x + 4)$ **5.** $(2x - 5)(x - 3)$
6. $(2x - 3)(x - 8)$ **7.** 3, −4 **8.** −4, 7 **9.** 3, 6

Check Understanding **1a.** −4, 4 **b.** none **c.** −4, 2
2a. Since 1 and −3 are the zeroes of the denominator and neither is a zero of the numerator, $x = 1$ and $x = -3$ are vertical asymptotes. **b.** The graph of this function is the same as the graph of $y = \frac{1}{x + 3}$, except that it has a hole at $x = 2$. The vertical asymptote is $x = -3$. **c.** The graph of this function is the same as the graph of $y = x - 1$, except that it has a hole at $x = -1$. **3a.** $y = -2$ **b.** $y = 2$

4.

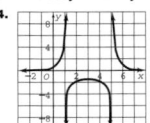

5a. Answers may vary. Sample: Graph $y = 8$ and use the Intersection feature to find that the graphs intersect at $x = 16,103.2$. So the number of discs produced must be greater than 16,103. **b.** $x = 100$; $y = 0.25$ **c.** Answers may vary. Sample: The vertical asymptote means that if you produce 100 or fewer discs you won't sell any, since the first 100 are samples. The horizontal asymptote means that the average cost will never go below $.25, since that is how much each disc costs to produce.

Checkpoint Quiz 1 **1.** $z = 5xy$ **3.** $z = \frac{100}{xy}$ **5.** Answers may vary. Sample: $y = \frac{1}{x} + 5$ is a vertical translation of $y = \frac{1}{x}$ up 5 units.

7.

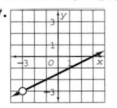

Lesson 9-4   pp. 499–501
Check Skills You'll Need **1.** $(2x - 1)(x - 1)$
2. $(2x + 3)(2x - 3)$ **3.** $(5x + 1)(x + 1)$
4. $10(x + 1)(x - 1)$ **5.** $\frac{5}{16}$ **6.** $\frac{1}{3}$ **7.** $\frac{1}{8}$ **8.** $\frac{6}{35}$ **9.** $\frac{5}{32}$
10. $\frac{3}{7}$ **11.** $\frac{3}{8}$ **12.** $\frac{2}{3}$

Check Understanding **1a.** $-\frac{3}{x}$; $x \neq 0$, $y \neq 0$
b. $\frac{-3(x + 2)}{(x - 2)(x - 4)}$; $x \neq 2$ or 4 **c.** $\frac{2x + 1}{x - 3}$; $x \neq 2$ or 3
2a. $\frac{2r}{5}$ **b.** As m gets larger, the ratio gets larger.
3. $\frac{a - 2}{a(a - 1)}$; $a \neq 0, 1, -1,$ or -2 **4.** $\frac{3(a + 5)(a - 3)}{(a + 1)(a + 4)}$; $a \neq -1, -4,$ or 4

Lesson 9-5   pp. 504–510
Check Skills You'll Need **1.** 21 **2.** 30 **3.** 187 **4.** 210
5. $\frac{17}{38}$ **6.** $\frac{19}{75}$ **7.** $\frac{11}{8}$ **8.** $\frac{137}{180}$

Check Understanding **1.** 4 cm **2a.** $6(x - 5)(x + 5)(x + 2)$
b. $10(x + 2)(x - 2)(x + 1)$ **3.** $\frac{3x^2 - 18x + 4}{(x - 6)(x + 2)}$
4a. $\frac{-3x^2 - 21x - 4}{6(x + 5)(x + 7)}$ **b.** $\frac{-x^2 + 5x + 2}{(3x - 1)(x - 2)(x + 2)}$ **5a.** $\frac{1}{xy}$
b. $\frac{6y}{2y - 1}$ **c.** $\frac{x^3 - 4x + x + 2}{2x^2 + 4x}$

Checkpoint Quiz 2 **1.** $\frac{3(x - 8)}{25(x - 4)}$ **2.** $\frac{3}{5}$ **3.** 2 **4.** $\frac{y(y - 5)}{2(y + 4)}$
5. $\frac{4(6y^2 + x^2)}{9x^3 y^3}$ **6.** $\frac{41}{15(y + 5)}$ **7.** $\frac{5xy - 12}{2y(y + 2)}$
8. $\frac{3x^3 - x^2 - 11x}{x(4y + 5)}$ **9.** $\frac{2x}{y}$ **10.** $\frac{y(3x + 1)}{x(4y + 5)}$

Lesson 9-6   pp. 512–514
Check Skills You'll Need **1.** $15t^2$ **2.** 8 **3.** $3h^3$
4. $(y + 2)(y - 1)$ **5.** $z(2z + 1)$ **6.** $(k + 2)(k - 2)$

Check Understanding **1.** no solution **b.** −3, 2 **2.** 2, −2
3. 10 mi/h downhill, 6 mi/h uphill **4a.** Maria: 6.75 h, Paco: 13.5 h **b.** Adrian: 4.5 h, Phillip: 9 h

Lesson 9-7   pp. 519–522
Check Skills You'll Need **1.** $\frac{7}{36}$ **2.** $\frac{25}{36}$ **3.** $\frac{1}{4}$ **4.** 72

Check Understanding **1.** Independent; the number of marbles is the same after the marble is replaced.
2a. $\frac{1}{25}$ or 4%; **b.** $\frac{1}{40}$ or 2.5% **b.** $\frac{1}{1000}$ or 0.1% **3a.** Not mutually exclusive since 2 is both even and prime. **b.** Mutually exclusive since no number is both even and less than 2. **4a.** about 0.26 or about 26% **b.** about 0.47 or about 47% **c.** about 0.79 or about 79% **5a.** $\frac{5}{8}$ **b.** $\frac{3}{8}$

Chapter 10
Diagnosing Readiness   p. 532
1. quadratic; $-x^2$, $6x$, 1 **2.** linear; 0, $-12x$, -18
3. linear; 0, x, $-\frac{13}{4}$ **4.** quadratic; $-8x^2$, $28x$, 0
5. quadratic; $-2x^2$, $-3x$, $+6$ **6.** linear; $-x$, -10

---

7.   **8.**

9.   **10.**

11. 16 **12.** $\frac{25}{4}$ **13.** 49

14. $y = (x + 3)^2 - 2$

15. $y = 2(x - 1)^2 + 8$

16. $y = -3\left(x - \frac{1}{6}\right)^2 - \frac{1}{12}$

17. $\frac{1}{2}$ **18.** $\frac{1}{2}$ **19.**

20.   **21.**

Lesson 10-1   pp. 535–538
Check Skills You'll Need **1.** −2, 6 **2.** −3, −1.5 **3.** −4, 3
4. ±2, −4 **5.** 3, 9 **6.** ±0.5, 1

Check Understanding

1a. 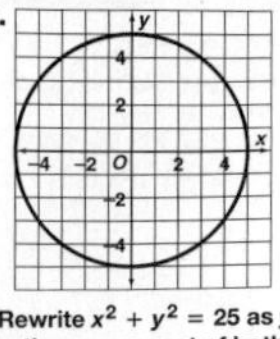

The graphs are the same.

b. Rewrite $x^2 + y^2 = 25$ as $y^2 = 25 - x^2$. Then take the square root of both sides, which gives you $y = \pm\sqrt{25 - x^2}$. **c.** When $x = 6$, $25 - x^2 = -11$. $\sqrt{-11}$ is not a real number.

2a. 4 units; 3 units; an ellipse is oblong instead of round. It has 2 axes of symmetry rather than infinitely many. **b.** (1, −2.9), (−1, 2.9), (−1, −2.9)

c. 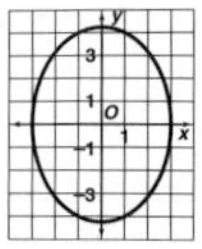

It is an ellipse with center (0, 0). The x-intercepts are 3 and −3 and the y-intercepts are $3\sqrt{2}$ and $-3\sqrt{2}$.

3a. No; there are vertical lines that intersect the graph in more than one point. **b.** Answers may vary. Sample: Solving $x^2 - y^2 = 9$ for y gives $y = \pm\sqrt{x^2 - 9}$. For $-3 < x < 3$, the value of $x^2 - 9$ is negative and $\sqrt{x^2 - 9}$ is not a real number. **c.** $y = x$ and $y = -x$; asymptotes

4. center: (0, 0); no x-intercepts, y-intercepts: −4, 4; domain: all real numbers, range: all y such that $y \geq 4$ or $y \leq -4$ **5a.** Answers may vary. Sample: All equations have an x^2-term, a y^2-term, and no other terms on the left side. There is a positive constant term and nothing else on the right side. **b.** Answers may vary. Sample: The related domains and ranges are all different. The absolute values of the coefficients of x^2 and y^2 are equal for $x^2 - y^2 = 1$, but the signs of the coefficients are different. The absolute values of the coefficients of x^2 and y^2 are equal for $x^2 + y^2 = 16$, and the signs are the same. The absolute values of the coefficients of x^2 and y^2 are different for $9x^2 + 25y^2 = 225$, but the signs are the same.

Lesson 10-2 pp. 543–546

Check Skills You'll Need **1.** 8 **2.** 4 **3.** 3 **4.** $\frac{1}{8}$ **5.** $2\sqrt{2}$ **6.** $\sqrt{65}$ **7.** $\sqrt{73}$

Check Understanding **1.** $x = \frac{1}{8}y^2$ **2.** $x = \frac{1}{2}y^2$ **3.** $y = \frac{1}{33}x^2$ **4.** (0, 3), $y = -3$ **5.** (−3, −1), (−3, −1.75), $y = -\frac{1}{4}$

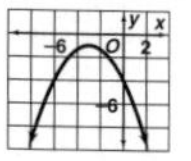

Lesson 10-3 pp. 549–552, 554

Check Skills You'll Need **1.** 4 **2.** 7 **3.** $2\sqrt{5}$ **4.** $4\sqrt{3}$ **5.** $6\sqrt{2}$ **6.** 1 **7.** 4 **8.** 9

Check Understanding **1.** $(x - 5)^2 + (y + 2)^2 = 64$ **2a.** $(x + 5)^2 + (y + 3)^2 = 1$ **b.** $(x - 2)^2 + (y - 3)^2 = 9$ **3.** $x^2 + (y + 4)^2 = 1$ **4.** (−8, −3), 11

5. 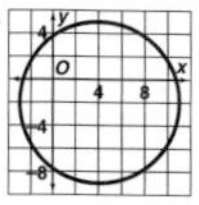

Checkpoint Quiz 1 **1.** (0, 0), $\left(0, \frac{1}{12}\right)$, $y = -\frac{1}{12}$;

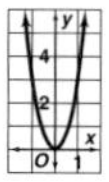

2. (0, −2), $\left(\frac{1}{16}, -2\right)$, $x = -\frac{1}{16}$; 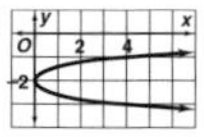

3. (3, −1), $\left(3, -\frac{3}{4}\right)$, $y = -\frac{5}{4}$; 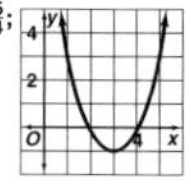

4. $(x + 6)^2 + (y - 3)^2 = 64$ **5.** 4 units left and 6 units up

Lesson 10-4 pp. 556–558

Check Skills You'll Need **1.** ±4 **2.** $\pm 4\sqrt{3}$ **3.** ±6 **4.** 34 **5.** −16 **6.** 7

Check Understanding **1.** $\frac{x^2}{9} + \frac{y^2}{36} = 1$ **2.** $\frac{x^2}{36} + \frac{y^2}{225} = 1$

3. $(2\sqrt{2}, 0)$, $(-2\sqrt{2}, 0)$; 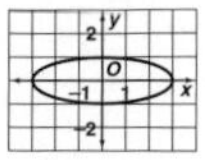

4. $\frac{x^2}{64} + \frac{y^2}{81} = 1$

Lesson 10-5 pp. 562–565, 568

Check Skills You'll Need **1.** $y = -\frac{5}{2}x$ **2.** $y = \frac{1}{3}x$ **3.** $y = \pm 2\sqrt{x^2 - 4}$ **4.** $y = \pm\frac{3}{5}\sqrt{x^2 + 25}$ **5.** $y = \pm\frac{3}{2}\sqrt{x^2 - 36}$

Check Understanding **1.** 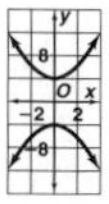

2. $(\sqrt{34}, 0)$, $(-\sqrt{34}, 0)$; 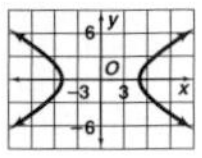

3. $\frac{x^2}{4.770 \times 10^{12}} - \frac{y^2}{3.668 \times 10^{12}} = 1$

Checkpoint Quiz 2 **1.** $\frac{x^2}{25} + \frac{y^2}{16} = 1$ **2.** $\frac{x^2}{25} + \frac{y^2}{29} = 1$ **3.** $\frac{x^2}{100} + \frac{y^2}{149} = 1$ **4.** $(\sqrt{65}, 0)$, $(-\sqrt{65}, 0)$

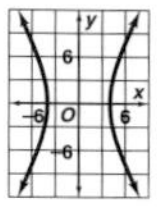

5. $(0, 2\sqrt{34})$, $(0, -2\sqrt{34})$ 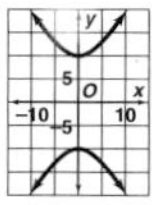

6. $(\sqrt{85}, 0)$, $(-\sqrt{85}, 0)$ 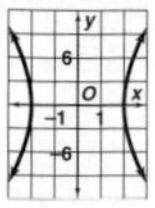

7. $(0, \sqrt{89})$, $(0, -\sqrt{89})$ 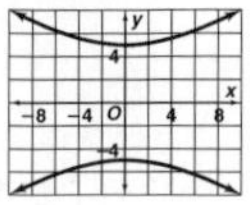

8. $\frac{x^2}{121} - \frac{y^2}{104} = 1$ **9.** $\frac{x^2}{16} - \frac{y^2}{9} = 1$ **10.** $\frac{y^2}{64} - \frac{x^2}{12.25} = 1$

Lesson 10-6 pp. 570–573

Check Skills You'll Need **1.** $y = x^2$; 4 units up **2.** $y = x^2$; 3 units right and 2 units down **3.** $y = x^2$; 1 unit up **4.** $y = x^2$; 5 units left, 6 units up **5.** $y - 8 = (x - 3)^2$ **6.** $y - 32 = (x + 5)^2$ **7.** $y - 3 = 2(x + 2)^2$ **8.** $y - 6 = 4\left(x - \frac{3}{2}\right)^2$

Check Understanding **1.** $\frac{(x - 1)^2}{25} + \frac{(y + 4)^2}{4} = 1$ **2.** $\frac{(y - 3)^2}{16} - \frac{(x - 2)^2}{33} = 1$ **3.** $\frac{(x - 100)^2}{784} - \frac{y^2}{9216} = 1$ **4.** circle with center (6, −2) and radius $4\sqrt{3}$;

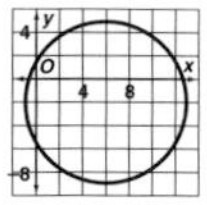

Chapter 11

Diagnosing Readiness pp. 586

1. 9, 11, 13, 15 **2.** 1, 6, 11, 16 **3.** 0.9, 1.1, 1.3, 1.5 **4.** −2, −7, −12, −17 **5.** $3\frac{1}{3}$, $7\frac{1}{3}$, $11\frac{1}{3}$, $15\frac{1}{3}$ **6.** −12, −15, −18, −21 **7.** 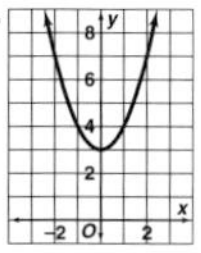

8. 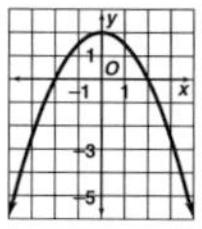

9. 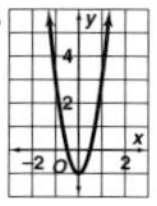

10. 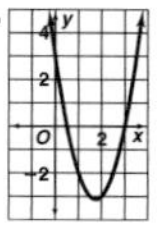

11. 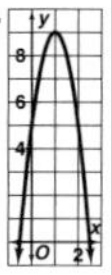

12. 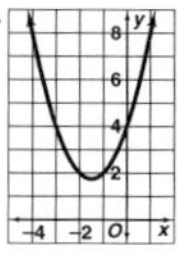

13. 4 **14.** −4 **15.** 0.4 **16.** 50 **17.** $5x^2$ **18.** $-0.3y^4$ **19.** x^3y^5 **20.** $11y^{12}$ **21.** $\frac{4}{3}$ **22.** $\frac{3}{4}$ **23.** $\frac{5}{3}$ **24.** $\frac{5}{18}$

Lesson 11-1 pp. 588–590

Check Skills You'll Need **1.** 13, 15; add 2. **2.** −14, −16; subtract 2. **3.** 3125, 15,625; multiply by 5. **4.** 20, 15; subtract 5. **5.** 8, 4; divide by 2. **6.** 20, 23; add 3. **7.** 128, 256; multiply by 2. **8.** −19, −23; subtract 4.

Check Understanding **1a.** Add 7; 55, 62, 69. **b.** Divide by 3; 3, 1, $\frac{1}{3}$. **2a.** 3.2 ft **b.** 10th bounce **3.** 22, 30 **4a.** 1, 4, 9, 16, 25, 36; 400 **b.** $a_n = n^2$ **c.** No; a_1 is not given.

Lesson 11-2 pp. 594–595

Check Skills You'll Need **1.** Subtract 2. **2.** Add 17. **3.** Add $\frac{3}{7}$. **4.** Subtract $\frac{1}{4}$.

Check Understanding **1a.** no **b.** yes; −3 **2a.** The first term in the sequence, 1100, was the amount of money with *no* participants, so there is one more term than the number of participants. **b.** 149 **3a.** 40.5 **b.** $\frac{a_6 + a_7}{2}$

Lesson 11-3 pp. 600–602, 605

Check Skills You'll Need **1.** 16 **2.** 21 **3.** 1000 **4.** $\frac{100}{3}$

Check Understanding **1a.** 5, 15, 45, 135, 405, 1215, 3645, 10,935, 32,805, 98,415; the tenth term is the ninth term times 3. **b.** Geometric; the common ratio is −4. **c.** Arithmetic; the common difference is +12. **2a.** 4,261,625,379 **b.** −34 **3a.** 40 **b.** 7.5 **c.** 378

Checkpoint Quiz 1 **1.** arithmetic; 15 **2.** geometric; 3 **3.** arithmetic; −3 **4.** geometric; 0.5 **5.** geometric; −0.5 **6.** arithmetic; −2 **7.** 6.25 **8.** 82 **9.** 1 **10.** To find the arithmetic mean, add the terms and divide by 2. To find the geometric mean, multiply the terms and find the square root of the product.

Lesson 11-4 pp. 607–609

Check Skills You'll Need **1.** 25 **2.** −42 **3.** $a_n = 2 + 2n$ **4.** $a_n = -2 + 3n$ **5.** $a_n = -11 - 6n$ **6.** $a_n = 19 - 9n$

Check Understanding **1a.** 0.3 + 0.6 + 0.9 + 1.2 + 1.5 + 1.8 + 2.1 + 2.4 + 2.7 + 3.0; 16.5 **b.** 100 + 125 + 150 + 175 + 200 + 225; 975 **2a.** 31 **b.** 252 **3a.** $\sum_{n=1}^{6} n$ **b.** $\sum_{n=1}^{9} (5n - 2)$ **4a.** 10, −2, 7; 25 **b.** 4, $\frac{3}{2}$, 3; 9 **c.** 4, 4, 25; 58

Lesson 11-5 pp. 614–616, 619

Check Skills You'll Need **1.** $193\frac{3}{4}$ **2.** 120 **3.** −22 **4.** −75 **5.** $\frac{12}{5}$ **6.** $\frac{4}{3}$ **7.** $\frac{2}{3}$ **8.** $\frac{99}{16}$

Check Understanding **1a.** $a_1 = -45$, $r = -3$, $n = 5$; −2745 **b.** $a_1 = \frac{1}{3}$, $r = \frac{1}{3}$, $n = 4$; $\frac{40}{81}$ **2a.** To find the amount 20% larger than a given amount, multiply by 1.2, which is equivalent to 120%. **b.** The common ratio becomes 1.25. **c.** Yes; they will have $1407.35. **3a.** yes **b.** no **4.** a. 2 **b.** 2

Checkpoint Quiz 2 **1.** arithmetic; 900 **2.** geometric; 29,524 **3.** geometric; −7.9375 **4.** arithmetic; 1200 **5.** geometric; 239.0625 **6.** arithmetic; 6150 **7.** $\frac{15}{14}$ **8.** 4 **9.** Answers may vary. Sample: $\frac{1}{2} + \frac{1}{4} + \frac{1}{8}$ **10.** No; the common difference causes arithmetic series to diverge.

Lesson 11-6 pp. 623–625

Check Skills You'll Need **1.** 4 ft^2 **2.** 2.75 m^2 **3.** 0.62 cm^2 **4.** $34\frac{7}{16}$ $in.^2$

Check Understanding **1a.** 1545; it is much larger. **b.** 1367.5; the mean is most accurate; it is between the other measures known to be smaller and larger than the actual value.

2a. 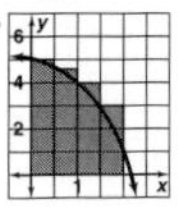

b. The left side values give the height of the circumscribed rectangles. **c.** 0.5(5) + 0.5(4.75) + 0.5(4) + 0.5(2.75) = 8.25 $units^2$; it is greater than Example 2. **3a.** $4\frac{1}{3}$ **b.** $8\frac{2}{3}$ **c.** $5\frac{1}{4}$

Chapter 12

Diagnosing Readiness p. 634

1. 120 **2.** 720 **3.** 144 **4.** 1 **5.** 6 **6.** 35 **7.** $a^5 + 5a^4b + 10a^3b^2 + 10a^2b^3 + 5ab^4 + b^5$ **8.** $j^3 + 9j^2k + 27jk^2 + 27k^3$ **9.** $m^2 + 1.4m + 0.49$ **10.** $0.000064 + 0.00192t + 0.024t^2 + 0.16t^3 + 0.6t^4 + 1.2t^5 + t^6$ **11.** ±0.1 **12.** ±0.071 **13.** ±0.063 **14.** ±0.051 **15.** ±0.048 **16.** ±0.036 **17.** 0.08 **18.** 0.125 **19.** 0.085 **20.** 0.95 **21.** 0.06

Lesson 12-1 pp. 636–639

Check Skills You'll Need **1.** yes **2.** no **3.** no **4.** $\frac{1}{18}$ **5.** $\frac{1}{4}$ **6.** 1

Check Understanding

1.

Type	Number
Acute	13
Right	7
Obtuse	5
Total	25

2. 0.857

3. Answers may vary. Sample:

Rolling One Number Cube

Numbers	1	2	3	4	5	6
Frequency	1	1	1	1	1	1
Probability	$\frac{1}{6}$	$\frac{1}{6}$	$\frac{1}{6}$	$\frac{1}{6}$	$\frac{1}{6}$	$\frac{1}{6}$

4a. The Plant Color Distribution would be most useful for avoiding white plants because it shows the total probability of growing green plants, which is the desired outcome.

b.

Genotype

Event	GG	GW	WW
Frequency	1	2	1
Probability	$\frac{1}{4}$	$\frac{1}{2}$	$\frac{1}{4}$

Plant Color

Event	Green	White
Frequency	3	1
Probability	$\frac{3}{4}$	$\frac{1}{4}$

Lesson 12-2 pp. 642–644

Check Skills You'll Need **1.** $\frac{1}{16}$ **2.** $\frac{1}{16}$ **3.** $\frac{3}{16}$ **4.** $\frac{9}{16}$ **5.** $\frac{7}{16}$ **6.** $\frac{9}{16}$

Check Understanding **1.** $\frac{7}{14}$ or $\frac{1}{2}$ **2.** ≈ 0.018 **3.** 0.9 **4.** 0.33

Lesson 12-3 pp. 648–655

Check Skills You'll Need
1. 0.2 0.3 0.6 0.7 0.8 0.9 1.2; 0.7 **2.** 11 15 17 18 21 21 23; 18 **3.** 2.6 3.9 7.8 9.1 10.4 11.7 15.6; 9.1 **4.** 76 80 82 84 86 86 89; 84

Check Understanding **1.** ≈ 3.6, 3.7, 2.8 **2.** ≈ 73.42; 73.5; 61, 70, 77, 83, 85

3. 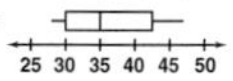

4. 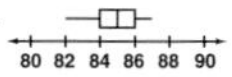

$Q_1 = 84$, $Q_2 = 85$, $Q_3 = 86$

5a. 21 **b.** 65 **c.** 71 **6a.** Yes; it is unlikely that the water temperature of a lake would change by 25°F. **b.** No; 98 would represent the busiest night of the week and it may relate to a weekly event.

Checkpoint Quiz 1

1. 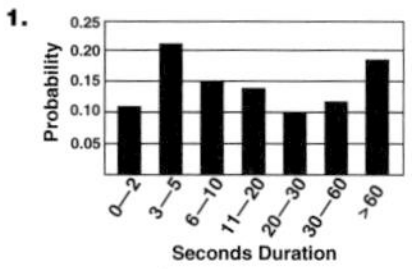

2. 0.385 **3.** No; when $x = 1$, $P(x) = -\frac{1}{2}$, and probability is never negative. **4.** $\frac{12}{57}$ **5.** $\frac{5}{8}$ **6.** $\frac{23}{43}$ **7.** $\frac{45}{68}$ **8.** 5.69, 5, 4 **9.** 3.82, 2.85, no mode

Lesson 12-4 pp. 656–660

Check Skills You'll Need **1.** 4.9 **2.** 2.5 **3.** 10.5 **4.** 9 **5.** 7 **6.** 8.03

Check Understanding **1a.** range: 14, interquartile range: 6
b. Yes; answers may vary.

1	2	3	4	5	6	7	8	9	10
1	1	1	1	1	10	10	10	10	10

c. Yes; sample:

1	2	3	4	5	6	7	8	9	10
3	3	3	5	5	6	6	8	8	8

2. 80, ≈ 18.7 **3.** 8, 4.0 **4a.** 1 **b.** No; three standard deviations from the mean is 46.3, which is less than 48. **5.** 100

Lesson 12-5 pp. 663–666

Check Skills You'll Need **1.** $\frac{1}{2}$ **2.** $-\frac{1}{3}$ **3.** $\frac{1}{6}$ **4.** $-\frac{1}{11}$ **5.** $\frac{\sqrt{2}}{10}$ **6.** $-\frac{1}{9}$

Check Understanding **1.** 52% **2a.** Yes; the sample is biased because it overrepresents students who live in a warm climate. **b.** Answers may vary. Sample: Every 10 years, the United States conducts a census of the population to find exactly how many people live in the country.

3. B; a larger sample has less variation, which corresponds to a smaller standard deviation. 4a. 100 b. 625 c. 2500 5. 71%, ±9%, 62% to 80%

Lesson 12-6 pp. 671–677

Check Skills You'll Need 1. 6 2. 1 3. 10 4. $x^3 + 6x^2 + 12x + 8$ 5. $w^4 - 4w^3y + 6w^2y^2 - 4wy^3 + y^4$ 6. $m^3 + 3m^2n + 3mn^2 + n^3$ 7. $t^4 + 12t^3s + 54t^2s^2 + 108ts^3 + 81s^4$ 8. $a^5 + 10a^4b + 40a^3b^2 + 80a^2b^3 + 80ab^4 + 32b^5$ 9. $p^6 + 6p^5q + 15p^4q^2 + 20p^3q^3 + 15p^2q^4 + 6pq^5 + q^6$

Check Understanding 2a. P (one prize) = $3(0.4)^1(0.6)^2 = 0.432$; $1(0.6)^3$, P(no prize) = 0.216 b. 1 3a. 0.2637 b. 0.2335 4. 0.9933

Checkpoint Quiz 2 1. $33.8\overline{3}$, 20, 6.20 2. 11, 5, 1.63 3. 2.375, 4, 1.41 4. 228 5a. This survey may be biased because it overrepresents people who shop for CDs online and entirely misses those who do not have internet access. b. Answers may vary. Sample: Survey a random selection of students in homerooms for each grade level. 6a. 0.3441 ≈ 34.4% b. ±3.8% c. 30.6% to 38.2% 7. 25 8. 0.343 9. 0.4096 10. 0.0768

Lesson 12-7 pp. 678–680

Check Skills You'll Need 1. 8, 10, 14, 16 2. 14.7, 15.7, 17.7, 18.7 3. 4, 5.5, 8.5, 10 4. 18.6, 20.3, 23.7, 25.4 5. 15.7, 16.6, 18.4, 19.3 6. 30.7, 31.9, 34.3, 35.5

Check Understanding 1a. 71% b. 88%

2.

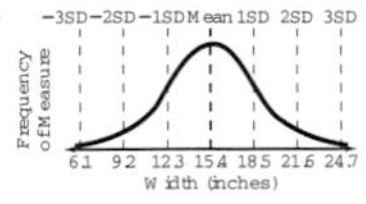

3a. 68 responses b. 13 or 14 responses 4a. 47 or 48 students b. 76 is about 1SD above the mean. About 13.5% + 2.5% should receive grades above 76. 16% of 140 is about 22.

Chapter 13

Diagnosing Readiness p. 694

1. vertical asymptote $x = 3$ 2. hole at $x = 1$ 3. vertical asymptotes $x = -\frac{1}{2}$ and $x = 4$ 4. $\frac{2b}{a}$ 5. $\frac{55}{18}$ 6. $\frac{3}{2(c + d)}$ 7. $\frac{c}{16}$ 8. $\frac{c + 4}{9}$ 9. $\frac{16}{x}$ 10. $\frac{15}{7}$ 11. 6

12. $(x - 1)^2 + (y + 4)^2 = 16$;

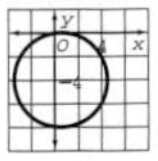

13. $\frac{(x - 2)^2}{9} + \frac{(y - 5)^2}{4} = 1$;

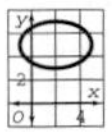

14. $y = \frac{1}{32}x^2 - 3$;

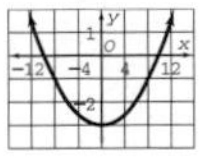

15. $\frac{(y - 1)^2}{9} - \frac{(x - 6)^2}{16} = 1$;

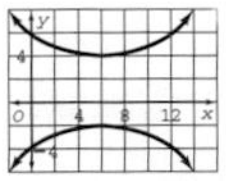

16. 4, 1; $a_n = 19 - 3n$; explicit or $a_1 = 16$, $a_n = a_{n-1} - 3$; recursive 17. −216, −343; $a_n = -n^3$; explicit 18. $\frac{1}{9}, \frac{1}{27}$; $a_n = 9\left(\frac{1}{3}\right)^{n-1}$; explicit or $a_1 = 9$, $a_n = \frac{1}{3} \cdot a_{n-1}$; recursive

Lesson 13-1 pp. 696–699

Check Skills You'll Need 1. yes 2. yes 3. no 4. yes 5. no 6. no 7. yes 8. yes

Check Understanding 1a. from −3 to 1 or 0 to 4; 4 b. from −4 to −1 or 0 to 3; 3 2a. not periodic b. periodic; 4 3a. 1.5 b. 1.5

4.

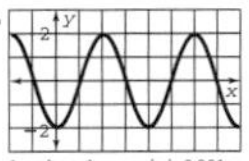

1 unit on the x-axis is 0.001 s

Lesson 13-2 pp. 704–708

Check Skills You'll Need

1. 2. 3. 4. 5. 6.

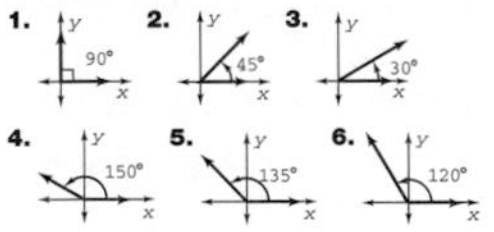

Check Understanding 1. 90°; 180°; 270°

2a. b.

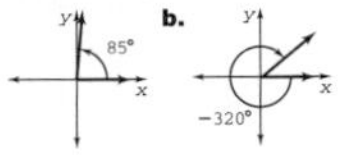

c.

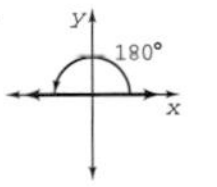

3a. 558° b. No; 40° is coterminal with 400° and 760°. c. Answers may vary. Sample: The difference between measures of two coterminal angles is a multiple of 360°.

4a. b.

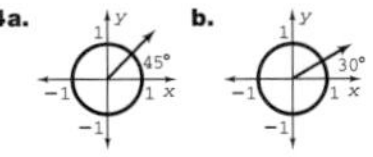

0.707, 0.707 0.87, 0.5

c.

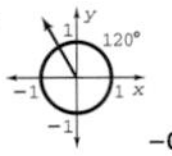

−0.5, 0.87

5a. −0.5, −0.87; −0.5, −0.87; the values are equal and are the rounded decimal equivalents of $-\frac{1}{2}$ and $-\frac{\sqrt{3}}{2}$. b. $-\frac{\sqrt{2}}{2}, \frac{\sqrt{2}}{2}$; −0.707, 0.707 c. $-\frac{\sqrt{3}}{2}, \frac{1}{2}$

Lesson 13-3 pp. 712–719

Check Skills You'll Need 1. 25.1 in. 2. 219.9 m 3. 50.3 mi 4. 10.7 ft 5. 31.4 mm 6. 19.8 cm

Check Understanding 1a. ≈1.48 radians b. ≈143.24° 2a. 90° b. $\frac{5\pi}{4}$ radians c. ≈114.59° d. $\frac{5\pi}{6}$ radians

3a. 0.71, 0.71; these values are the rounded decimal equivalent of $\frac{\sqrt{2}}{2}$. b. π radians = 180°, so $\frac{\pi}{4}$ radians becomes $\frac{180°}{4}$, which is 45°. 4. 6.3 in. 5a. ≈3.14 units b. ≈4.19 units c. ≈6.28 units d. ≈10.47 units

Checkpoint Quiz 1 1. 5, 1 2. 4, 2 3. $-\frac{\sqrt{2}}{2}, \frac{\sqrt{2}}{2}$ 4. $-\frac{1}{2}, -\frac{\sqrt{3}}{2}$ 5. 0, −1 6. $\frac{1}{2}, \frac{\sqrt{3}}{2}$ 7. $-\pi$ radians 8. $\frac{\pi}{5}$ radians 9. 180° 10. 240°

Lesson 13-4 pp. 720–724

Check Skills You'll Need 1. 2 2. all real numbers 3. 1 4. all real numbers between −1 and 1, inclusive

Check Understanding 1a. yes; at 450° b. Yes; the y-values repeat at regular intervals. 2a. 1 b. 360°, 2π radians c. domain: all real numbers, range: all real numbers between −1 and 1, inclusive 3a. 2π b. $\frac{2\pi}{3}$ 4a. 4 b. 3

5a.

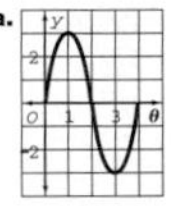

b. zero-min-zero-max-zero

c.

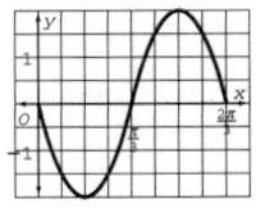

6a. b.

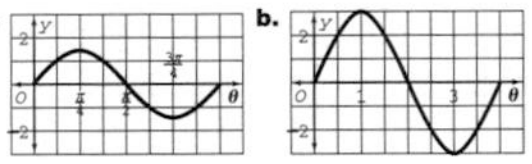

7. $y = \sin 0.010\theta$, $y = \sin 0.011\theta$

Lesson 13-5 pp. 729–731

Check Skills You'll Need 1. 1 2. 0 3. −1 4. 0

Check Understanding 1. They are the same curve translated $\frac{\pi}{2}$ units horizontally.

2a.

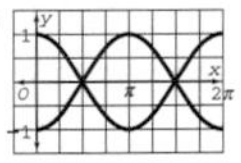

They are reflections of each other over the x-axis.

b. min-zero-max-zero-min

c.

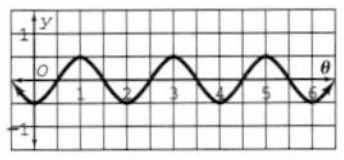

3a. $y = 4 \cos \frac{1}{3}\theta$ b. $y = 2.5 \cos \frac{\pi}{4}\theta$ 4a. 1.1, 2.0, 4.3, 5.1 b. 2.2, 4.1 c. $0 \le \theta < 2.2$ and $4.1 < \theta \le 2\pi$; $2.2 < \theta < 4.1$

Lesson 13-6 pp. 735–737

Check Skills You'll Need 1. 0.87, 0.5; 1.74 2. 0.5, 0.87; 0.58 3. 1, 0; undefined 4. 0.5, −0.87; −0.58 5. 1, 0; undefined 6. 0, 1; 0

Check Understanding 1a. 0.4, −0.4 b. The terminal side of $\frac{\pi}{2}$ lies on the line $x = 0$, which cannot intersect $x = 1$.

2a. b.

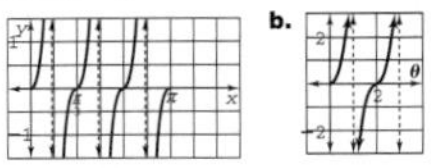

3a. 46.6 ft b. 8°

Lesson 13-7 pp. 742–748

Check Skills You'll Need

1. 2.

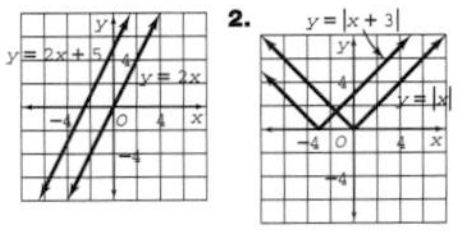

horizontal or vertical horizontal

3. 4.

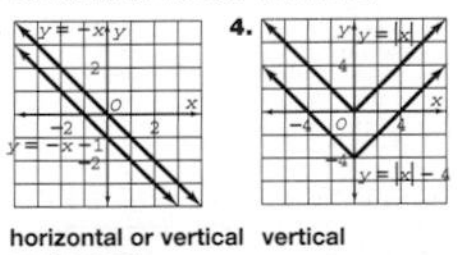

horizontal or vertical or diagonal vertical

5. 6.

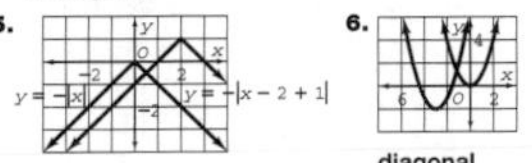

diagonal diagonal

Check Understanding 1a. 5; 5 units to the right b. −3; 3 units to the left

2a. b.

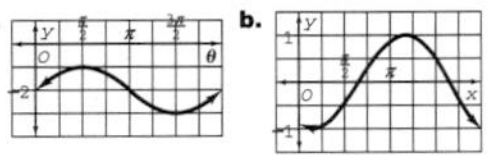

(b) is a phase shift.

3a. b.

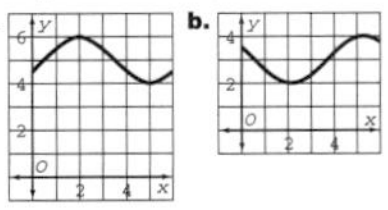

4a. b.

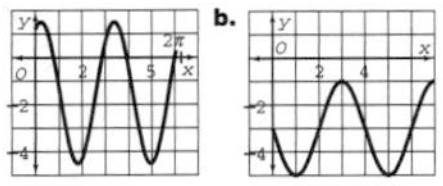

5a. $y = \cos x + \frac{\pi}{2}$ b. $y = 2 \sin\left(x - \frac{\pi}{4}\right)$ 6a. 86.5° b. day 100

Checkpoint Quiz 2

1.

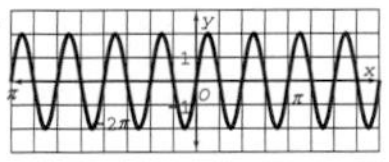

2.

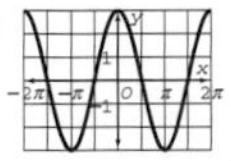

3.

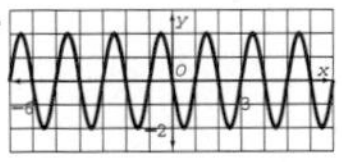

4.

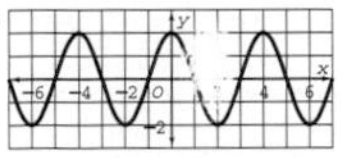

5.

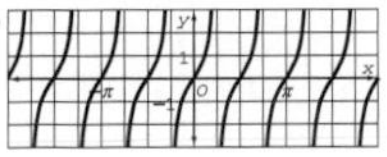

6.

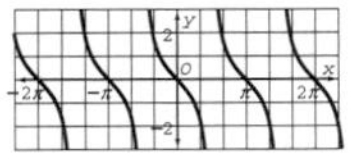

7.

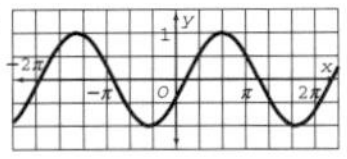

8.

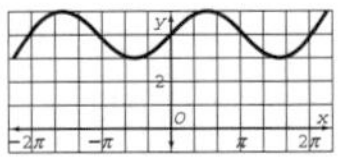

9.

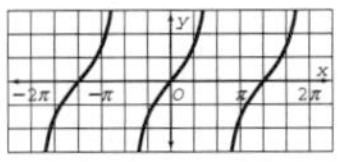

10.

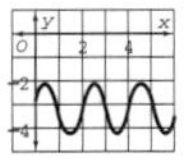

Lesson 13-8 pp. 749–752

Check Skills You'll Need 1. $\frac{13}{9}$ 2. $-\frac{8}{5}$ 3. 2π 4. $\frac{15}{4m}$ 5. $-\frac{1}{14}$

6. 7.

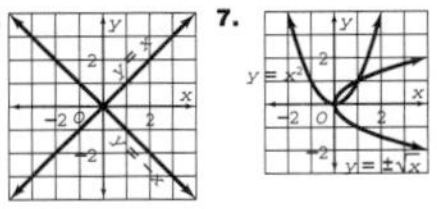

8. 9.

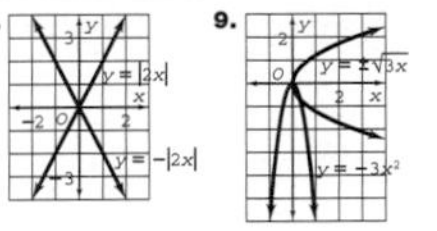

Check Understanding 1a. $\frac{8}{15}$ b. ≈0.7 2a. 2 b. 1 c. 2 3a. −1.003 b. −2.403 c. undefined

4.

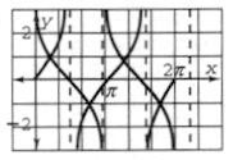

5. 1.4142 6. 6.9 ft; 8.5 ft; 68.8 ft

Chapter 14

Diagnosing Readiness p. 762

1. $\pm\frac{5}{2}$ 2. $\pm\sqrt{23}$ 3. $\pm\frac{4\sqrt{15}}{3}$ 4. $\pm\frac{\sqrt{22}}{2}$ 5. $\pm\sqrt{30}$ 6. ±2 7. Domain of f is $\{x \mid x \in R\}$, range of f is $\{y \mid y \in R\}$; $f^{-1}(x) = \frac{x - 2}{5}$, domain of f^{-1} is $\{x \mid x \in R\}$, range of f^{-1} is $\{y \mid y \in R\}$. f^{-1} is a function. 8. Domain of f is $\{x \mid x \in R, x \ge -3\}$, range of f is $\{y \mid y \in R, y \ge 0\}$; $f^{-1}(x) = x^2 - 3$, domain of f^{-1} is $\{x \mid x \in R\}$, range of f^{-1} is $\{y \mid y \in R, y \ge -3\}$. f^{-1} is a function. 9. Domain of f is $\left\{x \mid x \in R, x \ge \frac{4}{3}\right\}$, range of f is $\{y \mid y \in R, y \ge 0\}$; $f^{-1}(x) = \frac{x^2 + 4}{3}$, domain of f is $\{x \mid x \in R, x \ge 0\}$, range of f^{-1} is $\left\{y \mid y \in R, y \ge \frac{4}{3}\right\}$. f^{-1} is a function. 10. Domain of f is $\{x \mid x \in R, x \ne 0\}$, range of f is $\{y \mid y \in R, y \ne 0\}$; $f^{-1}(x) = \frac{5}{x}$, domain of f^{-1} is $\{x \mid x \in R, x \ne 0\}$, range of f^{-1} is $\{y \mid y \in R, y \ne 0\}$. f^{-1} is a function. 11. Domain of f is $\{x \mid x \in R, x \ne 1\}$, range of f is $\{y \mid y \in R, y \ne 0\}$; $f^{-1}(x) = \frac{10}{x} + 1$, domain of f^{-1} is $\{x \mid x \in R, x \ne 0\}$, range of f^{-1} is $\{y \mid y \in R, y \ne 1\}$. f^{-1} is a function. 12. Domain of f is $\{x \mid x \in R, x \ne 0\}$, range of f is $\{y \mid y \in R, y \ne -1\}$; $f^{-1}(x) = \frac{10}{x + 1}$, domain of f^{-1} is $\{x \mid x \in R, x \ne -1\}$, range of f^{-1} is $\{y \mid y \in R, y \ne 0\}$. f^{-1} is a function. 13. −1.5 14. 0.002 15. ≈1.065 16. ≈18,257 17. $\approx 3 \times 10^{-5}$ 18. 5 19. 0.67, 0.74, 1.11 20. −0.26, −0.97, 3.73 21. 0.96, 0.28, 0.29 22. −0.87, 0.5, −0.58

Lesson 14-1 pp. 764–766

Check Skills You'll Need 1. Yes; $2x + 3x = (2 + 3)x$ by the Dist. Prop. and $(2 + 3)x = 5x$ by arithmetic. 2. Yes; $-(4x - 10) = 10 - 4x$ by the opposite of a difference prop. 3. No; for $x = 0$, $\frac{4x^2}{x}$ is not defined, but $4x = 0$. 4. No; for $x = 1$, $\frac{x^2 + 1}{x - 1}$ is not defined, but $x + 1 = 2$.

Check Understanding **1.** $1 + \cot^2\theta = 1 + \left(\frac{\cos\theta}{\sin\theta}\right)^2 = 1 + \frac{\cos^2\theta}{\sin^2\theta} = 1 + \frac{1 - \sin^2\theta}{\sin^2\theta} = 1 + \frac{1}{\sin^2\theta} - \frac{\sin^2\theta}{\sin^2\theta} = 1 + \csc^2\theta - 1 = \csc^2\theta$ **2.** $\sec^2\theta - \sec^2\theta\cos^2\theta = \left(\frac{1}{\cos\theta}\right)^2 - \left(\frac{1}{\cos\theta}\right)^2\cos^2\theta = \frac{1}{\cos^2\theta} - \frac{1}{\cos^2\theta}\cdot\cos^2\theta = \frac{1}{\cos^2\theta} - \frac{\cos^2\theta}{\cos^2\theta} = \frac{1 - \cos^2\theta}{\cos^2\theta} = \frac{\sin^2\theta}{\cos^2\theta} = \tan^2\theta$ **3.** $\csc\theta$

Lesson 14-2 pp. 769–772

Check Skills You'll Need **1.** $f^{-1}(x) = x - 1$ **2.** $f^{-1}(x) = \frac{x + 3}{2}$ **3.** $f^{-1}(x) = \pm\sqrt{x - 4}$ **4.** 0.5 **5.** $\frac{\sqrt{2}}{2}$ **6.** $-\frac{\sqrt{2}}{2}$ **7.** 0 **8.** −1 **9.** $-\frac{\sqrt{3}}{2}$

Check Understanding **1.** none, $\frac{\pi}{2} + \pi n$, none **2a.** $120° + n\cdot360°$ and $240° + n\cdot360°$ **b.** $150° + n\cdot360°$ and $210° + n\cdot360°$ **c.** $45° + n\cdot360°$ and $315° + n\cdot360°$ **3a.** $0.46 + 2\pi n$ and $2.69 + 2\pi n$ **b.** $-0.82 + 2\pi n$ and $3.96 + 2\pi n$ **4a.** $0.41 + 2\pi n$ and $3.56 + 2\pi n$ **b.** $-0.63 + 2\pi n$ and $2.51 + 2\pi n$ **5.** $-\frac{\pi}{6}$ and $\frac{7\pi}{6}$ **6.** $\frac{\pi}{2}$ and $\frac{3\pi}{2}$ **7a.** $\frac{1}{2}$ s; 3 s **b.** At 2 s; the toy will reach a maximum at 4 in. and then come back down, again hitting 2 in. at 2 s. **c.** Let $y_1 = -4\cos\frac{2\pi}{3}t$ and let $y_2 = 2$. Graph. Trace and calculate the intersection.

Lesson 14-3 pp. 778–785

Check Skills You'll Need **1.** s **2.** r **3.** a **4.** t

Check Understanding **1.** 180 m **2.**

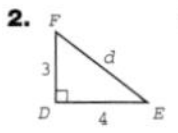

$\frac{3}{5} = 0.6, \frac{5}{3} \approx 1.67$

3a. Answers may vary. Sample: An advantage is that simplification of the equation is easier. A disadvantage is that you have to press an extra button on the calculator to get the cotangent function. **b.** ≈34.29 ft **4a.** 23.58° **b.** 56.25° **5.**

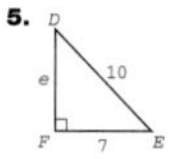

$e \approx 7.14$; $m\angle E \approx 45.6°$, $m\angle D \approx 44.4°$

Checkpoint Quiz 1 **1.** $\csc\theta$ **2.** $\tan^2\theta$ **3.** $-\csc^2\theta$ **4.** 2.25 **5.** 0.320 **6.** 1.345 **7.** $a \approx 7.7$, $m\angle A \approx 29.0°$, $m\angle B \approx 61.0°$ **8.** $c \approx 10.0$, $m\angle A \approx 51.9°$, $m\angle B \approx 38.1°$ **9.** $a \approx 19.6$, $m\angle A \approx 34.0°$, $m\angle B \approx 56.0°$

Lesson 14-4 pp. 787–789

Check Skills You'll Need **1.** $\frac{1}{12}$ **2.** $\frac{\sqrt{2}}{8}$ **3.** $\frac{\sqrt{3}}{20}$ **4.** $\frac{1}{24}$ **5.** $\frac{\sqrt{2}}{16}$ **6.** $\frac{\sqrt{3}}{18}$ **7.** 6 cm² **8.** 45 in.² **9.** 32.8 mm² **10.** 10.03 ft²

Check Understanding **1.** 36.6 in.² **2.** 31.0 yd **3.** 68.4° **4.** 56.4

Lesson 14-5 pp. 794–796

Check Skills You'll Need **1.** 26.2° **2.** 18.1 **3.** 52.1°

Check Understanding **1.** 6.4 **2.** 75.3° **3.** 30.7°

Lesson 14-6 pp. 800–804

Check Skills You'll Need **1.** $\sin\theta$ **2.** $\cos\theta$ **3.** $\tan\theta$ **4.** 1 **5.** $\sec^2\theta$ **6.** $\csc^2\theta$

Check Understanding **1.** $\cos\left(\theta - \frac{\pi}{2}\right) = \cos\left(-\left(\frac{\pi}{2} - \theta\right)\right) = \cos\left(\frac{\pi}{2} - \theta\right) = \sin\theta$ **2.** $0 + 2\pi n, \pi + 2\pi n$ **3.** $\sec(90° - A) = \csc A$ **4.** $\frac{\sqrt{6} - \sqrt{2}}{4}$ **5.** $-2 - \sqrt{3}$

Checkpoint Quiz 2 **1.** 36.1 cm² **3.** 34.9 m² **5.** $a = 8.2$ ft, $m\angle B = 69.7°$, $m\angle C = 83.3°$ **7.** cos 80° **9.** sin 80°

Lesson 14-7 pp. 807–809

Check Skills You'll Need **1.** $\cos A\cos B + \sin A\sin B$ **2.** $\cos A\cos B - \sin A\sin B$ **3.** $\frac{\tan A - \tan B}{1 + \tan A\tan B}$ **4.** $\sin A\cos B - \cos A\sin B$ **5.** $\sin A\cos B + \cos A\sin B$ **6.** $\frac{\tan A + \tan B}{1 - \tan A\tan B}$

Check Understanding **1.** $\frac{\sqrt{3}}{2}$ **2.** $2\cos 2\theta = 2(2\cos^2\theta - 1) = 4\cos^2\theta - 2$ **3a.** $\frac{1}{2}$ **b.** $-\frac{\sqrt{3}}{3}$ **4.** $-\frac{3}{5}, -\frac{4}{3}$

Selected Answers

Chapter 1

Lesson 1-1 pp. 4–10

EXERCISES **1.** natural numbers, whole numbers, integers, rational numbers, real numbers **3.** irrational numbers, real numbers **9.** whole numbers, integers **11.** rational numbers **13.**

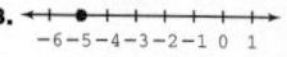

15.

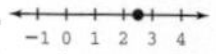

17. > **19.** > **25.** $-\frac{1}{4} > -\frac{1}{3}$, $-\frac{1}{3} < -\frac{1}{4}$ **27.** $-2.\overline{3} < 2.\overline{1}$, $2.\overline{1} > -2.\overline{3}$ **35.** $-3\frac{3}{5}, \frac{5}{18}$ **37.** $\frac{7}{2}, -\frac{2}{7}$ **43.** Dist. Prop. **45.** Assoc. Prop. of Mult. **53.** 10.3 **55.** −25 **61.** −5 **69.** natural numbers, whole numbers, integers, rational numbers, real numbers **71.** irrational numbers, real numbers **75.** > **77.** < **83.** Answers may vary. Sample: 4 is a whole number, but $\frac{1}{4}$ is not a whole number. **85.** 0 is a whole number, and since −0 = 0, the opposite of 0 is a whole number. **103.** −3.8 **105.** 0 **109.** $\frac{35}{3}$, or $11\frac{2}{3}$ **111.** 5

Lesson 1-2 pp. 12–17

EXERCISES **1.** −30 **3.** 368 **9.** 1 ft **11.** 64 ft **13.** 0.013 mm **15.** 0.4 mm **17.** $1210 **19.** $1464.10 **21.** $4a$ **23.** $-9a + b$ **37.** $4a$ **39.** 17 **41.** 66 **47.** $-\frac{3}{4}a^2 + 2b^2$ **49.** $\frac{7y^2}{12} + \frac{2y}{15}$ **55.** C **57.** G **63.** Assoc. Prop. of Add., Comm. Prop. of Add., Assoc. Prop. of Add., Identity Prop. of Mult., Dist. Prop. of Add. **75.** $-4.3, -|3.4|, |-3.4|, |-4.3|$ **77.** $-\sqrt{\frac{1}{8}}, -\sqrt{\frac{1}{10}}, \sqrt{\frac{1}{16}}, \sqrt{\frac{1}{4}}$ **79.** > **81.** <

Lesson 1-3 pp. 18–25

EXERCISES **1.** 23 **3.** $\frac{17}{2}$ **9.** 8 **11.** 2 **17.** $h = \frac{2A}{b}$ **19.** $w = \frac{V}{lh}$ **23.** $x = \frac{c}{a + b}, a \neq -b$ **25.** $x = a(c - b)$ or $ac - ab, a \neq 0$ **29.** 4 h **31.** width = 4.5 cm, length = 7.5 cm **37.** 3 **39.** $\frac{3}{2}$ **43.** $r_2 = \frac{Rr_1}{r_1 - R}$ **45.** $v = \frac{h + 5t^2}{t}$ **51.** ≈2.97 m **55.** $x = ab - b^2 - a, b \neq 0$ **57.** $x = \frac{b + d}{c - a}, a \neq c$ **73.** −7 **75.** −20 **77.** $7x^2 - 2x$ **79.** $2y - 7x$

Technology p. 25

1a. month 17 **b.** 41 months **c.** $187.74 **d.** $687.74 **e.** 7 payments **f.** E3 = B3 + (B3·0.018) − (B3·0.05), or B3·0.968

Lesson 1-4 pp. 26–31

EXERCISES **1.** $x \leq -\frac{1}{2}$

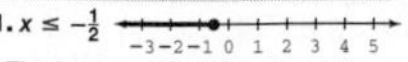

3. $a > 11$ **15.** The longest side is less than 21 cm. **17.** 4546 or more chips **19.** $-4 \leq x \leq 2$

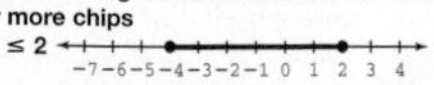

21. $-5 < x \leq 6$ **23.** All real numbers are solutions.

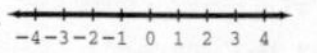

25. $x \leq -3$ or $x \geq 9$ **27.** between $4\frac{1}{2}$ and $5\frac{1}{2}$ days **29.** $z \geq 6$ **31.** $x \geq -48$ **37.** between $204,000 and $254,000 **39.** Dist. Prop.; arithmetic; Sub. Prop. of Inequality; Mult. Prop. of Inequality **41.** $-1 < x < 8$ **43.** no solutions **63.** no solution **65.** −20 **67.** $-2x + 14y$ **69.** $1.01 - 0.1k$

Lesson 1-5 pp. 33–38

EXERCISES **1.** −6, 6 **3.** −6, 12 **11.** $\frac{2}{3}$ **13.** −4, 8 **17.** $x \leq -3$ or $x \geq 13$

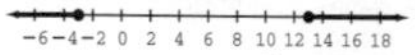

19. $-5 \leq x \leq 8$ **23.** $-2\frac{2}{3} < y < 3\frac{1}{3}$

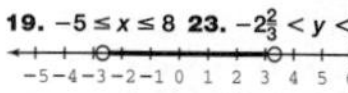

25. no solution **29.** $|k - 50.5| \leq 0.5$ **31.** $|b - 52.5| \leq 2.5$ **35.** $-\frac{3}{2}, -1$ **37.** $-\frac{1}{3}$ **45.** $x \leq -8$ or $x \geq 5$ **47.** $t < -\frac{3}{2}$ or $t > 2$ **55.** $|C - 28.75| \leq 0.25$; $28.5 \leq C \leq 29.0$ **59.** $|x - 9.55| \leq 0.02$, $9.53 \leq x \leq 9.57$ **73.** $y < 6$

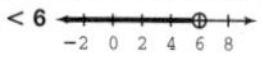

75. $a \geq 4$ **79.** 36 **81.** Inverse Prop. of Add.

Lesson 1-6 pp. 39–45

EXERCISES **1.** $\frac{161}{340}$ or about 47%; $\frac{179}{340}$ or about 53% **7.** $\frac{1}{2}$, or 50% **9.** $\frac{4}{5}$, or 80% **11.** $\frac{19}{125}$, or 15.2% **13.** $\frac{14}{25}$, or 56% **15.** {Gg, Gg, g, g}; $\frac{1}{2}$, or 50% **17.** $\frac{1}{16}$, or 6.25% **19.** $\frac{1}{4}$, or 25% **21a.** 1 **b.** 0 **25.** $\frac{52}{147}$, or 35.4% **27.** $\frac{31}{147}$, or 21.1% **29.** $\frac{1}{2}$ **31.** 0 **35.** $\frac{4}{9}$ **37.** $\frac{4}{9}$ **39.** ≈6.4% **53.** $-\frac{5}{3}, 5$ **55.** −5, 9 **59.** $-2 \leq x \leq 6$ **61.** $-5 < x < 1$

Chapter Review pp. 47–49

1. additive inverse **2.** sample space **3.** solution of an equation **4.** compound inequality

5. reciprocal **6.** experimental probability **7.** theoretical probability **8.** extraneous solution **9.** simulation **10.** absolute value **11.** real numbers, irrational numbers **12.** real numbers, rational numbers, integers **13.** real numbers, rational numbers, integers, whole numbers, natural numbers **14.** real numbers, irrational numbers **15.** real numbers, rational numbers **16.** > **17.** > **18.** > **19.** < **20.** 3.4; $-\frac{1}{3.4}$

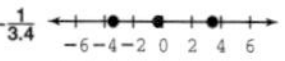

21. $-4 - \pi$; $\frac{1}{4 + \pi}$

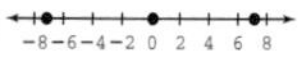

22. $-1\frac{7}{8}$; $\frac{8}{15}$

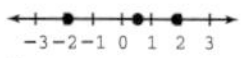

23. $-\sqrt{12}$; $\frac{1}{\sqrt{12}}$

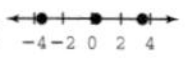

24–28. Answers may vary. Samples: **24.** $(x + 3)(1) = x + 3$ **25.** $(2x + 7) + 3y = 2x + (7 + 3y)$ **26.** $3(2x - 4) = 6x - 12$ **27.** $(5x)(3y) = (3y)(5x)$ **28.** $10z + 0 = 10z$ **29.** 4 **30.** 19 **31.** $5b$ **32.** 11 **33.** 10 **34.** 5 **35.** 4 **36.** −8 **37.** $\frac{b - a^2}{a}$, $a \neq 0, b \neq c$ **38.** 10 cm, 6 cm **39.** 525 mi/h **40.** 70°, 110° **41.** $z \leq \frac{2}{5}$

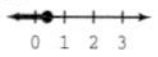

42. $x > 2$

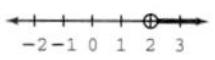

43. $y > 4.5$

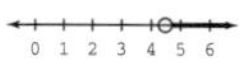

44. $-1 \leq x \leq 1$

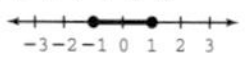

45. $x \leq \frac{3}{2}$ or $x > 6$

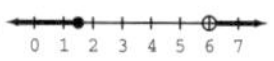

46. $y \geq \frac{5}{3}$

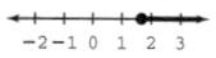

47. $155,850 ≤ A ≤ $415,850 **48.** 1 **49.** $\frac{1}{5}$, 9 **50.** no solutions **51.** $-\frac{1}{3} \leq x \leq \frac{5}{3}$

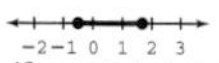

52. $y < 0$ or $y > 18$

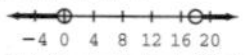

53. $x < -4$ or $x > 6$

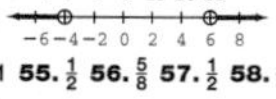

54. $|x - 43.6| \leq 0.1$ **55.** $\frac{1}{2}$ **56.** $\frac{5}{8}$ **57.** $\frac{1}{2}$ **58.** $\frac{3}{8}$ **59.** $\frac{5}{8}$ **60.** about 9%

CHAPTER 2

Lesson 2-2 pp. 55–61

EXERCISES

1.

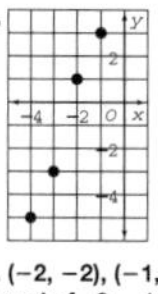

5. (−2, −2), (−1, 1), (1, 1), (1, 0), (3, 3), (3, −2); domain {−2, −1, 1, 3}, range {−2, 0, 1, 3} **9.** domain range **13.** function **15.** function

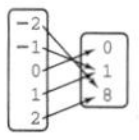

17. not a function **19.** function **23.** 13, 7, −3.5, −14 **25.** −2, −4, −7.5, −11

33.

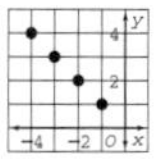

domain {−4, −3, −2, −1}, range {1, 2, 3, 4} **35.** domain $\left\{-\frac{3}{2}, \frac{1}{2}, \frac{3}{2}, \frac{5}{2}\right\}$, range $\left\{-\frac{1}{2}, \frac{1}{2}\right\}$ **37.** domain {−2, −1, 0, 9}, range {2, 5, 7}, not a function **39.** domain {−3.2 to 3.2}, range {−1 to 1}, not a function **41.** C **43.** yes **45.** no **47.** $v(r) = \frac{4}{3}\pi r^3$; about 4849 cm³ **67.** $\frac{2}{11}$ **69.** 0 **73.** $x = -6$; $x = 14$

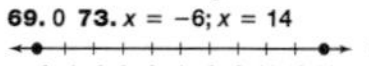

77. 50% increase

Lesson 2-2 pp. 62–70

EXERCISES

1.

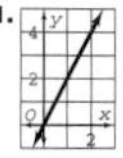

9a.

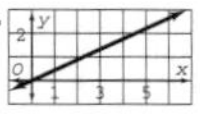

$y = 0.23x$, domain $\{x \mid x \in \mathbb{R}$ and $x \geq 0\}$, range $\{y \mid y \in \mathbb{R}$ and $y \geq 0\}$ **b.** x-intercept (0, 0), y-intercept (0, 0); when no miles have been driven, there is no cost. **c.** 0.23 represents a cost of $.23 per mile driven. **11.** −1 **13.** 3 **21.** $\frac{5}{6}x - y = \frac{19}{3}$

23. $y = -2$ **27.** $y - 0 = \frac{5}{4}(x - 1)$ **29.** $y + 1 = -\frac{4}{3}(x - 0)$ **33.** $\frac{3}{2}$ **35.** $-\frac{A}{B}$ **39.** $y = \frac{5}{2}x + \frac{13}{2}$

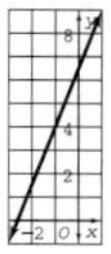

41. $x = 1$

43.

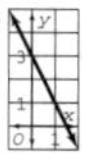

51. $\frac{1}{3}$ **53.** $-\frac{1}{4}$ **55.** −1, (0, 1000), (1000, 0) **57.** 5, (0, −1), $\left(\frac{1}{5}, 0\right)$ **63.** $-\frac{5}{13}$ **65.** $-\frac{7}{10}$ **67.** $y = 3x + 2$ **71.** $y = -1$

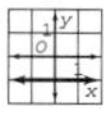

73. $y = \frac{5}{6}x + \frac{10}{3}$ **91.** domain {−2, 1, 2, 3, 4}, range {−2, −1, 2, 3}; not a function **93.** domain {−3, 0, 1, 7}, range {−10, −5, −1, 3}; not a function **95.** multiplicative inverses **97.** additive inverses, additive identity

Extension p. 71

1.

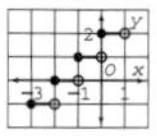

5. $f(x) = \begin{cases} -3x - 10, \text{ if } x \leq -2 \\ \frac{1}{2}x - 3, \text{ if } -2 < x < 2 \\ 2x - 6, \text{ if } x \geq 2 \end{cases}$

Lesson 2-3 pp. 72–77

EXERCISES **1.** yes; $k = 2, y = 2x$ **3.** no **9.** yes; $k = 12$ **11.** yes; $k = -2$ **17.** $k = \frac{2}{7}; -\frac{10}{7}$ **19.** $k = -1$; 5 **25.** 4 **27.** $\frac{5}{3}$ **29.** yes; $k = \frac{2}{3}, y = \frac{2}{3}x$ **31.** no **33.** $y = 2x$ **35.** $y = -\frac{9}{2}x$ **41.** 9 **43.** 90 **47.** Yes; $y = -\frac{5}{6}x$ contains the point $\left(15, -12\frac{1}{2}\right)$.

65.

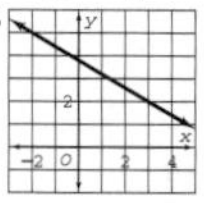

69.

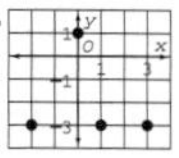

domain {0, 1, −2, 3}, range {1, −3} **71.** domain {1, 2, 4, 5}, range {−2, −1, 1, 2} **73.** 72%

Checkpoint Quiz 1 **1.** (9, 0), (0, −3) **2.** $\left(-\frac{5}{7}, 0\right)$, (0, 5) **3.** (0, 0) **4.** $\left(-\frac{5}{2}, 0\right)$, (0, 10) **5.** $y = 2x - 9$ **6.** $y = 4x - 2$ **7.** $y = -\frac{3}{5}x - 2$ **8.** $y = -\frac{2}{3}x + 2$ **9a.** $y = 27x$ **b.**

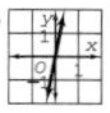

Both intercepts are 0 when no one has bought any tickets. **c.** Answers may vary. Sample: No; the number of people must be a whole number. **10.** A

Lesson 2-4 pp. 78–85

EXERCISES

1. $d = 62.5h + 15$

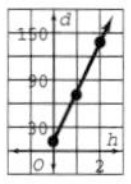

3. $h = 8y + 60$ **5.** $y = 0.5x + 0.75$; 3.25 lb **7.** $y = 1.75x + 1.75$; $8.40 **9.**

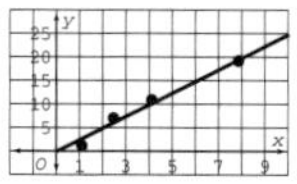

Linear model is reasonable; models may vary. Sample: $y = 2.6x - 0.6$ **11.** not reasonable

13a.

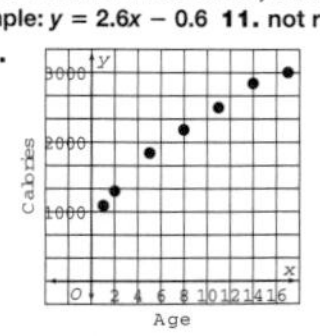

Answers may vary. Sample: $y = 119x + 1111$ **b.** 3015 Cal **c.** Answers may vary. Sample: No; adults need fewer Calories, not more. **15.** $y = -4x + 10$ **17.** $y = 7.5x + 2.5$ **23.** 85.8 **25.** 13 **37.** −3; 15 **39.** $\frac{42}{5}$; −42 **41.** range {1, 3.5, 5, 6, 8} **43.** range $\left\{-\frac{7}{2}, -\frac{5}{2}, -2, -\frac{5}{4}, 0\right\}$

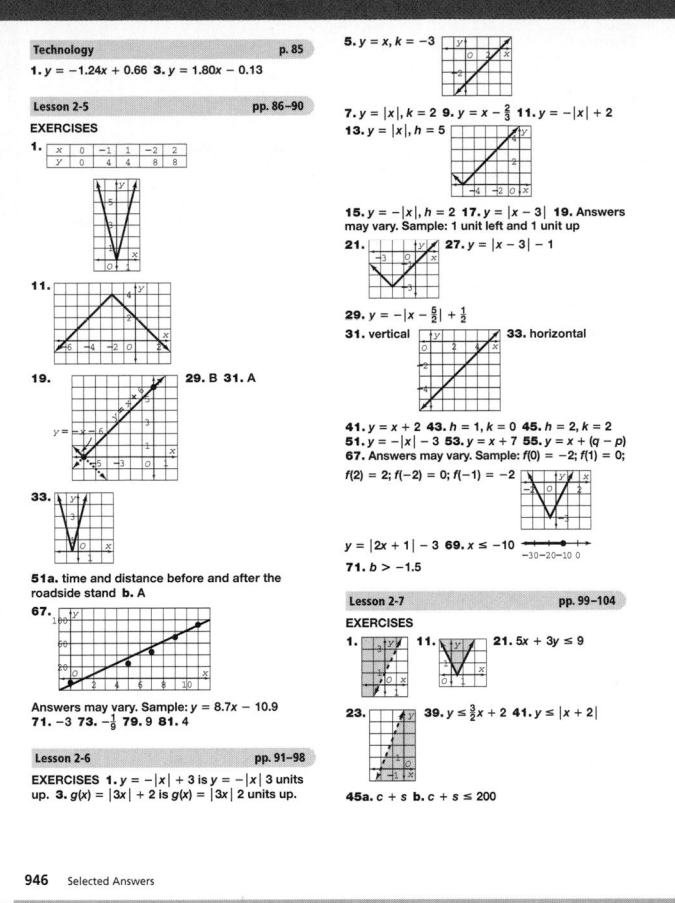

Technology p. 85

1. $y = -1.24x + 0.66$ 3. $y = 1.80x - 0.13$

Lesson 2-5 pp. 86–90

EXERCISES

1.

x	0	−1	1	−2	2
y	0	4	4	8	8

11.

19. 29. B 31. A

$y = -x - 6$

33.

51a. time and distance before and after the roadside stand b. A

67.

Answers may vary. Sample: $y = 8.7x - 10.9$
71. −3 73. −$\frac{1}{9}$ 79. 9 81. 4

Lesson 2-6 pp. 91–98

EXERCISES 1. $y = -|x| + 3$ is $y = -|x|$ 3 units up. 3. $g(x) = |3x| + 2$ is $g(x) = |3x|$ 2 units up.

5. $y = x, k = -3$

7. $y = |x|, k = 2$ 9. $y = x - \frac{2}{3}$ 11. $y = -|x| + 2$
13. $y = |x|, h = 5$

15. $y = -|x|, h = 2$ 17. $y = |x - 3|$ 19. Answers may vary. Sample: 1 unit left and 1 unit up.
21. 27. $y = |x - 3| - 1$

29. $y = -|x - \frac{5}{2}| + \frac{1}{2}$
31. vertical 33. horizontal

41. $y = x + 2$ 43. $h = 1, k = 0$ 45. $h = 2, k = 2$
51. $y = -|x| - 3$ 53. $y = x + 7$ 55. $y = x + (q - p)$
67. Answers may vary. Sample: $f(0) = -2$; $f(1) = 0$; $f(2) = 2$; $f(-2) = 0$; $f(-1) = -2$

$y = |2x + 1| - 3$ 69. $x \le -10$
71. $b > -1.5$

Lesson 2-7 pp. 99–104

EXERCISES

1. 11. 21. $5x + 3y \le 9$

23. 39. $y \le \frac{3}{2}x + 2$ 41. $y \le |x + 2|$

45a. $c + s$ b. $c + s \le 200$

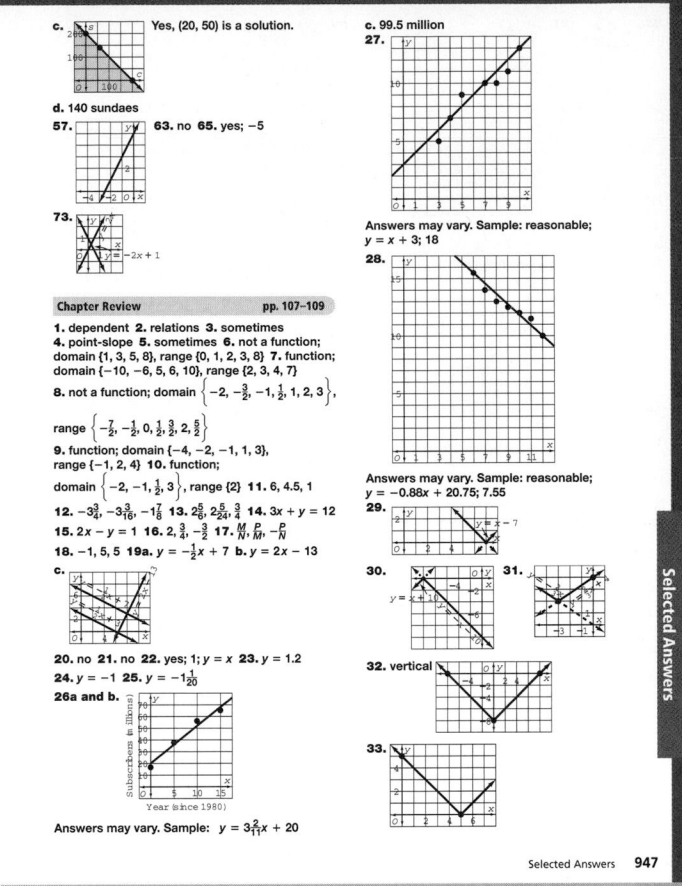

c. Yes, (20, 50) is a solution.
d. 140 sundaes
57. 63. no 65. yes; −5
73.

$y = -2x + 1$

Chapter Review pp. 107–109

1. dependent 2. relations 3. sometimes
4. point-slope 5. sometimes 6. not a function; domain {1, 3, 5, 8}, range {0, 1, 2, 3, 8} 7. function; domain {−10, −6, 5, 6, 10}, range {2, 3, 4, 7}
8. not a function; domain $\left\{ -2, -\frac{3}{2}, -1, \frac{1}{2}, 1, 2, 3 \right\}$,
range $\left\{ -\frac{7}{2}, -\frac{1}{2}, 0, \frac{1}{2}, \frac{3}{2}, 2, \frac{5}{2} \right\}$
9. function; domain {−4, −2, −1, 1, 3}, range {−1, 2, 4} 10. function; domain $\left\{ -2, -1, \frac{1}{2}, 3 \right\}$, range {2} 11. 6, 4.5, 1
12. $-3\frac{9}{4}, -3\frac{3}{16}, -1\frac{7}{8}$ 13. $2\frac{5}{8}, 2\frac{5}{24}, \frac{3}{4}$ 14. $3x + y = 12$
15. $2x - y = 1$ 16. $2, \frac{3}{4}, -\frac{1}{2}$ 17. $\frac{M}{N}, \frac{P}{M}, -\frac{P}{N}$
18. −1, 5, 5 19a. $y = -\frac{1}{2}x + 7$ b. $y = 2x - 13$
c.

20. no 21. no 22. yes; 1; $y = x$ 23. $y = 1.2$
24. $y = -1$ 25. $y = -1\frac{1}{20}$
26a and b.

Answers may vary. Sample: $y = 3\frac{2}{11}x + 20$

c. 99.5 million
27.

Answers may vary. Sample: reasonable; $y = x + 3$; 18
28.

Answers may vary. Sample: reasonable; $y = -0.88x + 20.75$; 7.55
29.

30. 31.

$y = x + 1$

32. vertical

33.

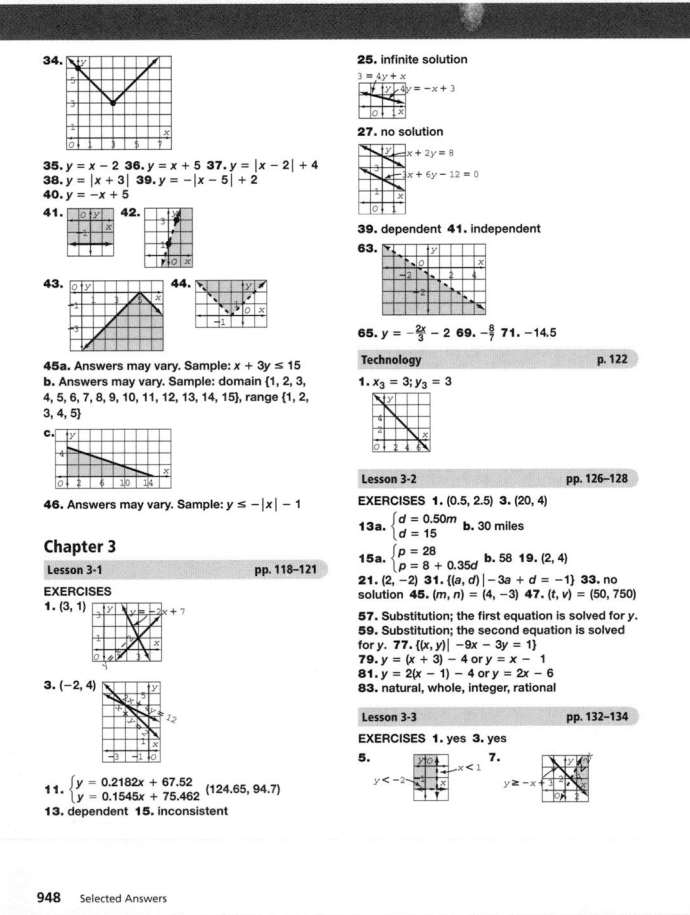

34.

35. $y = x - 2$ 36. $y = x + 5$ 37. $y = |x - 2| + 4$
38. $y = |x + 3|$ 39. $y = -|x - 5| + 2$
40. $y = -x + 5$
41. 42.

43. 44.

45a. Answers may vary. Sample: $x + 3y \le 15$
b. Answers may vary. Sample: domain {1, 2, 3, 4, 5, 6, 7, 8, 9, 10, 11, 12, 13, 14, 15}, range {1, 2, 3, 4, 5}
c.

46. Answers may vary. Sample: $y \le -|x| - 1$

Chapter 3

Lesson 3-1 pp. 118–121

EXERCISES

1. (3, 1)

3. (−2, 4)

11. $\begin{cases} y = 0.2182x + 67.52 \\ y = 0.1545x + 75.462 \end{cases}$ (124.65, 94.7)
13. dependent 15. inconsistent

25. infinite solution
$3 = 4y + x$

27. no solution

39. dependent 41. independent
63.

65. $y = -\frac{2x}{3} - 2$ 69. $-\frac{8}{7}$ 71. −14.5

Technology p. 122

1. $x_3 = 3; y_3 = 3$

Lesson 3-2 pp. 126–128

EXERCISES 1. (0.5, 2.5) 3. (20, 4)
13a. $\begin{cases} d = 0.50m \\ d = 15 \end{cases}$ b. 30 miles
15a. $\begin{cases} p = 28 \\ p = 8 + 0.35d \end{cases}$ b. 58 19. (2, 4)
21. (2, −2) 31. {(a, d) | −3a + d = −1} 33. no solution 45. (m, n) = (4, −3) 47. (t, v) = (50, 750)
57. Substitution; the first equation is solved for y.
59. Substitution; the second equation is solved for y. 77. {(x, y) | −9x − 3y = 1}
79. $y = (x + 3) - 4$ or $y = x - 1$
81. $y = 2(x - 1) - 4$ or $y = 2x - 6$
83. natural, whole, integer, rational

Lesson 3-3 pp. 132–134

EXERCISES 1. yes 3. yes
5. 7.

$y < -2$ $x < 1$ $y \ge -x$

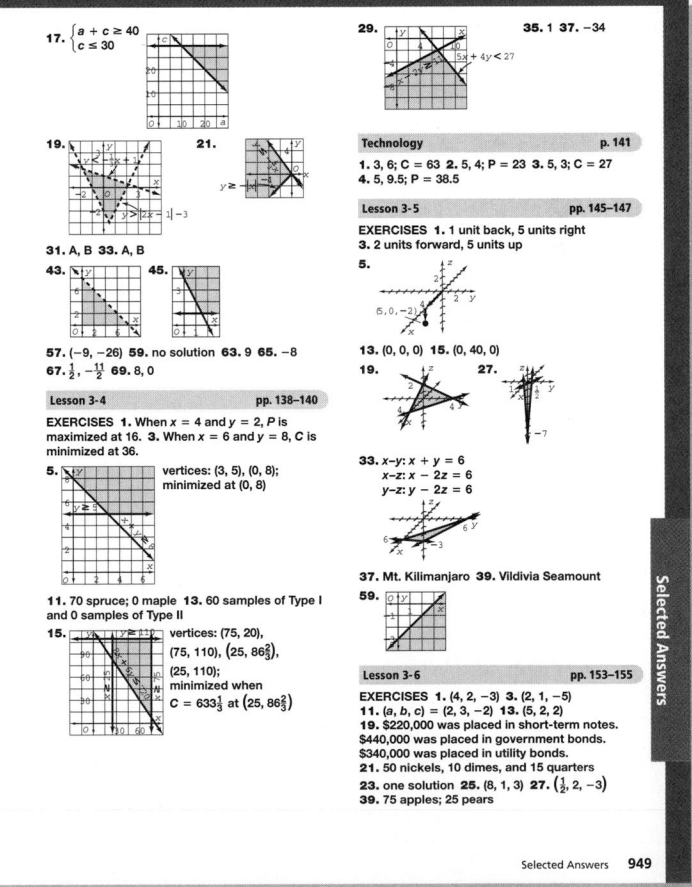

17. $\begin{cases} a + c \ge 40 \\ c \le 30 \end{cases}$

19. 21.

$y \ge -\frac{3}{2}$

31. A, B 33. A, B
43. 45.

57. (−9, −26) 59. no solution 63. 9 65. −8
67. $\frac{1}{2}, -\frac{11}{2}$ 69. 8, 0

Lesson 3-4 pp. 138–140

EXERCISES 1. When $x = 4$ and $y = 2$, P is maximized at 16. 3. When $x = 6$ and $y = 8$, C is minimized at 36.
5.

vertices: (3, 5), (0, 8); minimized at (0, 8)

11. 70 spruce; 0 maple 13. 60 samples of Type I and 0 samples of Type II
15.

vertices: (75, 20), (75, 110), (25, 86$\frac{2}{3}$), (25, 110); minimized when $C = 633\frac{1}{3}$ at (25, 86$\frac{2}{3}$)

29. 35. 1 37. −34

$5x + 4y < 27$

Technology p. 141

1. 3, 6; C = 63 2. 5, 4; P = 23 3. 5, 3; C = 27
4. 5, 9.5; P = 38.5

Lesson 3-5 pp. 145–147

EXERCISES 1. 1 unit back, 5 units right
3. 2 units forward, 5 units up
5.

(5, 0, −2)

13. (0, 0, 0) 15. (0, 40, 0)
19. 27.

33. x–y: $x + y = 6$
x–z: $x - 2z = 6$
y–z: $y - 2z = 6$

37. Mt. Kilimanjaro 39. Vildivia Seamount
59.

Lesson 3-6 pp. 153–155

EXERCISES 1. (4, 2, −3) 3. (2, 1, −5)
11. (a, b, c) = (2, 3, −2) 13. (5, 2, 2)
19. $220,000 was placed in short-term notes. $440,000 was placed in government bonds. $340,000 was placed in utility bonds.
21. 50 nickels, 10 dimes, and 15 quarters
23. one solution 25. (8, 1, 3) 27. ($\frac{1}{2}$, 2, −3)
39. 75 apples; 25 pears

T883

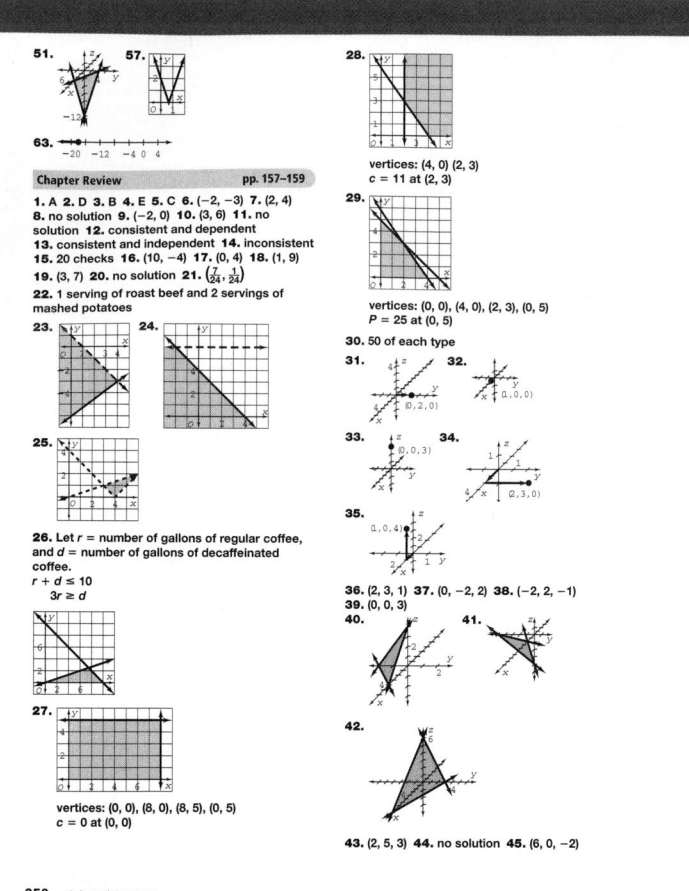

Page 950

51. 57.

63. number line: -20 -12 -4 0 4

Chapter Review pp. 157–159

1. A 2. D 3. B 4. E 5. C 6. $(-2, -3)$ 7. $(2, 4)$
8. no solution 9. $(-2, 0)$ 10. $(3, 6)$ 11. no solution 12. consistent and dependent 13. consistent and independent 14. inconsistent 15. 20 checks 16. $(10, -4)$ 17. $(0, 4)$ 18. $(1, 9)$ 19. $(3, 7)$ 20. no solution 21. $\left(\frac{7}{24}, \frac{1}{24}\right)$
22. 1 serving of roast beef and 2 servings of mashed potatoes

23. 24.

25.

26. Let r = number of gallons of regular coffee, and d = number of gallons of decaffeinated coffee.
$r + d \le 10$
$3r \ge d$

27. vertices: $(0, 0)$, $(8, 0)$, $(8, 5)$, $(0, 5)$ $c = 0$ at $(0, 0)$

28. vertices: $(4, 0)$ $(2, 3)$ $c = 11$ at $(2, 3)$

29. vertices: $(0, 0)$, $(4, 0)$, $(2, 3)$, $(0, 5)$ $P = 25$ at $(0, 5)$

30. 50 of each type

31. 32.

33. 34.

35.

36. $(2, 3, 1)$ 37. $(0, -2, 2)$ 38. $(-2, 2, -1)$ 39. $(0, 0, 3)$

40. 41.

42.

43. $(2, 5, 3)$ 44. no solution 45. $(6, 0, -2)$

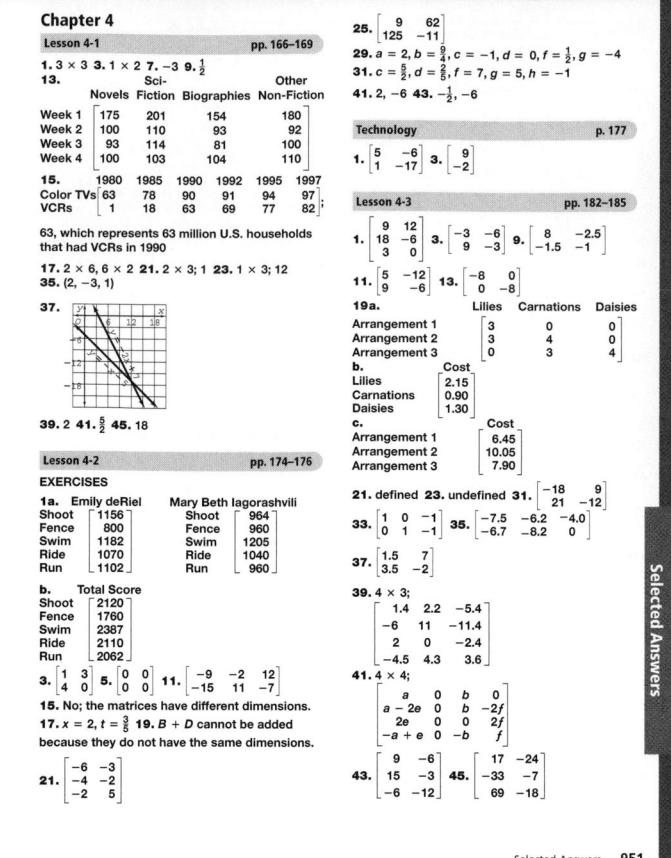

Page 951

Chapter 4

Lesson 4-1 pp. 166–169

1. 3×3 3. 1×2 7. -3 9. $\frac{1}{2}$

13.

	Novels	Sci-Fiction	Biographies	Other Non-Fiction
Week 1	175	201	154	180
Week 2	100	110	93	92
Week 3	93	114	81	100
Week 4	100	104	104	110

15.

	1980	1985	1990	1992	1995	1997
Color TVs	63	78	90	91	94	97
VCRs	1	18	63	69	77	82

63, which represents 63 million U.S. households that had VCRs in 1990

17. $2 \times 6, 6 \times 2$ 21. $2 \times 3; 1$ 23. $1 \times 3; 12$
35. $(2, -3, 1)$

37.

39. 2 41. 1 45. 18

Lesson 4-2 pp. 174–176

EXERCISES

1a.

Emily deRiel		Mary Beth Iagorashvili	
Shoot	1156	Shoot	964
Fence	800	Fence	960
Swim	1182	Swim	1205
Ride	1070	Ride	1040
Run	1102	Run	960

b.

	Total Score
Shoot	2120
Fence	1760
Swim	2387
Ride	2110
Run	2062

3. $\begin{bmatrix} 1 & 3 \\ 4 & 0 \end{bmatrix}$ 5. $\begin{bmatrix} 0 & 0 \\ 0 & 0 \end{bmatrix}$ 11. $\begin{bmatrix} -9 & -2 & 12 \\ -15 & 11 & -7 \end{bmatrix}$
15. No; the matrices have different dimensions.
17. $x = 2, t = \frac{9}{5}$ 19. $B + D$ cannot be added because they do not have the same dimensions.
21. $\begin{bmatrix} -6 & -3 \\ -4 & -2 \\ -2 & 5 \end{bmatrix}$

25. $\begin{bmatrix} 9 & 62 \\ 125 & -11 \end{bmatrix}$
29. $a = 2, b = \frac{9}{2}, c = -1, d = 0, f = \frac{1}{2}, g = -4$
31. $c = \frac{5}{2}, d = \frac{9}{2}, f = 7, g = 5, h = -1$
41. $2, -6$ 43. $-\frac{1}{2}, -6$

Technology p. 177

1. $\begin{bmatrix} 5 & -6 \\ 1 & -17 \end{bmatrix}$ 3. $\begin{bmatrix} 9 \\ -2 \end{bmatrix}$

Lesson 4-3 pp. 182–185

1. $\begin{bmatrix} 9 & 12 \\ 18 & -6 \\ 3 & 0 \end{bmatrix}$ 3. $\begin{bmatrix} -3 & -6 \\ 9 & -3 \end{bmatrix}$ 9. $\begin{bmatrix} 8 & -2.5 \\ -1.5 & -1 \end{bmatrix}$
11. $\begin{bmatrix} 5 & -12 \\ 9 & -6 \end{bmatrix}$ 13. $\begin{bmatrix} -8 & 0 \\ 0 & -8 \end{bmatrix}$

19a.

	Lilies	Carnations	Daisies
Arrangement 1	3	0	0
Arrangement 2	3	4	0
Arrangement 3	0	3	4

b.

	Cost
Lilies	2.15
Carnations	0.90
Daisies	1.30

c.

	Cost
Arrangement 1	6.45
Arrangement 2	10.05
Arrangement 3	7.90

21. defined 23. undefined 31. $\begin{bmatrix} -18 & -7 \\ 21 & -12 \end{bmatrix}$
33. $\begin{bmatrix} 1 & 0 & -1 \\ 0 & 1 & 0 \end{bmatrix}$ 35. $\begin{bmatrix} -7.5 & -6.2 & -4.0 \\ -6.7 & -8.2 & -4 \end{bmatrix}$
37. $\begin{bmatrix} 1.5 & 7 \\ 3.5 & -2 \end{bmatrix}$
39. 4×3; $\begin{bmatrix} 1.4 & 2.2 & -5.4 \\ -6 & 11 & -11.4 \\ 0 & -2.4 \\ -4.5 & 4.3 & 3.6 \end{bmatrix}$
41. 4×4; $\begin{bmatrix} a & 0 & b & 0 \\ a-2e & 0 & b & -2f \\ 2e & 0 & 2f \\ -a+e & 0 & -b & f \end{bmatrix}$
43. $\begin{bmatrix} 9 & -6 \\ 15 & -3 \\ -6 & -12 \end{bmatrix}$ 45. $\begin{bmatrix} 17 & -24 \\ -33 & -7 \\ 69 & -18 \end{bmatrix}$

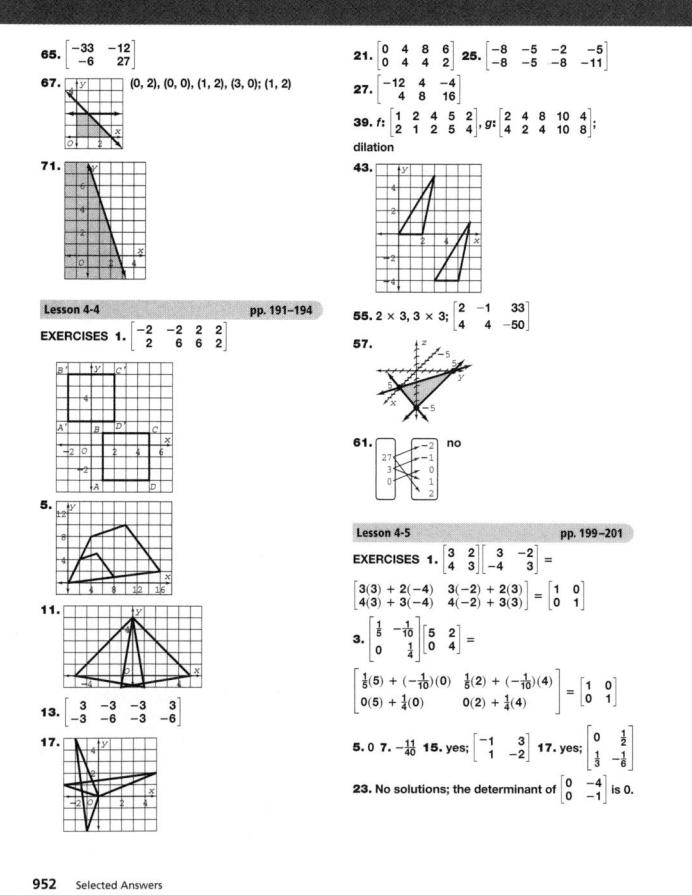

Page 952

65. $\begin{bmatrix} -33 & -12 \\ -6 & 27 \end{bmatrix}$

67. $(0, 2), (0, 0), (1, 2), (3, 0); (1, 2)$

71.

Lesson 4-4 pp. 191–194

EXERCISES 1. $\begin{bmatrix} -2 & -2 & 2 \\ 2 & 6 & 6 \end{bmatrix}$

5.

11.

13. $\begin{bmatrix} 3 & -3 & -3 & 3 \\ -3 & -6 & -3 & -6 \end{bmatrix}$

17.

21. $\begin{bmatrix} 0 & 4 & 8 & 6 \\ 0 & 4 & 4 & 2 \end{bmatrix}$ 25. $\begin{bmatrix} -8 & -5 & -2 & -5 \\ -8 & -5 & -8 & -11 \end{bmatrix}$
27. $\begin{bmatrix} -12 & 4 & -4 \\ 4 & 8 & 16 \end{bmatrix}$
39. $f: \begin{bmatrix} 1 & 2 & 4 & 5 & 2 \\ 2 & 1 & 2 & 5 & 4 \end{bmatrix}$ $g: \begin{bmatrix} 2 & 4 & 8 & 10 & 4 \\ 4 & 2 & 4 & 10 & 8 \end{bmatrix}$; dilation

43.

55. $2 \times 3, 3 \times 3$; $\begin{bmatrix} 2 & -1 & 33 \\ 4 & 4 & -50 \end{bmatrix}$

57.

61. no

Lesson 4-5 pp. 199–201

EXERCISES 1. $\begin{bmatrix} 3 & 2 \\ 4 & 3 \end{bmatrix}\begin{bmatrix} 3 & -2 \\ -4 & 3 \end{bmatrix} = \begin{bmatrix} 3(3)+2(-4) & 3(-2)+2(3) \\ 4(3)+3(-4) & 4(-2)+3(3) \end{bmatrix} = \begin{bmatrix} 1 & 0 \\ 0 & 1 \end{bmatrix}$
3. $\begin{bmatrix} \frac{1}{5} & -\frac{1}{10} \\ 0 & \frac{1}{4} \end{bmatrix}\begin{bmatrix} 5 & 2 \\ 0 & 4 \end{bmatrix} = \begin{bmatrix} \frac{1}{5}(5)+(-\frac{1}{10})(0) & \frac{1}{5}(2)+(-\frac{1}{10})(4) \\ 0(5)+\frac{1}{4}(0) & 0(2)+\frac{1}{4}(4) \end{bmatrix} = \begin{bmatrix} 1 & 0 \\ 0 & 1 \end{bmatrix}$
5. 0 7. $-\frac{11}{40}$ 15. yes; $\begin{bmatrix} -1 & 3 \\ 1 & -2 \end{bmatrix}$ 17. yes; $\begin{bmatrix} 0 & \frac{1}{2} \\ \frac{1}{3} & 0 \end{bmatrix}$
23. No solutions; the determinant of $\begin{bmatrix} 0 & -4 \\ 0 & -1 \end{bmatrix}$ is 0.

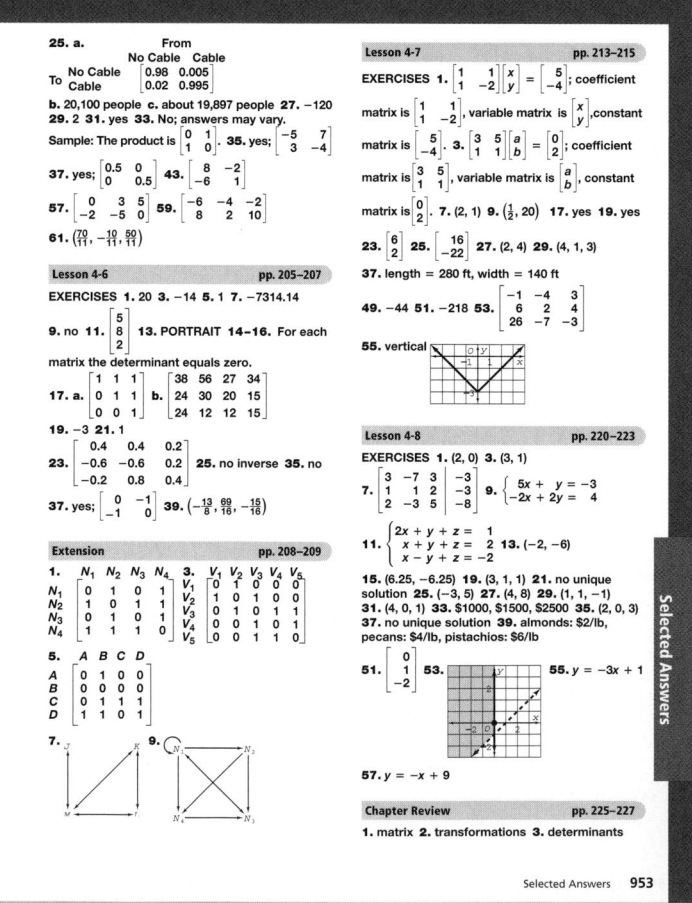

Page 953

25. a.

	From	
To	No Cable	Cable
No Cable	0.98	0.005
Cable	0.02	0.995

b. 20,100 people c. about 19,897 people 27. -120
29. 2 31. yes 33. No; answers may vary. Sample: The product is $\begin{bmatrix} 0 & 1 \\ 1 & 0 \end{bmatrix}$ 35. yes; $\begin{bmatrix} -5 & 7 \\ 3 & -4 \end{bmatrix}$
37. yes; $\begin{bmatrix} 0.5 & 0.5 \\ 0.5 & 0.5 \end{bmatrix}$ 43. $\begin{bmatrix} 8 & -2 \\ -6 & 1 \end{bmatrix}$
57. $\begin{bmatrix} 0 & 3 & 5 \\ -2 & -5 & 0 \end{bmatrix}$ 59. $\begin{bmatrix} -6 & -4 & -2 \\ 8 & 2 & 10 \end{bmatrix}$
61. $\left(\frac{70}{11}, -\frac{10}{11}, \frac{50}{11}\right)$

Lesson 4-6 pp. 205–207

EXERCISES 1. 20 3. -14 5. 1 7. -7314.14
9. no 11. $\begin{bmatrix} 5 \\ 8 \\ 2 \end{bmatrix}$ 13. PORTRAIT 14–16. For each matrix the determinant equals zero.
17. a. $\begin{bmatrix} 1 & 1 & 1 \\ 0 & 1 & 1 \\ 0 & 0 & 1 \end{bmatrix}$ b. $\begin{bmatrix} 38 & 56 & 27 & 34 \\ 24 & 30 & 20 & 15 \\ 24 & 12 & 12 & 15 \end{bmatrix}$
19. -3 21. 1
23. $\begin{bmatrix} 0.4 & 0.4 & 0.2 \\ -0.6 & -0.6 & 0.2 \\ -0.2 & 0.8 & 0.4 \end{bmatrix}$ 25. no inverse 35. no
37. yes; $\begin{bmatrix} 0 & -1 \\ 1 & 0 \end{bmatrix}$ 39. $\left(-\frac{13}{8}, \frac{69}{16}, -\frac{15}{16}\right)$

Extension pp. 208–209

1.

	N1	N2	N3	N4
N1	0	1	0	1
N2	1	0	1	1
N3	1	1	0	1
N4	1	1	1	0

3.

	V1	V2	V3	V4	V5
V1	0	1	0	0	0
V2	1	0	0	0	0
V3	0	0	0	1	1
V4	0	0	1	0	1
V5	0	0	1	1	0

5.

	A	B	C	D
A	0	1	0	0
B	0	0	0	0
C	0	1	1	1
D	1	1	0	1

7. 9.

Lesson 4-7 pp. 213–215

EXERCISES 1. $\begin{bmatrix} 1 & 1 \\ 1 & -2 \end{bmatrix}\begin{bmatrix} x \\ y \end{bmatrix} = \begin{bmatrix} 5 \\ -4 \end{bmatrix}$; coefficient matrix is $\begin{bmatrix} 1 & 1 \\ 1 & -2 \end{bmatrix}$, variable matrix is $\begin{bmatrix} x \\ y \end{bmatrix}$, constant matrix is $\begin{bmatrix} 5 \\ -4 \end{bmatrix}$. 3. $\begin{bmatrix} 3 & 5 \\ 1 & 1 \end{bmatrix}\begin{bmatrix} a \\ b \end{bmatrix} = \begin{bmatrix} 0 \\ 2 \end{bmatrix}$; coefficient matrix is $\begin{bmatrix} 3 & 5 \\ 1 & 1 \end{bmatrix}$, variable matrix is $\begin{bmatrix} a \\ b \end{bmatrix}$, constant matrix is $\begin{bmatrix} 0 \\ 2 \end{bmatrix}$. 7. $(2, 1)$ 9. $\left(\frac{1}{2}, 20\right)$ 17. yes 19. yes
23. $\begin{bmatrix} 6 \\ 2 \end{bmatrix}$ 25. $\begin{bmatrix} 16 \\ -22 \end{bmatrix}$ 27. $(2, 4)$ 29. $(4, 1, 3)$
37. length = 280 ft, width = 140 ft
49. -44 51. -218 53. $\begin{bmatrix} -1 & -4 & 3 \\ 6 & 2 & 4 \\ 26 & -7 & -3 \end{bmatrix}$
55. vertical

Lesson 4-8 pp. 220–223

EXERCISES 1. $(2, 0)$ 3. $(3, 1)$
7. $\begin{bmatrix} 3 & -7 & 3 \\ 1 & 1 & -3 \\ 2 & -3 & 5 \end{bmatrix}\begin{vmatrix} 1 \\ -3 \\ -8 \end{vmatrix}$ 9. $\begin{cases} 5x + y = -3 \\ -2x + 2y = 4 \end{cases}$
11. $\begin{cases} 2x + y + z = 1 \\ x + y + z = 2 \\ x - y + z = -2 \end{cases}$ 13. $(-2, -6)$
15. $(6.25, -6.25)$ 19. $(3, 1, 1)$ 21. no unique solution 25. $(-3, 5)$ 27. $(4, 8)$ 29. $(1, 1, -1)$
31. $(4, 0, 1)$ 33. $1000, $1500, $2500 35. $(2, 0, 3)$
37. no unique solution 39. almonds: $2/lb, pecans: $4/lb, pistachios: $6/lb
51. $\begin{bmatrix} 0 \\ 1 \\ -2 \end{bmatrix}$ 53. 55. $y = -3x + 1$
57. $y = -x + 9$

Chapter Review pp. 225–227

1. matrix 2. transformations 3. determinants

4. equal matrices **5.** zero matrix **6.** matrix equation **7.** square matrix **8.** preimage **9.** scalar product **10.** identity matrix **11.** $2 \times 3; -7$ **12.** $3 \times 2; -5$ **13.** $3 \times 3; 78$ **14.** 226 **15.** 50

16. about 9% **17.** $\begin{bmatrix} 1 & -8 & 12 \end{bmatrix}$ **18.** $\begin{bmatrix} t - 1 \\ 3 \end{bmatrix}$

19. $\begin{bmatrix} -3 & 10 \\ -3 & 3 \end{bmatrix}$ **20.** $\begin{bmatrix} 2 & 8 & 13 \\ 33 & 0 & -7 \end{bmatrix}$

21. $x = -2, w = 8, r = 4, t = -1$

22. $t = -4, y = \frac{11}{2}, r = 4, w = 5$

23. $\begin{bmatrix} 18 & 3 & 0 & 24 \\ -12 & 9 & 21 & 33 \end{bmatrix}$ **24.** $\begin{bmatrix} -9 & 7 \\ -8 & -8 \end{bmatrix}$

25. does not exist **26.** $\begin{bmatrix} -8 & 10 & 21 & 41 \\ -28 & 10 & 28 & 28 \end{bmatrix}$

27. $\begin{bmatrix} -14 & -2 \\ 43 & 4 \end{bmatrix}$ **28.** $\begin{bmatrix} 4 & -1 & 2 \\ -1 & -2 & 3 \end{bmatrix}$

29. $\begin{bmatrix} 0 & -5 & -2 \\ 5 & 4 & 9 \end{bmatrix}$ **30.** $\begin{bmatrix} -3 & 2 & -1 \\ 1 & 0 & 5 \end{bmatrix}$

31. $\begin{bmatrix} 1 & 0 & 5 \\ 3 & -2 & 1 \end{bmatrix}$ **32.** $\begin{bmatrix} 1 & 0 & 5 \\ -3 & 2 & -1 \end{bmatrix}$

33. $\begin{bmatrix} 1.5 & -1 & 0.5 \\ 0.5 & 0 & 2.5 \end{bmatrix}$ **34.** $\begin{bmatrix} 6 & -4 & 2 \\ 2 & 0 & 10 \end{bmatrix}$

35. $\begin{bmatrix} -1 & 0 & -5 \\ 3 & -2 & 1 \end{bmatrix}$ **36.** 24; $\begin{bmatrix} \frac{1}{6} & -\frac{1}{24} \\ 0 & \frac{1}{4} \end{bmatrix}$

37. 0; does not exist **38.** 42; $\begin{bmatrix} \frac{5}{42} & -\frac{1}{42} \\ -\frac{4}{21} & \frac{5}{21} \end{bmatrix}$

39. 6; $\begin{bmatrix} \frac{1}{3} & -\frac{2}{3} & 0 \\ -\frac{1}{6} & \frac{1}{3} & -\frac{1}{2} \\ \frac{1}{3} & \frac{1}{3} & 0 \end{bmatrix}$ **40.** $\begin{bmatrix} 1 & 2 \\ -1 & 0 \end{bmatrix}$ **41.** $\begin{bmatrix} -4 \\ -7 \end{bmatrix}$

42. $\begin{bmatrix} 2 \\ 2 \end{bmatrix}$ **43.** $\begin{bmatrix} 2 & 1 \\ 3 & 2 \end{bmatrix}$ **44.** no unique solution **45.** no unique solution **46.** 3 small canoes, 2 large canoes **47.** $(4, -7)$ **48.** $(6, 0, -2)$

Chapter 5

Lesson 5-1 pp. 237–239

EXERCISES **1.** linear; none, x, 4 **3.** quadratic; $3x^2$, $-6x$, none **11.** $(-1, 0), x = -1$ **13.** $P'(6, 9)$, $Q'(2, 1)$ **17.** $y = x^2 - 5x + 2$ **19.** $y = x^2 + 2x$ **21a.** $y = -16x^2 + 33x + 46$, where x is the number of seconds after release and y is the height in ft. **b.** 28.5 ft

23. $y = 4x^2$ **25.** no **27.** $\left(-\frac{1}{2}, -\frac{1}{2}\right), x = -\frac{1}{2}$ **29.** $\left(\frac{1}{2}, 0\right), x = \frac{1}{2}$ **31.a.** $y = -0.01467x^2 + 1.312x + 9.795$ **b.** March of 1993 **33.** 8 **35.** $-\frac{11}{8}$ **49.** $\left[\begin{array}{cc|c} 3 & -1 & 7 \\ 2 & 2 & 10 \end{array}\right]$; $(3, 2)$ **51.** $\begin{bmatrix} 0 & -4 & 17 & -4 \end{bmatrix}$ **53.** $(2, 5)$ **55.** $(-1, -1)$ **57.** $\frac{1}{2}$

Technology p. 240

1. linear: $y = 3.090x - 0.9375$; quadratic: $y = 0.1457x^2 - 0.6930x + 9.0852$; the quadratic model is better. The residuals are closer to zero for the quadratic model.

Lesson 5-2 pp. 244–247

EXERCISES

1. 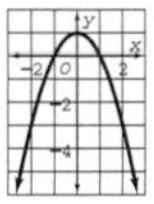 **3.** 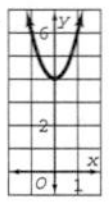 **11.** 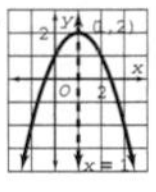

13. 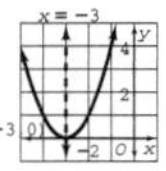 **23.** 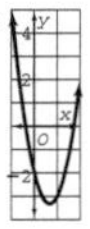

min, $-\frac{10}{3}$

25. 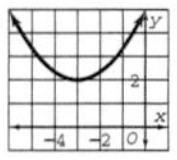

min, 2

29. 2 s; 64 ft

31. 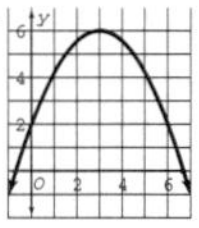 **33.** 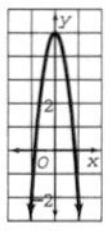

37. B **39.** A **45.** -3 **47.** 2 **49.** $y = -4x^2 - 3$ **51.** $y = 10x^2 - 1$ **55.** 25 ft by 50 ft, area = 1250 ft^2

57. $y = x^2 + 1$; up **59.** $y = -\frac{1}{2}x^2 + 1$; down **81.** $\begin{bmatrix} 3 & -4 \\ 3 & 0 \end{bmatrix}$ **83.** Let x = amount of storage space and y = amount of space to be covered by the roof. $x \geq 40{,}000$; $y \leq 25{,}000$

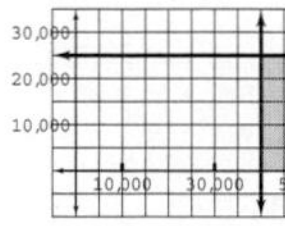

Lesson 5-3 pp. 251–254

EXERCISES

1. 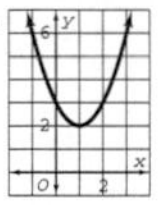

13. $y = \frac{1}{4}x^2$ **15.** $y = -(x - 2)^2$ **17.** $y = (x - 2)^2$ **19.** $y = 6(x + 3)^2 - 2$ **21.** $(-20, 0), -600$ **23.** $(-5.5, 0)$, 726 **27.** $y = (x - 2)^2 + 2$ **29.** $y = 6x^2 - 10$

37. 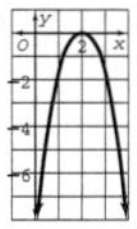

43. $y = -7(x - 1)^2 + 2$ **45.** $y = -\frac{1}{2}(x + 3)^2 + 6$ **51.** $y = 25x^2 + 60x + 27$ **53.** $y = 2x^2 + 22x$ **59.** yes **61.** no; $y = -3\left(x + \frac{1}{3}\right)^2 + \frac{4}{3}$ **69.** $a = 3$, $k = -1$ **71.** $a = \frac{1}{5}, k = 1$

91. 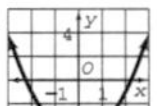 **93.** 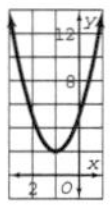

95. $\begin{bmatrix} -4 \\ 0 \end{bmatrix}$

Lesson 5-4 pp. 259–261

EXERCISES **1.** 3; $3(a^2 + 3)$ **3.** x; $x(x - 2)$ **7.** $(x + 1)(x + 2)$ **9.** $(x + 2)(x + 5)$ **13.** $(x - 1)(x - 2)$ **15.** $(r - 2)(r - 9)$ **19.** $(x - 7)(x + 2)$ **21.** $(x - 8)(x + 5)$ **25.** $(3x + 4)(x + 9)$ **27.** $(r + 2)(5r + 13)$ **31.** $(x + 4)(3x - 5)$ **33.** $(x - 2)(7x + 6)$ **37.** $(x + 1)^2$ **39.** $(x - 9)^2$ **47.** $5x - 1$ by $5x - 1$ **49.** $(x + y)^2 - y^2$; $x(x + 2y)$ **51.** $9(x + 2)(x - 2)$ **53.** $3(2y + 5)(2y - 5)$ **67.** $(x - 70)$ ft **85.** $y = (x - 1)^2$ **87.** $y = 5x^2 - 1$ **89.** -29 **91.** penny: 2.5 g, nickel: 5 g, dime 2.3 g

Lesson 5-5 pp. 266–268

EXERCISES **1.** $-4, -2$ **3.** $-1, \frac{3}{2}$ **7.** $-4, 4$ **9.** $-4, 4$ **13.** 0, 4 **15.** $-\frac{7}{2}, \frac{7}{2}$ **21.** $-1.32, 8.32$ **23.** -1.67, -1.5 **33a.** $\frac{5\sqrt{10}}{9}$ or about 1.76 s **b.** $\frac{10\sqrt{10}}{3}$ or about 10.54 s **35.** 3 ft **37.** 3, 8 **39.** $-\frac{1}{2}, 3$ **55.** $(0, -2), (2, 2)$ **59.** Answers may vary. Sample: $x^2 + x - 6 = 0$, $2x^2 - 12 = -2x$ **61.** Answers may vary. Sample: $6x^2 - 7x + 2 = 0$, $18x^2 - 21x = -6$ **75.** $(5z + 3)(5z - 3)$ **77.** 3×3; 5 **79.** 3×3; 0 **81.** Comm. Prop. of Add. **83.** Additive Inverse Prop.

Extension p. 269

1. 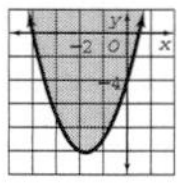

Lesson 5-6 pp. 274–276

EXERCISES **1.** $2i$ **3.** $i\sqrt{15}$ **11.** $2 + i\sqrt{3}$ **13.** $6 - 2i\sqrt{7}$ **15.** $7 - 5i$ **19.** 2 **21.** $2\sqrt{2}$ **25.** $-5 + 3i$ **27.** $3 + 2i$ **29.** $6 + 3i$ **31.** $7 + 4i$ **35.** 10 **37.** $9 + 58i$ **41.** $\pm 5i$ **43.** $\pm\frac{8i\sqrt{3}}{3}$ **47.** $-i, -1 - i, i$ **49.** $1 - i, 1 - 3i, -7 - 7i$ **51.** $\pm 7i$ **57.** $288i$ **59.** $10 - 4i$ **81.** $-2.351, 0.851$ **83.** $-5.562, -1.438$

85. 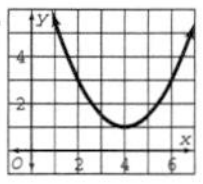 **87.** 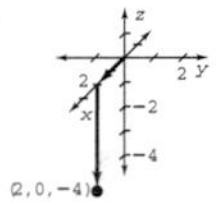

Lesson 5-7 pp. 281–283

EXERCISES **1.** $-4, -2$ **3.** $-1, 3$ **7.** 81 **9.** 144 **13.** $-4, 7$ **15.** $-3 \pm 4i\sqrt{2}$ **23.** $2 \pm \frac{\sqrt{15}}{3}$ **25.** $-4, \frac{7}{2}$ **29.** $y = -(x - 2)^2 + 3$ **31.** $y = (x + 2)^2 - 3$ **35.** $y = \frac{1}{2}(x - 5)^2 - \frac{1}{2}$; $\left(5, -\frac{1}{2}\right)$ **37a.** $(60, 5000)$ **b.** \$5000 **c.** \$60 **41.** $-20, 20$ **43.** $-16, 16$ **51.** $-12 \pm 3\sqrt{17}$ **53.** $\frac{1}{4} \pm \frac{\sqrt{57}}{12}$ **69.** $-2 + 2i$ **71.** $84 + 5i$ **73.** $y = -\frac{1}{2}x^2 + x + 2$ **75.** $(2, 0)$ **77.** $(3, 1)$

Lesson 5-8 pp. 289–291

EXERCISES **1.** 1, 3 **3.** $-\frac{7}{2}, 1$ **13.** $3 \pm i\sqrt{2}$ **15.** $-\frac{3}{2} \pm \frac{i\sqrt{11}}{2}$ **23.** $\frac{5}{3} \pm \frac{\sqrt{10}}{3}$; 0.61, 2.72 **25.** $-\frac{1}{6}, 1$ **31.** -4; two, imaginary **33.** 0; one, real **41.** 1,10 **43.** $-\frac{3}{2}, \frac{1}{2}$ **53a.** $w(18 - w) = 36$ **b.** 2.29 in. by 15.71 in. **57.** two **59.** none **67a.** $x^2 = 100\pi$ **b.** 17.72 cm **81.** $-2, 10$ **83.** $\frac{3 \pm \sqrt{41}}{2}$ **85.** $\begin{bmatrix} 3 & 0 & 4 & -2 \\ 0 & -3 & 2 & -4 \end{bmatrix}$ **87.** $\begin{bmatrix} -16 & 52 \\ -7 & 24 \end{bmatrix}$

Chapter Review pp. 293–295

1. perfect square trinomial **2.** quadratic formula **3.** vertex form of a quadratic function **4.** zero of a function **5.** discriminant **6.** quadratic; $-2x^2$, $5x$, 3 **7.** quadratic; $-x^2$, x, 3 **8.** linear; none, $-4x$, 3 **9.** $(0, -1), x = 0$, $(2, 3)$ and $(-1, 0)$ **10.** $(-2, 1), x = -2$, $(-2, 1)$ and $(-4, 0)$ **11.** $(1, -4), x = 1$, $(3, -1)$ and $\left(2, -3\frac{1}{4}\right)$ **12a.** $y = 614x^2 - 342x + 4962$, where $x = 0$ corresponds to 1995 and y is in thousands. **b.** around 1999 **c.** $y = -25.5x^2 + 917.8x + 4776.7$ **d.** around 2007 **e.** ≈13,000,000

13. 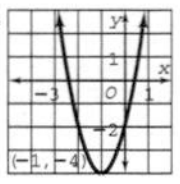

vertex $(-1, -4)$, y-intercept: -2; $x = -1$

14. 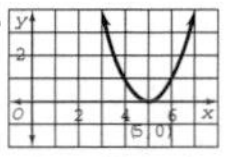

vertex $(5, 0)$, y-intercept: 25; $x = 5$

15. 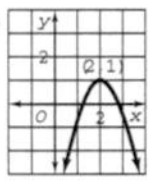

vertex $(2, 1)$, y-intercept: -7; $x = 2$

16. 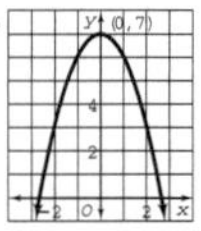

vertex $(0, 7)$, y-intercept: 7; $x = 0$

17. $y = \left(x + \frac{1}{2}\right)^2 - 12\frac{1}{4}$; minimum: $-12\frac{1}{4}$
18. $y = -(x - 1)^2 + 3$; maximum: 3
19. $y = 2(x + 2)^2 - 11$; minimum: -11
20. $y = -0.5(x - 0)^2 + 5$; maximum: 5
21. $y = -\frac{1}{2}(x - 1)^2 + 2$; maximum: 2
22. $y = \frac{4}{9}(x - 3)^2 - 1$; minimum: -1
23. $y = \frac{1}{2}(x - 0)^2 - 2$; minimum: -2
24. 0, 7 **25.** $-4, 2$ **26.** $-6, 0$ **27.** $2 - 2\sqrt{2}, 2 + 2\sqrt{2}$ **28.** $-1, 4$ **29.** $-0.85, 5.85$ or $\frac{5 \pm 3\sqrt{5}}{2}$ **30.** $\frac{2}{3}, 4$ **31.** $-1, 4$ **32.** -4 **33.** 3 **34.** $\frac{3}{2}$ **35.** $-3, 3$ **36.** $-\frac{1}{3}, \frac{5}{2}$ **37.** $-\frac{3}{2}, -\frac{1}{2}$ **38.** $-2.61, 1.28$ or $\frac{-2 \pm \sqrt{34}}{3}$ **39.** $5i$ **40.** $-1 + i\sqrt{2}$ **41.** $-4 - i$ **42.** $3i\sqrt{3}$ **43.** $4 + 8i\sqrt{2}$ **44.** $\sqrt{10}$ **45.** $\sqrt{13}$ **46.** 4 **47.** $-4 + 6i$ **48.** $51 + 21i$ **49.** $8 + 6i$ **50.** $2 + 16i$

51. $-2 + i$; 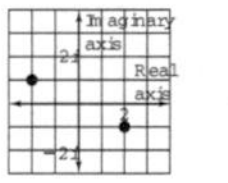 **52.** $4 - 3i$; 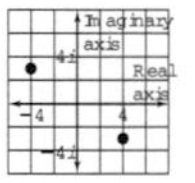

53. $7 + 4i$; 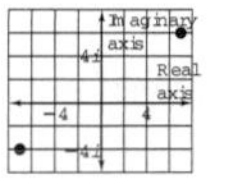 **54.** $2i$; 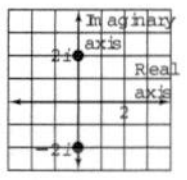

55. $-2i, 2i$ **56.** $-5i, 5i$ **57.** $-2i, 2i$ **58.** $\frac{-i\sqrt{6}}{3}, \frac{i\sqrt{6}}{3}$ **59.** $-i, -1 - i, i$ **60.** $i, 1 + i, -i$ **61.** $-1, \frac{1}{3}$ **62.** $-\frac{3}{2} + \frac{i\sqrt{91}}{2}, -\frac{3}{2} - \frac{i\sqrt{91}}{2}$

63. $1 + i\sqrt{3}, 1 - i\sqrt{3}$ **64.** $\frac{1}{2} + \frac{3i\sqrt{3}}{2}, \frac{1}{2} - \frac{3i\sqrt{3}}{2}$ **65.** $-\frac{3}{4} + \frac{\sqrt{73}}{4}, -\frac{3}{4} - \frac{\sqrt{73}}{4}$ **66.** $-\frac{3}{4}, 1$ **67.** $y = \left(x + \frac{3}{2}\right)^2 - \frac{13}{4}$; $\left(-\frac{3}{2}, -\frac{13}{4}\right)$ **68.** $y = 2\left(x - \frac{1}{4}\right)^2 - \frac{9}{8}$; $\left(\frac{1}{4}, -\frac{9}{8}\right)$ **69.** $y = \left(x + \frac{1}{2}\right)^2 + \frac{7}{4}$; $\left(-\frac{1}{2}, -\frac{7}{4}\right)$ **70.** 2 real solutions; $3 + \sqrt{7}, 3 - \sqrt{7}$ **71.** 2 imaginary solutions; $\frac{7}{4} + \frac{i\sqrt{3i}}{4}, \frac{7}{4} - \frac{i\sqrt{3i}}{4}$ **72.** 2 real solutions; $3 + \sqrt{5}, 3 - \sqrt{5}$

Chapter 6

Lesson 6-1 pp. 303–305

EXERCISES **1.** $10x + 5$; degree 1, 2 terms **3.** $2m^2 + 7m - 3$; degree 2, 3 terms **13.** $y = x^3 + 1$ **15.** $y = 1.5x^3 + x^2 - 2x + 1$ **19.** $y = x^3 - 10x^2$; 2023 **21.** $y = -0.03948x^3 + 2.069x^2 - 17.93x + 106.9$; 206.07 **25.** $x^3 + 4x$; degree 3, 2 terms **27.** 7; degree 0, 1 term **33.** $-c^2 + 16$; binomial **35.** $16x^2 - x - 5$; trinomial **47.** $30x^3 - 10x^2$; binomial **49.** $b^3 - 6b^2 + 9b$; trinomial **67.** 2

69. 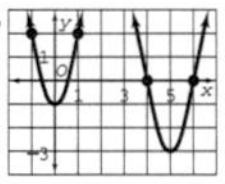 5, −3)

71. $\begin{bmatrix} 2 & -3 & -6 \\ 5 & -2 & 0 \end{bmatrix}$

Extension p. 306

1. (↗,↗) **2.** (↗,↗) **3.** (↗,↘) **4.** (↗,↗) **5.** (↘,↗) **6.** (↗,↗) **7.** (↗,↘) **8.** (↘,↗) **9.** (↘,↘) **10.** (↘,↘)

Lesson 6-2 pp. 311–313

EXERCISES **1.** $x^2 + x - 6$ **3.** $x^3 - 7x^2 + 15x - 9$ **7.** $x(x - 6)(x + 6)$ **9.** $5x(2x^2 - 2x + 3)$ **13.** $(-3.2, 24.2), (0.5, -1.4), 0, -5, 1$ **15a.** $h = x$, $\ell = 16 - 2x, w = 12 - 2x$ **b.** $V = x(16 - 2x)(12 - 2x)$

c. 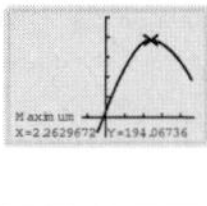

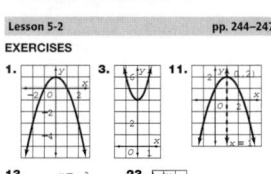

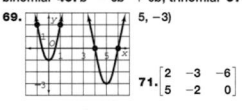

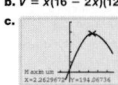

194 $in.^3$, 2.26 in.

17. 2, −9 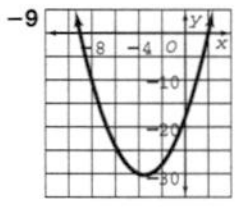

21. $y = x^3 - 18x^2 + 107x - 210$ **23.** $x^3 + 9x^2 + 15x - 25$ **29.** -3 (mult. 3) **31.** $-1, 0, \frac{1}{2}$ **37.** 2 x^3 blocks, 15 x^2 blocks, 31 x blocks, 12 unit blocks **39.** $V = 12x^3 - 27x$ **41.** $y = -2x^3 + 9x^2 - x - 12$ **43.** $y = 3x(x - 8)(x - 1)$ **45.** $y = x^2(x + 4)(x - 1)$ **47.** $(2.5, 10.5), (5.1, -7.1), \frac{3}{2}, 4, 6$ **49.** $(-0.05, 2.98)$, $(0.88, -6.17)$, 1.5 **51.** Answers may vary. Sample: $y = x^3 - 3x^2 - 10x$ **53.** $y = x^4 - 4x^3 - 7x^2 + 22x + 24$ **55.** 0 (mult. 2), -1 (mult. 2) **71.** $-7x^4 - x^3$; quartic binomial **73.** $(x + 4)(x + 1)$ **75.** $(x - 6)(x - 6)$ **77.** -11

Lesson 6-3 pp. 318–320

EXERCISES **1.** $x - 8$ **3.** $x^2 + 4x + 3$, R 5 **9.** no **11.** yes **13.** $x^2 + 4x + 3$ **15.** $x^2 - 11x + 37$, R -128 **23.** $y = (x + 1)(x + 3)(x - 2)$ **25.** $\ell = x + 3$ and $h = x$ **27.** 0 **29.** 0 **37.** $x^2 + 4x + 5$ **39.** $x^4 - x^3 + x^2 - x + 1$ **43.** yes **45.** no **49.** yes **51.** no **53.** $x^3 - 2x^2 - 2x + 4$, R -35 **55.** $x^3 - 4x^2 + x$ **65.** $y = x^2 + 2x - 15$ **67.** $y = x^3 - 6x^2 + 3x + 10$ **69.** 24 **71.** $23 - 11i$ **73.** none exists

Lesson 6-4 pp. 324–326

EXERCISES **1.** $-2, 1, 5$ **3.** 0, 1 **13.** $(x - 10)(x^2 + 10x + 100)$ **15.** $3, \frac{-3 \pm 3i\sqrt{3}}{2}$ **17.** $5, \frac{-5 \pm 5i\sqrt{3}}{2}$ **21.** $(x^2 - 7)(x - 1)(x + 1)$ **23.** $(x^2 - 3)(x - 2)(x + 2)$ **27.** $\pm 3, \pm 1$ **29.** $\pm 4, \pm 2i$ **33.** $-1, 3.24, -1.24$ **35.** $-2, -3$, 1 2 **41.** about 3.58 cm, about 2.83 cm **43.** $\frac{4}{3}, \frac{-2 \pm 2i\sqrt{3}}{3}$ **45.** $\pm 5, \pm i\sqrt{2}$ **61.** $V = x^2(4x - 2)$, 4 in. by 4 in. by 16 in. **63.** $-\frac{5}{2}, 1, y = (2x + 5)(x - 1)$ **65.** $-1, 2, 2, y = (x + 1)(x - 2)^2$ **77.** $2x^2 + x - 3$ R 2 **79.** ± 6 **81.** $\begin{bmatrix} 0 \\ -5 \end{bmatrix}$

Extension p. 328

1. pos. real roots: 1, neg. real roots: 2 or none
3. pos. real roots: 1, neg. real roots: 2 or none

5. pos. real roots: 1, neg. real roots: 3 or 1 **7.** pos. real roots: 1, neg. real roots: 1 **9.** pos. real roots: 4, 2, or none; neg. real roots: 1

Lesson 6-5 pp. 333–334

EXERCISES **1.** ±1, ±2; 1 **3.** ±1, ±2, ±4; −1 **7.** 2, $\pm i\sqrt{5}$ **9.** −3, 1, $\frac{7}{2}$ **13.** $-\sqrt{5}, \sqrt{13}$ **15.** $1+\sqrt{10}$, $2-\sqrt{2}$ **17.** $2-3i, -6i$ **19.** $x^3 - x^2 + 9x - 9 = 0$ **21.** $x^3 - 2x^2 + 16x - 32 = 0$ **25.** $\pm\frac{1}{12}, \pm\frac{1}{6}, \pm\frac{1}{4}, \pm\frac{1}{2}, \pm\frac{1}{3}, \pm\frac{2}{3}, \pm\frac{3}{4}, \pm1, \pm\frac{3}{2}, \pm2, \pm3, \pm6; \frac{1}{2}, \frac{3}{2}, \frac{2}{3}$ **27.** $\pm\frac{7}{3}, \pm\frac{1}{6}, \pm\frac{1}{2}, \pm\frac{1}{3}, \pm\frac{7}{6}, \pm1, \pm\frac{3}{2}, \pm3, \pm\frac{7}{2}, \pm7, \pm\frac{21}{2}, \pm21; \frac{1}{3}, -\frac{7}{2}, 1, 3$ **29.** $x^4 - 6x^3 + 14x^2 - 24x + 40 = 0$ **31.** $x^4 - 6x^3 + 2x^2 + 30x - 35 = 0$ **33.** Sometimes true; since −2 is a factor of 8, −2 is a possible root of the equation. **35.** Sometimes true; since $\sqrt{5}$ and $-\sqrt{5}$ are conjugates, they can be roots of a polynomial equation with integer coefficients. **43a–c.** Answers may vary. Sample: **a.** $x - 1 - \sqrt{2} = 0$ **b.** $x^2 - 2(1+\sqrt{2})x + (1+\sqrt{2})^2 = 0$ **c.** −1 **49.** $\pm\sqrt{5}, \pm 2i$ **51.** −1, 7 **53.** $\frac{3}{2} \pm \sqrt{5}$ **55.** (−6, 2)

Lesson 6-6 pp. 337–338

EXERCISES **1.** 3 complex roots; number of real roots: 1 or 3; possible rational roots: ±1 **3.** 4 complex roots; number of real roots: 0, 2, or 4; possible rational roots: 0 **9.** $-1, \frac{1 \pm i\sqrt{7}}{4}$ **11.** $4, \frac{1 \pm i\sqrt{3}}{2}$ **17.** 4 complex roots; number of real roots: 0, 2, or 4; possible rational roots: $\pm\frac{1}{2}, \pm1, \pm2, \pm\frac{13}{2}, \pm13, \pm26$ **19.** 3 complex roots; number of real roots: 1 or 3; possible rational roots: $\pm\frac{1}{3}, \pm\frac{2}{3}, \pm1, \pm\frac{4}{3}, \pm2, \pm3, \pm4, \pm6, \pm12$ **21.** $4, \pm 3i$ **23.** $-6, \frac{-1 \pm i}{2}$

29. −3.24, 1.24

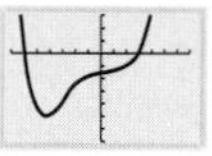

37. 3 (mult. 2) **39.** $\frac{3\ w\ i\sqrt{23}}{4}$
41. $y = 2x^2 + 24x + 75$

Lesson 6-7 pp 342–345

EXERCISES **1.** 120 **3.** 6,227,020,800 **11.** 56 **13.** 1680 **21.** 15 **23.** 1 **31.** 2600 **33.** true because of the Comm. Prop. of Add. **35.** False; answers may vary. Sample: (3 + 2)! = 120 and 3! + 2! = 8 **43.** 84 **45.** 5 **47.** permutation **49.** combination **51.** 210 **53.** 5 **55a.** 56 **b.** 56 **57.** 3024 **59.** 24 **81.** 3 complex roots; number of real roots: 1 or 3; possible rational roots: $\pm\frac{1}{12}, \pm\frac{1}{6}, \pm\frac{1}{4}, \pm\frac{1}{3}, \pm\frac{1}{2}, \pm\frac{2}{3}, \pm1, \pm2$ **83.** $y = -x^3 - 3x^2 + 6$; cubic trinomial **85.** $h(t) = 5t^2 - 3t$; quadratic binomial **89.** $4(x-1)^2$ **91.** $3(x-5)(x+5)$ **93.** maximum; 4.125

Lesson 6-8 pp. 349–351

EXERCISES **1.** $a^3 + 3a^2b + 3ab^2 + b^3$ **3.** $a^4 + 4a^3b + 6a^2b^2 + 4ab^3 + b^4$ **13.** $x^4 + 4x^3y + 6x^2y^2 + 4xy^3 + y^4$ **15.** $s^2 - 2st + t^2$ **21a.** about 25% **b.** about 21% **c.** about 12% **23.** $x^7 + 7x^6y + 21x^5y^2 + 35x^4y^3 + 35x^3y^4 + 21x^2y^5 + 7xy^6 + y^7$ **25.** $81x^4 - 108x^3y + 54x^2y^2 - 12xy^3 + y^4$ **43a.** about 31% **b.** about 16% **c.** about 16% **45.** ${}_8C_4x^4y^4$ **47.** 7, $7r^6s$ **49.** $80x^2$ **51.** $264x^{10}$ **59a.** $(s+0.5)^3$ **b.** $s^3 + 1.5s^2 + 0.75s + 0.125$ **61.** 13, d^{12}, $12d^{11}e$ **63.** 6, $32a^5$, $80a^4b$ **75.** 20 **77.** 35 **81.** 20.75; −12.60; −3, 1, 4 **83.** $y = (x-3)^2 - 7$ **85.** $y = -4(x-0)^2 + 9$

Chapter Review pp. 353–355

1. degree **2.** standard form of a polynomial **3.** multiplicity **4.** complex conjugates **5.** combinations **6.** $3p^3 - 2p$; degree 3, 2 terms **7.** $-5x^9 + 3$; degree 9, 2 terms **8.** $-x^5 - x^3 + x$; degree 5, 3 terms **9.** $4x^3 + 2x^2 + 2x$; degree 3, 3 terms **10.** $x^7 + x^4 - x^2 + x + 5$; degree 7, 5 terms **11.** s; degree 1, 1 term **12.** cubic: $y = 62.26851852x^3 - 303.1944444x^2 + 481.8148148x - 248.5222222$; quartic: $y = 984.375x^4 - 6631.481481x^3 + 16{,}498.68056x^2 - 17{,}954.68519x + 7208.877778$;

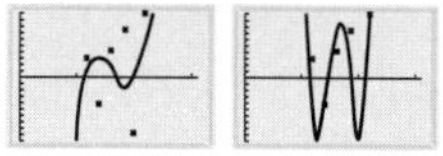

The quartic model better fits the data.
13. $x(x-4)(x+3)$; −3, 0, 4; rel. max. = 12.60, rel. min. = −20.75 **14.** $(2-x)(2+x)$; −2, 2; rel. max. = 4 **15.** $x^3(x+2)^4$; 0 (mult. 3), −2 (mult. 4); rel. max. = 0, rel. min. = −1.07 **16.** $f(x) = x^4 + 3x^3 - 4x^2 - 12x$ **17.** $f(x) = x^3 - 4x^2 + 5x - 2$ **18.** $f(x) = x^4 + 2x^3 - 3x^2$ **19.** $f(x) = x^3 + 6x^2 + 12x + 8$ **20.** $x^2 + 5x + 8$, R 12; check students' work. **21.** $x^3 - x^2 + x - 2$, R 4; check students' work. **22.** $(x+1)(x-3)(x-1)$ **23.** $(x-3)^2(x+2)$ **24.** 93 **25.** −30 **26.** 77 **27.** −9 **28.** −1, 1.38, 3.62 **29.** −1.78 **30.** 0 **31.** −1.52 **32.** −1.63 **33.** no solution **34.** $(x-2)(x^2+2x+4)$; $2, -1 \pm i\sqrt{3}$ **35.** $t^4(2t-1)(2t+1)$; $0, \frac{1}{2}, -\frac{1}{2}$ **36.** $(2x+1)(4x^2-2x+1)$; $-\frac{1}{2}, \frac{1 \pm i\sqrt{3}}{4}$ **37.** $x(x-4)(x-1)$; 0, 1, 4 **38.** $x(x^2-2x-5)$; $0, 1 \pm \sqrt{6}$ **39.** $(x+2)^2(x^2-2x+4)^2$; $-2, 1 \pm i\sqrt{3}$ **40.** 3 complex roots; number of real roots: 3 or 1; possible rational roots: ±1, ±2, ±3, ±6; roots 1, 2, 3 **41.** 4 complex roots; number of real roots: 4, 2, or 0; possible rational roots: $\pm1, \pm2, \pm4, \pm8, \pm\frac{1}{2}, \pm\frac{1}{5}, \pm\frac{2}{5}, \pm\frac{4}{5}, \pm\frac{8}{5}, \pm\frac{1}{10}$; roots: $-1, -\frac{1}{2}, \frac{4}{5}, 2$ **42.** 4 complex roots; number of real roots: 4, 2, or 0; possible rational roots: ±1, ±7; roots: ±1.26, ±2.10 **43.** 4 complex roots; number of real roots: 4, 2, or 0; possible rational roots: ±1, ±2, ±4; roots: −1, −2 **44.** 3 complex roots; number of real roots: 3 or 1; possible rational roots: ±1, ±5; roots: $-1, 2 \pm i$ **45.** 4 complex roots; number of real roots: 4, 2, or 0; possible rational roots: ±1, ±2, ±3, ±6; roots: $\pm\sqrt{3}, 1 \pm i$ **46.** $x^3 - 2x^2 + x - 2$ **47.** $x^4 - 16x^3 + 91x^2 - 216x + 182$ **48.** $x^4 - 10x^3 + 39x^2 - 70x + 50$ **49.** $x^5 - 6x^4 + 11x^3 - 24x^2 + 28x$ **50.** $x^4 - 8x^3 + 23x^2 - 42x + 30$ **51.** $x^4 - 12x^2 + 35$ **52.** 72 **53.** 24 **54.** 35 **55.** 30 **56.** 2 **57.** 120 **58.** $4320x^3y^3$ **59.** 27%

Chapter 7

Lesson 7-1 pp. 366–367

EXERCISES **1.** 15, −15 **3.** none **5.** −4 **7.** $-\frac{1}{2}$ **9.** 2, −2 **11.** 0.3, −0.3 **13.** 6 **15.** no real root **21.** $4|x|$ **23.** $x^4|y^9|$ **29.** 1.34 in. **31.** 0.48 cm **33.** 10, −10 **35.** 0.5, −0.5 **37.** $\sqrt[3]{-64}, \sqrt[6]{64}, -\sqrt[3]{-64}, \sqrt{64}$ **39.** 0.5 **41.** 0.2 **59.** Some; they are equal for $x \geq 0$. **61.** Some; they are equal for $x \geq 0$. **75.** $x^5 + 5x^4y + 10x^3y^2 + 10x^2y^3 + 5xy^4 + y^5$ **77.** $729x^6 - 7290x^5 + 30{,}375x^4 - 67{,}500x^3 + 84{,}375x^2 - 56{,}250x + 15{,}625$ **79.** $y = x(2x-7)(2x+7)$ **81.** $y = 4x(x+1)^2$ **83.** $y = 3(x-0)^2 - 7$ **85.** $y = \frac{1}{4}(x+4)^2 - 5$

Lesson 7-2 pp. 371–373

EXERCISES **1.** 16 **3.** −9 **9.** $2x\sqrt{5x}$ **11.** $5x^2\sqrt{2x}$ **17.** $2\sqrt[3]{12}$ **19.** $7x^3y^4\sqrt{6y}$ **23.** 10 **25.** $2x^2y^2\sqrt{2}$ **27.** $\frac{\sqrt{2x}}{2}$ **29.** $\frac{\sqrt[3]{4x}}{2}$ **35.** $r = \frac{\sqrt{Gm_1m_2F}}{F}$ **37.** $10\sqrt{2}$ **39.** $3x^6y^5\sqrt{2y}$ **55.** 212 mi/h greater **77.** $-9c^{24}d^{32}$ **79.** $2y^5$ **85.** $x^2 - 3x + 9$, a factor **87.** $2x^3 + x^2 + 2x$, R 10, not a factor **89.** 25 **91.** $\frac{121}{4}$

Lesson 7-3 pp. 376–378

EXERCISES **1.** $6\sqrt{6}$ **3.** cannot combine **7.** $33\sqrt{2}$ **9.** $7\sqrt{2}$ **13.** $8 + 4\sqrt{5}$ **15.** $63 - 38\sqrt{2}$ **19.** 14 **21.** −40 **23.** $-2 + 2\sqrt{3}$ **25.** $13 + 7\sqrt{3}$ **27.** $13\sqrt{2}$ **29.** $48\sqrt{2x}$ **47.** $14\sqrt{7}\ m$ **63.** $3\sqrt[3]{2}$ **65.** 4 **71.** $2, -1 \pm i\sqrt{3}$ **73.** $\frac{1}{5}, \frac{-1 \pm i\sqrt{3}}{10}$

Lesson 7-4 pp. 382–384

EXERCISES **1.** 6 **3.** 7 **11.** $\sqrt[5]{x}$ **13.** $\sqrt[5]{y^2}$ or $(\sqrt[5]{y})^2$ **17.** $\sqrt[5]{y^6}$ or $(\sqrt[5]{y})^6$ **19.** $7^{\frac{1}{2}}x^{\frac{3}{2}}$ **27.** ≈15.1 m **29.** ≈1.6 m **31.** 16 **33.** 64 **39.** $\frac{1}{x^4}$ **41.** $\frac{5}{x^{\frac{2}{3}}}$ **51.** −3 **53.** 729 **63.** 635.87 **65.** $x^{\frac{1}{2}}$ **67.** $x^{\frac{1}{2}}$ **95.** $4\sqrt[3]{3}$ **97.** $1 + 3\sqrt{5}$ **101.** $4x(x^2 - 2x + 4)$ **103.** $(x-9)^2$

Lesson 7-5 pp. 388–390

EXERCISES **1.** 16 **3.** 22 **7.** 3 **9.** 18 **13.** 30.6 ft **15.** 3 **17.** −3, −4 **21.** $\frac{81}{16}$ **23.** −1, −6 **31.** $s = \sqrt{A}$; $4\sqrt{2}$ m, or about 5.7 m **35.** 4 **37.** 23 **65.** 16 **67.** $6\sqrt{2}$ **75.** 7 **77.** 60 **85.** 3, 4 **87.** −5, −4

Lesson 7-6 pp. 394–398

EXERCISES **1.** $x^2 + 3x + 5$ **3.** $-x^2 + 3x + 5$ **13.** $2x^2 + 2x - 4$; domain: all real numbers **15.** $2x^2 - 2$; domain: all real numbers **21.** $x^2 + 5$; 14, 9 **23.** 104 **25.** 16 **31.** 1 **33.** −3 **43a.** $f(x) = 0.9x$ **b.** $g(x) = x - 2000$ **c.** $14,200 **d.** $14,400 **45.** $x^2 - x + 7$ **47.** $x^2 - 5x - 3$ **51.** $-3x^2 + 2x + 16$, domain: all real numbers **53.** $3x^3 + 8x^2 - 4x + 16$, domain: all real numbers **59.** −4 **61.** 2 **63.** $3x^2, 9x^2$ **65.** $12x^2 + 2, 6x^2 + 4$ **71a.** $P(x) = 5295x - 1000$ **b.** $158,750

73. $(f+g)(x) = f(x) + g(x)$ Def. of Function Add.
$= 3x - 2 + (x^2 + 1)$ Substitution
$= x^2 + 3x - 2 + 1$ Comm. Prop.
$= x^2 + 3x - 1$ arithmetic

75. $(f \circ g)(x) = f(g(x))$ def. of comp. functions
$= f(x^2 + 1)$ substitution
$= 3(x^2 + 1) - 2$ substitution
$= 3x^2 + 3 - 2$ Dist. Prop.
$= 3x^2 + 1$ arithmetic

93. −3 **95.** 3 **99.** $x^6 + 6x^5y + 15x^4y^2 + 20x^3y^3 + 15x^2y^4 + 6xy^5 + y^6$ **101.** $128x^7 - 1344x^6y + 6048x^5y^2 - 15{,}120x^4y^3 + 22{,}680x^3y^4 - 20{,}412x^2y^5 + 10{,}206xy^6 - 2187y^7$ **107.** $-2 + 19i\sqrt{2}$ **109.** $-8 - 36i$

Lesson 7-7 pp. 404–406

EXERCISES

1.

x	0	1	0	2
y	1	2	3	4

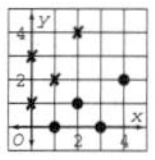

5. $y = \frac{1}{3}x - \frac{1}{3}$; yes **7.** $y = -\frac{1}{3}x + \frac{4}{3}$; yes

15.

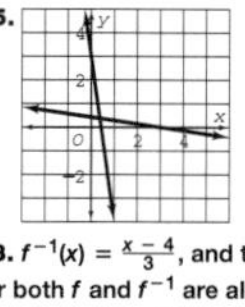

23. $f^{-1}(x) = \frac{x-4}{3}$, and the domain and range for both f and f^{-1} are all real numbers; f^{-1} is a function. **25.** $f^{-1}(x) = x^2 - 7$, domain $f\{x|x \in R, x \geq -7\}$, range $f\{y|y \in R, y \geq 0\}$, domain $f^{-1}\{x|x \in R, x \geq 0\}$, and range $f^{-1}\{y|y \in R, y \geq -7\}$; f^{-1} is a function. **29a.** $F = \frac{9}{5}(C - 32)$; yes **b.** −3.89°F **31.** 10 **33.** 0.2 **35.** $f^{-1}(x) = \pm\sqrt{\frac{2x+8}{3}}$; no **37.** $f^{-1}(x) = \frac{x^2 - 6x + 10}{2}$; yes **47.** $f^{-1}(x) = x^2$, domain of $f\{x|x \in R, x \geq 0\}$, range of $f\{y|y \in R, y \geq 0\}$, domain of $f^{-1}\{x|x \in R, x \geq 0\}$, range of $f^{-1}\{y|y \in R, y \geq 0\}$, and f^{-1} is a function. **49.** $f^{-1}(x) = 3 - x^2$, domain of $f\{x|x \in R, x \leq 3\}$, range of $f\{y|y \in R, y \geq 0\}$, domain of $f^{-1}\{x|x \in R, x \geq 0\}$, range of $f^{-1}\{y|y \in R, y \leq 3\}$, and f^{-1} is a function. **59a–b.** Answers may vary. Sample:

a.

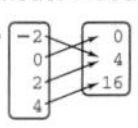

b.

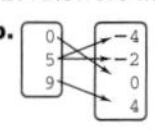

61. $n = s\sqrt{2}$; $3\sqrt{2}$ in. ≈ 4.2 in. **75.** $2x + 7$ **77.** $x + 14$ **81.** −2 **83.** 3 **89.** $\pm1, \pm2, \pm4, \pm\frac{1}{3}, \pm\frac{2}{3}, \pm\frac{4}{3}$; roots are $\frac{2}{3}$, 2, −1. **91.** $\pm1, \pm2, \pm3, \pm5, \pm6, \pm10, \pm15, \pm30, \pm\frac{1}{2}, \pm\frac{3}{2}, \pm\frac{5}{2}, \pm\frac{15}{2}$; roots are $5, -\frac{3}{2}, 2$.

Technology pp. 409

1.

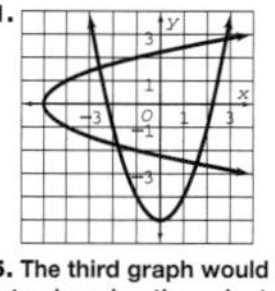

5. The third graph would be the same as the first. Interchanging the pairs twice restores the original pairs.

Lesson 7-8 pp. 411–413

EXERCISES

1.

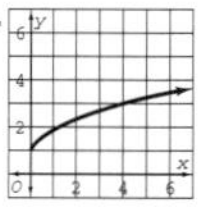

9.

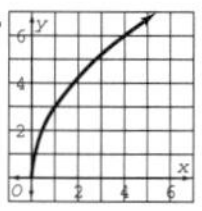

17.

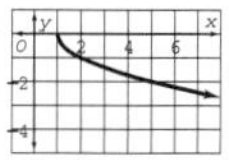

25.

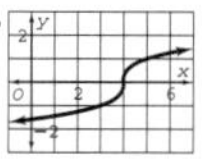

31. $y = -4\sqrt{x+2}$; the graph is the graph of $y = -4\sqrt{x}$ translated 2 units to the left. **33.** $y = 4\sqrt[3]{x+2}$; the graph is the graph of $y = 4\sqrt[3]{x}$ translated 2 units to the left.

37.

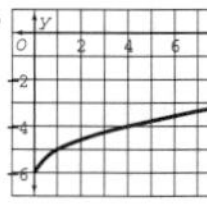

domain: $x \geq 0$, range: $y \geq -6$

53a. $y = \sqrt{x-5} - 2$ **b.** $y = \sqrt{x-1} - 5$ **55.** $y = 5\sqrt{x-4} - 1$; the graph is the same as $y = 5\sqrt{x}$, translated 4 units to the right and 1 down. **57.** $y = -2\sqrt[3]{x - \frac{1}{4}}$; the graph is the graph of $y = -2\sqrt[3]{x}$ translated $\frac{1}{4}$ unit to the right. **77.** $y = \frac{3(x+3)}{2}$; yes **79.** $y = (x+4)^2 - 3$; yes **83.** $\frac{\sqrt[3]{12xy^2}}{2y}$ **85.** $\frac{\sqrt[3]{48x^3y^4}}{2y}$ **87.** $\frac{-3 \pm 3\sqrt{5}}{2}$ **89.** $-5 \pm \sqrt{14}$

Chapter Review pp. 415–417

1. radicand **2.** index **3.** rationalize the denominator **4.** are not **5.** rational exponents **6.** composite function **7.** rational exponents **8.** inverse functions **9.** a radical equation **10.** principal root **11.** 12 **12.** −0.4 **13.** 7 **14.** 0.5 **15.** −3 **16.** $7|xy^5|$ **17.** $-4y^3$ **18.** $(a-1)^2$ **19.** $3x^3$ **20.** $(y+3)^2$ **21.** $4x^4y^2\sqrt{2xy}$ **22.** 20 **23.** $6\sqrt[3]{2}$ **24.** $10x^2y\sqrt[3]{12y^2}$ **25.** $7x^2\sqrt{2}$ **26.** $15x^3y^2\sqrt{x}$ **27.** $6xy\sqrt[4]{2y}$ **28.** 4 **29.** $2y\sqrt[3]{y}$ **30.** $5x$ **31.** $6xy\sqrt{3x}$ **32.** $3a^2b\sqrt[3]{b}$ **33.** $\frac{2\sqrt{3}}{3}$ **34.** $\frac{x\sqrt{6x}}{4}$ **35.** $\frac{\sqrt[3]{5x^2}}{x^2}$ **36.** $\frac{a^3\sqrt{ab}}{4b}$ **37.** $\frac{y\sqrt[3]{150x}}{10x^2}$ **38.** $6\sqrt{3}$ **39.** $7 - 3\sqrt{3}$ **40.** 43 **41.** $2\sqrt{2x}$ **42.** $\frac{42 - 12\sqrt{3}}{37}$ **43.** $-\frac{\sqrt{2}+\sqrt{10}}{4}$ **44.** $\sqrt[5]{3}$ **45.** $\sqrt[3]{x^2}$ **46.** $\sqrt[4]{\frac{1}{8}}$ **47.** $\sqrt[5]{3}$ **48.** $\sqrt[4]{\frac{1}{p^9}}$ **49.** 81 **50.** 216 **51.** x **52.** $x^{\frac{1}{9}}$ **53.** $\frac{y^4}{x^6}$ **54.** −42 **55.** 2 **56.** 121 **57.** $x^2 - x + 7$ **58.** $-x^2 + 5x + 3$ **59.** $2x^3 - x^2 - 11x + 10$ **60.** $x^2 - 5x - 3$ **61.** $\frac{x^2 - 3x + 2}{2x + 5}, x \neq -\frac{5}{2}$ **62.** 1 **63.** 25 **64.** 9 **65.** 1 **66.** $c^2 - 6c + 9$ **67.** $y = \frac{1}{6}x - \frac{1}{3}$; yes **68.** $y = \left(\frac{x-1}{2}\right)^{\frac{1}{3}}$; yes **69.** $y = \pm\sqrt[4]{x} + 2$; no **70.** $y = x^2 - 2$; yes **71.** 5 **72.** −5 **73.** 6 **74.** t

75.

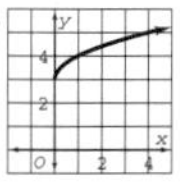

76.

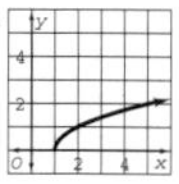

77.

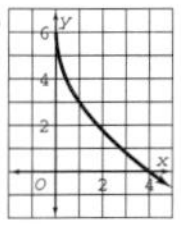

78.

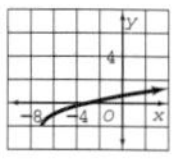

Chapter 8

Lesson 8-1 pp. 426–429

EXERCISES

1.

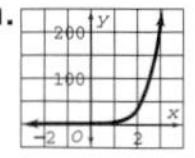

9a. 1.0126 **b.** $y = 6.08(1.0126)^x$ where $x = 0$ corresponds to 2000. **11.** $y = 2.5(7)^x$ **13.** $y = 5(0.6)^x$ **17.** exponential decay **19.** exponential decay

25.

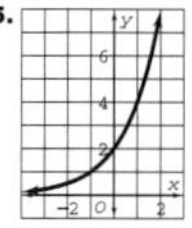

$y = 0$ is the horizontal asymptote.

33. $y = 12{,}000(0.9)^x$; 6377 **35a.** $y = 6500(0.857)^x$ **b.** about $4090 **37.** 63% increase **39.** 35% decrease **43a.** 5.6% **b.** 0.0017% **47.** 6 **49.** 0.45 **65.**

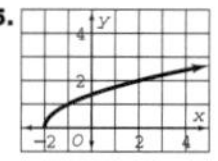

69. $84r^2\sqrt[3]{9r^2}$ **71.** Answers may vary. Sample: $y = x^3 - 5x^2 + 4x$ **73.** Answers may vary. Sample: $y = x^3 - 7x^2 + 10x$ **75.** $y = -5x^2 + 2$ **77.** $y = 10x^2 + 2$

Technology p. 430

1. $y = 6.25(0.5)^x$

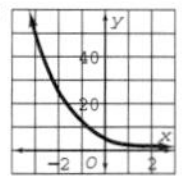

5. As the temperature of the coffee approaches the temperature of the room, the room temperature ceases to affect the coffee temperature.

Lesson 8-2 pp. 434–437

EXERCISES **1.** Asymptote is $y = 0$.

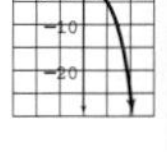

9.

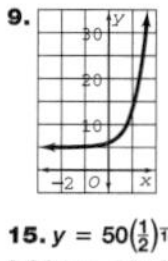

15. $y = 50\left(\frac{1}{2}\right)^{\frac{1}{14.3}x}$; 0.85 mg **17.** $y = 24\left(\frac{1}{2}\right)^{\frac{1}{5730}x}$; 0.64 mg **19.** 403.4288 **21.** 1 **25.** $448.30 **27.** 0

33. $y = -3^x$; $y = -3^{(x-8)} + 2$ **35.** $y = -3\left(\frac{1}{3}\right)^x$; $y = -3\left(\frac{1}{3}\right)^{x+5} - 1$ **37.** 8.7 yr **41.** \$399.97
43. exponential growth **45.** exponential growth
57. $y = -2(4)^x$ **59.** $y = 8(0.5)^x$ **63.** $-\sqrt[3]{4}$
65. $2(\sqrt[4]{2} + \sqrt[4]{8})$ **71.** $x^2 - x - 6$ **73.** $x^2 + x + 1$
77. $x + y = -2, x + 4z = -2, y + 4z = -2$
79. $x - y = 8, x + 2z = 8, -y + 2z = 8$

Lesson 8-3 pp. 441–444

EXERCISES **1.** The earthquake in Missouri released about 1.97 times more energy. **3.** The earthquake in Missouri released about 8,759,310 times more energy. **7.** $3 = \log 1000$ **9.** $\log \frac{1}{10} = -1$ **15.** $\frac{1}{2}$ **17.** $\frac{3}{2}$ **27.** 6.3×10^{-3} **29.** 7.9×10^{-4}

35.
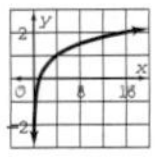

41. 0.6990; 0 **43.** −1.0969; −2 **53.** $128 = 2^7$
55. $16{,}807 = 7^5$ **63.** $y = 4^x$ **65.** $y = 10^x$

73.
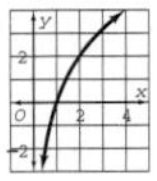

75. domain $\{x \mid x \in R \text{ and } x > 0\}$, range $\{y \mid y \in R\}$
77. domain $\{x \mid x \in R \text{ and } x \geq 3\}$, range $\{y \mid y \in R\}$

97.
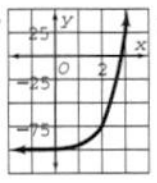
$y = -100$

101. $4\sqrt{w^3}$ **103.** $\sqrt[n]{x^p}$ **105.** −0.162, 6.162
107. $(2x - 3)(2x - 1)$ **109.** $(5x - 2)(x + 3)$

Lesson 8-4 pp. 449–451

EXERCISES **1.** Product Property **3.** Power Property **11.** log 14 **13.** log 972 **19.** $3 \log x + 5 \log y$ **21.** $\log_4 5 + \frac{1}{2} \log_4 x$ **31.** 9 dB **33.** −2 **35.** 6 **45.** 1.4772 **47.** 2.097 **56.** Answers may vary. Sample: $\log 150 = \log \frac{300}{2} = \log 300 - \log 2$
57. 12 dB **59.** False; $\frac{1}{2} \log_3 3 = \log_3 3^{\frac{1}{2}}$, not $\log_3 \frac{3}{2}$.
61. False; the two logs have different bases.

73. $\log_3 \sqrt[4]{2x}$ **75.** $\log \frac{3}{2}$ **79.** $3 \log 2 + \frac{3}{2} \log x - 3 \log^5$ **81.** $\log 2 + \frac{1}{2} \log 4 + \frac{1}{2} \log r - \log s$
97. $3 = \log_5 125$ **99.** $-3 = \log_5 \frac{1}{125}$ **101.** $\frac{64}{7}$
103. $-\sqrt{3}, \sqrt{5}$ **105.** $-2i, -4 - i$

Technology p. 452

3. Since the graphs are equivalent it is an identity; therefore the expressions are equal for all values of $x > 1$.

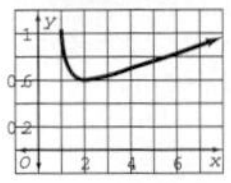

5a.
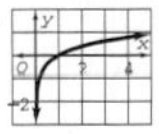

Lesson 8-5 pp. 456–460

EXERCISES **1.** 1.585 **3.** 2.732 **11.** 3.170; $\log_8 729.5$ **13.** 3.631; $\log_8 1901.1$ **19.** 2.3219
21. 0.0499 **27.** 0.5690 **29.** 4.7027 **33.** 0.05
35. 33 **43.** 223,606.8 **45.** $\frac{1}{4}$ **51.** $2 = 10\left(\frac{1}{2}\right)^{\frac{x}{1.17}}$, 2.7 minutes **53.** −1 **55.** $\frac{1}{2}$ **61a.** Florida growth factor = 1.0213, $y = 15{,}982{,}378\,(1.0213)^x$; New York growth factor = 1.0054, $y = 18{,}976{,}457 \cdot (1.0054)^x$ **b.** 2011 **69.** $\frac{\log 8}{\log 3}$ **71.** $\frac{\log 3.3}{\log 9}$ **77a.** top up: 10^{-5} W/m², top down: $10^{-2.5}$ W/m² **b.** 99.67%
79. 2.9315 **81.** 0.6225 **113.** $\log 2 + 3 \log x - 2 \log y$ **115.** $3 \log_3 3 + 3 \log_3 x$ **119.** $x^2 + 3x - 1$
121. $3x^3 - 3x$ **123.** $\pm 2, \pm 2i$ **125.** −2, −1, 3
127. $\frac{679 + x}{6} = 133$

Extension p. 461

1. not a good model

Lesson 8-6 pp. 464–467

EXERCISES **1.** ln 125 **3.** ln 4 **11.** 24.13
13. 25 seconds **15.** 0.135 **17.** 1488.979
23. 2.890 **25.** 2.401 **29.** 6 years **31.** 1 **33.** 10
39. 10.8 **41.** sometimes **43.** always
45. 19.8 hours **47.** 3.6 **49.** 9.4 **55.** 180.77
57. 29.61 **71.** 4 **73.** 0.272 **79.** $y = \frac{x-7}{5}$; yes
81. $y = \pm\sqrt{5 - x}$; no

Chapter Review pp. 469–471

1. growth factor **2.** common logarithm **3.** asymptote **4.** logarithm **5.** exponential equation **6.** exponential growth; 400%

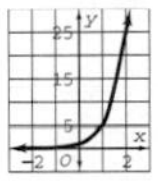

7. exponential growth; 300%

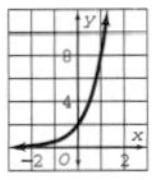

8. exponential growth; 280%

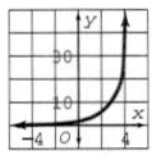

9. exponential decay; −75%

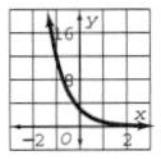

10. $y = \frac{25}{7}\left(\frac{7}{5}\right)^x$ **11.** $y = 0.0015(10)^x$
12. $y = 2.25\left(\frac{1}{3}\right)^x$ **13.** $y = \left(\frac{1}{3}\right)^x$
14. $y = 12{,}500(0.91)^x$; \$7800 **15.** $y = 50(1.03)^x$; \$58
16. $y = 1500(0.2)^x$; 2.4 **17.** $y = 2(1.4)^x$; 7.6832
18. $y = 3^x$ reflected over the x-axis and translated up 1 unit

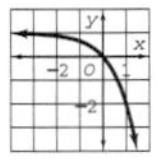

19. $y = 8^x$ translated down 1 unit

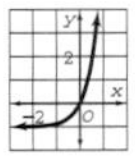

20. $y = 2(2)^x$ translated left 1 unit and up 3 units

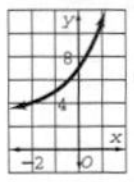

21. $y = 2\left(\frac{1}{3}\right)^x$ reflected over the x-axis and translated right 2 units

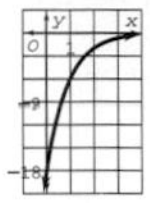

22. \$1100.76 **23.** \$291.91 **24.** \$645.23
25. 2.7183 **26.** 0.3679 **27.** 148.4132 **28.** 0.6065
29. $y = 3\left(\frac{1}{2}\right)^{\frac{t}{1620}}$; ≈2.946 mg **30.** 2.0×10^{-6}
31. 7 **32.** $2 = \log_6 36$ **33.** $-3 = \log_2 0.125$
34. $3 = \log_3 27$ **35.** $-3 = \log 0.001$ **36.** 6
37. −2 **38.** −5 **39.** 0

40.
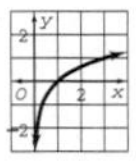
41.
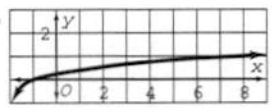

42.
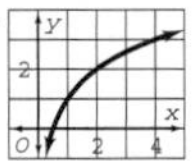
43.
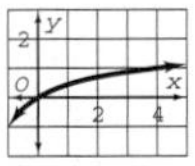

44. log 24 **45.** $\log_2 \frac{5}{3}$ **46.** $\log_3 7x^4$ **47.** $\log \frac{z}{y}$
48. $2 \log_4 x + 3 \log_4 y$; Product and Power Properties **49.** $\log 4 + 4 \log 5 + \log t$; Product and Power Properties **50.** $\log_3 2 - \log_3 x$; Quotient Property **51.** $2 \log (x + 3)$; Power Property **52.** 1.76 dB **53.** 2.38 **54.** 3.26 **55.** 4.65
56. 1.37 **57.** 1 **58.** ≈0.66 **59.** ≈0.67 **60.** ≈3.06
61. $\frac{10}{3}$ **62.** 8 **63.** 50 **64.** 7,625,597,484,987
65. $\log_5 91.68$ **66.** about 18.2 hours **67.** 0.83
68. 2.26 **69.** 4.31 **70.** 0.00018 **71.** 3.77 **72.** 6.03
73. 3.4%

Chapter 9

Lesson 9-1 pp. 481–483

EXERCISES **1.** $y = \frac{11}{x}$ **3.** $y = \frac{1}{x}$ **7.** direct; $y = 5x$
9. direct; $y = 2x$ **13.** $y = \frac{100}{x}$; 10 **15.** $y = -\frac{5}{3x}$; $-\frac{1}{6}$
17. A varies jointly with b and h. **19.** V varies jointly with B and h. **25.** $z = 10xy$; 360
27. $z = \frac{4}{xy}$; $\frac{1}{9}$ **29.** 18 **31.** $\frac{1}{4}$ **35.** 7200 rpm **37.** $18\frac{2}{3}$
39. 2 **43.** 2.625 **45.** 8 **49.** 32 **51.** $\frac{40}{3}$ **53.** 32
55. quartered; divided by 16 **65.** $\frac{e^5}{4} \approx 37.1$
67. $\frac{e^2}{8} \approx 0.92$ **69.** $42x^2\sqrt[3]{6}$ **71.** $|x^5|y^{50}$
73. $2m^2|n|\sqrt[4]{4}$

Technology p. 484

1.
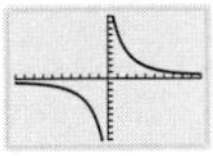

Lesson 9-2 pp. 488–490

EXERCISES

1.
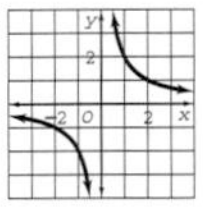

5. The graph of $y = \frac{1}{x}$ is closer to the axes.
7. The branches of $y = \frac{8}{x}$ are in Quadrants I and III. The branches of $y = -\frac{8}{x}$ are in Quadrants II and IV. Each graph is a 90° rotation about the origin of the other graph. **11.** 7.67 ft **13.** 1.84 ft

15.
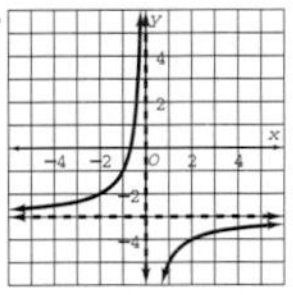

23. $y = \frac{2}{x + 2} + 3$ **27.** $y = \frac{0.5}{x}$ **29.** $y = -\frac{8.3}{x}$

33.
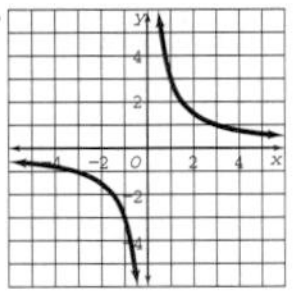

41.
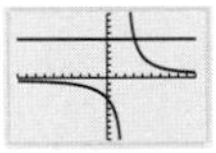
(3, 6)

61. h varies directly with V and inversely with the square of s. **63.** w varies directly with V and inversely with the product of ℓ and h. **65.** growth, 4 **67.** decay, 0.8 **69.** $79 - 20\sqrt{3}$ **71.** $50 + 35\sqrt{2}$

Lesson 9-3 pp. 495–498

EXERCISES **1.** $x = 0, x = 2$ **3.** $x = 1, x = -1$
11. hole at $x = -5$ **13.** vertical asymptote at $x = -1$, hole at $x = 2$ **19.** $y = 0$ **21.** $y = 1$

25.
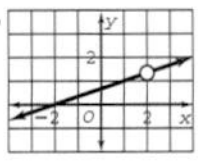

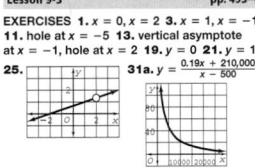

31a. $y = \frac{0.19x + 210{,}000}{x - 500}$

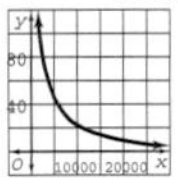

b. \$46.88; \$14.68 **c.** more than 21,916 discs **d.** $x = 500$, $y = 0.19$ **33.** vertical asymptote at $x = -2$

35.
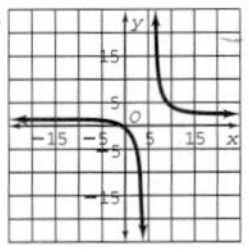

43a. $y = \frac{20{,}000x + 200{,}000}{x + 1}$

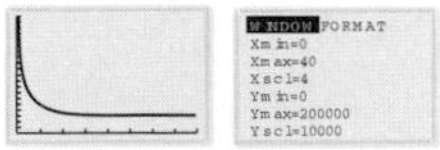

b. \$65,000; \$25,806.45
45a. The increase in production workers' average hourly wage is greater. **b.** rational

c. $R(x) = \frac{M(x)}{A(x)}$

d.
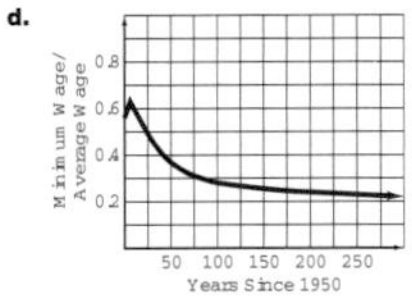

around the year 2106
51. vertical: $x = 0$, horizontal: $y = 4$ **53.** vertical: $x = -1$, horizontal: $y = 1$

Lesson 9-4 pp. 501–503

EXERCISES **1.** $\frac{1}{2x - 1}$; $x \neq 0$ or $\frac{1}{2}$ **3.** $b + 1$; $b \neq 1$
7. $\frac{7}{15x^2}$; $x \neq 0, y \neq 0$ **9.** $\frac{4}{3}$; $y \neq \frac{1}{2}$ or 3 **13.** $\frac{2}{3x^2y^2}$; $x \neq 0, y \neq 0$ **15.** $\frac{5(x + y)}{3}$; $x \neq y$ **19.** $\frac{(x - 8)}{(x - 10)}$; $x \neq -3$ or 10 **21.** $\frac{y(y + 3)}{12(y + 4)}$; $x \neq 0, y \neq -4$ or 3
27. $\frac{a + 3}{(a - 3)(a - 3)}$; $a \neq -4$, −3, or 3 **29.** $\frac{4}{x}$; $x \neq 0$, −5, 4, or 1 **33.** $\frac{(x - 1)^3}{(x + 4)}$, $x \neq -4, 0, 1$ **35.** $\frac{18x^5}{y^2}$, $y \neq 0$
37a. 1.2 m/s² **b.** 2.68 m/s² **49.** vertical asymptotes at $x = -\frac{2}{3}$ and $x = -1$ **51.** 3 **53.** $\frac{3}{2}$
55. $x = 22$

Lesson 9-5 pp. 507–510

EXERCISES **1.** $\frac{120}{59} \approx 2.03$ in. **5.** $(x - 1)(x + 1)(x + 1)$ **7.** $18(2x - 7)(x + 3)$ **11.** $\frac{2(d - 2)}{2d + 1}$
13. $\frac{7x^2 + 20x - 18}{(x - 3)(x + 3)(x + 4)}$ **17.** $\frac{-3(2y + 1)}{2y - 1}$
19. $\frac{x^2 - 24}{3x(x + 3)}$ **23.** $\frac{15}{28}$ **25.** $\frac{b}{9}$ **31.** $\frac{3x - 8}{4x^2}$
33. $\frac{2x^3 - x^2 + 1}{x^2(x + 1)(x - 1)}$ **45.** $\frac{2x - 5y}{2(3x + 2y)}$ **47.** x **63.** $\frac{1}{4xy}$; $a \neq 0, b \neq 0, x \neq 0, y \neq 0$ **65.** $\frac{12x}{x + 3}$; $x \neq -3$, 2, or 3
69. $\log_{10} p^7q$ **71.** 30 **73.** $\frac{15}{4}$

Lesson 9-6 pp. 514–517

EXERCISES **1.** 5 **3.** 10 **11.** 10 **13.** 2
23. passenger train: 112 mi/h, freight train: 92 mi/h **25.** $1\frac{5}{7}$ h **27.** $E = mc^2$ **29.** $c = \sqrt{a^2 - b^2}$
39. 3 **41.** no solution **65.** $\frac{-y - 13}{4(y + 1)}$
67. $\frac{-3x^2 + 8x + 3}{(2x - 2)(x + 3)}$ **69.** $x = -1$ **71.** $x = -6$
73. $y = \pm\sqrt{x - 1}$; no

Lesson 9-7 pp. 522–525

EXERCISES **1.** independent **3.** dependent **5.** $\frac{1}{6}$
7. 0.54 **11.** Mutually exclusive since if the numbers are equal, then the sum is even.
13. 47% **15.** $\frac{14}{15}$ **17.** $\frac{26}{35}$ **19.** $\frac{1}{2}$ **21.** $\frac{5}{6}$ **27.** $\frac{7}{12}$
29. $\frac{31}{56}$ **31.** 13% **33.** 98% **37.** $\frac{4}{15}$ **39.** $\frac{1}{15}$ **41.** $\frac{1}{11}$
43. $\frac{7}{15}$ **45a.** $\frac{1}{4}$ **b.** $\frac{1}{64}$ **59.** $\frac{3}{7}$ **61.** $\frac{1}{6}$ **63.** $\frac{e^6}{2} \approx 201.71$
65. $\pm e^2 \approx \pm 7.39$

Chapter Review pp. 527–529

1. mutually exclusive **2.** simplest form **3.** independent events **4.** branch **5.** point of discontinuity **6.** $y = \frac{150}{x}$; 30 **7.** $y = \frac{60}{x}$; 12
8. $y = \frac{180}{x}$; 36 **9.** $y = \frac{72}{x}$ **10.** not possible
11. $y = -2x$ **12.** $z = \frac{7}{4}xy$; 56 **13.** $z = \frac{4x}{y}$; 2
14. $z = \frac{x^3}{y}$; 8 **15.** R varies jointly with k, m and the square of n. **16.** W varies inversely with the square of d. **17.** P varies directly with x and inversely with the product of z and the square of y.

18.
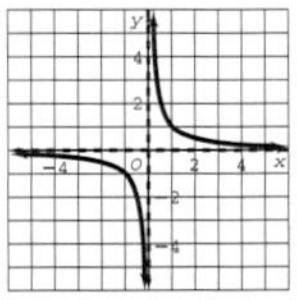

19.
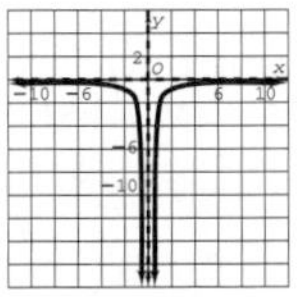

20.
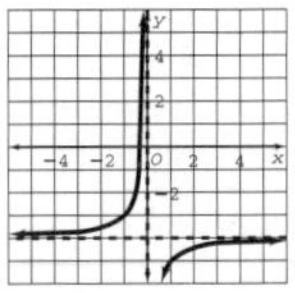

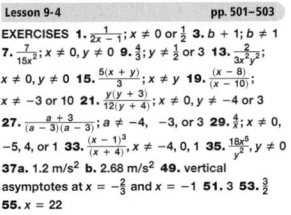

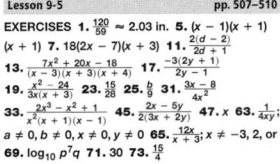

21.

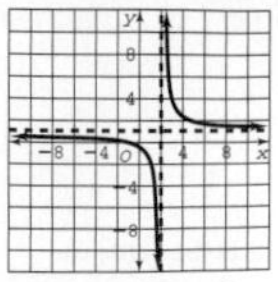

22. $y = \frac{4}{x} + 3$ 23. $y = \frac{4}{x-2} + 2$ 24. $y = \frac{4}{x+3} - 4$

25. about 31,056 headsets

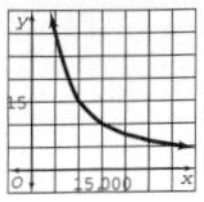

26. −7 vertical asymptote $x = -7$, horizontal asymptote $y = 0$

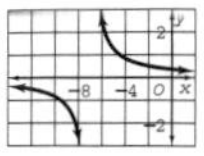

27. −2, 1

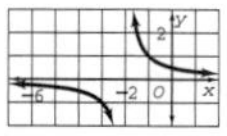

vertical asymptote $x = -2$, horizontal asymptote $y = 0$, hole at $x = 1$

28. 1, −1

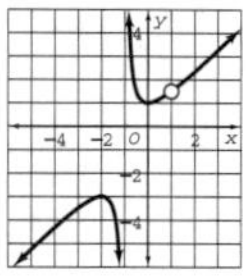

vertical asymptote $x = -1$, hole at $x = 1$

29. no points of discontinuity

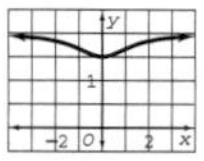

horizontal asymptote $y = 2$

30. $\frac{(x-1)(x+1)}{x+3}$; $x \neq -4, -3,$ or 6

31. $\frac{(2x-1)(x+1)}{x+4}$; $x \neq -4, -1,$ or 0 32. $\frac{r}{3}$

33. 12 cm 34. $\frac{3(3x-4)}{(x-2)(x+2)}$

35. $\frac{-x^2+3x+2}{x(x+1)(x-1)(x+3)}$ 36. $\frac{8}{15}$ 37. $\frac{1}{4(x+y)}$

38. −1 39. no solution 40. −12, 9 41. Jessica: 10 mi/h, William: 8 mi/h 42. dependent

43. independent 44. not mutually exclusive

45. not mutually exclusive 46. $\frac{1}{3}$ 47. $\frac{2}{3}$ 48. $\frac{5}{6}$

Chapter 10

Lesson 10-1 pp. 538–541

EXERCISES

1.

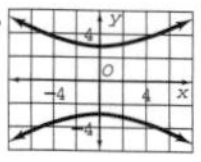

Hyperbola: center (0, 0), y-intercepts at $\pm\frac{5\sqrt{3}}{3}$, no x-intercepts, the lines of symmetry are the x- and y-axes; domain: all real numbers, range: $y \geq \frac{5\sqrt{3}}{3}$ or $y \leq -\frac{5\sqrt{3}}{3}$. 17. center (0, 0), x-intercepts at ±3, y-intercepts at ±2; domain: $-3 \leq x \leq 3$, range: $-2 \leq y \leq 2$ 19. center (0, 0), x-intercepts at ±3, no y-intercepts; domain: $x \leq -3$ or $x \geq 3$, range: all real numbers

23. 19 25. 18

29.

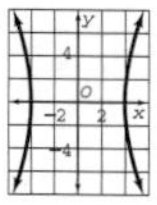

Hyperbola: center (0, 0), x-intercepts ±4, the lines of symmetry are the x- and y-axes; domain: $x \leq -4$ or $x \geq 4$, range: all real numbers.

35, 37. Answers may vary. Samples are given.

35. (2, 4) 37. $(-2, 2\sqrt{2})$

41. $x^2 + y^2 = 36$

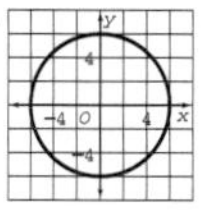

57. $\frac{1}{2}$ 59. $\frac{2}{3}$ 61. $z = -4xy$; 24 63. $z = -\frac{1}{2}xy$; 3

65. $y = \frac{1}{2}(4^x)$ 67. $y = \frac{1}{3}(3)^x$ 71. $p^6 + 6p^5q + 15p^4q^2 + 20p^3q^3 + 15p^2q^4 + 6pq^5 + q^5$

73. $243 - 405x - 270x^2 - 90x^3 + 15x^4 - x^5$

Technology p. 542

1.

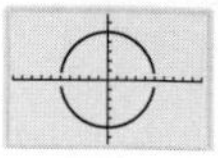

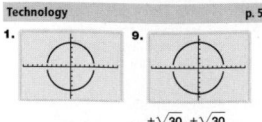

9.

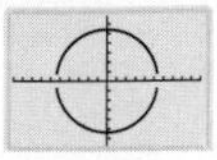

$\pm\sqrt{30}, \pm\sqrt{30}$

Lesson 10-2 pp. 546–548

EXERCISES 1. $y = \frac{1}{8}x^2$ 3. $x = -\frac{1}{12}y^2$ 7. $x = \frac{1}{24}y^2$

9. $y = \frac{1}{28}x^2$ 13. $y = \frac{1}{6}x^2$ 17. $\left(0, \frac{1}{4}\right)$, $y = -\frac{1}{4}$

19. $\left(-\frac{1}{2}, 0\right)$, $x = \frac{1}{2}$

25. (0, 0), (0, −1), $y = 1$

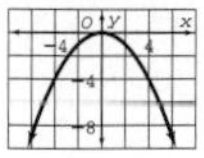

37. $y = \frac{1}{400}x^2$ 39. $x = -\frac{1}{28}y^2$ 43. $x = -\frac{1}{8}y^2$

45. $x = y^2$

47.

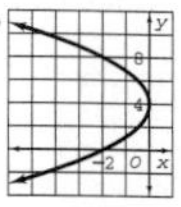

53. $y = -\frac{1}{6}(x-1)^2 + 1$

67.

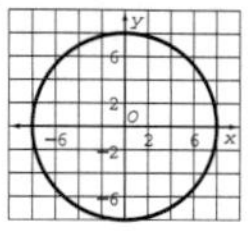

71. $x = 0$ and $y = 4$ 73. $x = 1$ and $y = 0$

Lesson 10-3 pp. 552–554

EXERCISES 1. $x^2 + y^2 = 100$ 3. $(x-2)^2 + (y-3)^2 = 20.25$ 9. $x^2 + (y+1)^2 = 9$

11. $(x-2)^2 + (y+4)^2 = 25$ 17. $(x+3)^2 + (y-4)^2 = 9$ 19. (−1, −1), 1 21. (3, −1), 6

27.

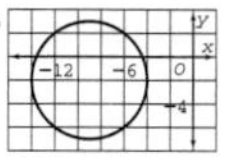

35. $x^2 + y^2 = 16$ 37. $x^2 + y^2 = 25$ 45. $(x+6)^2 + (y-13)^2 = 49$ 47. $(x+2)^2 + (y-7.5)^2 = \frac{9}{4}$

55. (0, 0), $\sqrt{2}$ 57. (0, 0), $\sqrt{14}$

65. circle; $(x-4)^2 + (y-3)^2 = 16$;

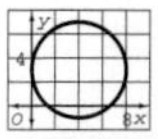

77. $x = -\frac{1}{12}y^2$ 79. $x = 2, x = 3$ 81. 4 83. −3

Extension p. 555

1.

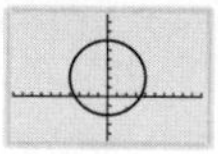

Lesson 10-4 pp. 559–561

EXERCISES 1. $\frac{x^2}{16} + \frac{y^2}{9} = 1$ 3. $\frac{x^2}{9} + y^2 = 1$

9. $\frac{x^2}{2.25} + \frac{y^2}{0.25} = 1$ 11. $\frac{x^2}{36} + \frac{y^2}{100} = 1$

19. (0, 4), (0, −4)

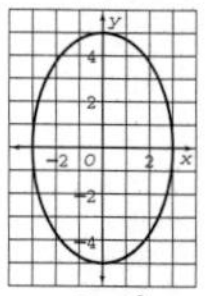

27. $\frac{x^2}{100} + \frac{y^2}{64} = 1$ 29. $\frac{x^2}{89} + \frac{y^2}{64} = 1$ 33. $(\sqrt{5}, 0)$, $(-\sqrt{5}, 0)$ 35. $(0, 4\sqrt{2})$, $(0, -4\sqrt{2})$ 45. $\frac{x^2}{16} + y^2 = 1$

47. $\frac{x^2}{4} + \frac{y^2}{16} = 1$ 51. $\frac{x^2}{25} + \frac{y^2}{4} = 1$ 53. $\frac{x^2}{702.25} + \frac{y^2}{210.25} = 1$ 73. $(x-2)^2 + (y+3)^2 = 36$

75. $\frac{1}{2x - 3x^4}$; $x \neq 0$, $\sqrt[3]{\frac{2}{3}}$ 79. $\log_3 6$ 81. log 320

Lesson 10-5 pp. 566–568

EXERCISES

1.

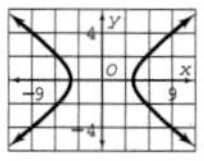

11. $(0, \sqrt{113})$, $(0, -\sqrt{113})$;

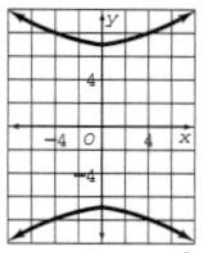

19. $\frac{x^2}{69{,}169} - \frac{y^2}{96{,}480} = 1$ 21. $\frac{x^2}{192{,}432{,}384} - \frac{y^2}{170{,}203{,}465} = 1$ 23. $\frac{x^2}{9} - \frac{y^2}{16} = 1$ 25. $y^2 - \frac{x^2}{3} = 1$

27.

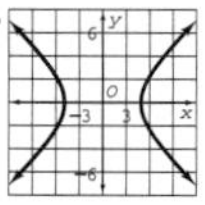

31. $\frac{y^2}{9} - x^2 = 1$

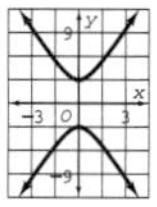

33. $y = \pm\frac{1}{2}\sqrt{2x^2 - 8}$; (2, 0), (−2, 0)

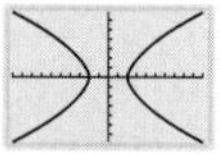

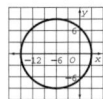

39. (0, ±1), $y = \pm x$ 41. (0, ±8), $y = \pm 2x$

55. $(0, \pm\sqrt{3})$, $(\pm\sqrt{2}, 0)$ 57. $\frac{3}{10x}$ 59. $\frac{x+3}{x-3}$ 61. 125

Lesson 10-6 pp. 573–576

EXERCISES

1. $\frac{(x+2)^2}{9} + \frac{(y-1)^2}{4} = 1$ 3. $\frac{x^2}{36} + \frac{(y+4)^2}{25} = 1$

5. $\frac{(x+3)^2}{16} - \frac{(y+3)^2}{9} = 1$ 7. $\frac{(x+1)^2}{9} - \frac{(y-2)^2}{40} = 1$

11. $\frac{(x-175)^2}{1936} - \frac{y^2}{28{,}689} = 1$

13. $(x+6)^2 + y^2 = 81$; center (−6, 0), radius 9

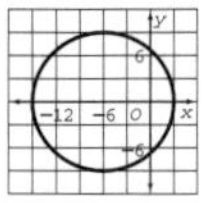

29. $(x+6)^2 + (y-9)^2 = 81$

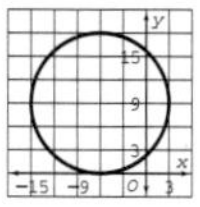

33. $\frac{(x-1)^2}{9} + \frac{(y+1)^2}{16} = 1$ 35. $(x+4)^2 + (y+4)^2 = 25$ 37. $(x-8)^2 + (y-2)^2 = 4$

39. $y - 5 = 4(x-3)^2$

49. ellipse, $\frac{x^2}{9} + \frac{y^2}{36} = 1$

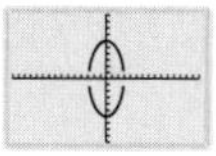

65. $(0, \sqrt{21})$, $(0, -\sqrt{21})$

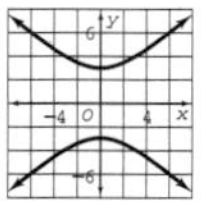

67. −1, 4 69. −0.4315, 1.9315 71. 2 73. 8

Extension p. 577

1. (−8, 0), (8, 0) 3. $\left(\pm\frac{21+\sqrt{41}}{10}, \frac{9-21\sqrt{41}}{50}\right)$, $\left(\pm\frac{21-\sqrt{41}}{10}, \frac{9+21\sqrt{41}}{50}\right)$ 7. quadratic, quadratic; (±2, 0) 9. linear, quadratic; (0, 2), $\left(-\frac{100}{29}, -\frac{42}{29}\right)$

Chapter Review pp. 579–581

1. directrix 2. major axis 3. standard form of an equation of a circle 4. radius 5. transverse axis

6. ellipse; x-axis and y-axis; domain: $-7 \leq x \leq 7$ range: $-11 \leq y \leq 11$

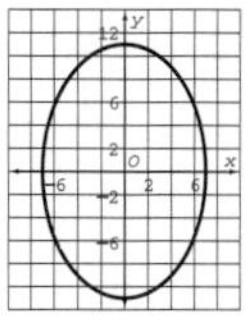

7. circle; every line through the center; domain: $-2 \leq x \leq 2$ range: $-2 \leq y \leq 2$

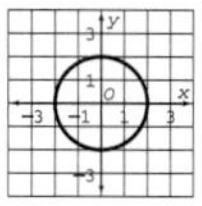

8. hyperbola; x-axis and y-axis; domain: $x \leq -5$ or $x \geq 5$ range: all real numbers

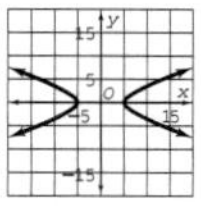

9.

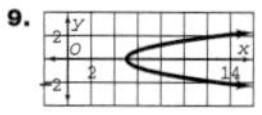

parabola; x-axis; domain: $x \geq 5$, range: all real numbers 10. center (0, 0); (±4, 0); domain: $x \geq 4$ or $x \leq -4$, range: all real numbers 11. center (0, 0); (0, ±2), (±3, 0); domain: $-3 \leq x \leq 3$, range: $-2 \leq y \leq 2$ 12. $y = \frac{1}{8}x^2 + 1$ 13. $x = -\frac{1}{12}y^2 - 1$

14. $x = \frac{1}{20}y^2$ 15. $y = -\frac{1}{20}x^2$ 16. $y = \frac{1}{24}x^2$

17. $y = \frac{1}{10}x^2$ 18. $y = 3x^2$

19. $\left(0, \frac{1}{20}\right)$, $y = -\frac{1}{20}$

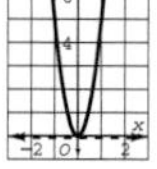

20. $\left(\frac{1}{8}, 0\right)$, $x = -\frac{1}{8}$

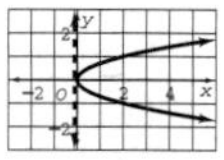

21. (−2, 0), $x = 2$

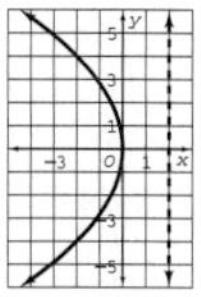

22. $x^2 + y^2 = 16$ 23. $(x-8)^2 + (y-1)^2 = 25$

24. $(x+3)^2 + (y-2)^2 = 100$ 25. $(x-5)^2 + (y+3)^2 = 64$ 26. $(x-3)^2 + (y-1)^2 = 9$

27. $(x+1)^2 + y^2 = 4$

28. center (1, 0), radius 8, right 1

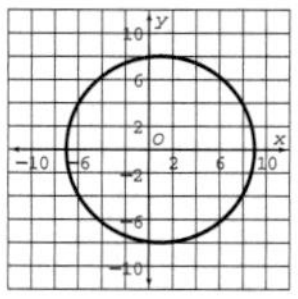

29. center (−7, −3), radius 7, left 7 and down 3

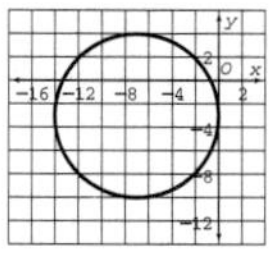

30. $\frac{x^2}{17} + \frac{y^2}{16} = 1$ 31. $\frac{x^2}{25} + \frac{y^2}{29} = 1$ 32. $\frac{x^2}{9} + \frac{y^2}{10} = 1$

33. $\frac{x^2}{40} + \frac{y^2}{36} = 1$ 34. $\frac{x^2}{64} + \frac{y^2}{16} = 1$

35.

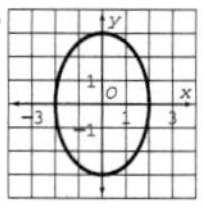

foci (0, ±2.2)

36. foci (±16.2, 0)

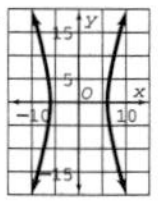

37. foci (0, ±23.9)

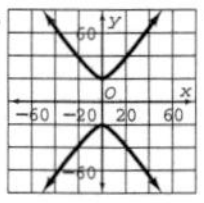

38. foci (±14.2, 0)

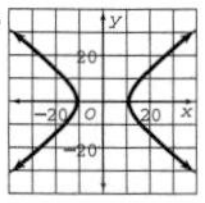

39. $\dfrac{x^2}{1.148 \times 10^{10}} - \dfrac{y^2}{3.395 \times 10^{10}} = 1$

40. $\dfrac{(x-3)^2}{4} + \dfrac{(y+2)^2}{9} = 1$ 41. $\dfrac{(x-6)^2}{9} - \dfrac{(y-3)^2}{16} = 1$

42. $\dfrac{(x-77.5)^2}{1640.25} - \dfrac{y^2}{4366} = 1$

43. hyperbola; center (0, −2), foci $(0, -2 \pm 2\sqrt{10})$

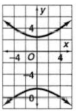

44. circle, center $\left(-\frac{3}{2}, 2\right)$, radius $\frac{\sqrt{61}}{2}$

45. parabola; vertex $\left(-\frac{1}{2}, -\frac{169}{4}\right)$

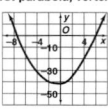

46. ellipse; center (1, −2), foci $\left(\frac{3 \pm \sqrt{51}}{3}, -2\right)$

Chapter 11

Lesson 11-1 pp. 591–593

EXERCISES 1. Subtract 3; 65, 62, 59. 3. Add one more to each term (add 3, add 4, add 5, etc.); 25, 33, 42.

11.

13. $a_n = a_{n-1} - 2, a_1 = 43$; 33 15. $a_n = a_{n-1} - 5, a_1 = 6$; −14 19. $a_n = \frac{1}{n-1}; \frac{1}{13}$ 21. $a_n = 4n - 1$; 47 25. explicit; 0, 1, 3, 6, 10 27. recursive; −2, 6, −18, 54, −162 33. 20, 23; $a_n = 3n + 2$; explicit or $a_n = a_{n-1} + 3, a_1 = 5$; recursive 35. 216, 343; $a_n = n^3$; explicit 45. 26, 677; 458, 330; 2.1×10^{11} 47. 25, 36, 49, 64 51a. 25 boxes b. 110 boxes c. 9 levels 57a. 15, 21 b. $a_n = a_{n-1} + n, a_1 = 1$ c. Yes; the formula yields the same value as the recursive formula. 63. $(x + 4)^2 + (y + 2)^2 = 5$

64. $\frac{(x+1)^2}{36} + \frac{(y+2)^2}{36} = 1$ 65. $xy = 20$ 66. $xy = 10$ 67. $xy = 117$ 68. $xy = 27$ 69. $xy = 10$ 70. $xy = 72$ 71. $xy = -\frac{1}{4}$ 72. $xy = 100$

Lesson 11-2 pp. 596–598

EXERCISES 1. no 3. no 11. 127 13. 12.5 21. −7.5 23. 13 31. 4 33. 13 47. 15 49. 22 53. $a_n = 0 + 6(n-1), a_n = a_{n-1} + 6, a_1 = 0$ 55. $a_n = -4 + 4(n-1), a_n = a_{n-1} + 4, a_1 = -4$ 63. −4, −10, −16 65. −8, −17, −26 71a. $20, $45, $75, $110, $150, $195, $245, $300, $360, $425, $495 b. $a_n = a_{n-1} + $20 + $5(n-1), a_1 = $20 c. $495 93. recursive: −2, −7, −12, −17, −22 95. explicit; 0, 3, 8, 15, 24 97. $(0, -\sqrt{5})$ and $(0, \sqrt{5})$ 99. $(1 - \sqrt{21}, 0)$ and $(1 + \sqrt{21}, 0)$ 101. $r = \frac{\sqrt[3]{6\pi^2 v}}{2\pi}$

Extension p. 599

1a. fifth b. seventh c. sixth d. fourth 3a. 1, 1, 2, 3, 5, 8, 13, 21, 34, 55 b. 143; 13; the answer is the seventh term. c. Check students' work; the answer is the seventh term. d. It will be 11 times the seventh term.

Lesson 11-3 pp. 602–605

EXERCISES 1. yes; 2; 16, 32 3. yes; −2; 16, −32 13. $a_n = 5 \cdot (-3)^{n-1}$; 5, −15, 45, −135, 405 15. $a_n = \frac{1}{2}\left(\frac{1}{3}\right)^{n-1}; \frac{1}{2}, \frac{1}{3}, \frac{2}{9}, \frac{4}{27}, \frac{8}{81}$ 23. 1530 25. 1.5

---

29. arithmetic; 125, 150 31. arithmetic; 50, 55 37. 6561, 2187, 729 39. 10, 8, 6.4 43. 12,288 45. 201,326,592 49. 16 51. 10 59. 7 69. $a_n = 26 - 9n$; as $a_n = a_{n-1} - 9, a_1 = 17$ 71. $x^2 + y^2 = 9$ 75. $x = -1$

Lesson 11-4 pp. 610–612

EXERCISES 1. 21 + 18 + 15 + 12 + 9 + 6 + 3; 84 3. 100 + 99 + 98 + 97 + 96 + 95; 585 7. 32 9. 264 13. $\sum_{n=1}^{4} 2n$ 15. $\sum_{n=1}^{7}(n + 4)$ 19. 5, 1, 9; 25 21. 6, 4, −1; 9 25. sequence; infinite 27. series; finite 33a. 91 b. 83 35. 110 37. 5150 55. $a_n = 1(2)^{n-1}$; 1, 2, 4 57. $a_n = -1(-1)^{n-1}$; −1, 1, −1

61.

ellipse: x- and y-axes; domain: −6 ≤ x ≤ 6; range: $-2\sqrt{3} \le y \le 2\sqrt{3}$ 65. $\frac{c-2}{c-5}$

Lesson 11-5 pp. 616–619

EXERCISES 1. 255 3. 381 9. converges; has a sum 11. converges; has a sum 19. 1 21. $\frac{8}{3}$ 25. arithmetic; 420 27. geometric; 96.47 33. 4 35. no sum 41. $\frac{1}{8}$ 57. 140 59. 1375 61. (−1, 0), x = 1;

63. $\frac{7c - 4}{2c^2}$ 65. $\frac{x^2 + 6x + 4}{(x + 6)(x - 6)}$

Extension pp. 620–621

1. $1 + 3 + 5 + 7 + 9 + 11 \overset{?}{=} 6^2$, 36 = 36; $1 + 3 + 5 + 7 + 9 + 11 + 13 \overset{?}{=} 7^2$, 49 = 49; $1 + 3 + 5 + 7 + 9 + 11 + 13 + 15 \overset{?}{=} 8^2$, 64 = 64

---

3. For n = 1, $\frac{1}{1(1 + 1)} = \frac{1}{1 + 1}$
Assume
$\frac{1}{1 \cdot 2} + \frac{1}{2 \cdot 3} + \frac{1}{3 \cdot 4} + \cdots + \frac{1}{k(k + 1)} = \frac{k}{k + 1}$
Prove
$\frac{1}{1 \cdot 2} + \frac{1}{2 \cdot 3} + \frac{1}{3 \cdot 4} + \cdots + \frac{1}{(k + 1)((k + 1) + 1)} = \frac{k + 1}{(k + 1) + 1}$
Proof
$\frac{1}{1 \cdot 2} + \frac{1}{2 \cdot 3} + \frac{1}{3 \cdot 4} + \cdots + \frac{1}{k(k + 1)} + \frac{1}{(k + 1)((k + 1) + 1)} = \frac{k}{k + 1} + \frac{1}{(k + 1)((k + 1) + 1)} = \frac{k(k + 2)}{(k + 1)(k + 2)} + \frac{1}{(k + 1)((k + 1) + 1)} = \frac{k(k + 2) + 1}{(k + 1)((k + 1) + 1)} = \frac{(k + 1)^2}{(k + 1)((k + 1) + 1)} = \frac{k + 1}{(k + 1) + 1}$

Technology p. 622

1. 1780 3. $7\frac{7}{8}$ 5. 62

Lesson 11-6 pp. 625–627

EXERCISES 1. total produced 3. miles 7. 110 units² 9. $A = \sum_{n=1}^{5} 1f(a_n)$ a. 0.5 units² b. 2.5 units² 11. $A = \sum_{n=1}^{2} 1f(a_n)$ a. 3 units² b. 7 units² 19. 2.5 units² 21. 3.3 units²

25. 43 units²

33. 7.5 units² 35. 3.46 units² 51. has a sum 53. $\frac{x^2}{16} - \frac{y^2}{9} = 1$;

57. $\frac{3}{14}$

Chapter Review pp. 629–631

1. limits 2. circumscribed rectangles 3. sequence 4. converges 5. common ratio 6. $a_n = a_{n-1} + 17, a_1 = 5$; 73, 90, 107 7. $a_n = -7a_{n-1}, a_1 = 1$; 2401; −16,807; 117,649 8. $a_n = a_{n-1} + 9, a_1 = -2$; 34, 43, 52 9. $a_n = 3n - 2$; 34 10. $a_n = 2^n$; 4096 11. $a_n = 6n^2 - 30$; 834 12. Answers may vary. Sample: If the formula uses the previous term, then it is recursive; otherwise it is explicit. 13. no 14. yes; d = 15; $a_{32} = 468$ 15. yes; d = 3; $a_{32} = 100$ 16. 5 17. 101.5 18. −4.9 19. 5 20. −10.5, −8, −5.5 21. 1.4, 0.8, 0.2 22. 11 23. 0.5 24. If the terms of the sequence have a common difference, then the sequence is arithmetic. 25. yes; $r = \frac{1}{2}, a_n = 1\left(\frac{1}{2}\right)^{n-1}$; $\frac{1}{16}, \frac{1}{32}$ 26. no 27. yes; r = 1.2, $a_n = 3(1.2)^{n-1}$, 6.2208, 7.46496 28. 6 29. 20 30. 0.04 31. −10, −5, −2.5 32. $-\frac{1}{3}, -\frac{2}{3}, -\frac{4}{3}$ 33. $3\frac{1}{2}, 12\frac{1}{4}, 42\frac{7}{8}$ 34. $\sum_{n=1}^{6} 13 - 3n$; 20 35. $\sum_{n=1}^{7} 45 + 5n$; 455 36. $\sum_{n=1}^{11} 4.6 + 1.4n$; 143 37. $\sum_{n=1}^{8} 23 - 2n$; 112 38. 3, −3, 26; 27 39. 9, 4, 8; 54 40. 11, $-\frac{19}{3}, -10; -\frac{220}{3}$ 41. No; she will have only 1150 available by the end of the fifth year. 42. $4\frac{121}{243}$ 43. 31 44. 53.125 45. $14\frac{7}{18}$ 46. converges; S = 187.5 47. diverges; no sum 48. diverges; no sum 49. converges; S = 2 50. $A = \sum_{n=1}^{4} 1 \cdot f(a_n)$ a. 1 unit² b. 5 units² c. $\frac{8}{3}$ units² 51. $A = \sum_{n=1}^{4} 1 \cdot f(a_n)$ a. 3 units² b. 11 units² c. 6 units² 52. $A = \sum_{n=1}^{5} 1 \cdot f(a_n)$ a. 6 units² b. 14 units² c. 10.6 units² 53. $A = \sum_{n=1}^{5} 1 \cdot f(a_n)$ a. 7 units² b. 9 units² c. 8 units² 54. $A = \sum_{n=1}^{2} 1 \cdot f(a_n)$ a. 9 units² b. 17 units² c. 12 units² 55. $A = \sum_{n=1}^{2} 1 \cdot f(a_n)$ a. 7 units² b. 11 units² c. $8\frac{2}{3}$ units²

Chapter 12

Lesson 12-1 pp. 636–639

EXERCISES

1.
Object	Frequency
Rock	11
Paper	10
Scissors	15
Total	36

3. 0.11 5. 0.53

7.
Number of Days Per Month				
Days	28	29	30	31
Frequency	3	1	16	28
Probability	$\frac{3}{48}$	$\frac{1}{48}$	$\frac{16}{48}$	$\frac{28}{48}$

9. 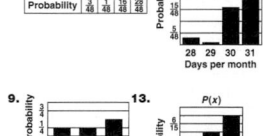 13.

25. 4 units² 27. 29. dependent

Lesson 12-2 pp. 644–646

EXERCISES 1. 0.9 3. $0.\overline{6}$ 5. 0.406 9. 45%

11. M = male, F = female, R = right, L = Left

0.1, 0.114

17. 0.194 19. P(C) 21. P(R|W) 31. center (0, 0), x-intercepts (2, 0), (−2, 0) y-intercepts (0, 4), (0, −4); domain: {x | −2 ≤ x ≤ 2}, range: {y | −4 ≤ y ≤ 4} 33. 0.830 35. 3.465

Extension p. 647

1. 0.9508 3. 0.9998 7. 0.08 9. 0.84

Lesson 12-3 pp. 652–654

EXERCISES 1. 4.36, 3, 1 3. 600.3, 535.5, 499

5.

7.

9. 6, 18 11. 0. 15. 381; this value raises the mean. 17. 60th 27. ≈0.20 29. yes; −9 31. no

33.

35.

37. 16 39. 43.5 41.

Lesson 12-4 pp. 660–662

EXERCISES 1. 5, 2.5 3. 704, 461 5. 15.1, 3.5 7. 10,567.45; 435.16 9. 3 standard deviations 11. −1.4 13. 0 15. 14.6, 52.3; the bird speeds are more spread out than the cat speeds. 17. 1998: ≈7656; 1999: ≈6945 21a. 53.8, 3.4 b. 7; 9; 10 23. ≈75.8; ≈8.7 25. ≈0.007; ≈0.08 35.

Lesson 12-5 pp. 666–669

EXERCISES 1. 73% 3. 92% 5. very little bias 7. C; this sample has the smallest standard deviation, which most likely indicates a larger sample. 9. ±7% 11. ±3% 13. 400 15. ±4%; 55% to 63% 17a. 63% b. ±5% c. 58% to 68% 19a. 94% b. ±18% c. 76% to 100% 27. 31%, ±13% 29. 63%, ±5% 39. ≈6.6, ≈5.1 41. $\sum_{n=1}^{8}(49 - 8n)$ 43. $\sum_{n=1}^{10}(-33 + 6n)$ 45. $\frac{x^2}{25} + \frac{y^2}{36} = 1$

Lesson 12-6 pp. 674–676

EXERCISES 1. Each guess is a trial. There are 5 trials. Each correct answer is a success. The probability of a success on a single trial is 0.5. Check students' designs and simulations. 5. 25% 7. 0% 9. 0.1361 11. 0.0015

---

13. P(0) = 0.0156
P(1) = 0.0938
P(2) = 0.2344
P(3) = 0.3125
P(4) = 0.2344
P(5) = 0.0938
P(6) = 0.0156

15. 0.2824 17. 0.1109 19. 0.2051 25a. $_{40}C_3 \cdot \left(\frac{1}{7}\right)^3\left(\frac{6}{7}\right)^{37} = 0.0960 \approx 9.6\%$ 33. Sample B was larger because it had a smaller standard deviation. 35. ≈18.18 37. 85.3125 39. $\frac{x^2}{400} - \frac{y^2}{441} = 1$ 41. (x + 3)(x − 2) 43. 3(x + 1)(x + 3)

Lesson 12-7 pp. 681–684

EXERCISES 1. 43% 3. 43 men

5.

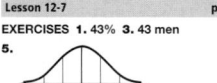

9. 79.1 11. 68% 15. 32% 19. 2.5% 21. 100% 23. 50% 27a. 209 b. 41 c. 127 – 250 41. total number of bus passengers over x hours 45. $y = \frac{6}{5}x$ 47. $y = -\frac{9}{x}$

Technology p. 685

1. 0.543 3. 0.002 5a. 0.419 b. 0.116

Chapter Review pp. 687–689

1. sample 2. outlier 3. probability distribution 4. binomial experiment 5. measures of variation

6a.
Winner	Freq.
Player 1	8
Player 2	4
Ties	3
Total	15

b. P(Player 2 wins) = $\frac{4}{15}$

9. $\frac{3}{14}$ 10. $\frac{3}{8}$ 11.

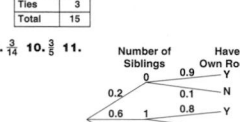

12. 0.9 **13.** 0.2 **14.** 14.4; 14; 12, 13, 14

15.

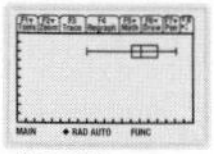

$0 \le x \le 20$
$0 \le y \le 10$

16. 20th percentile = 13, 90th percentile = 18 **17.** 53rd percentile **18.** 8 **19.** 6 **20.** 0.26 **21.** 2 **22.** −2.45 **23a.** 76% **b.** ±14% **c.** from 62% to 90% **24.** Each guess is a trial. There are 4 trials. Since there are 2 equally possible answers, the probability of success is 0.5. Let 1 represent a correct response and 2 an incorrect response. Generate 4 random numbers, either 1 or 2, 10 times. The probability is one tenth the number of times there are exactly three 1's. **25.** 0.137

27.

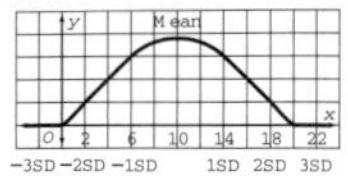

Chapter 13

Lesson 13-1 pp. 699–702

EXERCISES **1.** 5 **3.** 4 **5.** periodic; 12 **7.** not periodic **11.** 3 **13.** 2

15.

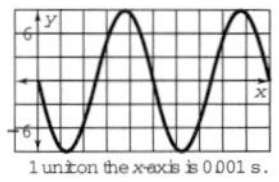

1 unit on the x-axis is 0.001 s.

17. Answers may vary. Sample: Yes; average monthly temperatures for three years should be cyclical due to the variation of the seasons. **19.** Answers may vary. Sample: Yes; traffic that passes through an intersection should be at the same levels for the same times of day for two consecutive work days. **21a.** 1 s **b.** 3 mV **23.** 3, −3, 4;

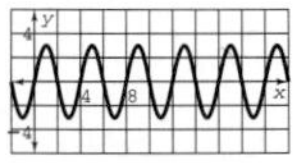

27. 2 weeks **29.** 1 hour

41.

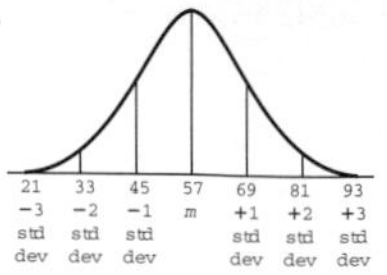

43. 14, 16; $a_n = 2n + 2$; explicit or $a_1 = 4$, $a_n = a_{n-1} + 2$; recursive

45. $(x + 3)^2 = 20(y - 2)$

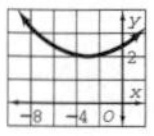

Lesson 13-2 pp. 708–710

EXERCISES 1. 45° **3.** 240°

7.

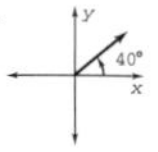

13. 215° **15.** 4° **21.** $\frac{1}{2}, \frac{\sqrt{3}}{2}$; 0.50, 0.87 **25.** $\frac{\sqrt{3}}{2}, \frac{1}{2}$; 0.87, 0.50 **27.** $\frac{\sqrt{3}}{2}, -\frac{1}{2}$; 0.87, −0.50 **29.** 1.00, 0.00 **31.** 0.71, −0.71 **37–39.** Answers may vary. Samples: **37.** 405°, −315° **39.** 45°, −315° **45.** II **47.** negative *x*-axis **51a.** 0.77, 0.77, 0.77 **b.** The cosines of the three angles are equal because the angles are coterminal. **69.** periodic; 3 **71.** periodic; 6

Lesson 13-3 pp. 715–719

EXERCISES **1.** $-\frac{5\pi}{3}$, −5.24 **3.** $-\frac{\pi}{2}$, −1.57 **7.** 540° **9.** −120° **15.** $\frac{1}{2}, \frac{\sqrt{3}}{2}$ **17.** $-\frac{1}{2}, \frac{\sqrt{3}}{2}$ **21.** 10.5 m **23.** 25.1 in. **27.** ≈32 ft **29.** ≈42.2 in. **31.** III **33.** positive *y*-axis

37.

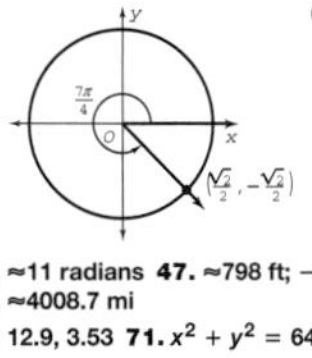

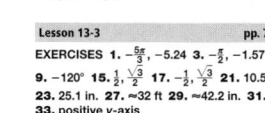

0.71, −0.71

45. ≈11 radians **47.** ≈798 ft; −55°, 665° **51.** ≈4008.7 mi **69.** 12.9, 3.53 **71.** $x^2 + y^2 = 64$

Lesson 13-4 pp. 724–727

EXERCISES 1. $\frac{1}{2}$ **3.** ≈0.9 **7.** 1 **9.** ≈−0.8 **13.** 3; 2, $\frac{2\pi}{3}$ **15.** 2; 3, π

17.

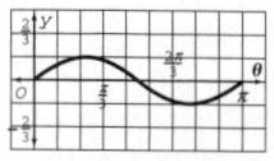

$y = \frac{1}{3}\sin 2\theta$

23.

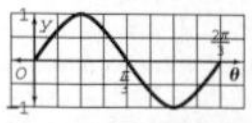

29. 2π; $y = -3\sin\theta$ **35.** 5; 1, $\frac{2\pi}{5}$ **43a.** $\frac{1}{440}$ **b.** 0.001 **c.** 880π

45. $\frac{2\pi}{5}$, 3.5

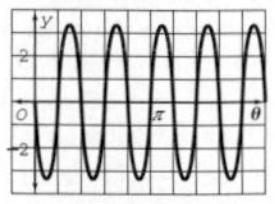

67. $\frac{5\pi}{6}$ radians, 2.62 radians **69.** $\frac{16\pi}{9}$ radians, 5.59 radians **71.** 49% **73.** $a_n = 12 + 3n$; 57

Technology p. 728

1. 2π radians, 360°; 0 **3.** $\frac{2\pi}{3}$ radians, 120°; −1 **5.** 2π radians, 360°; −0.5

Lesson 13-5 pp. 732–734

EXERCISES **1.** 2π, 3; max: 3, min: −3, zeros: $\frac{\pi}{2}, \frac{3\pi}{2}$ **3.** π, 1; max: 1, min: −1, zeros: $\frac{\pi}{4}, \frac{3\pi}{4}, \frac{5\pi}{4}, \frac{7\pi}{4}$

5.

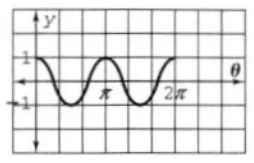

11. $y = \frac{\pi}{2}\cos\frac{2\pi}{3}\theta$ **13.** $y = -3\cos 2\theta$ **17.** 1.98, 4.30 **19.** 2.52 **23.** π, $-1 \le y \le 1$, 1 **25.** 4π, $-\frac{1}{3} \le y \le \frac{1}{3}, \frac{1}{3}$ **31.** 1.83, 2.88, 4.97, 6.02 **33a.** 3.79, 5.64 **b.** 10.07, 11.92; these values are the sums of the values from part (a) and 2π. **35a.** 5.5 ft; 1.5 ft **b.** about 12 h 22 min **c.** $y = 1.5\cos\frac{2\pi t}{742}$ **d.** 12:17 A.M.–7:49 A.M., 12:39 P.M.–8:11 P.M. **49.** about 1111 **51.** about 83 **53.** $a_n = 12(-0.3)^{n-1}$; 12, −3.6, 1.08, −0.324, 0.0972

Lesson 13-6 pp. 737–740

EXERCISES **1.** 0 **3.** −1 **9.** π **11.** $\frac{\pi}{5}$, $\theta = -\frac{\pi}{10}, \frac{\pi}{10}$ **13.** $\frac{\pi}{4}$, $\theta = -\frac{\pi}{8}, \frac{\pi}{8}$ **15.**

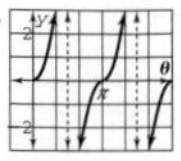

19.

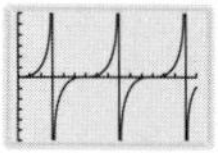

50, undefined, −50

23. 6

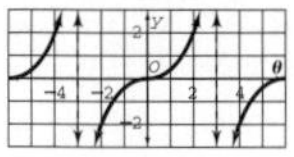

27. 2.03, 5.18 **33.** 200 **35.** 135 **39.** $y = -\tan\left(\frac{1}{2}x\right)$ **53.** 1.32, 4.97 **55.** 1.93, 4.35 **59.** 5.9, 6, 4 and 6

Lesson 13-7 pp. 746–748

EXERCISES **1.** −1; 1 unit to the left **3.** 1.6; 1.6 units to the right

7.

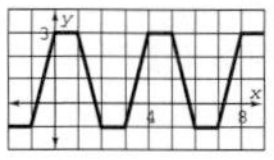

11.

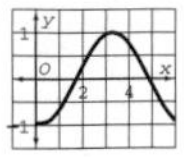

17. 3, 2π; 1 unit up **19.** 1, 2π; $\frac{\pi}{2}$ units left and 2 units up

21.

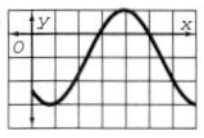

25.

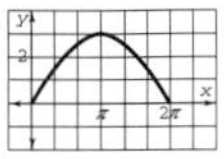

31. $y = \sin(x + \pi)$ **33.** $y = \sin x + 3$

37a.

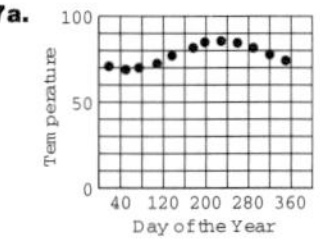

b. $8.5\cos\frac{2\pi}{365}(x - 228) + 77.5$ **39.** $y = \cos(x + 3) + \pi$ **41.** $y = 2\cos\left(x - \frac{\pi}{3}\right) - 1$; $y = 2\sin\left(x + \frac{\pi}{6}\right) - 1$ **61.** $\frac{\pi}{6}$; $\theta = -\frac{\pi}{12}, \frac{\pi}{12}$

Selected Answers

63. $\frac{2\pi}{3}$; $\theta = -\frac{\pi}{3}, -\frac{\pi}{3}$ **65.** 0.0064 **67.** ≈0.136 **69.** 62 **71.** −335,923

Lesson 13-8 pp. 752–755

EXERCISES **1.** 1.02 **3.** −0.70 **5.** $\frac{3}{4}$ **7.** $-\frac{5}{3}$ **9.** $\sqrt{2}$ **11.** 0 **21.** −7.02 **23.** 1

29.

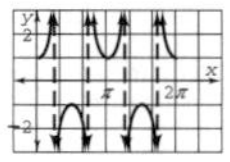

33. 1.1547 **35.** −2.9238

47.

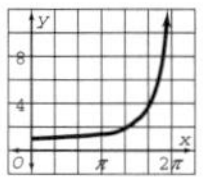

51. C **53.** D

61.

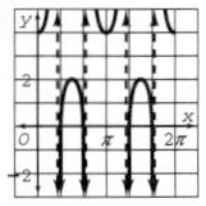

3 units up

83. 2, 2π; 5 units down **85.** 3, 2π; $\frac{\pi}{6}$ units left, 4 units up

87.

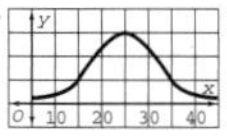

89a. $\sum_{n=-1}^{2}(1)f(a_n)$, 3 units^2

b. $\sum_{n=-1}^{2}(1)f(a_n)$, 18 units^2

Chapter Review pp. 757–759

1. period **2.** unit circle **3.** tangent function **4.** phase shift **5.** secant function **6.** periodic; 4, 2 **7.** Answers may vary. Sample:

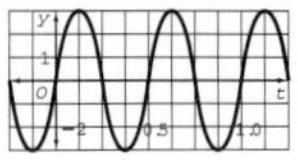

8. −225°

9.

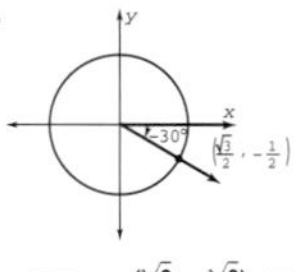

10. 240° **11.** $\left(\frac{\sqrt{2}}{2}, -\frac{\sqrt{2}}{2}\right)$; (0.71, −0.71) **12a.** $\frac{\pi}{3}$ **b.** $\frac{1}{2}, \frac{\sqrt{3}}{2}$ **13a.** $-\frac{\pi}{4}$ **b.** $\frac{\sqrt{2}}{2}, -\frac{\sqrt{2}}{2}$ **14a.** π **b.** −1, 0 **15a.** 360° **b.** 1, 0 **16a.** 150° **b.** $-\frac{\sqrt{3}}{2}, \frac{1}{2}$ **17a.** −135° **b.** $-\frac{\sqrt{2}}{2}, -\frac{\sqrt{2}}{2}$ **18.** 26.2 ft

19.

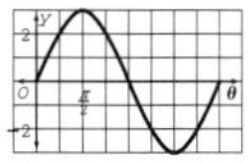

20.

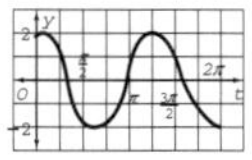

21.

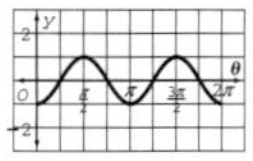

22. 3 cycles; 1, $\frac{2\pi}{3}$; $y = -\sin 3\theta$ **23.** $y = 4\sin 4\theta$ **24.** $y = 3\cos 2\theta$ **25.** $y = 2\cos 2\theta$ **26.** 3.91, 5.45 **27.** 0.16, 1.84, 4.16, 5.84 **28.** 0.59, 0.98, 2.16, 2.55, 3.73, 4.12, 5.30, 5.69

29.

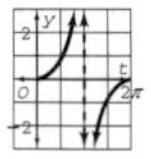

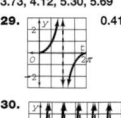

0.41, 1

30.

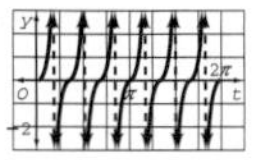

−1, undefined

31.

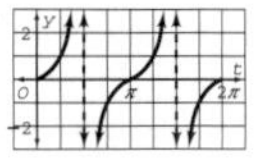

2, undefined

32.

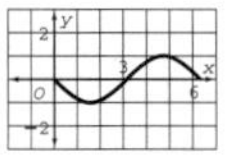

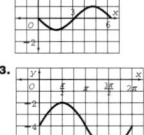

33.

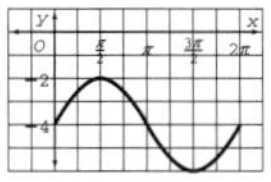

35. $y = \sin\left(x - \frac{\pi}{4}\right)$ **36.** $y = \cos x - 2$ **37.** $\sqrt{2}$ **38.** $-\frac{\sqrt{3}}{3}$ **39.** 2

40.

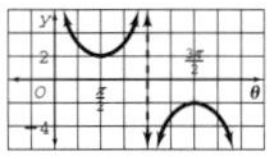

41.

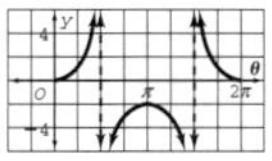

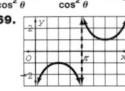

Chapter 14

Lesson 14-1 pp. 766–768

EXERCISES **1.** $\cos\theta\cot\theta = \cos\theta\left(\frac{\cos\theta}{\sin\theta}\right) = \frac{1 - \sin^2\theta}{\sin\theta} = \frac{1}{\sin\theta} - \sin\theta$ **3.** $\cos\theta\tan\theta = \cos\theta\left(\frac{\sin\theta}{\cos\theta}\right) = \sin\theta$ **9.** 1 **11.** $\tan^2\theta$ **21.** $\sec\theta$ **23.** $\sec^2\theta$ **39.** $\pm\sqrt{1 - \cos^2\theta}$ **41.** $\frac{\pm\sqrt{1 - \sin^2\theta}}{\sin\theta}$ **45.** $\sin^2\theta\tan^2\theta = \sin^2\theta\left(\frac{\sin^2\theta}{\cos^2\theta}\right) = (1 - \cos^2\theta)\left(\frac{\sin^2\theta}{\cos^2\theta}\right) = \frac{\sin^2\theta - \sin^2\theta\cos^2\theta}{\cos^2\theta} = \frac{\sin^2\theta}{\cos^2\theta} - \frac{\sin^2\theta\cos^2\theta}{\cos^2\theta} = \tan^2\theta - \sin^2\theta$

69.

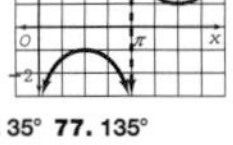

75. 35° **77.** 135°

Lesson 14-2 pp. 773–776

EXERCISES **1.** $-\frac{\pi}{2} + 2\pi n$ **3.** $\frac{\pi}{2} + 2\pi n$ **5.** $30° + n \cdot 360°$ and $210° + n \cdot 360°$ or $30° + n \cdot 180°$ **7.** $120° + n \cdot 360°$ and $300° + n \cdot 360°$ or $120° + n \cdot 180°$ **9.** $0.46 + 2\pi n$ and $2.69 + 2\pi n$

17. $\frac{\pi}{6}, \frac{11\pi}{6}$ **19.** $\frac{\pi}{4}, \frac{3\pi}{4}$ **27.** $\frac{\pi}{2}, \frac{3\pi}{2}$ **29.** $\frac{\pi}{4}, \frac{3\pi}{4}, \frac{5\pi}{4}, \frac{7\pi}{4}$ **35.** $30° + n \cdot 360°$ and $150° + n \cdot 360°$ **37.** $210° + n \cdot 360°$ and $330° + n \cdot 360°$ **39.** $\frac{3\pi}{2}$ **41.** 0.34, 2.80 **47.** $\frac{\pi}{2} + 2\pi n, \frac{3\pi}{2} + 2\pi n$ **49.** $\frac{\pi}{4} + \frac{\pi}{2}n$ **59.** $0.79 + \pi n, 2.36 + \pi n$ **61.** $0.79 + \pi n, 2.36 + \pi n$ **65.** $\frac{3\pi}{2} + 2\pi n$ **83.** $\tan^2\theta$ **85.** 1 **89.** $y = 3\cos\theta$ **91.** $y = \frac{\pi}{4}\cos\frac{2}{3}\theta$

Technology p. 777

1.

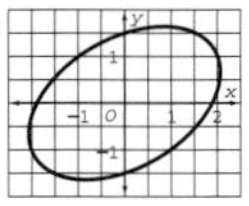

Lesson 14-3 pp. 782–785

EXERCISES **1a.** 8333 ft **b.** 8824 ft **3a.** $\frac{9}{41} \approx 0.22$ **b.** $\frac{40}{41} \approx 0.98$ **c.** $\frac{40}{9} \approx 4.44$ **d.** $\frac{41}{9} \approx 4.56$ **e.** $\frac{9}{41} \approx 0.22$ **f.** not defined **5.** 41.8 **7.** 10.6 **9.** 45.0°, 315.0° **11.** 48.6°, 131.4° **19.** $c \approx 7.8$, $\angle A = 39.8°$, $\angle B = 50.2°$ **21.** $c \approx 10.2$, $\angle A = 52.6°$, $\angle B = 37.4°$ **25.** $\cos\theta = \frac{\sqrt{55}}{8}$, $\tan\theta = \frac{3\sqrt{55}}{55}$, $\csc\theta = \frac{8}{3}$, $\sec\theta = \frac{8\sqrt{55}}{55}$, $\cot\theta = \frac{\sqrt{55}}{3}$ **35.** $a = 15$, $m\angle A \approx 61.9°$, $m\angle B \approx 28.1°$ **37.** $a \approx 7.9$, $b \approx 6.2$, $m\angle B = 38°$ **41.** 35.5° **43.** 20.3 m^2 **61.** no solution **63.** $0 + n \cdot 360°$ and $180° + n \cdot 360°$

65.

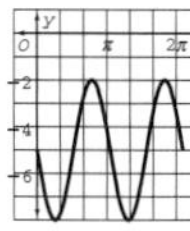

Lesson 14-4 pp. 789–792

EXERCISES **1.** 18.7 cm^2 **3.** 81.9 m^2 **5.** 10.9 **7.** 7.4 **11.** 33.5° **13.** 27.0° **17.** $m\angle D = 100°$, $e = 22.3°$, $f = 34.2$ **19.** $m\angle T = 29.3°$, $m\angle R = 26.7°$, $r = 8.3$ **27.** 7.5 mi, 7.9 mi **29.** 65° **31.** 44.5 **33.** 49.4 **39.** 28.0 ft **41.** 4.0 cm **51.** 24.6°, 204.6° **53.** 54.7°, 234.7° **55.** $b = 3\sqrt{2}$, $m\angle A = 45°$, $m\angle C = 45°$ **57.** $b = 8.3$, $m\angle A = 11.1°$, $m\angle C = 78.9°$

Selected Answers

61. 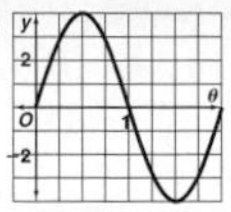 63. $\frac{7}{5}$

Extension p. 793

1. 70.4 and 47.6°, or 109.6° and 8.4° 3. 87.3° and 44.7°, or 92.7° and 39.3° 5. 44.0° and 112.4°, or 136.0° and 20.4°

Lesson 14-5 pp. 796–799

EXERCISES 1. 37.1 3. 13.7 7. 47.3° 9. 125.1° 13. 60.4° 15. 71.7° 19. $c^2 = a^2 + b^2 - 2ab\cos C$ 21. $\frac{\sin A}{a} = \frac{\sin B}{b}$ 25. $m\angle A = 50.1°$, $m\angle B = 56.3°$, $m\angle C = 73.6°$ 27. $m\angle A = 90°$, $m\angle B = 36.9°$, $m\angle C = 53.1°$ 31. 38.9 ft 33. 77.2° 35. 57.1° 37. 8.8 cm 41. 32.6° 43. 67.2° 47. 109 cm 59. 17.1 in. 61. 26.3 in. 63. $2\pi, x = \pm\pi$ 65. $\frac{\pi}{3}, x = \pm\frac{\pi}{6}$

Lesson 14-6 pp. 804–806

EXERCISES 1. $\csc\left(\theta - \frac{\pi}{2}\right) = \csc\left(-\left(\frac{\pi}{2} - \theta\right)\right) = -\csc\left(\frac{\pi}{2} - \theta\right) = -\sec\theta$ 9. $\frac{\pi}{4}, \frac{3\pi}{4}, \frac{5\pi}{4}, \frac{7\pi}{4}$ 15. $\sec A$ 17. 0 19. −1 21. $\frac{\sqrt{2} - \sqrt{6}}{4}$ 23. $2 - \sqrt{3}$ 37. $\sin(A - B) = \sin(A + (-B)) = \sin A\cos(-B) + \cos A\sin(-B) = \sin A\cos B - \cos A\sin B$ 45. $\sin 5\theta$ 47. $\cos 5\theta$ 51. $(5\cos\theta - 5\sqrt{3}\sin\theta, 5\sin\theta + 5\sqrt{3}\cos\theta)$ 65. 9.8 ft 67. 21.1 mm 69. $\frac{4\pi}{9}$ and 1.40 71. $-\frac{\pi}{12}$ and −0.26 75. 45.2 77. 57.6

Lesson 14-7 pp. 810–811

EXERCISES 1. $-\frac{\sqrt{3}}{2}$ 3. $-\sqrt{3}$ 9. $\sin 2\theta = \sin(\theta + \theta) = \sin\theta\cos\theta + \cos\theta\cdot\sin\theta = 2\sin\theta\cos\theta$ 11. $\frac{\sqrt{2 + \sqrt{3}}}{2}$ 13. $\frac{\sqrt{2 - \sqrt{3}}}{2}$ 19. $\frac{3\sqrt{10}}{10}$ 21. 3 23. $\frac{4\sqrt{17}}{17}$ 25. −4 27. $\sin 2R = 2\sin R\cos R = 2\frac{r}{t}\cdot\frac{s}{t} = \frac{2rs}{t^2}$ 29. $\sin 2S = 2\sin S\cos S = 2\cdot\frac{s}{t}\cdot\frac{r}{t} = \frac{2sr}{t^2} = 2\sin R\cos R = \sin 2R$ 35. $-\frac{7}{25}$ 37. $-\frac{25}{24}$ 43. $\sin\theta(4\cos\theta - 3) = 0$; 0, π, 0.723, 5.560 47. $-\cos\theta$ 63. $\frac{\sqrt{3}}{2}$ 65. 12, about 4.1

Chapter Review pp. 813–815

1. Law of Sines 2. trigonometric ratios for a right triangle 3. Law of Cosines 4. trigonometric identity 5. Law of Sines 6. $\sin\theta\tan\theta = \frac{\sin^2\theta}{\cos\theta} = \frac{1 - \cos^2\theta}{\cos\theta} = \frac{1}{\cos\theta} - \frac{\cos^2\theta}{\cos\theta} = \frac{1}{\cos\theta} - \cos\theta$ 7. $\cos^2\theta\cot^2\theta = (1 - \sin^2\theta)\cot^2\theta = \cot^2\theta - \sin^2\theta\cot^2\theta = \cot^2\theta - \sin^2\theta\cdot\frac{\cos^2\theta}{\sin^2\theta} = \cot^2\theta - \cos^2\theta$ 8. $\cos^2\theta$ 9. 1 10. 1 11. −60° 12. 60° 13. −30° 14. 30° 15. $0.34 + 2\pi n$, $2.80 + 2\pi n$ 16. $-1.11 + 2\pi n$, $2.03 + 2\pi n$ 17. $2.27 + 2\pi n$, $4.02 + 2\pi n$ 18. $0.20 + 2\pi n$, $6.08 + 2\pi n$ 19. $\frac{\pi}{3}, \frac{5\pi}{3}$ 20. $\frac{\pi}{6}, \frac{7\pi}{6}$ 21. $0, \frac{\pi}{2}, \pi$ 22. $\frac{3}{5}$, 0.6 23. $\frac{4}{5}$, 0.8 24. $\frac{3}{4}$, 0.75 25. $3\sqrt{10}$, 18.4°, 71.6° 26. 16, 36.9°, 53.1° 27. 37.7, 43.3°, 46.7° 28. 13.14 m² 29. 92.12 ft² 30. 57.81 m² 31. 7.1 in. 32. 54.3° or 125.7° 33. 21.4 ft 34. 43.9° 35. 52.2° 36. $\cos\left(\theta + \frac{\pi}{2}\right) = \cos\theta\cdot\cos\left(\frac{\pi}{2}\right) - \sin\theta\cdot\sin\left(\frac{\pi}{2}\right) = \cos\theta\cdot 0 - \sin\theta\cdot 1 = -\sin\theta$ 37. $\sin^2\left(\theta - \frac{\pi}{2}\right) = \sin^2\left(-\left(\frac{\pi}{2} - \theta\right)\right) = \left(-\sin\left(\frac{\pi}{2} - \theta\right)\right)\cdot\left(-\sin\left(\frac{\pi}{2} - \theta\right)\right) = (-\cos\theta)(-\cos\theta) = \cos^2\theta$ 38. $\frac{\pi}{2}$ 39. 0 40. $\frac{\sqrt{3}}{2}$ 41. 0 42. $-\sqrt{3}$ 43. −1 44. $\sqrt{3}$ 45. $\frac{\sqrt{3}}{2}$

Extra Practice

CHAPTER 1 1. > 3. > 9. −102, $\frac{1}{102}$ 11. $-2\frac{3}{4}, \frac{4}{11}$ 21. 28 23. 14 25. 2 27. −11

31. $t \le -1$ 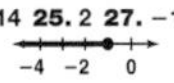

−4 −2 0

33. $a < -\frac{7}{2}$ 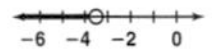

−6 −4 −2 0

37. $-2 \le z < 1$ 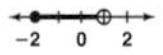

−2 0 2

39. $x < -2, x > 8$

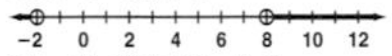

−2 0 2 4 6 8 10 12

43. −11, 15.5 45. −5, 9

49. $t \le -5.5, t \ge -1.5$ 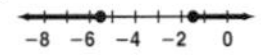

−8 −6 −4 −2 0

51. $-11 \le w \le -1$

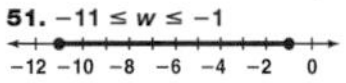

−12 −10 −8 −6 −4 −2 0

55. 1 57. $\frac{4}{9}$

CHAPTER 2 1. Yes; each x-value has exactly one y-value. 3. No; the x-value 1 has two y-values. 15. $3x - y = -7$ 17. $3x - 4y = -26$ 21. $y - 2 = -1(x - 0)$ 23. $y - 0 = \frac{1}{2}(x - 3)$ 27. 2, −5, 2.5 29. 0, 4, none 35. $3x - y = -9$ 37. $8x - 2y = 7$ 43. $y = \frac{7}{3}x$ 45. $y = 2.5x$

51. 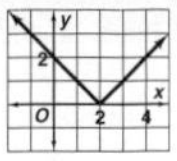 59. 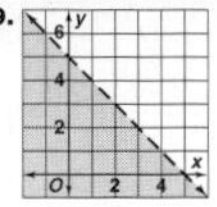

CHAPTER 3

1. 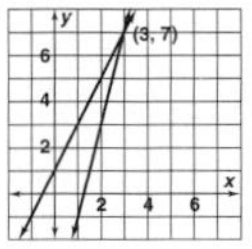

(3, 7)

7. (1, 4) 9. (6, −3)

13. 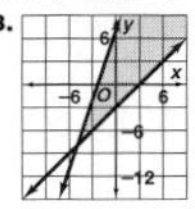

17. (0, 0) 19. 50 chef's salads and 50 Caesar salads

29. 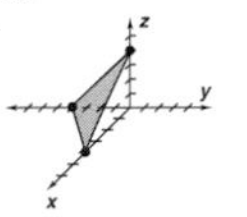

35. (2, 1, 3) 37. (2, 3, −6)

CHAPTER 4 1. 2 × 3; 6 3. 2 × 3; −83 7. $\begin{bmatrix} 4 & 67 \\ 12 & 18 \end{bmatrix}$ 9. $\begin{bmatrix} -6 & -1 & 0 \\ 17 & -11 & -8 \end{bmatrix}$ 11. $\begin{bmatrix} -62 & 121 \\ 43 & -54 \end{bmatrix}$ 13. $\begin{bmatrix} 5 & -7 & 7 \\ 2 & 1 & -2 \end{bmatrix}$ 15. $\begin{bmatrix} -26 & 7 & 5 \\ -4 & -7 & 25 \end{bmatrix}$ 17. $\begin{bmatrix} 16 & 2 \\ -4 & 10 \end{bmatrix}$ 27. $\begin{bmatrix} 5 & 10 & 20 \\ 25 & -5 & 15 \end{bmatrix}$ 29. $\begin{bmatrix} 3 & 4 & 6 \\ -2 & -8 & -4 \end{bmatrix}$ 31. $\begin{bmatrix} \frac{68}{15} & -\frac{34}{15} \\ -\frac{16}{15} & \frac{83}{15} \end{bmatrix}$ 33. $\begin{bmatrix} 2 \\ 7 \end{bmatrix}$ 35. (9, 1)

CHAPTER 5 1. linear; none, 3x, 4 3. linear; none, $-\frac{3}{2}x, \frac{1}{2}$ 7. 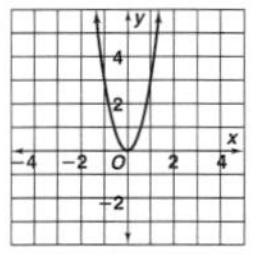

15. $(x + 9)(x - 6)$ 17. $(x - 6)(x + 6)$ 27. 0.24, −4.24 29. 0.41, −2.41 35. $8 - 3i$ 37. $1 - 3i$ 41. $\pm 4i$ 43. $\pm i\sqrt{10}$ 47. $-i, -1 - i, i$

49. −1, −4 51. $\frac{5}{4} \pm \frac{\sqrt{17}}{4}$ 59. 108; 2, real 61. 25; 2, real

CHAPTER 6 1. $-4a^2 + 3a$; quadratic binomial 3. $-2n^3 + 3n^2 - n - 3$; cubic polynomial of 4 terms 7. $y = x^3 - 4x^2 + x + 6$ 9. $y = x^3 + 2x^2 - x - 2$ 15. $x^2 - 2x - 2$ 17. $2x^2 + 2x$ 21. 0, −2, 5 23. 2 27. $-2, \pm i\sqrt{3}$ 29. $-1, \frac{-5 \pm \sqrt{13}}{6}$ 33. 720 35. 210 45. permutation; 60,480 orders 47. combination; 6 ways 49. $81x^4 + 216x^3 + 216x^2 + 96x + 16$ 51. $16x^4 + 160x^3y + 600x^2y^2 + 1000xy^3 + 625y^4$

CHAPTER 7 1. $6x^2$ 3. $3|x^3|$ 9. $6x^3\sqrt{2x}$ 11. $10a^2$ 15. $5\sqrt{7}$ 17. $3\sqrt{7x}$ 21. $\frac{y^9}{x^{20}}$ 23. $\frac{y^3}{2x^5}$ 29. no solution 31. 3, 7 35. 1 37. 64 45. $f^{-1}(x) = x^2 - 4, x \ge 0$; domain of f: $\{x \ge -4\}$, range of f: $\{y \ge 0\}$, domain of f^{-1}: $\{x \ge 0\}$, range of f^{-1}: $\{y \ge -4\}$; f^{-1} is a function.

51. 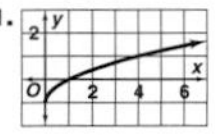

CHAPTER 8 1. $y = 4(2.5)^x$ 3. $y = \frac{2}{3}(3)^x$ 7. exponential growth 9. exponential decay

17. 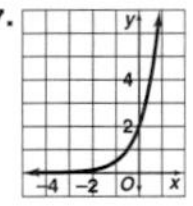

25. $\log_9 729 = 3$ 27. $\log_{\frac{1}{2}}\frac{1}{16} = 4$ 41. log 24 43. $\log x^7$ 47. $\log_b 2 + 2\log_b x + 3\log_b y$ 49. $5(\log_b 4 + \log_b m + \log_b n)$ 53. 8 55. 50,000

CHAPTER 9 1. $y = \frac{6}{x}$ 3. $y = \frac{40}{x}$

7. 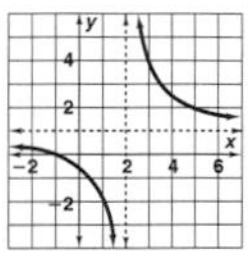

15. 0 17. −2, 1 23. $x + 3; x \ne -6$ 25. $x + 2; x \ne -3, 4$ 29. $\frac{14x - 3}{2(x + 2)}$ 31. $\frac{8x - 3}{x(x + 3)}$ 35. −4 37. −5, 4 41. independent 43. dependent

CHAPTER 10 1. 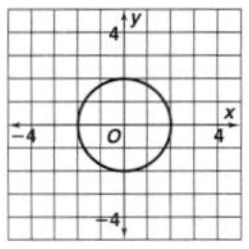

Circle; every line through (0, 0) is a line of symmetry, radius 2; domain: $-2 \le x \le 2$, range: $-2 \le y \le 2$. 7. $y = \frac{1}{12}x^2$ 9. $y = -\frac{1}{8}x^2$ 17. (4, 0), $x = -4$;

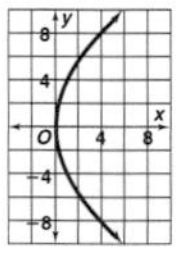

25. $(x + 4)^2 + (y + 6)^2 = 4$ 27. $(x - 1)^2 + (y - 4)^2 = 25$ 31. (−6, −9), 12 33. (−8, 1), 10 37. $(\pm 4\sqrt{2}, 0)$

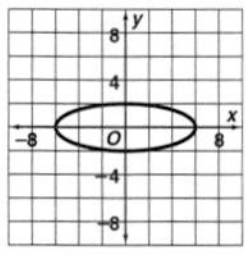

49. ellipse; center (0, 0), foci $(\pm 3\sqrt{3}, 0)$

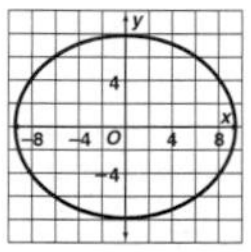

CHAPTER 11 1. explicit; 5, 8, 11, 14, 17 3. explicit; 15, 40, 75, 120, 175 7. 9, 11, 13; $a_n = 2n + 1$; $a_1 = 3, a_n = a_{n-1} + 2$ 9. −7.5, −6, −4.5; $a_n = -13.5 + 1.5n$; $a_1 = -12, a_n = a_{n-1} + 1.5$ 13. 15 15. −4.5 17. $a_n = -27\left(\frac{1}{3}\right)^{n-1}$; −27, −9, −3, −1, $-\frac{1}{3}$ 19. $a_n = -5(3)^{n-1}$; −5, −15, −45, −135, −405 23. $\sum_{n=1}^{10}(3n + 1)$; 175 25. $\sum_{n=1}^{20}(-n + 98)$; 1750

27. 6, 2, −3; −3 29. 8, 4, 25; 116 31. $\frac{9}{4}$ 33. 1 37. geometric; 3069 39. arithmetic; −1110 41. 0 + 1 = 1; 1 + 8 = 9 43. 3 + 4 = 7; 4 + 5 = 9

CHAPTER 12 1. 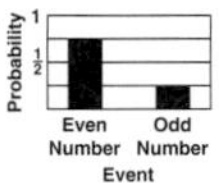

Probability
1
1/2
Even Number
Odd Number
Event

3. $\frac{39}{80}$ 5. $\frac{25}{80}$ 9. 25.8, 21, 24 11. 4.8, 4.2, 6.1 13. 25.429, 11, 8, 3.81 15. 99.71, 5, 3, 1.578 17. ±6% 19. ±3% 23. 0.2787 ≈ 28% 25. 0.0003 ≈ 0.03% 29. $P(k = 0) = 0.0467$
$P(k = 1) = 0.1866$
$P(k = 2) = 0.3110$
$P(k = 3) = 0.2765$
$P(k = 4) = 0.1382$
$P(k = 5) = 0.0369$
$P(k = 6) = 0.0041$

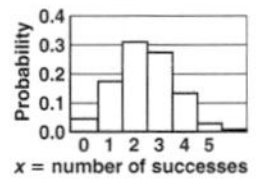

Probability
0.4
0.3
0.2
0.1
0.0
0 1 2 3 4 5
x = number of successes

35. 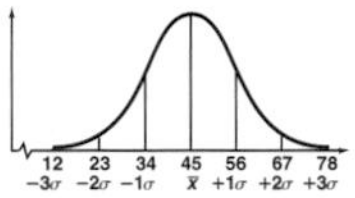

12 23 34 45 56 67 78
−3σ −2σ −1σ x̄ +1σ +2σ +3σ

CHAPTER 13 1. 4, $1\frac{1}{2}$ 3. 4, 2 11. $\frac{3\pi}{2}$, 4.71 13. $\frac{-55\pi}{18}$, −9.60 17. −115° 19. −540° 23. 1, $\frac{\pi}{2}$ 25. 2, 8π

29. 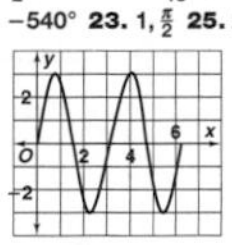 35. 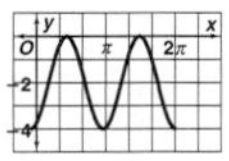

39. −1.5299 41. −1

CHAPTER 14 1. $60° + n\cdot 360°$ and $120° + n\cdot 360°$ 3. $60° + n\cdot 360°$ and $240° + n\cdot 360°$ 5. no solution 7. 1.313 13. $\frac{3\pi}{2}$ 15. 0, π, 2.6779, 5.8195, 2π 19. $b = 5.7$, $\angle A = 51.1°$, $\angle B = 38.9°$

21. $c = 4.5$, $\angle A = 26.6°$, $\angle B = 63.4°$ 25. $\frac{12}{13}$, 0.923 27. $\frac{12}{5}$, 2.4 29. 11.3 31. 46.3 33. $\frac{\sqrt{6} - \sqrt{2}}{4}$ 35. $\frac{\sqrt{3}}{2}$ 39. 1 41. −1 45. $\frac{\sqrt{2 - \sqrt{3}}}{2}$ 47. $\frac{\sqrt{2 + \sqrt{2}}}{2}$

Skills Handbook

p. 836 1. $\left(13, 6\frac{1}{2}\right)$ 3. 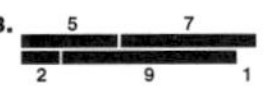

5 7
2 9 1

p. 837 1. 23 pigs and 17 ducks 3. 45 mi

p. 838 1. ten of each coin

p. 839 1. 12 slices 3. 204

p. 840 1. Leon 3. 15 students

p. 841 1. $85\frac{1}{3}$ cm

3. 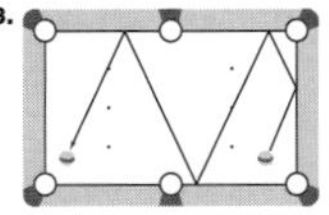

p. 842 1. 46% 3. 29.4% 13. 0.4 15. 1.5 19. 12.5 21. 75

p. 843 1. $1\frac{2}{5}$ 3. $6\frac{5}{6}$

p. 844 1. 3 to 4 3. 9.5 g/oz 7. 8 9. 1.8

p. 845 1. 1 3. −38

p. 846 1. 14.4 3. 84 13. $\ell = \frac{P}{2} - w$ 15. $b = c - 2a$

p. 847 1. 14 m² 3. 30 cm² 5. 91.1 ft³ 7. 314.2 in.³ 9. 110.5 in.² 11. 121.5 ft²

p. 848 1. I 3. IV 13. $\frac{3}{4}$ 15. 0 19. $\left(5, -\frac{3}{2}\right)$ 21. $\left(\frac{5}{2}, -1\right)$

p. 849 1. −1 3. 6

13. $x \le 6$

15. $y \ge -2$

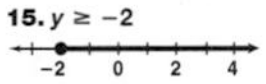

−2 0 2 4

p. 850 1. 8, −8 3. 5, −13

13. $-3 \le x \le 15$

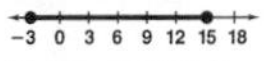

−3 0 3 6 9 12 15 18

15. $r \le -7$ or $r \ge 7$

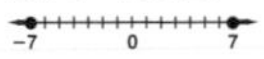

−7 0 7

p. 851

1. 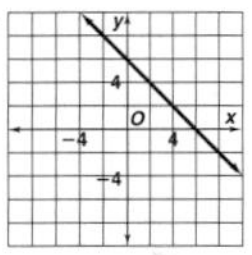

p. 852 1. x^3 3. a^4b 5. $\frac{1}{c^4}$ 7. $\frac{x^5}{y^7z^3}$ 9. d^8 11. r^5s^8

p. 853 1. $x^2 + 10x - 5$ 3. $12x^4 - 20x^3 + 36x^2$ 7. $(a - 6)(a - 2)$ 9. $(n - 4)(n + 2)$

p. 854 1. 1.34×10^6 3. 7.75×10^{-4} 11. 6.4×10^5 13. $\approx 8.52 \times 10^2$

p. 855 1. 6 3. $3\sqrt{2}$

p. 856 1. 10 3. 15 11. 10 13. 22.7

p. 857

1. 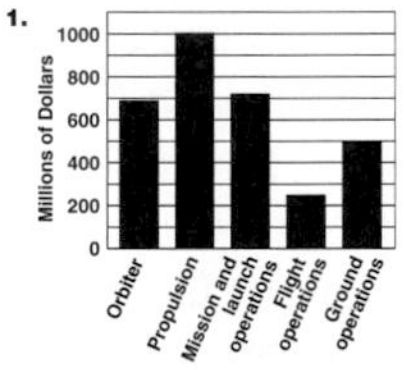

Millions of Dollars
1000
800
600
400
200
0
Orbiter
Propulsion
Mission and launch operations
Flight operations
Ground operations

p. 858 1. 3.8, 5, 5 3. 4.0, 2.4, 2.4

p. 859 1. $\frac{a}{3b^2}$ 3. $\frac{1}{2}$ 5. $4x$ 7. $\frac{2}{h}$

CHAPTER 1

LESSON 1-1

pages 8–10   Exercises

83. Answers may vary. Sample: 4 is a whole number, but $\frac{1}{4}$ is not a whole number.

84. Answers may vary. Sample: 7 is a natural number, but -7 is not a natural number.

85. 0 is a whole number, and since $-0 = 0$, the opposite of 0 is a whole number.

86. Answers may vary. Sample: The integer -1 has -1 as its reciprocal, so -1 is an integer whose reciprocal is an integer.

87. Answers may vary. Sample: $\sqrt{2}$ and $\sqrt{2}$ are irrational numbers, but their product, 2, is a rational number.

page 11   Investigation

4. Answers may vary. Sample: The formula that uses an infinite product gives $\frac{131,072}{43,659} \approx 3.00217596$ if you use 10 factors. The continued fraction gives ≈ 3.14146342 if you go to the bottom level shown. The continued fraction approximations appear to be getting close to π faster than the infinite sum and infinite product approximations, but the calculations are more complicated for the continued fraction.

LESSON 1-3

pages 21–23   Exercises

67b. Solutions are rational when $\frac{c-b}{a} \geq 0$, $a \neq 0$, and $\frac{c-b}{a}$ is a perfect square (a whole number perfect square or, in simplest form, a fraction whose numerator and denominator are whole number perfect squares), since $x^2 = \frac{c-b}{a}$ ($a \neq 0$), $x = \sqrt{\frac{c-b}{a}}$ or $x = -\sqrt{\frac{c-b}{a}}$. For $\sqrt{\frac{c-b}{a}}$ and $-\sqrt{\frac{c-b}{a}}$ to be rational, $\frac{c-b}{a}$ must be nonnegative and also $\frac{c-b}{a}$ must be a perfect square.

LESSON 1-4

pages 29–31   Exercises

11.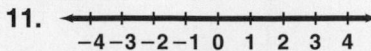
$-4\ -3\ -2\ -1\ 0\ 1\ 2\ 3\ 4$

12.
$-4\ -3\ -2\ -1\ 0\ 1\ 2\ 3\ 4$

61. [4] Answer includes all of the following six parts of the explanation (or equivalent statements), which consist of solving each compound inequality, graphing each compound inequality, and explaining why the choices of *or* and *and* result in solutions of *all real numbers* and *no real numbers*.

$x + 5 > 0 \ \boxed{} \ x - 3 < 0$
$\quad x > -5 \ \boxed{} \ x < 3$
$-5\ -4\ -3\ -2\ -1\ 0\ 1\ 2\ 3$

The solutions to the two simple inequalities overlap. By writing *or* in the box, the solution is any value on either of the two arrows, or all real numbers.

$x + 5 < 0 \ \boxed{} \ x + 5 > 0$
$\quad x < -5 \ \boxed{} \ x > -5$
$-9\ -8\ -7\ -6\ -5\ -4\ -3\ -2\ -1$

The solutions to the two simple inequalities do not overlap. By writing *and* in the box, the solution is any point on both arrows, or no real numbers.

[3] omits one or two parts of the six parts of the explanation

[2] omits three or four of the six parts of the explanation

[1] includes at least one of the six parts of the explanation

LESSON 1-5

pages 36–38   Exercises

24. $-2 < x < 6$
$-10\ -8\ -6\ -4\ -2\ 0\ 2\ 4\ 6\ 8\ 10$

25. no solution

26. $-3\frac{1}{2} \leq w \leq \frac{1}{2}$
$-5\ -4\ -3\ -2\ -1\ 0\ 1\ 2\ 3$

27. $t \geq -\frac{11}{15}$ or $t \leq \frac{17}{15}$
$-1\ -\frac{12}{15}\ -\frac{9}{15}\ -\frac{6}{15}\ -\frac{3}{15}\ 0\ \frac{3}{15}\ \frac{6}{15}\ \frac{9}{15}\ \frac{12}{15}\ 1\ 1\frac{3}{15}\ 1\frac{6}{15}$

44. $-6 \leq x \leq 8\frac{2}{3}$
$-8\ -6\ -4\ -2\ 0\ 2\ 4\ 6\ 8\ 10\ 12$

45. $x \leq -8$ or $x \geq 5$
$-12\ -10\ -8\ -6\ -4\ -2\ 0\ 2\ 4\ 6\ 8$

46. All real numbers are solutions.
$-4\ -3\ -2\ -1\ 0\ 1\ 2\ 3\ 4$

47. $t < -\frac{3}{2}$ or $t > 2$
$-4\ -3\ -2\ -1\ 0\ 1\ 2\ 3\ 4$

48. All real numbers are solutions.
$-4\ -3\ -2\ -1\ 0\ 1\ 2\ 3\ 4$

49. $x < -\frac{1}{2}$ or $x > \frac{3}{2}$
$-4\ -3\ -2\ -1\ 0\ 1\ 2\ 3\ 4$

50. $x \leq -8.4$ or $x \geq 9.6$
$-12\ -8\ -4\ 0\ 4\ 8\ 12$

56. The graph of $|x| < a$ (where $a > 0$) is the set of all points on the number line that lie between the points for a and $-a$. The graph of $|x| > a$ has two parts: the left part consists of the points to the left of the point for $-a$, and the right part consists of the points to the right of the point for a.

64. $(-6 \leq x \leq -5)$ or $(5 \leq x \leq 6)$
$-8\ -6\ -4\ -2\ 0\ 2\ 4\ 6\ 8$

65. $(x \leq -6)$ or $(-5 < x < 5)$ or $(x \geq 6)$
$-6\ -4\ -2\ 0\ 2\ 4\ 6$

66. $x \geq \frac{5}{2}$
$-2\ -1\ 0\ 1\ 2\ 3\ 4\ 5\ 6$

page 38   Checkpoint Quiz 2

1.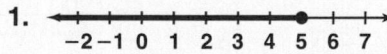
$-2\ -1\ 0\ 1\ 2\ 3\ 4\ 5\ 6\ 7$

2.
$-2\ -1\ 0\ 1\ 2\ 3\ 4\ 5\ 6\ 7$

3.
$-4\ -3\ -2\ -1\ 0\ 1\ 2\ 3\ 4\ 5$

4.
$-6\ -5\ -4\ -3\ -2\ -1\ 0\ 1\ 2\ 3\ 4$

5.
$-16\ -14\ -12\ -10\ -8\ -6\ -4\ -2\ 0\ 2\ 4\ 6\ 8$

6.
$-4\ -3\ -2\ -1\ 0\ 1\ 2\ 3\ 4$

LESSON 1-6

pages 42–45   Exercises

5. Answers may vary. Sample: Generate 100 random numbers with a calculator. Record the first five digits of each number. Let 0 and 1 represent correct answers and the other digits incorrect answers. Tally the recorded numbers with exactly one digit that represents a correct answer. Tally the recorded numbers with exactly two digits that represent correct answers. Tally the recorded numbers with exactly three digits that represent correct answers. The tally totals, as percents, give the experimental probabilities. They should be in the neighborhood of 40%, 20%, and 5%, respectively.

CHAPTER 2

LESSON 2-1

page 55   Check Skills You'll Need

1.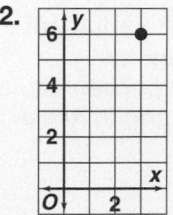

2.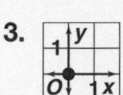

3.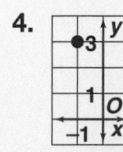

4.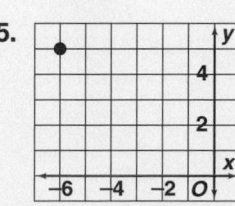

5.

page 55   Check Understanding

1a.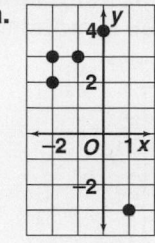

b.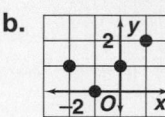

pages 59–61   Exercises

8.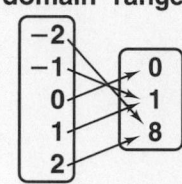

domain   range

9.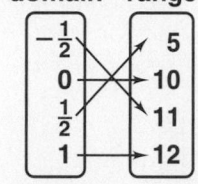

domain   range

10.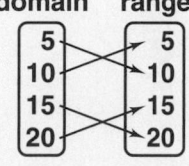

domain   range

11. domain   range
    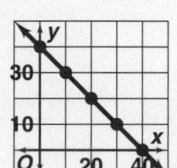

22. −7, −3, 4, 11

23. 13, 7, −3.5, −14

24. 4.5, 6.5, 10, 13.5

25. −2, −4, −7.5, −11

26. 21, 13, −1, −15

27. −13, −9, −2, 5

28. $29\frac{1}{3}, 17\frac{1}{3}, -3\frac{2}{3}, -24\frac{2}{3}$

29. $-\frac{23}{6}, -\frac{13}{6}, \frac{3}{4}, \frac{11}{3}$

30. $-\frac{9}{2}, -\frac{7}{2}, -\frac{7}{4}, 0$

59. domain: {all integers}, range: {all integers}; function, each integer pairs to a unique even integer.

60. domain: {all integers}, range: {all integers}; function each integer pairs with its opposite.

61. domain: {all integers}, range: {all integers}; not a function, each nonzero integer pairs with a pos. and neg. even integer.

65. [4] Yes; $S(c) = 6c^2$; $S(2.5) = 6(2.5)^2 = 37.5$; the surface area is 37.5 cm².

   [3] minor computational error

   [2] includes only function

   [1] no work shown

73. −6, 14
    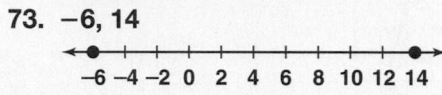

74. $-2 \le b \le 2$

75. $y \ne 6$

LESSON 2-2

page 62   Check Skills You'll Need

1. $\frac{17}{3}, 7, \frac{23}{3}, \frac{29}{3}$

2. $-\frac{16}{5}, -2, -\frac{7}{5}, \frac{2}{5}$

3. −5, 1, 4, 13

4. $-9, -8, -\frac{15}{2}, -6$

page 63   Check Understanding

2a.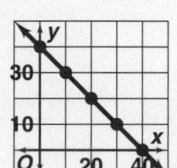

$y = 40 - x$
x-intercept (40, 0),
y-intercept (0, 40).
When there are 0 children, the train holds 40 adults. When there are 0 adults, the train holds 40 children.

pages 67–70   Exercises

1.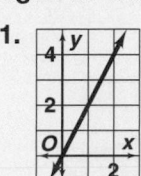

2.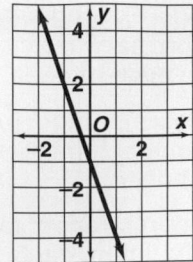

3.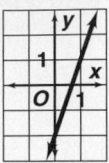

4.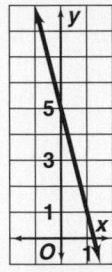

5.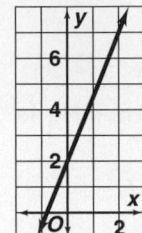

6.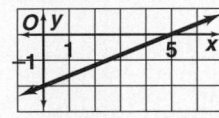

7.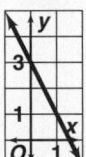

8.

10a.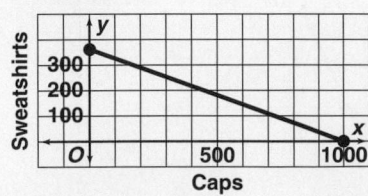

b. The *x*-intercept is the point that represents selling 1000 caps and

T894

0 sweatshirts in order to raise the $4500. The *y*-intercept represents selling 0 caps and 360 sweatshirts to raise the $4500.

40. $y = 10$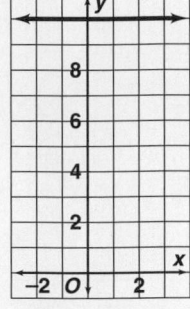

41. $x = 1$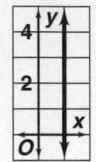

42.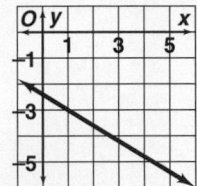

43.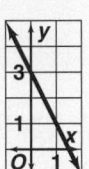

44.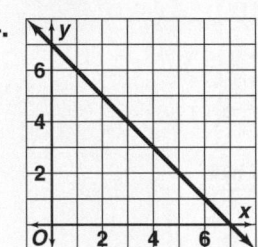

45.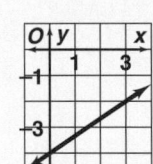

46.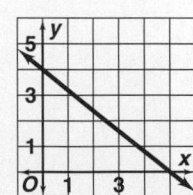

47.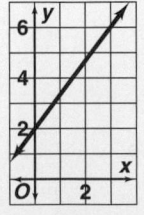

48.

49.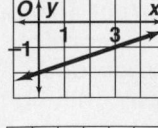

50.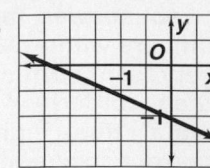

81a.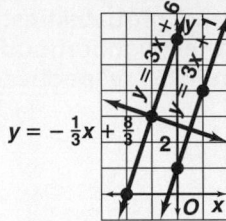

$y = -\frac{1}{3}x + \frac{8}{3}$

82. The equation of the line connecting (1, 3) to (−2, 6) is $y = -x + 4$. The equation of the line connecting (1, 3) to (3, 5) is $y = x + 2$. The slopes are negative reciprocals so the lines are perpendicular. Therefore by def. of a right triangle it is a right triangle.

83. The slope of the line connecting (2, 5) to (4, 8) is $\frac{3}{2}$, (2, 5) to (5, 3) is $-\frac{2}{3}$, (4, 8) to (7, 6) is $-\frac{2}{3}$, and (5, 3) to (7, 6) is $\frac{3}{2}$. Since the adjacent sides' slopes are negative reciprocals they are perpendicular. By the def. of a rectangle, it is a rectangle.

84. $p: y = 4x + 16$
$q: y = -\frac{1}{4}x + \frac{13}{4}$
$r: y = 4$

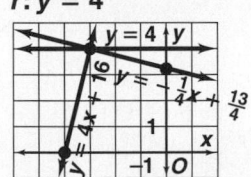

LESSON 2-3

pages 74–77   Exercises

65.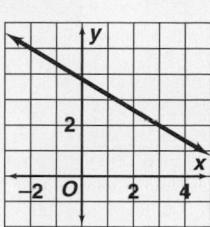

66.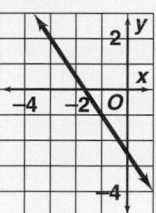

67.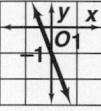

68.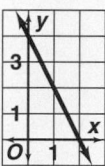

LESSON 2-4

pages 78–80   Check Understanding

1b.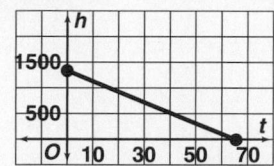

The h-intercept (0, 1350) represents the starting height at time 0.

4a.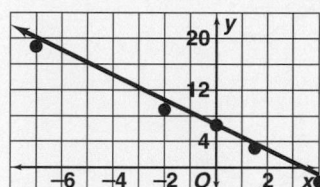

A linear model is reasonable; models may vary. Sample: $y = -1.92x + 6$

b.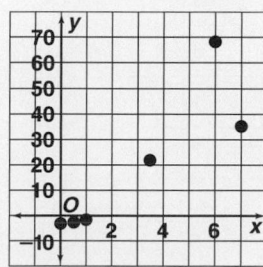

not reasonable

---

pages 81–84   Exercises

1. $d = 62.5h + 15$

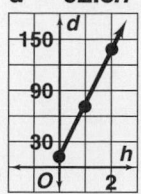

2a. $y = -50t + 1000$

b.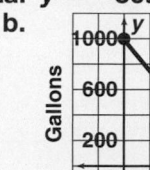

The y-intercept (0, 1000) represents the filled pool, and the t-intercept (20, 0) represents the time needed to empty the pool.

8.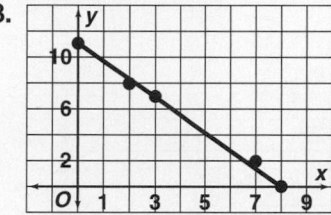

Linear model is reasonable; models may vary. Sample: $y = -1.3x + 11$

9.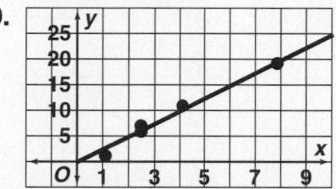

Linear model is reasonable; models may vary. Sample: $y = 2.6x - 0.6$

10.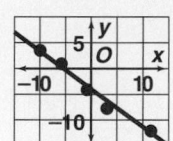

Linear model is reasonable; models may vary. Sample: $y = -0.75x - 3.75$

11.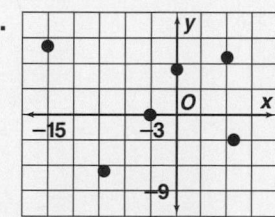

not reasonable

12a.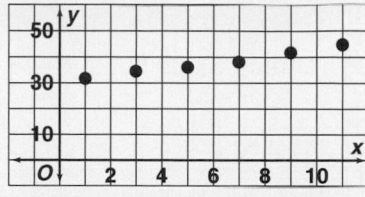

Linear model is reasonable.

13a.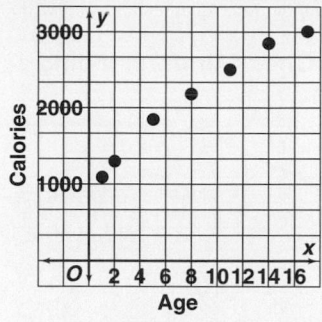

Answers may vary. Sample: $y = 110x + 1170$

14a.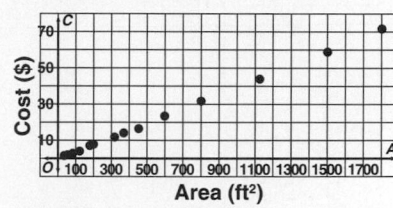

19c. Answers may vary. Sample:

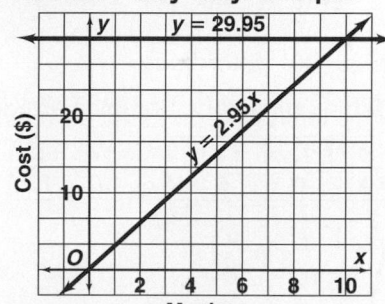

Either way, you will average the same costs over the long run.

27a.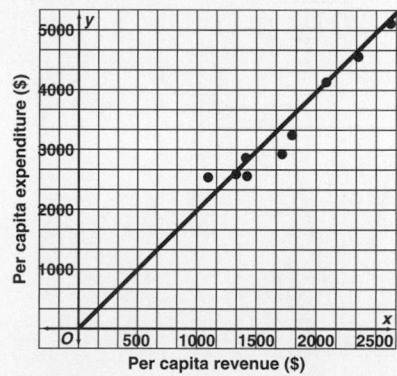

LESSON 2-5

page 86 Check Skills You'll Need

3.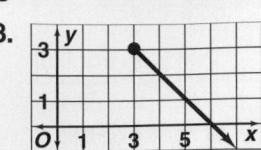

page 87 Check Understanding

2b.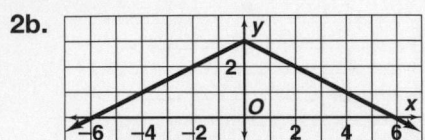

3a.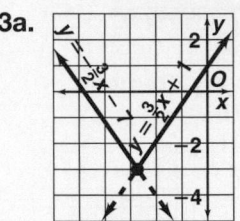

b.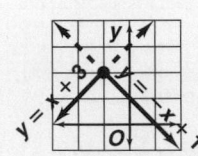

pages 88–90 Exercises

1–9. Tables may vary. Samples are given.

1.

x	0	−1	1	−2	2
y	0	4	4	8	8

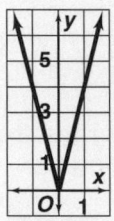

2.

x	−2	−1	0	1	2
y	7	3	−1	3	7

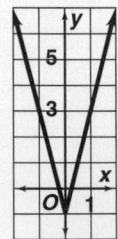

3.

x	−1	0	¼	1	2
y	5	1	0	3	7

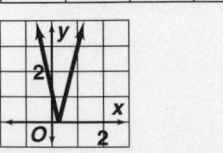

4.

x	−2	−1	0	1	2
y	6	3	0	3	6

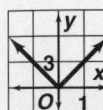

5.

x	−2	−1	0	1	2
y	8	5	2	5	8

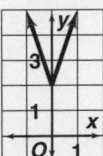

6.

x	−1	0	⅔	1	2
y	5	2	0	1	4

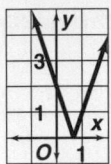

7.

x	−2	−1	0	1	2
y	−4	−2	0	−2	−4

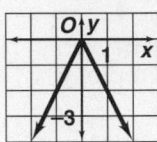

8.

x	−2	−1	0	1	2
y	1	3	5	3	1

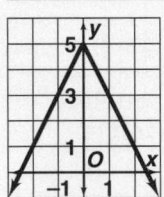

9.

x	−4	−3	−$\frac{5}{2}$	−1	0
y	−3	−1	0	−3	−5

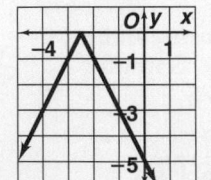

10.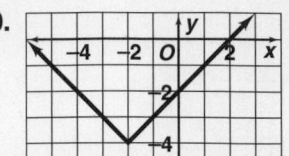

11.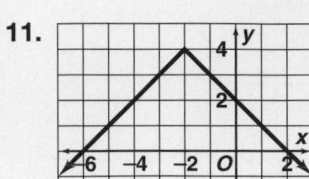

12.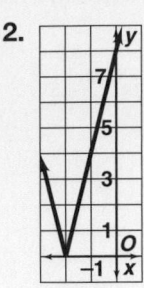

13.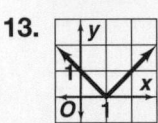

14.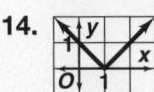

15.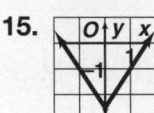

16.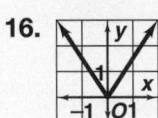

17.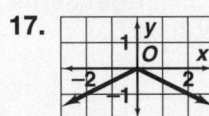

18.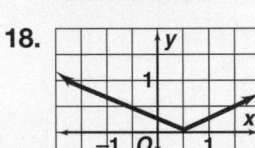

19.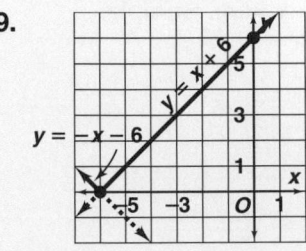

20.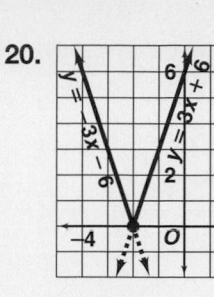

21.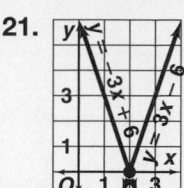

22. $y = -x + 5$
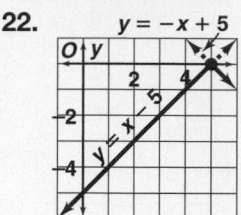

23.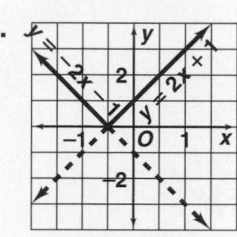

24.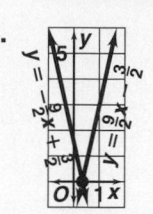

25.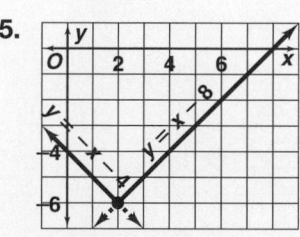

26.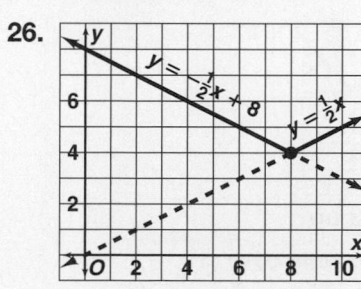

27.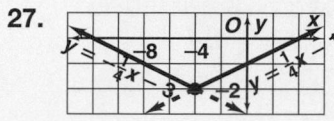

28.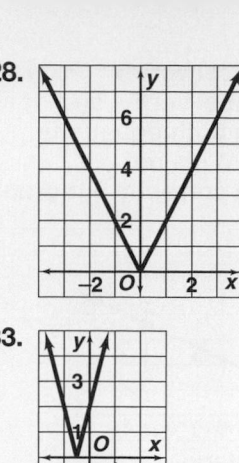

33.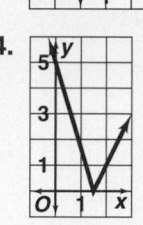

34.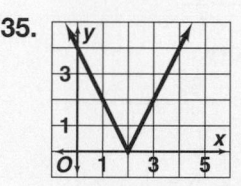

35.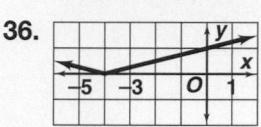

36.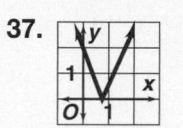

37.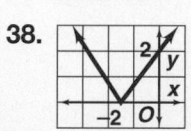

38.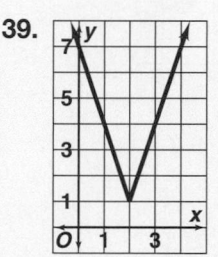

39.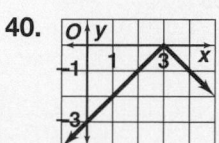

40.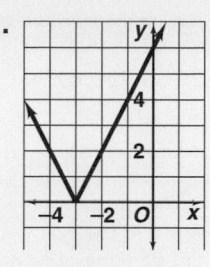

41.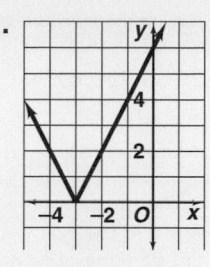

42.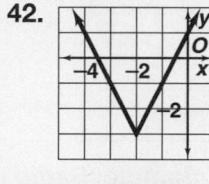

43.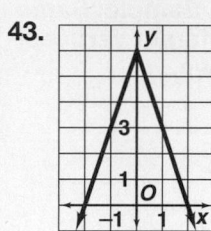

44.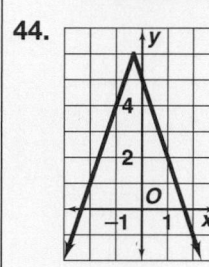

45.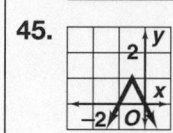

46.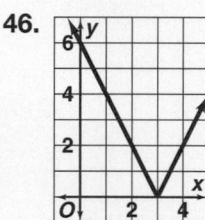

47.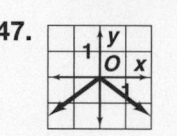

48.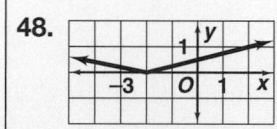

49.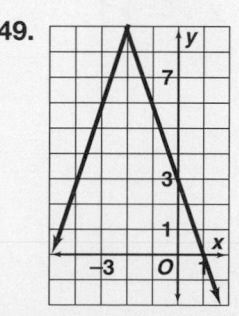

50.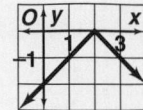

52a.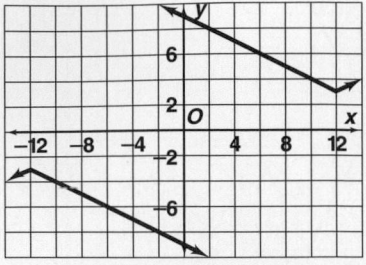

b. Answers may vary. Sample: Same shape and size, different vertices, and one points down.

53.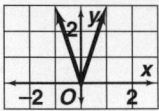

54.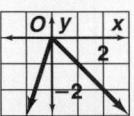

55.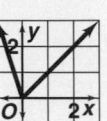

56.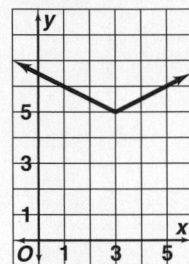

57.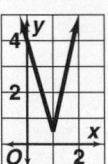

58.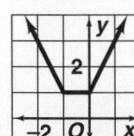

66. [4] $y = -5x - 1$, $y = 5x + 1$

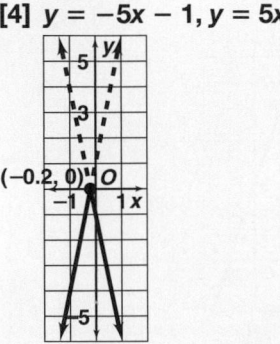

[3] does not label vertex
[2] does not label vertex and does not include both equations
[1] $y = -|5x + 1|$ is not interpreted correctly but graph is correct

67.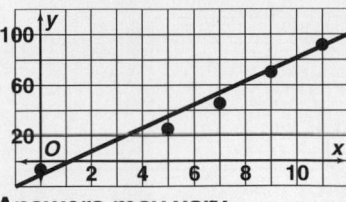

Answers may vary.
Sample: $y = 8.7x - 10.9$

68.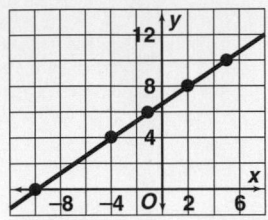

Answers may vary.
Sample: $y = \frac{2}{3}x + 6\frac{2}{3}$

69.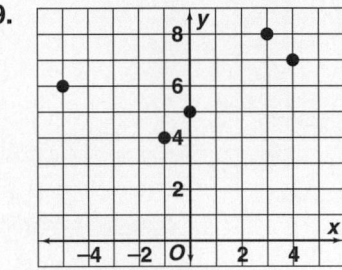

not reasonable

70.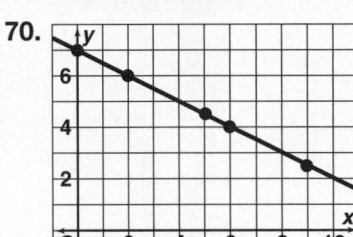

Answers may vary.
Sample: $y = -0.5x + 7$

LESSON 2-6

pages 95–98   Exercises

8. $y = -|x|$, $k = 6$

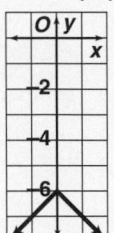

37. diagonal

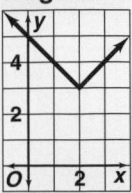

38. diagonal

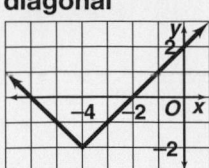

39. diagonal

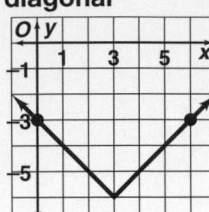

56.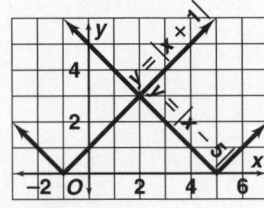

6 right

57.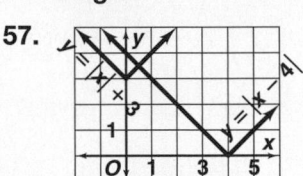

4 right, 3 down

58.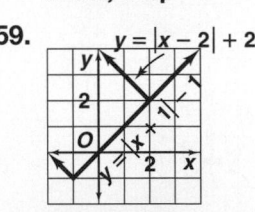

3 left, 1 up

59. $y = |x - 2| + 2$

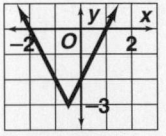

3 right, 3 up

67. Answers may vary.
Sample: $f(0) = -2$;
$f(1) = 0$; $f(2) = 2$;
$f(-2) = 0$; $f(-1) = -2$

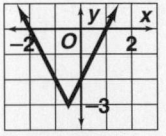

$y = |2x + 1| - 3$

68. Answers may vary.
Samples: $f(0) = 1$;
$f(1) = \frac{8}{9}$; $f(3) = \frac{2}{3}$;
$f(-1) = \frac{10}{9}$; $f(-3) = \frac{4}{3}$

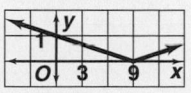

69. $x \leq -10$

70. $a > 4.5$

71. $b > -1.5$

page 98   Checkpoint Quiz 2

1.

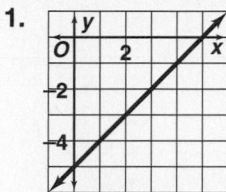

2.

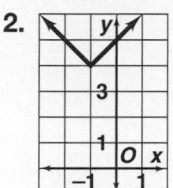

3.

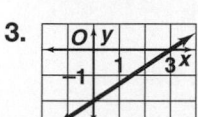

4.

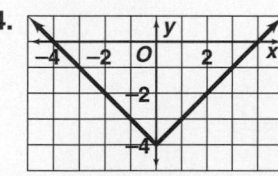

5.

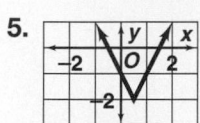

6.

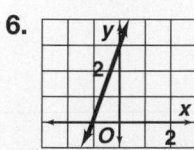

LESSON 2-7

page 99   Check Skills You'll Need

1. $p \leq 1.25$

2. $t > 13$

3. $t \leq -3$

4. $c = \pm 4.5$

5. $b = 2, 8$

6. $h \leq -3.5$ or $h \geq 3.5$

page 99   Investigation

1. and 2a.

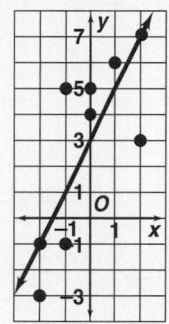

2b. on the line: $(-2, -1)$, $(2, 7)$
above the line: $(-1, 5)$, $(0, 4)$, $(0, 5)$,
$(1, 6)$
below the line: $(-2, -3)$,
$(-1, -1)$, $(2, 3)$

pages 102–104   Exercises

10a. $y \geq 20x$ if $x \leq 6$
$y \geq 15x$ if $x > 6$

b. Answers may vary. Sample:

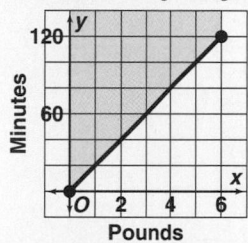

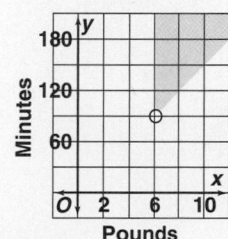

11.

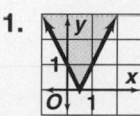

12.

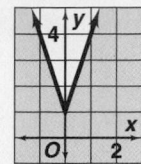

13.

14.

15.

16.

17.

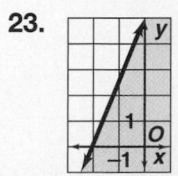

18.

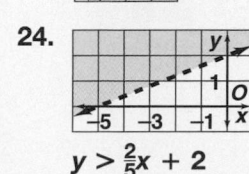

19.

23.

24.

$y > \frac{2}{5}x + 2$

25.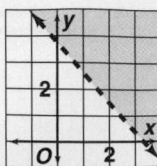

26.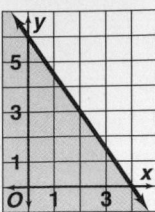

27.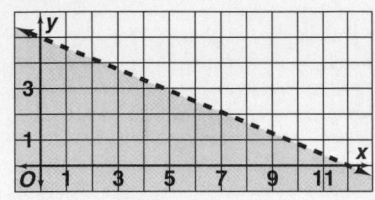

28.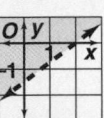

29.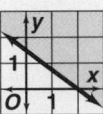

30.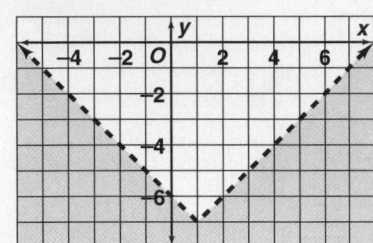

31.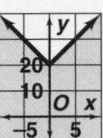

32.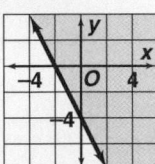

33.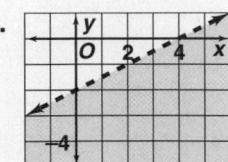

34.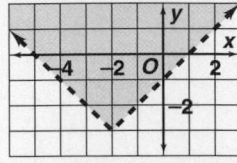

35.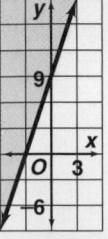

36.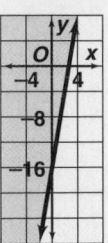

37.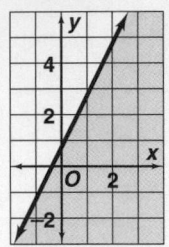

45c.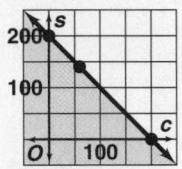

Yes, (20, 50) is a solution.

47.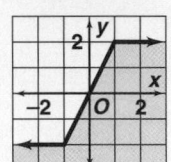

48.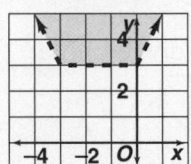

49.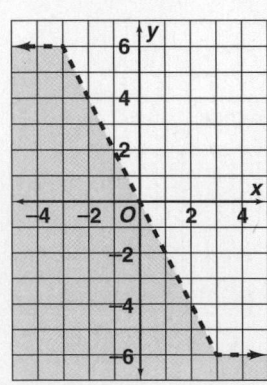

50.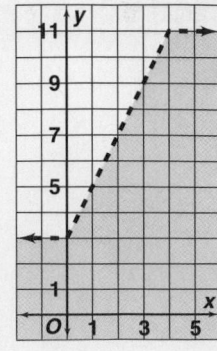

page 110   Chapter Test

1. domain {0, 1, 2, 3, 4},
   range {−16, −9, −4, −1, 0}

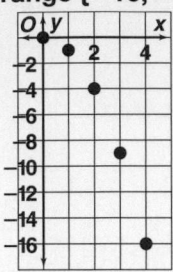

2. domain {3, 4, 5, 6, 7},
   range {2, 3, 4, 5, 6}

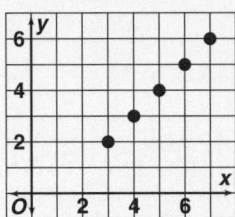

23. Answers may vary. Sample:
   a. $y = -x$
   b. $y = x + 15$
   c. $y = x$
   d. $y = -x - 5$
   e. rectangle

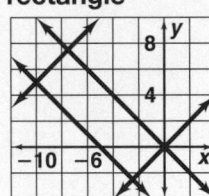

27.

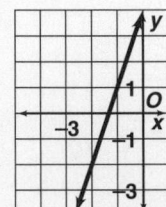

T900

28.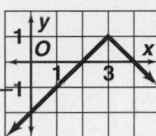

29.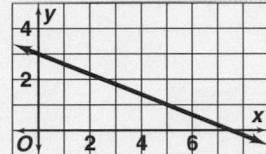

30.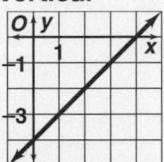

31a–b.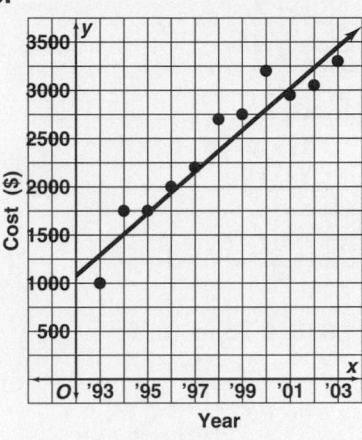

Answers may vary. Sample:
$y = 225x + 625$, where 1990 corr.
to $x = 0$.

c. Answers may vary. Sample: $4000

32. vertical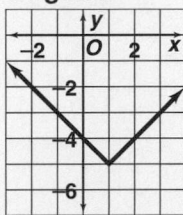

33. diagonal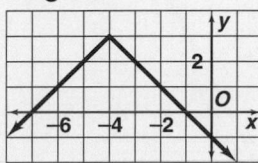

34. diagonal

35. vertical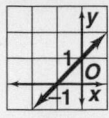

36. vertical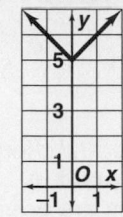

37. diagonal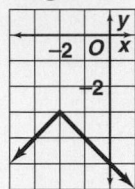

38.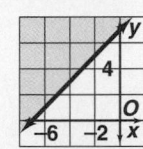

39.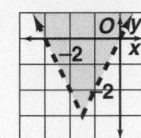

40.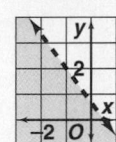

41.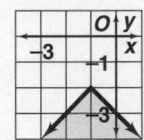

page 111 Standardized Test Prep

15. [2]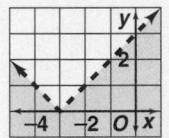

The parent function is $y = |x|$,
and $y = |x + 3|$ is $y = |x|$
shifted 3 units to the left.

[1] includes only graph

16. [2] The constant of variation is -1
and when $y = 3$, $x = -3$.

[1] only includes either -1 OR -3

17. [4] a. $y = 2x + 10$

b. $y = -\frac{1}{2}x + \frac{3}{2}$

c.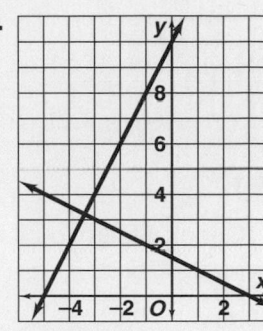

[3] does 2 parts

[2] does only one part

[1] has computational errors in all
parts

CHAPTER 3

page 114 Diagnosing Readiness

13.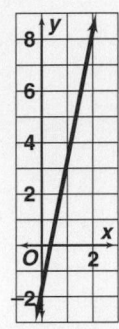

15. $y = 6x$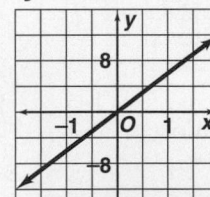

16.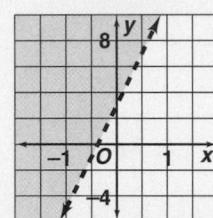

17.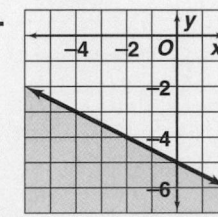

18.

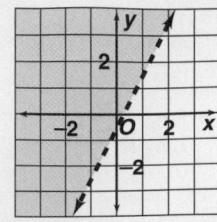

LESSON 3-1

page 116   Check Skills You'll Need

1.

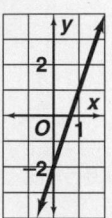

2.

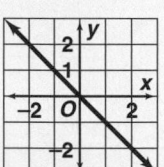

3.

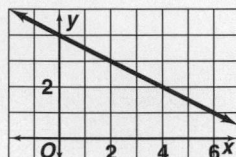

4, 5, 6.

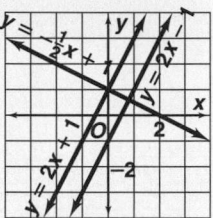

page 116   Investigation

1a.

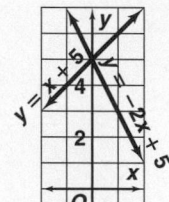

b.

---

c.

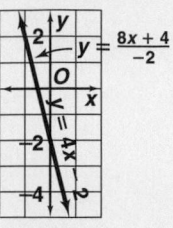

2a. (a): one; (b): none;
(c): all

b. If the slopes are not equal then
the graphs have one point in
common. If the slopes are equal,
they either have no points or all
points in common.

pages 118–121   Exercises

6. (3, −4)

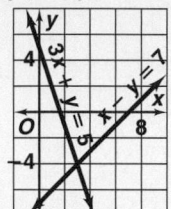

7. (3, 6)

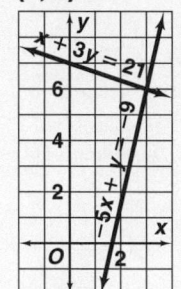

8. (0, 0)

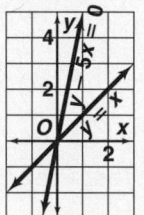

9.

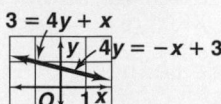

25. infinite solution

---

26. $\left(\frac{4}{3}, \frac{7}{6}\right) \approx (1.5, 1)$

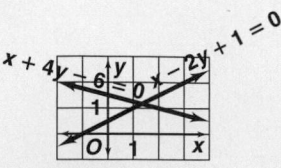

27. no solution

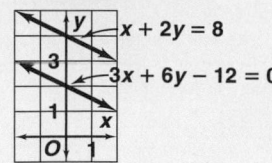

28. (6, 4)

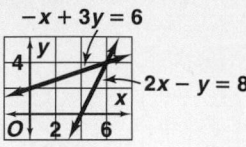

29. (2, −3)

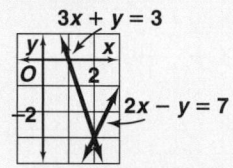

30. (1.875, 0.75) $\approx$ (2, 1)

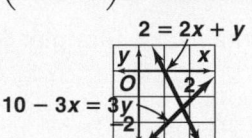

31. $\left(\frac{16}{9}, -\frac{14}{9}\right) \approx (1.5, -1.5)$

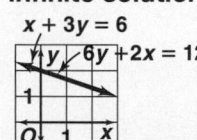

32. $\left(\frac{1}{3}, \frac{3}{5}\right)$

33. infinite solutions

34. (4, 2)

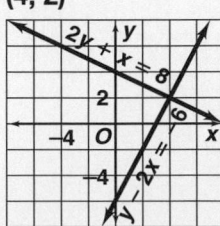

---

35. (1.7, 2.6)

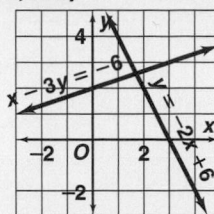

36. no solution

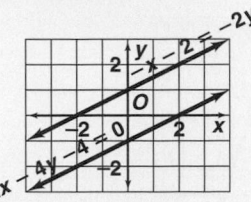

37a. $\begin{cases} c = 3 + 0.40b \\ c = 9.00 \end{cases}$

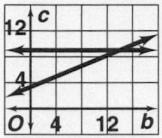

44b. The cost would be the same for a 6-day stay.

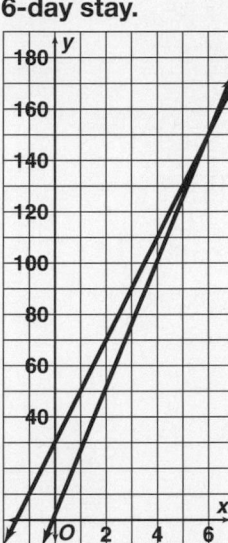

45. $\begin{cases} y = 6x + 80 \\ y = 4x + 100 \end{cases}$

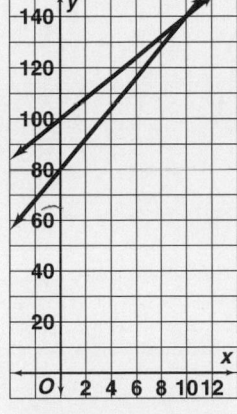

After 10 minutes the numbers of flyers will be equal.

62.

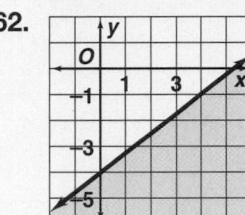

63.

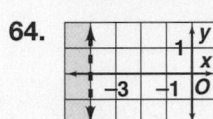

64.

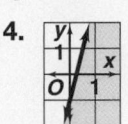

LESSON 3-3

page 130 Check Skills You'll Need

4.

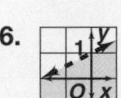

5.

6.

7.

8.

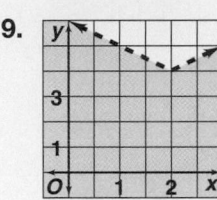

9.

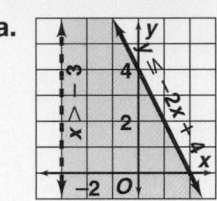

page 131 Check Understanding

1a.

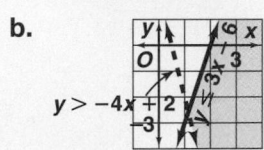

b. $y > -4x + 2$

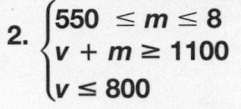

2. $\begin{cases} 550 \le m \le 8 \\ v + m \ge 1100 \\ v \le 800 \end{cases}$

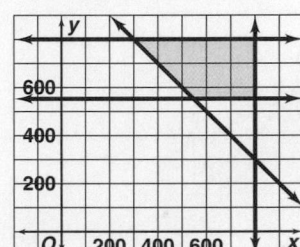

3a. $y \le |x + 5|$

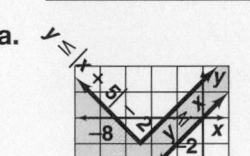

b. $y \le |x - 4|$
$y \ge -2x + 4$

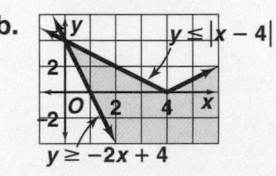

T903

2. $\begin{cases} m + 5 \le 150 \\ m \ge 60 \end{cases}$

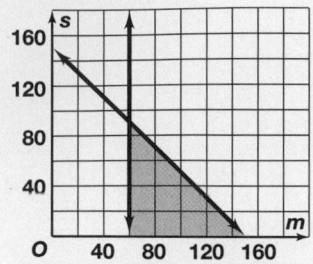

3.

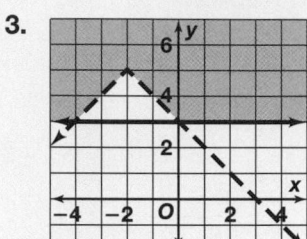

pages 132–134 Exercises

10. no solution

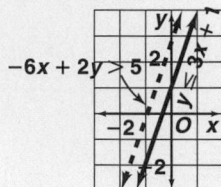

$-6x + 2y > 5$

11.

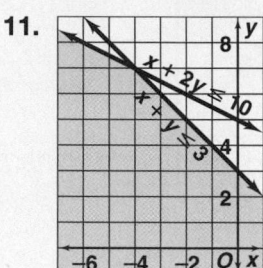

$x + 2y \le 10$

$x + y \ge 3$

12. $-x - y \le 2$ $y - 2x > 1$

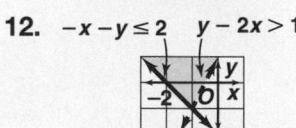

13. $y > -2x$ $-2x + y \le -2$

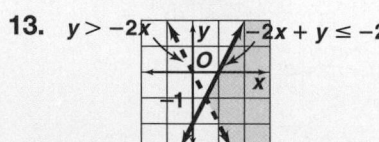

14.

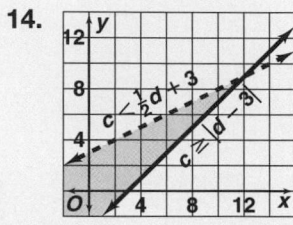

$c < \frac{1}{2}d + 3$

$c \ge |d - 3|$

---

15. $2x + y > 1$ $y + 3x < 1$

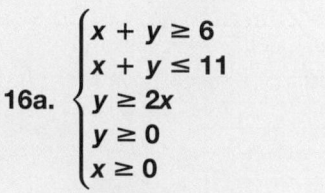

16a. $\begin{cases} x + y \ge 6 \\ x + y \le 11 \\ y \ge 2x \\ y \ge 0 \\ x \ge 0 \end{cases}$

b.

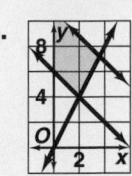

17. $\begin{cases} a + c \ge 40 \\ c \le 30 \end{cases}$

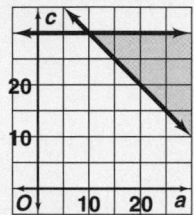

18.

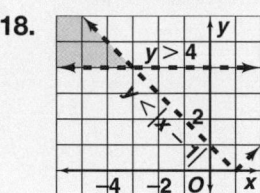

$y > 4$

19.

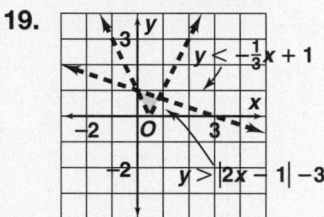

$y < -\frac{1}{3}x + 1$

$y > |2x - 1| - 3$

20.

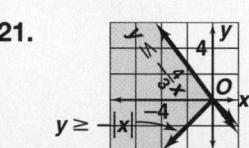

$y \ge |x + 2|$

$y > x - 2$

21.

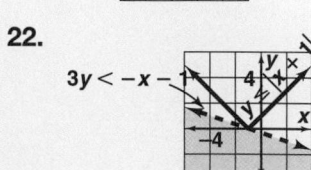

$y \ge -|x|$

22.

$3y < -x - 1$

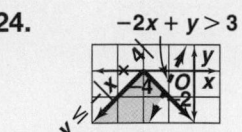

$y \le |x + 1|$

23.

$y \le -|x - 3|$

$y > -2$

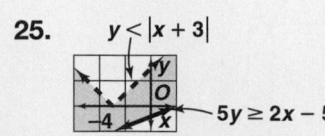

---

24. $-2x + y > 3$

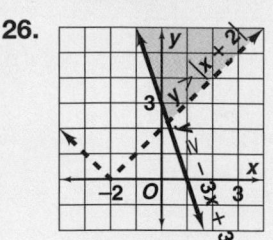

25. $y < |x + 3|$

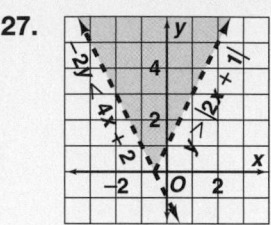

$5y \ge 2x - 5$

26.

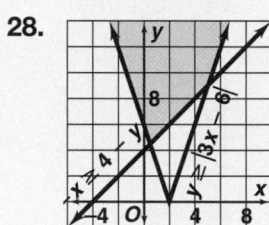

27.

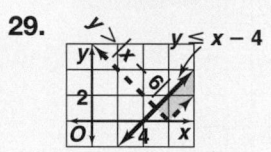

28.

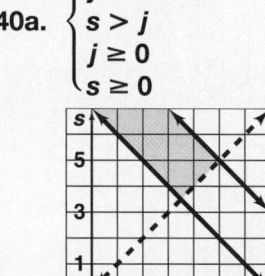

29. $y \le x - 4$

40a. $\begin{cases} j + s \ge 7 \\ j + s \le 10 \\ s > j \\ j \ge 0 \\ s \ge 0 \end{cases}$

b. (0, 7) (0, 8) (0, 9) (0, 10) (1, 6) (1, 7) (1, 8) (1, 9) (2, 5) (2, 6) (2, 7) (2, 8) (3, 4) (3, 5) (3, 6) (3, 7) (4, 5) (4, 6)

c. **Only whole numbers of juniors and seniors make sense.**

41. Answers will vary. Possible solution:
$$\begin{cases} x < 5 \\ y \geq 1 \end{cases}$$

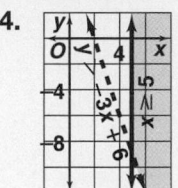

42. Answers may vary. Sample: If the isolated variable is greater than the remaining expression, the half-plane above the boundary line is shaded. If the variable is less than the remaining expression, then the half-plane below the line is shaded.

43.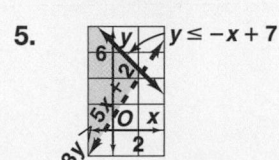

44.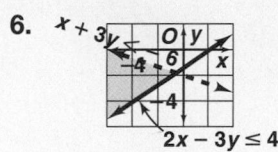

45.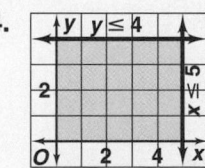

46.

47.

48.

49. $$\begin{cases} y \geq |x| - 2 \\ y \leq -|x| + 2 \end{cases}$$

50. $$\begin{cases} y \leq 3 \\ y \geq 0 \\ y \leq 3x + 9 \\ y \leq -3x + 9 \end{cases}$$

51. $$\begin{cases} y \leq 4 \\ y \geq 0 \\ y \leq 2x \\ y \geq 2x - 8 \end{cases}$$

56. **[2]** For the first inequality, $-2(2) + 3 = -1$ and $-2 < -1$, so $(2, -2)$ satisfies the inequality. For the second inequality, $2 - 4 = -2$ and $-2 \geq -2$, so $(2, -2)$ satisfies the inequality. Since $(2, -2)$ satisfies both inequalities, it is a solution to the system.

[1] omits one or two of the three explanations above

LESSON 3-4

page 135   Check Skills You'll Need

4.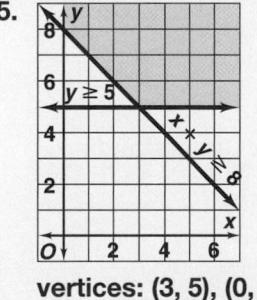

5.

$y \leq -x + 7$

6.

$2x - 3y \leq 4$

pages 138–140   Exercises

4.

vertices: (0, 0), (5, 0), (5, 4), (0, 4)
maximized at (5, 4)

5.

vertices: (3, 5), (0, 8)
minimized at (0, 8)

6.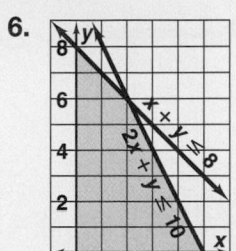

vertices: (0, 0), (5, 0), (2, 6), (0, 8)
maximized at (5, 0)

7.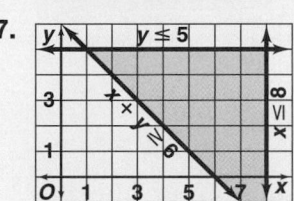

vertices: (1, 5), (8, 5), (8, −2), (1, 5)
minimized at (8, −2)

8.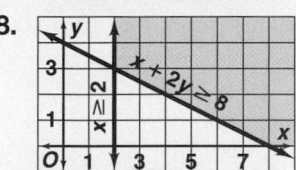

vertices: (8, 0), (2, 3)
minimized at (8, 0)

9.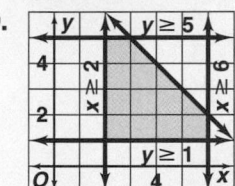

vertices: (2, 1), (6, 1), (6, 2), (2, 5), (3, 5)
maximized at (6, 2)

14.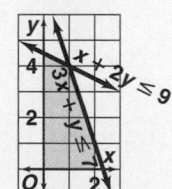

vertices: (0, 0), (1, 4), (0, 4.5), $\left(\frac{7}{3}, 0\right)$; maximized when $P = 6$ at (1, 4)

15.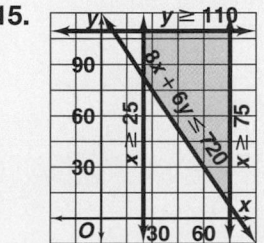

vertices: (75, 20), (75, 110), $\left(25, 86\frac{2}{3}\right)$, (25, 110); minimized when $C = 633\frac{1}{3}$ at $\left(25, 86\frac{2}{3}\right)$

16.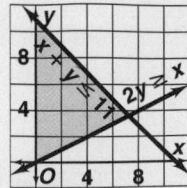

vertices: $(0, 0)$, $\left(7\frac{1}{3}, 3\frac{2}{3}\right)$, $(0, 11)$; maximized when $P = 29\frac{1}{3}$ at $\left(7\frac{1}{3}, 3\frac{2}{3}\right)$

17.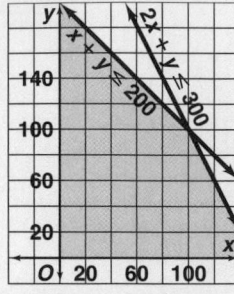

vertices: $(0, 0)$, $(150, 0)$, $(100, 100)$, $(0, 200)$; maximized when $P = 400$ at $(0, 200)$

18.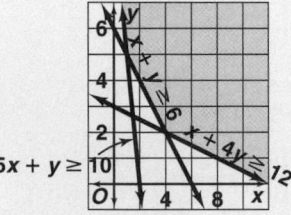

vertices: $(12, 0)$, $(0, 10)$, $(4, 2)$, $(1, 5)$; minimized when $C = 80,000$ at $(4, 2)$

19.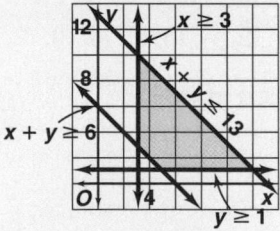

vertices: $(3, 3)$, $(3, 10)$, $(5, 1)$, $(12, 1)$; maximized when $C = 80,000$ at $(4, 2)$

21.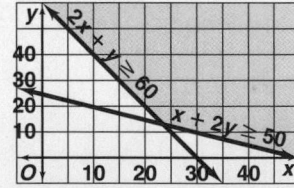

vertices: $(0, 60)$, $\left(23\frac{1}{3}, 13\frac{1}{3}\right)$, $(50, 0)$; minimized when $x = 23\frac{1}{3}$ and $y = 13\frac{1}{3}$
Round to $(23, 14)$ and $(24, 13)$; $(24, 13)$ gives you a minimum cost of $261.00.

34a.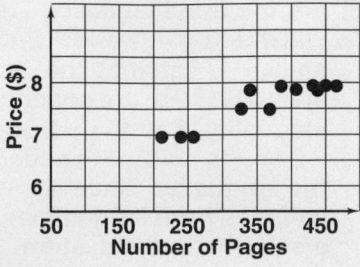

LESSON 3-5

page 142 Check Skills You'll Need

5.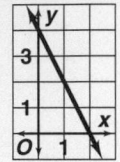

6.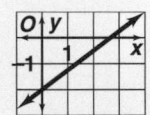

7.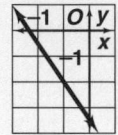

8.

page 143 Additional Examples

1.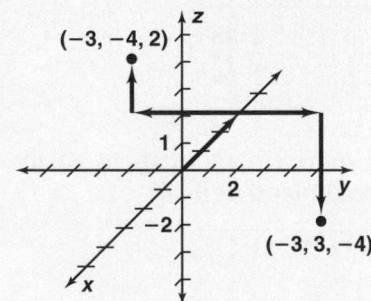

page 144 Check Understanding

1a. $(0, -4, -2)$

b.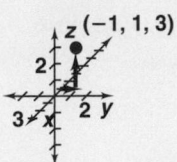

c.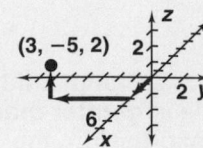

d.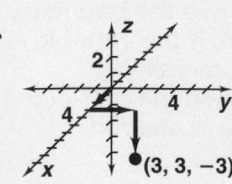

pages 145–147 Exercises

8.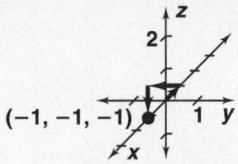

9.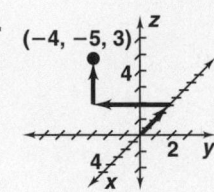

10.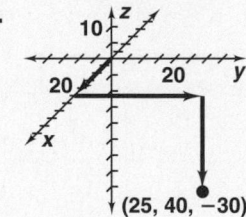

11.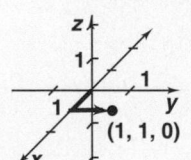

12.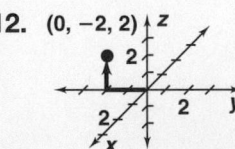

19.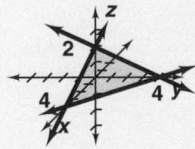

20.

21.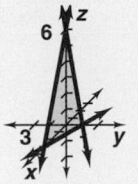

22.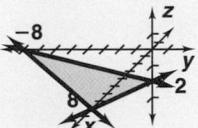

23.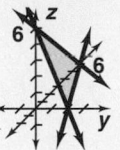

24.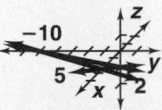

25. Sample: Balcony represents vertical direction, row is backward or forward, and seat is left or right.

26a. $0.05x + 0.25y + 0.40z \le 20$

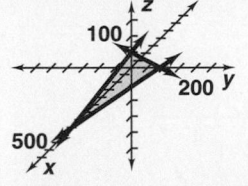

b. Answers may vary. Sample: 200 balloons, 40 streamers, 0 noisemakers

c. Finite; the equation can only have whole number solutions.

27.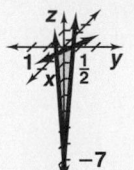

28.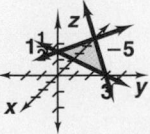

29.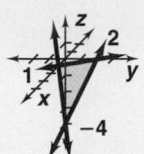

30.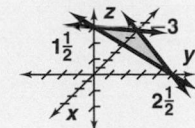

31.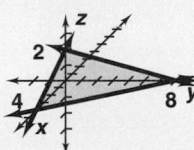

32.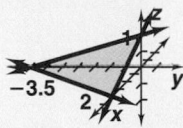

33. x–y: $x + y = 6$
x–z: $x - 2z = 6$
y–z: $y - 2z = 6$

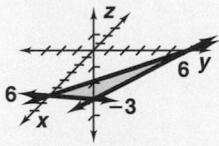

34. x–y: $-2x + y = 10$
x–z: $-2x + 5z = 10$
y–z: $y + 5z = 10$

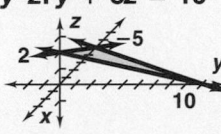

35. x–y: $-3x - 8y = 24$
x–z: $-x - 4z = 8$
y–z: $-2y - 3z = 6$

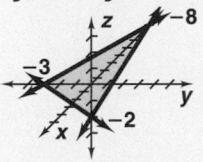

36. x–y: $x + 5y = 5$
x–z: $x - z = 5$
y–z: $5y - z = 5$

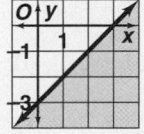

50.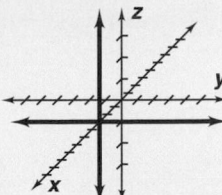

51.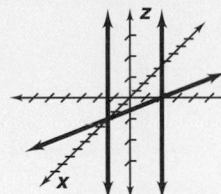

52.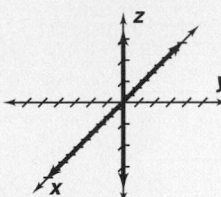

59.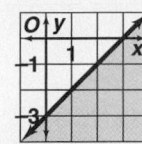

60.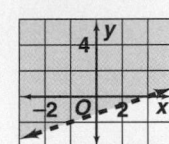

61.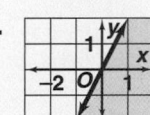

LESSON 3-6

pages 153–155   Exercises

49. **[2]** The three equations include parallel planes, so there is no point common to all three planes.

[1] not explained in terms of intersecting planes

53.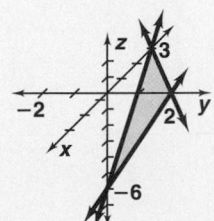

54.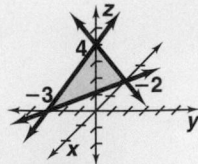

55.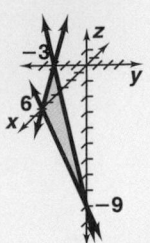

62.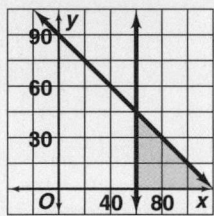

63.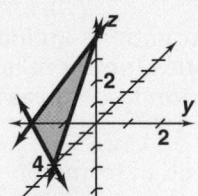

64.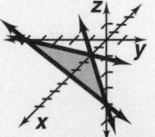

65.

66.

67.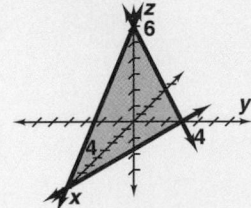

page 156   Test-Taking Strategies

3b.

pages 157–159   Chapter Review

40.

41.

42.

---

page 160   Chapter Test

1. independent

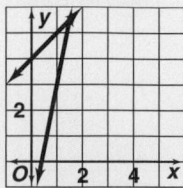

2. inconsistent

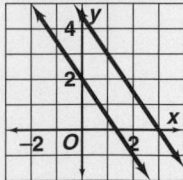

8.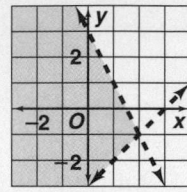

9.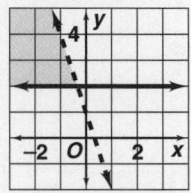

10.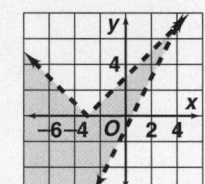

11.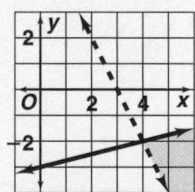

12.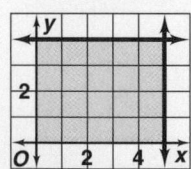

vertices: (0, 0), (6, 0), (6, 5), (0, 5)
$P = 17$ at (6, 5)

13.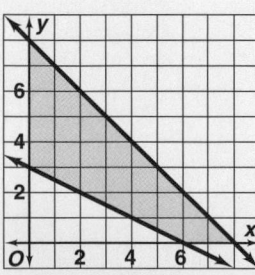

vertices: (0, 3), (6, 0), (8, 0), (0, 8)
$C = 6$ at (6, 0)

22.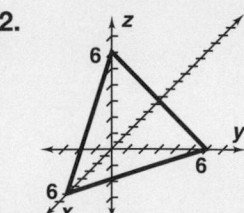

23.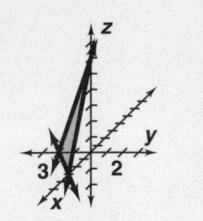

24.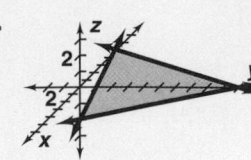

25.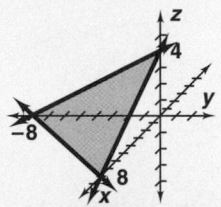

26. x = number of balloons
y = number of party favors
z = number of streamers
$0.06x + 0.48y + 0.08z = 24$

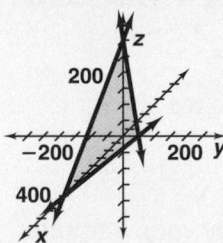

29. x = amount in growth fund,
y = amount in income fund,
z = amount in money market fund,
$x + y + z = 50{,}000$
$1.12x + 1.08y + 1.05z = 54{,}500$
$y = 2z$, $x = \$20{,}000$, $y = \$20{,}000$;
$z = \$10{,}000$

30. x = amount of sales,
y = pay,
$y = 0.15x + 200$
$y = 0.10x + 300$,
$x = \$2000$

31. c = number of cots
t = number of tables
h = number of chairs
$10c + 10t + 40h = 1950$
$20c + 20h = 1800$
$10c + 5t + 20h = 1350$
A cot cost \$75, a table cost \$60,
and a chair cost \$15.

CHAPTER 4

page 162 Diagnosing Readiness

11.

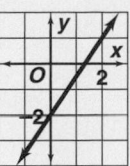

12.

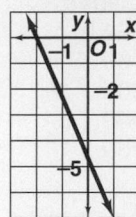

13.

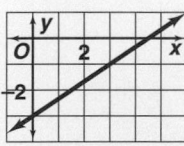

14.

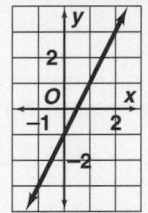

15.

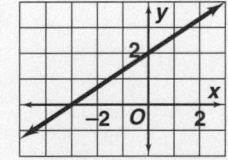

16.

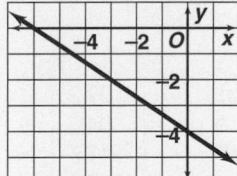

17.

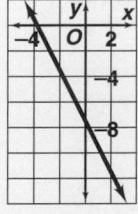

18.

LESSON 4-1

page 165 Check Understanding

3a.

	China	Russia	United States
Production	33	41	73
Consumption	34	26	95

b. Add a new column for each additional country.

c. A $c \times d$ matrix has c rows and d columns, while a $d \times c$ matrix has d rows and c columns.

pages 166–169 Exercises

12.

	Novels	Biogr.	Sci-Fi	Nonfiction
Week 1	175	100	93	100
Week 2	154	93	81	104
Week 3	201	110	114	103
Week 4	180	92	100	110

13.

	Week 1	Week 2	Week 3	Week 4
Novels	175	154	201	180
Biogr.	100	93	110	92
Sci-Fi	93	81	114	100
Nonfiction	100	104	103	110

14a.

$H =$

	Videodisc Players	Modems	Networks	CD-ROMs
Elementary	25.9	35.1	26.4	37.9
Junior High	9.2	11.0	9.0	11.0
Senior High	10.7	14.5	12.9	14.0

b. 9.0; millions of networks in the junior high schools

15.

	1980	1985	1990	1992	1995	1997
Color TVs	63	78	90	91	94	97
VCRs	1	18	63	69	77	82

63, which represents 63 million U.S. households that had VCRs in 1990

16.

	Color TVs	VCRs
1980	63	1
1985	78	18
1990	90	63
1992	91	69
1995	94	77
1997	97	82

91, which represents 91 million U.S. households that had color TVs in 1992

29a. Answers may vary. Sample:

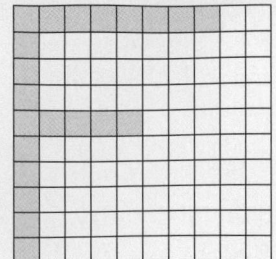

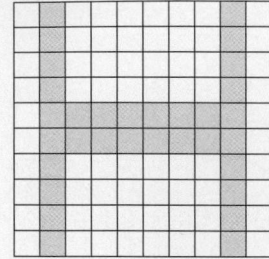

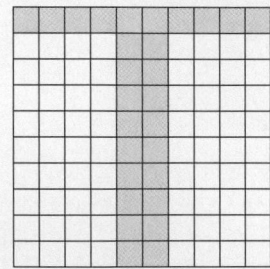

b. Answers may vary. Sample:

$$F = \begin{bmatrix} 1 & 1 & 1 & 1 & 1 & 1 & 1 & 1 & 0 & 0 \\ 1 & 0 & 0 & 0 & 0 & 0 & 0 & 0 & 0 & 0 \\ 1 & 0 & 0 & 0 & 0 & 0 & 0 & 0 & 0 & 0 \\ 1 & 0 & 0 & 0 & 0 & 0 & 0 & 0 & 0 & 0 \\ 1 & 1 & 1 & 1 & 1 & 0 & 0 & 0 & 0 & 0 \\ 1 & 0 & 0 & 0 & 0 & 0 & 0 & 0 & 0 & 0 \\ 1 & 0 & 0 & 0 & 0 & 0 & 0 & 0 & 0 & 0 \\ 1 & 0 & 0 & 0 & 0 & 0 & 0 & 0 & 0 & 0 \\ 1 & 0 & 0 & 0 & 0 & 0 & 0 & 0 & 0 & 0 \\ 1 & 0 & 0 & 0 & 0 & 0 & 0 & 0 & 0 & 0 \end{bmatrix}$$

$$H = \begin{bmatrix} 0 & 1 & 0 & 0 & 0 & 0 & 0 & 0 & 1 & 0 \\ 0 & 1 & 0 & 0 & 0 & 0 & 0 & 0 & 1 & 0 \\ 0 & 1 & 0 & 0 & 0 & 0 & 0 & 0 & 1 & 0 \\ 0 & 1 & 0 & 0 & 0 & 0 & 0 & 0 & 1 & 0 \\ 0 & 1 & 1 & 1 & 1 & 1 & 1 & 1 & 1 & 0 \\ 0 & 1 & 1 & 1 & 1 & 1 & 1 & 1 & 1 & 0 \\ 0 & 1 & 0 & 0 & 0 & 0 & 0 & 0 & 1 & 0 \\ 0 & 1 & 0 & 0 & 0 & 0 & 0 & 0 & 1 & 0 \\ 0 & 1 & 0 & 0 & 0 & 0 & 0 & 0 & 1 & 0 \\ 0 & 1 & 0 & 0 & 0 & 0 & 0 & 0 & 1 & 0 \end{bmatrix}$$

$$T = \begin{bmatrix} 1 & 1 & 1 & 1 & 1 & 1 & 1 & 1 & 1 & 1 \\ 0 & 0 & 0 & 0 & 1 & 1 & 0 & 0 & 0 & 0 \\ 0 & 0 & 0 & 0 & 1 & 1 & 0 & 0 & 0 & 0 \\ 0 & 0 & 0 & 0 & 1 & 1 & 0 & 0 & 0 & 0 \\ 0 & 0 & 0 & 0 & 1 & 1 & 0 & 0 & 0 & 0 \\ 0 & 0 & 0 & 0 & 1 & 1 & 0 & 0 & 0 & 0 \\ 0 & 0 & 0 & 0 & 1 & 1 & 0 & 0 & 0 & 0 \\ 0 & 0 & 0 & 0 & 1 & 1 & 0 & 0 & 0 & 0 \\ 0 & 0 & 0 & 0 & 1 & 1 & 0 & 0 & 0 & 0 \\ 0 & 0 & 0 & 0 & 1 & 1 & 0 & 0 & 0 & 0 \end{bmatrix}$$

LESSON 4-2

pages 174–176 Exercises

1a.

	Emily deRiel		Mary Beth Iagorashvil
Shoot	1156		964
Fence	800		960
Swim	1182		1205
Ride	1070		1040
Run	1102		960

b.

	Total Score
Shoot	2120
Fence	1760
Swim	2387
Ride	2110
Run	2062

18. $\begin{bmatrix} 0 & 5 \\ 8 & -6 \\ 0 & 5 \end{bmatrix}$

19. *B* and *D* cannot be added because they do not have the same dimensions.

20. $\begin{bmatrix} 6 & 3 \\ -3 & 3 \end{bmatrix}$

21. $\begin{bmatrix} -6 & -3 \\ -4 & -2 \\ -2 & 5 \end{bmatrix}$

22. $\begin{bmatrix} -4 & 1 \\ -3 & -1 \end{bmatrix}$

23a.

	James Gregory		Velizar Iliev
Shoot	1132		1072
Fence	760		910
Swim	1173		1177
Ride	1100		1100
Run	1114		1118

	Chad Senior
Shoot	1072
Fence	610
Swim	1285
Ride	1070
Run	1174

b.

	Total Score
Shoot	3276
Fence	2280
Swim	3635
Ride	3270
Run	3406

c. Answers may vary. Sample:

	Iliev minus Senior
Shoot	0
Fence	300
Swim	-108
Ride	30
Run	-56

Fencing; 300

27a.

	Plant 1	
	Plastic	Rubber
1-color	1000	1400
3-color	2600	3800

	Plant 2	
	Plastic	Rubber
1-color	1200	3600
3-color	1800	4800

b.

	Plant 1 − Plant 2	
	Plastic	Rubber
1-color	-200	-2200
3-color	800	-1000

Plant 1; Plant 2

LESSON 4-3

pages 182–185   Exercises

19a.

	Lilies	Carnations	Daisies
Arrangement 1	3	0	0
Arrangement 2	3	4	0
Arrangement 3	0	3	4

b. Cost

Lilies	2.15
Carnations	0.90
Daisies	1.30

c.

	Cost
Arrangement 1	6.45
Arrangement 2	10.05
Arrangement 3	7.90

53. No; AB will be a 2×2 matrix and BA will be a 3×3 matrix, and equal matrices must have the same dimensions. Answers may vary. Sample: Let A be the

matrix $\begin{bmatrix} 0 & 1 & 2 \\ 3 & 0 & 0 \end{bmatrix}$, and let B be the matrix $\begin{bmatrix} 1 & 0 \\ 2 & 4 \\ 3 & 1 \end{bmatrix}$. Then

$AB = \begin{bmatrix} 8 & 6 \\ 3 & 0 \end{bmatrix}$ and $BA = \begin{bmatrix} 0 & 1 & 2 \\ 12 & 2 & 4 \\ 3 & 3 & 6 \end{bmatrix}$.

54.

	Thursday	Friday	Saturday
Revenue	[2100	1950	2570]

63. **[2]** $3Y + 2\begin{bmatrix} -1 & -3 \\ 2 & 5 \end{bmatrix} = \begin{bmatrix} 13 & -9 \\ 4 & 16 \end{bmatrix}$

$3Y + \begin{bmatrix} -2 & -6 \\ 4 & 10 \end{bmatrix} = \begin{bmatrix} 13 & -9 \\ 4 & 16 \end{bmatrix}$

$3Y = \begin{bmatrix} 13 & -9 \\ 4 & 16 \end{bmatrix} - \begin{bmatrix} -2 & -6 \\ 4 & 10 \end{bmatrix}$

$\frac{1}{3} \cdot 3Y = \begin{bmatrix} 15 & -3 \\ 0 & 6 \end{bmatrix} \cdot \frac{1}{3}$

$Y = \begin{bmatrix} 5 & -1 \\ 0 & 2 \end{bmatrix}$

[1] fails to show work OR makes a computational error

64. **[4]** No; in the case of $M \times N$, $-3 \times 0 + 4 \times -2 = -8$ for element MN_{11}. In $N \times M$, $0 \times -3 + 1 \times 1 = 1$ for element NM_{11}. Therefore, since the first elements of MN and NM are not equal, $M \times N \neq N \times M$.

[3] recognizes the results are not the same and attempts to explain why

[2] recognizes that $M \times N \neq N \times M$ but does not explain

[1] understands what $M \times N$ and $N \times M$ mean but cannot properly relate it to problem

67.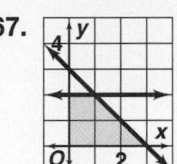

(0, 2), (0, 0), (1, 2), (3, 0); (1, 2)

68.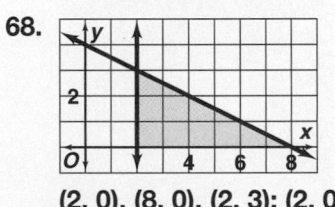

(2, 0), (8, 0), (2, 3); (2, 0)

69.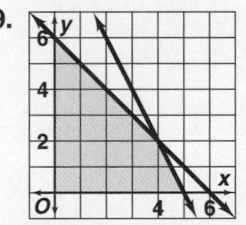

(0, 0), (5, 0), (4, 2), (0, 6); (5, 0)

70.

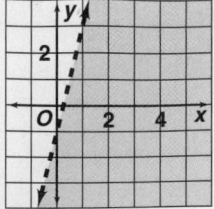

71.

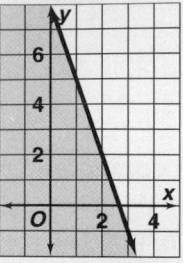

72.

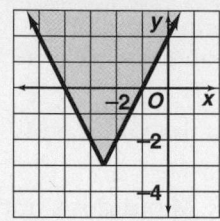

LESSON 4-4

page 187   Check Skills You'll Need

1.

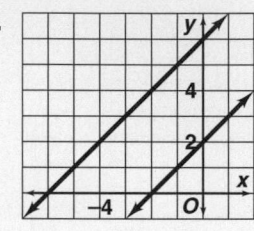

$y = x + 6$

2.

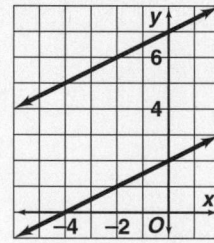

$f(x) = \frac{1}{2}x + 7$

3.

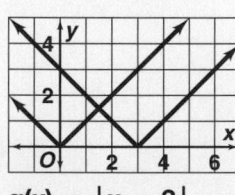

$g(x) = |x - 3|$

4.

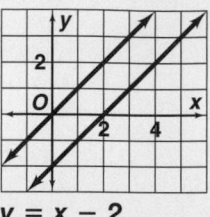

$y = x - 2$

5.

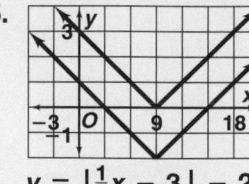

$y = \left|\frac{1}{3}x - 3\right| - 2$

6.

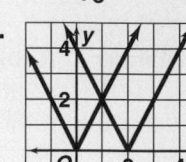

$f(x) = |-2x + 4|$

page 187   Investigation

2.

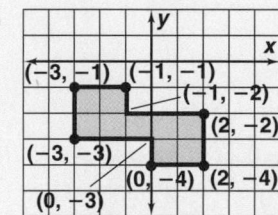

3. Original figure: $(-7, 5)$, $(-5, 5)$, $(-5, 4)$, $(-2, 4)$, $(-2, 2)$, $(-4, 2)$, $(-4, 3)$, $(-7, 3)$. Image: $(-3, -1)$, $(-1, -1)$, $(-1, -2)$, $(2, -2)$, $(2, -4)$, $(0, -4)$, $(0, -3)$, $(-3, -3)$

4. Going from the original figure to the new figure, the *x*-coordinate of a point on the original increases by 4, and the *y*-coordinate of the point decreases by 6.

5. $(3, 8)$, $(5, 8)$, $(5, 7)$, $(8, 7)$, $(8, 5)$, $(6, 5)$, $(6, 6)$, $(3, 6)$

6. 2 units down and 4 units right:
$(0, 0)$, $(2, 0)$, $(2, 2)$, $(-1, 2)$, $(-1, 3)$, $(-3, 3)$, $(-3, 1)$, $(0, 1)$;
5 units down and 7 units right: $(0, 0)$, $(2, 0)$, $(2, -1)$, $(5, -1)$, $(5, -3)$, $(3, -3)$, $(3, -2)$, $(0, -2)$

7. Sample: repetition of 2 right and 1 up, 2 left and 1 down, 3 left and 3 up, and 3 right and 3 down

1c.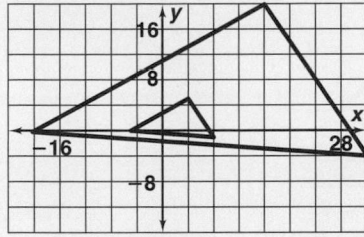

2a.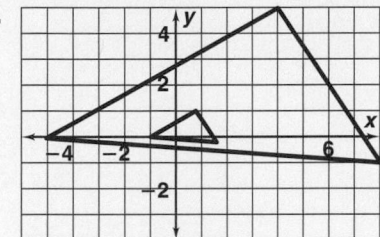

b.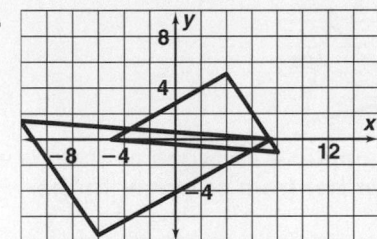

c.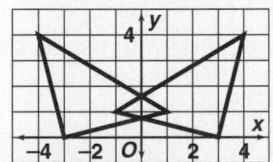

3a.

b.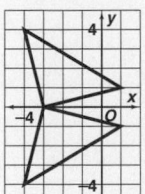

c.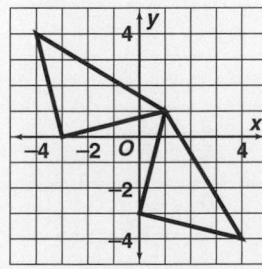

d.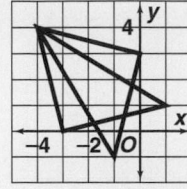

4a.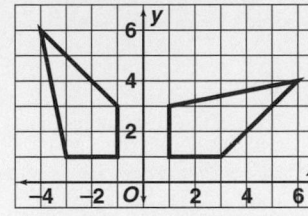

b.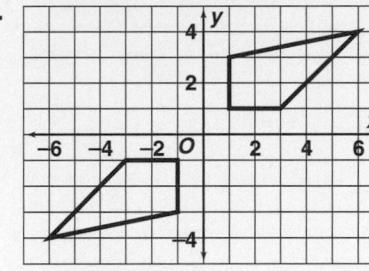

c.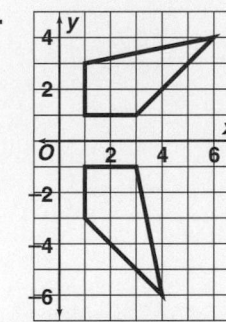

d.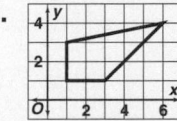

pages 191–194   Exercises

1.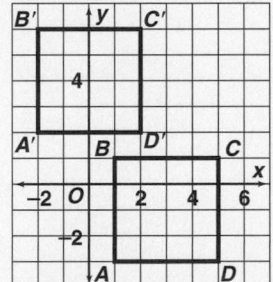

2.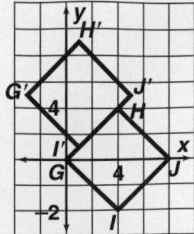

4.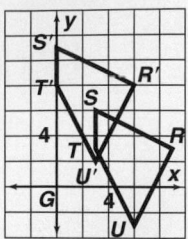

5.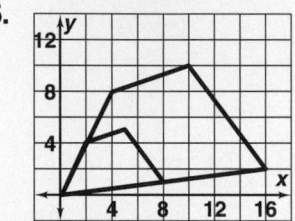

6.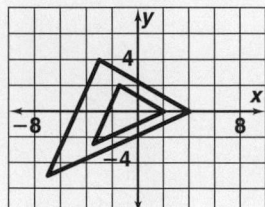

7.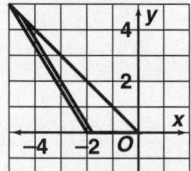

8.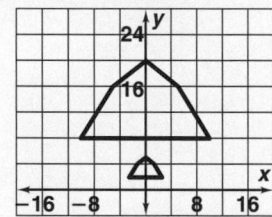

9.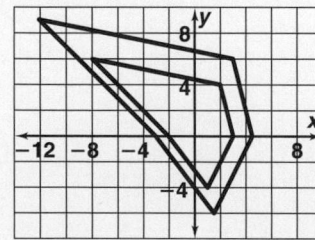

17.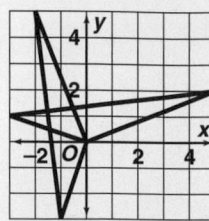

18.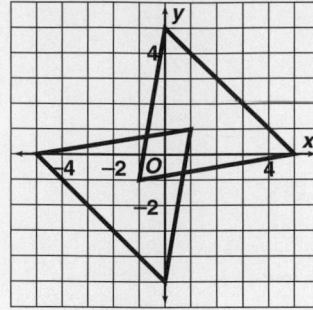

19.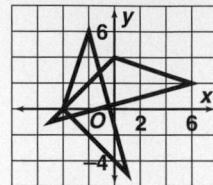

35a.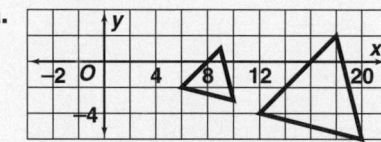

b. **Answers may vary. Sample: It enlarges or shrinks a figure and moves it farther from or closer to the origin.**

36.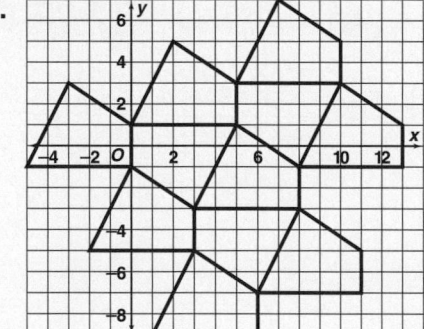

39. $f: \begin{bmatrix} 1 & 2 & 4 & 5 & 2 \\ 2 & 1 & 2 & 5 & 4 \end{bmatrix}$, $g: \begin{bmatrix} 2 & 4 & 8 & 10 & 4 \\ 4 & 2 & 4 & 10 & 8 \end{bmatrix}$;

dilation

40. $f: \begin{bmatrix} -5 & -3 & -2 & -1 & 1 & -1 & -2 & -3 \\ 2 & 1 & -1 & 1 & 2 & 3 & 5 & 3 \end{bmatrix}$,

$g: \begin{bmatrix} -3 & -1 & 0 & 1 & 3 & 1 & 0 & -1 \\ -2 & -3 & -5 & -3 & -2 & -1 & 1 & -1 \end{bmatrix}$;

translation

41. $f: \begin{bmatrix} -5 & -2 & 1 \\ 3 & 0 & 3 \end{bmatrix}$, $g: \begin{bmatrix} -1 & 2 & 5 \\ 1 & -2 & 1 \end{bmatrix}$;

translation

42. $f: \begin{bmatrix} 0 & 4 & 4 \\ 0 & 2 & 4 \end{bmatrix}$, $g: \begin{bmatrix} 0 & -4 & -4 \\ 0 & -2 & -4 \end{bmatrix}$;

rotation

43.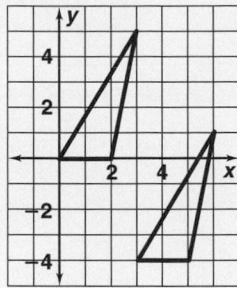

44.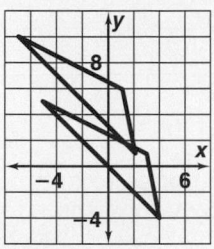

45a. **Check students' work.**

b. **Translate the vertices of *ABCD* down 12 units.**
$\begin{bmatrix} 0 & 0 & 0 & 0 \\ -12 & -12 & -12 & -12 \end{bmatrix}$;
coordinates of pre-image: (5, 8), (6, 8), (6, 9), (5, 9),
coordinates of image: (5, −4), (6, −4), (6, −3), (5, −3)

c. $\begin{bmatrix} 11 & 12 & 12 & 11 \\ 2 & 2 & 3 & 3 \end{bmatrix}$

46. $\begin{bmatrix} -6 & 1 & -10 \\ 0 & 6 & 6 \end{bmatrix}$

47. $\begin{bmatrix} 0 & 2 & 0 \\ -4 & -7 & -10 \end{bmatrix}$

48. $\begin{bmatrix} 5 & 10 & 2 & 6 \\ 17 & 6 & 6 & 2 \end{bmatrix}$

49. $\begin{bmatrix} -3 & -1.5 & -2 & -4 \\ 3 & 4.5 & 5 & 3.5 \end{bmatrix}$

55. 2×3; $\begin{bmatrix} 2 & -1 & 33 \\ 4 & 4 & -50 \end{bmatrix}$

56. undefined, because the number of columns in the first matrix is not equal to the number of rows in the second matrix

57.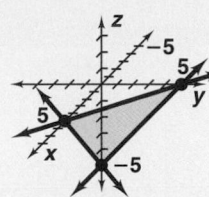

58.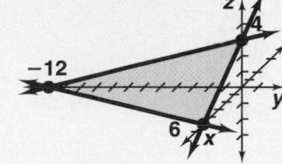

59.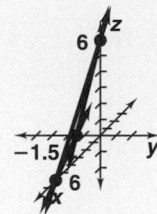

60. 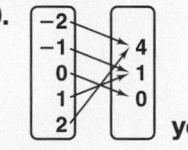 yes

61. 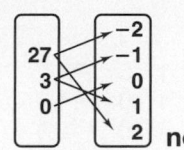 no

62. 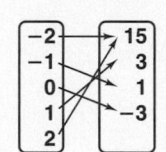 yes

63. 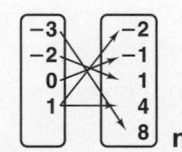 no

pages 199–201   Exercises

1. $\begin{bmatrix} 3 & 2 \\ 4 & 3 \end{bmatrix}\begin{bmatrix} 3 & -2 \\ -4 & 3 \end{bmatrix} =$

$\begin{bmatrix} 3(3) + 2(-4) & 3(-2) + 2(3) \\ 4(3) + 3(-4) & 4(-2) + 3(3) \end{bmatrix}$

$= \begin{bmatrix} 1 & 0 \\ 0 & 1 \end{bmatrix}$

2. $\begin{bmatrix} -3 & 7 \\ -2 & 5 \end{bmatrix}\begin{bmatrix} -5 & 7 \\ -2 & 3 \end{bmatrix} =$

$\begin{bmatrix} -3(-5) + 7(-2) & -3(7) + 7(3) \\ -2(-5) + 5(-2) & -2(7) + 5(3) \end{bmatrix} = \begin{bmatrix} 1 & 0 \\ 0 & 1 \end{bmatrix}$

3. $\begin{bmatrix} \frac{1}{5} & -\frac{1}{10} \\ 0 & \frac{1}{4} \end{bmatrix} \begin{bmatrix} 5 & 2 \\ 0 & 4 \end{bmatrix} =$

$\begin{bmatrix} \frac{1}{5}(5) + (-\frac{1}{10})(0) & \frac{1}{5}(2) + (-\frac{1}{10})(4) \\ 0(5) + \frac{1}{4}(0) & 0(2) + \frac{1}{4}(4) \end{bmatrix} = \begin{bmatrix} 1 & 0 \\ 0 & 1 \end{bmatrix}$

25a.

	From	
	No Cable	**Cable**

To $\begin{array}{l} \text{No Cable} \\ \text{Cable} \end{array}$ $\begin{bmatrix} 0.98 & 0.005 \\ 0.02 & 0.995 \end{bmatrix}$

b. about 20,100 people
c. about 19,897 people

50. det $M = ad - bc$ and det $N = eh - fg$. Next,

$MN = \begin{bmatrix} ae + bg & af + bh \\ ce + dg & cf + dh \end{bmatrix}$, and

det $MN = (ae + bg)(cf + dh) - (af + bh)(ce + dg)$
$= acef + adeh + bcfg + bdgh - acef$
$\quad - adfg - bceh - bdgh$
$= adeh - bceh + bcfg - adfg.$
But det $M \cdot$ det $N = (ad - bc)(eh - fg)$
$= adeh - bceh - adfg + bcfg.$
So det $M \cdot$ det $N =$ det $MN.$

LESSON 4-6

page 203   Check Understanding

3a. The matrices $\begin{bmatrix} 0 & 0 & 1 \\ 0.2 & -0.2 & 0 \\ 0 & -1 & 1 \end{bmatrix}$ and $\begin{bmatrix} 1 & 5 & -1 \\ 1 & 0 & -1 \\ 1 & 0 & 0 \end{bmatrix}$ have

a product of $\begin{bmatrix} 1 & 0 & 0 \\ 0 & 1 & 0 \\ 0 & 0 & 1 \end{bmatrix}$, so they are inverses.

b. The matrices $\begin{bmatrix} 0 & 1 & 0 \\ 1 & 0 & 1 \\ 0 & 1 & 0 \end{bmatrix}$ and $\begin{bmatrix} 3 & 4 & 1 \\ -2 & 0 & 2 \\ 1 & 5 & 3 \end{bmatrix}$ have a

product of $\begin{bmatrix} -2 & 0 & 2 \\ 4 & 9 & 4 \\ -2 & 0 & 2 \end{bmatrix}$, so they are not inverses.

pages 208–209   Extension

7.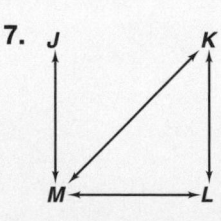

8.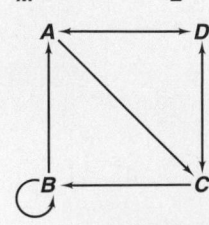

9.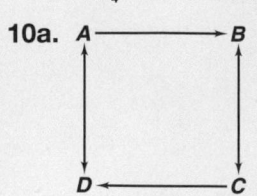

10a.

b.

$$T = \begin{array}{c} \\ A \\ B \\ C \\ D \end{array} \begin{array}{cccc} A & B & C & D \\ \begin{bmatrix} 0 & 1 & 0 & 1 \\ 0 & 0 & 1 & 0 \\ 0 & 1 & 0 & 1 \\ 1 & 0 & 0 & 0 \end{bmatrix} \end{array}$$

c. $\begin{bmatrix} 1 & 0 & 1 & 0 \\ 0 & 1 & 0 & 1 \\ 1 & 0 & 1 & 0 \\ 0 & 1 & 0 & 1 \end{bmatrix}$;

the matrix models trips from one house to another that can be travelled using exactly two paths.

LESSON 4-7

page 210   Check Understanding

1a. $\begin{bmatrix} 3 & 2 \\ 0 & 1 \end{bmatrix} \begin{bmatrix} x \\ y \end{bmatrix} = \begin{bmatrix} 16 \\ 5 \end{bmatrix}$; coefficient matrix is $\begin{bmatrix} 3 & 2 \\ 0 & 1 \end{bmatrix}$,

variable matrix is $\begin{bmatrix} x \\ y \end{bmatrix}$, constant matrix is $\begin{bmatrix} 16 \\ 5 \end{bmatrix}$.

b. $\begin{bmatrix} 1 & -1 & 1 \\ 1 & -2 & -1 \\ 2 & -1 & 2 \end{bmatrix} \begin{bmatrix} x \\ y \\ z \end{bmatrix} = \begin{bmatrix} 0 \\ 5 \\ 8 \end{bmatrix}$; coefficient matrix is

$\begin{bmatrix} 1 & -1 & 1 \\ 1 & -2 & -1 \\ 2 & -1 & 2 \end{bmatrix}$, variable matrix is $\begin{bmatrix} x \\ y \\ z \end{bmatrix}$, constant matrix

is $\begin{bmatrix} 0 \\ 5 \\ 8 \end{bmatrix}$.

pages 213–215   Exercises

1. $\begin{bmatrix} 1 & 1 \\ 1 & -2 \end{bmatrix} \begin{bmatrix} x \\ y \end{bmatrix} = \begin{bmatrix} 5 \\ -4 \end{bmatrix}$; coefficient matrix is $\begin{bmatrix} 1 & 1 \\ 1 & -2 \end{bmatrix}$,

variable matrix is $\begin{bmatrix} x \\ y \end{bmatrix}$, constant matrix is $\begin{bmatrix} 5 \\ -4 \end{bmatrix}$.

2. $\begin{bmatrix} -3 & 1 \\ 1 & 0 \end{bmatrix} \begin{bmatrix} x \\ y \end{bmatrix} = \begin{bmatrix} -7 \\ 2 \end{bmatrix}$; coefficient matrix is $\begin{bmatrix} -3 & 1 \\ 1 & 0 \end{bmatrix}$,

variable matrix is $\begin{bmatrix} x \\ y \end{bmatrix}$, constant matrix is $\begin{bmatrix} -7 \\ 2 \end{bmatrix}$.

3. $\begin{bmatrix} 3 & 5 \\ 1 & 1 \end{bmatrix}\begin{bmatrix} a \\ b \end{bmatrix} = \begin{bmatrix} 0 \\ 2 \end{bmatrix}$; coefficient matrix is $\begin{bmatrix} 3 & 5 \\ 1 & 1 \end{bmatrix}$, variable matrix is $\begin{bmatrix} a \\ b \end{bmatrix}$, constant matrix is $\begin{bmatrix} 0 \\ 2 \end{bmatrix}$.

4. $\begin{bmatrix} 1 & 3 & -1 \\ 1 & 0 & 2 \\ 0 & 2 & -1 \end{bmatrix}\begin{bmatrix} x \\ y \\ z \end{bmatrix} = \begin{bmatrix} 2 \\ 8 \\ 1 \end{bmatrix}$; coefficient matrix is $\begin{bmatrix} 1 & 3 & -1 \\ 1 & 0 & 2 \\ 0 & 2 & -1 \end{bmatrix}$, variable matrix is $\begin{bmatrix} x \\ y \\ z \end{bmatrix}$, constant matrix is $\begin{bmatrix} 2 \\ 8 \\ 1 \end{bmatrix}$.

5. $\begin{bmatrix} 1 & -1 & 1 \\ 2 & 0 & 1 \\ 0 & 1 & 3 \end{bmatrix}\begin{bmatrix} r \\ s \\ t \end{bmatrix} = \begin{bmatrix} 150 \\ 425 \\ 0 \end{bmatrix}$; coefficient matrix is $\begin{bmatrix} 1 & -1 & 1 \\ 2 & 0 & 1 \\ 0 & 1 & 3 \end{bmatrix}$, variable matrix is $\begin{bmatrix} r \\ s \\ t \end{bmatrix}$, constant matrix is $\begin{bmatrix} 150 \\ 425 \\ 0 \end{bmatrix}$.

6. $\begin{bmatrix} 1 & 2 \\ 2 & 3 \end{bmatrix}\begin{bmatrix} x \\ y \end{bmatrix} = \begin{bmatrix} 11 \\ 18 \end{bmatrix}$; coefficient matrix is $\begin{bmatrix} 1 & 2 \\ 2 & 3 \end{bmatrix}$, variable matrix is $\begin{bmatrix} x \\ y \end{bmatrix}$, constant matrix is $\begin{bmatrix} 11 \\ 18 \end{bmatrix}$.

page 228   Chapter Test

1.

	Years	Vetoes	Overrides
Kennedy	3	21	9
Johnson	5	30	0
Nixon	5.5	43	7
Ford	2.5	66	12
Carter	4	31	2
Reagan	8	78	9
Bush	4	46	1
Clinton	8	38	2

10. $\begin{bmatrix} 4 & 6 & 3 & 1 \\ -5 & -1 & 1 & -3 \end{bmatrix}$

11. $\begin{bmatrix} -1 & 3 & 5 & 1 \\ 2 & 4 & 1 & -1 \end{bmatrix}$

12. $\begin{bmatrix} -1 & 3 & 5 & 1 \\ -2 & -4 & -1 & 1 \end{bmatrix}$

13.

14. Answers may vary. Sample: $\begin{bmatrix} 1 & 2 \\ 1 & 2 \end{bmatrix}$

15. Answers may vary. Sample: Two matrices can be multiplied if and only if the number of columns of the first matrix equals the number of rows of the second matrix. The product matrix will have the same number of rows as the first matrix and columns as the second matrix.

22. $\begin{bmatrix} \frac{5}{43} & -\frac{4}{43} \\ \frac{7}{86} & \frac{3}{36} \end{bmatrix}$

23. $\begin{bmatrix} \frac{2}{15} & \frac{1}{9} \\ -\frac{1}{5} & 0 \end{bmatrix}$

24. $\begin{bmatrix} 2 & \frac{1}{2} \\ 0 & \frac{1}{4} \end{bmatrix}$

25. $\approx \begin{bmatrix} 0.1923 & 0.2846 & -0.2231 \\ 0.2115 & 0.2731 & -0.0654 \\ -0.1538 & -0.1077 & 0.1385 \end{bmatrix}$

26. $\begin{bmatrix} -1 & 0.5 & 0.5 \\ 2 & -1.5 & 0.5 \\ 0 & 0.5 & -0.5 \end{bmatrix}$

page 229   Standardized Test Prep

14. [2] translation matrix = $\begin{bmatrix} -7 & -7 & -7 \\ 2 & 2 & 2 \end{bmatrix}$

new image matrix = $\begin{bmatrix} -8 & -3 & -2 \\ 2 & 9 & 4 \end{bmatrix}$

[1] includes only new image matrix and not translation matrix OR includes both but makes minor computational error

15. [4] a. $\begin{bmatrix} 2 & 3 & 3 \\ 3 & 3 & 3 \\ 4 & 1 & 2 \end{bmatrix}\begin{bmatrix} a \\ b \\ c \end{bmatrix} = \begin{bmatrix} 24 \\ 27 \\ 20 \end{bmatrix}$

b. $\begin{bmatrix} a \\ b \\ c \end{bmatrix} = \begin{bmatrix} 3 \\ 4 \\ 2 \end{bmatrix}$

c. 3 oz of Food A, 4 oz of Food B, and 2 oz of Food C

[3] conclusion in part (c) not stated

[2] either the original coefficient matrix stated incorrectly OR the equation solved incorrectly

[1] any two parts incorrect

CHAPTER 5

LESSON 5-1

page 232 Diagnosing Readiness

7.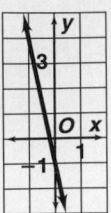

8.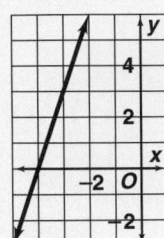

9.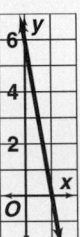

10.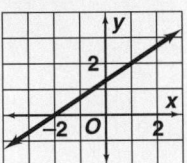

11.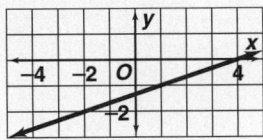

12.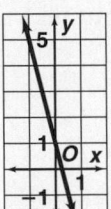

13.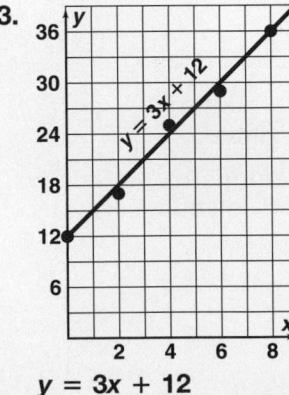

$y = 3x + 12$

14.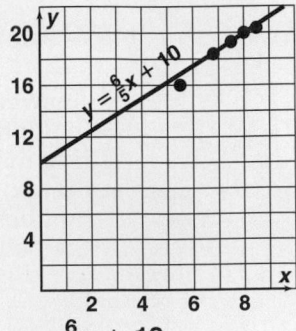

$y = \frac{6}{5}x + 10$

15.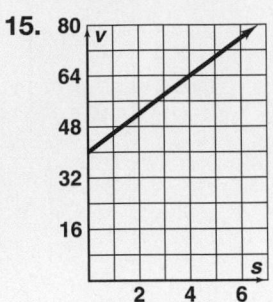

$v = 6s + 40$

16. $y = |x|$

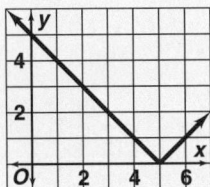

LESSON 5-2

page 241 Check Skills You'll Need

7.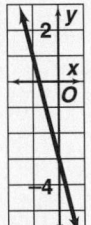

8.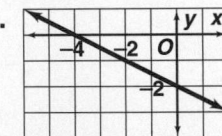

9.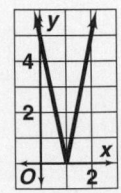

page 241 Check Understanding

1a.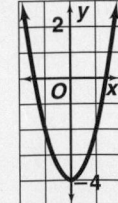

b.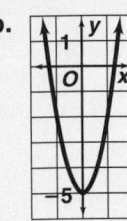

pages 244–247 Exercises

10.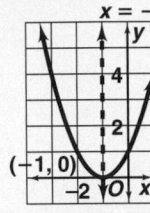

11.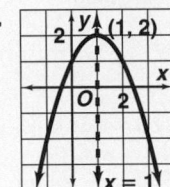

12.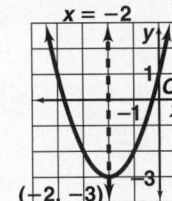

13.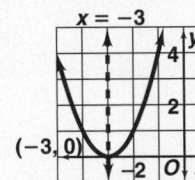

14.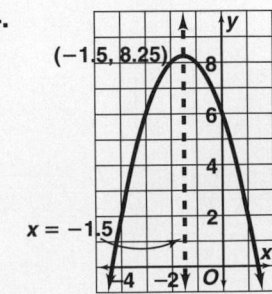

15.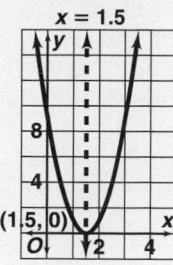
$x = -1$
$(-1, -2)$

16.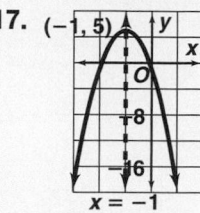
$x = 1.5$
$(1.5, 0)$

17.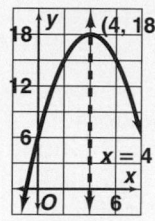
$(-1, 5)$
$x = -1$

18.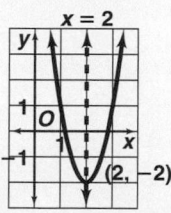
$(4, 18)$
$x = 4$

19.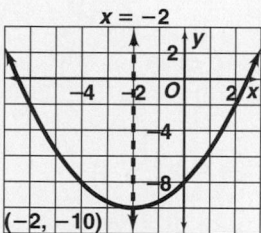
$x = 2$
$(2, -2)$

20.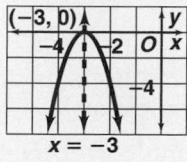
$x = -2$
$(-2, -10)$

21.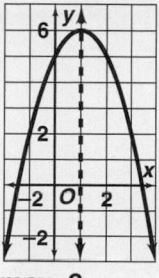
$(-3, 0)$
$x = -3$

22.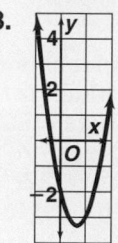
max, 6

23.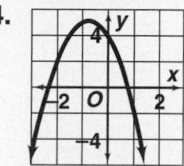
min, $-\frac{10}{3}$

24.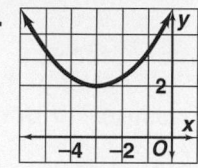
max, $\frac{41}{8}$

25.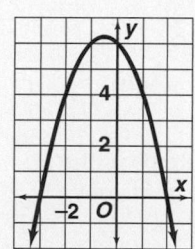
min, 2

26.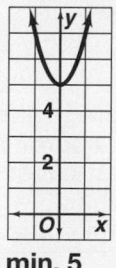
max, $6\frac{1}{4}$

27.
min, 5

LESSON 5-3

page 248 Check Skills You'll Need

1. $y = -x$
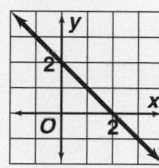

2. $y = |3x|$
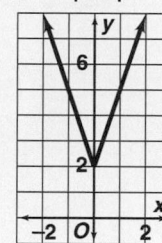

3. $y = -|x|$
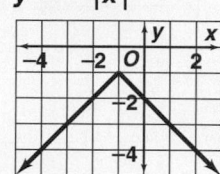

page 248 Investigation

1. $y = (x - 2)^2 = x^2 - 4x + 4$;
$y = (x + 3)^2 - 1 =$
$x^2 + 6x + 9 - 1 = x^2 + 6x + 8$;
$y = -3(x + 2)^2 + 4 =$
$-3(x^2 + 4x + 4) + 4 =$
$-3x^2 - 12x - 12 + 4 =$
$-3x^2 - 12x - 8$;
$y = 2(x + 3)^2 + 1 =$
$2(x^2 + 6x + 9) + 1 =$
$2x^2 + 12x + 18 + 1 =$
$2x^2 + 12x + 19$

2a. column 2: 2, -3, -2, -3;
column 4: 2, -3, -2, -3

b. $-\frac{b}{2a} = h$

pages 251–254 Exercises

36.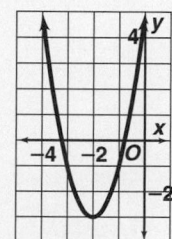

37.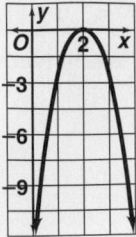

38.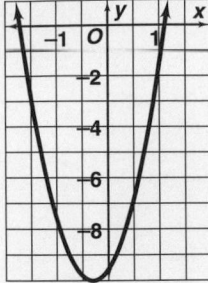

39.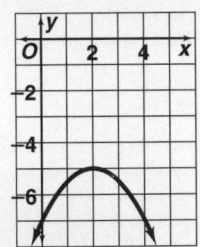

40.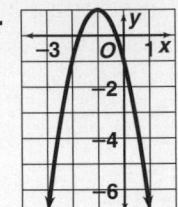

41.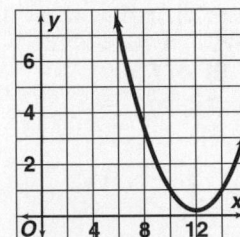

91.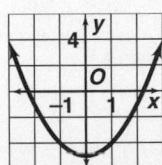

92.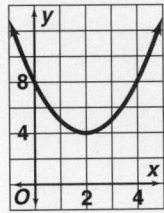

93.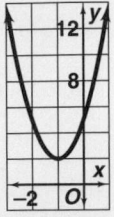

LESSON 5-4

pages 259–261   Exercises

84. **[4] a.** By entering two given lists into a graphing calculator and then having it calculate the quadratic regression, you get $h = -16t^2 + 22t + 3$ as the quadratic model for the ball's height as a function of time.

   b. $-16t^2 + 22t + 3$
   ① Multiply $a \times c$.
      $-16 \times 3 = -48$
   ② Find factors of -48 that add to be 22. $-1, 48; -2, 24; -3, 16; -4, 12 \ldots$
      $-2 + 24 = 22$
   ③ Rewrite as $-16t^2 - 2t + 24t + 3$.
   ④ Find common factors.
      $-2t(8t + 1) + 3(8t + 1)$
   ⑤ Rewrite using Distributive Property.
      $(8t + 1)(-2t + 3)$

   [3] appropriate steps, with one computational error

   [2] explanation in either part (a) OR (b)

   [1] correct solution, without explanation of steps

LESSON 5-5

pages 266–268   Exercises

64. Solve $(x - 4)(x - 6) = 0$ to find that the zeros of $y = x^2 - 10x + 24$ are 4 and 6. Average 4 and 6 to get 5. This is the x-coordinate of the vertex. Substitute 5 for x in $x^2 - 10x + 24$ to find that -1 is the y-coordinate of the vertex. The vertex is $(5, -1)$.

66a. Answers may vary. Sample: If $x \neq h$, then $x - h$ will be nonzero, $(x - h)^2$ will be positive, and $a(x - h)^2$ will be positive. Adding a positive to k will always result in a number greater than k. So the point (h, k) is the lowest point when $x = h$ on the graph of $y = (x - h)^2 + k$.

   b. No; $(x - h)^3$ can be negative.

LESSON 5-6

pages 274–276   Exercises

67a. row 2: 2, 5, $\sqrt{5}$, $\sqrt{5}$
     row 3: 6, 10, $\sqrt{10}$, $\sqrt{10}$
     row 4: -12, 100, 10, 10

   b. Answers may vary. Sample: The sum of a complex number $a + bi$ and its conjugate is $2a$. The product of $a + bi$ and its conjugate is the square of the absolute value of $a + bi$. The absolute values of a complex number and its conjugate are equal.

   c.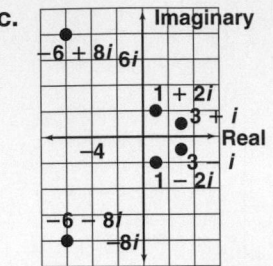

   They are symmetric images of each other with respect to the real axis.

   d. True; the additive inverse of $a + bi$ is $-a - bi$, and the conjugate of $-a - bi$ is $-a + bi$. The conjugate of $a + bi$ is $a - bi$ and the additive inverse of $a - bi$ is $-a + bi$.

74.
   $(3 + 4i)^1 = 3 + 4i$ and $3^2 + 4^2 = 25$;
   $(3 + 4i)^2 = -7 + 24i$ and $(-7)^2 + (24)^2 = 625 = 25^2$;
   $(3 + 4i)^3 = -117 + 44i$ and $(-117)^2 + (44)^2 = 15{,}625 = 25^3$;
   $(3 + 4i)^4 = -527 - 336i$ and $(-527)^2 + (-336)^2 = 390{,}625 = 25^4$;
   $(3 + 4i)^5 = -237 - 3116i$ and $(-237)^2 + (-3116)^2 = 9{,}765{,}625 = 25^5$

80. **[4]**
   $x^4 - 16 = (x^2 - 4)(x^2 + 4) = (x - 2)(x + 2)(x^2 + 4)$

$x - 2 = 0$	$x + 2 = 0$	$x^2 = -4$
$x = 2$	$x = -2$	$x = \sqrt{-4}$
		$x = \pm 2i$

   [3] appropriate methods, with one computational error

   [2] initial factoring correct but solvings are incorrect

   [1] answer only, without work shown

page 277 Investigation

1.

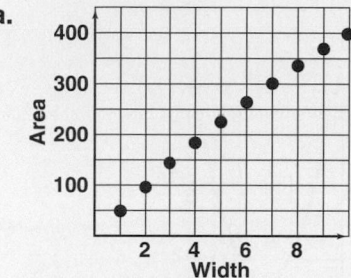

$x^2 + 4x + 4$;
$(x + 2)(x + 2)$

2.

$x^2 + 12x + 36$;
$(x + 6)(x + 6)$

3.

$x^2 + 2x + 1$;
$(x + 1)(x + 1)$

10. Answers may vary. Sample:
First subtract 6 from each side,
which gives you $x^2 + 6x = -6$.
By completing the square on the
left side you get $x^2 + 6x + 9$, but
you also have to add 9 to the right
side to keep the sides equal.
$x^2 + 6x + 9$ factors into $(x + 3)^2$,
so you now have $(x + 3)^2 = 3$. To
solve for x you take the square
root of each side and subtract 3
from each side. This gives you
$x = -3 \pm \sqrt{3}$.

LESSON 5-7

page 279   Check Understanding

4a. $x^2 - 8x + 36 = 0$; $(4 + 2i\sqrt{5})^2 -$
$8(4 + 2i\sqrt{5}) + 36 = 16 + 2(8i\sqrt{5}) +$
$(2i\sqrt{5})^2 - 32 - 16i\sqrt{5} + 36 =$
$(16 - 20 - 32 + 36) + (16i\sqrt{5} -$
$16i\sqrt{5}) = 0$; $(4 - 2i\sqrt{5})^2 - 8(4 -$
$2i\sqrt{5}) + 36 = 16 + 2(-8i\sqrt{5}) +$
$(-2i\sqrt{5})^2 - 32 + 16i\sqrt{5} + 36 =$
$16 - 20 - 32 + 36 + (-16i\sqrt{5} +$
$16i\sqrt{5}) = 0$

b. The graph of $y = x^2 - 8x + 36$ has
no x-intercepts, so the equation
has no real solutions.

page 281–283   Exercises

49. row 2: 47, 46, 45, 44, 43, 42, 41, 40
row 3: 96, 141, 184, 225, 264, 301,
336, 369, 400

a.

$A = -w^2 + 50w$

b. Check students' work.

c. The numbers w such that
$0 < w < 50$; since the perimeter
is 100 the width would have to
be less than 50, and since length
can't be negative it would have
to be greater than 0.

d. 625 units^2; 25 units by 25 units

e. $A = w(50 - w)$; yes; both
equations are quadratic and
model the same situation.

67. [2] $\quad x^2 + 36 \qquad\qquad = 14x$
$\quad\underline{-36 - 14x \quad -14x - 36}$
$\qquad x^2 - 14x \qquad = \qquad -36$
$x^2 - 14x + (-7)^2 = -36 + (-7)^2$
$\quad x^2 - 14x + 49 = 13$
$\qquad\qquad (x - 7)^2 = 13$
$\qquad\qquad x - 7 = \pm\sqrt{13}$
$\qquad\qquad\quad x = 7 \pm \sqrt{13}$

[1] one computational error, OR
correct answer without work
shown

68. [4] $3x^2 + 7x = 6$ Move variables
to the left side and constant to
the right by using the Addition
Property of Equality.

$x^2 + \frac{7}{3}x = 2$ Divide each side
by 3.

$x^2 + \frac{7}{3}x + \frac{49}{36} = \frac{121}{36}$ Add the
square of $\frac{1}{2} \cdot \frac{7}{3}$ to each side.

$(x + \frac{7}{6})^2 = \frac{121}{36}$ Factor left side.

$x + \frac{7}{6} = \pm\frac{11}{6}$ Take the square
root of each side.

$x = -\frac{7}{6} \pm \frac{11}{6}$ Add $-\frac{7}{6}$ to each
side.

$x = -3, \frac{2}{3}$ Simplify $-\frac{7}{6} - \frac{11}{6}$
and $-\frac{7}{6} + \frac{11}{6}$.

[3] appropriate methods, but with
one computational error

[2] correct listing of steps with
incorrect explanations

[1] correct solution, without work
shown

LESSON 5-8

pages 289–291   Exercises

79. [2] For an equation of the form
$ax^2 + bx + c = 0$, where
$a \neq 0$, the discriminant is
the number $b^2 - 4ac$. If the
discriminant is negative,
then there are 2 imaginary
solutions; if it is zero, then
there is 1 real solution; if it is
positive, then there are 2 real
solutions.

[1] only states that the
discriminant is $b^2 - 4ac$

80. [4] Rewrite the equation as $3x^2 -$
$x - 4 = 0$. Then use $a = 3$,
$b = -1$ and $c = -4$ in the
quadratic formula. You get

$\dfrac{-(-1) \pm \sqrt{(-1)^2 - 4(3)(-4)}}{2(3)} =$

$\dfrac{1 \pm \sqrt{1 - (-48)}}{6} = \dfrac{1 \pm \sqrt{49}}{6} =$

$\dfrac{1 \pm 7}{6} = \dfrac{1 + 7}{6}, \dfrac{1 - 7}{6}$ or $\dfrac{4}{3}, -1$

[3] appropriate methods, with one
computational error

[2] insufficient explanation and
computational error

[1] correct solution, without work
shown

page 296   Chapter Test

2.

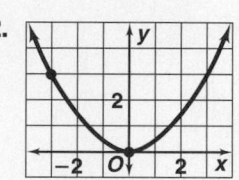

3.

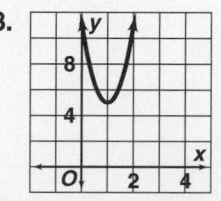

4.

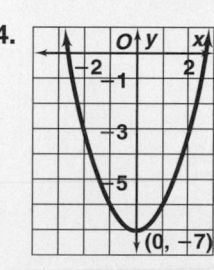

$x = 0, (0, -7)$

5.

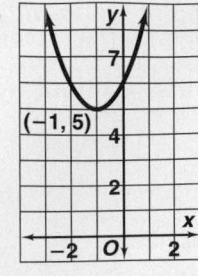

$x = -1, (-1, 5)$

6.

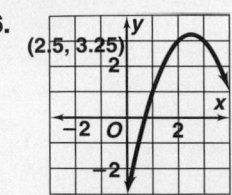

$x = 2.5, (2.5, 3.25)$

7.

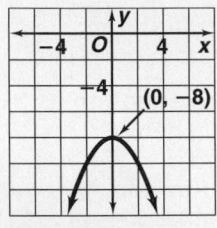

$x = 0, (0, -8)$

17.

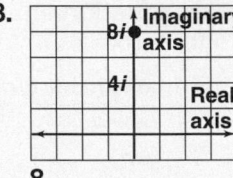

$\sqrt{53}$

18.

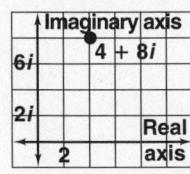

8

19.

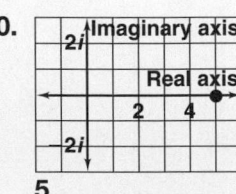

$4\sqrt{5}$

20.

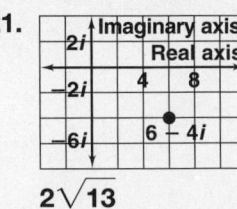

5

21.

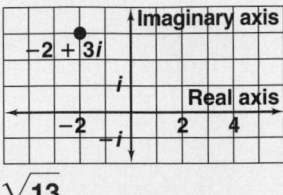

$2\sqrt{13}$

22.

$\sqrt{13}$

33. $y = (x - 3)^2 - 4;$

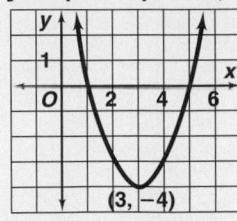

34. $y = -(x - 4)^2 + 6;$

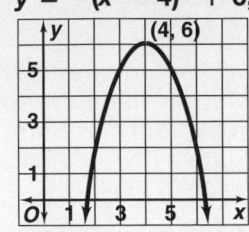

35. $y = 2(x - \frac{3}{4})^2 - 2\frac{1}{8};$

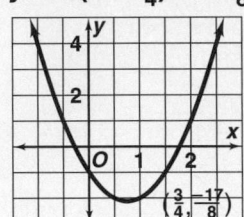

36. $y = -\frac{1}{2}(x - 4)^2 - 1;$

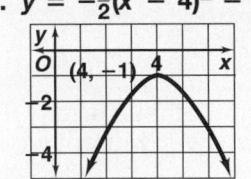

CHAPTER 6

page 298 Diagnosing Readiness

6.

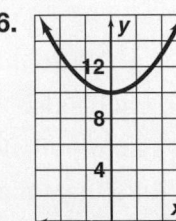

LESSON 6-1

pages 303–305 Exercises

13. $y = x^3 + 1$

14. $y = 12x^3 - 50x^2 + 60x - 12$

15. $y = 1.5x^3 + x^2 - 2x + 1$

16. $y = -3x^3 - 10x^2 + 100$

17a. males: $y = -0.002571x^2 + 0.2829x + 67.21$
females: $y = -0.002286x^2 + 0.2514x + 74.82$

   b. males: $y = 0.00008333x^3 - 0.007571x^2 + 0.3545x + 67.11$
females: $y = 0.00008333x^3 - 0.007286x^2 + 0.3231x + 74.72$

   c. The cubic model is a better fit.

18. $y = x^3 - 2x^2;$ 4335

19. $y = x^3 - 10x^2;$ 2023

20. $y = -0.5x^3 + 10x^2;$ 433.5

21. $y = -0.03948x^3 + 2.069x^2 - 17.93x + 106.9;$ 206

22. $y = -0.007990x^3 + 0.4297x^2 - 6.009x + 43.57;$ 26.3

23. $y = 0.01002x^3 - 0.3841x^2 + 5.002x + 2.132;$ 25.4

59b.

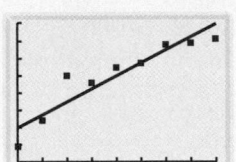

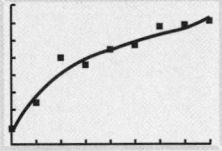

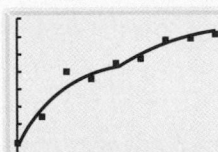

The quartic model fits best.

65. [2] If it is in standard form, the degree is the exponent on the first variable.

[1] incorrect reason for why it is easier to find in standard form

69.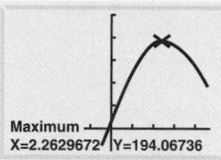

(5, −3)

70. $\begin{bmatrix} 1 & -3 & 1 & 5 \\ -8 & -3 & 0 & -3 \end{bmatrix}$

71. $\begin{bmatrix} 2 & -3 & -6 \\ 5 & -2 & 0 \end{bmatrix}$

72. $\begin{bmatrix} -2 & -1 & -2 & -1 \\ -3 & -3 & -4 & -4 \end{bmatrix}$

LESSON 6-2

pages 311–313   Exercises

15c.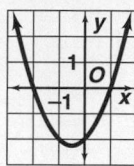

194 in.^{3}, 2.26 in.

16. 1, −2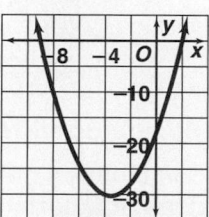

17. 2, −9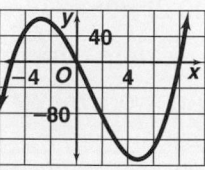

18. 0, −5, 8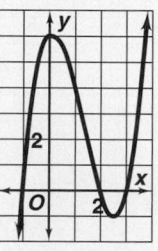

19. −1, 2, 3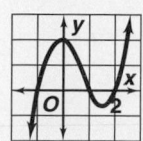

20. −1, 1, 2

LESSON 6-3

LESSON 6-3

pages 318–320   Exercises

64. [2]
$$\begin{array}{r} x^2 - 6x - 7 \\ x - 1\overline{\smash{\big)}\,x^3 - 7x^2 - x + 7} \\ \underline{x^3 - x^2} \\ -6x^2 - x \\ \underline{-6x^2 + 6x} \\ -7x + 7 \\ \underline{-7x + 7} \\ 0 \end{array}$$

$x^2 - 6x - 7 = 0$
$(x + 1)(x - 7) = 0$
$x = 1, -1, 7$

[1] incorrect illustration of division or incorrect list of zeros

LESSON 6-4

page 321   Check Skills You'll Need

1. (1, 4)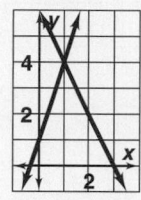

2. $\left(1, \frac{2}{3}\right)$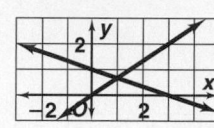

3. no points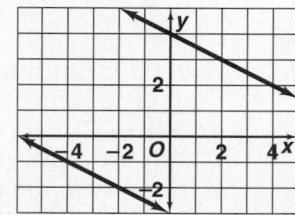

pages 324–326   Exercises

75. [4] $8x^3 - 27 = (2x)^3 - (3)^3 =$
$(2x - 3)(4x^2 + 6x + 9).$
If $2x - 3 = 0$, then $x = \frac{3}{2}$.
If $4x^2 + 6x + 9 = 0$, then $x =$
$\dfrac{-6 \pm \sqrt{36 - 144}}{8} =$

$\dfrac{-6 \pm \sqrt{-108}}{8} =$

$\dfrac{-6 \pm 6i\sqrt{3}}{8} =$

$\dfrac{-3 \pm 3i\sqrt{3}}{4}.$

[3] minor computational errors

[2] $(2x - 3) = 0$ and
$4x^2 + 6x + 9 = 0$ written
and solved for x in the first
equation but not in the second

[1] answer correct, without work shown

LESSON 6-5

pages 333–334   Exercises

47. [4] The three factors are $(x + 4)$,
$(x + 4i)$, $(x - 4i)$.
$(x + 4)(x + 4i)(x - 4i) =$
$(x + 4)(x^2 + 16) =$
$x^3 + 4x^2 + 16x + 64.$
The leading coefficient
is $\frac{3}{2}$, so the equation is
$\frac{3}{2}x^3 + 6x^2 + 24x + 96 = 0.$

[3] leaves the answer as
$x^3 + 4x^2 + 16x + 64 = 0$ OR
makes minor errors

[2] identifies $(x + 4)$, $(x + 4i)$, and
$(x - 4i)$ as factors

[1] identifies the third root as $4i$

LESSON 6-6

pages 337–338   Exercises

17. 4 complex roots
number of real roots: 0, 2, or 4
possible rational roots: $\pm\frac{1}{2}$, ±1,
±2, $\pm\frac{13}{2}$, ±13, ±26

18. 5 complex roots
number of real roots: 1, 3, or 5
possible rational roots: ±1, ±2,
±3, ±6, ±9, ±18

19. 3 complex roots
number of real roots: 1 or 3
possible rational roots: $\pm\frac{1}{3}$, $\pm\frac{2}{3}$,
±1, $\pm\frac{4}{3}$, ±2, ±3, ±4, ±6, ±12

20. 6 complex roots
number of real roots: 0, 2, 4, or 6
possible rational roots: $\pm\frac{1}{4}$, $\pm\frac{1}{2}$,
$\pm\frac{3}{4}$, ±1, $\pm\frac{3}{2}$, ±2, ±3, ±4, ±6, ±8,
±12, ±24

LESSON 6-7

page 346   Investigation

5.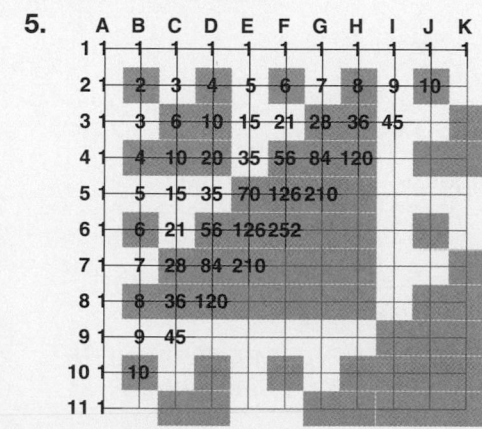

7a.

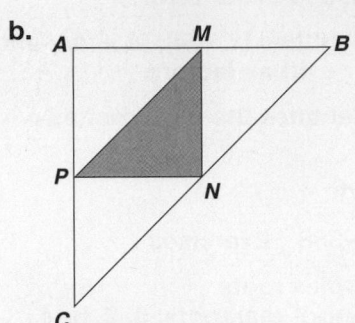

	A	B	C	D	E	F	G	H	I	J	K
1	1	1	1	1	1	1	1	1	1	1	1
2		2	3	4	5	6	7	8	9	10	
3		3	6	10	15	21	28	36	45		
4		4	10	20	35	56	84	120			
5		5	15	35	70	126	210				
6		6	21	56	126	252					
7		7	28	84	210						
8		8	36	120							
9		9	45								
10		10									
11											

b.

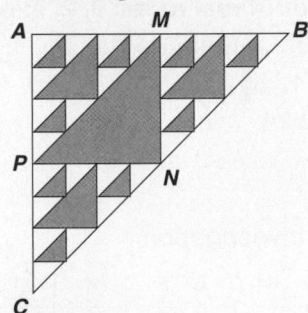

Begin with a large isosceles right triangle, $\triangle ABC$. Connect midpoints of all sides to form 4 congruent triangles. Shade $\triangle MNP$ (the "middle" triangle). Now repeat the process in each unshaded triangle by connecting midpoints and shading the "middle" triangle. After two repetitions of the process, the pattern is the same as the shaded grid.

LESSON 6-8

pages 349–351   Exercises

3. $a^4 + 4a^3b + 6a^2b^2 + 4ab^3 + b^4$

4. $x^5 - 5x^4y + 10x^3y^2 - 10x^2y^3 + 5xy^4 - y^5$

5. $a^6 - 6a^5b + 15a^4b^2 - 20a^3b^3 + 15a^2b^4 - 6ab^5 + b^6$

6. $x^7 - 7x^6y + 21x^5y^2 - 35x^4y^3 + 35x^3y^4 - 21x^2y^5 + 7xy^6 - y^7$

67. Answers may vary. Sample: A coin is tossed five times with the probability of heads on each toss 0.5. Write an expression for the probability of exactly 2 heads being tossed.

68a. $(k + 1)! =$
$(k + 1) \cdot (k) \cdot (k - 1) \cdot \ldots \cdot 1 =$
$(k + 1)[(k) \cdot (k - 1) \cdot \ldots \cdot 1] =$
$(k + 1) \cdot k!$

b. The derivation below finds a common denominator for the fractions that represent $_nC_k$ and $_nC_{k+1}$, and then uses algebra to show that $_nC_k + {_nC_{k+1}} = {_{n+1}C_{k+1}}$. In addition, the identity from part (a) is used three times.

$$_nC_k + {_nC_{k+1}} = \frac{n!}{k!\,(n-k)!}$$

$$+ \frac{n!}{(k+1)!\,(n-k-1)!} =$$

$$\frac{(k+1)n!}{(k+1)!\,(n-k)!} + \frac{(n-k)n!}{(k+1)!\,(n-k)!} =$$

$$\frac{(k+1+n-k)n!}{(k+1)!\,(n-k)!} = \frac{(n+1)n!}{(k+1)!\,(n-k)!} =$$

$$\frac{(n+1)!}{(k+1)!\,(n-k)!} =$$

$$\frac{(n+1)!}{(k+1)!\,((n+1)-(k+1))!} =$$

$$_{n+1}C_{k+1}$$

c. If you consider the row of Pascal's Triangle containing just 1 to be row zero, $_4C_2$ is 6, the third entry in the fourth row. $_4C_3$ is 4, the fourth entry in the fourth row. $_5C_3$ is 10, the fourth entry in the fifth row. $_4C_2 + {_4C_3} = 6 + 4 = 10 = {_5C_3}$

73. [2] $_7C_1x^6y^1$ or $7x^6y$

[1] provides some expression in x and y without the correct coefficients

74. [4] The sixth term is $_7C_5(2x)^2(-3y)^5 = 21(4x^2)(-243y^5) = -20,412x^2y^5$

[3] incorrect coefficient but correct exponents for x and y

[2] $_7C_6(2x)^2(-3y)^5$ correct, but not the rest of the answer

[1] presents some expression in x and y

page 356   Chapter Test

5. $-1.62, 0, 0.62$

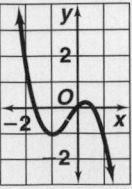

6. $-5, -2, -1, 1$

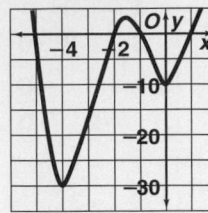

7. $0.65, -3.04$

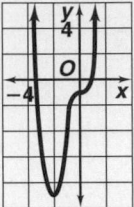

8. $-1.26, 1$

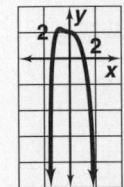

9. $-0.73, 1, 2.73$

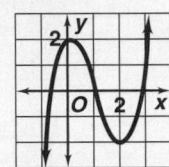

page 357   Standardized Test Prep

17. [2] a. combination because order does not matter

   b. 27,405

   [1] answers either part (a) OR (b)

18. [4] Answers may vary. Sample:

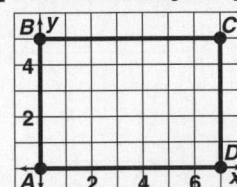

$$\begin{bmatrix} 1 & 0 \\ 0 & -1 \end{bmatrix} \times \begin{bmatrix} 0 & 0 & 7 & 7 \\ 0 & 5 & 5 & 0 \end{bmatrix} = \begin{bmatrix} 0 & 0 & 7 & 7 \\ 0 & -5 & -5 & 0 \end{bmatrix}$$

x-axis reflection

$$\begin{bmatrix} 0 & -1 \\ 1 & 0 \end{bmatrix} \times \begin{bmatrix} 0 & 0 & 7 & 7 \\ 0 & -5 & -5 & 0 \end{bmatrix} =$$
$$\begin{bmatrix} 0 & 5 & 5 & 0 \\ 0 & 0 & 7 & 7 \end{bmatrix}$$
90° rotation

[3] error in matrix calculation

[2] performs either reflection OR rotation

[1] correct answer, without work shown

CHAPTER 7

page 360 Diagnosing Readiness

19.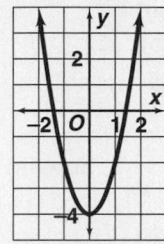

20.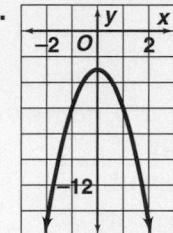

21.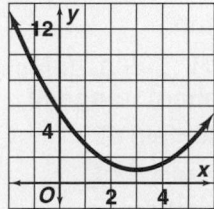

22.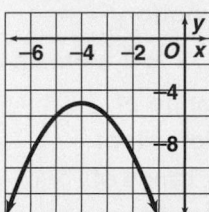

23.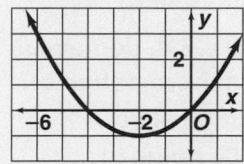

24.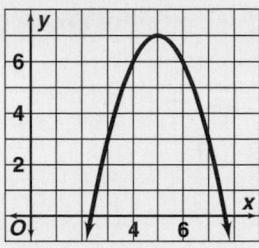

LESSON 7-1

page 367 Standardized Test Prep

74. [2] $\sqrt{x^2 y^4}$ equals $\sqrt[3]{x^3 y^6}$ whenever $y = 0$, regardless of the value of x. This is true because $x^2 y^4$ and $x^3 y^6$ will be 0 whenever $y = 0$. $\sqrt{x^2 y^4}$ also equals $\sqrt[3]{x^3 y^6}$ if $y \neq 0$ and $x \geq 0$. This is true because $\sqrt{x^2 y^4} = |x| y^2$ and $\sqrt[3]{x^3 y^6} = xy^2$, and, for $y \neq 0$, $|x| y^2 = xy^2$ when $x \geq 0$.

[1] answer only, with no explanation

LESSON 7-6

page 392 Check Skills You'll Need

1. D: {0, 2, 4},
   R: {−5, −3, −1}

2. D: {−1, 0, 1},
   R: 0

3. D: all real numbers,
   R: all real numbers

4. D: all real numbers,
   R: all real numbers ≥ 0

LESSON 7-7

page 400 Check Skills You'll Need

1.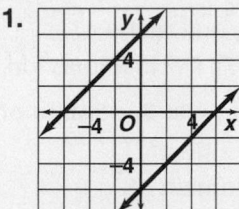

2.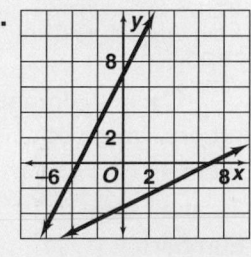

3.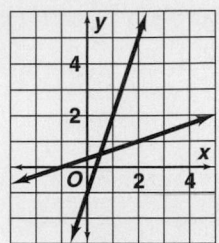

4.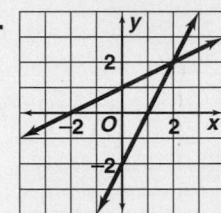

5.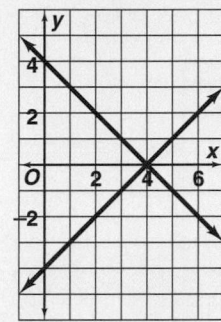

6.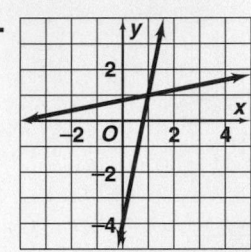

pages 404–406 Exercises

1.

x	0	1	0	2
y	1	2	3	4

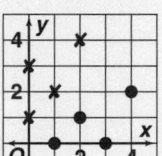

2.

x	0	1	2	3
y	1	2	3	4

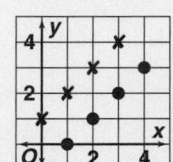

3.

x	0	1	4	9
y	0	1	2	3

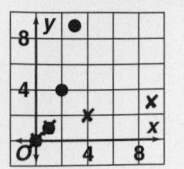

4.

x	2	2	2	2
y	−3	−2	−1	0

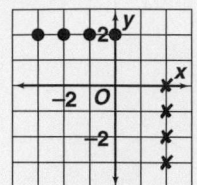

14.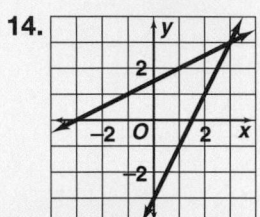

15.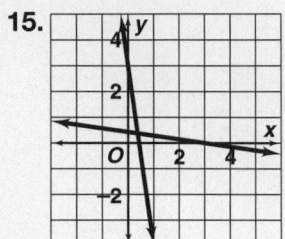

16.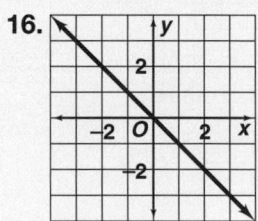

17.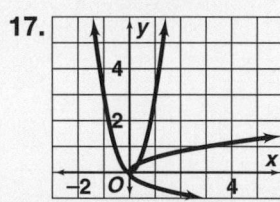

18.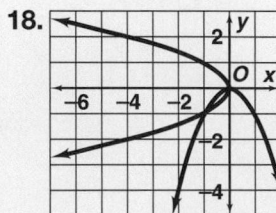

19.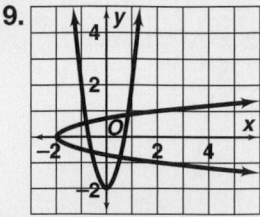

20.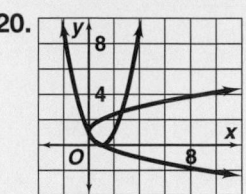

21.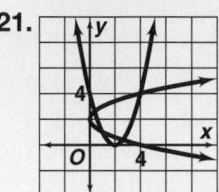

22.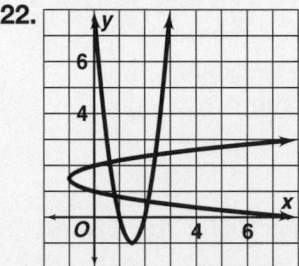

23. $f^{-1}(x) = \frac{x - 4}{3}$, and the domain and range for both f and f^{-1} are all real numbers; f^{-1} is a function.

24. $f^{-1}(x) = x^2 + 5, x \geq 0$, domain of $f: \{x \mid x \geq 5\}$, range of $f: \{y \mid y \geq 0\}$, domain of $f^{-1}: \{x \mid x \geq 0\}$, and range of $f^{-1}: \{y \mid y \geq 5\}$; f^{-1} is a function.

25. $f^{-1}(x) = x^2 - 7, x \geq 0$, domain of $f: \{x \mid x \geq -7\}$, range of $f: \{y \mid y \geq 0\}$, domain of $f^{-1}: \{x \mid x \geq 0\}$, and range of $f^{-1}: \{y \mid y \geq -7\}$; f^{-1} is a function.

26. $f^{-1}(x) = \frac{3 - x^2}{2}, x \geq 0$, domain of $f: \{x \mid x \leq \frac{3}{2}\}$, range of $f: \{y \mid y \geq 0\}$, domain of $f^{-1}: \{x \mid x \geq 0\}$, and range of $f^{-1}: \{y \mid y \leq \frac{3}{2}\}$; f^{-1} is a function.

27. $f^{-1}(x) = \pm\sqrt{\frac{x - 2}{2}}, x \geq 2$, domain of f: all real numbers, range of $f: \{y \mid y \geq 2\}$, domain of $f^{-1}: \{x \mid x \geq 2\}$, and range of f^{-1}: all real numbers; f^{-1} is not a function.

28. $f^{-1}(x) = \pm\sqrt{1 - x}, x \leq 1$, domain of f: all real numbers, range of $f: \{y \mid y \leq 1\}$, domain of $f^{-1}: \{x \mid \leq 1\}$, and range of f^{-1}: all real numbers; f^{-1} is not a function.

47. $f^{-1}(x) = x^2, x \leq 0$, domain of $f: \{x \mid x \geq 0\}$, range of $f: \{y \mid y \leq 0\}$, domain of $f^{-1}: \{x \mid x \leq 0\}$, range of $f^{-1}: \{y \mid y \geq 0\}$, and f^{-1} is a function.

48. $f^{-1}(x) = (x - 3)^2, x \geq 3$, domain of $f: \{x \mid x \geq 0\}$, range of $f: \{y \mid y \geq 3\}$, domain of $f^{-1}: \{x \mid x \geq 3\}$, range of $f^{-1}: \{y \mid y \geq 0\}$, and f^{-1} is a function.

49. $f^{-1}(x) = 3 - x^2, x \geq 0$, domain of $f: \{x \mid x \leq 3\}$, range of $f: \{y \mid y \geq 0\}$, domain of $f^{-1}: \{x \mid x \geq 0\}$, range of $f^{-1}: \{y \mid y \leq 3\}$, and f^{-1} is a function.

50. $f^{-1}(x) = x^2 - 2, x \geq 0$, domain of $f: \{x \mid x \geq -2\}$, range of $f: \{y \mid y \geq 0\}$, domain of $f^{-1}: \{x \mid x \geq 0\}$, range of $f^{-1}: \{y \mid y \geq -2\}$, and f^{-1} is a function.

51. $f^{-1}(x) = \pm\sqrt{2x}, x \geq 0$, domain of f: all real numbers, range of $f: \{y \mid y \geq 0\}$, domain of $f^{-1}: \{x \mid x \geq 0\}$, range of f^{-1}: all real numbers, and f^{-1} is not a function.

52. $f^{-1}(x) = \pm\frac{1}{\sqrt{x}}, x \geq 0$, domain of $f: \{x \mid x \neq 0\}$, range of $f: \{y \mid y > 0\}$, domain of $f^{-1}: \{x \mid x > 0\}$, range of $f^{-1}: \{y \mid y \neq 0\}$, and f^{-1} is not a function.

53. $f^{-1}(x) = \pm\sqrt{x} + 4$, domain of f: all real numbers, range of $f: \{y \mid y \geq 0\}$, domain of $f^{-1}: \{x \mid x \geq 0\}$, range of f^{-1}: all real numbers, and f^{-1} is not a function.

54. $f^{-1}(x) = 7 + \sqrt{x}$, $x \geq 0$, domain of f: all real numbers, range of f: $\{y \mid y \geq 0\}$, domain of f^{-1}: $\{x \mid x \geq 0\}$, range of f^{-1}: all real numbers, and f^{-1} is not a function.

55. $f^{-1}(x) = \pm\sqrt{\frac{1}{x}} - 1$, $x > 0$, domain of f: $\{x \mid x \neq -1\}$, range of f: $\{y \mid y > 0\}$, domain of f^{-1}: $\{x \mid x > 0\}$, range of f^{-1}: $\{y \mid y \neq -1\}$, and f^{-1} is not a function.

56. $f^{-1}(x) = \left(-\frac{x-4}{2}\right)^2$, $x \leq 4$, domain of f: $\{x \mid x \geq 0\}$, range of f: $\{y \mid y \leq 4\}$, domain of f^{-1}: $\{x \mid x \leq 4\}$, range of f^{-1}: $\{y \mid y \geq 0\}$, and f^{-1} is a function.

57. $f^{-1}(x) = \left(\frac{3}{x}\right)^2$, $x > 0$, domain of f: $\{x \mid x > 0\}$, range of f: $\{y \mid y > 0\}$, domain of f^{-1}: $\{x \mid x > 0\}$, range of f^{-1}: $\{y \mid y > 0\}$, and f^{-1} is a function.

58. $f^{-1}(x) = -\frac{1}{2}\left(\frac{1}{x}\right)^2$, $x > 0$, domain of f: $\{x \mid x < 0\}$, range of f: $\{y \mid y > 0\}$, domain of f^{-1}: $\{x \mid x > 0\}$, range of f^{-1}: $\{y \mid y < 0\}$, and f^{-1} is a function.

page 407   Technology

1.
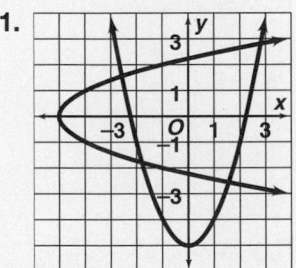

LESSON 7-8

page 408   Check Skills You'll Need

1.
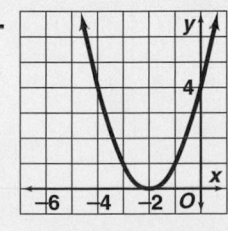

2.
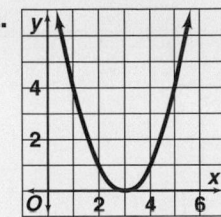

3.
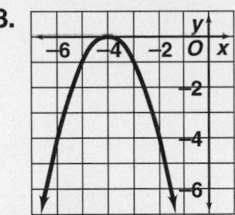

4.
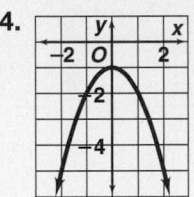

5.
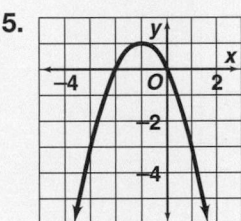

6.
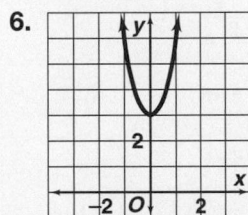

pages 411–413   Exercises

1.
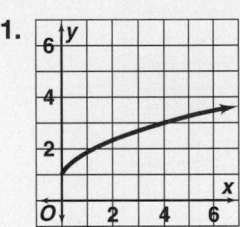

2.
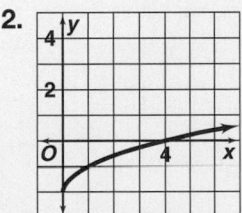

3.
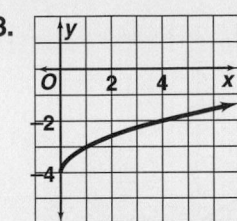

4.
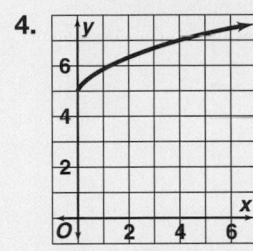

5.
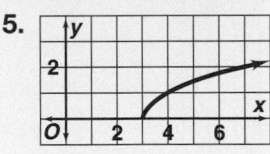

6.
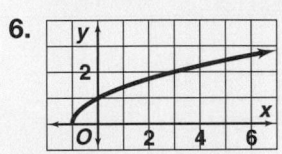

7.
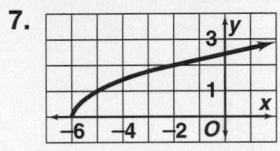

8.
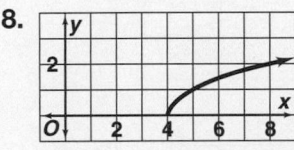

9.
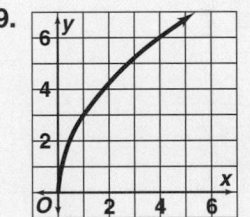

10.
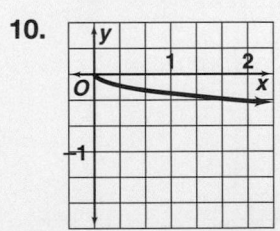

11.
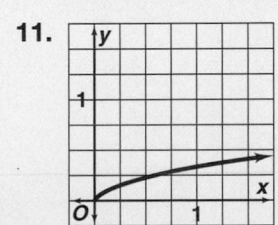

12.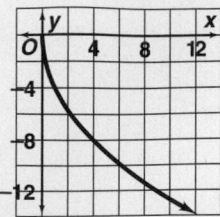

13.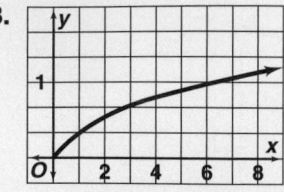

14.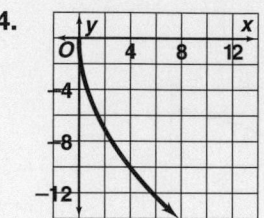

15.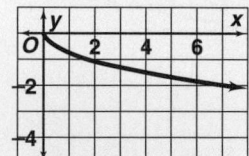

16.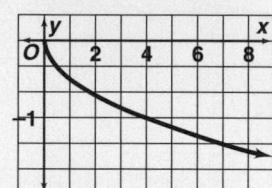

17.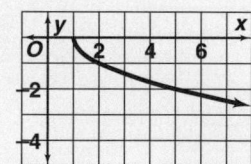

18.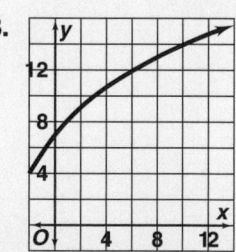

19.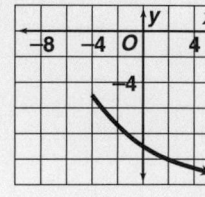

20.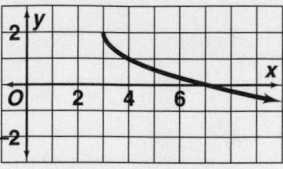

21.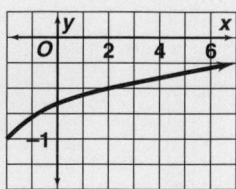

22.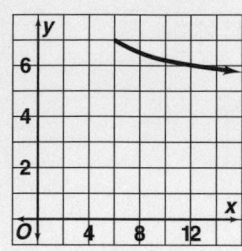

24.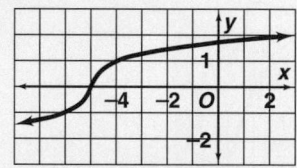

25.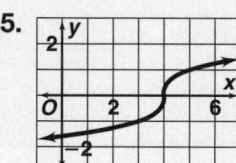

26.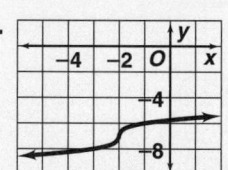

27.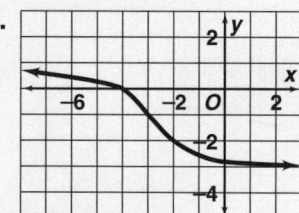

28.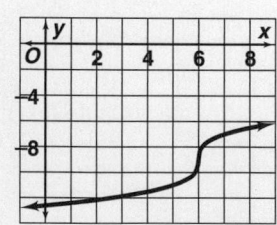

29.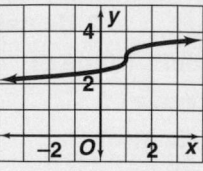

36.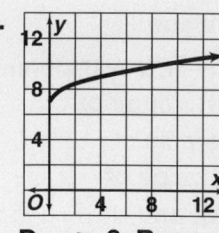

D: $x \geq 0$, R: $y \geq 7$

37.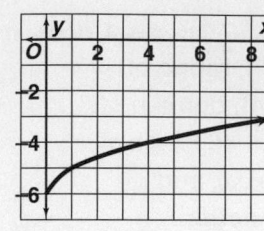

D: $x \geq 0$, R: $y \geq -6$

38.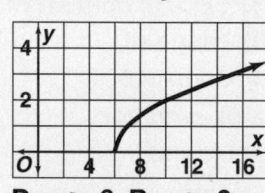

D: $x \geq 6$, R: $y \geq 0$

39.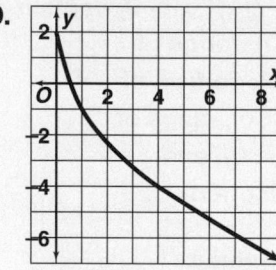

D: $x \geq 0$, R: $y \leq 2$

40.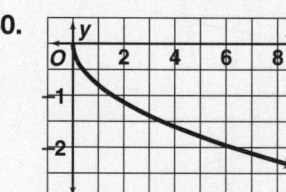

D: $x \geq 0$, R: $y \leq 0$

41.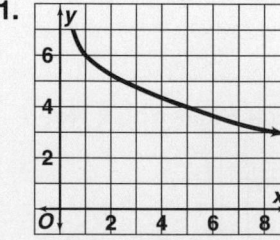

D: $x \geq \frac{1}{2}$, R: $y \leq 7$

42.

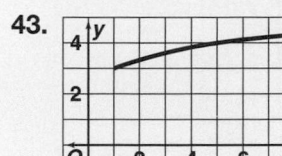

D: all real numbers,
R: all real numbers

43.

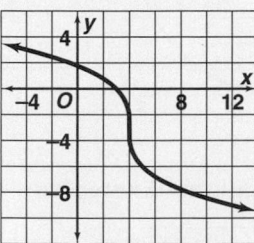

D: $x \geq 1$, R: $y \geq 3$

44.

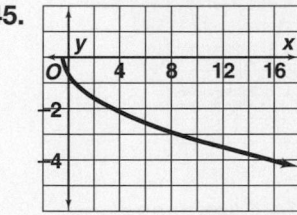

D: all real numbers,
R: all real numbers

45.

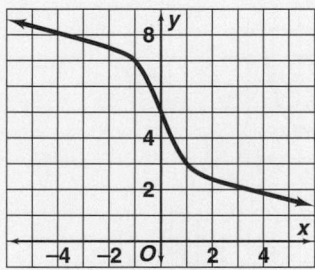

$x \geq -\frac{1}{2}$, R: $y \leq 0$

46.

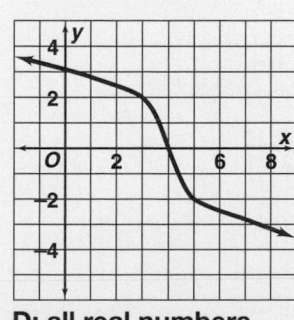

D: all real numbers,
R: all real numbers

47.

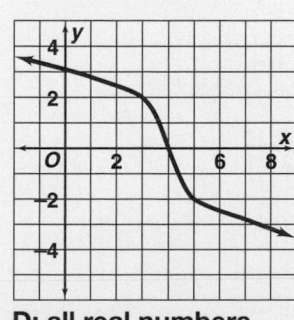

D: all real numbers,
R: all real numbers

48.

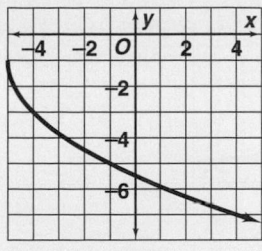

D: $x \geq -5$, R: $y \leq -1$

49.

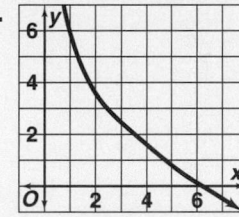

D: all real numbers,
R: all real numbers

50.

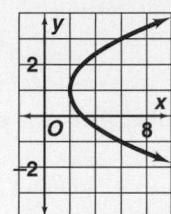

D: $x \geq \frac{3}{4}$, R: $y \leq 7$

54a.

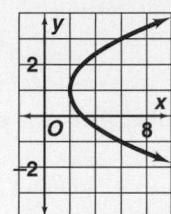

b. Both domains are $x \geq 2$. The range of $y = \sqrt{x - 2} + 1$ is $y \geq 1$. The range of $y = -\sqrt{x - 2} + 1$ is $y \leq 1$.

55. $y = 5\sqrt{x - 4} - 1$; the graph is the same as $y = 5\sqrt{x}$, translated 4 units to the right and 1 down.

56. $y = 6\sqrt{x + 3} + 4$; the graph is the graph of $y = 6\sqrt{x}$ translated 3 units to the left and 4 up.

57. $y = -2\sqrt[3]{x - \frac{1}{4}}$; the graph is the graph of $y = -2\sqrt[3]{x}$ translated $\frac{1}{4}$ unit to the right.

58. $y = \frac{1}{2}\sqrt{x - 1} - 2$; the graph is the same as $y = \frac{1}{2}\sqrt{x}$ translated 1 unit right and 2 down.

59. $y = 10 - \frac{1}{3}\sqrt[3]{x + 3}$; the graph is the same as $y = -\frac{1}{3}\sqrt[3]{x}$ translated 3 units to the left and 10 up.

60. $y = \frac{1}{3}\sqrt{x + 9} + 5$; the graph is the same as $y = \frac{1}{3}\sqrt{x}$, translated 9 units to the left and 5 up.

63. If $a > 0$, the graph is stretched vertically by a factor of a. If $a < 0$, the graph is reflected over the x-axis and stretched vertically by a factor of $|a|$.

64. $y = -\sqrt{2}\sqrt{x + 4}$; the graph is the graph of $y = -\sqrt{2x}$ translated 4 units to the left; domain: $x \geq -4$, range: $y \leq 0$.

65. $y = -\sqrt{8}\sqrt{x - \frac{3}{4}}$; the graph is the graph of $y = -\sqrt{8x}$ translated $\frac{3}{4}$ units to the right; domain: $x \geq \frac{3}{4}$, range: $y \leq 0$.

66. $y = \sqrt{3} \cdot \sqrt{x - \frac{5}{3}} + 6$; the graph is the graph of $y = \sqrt{3x}$ translated $\frac{5}{3}$ units to the right and 6 units up; domain: $x \geq \frac{5}{3}$, range: $y \geq 6$.

67. $y = -\sqrt{12} \cdot \sqrt{x + \frac{2}{3}} - 3$; the graph is the graph of $y = -\sqrt{12x}$ translated $\frac{2}{3}$ units to the left and 3 units down; domain: $x \geq -\frac{2}{3}$, range: $y \geq -3$.

68a.

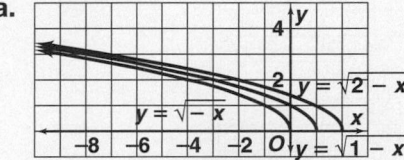

$y = \sqrt{2} - x$
$y = \sqrt{-x}$
$y = \sqrt{1} - x$

b. The graph of $y = \sqrt{h - x}$ is a reflection of the graph of $y = \sqrt{x - h}$ in the line $x = h$.

page 418   Chapter Test

32.

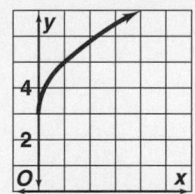

D: real numbers ≥ 0,
R: real numbers ≥ 3

33.

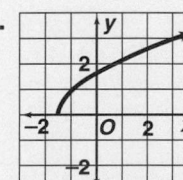

D: real numbers $\geq -\frac{3}{2}$,
R: real numbers ≥ 0

34.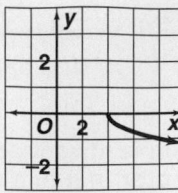

D: real numbers ≥ 4,
R: real numbers ≤ 0

35.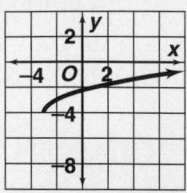

D: real numbers ≥ $-\frac{3}{2}$,
R: real numbers ≥ -4

CHAPTER 8

LESSON 8-1

page 426–429   Exercises

24–31. $y = 0$ is the horizontal asymptote.

24.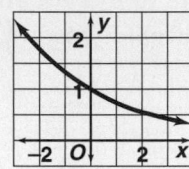

25.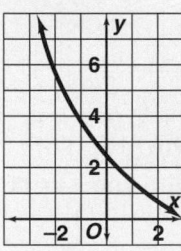

26.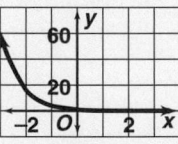

27.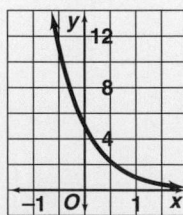

28.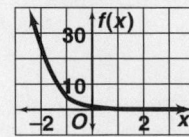

29.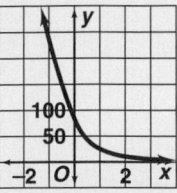

30.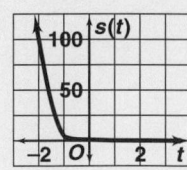

31.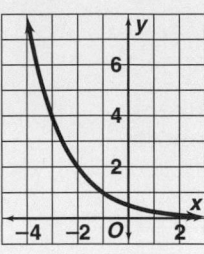

63. [2]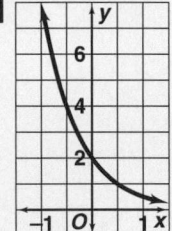

[1] general form of graph correct, but not exact

64. [4] $y = ab^x$

$54 = ab^2$

$a = \dfrac{54}{b^2}$

$2 = \dfrac{54}{b^2} \cdot b^{\frac{1}{2}}$

$2 = \dfrac{54}{b^{\frac{3}{2}}}$

$2b^{\frac{3}{2}} = 54$

$b^{\frac{3}{2}} = 27$

$b = 27^{\frac{2}{3}}$

$b = 9$

$a = \dfrac{54}{9^2}$

$a = \dfrac{2}{3}$

$y = \dfrac{2}{3} \cdot 9^x$

[3] appropriate methods with one computational error

[2] starts problem correctly, but fails to finish it properly

[1] correct answer, without work shown

LESSON 8-2

page 432   Check Understanding

2a.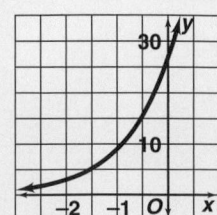

b.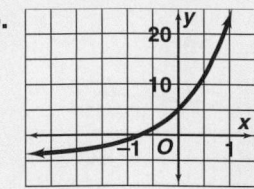

c.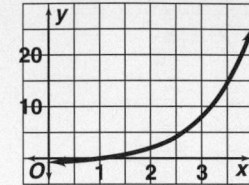

page 432   Additional Examples

2.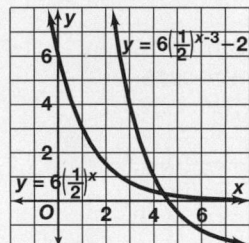

pages 434–437   Exercises

9.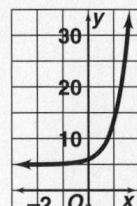

10.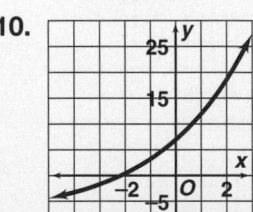

11.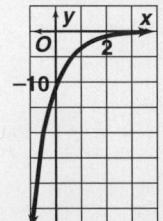

12.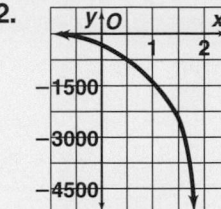

13.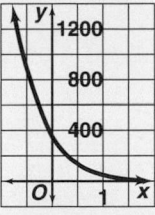

14.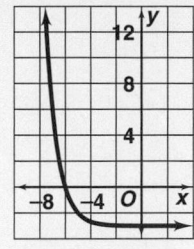

page 437   Checkpoint Quiz 1

8.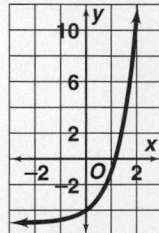

9. Answers may vary. Sample: The population of Smallville was 1200 in 1990. It was growing at a rate of 1% per year. Find the population in 2010.

LESSON 8-3

page 438   Check Skills You'll Need

5.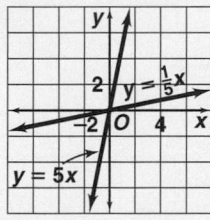

6.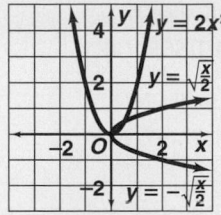

7.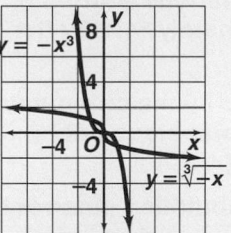

8.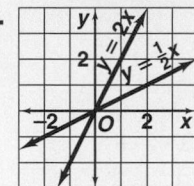

page 438   Check Understanding

1. The earthquake in California released about 1265 times as much energy as the earthquake in Alabama.

LESSON 8-4

pages 449–451   Exercises

79. $3 \log 2 + \frac{3}{2} \log x - 3 \log 5$

80. $3 \log m - 4 \log n + 2 \log p$

81. $\log 2 + \frac{1}{2} \log 4 + \frac{1}{2} \log r - \log s$

82. $\frac{1}{2} \log_b x + \frac{2}{3} \log_b y - \frac{2}{5} \log_b z$

83. $\frac{5}{2} \log_4 x + \frac{7}{2} \log_4 y - \log_4 z$
    $- 4 \log_4 w$

84. $\frac{1}{2} \log (x^2 - 4) - 2 \log (x + 3)$

85. $\frac{1}{2} \log x + \frac{1}{4} \log 2 - \log y$

86. $\log_3 x + \log_3 y - 6 \log_3 z$

87. $\frac{1}{2} \log_7 (r + 9) - 2 \log_7 s - \frac{1}{3} \log_7 t$

95. [4] 1) $\log \frac{24}{2} = \log 24 - \log 2$;
        Quotient Property

    2) $\log 2 \cdot 6 = \log 2 + \log 6$;
       Product Property

    3) $\log 144^{\frac{1}{2}} = \frac{1}{2} \log 144$;
       Power Property

    4) $\log 3 \cdot 2^2 = \log 3 + 2 \log 2$;
       Product and Power
       Properties

[3] log 12 written three ways

[2] log 12 written two ways OR written 4 ways but properties not named

[1] log 12 written only 2 ways and properties not named

page 472   Chapter Test

1.

x	0	1	2	3	4	5
y	3	0.75	0.19	0.05	0.01	0.00

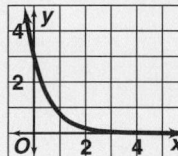

2.

x	0	1	2	3	4	5
y	−1	−6	−36	−216	−1296	−7776

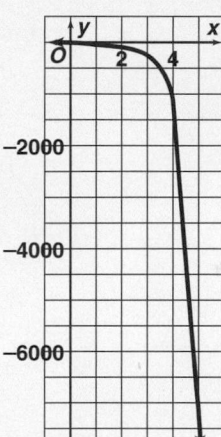

3.

x	0	1	2	3	4	5
y	0.1	1	10	100	1000	10,000

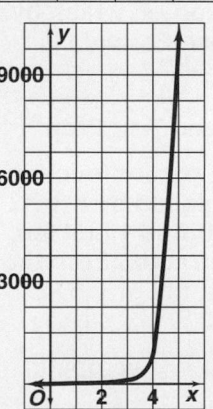

4.

x	0	1	2	3	4	5
y	100	200	400	800	1600	3200

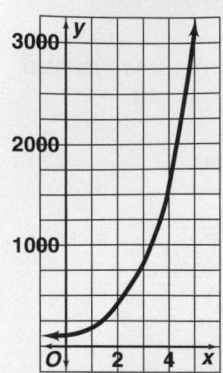

20.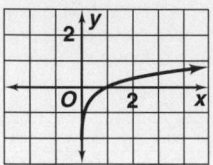

21.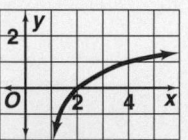

22.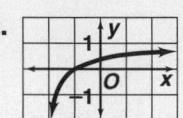

23.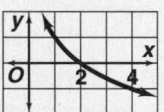

32. Answers may vary. Sample: Taking common logarithms of both sides gives $2x = \frac{\log 4}{\log 3}$. Taking logarithms to the base 3 of both sides gives $2x = \log_3 4$, which by the Change of Base Formula is equivalent to $2x = \frac{\log 4}{\log 3}$.

page 473   Standardized Test Prep

16. **[2]** Since x, in the parent function $y = 10^x$, is replaced by $x + 1$, the graph is shifted 1 unit left. Since 3 is subtracted from the function value, the graph is shifted down 3.

[1] leaves out one or two points

17. **[4]** $A = 1000e^{(0.055)(1)}$
$\approx 1000(1.0565406)$
≈ 1056.54
$A = 1000e^{(0.055)(4)}$
$\approx 1000(1.2460767)$
≈ 1246.08

There will be approximately $1057 after one year; approximately $1246 after 4 years.

[3] one error in one computation (the second steps not required)

[2] one computation incorrect

[1] one equation incorrect

18. **[4]** $\begin{bmatrix} 1 & 2 & 3 \\ 2 & 1 & 3 \\ 2 & 3 & 1 \end{bmatrix} =$
$1 \cdot 1 \cdot 1 + 2 \cdot 3 \cdot 2 +$
$3 \cdot 2 \cdot 3 - (2 \cdot 1 \cdot 3 +$
$3 \cdot 3 \cdot 1 + 1 \cdot 2 \cdot 2) =$
$31 - 19 = 12$

[3] evaluation set up correctly, one computational error

[2] evaluation set up correctly, evaluated improperly

[1] answer only, without work shown

CHAPTER 9

page 484   Technology

1.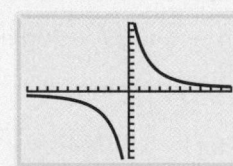

2.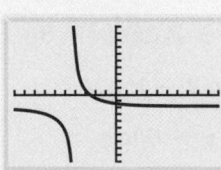

3.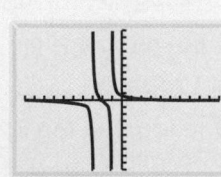

4.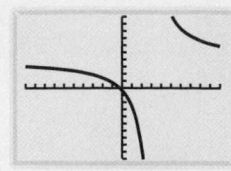

5.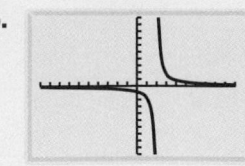

6.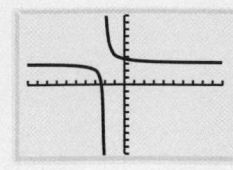

7.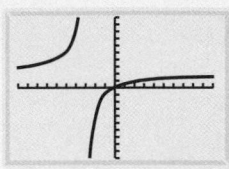

8.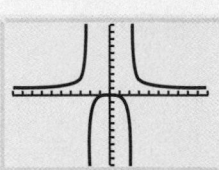

9.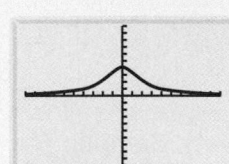

10.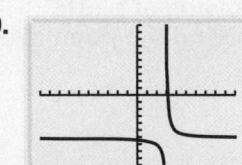

11.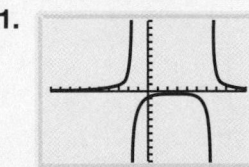

12.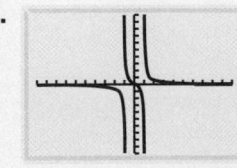

LESSON 9-2

pages 485–488　Check Understanding

5. $x = -7$ and $y = -3$

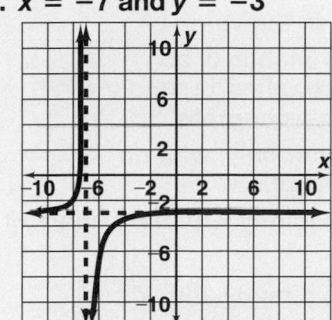

6b.

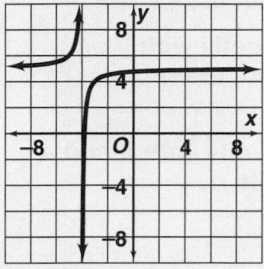

pages 488–490　Exercises

1.

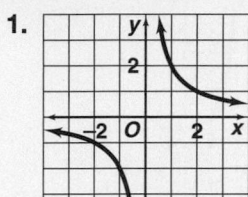

2.

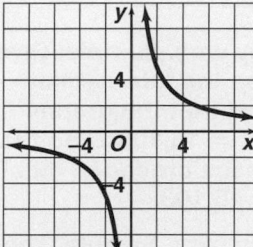

3.

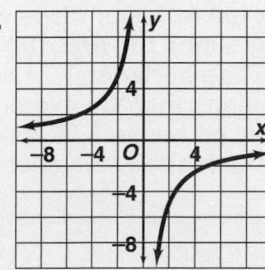

14.

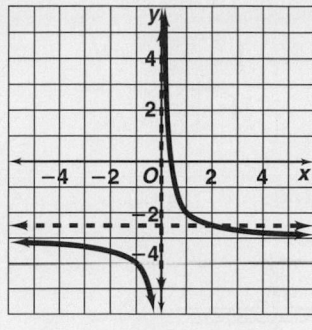

15.

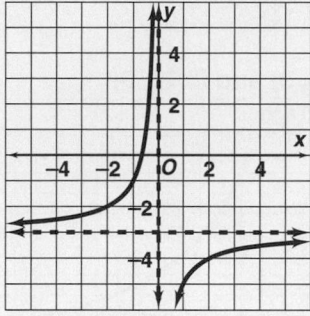

16.

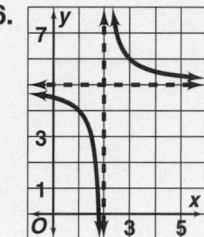

17.

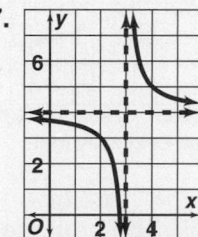

18.

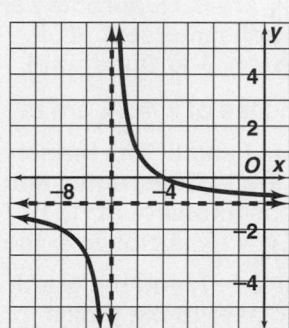

19.

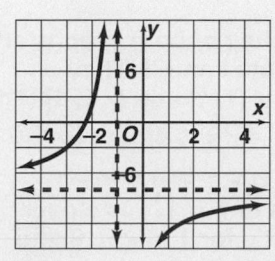

20.

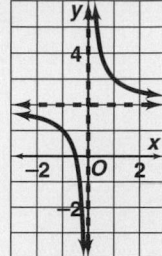

21.

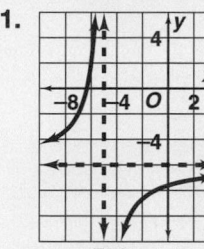

25a. $c = \dfrac{750}{a}$

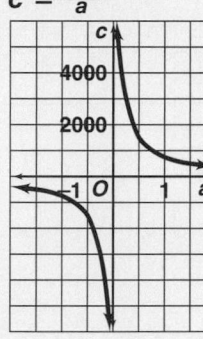

$a = 0, c = 0$

b. Answers may vary. Sample:
If the number of awards is large,
the amount of money available
for each award approaches 0.
If there are a small number of
awards, then the amount of
money available for each award
gets larger.

33.

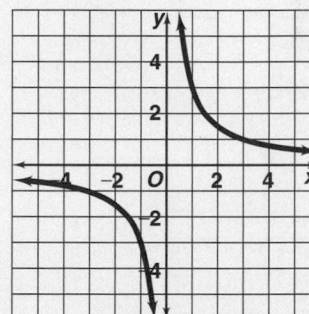

34.

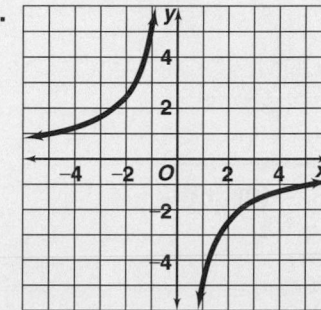

35.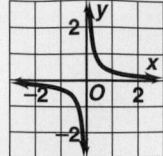

36.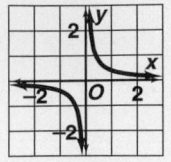

37.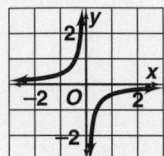

38.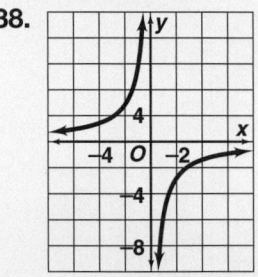

41.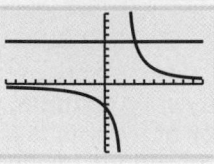

(3, 6)

42.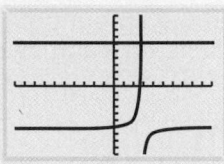

(2.92, 6.2)

43.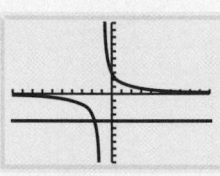

(−1.75, −4)

44.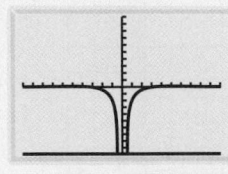

(−0.45, −10) and
(0.45, −10)

45.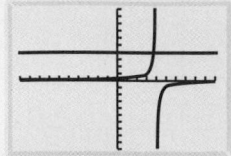

(3.76, 4.2)

46.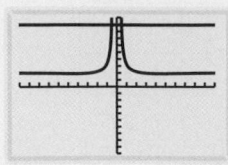

(−0.76, 9) and (0.76, 9)

47a. $m = \dfrac{10{,}000}{g}$

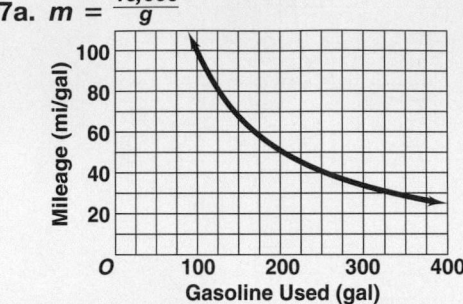

b. $m = \dfrac{10{,}000}{g - 50}$

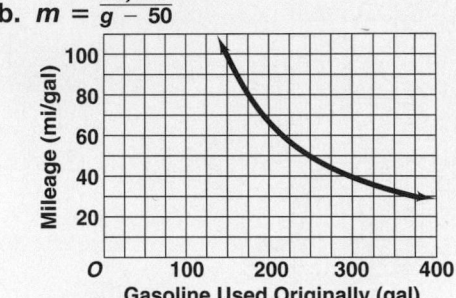

48. The branches of $y = \frac{1}{x}$ are in
Quadrants I and III. The branches
of $y = \left|\frac{1}{x}\right|$ are in Quadrants I and
II. The graphs intersect at all
points on $y = \frac{1}{x}$ in Quadrant I.

49. The branches of $y = \frac{1}{x^2}$ are in
Quadrants I and II. The branches
of $y = \frac{1}{x}$ are in Quadrants I and III.
The graphs intersect at (1, 1). The
graph of $y = \frac{1}{x^2}$ is closer to the
x-axis for $x > 1$, and the graph of
$y = \frac{1}{x}$ is closer to the y-axis for
$0 < x < 1$.

50. The branches of both graphs are
in Quadrants I and II. They
intersect at (1, 1) and (−1, 1). The
graph of $y = \frac{1}{x^2}$ is closer to the
x-axis for $x > 1$ and $x < −1$.
The graph of $y = \left|\frac{1}{x}\right|$ is closer
to the y-axis for $1 < x < 0$ and
$0 < x < 1$.

page 490   Standardized Test Prep

58. [2] When $x − 2 = 0$, $-\dfrac{3}{x - 2}$ is
undefined, so $x = 2$ is an
asymptote. As x becomes
larger, the value of $-\dfrac{3}{x - 2}$
approaches 0, so y
approaches 11, and $y = 11$
is an asymptote.

[1] answer only, with no
explanation

60. V varies jointly with the square of
s and h.

61. h varies directly with V and
inversely with the square of s.

62. B varies directly with V and
inversely with h.

63. w varies directly with V and
inversely with the product of
ℓ and h.

64. b varies directly with A and
inversely with h.

LESSON 9-3

pages 492–495   Check Understanding

4.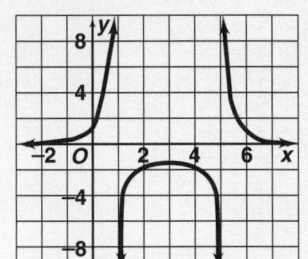

5a. Answers may vary. Sample: Graph
$y = 8$ and use the Intersection
feature to find that the graphs
intersect at $x = 16{,}103.2$. So the
number of discs produced must be
greater than 16,103.

c. Answers may vary. Sample: The
vertical asymptote means that if
you produce 100 or fewer discs you
won't sell any, since the first 100
are samples. The horizontal
asymptote means that the average
cost will never go below $.25, since
that is how much each disc costs
to produce.

35.

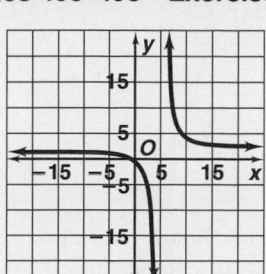

36.

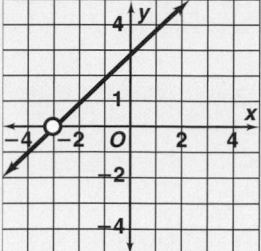

37.

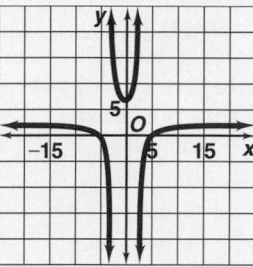

38.

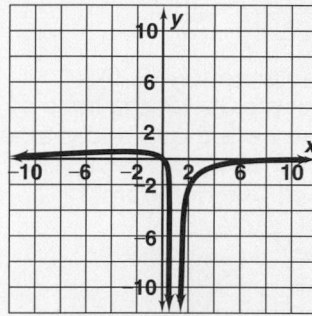

39.

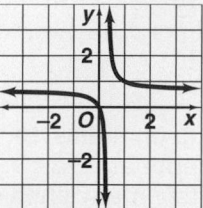

40.

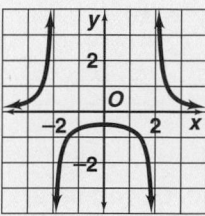

43a. $y = \dfrac{20{,}000x + 200{,}000}{x + 1}$

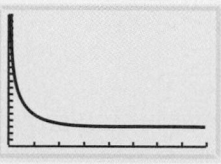

WINDOW FORMAT
Xmin=0
Xmax=40
Xscl=4
Ymin=0
Ymax=200000
Yscl=10000

45d.

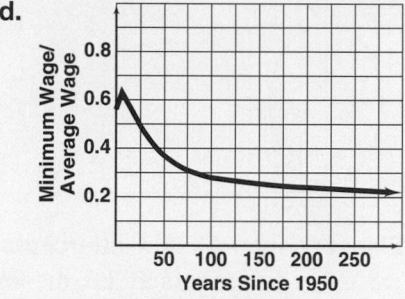

page 498   Checkpoint Quiz 1

9.

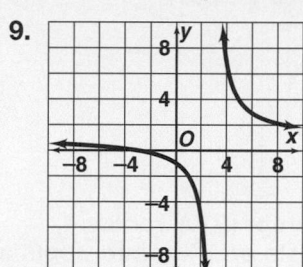

LESSON 9-5

page 504   Investigation

2. Since the denominators are the same, add the numerators and simplify.

3. Answers may vary. Sample: You have to get a common denominator, find the corresponding numerators and then add numerators for both rational expressions and fractions.

page 530   Chapter Test

7.

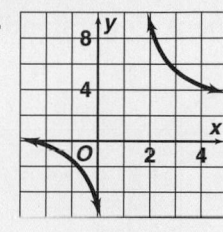

$y = \dfrac{7}{x - 1} + 2$

8.

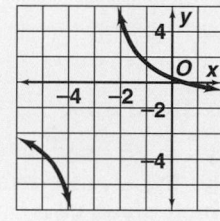

$y = \dfrac{7}{x + 3} - 2$

18. $-\dfrac{2x - 1}{(x + 4)(2x + 1)}; x \neq -4,$

$-3, -\dfrac{1}{2},$ or 0

CHAPTER 10

page 532   Diagnosing Readiness

19.

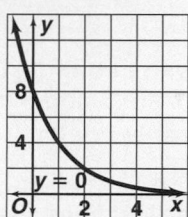

20.

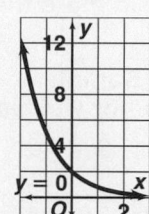

21.

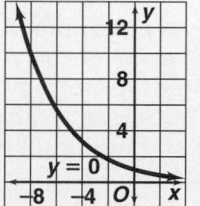

LESSON 10-1

pages 536–538 Check Understanding

1a.

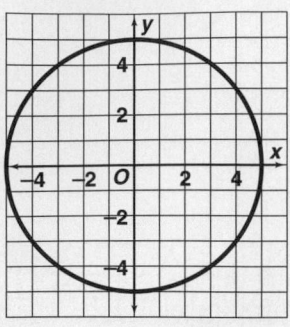

The graphs are the same.

b. Rewrite $x^2 + y^2 = 25$ as $y^2 = 25 - x^2$. Then take the square root of both sides, which gives you $y = \pm\sqrt{25 - x^2}$.

2c.

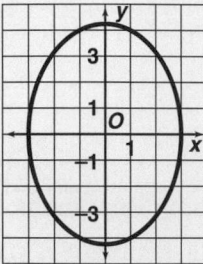

It is an ellipse with center $(0, 0)$. The x-intercepts are 3 and -3 and the y-intercepts are $3\sqrt{2}$ and $-3\sqrt{2}$.

3a. No; there are vertical lines that intersect the graph in more than one point.

b. Answers may vary. Sample: Solving $x^2 - y^2 = 9$ for y gives $y = \pm\sqrt{x^2 - 9}$. For $-3 < x < 3$, the value of $x^2 - 9$ is negative and $\sqrt{x^2 - 9}$ is not a real number.

5a. Answers may vary. Sample: All equations have an x^2-term, a y^2-term, and no other terms on the left side. There is a positive constant term and nothing else on the right side.

b. Answers may vary. Sample: The related domains and ranges are all different. The absolute values of the coefficients of x^2 and y^2 are equal for $x^2 - y^2 = 1$, but the signs of the coefficients are different. The absolute values of the coefficients of x^2 and y^2 are equal for $x^2 + y^2 = 16$, and the signs are the same. The absolute values of the coefficients of x^2 and y^2 are different for $9x^2 + 25y^2 = 225$, but the signs are the same.

T936

pages 538–541 Exercises

1.

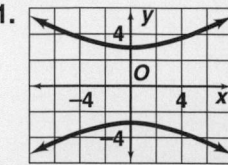

Hyperbola: center $(0, 0)$, y-intercepts at $\pm\frac{5\sqrt{3}}{3}$, no x-intercepts, the lines of symmetry are the x- and y-axes; domain: all real numbers, range: $y \geq \frac{5\sqrt{3}}{3}$ or $y \leq -\frac{5\sqrt{3}}{3}$.

2.

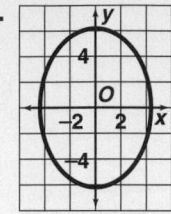

Ellipse: center $(0, 0)$, x-intercepts at $\pm3\sqrt{2}$, y-intercepts at ±6, the lines of symmetry are the x- and y-axes; domain: $-3\sqrt{2} \leq x \leq 3\sqrt{2}$, range $-6 \leq y \leq 6$.

3.

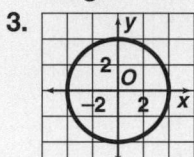

Circle: center $(0, 0)$, radius 4, x-intercepts at ±4, y-intercepts at ±4, there are infinitely many lines of symmetry; domain: $-4 \leq x \leq 4$, range: $-4 \leq y \leq 4$.

4.

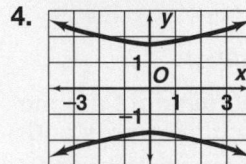

Hyperbola: center $(0, 0)$, y-intercepts at $\pm\sqrt{3}$, no x-intercepts, the lines of symmetry are the x- and y-axes; domain: all real numbers, range: $y \leq -\sqrt{3}$ or $y \geq \sqrt{3}$.

5.

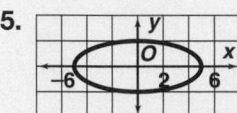

Ellipse: center $(0, 0)$, y-intercepts at ±2, x-intercepts at ±5, the lines of symmetry are the x- and y-axes; domain: $-5 \leq x \leq 5$, range: $-2 \leq y \leq 2$.

6.

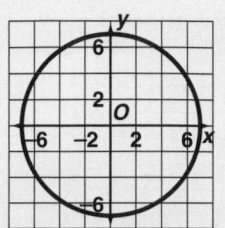

Circle: center $(0, 0)$, radius 7, x- and y-intercepts at ±7, there are infinitely many lines of symmetry; domain: $-7 \leq x \leq 7$, range: $-7 \leq y \leq 7$.

7.

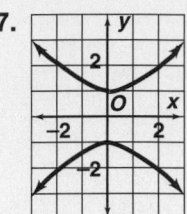

Hyperbola: center $(0, 0)$, y-intercepts at ±1, the lines of symmetry are the x- and y-axes; domain: all real numbers, range: $y \leq -1$ or $y \geq 1$.

8.

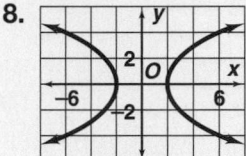

Hyperbola: center $(0, 0)$, x-intercepts at ±2, the lines of symmetry are the x- and y-axes; domain: $x \leq -2$ or $x \geq 2$, range: all real numbers.

9.

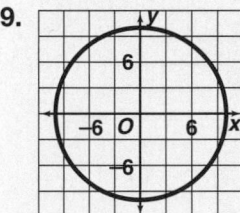

Circle: center $(0, 0)$, radius 10, x- and y-intercepts at ±10, there are infinitely many lines of symmetry; domain: $-10 \leq x \leq 10$, range: $-10 \leq y \leq 10$.

10.

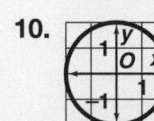

Circle: center $(0, 0)$, radius 2, x- and y-intercepts at ±2, there are infinitely many lines of symmetry; domain: $-2 \leq x \leq 2$, range: $-2 \leq y \leq 2$.

11.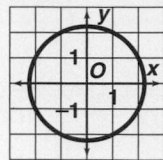

Ellipse: center (0, 0), *x*-intercepts at ±4, *y*-intercepts at ±2, the lines of symmetry are the *x*- and *y*-axes; domain: $-4 \le x \le 4$, range: $-2 \le y \le 2$.

12.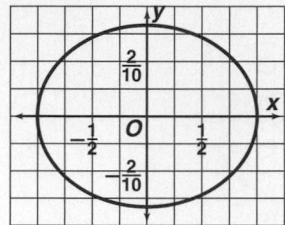

Circle: center (0, 0), radius $\sqrt{5}$, *x*- and *y*-intercepts at $\pm\sqrt{5}$, there are infinitely many lines of symmetry; domain: $-\sqrt{5} \le x \le \sqrt{5}$, range: $-\sqrt{5} \le y \le \sqrt{5}$.

13.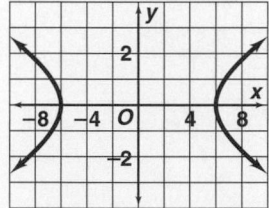

Ellipse: center (0, 0), *x*-intercepts at ±1, *y*-intercepts at $\pm\frac{1}{3}$, the lines of symmetry are the *x*- and *y*-axes; domain: $-1 \le x \le 1$, range: $-\frac{1}{3} \le y \le \frac{1}{3}$.

14.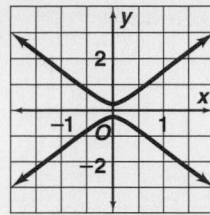

Hyperbola: center (0, 0), *x*-intercepts at ±6, the lines of symmetry are the *x*- and *y*-axes; domain: $x \le -6$, or $x \ge 6$ range: all real numbers.

15.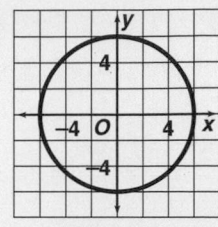

Hyperbola: center (0, 0), *y*-intercepts at $\pm\frac{1}{2}$, the lines of symmetry are the *x*- and *y*-axes; domain: all real numbers, range: $y \le -\frac{1}{2}$ or $y \ge \frac{1}{2}$.

16.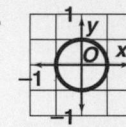

Ellipse: center (0, 0), *x*-intercepts at ±2, *y*-intercepts at ±6, the lines of symmetry are the *x*- and *y*-axes; domain: $-2 \le x \le 2$, range: $-6 \le y \le 6$.

33a. All lines in the plane that pass through the center of a circle are axes of symmetry of the circle.

b. The axes of symmetry of an ellipse intersect at the center of the ellipse. The same is true for a hyperbola. This can be confirmed using, for example, $4x^2 + 9y^2 = 36$ and $4x^2 - 9y^2 = 36$.

34a. Let the lamp sit in a normal, upright position, but close enough to the wall for the bottom rim of the shade to almost touch the wall.

b. Hold the lamp so that the shade contacts the wall along a vertical line.

c. Hold the lamp at an angle so that the light from the top of the shade gives a closed, curved oblong area of light on the wall.

d. Hold the lamp so that the circular top rim of the shade is parallel to the wall.

41.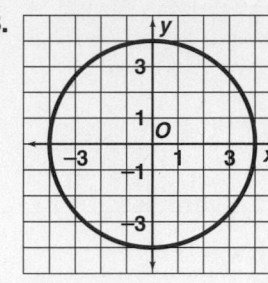

$x^2 + y^2 = 36$

42.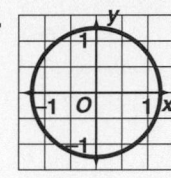

$x^2 + y^2 = \frac{1}{4}$

43.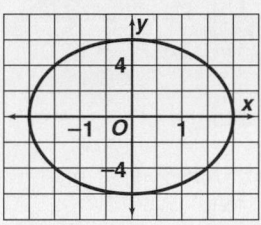

$x^2 + y^2 = 16$

44.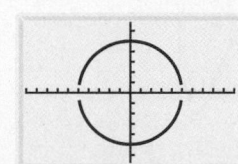

$x^2 + y^2 = 1.5625$

page 542   Technology

1.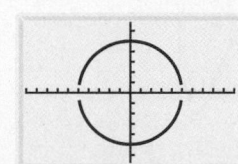

2.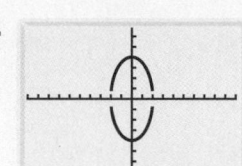

3.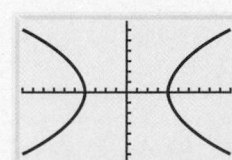

4.

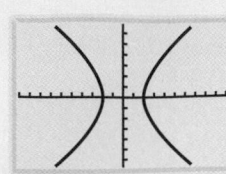

5.

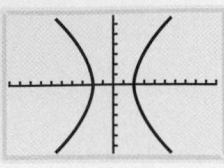

6.

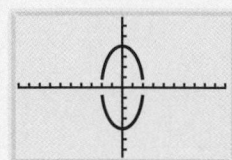

LESSON 10-2

pages 546–548   Exercises

24. $(0, 0)$, $(6, 0)$, $x = -6$

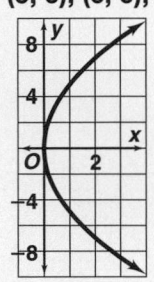

25. $(0, 0)$, $(0, -1)$, $y = 1$

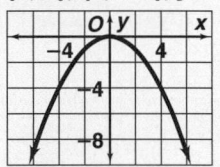

26. $(0, 0)$, $(3, 0)$, $x = -3$

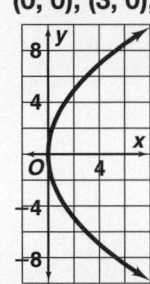

27. $(0, 0)$, $\left(\frac{25}{4}, 0\right)$, $x = -\frac{25}{4}$

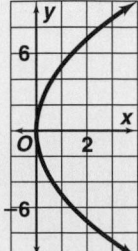

28. $(0, 0)$, $(0, 1)$, $y = -1$

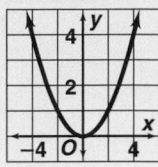

29. $(0, 0)$, $(0, -1)$, $y = 1$

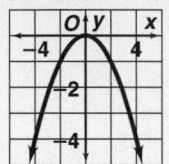

30. $(2, 0)$, $(2, 1)$, $y = -1$

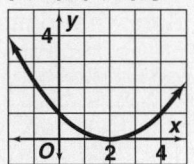

31. $(0, 0)$, $(-2, 0)$, $x = 2$

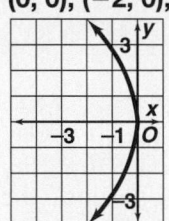

32. $(-2, 4)$, $\left(-2, \frac{17}{4}\right)$, $y = \frac{15}{4}$

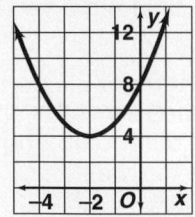

33. $(-3, 0)$, $\left(-\frac{3}{2}, 0\right)$, $x = -\frac{9}{2}$

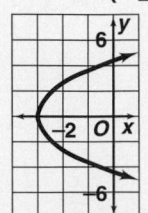

34. $(4, 0)$, $(4, -6)$, $y = 6$

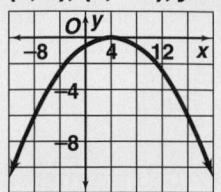

35. $(3, -1)$, $(6, -1)$, $x = 0$

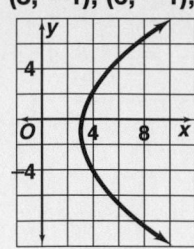

46.

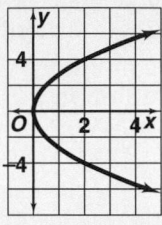

47.

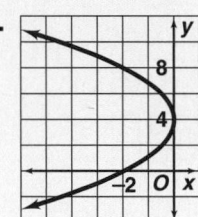

48.

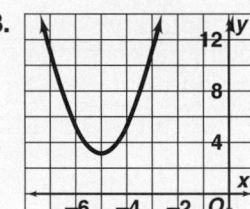

49.

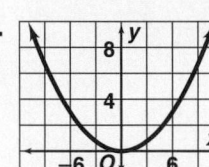

50.

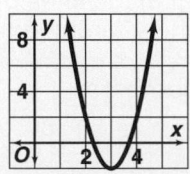

T938

51.

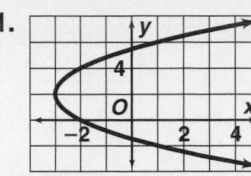

LESSON 10-3

pages 552–554   Exercises

27.

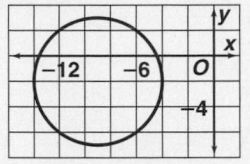

28.

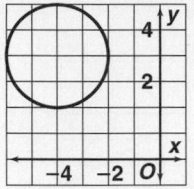

29.

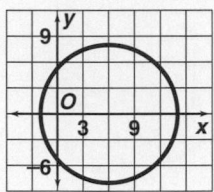

30.

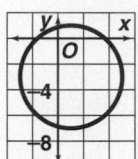

31.

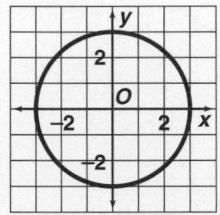

32.

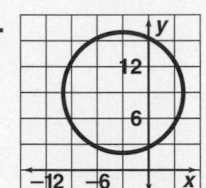

33.

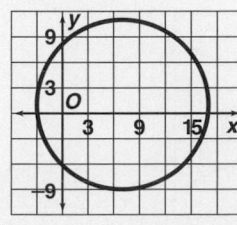

34.

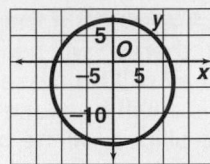

67. Let $P(x, y)$ **be any point on the circle centered at the origin and having radius** r. **If** $P(x, y)$ **is one of the points** $(r, 0), (-r, 0), (0, r),$ **or** $(0, -r),$ **substitution shows that** $x^2 + y^2 = r^2$. **If** $P(x, y)$ **is any other point on the circle, drop a perpendicular** $\overline{PK}$ **from** P **to the** x-**axis (**K **on the** x-**axis).** $\triangle OPK$ **is a right triangle with legs of lengths** $|x|$ **and** $|y|$ **and with hypotenuse of length** r. **By the Pythagorean Theorem,** $|x|^2 + |y|^2 = r^2$. **But** $|x|^2 = x^2$ **and** $|y|^2 = y^2$. **So** $x^2 + y^2 = r^2$.

69a.

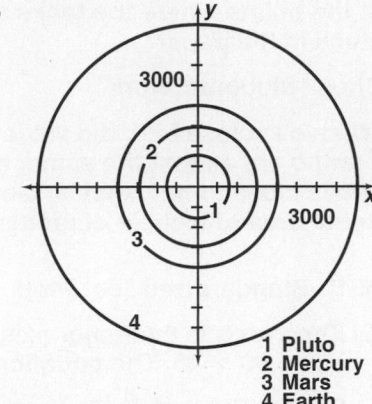

1 Pluto
2 Mercury
3 Mars
4 Earth

b. Earth: $x^2 + y^2 = 15{,}705{,}369$
  Mars: $x^2 + y^2 = 4{,}456{,}321$
  Mercury: $x^2 + y^2 = 2{,}296{,}740$
  Pluto: $x^2 + y^2 = 511{,}225$

page 555   Extension

7.

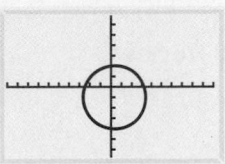

8.

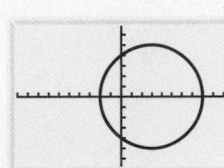

LESSON 10-4

pages 559–561   Exercises

9. $\dfrac{x^2}{2.25} + \dfrac{y^2}{0.25} = 1$

10. $\dfrac{x^2}{64} + \dfrac{y^2}{256} = 1$

11. $\dfrac{x^2}{36} + \dfrac{y^2}{100} = 1$

12. $\dfrac{x^2}{12.25} + \dfrac{y^2}{25} = 1$

13. $\dfrac{x^2}{196} + \dfrac{y^2}{49} = 1$

14. $x^2 + \dfrac{y^2}{16} = 1$

15. $\dfrac{x^2}{256} + \dfrac{y^2}{56.25} = 1$

16. $\dfrac{x^2}{900} + \dfrac{y^2}{400} = 1$

17. $x^2 + \dfrac{y^2}{6.25} = 1$

18. $(0, \sqrt{5}), (0, -\sqrt{5})$

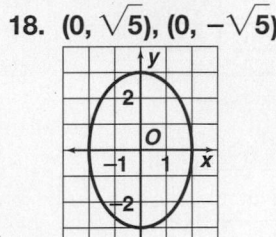

19. $(0, 4), (0, -4)$

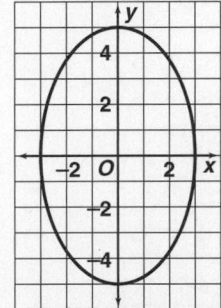

20. $(4\sqrt{2}, 0), (-4\sqrt{2}, 0)$

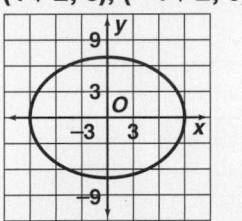

21. $(8, 0), (-8, 0)$

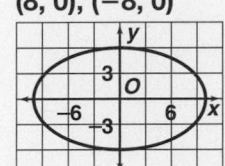

22. $(0, 6), (0, -6)$

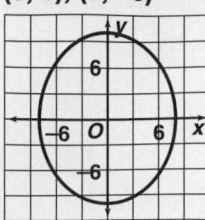

23. $(0, \sqrt{6}), (0, -\sqrt{6})$

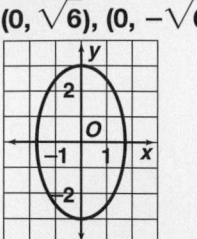

24. $(2\sqrt{3}, 0), (-2\sqrt{3}, 0)$

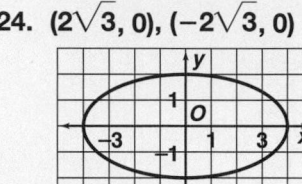

25. $(9, 0), (-9, 0)$

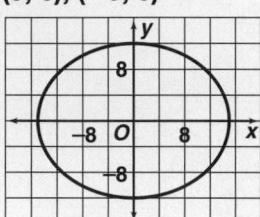

26. $(3\sqrt{15}, 0), (-3\sqrt{15}, 0)$

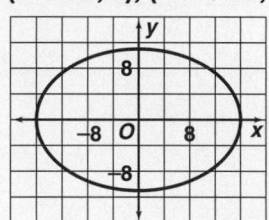

41a. 0.9;

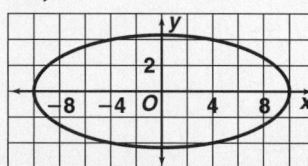

b. 0.1;

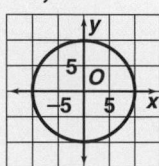

c. The shape is close to a circle.

d. The shape is close to a line segment.

43a. Yes; since $c^2 = a^2 - b^2$, if the foci are close to 0, then c^2 will be close to 0 and a^2 will be close to b^2. This means a will be close to b and hence the ellipse will be close to a circle.

b. If F_1 and F_2 are considered distinct pts., then a circle is not an ellipse. If F_1 and F_2 are the same pt., then a circle is an ellipse.

48. The vertices are the points farthest from the center and the co-vertices are the points closest to the center.

64a. The vertices are at the points where the curve intersects the line through the holes made by the tacks. The co-vertices are the points where the curve intersects the perpendicular bisector of the segment connecting the vertices.

b. at the points where the tacks are stuck in the paper

c. Check students' work.

65. When c is close to 0, the values of a and b are almost the same, and πab is close to πa^2, that is, close to the area of a circle of radius a.

page 561   Standardized Test Prep

72. [2] The x-axis is the major axis since $50 > 40$. The equation is of the form $\frac{x^2}{a^2} + \frac{y^2}{b^2} = 1$.
$2a = 50$, so $a = 25$, and $2b = 40$, so $b = 20$. Therefore, $a^2 = 625$ and $b^2 = 400$. The equation is $\frac{x^2}{625} + \frac{y^2}{400} = 1$.
[1] answer only OR minor error in calculating a^2 and b^2

page 561   Mixed Review

75. $\frac{1}{2x - 3x^4}; x \neq 0, \sqrt[3]{\frac{2}{3}}$

76. $\frac{x - 6}{x - 1}; x \neq 1, -6$

77. $\frac{x - 5}{x^2 - 2x + 4}; x \neq -2$

LESSON 10-5

pages 566–568   Exercises

1.

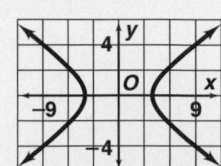

2.

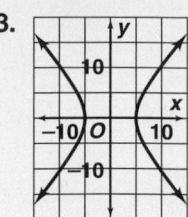

3.

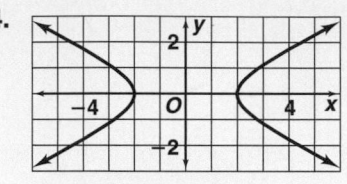

4.

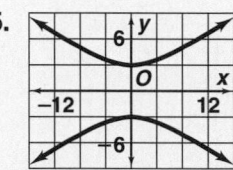

5.

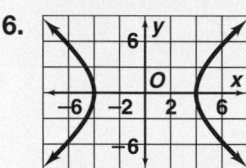

6.

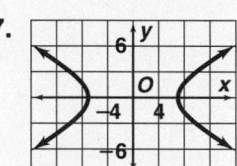

7.

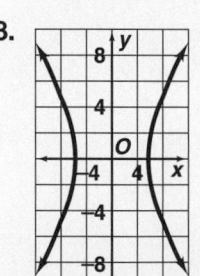

8.

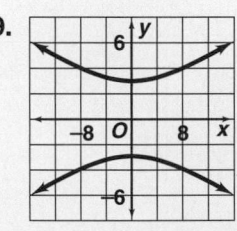

9.

10. $(0, \sqrt{97})$, $(0, -\sqrt{97})$;

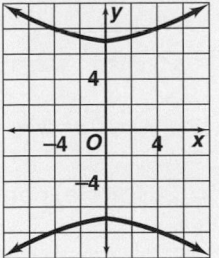

11. $(0, \sqrt{113})$, $(0, -\sqrt{113})$;

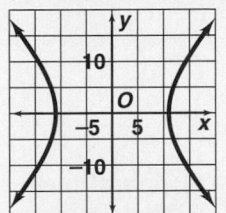

12. $(\sqrt{265}, 0)$, $(-\sqrt{265}, 0)$;

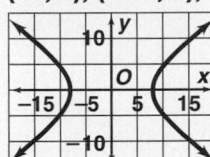

13. $(10, 0)$, $(-10, 0)$;

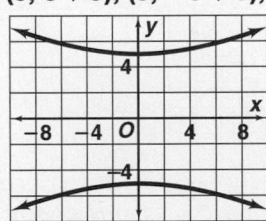

14. $(0, 5\sqrt{5})$, $(0, -5\sqrt{5})$;

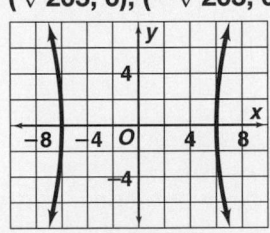

15. $(\sqrt{205}, 0)$, $(-\sqrt{205}, 0)$

16. $(0, \sqrt{29})$, $(0, -\sqrt{29})$

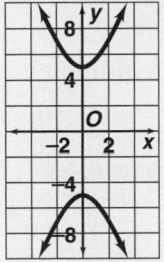

17. $(2\sqrt{11}, 0)$, $(-2\sqrt{11}, 0)$

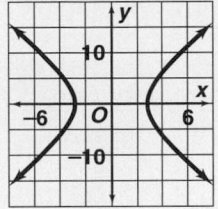

18. $(0, 4\sqrt{3})$, $(0, -4\sqrt{3})$

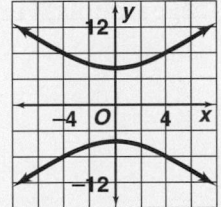

27.

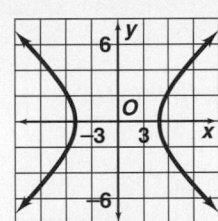

28.

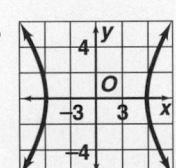

29.

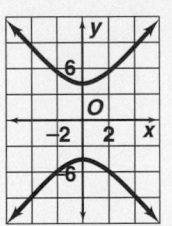

30. $\dfrac{y^2}{20.25} - \dfrac{x^2}{4} = 1$

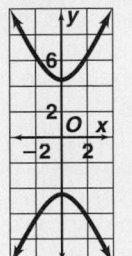

31. $\dfrac{y^2}{9} - x^2 = 1$

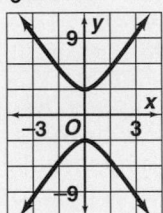

32. $\dfrac{x^2}{32} - \dfrac{y^2}{64} = 1$

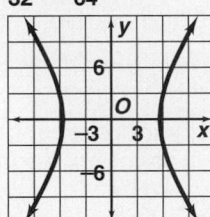

33. $y = \pm\sqrt{\dfrac{x^2}{2} - 2}$; $(2, 0)$, $(-2, 0)$

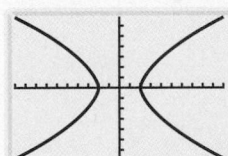

34. $y = \pm\sqrt{x^2 - 1}$; $(1, 0)$, $(-1, 0)$

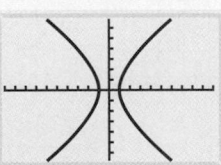

35. $y = \pm\sqrt{3x^2 - 2}$; $(-0.816, 0)$, $(0.816, 0)$

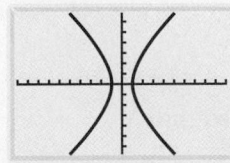

37. Answers may vary. Sample: Similarities—Both have two axes of symmetry that intersect at the center of the figure. Both have two foci that lie on the same line as the two "principal" vertices. Differences—An ellipse consists of points whose distances from the foci have a constant sum, but a hyperbola consists of points whose distances from the foci have a constant difference. An ellipse is a closed curve, but a hyperbola is not and has two separate branches that do not touch. Hyperbolas have asymptotes, but ellipses do not. An ellipse intersects both its axes of symmetry, but a hyperbola intersects only one of its axes of symmetry.

47a. For the x-values in those rows, the value of $x^2 - 9$ is negative and so $\sqrt{x^2 - 9}$ is not a real number.

b. As x increases, y increases, but the difference between x and y gets closer to zero.

c. No; for positive values of x greater than 3, $x = \sqrt{x^2}$ and $\sqrt{x^2} \neq \sqrt{x^2 - 9}$.

d. $y = x, y = -x$;

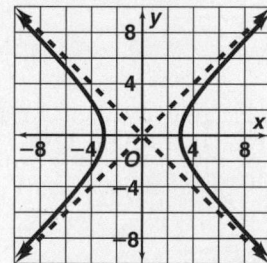

48a. If the hyperbola $\frac{y^2}{a^2} - \frac{x^2}{b^2} = 1$ crossed either $y = \frac{a}{b}x$ or $y = -\frac{a}{b}x$, then there would have to be a value of x and a value of y for which $\frac{a}{b}\sqrt{x^2 + b^2} = \frac{a}{b}x$ or $\frac{a}{b}\sqrt{x^2 + b^2} = -\frac{a}{b}x$. That would require that $\sqrt{x^2 + b^2} = x$ or $\sqrt{x^2 + b^2} = -x$. But squaring these equations gives $x^2 + b^2 = x^2$. This would mean that $b^2 = 0$ and hence $b = 0$. But for any hyperbola, $b > 0$. So the hyperbola never intersects its asymptotes.

b. Yes; multiply both sides by $\frac{1}{4}$ to obtain $\frac{y^2}{64} - \frac{x^2}{36} = 1$. This equation is clearly an equation of a hyperbola. Yes; multiply both sides by -1 to obtain $\frac{x^2}{9} - \frac{y^2}{16} = 1$. This equation is clearly an equation of a hyperbola.

pages 567–568   Standardized Test Prep

52. [2] $\frac{x^2}{a^2} - \frac{y^2}{b^2} = 1$ or $\frac{y^2}{a^2} - \frac{x^2}{b^2} = 1$; divide both sides by 1225 and then simplify, which leaves you with $\frac{x^2}{49} - \frac{y^2}{25} = 1$.

[1] answer correct, but no explanation

LESSON 10-6

pages 573–576   Exercises

12. $y = (x - 4)^2 + 3$; parabola, vertex (4, 3)

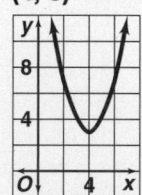

13. $(x + 6)^2 + y^2 = 81$; circle, center (−6, 0), radius 9

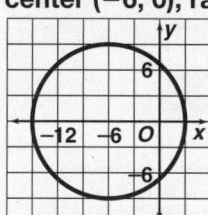

14. $\frac{(x + 1)^2}{3} + \frac{(y - 3)^2}{9} = 1$; ellipse, center (−1, 3), foci (−1, 3 ± $\sqrt{6}$)

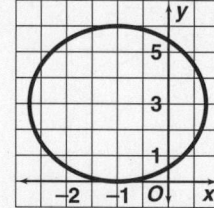

15. $(x - 1)^2 + (y + 3)^2 = 13$; circle, center (1, −3), radius $\sqrt{13}$

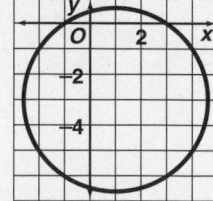

16. $(y - 2)^2 - (x - 3)^2 = 1$; hyperbola, center (3, 2), foci (3, 2 ± $\sqrt{2}$)

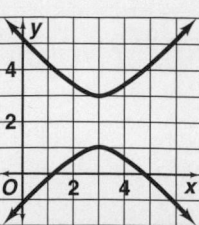

17. $\frac{(x - 1)^2}{4} - (y + 1)^2 = 1$; hyperbola, center (1, −1), foci (1 ± $\sqrt{5}$, −1)

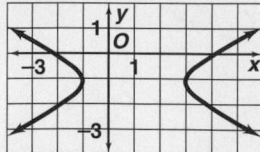

18. $x^2 + (y + 7)^2 = 36$; circle, center (0, −7), radius 6

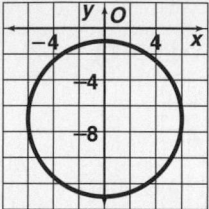

19. $x - 3 = \frac{1}{2}(y - 2)^2$; parabola, vertex (3, 2)

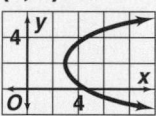

20. $\frac{(x + 2)^2}{9} + \frac{(y - 3)^2}{4} = 1$; ellipse, center (−2, 3), foci (−2 ± $\sqrt{5}$, 3)

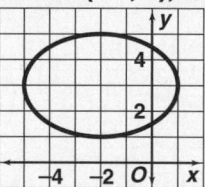

21. $(x + 3)^2 - (y - 5)^2 = 1$; hyperbola, center (−3, 5), foci (−3 ± $\sqrt{2}$, 5)

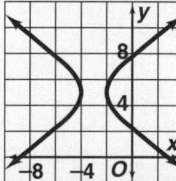

22. $\frac{(x - 1)^2}{16} + \frac{y^2}{4} = 1$; ellipse, center (1, 0), foci (1 ± $2\sqrt{3}$, 0)

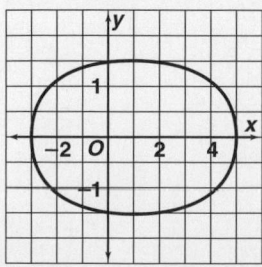

23. $\frac{x^2}{4} - \frac{(y+3)^2}{9} = 1$; hyperbola, center $(0, -3)$,

foci $(\pm\sqrt{13}, -3)$

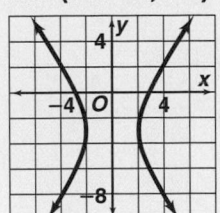

29. $(x+6)^2 + (y-9)^2 = 81$

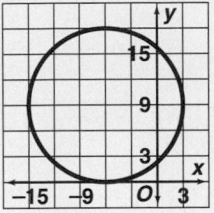

30. $\frac{(x-3)^2}{36} + \frac{(y-2)^2}{9} = 1$

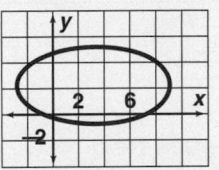

31. $y = \frac{1}{20}(x-2)^2 - 3$

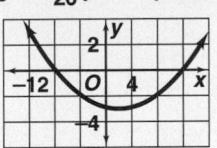

32. $\frac{(y+3)^2}{4} - \frac{(x-6)^2}{5} = 1$

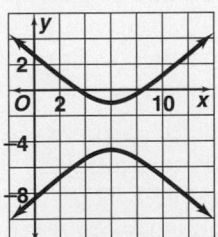

49.

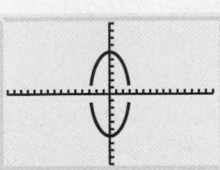

ellipse, $\frac{x^2}{9} + \frac{y^2}{36} = 1$

50.

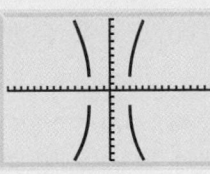

hyperbola, $\frac{x^2}{9} - \frac{y^2}{36} = 1$

51.

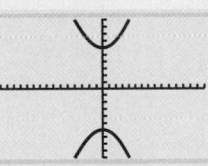

hyperbola, $\frac{y^2}{36} - \frac{x^2}{9} = 1$

52.

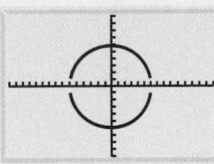

circle, $x^2 + y^2 = 36$

53.

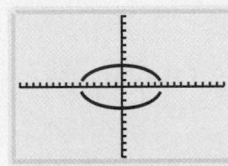

ellipse, $\frac{x^2}{36} + \frac{y^2}{9} = 1$

54.

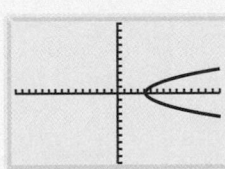

parabola, $x = y^2 + 4$

pages 579–581   Chapter Review

6.

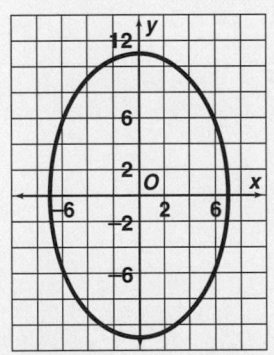

ellipse; x-axis and y-axis;
domain: $-7 \le x \le 7$
range: $-11 \le y \le 11$

7.

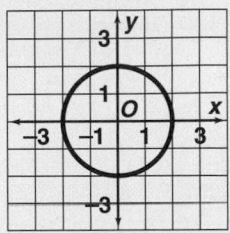

circle; every line through the center;
domain: $-2 \le x \le 2$
range: $-2 \le y \le 2$

8.

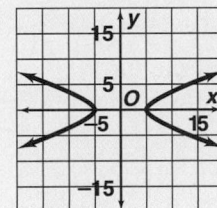

hyperbola; x-axis and y-axis;
domain: $x \le -5$ or $x \ge 5$
range: all real numbers

9.

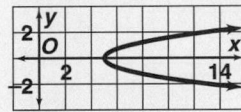

parabola; x-axis;
domain: $x \ge 5$
range: all real numbers

page 582   Chapter Test

6. focus $\left(0, \frac{1}{12}\right)$, directrix $y = -\frac{1}{12}$

7. focus $\left(-\frac{1}{8}, 0\right)$, directrix $x = \frac{1}{8}$

8. focus $\left(-\frac{1}{20}, 0\right)$, directrix $x = \frac{1}{20}$

9. focus $\left(0, \frac{1}{18}\right)$, directrix $y = -\frac{1}{18}$

14. center $(2, 3)$, radius 6;

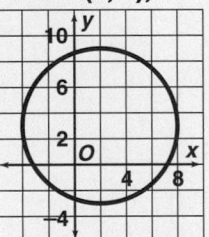

15. center $(-5, -8)$, radius 10;

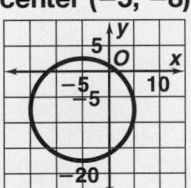

16. center (1, −7), radius 9;

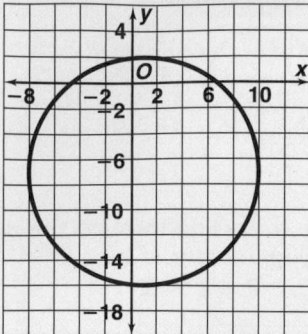

17. center (−4, 10), radius 11;

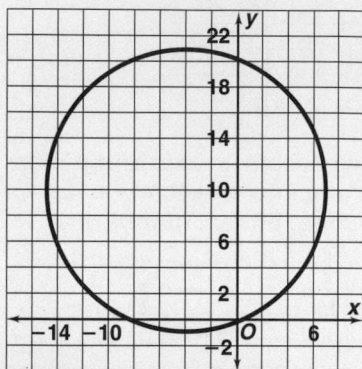

21. foci (±3 √5, 0);

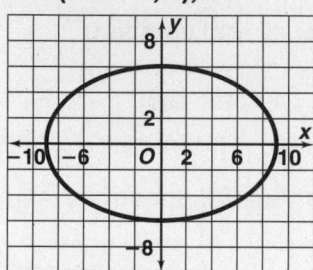

22. foci (0, ±4 √6)

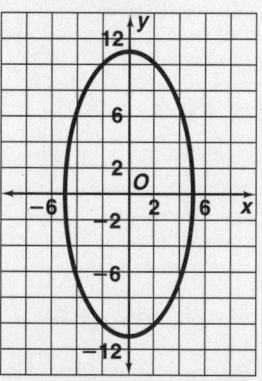

23. foci (0, ±4 √3)

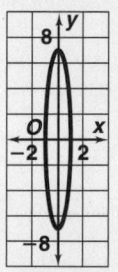

24. foci (0, ±√3)

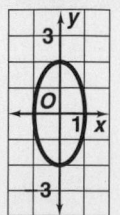

26. foci (±2 √61, 0)

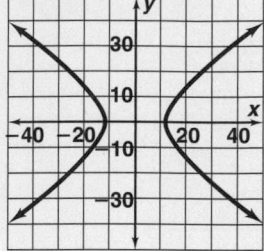

27. foci (0, ±√569)

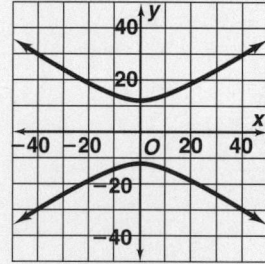

28. foci (±2 √17, 0)

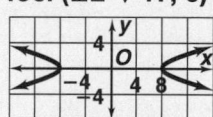

29. foci (0, ±√226)

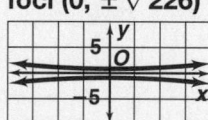

31. $\frac{x^2}{16} + \frac{y^2}{9} = 1$

32. $\frac{(x + 2)^2}{16} + \frac{(y - 7)^2}{9} = 1$

33. $\frac{(x - 3)^2}{25} + \frac{(y + 2)^2}{36} = 1$

34. $\frac{x^2}{9} - \frac{(y - 7)^2}{16} = 1$

35. $\frac{y^2}{25} - \frac{(x - 2)^2}{24} = 1$

36. $(x + 4)^2 - \frac{(y + 1)^2}{15} = 1$

37. parabola; vertex (2, 1)

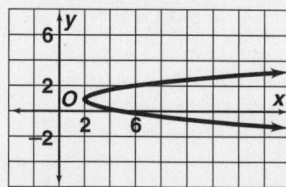

38. circle; center (2, 3), radius 3

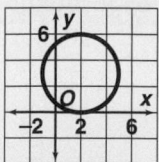

39. ellipse; center (2, 3), foci (2, 3 ±2√3);

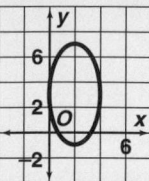

40. hyperbola; center (2, 3), foci (2 ± 2√5, 3)

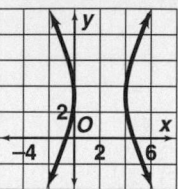

page 583 Cumulative Review

14. [2] $x^2 - 2x = 0$
$x(x - 2) = 0$
$x = 0$ or $x - 2 = 0$
                      $x = 2$
The zeros are 0 and 2.

[1] only 1 correct

15. [4] a. $y = 3x + 2$; slope = 3; the slope of a perpendicular line is $-\frac{1}{3}$. Select any y-intercept: −1. The equation is $y = -\frac{1}{3}x - 1$.

b. $y = 3x + 2$; slope of parallel line = 3; select any y-intercept: 4. The equation is $y = 3x + 4$.

[3] only takes reciprocal of slope in (a) OR only makes it negative

[2] takes the negative reciprocal of the slope in (b) and leaves the slope in (a)

[1] performs the error mentioned in [3] AND (b) is incorrect

CHAPTER 11

page 586 Diagnosing Readiness

10.
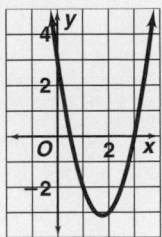

11.
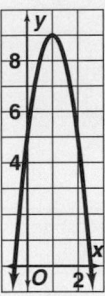

12.
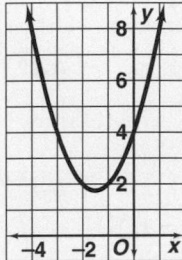

LESSON 11-1

page 588 Check Skills You'll Need

2. $-14, -16$; subtract 2.

3. 3125, 15,625; multiply by 5.

4. 20, 15; subtract 5.

5. 8, 4; divide by 2.

6. 20, 23; add 3.

page 588 Investigation

3.
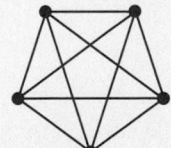 , 10 calls

pages 591–593 Exercises

3. Add one more to each term (add 3, add 4, add 5, etc.); 25, 33, 42.

4. Add 3; 16, 19, 22.

5. Divide by 10; 0.001, 0.0001, 0.00001.

6. Multiply by $\frac{1}{2}$; $\frac{1}{64}$, $\frac{1}{128}$, $\frac{1}{256}$.

7. Multiply by -2; -128, 256, -512.

---

8. Each term is the preceding term multiplied by n; 720, 5040, 40,320.

9. Every odd-numbered term is 0, and every even-numbered term is $\frac{1}{n-1}$; 0, $\frac{1}{7}$, 0.

10.
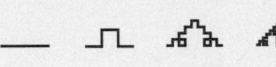

11.

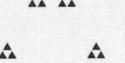

24. recursive; 3, 9, 21, 45, 93

25. explicit; 0, 1, 3, 6, 10

26. explicit; $-24, -21, -16, -9, 0$

27. recursive; $-2, 6, -18, 54, -162$

28. explicit; $-6, -18, -38, -66, -102$

29. explicit; 3, 9, 19, 33, 51

33. 20, 23; $a_n = a_{n-1} + 3$, $a_1 = 5$; recursive

34. 96, 192; $a_n = 2a_{n-1}$, $a_1 = 3$; recursive

35. 216, 343; $a_n = n^3$; explicit

36. 4096, 16,384; $a_n = 4^n$; explicit

37. 144, 169; $a_n = (n + 6)^2$; explicit

38. -1, 1; $a_n = -1(a_{n-1})$, $a_1 = -1$; recursive

39. -1, $-\frac{1}{2}$; $a_n = \frac{a_{n-1}}{2}$; recursive

40. $-47, -40$; $a_n = a_{n-1} + 7$; recursive

41. $-11, -19$; $a_n = a_{n-1} - 8$; recursive

LESSON 11-2

pages 596–598 Exercises

72.
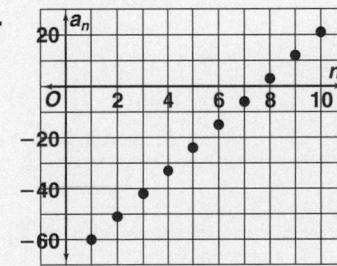

73.
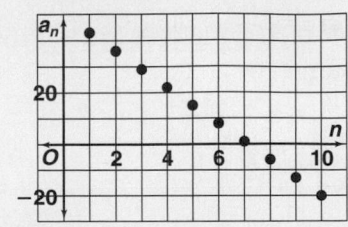

LESSON 11-3

pages 603–605 Exercises

58d.
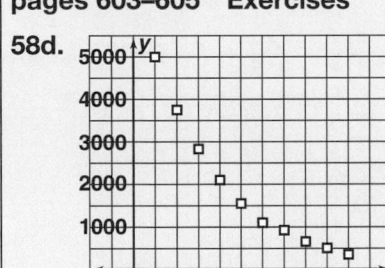

LESSON 11-5

pages 616–619 Exercises

30a.
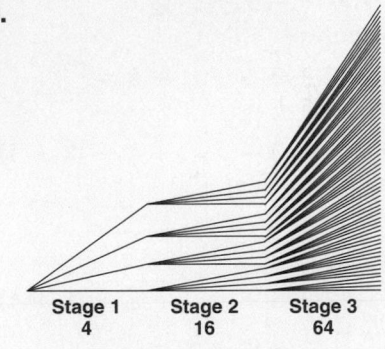

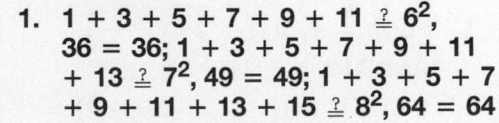

4, 16, 64

page 621 Extension

1. $1 + 3 + 5 + 7 + 9 + 11 \stackrel{?}{=} 6^2$, $36 = 36$; $1 + 3 + 5 + 7 + 9 + 11 + 13 \stackrel{?}{=} 7^2$, $49 = 49$; $1 + 3 + 5 + 7 + 9 + 11 + 13 + 15 \stackrel{?}{=} 8^2$, $64 = 64$

2. a. $2(1) \stackrel{?}{=} 1(1 + 1)$, $2 = 2$

   b. $2 + 4 + 6 + \ldots + 2k = k(k + 1)$

   c. $2 + 4 + 6 + \ldots + 2k + 2(k + 1) = (k + 1)[(k + 1) + 1]$

   d. $2 + 4 + 6 + \ldots + 2k + 2(k + 1)$
   $= (2 + 4 + 6 + \ldots + 2k) + 2(k + 1)$
   $= k(k + 1) + 2(k + 1)$
   $= (k + 1)(k + 2)$
   $= (k + 1)[(k + 1) + 1]$

3. For $n = 1$, $\frac{1}{1(1+1)} = \frac{1}{1+1}$

Assume
$$\frac{1}{1\cdot2} + \frac{1}{2\cdot3} + \frac{1}{3\cdot4} + \ldots + \frac{1}{k(k+1)} = \frac{k}{k+1}$$

Prove
$$\frac{1}{1\cdot2} + \frac{1}{2\cdot3} + \frac{1}{3\cdot4} + \ldots + \frac{1}{k(k+1)} + \frac{1}{(k+1)((k+1)+1)} = \frac{k+1}{(k+1)+1}$$

Proof
$$\frac{1}{1\cdot2} + \frac{1}{2\cdot3} + \frac{1}{3\cdot4} + \ldots + \frac{1}{k(k+1)} + \frac{1}{(k+1)((k+1)+1)} =$$
$$\frac{k}{k+1} + \frac{1}{(k+1)((k+1)+1)} =$$
$$\frac{k(k+2)}{(k+1)(k+2)} + \frac{1}{(k+1)((k+1)+1)} =$$
$$\frac{k(k+2)+1}{(k+1)((k+1)+1)} =$$
$$\frac{k^2+2k+1}{(k+1)((k+1)+1)} =$$
$$\frac{(k+1)^2}{(k+1)((k+1)+1)} = \frac{k+1}{(k+1)+1}$$

4. For $n = 1$, $1 = \frac{1(1+1)}{2}$

Assume
$$1 + 2 + 3 + \ldots + k = \frac{k(k+1)}{2}$$

Prove
$$1 + 2 + 3 + \ldots + k + (k+1) = \frac{(k+1)((k+1)+1)}{2}$$

Proof
$$1 + 2 + 3 + \ldots + k + (k+1) =$$
$$\frac{k(k+1)}{2} + (k+1) =$$
$$\frac{k(k+1) + 2(k+1)}{2} =$$
$$\frac{(k+1)(k+2)}{2} = \frac{(k+1)((k+1)+1)}{2}$$

5. For $n = 1$, $3(1) - 2 = \frac{1(3(1)-1)}{2}$

Assume
$$1 + 4 + 7 + \ldots + (3k-2) = \frac{k(3k-1)}{2}$$

Prove
$$1 + 4 + 7 + \ldots + (3k-2) + (3(k+1)-2) = \frac{(k+1)(3(k+1)-1)}{2}$$

Proof
$$1 + 4 + 7 + \ldots + (3k-2) + (3(k+1)-2) = \frac{k(3k-1)}{2} +$$
$$3(k+1) - 2 =$$
$$\frac{k(3k-1) + 6(k+1) - 4}{2} =$$
$$\frac{3k^2 - k + 6k + 6 - 4}{2} =$$
$$\frac{3k^2 + 5k + 2}{2} =$$
$$\frac{(k+1)(3k+2)}{2} =$$

$$\frac{(k+1)(3k+3-1)}{2} =$$
$$\frac{(k+1)(3(k+1)-1)}{2}$$

6. For $n = 1$, $\left(\frac{1}{2}\right)^1 = 1 - \left(\frac{1}{2}\right)^1$

Assume
$$\frac{1}{2} + \left(\frac{1}{2}\right)^2 + \left(\frac{1}{2}\right)^3 + \left(\frac{1}{2}\right)^4 + \ldots + \left(\frac{1}{2}\right)^k = 1 - \left(\frac{1}{2}\right)^k$$

Prove
$$\frac{1}{2} + \left(\frac{1}{2}\right)^2 + \left(\frac{1}{2}\right)^3 + \left(\frac{1}{2}\right)^4 + \ldots + \left(\frac{1}{2}\right)^k + \left(\frac{1}{2}\right)^{k+1} = 1 - \left(\frac{1}{2}\right)^{k+1}$$

Proof
$$\frac{1}{2} + \left(\frac{1}{2}\right)^2 + \left(\frac{1}{2}\right)^3 + \left(\frac{1}{2}\right)^4 + \ldots + \left(\frac{1}{2}\right)^k + \left(\frac{1}{2}\right)^{k+1} = 1 - \left(\frac{1}{2}\right)^k +$$
$$\left(\frac{1}{2}\right)^{k+1} = 1 - \left(\frac{1}{2}\right)^k\left(1 - \frac{1}{2}\right) = 1 -$$
$$\left(\frac{1}{2}\right)^k\left(\frac{1}{2}\right) = 1 - \left(\frac{1}{2}\right)^{k+1}$$

7. For $n = 1$, $1^2 + 1$ is divisible by 2.

Assume
$k^2 + k$ is divisible by 2; that is $k^2 + k = 2N$, where N is an integer.

Prove
$(k+1)^2 + (k+1)$ is divisible by 2.

Proof
$(k+1)^2 + (k+1) =$
$k^2 + 2k + 1 + k + 1 =$
$k^2 + k + 2k + 2 = 2N +$
$2k + 2 = 2(N + k + 1)$.
Since $(N + k + 1)$ is an integer, $(k+1)^2 + (k+1)$ is divisible by 2.

8. For $n = 1$, $1(1+1) = 2$
and $\frac{1(1+1)(1+2)}{3} = 2$

Assume
$$1\cdot2 + 2\cdot3 + 3\cdot4 + \ldots + k(k+1) = \frac{k(k+1)(k+2)}{3}$$

Prove
$$1\cdot2 + 2\cdot3 + 3\cdot4 + \ldots + k(k+1) + (k+1)((k+1)+1) = \frac{(k+1)((k+1)+1)((k+1)+2)}{3}$$

Proof
$$1\cdot2 + 2\cdot3 + 3\cdot4 + \ldots + k(k+1) + (k+1)((k+1)+1) = \frac{k(k+1)(k+2)}{3} + (k+1)((k+1) + 1) =$$
$$\frac{k(k+1)(k+2)}{3} + (k+1)(k+2) =$$
$$(k+1)(k+2)\left(\frac{k}{3} + 1\right) =$$
$$\frac{(k+1)((k+2)(k+3))}{3} =$$
$$\frac{(k+1)((k+1)+1)((k+1)+2)}{3}$$

9. For $n = 1$, $1^2 = \frac{1(1+1)(2\cdot1+1)}{6}$

Assume
$$1^2 + 2^2 + 3^2 + \ldots + k^2 = \frac{k(k+1)(2k+2)}{6}$$

Prove
$$1^2 + 2^2 + 3^2 + \ldots + k^2 + (k+1)^2 = \frac{(k+1)((k+1)+1)(2(k+1)+2)}{6}$$

Proof
$$1^2 + 2^2 + 3^2 + \ldots + k^2 + (k+1)^2 = \frac{k(k+1)(2k+1)}{6} +$$
$$(k+1)^2 = (k+1)\left(\left(\frac{k(2k+1)}{6}\right) +$$
$$(k+1)\right) = (k+1)\left(\frac{2k^2 + k + 6k + 6}{6}\right) =$$
$$\frac{(k+1)(k+2)(2k+3)}{6} =$$
$$\frac{(k+1)((k+1)+1)(2(k+1)+1)}{6}$$

10. For $n = 1$, $a_1r^{1-1} = a_1r^0 = a_1 = a_1\cdot\frac{1-r}{1-r} = \frac{a_1(1-r^1)}{1-r}$

Assume
$$a_1 + a_1r + a_1r^2 + \ldots + a_1r^{k-1} = \frac{a_1(1-r^k)}{1-r}$$

Prove
$$a_1 + a_1r + a_1r^2 + \ldots + a_1r^{k-1} + a_1r^{(k+1)-1} = \frac{a_1(1-r^{k+1})}{1-r}$$

Proof
$$a_1 + a_1r + a_1r^2 + \ldots + a_1r^{k-1} + a_1r^{(k+1)-1} = \frac{a_1(1-r^k)}{1-r} + a_1r^k =$$
$$a_1\left(\frac{1-r^k}{1-r} + r^k\right) =$$
$$a_1\left(\frac{(1-r^k) + (1-r)r^k}{1-r}\right) =$$
$$a_1\left(\frac{1 - r^k + r^k - r^{k+1}}{1-r}\right) = \frac{a_1(1-r^{k+1})}{1-r}$$

LESSON 11-6

pages 625–627   Exercises

9. $A = \displaystyle\sum_{n=1}^{2} 1f(a_n)$

a. 0.5 units^2

b. 2.5 units^2

10. $A = \displaystyle\sum_{n=1}^{2} 1f(a_n)$

a. 5 units^2

b. 9 units^2

11. $A = \displaystyle\sum_{n=1}^{2} 1f(a_n)$

a. 3 units^2

b. 7 units^2

12. $A = \sum\limits_{n=1}^{2} 1f(a_n)$

a. 3 units^2

b. 7 units^2

13. $A = \sum\limits_{n=1}^{2} 1f(a_n)$

a. $10\frac{1}{3}$ units^2

b. $13\frac{1}{3}$ units^2

14. $A = \sum\limits_{n=1}^{2} 1f(a_n)$

a. 5 units^2

b. 25 units^2

15. $A = \sum\limits_{n=1}^{2} 1f(a_n)$

a. 6.75 units^2

b. 7.75 units^2

16. $A = \sum\limits_{n=1}^{2} 1f(a_n)$

a. 5 units^2

b. 9 units^2

17. $A = \sum\limits_{n=1}^{2} 1f(a_n)$

a. 5 units^2

b. 9 units^2

24.

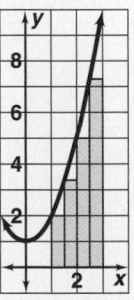

8.75 units^2

25.

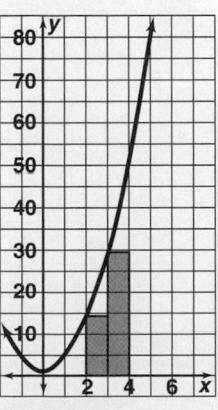

43 units^2

26.

28.75 units^2

27.

50 units^2

28.

16.875 units^2

29.

19.5 units^2

30a.

b. 3 units^2

c.

12 units^2

d. 7.5 units^2; the mean best approximates the area because it is between the other measures known to be larger and smaller than the actual value.

31a. Answers may vary. Sample:

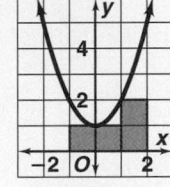

Xmin:0   Ymin:0
Xmax:200   Ymax:70
Xscl:25   Yscl:10

0.37 mile

b. Answers may vary. Sample: Using inscribed rectangles will result in an estimate smaller than the actual number.

page 632   Chapter Test

35.

2 units^2

36.

4 units^2

37.

9 units^2

38. Answers may vary. Sample: You could find the sum of the circumscribed rectangles and the sum of the inscribed rectangles and average the numbers.

CHAPTER 12

LESSON 12-1

pages 637–638   Check Understanding

3. Answers may vary.
Sample:

Rolling One Number Cube

Number	1	2	3	4	5	6
Frequency	1	1	1	1	1	1
Probability	$\frac{1}{6}$	$\frac{1}{6}$	$\frac{1}{6}$	$\frac{1}{6}$	$\frac{1}{6}$	$\frac{1}{6}$

4a. The Plant Color Distribution would be most useful for avoiding white plants because it shows the total probability of growing green plants, which is the desired outcome.

b.

Genotype

Event	GG	Gw	ww
Frequency	1	2	1
Probability	$\frac{1}{4}$	$\frac{1}{2}$	$\frac{1}{4}$

Plant Color

Event	Green	White
Frequency	3	1
Probability	$\frac{3}{4}$	$\frac{1}{4}$

pages 639–641   Exercises

6.

Outcome	Probability
Red	$\frac{1}{7}$
Green	$\frac{3}{7}$
Blue	$\frac{2}{7}$
Yellow	$\frac{1}{7}$

8.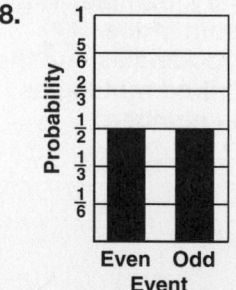

9.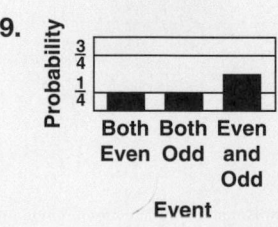

10. Answers may vary. Sample design: Use random numbers. Assign numbers 1 to 1000 to each event, based on its probability.

Age	Probability	Cumulative Probability	Assigned Numbers
<20	0.051	0.051	1–51
20–29	0.176	0.227	52–227
30–39	0.211	0.438	228–438
40–49	0.211	0.649	439–649
50–59	0.156	0.805	650–805
60–69	0.096	0.901	806–901
70–79	0.070	0.971	902–971
≥ 80	0.029	1	972–1000

Random numbers generated: 697, 420, 488, 567, 272, 396, 474, 870, 896, 282, 464, 681, 274, 663, 681, 282, 376, 363, 860, 129
Results of simulation:
Age 20–29: 1, Age 30–39: 8;
Age 40–49: 4, Age 50–59: 4;
Age 60–69: 3

11. Answers may vary. Sample design: Use random numbers. Assign numbers 1 to 1000 to each event, based on its probability.

Type	Prob.	Cum. Prob.	Assigned Numbers
Luxury	0.165	0.165	1–165
Large	0.076	0.241	166–241
Midsize	0.527	0.768	242–768
Small	0.232	1	769–1000

Random numbers generated: 612, 904, 249, 194, 435, 772, 93, 236, 80, 370, 849, 468, 819, 800, 371, 14, 396, 278, 303, 662, 637, 572, 700, 196, 810, 314, 496, 408, 737, 624
Results of simulation: 3 luxury cars, 3 large cars, 18 midsize cars, and 6 small cars

14a.

Weather Conditions in Dayton, Ohio

Type	Frequency	Probability
Clear	82	0.225
Partly Cloudy	118	0.323
Mostly Cloudy	34	0.093
Rain	75	0.205
Light Snow	45	0.123
Snow	11	0.030

b. The independent variable is the type of weather. The dependent variable is the probability that a type of weather occurs.

c. $\frac{131}{365}$ OR 0.359

16a. The independent variable is the amount of gas in the tank; the dependent variable is the percent of people who fill their tanks when they have a given amount of gas.

b.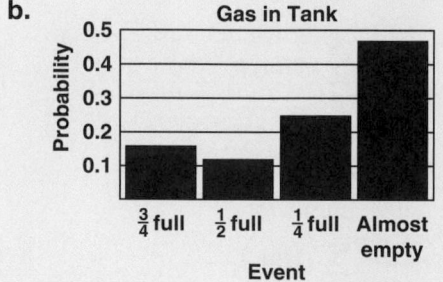

c. 0.28 or 28%

19. Answers may vary. Sample:

a.

Calls	$P(c)$	Cum. Prob.	Assigned #s
0	0.21	0.21	1–21
1	0.30	0.51	22–51
2	0.18	0.69	52–69
3	0.13	0.82	70–82
4	0.09	0.91	83–91
5	0.05	0.96	92–96
6	0.03	0.99	97–99
7	0.01	1.00	100

b. There were six hours in which 3 calls were received, and two in which 4 calls were received. A total of ten callers would have to wait.

d. An additional response team would reduce the probability of having to wait from $\frac{10}{47}$ to $\frac{2}{47}$, a considerable improvement.

LESSON 12-2

pages 646–648   Exercises

29.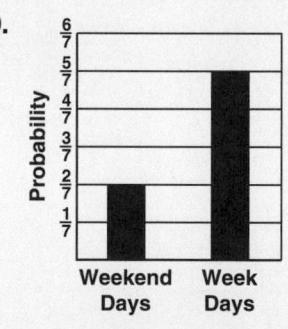

LESSON 12-4

page 656   Investigation

5a. Sets 2 and 4

  b. Sets 2 and 3

6a. The three sets have the same mean, median, and mode. The difference between the extreme values is the same for Sets 2 and 4, although Set 2 is less spread out. The difference $Q_3 - Q_1$ is the same for Sets 2 and 3, although Set 3 is less spread out. Set 4 is the most spread out, with all but two values 40 or more away from the mean. Set 1 is the least spread out, with all its values 3 or less away from the mean.

  b.
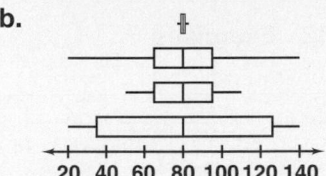

page 657   Check Understanding

1b. Yes; examples may vary. Sample:

  1 2 3 4 5 6 7 8 9 10;
  1 1 1 1 1 10 10 10 10 10

 c. Yes; examples may vary. Sample:

  1 2 3 4 5 6 7 8 9 10;
  3 3 3 5 5 6 6 8 8 8

LESSON 12-6

page 671   Check Skills You'll Need

5. $w^4 - 4w^3y + 6w^2y^2 - 4wy^3 + y^4$

6. $m^3 + 3m^2n + 3mn^2 + n^3$

7. $t^4 + 12t^3s + 54t^2s^2 + 108ts^3 + 81s^4$

8. $a^5 + 10a^4b + 40a^3b^2 + 80a^2b^3 + 80ab^4 + 32b^5$

9. $p^6 + 6p^5q + 15p^4q^2 + 20p^3q^3 + 15p^2q^4 + 6pq^5 + q^6$

page 671   Investigation

2b. Answers may vary. Sample:

Score	Frequency
0	0
10	0
20	1
30	2
40	2
50	2
60	1
70	2
80	0
90	0
100	0

pages 674–677   Exercises

12. $P(0) = 0.1176$
$P(1) = 0.3025$
$P(2) = 0.3241$
$P(3) = 0.1852$
$P(4) = 0.0595$
$P(5) = 0.0102$
$P(6) = 0.0007$

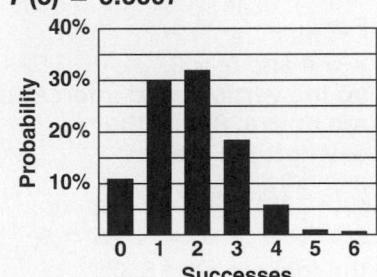

13. $P(0) = 0.0156$
$P(1) = 0.0938$
$P(2) = 0.2344$
$P(3) = 0.3125$
$P(4) = 0.2344$
$P(5) = 0.0938$
$P(6) = 0.0156$

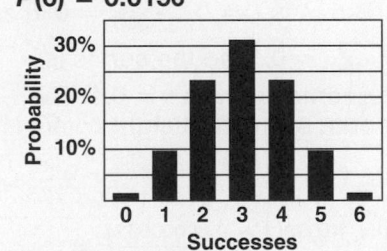

14. $P(0) = 0.000001$
$P(1) = 0.000054$
$P(2) = 0.0012$
$P(3) = 0.0146$
$P(4) = 0.0984$
$P(5) = 0.3543$
$P(6) = 0.5314$

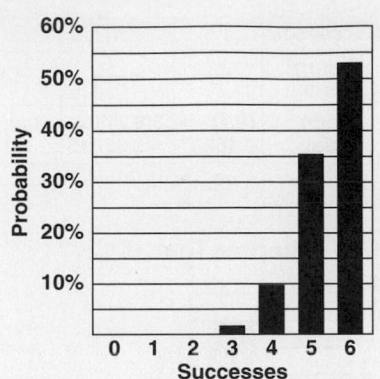

25a. $_{40}C_3\left(\frac{1}{7}\right)^3\left(\frac{6}{7}\right)^{37} \approx 0.0960 = 9.6\%$

  b. Answers may vary. Sample: Generate 40 numbers ranging from 1 to 7. Let the number 4 represent Wednesday birthdays. Repeat 10 times. Count the number of runs that 4 came up exactly 3 times; divide that number by 10 to get the probability that exactly 3 of 40 people will have Wednesday birthdays. 10%

  c. 10 runs is too few to get an accurate probability.

26. Answers may vary. Sample: 60% of the summer days in Eastport are sunny. What is the probability of a week containing just two sunny days?

LESSON 12-7

page 679   Check Understanding

2.
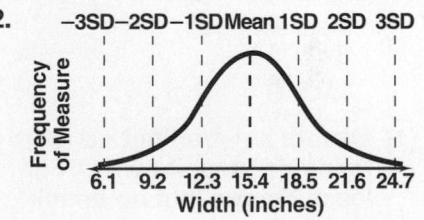

pages 687–689   Chapter Review

7.

Product	Freq.	Prob.	Product	Freq.	Prob.
1	1	$\frac{1}{36}$	12	4	$\frac{4}{36}$
2	2	$\frac{2}{36}$	15	2	$\frac{2}{36}$
3	2	$\frac{2}{36}$	16	1	$\frac{1}{36}$
4	3	$\frac{3}{36}$	18	2	$\frac{2}{36}$
5	2	$\frac{2}{36}$	20	2	$\frac{2}{36}$
6	4	$\frac{4}{36}$	24	2	$\frac{2}{36}$
8	2	$\frac{2}{36}$	25	1	$\frac{1}{36}$
9	1	$\frac{1}{36}$	30	2	$\frac{2}{36}$
10	2	$\frac{2}{36}$	36	1	$\frac{1}{36}$

26.

Successes	5	4	3	2	1	0
$(p + q)^5$ term	$1p^5$	$5p^4q$	$10p^3q^2$	$10p^2q^3$	$5pq^4$	$1q^5$
Term value	$(0.7)^5 =$ 0.16807	$5(0.7)^40.3$ $= 0.36015$	$10(0.7)^3(0.3)^2$ $= 0.3087$	$10(0.7)^2(0.3)^3$ $= 0.1323$	$5(0.7)(0.3)^4$ $= 0.02835$	$(0.3)^5 =$ 0.00243

page 690   Chapter Test

1.

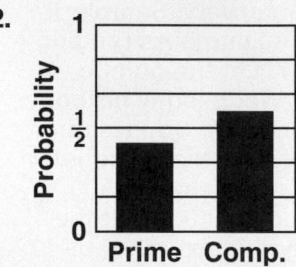

2.

3. Sample: Suppose two hybrid Aa parent plants are crossed. The offspring can be described by the sample space {AA, Aa, aa} or by the sample space {dominant, recessive}.

page 691   Standardized Test Prep

13. [2]

$$\frac{x}{6} = \frac{(x + 4)}{9}$$

$$(6)(9)\frac{x}{6} = (6)(9)\frac{(x + 4)}{9}$$

$$9x = 6(x + 4)$$

$$9x = 6x + 24$$

$$3x = 24$$

$$x = 8$$

Check

$$\frac{8}{6} \stackrel{?}{=} \frac{(8 + 4)}{9}$$

$$\frac{4}{3} \stackrel{?}{=} \frac{12}{9}$$

$$\frac{4}{3} = \frac{4}{3}$$

[1] correct solution but no more than one step shown OR at least 2 steps, but no check

14. [2]

$$9 \log 3 - 3 \log 9 = \log 27$$
$$9 \log 3 - 3 \log 3^2 = \log 3^3 \quad \text{factoring}$$
$$9 \log 3 - (3)(2)\log 3 = 3 \log 3 \quad \text{Power Prop. of Logs}$$
$$9 \log 3 - 6 \log 3 = 3 \log 3 \quad \text{Simplify.}$$
$$3 \log 3 = 3 \log 3$$

OR

$$\log 3^9 - \log 9^3 = \log 3^3 \quad \text{Power Prop. of Logs}$$
$$\log 3^9 - \log (3^2)^3 = \log 3^3 \quad \text{factoring}$$
$$\log \frac{3^9}{3^6} = \log 3^3 \quad \text{Quotient Prop. of Logs}$$
$$\log 3^3 = \log 3^3 \quad \text{Simplify.}$$

[1] only one step shown

15. [4] Vertices and intercepts are at $(\pm a, 0)$, asymptotes are $y = \pm\frac{b}{a}x$, and foci are at $(\pm c, 0)$.
For $\frac{x^2}{16} - \frac{y^2}{9} = 1$,
$a = 4$ and $b = 3$,
so the vertices and intercepts are at $(\pm 4, 0)$ and the asymptotes are at
$y = \pm\frac{3}{4}x$. Since
$c = \sqrt{a^2 + b^2} = \sqrt{25} = 5$,
the foci are at $(\pm 5, 0)$.

[3] 3 parts correct

[2] 2 parts correct

[1] 1 part correct

16. [4] There is no common difference: $1000 - 10,000 \neq 100 - 1000$.
But $\frac{1000}{10,000} = 0.1$, $\frac{100}{1000} = 0.1$, and $\frac{10}{100} = 0.1$, so the series is geometric with $r = 0.1$. The sum of the first eight terms is

$$S_8 = \frac{a_1(1 - r^8)}{1 - r} = \frac{10,000(1 - 0.1^8)}{1 - 0.1} =$$

$$\frac{10,000(1 - 0.00000001)}{0.9} =$$

$$\frac{10,000(0.99999999)}{0.9} =$$

$$10,000(1.11111111) = 11,111.1111$$

[3] r incorrect, OR the sum incorrect OR little explanation of why the series is geometric

[2] 2 of the above incorrect OR 1 incorrect and little explanation of why the series is geometric

[1] series treated as arithmetic, but with computations formally correct

CHAPTER 13

LESSON 13-1

page 696   Investigation

2.

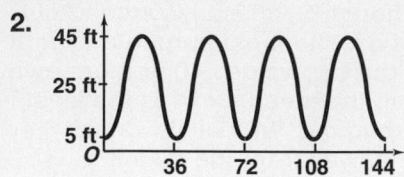

pages 699–702   Exercises

33a.

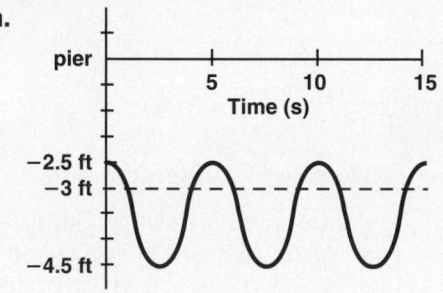

41.

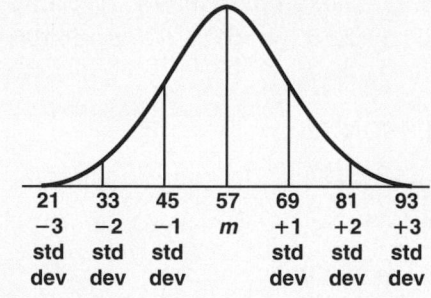

LESSON 13-2

pages 708–710   Exercises

7.

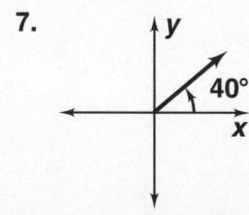

8.

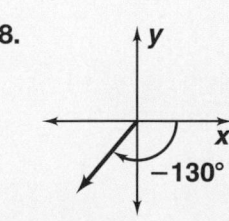

9.

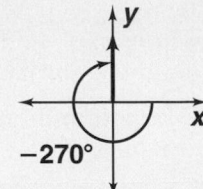

$-270°$

10.

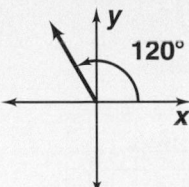

$120°$

11.

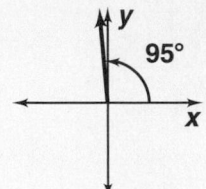

$95°$

53.

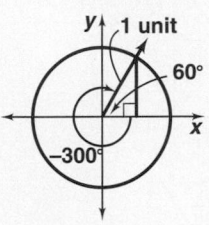

1 unit
$60°$
$-300°$

$\frac{1}{2}, \frac{\sqrt{3}}{2}$

54.

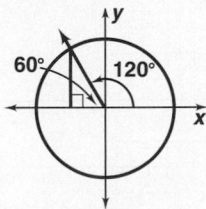

$60°$ $120°$

$-\frac{1}{2}, \frac{\sqrt{3}}{2}$

55.

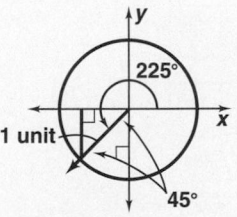

$225°$
1 unit
$45°$

$-\frac{\sqrt{2}}{2}, -\frac{\sqrt{2}}{2}$

56.

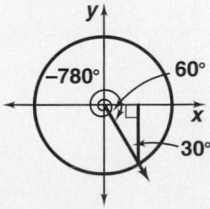

$-780°$ $60°$
$30°$

$\frac{1}{2}, -\frac{\sqrt{3}}{2}$

57.

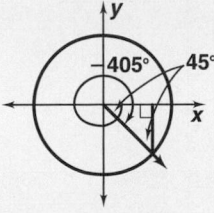

$-405°$ $45°$

$\frac{\sqrt{2}}{2}, -\frac{\sqrt{2}}{2}$

58.

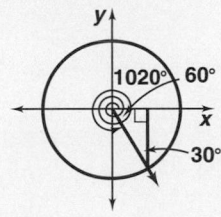

$1020°$ $60°$
$30°$

$\frac{1}{2}, -\frac{\sqrt{3}}{2}$

page 710   Standardized Test Prep

67. [2]

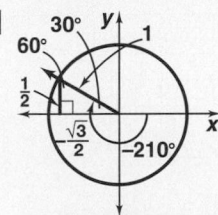

$30°$
$60°$
$\frac{1}{2}$
$\frac{\sqrt{3}}{2}$
$-210°$
1

The terminal side forms an angle of 30° with the negative x-axis. Using the unit circle, $r = 1$, $x = -\frac{\sqrt{3}}{2}$, and $y = \frac{1}{2}$.

So $\sin(-210°) = \frac{x}{r} = \frac{-\frac{\sqrt{3}}{2}}{1} = -\frac{\sqrt{3}}{2}$.

[1] answer only, with no work shown

68. [4]

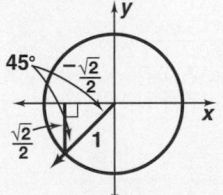

$45°$ $-\frac{\sqrt{2}}{2}$
$\frac{\sqrt{2}}{2}$ 1

The terminal side forms an angle of 45° with the negative x-axis, so $\sin(-135°) = -\frac{\sqrt{2}}{2}$ and $\cos(-135°) = -\frac{\sqrt{2}}{2}$.

Then $[\sin(-135°)]^2 + [\cos(-135°)]^2 = \left[-\frac{\sqrt{2}}{2}\right]^2 + \left[-\frac{\sqrt{2}}{2}\right]^2 = \frac{2}{4} + \frac{2}{4} = \frac{4}{4} = 1$.

[3] one computational error

[2] incomplete explanation with correct answer

[1] answer only, with no work shown

LESSON 13-3

pages 715–719   Exercises

13.

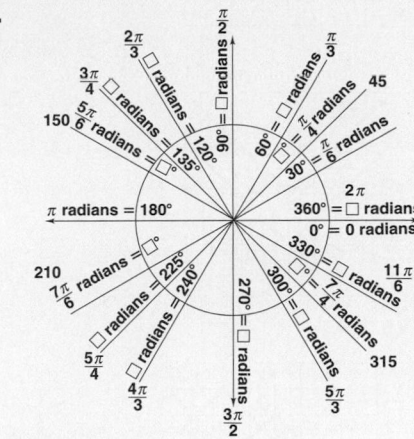

LESSON 13-5

pages 732–734   Exercises

34a.

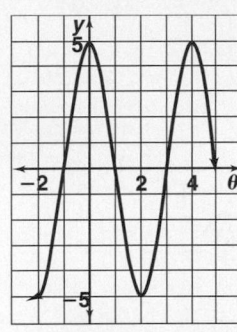

b. Answers may vary. Sample: 0 s, 4 s, 8 s, 12 s

LESSON 13-7

page 742   Check Skills You'll Need

1.

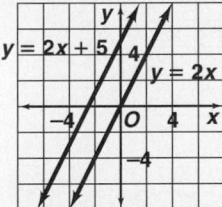

$y = 2x + 5$
$y = 2x$

vertical

2.

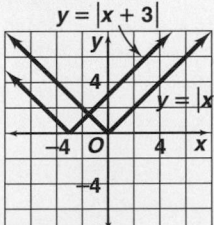

$y = |x + 3|$
$y = |x|$

horizontal

3.

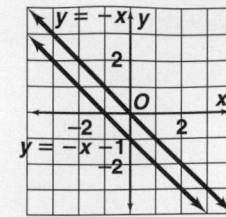

$y = -x$ y

$y = -x - 1$

vertical

4.

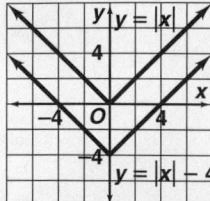

$y = |x|$

$y = |x| - 4$

vertical

5.

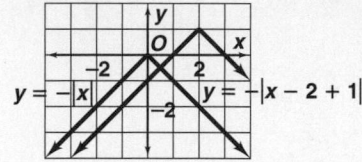

$y = -|x|$ $y = -|x - 2 + 1|$

diagonal

6.

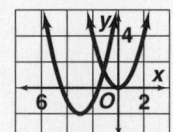

diagonal

pages 746–748   Exercises

11.

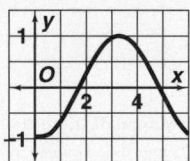

12.

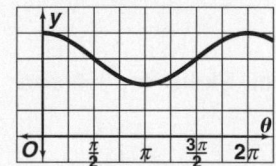

13.

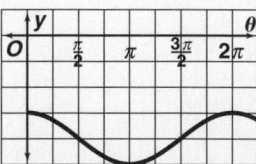

14.

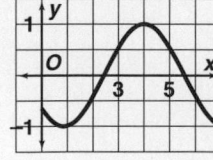

15.

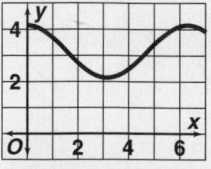

16.

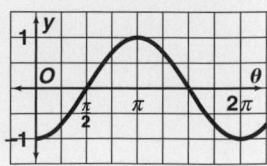

21.

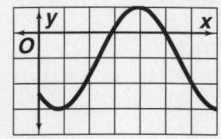

22.

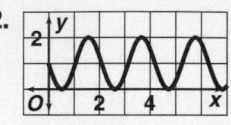

23.

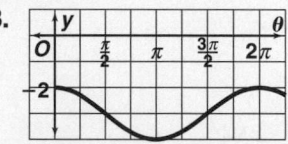

24.

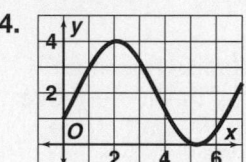

25.

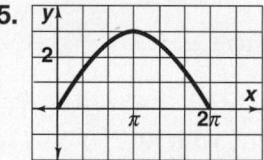

26.

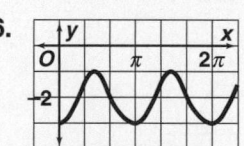

27.

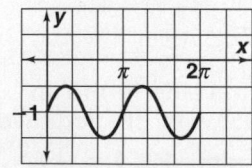

28.

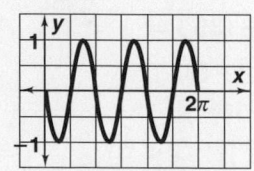

29.

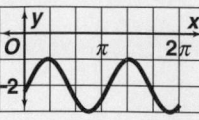

30.

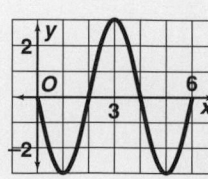

37a.

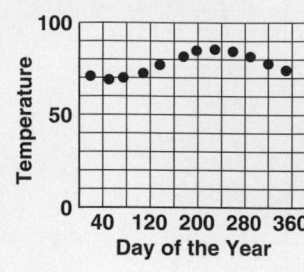

47.

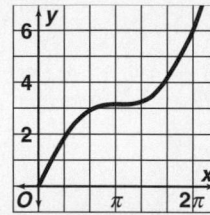

48.

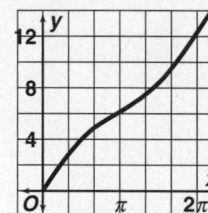

49.

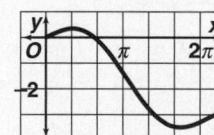

50.

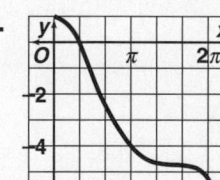

51.

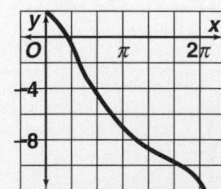

52.

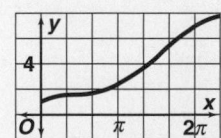

53.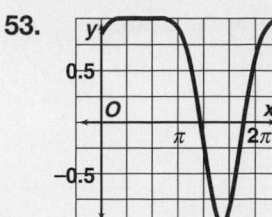

54.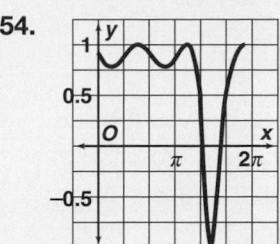

page 748 Checkpoint Quiz 2

1.

2.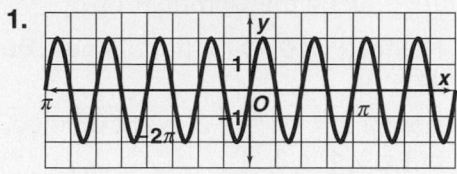

3.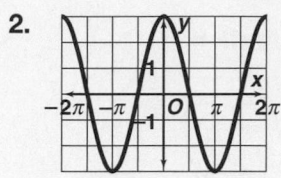

4.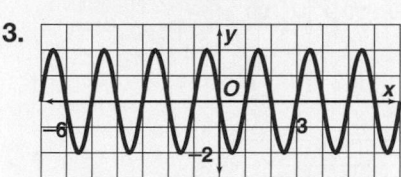

5.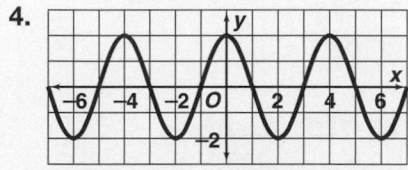

6.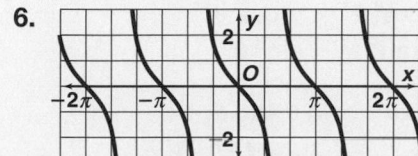

7.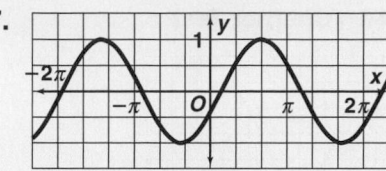

8.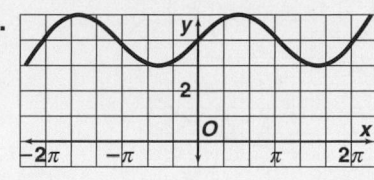

9.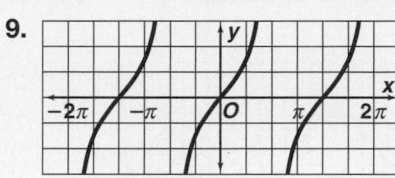

10.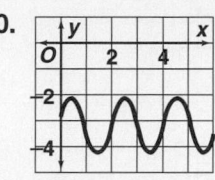

LESSON 13-8

page 749 Check Skills You'll Need

6.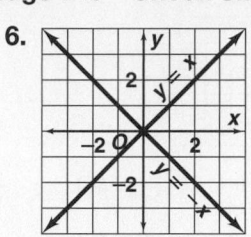

7.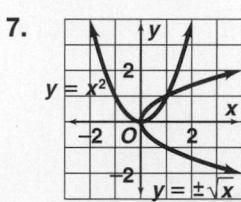

8.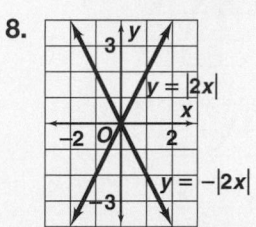

9.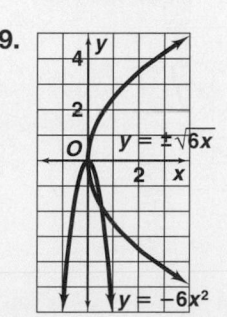

41a.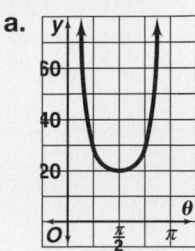

61.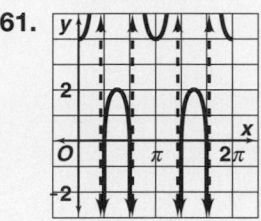

3 units up

62.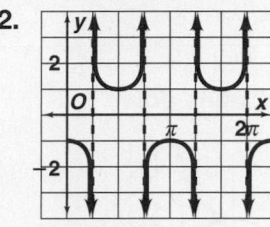

$\frac{\pi}{2}$ unit left

63.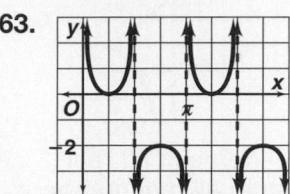

1 unit down

64.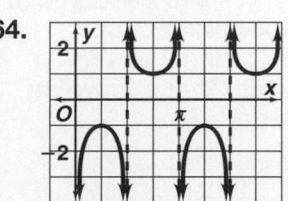

$\frac{\pi}{2}$ unit right

65.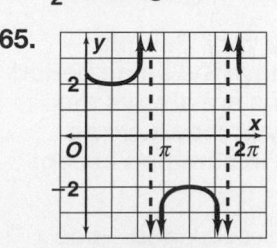

4 units right

T953

66. 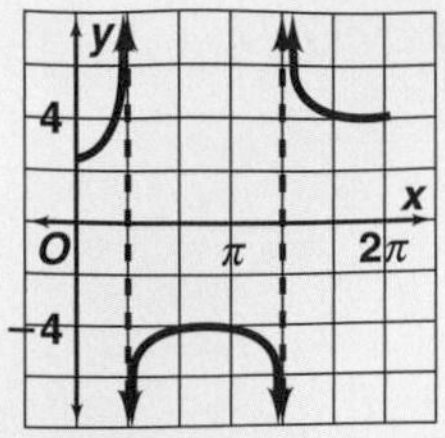

2 units left, 1 unit down

67. 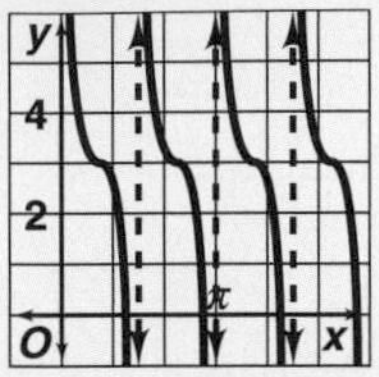

π units left, 3 units up

68. 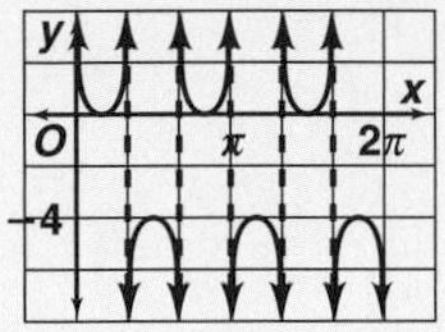

$\frac{\pi}{6}$ units right, 2 units down

69a. 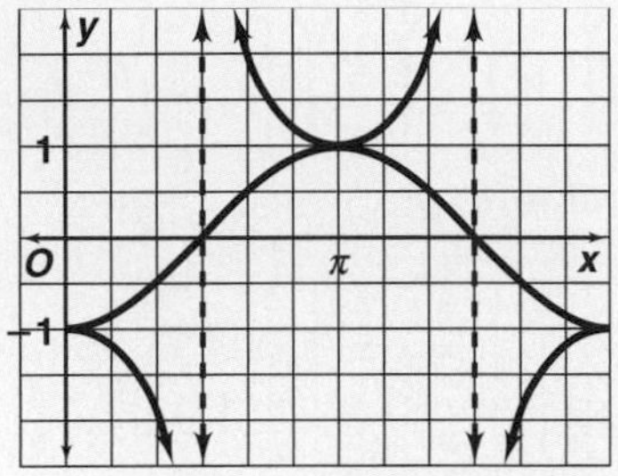

b. $y = -\cos x$—domain: all real numbers; range: all real numbers between -1 and 1, inclusive; period: 2π; $y = -\sec x$—domain: all real numbers except odd multiples of $\frac{\pi}{2}$; range: all real numbers except those between -1 and 1; period: 2π

c. Multiples of π; $\sec(n\pi) = \frac{1}{\cos(n\pi)} = \frac{1}{\pm 1} = \pm 1 = \cos(n\pi)$.

d. Answers may vary. Sample: The graphs have the same period and their signs are always the same. However, they have no range values in common except 1 and -1.

e. The signs of $-\sec x$ and $-\cos x$ are the same because reciprocals have the same sign.

page 760 Chapter Test

23. 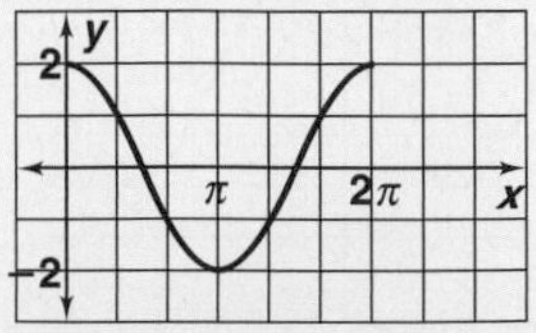

24. 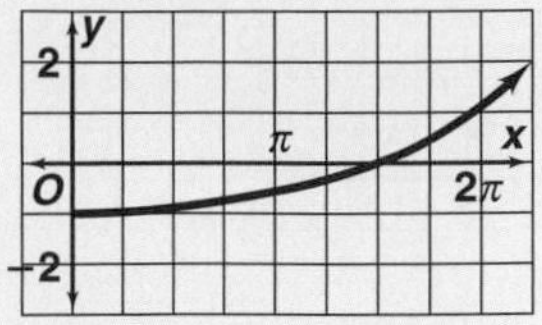

25. 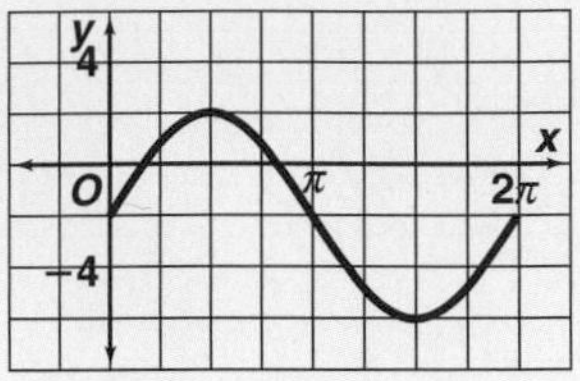

26. 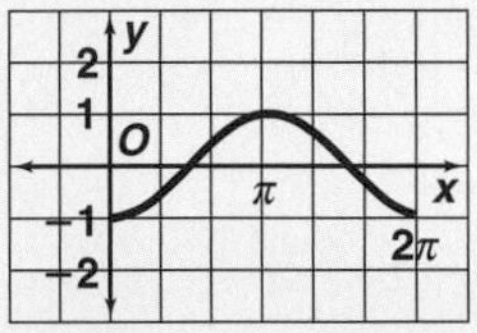

27. 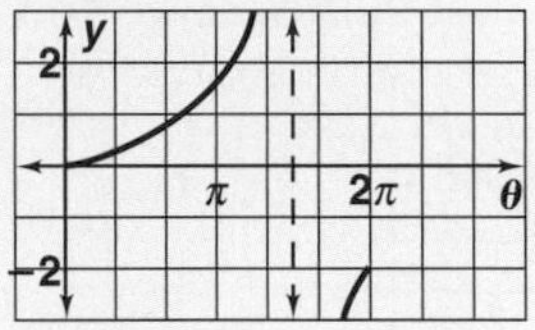

28. 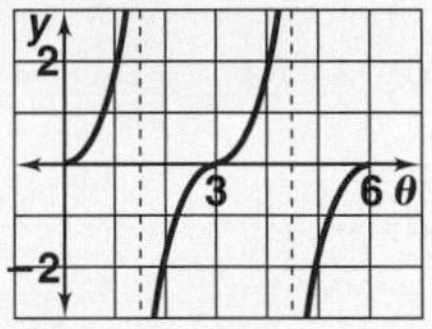

41. 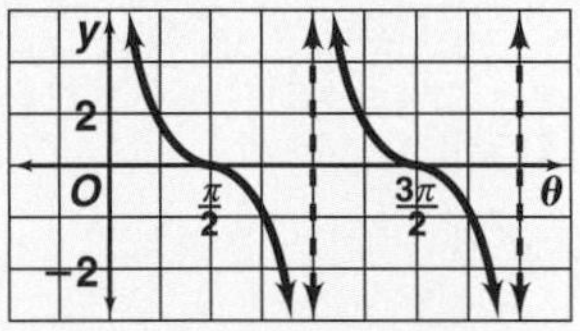

42. 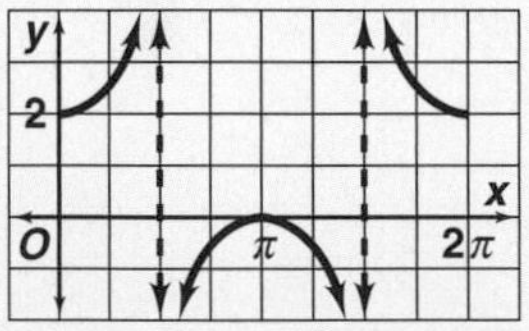

43. 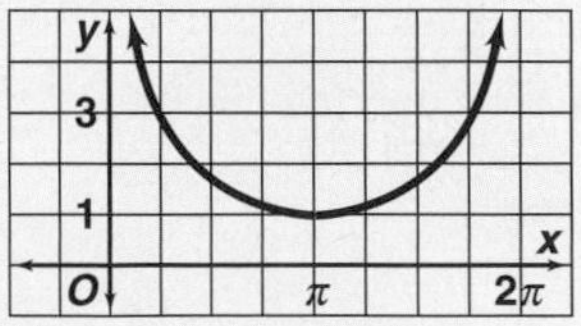

44. 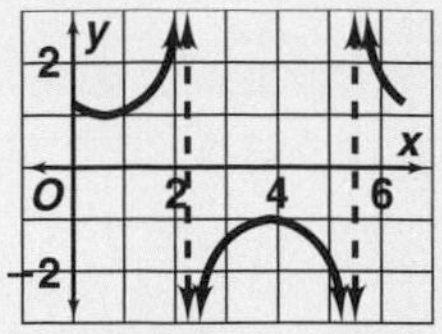

CHAPTER 14

LESSON 14-1

page 764 Check Skills You'll Need

1. Yes; $2x + 3x = (2 + 3)x$ by the Dist. Prop. and $(2 + 3)x = 5x$ by addition.
2. Yes; $-(4x - 10) = -4x + 10$ by the Dist. Prop. and $-4x + 10 = 10 - 4x$ by the Comm. Prop.
3. No; for $x = 0$, $\frac{4x^2}{x}$ is not defined, but $4x = 0$.
4. No; for $x = 1$, $\frac{x^2 + 1}{x - 1}$ is not defined, but $x + 1 = 2$.

page 764 Investigation

1. 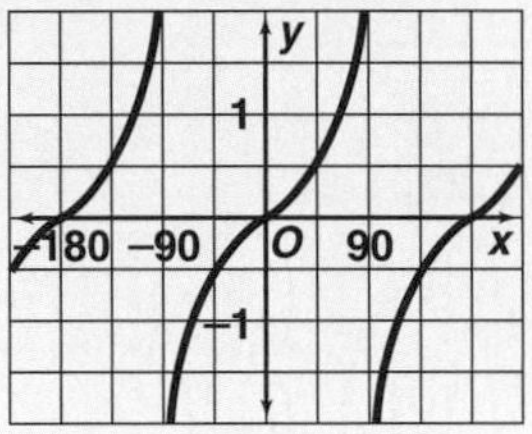

2. 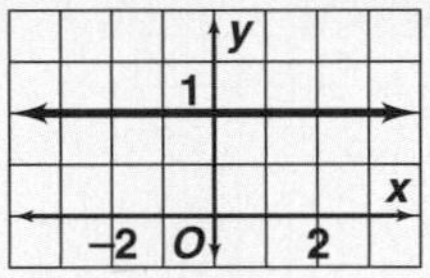

pages 766–768 Exercises

45. $\sin^2\theta \tan^2\theta = \sin^2\theta\left(\frac{\sin^2\theta}{\cos^2\theta}\right)$

$= (1 - \cos^2\theta)\left(\frac{\sin^2\theta}{\cos^2\theta}\right)$

$= \frac{\sin^2\theta - \sin^2\theta\cos^2\theta}{\cos^2\theta}$

$= \frac{\sin^2\theta}{\cos^2\theta} - \frac{\sin^2\theta\cos^2\theta}{\cos^2\theta}$

$= \tan^2\theta - \sin^2\theta$

46. $\sec\theta - \sin\theta\tan\theta$

$= \frac{1}{\cos\theta} - \sin\theta\left(\frac{\sin\theta}{\cos\theta}\right)$

$= \frac{1}{\cos\theta} - \frac{\sin^2\theta}{\cos\theta} = \frac{1 - \sin^2\theta}{\cos\theta} = \frac{\cos^2\theta}{\cos\theta}$

$= \cos\theta$

47. $\sin\theta\cos\theta\left(\dfrac{\sin\theta}{\cos\theta}+\dfrac{\cos\theta}{\sin\theta}\right)$

$$=\dfrac{\sin^2\theta\cos\theta}{\cos\theta}+\dfrac{\cos^2\theta\sin\theta}{\sin\theta}$$

$$=\sin^2\theta+\cos^2\theta=1$$

48. $\dfrac{1-\sin\theta}{\cos\theta}\cdot\dfrac{\cos\theta}{\cos\theta}=\dfrac{(1-\sin\theta)\cos\theta}{\cos^2\theta}$

$$=\dfrac{(1-\sin\theta)\cos\theta}{1-\sin^2\theta}$$

$$=\dfrac{(1-\sin\theta)\cos\theta}{(1-\sin\theta)(1+\sin\theta)}$$

$$=\dfrac{\cos\theta}{1+\sin\theta}$$

49. $\dfrac{\sec\theta}{\cot\theta+\tan\theta}$

$$=\dfrac{\dfrac{1}{\cos\theta}}{\dfrac{\cos\theta}{\sin\theta}+\dfrac{\sin\theta}{\cos\theta}}\cdot\dfrac{\sin\theta\cos\theta}{\sin\theta\cos\theta}$$

$$=\dfrac{\sin\theta}{\cos^2\theta+\sin^2\theta}=\dfrac{\sin\theta}{1}=\sin\theta$$

50. $(\cot\theta+1)^2=\cot^2\theta+2\cot\theta+1=\cot^2\theta+1+2\cot\theta=\csc^2\theta+2\cot\theta$

57. $\dfrac{\cot\theta\sin\theta}{\sec\theta}+\dfrac{\tan\theta\cos\theta}{\csc\theta}$

$$=\dfrac{\left(\dfrac{\cos\theta}{\sin\theta}\right)\sin\theta}{\dfrac{1}{\cos\theta}}+\dfrac{\left(\dfrac{\sin\theta}{\cos\theta}\right)\cos\theta}{\dfrac{1}{\sin\theta}}$$

$$=\dfrac{\cos\theta}{\dfrac{1}{\cos\theta}}+\dfrac{\sin\theta}{\dfrac{1}{\sin\theta}}$$

$$=\cos^2\theta+\sin^2\theta=1$$

58. $\sin^2\theta\tan^2\theta+\cos^2\theta\tan^2\theta$
$=\tan^2\theta(\sin^2+\cos^2\theta)$
$=\tan^2\theta(1)=\tan^2\theta$
$=\sec^2\theta-1$

67. [2] Replace $\tan\theta$ and $\sec\theta$ with their equivalents. This results in
$$\dfrac{\dfrac{\sin\theta}{\cos\theta}}{\cos\theta-\dfrac{1}{\cos\theta}}.$$
Combine the terms in the denominator by multiplying the first term by $\dfrac{\cos\theta}{\cos\theta}$, so the terms have a common denominator. This leaves
$$\dfrac{\dfrac{\sin\theta}{\cos\theta}}{\dfrac{\cos^2\theta-1}{\cos\theta}}.$$
Invert and multiply:
$$\dfrac{\sin\theta}{\cos\theta}\cdot\dfrac{\cos\theta}{\cos^2\theta-1}.$$
Simplify and substitute $-\sin^2\theta$ for $\cos^2\theta-1$, which yields $-\dfrac{1}{\sin\theta}$. The final answer is $-\csc\theta$.

[1] omits explanation OR includes minor error

68.[4] Using the Pythagorean identities, $1-\sin^2x$ is replaced by $\cos^2x$.

This leaves $\dfrac{\cos x}{\cos^2 x}=\sec x$. The next step is to simplify, leaving $\dfrac{1}{\cos x}=\sec x$, and since $\dfrac{1}{\cos x}=\sec x$, then $\sec x=\sec x$, which proves the identity.

[3] appropriate methods with minor error

[2] correct steps without explanation

[1] steps with a minor error and without explanation

page 768   Mixed Review

73.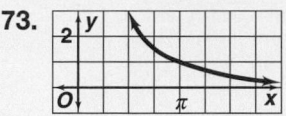

74.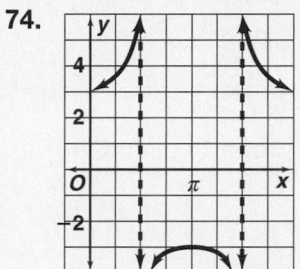

83.

```
      ┌───┬──────┐
●─────┤   │      ├─────●
      └───┴──────┘
  ├──┼──┼──┼──┼──┼──┤
 290 300 310 320 330 340 350
```

84.

```
      ┌─┬─┐
●─────┤ │ ├──────────────●
      └─┴─┘
  ├──┼──┼──┼──┼──┼──┤
 10  30  50  70  90 110
```

LESSON 14-3

pages 782–785   Exercises

35. $a=15$, $m\angle A\approx61.9°$, $m\angle B\approx28.1°$

36. $c\approx12.2$, $m\angle A\approx35.0°$, $m\angle B\approx55.0°$

37. $a\approx7.9$, $b\approx6.2$, $m\angle B=38°$

38. $a\approx3.9$, $c\approx6.9$, $m\angle B=55.8°$

39. $a\approx26.8$, $c\approx28.1$, $m\angle A\approx72.8°$

40. $a\approx19.8$, $b=2.9$, $m\angle A=81.7°$

46. Using inverse sine, you can find that $\theta=30°$. Since sine is positive in the first and second quadrants, another solution is 150°. All the solutions would be $30°+n\cdot360°$ and $150°+n\cdot360°$.

47.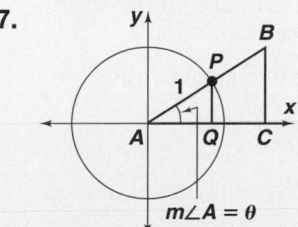

$m\angle A=\theta$

Since $\triangle APQ$ and $\triangle ABC$ are similar triangles,
$\dfrac{AQ}{AP}=\dfrac{AC}{AB}$. So, since $\cos\theta=AQ$,
$$\cos\theta=AQ=\dfrac{AQ}{1}=$$
$$\dfrac{AQ}{AP}=\dfrac{AC}{AB}=\cos A.$$

59. [2] $\tan\angle A=\dfrac{135}{95}$
$m\angle A=\tan^{-1}1.421$
$m\angle A=54.9°$
$\tan\angle B=\dfrac{95}{135}$
$m\angle B=\tan^{-1}0.7037$
$m\angle B=35.1°$

[1] answer only, without work shown

LESSON 14-6

pages 804–806   Exercises

1. $\csc\left(\theta-\dfrac{\pi}{2}\right)=\dfrac{1}{\sin\left(\theta-\dfrac{\pi}{2}\right)}$

$$=\dfrac{1}{\sin\left(-\left(\dfrac{\pi}{2}-\theta\right)\right)}$$

$$=\dfrac{1}{\sin\left(\dfrac{\pi}{2}-\theta\right)}$$

$$=\dfrac{1}{-\cos\theta}$$

$$=-\sec\theta$$

2. $\sec\left(\theta-\dfrac{\pi}{2}\right)=\dfrac{1}{\cos\left(\theta-\dfrac{\pi}{2}\right)}$

$$=\dfrac{1}{\cos\left(-\left(\dfrac{\pi}{2}-\theta\right)\right)}$$

$$=\dfrac{1}{\cos\left(\dfrac{\pi}{2}-\theta\right)}$$

$$=\dfrac{1}{\sin\theta}$$

$$=\csc\theta$$

3. $\cot\left(\dfrac{\pi}{2}-\theta\right)=\dfrac{\cos\left(\dfrac{\pi}{2}-\theta\right)}{\sin\left(\dfrac{\pi}{2}-\theta\right)}$

$$=\dfrac{\sin\theta}{\cos\theta}$$

$$=\tan\theta$$

4. $\csc\left(\dfrac{\pi}{2}-\theta\right)=\dfrac{1}{\sin\left(\dfrac{\pi}{2}-\theta\right)}$

$$=\dfrac{1}{\cos\theta}$$

$$=\sec\theta$$

5. $\tan\left(\theta-\dfrac{\pi}{2}\right)=\tan\left(-\left(\dfrac{\pi}{2}-\theta\right)\right)$

$$=-\tan\left(\dfrac{\pi}{2}-\theta\right)$$

$$=-\cot\theta$$

6. $\sec\left(\dfrac{\pi}{2}-\theta\right)=\dfrac{1}{\cos\left(\dfrac{\pi}{2}-\theta\right)}$

$$=\dfrac{1}{\sin\theta}$$

$$=\csc\theta$$

37. $\sin (A - B) = \sin (A + (-B))$
$= \sin A \cos (-B) + \cos A \sin (-B)$
$= \sin A \cos B - \cos A \sin B$

38. $\tan (A - B) = \tan (A + (-B))$
$= \dfrac{\tan A + \tan(-B)}{1 - \tan A \tan (-B)}$
$= \dfrac{\tan A - \tan B}{1 + \tan A \tan B}$

39. $\cos (A + B) = \cos (A - (-B))$
$= \cos A \cos (-B) + \sin A \sin (-B)$
$= \cos A \cos B - \sin A \sin B$

40. $\tan (A + B) = \tan (A - (-B))$
$= \dfrac{\tan A - \tan (-B)}{1 + \tan A \tan (-B)}$
$= \dfrac{\tan A + \tan B}{1 - \tan A \tan B}$

41. $\sin \left(x + \dfrac{\pi}{3}\right) + \sin \left(x - \dfrac{\pi}{3}\right)$
$= \sin x \cos \dfrac{\pi}{3} + \cos x \sin \dfrac{\pi}{3}$
$\quad + \left[\sin x \cos \dfrac{\pi}{3} - \cos x \sin \dfrac{\pi}{3}\right]$
$= \sin x \cos \dfrac{\pi}{3} + \cos x \sin \dfrac{\pi}{3}$
$\quad + \sin x \cos \dfrac{\pi}{3} - \cos x \sin \dfrac{\pi}{3}$
$= 2 \sin x \cos \dfrac{\pi}{3}$
$= 2 \sin x \cdot \dfrac{1}{2}$
$= \sin x$

42. $\sin\left(\dfrac{3\pi}{2} - x\right)$
$= \sin \dfrac{3\pi}{2} \cos x - \cos \dfrac{3\pi}{2} \sin x$
$= -1 \cos x - 0 \cdot \sin x$
$= -\cos x$

43. Answers may vary. Sample:
$\sin (30° + 60°) \overset{?}{=} \sin 30° + \sin 60°$
$\sin (90°) \overset{?}{=} \sin 30° + \sin 60°$
$1 \neq \dfrac{1}{2} + \dfrac{\sqrt{3}}{2}$

53. $\cos (\pi - \theta)$
$= \cos \pi \cos \theta + \sin \pi \sin \theta$
$= \cos \pi \cos \theta = -\cos \theta$

54. $\sin (\pi - \theta)$
$= \sin \pi \cos \theta - \cos \pi \sin \theta$
$= -\cos \pi \sin \theta = \sin \theta$

55. $\sin (\pi + \theta)$
$= \sin \pi \cos \theta + \cos \pi \sin \theta$
$= -\sin \theta$

56. $\cos (\pi + \theta)$
$= \cos \pi \cos \theta - \sin \pi \sin \theta$
$= -\cos \theta$

57. Given a parallelogram with adjacent sides x_1 and x_2 forming angle θ, and diagonals of d_1 and d_2, then by the Law of Cosines:
$d_1^2 + d_2^2 = x_1^2 + x_2^2 - 2x_1x_2 \cos \theta$
$\quad + [x_1^2 + x_2^2 - 2x_1x_2 \cos(\pi - \theta)]$
$= 2x_1^2 + 2x_2^2 - 2x_1x_2 \cos \theta -$
$\quad 2x_1x_2 [\cos \pi \cos \theta +$
$\quad \sin \pi \sin \theta]$

$= 2x_1^2 + 2x_2^2 - 2x_1x_2 \cos \theta -$
$\quad 2x_1x_2 [-\cos \theta]$
$= 2x_1^2 + 2x_2^2 - 2x_1x_2 \cos \theta +$
$\quad 2x_1x_2 \cos \theta$
$= 2x_1^2 + 2x_2^2 = 2(x_1^2 + x_2^2)$

63. [2] $\sin (165°) = \sin (15°)$
$= \sin (45° - 30°)$
$= \sin 45° \cdot \cos 30° -$
$\quad \cos 45° \sin 30°$
$= \dfrac{\sqrt{2}}{2} \cdot \dfrac{\sqrt{3}}{2} - \dfrac{\sqrt{2}}{2} \cdot \dfrac{1}{2}$
$= \dfrac{\sqrt{6}}{4} - \dfrac{\sqrt{2}}{4} = \dfrac{\sqrt{6} - \sqrt{2}}{4}$

[1] incorrect property used OR minor error

64. [2] $\cos \left(\dfrac{\pi}{6}\right) = \cos \left(\dfrac{\pi}{2} - \dfrac{\pi}{3}\right)$
$= \cos \left(\dfrac{\pi}{2}\right) \cos \left(\dfrac{\pi}{3}\right) +$
$\quad \sin \left(\dfrac{\pi}{2}\right) \sin \left(\dfrac{\pi}{3}\right)$
$= 0 \cdot \dfrac{1}{2} + 1 \cdot \dfrac{\sqrt{3}}{2} = \dfrac{\sqrt{3}}{2}$

[1] incorrect property used OR minor error

LESSON 14-7

pages 810–811   Exercises

31. $\tan \dfrac{R}{2} = \sqrt{\dfrac{1 - \cos R}{1 + \cos R}}$
$= \sqrt{\dfrac{1 - \dfrac{s}{t}}{1 + \dfrac{s}{t}}}$
$= \sqrt{\dfrac{t - s}{t + s} \cdot \dfrac{t + s}{t + s}}$
$= \sqrt{\dfrac{t^2 - s^2}{(t + s)^2}}$
$= \sqrt{\dfrac{r^2}{(t + s)^2}}$
$= \dfrac{r}{t + s}$

32. $\tan^2 \dfrac{s}{2} = \left(\tan \dfrac{s}{2}\right)^2$
$= \left(\pm \sqrt{\dfrac{1 - \cos s}{1 + \cos s}}\right)^2$
$= \dfrac{1 - \cos s}{1 + \cos s}$
$= \dfrac{1 - \dfrac{r}{t}}{1 + \dfrac{r}{t}}$
$= \dfrac{t - r}{t + r}$

33. No; since the sine function is periodic, A and B can have many different values.

50. Answers may vary. Sample:
No; the graphs
of $y = \dfrac{\tan \theta}{4}$ and
$y = \tan \dfrac{\theta}{4}$ are only equal at certain finite values.

51–56. Answers may vary.

51. $4 \sin \theta \cos \theta (\cos^2 \theta - \sin^2 \theta)$

52. $8 \cos^4 \theta - 8 \cos^2 \theta + 1$

53. $\dfrac{4 \tan \theta (1 - \tan^2 \theta)}{\tan^4 \theta - 6 \tan^2 \theta + 1}$

54. $\pm \sqrt{\dfrac{1}{2} - \dfrac{1}{2}\sqrt{\dfrac{1}{2} + \dfrac{\cos \theta}{2}}}$

55. $\pm \sqrt{\dfrac{1}{2} + \dfrac{1}{2}\sqrt{\dfrac{1}{2} + \dfrac{1}{2} \cos \theta}}$

56. $\pm \sqrt{\dfrac{1 \pm \sqrt{\dfrac{1}{2} + \dfrac{1}{2} \cos \theta}}{1 \pm \sqrt{\dfrac{1}{2} + \dfrac{1}{2} \cos \theta}}}$

57a. $\tan \dfrac{A}{2} = \pm \sqrt{\dfrac{1 - \cos A}{1 + \cos A}}$
$= \pm \sqrt{\dfrac{1 - \cos A}{1 + \cos A} \cdot \sqrt{\dfrac{1 + \cos A}{1 + \cos A}}}$
$= \pm \sqrt{\dfrac{1 - \cos^2 A}{(1 + \cos A)^2}}$
$= \pm \sqrt{\dfrac{\sin^2 A}{(1 + \cos A)^2}}$
$= \dfrac{\sin A}{1 + \cos A}$

Since $\tan \dfrac{A}{2}$ and $\sin A$ always have the same sign where $\tan \dfrac{A}{2}$ is defined, only the positive sign occurs.

b. $\tan \dfrac{A}{2} = \pm \sqrt{\dfrac{1 - \cos A}{1 + \cos A}}$
$= \pm \sqrt{\dfrac{1 - \cos A}{1 + \cos A} \cdot \sqrt{\dfrac{1 - \cos A}{1 - \cos A}}}$
$= \pm \sqrt{\dfrac{(1 - \cos A)^2}{1 - \cos^2 A}}$
$= \pm \sqrt{\dfrac{(1 - \cos A)^2}{\sin^2 A}}$
$= \dfrac{1 - \cos A}{\sin A}$

Since $\tan \dfrac{A}{2}$ and $\sin A$ always have the same sign where $\tan \dfrac{A}{2}$ is defined, only the positive sign occurs.

60. [2] $\sin \dfrac{135°}{2} = \sqrt{\dfrac{1 - \cos 135°}{2}}$
$= \sqrt{\dfrac{1 - \dfrac{-\sqrt{2}}{2}}{2}}$
$= \sqrt{\dfrac{\dfrac{2 + \sqrt{2}}{2}}{2}}$
$= \dfrac{\sqrt{2 + \sqrt{2}}}{2}$

[1] appropriate methods with minor error

61. [4] $\tan \theta = \frac{0.5}{1} = 0.5 = \frac{1}{2}$

$\tan 2\theta = \frac{2 \tan \theta}{1 - \tan^2 \theta}$

$= \frac{2(\frac{1}{2})}{1 - (\frac{1}{2})^2} = \frac{1}{1 - \frac{1}{4}}$

$= \frac{1}{\frac{3}{4}} = \frac{4}{3}$

[3] appropriate method with minor error

[2] correct answer without work shown

[1] recognized using double-angle identities but did not apply them properly

page 812   Test-Taking Strategies

5. $A = 0, B = 2\pi$
$A = \frac{\pi}{4}, B = \frac{7\pi}{4}$
$A = 2\pi, B = 0;$
$A + B = 2\pi$
$\sin (A + B) = 0$
$\sin A + \sin B =$
$\sin (2\pi - B) + \sin B =$
$(\sin 2\pi \cdot \cos B - \cos 2\pi \cdot \sin B) +$
$\sin B = (0 \cdot \cos B - 1 \cdot \sin B) +$
$\sin B = -\sin B + \sin B = 0$

page 816   Chapter Test

15. $\frac{4}{6.4}$, 0.62

16. $\frac{6.4}{5}$, 1.28

17. $\frac{5}{4}$, 1.25

18. $\frac{6.4}{5}$, 1.28

19. $\frac{6.4}{4}$, 1.60

20. $\frac{5}{4}$, 1.25

21. 8, 36.9°, 53.1°

22. 15.6, 50.2°, 39.8°

23. 46.5, 24.3°, 65.7°

24. 6.1, 25.3°, 64.7°

34. $-\sin \left(\theta - \frac{\pi}{2}\right) = -\sin \left(-\left(\frac{\pi}{2} - \theta\right)\right)$
$= \sin \left(\frac{\pi}{2} - \theta\right) = \cos \theta$

35. $\csc \left(\theta + \frac{\pi}{2}\right) =$

$\dfrac{1}{\sin \theta \cos \frac{\pi}{2} + \cos \theta \sin \frac{\pi}{2}}$

$= \dfrac{1}{\sin \theta \, (0) + \cos \theta \, (1)}$

$= \dfrac{1}{\cos \theta} = \sec \theta$

36. $\csc \left(\theta - \frac{\pi}{2}\right) = \dfrac{1}{\sin \left(-(\frac{\pi}{2} - \theta)\right)}$

$= \dfrac{1}{-\sin \left(\frac{\pi}{2} - \theta\right)}$

$= \dfrac{1}{-\cos \theta}$

$= -\sec \theta$

37. $\cos \left(-\theta - \frac{\pi}{2}\right) =$

$\cos (-\theta) \cos \frac{\pi}{2} + \sin (-\theta) \sin \frac{\pi}{2} =$

$\cos (\theta)(0) + \sin (-\theta)(1) = \sin (-\theta)$

pages 817–819   Standardized Test Prep

34. [2] $\dfrac{\sin C}{6} = \dfrac{\sin 56°}{8}$

$m\angle C = \sin^{-1} \left(\dfrac{6 \sin 56°}{8}\right)$

$m\angle C \approx 38.4°$

[1] correct equation, incorrect final answer

35. [2]

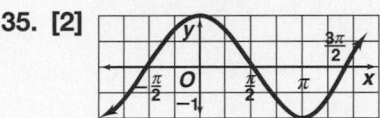

[1] graph translated $\frac{\pi}{2}$ to the right

36. [2]

$\underline{-2}\big|\quad 2 \quad\quad 4 \quad\; 5 \quad\quad\; 9 \quad -2$

$\quad\quad\quad\quad\quad\quad -4 \quad 0 \; -10 \quad\; 2$

$\quad\quad\quad\; 2 \quad\quad 0 \quad 5 \quad -1 \quad\big|\,\underline{0}$

$2x^3 + 5x - 1$

[1] minor arithmetic error

37. [2] $y = \dfrac{4x + 9}{x + 2}$; the graph of $y = \frac{1}{x}$ is a hyperbola whose asymptotes are the coordinate axes. So, substituting $y - 4$ for y and $x + 2$ for x gives a hyperbola with the desired asymptotes.

[1] missing or incorrect explanation

38. [2] $(5 + 2i)(-3 + i) =$
$-15 - 6i + 5i + 2i^2$
$= -15 - i - 2$
$= -17 - i$

[1] minor arithmetic error

39. [2] $A = Pe^{rt}$
$= 600e^{(0.05)(1.5)}$
$\approx \$646.73$

[1] incorrectly substitutes values into equations

40. [2] Yes; the three events can be used to form a probability distribution since they make up the entire sample space and their probabilities can be computed.

[1] only either the sample space OR probabilities are mentioned

41. [2] $\left(\frac{1}{6}\right)^3 \cdot 6 = \frac{1}{36} \approx 0.028$

[1] $\frac{1}{6^3}$ left as final answer

42. [2] $\begin{bmatrix} \frac{3}{40} & \frac{2}{40} \\ \frac{-11}{40} & \frac{6}{40} \end{bmatrix}$

[1] a number other than 40 is used for the determinant OR 1 sign error

43. [4] $a^2 = 23^2 + 19^2 - 2 \cdot 23 \cdot 19 \cos 65° \approx 520.6316$
$a \approx 22.82$

[3] correct formula, incorrect entry

[2] incorrect formula, correct computation

[1] correct formula, 2 incorrect entries

44. [4] 1 year, 4.5% continuously:
$A = 350e^{(0.045)} \approx 366.11$
5 years, 4.5% continuously:
$A = 350e^{(0.045)5} \approx 438.31$
1 year, 5% monthly
$A = 350\left(1 + \frac{0.05}{12}\right)^{12} \approx 367.91$
5 years, 5% monthly
$A = 350\left(1 + \frac{0.05}{12}\right)^{(5)(12)} \approx 449.18$

[3] one incorrect use of formula

[2] two incorrect uses of formula

[1] attempt to solve only one portion of problem

CHAPTER 2

page 823   Extra Practice

35. $3x - y = -9$

36. $4x - 6y = -9$

37. $8x - 2y = 7$

38. $x + y = 1$

51.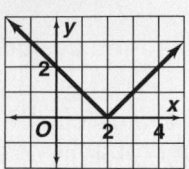

52.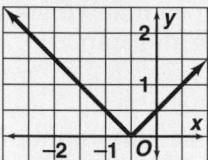

53.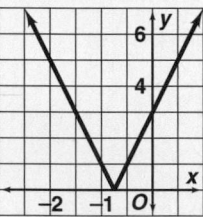

54.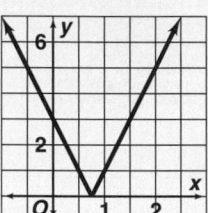

55.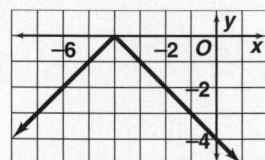

56.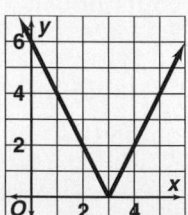

57.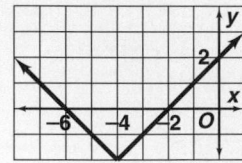

58.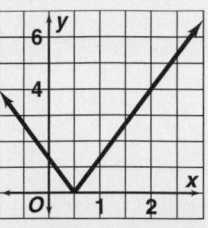

59.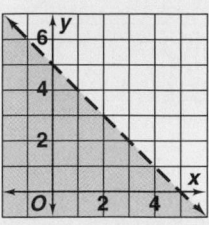

60.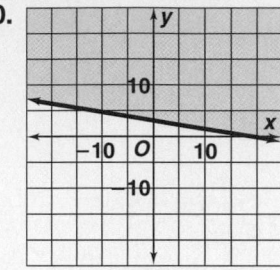

61.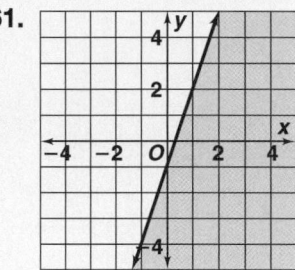

62.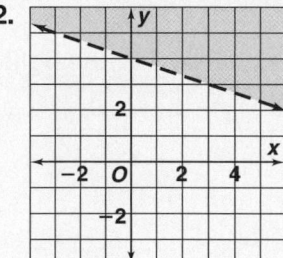

63.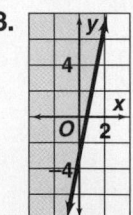

64.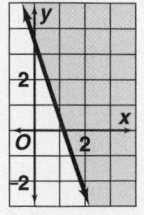

65.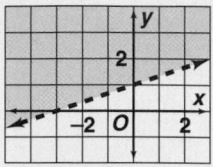

66.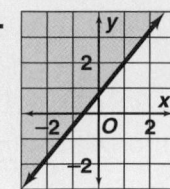

CHAPTER 3

page 824   Extra Practice

20–23.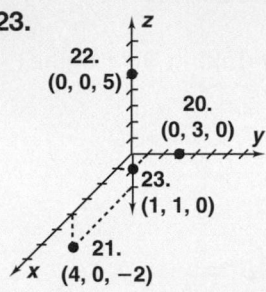

22. (0, 0, 5)
20. (0, 3, 0)
23. (1, 1, 0)
21. (4, 0, −2)

24–28.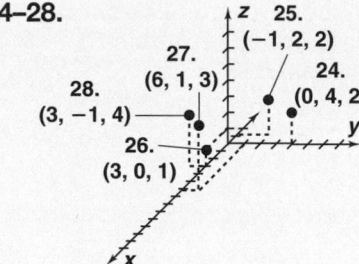

25. (−1, 2, 2)
27. (6, 1, 3)
24. (0, 4, 2)
28. (3, −1, 4)
26. (3, 0, 1)

29.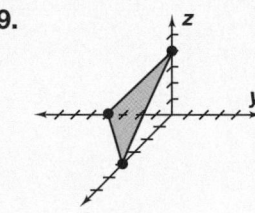

30.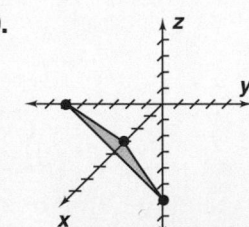

31.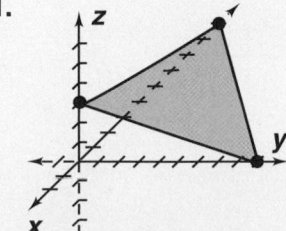

32.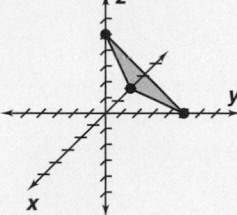

33.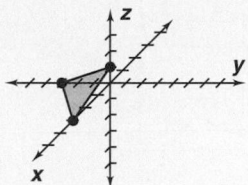

34.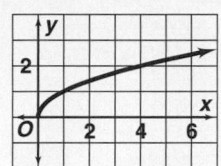

CHAPTER 7

page 828   Extra Practice

50.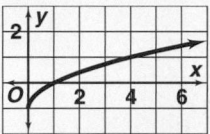

51.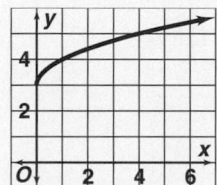

52.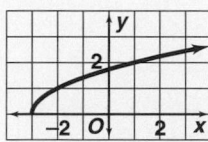

53.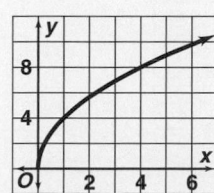

54.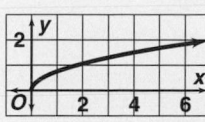

55.

56.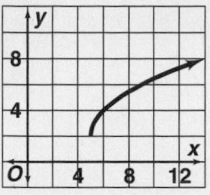

57.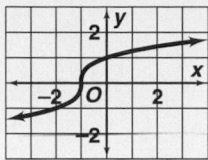

58.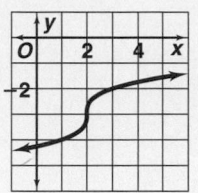

CHAPTER 8

page 829   Extra Practice

33.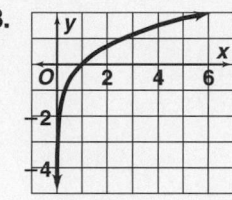

34.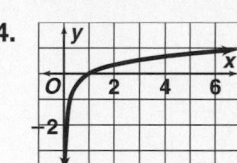

35.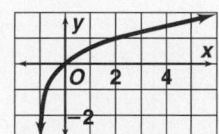

36.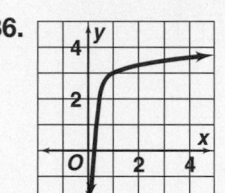

37.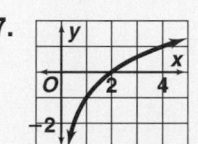

38.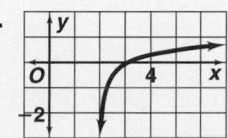

39.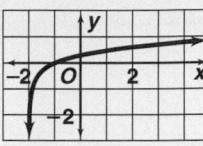

40.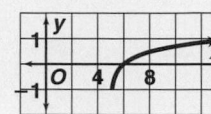

CHAPTER 10

page 831   Extra Practice

1.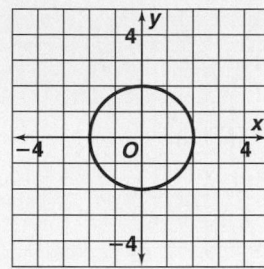

Circle; every line through
(0, 0) is a line of symmetry,
radius 2; domain: $-2 \leq x \leq 2$,
range: $-2 \leq y \leq 2$.

2.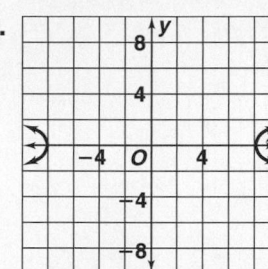

hyperbola; $x = 0, y = 0$;
domain: $|x| \geq 8$,
range: all real values of y

3.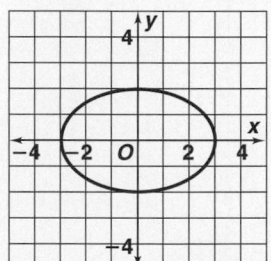

ellipse; $x = 0, y = 0$;
domain: $-3 \leq x \leq 3$,
range: $-2 \leq y \leq 2$

4.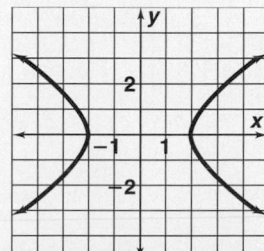

hyperbola; $x = 0, y = 0$;
domain: $x \leq -2, x \geq 2$,
range: all real values of y

5.

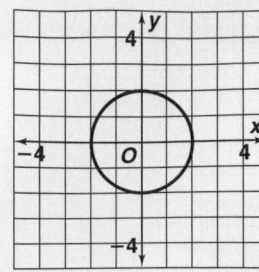

circle; every line through (0, 0) is a line of symmetry, radius 2; domain: $-2 \le x \le 2$, range: $-2 \le y \le 2$

6.

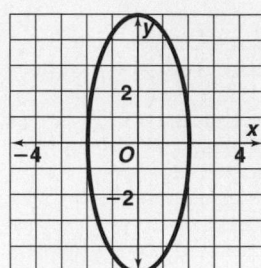

ellipse; $x = 0, y = 0$; domain: $-2 \le x \le 2$, range: $-5 \le y \le 5$

16. $\left(0, \frac{1}{16}\right), y = -\frac{1}{16}$;

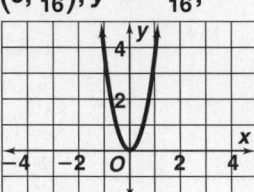

17. $(4, 0), x = -4$;

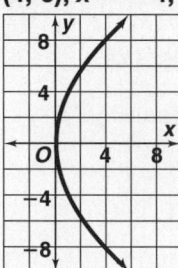

18. $\left(0, -\frac{1}{40}\right), y = \frac{1}{40}$;

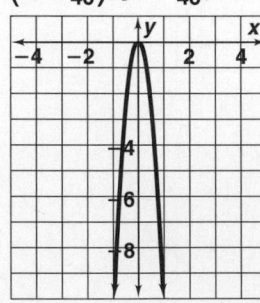

19. $(2, 0), x = -2$;

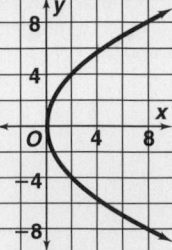

20. $\left(0, \frac{3}{2}\right), y = -\frac{3}{2}$;

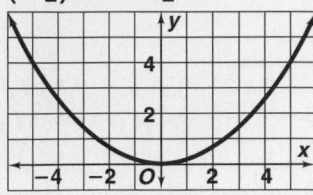

21. $(5, 0), x = -5$;

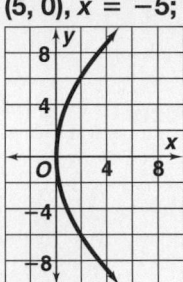

22. $(0, -1), y = 1$;

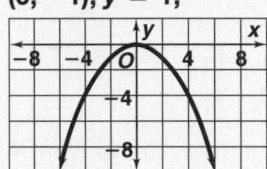

23. $\left(0, -\frac{1}{2}\right), y = \frac{1}{2}$;

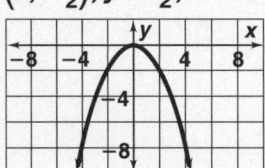

36. $(0, \pm 4)$

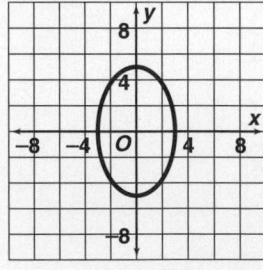

37. $(\pm 4\sqrt{2}, 0)$

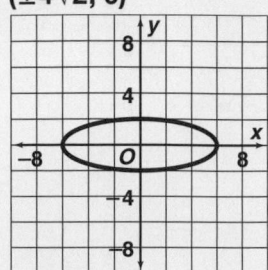

38. $(0, \pm\sqrt{21})$

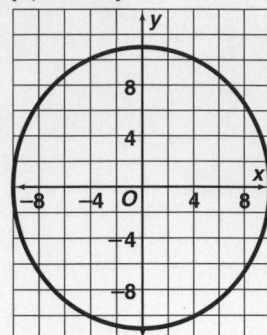

39. $(\pm\sqrt{17}, 0)$

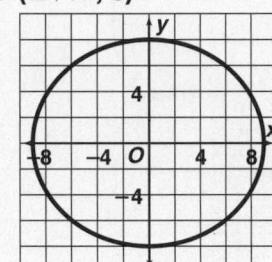

40. $(0, \pm\sqrt{95})$

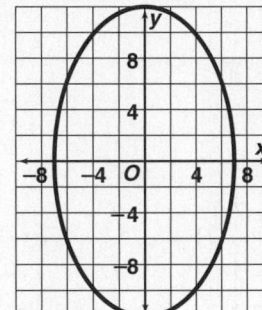

41. $(\pm\sqrt{3}, 0)$

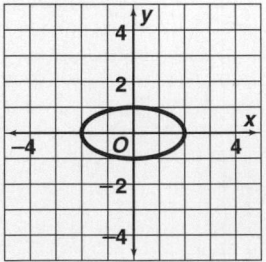

42.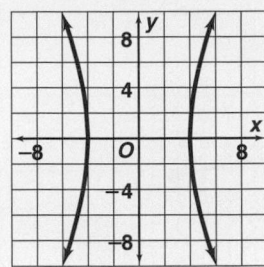

43.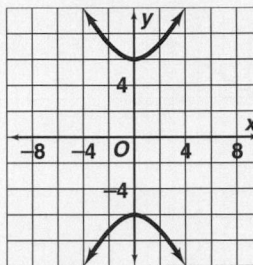

44.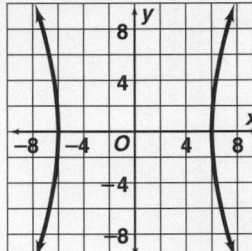

45.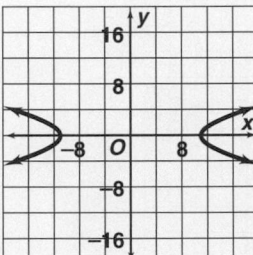

46.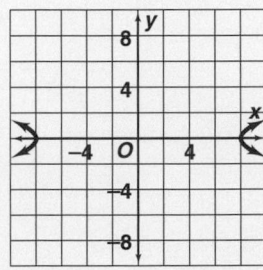

47.

CHAPTER 12

page 833   Extra Practice

28. $P(k = 0) = 0.3277$
$P(k = 1) = 0.4096$
$P(k = 2) = 0.2048$
$P(k = 3) = 0.0512$
$P(k = 4) = 0.0064$
$P(k = 5) = 0.00032$

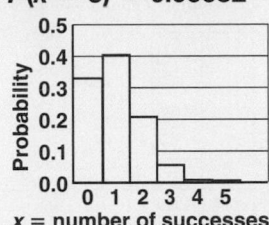

x = number of successes

29. $P(k = 0) = 0.0467$
$P(k = 1) = 0.1866$
$P(k = 2) = 0.3110$
$P(k = 3) = 0.2765$
$P(k = 4) = 0.1382$
$P(k = 5) = 0.0369$
$P(k = 6) = 0.0041$

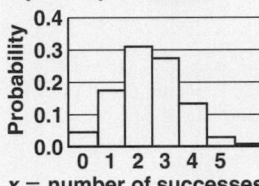

x = number of successes

30. $P(k = 0) = 0.00243$
$P(k = 1) = 0.0284$
$P(k = 2) = 0.1323$
$P(k = 3) = 0.3087$
$P(k = 4) = 0.3602$
$P(k = 5) = 0.16807$

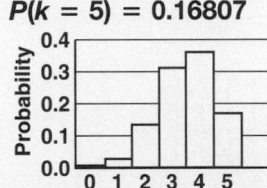

x = number of successes

31. $P(k = 0) = 0.4096$
$P(k = 1) = 0.4096$
$P(k = 2) = 0.1536$
$P(k = 3) = 0.0256$
$P(k = 4) = 0.0016$

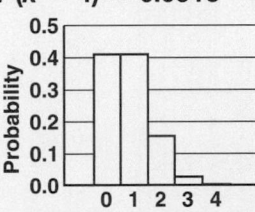

x = number of successes

32. $P(k = 0) = 0.0777$
$P(k = 1) = 0.2592$
$P(k = 2) = 0.3456$
$P(k = 3) = 0.2304$
$P(k = 4) = 0.0768$
$P(k = 5) = 0.01024$

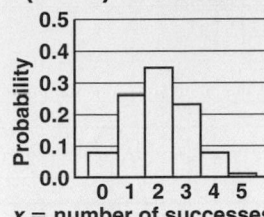

x = number of successes

33. $P(k = 0) = 0.000064$
$P(k = 1) = 0.001536$
$P(k = 2) = 0.01536$
$P(k = 3) = 0.08192$
$P(k = 4) = 0.24576$
$P(k = 5) = 0.3932$
$P(k = 6) = 0.262144$

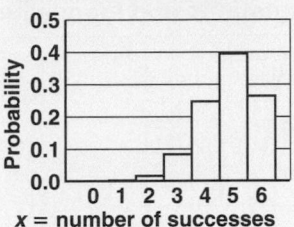

x = number of successes

CHAPTER 13

page 834   Extra Practice

28.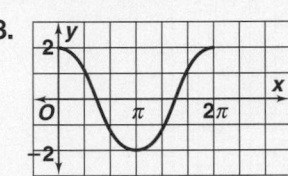

29.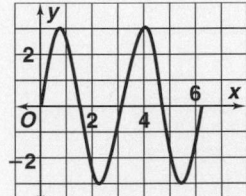

30.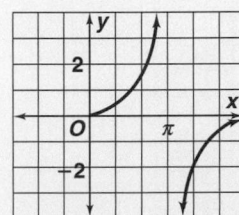

31.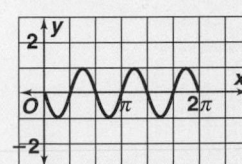

32.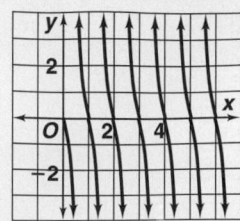

33.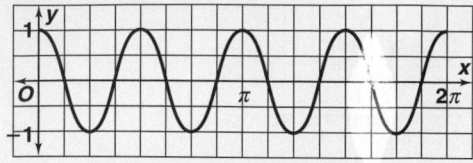

SKILLS HANDBOOK

page 851 Graphing Two-Variable
Equations and Inequalities

10.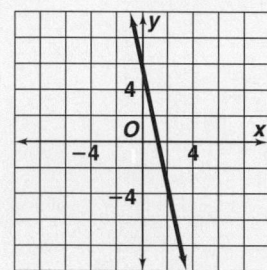

11.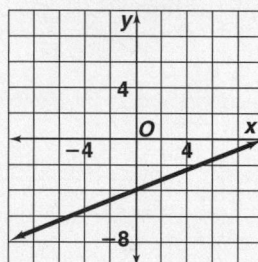

12.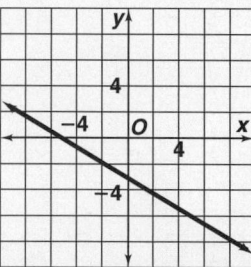

13.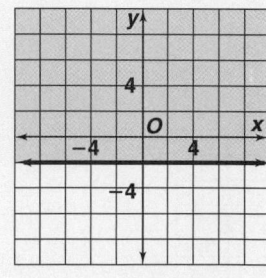

14.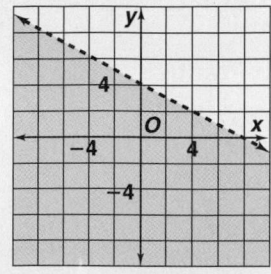

15.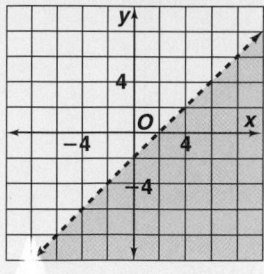

16.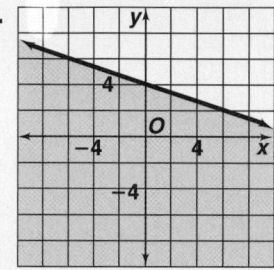

17.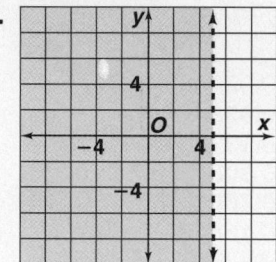

18.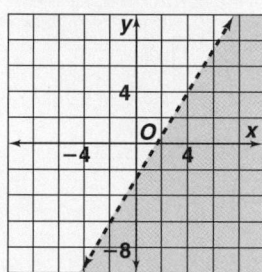

19.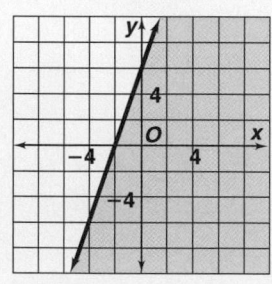

20.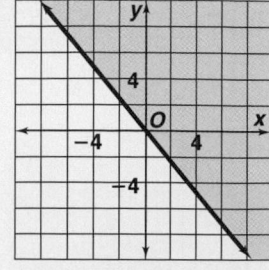

21.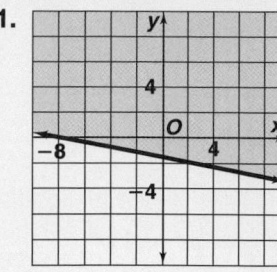

22.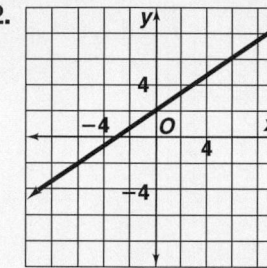

23.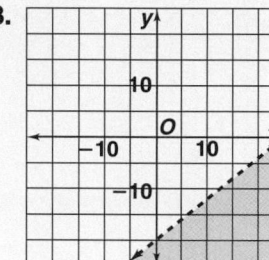

24.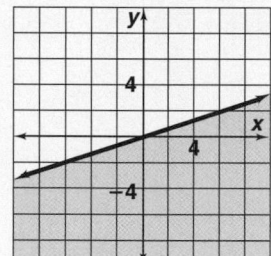

Index

Index

trigonometric, 766

variable, 12–13

Extended response exercises, 31, 38, 45, 61, 90, 98, 111, 121, 140, 185, 194, 229, 239, 261, 276, 283, 291, 313, 326, 334, 351, 357, 373, 378, 406, 413, 429, 451, 467, 473, 483, 490, 517, 576, 583, 598, 605, 641, 655, 669, 676, 684, 691, 702, 710, 727, 740, 748, 768, 776, 811, 819

Extensions

The Ambiguous Case, 793

Comparing Conditional Probabilities, 647

Descarte's Rule of Signs, 328

End Behavior, 306

The Fibonacci Sequence, 599

Linear and Exponential Models, 461

Lissajous Figures, 777

Mathematical Induction, 620–621

Networks, 208–209

Piecewise Functions, 71

Quadratic Inequalities, 269

Solving Quadratic Systems, 577

Using Parametric Form, 555

Extraneous solutions, 34, 48, 49, 387–388, 511–512, 529

F _____

Factor

decay, 425–426, 469

greatest common, 255

growth, 422–425, 469

linear, 307

prime, 307

Factor Theorem, 309, 354

Factorial notation, 339, 355

Factoring

defined, 255

difference of cubes, 322, 354

difference of squares, 259, 294

greatest common factor, 255

perfect square trinomial, 258, 294

polynomial, 307–310, 314–317, 322–324, 354, 853

quadratic expression, 255–258

quadratic trinomial, 256–258

sum of cubes, 322, 354

Families of functions, 91, 109

Feasible region, 136, 158

Fibonacci sequence, 599

Finite geometric series, 614–615, 631

Finite graph, 208–209

Foci

of ellipse, 556, 558, 580

of hyperbola, 563–565, 581

of parabola, 543, 545–546, 579

FOIL, 234

Formula(s), 865–870

for binomial probability, 673

Change of Base Formula, 453–454

for conditional probability, 643, 687

for continuously compounded interest, 433–434

for converting between radians and degrees, 713

evaluating, 846

explicit formulas, 590, 595, 601, 629

Law of Cosines, 794

Law of Sines, 788

for length of intercepted arc, 714

for margin of error, 665

Quadratic Formula, 285–289, 295

recursive formulas, 590, 595, 599, 601, 629

slope formula, 64, 848

solving for one variable, 19, 846

spreadsheet formulas, 25

for standard deviation, 657

for sum of arithmetic series, 608

for sum of geometric series, 614, 616

Fractal, 273, 275, 591

Fractal geometry, 591

Fraction, 843

complex, 506–507

Frequency table, 636–637

Function(s). *See also* Equation(s), Graph(s).

absolute value, 86–88, 109

addition of, 392, 417

composition of, 393–394, 399, 417

cube root, 410

defined, 57, 107

discrete, 57, 107

division of, 392–393, 417

exponential, 422–426, 430–434, 469

families of, 91, 109

inverse, 400–403, 407–408, 417

linear, 62, 108, 461

logarithmic, 440–441, 462–464, 471

maximum and minimum values of, 135–138, 243, 309

multiplication of, 392–393, 417

notation, 58, 107, 402–403

objective, 135, 158

operations with, 392–394, 417

parent, 91, 109

periodic, 696–699, 757

piecewise, 71

polynomial, 300–303, 306, 309–310, 317, 335–337, 354

quadratic, 234–236, 241–243, 248–251, 280–281, 294

radical, 408–411, 417

rational, 484, 491–495, 528

rules, 58

square root, 409–410

step, 71

subtraction of, 392, 417

translations. *See* Translations.

trigonometric. *See* Trigonometric function.

vertical-line test, 57

Function notation, 58, 107, 402–403

Function rules, 58

Fundamental Theorem of Algebra, 335–337, 355

G _____

Gauss, Carl Friedrich, 335

GCF (greatest common factor), 255

Genetics, 41

Geometric mean, 602, 630

Geometric probability, 42, 49

Geometric sequence, 600–602, 630

Geometric series, 613, 614–616, 631

Geometry, 14–15, 17, 20, 22, 30, 38, 42–43, 48, 60, 69, 73, 76, 83, 126, 133, 146, 154–155, 186–191, 192, 201, 214, 223, 238, 260, 275, 282, 291, 305, 311–312, 318, 324–325, 343, 350, 356, 366, 372, 377, 389, 396, 399, 404, 405, 418, 436, 480, 590, 592, 593, 598, 613, 717, 739–740, 754, 783–784, 791, 798

Geometry Review

formulas, 870

Geometric Transformations, 186

Radical Expressions in Formulas, 391

Special Right Triangles, 703

Glossary, 871–913

Golden ratio, 265, 287

Graphing calculator

! option, 339

absolute value function, 87

area under a curve, 625

box-and-whisker plot, 651

CALC feature, 265

circle, 555

comparing models of data, 302

conic sections, 542

cube roots, 365

CubicReg feature, 302

data, fitting curves to, 302, 430

determinant of a matrix, 203

Disp feature, 555

DispGraph feature, 555

DrawInv feature, 407

evaluating a series, 622

exponential functions transformed into linear functions, 461

exponents, entering, 380

ExpReg feature, 430

factorial, 339

geometric sequence, 600

graphing two equations simultaneously, 452

Intersect feature, 141, 321

inverse of function, 407

line of best fit, 85

linear programming, 141

LinReg feature, 85, 240, 302

LIST feature, 649

matrix determinant, evaluating, 203

matrix equation, 211

matrix operation, 177

measures of central tendency, 649

Param feature, 555

parametric equation, 122, 407

parametric form, 555

PRB menu, 339, 341

PRGM menu, 555

Prompt feature, 555

quadratic inequality, 269

QuadReg feature, 240, 302

Radian feature, 555

random numbers, 40, 639

rational function, 484

residuals, 240

root, finding, 365

rref feature, 220

Shade command, 269

solving polynomial equation, 321

STAT PLOT feature, 461, 600, 649, 651

Index

M

146, 155, 161, 169, 176, 185, 194, 206, 215, 223, 229, 239, 247, 261, 268, 276, 283, 291, 297, 313, 319, 326, 334, 338, 351, 357, 367, 373, 378, 384, 397, 405–406, 413, 419, 429, 436–437, 444, 451, 466–467, 468, 473, 483, 490, 497, 503, 509–510, 517, 531, 540–541, 548, 561, 567, 583, 593, 598, 604, 612, 627, 633, 641, 646, 654–655, 668–669, 683, 691, 701–702, 710, 718–719, 727, 734, 740, 748, 761, 768, 776, 784–785, 805–806, 811, 817–819

Multiple events, probability of, 519–522, 529

Multiple representations, 78, 80, 85, 86, 91, 100, 117, 131, 135–137, 236, 240, 302, 308, 327, 425–426, 441, 455, 467, 478, 485, 535–536, 638, 737, 745, 747

Multiple zeros, multiplicity, 310, 354

Multiplication
of binomial radical expressions, 375–376, 416
of binomials, 234, 853
of complex numbers, 272
of fractions, 843
of functions, 392–393, 417
of matrices, 180–182, 226
of radical expressions, 368–369, 375–376, 416
of rational expressions, 500
scalar, 178–179, 226
simplifying algebraic expressions, 13
of square roots, 262

Multiplication Counting Principle, 339

Multiplication property
of equality, 18
of inequality, 26
of square roots, 262

Multiplicative identity matrix, 195, 227

Multiplicative identity property of scalar multiplication, 179

Multiplicative inverses
of matrices, 195–197, 203, 212, 227
reciprocals, 7, 47–48

Multiplicative Property of Zero
matrix multiplication, 182
real number multiplication, 13
scalar multiplication, 179

Mutually exclusive events, probability of, 521, 529

N

n **factorial,** 339, 355

NCTM, 2A, 52A, 114A, 162A, 232A, 298A, 360A, 420A, 476A, 532A, 586A, 634A, 694A, 762A

Natural logarithm, 462–464, 471

Natural numbers, 5

Need Help?, 12, 14, 26, 35, 62, 69, 74, 87, 89, 93, 97, 99, 101, 116, 125, 130, 144, 148, 151, 154, 179, 187, 190, 192, 196, 203, 210, 211, 212, 222, 234, 242, 248, 255, 259, 265, 271, 280, 286, 307, 308, 309, 314, 323, 365, 375, 381, 387, 392, 401, 408, 422, 431, 436, 441, 453, 454, 464, 489, 499, 501, 505, 506, 512, 524, 543, 544, 546, 563, 570, 572, 590, 602, 614, 624, 637, 671, 673, 679, 707, 717, 721, 722, 735, 766, 784, 787, 796, 809

Negative angle identities, 801, 815

Networks, 208–209

Normal curves, 679–680, 689

Normal distribution, 678–680, 689

Notation
factorial, 339, 355
function, 58, 107, 402–403
scientific, 854
summation, 609, 630

*n***th root,** 363–364

Number line, 6

Number(s)
complex, 270–273, 332, 355
imaginary, 270–273
irrational, 5–6, 271, 331, 355
natural, 5–6, 271
random, 40, 43, 639, 864
rational, 5–6, 271
real, 5–8, 271
whole, 5–6, 271

O

Objective function, 135, 158

Open-Ended, 16, 23, 31, 37, 44, 48, 50, 60, 69, 75, 82, 89, 96, 103, 109–110, 120, 127, 133, 139, 145, 154, 160, 169, 175, 176, 184, 187, 201, 205, 214, 221, 228, 238, 245, 253, 260, 266–267, 275, 290, 296, 303, 312, 319, 325, 326, 333, 337, 343, 356, 366, 372, 377, 383, 390, 396, 405, 412, 418, 419, 428, 435, 437, 442, 449, 450, 458, 466, 472, 482, 489, 502, 508, 516–517, 524, 530, 540, 547, 553, 555, 560, 566, 575, 582, 592, 596, 599–600, 603, 611, 617, 619, 626, 627, 632, 640, 645, 655, 662, 667, 675, 677, 683, 684, 690, 700, 709, 717, 726, 739, 747, 760, 767, 775, 777, 783, 785, 791, 797, 805, 810, 816

Opposites
additive inverse, 7, 47–48
additive inverse matrices, 171
simplifying algebraic expressions, 13

Or (compound inequality), 28, 48

Order of operations, 845

Ordered pair, 54–56

Ordered triple, 142, 159

Ordinate, 54

Origin, 54, 142

Outlier, 652, 688

P

Pacing Options, 2A, 52A, 114A, 162A, 232A, 298A, 360A, 420A, 476A, 532A, 586A, 634A, 694A, 762A

Parabola(s)
axis of symmetry, 235, 293, 543
conic sections, 535, 543–545
defined, 235, 543, 579
directrix, 543, 545–546, 579
equation, 248–251, 543–545
focus, 543, 545–546, 579
graphing, 235, 241–242, 249–250, 543–546
maximums and minimums, 243
translations of, 248–251
vertices, 235, 243, 293

Parallel lines, 66

Param feature, graphing calculator, 555

Parametric equation, 122, 407, 555, 777

Parametric form, 555

Parent function, 91, 109, 744

Pascal, Blaise, 347

Pascal's Triangle, 346–348, 355

Paths, finite graphs, 208–209

Patterns, *See also* Sequences, Series. 248, 588, 591

Percent, 842

Percentiles, 651, 688

Perfect square trinomial, 258, 278–280, 294

Perimeter, 14

Periodic cycle, 696, 697, 757

Periodic functions. *See also* Trigonometric functions.
amplitude of, 698–699, 757
cycle, 697
identifying, 696–697
translations, 742–746, 759

Period
of cosine function, 730
of function, 697
of sine function, 721
of tangent function, 736

Permutations, 339–340, 355

Perpendicular lines, 66, 67

Phase shift, 742, 759

Pi (π), 11

Piecewise function, 71

Plane, sketching, 144

Point in Time
dating lunar rocks, 467
finding *Titanic,* 541
murals, 207
Otis Boykin, 702
the sun's movements, 605

Point of discontinuity, 491–493, 528

Point-slope form, 65–66, 108

Polynomial equations
Descartes's Rule of Signs, 328
Fundamental Theorem of Algebra, 335–337, 355
Imaginary Root Theorem, 332, 355
imaginary roots, 332
Irrational Root Theorem, 331, 355
irrational roots, 331
number of roots, 335–337
Rational Root Theorem, 329–331, 355
rational roots, 329–331
solving by factoring, 322–324, 354
solving by graphing, 321–322
solving higher-degree equations, 324
writing equations from roots, 332, 355

Polynomial function(s)
defined, 301, 353
end behavior, 306
evaluating, 317
Factor Theorem, 309
graphing, 300, 306
modeling data, 302–303
multiple zeros, multiplicity, 310, 354

Index

T973

Acknowledgments

STAFF CREDIT

The people who made up the High School Mathematics team—representing design services, editorial, editorial services, market research, marketing services, online services & multimedia development, production services, project office, and publishing processes—are listed below. Bold type denotes the core team members.

Leora Adler, Carolyn Artin, Stephanie Bradley, Amy D. Breaux, **Peter Brooks,** Judith Buice, Ronit Carter, **Lisa J. Clark,** Bob Cornell, Carol Dance, Sheila DeFazio, Marian DeLollis, Jo DiGiustini, Delphine Dupee, Emily Ellen, Janet Fauser, Debby Faust, Suzanne Feliciello, Frederick Fellows, Jonathan Fisher, **Paula Foye,** Paul Frisoli, Patti Fromkin, Melissa Garcia, Jonathan Gorey, Jennifer Graham, Barbara Hardt, Daniel R. Hartjes, Richard Heater, Kerri Hoar, Jayne Holman, Karen Holtzman, Angela Husband, Kevin Jackson-Mead, Albert Jacobson, Misty-Lynn Jenese, Carolyn Lock, Diahanne Lucas, Catherine Maglio, Cheryl Mahan, Barry Maloney, Meredith Mascola, Ann McSweeney, **Eve Melnechuk,** Sandy Morris, **Cindy Noftle,** Marsha Novak, **Marie Opera,** Jill Ort, Michael Oster, Steve Ouellette, Dorothy M. Preston, Rashid Ross, Donna Russo, **Malti Sharma, Dennis Slattery,** Kathryn Smith, Lisa Smith-Ruvalcaba, Emily Soltanoff, **Deborah Sommer,** Mark Tricca, Nate Walker, Diane Walsh, **Joe Will,** Amy Winchester, Carol Zacny

Cover Design: Brainworx Studio

Cover Photos: Water drops, Martin Dohrn/Science Photo Library/Photo Researchers, Inc.
Spiral staircase, Bryan Reinhart/Masterfile Corporation

Technical Illustration: Argosy Illustration; Nesbitt Graphics, Inc.

ILLUSTRATION

Tina Adams: 575 br

ANCO/Outlook: 325, 540, 772 Argosy Illustration: 89

Kenneth Batelman: 75, 139, 175, 208, 236, 302, 344, 423, 497, 651, 737

Carol Dance: 82

Dorling Kindersley Ltd./Richard Bonson: 474 br, 474 bl, 475b, 585 m

Dorling Kindersley Ltd.: 475 t

Jim DeLapine: 497

Kathleen Dempsey: 168

GeoSystems Global Corporation: 146

John Edwards Inc.: 79, 97, 183, 222 b, 465, 639, 662 tl

Suzanne Feliciello: 667 b

Dennis Harms: 170, 178, 346, 379, 637 b

Lois Leonard Stock: 186

Seymour Levy: 137, 145

Ron Magnes: 198, 199, 200

Steve McEntee: 649

Jim Nuttle: 56

Marie Opera: 124, 189

Lisa Smith-Ruvalcaba: 672

Brucie Rosch: 9, 152, 165, 184 b, 345, 364, 448, 640, 667 t, 747

Olyna Serbyn: 127

Gary Torrisi: 204, 702, 791 t, 561, 591 b, 592 l

Roberta Warshaw: 97, 139, 346, 727, 592 br

J/B Woolsey Associates: 167, 222 t, 311 mr, 312, 325 l, 342, 365, 541 br, 642, 653, 665, 682 b, 745

XNR Productions: 94, 554

PHOTO RESEARCH

Sharon Donahue

PHOTOGRAPHY

Front Matter

Page vii, AP Photo/Doug Mills; **viii,** AP Photo/Brietling Orbiter; **ix,** Bob Daemmrich/Stock Boston; **x,** SPARC; **xi,** SuperStock, Inc.; **xii,** © 2000 by Consumers Union of the United States, Inc., Yonkers, New York 10703-1057, a nonprofit organization. Reprinted with permission from the March 2000 issue of *Consumer Reports,* for educational purposes only.; **xiii,** Stone/Getty Images, Inc.; **xiv,** NASA; **xv,** Bob Daemmrich Photography, Inc.; **xvi,** Stone/Getty Images, Inc.; **xvii,** Stone/Getty Images, Inc.; **xviii,** Raymond Gehman/Corbis; **xix,** Lawrence Migdale/Photo Researchers, Inc.; **xx,** Stone/Getty Images, Inc.

Chapter 1

Pages 2, 3, Chris Hondoros/Newsmakers/Getty Images, Inc.; **4,** Art Institute of Chicago, Illinois/Lauros-Giraudon, Paris/SuperStock, Inc.; **6,** Jeff Greenberg/PhotoEdit; **13,** Charles Gupton/Stock Boston; **15,** Bob Daemmrich Photography, Inc.; **16,** Jonathan Nourock/Stone/Getty Images, Inc.; **20,** Bob Daemmrich/Stock Boston; **21,** SuperStock, Inc.; **22,** AP Photo/Doug Mills; **24,** Jeff Henry/Peter Arnold, Inc.; **28,** Bob Daemmrich/Stock Boston; **29,** Juneberg Clark/Photo Researchers, Inc.; **30,** Jon Riley; **36,** Corbis; **37,** Northeast River Forecast Center/NOAA; **39 l,** Richard Haynes; **39 m, r, 40,** Ken O'Donoghue; **44,** Tim Davis/Allstock/PictureQuest.

Chapter 2

Pages 52, 53, Bridge design by Vebjorn Sand/Photo by Terje S. Johansen; **55,** Richard Megna/Fundamental Photographs; **56,** Jim Chatwin/Index Stock Imagery/PictureQuest; **58,** Dirk Weisheit/DDB Stock Photo; **61,** Bob Rowan/Corbis; **63,** Le Figaro/Liaison/Getty Images, Inc.; **66 t,** Patrick Ingrand/Stone/Getty Images, Inc.; **66 b,** Pearson Education, Inc., Silver Burdett & Ginn; **69,** Texas Instruments; **76,** Vanessa Vick/Photo Researchers, Inc.; **77 l,** Stacy Pick/Stock Boston; **77 r,** George A. Robinson/Stone/Getty Images, Inc.; **78,** AP Photo/Brietling Orbiter; **80,** Stone/Getty Images, Inc.; **82,** PhotoDisc, Inc./Getty Images, Inc.; **88,** Martin Rogers/Stock Boston/PictureQuest; **89,** Russ Lappa; **92,** Bill Aron/PhotoEdit; **94,** British Museum; **95 both,** © The Design Library, New York; **100 t,** Joe Sohm/Stock Boston; **100 b,** M. Grecco/Stock Boston; **112 t all,** © John T. Fowler. All rights reserved; **112–113,** Dorling Kindersley Ltd.; **113 tl,** Bridge design by Vebjorn Sand/Photo by Terje S. Johansen; **113 tm,** Getty Images, Inc.; **113 tr,** L'Institute Bibliothèque, Paris.

Chapter 3

Pages 114, 115, Renee Lynn/Photo Researchers, Inc.; **117,** AP Photo/Thomas Kienzle; **119 l,** PhotoDisc, Inc./Getty Images, Inc.; **119 m,** Corbis Digital Stock; **119 r,** Stone/Getty Images, Inc.; **120,** David Young-Wolff/PhotoEdit; **124,** PhotoDisc, Inc./Getty Images, Inc.; **131,** Bob Daemmrich/Stock Boston; **133,** Bob Daemmrich/Stock Boston; **137 both,** Mark Thayer; **139,** Bob Daemmrich Photo, Inc.; **142,** David Weintraub/Stock Boston; **143,** Mark Thayer; **145,** Zigy Kaluzny/Stone/Getty Images, Inc.; **147 l,** Jose L. Pelaze/Corbis Stock Market; **147 r,** 1992 SIU Biomed Comm/Custom Medical Stock Photo; **149,** Pearson Education, Inc.; **153,** AP Photo/Paul Sakuma; **154,** Stone/Getty Images, Inc.

Chapter 4

Pages 162, 163, 165, Michael Newman/PhotoEdit; **166,** AP Photo/L.G. Patterson; **170,** Frank Siteman/Stock Boston; **175,** AP Photo/John Bazemore; **178,** Jeff Greenberg/Omni-Photo Communications, Inc.; **181 both,** Andrew Syred/Science Photo Library/Photo Researchers, Inc.; **184,** Atlantic Feature © 1996 by Mark Parisi; **189,** Russ Lappa; **189 inset,** William Taufic/Corbis Stock Market; **191,** George Holton, Photo Researchers, Inc.; **193,** Jerry Clapsaddle; **198,** *New York Times;* **205,** AP Photo/*The Daily Times,* Marc F. Henning; **206,** AP Photo/*Lincoln Journal Star,* Robert Becker; **207 both,** SPARC; **212,** Russ Lappa; **214,** David Simson/Stock Boston; **230 cacao tree;** Dag Sundberg/Image Bank/Getty Images, Inc.; **230 cocoa pods,** Jeremy Horner/Corbis; **230 the rest,** Hershey Foods Corporation. Photos provided by JPL Productions; **231 tr,** Dorling Kindersley Ltd.; **231 m all,** Hershey Foods Corporation. Photos provided by JPL Productions; **231 bl,** Dorling Kindersley Ltd.; **231 br,** Greg Pease/Getty Images, Inc.

Chapter 5

Pages 232, 233, Pearson Education, Inc./PH College; **235,** Jon Chomitz; **238 t,** Fish & Wildlife Service; **238 b,** AP Photo/*St. Cloud Times,* Paul Middlestaedt; **243,** Marty Katz/The Image Works; **245,** Michael Newman/PhotoEdit; **246,** James L. Stanfield/National Geographic Image Collection; **247,** Michael Epstein/PhotoEdit; **250,** SuperStock, Inc.; **252,** Finagle A Bagel; **259,** Doug Menuez/PhotoDisc, Inc./Getty Images, Inc.; **260,** Jeff Greenberg/Visuals Unlimited; **264,** Mike McMillan/Spotfire Images; **265,** *Portrait of a Man,* 1773–1775, 12″ × 16¼″, Museo De Zaragoza; **266,** Asian Art Museum of San Francisco, The Avery Brundage Collection, B60 M427; **273,** Prentice Hall; **274,** © *Robotman* reprinted by permission of Newspaper Enterprise Association, Inc.; **275,** Prentice Hall; **277,** Jon Chomitz; **279,** Courtesy of Craig Smorynski; **280,** Michael Newman/PhotoEdit; **282,** Prentice Hall; **283,** Petyer Pearson/Stone/Getty Images, Inc.; **284,** Prentice Hall; **287,** Stone/Getty Images, Inc.; **288,** Reuters New Media Inc./Corbis; **290,** AP/Wide World Photos.

Chapter 6

Pages 298, 299, AP Photo/Eric Risberg; **302,** National Geographic Society; **308,** Spencer Grant/Stock Boston; **311,** Greg Pease/Stone/Getty Images, Inc.; **312,** Bob Daemmrich/Stock Boston/PictureQuest; **316,** Museo Archeologico, Florence, Italy/Art Resource, New York; **318,** Christie's Images, London/Bridgeman Art Library/SuperStock, Inc.; **320,** Corbis Digital Stock; **322,** Nik Kleinberg/Stock Boston; **325,** James A. Sugar/Corbis; **328,** Craig Smorynski; **335,** C. Marvin Lang; **340,** Stone/Getty Images, Inc.; **341,** PhotoEdit; **343 t,** © 2000 by Consumers Union of the United States, Inc., Yonkers, New York 10703-1057, a nonprofit organization. Reprinted with permission from the March 2000 issue of *Consumer Reports,* for educational purposes only; **343 b,** *Peanuts* reprinted by permission of United Feature Syndicate, Inc.;

347, Jean-Loup Charmet/Photo Researchers, Inc.; **349,** Andy Lyons/Allsport/Getty Images, Inc.; **350,** Stone/Getty Images, Inc.; **358 tl,** Colorsport; **358 bl,** Dorling Kindersley Ltd.; **358–359,** Glyn Kirk/Action Plus; **359 tl,** Colorsport; **359 tr,** Allsport/Getty Images, Inc.; **359 br,** Vincent Laforet/Allsport/Getty Images, Inc.

Chapter 7

Pages 360, 361, U.S. Space & Rocket Center; **366,** Stone/Getty Images, Inc.; **371,** Sidney Harris; **372,** Stone/Getty Images, Inc.; **377,** Judy Canty/Stock Boston; **380,** Jason Grow/Corbis Saba; **383,** An Keren/Sovfoto/Eastfoto/ PictureQuest; **386,** Jean-Claude LeJeune/Stock Boston; **389,** Russ Lappa; **394,** Robert Brenner/PhotoEdit; **395 l,** Amy C. Etra/PhotoEdit; **395 r,** Robert Fried/Stock Boston; **397,** Stone/Getty Images, Inc.; **403,** AP Photo/*The Saginaw News,* Bernie Eng; **405,** Tony Freeman/PhotoEdit; **406,** Bob Daemmrich/The Image Works; **410,** PhotoDisc, Inc./Getty Images, Inc.; **412,** Ringling Bros. and Barnum & Bailey Combined Shows, Inc.

Chapter 8

Pages 420, 421, Richard Pasley/Stock Boston; **423,** Spencer Grant/PhotoEdit; **424,** AP Photo/University of Illinois, Mark Jones; **428,** AP Photo/Bob Care; **432,** Peter Berndt, MD/Custom Medical Stock Photo; **435,** Bill Aron/PhotoEdit; **436,** Laura Dwight/Omni-Photo Communications, Inc.; **438,** AP Photo/Lauren McFalls; **440,** L. S. Stepanowicz/Bruce Coleman, Inc.; **443,** James King-Holmes/ Science Photo Library/Photo Researchers, Inc.; **448,** John Neubauer/ PhotoEdit; **450,** Reuters New Media Inc./Corbis; **455,** Jeff Greenberg/PhotoEdit; **457,** Andrew Rafkind/Stone/Getty Images, Inc.; **458,** Catherine Karnow/Corbis; **459,** Andy Sacks/Stone/Getty Images, Inc.; **463,** NASA; **466,** David Young-Wolff/PhotoEdit; **467,** NASA; **467 inset,** NASA/Bruce Coleman, Inc.; **474 l,** Photograph by Halliday Historic Photograph Co., circa 1905. Courtesy of Society for the Preservation of New England Antiquities; **474 r,** Peter Vanderwarker Photographs; **474–475 b,** Dorling Kindersley Ltd.

Chapter 9

Pages 476, 477, David Breashears/Arcturus Motion Pictures; **479,** Kevin Dodge/Masterfile Corporation; **482,** Bob Daemmrich/Stock Boston; **486,** Robert Freck/Stone/Getty Images, Inc.; **489,** Comstock Images; **495,** Dennis O'Clair/Stone/Getty Images, Inc.; **500,** Tom Dietrich/Stone/Getty Images, Inc.; **502,** 1992 Jeffrey Muir Hamilton/Stock Boston; **504 both,** Mark Thayer; **509,** Bob Daemmrich Photo, Inc.; **513,** Courtesy of Lightning Cycle Dynamics, Inc.; **516 t,** Reprinted with special permission of King Features Syndicate; **516 b,** Morton Beebe/Corbis; **519 all,** Jon Chomitz; **520,** Mark C. Burnett/Stock Boston; **522,** Prentice Hall; **523,** Pitney Bowes, Inc.; **525,** H. Dratch/The Image Works.

Chapter 10

Pages 532, 533, NASA; **535, 536 both,** Jeff Smith; **539,** Richard Pasley/Stock Boston; **540,** Peter L. Chapman/Stock Boston; **541,** Painting by Ken Marschall from *Titanic: An Illustrated History* © 1992, A Madison Press Book; **545,** Stone/Getty Images, Inc.; **547 t,** Prentice Hall; **547 b,** Woody Woodworth/SuperStock, Inc.; **549,** Molly & Georg Gerster/Comstock Images; **551,** Michael Rosenfeld/Stone/ Getty Images, Inc.; **553,** Susan Van Etten/Stock Boston; **557,** NASA Langley Research Center; **559,** Ken O'Donoghue; **567,** Ed Young/Science Photo Library/Photo Researchers, Inc.; **575,** Collection of the Lowe Art Museum, University of Miami. Museum purchase in memory of Shelia Simrod Friedman, #92.0094; **584 t,** Dorling Kindersley Ltd.; **584–585,** NASA; **585 t,** NASA.